Handbook of Heat and Mass Transfer

Volume 3: Catalysis, Kinetics, and Reactor Engineering

Nicholas P. Cheremisinoff, Editor

in collaboration with:

B. D. Adkins
O. M. Alfano
P. Andow
H. Angélino
A. Baiker
A. A. C. M. Beenackers
A. Căluşaru
A. E. Cassano
B. H. Davis
K. Endo
M. E. Findley
P. Forzatti
M. Friederick
E. Furimsky
M. A. Galan
J. W. Geus
G. H. Graaf
T. M. Grigor'eva
W. Haarde
M. Harada
Y. Hatate
J. L. Hudson
S. L. Karwa
I. G. Kevrekidis
K. Kida
M. A. Kohler
J. A. Kolbanovskii
T. J. Kotas
E. G. M. Kuijpers
D. Kunzru
C. Laguérie
W. K. Lee
A. A. Levitskii
L. Lietti
S.-X. Lin
H. Matsuyama
B. J. McCoy
D. Mewes
D. R. Milburn
Y. Miyake
S. Nagai
N. Nishio
B. A. Ogunnaike
E. O'Shima
W. Ostendorf
T. Otsu
J.-E. A. Otterstedt
L. S. Polak
R. A. Rajadhyaksha
K. H. Row
J. Shiozaki
J. M. Smith
Y. Sonoda
E. J. Stamhuis
B. Tabis
R. L. Tatuzov
J. R. Too
E. Tronconi
S. H. Ungureanu
L. L. Upson
P. C. M. van Stiphout
C. G. Vayenas
X. E. Verykios
G.-X. Wang
S. Whitaker
G.-H. Yang
Y. Yoshimura

Handbook of Heat and Mass Transfer

Volume 3: Catalysis, Kinetics, and Reactor Engineering

ISBN 0-87201-442-8

Library of Congress Cataloging-in-Publication Data
(Revised for vol. 3)
Handbook of heat and mass transfer.
Includes bibliographies and indexes.
Contents: v. 1. Heat transfer operations—v. 2. Mass transfer and reactor design—v. 3. Catalysis, kinetics, and reactor engineering.
1. Heat—Transmission—Handbooks, manuals, etc.
2. Mass transfer—Handbooks, manuals, etc.
I. Cheremisinoff, Nicholas P.
TJ260.H36 1986 621.402′2 84-25338
ISBN 0-87201-411-8 (v. 1)

Series ISBN 0-87201-338-3

CONTENTS

Section II: Multiphase Reactor Operations

Section III: Advanced Methods of Systems Analysis

HANDBOOK OF HEAT AND MASS TRANSFER

VOLUME 1: HEAT TRANSFER OPERATIONS

Heat Transfer Mechanisms
Industrial Operations and Design

VOLUME 2: MASS TRANSFER AND REACTOR DESIGN

Mass Transfer Principles
Distillation and Extraction
Multiphase Reactor Systems
Special Applications and Reactor Topics

VOLUME 3: CATALYSIS, KINETICS, AND REACTOR ENGINEERING

Catalyst Technology
Multiphase Reactor Operations
Advanced Methods of Systems Analysis

VOLUME 4: COMBUSTION SCIENCE AND TECHNOLOGY

VOLUME 5: MULTIPHASE REACTOR OPERATIONS

VOLUME 6: MULTIPHASE REACTOR DESIGN

VOLUME 7: RADIATION TECHNOLOGY

CONTRIBUTORS TO THIS VOLUME

B. D. Adkins, Kentucky Energy Cabinet Laboratory, Lexington, Kentucky, USA.

O. M. Alfano, Instituto de Desarrollo Tecnologico para la Industria Quimica, Universidad Nacional del Litoral and Consejo National da Investigaciones, Cientificas Y Tecnicas, Argentina.

P. Andow, KBC Process Automation, Chilworth Research Centre, Southampton, United Kingdom

H. Angélino, Laboratoire de Genie Chimique, ENSIGC-Chemin de la Loge, Cedex, France.

A. Baiker, Dept. of Industrial and Engineering Chemistry, Swiss Federal Institute of Technology (ETM), Zurich, Switzerland.

A. A. C. M. Beenackers, Dept. of Chemical Engineering, State University of Groningen, Groningen, The Netherlands.

A. Căluşaru, Institute of Chemical Research, Bucharest, Romania.

A. E. Cassano, Instituto de Desarrollo Tecnologico para la Industria Quimica, Universidad Nacional del Litoral and Consejo National de Investigaciones, Cientificas Y Tecnicas, Argentina.

B. H. Davis, Kentucky Energy Cabinet Laboratory, Lexington, Kentucky, USA.

K. Endo, Dept. of Applied Chemistry, Faculty of Engineering, Osaka City University, Osaka, Japan.

M. E. Findley, Dept. of Chemical Engineering, University of Missouri-Rolla, Rolla, Missouri, USA.

P. Forzatti, Dipartimento di Chimica Industriale ed Ingegneria Chimica "G. Natta" de Politecnico, Milano, Italy.

M. Friederick, Institut fur Verfah Renstechnik, Universitat Hannover, Hannover, Federal Republic of Germany.

E. Furimsky, Energy Research Laboratories, Canada Centre for Mineral & Energy Technology (CANMET) Energy, Mines and Resources, Ottawa, Ontario, Canada.

M. A. Galan, Facultad de Ciencias, Universidad de Cadiz, Spain.

J. W. Geus, Dept. of Inorganic Chemistry, State University of Utrecht, The Netherlands.

G. H. Graaf, Dept. of Chemical Engineering, State University of Groningen, Groningen, The Netherlands.

T. M. Grigor'eva, A. V. Topchiev Inst. of Petrochemical Synthesis, Academy of Sciences of the USSR, Moscow, USSR.

W. Haarde, Institut fur Verfah Renstechnik, Universitat Hannover, Hannover, Federal Republic of Germany.

M. Harada, Institute of Atomic Energy, Kyoto University, Kyoto, Japan.

Y. Hatate, Dept. of Chemical Engineering, Kagoshima University, Japan.

J. L. Hudson, Dept. of Chemical Engineering, University of Virginia, Charlottesville, Virginia, USA.

S. L. Karwa, Dept. of Chemical Technology, University of Bombay, Matunga, Bombay, India.

I. G. Kevrekidis, Dept. of Chemical Engineering, Princeton University, Princeton, New Jersey, USA.

K. Kida, Dept. of Applied Chemistry, Faculty of Engineering, Kumamoto University, Kumamoto, Japan.

M. A. Kohler, Dept. of Industrial and Engineering Chemistry, Swiss Federal Institute of Technology (ETH), Zurich, Switzerland.

Ju. A. Kolbanovskii, A. V. Topchiev Inst. of Petrochemical Synthesis, Academy of Sciences of the USSR, Moscow, USSR.

T. J. Kotas, Dept. of Mechanical Engineering, Queen Mary College, University of London, London, United Kingdom.

E. G. M. Kuijpers, Harshaw Chemie B. V., De Meern, The Netherlands.

D. Kunzru, Dept. of Chemical Engineering, Indian Institute of Technology, Kanpur, India.

C. Laguérie, Laboratoire de Geneie Chimique, ENSIGC-Chemin de la Loge, Toulouse, Cedex, France.

W. K. Lee, Dept. of Chemical Engineering, Korea Advanced Institute of Science and Technology, Seoul, Korea.

A. A. Levitskii, A. V. Topchiev Inst. of Petrochemical Synthesis, Academy of Sciences of the USSR, Moscow, USSR.

L. Lietti, Dipartimento di Chimica Industriale ed Ingegneria Chimica "G. Natta" de Politecnico, Milano, Italy.

S.-X. Lin, University of Petroleum, China, Dongying, Shandong, People's Republic of China.

H. Matsuyama, Dept. of Chemical Engineering, Kyushu University, Japan.

B. J. McCoy, Dept. of Chemical Engineering, University of California, Davis, California, USA.

D. Mewes, Institut fur Verfah Renstechnik, Universitat Hannover, Hannover, Federal Republic of Germany.

D. R. Milburn, Kentucky Energy Cabinet Laboratory, Lexington, Kentucky, USA.

Y. Miyake, Kyoto Institute of Technology, Kyoto, Japan.

S. Nagai, Dept. of Fermentation Technology, Faculty of Engineering, Hiroshima University, Hiroshima, Japan.

N. Nishio, Dept. of Fermentation Technology, Faculty of Engineering, Hiroshima University, Hiroshima, Japan.

B. A. Ogunnaike, Dept. of Chemical Engineering, University of Lagos, Lagos, Nigeria.

E. O'Shima, Research Laboratory of Resources Utilization, Tokyo Institute of Technology, Tokyo, Japan.

W. Ostendorf, Institut fur Verfah Renstechnik, Universitat Hannover, Hannover, Federal Republic of Germany.

T. Otsu, Dept. of Applied Chemistry, Faculty of Engineering, Osaka City University, Osaka, Japan.

J.-E. A. Otterstedt, Department of Engineering Chemistry, Chalmers University of Technology, Gothenberg, Sweden.

L. S. Polak, A. V. Topchiev Inst. of Petrochemical Synthesis, Academy of Sciences of the USSR, Moscow, USSR.

R. A. Rajadhyaksha, Dept. of Chemical Technology, University of Bombay, Matunga, Bombay, India.

K. H. Row, Dept. of Chemical Engineering, Korea Advanced Institute of Science & Technology, Seoul, Korea.

J. Shiozaki, Yamatake Honeywell Co., Ltd., Tokyo, Japan.

J. M. Smith, Dept. of Chemical Engineering, University of California, Davis, California, USA.

Y. Sonoda, Dept. of Applied Chemistry, Faculty of Engineering, Kumamoto University, Kumamoto, Japan.

E. J. Stamhuis, Dept. of Chemical Engineering, State University of Groningen, Groningen, The Netherlands.

B. Tabis, Dept. of Chemical Engineering and Physical Chemistry, Technical University of Cracow, Cracow, Poland.

R. L. Tatuzov, A. V. Topchiev Institute of Petrochemical Synthesis, Academy of Sciences of the USSR, Moscow, USSR.

J. R. Too, Dept. of Chemical Engineering, The Catholic University of America, Washington, DC, USA.

E. Tronconi, Dipartimento di Chimica Industriale ed Ingegneria Chimica "G. Natta" de Politecnico, Milano, Italy.

S. H. Ungureanu, Politechnical Institute of Iasi, Faculty of Chemical Technology, Iasi, Romania.

L. L. Upson, Katalistiks b.v., Leiderdorp, The Netherlands.

P. C. M. van Stiphout, Dept. of Inorganic Chemistry, State University of Utrecht, The Netherlands.

C. G. Vayenas, Institute of Chemical Engineering and High Temperature Chemical Processes, Dept. of Chemical Engineering, University of Patras, Patras, Greece.

X. E. Verykios, Institute of Chemical Engineering and High Temperature Chemical Processes, Dept. of Chemical Engineering, University of Patras, Patras, Greece.

G.-X. Wang, University of Petroleum, China, Dongying, Shandong, People's Republic of China.

S. Whitaker, Dept. of Chemical Engineering, University of California, Davis, California, USA.

G.-H. Yang, University of Petroleum, China, Dongying, Shandong, People's Republic of China.

Y. Yoshimura, National Chemical Laboratory for Industry, Tsukuba, Ibaraki, Japan.

ABOUT THE EDITOR

Nicholas P. Cheremisinoff, Ph.D., heads the product development group of the Elastomers Division of Exxon Chemical Co., Linden, N.J. He has extensive experience in analyzing multiphase flows and in designing reactor operations for manufacturing specialty chemicals and synthetic fuels production. Dr. Cheremisinoff received his B.S., M.S., and Ph.D. degrees in chemical engineering from Clarkson College of Technology. He is the author, co-author, and editor of more than forty volumes; including Gulf Publishing Company's multivolume *Encyclopedia of Fluid Mechanics*, and the *International Journal of Engineering Fluid Mechanics.*

PREFACE

This third volume of the *Handbook of Heat and Mass Transfer* has two overall objectives: The first is to apply the fundamental principles of transport phenomena detailed in Volumes 1 and 2 to complex, multiphase reactor operations; and the second is to introduce additional topics important to catalyst selection criteria and overall reactor control and operation not previously covered. This series is intended to complement the *Encyclopedia of Fluid Mechanics,* which is an extensive treatise on the dynamics of flow phenomena of applied interest.

Transport phenomena embrace all three subjects of flow dynamics, heat transport, and mass exchange, which play dominant roles in the kinetic responses of industrial reactor operations. In the first two volumes of this handbook the three subjects were closely related in a general overview. The balance of this series, starting with this volume, will apply principles to specific reactor types and designs. Scale-up methodology and advanced control theory are emphasized.

This volume is organized into three main sections. Section I, "Catalyst Technology," contains eight chapters covering the properties, uses, and selection of major industrial catalysts. Emphasis is placed largely on solid catalyst systems, because liquid catalysts, particularly for polymerization type reactions, are best treated in a subsequent volume. Topics discussed are catalyst properties, activity, selectivity, catalyst technology in petroleum manufacturing, and experimental methods for studying desorption from catalyst surfaces.

Section II, "Multiphase Reactor Operations," comprises fourteen chapters covering design methodology, scale-up criteria, and operational characteristics of principal reactor types and processes. Systems covered include agitated multiphase catalytic reactors; packed-bed, fluidized bed, and gasification reactors; and slurry polymerization reactors. In addition, reactor operations covering light-sensitized reactions (photoreactors) and solvent extraction are treated. A final chapter is devoted to the promising area of separation by gas-liquid chromatography.

Section III, "Advanced Methods of Systems Analysis," which also comprises fourteen chapters, addresses two broad areas—principles of kinetic and thermodynamic modeling and application of modeling to predict reactor response and operational control. The first chapter in this section covers the second law analysis. The second chapter describes the use of tomographic measurement techniques as an advanced tool for studying reactor response. Two chapters focus on the dynamics and modeling of CSTRs and tubular reactors. Eight chapters cover principles, methodology, and application of computer-aided techniques in predicting the sensitivity of reactors and in overall controller design theory. The balance of this section is devoted to principles and illustration of fault diagnosis analysis. On this subject, although industry's benefits to mankind are great, its risks are also enormous. Many plants retain large inventories of hazardous materials, and operate at high temperatures and pressures. Although plant failures are comparatively rare, the examples of Bhopal, India, Three Mile Island, USA, and Sevesco, Italy remind us they can be catastrophic. Fault diagnosis is a tool that is being more heavily used in plant operations planning to avoid such reoccurrences.

To ensure the highest degree of reliability, the services of sixty-seven specialists were enlisted. This work presents the efforts of these experts. It also incorporates the experience and advise of scores of engineers and scientists who aided with advice and suggestions in reviewing and refereeing the material presented. Each contributor is to be regarded as responsible for the statements presented in his or her respective chapter(s). These individuals are to be congratulated for devoting their time and efforts to this volume. Without their diligence this work could not have been made available to the users. Similarly, special thanks is expressed to Gulf Publishing Company and its outstanding staff for the production of this series.

Nicholas P. Cheremisinoff

SECTION I

CATALYST TECHNOLOGY

CONTENTS

CHAPTER 1

CHARACTERIZATION OF CATALYSTS

A. Baiker and M. A. Kohler

Department of Industrial and Engineering Chemistry
Swiss Federal Institute of Technology (ETH)
Zurich, Switzerland

CONTENTS

INTRODUCTION

The characterization of catalysts is important in the manufacture of catalysts and for the optimization of industrial catalytic processes [1]. The primary purpose of this characterization is to provide a basis for understanding the interrelationship between activity and selectivity of a catalyst,

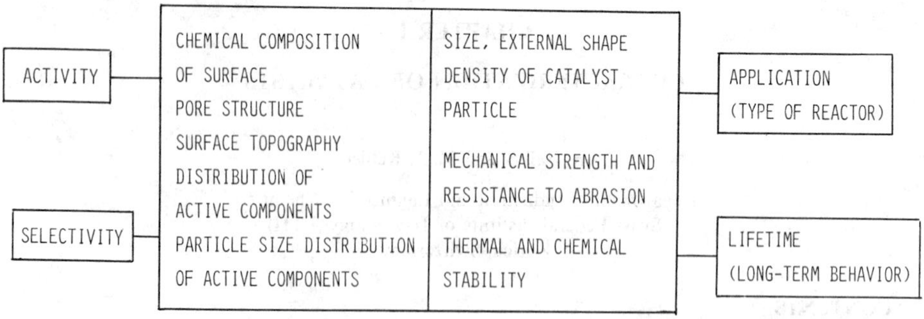

Figure 1. Relationship between physical and chemical properties of industrial catalysts and their performance.

and its physical and chemical properties. Thus, catalyst characterization is not only part of any worthwhile catalytic research or development program, but also a matter of commercial interest (e.g., a catalyst manufacturer needs to demonstrate that his product meets a certain set of specifications).

Ideally, a catalyst should be characterized under exactly the same conditions as those under which it will be used in practice. However, this cannot always be realized, since many characterization methods cannot be applied under reaction conditions. The chemical composition and the surface and pore structure of industrial catalysts are generally complex, because of the requirements with respect to activity, selectivity, and lifetime. Moreover, an ideal catalyst must satisfy criteria of technical application such as optimal particle size, external shape, mechanical strength, density, and thermal conductivity. The relationship between these requirements and the physical and chemical properties is shown in a very simplified manner in Figure 1.

Since the behavior of a catalyst depends also on several parameters of the reactor in which it will be used (e.g., heat transfer, mass transfer), understanding of the catalytic reactor is essential too, so that the significance of the data can be gauged [2].

Among the many techniques now in use for the characterization of catalysts, only a few have been standardized. These include the determination of the solid and apparent density pycnometrically, the total surface area by the Brunauer-Emmett-Teller (BET) method, and the determination of the pore-size distribution by nitrogen-capillary condensation and mercury porosimetry. Other routine measurements include the determination of the metal-surface area by selective gas-adsorption (chemisorption), and of the mean particle size by X-ray diffraction line-broadening. Several other methods are used for specific problems of characterization [3–7]. Spectroscopic methods have found increasing use during the past two decades, and their potential has not yet been exhausted.

As a rule, several different methods must be used to characterize a catalyst sufficiently. Table 1 lists the most important techniques used for industrial catalysts. Some methods have overlapping areas of application which does not imply, of course, that all methods are equally suited for a given investigation. A proper strategy should therefore be worked out at the start of any investigation.

In this survey, the most important techniques used for characterization of industrial catalyst are compiled in a way that macroscopic properties of a catalyst are discussed first, and methods analyzing microscopic details are described subsequently. As a result, the physical (bulk) properties are analyzed at the beginning followed by chemical bulk methods, while surface specific techniques are discussed later. A schematic view of most typical steps in catalyst characterization is given in Figure 2, and this survey follows, roughly, this guide: Path A concerns the physical properties of the catalyst, path B deals with the bulk of the solid, while path C analyzes the nature of the catalyst surface. The corresponding techniques are listed in parenthesis. It is clear that the importance of a particular method depends on the catalytic system to be investigated, and thus is not necessarily proportional to the weight attributed in this chapter.

Table 1
Characteristic Properties of Industrial Catalysts and Methods for Their Determination

Characteristic Properties	Methods of Measurements
Total surface area	Gas adsorption (sorption methods, mercury porosimetry)
Component surface area	Selective gas adsorption
Metal particle size	Selective gas adsorption, x-ray
Dispersion	Diffraction, electron microscopy, (magnetization measurements)
Functional groups	Selective adsorption and titration, infrared UV- and visible spectroscopy
Pore-size distribution, pore volume, apparent and solid density	Gas adsorption and mercury porosimetry, mercury and helium pycnometry
Mechanical strength and abrasion resistance	Press tests, special abrasion tests
Surface topography, local distribution and shape of metal particles	Transmission and scanning electron microscopy
Identification of solid phases (bulk analysis)	X-ray diffraction
Phase transformations and solid reactions	Differential thermoanalysis, calorimetry, x-ray diffraction
Chemical composition of bulk and surface layers, concentration depth profiles	Electron-probe microanalysis, photoelectron spectroscopy (XPS), auger electron spectroscopy, secondary-ion mass spectroscopy
Type of chemisorbed species and their interaction with catalyst surface	Temperature-programmed desorption secondary-ion mass spectroscopy, infrared, UV- and visible spectroscopy
Reduction behavior, surface heterogeneity, promoter influences	Temperature-programmed reduction and surface reaction, thermogravimetry

PHYSICAL PROPERTIES OF CATALYSTS

Mechanical Properties

Industrial catalysts are manufactured in various geometrical shapes (e.g., pellets, spheres, extrudates) depending on their use, and these must frequently satisfy stringent requirements with respect to mechanical strength and resistance to abrasion.

The lifetimes of catalysts are frequently limited, in practice, by their mechanical properties. Catalyst particles used in a fixed-bed reactor may fail due to insufficient mechanical strength to withstand the pressures that occur in the bed even at high temperatures, while abrasion problems are additionally important when the catalyst are used in a fluidized-bed reactor.

It is generally found that, other things being equal, mechanical strength falls with increasing porosity. However, there are other factors such as pore size distribution and pore shape, particle or grain size distribution, and the nature of the particle junctions (pressing and heating procedures during the preparation), which may cause the strength to vary. Various methods are known for investigating mechanical strength [8–10]. One frequently used method consists in compressing a bed of the catalyst particles with a piston and measuring the dislocation of the piston as a function of the applied pressure. Others include the energy required for the impact rupture of a specimen (conveniently expressed per unit cross-sectional area of the specimen), or the pressure drop of a gas flowing through a bed of catalyst, since it can give information about the size of crushed particles.

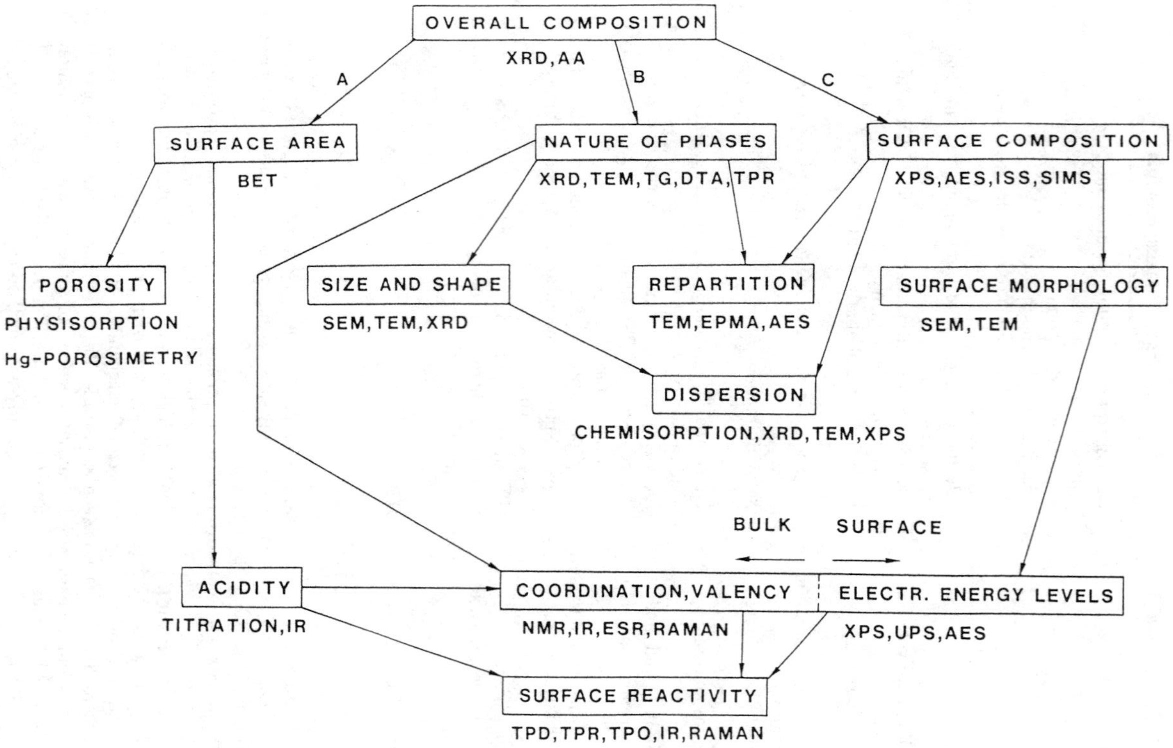

Figure 2. General scheme for the characterization of industrial catalysts: AA, atomic absorption spectroscopy; AES, auger electron spectroscopy; EPMA, electron probe microanalysis; ESR, electron spin resonance spectroscopy; DTA, differential thermoanalysis; ISS, ion scattering spectroscopy; IR, infrared spectroscopy; NMR, nuclear magnetic resonance spectroscopy; SEM, scanning electron microscopy; SIMS, secondary-ion mass spectroscopy; TEM, transmission electron microscopy; TG, thermogravimetry; TPD, temperature programmed desorption; TPO, temperature programmed oxidation; TPR, temperature programmed reduction; UPS, ultraviolet photoelectron spectroscopy; XPS, X-ray photoelectron spectroscopy; XRD, X-ray diffraction.

When solids come into contact under conditions of rubbing, impact, or even static loading, some degradation at the surface occurs (abrasive wear). The resistance of catalyst particles is tested by subjecting them to a particular abrasive motion, for example, the turning motion of a rotating tube. Special deflector plates are often attached within the tube to intensify the abrasive motion [5]. Such tests are, however, hardly sufficient for use in fluidized-bed reactors. In this case, direct testing in the reactor is recommended.

Thermal Properties

The thermal and thermomechanical properties of catalyst materials are important inasmuch as they control the heat transport properties into or out of a catalyst or the extent to which a catalyst bed may depart from isothermal conditions, respectively. This is a problem of considerable importance in catalytic reactor design and operation, and will be discussed in more detail at the end of this chapter. On the other hand, the thermal shock resistance of the material is important in determining the mechanical stability of the catalyst under conditions of thermal cycling or other forms of non-steady temperature operation.

For practical purposes, temperatures between room temperature and a few hundred °C are interesting. For most substances in this range, the thermal conductivity is a relatively slowly changing function of temperature, as demonstrated by the data in Figure 3.

The method used for measuring the thermal conductivity depends on the physical form in which the material is available [11] and a number of techniques are described in detail in the literature [12, 13].

Catalyst particles may be subject to thermal shock due to temperature variations during preparation, operation, or regeneration. Failure may be assisted by the presence of macroscopic or microscopic internal stresses already present. There are two main approaches to the problem: The first

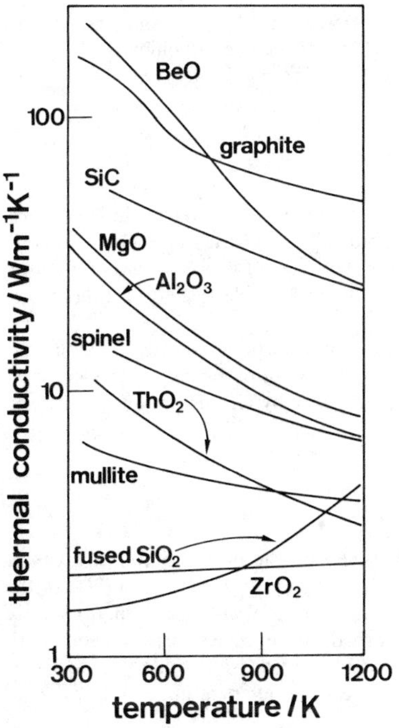

Figure 3. Thermal conductivity data for some non-porous non-metallic materials. (Reproduced with permission from Ref. [21].)

considers the question of crack initiation, the second deals with crack propagation. When considering brittle materials in general, the decision as to which technique is the most appropriate is dependent upon what performance criteria are acceptable [2]. Resistance to crack initiation is favored by materials of high strength, high thermal conductivity, low coefficient of thermal expansion, low elastic modulus, and low Poisson's ratio, while resistance to crack propagation is increased by low strength, high elastic modulus, high fracture surface energy and low Poisson's ratio. Therefore, other things being equal, the traditional approach has been to aim at high strength materials for conditions of mild thermal shock, and at low strength materials for conditions of severe thermal shock [2, 14, 15].

Pycnometry—Solid and Apparent Density

The solid and apparent density of a catalyst are properties that are frequently specified by the manufacturer. The solid density is that of the material from which the porous solid is formed, while the apparent unit density refers to an individual catalyst unit (tablet, bead, grain, etc.), taking the unit as defined by its external geometric surface.

Both densities are determined pycnometrically, i.e., by measuring the volume of gas or liquid that is displaced by the solid. The solid density is usually measured with helium since it has an effective atomic diameter of only about 0.2 nm and therefore can penetrate into extremely fine pores. Care must be taken to avoid adsorption of the helium by using higher temperatures. Analogous measurements with mercury are carried out to determine the apparent density.

If the solid (ρ_w) and the apparent (ρ_s) densities are known, then the specific pore volume V_p can be calculated from

$$V_p = 1/\rho_w - 1/\rho_s \tag{1}$$

Frequently, the bulk density, which is important in practice, is specified by the manufacturer. This quantity, which indicates how much catalyst can be packed in a given reactor volume, is also measured by a displacement method.

Gas Adsorption (Physisorption) Methods

Gas adsorption is mainly used for the measurement of surface area, but certain techniques, such as capillary condensation, can also provide information about the pore structure (pore size distribution, pore volume). Depending on the type of interaction between adsorbed species (molecules, atoms) and the surface of the solid, a distinction is made between non-selective adsorption (physisorption) and selective adsorption (chemisorption).

For measurements of the total surface area of a solid, the physisorption is generally used, and this procedure is described in this chapter. The fraction covered by a particular component (e.g., metal surface on metal/support catalysts) can be determined only by chemisorption and will be discussed later.

Physisorption—Determining the Total Surface Area

The principle of measuring the total surface area of a solid by the physisorption of a gas or vapor consists of determining the number of gas molecules required to cover the surface of the solid with a monolayer of the adsorbate. If the area occupied by one molecule is known, the surface area of the solid can be calculated from the number of adsorbed gas molecules measured volumetrically or gravimetrically. Adsorption of a gas is usually characterized by an isotherm, which represents the amount of gas adsorbed on the solid in equilibrium at a given temperature as a function of the pressure.

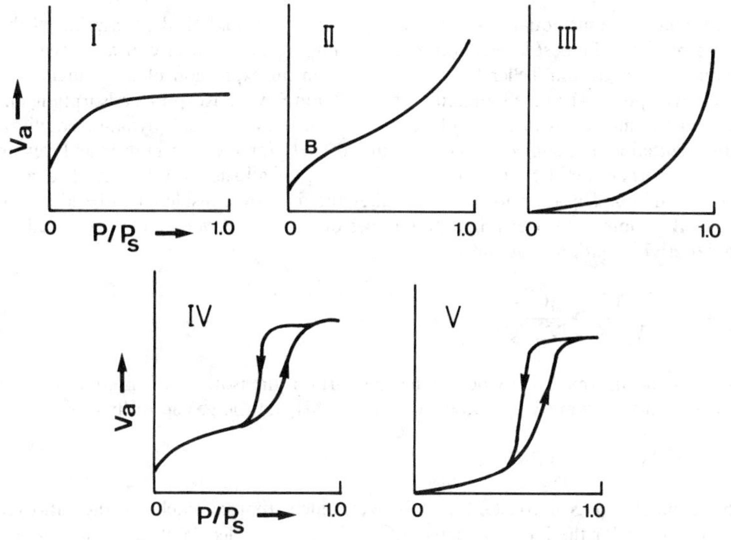

Figure 4. Classification of adsorption isotherms according to Brunauer et al. [16].

The large number of different measured physisorption isotherms can be grouped into a few characteristic types of curves if the pressure P of the gas is referred to the saturation pressure P_s. The five most important types [16] are shown in Figure 4. In all these types of isotherms, the amount of adsorbed gas increases with the relative gas pressure (P/P_s) and at some point corresponds to a monolayer which, upon further gas adsorption, becomes a multilayer adsorption and, finally, a condensed phase.

It is generally admitted that Type I isotherm is characteristic of microporous adsorbents (activated carbon, fine-pore silica gel, zeolites), but rarely occurs with nonporous solids [5, 17]. It is normally called a Langmuir isotherm and corresponds to the one expected in reversible chemisorption. The asymptotic value (plateau) was ascribed by Langmuir [18] to the formation of a monolayer. Isotherms of types II and III are observed for macroporous adsorbents. Type II is called a sigmoidal isotherm and occurs frequently with the point B indicating the so-called knee of the curve, which usually corresponds to a fully developed monolayer on the solid. On the contrary, Type III is rather unusual and corresponds to very weak adsorbate-adsorbent interactions (forces of attraction between gas molecules greater than the adsorptive binding force).

Isotherms of the Types IV and V are obtained with mesoporous systems. Type IV is often observed with porous solids such as industrial catalysts. The sharp rise in the amount of adsorbed gas at higher relative pressures is attributable to capillary condensation of the gas in the pores. A hysteresis effect is usually found, i.e., the adsorption and desorption branches of the isotherm do not coincide. The capillary condensation region of the curve can be used to find the pore size distribution, as described in detail below. Type V correspond to the Type III isotherm in the lower relative pressure range, and to capillary condensation in the higher range; it is seldom seen in practice.

In practice, the shape of the isotherm therefore gives a rather good idea of the mean size of the pores present in the solid. Sometimes, however, an isotherm cannot be related to one definite group of this classification because different types of pores are present in the adsorbent.

Another easy way to get information on the porous texture of a catalyst based on the shape of the hysteresis loop has been described by de Boer [17, 19], although this classification is difficult due to the complex pore structure found in many industrial catalysts.

BET-Method. Various equations have been proposed for analytical description of the adsorption isotherms [20], the best known and the most important for surface measurements being that of Brunauer. Emmett, and Teller [21]. It is based on an expansion of the Langmuir theory to multilayer adsorption. As in the Langmuir theory of monolayer adsorption, adsorption, and desorption rates of gas molecules in a monolayer are assumed to be equal (dynamic equilibrium). The adsorption enthalpy is assumed to have a value of ΔH_1 for the first molecular layer and to decrease to the normal latent heat of condensation ΔH_c for all successive layers. The conditions of evaporation and condensation for all layers after the first are considered to be identical to those of a liquid. By summation over a infinite number of adsorbed layers under the stated conditions, the familiar BET equation is obtained:

$$\frac{P}{V_a(P_s - P)} = \frac{1}{V_m \cdot C} + \frac{(C-1)P}{V_m \cdot C \cdot P_s'} \qquad (2)$$

Here, C is a constant that largely determines the form of the isotherm. It is coupled exponentially to the heats of adsorption (ΔH_1) and condensation (ΔH_c) of the gas according to

$$C = \psi \exp[(\Delta H_c - \Delta H_1)/RT] \qquad (3)$$

In this equation, ψ is a constant that is determined approximately by the ratio j_m/j_c of the partition functions for the internal degrees of freedom in a molecule of the monolayer (j_m) and of the condensed phase (j_c), V_a is the total volume of the adsorbed gas, V_m the volume of the adsorbed monolayer, and P_s the saturation pressure of the gas at the temperature at which the adsorption measurement is carried out.

The C-value is thus characteristic of the intensity of the adsorbate-adsorbent interaction: The larger the constant C, the more the form of the isotherm corresponds to Type II, which is frequently observed in the adsorption of nitrogen and rare gases. For small values of C, the shape of the curve approaches that of Type III. In this case, there is a strong tendency for multilayer adsorption to occur before the monolayer is completed, which contradicts the assumptions of the BET model. Equation 2 assumes that for P equal P_s, the adsorbed layer is infinitely thick. The resulting equation in case that the adsorbed film is limited to a finite number of molecular layers has also been discussed in the literature [5, 17].

If an isotherm can be described by Equation 2, a plot of $P/V_a(P_s - P)$ versus P/P_s should give a straight line, and its intersection with the axis and the slope can be used to calculate V_m and C. However, the theoretical and experimental isotherms coincide only over a limited pressure range. This limitation is the result of the assumptions on which the BET-theory is based. Indeed, it considers neither the heterogeneity of the solid surface, which mainly affects the low pressure range of the isotherm, nor the lateral interactions between the adsorbed molecules, which become more and more important as the pressure increases. Consequently, the BET equation (2) is normally able to describe a physical adsorption isotherm in the relative pressure range between 0.05 and 0.35 for Type II and IV isotherms. A poorer description is obtained for the Type I, III and V isotherms, but, in practice, they are often analyzed by the BET method. Figures 5 and 6 show the experimental isotherms, together with the BET representations, for two solids that differ morphologically.

The V_m-value is directly proportional to the specific surface area of the adsorbent and S_{BET} is calculated by

$$S_{BET} = V_m N_A A_m / V_{mol} \qquad (4)$$

where N_A is the Avogadro number and V_{mol} the molar volume of the gas. The cross-sectional area A_m of an adsorbed gas molecule can be estimated from the density of the condensed phase of the gas [22, 23], provided certain assumptions are made about the geometrical arrangement of the molecules in the layer of the adsorbate. In practice, a cross-sectional area of 0.162 nm^2 is usually applied for nitrogen [22].

In principle, any condensable gas can be used for the BET method, but for reliable measurements the gas molecule should be small and have, if possible, a spherical structure. Therefore, nitrogen

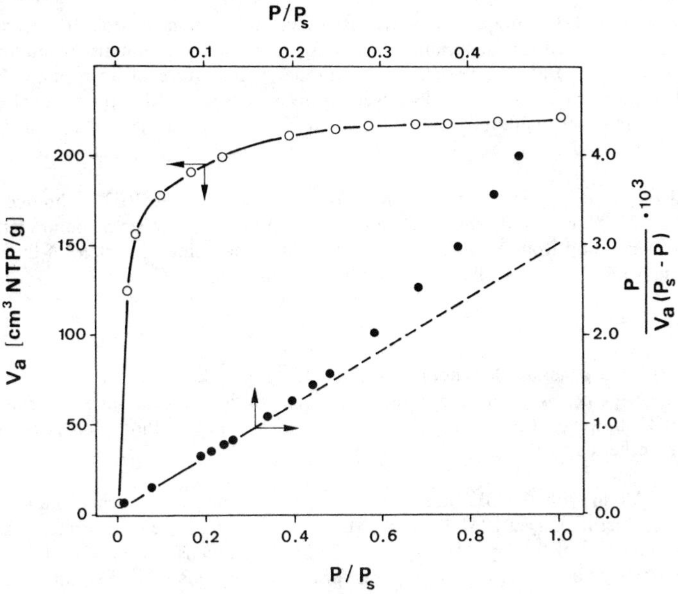

Figure 5. Isotherm and BET diagram of nitrogen adsorption on fine-pore silica.

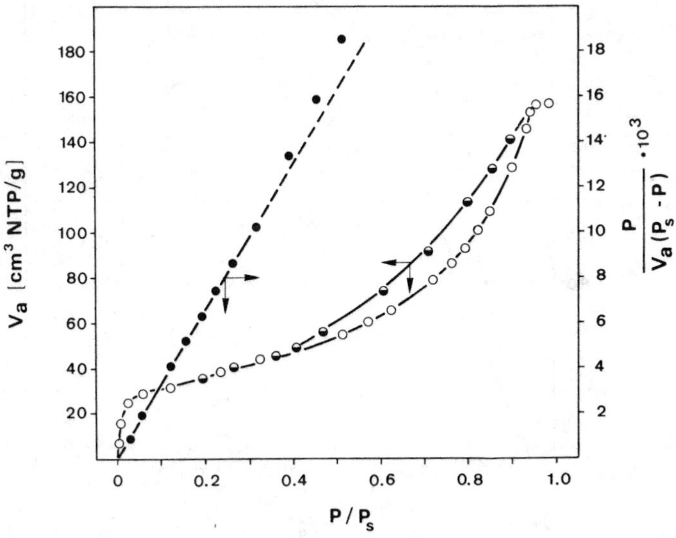

Figure 6. Isotherm and BET diagram of nitrogen adsorption on a silica supported copper catalyst.

is normally used, and, less frequently, krypton, argon, and carbon dioxide. If surfaces of a few square meters only have to be determined accurately, krypton and argon are advantageous, since they have a lower saturation pressure at the normal temperature of adsorption (77K, liquid nitrogen). This means that a substantially lower gas pressure is required in the volumetric measurement apparatus in order to fulfill the suitable relative pressure range ($0.05 < P/P_s < 0.35$). The fraction of the gas molecules that are adsorbed is thereby increased and the accuracy of the method is improved.

Based on the same physical principle, numerous variations of the BET technique have been developed [24, 25]. Substantial simplification results from the so-called single point method, where the monolayer is found from a single experimental point and using the origin of the coordinate. For isotherms with $C \gg 1$, the BET equation (2) is simplified to

$$V_m = V_a(P_s - P)/P_s \qquad (5)$$

Since the BET line generally does not pass through the origin, the surface determined by Equation 5 is usually a few percent smaller than in the case of the multipoint technique. As a rule, the larger the constant C, however, the more accurate is the single point method, and good accuracy is achieved for isotherms with C greater than about 50 [5].

"*t-Method*" Along with the BET method, several less common empirical methods have been proposed for isotherm analysis [24]. From the volume of the adsorbate on a surface of known area S, the mean thickness of the layer $t = V_a/S$ can be found. Lippens and de Boer [26, 27] noticed that in measurements of nitrogen adsorption on various non-porous solids a common curve $t(P/P_s)$

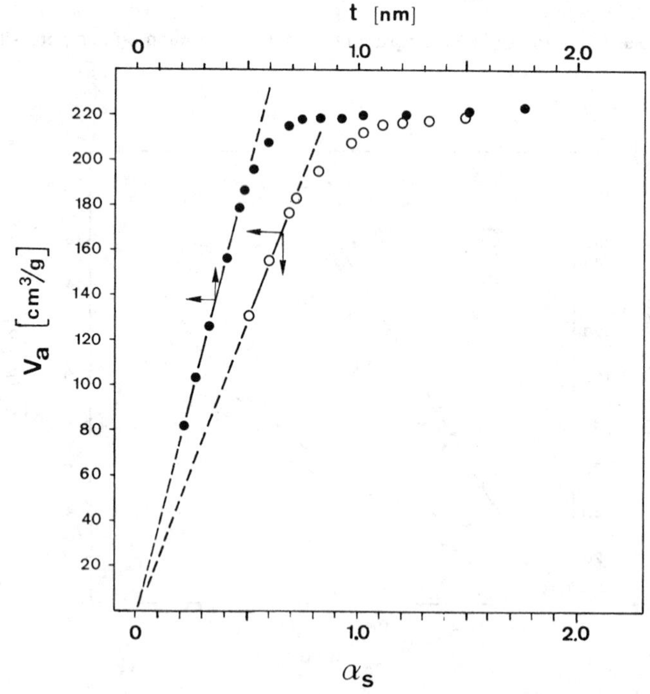

Figure 7. t and α_s diagrams of nitrogen adsorption on fine pore silica. Corresponding isotherm is plotted in Figure 5.

was obtained, which means that the layer thickness is practically independent on the solid but is merely a function of the relative pressure and the geometrical arrangement of the molecules in the layer. The proposed values for the statistical thickness t of the adsorbate layer [24, 26, 27] differ according to the selected molecular arrangement in the layer, but the values by Lippens and de Boer [26] have proven themselves in practice. An analytical method for determining t as a function of the relative pressure

$$t = t_m \left[\frac{5}{\ln(P_s/P)} \right]^{1/3} \qquad (6)$$

has been proposed by Halsey [28], with t_m being the thickness of the monolayer. Values of 0.35 nm [27] and 0.43 nm [29] have been proposed for t_m, depending on the geometrical arrangement of the molecules in the monolayer.

As long as the multilayer of adsorbate is formed unhindered on the solid, the V_a/t plot is a straight line passing through the origin, the slope of which is a measure of the adsorbent surface area (Figures 7 and 8) according to

$$S_t = 15.5 V_a/t \qquad (7)$$

At higher relative pressures (higher t-values), deviations from the straight line may occur:

1. An upward deviation indicates the presence of capillary condensation in the pores of the adsorbent; this is characteristic of cylinder-shaped pores, "ink-bottle" pores or spheroidal cavities.
2. A downward deviation is observed when micropores or slit-shaped pores are present in the solid [17], which may be gradually filled upon increasing the relative pressure, without capillary condensation taking place.

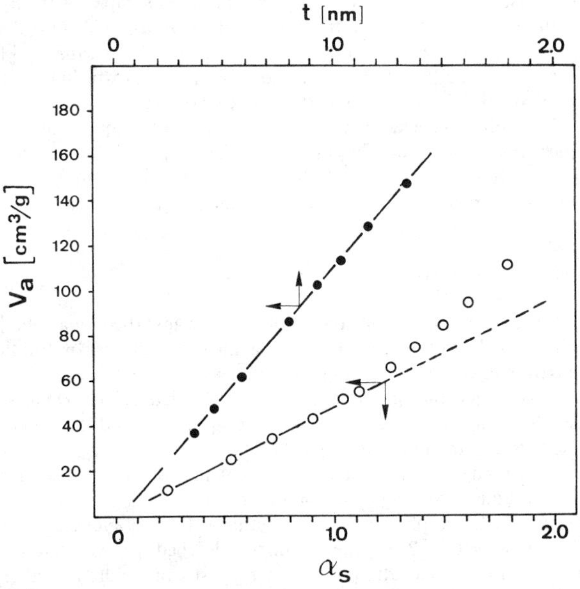

Figure 8. t and α_s diagrams of nitrogen adsorption on silica supported copper catalyst corresponding isotherm is plotted in Figure 6.

The "t-curve" is thus an interesting tool in textural studies for it gives additional valuable information about the shape of the pores in a catalyst. In the common range of validity $0.05 > P/P_s > 0.35$, relatively good agreement between the surfaces determined by the BET and the t-method is frequently obtained.

"*α_s-Method*". The same principle of comparing an experimental isotherm to a standard isotherm is applied in a slightly different way by Sing [30, 31]. Here, the volume V_a of gas adsorbed on the solid is plotted as a function of a parameter α_s, which is defined as the ratio $V_a/V_a(0.4)$ measured at the same relative pressure on a nonporous reference sample. $V_a(0.4)$ is the volume of gas adsorbed at a relative pressure 0.4. With nitrogen, below this relative pressure, the formation of a monolayer and the filling of micropores (pore width 2 nm) occurs. From the slope of the resulting straight line, the surface S_a can be calculated using the expression

$$S_\alpha = KV_a/\alpha_s \tag{8}$$

The constant K is generally determined by reference measurements on samples of the same material with known BET surfaces. A value of 2.89 for silica is given in the literature [32].

Below a relative pressure of about 0.4 ($\alpha_s = 1$), the $V_a(\alpha_s)$ diagrams of nonporous materials normally cannot be distinguished from those of materials having mainly mesopores (2–50 nm) and macropores (50 nm), so that comparable values for the total surface areas are obtained as in the BET method. The shapes of α_s-plots are essentially the same as for the t-plots (Figures 7 and 8) and deviations from linearity are explained the same way as above. The "α_s-method" is thus, among other things, also suitable for verification of the presence of micropores (in the region of low relative pressures, i.e., for α_s below 1, see Figure 8). There are, however, two main differences between the two techniques: According to Lippens and de Boer [26, 27], the t-curve is nearly independent of the nature of the adsorbent and consequently the standard isotherm is obtained by averaging several reduced isotherms corresponding to a series of nonporous solids. On the other hand, Sing [30, 31] chooses the standard isotherm adapted to the nature of the test sample. Secondly, the "α_s-method" is independent of the BET method, while the "t-method" obviously falls into the field of the BET method by using, in the definition of t, the value V_m of the monolayer capacity [17]. This question has been much debated in the literature, but Lecloux [17] has shown that the t- and α_s-methods are strictly relevant to the BET-theory and that these two methods are two equivalent ways of analyzing adsorption isotherms. The different values obtained for the isotherms in Figures 4 and 5 by applying the three techniques are: fine pore silica, $S_{BET} = 728\ m^2/g$, $S_\alpha = 693\ m^2/g$, $S_t = 606\ m^2/g$; Cu/SiO_2 catalyst, $S_{BET} = 131\ m^2/g$, $S_\alpha = 125\ m^2/g$, $S_t = 168\ m^2/g$. These values are thus mainly influenced by the standard isotherms adapted for the calculations.

Methods and Sample Preparation

Various methods are used to determine the amount of gas adsorbed on a solid [20, 24], the most common of which being the volumetric and the gravimetric methods. In addition, flow methods have proven themselves primarily for chemisorption measurements.

In the volumetric technique, the amount of gas adsorbed is determined by measuring the decrease in pressure of the adsorbate gas in the system. Various apparatus and the experimental procedure are thoroughly described in the literature [20, 24, 33].

For gravimetric measurements, either quartz spring balances or electronic microbalances are used, both permitting continuous recording of the sample weight.

Two different principles are applied in the flow method—the *continuous* and the *pulse techniques*. In the method of continuous flow [2, 34], the amount of adsorbed species is determined by measuring the difference in adsorbate concentration in a carrier gas stream before and after contact with the solid using a suitable detector (e.g., heat conductivity cells). In the pulse method [2, 35] the adsorbate is fed discontinuously (pulse like) into a continuous stream of carrier gas, and the amount adsorbed is detected analogously as above. This method is widely applied in industry since it is substantially faster than volumetric or gravimetric methods. However, the results of such dynamic measurements should be analyzed carefully since dynamic methods do not necessarily determine equilibrium values (isotherms).

For any measurement, preparation of the sample, i.e., removal of adsorbed contaminants by heating under vacuum or in an inert atmosphere, is of crucial importance. The higher the temperature selected and the better the vacuum, the more complete will be the removal of the contaminants, but surface changes such as sintering (possible even far below the melting point of the material) can occur. Optimum heating conditions must therefore be determined, often experimentally on the basis of maximum surface area. For measurements of physisorption on inorganic catalysts, temperatures between 150 and 200°C are suitable, but higher temperatures often must be selected for chemisorption measurements.

Capillary Condensation—Determining the Mesopore-Size Distribution

In the adsorption of a gas on a porous solid, the adsorption on the surface is frequently superimposed on condensation in the pores. A distinction is made between condensation in the micropores (pore size 2 nm) and true capillary condensation in the mesopores.

Brunauer et al. [36] have modified the "t-method" to determine the pore volume and the size distribution of the micropores. Below a relative pressure of about 0.4, the nitrogen isotherms in the V_a(t)-diagram of nonporous solids and those with mesopores and macropores (but not micropores) normally are scarcely distinguishable. On the other hand, the micropore size distribution is found from the decrease in the slope of the V_a(t)-curve by dividing the plot into steps, each corresponding to an increase Δt in the thickness of the adsorbed layer. The slopes of the tangents drawn at the beginning and the end of each step are a measure of the pore surface as a function of the pore width, and the pore volume distribution can be found by selecting a pore model [17]. Although, the soundness of Brunauer's approach has been questioned, in particular by Gregg and Sing [20] and Dubinin [37], this analysis of the V_a(t) plot is presently the only means for calculating the micropore size distribution from an isotherm.

In mesopores, sorption of a gas or vapor around its normal liquefaction temperature generally shows hysteresis (compare Figure 6); less gas is taken up at a given relative pressure after an increase in pressure from a low value than after a decrease in pressure from saturation. Although hysteresis is a source of information on the size and even shape of the adsorbent pores, it is also of fundamental difficulty for the interpretation of sorption measurements.

One approach to capillary condensation proposed by Kelvin [20] relates the mean radius r of the liquid meniscus (see Figure 9) to the surface tension σ, the molar volume V_{mol} of the condensed phase, the gas constant R, the absolute temperature T, and the contact angle θ between the condensed phase and the surface of the solid:

$$r[P] = \frac{2\sigma \cdot V_{mol} \cdot \cos\theta}{RT \ln(P/P_s)} \qquad (9)$$

The mean radius r of the liquid meniscus is found from the two main radii r_1 and r_2 of the liquid surface (see Figure 9) according to

$$2/r = 1/r_1 + 1/r_2 \qquad (10)$$

It is clear from Figure 9 that only r_1 is significant for the condensation (adsorption branch of the isotherm), while both r_1 and r_2 are significant for the evaporation (desorption branch). A continuous, cylindrical mesopore fills with condensate when $r[P] \geq 2r_1$ and empties when $r[P] \leq r_1 = r_2$. As Figure 9 shows, in finding the pore radius by the Kelvin equation it is necessary to consider the thickness t of the adsorbate layer, which can be determined by Equation 6. The mesopore radius is then calculated from either the adsorption branch (Equation 11) or the desorption branch (Equation 12) of the isotherm and the Kelvin equation.

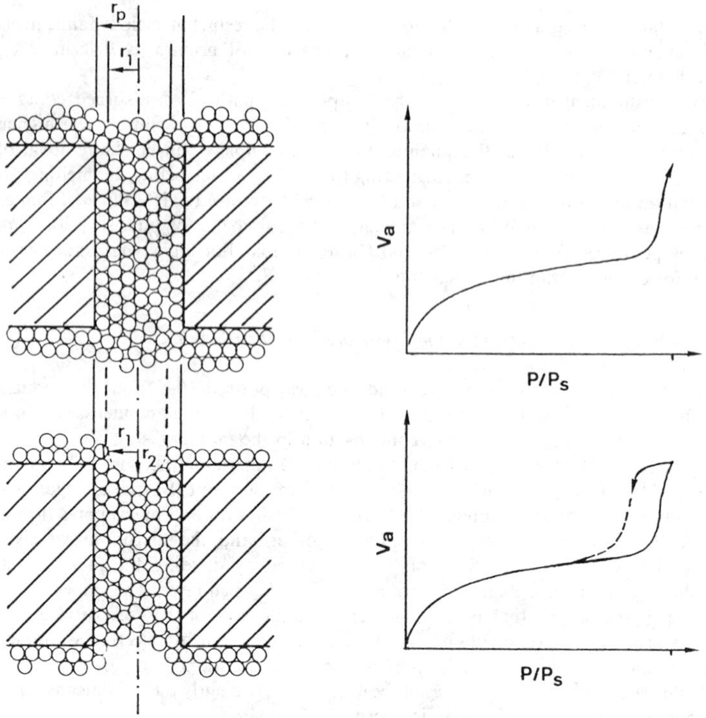

Figure 9. Nitrogen adsorption and desorption in continuous cylindrical mesopores.

$$r_p = -\frac{\sigma \cdot V_{mol} \cdot \cos\theta}{RT\ \ln(P/P_s)_a} + t \tag{11}$$

$$r_p = -\frac{2\sigma V_{mol} \cdot \cos\theta}{RT\ \ln(P/P_s)_d} + t \tag{12}$$

As a substantial simplification, the assumption of $\theta = 0$ seems justified for complete wetting and filled pores, i.e., for the desorption branch (evaporation), but is controversial for the adsorption branch.

For a symmetrical pore geometry, calculation of the size distribution of the mesopores from either adsorption or desorption data permits simple determination of the mesopore surface area. The gas volumes adsorbed or desorbed upon a change in relative pressure are taken from the isotherms and Equation 11 or 12 is applied. Assuming a certain pore geometry, the contributions of pores of various sizes to the total surface area can be found from the pore radius distribution ($\sum \Delta V_p = f[r_p]$) by stepwise computational methods [20, 33, 38–40]. The computational method most frequently used in practice was proposed by Pierce [38], and Figure 10 shows the integral and differential pore radius distribution calculated by this method for the Cu/SiO_2 catalyst already described in the isotherm of Figure 6. The corresponding mesopore surface area was calculated to 99 m^2/g, which is considerably smaller than the measured BET surface area (131 m^2/g).

This discrepancy between the cumulative pore surface area and the BET area is typical for the Pierce technique. From the thermodynamics of vapor sorption in capillaries, it appears that the

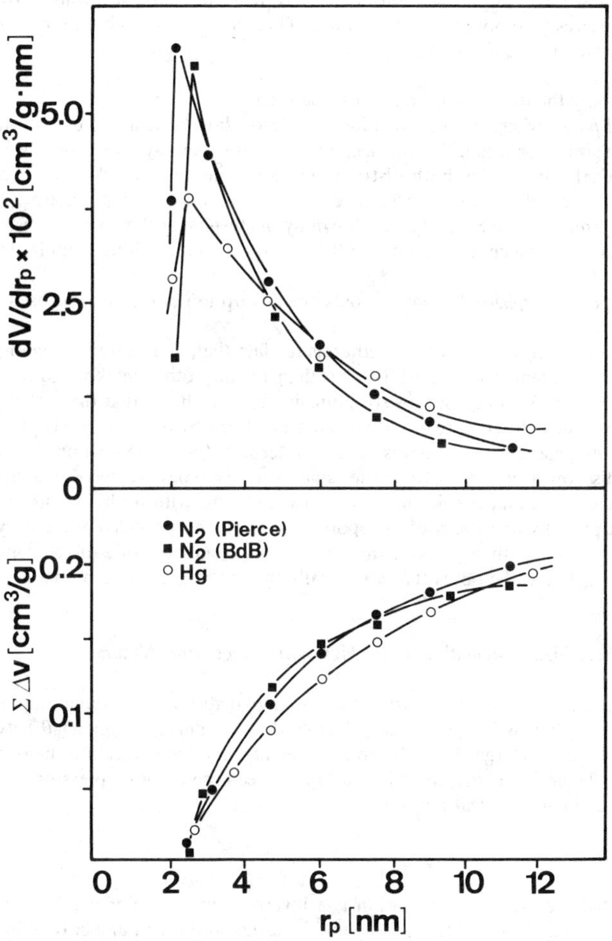

Figure 10. Integral and differential pore-radius distribution of silica supported copper catalyst determined by nitrogen capillary condensation and Hg-porosimetry, respectively. The pore radius distributions determined by capillary condensation were derived from the measured isotherm (Figure 6) using the methods of Pierce [38] and Broekhoff and de Boer [41], respectively.

Kelvin equation is problematic for calculation of the pore size distribution, since it does not account for multilayer adsorption that occurs even on nonporous solids [17, 33, 41]. Moreover, for a porous solid, the thickness of the adsorbed layer t also depends on the curvature radius of the surface, i.e., on the shape and the size of the pore in which the adsorption occurs [17]. Broekhoff and de Boer [19, 33, 41] have developed a complete thermodynamical analysis of these phenomenon and a corresponding method of isotherm data analysis. Unfortunately, this approach has been too largely ignored by subsequent authors in the field.

The main limitation of the applicability of the Broekhoff-de Boer (BdB) method comes from the irreversible nature of vapor sorption in mesopores. In fact, theoretical [42] and experimental [43] evidences are available to demonstrate that in general both adsorption and desorption branches are irreversible and thus that application of either of these branches will lead to over- or underestimates of pore sizes if no pore model is adopted. This uncertainty has been removed by choosing specific simple pore models including

1. *Slit pores*, only the desorption branch can be used.
2. *Cylindrical pores*, where both adsorption and desorption branch can be used for calculation of the pore size distribution. Ideally, i.e., if the actual porous system is very well described by the cylindrical pore model, both distribution curves should coincide, and in both cases the cumulative pore surface should be nearly equal to S_{BET} (unless micropores are present, in which case S_{cum} is smaller than S_{BET}). This is shown by the results for the pore size distribution of the Cu/SiO_2 catalyst, which are included in Figure 9, and the resulting cumulative pore surface of about 125 m^2/g.
3. *Ink-bottle pores* or *spheroidal cavities*, only the adsorption branch can be used.

One of the main interests of the BdB method is the fact that, in all cases, the cumulative specific surface is more consistent with the BET-value than for any other method. Moreover, by using synthetic samples of well defined porous structure, it has been shown that this technique gives pore size distributions much closer to reality than those identified by other methods [17, 44].

The absence of hysteresis in isotherms is often interpreted as an indication that no mesopores are present. This conclusion is not definite, since various types of closed-end mesopores (e.g., hemispherical, spherical, and cuneiform pores) give isotherms with no hysteresis. A more reliable indication of the presence or absence of mesopores in such cases is provided by mercury porosimetry. There is still no complete theory about this hysteresis, presumably due to the complexity of the interconnections between the pores that are usually present in porous materials.

Porosimetry—Pore Size Distribution in the Mesopore Range, Pore Volume

Mercury porosimetry is used to measure the pore size distribution in the mesopore and macropore range. The method is based on the principle that the angle of contact θ between mercury and a nonwetable solid is larger than 90°, so that the mercury penetrates into the pores only under pressure. In the classical analysis, the relationship between the required pressure gradient and the pore radius, assuming cylindrical pores, is

$$P = -2\sigma \cos \theta / r_p \tag{13}$$

which implies that the mercury penetration is a reversible process. For many nonwetable solids, the angle of contact varies from 110° to 140°, and investigations on a number of industrial catalysts have established a mean contact angle of about 130° [45].

Limitations to the technique arise mainly from the very high pressures needed for penetration into small pores (up to 3.5×10^8 Pa). It is therefore necessary to consider the compressibility of the mercury, which is done by blank measurements without sample.

Under these pressures it is more difficult to reach pressure equilibrium, in particular if some "ink-bottle" pores are present. Moreover, the higher the pressure, the larger the possible variation of the contact angle θ [17], which is also sensitive to the roughness and the curvature of the solid surface (the latter being more important with narrower pores). Modifying or breaking down of the porous texture of the sample also have to be considered: The presence of large cavities with bottleneck type constricted openings makes the solid very sensitive to crushing or squeezing.

Determining the pore size distribution requires measuring the amount of mercury that penetrates into the pores at a given pressure. Automatic equipment for this measurement is commercially available, the maximum pressure being about 3.5×10^8 Pa, which corresponds to a pore diameter of about 4 nm based on the contact angle being 130°. In practice, mercury porosimetry is mainly used for the pore size range of 5 to 15,000 nm. In this range, which is available to both capillary condensation and mercury porosimetry, there is often a relatively good agreement on the resulting pore size distributions [46], as illustrated by the results in Figure 10. This agreement is surprising

in view of the simplifying assumptions (contact angle, pore geometry) that must be made in analyzing the data with both methods.

Various models exist for calculating the surface area from porosimetry data. For cylindrical pores, Goodsel [47] gives

$$S_p = -\frac{1}{m \cdot \sigma \cdot \cos\theta} \int_0^{V_p} P \, dV \tag{14}$$

where m is the weight of the sample.

The value of the total pore volume is found by integration of the pore-radius distribution (Equation 14). Other geometric pore models also have been incorporated and Rootare and Prenzlow [48] proposed a method of analysis in which a particular pore geometry need not be postulated. Their expression is calculating the specific surface area by

$$S_p = \frac{2}{m} \int_0^{V_p} \frac{dV}{r_p} \tag{15}$$

The integral is calculated from the measured curve dV(P). For many catalysts, the surface areas determined by these last two methods [47, 48] are in good agreement, but they can be compared to the BET surface areas only to a very limited extent [46]. Additionally, it should be emphasized that the accuracy of the pore size distribution, as determined by both capillary condensation and porosimetry, is often overestimated [20].

BULK CHEMICAL COMPOSITION AND MORPHOLOGY

So far, primary attention was given to those methods that can provide information about the characteristic physical properties of a catalyst. This chapter emphasizes techniques analyzing the chemical properties of the bulk material.

X-Ray Diffraction—Identification of Solid Phases, Phase Transformations, Lattice Constants, Mean Particle Size

X-rays, incident on a crystalline solid, may cause diffractions due to elastic scattering of the ray quanta on the electrons of the chemical building blocks (atoms, ions) of the substance. The lattice structure, i.e., the three-dimensional arrangement of the building blocks, therefore can be referred to the resulting diffraction pattern. The quantitative description of the elastic X-ray scattering by extended objects is summarized in various textbooks such as [49].

The basis for evaluating diffraction diagrams resulting from a parallel, monochromatic beam of wave length λ is the Bragg equation

$$2d_{hkl} \sin\theta = n \cdot \lambda \tag{16}$$

where θ is the angle of incidence with respect to a set of lattice planes h, k, l having an interplane distance d_{hkl} and n is the order of diffraction. Constructive interference may be achieved with monochromatic radiation by varying the angle of incidence either by rotating the crystal (rotating crystal method) or by transmission of the radiations through a large number of small, randomly orientated crystals (powder method). The latter technique is often used to investigate industrial catalysts.

In the common Debye-Scherrer method (Figure 11), radiation from an X-ray source (after elimination of the K-radiation and collimation of the remaining K-radiation in a pinhole system) is incident on the powder specimen, which is mounted in the center of a thin-walled capillary tube. The primary X-ray beam should be selected to avoid fluorescence problems and should be as monochromatic as possible. For instance, nickel-filtered Cu Kα is often used with platinum, palladium, and nickel; and iron-filtered Co Kα or zirconium-filtered Mo Kα with iron. A monochromator can

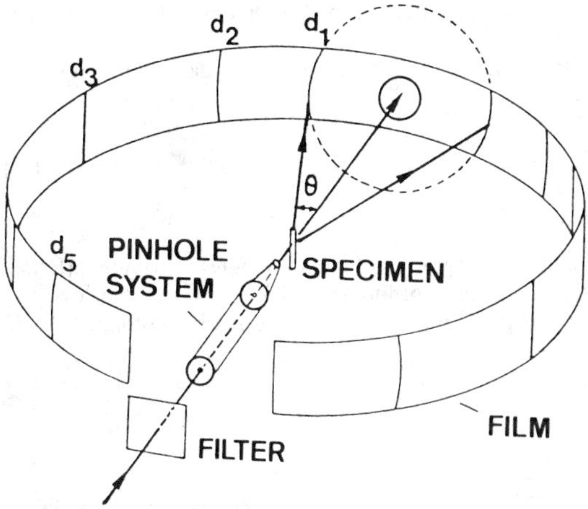

Figure 11. Principle of the Debye-Scherrer powder method.

also be used, but with considerable loss of intensity [49]. For the measurement, the Bragg reflection condition is satisfied for all possible lattice planes (h, k, l) in that the specimen contains enough crystallites and that the sample is usually rotated about its cylindrical axis. The resulting coaxial reflection cones produce more or less defined lines on the cylindrically arranged strip of film (Figure 11) and the angle θ can be evaluated in a simple manner from the distance between two associated lines of interference. The interplane distance d_{hkl} is then calculated using Equation 16.

This technique also provides a very useful tool for investigating thermally-induced phase-transitions and recrystallization processes. The most elegant method is by high temperature X-ray diffraction [49], where the specimen is heated linearly at a given rate and the interference lines are recorded simultaneously on a film. Figure 12 presents a high temperature scan showing the phase changes of a kaolin support.

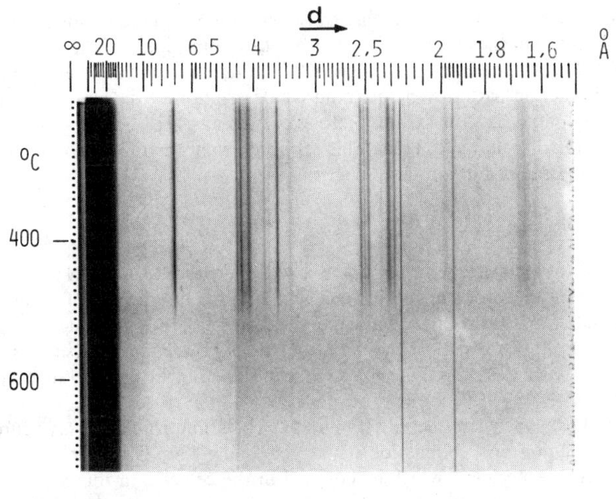

Figure 12. High-temperature X-ray film scan (Guinier-Lenne camera) showing the phase transition of kaolin support material at about 500 K. Heating rate, 1°C/min.

In powder diffractometry, a different technique of supporting the sample, i.e., to press the finely ground powder into a metal plate with a window or recess, is used. Care must be taken to obtain a uniform surface for maximum clarity of the reflection lines. Finely divided metals may react with air and protection from air may be desirable (especially with reduced dispersed metal catalysts). Considerably higher accuracy of the diffracted emission detection is achieved with quantum detectors such as Geiger, scintillation, or semiconductor counters. The angle of the individual interferences can be read directly (Figure 13).

In order to carry out qualitative analysis of catalysts of complex or unknown composition, the calculated values of d (Debye-Scherrer method) or the measured values of θ (powder diffractometry) for a given wavelength of the X-ray beam are compared with values from the literature or with reference samples. Systematically compiled collections of structural and diffraction data of crystals are available. The most comprehensive of these are the "Powder Diffraction File," also known as the "ASTM File," and "Crystal Data," published by the U.S. Joint Committee on Powder Diffraction.

Information about the lattice constant of a component (metal on support) may be helpful in the manufacture of catalysts or the investigation of deactivated samples, since such data permit conclusions about the presence or absence of foreign atoms or ions in the crystal lattice of the active component [50, 51]. For cubic crystals, the lattice constant a_0 is given by

$$\sin^2 \theta = [\lambda/2a_0]^2(h^2 + k^2 + l^2) \tag{17}$$

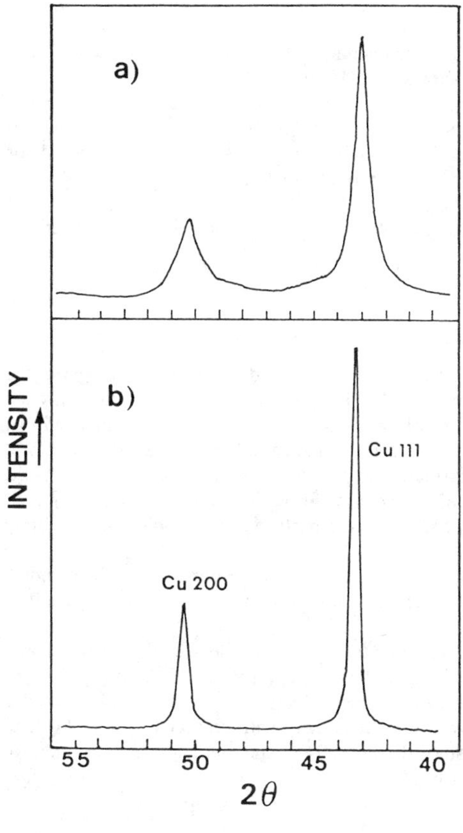

Figure 13. Illustration of XRD line-broadening. The X-ray reflections (Cu Kα shown in a) were obtained from a fresh silica supported copper catalyst; The patterns are shown in b) from the same catalyst after deactivation due to sintering. The mean copper particle size determined from the line-broadening was 12 nm for the fresh catalyst (a), and 38 nm for the deactivated catalyst (b).

Determining the lattice constants from powder patterns is more difficult for crystals of tetragonal or hexagonal symmetry (crystals defined by two lattice constants), and for rhombic, monoclinic, and triclinic crystals the method is quite involved.

For catalysis, the use of powder diffractometry to determine the particle size of specific components, e.g., the metal particle size on metal/support catalysts, is of particular importance. For small crystalline particles, the number of parallel lattice planes decreases, resulting in a broadening of the Bragg reflections (diffraction lines), since the reflection conditions (Equation 16) are less stringent. This behavior is illustrated in Figure 13, which depicts the most prominent copper reflections of two supported copper catalysts with different mean copper particle size. X-ray diffraction line broadening becomes experimentally significant when the crystallite size falls below about 100 nm, it is particularly applicable to metal crystallites of 3–50 nm. Below 3 nm the line is very broad and tends to become lost, although with modern step-scanning techniques the lower limit can be reduced to about 2 nm. Above 50 nm the change in peak shape is small and the method is therefore insensitive.

There are factors other than crystallite size that can contribute to the observed line width. In addition to pure instrumental factors (the most important contribution) there are matters such as strain, stacking and twin faults [49] or distortion of the diffraction line profile by a catalyst support [2]. If only the particle size contributes significantly to the line width in excess of the instrumental width, and if one is only interested in the estimation of the average crystallite size, the interpretation of the data is simple. Assuming that the line shapes are Gaussian (squares of the factors are additive) the line width B_d due to particle size broadening is given by [52]

$$B_d^2 = B_{obs}^2 - B_{inst}^2 \tag{18}$$

where B_{obs} is the observed width and B_{inst} is the instrumental width, which is obtained by a calibration procedure using a material of large crystals ($100 < d < 1{,}000$ nm) of good crystalline perfection such as magnesium oxide or quartz powder. The instrumental broadening is a function of the glancing angle θ, which must be considered in the calibration. For certain types of diffractometers, the corresponding curves can be found in the literature [53]. An improved method for correcting the measured peak width that is used frequently in practice was proposed by Wagner and Aqua [54].

From B_d, the mean crystallite diameter d_{hkl} is given by the relation originally derived by Scherrer [55].

$$d_{hkl} = \frac{K \cdot \lambda}{\beta \cdot \cos \theta} \tag{19}$$

where λ is the X-ray wavelength, and K is a constant whose value depends on the shape of the particle and the method used to measure the peak width. In principle, two different methods can be used to measure the peak width. Either the width of the peak is measured at half its height or the integrated peak-area is divided by the peak height. In the first case, K is between 0.84 and 0.89, depending on the shape of the particle. If no information about the shape of the particle is available, spherical shape is usually assumed and a value of 0.9 is chosen for K. In the second case (integrated peak-area), K varies between 1.0 and 1.16, depending on the particle shape, and a value of unity is usually selected [49].

In selecting reflections for measurement, two-dimensional lattice reflections should be avoided. These result from crystals in which the order in one dimension has been lost such as layer lattice metal hydroxides, clays, and carbon black.

Various disturbing factors may appear in the determination of the particle size in multicomponent systems such as metal/support catalysts. For example, the diffraction peaks of the metal and the support may overlap in the diffraction pattern, or the metal load may be too small to yield a diffraction peak that can be analyzed. The lower limit sensitivity with respect to the metal load depends on the atomic number of the metal, since the intensity of the diffracted radiation is proportional to the square of the atomic number [49].

Diffractometric determination of the mean particle size has the advantage over other methods (electron microscopy and chemisorption, both described later in this survey) that extensive pretreatment of the specimen is unnecessary. However, the accuracy of the method is limited to about $\pm 15\%$ depending on the system investigated and should not be overestimated. Adams et al. [56] have carried out a comparative study of the three methods.

In addition to the Debye-Scherrer camera and the diffractometer, other powder methods [49] are also used for the investigation of industrial catalysts, depending on the problem. Small-angle X-ray scattering [57] and magnetic methods [58] may be applied to smaller crystallites in the 1–10 nm range, but these methods are much more demanding with respect to data evaluation and are rarely used in industry.

Thermoanalytic Methods—Thermal Stability, Reduction Behavior, and Phase Transformations

Various thermoanalytic methods are known [59], and the two most important aids for the investigation of industrial catalysts are thermogravimetry (TG, DTG) and differential thermoanalysis (DTA, DSC).

In thermogravimetry (TG), the weight of a specimen is measured at a continuously changing temperature. Thus, a TG apparatus consists essentially of a sensitive microbalance connected to an analog-electronic display and a furnace with a programmable temperature profile. DTG curves are obtained from the TG measurements by differentiation. Important characteristics are the sensitivity of the measurement and the maximum permissible weight of the sample.

The main applications of thermogravimetry include studies of the preparation and reduction of supported metal catalysts [60, 61]. Important variables such as the heating rate, the temperature range, the feed rate, and the compostion of the gas during calcination and reduction can be varied and their effect on, for example, metal dispersion can be investigated.

Furthermore, TG studies can provide information about the thermal stability of a solid material (e.g., when gaseous products are formed above the decomposition temperature of a component). TG is also suitable for studies of adsorption and desorption, where the catalyst is exposed to a reactant gas (similar to TPD described below) and the desorption or adsorption are traced as a function of temperature on basis of the loss or increase in weight of the specimen. An illustrating example of the potential of thermoanalytical measurements is shown in Figure 14. The poisoning of a copper catalyst originating from surface nitride formation in the presence of ammonia was studied using TG and DTA [62]. The TG curve (Figure 14A) depicts the formation and decomposition of the copper nitride as a function of temperature and provides information about the kinetics of the nitride formation and decomposition. The DTA curve shown in Figure 14B reflects the enthalpy changes occurring during the decomposition of the copper nitride. From this curve the heat of decomposition ($Cu_3N_{(s)} \rightarrow 3\ Cu_{(s)} + \frac{1}{2}\ N_2$) was calculated to 88 ± 5 kJ/mol [62]. Agglomeration or adsorption of foreign species during catalyst poisoning is often associated with a change in weight and can be investigated efficiently with thermogravimetry.

In differential thermoanalysis (DTA), the difference in temperature between the sample and an inert reference substance (e.g., γ-alumina, quartz) is measured continuously as a function of the reference temperature [59]. The temperatures are usually monitored with unsheathed thermocouples embedded in the powdered samples, and a linear temperature increase in the range 0–50 K min^{-1} with a typical maximum temperature of 1,300°C is often selected [2, 59]. Any transformation or chemical reaction in the sample under study that causes a liberation or adsorption of heat results in a positive or negative peak in the plot of the differential temperature versus reference temperature.

The DTA method can be used, among other things, for catalyst screening [63] or adsorption and desorption processes, e.g., in catalyst deactivation [62, 64]. It is often combined in practice with the TG method to follow reduction, dehydration and decomposition processes (thermal stability) [65, 66]. Figure 15 illustrates the combined use of TG, DTG and DTA for the investigation of the reduction of a V_20_5 catalyst in a hydrogen atmosphere [66].

The technique of differential scanning calorimetry (DSC) is closely related to DTA: In DSC, the specimen and the reference material are forced to follow the same temperature program. A "thermal

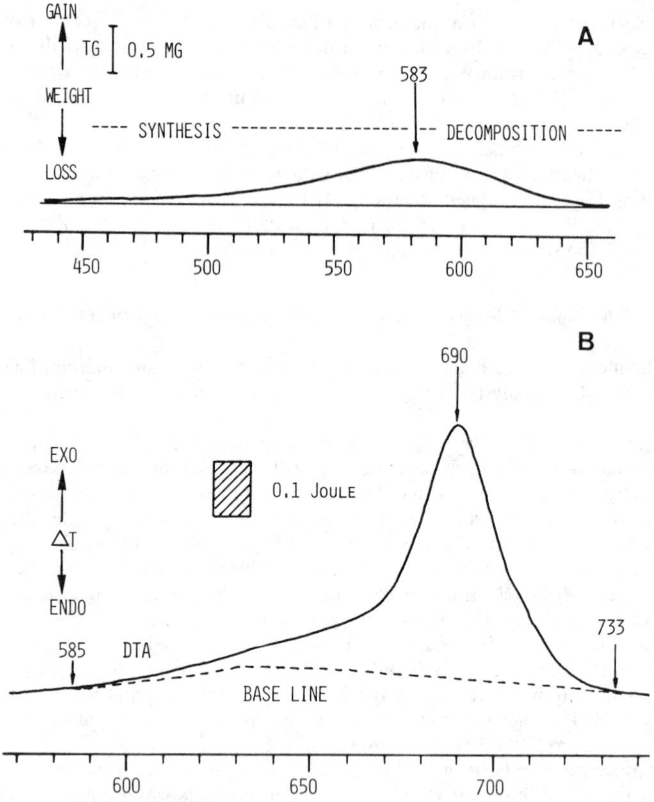

Figure 14. Poisoning of a copper catalyst by surface nitride formation investigated by means of thermogravimetry (TG) and thermoanalysis (DTA) [62]. A) shows the weight gain and loss of the catalyst when exposed to ammonia due to the formation and decomposition of the copper nitride as function of temperature. B) depicts the heat liberated during the exothermic decomposition of the copper nitride.

event" requires an incremental addition or removal of heat to or from the specimen, which is the experimental parameter measured as a function of the temperature.

The DSC technique thus permits direct quantitative determination of caloric quantities. Its range of application coincides essentially with that of the classic DTA method. Typical examples include conversion of gibbsite to boehmite [67], a variety of zeolite dehydration studies [68] or the decomposition of nitride layers on supported copper and nickel catalysts [62, 69] illustrated above.

Temperature Programmed Reduction (TPR)

Temperature programmed reduction has gained increasing importance for the characterization of catalysts since its first application by Robertson et al. [70]. The technique has been applied successfully to study the influence of pretreatment procedures, of support material, and of chemical changes due to promoters action. Therefore, the TPR method is also suitable for quality control of different catalyst charges since deviations from manufacture often result in different profiles of reduction.

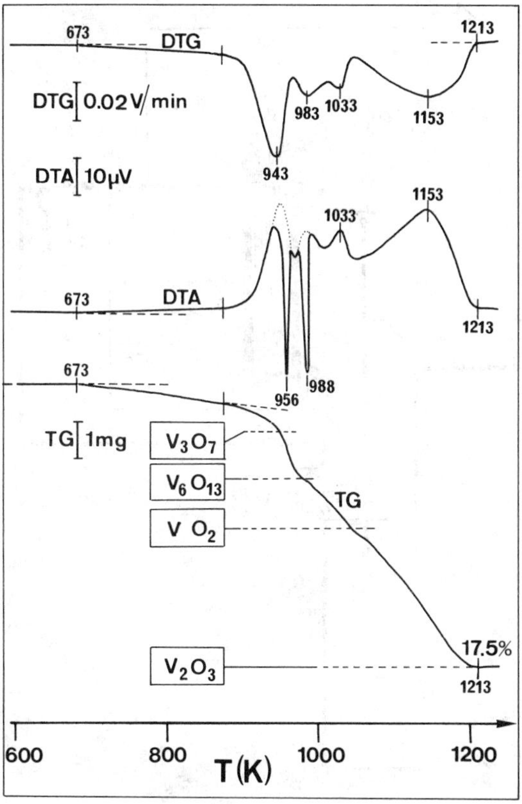

Figure 15. Illustration of the combined use of TG, DTG, and DTA for the investigation of the reduction of a V_2O_5 catalyst in a hydrogen atmosphere [66]. The two endothermic peaks in the DTA curve appearing at 956 and 988 K are attributed to partial melting of some phases (V_2O_5 and V_3O_7) during reduction.

At the beginning of a TPR experiment, gas flows over a fixed amount of solid at a temperature low enough to prevent reaction. In principle, any reducing gas can be used, but diluted hydrogen (e.g., 5% H_2, 95% He or N_2) is commonly applied. The temperature of the solid is then increased at linear rate and the rate of reaction is monitored. This can be achieved by measuring concentration or pressure changes in the gas phase or weight changes of the solid. The convenient method is to detect the hydrogen uptake by the difference in thermal conductivity of the gas before and after the reduction [71]. An essential extension of the TPR technique has been achieved by mass analysis of the gases produced during the reduction [72]. A typical construction of a TPR apparatus is shown schematically in Figure 16. Detailed information about the experimental method and the instrumentation is given in Reference 74.

The sensitivity of TPR is high, typically hydrogen uptakes of 1 μmol and a few miligrams of reducible species are adequate [71], depending on the operating variables. In an extensive study on parameter sensitivity, Monti and Baiker [73] demonstrated that optimal sensitivity can only be obtained if the operating conditions are properly selected. For this purpose, a characteristic number

$$K = S_0/V^*c_0 \tag{20}$$

was defined, where S_0 is the amount of reducible species, V^* is the total flow rate of the reducing gas and c_0 is the initial hydrogen concentration. For common heating rates between 0.1 and 0.3 K/s, the limiting values for K were found to be $55 < K < 140$ s.

Different methods for estimating the kinetic parameters of the reduction from TPR measurements were proposed in the literature [73, 74]. For measurements in which the operating variables

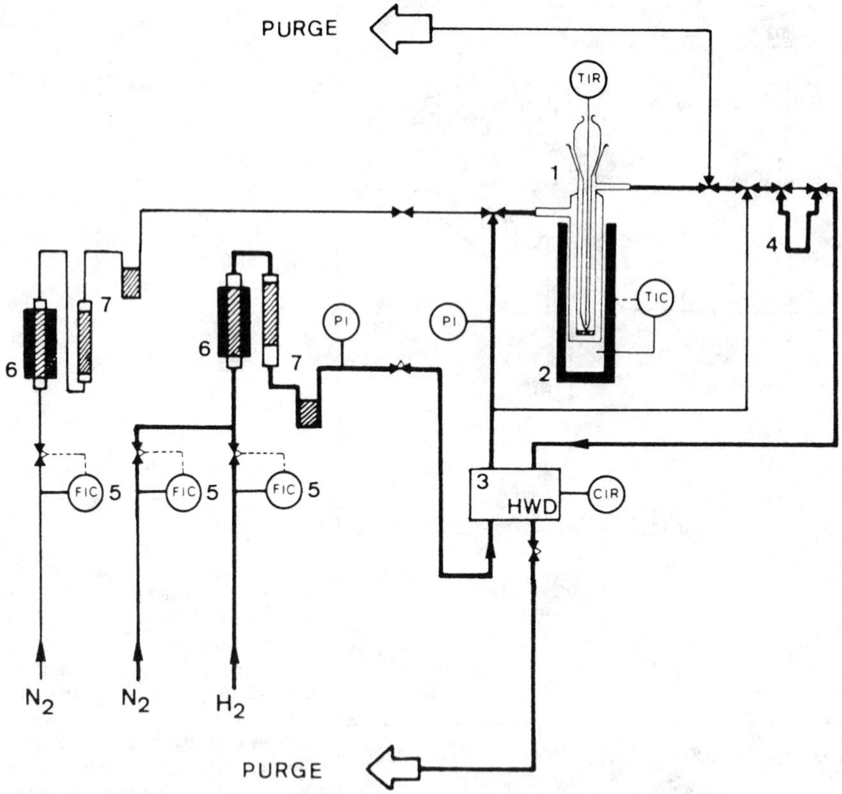

Figure 16. Experimental set up used for TPR measurements: (1) reactor; (2) temperature controlled furnace; (3) hot wire detector; (4) cooling trap; (5) flow controller; (6) copper filled furnace for removal of traces of oxygen; (7) molecular sieve packings; FIC, flow control; PI, pressure gauges; TIC, temperature control, TIR, temperature recording; CIR, concentration recording.

were optimized good accordance was found between measured reduction profiles and profiles simulated using the estimated kinetic parameters [73].

A variety of experimental examples that demonstrate the potential of TPR in catalytic research have been compiled [71, 74]. Figure 17 illustrates, as an example, how information concerning the reduction or the metal/support interaction can be obtained by the TPR technique. Curve a) is the reduction profile of pure CuO and curve b) that of CuO supported on γ-Al_2O_3. The supported CuO is reduced at considerably higher temperature only, which is presumably due to the presence of $CuAl_2O_4$ at the phase boundary between the copper particles and the support.

The potential of TPR to "fingerprint" the phase composition of an oxidic catalyst is illustrated in Figure 18. Note the marked change in the shape and location of the profiles of the different vanadium oxide phases. Frequently the reduction is structure sensitive, i.e., catalysts of the same chemical composition, but different distribution of the crystal faces exposed on the surface, yield markedly different reduction profiles. This behavior is illustrated in Figure 19 showing the reduction profiles of two V_2O_5 catalysts with different grain morphology. Sample A consisted of well-developed platelets exposing predominantly the (010) faces, whereas sample B contained agglomerates of needle-type grains.

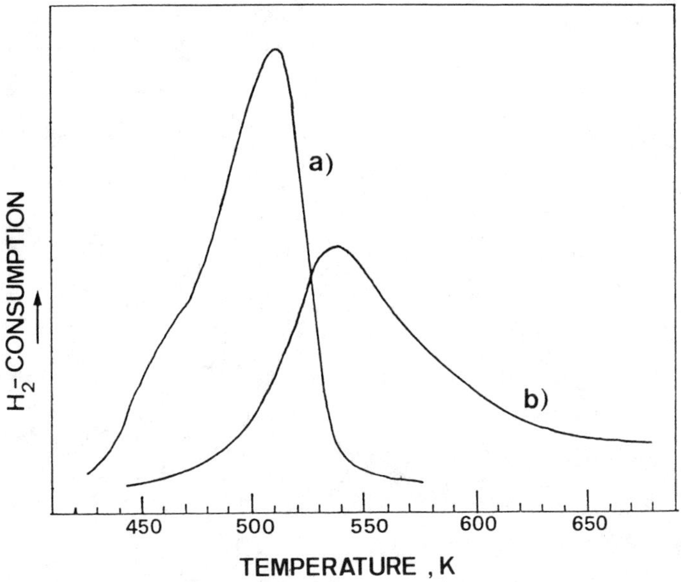

Figure 17. Metal-support interaction as seen by TPR. Curve a) shows the reduction profile of pure CuO, and curve b) of alumina supported CuO. Heating rate 10.7 K/min.

The TPR technique has been adopted to study other temperature programmed reactions, such as temperature programmed oxidation (TPO) [77], temperature programmed sulfidation (TPS) [78], and temperature programmed methanation (TPM) [79]. In this case hydrogen in the carrier gas is replaced by O_2, H_2S, and CO, respectively. In principle any reacting gas may be used in a similar technique to fingerprint the reactivity of the solid with this gas.

Electron Spin Resonance Spectroscopy (ESR)

The electron spin resonance technique has been extensively used to study paramagnetic species that exist on various solids. Such species may be free radicals and radical ions adsorbed on the surface, or more importantly, transition metal ions with unpaired electrons contained within the catalyst. It is based on the following principle: For any unpaired electron, the application of an external magnetic field causes the magnetic vector to precess, which results in two Zeeman levels corresponding to different orientations of the electron magnetic moment with respect to the applied field [2, 80]. The application of an electromagnetic field H of an appropriate frequency γ (commonly required wavelength about 3 cm, the microwave region) then induces a transition (spin flip) between the two Zeeman levels, at resonance

$$h\gamma = g\beta H \tag{21}$$

where β is the Bohr magneton. The sample is exposed to microwaves of a fixed frequency and the absorption of the radiation is measured as a function of the applied magnetic field usually in the derivative form). Information about the chemical environment is gained from the difference between the Lande g-factor (which is a physical property of the electron) in the free electron and in the bound state.

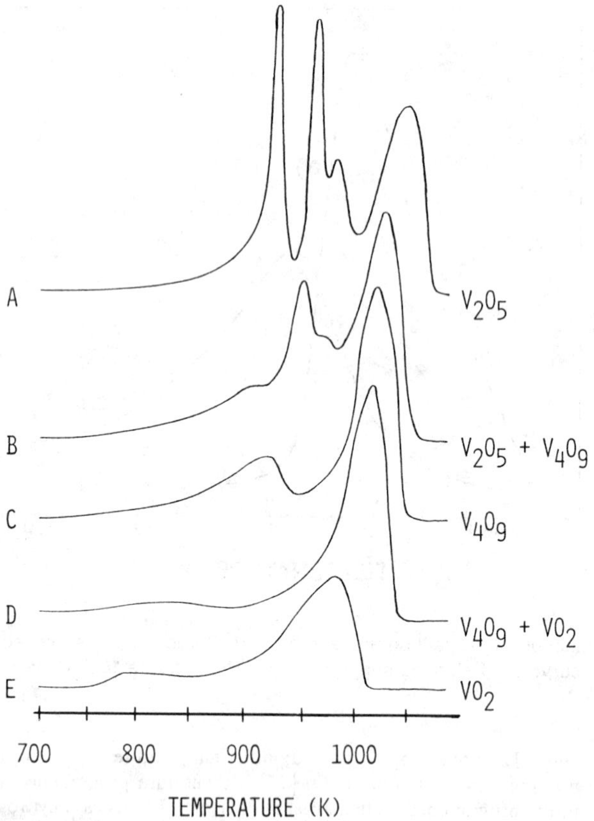

Figure 18. Reduction profiles of different Vanadium oxide phases [75]. Heating rate, 10 K/min.

A number of other interactions contribute to ESR absorption spectra such as the interaction between the electron magnetic moment with the magnetic moment of the nucleus (hyperfine splitting) or interaction between the d electrons with the electronic field via spin-orbit coupling (crystal field splitting). For more information, the reader is referred to the reviews [80, 81].

It is apparent that ESR is limited to applications involving paramagnetic species having relaxation times compatible with reasonably well-resolved spectra, and for ease of interpretation, preferably only one unpaired electron. In industrial catalysts, these conditions are seldom fulfilled and the interpretation of ESR data is often difficult. Thus, the application of this technique for the investigation of industrial catalysts has been rather small so far. However, ESR is most valuable when applied together with other techniques such as TPR and other electron or optical spectroscopies. For example, ESR has been used to characterize the nature of Cr ions in an industrial chromium oxide/silica catalyst [82] (in conjunction with IR-spectroscopy) and to determine the nature of copper species supported on alumina [83] (with TPR). In the latter study, considerable information gained from the analysis of the hyperfine structure allowed detailed interpretation of the nature of the copper species.

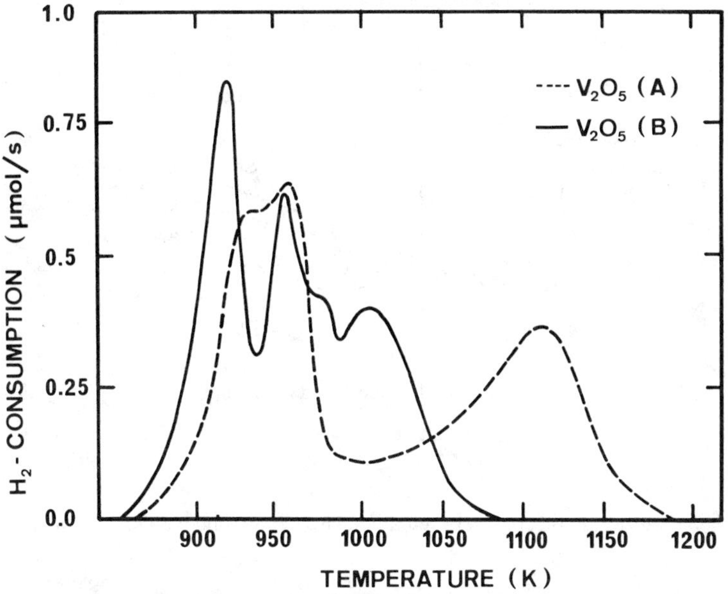

Figure 19. Influence of the grain morphology of V_2O_5 on its reduction behavior. Heating rate, 9 K/s. Sample A consisted of well-developed platelets with the large faces corresponding to (010) planes; sample B contained poorly defined agglomerates of needle-type grains. Morphologies of the samples are shown in Ref. [76].

ESR also proved to be a powerful method for the characterization of supported vanadium oxide layer catalysts [84]. From the analysis of the spectra estimates of the V=O bond strength, and the delocalization of the V^{4+} unpaired electron onto the coordinatively bound oxygen ligands were obtained.

Nuclear Magnetic Resonance Spectroscopy (NMR)

Nuclear magnetic resonance is an important tool in the analysis of organic and inorganic liquids. However, the application of NMR techniques to solids and relatively immobile species is complicated by the strong dipolar interactions characteristics for most oriented molecules [80] and that result in line width of typically several thousand Hertz. Under such conditions it is obviously not possible to measure chemical shifts and spin-spin couplings amounting to only a few hundred Hertz. Using conventional spectrometers, one must therefore be content with data on relaxation times (e.g., for adsorbed species) and a limited amount of structural information.

The results of Vaughan and Waugh (reviewed in [80, 85]), however, show that it is possible to electronically (quantum mechanically) average out the dipolar interactions in solid samples, and at least medium resolution spectra with line width in the order 10 Hz are thus possible. NMR spectroscopy is undergoing rapid modifications that could greatly expand the applications in heterogeneous catalysis.

NMR spectroscopy may in principle be applied to all nuclei with a non-zero order nuclear spin. Such nuclei possess a magnetic moment and angular momentum. The theory on which the technique is based is outlined in detail in several reviews [80, 85, 86]. A number of techniques are then

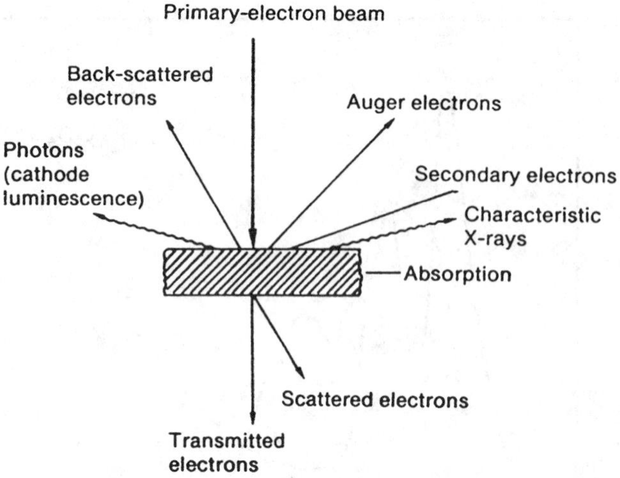

Figure 20. Interactions between an electron beam and a solid specimen.

implemented to make use of the unique combination of field and orientation dependence of each interaction to remove or attenuate unwanted broadening including sample spinning, multipulse sequencing, magic angle spinning (MAS) and others [85]. Since NMR is a relatively insensitive technique, only selected nuclei are suitable such as ^{29}Si [87], ^{27}Al, and ^{63}Cu. However, the expanding application of MAS-NMR to these nuclei suggests that the applicability of the method will continue to grow in importance (dominantly in research).

Electron-Probe Microanalysis (EPMA)

The interactions that occur when electrons strike a solid are shown schematically in Figure 20. They will be discussed in detail in following chapters involving spectroscopic methods. In electron-probe microanalysis [4, 88] the characteristic X-rays emitted from a solid excited by high-energy electrons, which appear as discrete X-ray lines superimposed on the "bremsstrahlung" spectrum, are used for chemical analysis. The excitation range of the electron beam is about 1 μm^3 is the limiting factor of the attainable lateral resolution and surface sensitivity. EPMA has therefore to be considered as a bulk analysis technique rather than as a surface analytical tool.

In order to produce characteristic radiation, an electron must be ejected from a lower shell (K, L, or M). The required primary-electron energy E_0 must be greater than the ionization energy E_1 for the corresponding subshell with the quantum numbers n, l. The positive hole resulting from ionization is filled with an electron from higher shells, and the energy released in this process is emitted in a radiative transition as X-ray quantum with a probability w (X-ray fluorescence yield). The selection rules for the transitions are $\Delta l = \pm 1$ and $\Delta j = 0, \pm 1$. The most common transitions are shown in Figure 21 in an energy-level diagram with the customary nomenclature.

The characteristic radiation is element-specific and its wavelength has a fixed relationship to the atomic number of the excited or ionized atoms. Qualitative elemental analysis of the surface of a solid thus necessitates determining the wavelength or energy of the characteristic radiation. This requires spectral analysis of the emitted radiation, which is possible by either diffraction of the X-rays on single crystals (wave-length dispersion, crystal spectrometer), or by direct measurement of the X-ray quanta energy (energy dispersive X-ray analyzer, EDX).

In the present state of the art, crystal spectrometers can detect the elements from beryllium to uranium, and energy dispersive spectrometers those from carbon to uranium. Only the K-lines of

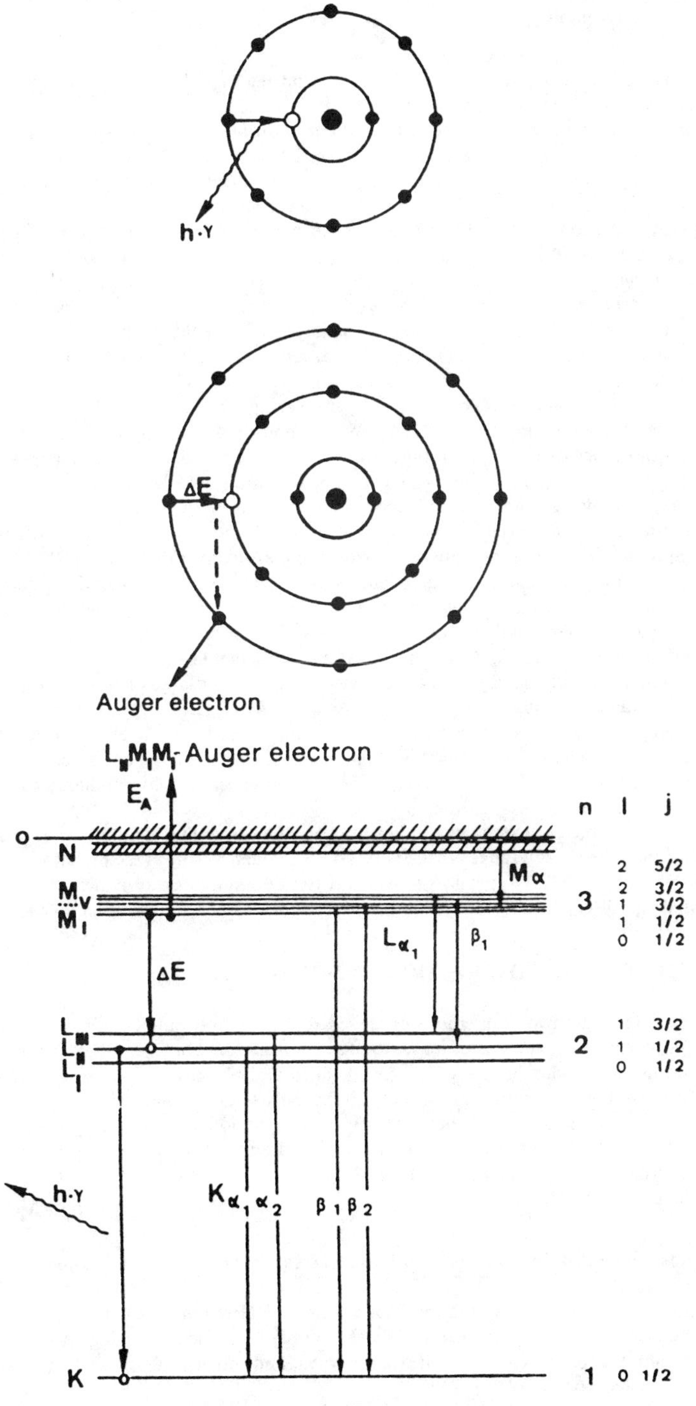

Figure 21. Diagram of electron transition used in electron microanalysis (EPMA) and Auger electron spectroscopy (AES).

the elements beyond Na (atomic number 11) can be detected by EDX in practice because of absorption losses in the entrance window of the detector.

In order to make an analysis of the elemental composition of a solid specimen, a focused beam of electrons is scanned horizontally over the sample. The resulting distribution of the characteristic X-rays as a function of the position on the sample surface is displayed on a synchronously operating cathode-ray oscilloscope in light-dark contrast. In addition to determining the areal distribution, the concentration profiles of elements also can be measured. The application of the method is wide-spread in catalysis, although limitations may arise from the bulk character of the analysis. Moreover, detection of lighter elements is more difficult, because the intensity of the characteristic X-rays is proportional to the square of the atomic number.

Modern instruments for electron-probe microanalysis are usually coupled with a scanning electron microscope (SEM) such that there are no great reductions in either method. Typical examples that illustrate the combined use of these methods are available [4].

Quantitative EPMA analysis is carried out by measuring the intensity of the characteristic X-ray radiation. The mass fraction of an element can be found by comparing the line intensities of the investigated substance to a calibrated standard. If no standard with a chemical composition similar to the test specimen is available, pure-element standards are used [2, 4, 88].

For quantitative determination of the elemental composition, the surface of the solid must meet certain requirements. The specimen must be stable in high vacuum and exhibit no changes, such as local vaporization or sintering, under electron bombardment. Furthermore, the electron bombardment must not produce any charge phenomena that result in a change of the diameter of the electron beam and the excitation voltage. In order to hold the excitation conditions constant over all points of measurement and comparable to the standard specimen, the surface roughness of the samples should not exceed the micron range. If surface irregularities exist that for some reason cannot be eliminated, the signal must be integrated over a rather large area, since a local measurement may be altered by roughness.

In preparing the specimen, attention must be given especially to its electrical conductivity. If nonconductive materials are to be investigated, the sample surface must be coated, e.g., with a thin film (a few tenths of nm) of carbon or gold (by vapor deposition), to conduct away the charge resulting from the electron bombardment.

Generally, use of the electron-beam microprobe provides useful information on a catalyst whenever resolution in the micron range is called for. This is frequently true in the preparation, activation, and poisoning of catalysts. Typical examples are the determination of concentration profiles in impregnated catalysts [89, 90] and the deposition of poisons and fouling components [91, 92].

SURFACE CHEMICAL COMPOSITION AND MORPHOLOGY

Most of the characterization methods discussed so far are only suitable for the investigation of the bulk properties of a solid catalyst. Although information about the bulk properties is important and useful, we should stress that the chemical and physical properties of the surface of a solid catalyst are the most important factors governing its activity and selectivity behavior. Next we focus on characterization techniques that provide information about surface properties. Different definitions for the term "surface" have been given in the literature, depending on the context in which this term was used. Here we shall use the term surface meaning several top atomic layers and not the outermost atomic layer.

Selective Adsorption and Titration—Metal Surface Area, and Degree of Dispersion

In contrast to measurement of the total surface area, determining the surface area of one component of the catalyst (usually the metal surface) can only be carried out using selective adsorption (chemisorption). Hydrogen, carbon monoxide, oxygen, and nitrous oxide are the most commonly used gases for chemisorption [93].

The use of chemisorption for surface area measurements essentially requires the reliable and reproducible determination of gas uptakes to cover one component of the solid with a monolayer of adsorbate, which is done by either volumetry, gravimetry, or the dynamic flow method as previously described. It is important to recognize that the monolayer uptake, although a high coverage situation, is a model used to define the corresponding chemisorption stoichiometry, with the stoichiometric factor X_m being defined as the average number of surface metal atoms associated with the adsorption of each adsorbate molecule.

The stoichiometric factor usually presents no problem when hydrogen is used as the adsorbate gas, since H_2 is generally dissociatively adsorbed on the catalytically important transition metals, i.e., it is chemisorbed with a stoichiometric factor of 2 (referred to the H_2 molecule) as evidenced by numerous studies [4].

With other adsorbates, difficulties frequently arise with respect to the stoichiometric factor because the molecules may be chemisorbed differently, depending on the surface geometry and the coverage. Examples of IR-studies of CO chemisorbed on Pd/SiO_2 are known to show two different absorption bands for the CO-stretching vibration corresponding to the bridged Pd—(CO)—Pd and the linear form Pd=C=O. In the size range < 10 nm, the surface geometry and therefore the stoichiometric ratio frequently depends on the particle size. An example is the increase of the stoichiometric factor from 1 to 2 with increasing particle size that was observed in the chemisorption of CO on a supported platinum catalyst [94]. This influence of particle size disappears for metal particles larger than about 10 nm, as frequently used in industrial catalysts, and constant stoichiometry is then more likely.

The value of the stoichiometric factor X_m can be determined, e.g., by chemisorption measurements on metal powders having known BET surface areas. Another method consists in determining the particle size from the measured metal surface area of the supported metal catalyst, assuming a particular regular geometric shape (e.g., sphere, cube) and comparing this particle size with that determined by X-ray diffraction line-broadening or electron microscopy.

From the amount of adsorbed gas measured it is then possible to calculate the number of accessible surface atoms (N_s) of the component (usually metal) from

$$N_s = V_m N_A X_m / V_{mol} \tag{22}$$

where V_m = volume of the chemisorbed monolayer
V_{mol} = molar volume of the adsorbate
N_A = Avogadro number

Another problem that exists with determining metal surface area from chemisorption measurements is the uncertainty concerning the heterogeneity of the dispersed metal surface, since knowledge of the number Φ_s of atoms per unit surface area is required. For a polycrystalline surface it is usual to evaluate the corresponding metal surface by assuming that the surface consists of equal proportions of the main low index planes, i.e., (111), (100), and (110) for cubic face centered and (110), (100), and (211) for cubic body centered metals. Values of the area occupied by a single accessible atom so obtained are listed in the literature for many catalyst materials. Typical concentrations of surface atoms are in the order of $1 - 1.6 \times 10^{19}$ atoms/m^2 [2]. The surface is then calculated from

$$S_M = N_s/\Phi_s \tag{23}$$

When the weight fraction of the metal in catalyst is known, the "degree of dispersion" D of the metal, i.e., the ratio of the surface atoms to the total number of metal atoms N_T (volume + surface atoms), can be calculated from N_s as determined by Equation 20:

$$D = N_s/N_T \tag{24}$$

The degree of dispersion is an important property of supported metal catalysts since it can affect selectivity and activity of the sample.

Although chemisorption, in contrast to the physisorption previously described, is restricted to a monolayer, the criteria for the presence of such a layer are not necessarily clearer in the case of chemisorption. It is often difficult to distinguish between chemisorbed and physisorbed adsorbate, in particular with weak chemisorptive bonding with the surface of the solid. Furthermore, gas adsorption on a dispersed metal catalyst is frequently slow, and considerable time may be required for a complete "adsorption equilibrium." As an example, the slow hydrogen adsorption on a supported noble metal at room temperature often needs 10 – 15 minutes for completion [2] and extreme values such as 3 hours (H_2 adsorption on ruthenium at 294 K [95]) are known.

The procedure of chemisorption measurements, as first reported by Emmett and Brunauer [96] is illustrated in Figure 22 using an alumina supported Pt catalyst and carbon monoxide as the adsorbate. It is important to first remove surface contaminations by completely reducing the catalyst with hydrogen. Then, CO is adsorbed at room temperature (298 K), where CO is both chemisorbed and physisorbed (isotherm I in Figure 22). The catalyst sample is evacuated subsequently to desorb the physisorbed species from the surface. Then, a new isotherm II corresponding to the physisorbed fraction of the adsorbate alone is measured. In this case, repeated evacuation followed by adsorption results in a reproducible isotherm II. The amount of chemisorbed CO is then calculated from the difference between the two isotherms (see Figure 22).

The presence of a support material or other components may limit the chemisorptive measurement of the metal surface since chemisorptive processes are generally not completely selective, and therefore part of the adsorbate may chemisorb on the support or other components. For example,

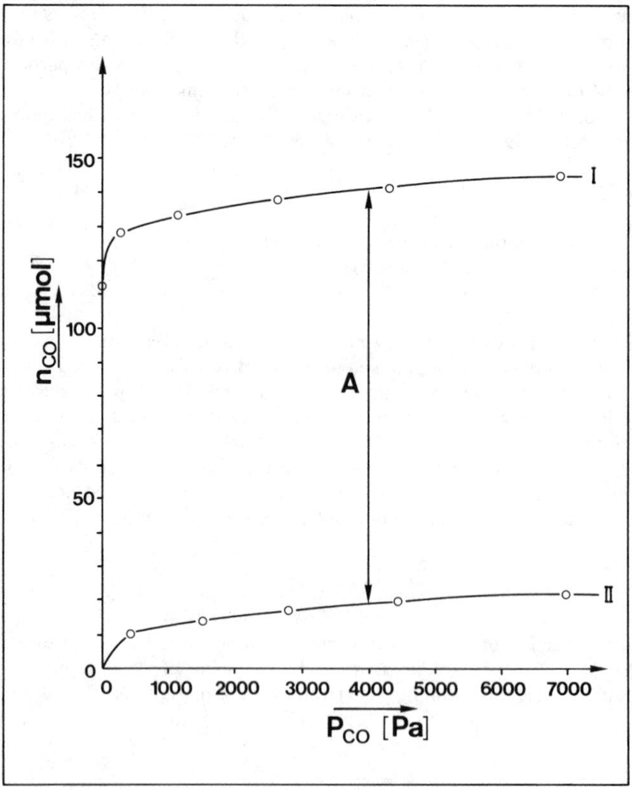

Figure 22. Determination of the chemisorbed fraction in adsorption measurements. Example: CO adsorption on an alumina supported platinum catalyst.

the frequently used adsorbate gases H_2, O_2, and CO_2 may be adsorbed on silica or alumina supports [97] to an extent that cannot be neglected. For this reason, chemisorption on other components must be checked in the case of multicomponent catalysts and, if necessary, corrections made for the gas that is chemisorbed on these components.

Various metals either take up hydrogen in true solution as dissolved hydrogen atoms (e.g., Ni, Co, Fe, Mn, Cu, Ag, Pt), or form hydrides (e.g., Pd, Ti, Ta, V). Although the hydrogen uptake of the former metals is relatively modest, it is often substantial for the latter metals forming hydrides.

Another phenomenon that may occur particularly in the chemisorption of H_2 on supported metal catalysts is the so-called "spillover effect," i.e., the migration on the support material of hydrogen initially chemisorbed dissociatively on the metal surface. For platinum supported on carbon or materials contaminated with carbon, this spillover of hydrogen can yield erroneously high results for the platinum surface area.

Despite these problems, chemisorptive determination of the metal surface area of transition metals with hydrogen are generally more reliable than with oxygen or carbon monoxide, since the criteria for the monolayer coverage and stoichiometric factor are quite certain [93]. In the chemisorption of oxygen on various transition metals problems arise with respect to limiting the chemisorption to the outermost atomic layer of the metal surface. This makes the definition of a criterion for monolayer adsorption very difficult. For oxygen adsorption, the stoichiometric factor commonly depends also on the degree of coverage, the temperature, and the particle size. The same problem arises with CO, where additional difficulties may be introduced by the formation of volatile metal carbonyls, e.g., nickel carbonyl can be formed by passing CO over finely dispersed nickel at 100 kPa and 360 K.

Titration Methods. Along with these direct chemisorption methods, so-called "titration methods" are used for determining the metal surfaces of dispersed platinum [98] and palladium [99]. The principle is the "titration" of gas previously chemisorbed on the metal by reaction with another gas. Previously chemisorbed O_2 is usually titrated with hydrogen in accordance with

$$O^* + \tfrac{3}{2}\,H_2 \longrightarrow H^* + H_2O \qquad (25)$$

and, alternatively, H_2-chemisorption is analyzed by subsequent titration with oxygen:

$$2\,H^* + O_2 \longrightarrow O^* + H_2O \qquad (26)$$

Although the stoichiometry of these reactions implies a greater sensitivity than direct H_2-chemisorption, the latter is generally preferable due to less uncertainties (catalyst pretreatment, reversibility of Reactions 25 and 26). Of course, the tritration methods sometimes offer advantages, namely, when the catalyst must be pretreated at lower temperatures due to sintering.

A special case of surface reaction is applied in the titration with nitrous oxide on copper catalysts according to

$$2\,Cu + N_2O \longrightarrow Cu_2O + N_2 \qquad (27)$$

where the amount of reacted N_2O is determined chromatographically via the evolving nitrogen. The pulse chromatographic technique by Evans et al. [100] has found increasing interest in the last few years.

The titrimetric determination of acidic sites will not be discussed here, but a thorough description of these methods can be found in [101].

Electron Microscopy—Surface Morphology, Size, Shape, and Local Distribution of Components

Electron microscopy is primarily a useful tool to investigate the surface morphology and thus permits direct determinations of the shape, size distribution, and location of specific components (e.g., metal particles on metal/support catalysts). In this context, studies of changes produced by sintering, phase transitions, reduction behavior and deposition of foreign material may be of special interest.

In principle, information about the crystal structure of components in a catalyst aggregate is contained in diffracted beams from an irradiation by either X-rays or electrons. Since an electron beam is finely collimated fairly easily, a high level of spatial resolution is obtained by electron diffraction techniques.

The most important interactions between the primary electron beam and the solid specimen were shown in Figure 20. For catalyst investigation, interactions providing information about the surface morphology (secondary or back-scattered electrons) and the chemical composition (characteristic X-rays, Auger electrons, secondary ions) are of particular importance. A few new techniques for the surface analysis of solids that combine electron microscopy with spectroscopic techniques such as scanning Auger microprobe (SAM) will be discussed in connection with the spectroscopic methods.

Standard practice of electron microscope techniques are scanning electron microscopy (SEM) and transmission electron microscopy (TEM). Both methods are frequently applied for the investigation of industrial catalysts. For analytical purposes, it should be kept in mind that irradiation by an electron (or ion) beam will result in some sort of modification of the specimen by either heating or by removal of matter and the significance of this process depends on both the sample and the nature of the technique. For example, beam heating may be substantial for non-metallic substances due to the low thermal conductivity of these materials.

The physical principle of electron microscopy, the mode of operation, and the technical construction of the various types now in use are discussed thoroughly in the literature [102, 103]; therefore, only a few important points will be mentioned herein.

Scanning Electron Microscopy (SEM)

In scanning electron microscopy, the surface of the specimen is scanned from point to point by an electron beam focussed to 5–20 nm [4, 102]. Normal SEM operates with signals back-scattered from the sample and thus does not need specimen thickness limitations. The electrons collected are used to modulate the brightness in a cathode ray display screen, the scan of which is synchronized with the scan of the specimen, thus producing an image. The magnification, defined as the ratio of the image area on the oscilloscope tube to the scanned area of the specimen, can be adjusted electronically by beam-deflecting devices. The surface topography becomes visible because the secondary electron yield depends on the angle of the surface with respect to the incident beam and the electron collector system. The technique has a great practical importance in that the in-focus depth of the field is very large (typically about 15 μm at a magnification of 10^4). Samples of up to a few centimeters can be accommodated in normal instruments, so that a large field can be investigated. Nonconductive surfaces usually require coating by metal (gold) evaporation to prevent surface charging, which would lead to image distortion.

In conventional instruments, the lateral resolution is in the range of 10 nm, but considerably better resolutions can be obtained by special techniques such as scanning transmission electron microscopy (STEM) using very thin samples (<100 nm) and typical resolutions of 0.5 nm [2, 103].

As mentioned previously, elemental analysis by X-ray emission (i.e., energy dispersive X-ray analysis, EDX) is often fitted to a scanning electron microscope, and the elemental distribution revealed from the emitted X-rays is displayed as a line-scan or as a two-dimensional distribution. Although the analysis comprises a layer thickness in the micron range (unlike low energy incident beams are used) this combination can provide essential information about the catalyst morphology and composition.

Figure 23 illustrates the potential of SEM for the investigation of the grain and surface morphology of a catalyst. Two morphologically different molybdenum trioxide catalysts are shown. Catalyst A consists of large thin platelets of orthorombic MoO_3 exposing predominantly the (010) plane; catalyst B consists of microcrystalline MoO_3. The two catalysts were found to exhibit different activity for the selective reduction of nitric oxide with ammonia [104] and the partial oxidation of methanol to formaldehyd [105].

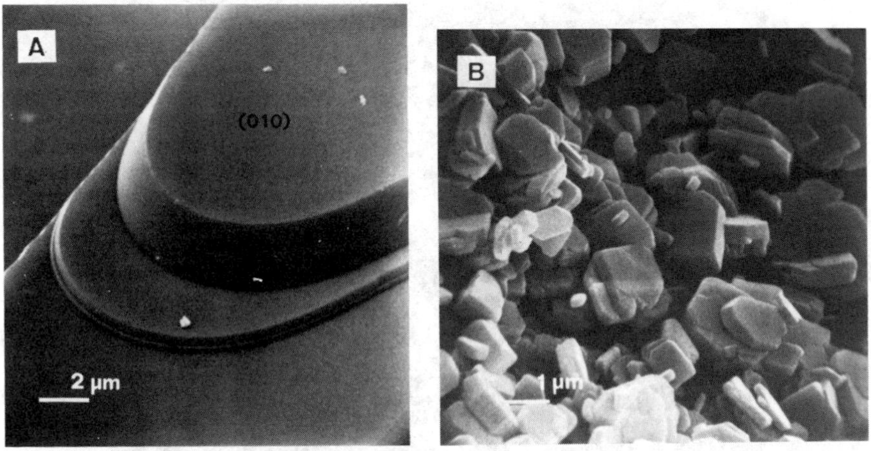

Figure 23. Example of the use of SEM for the investigation of the grain and surface morphology of a catalyst. Two morphologically different MoO_3 catalysts are shown that exhibited different activity for the selective reduction of nitric oxide with ammonia [104] and the partial oxidation of methanol to formaldehyde [105].

Transmission Electron Microscopy (TEM)

The beam of a transmission electron microscope is similar to that of an optical microscope, the difference being that the beam is one of electrons. Because of the strong interaction between high-energy primary electrons employed (100 keV – 1 MeV) and the solid specimen, the thickness of the sample is limited to typically 100–500 nm for TEM investigations, depending on the solid and the energy of the electron beam.

In studying catalyst structures, different techniques have been developed. The most frequently applied is obviously the direct observation of specimen morphology when the sample is a powder or in some other sort of subdivision. Estimation of average particle size and particle size distribution in dispersed metal catalysts is a frequent application of this technique. When the sample is of substantial macroscopic size so that electron beam penetration is not possible, information may be gained from a shadowed surface replica (e.g., carbon replica produced by two-step coating of the catalyst and carrying the detailed information) in transmission [106]. Interpretation of contrast features such as extinction contours, lattice images, and phase contrasts may also give some indication about the sample structure [2].

The best resolution of surface topography is around a few angstroms with conventional transmission electron microscopes. However, in the investigation of catalysts, the image contrast rather than the resolution is often the limiting factor. For crystalline specimens with particle sizes larger than about 3 nm, diffraction contrast is the dominant method for producing an image contrast. This depends on one or more operating Bragg reflections removing electrons from the beam, so that either the beam minus the diffracted electrons (bright field image) or the diffracted electrons (dark field image) are arranged to be collected through the objective aperture. For particles smaller than about 1.5 nm, the concept of phase contrast based on interference between the undeflected beam and scattered beams (i.e., scattering losses) is useful. In the broadest sense, the resulting contrast is therefore always a phase contrast.

TEM has been used extensively in catalysis to determine the distribution in size and location of metal particles on supported metal catalysts [e.g. 102, 103, 107]. A typical example showing the distribution, shape and location of finely dispersed Pt particles on alumina is shown in Figure 24.

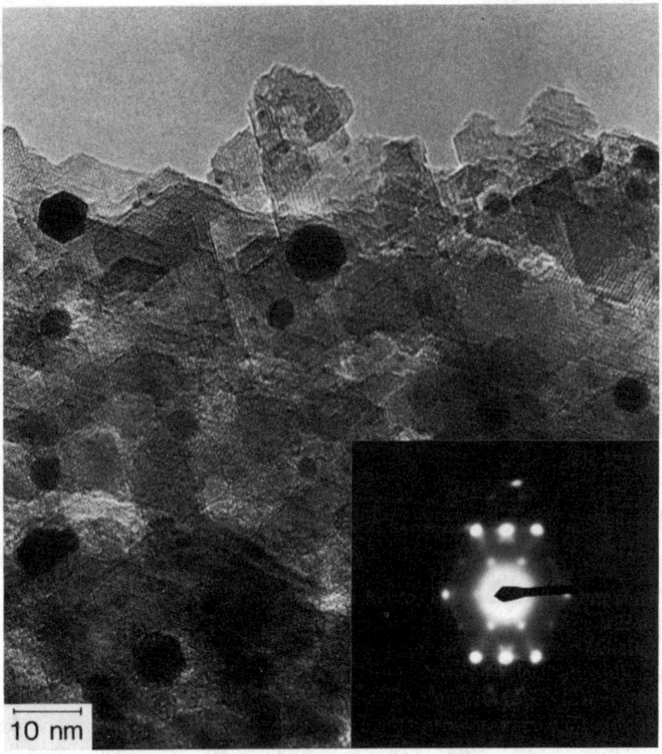

Figure 24. Transmission electron micrograph of alumina supported platinum catalyst. The platinum particles of less than 10 nm size exhibit a regular hexagonal shape (dark spots). The inset shows the electron diffraction patterns of the crystalline γ-alumina support.
Source: A. Reller, University of Zurich.

The method of determining particle size distribution is quite time consuming, since many electron micrographs must be evaluated to obtain representative statistical information about the entire surface of the catalyst.

If the mean particle size d, as determined by TEM, is to be compared with corresponding values obtained by X-ray line broadening or chemisorption measurements, care must be taken that the correct basis is chosen for the calculation of $\bar{d}$. Calculations may be based on the numerical average ($\bar{d} = \sum n_i d_i / \sum n_i$), the surface average ($\bar{d} = \sum n_i d_i^3 / \sum n_i d_i^2$), or the volume average ($\bar{d} = \sum n_i d_i^4 / \sum n_i d_i^3$). All three average diameters can be calculated from the TEM analysis, whereas X-ray diffraction line broadening gives the volume average and selective chemisorption gives the surface average only.

The combined use of high-resolution transmission electron microscopy and electron diffraction can provide a detailed morphological characterization of a catalyst. Figure 25 depicts the electron diffraction pattern and the high-resolution electron micrograph of a mixed-gel titania-silica catalyst [108]. Electron microscopy shows that the catalyst, which was used for the selective reduction of nitric oxide, consists of amorphous silica in which the titania is embedded as small crystalline domains of about 10 nm size. The metric evaluation of the diffraction pattern indicates that the titania domains adopts the structure of anatase.

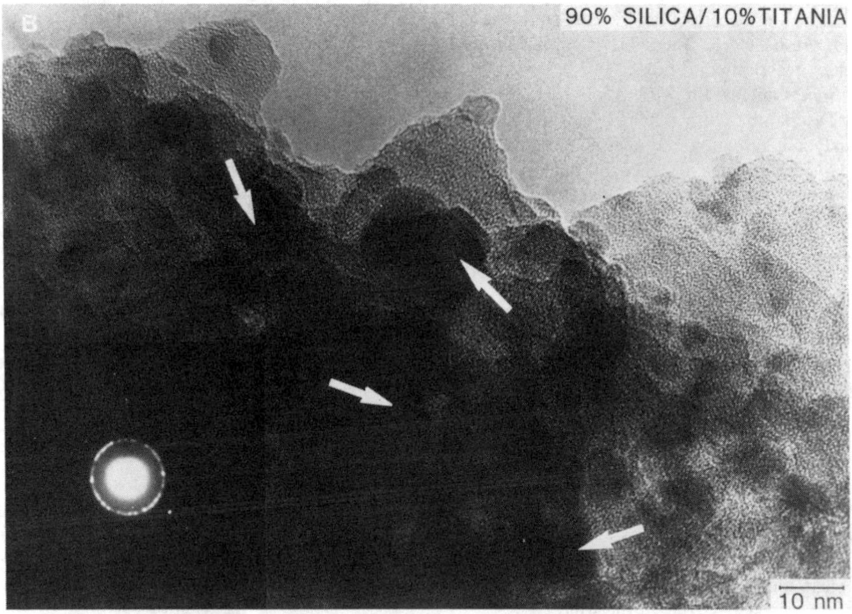

Figure 25. Electron diffraction pattern and high-resolution electron micrograph of mixed gel titania-silica catalyst [108]. Arrows point to crystalline domains of titania (anatase), which are embedded in the amorphous silica matrix.

Spectroscopic Methods

Chemical Composition of the Surface, Elemental Distribution and Concentration of Individual Components on the Catalyst Surface

Atomic identification in a solid is possible using methods that depend on an analysis based on some part of the electronic structure in the atoms considered. The atomic processes in question are described schematically in Figure 20. For example, one may measure the energy required to create a hole in a core electronic state (e.g., X-ray photoelectron spectroscopy), or one may determine the energy of an electronic transition involved in the recombination of the electron hole with an electron of higher energy (e.g., Auger electron emission).

This part of the survey discusses the most common methods used for investigating industrial catalysts, including photoelectron spectroscopy (XPS, UPS), Auger electron spectroscopy (AES) and, to a lesser extent since applied less frequently, ion scattering spectroscopy (ISS) and secondary-ion mass spectroscopy (SIMS). In addition to these more general methods several other techniques [2–4, 80] have proven to be useful for specific problems, such as infrared spectroscopy (IR) for characterizing certain functional centers on catalyst surfaces (e.g., OH groups on zeolites and silicates) and for identifying the structure of adsorbed species (as described later).

As a result of the wide range of specific applications, the number of both techniques and applications of spectroscopic methods is growing rapidly and other techniques, which are not or only superficially treated in this review, may be of certain interest for a specific investigation. In this case, the reader is referred to specialized literature cited in general reference books such as [2–4, 80, 109].

An inherent property of surface sensitive analytical techniques is that they are limited to ultrahigh vacuum (UHV) conditions. In practice, a specimen preparation chamber allowing the sample to be heated to approximately 750 K in controlled atmospheres before transferring to the spectrometer via a vacuum lock is very desirable. The conditions of measurement must be considered when interpreting experimental results, since the chemical and physical properties of a catalyst surface that are measured under UHV conditions are not necessarily representative for those that prevail under reaction conditions.

Spectrometers for XPS, AES, SIMS, and ISS investigations comprise essentially a stainless-steel UHV chamber with a holder for the solid specimen, a UHV pump, a source of excitation, and an analyzing system. UHV chambers are usually designed to carry various sources of excitation and analyzing systems attached by flanges. In that case, several different spectroscopic investigations may be done in the same apparatus.

Photoelectron Spectroscopy (XPS and UPS)

In photoelectron spectroscopy, the solid specimen is excited by a monochromatic photon beam. Either soft X-rays (XPS) of energy 1–20 keV, or ultraviolet radiation (UPS) of energy ≤ 60 eV are used for excitation. In either case, a photon of energy ($h\gamma$) can eject an electron with a binding energy less than ($h\gamma$) from the irradiated target. The relevant energy levels are shown in Figure 26. The kinetic energy of the photoelectrons emitted depends on the energy of the exciting photons ($h\gamma$), the electron work function of the spectrometer (ϕ_{sp}), and the binding energy E_B (in reference to the Fermi level) of the electrons in the solid according to

$$E_{kin} = h\gamma - E_B - \phi_{sp} \tag{28}$$

Since the work function of the electrons in the spectrometer (ϕ_{sp}) is constant, Equation 28 provides a clear identification between the kinetic energy of the emitted photoelectrons and the binding energy of the electrons in the solid.

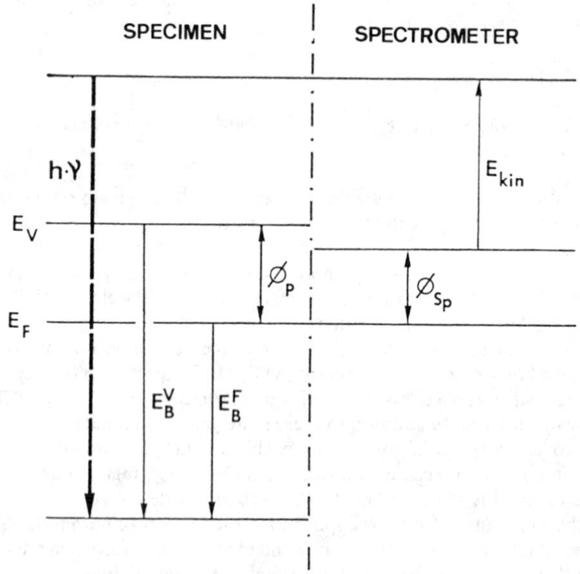

Figure 26. Relevant energy levels of photoelectron spectroscopy: E_B^V—binding energy referred to vacuum; E_B^F—binding energy referred to Fermi level; ϕ_{sp}—electron work function of the spectrometer; ϕ_p—electron work function of specimen.

X-ray photons are needed to excite core electrons and the most commonly used X-rays for this purpose are MgKα (1,254.6 eV) and AlKα (1,486.6 eV). Electrons ejected from the core levels thus have energies in the range 100–1,400 eV [108]. With ultraviolet irradiation, the most commonly used photon energies are He II (40.8 eV), Ne II (26.9 eV), He I (21.2 eV) and Ne I (16.8 eV) [2]. With these relatively low excitation energies, the technique is mainly restricted to investigation of valence electrons. Since the valence band is relatively broad, UPS spectral data are broad and the method is practically confined to obtaining fundamental information about the valence band structure [108].

Conversely, the core electron excitations in XPS result in sharp spectrum lines (on a rising background) which are specific for the chemical identity of the atoms from which the excitation occurred. More precisely, the peaks correspond to the various bound electron states in the system. They appear because some of the photoelectrons escape from the solid without energy loss. Recording of the spectra by cumulating the photoelectrons registered in the detector over a longer period of time results in statistical averaging of the response curve or clearly identified characteristic signals, respectively. Although the X-rays penetrate far into the solid, the mean free path for escape of an 100–1,400 eV electron without energy loss is typically only 0.5–3 nm, as seen in Figure 27 [110]. Secondary electron emission and inelastic losses account for much of the background in the spectrum, but the important information carried in the analysis (peaks) applies to a thin surface layer as a result of the short mean free path length. XPS is therefore inherently a specific surface technique.

With the aid of a XPS line energy table (listed for common irradiation sources) [111], the peak positions usually establish both element and core level of electron origin, particularly if more than one energy region is examined. This qualitative analysis of a sample surface can also provide essential information about impurities or poisons on catalysts. All elements except hydrogen can be detected.

The quantitative analysis aspects of XPS are even more important to catalysis: The XPS tables give the expected region for a particular core electron peak, but the precise binding energy depends on the chemical state of the parent atom (typical shift of about 1 eV per change in formal oxidation state [80]) and the chemical environment of the excited atoms. Although this shift does not reach

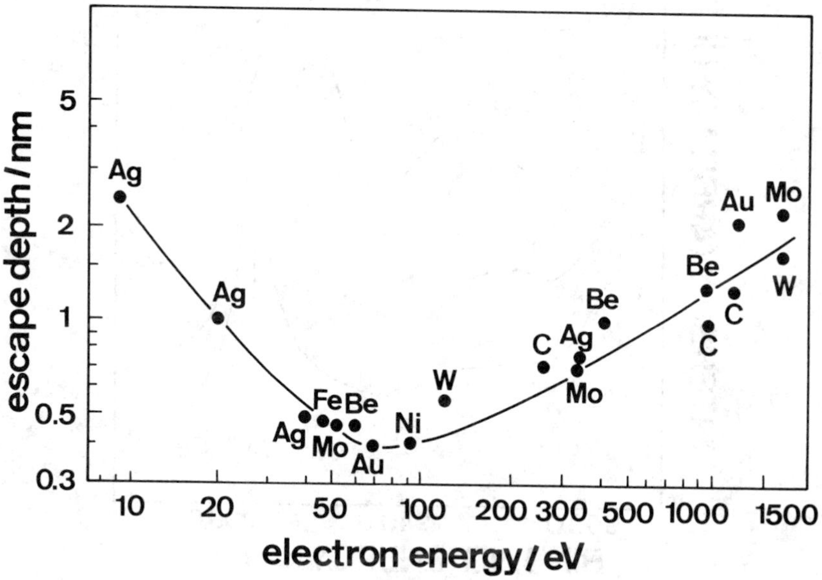

Figure 27. Escape depth for electrons for various materials as a function of the electron energy. (After Palmberg, P. W., *Anal. Chem.*, 45, 549 A (1923).)

the precision of other techniques such as NMR, it clearly reveals such phenomena as reduction of supported metal oxides. Figure 28 gives a typical example of CuO/silica reduction in H_2 at various states [112]. Association of higher binding energy with higher formal charge is a useful approximation, but does not include other sources of chemical shift such as reference level or matrix and final state effects (i.e., chemical environment of the emitting atom). The question of the reference level may be a problem that is usually overcome by referencing the characteristic peaks to a well known standard such as the Si(2p) line in supported catalysts (compare Figure 28). The shift originating from the chemical environment or appearing satellite peaks (so-called shake-up peaks commonly observed with diamagnetic compounds (Figure 28) can be the source of additional information gained from XPS data [112, 80, 109, 110, 112].

XPS has proven to be a powerful technique for investigating catalysts and their chemical structure. As a further example, the analysis of metal distribution in supported catalysts from relative surface (metal/support) abundances is mentioned: The departure of experimental data from a theoretical relationship based on uniform distribution can show the extent of metal accumulation on the external surface of the support [111, 113] or the extent of metal dispersion, respectively. Finally, we note that the great advantage of the surface sensitivity may also be a liability [80]. Since typical catalysts are porous, with most of the surface hidden from "XPS-view," caution is needed in assuming that the surface results are representative for what the molecules "see" of a catalyst surface.

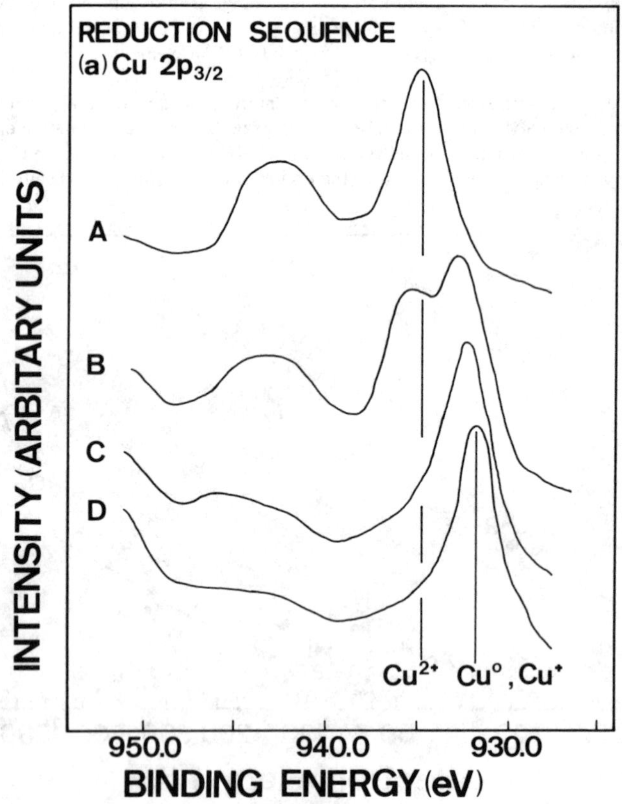

Figure 28. XPS study of the reduction of silica supported CuO. [112]. Note the shift in the binding energy of the Cu $2p_{3/2}$ electron upon reduction of Cu^{2+} to Cu^{+}, and Cu^0, respectively.

Auger Electron Spectroscopy (AES)

Analysis of the Auger electron is often combined with the XPS investigations. After a core electron has been ejected, the core hole will be filled with a more weakly bound electron. If the energy released by this transition is emitted as photon, the process is called X-ray fluorescence. However, the transition energy may be transferred to another electron (Auger electron) in a higher shell by a radiationless process (see Figure 21). The Auger electron then leaves the atom with a certain kinetic energy, which depends only on the atom from which it originates, not on the method of producing the core hole [80, 114]. The Auger-electron yield (a) and the X-ray fluorescence yield (w) are complementary ($a + w = 1$). As a consequence of the core holes produced in an XPS experiment, Auger peaks as well as photoemission peaks appear in an XPS spectrum.

The yield for the various types of Auger electrons is again a function of the atomic number: mainly K Auger electrons are produced from the lighter elements, while L and M Auger electrons prevail for the heavier elements. The energy range of Auger electrons is mainly in the order of 20–2,000 eV [115].

An Auger electron is characterized by the three energy levels involved in the transition, i.e., the ionized emptied state (X), the state (Y) from which an electron goes over to the ionized state, and the state (Z) from which the Auger electron is emitted (see Figure 21, $X = L_{II}$, $Y = M_I$, $Z = M_I$). Equation 29 approximately describes the relationship of the kinetic energy of the Auger electron E_A to the ionization energies of the corresponding shells $X(E_X)$, $Y(E_Y)$ and $Z(E_Z)$.

$$E_A = E_X - E_Y - E_Z \qquad (29)$$

Because the mean free path of the Auger electrons in the solid is also limited by inelastic losses, only a few atomic layers (typically 3–8 layers or 0.5–2 nm, compare Figure 27) contribute to the Auger signal. The surface specificity is thus in the same range as for XPS. UHV (10^{-7} Pa) is therefore required in order to keep the disturbing signals from contaminations as low as possible.

The experimental basis of AES is the measurement of the energy distribution N(E) of the Auger electrons leaving the solid specimen, where N(E) is the number of electrons with energies between E and $E + \Delta E$ that are recorded by the analyzer per unit time. In practice, recording of the differential distribution dN(E)/dE versus E is more common. Auger peaks are superimposed on a broad background originating from inelastic scattering of both primary excited electrons and various secondary electrons (compare XPS chapter). Considerable recording times of up to hours may thus be required to gain significant signals. However, as a rough guide, using electron counting and signal averaging methods, one can expect an elemental sensitivity down to about 1% of a monolayer.

The AES technique has potential for both element identification and for quantitative estimation. The identification is carried out from the Auger line energies corrected by subtraction of the work function of the analyzer material (typically in the range 4–5 eV). Particularly for the heavier metals, the total number of possible lines is quite large, but attention is usually confined to the most intense lines. A comprehensive tabulation of all Auger line energies for element of atomic numbers between 3 and 92 (hydrogen and helium cannot be identified) is available in [115].

Auger lines can also be used for quantitative determination. Considering surfaces of metals or alloys, for which the peak shapes of unknown specimens and calibration samples are almost identical [80, 109], it is valid to assume that the Auger peak height is directly proportional to the concentration. This is not generally true for metal derivates such as oxides, and measurements in terms of integrated peak areas are recommended in this case.

In examining the chemical shifts of metals versus their oxides, Wagner and Biloen [116] observed that Auger shifts are often several eV larger than photoline shifts. This difference is usually ascribed to the three electrons involved in the Auger process, all of which being subject to the influence of the chemical environment (valence states or other factors of chemical structure). Kowalczyk et al. [117] have shown that, indeed, changes in the modified Auger parameter α' [118] (i.e., the sum of the binding energy BE of a core level and KE of an Auger line derived from the core level) are proportional to the change in extra-atomic relaxation between different states. Comparing experimental Auger parameters to known α'-values in reference compounds [115, 118] thus opens a broad field of data interpretation about coordination and local environment of specific components. For example, significant differences in α' were identified for Cu-clusters of different size in/on zeolites [107] or supported on silica [112]. In the latter case, the resulting modified Auger parameter decreased approximately linearly with size of CuO and Cu-metal particles (in the range of about 1–5 nm).

Due to the high surface sensitivity of the Auger analysis, it may also be combined with ion sputtering (e.g., by bombardment with argon ions) to obtain a depth profile analysis of a catalyst. High-energy ions sputter away the surface layer (at typical rates of 10 nm min^{-1}) while the composition is measured simultaneously by AES. Depth profiles have a limited resolution because of possible homogenizing of the material during the argon-ion bombardment. Figure 29 depicts an example of depth profile measurements carried out on a Cu/ZrO_2 catalyst prepared from an amorphous Cu—Zr alloy [119]. The measurement of depth profiles in a catalyst precursor or a catalyst can provide information about thermally or chemically induced segregation processes in the surface and bulk region. Such segregation processes play an important role in catalyst activation and deactivation.

AES is also used in research for kinetic studies of adsorption and desorption of gases [114].

A further development of AES is the scanning Auger microprobe (SAM), where the surface of the solid specimen is scanned (see EPMA) by a monoenergetic primary-electron beam. Only the characteristic Auger electrons for elements of interest are then used to produce the electron-microscopic concentration diagram. The scanning Auger microprobe, with a lateral resolution of 1 μm (although resolutions of down to 50 nm have been achieved using special electron optics) and a surface sen-

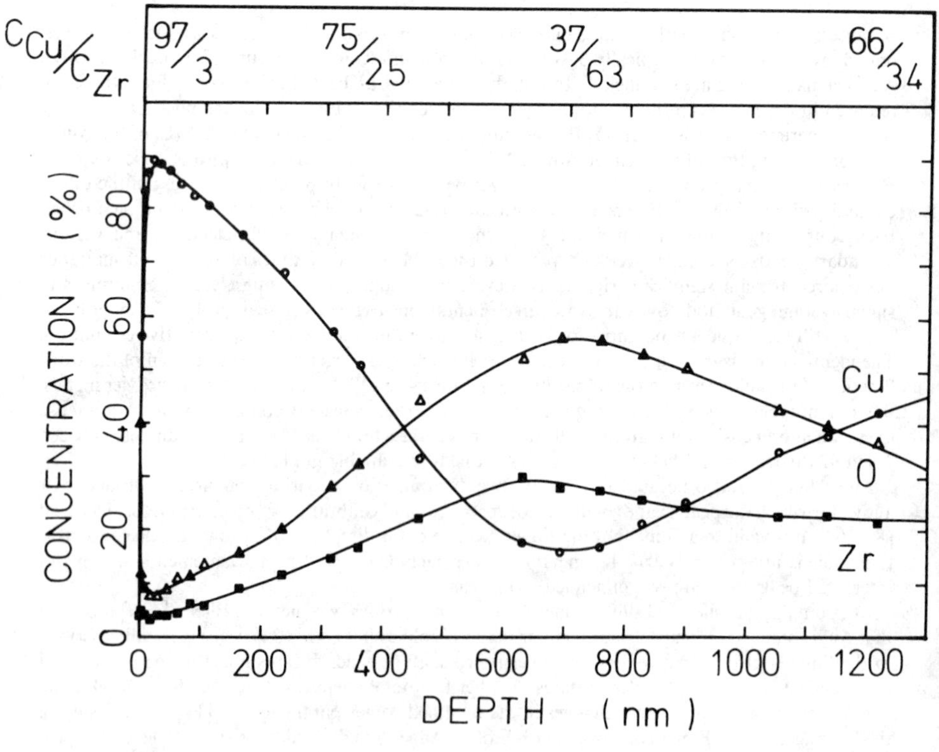

Figure 29. Depth concentration profiles determined for a zirconia supported copper catalyst by co[mbined] use of argon ion sputtering and AES [119].

sitivity of about 1 nm, is superior to the comparable EPMA. Concentration profiles also can be measured in addition to the areal distribution of elements on the surface of the solid.

Ion Scattering Spectroscopy (ISS)

Surface analytical methods involving the impact of an ion beam on the sample under investigation comprise two classes: In the first category, the energy of the reflected ions is analyzed and the results can be interpreted in terms of the specimen composition (ISS, and Rutherford backscattering spectroscopy RBS, the difference being in the energy of the incident ions). Secondary ion mass spectroscopy (SIMS), where secondary ions created by the primary ion beam are mass analyzed directly, falls into the second class (see next chapter).

When an ion with energy of 0.5–3 keV collides with a solid surface, the energy of the reflected ion may be calculated from the formula, which is strictly applicable to elastic collision between two isolated atoms (as long as there is no reaction in the chemical sense by bombarding with noble gas ions) [2, 120]. The mass of the target atom is then calculated from this relation taking the geometric configuration (scattering angle) into account. As the method relies on mass discrimination alone, no information about the chemical environment can be gained from ISS.

He^+ are commonly used as primary ions allowing unit mass resolution in the specimen up to about an atomic weight of 50 [120]. In principle, this limit can be improved using heavier ions (Ne^+, Ar^+).

The ion beam is collimated to irradiate an area of typically 1 mm^2 and curved parallel plate analyzers are commonly used. Since the incident beam consists of ions, considerable neutralization in the exciting beam occurs, much of which by an Auger type process. The intensity of the resulting signals is thus comparatively small.

Ion scattering spectroscopy is restricted to the analysis of one monolayer (surface specific) and the sensitivity is quite high in the order of 10^{-2} to 10^{-3} monolayers depending on the nature of the specimen elements. The technique is intrinsically destructive because surface atoms are continuously removed which, in turn, allows structural depth probing through the outer three or four atomic layers of the sample under investigation. Beyond this, statistical mixing causes loss of information. Although applications to catalysis are rather scarce today, the ISS technique combined with depth profiling has proven useful in delineating the layered structure of Co—Mo, Ni—Mo/alumina and Cu—Mn (hopcalite) catalysts [121].

Secondary-Ion Mass Spectroscopy (SIMS)

In secondary-ion mass spectroscopy [4, 122], the surface of the solid is bombarded with rare-gas ions of very low current density (typically Ar^+ of 2 keV at 10^{-9} A cm^{-2}). Various interactions from the fraction of the incident beam penetrating into the lattice of the solid (a small fraction is reflected) cause splitting of neutral atoms to secondary ions (apart from photons and secondary electrons). The ion emission step, grossly simplified, can be divided into the following steps: (1) transfer of energy of the primary ions to the surface particles of the solid; (2) ionization and separation of surface particles; and (3) electron exchange between emitted particles and the surface, including reneutralization. The ejected target particles thus consist of both neutral atoms and ions, but only the ionized fraction of the atoms and molecules that are removed (positive and negative secondary ions) is measured with a mass spectrometer. Monoatomic and multiatomic ions (cluster ions) are present, which may complicate the resulting SIMS spectrum considerably. For example, even a sample as simple as a nickel surface saturated with adsorbed oxygen yields the following species upon bombardment with Ar^+: Ni^+, Ni_2^+, Ni_3^+, NiO^+, Ni_2O^+, O^+, O_2^+ and some negatively charged ions are also often generated [2, 122].

Since the method depends on mass resolution, it can be applied over the complete range of atomic weights (including hydrogen) and can distinguish isotopes as well as chemical compounds by their fragment ions. Its sensitivity exceeds by far that of EPMA, XPS, AES, and ISS, typical sensitivities are in the range of 10^{-6} monolayer. Similar to ISS, the analysis is essentially confined to the topmost layer of atoms analyzed.

There are two different modes of operation depending on the application: In the static mode, sputtering is normally entirely restricted to the top three layers while in the dynamic mode substantial sputtering rates are achieved [123]. Quantitative analysis is still difficult since the yield appears to be the result of changes in proportion of ions and neutrals, which makes calibration difficult.

In addition to its importance for characterizing catalyst surfaces (mainly of oxidic catalysts, the oxidation of metals or their interaction with oxygen), in particular of the valence state of metal cations in surface compounds, the possibility of using SIMS to investigate the course of reactions is of interest. Benninghoven [122] presents an example of such an investigation for the oxidation of ethylene on an industrial silver catalyst. The formation of hydroxides, cyanides, nitrates, chlorides, and sulfates, as well as of several fatty acids on the surface of the catalyst, was demonstrated.

Despite the relative demanding and complex analysis of SIMS, it can be assumed that this technique will increasingly be used for the investigation of industrial catalysts and heterogeneous reactions.

Comparison of Important Techniques

XPS, AES, ISS, and SIMS are four important spectroscopic techniques that are applied for investigating industrial catalysts. The relevant differences in both principles and properties which, in turn, determine the range of applications of these techniques are compared in Table 2.

Electron/photon excitation (SEM, TEM, XPS, AES, etc.) is certainly more common than ion-beam irradiation, although specific information may require a special method exceptionally suited to the problem.

Table 2
Comparison of the Characteristic Properties and Performance of XPS, AES, ISS, and SIMS

Properties	XPS	AES	ISS	SIMS
Principle				
excitation	X-ray photons (Mg, AlK)	electrons (2–10 kV)	ions (0.2–2 kV)	ions (1–20 kV)
emission	photoelectrons	Auger electrons	ions	ions
Information depth (monolayers)	5–20	2–10	1	1–5
Sensitivity (fraction of monolayer)	$c \geq 10^{-2}$	$c \geq 10^{-3}$	$c \geq 10^{-2}$	$c \geq 10^{-6}$
Lateral resolution	1 mm	0.1 μm	0.5 mm	1 μm
Analyzed surface area (mm^2)	2–100	4×10^{-10}–10^{-2}	0.5–5	10^{-6}–10
Analysis of:				
elements	$Z > 1$	$Z > 2$	$Z > 1$	all
isotopes	no	no	yes	yes
chem. compounds	yes	in special cases	no	in special cases
Depth profiles	in combination with sputtering	in combination with sputtering	yes	yes
Distruction of sample	normally not	possible	normally yes	normally yes
Quantitative analysis				
without standard	±10–15%	±20–30%	limited	not possible
with standard	±5	+5–10%	possibility	possible

In this context, we cite a few additional methods used for such specific applications. The number of techniques is growing rapidly nowadays, and more and more sophisticated techniques will be available in the near future even for industrial applications.

Among these techniques are the extended X-ray absorption fine structure method EXAFS (allowing analysis of the local structure from photon irradiation), Rutherford backscattering spectroscopy RBS (ion-beam excitation, as already mentioned), Moessbauer spectroscopy (allowing determination of the nature of the metallic phase in highly dispersed bimetallic iron catalysts and particle size estimation of these clusters), and photoacoustic spectroscopy PAS (combining calorimetry and optical spectroscopy to measure the incident radiation directly). For more information, the reader is referred to the specialized literature [2, 4, 80, 120]. Some of these techniques are also included in the general scheme for characterization of industrial catalysts shown in Figure 2.

IDENTIFYING SURFACE SPECIES

The interaction of the reactants with the catalyst surface is of primary importance for heterogeneous reactions. Three main approaches to the identification of the surface species must be considered:

1. The desorption methods are based on desorption of chemisorbed species caused by external means (addition of energy) and thereby determining the type of the desorbing species and its rate of desorption.
2. Vibrational spectroscopic methods (IR, FTIR, Raman, UV-VIS) are directed towards determining the nature of bonding of adsorbed molecules and to identifying intermediate surface species.
3. Isotopic measurements: Surface species may be analyzed from isotopic identification from products. These techniques involve standard analyzing techniques such as IR, NMR, and MS as used in organic reactions. Since this method is very specific for a given application (and thus depends mainly on the imagination of the researcher), it is not discussed in this survey.

Temperature Programmed Desorption (TPD)

The desorption of a chemisorbed species can be affected by the addition of heat, electrons, ions, photons, or by an electrical field, each resulting in a corresponding set of different methods. Cvetanovic and Amenomiya [124] reviewed these methods of desorption. It is important to realize that all desorption techniques are structure-breaking; thus a potentially complex surface intermediate will be broken down into simpler gas phase species on desorption. All of the methods except one, temperature programmed desorption, require vacuum, which severely limits their use for industrial catalysts.

With the TPD method, the requirement of a vacuum can be circumvented by desorbing into a stream of inert carrier gas, the concentration of the released species being recorded as a function of temperature [125]. This method has since found wide application for industrial catalysts, primarily because it can be used under conditions approximating reaction conditions.

The basic structure of an apparatus suitable for TPD measurements is analogous to that for TPR experiments (Figure 16) and they are indeed combined in many cases [70, 126]. The system for chemical analysis usually consists of a GC detector followed by a cold trap for retention of the desorbed material, which is often combined with a mass spectrometer in order to obtain direct information about the desorbed species. A TPD measurement usually includes the following steps:

1. Pretreatment of the catalyst (desorption of foreign species and possibly reduction.)
2. Exposure to the reactant gas.
3. Desorption of the physisorbed fraction by extensive evacuation.
4. Heating of the catalyst sample using a linear temperature program. The desorbed species are transported to the detector by a stream of inert gas (normally He) and recorded.
5. Analysis of the desorbed species by gas chromatography or by mass spectroscopy.

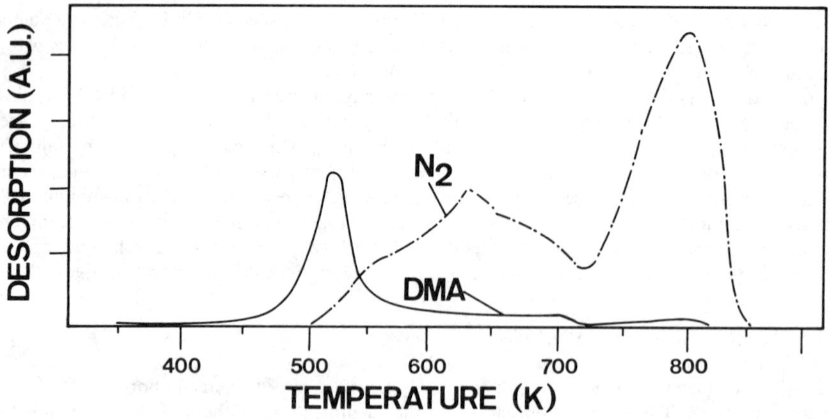

Figure 30. Desorption of nitrogen and dimethylamine (DMA) from a nickel catalyst which has been exposed to dimethylamine at 200°C [126]. The nitrogen desorption originates from the decomposition of nickel nitride that formed on the nickel surface during exposure to dimethylamine.

Figure 30 shows, as an example of a TPD spectrum, the desorption of nitrogen and dimethylamine from a nickel catalyst that had been previously exposed to dimethylamine [126]. The nitrogen desorption can be explained by the decomposition of nickel nitride that has formed on the nickel surface during exposure to dimethylamine. The nickel nitride decomposes above about 630 K and nitrogen is desorbed into the carrier gas. Nitride formation, as identified by TPD, among other things, plays a critical role in catalytic amination of alcohols, since it deactivates the catalyst.

Various studies [69, 127] are concerned with the quantitative analysis of TPD spectra, i.e., determining the desorption kinetics. Four basic cases can be differentiated: First and second order desorption kinetics with and without readsorption of the desorbed gas. In addition, kinetic models have been developed that also account for the surface heterogeneity [128]. Quantitative TPD analysis is quite difficult due to the numerous sources of uncertainties, some of the most important sources of errors being discussed by Brenner and Hucul [129].

Qualitative information is usually more important when investigating industrial catalysts, i.e., a precise determination of the desorption kinetic parameters is often not required.

The TPD technique, in particular when combined with other methods, has a broad range of applications; for example, metal/support interactions and promoter influences, as well as activation and deactivation processes, can be investigated.

Vibrational Spectroscopy Methods

Infrared Spectroscopy (IR)

This is one of the most important spectroscopic techniques used in catalysis. The main reasons for this popularity are the wide range of applications and the relatively low costs of equipment.

The technique is based on the vibrational transitions that occur when the system under investigation is exposed to electromagnetic radiation of a frequency equal to a natural vibration frequency of the system [4, 80, 130]. The commonly applied infrared spectra cover frequencies between 1.2×10^{13} to 1.2×10^{14} Hz, which are conveniently referred to wave numbers (inverse of the wavelength) in the range 400–4,000 cm^{-1}.

In each vibrational mode, all atoms of the molecule vibrate at the same frequency, but the motion is normally dominated by one particular bond or group of atoms. Interpretation of a given spectrum thus consists mainly in comparing the characteristic wave numbers to extensive tabulations in the literature [130, 131]. Frequency shifts, which are very common in IR studies may provide additional information about the environment of the characteristic groups [130].

The most powerful application is for powdered catalysts in transmission mode [131]. The sample is usually held in the form of a thin pressed waver through which the radiation passes. However, extensive scattering (more pronounced when larger particles are used) and absorption losses (e.g., in catalysts supported on silica or alumina) may cause problems and the sample preparation is thus very important (compare [4, 132]).

In situ infrared studies carried out at reaction temperatures and pressures has become increasingly interesting and may provide essential information about adsorption and reaction of surface species. A combined reactor/IR cell was designed, among others, by Hicks et al. [133]. For example, it allowed distinction of different CO adsorption sites on Cu/SiO_2 and identification of the relevant surface species in the hydrogenolysis of methyl formate over a similar catalyst [132]. An illustrating example from the latter study is given in Figure 31, showing the correlation between the characteristic absorption intensity (absorbance at 1,666 cm^{-1} due to methyl formate adsorbed on copper) versus the rate of hydrogenolysis measured simultaneously. It is clear from this analysis, that the surface species identified at this frequency (or another species in equilibrium with it) is involved in the rate determining step. By competitive adsorption measurements in the same study, it was then possible to identify the mechanism of catalyst poisoning (CO induced deposition of a formaldehyde type polymer).

Computerized dispersive spectrometers allowing signal averaging, substraction of spectra (baselines, pure support, gas-phase contributions etc.) are necessary to develop the full potential of these techniques.

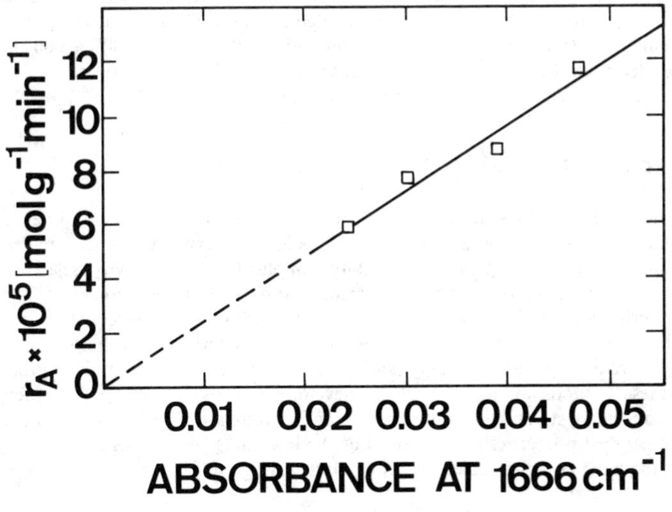

Figure 31. Correlation between IR signal from relevant surface reaction intermediate and simultaneously measured reaction rate data. The characteristic IR absorption signal due to methyl formate bound to the copper surface (absorbance at 1,666 cm^{-1}) was measured simultaneously with the rate of hydrogenolysis of methyl formate. The results indicate that the surface species is involved in the rate determining step. (Reproduced with permission from Ref. [132].)

Infrared spectroscopy may also be carried out in the reflection or emission mode, although these techniques are less frequently applied with industrial catalysts. However, multiple reflection techniques have been used with powdered catalysts with some success [134].

The FTIR technique makes use of an interferometer (e.g., Michelson interferometer) rather than a monochromator, and provides a number of advantages in the measurement of IR data: For polychromatic radiation, the interferometer output is the sum of the waves for all component frequencies, i.e., all not selectively absorbed frequencies reach the detector together (unlike monochromator spectrometers). A Fourier transform of the accumulated interferogram results yields the infrared spectrum. For the same signal to noise ratio, a great saving in time is achieved with FTIR spectrometers (Fallgett's advantage) and the absence of grating or filters yields a greater throughput of infrared energy (Jacquinot's advantage). These advantages make application of FTIR spectroscopy for in situ investigations of catalyst surfaces and adsorption thereon very attractive.

Raman Spectroscopy

When a molecule in the ground vibrational state absorbs energy from an incident photon radiation it is raised into a higher energy unstable state. The molecule then returns immediately into a lower energy state, most likely into the ground state. By far the greater part of the resulting energy scattering is thus the result of elastic collision (return to the ground state) between the incident photon and the molecule, which is known as Rayleigh scattering [80, 131]. On the other hand, a smaller part (in the order of 10^{-6} of the incident radiation) of the molecules may return to the first excited level and less energy is imparted to the emitted photon, and the wave number displacement from the incident radiation is referred to as the Raman shift. Raman spectroscopy is thus inherently an insensitive technique, and its application as a viable surface technique only makes sense by the use of powerful lasers [2, 131]. More information about this technique may therefore be found in the cited literature. However, the possibility of substantial surface enhancement of the Raman scattering as described in [135], may increase the number of applications in catalytic research.

Whereas infrared studies have been largely devoted to the study of the adsorption of relatively simple molecules, spectral studies in the ultraviolet and visible region (5,000–50,000 cm^{-1}) [4, 80] being due to electronic transitions, can be most valuable in the characterization of catalyst precursors or more complicated reaction intermediates [136].

CATALYST TESTING

As mentioned earlier, catalyst testing under reaction conditions should be an integrated part of any worthwhile catalyst characterization. The reasons for such experiments are deducted from the most important factors affecting industrial catalyst application, i.e., activity, selectivity, life-time (deactivation), and cost. The objective of laboratory catalyst testing is normally to define one or more of these criteria (excluding costs, which are usually not identified directly).

It has to be stressed in this context that most of the characterization techniques previously described cannot predict activity, selectivity, and life-time quantitatively for a given process. On the other hand, these methods are indispensible for developing catalysts, investigating reaction mechanisms, optimizing catalysts, and for catalyst screening (i.e., to relate experimental activities and selectivities to the catalyst properties as mentioned at the beginning of this survey).

Therefore, the most common objectives of catalyst testing are [2]:

1. Routine quality control of manufacturers or users of batches or samples of a particular catalyst involving, for example, standardized operation conditions.
2. Rapid screening of a series of catalysts in terms of activity and selectivity to establish an order of merit. A simple testing apparatus and relatively mild conditions may be applied and the results are often analyzed in terms of a single parameter (e.g., activity per mass, selectivity).
3. Optimization of a smaller number of catalyst to establish the performance of each sample under optimized reaction conditions. The effect of known poisons may also be investigated over a

longer period of time. In this context, deviations from ideal behavior may play an important part, as discussed later.

4. Development of a new catalyst. This objective requires more additional characterization methods in order to obtain satisfactory results.
5. Analysis of a particular reaction mechanism. The degree of sophistication in such an investigation can vary considerably and may involve a number of characterization techniques previously described including labelled compounds. The results normally assist the formulation of a suitable kinetic model or provide essential information for improving a catalyst (as discussed later).
6. Determination of a detailed kinetic model, e.g., for a deactivation or regeneration process. Such a kinetic model may then be used for other purposes than catalyst characterization such as reactor design.
7. Continuous long-term operation of a catalyst in order to simulate commercial reaction conditions. This test is normally carried out in a reactor configuration similar to a planned commercial plant (commonly of a reduced scale).

Selecting the Testing Reactor Type

The selection of the most suitable reactor type for catalyst testing depends principally on the kind of information required (objective), the reacting system, the reaction rate, the thermicity, and a finance factor. Depending on the specific application, many specialized reactor types have been developed and reviewed extensively in a number of publications [e.g., 137–139]. In this survey, only the three main types are shortly discussed: In the large group of non-steady state reactors (batch, semi-batch, and pulse reactor) only the batch type is presented while in the class of continuous reactors (plug-flow (PFR) and fluid-bed reactors) the two different types of PFR (i.e., differential and integral mode) will be discussed. The advantages and disadvantages of these reactors will be compared in Table 3. For more detailed information, we refer to the reviews [2, 138–141].

Autoclave batch reactors. These reactors are mainly applied for rapid catalyst screening in the high temperature and pressure range due to fast turnaround times (i.e., more experiments can be carried out in a space of time due to no time delay to reach steady state and fast clean-up and preparation times) and relatively low equipment and running costs. In practice, this type of catalyst testing reactor is essentially confined to liquid and three-phase reactions. Furthermore, it may be

Table 3
Comparison of Characteristic Parameters Determining the Application of Batch (Autoclave), Differential, and Integral Reactors for Catalyst Testing

Parameter	Batch-Reactor	Differential-Reactor	Integral-Reactor
Type of reactor	non-steady state	continuous	continuous
Typical conversion	10–100%	5% (<20%)	>20%
Kinetic measurements	less suited	well suited	less suited
Selectivity measurements	well suited	less suited	well suited
Intrareactor gradients	usually none	none	usually yes
Analysis	by sampling	demanding (small by-products)	by sampling
By-product accumulation	yes	none	little
Catalyst poisoning	can be strong	usually little	can be strong
Scale-up evaluation	suited	difficult	suited

of particular interest in the manufacture of pharmaceuticals and chemical specialities, which is still often carried out in batch reactors. Problems of selectivity (even at high conversions) and catalyst handling are thus studied very realistically in this case.

However, a number of serious disadvantages may make detailed studies including catalyst comparison almost impossible. They include:

1. The large thermal capacity results in long heat-up and cool-down times and temperature constants may be difficult to obtain. In order to obtain reliable kinetic data (i.e., well defined and equilibrated reaction conditions such as temperature, pressure, and starting point of the reaction), a catalyst injection system into a reaction mixture at the desired temperature is often applied. However, activity and selectivity in an industrial system may then be distorted.
2. The final composition of gas and liquid products are a time-averaged value and sampling during the course of reaction is normally required to gain reliable kinetic data, which can cause experimental problems. Problems may arise regarding the separation of the reaction products from the catalyst and the sample volume, which should be small compared to the total reactor volume. The analysis may also be difficult as a result of the pressure variations of reactants and products. This problem may be overcome by using a semi-batch mode, where one reactant (e.g., hydrogen in hydrogenations) is fed continuously to a constant pressure [138].
3. Accumulation of inhibitors and catalyst poisons can distort the product distribution or the achievable yields of products. In such a case, a continuous reactor may be desirable. In most applications, autoclave sizes of up to 1 liter volume equipped with a powerful stirrer have proved reasonable.

Differential plug flow reactor. Truly differential data (i.e., strictly the conversions are below about 5%, but conversions up to approximately 20% may be acceptable depending on the reaction system) are the most unequivocal in catalyst activity testing, since they allow useful rate calculation at fixed concentrations in a domain where mass and heat transfer influences and radial and axial dispersion effects are normally absent. As a result of the uniform conditions in the catalyst layer, the effect of most reaction parameters can be studied separately [138].

However, using a differential reactor in the single-pass mode [138, 139] may cause significant analytical problems due to the low conversions required. In the case of complex reaction systems with selectivity problems, these conversions may not be representative for the reaction behavior and specially prepared samples approaching the situation of higher conversions are then required for catalyst comparison (i.e., great experimental effort with sometimes doubtful results in terms of catalyst selectivity). Nevertheless, this technique is certainly most suited and commonly applied for analyzing the catalyst activity in selective gas-phase reactions [e.g., 132, 139].

In practice, these problems with single pass reactors are often not acceptable. The addition of a recycle—internal (e.g., Berty reactor) or external by means of a pump—often overcomes this problem in that the conversion per pass is maintained in a differential mode, but the overall conversion may be substantial. Furthermore, high recycle rate approach high mass velocities as typically used in industrial applications [138–140], and these types of reactor find wide application for catalyst screening and testing.

Integral plug flow reactor. The integral reactor normally eliminates the problems encountered in the differential mode, in particular, it allows good accuracy of the results under high conversion conditions. The selectivity behavior of different catalysts is thus easily compared from integral testing. Kinetic modeling of a reaction system is generally based on data obtained at high conversions (typically about 50% of equilibrium conversion), although numerical evaluation of the kinetic equation system is often required in this case. Of course, there are several disadvantages, the most important being the axial (and radial) non-uniformity of both concentrations and temperature. However, this type of reactor often closely approaches industrial conditions, in particular, when semi-technical integral reactors (diameter about 50 mm) are used. Catalyst life-time or deactivation and regeneration can be studied under almost technical conditions, which may be of interest in an advanced state of a catalyst investigation.

Deviations from Ideal Catalyst Behavior

The aim of catalyst activity testing in laboratory scale reactors is generally to obtain intrinsic kinetic data, i.e., activity and selectivity data that are not disguised by heat and mass transfer effects. A number of diagnostic analytical criteria and experimental methods have been developed to detect and minimize heat and mass transfer effects [141–143]. In order to apply these criteria properly some basic understanding of mass and heat transfer to and from the catalyst is necessary. Figure 32 illustrates schematically the crucial processes occurring during catalytic reactions on a porous catalyst pellet.

Heat and mass transfer limitations may arise from temperature and concentration gradients existing in three general domains: *intrareactor, interphase, and intraparticle.* The intrareactor domain refers to the macrogradients within the reactor as a whole and may originate from insufficient mixing of reactants (batch reactors), backmixing, by-passing effects and heat transfer resistance at the reactor wall (fixed-bed reactors). The interphase domain refers to the transport across the fluid film (boundary layer) separating the catalyst external surface from the bulk fluid, and the intraparticle domain refers to the processes of diffusion and conduction within individual catalyst particles. It is clear that reactor and catalyst particle geometry are important in industrial processes. The selection of a catalyst should therefore not only be based on its performance under ideal conditions. Criteria of application under process conditions must be considered, too.

An excellent review of mass (and partially heat) transfer evaluations and limitations has been presented by Satterfield [143], and thus we concentrate here only on two important criteria for estimating the influence of interphase and intraparticle mass transfer gradients.

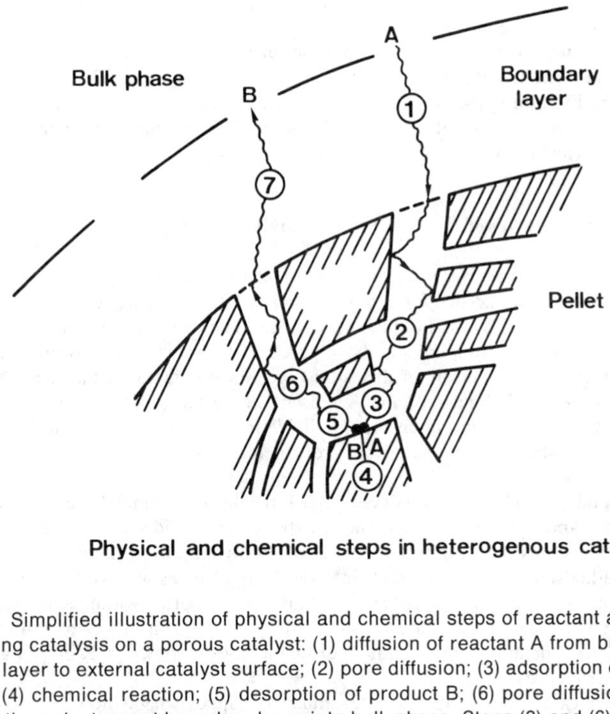

Physical and chemical steps in heterogenous catalysis.

Figure 32. Simplified illustration of physical and chemical steps of reactant and product molecules during catalysis on a porous catalyst: (1) diffusion of reactant A from bulk phase through boundary layer to external catalyst surface; (2) pore diffusion; (3) adsorption of A on active surface site; (4) chemical reaction; (5) desorption of product B; (6) pore diffusion; (7) diffusion of product B through stagnant boundary layer into bulk phase. Steps (2) and (6) are only relevant in porous catalyst systems.

Conditions for the absence of mass transfer limitations across the film surrounding the catalyst particle are negligible for a first order reaction and isothermal conditions if [143]:

$$\eta k_r/k_c a < 0.1 \tag{30}$$

where k_c = fluid-particle mass transfer coefficient
k_r = rate constant
a = specific surface of the particle
η = effectiveness factor as defined below

A comparison between typical film limitations shows [143], that heat transfer limitations normally occur long before mass transfer effects in many industrial applications.

The opposite situation is, however, usually found for intraparticle gradients. The effects of mass and heat transfer limitations within the porous structure of a catalyst particle are generally expressed in the form of an effectiveness factor, η, the ratio of observed to intrinsic rate (concentration and temperature in the particle identical to those on the particle surface). For n-th order reaction, η is shown to be a function of the Thiele modulus ψ

$$\psi = \frac{d_p}{2}\sqrt{\frac{k_r C_s^{n-s}}{D_e}} \tag{31}$$

where C_s = surface concentration
D_e = effective diffusivity of the reactant in the catalyst particle

Below ψ values of about 1, the effectiveness factor approaches unity, while above $\psi = 1$, η decreases with increasing ψ. For more details, see [143].

Application of the criteria just given requires information about parameters such as heat and mass transfer coefficients and effective diffusivity. Some procedures for estimating these parameters have been proposed in the literature [141–144]. However, the uncertainty in the estimations by means of correlations is sometimes rather critical. Thus, if possible, it is often advantageous to determine these parameters experimentally.

Determining Effective Diffusivity of Gases in Porous Catalysts

Many industrial catalytic processes operate in the intraparticle diffusion controlled regime as a result of the high reaction rates needed for commercial application. Consequently, the efficiency of porous catalysts is often limited by their diffusive properties. The theoretical prediction of the effective diffusivity of gases (and even more of liquids) in porous catalysts is frequently not possible with reasonable certainty. Part of the reason for this is that the diffusion flux may include contributions from several mechanisms, including bulk and Knudsen and surface diffusion, and the geometric models known for the pore structure often are unreliable for such predictions. Thus, data for the effective diffusivity of gases in porous catalysts are still more accurately derived from diffusion measurements.

Several experimental methods have been developed for the determination of effective diffusion coefficients of gases and vapors in porous solids. They can be broadly divided into steady and unsteady state methods. A further classification may be obtained by dividing these methods in single pellet and multi-pellet methods. The former methods include steady-state as well as unsteady-state measurements carried out on a single pellet, either sealed into, or supported within a custom built cell. The latter methods comprise unsteady-state measurements performed on a batch of porous particles. A rough classification of the most important measuring methods is shown in Table 4 together with pertinent literature references.

Table 5 gives an idea about the appropriate diffusivity ranges where the different measuring methods can be applied. Which method should be used for determining the diffusivity in a particular investigation cannot be answered rapidly, since many different factors must be considered, such as

Table 4
Survey of Experimental Methods for Determining Effective Diffusivity

Single Pellet (Diffusion Cell)		Multi-Pellet
Steady-State		Unsteady-State
Counter current diffusion flux [145–150] Permeability [151, 152]	Pulse-response [153–157] Transient desorption [158]	Time-lag [159, 160] Pulse-response in packed bed [161–163] Transient sorption-desorption [164–166]

Table 5
Appropriate Diffusivity Measuring Ranges

Method	Diffusivity $cm^2\,s^{-1}$
Single Pellet Methods	
counter current	10^{-1}–10^{-3}
permeability	10^{-3}–10^{-5}
pulse response	10^{-1}–10^{-3}
transient desorption	10^{-2}–10^{-8}
Multi-Pellet Methods	
time-lag	10^{-6}
pulse response in packed bed	$10^{-1} - 10^{-3}$
transient sorption-desorption	$10^{-6} - 10^{-14}$

the expected range of diffusivity, the geometrical shape and size of the catalyst samples, the adsorptive interaction of diffusing gases with the solid and the temperature at which the measurement is carried out. A discriminating factor is certainly the diffusivity measuring range. It is readily seen from Table 5 that, e.g., for measuring the intracrystalline diffusivity in zeolites only the time-lag and the transient sorption-desorption methods seem to be appropriate. Conversely, these methods are not well-suited to measure the effective diffusivity in most of other industrial catalysts, i.e. in the diffusivity range of 10^{-1}–10^{-5} $cm^2\,s^{-1}$.

Due to their wide application we will briefly discuss the most frequently used diffusivity determination methods that cover the range 10^{-1}–10^{-5} $cm^2\,s^{-1}$. These are the steady-state counterdiffusion method and the unsteady-state (dynamic) pulse-response method, both performed on single pellets in a diffusion cell.

Steady-State Counterdiffusion Method

The steady-state counterdiffusion method, which according to its inventors is often referred as the Wicke-Kallenbach method [145], has become one of the most widely applied methods for studying diffusion in porous solids such as catalysts. The principal experimental arrangement for steady-state counterdiffusion measurement is illustrated in Figure 33. Brief descriptions of apparatus of this type are reported in the literature [145–150]. For diffusivity measurements the porous sample is sealed into a diffusion cell in such a way that the axial faces of the cylindrical pellet are exposed

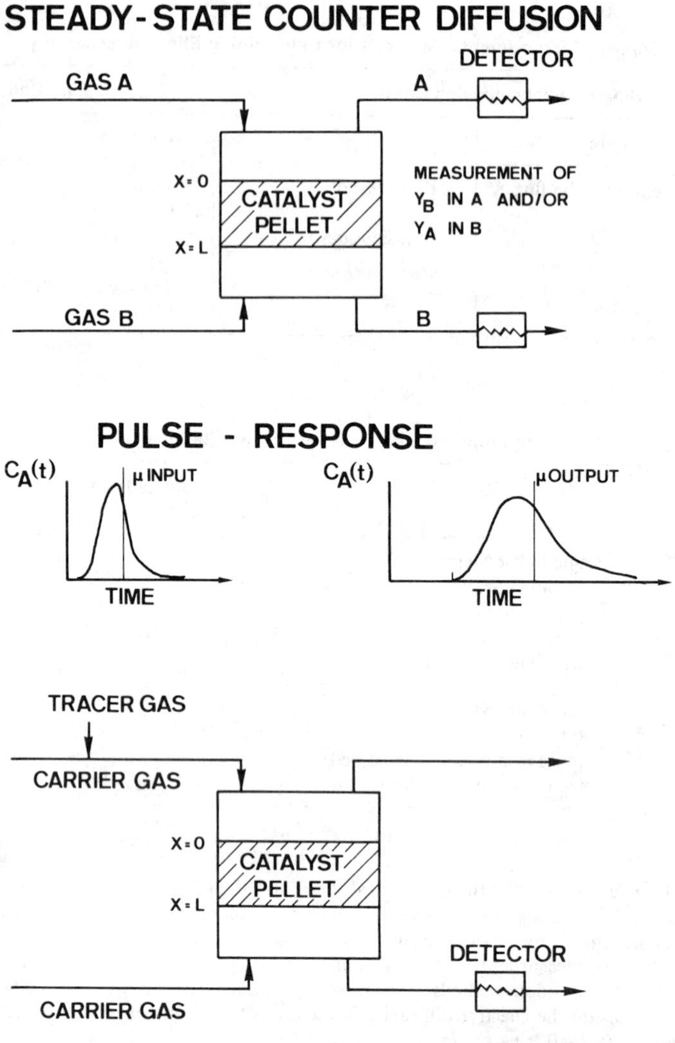

Figure 33. Principal experimental arrangements used for steady-state counter diffusion measurements and pulse-response measurements performed in a diffusion cell. μ_{input} and μ_{output} correspond to first moments of input pulse and output pulse, respectively.

to gas streams of different compositions under isobaric and isothermal conditions. Mostly, the counter diffusion of pure gases is measured. The effective diffusivity, D_e, can be determined from the known dimensions of the pellet, concentration difference, and diffusion rate employing the relationship given by Evans et al. [149].

$$N_A = \frac{D_e P}{RTL\beta} \ln\left[\frac{1 - \beta y_{A_L}}{1 - \beta y_{A_0}}\right] \tag{32}$$

where N_A and N_B = diffusion rates of components A and B, respectively
P = pressure
A = cross-sectional area of the pellet
R = universal gas constant
T = temperature
L = length of pellet
Y_{A_0}, Y_{A_L} = mole fractions of A at the upper and lower face of the cylindrical pellet

The diffusion rates N_A and N_B are determined by a mass balance over the cell.

When using this technique one has to account for the fact that due to the confined geometrical circumstances imposed, the diffusivities determined are likely to reflect only the flux through the major pores that interconnect the flat end faces of the pellet. Furthermore, due to the steady-state character of the method, dead-ended or laterally distributed micropores are not accounted for. These drawbacks can largely be circumvented by using the dynamic pulse-response method.

Pulse-Response Method

Dynamic pulse-response techniques employing measurements in a diffusion cell have become increasingly popular in recent years. The basic principle of the pulse-response method consists in the measurement of the tracer gas concentration as a function of time at the cell entrance and exit (or sometimes at the exit only) following the imposition of a concentration disturbance upstream from the cell. The principal experimental arrangement is shown in Figure 33. The effective diffusivity D_e is determined by analyzing the response of the disturbance. This is mostly done either by matching moments of a suitable mathematical model of the cell with observed moments, or by fitting an analytical solution of the model in the time domain. The methods of analyzing pulse-response data were reviewed by Ramachandran and Smith [167]. Different techniques have been proposed for pulse-response measurements in a diffusion cell arrangement. They differ in particular in the geometrical arrangement of the catalyst sample in the diffusion cell. Among these techniques, the one developed by Dogu and Smith [153, 154] is probably most frequently applied. This is to ascribe to the fact that this technique employs a Wicke-Kallenbach type cell, which makes it very flexible. Using the same cell steady-state counterdiffusion as well as permeability measurements can be conducted. Another advantage is that diffusivities can be determined by 1st moment analysis.

The pulse-response method is also used in packed-bed arrangements of porous particles such as in gas chromatographic columns [156, 157, 161–163]. However, in such multiparticle arrangements the evaluation of the pulse-response signals is considerably more complicated because axial dispersion and fluid-particle mass transfer must be accounted for before the effective diffusivity can be evaluated. The analysis of higher moments of the response signal becomes necessary in this case.

Finally, we note that each of the different measuring techniques has its own characteristics and this can lead to certain deviations in the measured diffusivity when measurements with different methods are compared. However, frequently these deviations are relatively small [156, 157] provided appropriate diffusivity measuring methods are used.

Reaction Mechanisms Based on Catalyst Testing

Catalyst testing provides one of the most powerful tools for investigating the reactions on a catalyst surface and for understanding the principles of reaction promotion by different components of a catalyst or their interrelation, respectively. Three principle aspects are outlined as follows:

1. Certain characteristic kinetic parameters such as activation energies and experimental reaction orders may provide information about the reaction mechanisms. In the reaction of NO with NH_3 over vanadium oxide for example, the Eley-Rideal mechanism is supported by the first order reaction with respect to NO and the zero order reaction with respect to ammonia [158]. Modeling of reaction rates according to standard models such as the Langmuir-Hinselwood approach can then elaborate the information in that, for example, mechanisms

can be excluded due to thermodynamical inconsistency of the estimated values for the entropy and heat of adsorption of the reactants [169].

2. Identification of intermediate- or by-products isolated during reactions may allow formulation or exclusion of reaction mechanism sequences (including activated states).
3. Isotope tracer investigations play a major role in that many generally accepted heterogeneous reaction mechanisms were elucidated by such reaction studies, in particular when they are combined with sophisticated characterization methods as presented earlier. In this context we cite again the investigation of the mechanism for the reaction of NO with NH_3 explaining in detail the role of the vanadium catalyst [168, 170] or the methanol production from synthesis gas over Cu/ZnO catalysts [171]. In the latter case, the nature and the role of different surface species was analyzed by a number of surface techniques including IR [172].

Based on these advantages, a detailed catalyst characterization by investigating a test reaction is generally considered to be an efficient, interesting, and rewarding task which should be part of most studies on industrial catalysts.

CONCLUDING REMARKS

As previously mentioned, there are numerous other methods of catalyst characterization that are not mentioned in this survey, since they are primarily applied for research purposes and less for the investigation of industrial catalysts. The number of these specific techniques is growing fast, although the principal methods suited to catalyst characterization appear to be almost exploited. However, many improvements still seem possible, mainly as a result of upgraded excitation and detection techniques. Combination of different methods (e.g., SAM) is also a likely field of principal future standard characterization techniques. In particular, more methods are needed for the investigation of catalysts *under reaction conditions*, and many techniques may be added to a reaction cell in a similar way as already described for the combined IR/reactor cell.

The importance of characterizing catalysts can hardly be overestimated, since it provides understanding of the relationship between physical and chemical properties of catalytically active solids and their activity and selectivity.

REFERENCES

1. Acres, G. J. K., *Platinum Metals Rev.*, *24*, 14 (1980).
2. Anderson, J. R., and Pratt, K. C., *Introduction to Characterization and Testing of Catalysts*, Academic Press, Australia (1985).
3. Anderson, J. R., *Structure of Metallic Catalysts*, Academic Press, London (1975).
4. Anderson, R. B., *Experimental Methods in Catalytic Research*, Vol. I; Academic Press, New York (1986); Anderson, R. B., and Dawson, P. T., *Experimental Methods in Catalytic Research*, Vol. II and III, Academic Press, New York (1976).
5. Baiker, A., *Chimia*, *35*, 408 (1981); *Int. Chem. Eng.*, *25*, 16 (1985).
6. Baiker, A., *Chimia*, *35*, 440 (1981); *Int. Chem. Eng.*, *25*, 30 (1985).
7. Baiker, A., *Chimia*, *35*, 485 (1981); *Int. Chem. Eng.*, *25*, 28 (1985).
8. Beaver, E. R., *AIChE Symp. Ser.*, *70*, 1 (1974).
9. Dart, J. C., *AIChE Symp. Ser.*, *70*, 5 (1974).
10. Adams, C. R., Sartor, A. F., and Welch, J. G., *AIChE Symp. Ser.*, *70*, 49 (1974).
11. Hoffmann, U., Emig, G., and Hofmann, H., *ACS Symp. Ser.*, *65*, 189 (1978).
12. Parrott, J. E., and Stuckes, A. D., *Thermal Conductivity of Solids*, Pion, London (1975).
13. Kulkarni, B. D., and Doraiswamy, L. K., *Catal. Rev.*, *22*, 431 (1980).
14. Krohn, D. A., Larson, D. R., and Hasselman, D. P. H., *J. Am. Chem. Soc.*, *56*, 490 (1973).
15. Garvie, R. G., *J. Amer. Cheramic Soc.*, *52*, 600 (1979).
16. Brunauer, S., Deming, L. S., Deming, W. E., and Teller, E., *J. Am. Chem. Soc.*, 62, 1723 (1940).
17. Lecloux, A. J., in J. R. Anderson, M. Boudart (Eds.) *Catalysis, Science & Technology*, Vol. 2, Springer Verlag, New York (1981), p. 171.

18. Langmuir, I., *J. Am. Chem. Soc.*, *38*, 2221 (1916).
19. de Boer, J. H., *The Structure and Properties of Porous Materials*, Butterworth, London (1958).
20. Gregg, S. S., and Sing, K. S. W., *Adsorption, Surface Area and Porosity*, Academic Press, New York (1967).
21. Brunauer, S., Emmett, P. H., and Teller, E., *J. Am. Chem. Soc.*, *60*, 309 (1938).
22. Emmett, P. H., and Brunauer, S., *J. Am. Chem. Soc.*, *59*, 1553 (1937).
23. Livingston, K. K., *J. Colloid Sci.*, *4*, 447 (1949).
24. Lecloux, A., in D. H. Everett, R. H. Otterwill (Eds.), *Surface Area Determination*, Butterworth, London (1970).
25. Meffert, A., and Langenfeld, A., *Z. Anal. Chem.*, *283*, 187 (1968).
26. Lippens, B. D., and de Boer, J. H., *J. Catal.*, *4*, 319 (1965).
27. Lippens, B. D., Linsen, B. G., and de Boer, J. H., *J. Catal.*, *3*, 32 (1964).
28. Halsey, G. D., *J. Chem. Phys.*, *16*, 931 (1948).
29. Shull, C. G., *J. Am. Chem. Soc.*, *70*, 1405 (1948).
30. Sing, K. S. W., *Chem. Ind. (London)*, 1520 (1968).
31. Sing, K. S. W., in D. H. Everett, R. H. Ottewill, *Surface Area Determination*, Butterworth, London, 25 (1970).
32. Bhambhani, M. R., Cutting, P. A., Sing, K. S. W., and Turk, D. H., *J. Colloid Interface Sci.*, *38*, 109 (1972).
33. Broekhoff, J. C. P., and Linsen, B. G., in B. G. Linsen, *Physical and Chemical Aspects of Adsorbents and Catalysts*, Academic Press, London (1970).
34. Benesi, H. A., Atkins, L. T., and Mosley, R. B., *J. Catal.*, *23*, 211 (1971).
35. Hansen, A., and Gruber, H., *J. Catal.*, *20*, 97 (1971).
36. Mikhail, R. S., Brunauer, S., and Bodor, E. E., *J. Colloid Interface Sci.*, *32*, 367 (1970).
37. Dubinin, M. M., *J. Colloid Interface Sci.*, *23*, 487 (1967)
38. Pierce, G., *J. Phys. Chem.*, *57*, 149 (1953).
39. Dollimore, D., and Heal, G. R., *J. Colloid Interface Sci.*, *33*, 508 (1971).
40. Roberts, B. F., *J. Colloid Interface Sci.*, *23*, 266 (1967).
41. Broekhoff, J. C. P., in B. Delmon, P. Grange, P. Jacobs, G. Ponclet (Eds.), *Preparation of Heterogeneous Catalysts*, Elsevier, Amsterdam, 663 (1979); J. C. P. Broekhoff, J. H. de Boer, *J. Catal.*, *9*, 8 and 15 (1967), *10*, 153, 368, 377 and 391 (1968)
42. Everett, D. H., and Haynes, J. M., in D. H. Everett (Ed.), *Colloid Science*, Vol. 1, The Chemical Society, London (1973).
43. Broekhoff, J. C. P., and van Beek, W. P., *J. Chem. Soc. Faraday Trans.*, 36 and 42 (1979).
44. De Wit, L. A., and Scholten, J. J. F., *J. Catal.*, *36*, 30 (1975).
45. Baiker, A., and Reithaar, A., *Ind. Eng. Chem., Prod. Res. Dev.*, *21*, 590 (1982).
46. Baiker, A., and Richarz, W., *Chem. Ing. Tech.*, *49*, 399 (1977).
47. Goodsel, A. J., *Powder Technol.*, *9*, 191 (1974).
48. Rootare, H. M., and Prenzlow, C. F., *J. Phys. Chem.*, *71*, 2733 (1967).
49. Klug, P. H., and Alexander, L. E., *X-ray Diffraction Procedures*, J. Wiley and Sons, New York (1974).
50. Westrick, R., *Chem. Anal.*, *21*, 2094 (1953).
51. Dry, M. E., and Ferreira, L. D., *J. Catal.*, *7*, 352 (1967).
52. Warren, B. E., *J. Appl. Phys.*, *12*, B 75 (1941).
53. Rau, R. C., in G. L. Clark (Ed.), *Enzyclopedia of X-Rays and -Rays*, Reinhold, New York (1963).
54. Wagner, C. N. J., and Aqua, E. N., *Advan. X-Ray Anal.*, *7*, 46 (1964).
55. Scherrer, P., *Göttingen Nachrichten*, *2*, 98 (1918).
56. Adams, C., Benesi, H., and Meisenheimer, R. J., *J. Catal.*, *1*, 336 (1962).
57. Brumberger, H. (Ed.), *Small-Angle-X-Ray Scattering*, Gordon and Breach (1967).
58. Selwood, P. W., *Adsorption and Collective Paramagnetism*, Academic Press, New York (1962).
59. Daniels, T., *Thermal Analysis*, Kogan Page, London (1973).
60. Batholomew, C. H., and Farrauto, R. J., *J. Catal.*, *45*, 41 (1976).
61. Morikawa, K., Shirasaki, T., and Okada, M., *Adv. Catal.*, *20*, 97 (1969).
62. Baiker, A., and Maciejewski, M., *J. Chem. Soc., Faraday Trans I*, *80*, 2331 (1984).

63. Papadatos, K., and Shelstad, K. A., *J. Catal.*, *28*, 116 (1973).
64. Arai, H., Seiyama, T., Harakawa, M., and Tominaga, H., in B. Delmon, G. F., Froment (Eds.), *Catalyst Deactivation*, Elsevier, Amsterdam (1980).
65. Coughlan, B., Narayanan, S., McCann, W. A., and Carroll, W. M., *J. Catal.*, *49*, 97 (1977).
66. Maciejewski, M., Reller, A., and Baiker, A., *Thermochim. Acta*, *96*, 81 (1985).
67. Rouquerol, J., Rouquerol, F., and Ganteaune, M., *J. Catal.*, *36*, 99 (1975).
68. Vucelic, V., Dondue, V., and Djurdjevic, P., *Thermochim. Acta*, *14*, 341 (1976).
69. Baiker, A., *Ind. Eng. Chem., Prod. Res. Dev.*, *20*, 615 (1981).
70. Robertson, S. D., McNicol, B. D., DeBaas, J. H., and Kloet, S. C., *J. Catal.*, *37*, 424 (1975).
71. Hurst, N. W., Gentry, S. J., Jones, A., and McNicol, B. D., *Catal. Rev.*, *24*, 233 (1982).
72. McCarty, J. G., and Wise, H., *J. Catal.*, *57*, 406 (1979).
73. Monti, D. A. M., and Baiker, A., *J. Catal.*, *83*, 323 (1983).
74. Jones, A., McNicol, B. D., *Temperature-Programmed Reduction for Solid Materials Characterization*, Marcel Dekker, New York, 1986.
75. Baiker, A., and Zollinger, P., *Appl. Catal.*, *10*, 231 (1984).
76. Baiker, A., and Monti, D., *J. Catal.*, *91*, 361 (1985).
77. Uda, T., Lin, T. T., and Keulks, G. W., *J. Catal.*, *62*, 26 (1980).
78. Arnoldy, P., van der Heijkant, J. A. M., Bok, G. D., and Moulijn, J. A., *J. Catal.*, *92*, 35 (1985).
79. Tomita, A., and Tamai, Y., *J. Catal.*, *97*, 293 (1972).
80. Delgass, W. N., Haller, G.L., Kellerman, R., and Lunsford, J. H., *Spectroscopy in Heterogeneous Catalysis*, Academic Press, New York (1979).
81. Gardner, C. L., and Casey, E. J., *Catal. Rev.*, *9*, 1 (1974).
82. Groeneveld, C., Wittgen, P. P. M. M., van Kersbergen, A. M., Mestrom, P. L. M., Nuitjen, C. E., and Schuit, G. C. A., *J. Catal.*, *59*, 153 (1979).
83. Baiker, A., Monti, D., and Wokaun, A., *Appl. Catal.*, *23*, 425 (1986).
84. Sharma, V. K., Wokaun, A., and Baiker, A., *J. Phys. Chem.*, *90*, 2715 (1986).
85. Haeberlen, U., *High Resolution NMR in Solids*, Academic Press, New York (1976).
86. Slichter, C. P., *The Principles of Magnetic Resonance*, 2nd ed., Springer Verlag, New York (1978).
87. Bodart, P., Nagy, J. B., Debras, G., Gabelica, Z., Derouane, E. G., and Jacobs, P. A., *Bull. Soc. Chim. Belg.*, *92*, 711 (1983).
88. Birks, L. S., *Electron Probe Microanalysis*, J. Wiley & Sons, New York (1971).
89. Chen, H. C., and Anderson, R.B., *Ind. Eng. Chem., Prod. Res. Dev.*, *12*, 122 (1973).
90. Baiker, A., and Holstein, W. L., *J. Catal.*, *84*, 178 (1983).
91. Harbord, N. H., *Platinum Metal Rev.*, *18*, 97 (1974).
92. Miyazaki, K., *J. Catal.*, *28*, 245 (1973).
93. Farrauto, R. J., *AIChE Symp. Ser.*, *70*, (143), 9 (1974).
94. Dorling, T. A., and Moss, R. L., *J. Catal.*, *7*, 378 (1967).
95. Dalla Betta, R. A., *J. Catal.*, *34*, 57 (1974).
96. Emmett, P. H., and Brunauer, S., *J. Am. Chem. Soc.*, *59*, 310 (1937).
97. Wanke, S. W., and Dougharty, N. A., *J. Catal.*, *24*, 367 (1972).
98. Benson, J. E., and Boudart, M., *J. Catal.*, *4*, 704 (1965).
99. Sermon, P. A., *J. Catal.*, *24*, 460 (1972).
100. Evans, J. W., Wainwright, M. S., Bridgewater, A. J., and Young, D. J., *Appl. Catal.*, *7*, 75 (1983).
101. Tanabe, K., *Solid Acids and Bases*, Kondansha-Academic Press, Tokyo, New York (1970).
102. Gundry, P. J., and Jones, G. A., *Electron Microscopy in the Study of Materials*, E. Arnold, London (1976).
103. Spence, J. C. H., *Experimental High-Resolution Microscopy*, Clarendon Press, Oxford (1981).
104. Baiker, A., Dollenmeier, P., and Reller, A., *J. Catal.*, *103*, 394 (1987).
105. Baiker, A., and Gasser, D., *Z. Phys. Chem., Neue Folge*, *149*, 119 (1986).
106. Brammer, I. S., and Dewey, M. A. P., *Specimen Preparation for Electron Microscopy*, Blackwell, Oxford (1966).
107. Sexton, B. A., Smith, T. D., and Sanders, J. V., *J. Electr. Spectrosc. Rel. Phenom.*, *35*, 27 (1985).
108. Baiker, A., Dollenmeier, P., Glinski, M., and Reller, A., *Appl. Catal.*, *35*, 365 (1987).

109. Brundle, C. R., and Baker, A. D., (Eds.), *Electron Spectrosopy: Theory, Techniques and Applications*, Vol. 2, Academic Press, London (1978).
110. Brundle, C. R., *Surf. Sci.*, *48*, 99 (1975).
111. Perkin-Elmer Corpn., *Handbook of X-ray Photoelectron Spectroscopy*, Physical Electronics Division (1979).
112. Kohler, M. A., Curry-Hyde, H. E., Sexton, B. A., Hughes, A. E., and Cant, N. W., *J. Catal.*, *108*, 323 (1987).
113. Sexton, B. A., Hughes, A. E., Foger, K., *J. Catal.*, *88*, 466 (1984).
114. Pentenero, A., *Catal. Rev.*, *5*, 199 (1971).
115. Coughlan, W. A., and Clausing, R. E., *Atomic Data*, *5*, 317 (1973).
116. Wagner, C. D., and Biloen, P., *Surf. Sci.*, *35*, 82 (1973).
117. Kowalczyk, S. P., Ley, L., McFeely, F. R., Pollak, R. A., and Shirley, D. A., *Phys. Rev. B*, *9*, 381 (1974).
118. Wagner, C. D., Galeand, L. H., and Raymond, R. H., *Anal. Chem.*, *51*, 466 (1979).
119. Vanini, F., Büchler, S., Xin-nan Yu, Erbudak, M., Schlapbach, L., and Baiker, A., Surf. Sci., *189/190*, 1117 (1987).
120. Buck, T. M., in A. W. Czanderna (Ed.), *Methods of Surface Analysis*, Elsevier, Amsterdam (1975).
121. Veprek, S., Cocke, D. L., Kehl, S., and Oswald, H. R., *J. Catal.*, *100*, 250 (1986).
122. Benninghofen, A., *Critical Review in Solid State Science*, CRC Press, Cleveland (1978).
123. Yu, M. L., and Reuter, W., *J. App. Phys.*, *52*, 1478 (1981). York (1974).
124. Cvetanovic, R. J., and Amenomiya, Y., *Catal. Rev.*, *6*, 21 (1972).
125. Amenomiya, Y., and Cvetanovic, R. J., *J. Phys. Chem.*, *67*, 144 (1963).
126. Baiker, A., Monti, D., and Yuan Son Fang, *J. Catal.*, *88*, 81 (1984).
127. Kovalinka, J. A., Scholten, J. J. F., and Rasser, J. C., *J. Catal.*, *48*, 365 (1977).
128. Tokoro, Y., Uchijiama, T., and Yoneda, Y., *J. Catal.*, *56*, 110 (1979).
129. Brenner, A., and Hucul, D. A., *J. Catal.*, *56*, 134 (1979).
130. Little, L. H., *Infrared Spectra of Adsorbed Species*, Academic Press, New York (1966).
131. Colthup, N. B., Daley, L. H., and Wiberley, S. E., *Introduction to Infrared and Raman Spectroscopy*, Academic Press, New York (1975).
132. Monti, D. M., Cant, N. W., Trimm, D. L., and Wainwright, M. S., *J. Catal.*, *100*, 17 (1986).
133. Hicks, R. F., Kellner, C. S., Savatsky, B. J., Hecker, W. C., and Bell, A. T., *J. Catal.*, *71*, 216 (1981).
134. Haller, G. L., Rice, R. W., and Wan, Z. C., *Catal. Rev.*, *13*, 259 (1976).
135. Wokaun, A., and Baiker, A., *Chimia*, *40*, 2 (1986).
136. Leftin, H. P., *J. Phys. Chem.*, *64*, 1714 (1960).
137. Mahoney, J. A., *NATO Adv. Study Inst. Ser.*, *Ser. E 52*, 487 (1981).
138. Doraiswamy, L. K., and Tajbl, D. G., *Catal. Rev.*, *10*, 177 (1974).
139. Sunderland, P., *Trans. Instn. Chem. Engers.*, *54*, 135 (1976).
140. Berty, J. M., *Catal. Rev.*, *20*, 75 (1979).
141. Butt, J. B., and Weekmann, V. W., *AIChE Symposium Series*, *70*, 27 (1974).
142. Maers, D. E., *Ind. Eng. Chem. Proc. Des. Dev.*, *10*, 541 (1974).
143. Satterfield, C. N., *Mass Transfer in Heterogeneous Catalysis*, Kreiger, New York (1981).
144. Kulkarni, B. D., and Doraiswamy, L. K., *Catal. Rev.*, *22*, 431 (1980).
145. Wicke, E., and Kallenbach, R., *Kolloid Z.*, *97*, 135 (1941).
146. Weisz, P. B., and Schwartz, A. B., *J. Catal.*, *1*, 399 (1962).
147. Youngquist, G. R., *Ind. Eng. Chem.*, *62*, 52 (1970).
148. Dullien, F. A. L., *Porous Media-Fluid Transport and Pore Structure*, Academic Press, New York, 1979.
149. Evans, R. B., Watson, G. B., and Mason, E. A., *J. Phys. Chem.*, *35*, 2076 (1961).
150. New, M., Baiker, A., and Richarz, W., *Chem. Ing. Tech.*, *51*, 972 (1979).
151. Smiljanic, D. D., *J. Catal.*, *46*, 214 (1977).
152. Otani, S., Wakao, N., and Smith, J. M., *A.I.CH.E.J.*, *11*, 439 (1965).
153. Dogu, G., and Smith, J. M., *A.I.Ch.E.J.*, *21*, 58 (1975).
154. Dogu, G., and Smith, J. M., *Chem. Eng. Sci.*, *31*, 123 (1976).

155. Gibilaro, L. G., and Waldram, S. P., *J. Catal.*, *67*, 392 (1980).
156. Baiker, A., New, M., and Richarz, W., *Chem. Eng. Sci.*, *37*, 643 (1982).
157. Cresswell, D. L., and Orr, N. H., in *Residence Time Distribution Theory in Chemical Engineering*, (Eds. A. Pethö, R. D. Noble), Verlag Chemie, Weinheim, (1982), pp. 41–74.
158. Gorring, R. L., and De Rosset, A. J., *J. Catal.*, *3*, 341 (1964).
159. Barrer, R. M., *J. Phys. Chem.*, *57*, 35 (1953).
160. Goodknight, R. C., I. Fatt, *J. Phys. Chem.*, *64*, 760 (1962).
161. Schanel, L., and Schneider, P., *Chem. Eng. J.*, *2*, 274 (1971).
162. Haines, H. W., and Sharma, P. N., *A.I.Ch.E.J.*, *19*, 1043 (1973).
163. Suzuki, M., and Smith, J. M., *A.I.Ch.E.J.*, *18*, 326 (1972).
164. Habgood, H. W., *Can. J. Chem.*, *36*, 1384 (1958).
165. Satterfield, C. N., and Margets, W. G., *AIChE J.*, *17*, 295 (1971).
166. Ma, Y. H., and Lee, T. Y., *Ind. Eng. Chem. Fundam.*, *16*, 44 (1977).
167. Ramachandran, P. A., and Smith, J. M., *Ind. Eng. Chem. Fundam.*, *17*, 148 (1978).
168. Inomata, M., Miyamoto, A., and Murakami, Y., *J. Catal.*, *62*, 140 (1980).
169. Boudart, M., Mears, D. E., Vannice, M. A., *Ind. Chim. Belg.*, *32*, 281 (1967).
170. Miyamoto, A., Kobayashi, K., Inomata, M., and Murakami, Y., *J. Phys. Chem.*, *86*, 2945 (1982).
171. Klier, K., *Adv. in Catal.*, *31*, 243 (1982).
172. Boccuzzi, F., Ghiotti, G., and Chiorino, A., *Surf. Sci.*, *156*, 933 (1985).

CHAPTER 2

PROPERTIES AND KINETICS OF ZEOLITE-TYPE CRACKING CATALYSTS

Guang-Xun Wang, Shi-Xiong Lin, and Guang-Hua Yang

University of Petroleum, China
Dongying, Shandong
People's Republic of China

CONTENTS

INTRODUCTION

More than half a century has passed since natural clay (montmorillonite) was used for the first time as a cracking catalyst to facilitate the conversion of gas oil to gasoline. The presence of a cracking catalyst in the oil vapor extensively modifies the mechanism of the hydrocarbon cracking reaction and greatly increases the reaction rate. At the same time, a greater yield of a better quality gasoline and more valuable gases are provided. However, the catalyst soon becomes deactivated during use due to carbonaceous deposition on its surface, which is formed in the cracking reaction. Fortunately, the activity of the coked catalyst can be readily restored by burning off the coke with air in a regenerator. This regenerated catalyst can be used for further cracking.

During the long period of process development in the field of fluid catalytic cracking (FCC), great strides have been made both in the evolution of catalyst manufacture and in the innovation of process technology. One of the most significant events in the chronicle of the catalytic cracking industry was probably the advent of cracking catalyst containing zeolite. In 1962, when a relatively minor proportion of zeolite crystals was incorporated into an amorphous silica-alumina matrix a brand-new catalyst was created.

The zeolite component in the catalyst has a remarkable catalytic activity, and its synergism with the matrix makes the zeolite catalyst superior to the amorphous silica-alumina catalyst in the following respects:

1. Remarkably higher activity and stability
2. Much better selectivity for gasoline
3. Less susceptibility to metal poisoning
4. Lower coke producing tendency.

The chief drawback is a slight reduction of the gasoline octane number.

Since then, the zeolite catalyst has been developed rapidly and has become dominant in the catalyst market. The incorporation of zeolite in the cracking catalyst has become a common practice, requisite in catalyst manufacture. The replacement of amorphous catalyst by zeolite-type catalyst has led to the revival of the fluid cracking process. One of the vital innovations achieved in the technology was the adoption of a short contact time riser reactor to supercede the dense bed reactor, in order to take full advantage of the zeolite cracking catalysts.

Modern cracking catalysts are sophisticated materials made by means of chemical synthesis. They are tailor-made to meet the requirements for processing heavy oil of various crackability and to accommodate the operating conditions for the ever-improving FCC processes. Recently, the main trends of cracking catalyst development are toward residuum cracking and/or octane enhancing capabilities [1–4].

In recent years, the world production of cracking catalysts has exceeded 320,000 tons annually, which would be sufficient to process at least 600 million tons of vacuum gas oil. The major catalyst manufacturers in the world are able to supply a range of products distinctive in property and add new catalyst designations to their product list year after year.

The wise choice and optimum use of the cracking catalyst calls for a comprehensive knowledge of the catalytic cracking process, involving the interaction of feedstock, catalyst and engineering. A vast amount of information is available both in the journal literature and in the patent literature. Excellent reviews on the catalytic aspects of contemporary FCC processes have been written by Venuto and Habib [5, 6], Corma and Wojciechowski [7], Maselli and Peters [8], and Otterstedt et al [9].

We intend to focus our discussion on the catalyst properties that are closely related to the performance in FCC units. Emphases are to be placed on the kinetics of catalytic cracking and the kinetics of catalyst regeneration. Special attention will be given to the latest developments in these fields, including the achievements in this country.

ROLE OF CRACKING CATALYST IN FCCU

In a fluid catalytic cracking unit, the catalyst should perform three basic functions: (1) provide sufficient number of active sites for the catalytic conversion of the feedstock, (2) transfer a part of heat evolved in coke burning from the regenerator to the reactor in order to support the endothermic cracking reaction; and (3) withstand and/or even positively depress the deleterious effects of the severe environments that prevail in the reactor and in the regenerator.

It may be instructive to make a brief description of a commercial reactor-regenerator system to show how the cracking catalyst plays its role and what impairments it suffers during its lifetime in the unit. As shown in Figure 1 the system consists of four sections: the riser reactor, the separator, the stripper and the regenerator. The catalyst recirculates periodically through these sections in the sequence mentioned above.

As soon as the red-hot regenerated catalyst at about 700°C enters at the base of the riser reactor, it meets a jet or jets of the preheated feedstock and steam, which is used to atomize and vaporize the feedstock. Drastic interaction between the catalyst and the feedstock begins suddenly. It is at the mixing zone that there occurs the major portion of the heat transfer process between the catalyst and the feedstock, mass transport into the pores of catalyst particles and the catalytic reaction including coke deposition on the catalyst. As a result, the catalyst is suddenly cooled down to a temperature of about 550°C. The evaporization and cracking of the feed causes about a threefold volume expansion, which provides the flow of the mixture up the riser to the separator. Time for the mixture to pass through the reactor is approximately 1 to 4 seconds.

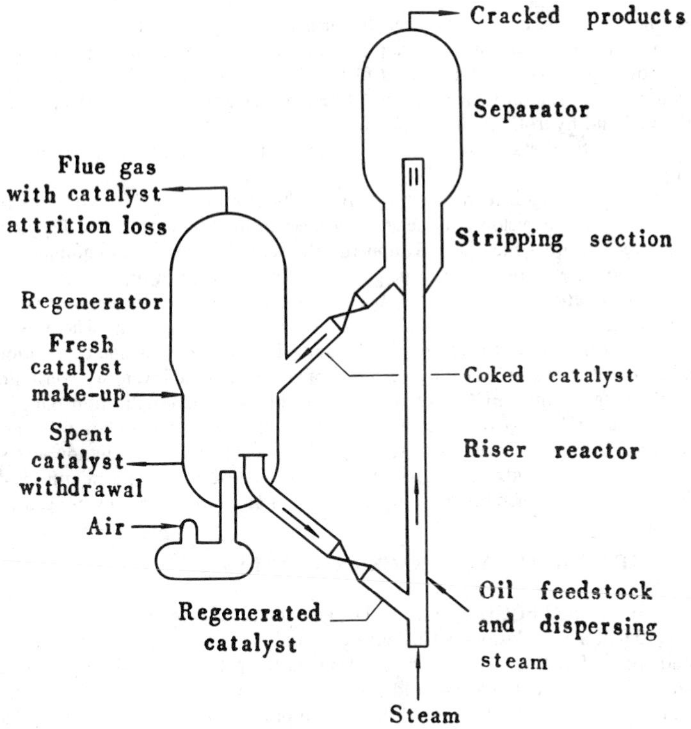

Figure 1. Circulation of fluid catalyst in FCC unit.

In spite of this short residence time, due to the high activity of zeolite catalyst, about 70% of the weight of the feed is converted into products, including the undesired yet necessary amount of coke, typically 4 to 5% of the weight of the feed, deposited on the basis of catalyst weight.

The coke deposition on the catalyst is, on the one hand, a nuisance in the sense of causing rapid catalyst deactivation by fouling the active sites on the catalyst surface, while on the other hand, it is a requisite in the sense of supplying all the energy needed to actuate the operation of the FCC complex.

Besides coke deposition, traces of metal elements existing in the feed are precipitated quantitatively on the catalyst. These metal contaminants will accumulate during the continued cycles of catalyst circulation and seriously affect the catalyst performance.

At the exit of the riser reactor, the coked catalyst carried by the gaseous oil products rushes into the separator, where it is quickly disengaged from the gaseous stream, in order to stop over-cracking, and then it flows into the stripping section, where the oil vapor entrapped in the interstices among catalyst particles and in the pores within the particles is recovered by steam stripping.

On entering the regenerator, the coked catalyst particles find themselves plunged into a fluidized bed of red-hot regenerated catalyst particles, which have already been in the regenerator for varying lengths of time. Owing to the very high rate of heat transfer, these new particles will be heated in milliseconds to approach the temperature of their neighbors. When the coke on the catalyst is burnt off, the catalyst activity is almost completely restored and having replenished with heat, it is ready for the next cycle.

In this manner, the cracking catalyst can be used repeatedly 5,000–10,000 times during its average lifetime of 2–3 months.

During regeneration, the coke is oxidized to form CO, CO_2, and H_2O. The steam from the burning of hydrogen constituent in the coke plus the atmospheric moisture carried into the regenerator by air blower produce an environment of 10–20% steam [8, 10]. The repeated exposure to heat and steam in the regenerator causes cumulative, irredeemable damage to the catalyst activity, known as thermal and hydrothermal deactivation.

In resid processing, the metal contamination is an important factor affecting the catalyst activity and selectivity.

Another loss of catalyst is due to attrition. Catalyst particles move at high speed (some 10–30 m/s) in the riser reactor and the cyclones for separating them from gaseous streams. They collide with each other at very high frequency [11, 12] and rub the walls of the process equipment. The fines produced by attrition are carried by the flue gas out of the regenerator and are lost.

For the sake of offsetting the effect due to catalyst deactivation, fresh catalyst is replenished periodically to maintain a constant level of catalyst activity in the FCC unit. The make-up rate is about 1% per day of the catalyst inventory in the unit. If the rate of loss due to attrition is lower than the make-up rate, the surplus catalyst is withdrawn to keep the inventory constant.

Therefore, the catalyst in a FCC unit is in a state of dynamic equilibrium. During smooth operation, everything is kept virtually constant. Though the catalyst population in the unit is a mixture of different ages, widely differing activities, different metal contamination levels, etc., the overall characteristics of the mixture is always kept nearly constant. Such a mixture is defined as an equilibrium catalyst, to differentiate from fresh catalyst and laboratory steam aged catalyst.

PROPERTIES OF ZEOLITE-TYPE CRACKING CATALYSTS

Aside from feedstock and FCCU operation, the performance of cracking process depends largely upon the properties of the catalyst used. Current FCC catalyst are featuring ever improving catalytic properties and special functions to meet the challenge of the petroleum and oil product market.

A successful FCC catalyst should have adequate activity to crack various feedstocks, including poor-quality, residual oil (resid). Its yield selectivity and product quality should be satisfactory and flexible to optimization. It should be stable both hydrothermally and mechanically to reduce its consumption in use. Its fluidizing characteristics should be able to assure ease of fluidization and transportation in the reactor and regenerator, and ease of separation from oil products and flue gases.

The resistivity towards metal contamination is one of the salient requirements during resid cracking. Compatibility with Ni or V passivating agents is also required.

The importance of regenerability (rate constant and activation energy of coke combustion) of the coked catalyst is noteworthy. Shorter time of exposure in regeneration environment will cause less hydrothermal deactivation in a smaller regenerator.

All FCC catalysts produce coke in the cracking reaction. An ideal catalyst is not what does not make coke at all. Coke is required for the heat balance of FCCU. Excessive coke due to resid processing and metal contamination is an important problem to be solved by catalyst innovation.

Catalysts containing ultrastable Y zeolite (USY) are more stable to heat than those containing rare earth exchanged Y zeolite (REY and REHY). They have lower hydrogen transfer activity and make higher octane gasoline.

Some catalysts have the SO_x reduction capability either by incorporating the SO_x sorbing ingredients into the catalyst or by adding them as an additive to the catalyst. Others have the CO combustion capability. The ZSM-5 containing catalysts are currently being tested on a limited basis to improve the gasoline octane.

Various analyses of zeolitic cracking catalyst is listed in Table 1.

Structure and Composition of Zeolite Y and USY

Zeolites are crystalline forms of aluminosilicates. The synthetic type X and Y zeolites resemble their natural counterpart, faujasite. They have open structures with relatively large cavities, known as supercages or cages. These cages are interconnected by windows of about 0.9 nm in diameter, allowing molecules with a cross-section smaller than 0.9 nm to enter the supercage.

Table 1
Analysis of FCC Catalyst

Analysis	Methods
Physical Properties	
Particle size distribution	Consecutive elutriation
Apparent bulk density	Weighing
Attrition index	Jersey or Davision apparatus
Pore volume distribution and surface area	Mercury intrusion and nitrogen adsorption
Zeolite unit cell size	XRD, IR
Zeolite content	XRD, Benesi
Crystalline alumina	XRD
Framework/Nonframework Al	^{27}Al NMR, IR
Chemical Composition	
SiO_2, Al_2O_3, RE_2O_3, La/Ce, Na_2O, Fe, Ni, V, $SO_4^=$, Cl^-,	Chemical or instrumental analysis
Catalytic tests	
Activity, selectivity, and stability	Microactivity test (MAT) and steam aging
Product yield and quality	MAT, pilot test
Regenerability	Kinetic experiment, DTG
Metal resistance	Metal impregnation and MAT

The structure of zeolite Y is depicted in Figure 2. The fundamental building blocks are SiO_4 and AlO_4 tetrahedra linked to each other by common oxygen atoms, which are denoted by the line segments. The joint points indicate the positions of either Si or Al atoms. Lowenstein's rule requires that each aluminum atom be bonded to four silicon atoms. This means that two AlO_4 tetrahedra can not be linked directly. They must be separated by at least one SiO_4 tetrahedron.

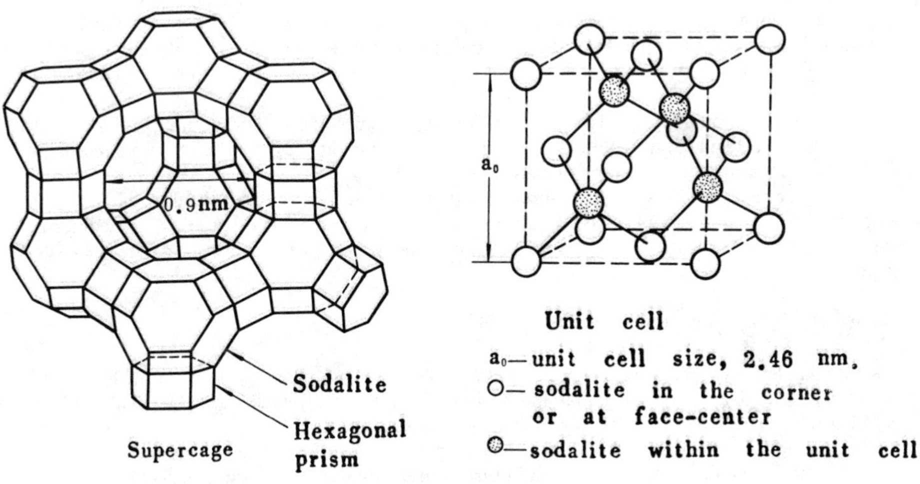

Figure 2. Structure of zeolite X and Y: left, the supercage; right, the unit cell.

There are 24 tetrahedra arranged to form a cubo-octahedron, known as a sodalite unit. This is a secondary building unit. There are 8 sodalite units linked by hexagonal prisms in a diamond-type array to form a unit cell, which is the elementary building block of zeolite Y. Shown in Figure 2 is the central part of a unit cell. The large 12-membered ring can be seen. It is the aperture allowing the oil molecules smaller than 0.9 nm in size to enter the super cage and the cracked oil molecules to leave. This is known as the shape selectivity of zeolite (molecular sieve effect).

Another type of shape selectivity is the space limitation for the reaction intermediate product (or transition state) formed in the supercage. Formation of an intermediate molecule larger than the space in the supercage will be prevented. This is advantageous to reduce the yield of coke or coke precursor, because they are usually greater than the supercage [13].

The faujasite product crystallized in its synthesis process is the sodium form zeolite. The chemical composition of a unit cell may be expressed as:

$$Na_n[(AlO_2)_n(SiO_2)_{192-n}].235\ H_2O$$

The total number of alumina and silica tetrahydra per unit cell is definite and equals to $24 \times 8 = 192$, but the atom ratio of silicon to alumina is subject to change, depending on the conditions during synthesis. Admittedly, the Si/Al ratio of zeolite Y is generally defined as between 2.5 and 5.0. Those with Si/Al ratio lower than 2.5 are referred to zeolite X, while those with ratio higher than 5.0 are regarded as in the range of ultrastable Y (USY).

The synthetic NaY looks like a white powder. Under the microscope, agglomerates of zeolite crystals with some intergrowth and impurities can be seen. To be used in catalyst manufacture, the crystal size should be controlled at about 1 micrometer. Though smaller crystals will exhibit higher activity, their inferior stability at high temperatures in the regenerator excludes them from practical application in catalyst formulations.

Because zeolite NaY has little carbocation activity and its sodium content makes it unstable in the regenerator, all sodium ions must be exchanged with hydrogen ions or cations of rare earth (RE) elements. Since Y zeolite is weak in acid solution, direct exchange with acid is considered inadequate. Therefore, HY zeolite is obtained in a circuitous way: first exchanging NaY with ammonium salt solution and then calcining the NH_4Y obtained to decompose it into HY and NH_3. The HY so obtained has moderate thermal stability, but if the decomposition of NH_4Y is carried out under specific operating conditions, its stability toward heat is greatly increased, and the process is called ultrastabilization.

During ultrastabilization, a number of aluminum atoms is removed from the zeolite framework and some silicon atoms move to the vacant positions left behind by the aluminum atoms previously removed. This avoids the collapse of the zeolite due to dealumination, which is the cause of permanent deactivation in the severe environment of the regenerator, and at the same time completes the process of ultrastabilization.

HY zeolite is a kind of solid acid. The acid sites of different strength and nature (Bronsted and Lewis acids) are regularly distributed on its intracrystalline surfaces. The relationship between acidity and cracking activity will be discussed later.

The displacement of Na with RE cations not only increases the hydrothermal stability of the exchanged zeolite, but also provide active acid sites. The presence of acid sites in REY zeolites is explained by the hydrolysis of RE polyvalent cation on the surface. For instance, a Bronsted acid site is produced as follows:

$$La^{3+}(H_2O)_n \longrightarrow La^{3+}(OH^-)(H_2O)_{n-1} + H^+$$

For the completeness of cation exchange, calcination of partially exchanged zeolite in the first stage is required. After calcination, the remaining Na ions are more readily exchanged. The final product is called rare earth Y zeolite (CREY) and sometimes simply REY.

The number of potential acid sites is determined by the number of negatively charged AlO_4 tetrahedra in the zeolite framework, which in turn depends upon the conditions of zeolite synthesis and various treatments to modify its properties. The aging of commercial catalyst in FCCU also changes the Al per unit cell in its zeolite component.

The number of Al atoms per unit cell or the Si/Al ratio in the zeolite framework can be measured directly by NMR and IR methods or for very pure zeolites by chemical analysis. However, the presence of impurities in the zeolite, or the presence of the matrix in cracking catalyst precludes determination of zeolite framework composition by direct elementary analysis.

The X-ray diffraction (XRD) is generally applied to determine the unit cell size a_0, from which Si/Al can be calculated [14].

$$Si/Al = (2.586 - a_0)/(a_0 - 2.419) \quad (1)$$

This method is based on the principle that the slight difference between the dimension of AlO_4 and SiO_4 tetrahedra causes a difference in unit cell size among various Si/Al ratio in the framework. The zeolite unit cell size a_0 becomes smaller as the AlO_4 is displaced by SiO_4 tetrahedra.

The XRD method for cracking catalyst is described in detail by ASTM D-3942-80.

Surface Acid Properties of Cation Exchanged Zeolites

The concepts of carbenium ion reaction mechanism were introduced to catalytic cracking by Greensfeld, Voge and associates [15]. According to IUPAC nomenclature rules, the ions that were formerly called carbonium ions should be called carbenium ions. The positively charged ions that contain so-called pentacoordinated carbon are called carbonium ions. The initiation of catalytic reaction of paraffins by zeolites has been explained with the pentacoordinated carbonium ions by Abbot [16].

Since the catalytic activity exhibited by zeolite catalysts is believed to be the carbocation capability with hydrocarbons, the surface acidity of cracking catalysts has long been a subject of extensive investigation. A great many methods [17, 18, 19] have been developed to measure the total amount of acid sites, to determine the acid strength distribution and to distinguish Bronsted sites and Lewis sites. The results obtained are useful in interpreting the catalyst behavior and in correlating the data observed in cracking reaction.

Unfortunately, these determinations are usually conducted at ambient temperatures or at elevated temperatures, considerably lower than those experienced in commercial operations. These findings can only show some general trends to catalyst activity and selectivity in relation to its acidity.

For zeolite containing catalysts the total acidity is comprised of two areas: the acid sites present in the zeolite and those in the matrix. If the matrix is made of synthetic amorphous Si/Al gel, the acidity of the matrix will constitute a considerable portion of the total acidity.

Zeolite HY, REY, and amorphous silica-alumina have Bronsted acid sites as prepared by the process. On heating above 500°C, Bronsted acids lose water to form Lewis acid. The reaction is partially reversible, and when the calcined catalyst contacts steam, only a part of the original Bronsted acidity is restored. Therefore both Bronsted acid sites and Lewis acid sites may be present and play their role in the catalytic cracking reaction.

The transformation of B-acids to L-acids may be postulated as in Figure 3. The labeled Al atom is the Lewis site, capable of accepting a pair of electrons for coordination.

Recently, magic angle spinning nuclear magnetic resonance (MAS NMR) of ^{29}Si and ^{27}Al in the zeolite has shown that Lewis acid centers due to tri-coordinated aluminum do not exist in the faujasite framework even after high temperature calcination [20, 21]. This discovery is contrary to traditional knowledge, but does not exclude the possibility of some Lewis acidity existing in the amorphous alumina occluded in the supercage. This may account for the presence of Lewis acid sites in USY zeolite.

The most common method used for the study of acid strength distribution is the classic Hammett indicator method using normal butylamine for titration. Judging color changes at the equivalent point demands experience and proficiency on the part of the analyst. Difficulty will be encountered in the case of titrating the colored catalyst, such as coked catalyst.

A new method free from the interference of catalyst color and ambient humidity, known as the Solvent Method, has been developed [22, 23]. The method is simple and reliable. The sample is pulverized and suspended in a series of selected solvents with various pK_a and then titrated with ethanol solution of NaOH, using an electroconductivity meter to indicate the equivalent point.

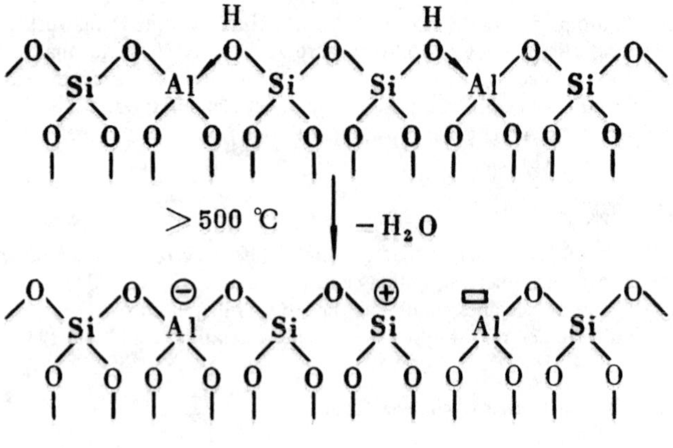

Figure 3. Transformation of Bronsted acids to Lewis acids.

The acid strength determined by the Solvent Method is expressed by the pK_a of the solvent used in titration. K_a is the equilibrium constant of the solvent and P means negative value of logarithm. Hammett acid strength H_0 is related to pK_a by an empirical equation:

$$H_0 = pK_a - 26 \tag{2}$$

A comparison of the experimental data obtained in the laboratory is shown in Table 2.

In the table, the effects of steam treatment and aging in FCCU on the acidity is clearly seen. The total acidity drops dramatically. The reduction of the strongest acid sites is prominent. Such information is usually correlated with catalyst performance.

Macroscopic Structure of Catalyst Particles

Commercial FCC catalysts look like free flowing, fine sand. Under the microscope, they appear to be a crowd of discrete, spheroidal globules, with various diameters between 20 and 120 μm. Over 50% by weight of catalyst particles fall in the range of 40 to 80 μm.

The average particle size and the distribution of particle size are among the important factors governing the state of fluidization and ease of catalyst transportation in FCCU. Therefore, their

Table 2
Effect of Catalyst Deactivation on Its Acid Strength Distribution

	Acidity, mmol/g							
	Hammett, Ho					Solvent pK_a		
Commercial catalyst MZ-3	**<−8.2**	**<−5.6**	**<−3.0**	**<+3.3**	**<+6.1**	**18**	**25**	**32**
Fresh catalyst	0.54	0.77	0.93	1.28	1.30	0.49	0.84	1.05
After 4 h, 800°C, 100% steam treatment	0	0.17	0.20	0.30	0.38	0.14	0.18	0.64
After 17 h, 800°C, 100% steam treatment	0	0.10	0.14	0.20	0.27	0.08	0.13	0.59
Equilibrium catalyst from FCC unit	0	0.12	0.15	0.25	0.33	0.10	0.16	0.57

Table 3
Comparison of Properties of Three Catalyst Categories Before and After Steaming

Catalyst Categories	REY Zeolite in Si/Al Gel Matrix	REY Zeolite in Kaolin Matrix	In-situ REY Zeolite in Kaolin Matrix
Chemical composition			
Al_2O_3, wt%	23.5	52.2	45
Na_2O, wt%	0.20	0.13	0.33
Physical properties			
Surface area, m^2/g	635	189	254
Pore volume, ml/g	0.47	0.25	0.28
Bulk density, g/ml	0.73	0.85	0.85
Attrition index, wt%	4.0	1.9	1.3
After 17 h., 800°C, 100% steam aging			
Surface area, m^2/g	149	78	168
Pore volume, ml/g	0.39	0.13	0.28

shape and size are carefully controlled in the process of spray drying the slurry of catalyst components—zeolite, matrix and/or binding material. The dried and calcined catalyst particles are rigid in mechanical strength. Their hardness in Moh's scale is between 6 and 7. They can retain their rigidity at very high temperature and withstand repeated thermal shocks. They are inspected in special test for their attrition resistivity. Inclusion of quartz crystals as an impurity in catalyst particles is undesirable for causing equipment erosion.

Mechanically strong as they are, they are porous in structure. These pores are open and interconnected to provide the accessibility to oil molecules during cracking and to oxygen molecules during regeneration. The exact description and modeling of the pore structure is a problem that remains unsolved in science. Generally, pore volume distribution and surface area of the pores are used to characterize catalyst pore structure. Nitrogen sorption test (BET method) can determine pore volume distribution for pores in the radius range 1.0–30.0 nm, while mercury intrusion porosity test can cover 3 nm–100 μm pore radii.

The data listed in Table 3 show the changes occurring in steam treatment. Decrease of surface areas is more serious than that of pore volumes. This is due to the collapse of the zeolite and the sintering of the matrix.

Normally, the coke deposition on FCC catalyst particles does not result in the blockage of pores in the matrix. This is shown in the pore volume distribution alteration by coking (Figure 4) [24].

Problem of Mass Transport during Residuum Cracking

For gas oil cracking on amorphous Si/Al FCC catalysts, the generally accepted concept concerning mass transport within catalyst particles is the absence of intraparticle diffusion limitation on the rate of cracking reaction [25]. Instantaneous vaporization of the liquid feed is assumed in the initial contact with the catalyst. The whole process is then treated as a vapor phase heterogeneous catalysis. The rate of intraparticle diffusion of oil molecules is considered kinetically insignificant for gas oil conversion.

When gas oil is cracked with fluid catalyst containing zeolite, the intracrystalline diffusion via the micropores of zeolite is worth discussing. For the pore sizes larger than molecular mean free path, ordinary or bulk diffusion of the vaporized feed oil molecules will take place. For those pore narrower than mean free path, Knudsen diffusion is dominant. Zeolite Y has rigid, regular and precisely defined pore structure, with apertures of about 0.9 nm. The diffusivity in zeolite pores of the oil molecules smaller than 0.9 nm in cross-section is expected to be several order of magnitude lower than that in the Knudsen region [26].

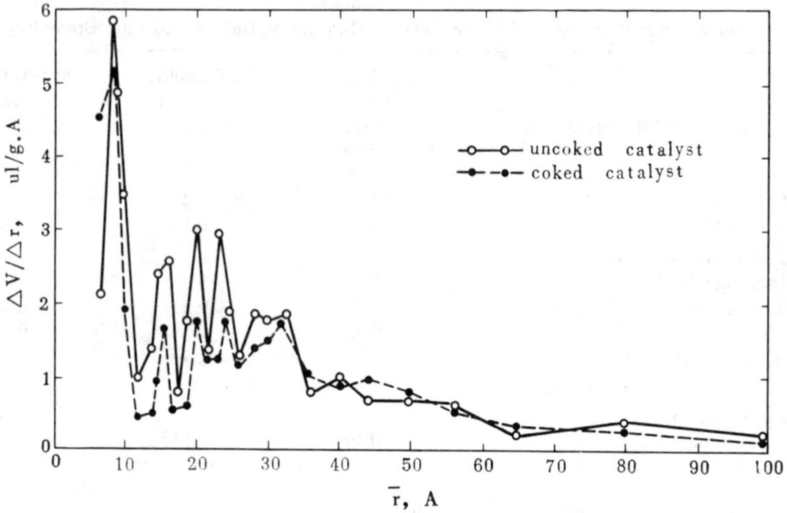

Figure 4. Change of pore size distribution of zeolite/kaolin catalyst after coke deposition. (After Shi and Li [24].)

Surface diffusion of the adsorbed molecules may play an important role in the mass transport during the process of cracking reaction with zeolite catalyst. However, little information is available on the subject.

Thomas and Barmby [27] calculated the rate of diffusion through the zeolite pores for gas oil molecules and found that the rate is much slower than is needed to account for the global rate of cracking reaction on catalyst particles. They believed with some reservation that the gas oil cracking reaction proceeds essentially on the outer surfaces of zeolite crystals rather than those deep in their interior. Since the possible contribution by surface diffusion or any other form of molecular mobility in zeolite pores has not been completely negated, the conclusion suggesting the existence of intracrystalline diffusion limitation on the reaction rate during gas oil cracking is not final.

Maselli and Peters [8] have studied the effect of zeolite crystal size on reaction rate by comparing the conversions of West Texas gas oil on catalysts containing 20% of either small (70 nm) or large (700 nm) zeolite crystals. Following results were obtained (Table 4). It was shown in the micro-activity test (MAT) that the reaction rate constant on the fresh catalyst containing small zeolite crystals is almost twice as that on the large ones. This seems to support the point of view that

Table 4
Effect of Zeolite Crystal Size on Catalyst Activity

Catalyst Composition	Zeolite Crystal Size	MAT Conversion, vol%	
		Fresh	Steam Aged
20% CREY zeolite,	700 nm	79 (3.76)*	77 (3.34)
80% clay and silica binder	70 nm	87 (6.69)	74 (2.84)

Adapted from References 8, 30
* *the number in parenthesis is proportional to the second order rate constant.*

diffusion of gas oil molecules into zeolite crystal is rate limiting, at least in sizes larger than 700 nm. The small crystals are not so stable as the large one in hydrothermal treatment.

During residual oil cracking, the feedstock is not capable of completely vaporizing under the condition of riser reaction operation. Both liquid and vapor must enter the pores in the catalyst particle and move through the matrix to reach the active sites of the zeolite.

Young and Rajagopalan [28, 29] considered the transport of residual oil in the catalyst particles as processes of molecular diffusion both in the vapor phase and in the liquid phase. They estimated the rate of liquid phase diffusion through amorphous Si/Al matrix and adopted the Weisz-Prater criterion to predict the presence of diffusion limitation in the matrix. In order to prove matrix diffusion limitation, MAT runs were conducted on different particle size fractions of a commercial catalyst. Both the dominant vapor-phase test and the dominant liquid-phase test showed no systematic increase in conversion with decreasing particle size (Table 5). Contrary to their expectation, these results suggest the absence of diffusion limitation in the liquid phase.

The authors of this chapter have an entirely different point of view concerning the mass transport phenomena during residual oil cracking. We propose that the interaction of catalyst particles with resid droplets should be split up into three steps:

1. The capture of catalyst particles by the oil droplets dispersed by the steam injection [30]. This was proved by our experiments studying the phenomenon that occurred when oil droplets were brought into contact with the catalyst at 700–800°C. No film boiling, which is known as Leidenfrost phenomenon, was observed in our laboratory. The residual oil wetted readily the outer surface of catalyst particle. The high frequency collision among the wetted or unwetted particles will, to certain extent, equilibrate the allocation of residual oil to every particles, though the gain of oil is in favor of smaller particles.
2. The imbibition of the unvaporized oil. The oil will vaporized on the periphery of catalyst particles. The remaining liquid is imbibed into the pores by the capillary action [31]. Though

Table 5
Effect of Catalyst Particle Size on MAT Activity (Standard Conversion, vol%)

		Average Particle Size, μm				
Catalyst	**Test Conditions**	**126**	**90**	**68**	**53**	**37**
Equilibrium Super DX, matrix vol. av. pore diam. = 45 nm	Residual oil, 500°C, WHSV = 16, C/O = 2, dominant vapor phase	67.1	65.0	64.2	63.0	—
Equilibrium Super DX, matrix vol. av. pore diam. = 45 nm	490°C+ fraction of a VGO, 427°C, WHSV = 16, C/O = 2, dominant liquid phase	53.5	54.0	50.6	—	52
Lab. steam aged Super DX, 8 h., 732°C, 30 psia steam, matrix vol. av. pore diam. = 45 nm	490°C+ fraction of a VGO, 427°C, WHSV = 16, C/O = 3, dominant liquid phase	75	68	69	—	69
Lab. aged Catalyst B, 8 h., 732°C, 30 psia steam, matrix vol. av. pore diam. = 8 nm	490°C+ fraction of a VGO, 427°C, WHSV = 16, C/O = 3, dominant liquid phase	72	—	71	72	76

Data adapted from References 8, 30

the temperature in the capillary may exceed oil bubbling point, in other words, the oil may be in a metastable state of superheating, the extremely small liquid volume in the capillary will provide little oportunity of producing a bubble nucleation [32]. The rate of mass transport in a capillary by liquid imbibition is several orders of magnitude higher than can be provided by molecular diffusion along the capillary filled with the stationary liquid.

3. The shrinking of liquid phase up to coke residue. The molecules in the liquid phase that contact directly with the catalytic sites will react first, and the reaction product must diffuse through the liquid phase to free surface for evaporation into the vapor phase. For the molecules that are in the vicinity of the active sites, they have to diffuse in opposite direction to reach the active sites. The distance of diffusion is within the size of pores and the concentration gradient is kept high, because the cracked products is constantly removed from the liquid phase by evaporation and the unconverted feedstock will become concentrated in the continually diminishing volume. This mode of diffusion accompanied with evaporative concentration is different from the diffusional processes occurring in the hydrocracking, where the oil and hydrogen molecules have to diffuse from the bulk liquid outside the catalyst pellets into their depth, while the cracked products, to diffuse out.

Our consideration of liquid imbibition by the catalyst particles is supported by the study of coke profile in the coked catalyst particles and the coke distribution among various catalyst particle sizes taken from the same coked catalyst sample [33]. For resid cracking, the radial profile of the coke derived from liquid phase (additive coke) suggested the thorough permeation of residual oil in the catalyst particles, though degree of saturation may vary with the distance of penetration.

Since liquid imbibition play a major role in mass transport of the liquid phase instead of liquid phase diffusion, it is easy to interpret the results of particle size test obtained by Maselli and Peters [8]. Each particle, no matter what size it is, will absorb on the average a volume of liquid defined by the catalyst/oil ratio in the MAT test. The rate of permeation is very high in comparison with the rate of cracking, so that catalyst particle size has no effect on the MAT conversion.

Microactivity Test (MAT) of FCC Catalysts

The activity of a catalyst can be theoretically defined by the kinetics of the catalyzed reaction. The rate constant and activation energy are the rigorous yardsticks to measure the catalytic activity. An endeavor is this direction has been made by Miale, Chen and Weisz [34]. They proposed the alpha test for FCC catalysts.

However, for the evaluation of commercial FCC catalysts, it is impractical to determine the rate constants of all the complex reactions involved in cracking process one by one. Moreover, cracking catalysts deactivate rapidly during cracking process due to coke deposition. It is very difficult to determine the intrinsic rate constant of individual cracking reaction free from the influence of deactivation by coking.

One of the most useful tools for evaluating FCC catalysts and predicting their commercial performance is the microactivity test (MAT), which is well documented in ASTM 3907-80. The conversion of the standard paraffinic gas oil during the test is regarded as a measure of catalytic activity. The product yield distribution of MAT is useful to describe the selectivity of the catalyst sample. The reduction in microactivity after hydrothermal treatment and metal contaminant impregnation of the catalyst sample gives valuable information of its hydrothermal stability and metal tolerance, respectively. At present, MAT is a routine test item for the catalyst supplier and the FCC operator.

Modification of test conditions will give data different from the originally obtained [35, 36]. Close observation of the specified test conditions is mandatory in conducting a MAT test.

The essence of MAT is a heterogeneous catalytic reaction on a quick decaying catalyst, performed in a fixed bed microreactor. The reactor is fed with an injection of standard gas oil by a syringe pump and the reaction products are collected in the process for analysis to determine the conversion and product yield. Since the reactor operates in an unsteady state due to catalyst deactivation, which also depends on the test conditions, the instantaneous conversion of gas oil in the reactor effluent decreases rapidly from the beginning of gas oil injection to the end. As a result of MAT, the conversion determined is a time average of the instantaneous conversion.

Table 6
Comparison of Laboratory Testing Conditions with Commercial Operation

Type of Test	Microactivity Test ASTM	Microactivity Test Modified		Test Using Confined Fluid Reactor		Commercial Riser Reactor
Preheating feedstock	slow	fast		fast		instantaneous
Feed dispersing agent	nil	N_2, He or steam		N_2 or steam		2–10% steam
Time on stream, s	75	37.5	7.2	5	30	2–5
WHSV	16	32	100	240	24	120–450*
Catalyst/oil ratio	3	3	5	3	5	4–2
Catalyst temperature, °C						
Before feed injection	483	510–550		500–600		700–800
Reaction temperature	470–480	490–530		490–550		500–550

* *In a riser reactor the catalyst particles flow concurrently with the oil vapors. The concept of space velocity is not applicable to this case. Suppose that the catalyst inventory in the riser were fixed, and then the calculated value would be 120–450.*

The reaction conditions of ASTM MAT and the modified version of activity tests are far away from those experienced in the commercial riser reactors. A comparison is made in Table 6, showing the significant differences between the reaction temperatures and between the lengths of catalyst time-on-stream or residence time in the reactor. This is the reason why the correlation of MAT with the commercial performance is not always precise and reliable, especially in the case of residual oil cracking.

Fresh cracking catalysts have very high activity. MAT of fresh catalysts will give conversion above 80%, which indicates the increasing significance of overcracking, and is not adequate for catalyst evaluation. MAT results after mild steam deactivation of fresh catalyst for example 800°C, 100% steam, 4 hr treatment, will give an indication of the inherent activity and selectivity, corresponding to the initial stage of catalyst introduction in FCCU.

Severe steam deactivation (800°C, 100% steam, 17 hr) simulates the effects of severe conditions in the regenerator on catalyst activity. The more stable the catalyst is, the more severe the conditions of the laboratory steam deactivation should be. The temperature and time of duration in steam deactivation are controlled accurately to produce repeatable determination of catalyst hydrothermal stability.

During steam deactivation, both matrix and zeolite undergo serious changes of their structure, acidity, etc. Liu et al have studied the kinetics of steam deactivation of a zeolite with high alumina Si/Al gel matrix [37, 38]. An empirical correlation of first order deactivation fits well with MAT conversion as catalyst activity (Table 7):

$$-\frac{dMA}{dt} = k_d MA \tag{3}$$

$$k_d(T) = A_m \exp(-E_M/RT) + A_Z \exp(-E_Z/RT) \tag{4}$$

where MA = microactivity, % conv.
t = time of 100% steam deactivation, day
k_d = deactivation rate constant, day^{-1}
A_M = frequency factor mainly due to matrix, day^{-1}
A_Z = frequency factor mainly due to zeolite, day^{-1}
E_M = activation energy of matrix deactivation, Joule/mole
E_Z = activation energy of zeolite deactivation, Joule/mole

Table 7
Changes of High Alumina CREY Catalyst after 4 h. Steam Deactivation

Temp. of Steam Deactivation, °C	Fresh	700	750	800	820	850
Microactivity test, % conversion	85.9	84.0	80.5	76.5	56.9	17.7
Deact. rate constant, 1/day	—	0.113	0.390	0.693	2.471	9.478
Total acidity, mmol/g	0.42	0.24	0.19	0.15	0.14	0.07
Strong acid, $Ho < -8.2$	0.16	0.06	0.04	0.02	0	0
Medium acid, $-8.2 < Ho < -3.0$	0.16	0.15	0.12	0.11	0.12	0.05
Weak acid, $-3.0 < Ho < +3.3$	0.10	0.03	0.03	0.02	0.02	0.02
Surface area, m^2/g	566	290	256	191	169	93
Relative crystallinity	100	69.5	61.4	43.9	28.1	0

Data adapted from Reference 38.

Metal contamination of FCC catalysts by Na, Ni and V compounds in the feedstock causes deactivation and poor selectivity toward more hydrogen and coke production. In order to simulate the equilibrium catalyst in this respect, various methods to deposit Ni and V on the fresh catalyst have been investigated by Mitchell [39]. The best procedure involves three steps: (1) calcining the fresh catalyst at 593°C; (2) impregnating the calcined catalyst by adding Ni and V naphthenates benzene solution to the point of incipient wetness; (3) steam aging of the impregnated catalyst at 732°C. The treated catalyst can simulate the catalytic properties of an equilibrium catalyst with same metal content, though an equilibrium catalyst is a heterogeneous mixture of widely different metal contents.

KINETICS OF CATALYTIC CRACKING REACTION ON ZEOLITE CATALYSTS

Pure Hydrocarbon Cracking

The mechanism of catalytic cracking of hydrocarbons has been thoroughly reviewed by Voge [40] and Haensel [41] and recently by Corma and Wojciechowski [7]. It is generally accepted that catalytic cracking both on the amorphous silica-alumina and the zeolite catalyst proceeds through carbenium ion type intermediates [40, 42–46].

The first valuable idea on the mechanism of catalytic cracking was that of Gayer, who showed in 1933 that a catalyst consisting of alumina supported on silica possesses acid properties [47]. This led to the speculation that these acid sites may in fact be the active centers of the catalytic reactions. In 1947 and later, Hansford and Thomas made the first attempt independently to explain the mechanism of catalytic cracking in terms of ionic reactions [48, 49].

The carbenium ion postulate is now known to agree with observed experimental phenomena and to explain the specific characteristics of catalytic cracking such as the follows:

1. The β-scission of the C—C bond
2. The preferential formation of products of $\geq C_3$ from linear hydrocarbons
3. The greater cracking reactivity of compounds containing a tertiary hydrogen
4. The rapid double bond shifts
5. The extensive skeletal isomerization
6. The hydrogen-transfer reaction
7. The high rate of dealkylation of alkylaromatics and the cracking occurs prominently next to the ring.

The reaction rate and selectivity of catalytic cracking on the zeolite catalysts differ much from that on the amorphous silica-alumina catalyst, although the mechanism of reaction is identical.

Table 8
Product Distribution from *n*-Hexadecane Cracking at 482°C

Catalyst	Silica-Alumina	REHX
Time on stream, sec.	2	2
LHSV	100	1,250
% Conversion	40.4	40.7
Product distribution, mole %		
C_1–C_2	1.1	—
C_3–C_4	59.8	43.1
C_5–C_{10}	38.7	55.9
C_{11}–C_{12}	0.5	0.9
Wt% carbon on catalyst	0.03	0.32
Instantaneous rate constant at 2 sec. (time on stream), moles/kg catalyst·hour	500	6,500

Data adapted from Reference 53.

Table 9
Composition of Gasoline from Virgin Gas-oil Cracking

Catalyst	Silica-Alumina	REX/SiO_2—Al_2O_3
% Paraffins	8.7	21.0
% Cycloparaffins	10.4	19.3
% Olefins	43.7	14.6
% Aromatics	37.3	45.0
Paraffins/olefins	0.20	1.44
% Conversion	49.5	73.4

Data adapted from Reference 27.

The differences of performance between these two types of catalyst can be illustrated by the data shown in Tables 8 and 9 [27, 53].

As shown in Table 8, the cracking rate of *n*-hexadecane on the REHX catalyst is more than ten times that on the amorphous silica-alumina catalyst, even though there is a higher coke buildup on the REHX catalyst. Others have reported that a series of zeolite catalysts are about 10,000 times more active than amorphous silica-alumina for the cracking of *n*-hexane [34]. The product distributions obtained in cracking of *n*-hexadecane with REHX and amorphous silica-alumina indicate that both distributions are characteristic of carbenium ion cracking, but the zeolite catalyst gives more products in the C_5 to C_{10} range, i.e., the range of gasoline, and fewer in the C_3 to C_4 range, as seen in Table 8. Nace [53] also concluded that the conversion level had only a small effect on product distribution. In comparison of gasoline composition from zeolite catalyst vs. amorphous silica-alumina catalyst (see Table 9), one can see that the ratio of paraffins to olefins in the gasoline from the zeolite catalyst is much greater than that from the amorphous silica-alumina catalyst. This indicates that the activity of zeolite catalyst for hydrogen-transfer reaction is much higher than that of amorphous silica-alumina catalyst.

A full explanation of the higher activity and better selectivity of zeolites compared with amorphous silica-alumina is lacking, but, according to many authors, strength and distribution of the acid sites and the crystalline structure of the zeolites give probably the most important effects on the reaction patterns [46, 50–53].

The high activity of zeolites may be due to the following effects:

1. Greater concentration of active sites in the zeolite. Katzer estimated a 50-fold concentration advantage in zeolite over amorphous silica-alumina [50].
2. Greater effective concentration of hydrocarbon in the vicinity of an acid site resulting from the strong adsorption in the micropore structure of a zeolite. Breck estimated that the concentration of *n*-heptane in the micropores of zeolite may be roughly 50 times that in a larger pores of amorphous silica-alumina at the cracking temperature [54].
3. Activating effects of the high electrostatic field potentials in the micropores of the zeolite on the hydrocarbon molecules [55].

The better selectivity of the zeolite can be explained by the distribution of acid site strengths. Moscou and Mone have studied the influence of acid strength on the selectivity of gas oil cracking [51]. They reported that the strongest acid sites were responsible for coke formation and the formation of light gases, whereas the acid sites of intermediate strength were responsible for reactions leading to hydrogen transfer and desired products. Similar suggestion has been reported by other authors. They suggest that any given reaction occurs on a specific narrow range of active site energies. For instance, the double bond isomerization reaction needs the weaker acid sites, the skeletal isomerization and hydrogen transfer reactions need the acid sites of intermediate strength, whereas the cracking reaction need the strongest acid sites [7]. In the case of the distributions of acid site strengths, the majority of acid sites in amorphous silica-alumina is found in the region of $H_0 < -8$ to -12, whereas the acid site strength distribution in zeolites lies mainly between -8 and -4 [46]. Thus, it can be said, that the relative activity for hydrogen transfer reaction to the activity for cracking reaction of zeolite is higher than that of amorphous silica alumina. In addition, the greater effective concentration of hydrocarbon in the micropores of the zeolite may also favor the intermolecular hydrogen transfer (probably second order reaction).

The effect of higher relative activity for hydrogen transfer is to stabilize or preserve gasoline range olefins formed by primary cracking of the parent molecule, prior to the "drain-off" by secondary cracking [6, 46]. The experimental data indicating the higher product ratio of $(C_5–C_{10})/(C_3–C_4)$ and the greater concentration of paraffins in gasoline, as shown in Tables 8 and 9, agree with the suggestion previously mentioned.

Another characteristic of the catalytic cracking reaction on the zeolite catalysts is the so called shape-selective catalysis. It is well known that the entry pore diameters of X- and Y-type zeolite range about 8–10 Å, one might expect that the diffusion rate of the reactant molecule into the micropore would be very sensitive to the size of the diffusing molecule relative to the pore size. In the extreme case, the large molecules might be excluded from the zeolite pore structure entirely and are cracked instead on the exterior surfaces of the zeolite crystallites or on the surface of the silica alumina matrix in which the crystallites are embedded. A range of four orders of magnitude in the effective coefficient for counter-diffusion in NaY has been reported [56]. For example, the effective diffusion coefficients into cyclohexane-saturated NaY at 25°C of toluene (molecule diameter = 6.8 Å) and 1,3,5-trimethylbenzene (molecule diameter = 8.4 Å) are about 3×10^{-6} and 4×10^{-9} m^2/s, respectively.

Nace [57] compared the cracking rates of a series of naphthenes with increasingly bulky ring structure over amorphous silica alumina and REHX catalysts. With amorphous catalyst, the cracking rate constant increased continuously with the size of naphthene reactant, with the C_{16}-naphthene (4-ring naphthene) showing 1.5-fold rate enhancement over the C_{12}-naphthene (triethyl-cyclohexane). With REHX catalyst, however, the cracking rate constant increased with reactant size initially, then decreased drastically with the 3- and 4-ring naphthenes. Correspondingly, the ratio of cracking rate constant k_{REHX}/k_{SiAl} dropped from a base value of 17 to a low of 2.4. This behavior indicates that the diffusional resistance in the intracrystalline pore structure of the zeolite become more important as the molecular size increases. On the basis of calculating the cracking rate of gas oil over zeolite catalyst in terms of rate per crystalline unit cell, Thomas and Barmly even suggested that many of the gas oil molecules were too large to enter the supercavity and the cracking reaction of these molecules took place primarily on the external surface [27]. On the subject concerning shape-selective catalysis, excellent reviews and descriptions have been made by Weisz and coworkers [26, 34, 58].

Many authors report that data for cracking of simple pure hydrocarbons fit a first-order law [40, 59–63], i.e., the rate of cracking reaction can be expressed by the following basic equation:

$$-dC_A/dt = kC_A \tag{5}$$

where C_A is the concentration of the reactant.

In cracking reaction, the ratio of the moles of products formed to the moles of feed reacted is greater than unity. Considering the dilution effect of the products formed, Nace derived an integrated first order flow reaction equation for obtaining the reaction rate constants [63]. Assuming the ratio mentioned above to be a constant, i, this integrated equation can be expressed as follows:

$$k = \frac{S}{P}[-i\ln(1-x) - (i-1)x] \tag{6}$$

where S = space velocity
P = total pressure
x = conversion

For the cracking reaction of n-hexadecane over REHX catalyst at 482°C, the cracking rate constant obtained from Equation 6 ranges only from 2,250 to 2,500, while the cracking conversion ranges from 11 to 37%. This implies that the first order reaction equation is acceptable to pure hydrocarbon cracking reaction provided that the conversion level is not too high.

Actually, the ratio of the moles of product formed to the moles of feed reacted increases considerably due to secondary reactions as the reaction proceeds, the exponent in Equation 5 tends to increase to above 1, although the basic cracking reaction of pure hydrocarbon is a first order reaction.

Gas Oil Cracking

Within the scope of petroleum refining, the term, gas oil, represents an intermediate fraction of the petroleum. Its boiling temperature range and composition are not well defined. Usually, as a feed of commercial catalytic cracking unit, gas oil is a vacuum distillate with boiling temperature range of about 300 to 520°C. It is a mixture consisting of thousands of hydrocarbon components as well as various N-, S-, and O-containing compounds.

Theoretically, the catalytic cracking reactions of gas oil also follow the carbenium ion mechanism as the catalytic cracking reactions of pure hydrocarbons do. Actually, many features of gas oil catalytic cracking reaction, especially the product distribution, show the ionic reaction characteristics. However, due to the multiplicity of reactants, the catalytic cracking reaction of gas oil is much more complicated and has its own characteristics other than that of pure hydrocarbon reaction. Some of the main characteristics of the gas oil catalytic cracking may be illustrated as followings:

1. The competition between different reactants for entry to the catalyst pores, adsorption on the acidic surface and reaction
2. The great molar expansion during cracking
3. The highly coupled networks of secondary reactions.

Furthermore, the rapid, time dependent decay of the catalyst activity from coke formation and the competition of thermal cracking reactions under higher reaction temperature will have important influences on the reaction process.

Characterization of Feed Stocks

It is necessary to obtain a reliable characterization of a gas oil used as a feedstock of catalytic cracking unit in order to develop credible correlations for predicting the cracking rate and product distribution. Evidently, to characterize a gas oil by its composition of individual hydrocarbon components is impossible. A great many chemical and physical measurements have been used for characterizing a variety of gas oil for catalytic cracking, such as:

1. The UOP characterization factor K—$K > 12.0$, highly crackable; $K = 11.5$, intermediate crackable; $K < 11.3$, refractory [64, 67].
2. Class composition, C_A, C_N, C_O, and C_P, which represent the percentages of carbon atom in aromatic, naphthene, olefin and paraffin respectively [65–67, 71].
3. Mono- and poly-nuclear aromatic distribution—the mononuclear aromatic fraction tends to give gasoline product, while the three- and four-ring fractions tend to form coke [65, 68].
4. Conradson Carbon Residue (CCR)—It is a measure of the tendency of the feedstock to form coke by deposition of high boiling, refractory feed components [70].
5. Elemental analysis—the higher ratio of H/C indicates higher crackability and selectivity of the feed, and the basic nitrogen content shows the extent of catalyst poisoning effect [66, 67, 71].

Besides the characterization methods mentioned above, there exist some other useful methods. The most important method that has been extensively investigated is the "lump" method. The principle of this method is to group various similar components into a few "lump" which are treated kinetically as pseudo-components. This will be discussed later.

Reaction Order

Although the catalytic cracking of pure hydrocarbons proceeds according to the first order rate law, the behavior of gas oil (a complex mixture of various hydrocarbons) cracking always shows a significant deviation from the first order reaction. Weekman and associates, working with zeolite catalysts, demonstrated that kinetics of gas oil catalytic cracking could be represented as a pseudo-second-order reaction [59, 72]. Wallaston et al also reported that the second-order expression could be used for cracking of gas oil as a whole [61]. The phenomenon that the apparent reaction order of gas oil cracking usually approach 2 can be explained by the following two reasons:

First, the gas oil is a complex mixture of different classes of pure hydrocarbons with a wide range of cracking rates. During reaction, the most reactive components such as naphthenes, paraffins and alkyl-mononuclear-aromatics are initially converted at very rapid rates. Thus, as the reaction proceeds, there is a progressive enrichment in concentration of more refractory hydrocarbon species, usually aromatics, especially the polyaromatics. In addition, there may also be some accumulation of refractory aromatics from hydrogen transfer reactions. As a result, the crackability of the reactant, involving unconverted original feed and reaction products, decreases with the extent of conversion. The change of aromatics content in cycle oil with conversion level illustrated in Figure 5 accounts for this phenomenon [6].

Second, the fact that the molar ratio of products formed to gas oil converted is greater than unity yields dilution effect in a flow reactor operated under constant total pressure. Furthermore, the ratio previously mentioned increases considerably due to secondary reactions as the reaction proceeds.

Luss and co-workers studied the reactions of mixtures. They concluded theoretically that in a situation in which many parallel first order, irreversible reactions occurred, even though each reaction would exhibit true first-order kinetics, the overall kinetics would lead to reaction orders higher than one if the range of conversion covered were wide enough [73].

Taking into account the change of crackability of the feed, Wojciechowski and co-workers retained the form of first order expression for gas oil cracking, but used the term, $k_0(C_A/C_{A_0})^W$, instead of the rate constant k in the first order expression. Where k_0 is the initial rate constant, C_{A_0} is the initial concentration of gas oil, and W is refractoriness of the feed [74]. Unfortunately, the necessary calculations thus brought forth are too complex to deal with.

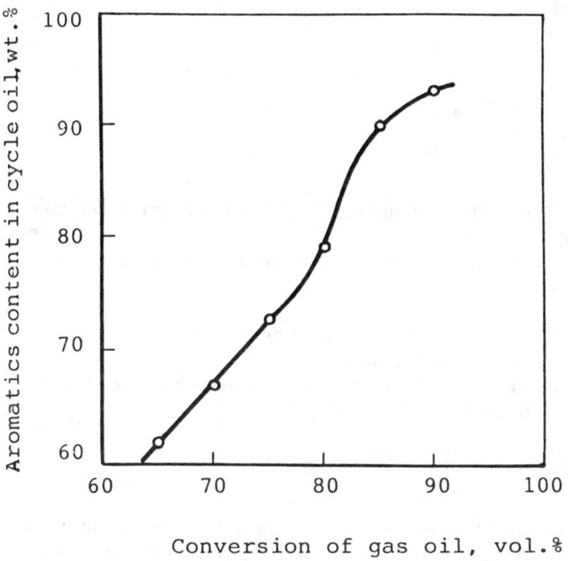

Figure 5. Change of aromatics content in cycle oil with conversion, original aromatics content in gas oil is 46 vol.%.

Catalyst Deactivation with Coke Deposition

The activity of cracking catalyst declines rapidly accompanied with the accumulation of carbonaceous deposits on the catalyst surface. This phenomenon has been the subject of a number of studies over the years because of its very significant economic importance. Several models have been proposed to describe the deactivation of catalyst due to coke deposition. Roughly, they can be classified as two categories, i.e., the deactivation related to time-on-stream and the deactivation related to the coke content on catalysts.

Voorhies [75], in his pioneering work, showed that the carbon weight percent on amorphous silica alumina catalyst, C_c, approximately followed a relation $C_c = at^n$, where t is the process time and a and n are constants. Voltz et al. [68] verified Voorhies' relation with a zeolite cracking catalyst and a wide variety of charge stocks. Wojciechowski and co-workers [7, 77, 78] discussed the time-on-stream theory of catalyst decay in detail and developed several relations according to this theory.

Froment and Bischoff [79] have argued that if catalyst activity decay is due to coke formation, then the catalyst activity cannot be a simple function of time. They suggested that the catalyst deactivation function should be related to the coke content rather than time-on-stream. Eberly [80] observed an independent space velocity effect on coke formation in a fixed bed reactor, using a much wider range of space velocities than originally reported by Voorhies. Lin et al. [81], cracking cumene over a LaY catalyst, found that the logarithm of decay function was proportional to the carbon weight percent of catalyst and that the Froment-Bischoff model of catalyst deactivation was adequate for representing this process. On the basis of the fact that the decay function for the main reaction and the coking reactions were found to be identical, he also suggested that the coking reactions and the main reaction occured on the same sites.

Although the theory of Froment and Bischoff may be more reasonable, but plant experience suggests an apparent independence of cracking activity and coking rate, and therefore the time-on-stream decay models are usually used for plant simulation. The acceptance of time-on-stream decay models, to certain extent, also due to their simplicity. The popular time-on-stream decay models may be illustrated as follows:

$$\phi = t_c^{-n} \qquad [61, 67] \tag{7}$$

$$\phi = \exp(-at_c) \qquad [72, 82] \tag{8}$$

$$\phi = (1 + Gt_c)^{-N} \qquad [76, 77] \tag{9}$$

where ϕ = catalyst decay function, i.e., the ratio of cracking rate constant at t_c to initial cracking rate constant
t_c = time in which the catalysts are exposed to the gas oil
n, G, N = parameters

Equation 7 has a theoretical deficit, i.e., it becomes unreasonable when $t_c < 1$, and it is only an empirical expression with certain limitation.

In practice, the catalysts are also deactivated by exposure to high temperature steam, metal contamination, and basic-nitrogen poisoning.

Kinetic Model

Kinetic models are useful for design, optimization, and control of commercial reactor. In addition, they provide guidance in the development of a new process and can reduce both time and capital requirements. Considerable effort has been devoted to developing adequate kinetic models for gas oil catalytic cracking.

One of the early attempts to describe the conversion of gas oil by a kinetic model was that due to Voorhies [75]. For a given catalyst, feedstock, and temperature, he found that the carbon weight percent on catalyst, C_c, was independently related to the catalyst-to-oil contact time, t_c, as shown in Equation 10.

$$C_c = At_c^n \tag{10}$$

He also found that there was a good realtion between the gas oil conversion, X, and the coke yield, C_f, as shown in Eq. 11

$$C_f = BX^m \tag{11}$$

Noting that C_f/C_c = catalyst to oil ratio C/O, an expression giving average conversion as a function of space velocity, V, and t_c was developed in the following form:

$$X = GV^{-p}t_c^{-q} \tag{12}$$

where G, p, and q are parameters. Obviously, Equation 12 is a simple empirical expression, but it had played a vital role in the design of many commercial catalytic cracking units in the past time.

Since that time, various kinetic models concerning gas oil conversion have been proposed by Blanding [60], Andrews [83], Weekman [72], and other investigators [61, 77]. For example, recognizing that the cracking reaction of gas oil follows the pseudo-second-order kinetics and the catalyst decay follows the first-order kinetics, Weekman has derived an expression for predicting the average conversion of gas oil, $\bar{X}$, in a fixed bed reactor as follows:

$$\bar{X} = \frac{1}{\lambda} \ln \frac{1 + A}{1 + Ae^{-\lambda}} \tag{13}$$

$$A = \frac{f\rho_0 k_0}{\rho_1 V} \tag{14}$$

where λ = deactivation parameter
f = void fraction in the bed
ρ_0 = initial charge density at reactor conditions
k_0 = initial rate constant
ρ_1 = density of liquid charge
V = liquid hourly space velocity

For the case of fluidized bed reactor, the conversion of gas oil at the bed exit, X_e, is expressed by Equation 15

$$X_e = \frac{A}{1 + \lambda + A} \tag{15}$$

Subsequently, Weekman has extended his models to include gasoline production and the subsequent recracking of gasoline [59]. A simplified reaction system was shown below as Equation 16

$$C_1 \longrightarrow a_1C_2 + a_2C_3 \tag{16a}$$

$$C_2 \longrightarrow C_3 \tag{16b}$$

Here, C_1, C_2, C_3 represent the gas oil charged, C_5–210°C gasoline fraction, and ($\leq C_4$ + coke) respectively. The a_1 and a_2 coefficients represent the mass of C_2 and C_3 produced per mass of C_1 converted respectively. Assuming that the kinetics of gas oil cracking and gasoline recracking could be represented as a second order reaction and a first order reaction respectively, Weekman developed the following gasoline selectivity model:

$$y_2 = r_1r_2 \exp(-r_2/y_1)[(1/r_2)\exp(r_2) - (y_1/r_2)\exp(r_2/y_1) - \mathrm{Ein}(r_2) + \mathrm{Ein}(r_2/y_1)] \tag{17a}$$

$$\mathrm{Ein}(x) = \int_{-\infty}^{x} (1/x)\exp(x)\,dx \tag{17b}$$

where y_1 = (1-conversion of gas oil)
y_2 = gasoline yield
$r_1 = K_1/K_0$
$r_2 = K_2/K_0$
K_0 = gas oil cracking rate
$K_1 = a_1K_0$
K_2 = gasoline cracking rate

In the derivation of Equation 17, two forms of catalyst decay function, the first order decay function and t^n decay function, have been used, however, the results obtained are almost identical. Since Equation 17 is independent of catalyst residence time, it holds for moving beds (or riser) and fluidized beds as well as for the instantaneous selectivity of fixed bed reactors, provided the gas oil and gasoline cracking activities decay at the same rate.

Because the gas oil feed contains many types of components, attempts have been made to group various similar components into a few "lumps." Satterfield [62] observed that, over a limited conversion range, the first-order kinetics could often be followed by a lump of species of similar reactivity. The fact that the reaction rate constants of properly lumped species are invariant with feedstock composition and source has been identified. Using these concepts, Jacob et al. [84] developed a comprehensive kinetic model using 10 major lumps to follow the catalytic cracking of virgin gas oils and recycle stocks. Only recently, Sha et al. [85] have developed an 11-lump model similar to that of Jacob et al. for improving the capability of prediction. In this model, the lump, C_{Ah}, in Jacob's model is further split into two lumps, i.e., the lump C_{Ah}, wt% carbon atoms among mono- and bi-aromatic rings in >340°C fraction, and the lump PC_{Ah}, wt% carbon atoms among polyaromatic rings (number of rings ≥ 3) in >340°C fraction. This kinetic model is schematically shown in Figure 6.

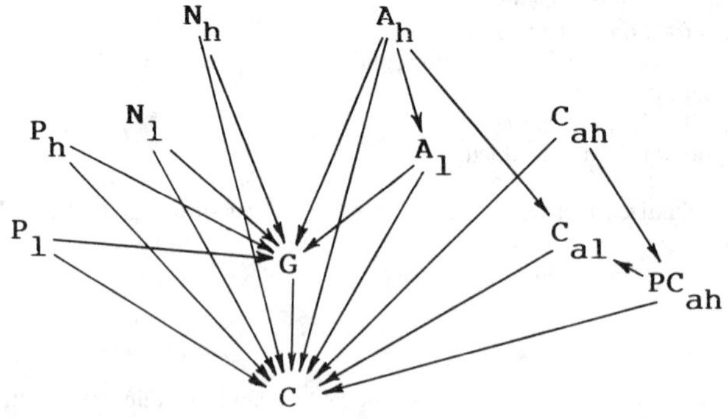

Figure 6. Lumped kinetic scheme. (After Sha, et al. [85].) P_h—wt% paraffinic molecules, higher than 340°C; P_l—wt% paraffinic molecules, 210–340°C; N_h—wt% naphthenic molecules, higher than 340°C; N_l—wt% naphthenic molecules, 210–340°C; A_h—wt% aromatic substituent groups, higher than 340°C; A_l—wt% aromatic substituent groups, 210–340°C; C_{ah}—wt% carbon atom among mono- and bi-aromatic rings, higher than 340°C; C_{al}—wt% carbon atom among mono- and bi-aromatic rings, 210–340°C; PC_{ah}—wt% carbon atom among polyaromatic rings, (number of rings equal to or greater than 3.); G—C_5–210°C gasoline; C—C_1–C_4 plus coke.

As shown in Figure 6, the key lumps comprise paraffins, naphthenes, bare aromatic rings, and aromatic substituent groups (side chains) in both light and heavy cycle oil cuts, as well as C_5–210°C gasoline (G-lump) and the aggregate H_2, H_2S, C_1 to C_4, coke (C-lump). Each reaction shown in Figure 6 is represented by first order kinetics. Thus the lumping model can be solved by means of the linear algebraical methodology. The fundamentals of this methodology have been discussed in detail by Wei et al. [86].

The model incorporates the terms to deal with the time-dependent catalyst deactivation during reaction.

From this kinetic model, predictions for gas oil conversion, gasoline yield, light fuel oil yield, and recycle oil can be obtained as a function of process variables. Additional relations are necessary for predictions of coke yield and the yields of individual gas components. In addition, the invariant kinetic parameters (rate constants and activation energies) allow the conversion and product selectivity to be calculated for the cracking of any charge stock for which the requisite molecular compositions have been determined. This makes it possible to minimize the required experimental work.

Some Kinetic Aspects of Resid Cracking

The Reaction Rate Consideration

As compared with gas oil cracking, the higher coking tendency and metal contents of the residual oil cause two major difficulties in FCCU, that is, the production of excessive coke and serious contamination of the catalyst. It may be expected that the reaction rate of the resid on the catalyst seriously deactivated by it should be low.

Nevertheless, when a FCC unit switches its feedstock from gas oil to atmospheric resid of 4–5% Conradson Carbon Residue and low metal content, no problem in respect of reaction rate is encountered. With regard to the riser reactor and its operating conditions, there is no distinction between the gas oil cracking and resid cracking except that more steam is used in the injection nozzles for better dispersion of the viscous resid. Slight lower conversions are obtained in the case of resid cracking. This implies that the rate of resid cracking would have been as high as that of gas oil cracking, if resid did not cause serious deactivation of the catalyst.

In fact, the commercial processes for resid cracking such as the HOC process (Kellogg), the RCC process (Ashland and UOP) and RFCC (Total) have their own features in design, but the contact time for the resid in the riser reactor is roughly the same as that for the gas oil [87–90].

Maselli and Peters [8] have provided some data to compare the rate of a vacuum gas oil and a 500°C plus residual oil on an active amorphous catalyst and a zeolite/inert mixture. For the amorphous catalyst, the first order rate constant of resid cracking is a factor of 1.4 greater than that of gas oil, while for the 15% zeolite/inert mixture, the reverse is true. Since most of resid cracking catalysts contain zeolite imbedded in a matrix of low activity, they may be something between two extremes previously mentioned. These data seems to support the conception that the rate of resid cracking on the heavily contaminated catalyst is approximately equal to that of gas oil.

Special Case of Gas-Liquid-Solid Reactor

Resid cracking in the riser reactor involves the reaction of a fraction of feedstock in liquid phase on the catalyst particles. The way of liquid transport to the active sites of the catalyst particles have been described in detail earlier in this chapter, including the wetting of the catalyst particles, the inhibition by the capillary action of the pores into the particles and the shrinking of the liquid phase in the pores. Conversely, if we suppose that the resid did not wet the particles or was not sucked into the particle, the catalyst would play a simple role of heat carrier and the reaction that occurs in the liquid phase would be purely thermal cracking. This would result in low reaction rate, poor product selectivity, and quality. In reality, this is not the case.

There are other features concerning the reaction in liquid state. First, the catalyst particles loaded with resid act as macrofluid in the reactor [91]. The ratio of oil to catalyst may differ from one particle to another, though the average ratio is governed by the catalyst/oil ratio of the riser operation. Secondly, since the liquid fraction moves concomitantly with the catalyst particle, the reaction time of the liquid will be equal to the residence time of the catalyst. The slip of catalyst in the ascending vapor causes a longer stay in the riser than does the oil vapor, while the backmixing of catalyst particles gives rise to a distribution of reaction time. Thirdly, the requirement of liquid phase conversion is contradictory to that of the vapor phase. The conversion of the liquid should be as complete as possible, because any unconverted feedstock will be carried over to the regenerator and treated as coke, whereas the conversion of the oil vapor should be controlled at an optimum to avoid both over- and undercracking.

Matrix "Feeds" Zeolite Theory

Residual oil from petroleum crudes is typically composed of very large molecules, including resins and asphaltenes in the form of colloidal micelle. The mass transport of these molecules in the matrix is not rate limiting. They may be precracked on the active, accessible sites provided by the matrix to form smaller molecules that can better penetrate into the pores of zeolite for selective conversion to gasoline range products. This is the theory of matrix feeds zeolite advocated by Davison reseachers. An experimental verification of this concept was performed by testing a fixed bed MAT reactor filled with a layer of amorphous catalyst on top of a zeolite catalyst. The result was compared with the situation where the sequence of two layers was inverted. The data showed a 45% increase in second order rate constant for the case where the amorphous catalyst was on the top, illustrating the beneficial effect of providing matrix cracking activity to "feed" the zeolite.

Debates Over Carbon Residue Contribution to Coke Yield

The Ramsbottom or Conradson Carbon Residue of cracking feedstock denotes its tendency of coking by heat. The relationship between coke yield in resid cracking and carbon residue in the feed has been studied by Knaus, et al. [92]. They made a distinction between the carbon derived from the substances that produced carbon residue and the carbon derived from all other substances. The partial coke yield derived from carbon residue was proportional to Ramsbottom carbon residue with a ratio factor of 1.1, and was independent on the selectivity of the catalyst used.

Dean et al. have denied the relationship between carbon residue in the feed and coke yield [89, 90]. They pointed out that if the regenerator temperature is not restricted by metallurgy or catalyst deactivation, the coke make is only marginally higher than that in a conventional gas oil cracker. They put special emphases on the instantaneous mixing of resid with regenerated catalyst by means of a powerful steam atomizer to effect the shattering of asphaltenes at the point of feed injection, and on the adoption of two-stage regeneration to protect the catalyst from premature hydrothermal deactivation.

Others have compromising views. They agreed that a varying proportion of carbon residue is converted to coke, depending on the quality of the feed, catalyst selectivity, and operation in FCCU [93, 94]. Indeed, it is one of the biggest problems to determine in a commercial cat cracker where the coke is coming from.

KINETICS OF CATALYST REGENERATION

The activity and selectivity of cracking catalysts decrease rapidly with coke deposition during cracking. It is necessary to "burn off" the coke deposit on the catalysts periodically. Normally, the coke content of the catalyst must be reduced from about 1% to about 0.5% for silica alumina catalysts and to lower than 0.2% for a zeolite type catalyst in a regenerator within a few minutes. Therefore, a study of the kinetics of catalyst regeneration plays an important role in designing and operating a catalytic cracking unit.

The Nature of Coke Deposit and the Coke Profile

The coke deposited on cracking catalysts is not pure carbon. It is generally agreed by all investigators that its molecular formula varies between $(C_1H_{0.4})_n$ and $(C_1H_1)_n$, i.e., it consists not only of carbon but also of a small amount of hydrogen. Actually, sulfur, nitrogen, and traces of metal elements may also be found in the coke on catalysts from commercial units.

X-ray diffraction studies show that approximately 50% of the carbon phase exists in pseudo-graphitic, or turbostratic structures. The remainder probably consists of relatively unorganized aromatic systems and of aliphatic and alicyclic appendages to poly-nuclear aromatic systems. There is no three-dimensional, or true crystallinity although the individual layers are similar to those in graphite [95]. By infrared examination, Eberly et al. [96] confirmed that besides condensed ring aromatic structures, there were also $—CH_3$ and $—CH_2$ groups in the coke deposited on silica alumina catalysts. This is consistent with Haldeman and Botty's study [95]. Furthermore, Eberly et al. found that the relative amount of aromatic, $—CH_2—$ and CH_3 groups depended to some extent on the feed composition.

Haldeman and Botty made a microscopic study of the distribution of coke on amorphous silica alumina catalyst and came to the conclusion that the coke was uniformly well dispersed with the steam-aged catalyst granules, but for the Ni-contaminated catalyst, a marked tendency to preferential deposition of carbon near the periphery of the catalyst granules did occur. Shi and Li [24] examined the coke distribution on the FCC zeolite catalyst (REY/Kaolin) by methanol adsorption study. Figure 4 shows the change of pore size distribution of this catalyst after coking by cumene at 500°C. It seems that the coke deposits both in the pores of different sizes in the REY molecular sieve and in the matrix. Calculation of adsorption data indicates that in this catalyst with a coke content of 2.4% there is no significant occlusion of catalyst pore space by carbon deposit.

Li [33] examined the radial distribution of the coke deposited on the FCC cracking catalysts by successive sampling and analysis of the outmost layer of the coked catalyst particles. They stirred the catalyst particles in an aqueous suspension. The fines formed by attrition of the catalyst particles were taken at definite intervals as samples representing the radial profile of the chemical composition. They found that the coke content in the periphery layer of definite thickness was much greater than that in the inner part of the catalyst particles for resid cracking catalysts. For gas oil cracking catalysts, however, the distribution of the coke deposit was essentially uniform throughout the whole catalyst particle. These features are shown in Figures 7 and 8. This result

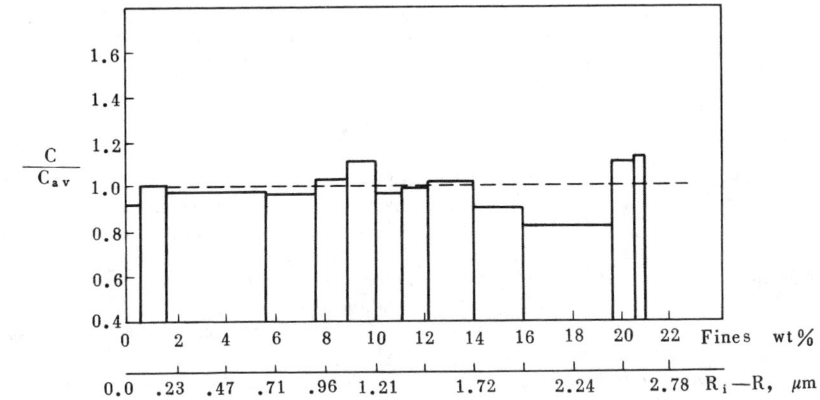

Figure 7. Radial coke distribution on catalyst particle during gas oil cracking. Conradson carbon residue of feed = 0.16%; initial average radius of catalyst particles R_i = 35 μm; average carbon content of catalyst C_{av} = 1.07%. (After Li [33].)

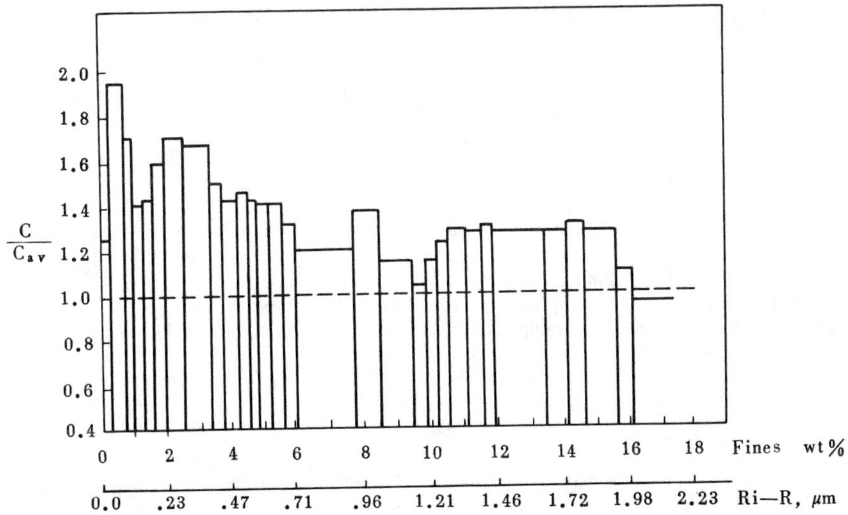

Figure 8. Radial coke distribution on catalyst particle during resid cracking. Conradson carbon residue of feed = 4.8%; initial average radius of catalyst particles R_i = 35 μm; average carbon content of catalyst C_{av} = 1.23%. (After Li [33].)

may be explained by the presence of a liquid reactant during the cracking reaction of the resid feed, which is rich in bituminous material and high boiling hydrocarbons.

Kinetics of Carbon Oxidation on Cracking Catalysts

A lot of literature on the kinetics of coke combustion of cracking catalysts has been published, most of them have concentrated on carbon oxidation kinetics on amorphous silica alumina catalysts at lower temperatures, e.g. <600°C. Recently, Lin, Wang, Yang and co-workers [97–99] have reported the results of their investigation on carbon oxidation kinetics on zeolite cracking catalysts at high temperatures up to 800°C.

Control Regions

Generally, three rate controlling steps may be encountered in the oxidation of carbon on cracking catalysts: (1) control by intrinsic carbon oxidation kinetics; (2) control by oxygen diffusion through the catalyst pores; and (3) intermediate control, i.e., control involving both reaction kinetics and oxygen diffusion. In general, however, the rate of carbon oxidation is not wholly controlled by either intrinsic carbon oxidation kinetics or oxygen diffusion, since both steps are operating with varying degrees of importance under different regeneration conditions. The higher the regeneration temperature and the larger the catalyst particle size, the more important role the diffusion step plays in the carbon oxidation process.

Weisz and Goodwin [100] investigated the effect of particle size and regeneration temperature on the transition of the control regions. With regard to the powdered catalyst having a 0.2 mm diameter, a straight line up to 575°C in the Arrhenius plot was obtained, which demonstrated that the oxidation process was kinetically controlled throughout the temperature range. For the beads of 4 mm diameter, however, the straight line shifted at about 475°C and diffusion control predominated at temperatures above 625°C. Weisz and Goodwin also suggested a criterion for evaluating the diffusion effect, i.e., if

$$\frac{dN}{dt} < OD/R^2 \tag{18}$$

where dN/dt was the combustion rate of carbon in terms of C moles per cubic cm catalyst per second, there was no significant effect of oxygen diffusion on the rate of carbon combustion.

Intrinsic Kinetics of Carbon Oxidation

For the FCC catalysts with a particle diameter 110 μm, the features of the control region is simpler. Mo et al. [99] and Lin et al. [97] investigated the kinetics of carbon combustion on silica alumina catalyst at higher temperatures. They concluded that the carbon combustion rate was controlled by the intrinsic burning rate of carbon even at a temperature up to 800°C for these catalysts. Figure 9 showed that straight lines were obtained in the Arrhenius plot throughout the temperature range.

The intrinsic carbon burning rate is the rate of the combustion of coke in the absence of appreciable diffusional restrictions. This rate has generally been observed to be proportional to the oxygen concentration [98, 101, 103, 105, 108, 110, 111], but the dependence of the reaction rate on the carbon concentration shows some controversy among investigators. Many authors regarded the carbon burning process as a first order reaction with respect to carbon concentration, however, Hughes and Shettigar [101] and Massoth [102] claimed that the surface reaction expression fitted the experimental data better than the first order reaction expression did. The kinetic expressions and values of the activation energy of carbon combustion proposed by individual authors are summarized in Table 10. Table 10 shows that the values of activation energy obtained range mostly from 140 to 160 KJ/mole.

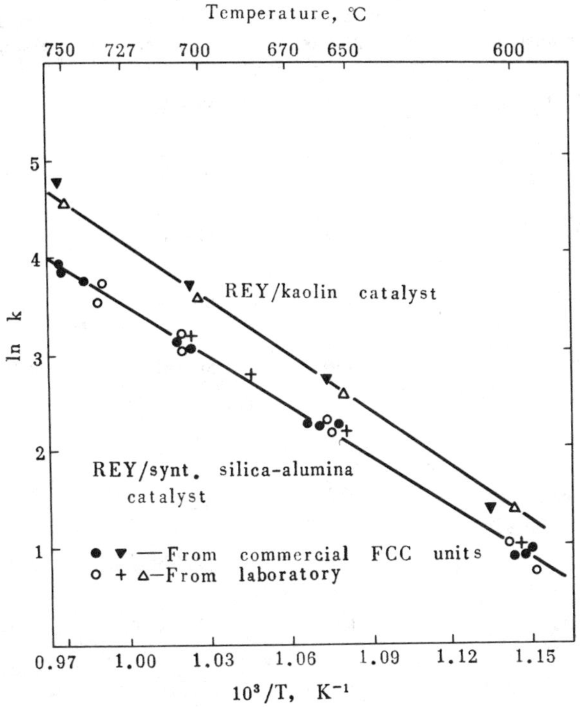

Figure 9. Arrhenius plot of carbon combustion rate. (After Mo et al. [99].)

The values of the carbon combustion rate constant k′ (k′ = kP_0, assuming P_0 to be constant, i.e., 0.21 atm.) against temperatures obtained by individual authors are plotted in Figure 10. It can be seen from Figure 10 that there are some differences between the k′ values obtained from different sources.

A prevailing concept that the combustion rate of carbon lacks of dependence either upon the nature of the coke deposit or upon the property of the cracking catalyst, and resembles the combustion rate of carbon in graphite [105], has been widely accepted by many authors. Recently, however, Mo et al. [100] and Lin et al. [111] found that difference in carbon combustion rates actually existed between different types of catalyst, i.e., the amorphous silica alumina type catalysts, the REY/Kaolin type catalysts, and the REY/Synthetic Si—Al type catalysts. They also found that if the catalysts of the same type were treated by steam at different conditions and then followed by coking, the combustion rate of carbon varied with the treating temperature and time. Figure 11 shows the changes of the rate constant k_c. Furthermore, by comparing with the data obtained by Gulbransen [108], they concluded that the carbon burning rate of the coke deposit in terms of the number of C atom per unit surface of carbon was about 2 to 3 times that of the graphite [111].

Taking account of the pseudo-graphitic structure of the coke deposit, Xiu et al. [112] examined the structure of coke isolated from different coked catalysts by X-ray diffraction analysis. The peaks showing the characteristics of the graphite 002 plane for the isolated coke from various samples were different in shape. Supposing that the degrees of the ordered structure of the coke samples could be characterized by the half peak width of these characteristic peaks, a certain relationship between the carbon burning rate and the half peak width was found. Figure 12 showed that the smaller the half peak width, i.e., the higher degree of the ordered structure of the coke, the lower the carbon combustion rate would be.

Table 10
Kinetic Expressions of Carbon Combustion

Kinetic Expression	Activation Energy, KJ/mole	Type of Catalyst	Temperature Range, °C	Ref.
$-\frac{dC}{dt} = (k_1 + k_2P_w)P_0C$	172	Si—Al	510–565	(103)
$-\frac{d(C/C_0)}{dt} = k_cP_0^{0.75}(C/C_0)$	144	Si—Al	500–580	(95)
$-\frac{dC}{dt} = k_cP_0C$	154	Si—Al	450–600	(105)
$-\frac{dC}{dt} = k_sS_0P_0(C/C_0)$	167	Si—Al	425–480	(102)
$\frac{d\alpha_c}{dt} = k_sP_0(1 - \alpha_c)^{2/3}$	136	Si—Al	420–545	(101)
$-\frac{dC}{dt} = k_cP_0C$	110	Cd—Y	400–570	(106)
$-\frac{dC}{dt} = k_cP_0C$	142	REY/Si—Al	500–650	(107)
$-\frac{dC}{dt} = k_cP_0C$	145	REY/Si—Al	600–750	(99)
$-\frac{dC}{dt} = k_cP_0C$	161	REY/kaolin	580–800	(99)

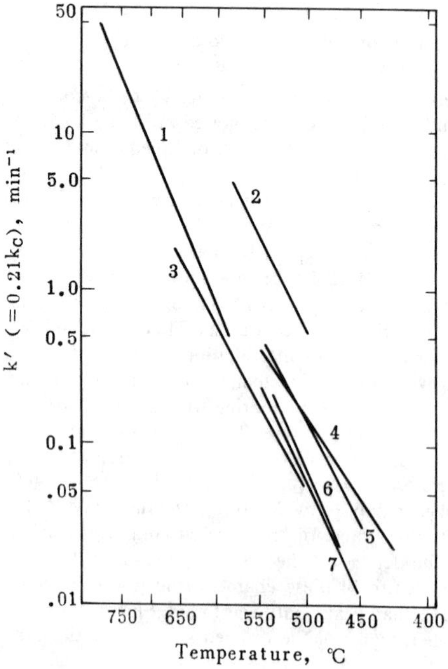

Figure 10. Carbon burning rate constants obtained by individual authors: 1—Mo et al. [99]; 2—Haldeman and Botty [95]; 3—Lin et al. [97]; 4—Hano et al. [106]; 5—Tone et al. [107]; 6—Weisz and Goodwin [100]; 7—Massoth [102].

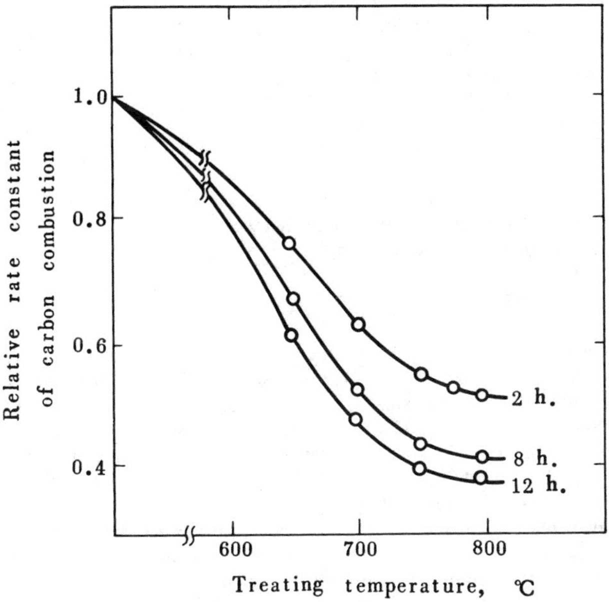

Figure 11. Influence of hydrothermal treating upon carbon burning rate (regeneration temperature 600°C). (After Lin et al. [111].)

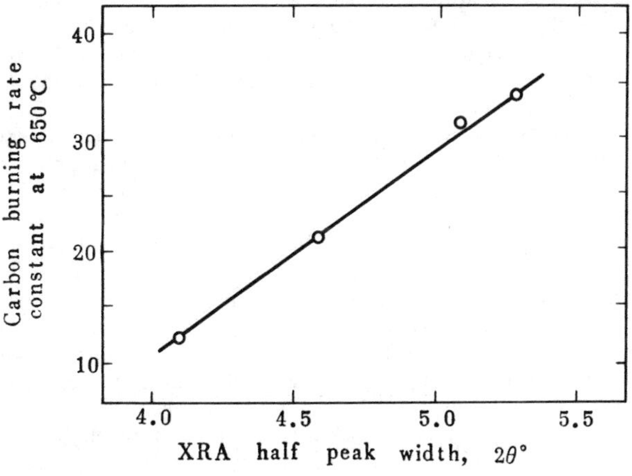

Figure 12. Relation between k_c and XRA half peak width. (After Xiu et al. [112].)

On the basis of the previous results and that the carbon burning rate constant of isolated coke remained the same as that of the coke originally on the catalyst (see Table 11), Lin et al. [111] concluded that the difference between carbon burning rates on different types of catalyst might result mainly from the different properties of the coke deposits. The properties of cracking catalyst affected the properties of the coke formed in cracking reaction, but it did not significantly affect

Table 11
Comparison of the k_c ($atm^{-1} \cdot min^{-1}$) at 650°C

Catalyst Sample No.	1	2	3
Coke on catalyst	31.8	21.3	13.0
Isolated coke	31.5	21.6	13.2

the carbon burning rate during regeneration. In reality, the regeneration reaction of cracking catalyst could be regarded as a non-catalytic reaction.

Effect of Contaminating Metals

Some contaminating metals have a significant effect on the carbon burning rate. Weisz and Goodwin [105] found the addition of 0.15% Cr_2O_3 to the silica alumina catalyst could raise the carbon burning rate constant fourfold. The catalytic effect of chromia was lost, however, if the sample was treated with high-temperature steam. This alteration was believed due to an irreversible change from a Cr^{6+} ion complex to a Cr^{3+} structure. Remizov [113] also investigated the effects of chromia on the carbon burning rate of zeolite catalysts under varied conditions. Tadashi Hano et al. [106] incorporated Co, Cr, and Cu in zeolite catalysts by ion-change, and found the carbon burning rates were significantly increased. Xiu et al. [112] investigated the effects of Fe, Ni, Cu, V, and Na on the carbon burning rate of zeolite catalysts. The rate constant of Cu-contaminated catalyst was about two times that of the non-contaminated catalyst. However, the rate constant of the coke isolated from the Cu-contaminated catalyst remained the same as that of the non-contaminated coked catalyst. This implied that a catalytic effect arose from the contaminating copper but not from the cracking catalyst itself.

It is interesting to note that the apparent activation energies of the catalyzed processes remain the same as those of uncatalyzed processes where the effect of the contaminating metal does not exist [104, 106, 112]. Weisz and Goodwin [105] supposed a complex catalytic mechanism to explain these experimental results. They supposed that a non-catalytic reaction of carbon and oxygen could occur very rapidly to produce an intermediate, X, via a reversible reaction, and the intermediate then underwent a catalytic conversion to the final product. If the major portion of the observed apparent activation energy was the thermodynamic free energy of the formation of the intermediate, X, and the kinetic activation energy of the formation of the final product was relatively small, then the observed apparent activation of the catalytic carbon burning reaction might remain the same as that of the noncatalytic reaction.

Carbon Combustion in Pellet Catalyst

At present the micro-bead cracking caralysts (mean diameter = 60 μm) are widely used in riser reactors and fluidized bed reactors. However, the pellet cracking catalysts (diameter = 3 mm) are still used in some old cracking units, e.g. Thermofor reactors. Therefore, the carbon combustion in the pellet catalyst will be discussed here briefly, although extensive literature concerning this problem exists.

The kinetics of carbon combustion in the pellet catalyst is more complicated than in the micro-bead catalyst, because the diffusion of oxygen into the inner pores may play an important role at higher regeneration temperatures. The regeneration temperatures normally adapted in commercial units are higher than 500°C, and a significant effect of oxygen diffusion may occur at such temperatures.

Several kinetic models for carbon oxidation in a single catalyst pellet have been proposed by individual investigators. Generally, these models can be split into two general groups: homogeneous models and retracting core models. In homogeneous models, oxygen is available to all the coke deposits throughout the particle, and a homogeneous type of gas-solid reaction occurs where the rate of carbon combustion is dominated by intrinsic kinetics. In retracting core models, the oxidation reaction becomes limited in various degrees by the mass transport of oxygen through the pores.

Three types of models may be included in the category of the retracting core model. A sharp interface unreacted shrinking core model was first postulated by Yagi and Kunii [114]. In this model, the oxygen will be immediately consumed at the reaction zone, and the reaction zone itself may be visualized in this case to consist of a sharp interface travelling from the outer solid surface towards the center with depletion of the coke. Bowen and Cheng [115], and Shettigar and Hughes [116] developed a finite thickness reaction zone unreacted shrinking core model. In this model, they assumed a narrow but finite thickness reaction zone between the product layer and unreacted core instead of one with a sharp interface. This indicates that the diffusing oxygen does not get consumed immediately on contact with the reaction zone but only after penetration of a small but finite length into the unreacted core. Szkely and Evans [117], and Sampath et al [118] developed a grain model. Basically, this model assumes that a porous pellet comprises an agglomeration of smaller particles and the reaction occurs with the particles making up the pellet by a sharp interface mechanism.

Conceptually, the sharp interface unreacted shrinking core model is best suited to explain the regeneration characteristics at high temperatures when diffusion should dominate the overall reaction process. The latter two models would be more suitable for the intermediate control region.

For all of the retracting core models the general assumption was made that, relative to gaseous reactant diffusion in the product layer, the unreacted core was stationary. This assumption of a pseudo steady state was justified because of the much faster rate of transport of the gaseous reactant towards the unreacted core as compared with the rate of movement of the core itself [119]. An assumption of isothermality throughout the pellet was also made. No significant discrepancies between the experiment and model arises from these assumptions when the carbon conversion is the basis for comparison. But, for predicting the temperature profile within the pellet, using the previous assumption would lead to erroneous results [120].

The CO_2/CO Product Ratio in Carbon Combustion

The heat required for the heat balance that allows the catalytic cracking unit to operate continuously is supplied by the burning of coke in the regenerator. In this process the combustion of CO is an important contributor to the overall energy balance. A well-controlled CO combustion in regeneration can be a valuable tool not only for optimizing the unit heat balance, but also for improving the flexibility to the operation of the unit.

Both CO and CO_2 are believed to be produced as the primary products in the oxidation of carbon on catalysts [121–123]. Arthur [122] studied the oxidation of graphite and coal char and proposed an equation for predicting the ratio of CO/CO_2 produced:

$$CO/CO_2 = 10^{3.4} \exp(-12{,}400/RT) \tag{19}$$

where T was the reaction temperature. This equation was derived by comparison of kinetic equations expressing the formation rates of CO and CO_2. The values of CO/CO_2 ratio at several temperatures calculated by equation(19) are shown in Table 12.

Weisz [123] examined the CO/CO_2 product ratio in the flue gas during regeneration of silica alumina catalysts of different sizes. He suggested that the original CO_2/CO ratio of the gaseous product leaving the carbon burning sites was just the same as that given by Arthur's equation, but CO_2/CO ratio would increase by conversion of CO to CO_2 when the gaseous product diffused

Table 12
Ratio of CO/CO_2 by Arthur's Equation

Temperature, K	CO/CO_2	CO_2/CO
823	1.3	0.77
873	2.0	0.5
923	2.9	0.34
973	4.1	0.24
1023	5.6	0.18

through the porous catalyst particle. The conversion of CO increased with the reaction temperature and the particle diameter of the catalyst.

In FCC units, combustion of CO may also occur in the voids of dense phase and in the dilute phase. For predicting the CO_2/CO ratio of flue gas leaving the regenerator a knowledge of kinetics of CO oxidation in gas phase is needed. Unfortunately, however, precise kinetic expression is not available yet due to the complexity of this reaction. The results calculated from different sources are scattered extensively. Experimentally, it has been reported that under low regenerator temperature operation (dense phase $< 700°C$), the CO_2/CO ratio of the gas leaving the dense phase is about 0.8–1.0 and is about 0.9–1.2 in the flue gas, if no combustion promotor is present [124]. Actually, the flue gas from the conventional FCCU regenerator has a CO_2/CO ratio of 1–2, depending on the degree of the after-burning inherent in catalyst combustion activity, and the quantity of metal poisons [125].

Kinetics of Hydrogen Oxidation on Cracking Catalyst

Coke deposits on cracking catalysts have a composition in the range of $CH_{0.4}$ to $CH_{1.0}$. Some authors showed that the water produced from the oxidation of hydrogen tended to occur earlier in the reaction than oxides of carbon from the oxidation of the carbon itself [102, 104, 126]. Since the reaction of the hydrogen constituent of the coke appeared not to have been investigated in detail, precise kinetic data of hydrogen oxidation had not been available till the publication of the paper in 1986 by Wang et al [127].

Wang et al investigated the kinetics of combustion of hydrogen in coke on a zeolite type catalyst at 600–750°C. In the case of measuring the hydrogen reaction velocity, the most difficult problem was that the reaction product, water, was readily adsorbed on the reactor wall, gas tubing, and the cracking catalyst itself. To circumvent this difficulty, special techniques, including a pulse reaction technique and a model reactor system, were developed. The reaction rate of hydrogen combustion was found linear to the partial pressure of both the oxygen and the hydrogen content. Thus, the kinetic equation for the combustion of hydrogen in coke could easily be expressed as follows:

$$-\frac{dH}{dt} = k_H P_0 H \tag{20}$$

The apparent activation energy of this reaction was found to be 157 KJ/mole. For temperatures below 700°C, a straight line was obtained in the Arrhenius plot, but for temperatures higher than 700°C this line was concave somewhat downward, which demonstrated that the combustion of hydrogen went so fast that the diffusion of oxygen might hinder the rate of reaction.

Wang et al. also derived an equation for predicting the relation between the conversion of carbon and the conversion of hydrogen during regeneration:

$$\alpha_H = 1 - (1 - \alpha_c)^m \tag{21}$$

where m was the ratio of k_H to k_c, and its value ranged from about 1.8 to 2.4 according to the regeneration temperatures. Figure 13 shows the relation between the two conversions in the process of regeneration. From Figure 13, all of the hydrogen in coke is burnt off while the conversion of carbon is approximately 85% during regeneration.

The previous results were in agreement with data from some commercial FCC units. For example, the operating data from a two-stage regenerator indicate that the carbon conversion and hydrogen conversion were 60.0% and 79.9% respectively and the rate constant ratio k_H/k_c was about 1.76.

Kinetic Model

The kinetic model of the coke combustion reaction has been studied by several authors.

Considering that the coke deposit had a pseudo graphitic structure, Sotirchos et al. [126] suggested that the coke deposit consisted of two solid phases, the graphitic carbon C and the aliphatic

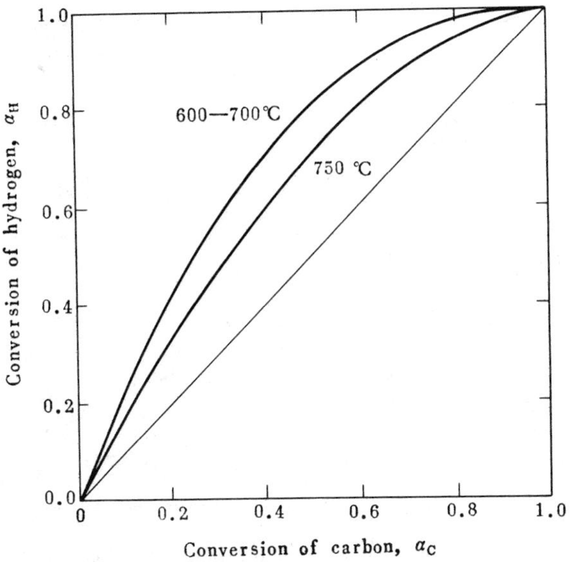

Figure 13. Conversion of carbon and hydrogen in the process of regeneration. (After Peng [130].)

hydrocarbon CH_2, and that the carbon combustion proceeded according to the following parallel reactions:

$$C + aO_2 \xrightarrow{r1} 2(1 - a)CO + (2a - 1)CO_2 \tag{22}$$

$$CH_2 + O_2 \xrightarrow{r2} CO + H_2O \tag{23}$$

where $a = \frac{1}{2}\left(1 + \frac{1}{1 + \lambda}\right)$

λ = ratio of CO to CO_2 determined by reaction temperature [122]

The rate r2 was assumed to be approximately 5r1, because precise kinetic data were not available.

Weisz and Goodwin [105] suggested an intermediate containing carbon and oxygen was produced during carbon combustion. This mechanism has been mentioned.

Wang et al. [127] and Mo et al. [99] proposed a series reaction model for describing the whole process of the carbon combustion reaction at high temperatures:

$$\text{Carbon in coke} \xrightarrow[O_2]{k_1} C_yO_x \xrightarrow[O_2]{k_2} CO + CO_2 \tag{24}$$

where C_yO_x was an intermediate. The kinetic equation derived from this model was:

$$\frac{d[CO + CO_2]}{dt} = \frac{k_1k_2C_0}{k_1 - k_2} \exp(-k_2t) - \exp(-k_1t) \tag{25}$$

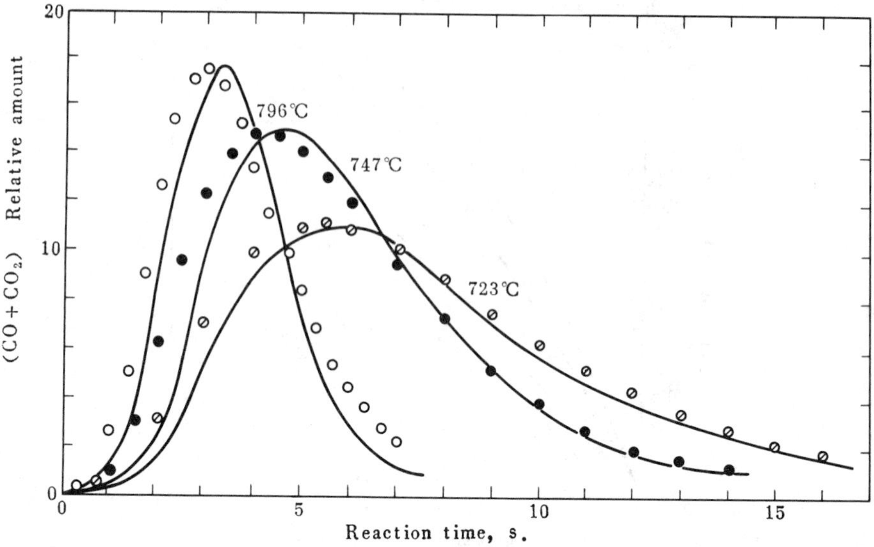

Figure 14. Effluent ($CO + CO_2$) diagram
Lines—experimental; circles—calculated by model (After Mo et al. [99].)

The results calculated by Equation 25 were quite in agreement with the experimental data at high temperatures as shown in Figure 14.

Some other experimental phenomena support the mechanism of forming an intermediate containing oxygen. Lin et al. [97] found a small content of oxygen in the coke isolated from partially regenerated coked catalyst. Panchenkov and Golovanov [128] studied the regeneration kinetics by a thermal balance method. At the beginning of the reaction, the coked catalyst sample didn't lose its weight, but a small gain in weight was observed. This abnormal phenomenon might be explained by the chemical adsorption of oxygen or the formation of some oxygen-containing intermediate. Wang et al. [129] passed on air pulse over a coked catalyst sample at an elevated temperature and followed this by purging with nitrogen. Carbon dioxide could still be detected in the effluent gas in a few minutes after the pulse, while the width of the air pulse was just a few seconds.

Based upon the previous discussion, we may conclude that a better kinetic model for the regeneration of coked cracking catalyst could be expressed as follows:

$$\text{Coke}\begin{cases}(\text{C}) \xrightarrow[O_2]{} C_yO_x \xrightarrow[O_2]{} a\text{CO} + b\text{CO}_2 \\ (\text{H}) \xrightarrow[O_2]{} H_2O\end{cases} \tag{26}$$

REFERENCES

1. Corbett, R. A., "Refining Catalyst Choices Expand Again," *Oil Gas J.*, *84*(41), 39 (1986).
2. Corbett, R. A., "More Refining Catalysts Available," *Oil Gas J.*, *83*(46), 127 (1985).
3. Aslund, L. R., "Unique Survey Spotlights Complex Catalyst World," *Oil Gas J.*, *82*(41), 55 (1984).
4. Corbett, R. A., "Octane Boosted by Special Catalyst Mechanisms," *Oil Gas J.*, *84*(41), 55 (1986).

5. Venuto, P. B., and Habib, E. T., "Catalyst-Feedstock-Engineering Interactions in Fluid Catalytic Cracking," *Catal. Rev.-Sci. Eng.*, *18*(1), 1 (1978).
6. Venuto, P. B., and Habib, E. T., "*Fluid Catalytic Cracking with Zeolite Catalysts*, Marcel Dekker, Inc., New York, 1979.
7. Corma, A., and Wojciechowski, B. W., "The Chemistry of Catalytic Cracking," *Catal. Rev.-Sci. Eng.*, *27*(1), 29 (1985).
8. Maselli, J. M., and Peters, A. W., "Preparation and Properties of Fluid Cracking Catalysts for Residual Oil Conversion," *Catal. Rev.-Sci. Eng.*, *26*(3 & 4), 525 (1984).
9. Otterstedt, J. E., Gevert, S. B., Jaras, S. G., and Menon, P. G., "Fluid Catalytic Cracking of Heavy (Residual) Oil Fractions: A Review," *Applied Catal.*, *22*, 159 (1986).
10. Chen, N. Y., Mitchell, T. O., Olson, D. H., and Pelrine, B. P., "Irreversible Deactivation of Zeolite Fluid Cracking Catalyst," *Ind. Eng. Chem., Prod. Res. Dev.* *16*(3), 244 (1977).
11. Yuu, S., "Collision Rate of Small Particles in a Homogeneous and Isotropic Turbulence," *AIChE J.*, *30*(5), 802 (1984).
12. Grimmett, E. S., "Kinetics of Particle Growth in the Fluidized Bed Calcination Process," *AIChE J.*, *10*(5), 717 (1964).
13. Rollmann, L. D., "Constraints on Carbon Formation in Zeolite Catalysts," *Progress in Catalyst Deactivation* (Figueiredo, ed.), Martinus Nijhoff Publishers, The Hague, 1981.
14. de Kroes, B., Groenboom, C. J., and Connor, P. O., "New Zeolites in FCC," *Ketjen Catalyst Symp.*, 1986.
15. Greensfelder, B. S., Voge, H. H., and Good, G. M., "Catalytic and Thermal Cracking of Pure Hydrocarbons," *Ind. Eng. Chem.*, *41*(11), 2573 (1949).
16. Abbot, J., and Wojciechowski, B. W., "Catalytic Cracking on HY and HZSM-5 of a Fischer-Tropsch Product," *Ind. Eng. Chem., Prod. Res. Dev.*, *24*, 501 (1985).
17. Benesi, H. A., and Winquist, B. H. C., *Advances in Catalysis*, *27*, 98 (1978).
18. Jacob, P. A., *Carboniongenic Activity of Zeolites*, Elsevier Publishing Co., Amsterdam, 1977, p. 33.
19. Forni, L., "Comparison of the Methods for the Determination of Surface Acidity of Solid Catalysts," *Catal. Rev.-Sci. Eng.*, *8*(1), 65 (1973).
20. Magee, J. S., Cormier, W. E., and Woltermann, G. M., "Octane Catalysts Contain Special Sieves," *Oil Gas J.*, *83*(21), 59 (1985).
21. Klinowske, J., *Progress in NMR Spec.*, *16*, 237 (1984).
22. Dong Songqi, Xia Wentao, Xie Liqun, Wang Tianshou and Wang Jianmin, "A Study on Acidic Properties of Cracking Catalysts," *J. East China Petroleum Institute*, *9*(2), 1 (1985).
23. Xia Wentao, Dong Sibqu, and Huang Zhenyun, "A New Method for Determining Catalyst Surface Acidity and Acid Strength Distribution," *Petroleum Processing* (Chinese), 11, 39 (1983).
24. Shi Jiqun and Li Li, "The Changes of the Pore Size Distribution in CRC-1 Zeolite Cracking Catalyst due to Coke Deposition," *J. East China Petroleum Institute*, *10*(4), 1 (1986).
25. Archibald, R. C., May N. C., and Greensfelder, B. S., "Experimental Catalytic and Thermal Cracking," *Ind. Eng. Chem.*, *8*, 1811 (1952).
26. Weisz, P. B., "Zeolites-New Horizons in Catalysis", *Chemtech.*, Aug. 1973, p. 498.
27. Thomas, C. L., and Barmby, D. S., "The Chemistry of Catalytic Cracking with Molecular Sieve Catalysts," *J. Catal*, *12*, 341 (1968).
28. Young, C. W., and Rajagopalan, K., "Techniques for Evaluating Heavy Oil Cracking Catalyst," *Ind. Eng. Chem., Proc. Des. Dev.*, *24*, 995 (1985).
29. Rajagopalan, K., Peters, A. W., and Edwards, G. C., "Influence of Zeolite Particles Size on Selectivity During Fluid Catalytic Cracking," *Applied Catal.*, *23*, 69 (1986).
30. Cheremisinoff, N. P., and Cheremisinoff, P. N., "Particulate Capture in Venturi Scrubbers," in *Hydrodynamics of Gas-Solids Fluidization*, Gulf Publishing Co., Houston, Texas, 1984, Chapt. 15.
31. Lee, S. Y., and Aris, R., "Supported Catalysis Prepared by Impregnation," *Catal. Rev.-Sci. Eng.*, *27*(2), 207 (1985).
32. Speedy, R. J., "Stability-Limit Conjecture," *J. Phys. Chem.*, *86*, 982 (1982).
33. Li Binghui, "*A Study of Coke Deposition and Distribution on FCC Catalysts during VGO and Resid Cracking*," Master dissertation, East China Petroleum Institute, 1987.

34. Miale, J. N., Chen, N. Y., and Weisz, P. B., "Catalysis by Crystalline Alumina-silicates," *J. Catal., 6*, 278 (1966).
35. Campagna, R. J., Wick, J. P., Brady, M. F., and Fort, D. L., "Fresh FCC Catalyst Tests Predict Performance," *Oil Gas J., 84*(12), 85 (1986).
36. Mauleon, J. L., and Courcell, J. C., "FCC Heat Balance Critical for Heavy Fuels." *Oil Gas J., 83*(42), 64 (1985).
37. Liu Fuying, Yan Zhengze, Weng Huixin, and Mao Xinjun, "Characterization of Zeolite-Containing Catalyst during Steam Deactivation." *Petroleum Processing* (Chinese), 3, 17 (1981).
38. Mao Xinjun, Weng Huixin, Yan Zhengze and Liu Fuying, "Relation Between Steam Deactivation and Surface Properties of Zeolite-Containing Cracking Catalyst," *Petroleum Processing* (Chinese), 6, 29 (1982).
39. Mitchell, B. R., "Metal Contamination of Cracking Catalyst-Synthetic Metal Deposition on Fresh Catalysts," *Ind. Eng. Chem., Prod. Res. Dev., 19*, 209 (1980).
40. Voge, H. H., "Catalytic Cracking," *Catalysis, Vol. 6* (P. H. Emmett ed.). Reinhold, New York, 1958, Chapt. 5.
41. Haensel, V., "Catalytic Cracking of Pure Hydrocarbons," *Advances in Catalysis, 3*, 179 (1951).
42. Greensfelder, B. S., and Voge, H. H., "Catalytic Cracking of Pure Hydrocarbons," *Ind. Eng. Chem., 37*(6), 514 (1945).
43. Greensfelder, B. S., and Voge, H. H., "Catalytic Cracking of Pure Hydrocarbons," *Ind. Eng. Chem., 37*(11), 1038 (1945).
44. Gladrow, E. M., Krebs, R. W., and Kimber, C. N., Jr., "Reactions of Hydrocarbons over Cracking Catalyst," *Ind. Eng. Chem., 45*(1), 142 (1953).
45. Eastwood, S. C., Plank, C. J., and Weisz, P. B., "New Development in Catalytic Cracking," Proceed. 8th World Petr. Congr., *4*, 245 (1971).
46. Oblad, A. G., "Molecular Sieve Cracking Catalysts," *Oil Gas J., 70*(13), 84 (1972).
47. Gayer, F. M., "The Catalytic Polymerization of Propylene," *Ind. Eng. Chem., 25*, 1122 (1933).
48. Hansford, R. C., "A Mechanism of Catalytic Cracking," *Ind. Eng. Chem., 39*, 848 (1949).
49. Thomas, C. L., "Chemistry of Cracking Catalysts," *Ind. Eng. Chem., 41*, 2564 (1949).
50. Gates, B. C., Katzer, J. R., and Schuit, G. C., *Chemistry of Catalytic Processes*, Academic, New York, 1977, Chart. 1.
51. Moscou, L., and Mone, R., "Structure and Catalytic Properties of Thermally and Hydrothermally Treated Zeolites Acid Strength Distribution of REX and REY," *J. Catal., 30*, 417 (1973).
52. Beaumont R., and Barthomeuf, D., "X, Y, Aluminum-Deficient and Ultrastable Faujasite-Type Zeolite II, "*J. Catal., 27*, 45 (1972).
53. Nace, D. M., "Catalytic Cracking over Crystalline Alumino-silicates," *Ind. Eng. Chem., Prod. Res. Dev., 8*, 24 (1969).
54. Breck, D. W., *Zeolite Molecular Sieves*, Wiley, New York, 1974.
55. Barrer, R. M., Buttitude, F. W., and Sutherland, J. W., "Structure of Faujasite and Properties of Its Inclusion Complexes with Hydrocarbons," *Trans. Faraday Soc., 53*, 1111 (1957).
56. Moore, R. M., and Katzer, J. R., "Counterdiffusion of Liquid Hydrocarbons in Type Y Zeolite," *AIChE J., 18*, 816 (1973).
57. Nace, D. M., "Catalytic Cracking over Crystalline Alumino-silicates," *Ind. Eng. Chem., Prod. Res. Dev., 9*, 203 (1970).
58. Weisz, P. B., Frilette, V. J., Mastman, R. W., and Mower, E. B., "Catalysis by Crystalline Alumino-silicates II. Molecular Shape Selective Reactions," *J. Catal., 1*, 307 (1962).
59. Weekman, V., Jr. and Nace, D. M., "Kinetics of Catalytic Cracking Selectivity in Fixed, Moving, and Fluid Bed Reactors," *AIChE J., 16*(3), 397 (1970).
60. Blanding, F. H., "Reaction Rates in Catalytic Cracking of Petroleum," *Ind. Eng. Chem., 45*(6), 1186 (1953).
61. Wallaston, E. G., Haflin, W. J., Ford, W. D., and D'Souza, G. J., "What Influences Cat Cracking," *Hydrocarbon Process., 54*(9), 93 (1975).
62. Satterfield, C. N., "Trickle-Bed Reactors," *AIChE J., 21*(2), 209 (1975).
63. Nace, D. M., "Catalytic Cracking over Crystalline Alumino-silicates II," *Ind. Eng. Chem., Proc. Res. Dev., 8*, 31 (1969).

64. Blazek, J. J., "Gains from FCC Revival Evident Now," *Oil Gas J.*, *71*(41), 65 (1973).
65. White, P. J., "Effect of Feed Composition on Catalytic Cracking Yields," *Oil Gas J.*, *66*(21), 112 (1968).
66. Voltz, S. E., Nace, D. M., Jacob, S. M., and Weekman, V. W., Jr., "Application of a Kinetic Model for Catalytic Cracking III," *Ind. Eng. Chem., Proc. Des. Dev.*, *11*(2), 261 (1972).
67. Nace, D. M., Voltz, S. E., and Weekman, V. W., Jr., "Application of a Kinetic Model for Catalytic Cracking," *Ind. Eng. Chem., Proc. Des. Dev.*, *10*(4), 530 (1971).
68. Voltz, S. E., Nace, D. M., and Weekman, V. W., Jr., "Application of a Kinetic Model for Catalytic Cracking," *Ind. Eng. Chem., Proc. Des. Dev.*, *10*(4), 538 (1971).
69. Pierce, W. L., Souther, R. P., Kaufman, T. G., and Ryan, D. F., "Innovations in Flexicracking," *Hydrocarbon Process.*, *51*(5), 92 (1972).
70. Cimbalo, R. N., Foster, R. L., and Wachtel, S. J., "Deposited Metals Poison FCC Catalyst," *Oil Gas J.*, *70*(20), 112 (1972).
71. Hemler, C. H., and Vermillion, W. L., "New Jobs for FCC," *Oil Gas J.*, *71*(45), 88 (1973).
72. Weekman, V. W., Jr., "A Model of Catalytic Cracking Conversion in Fixed, Moving, and Fluid-Bed Reactors," *Ind. Eng. Chem., Proc. Des. Dev.*, *7*(1), 90 (1968).
73. Golikeri, S., and Luss, D., "Analysis of Activation Energy of Grouped Parallel Reactions," *AIChE J.*, *18*(2), 277 (1972).
74. Kemp, R. R. D., and Wojciechowski, B. W., "The Kinetic of Mixed Feed Reactions," *Ind. Eng. Chem., Fundam.*, *13*, 332 (1974).
75. Voorhies, A., "Carbon Formation in Catalytic Cracking," *Ind. Eng. Chem.*, *37*, 318 (1945).
76. Wojciechowski, B. W., "The Kinetic Foundations and the Practical Application of the Time-on-stream Theory of Catalyst Decay," *Catal. Rev.-Sci. Eng.*, *9*(1) (1974).
77. Wojciechowski, B. W., "A Theoretical Treatment of Catalyst Decay," *Can. J. Chem. Eng.*, *46*, 48 (1963).
78. Best, D. A., and Wojciechowski, B. W., "Cumene Cracking on a Diffusional-limited Aging Catalyst," *J. Catal.*, *31*, 74 (1973).
79. Froment, G. F., and Bischoff, K. B., *Chemical Reactor Analysis and Design*, J. Wiley, New York, 1979.
80. Eberly, P. E., Kimberlin, C. N., Miller, W. H., and Drushel, H. V., "Coke Formation on Silica Alumina Cracking Catalysts," *Ind. Eng. Chem. Proc. Des. Dev.*, *5*, 193 (1966).
81. Lin Chen-chih, Park, S. W., and Hatcher, W. J., Jr., "Zeolite Catalyst Deactivation by Coking," *Ind. Eng. Chem., Proc. Des. Dev.*, *22*, 609 (1983).
82. Parakas, J. A., Shah, Y. T., Mckinney, J. D., and Carr, N. L., "Kinetic Model for Catalytic Cracking in a Transfer Line Reactor, "*Ind. Eng. Chem., Proc. Des, Dev.*, *15*(1), 165 (1976).
83. Andrews, J. M., "Cracking Characteristics of Catalytic Cracking Units," *Ind. Eng. Chem.*, *51*, 507 (1959).
84. Jacob, S. M., Gross, B., Voltz, S. E., and Weekman, V. W., Jr., "A Lumping and Reaction Scheme for Catalytic Cracking," *AIChE J.*, *22*(4), 701 (1976).
85. Sha, Y., Chen, X., Lin, J., Weng, H., Zhu, Z., and Mao, X., "Investigation of the Lumped Kinetic Model for Catalytic Cracking I," *Acta Petrolei Sinica* (*Petr. Process, Sect.*) (*Chinese*), *1*,(1), 3, (1985).
86. Wei, J., and Prater, C. D., "The Structure and Analysis of Complex Reaction System," *Adv. in Catal.*, *8*, 203 (1962).
87. Wrench, R. E., and Wilson, J. W., "FCCU upgrade to Heavy Oil Cracking Improves Margins," *Oil Gas J.*, *84*(40), 53 (1986).
88. Busch, L. E., Hettinger, W. P., Jr., and Krock, R. P., "Reduced Crude Oil Conversion in Commercial RCC and ART Process Operations," *NPRA AM-84-50* (1984).
89. Dean, R. R., Mauleon, J. L., and Letzsch, W. S., "Resid Puts FCC Process in New Perspective," *Oil Gas J.*, *80*(40), 75 (1982).
90. Dean, R. R., Mauleon, J. L., and Letzsch, W. S., "Total Introduces New FCC Process," *Oil Gas J.*, *80*(41), 168 (1982).
91. Levenspiel, O., "The Chemical Reactor Omnibook," OSU Book Stores, Inc., 1979, p. 61:2.
92. Knaus, J. A., Schwarzenbek, E. F., Atteridg, P. T., and Mahon, J. F., "Catalytic Cracking of Reduced Crudes," *Chem. Eng. Progress*, *57*(12), 37 (1961).

93. NPRA Q&A-2, *Oil Gas J.*, *81*(13), 114 (1983).
94. Murphy, J. R., and Chen, Y. L., "Interaction of FCC Variables Can Be Predicted," *Oil Gas J.*, *82*(36), 89 (1984).
95. Haldeman, R. C., and Botty, C., "On the Nature of the Carbon Deposit of Cracking Catalysts," *J. Phys. Chem.*, *63*, 489 (1959).
96. Eberly, P. E., Jr., Kimberlin, C. N., Jr., Miller, W. H., and Druchel, H. V., "Coke Formation on Silica-Alumina Cracking Catalysts," *Ind. Eng. Chem., Proc. Des. Dev.*, *5*, 193 (1966).
97. Lin Shi-xiong, Wang Guang-xun, Jia Kuan-he, Shi Ji-qun, Zhang Jian-fang, and Yang Guang-hua, "The Kinetics of Coke Deposition and Regeneration of Cracking Catalysts," *Acta Petrolei*, (special issue, Chinese), 93 (1982).
98. Wang Guang-xun, Lin Shi-xiong and Yang Guang-hua, "The Kinetics and Mechanism of Elimination of Carbonaceous Deposits on Cracking Catalysts in Regeneration," Proceedings of 32nd Chem. Eng. Conf., Vol. 2, p. 808, Vancouver, Canada, 1982.
99. Mo Wei-jian, Lin Shi-xiong and Yang Guang-hua, "Kinetics of Combustion of Carbon in Carbonaceous deposits on Zeolite Type Cracking Catalysts I & II", *Acta Petrolei Sinica* (*Petroleum Processing Section*) (Chinese), *2*, no. 2, 13 and no. 3, 11 (1986).
100. Weisz, P. B., and Goodwin, R. D., "Combustion of Carbonaceous Deposits within Porous Catalyst Particle. I," *J. Catal.*, *2*, 397 (1963).
101. Hughes, R., and Shettigar, U. R., "Regeneration of Silica-Alumina Catalyst Particles," *J. Appl. Chem., Biotechnol.*, *21*, 35 (1971).
102. Massoth, F. E., "Oxidation of Coked Silica-Alumina Catalyst." *Ind. Eng. Chem., Proc. Des. Dev.*, *6*, 200 (1967).
103. Johnson, M. F. L., and Mayland, H. C., "Carbon Burning Rates of Cracking Catalyst in the Fluidized State," *Ind. Eng. Chem.*, *47* (1955).
104. Dart, J. C., Savage, R. T., and Kirkbride, C. G., "Regeneration Characteristics of Clay Cracking Catalyst," *Chem. Eng. Progress*, *45*, 102 (1949).
105. Weisz, P. B., and Goodwin, R. B., "Combustion of Carbonaceous Deposits within Porous Catalyst Particles II," *J. Catal.*, *6*, 227 (1966).
106. Tadashi Hano, Fumiyuki Nakashio and Koichiro Kusunoki, "The Burning Rate of Coke Deposited on Zeolite Catalyst," *J. Chem. Eng., Japan*, *8*, 127 (1975).
107. Tone Setsuji, Miura Shln-ichi and Otake Tsutao, "Kinetics of Oxidation of Coke on Silica-Alumina Catalysts," *Bull. of Japan Petrol. Inst.*, *14*, 76 (1972).
108. Gulbransen, E. A., and Andrew, K. F., "Reactions of Artificial Graphite," *Ind. Eng. Chem.*, *44*, 1034 (1952).
109. Hughes, R., and Shettigar, U. R., "Regeneration of Coked Silica-Alumina Catalyst," *Ind. Eng. Chem., Proc. Des. Dev.*, *6*, 200 (1971).
110. Hargerbaumer, W. A., and Lee Rusell, "Combustion of Coke Deposit on Synthethic Bead Cracking Catalyst," *Oil Gas J.*, Mar. 15, 76 (1947).
111. Lin Shi-xiong, Wang Guang-xun, Jia Kuan-he, Shi Ji-qun and Yang Guang-hua, "Chemical Behavior of Coked FCC Catalysts During Regeneration," Proceedings, 3rd China-Japan-U.S.A. Symposium on Catalysis, Xiamen, China, 1987.
112. Xiu Mo, Jia Kuan-he and Yang Guang-hua, "Effects of the Contaminating Metals on Regeneration Kinetics of CRC-1 Catalyst," *J. East China Petrol. Inst.*, no. 3, (1987).
113. Remizov, F. G., Rabinovich, S. I., Asadulaeva, F. M., and Esipko, E. A., "The Effect of Chromia on Pellet Zeolite Cracking Catalysts," *Chem. and Technol. of Fuel and Lube Oil, USSR*, no. 9, 38 (1977).
114. Yagi, S., and Kunii, D., *J. Chem. Soc. Japan* (*Ind. Chem. Sect.*), *56*, 131 (1961).
115. Bowen, J. H., and Cheng, C. Y., "A Diffuse Interface Model for Fluid-Solid Reaction," *Chem. Eng. Sci.*, *24*, 1829 (1969).
116. Shettigar, U. R., and Hughes, R., "Prediction of Transient Temperature Distribution in Gas-Solid Reactions," *Chem. Eng. J.*, *3*, 93 (1972).
117. Szekely, J., and Evanx, J. W., "A Structural Model for Gas-Solid Reactions with a Moving Boundary-II," *Chem. Eng. Sci.* *26*, 1901 (1971).
118. Sampath, B. S., Ramachandran, P. A., and Hughes, R., "Modelling of Non-Catalytic Gas-Solid Reactions-I," *Chem. Eng. Sci.*, *30*, 125 (1975).

119. Bischoff, K. B., "Accuracy of the Pseudo Steady State Approximation for Moving Boundary Diffusion Problems," *Chem. Eng. Sci.*, *18*, 711 (1963).
120. Hughes, R., *Deactivation of Catalysts*, Academic Press INC., London, 1984, p. 231.
121. Laine, N. R., Vastola, F. J., and Walker, P. L., Jr., The Role of the Surface Complex in the Carbon–Oxygen Reaction, Proceed. of the 5th Conference on Carbon, Vol. 2, 211, 1963.
122. Arthur, J. R., "Reaction Between Carbon and Oxygen," *Trans. Faraday Soc.*, *47*. 164 (1951).
123. Weisz, P. B., "Combustion of Carbonaceous Deposits within Porous Catalyst Particles, III," *J. Catal.*, *6*, 425 (1966).
124. Upson, L. L., Principles of CO Combustion, Proceed. of the Katalistik's 7th Annual FCC Symposium, Venice, Italy, May. 12–13, (1986).
125. Chester, A. W., Schwartz, A. B., Stover, W. A., and McWilliams, J. P., "Catalyzing the Energy Balance of Cat Cracking," *Chemtech*, 50, (1981).
126. Sotirches, S. V., Mon, E., and Amundson, N. R., "Combustion of Coke Deposits in a Catalyst Pellet," *Chem. Eng. Sci.*, *38*, 55 (1983).
127. Wang Guang-xun, Lin Shi-xiong, Mo Weijian, Peng Chun-lan, Yang Guang-hua, "Kinetics of Combustion of Carbon and Hydrogen in Carbonaceous Deposits on Zeolite-type Cracking Catalysts," *Ind. Eng. Chem., Proc. Des. Dev.*, *25*, 626 (1986).
128. Panchenkov, G. M., and Galovanov, E. F., "Regeneration Kinetics of Silica-alumina Catalysts," *Trans. of Academy of Sciences, USSR, Tech. Sci. Sect.*, *3*, 384 (1952).
129. Wang Guang-xun, Lin Shi-xiong, and Yang Guang-hua, "Kinetics and Mechanism of Elimination of Carbonaceous Deposits on Cracking Catalysts in Regeneration," *J. East China Petrol. Inst.*, no. 3, 1 (1984).
130. Peng Chun-lan, Kinetics of Combustion of Hydrogen in Coke during Regeneration at High Temperature, M.S. Thesis, East China Petrol. Inst., 1984.

CHAPTER 3

INDUSTRIAL NICKEL CATALYSTS: PRODUCTION, CHARACTERIZATION AND USES

P. C. M. van Stiphout and J. W. Geus

Department of Inorganic Chemistry
State University of Utrecht
The Netherlands

E. G. M. Kuijpers

Harshaw Chemie B. V.
De Meern, The Netherlands

CONTENTS

INTRODUCTION

Nickel is one of the metals most frequently used for catalytic reactions. The main application of nickel catalysts lies in the hydrogenation of organic compounds as pioneered by Sabatier and Senderens [1]. Saturation of carbon-carbon double bonds is important with respect to the stabilization of product streams from crackers against undesired polymerization (gum formation). Cyclohexane, an important raw material, is produced by hydrogenation of benzene using nickel catalysts. Also primary products from the oxo reaction (hydroformylation) are processed with nickel catalysts. Finally, hydrogenation of carbon monoxide remaining after the low-temperature shift conversion in the ammonia process is carried out over nickel catalysts. Selective hydrogenation of unsaturated fatty oils is the basis of the edible oil and margarine industry. The development of nickel catalysts for this process, which took more than 50 years, has resulted in production of margarine and salad oils of an excellent chemical stability and of physical properties meeting the demands of consumers. Saturation of carbon-carbon double bonds in a non-selective hydrogenation process provides solid edible fats.

Besides hydrogenation of carbon-carbon double bonds reduction of nitro groups or cyanides to amines is performed over nickel catalysts. Introduction of NH_2 groups is in some cases also done with nickel catalysts by reacting alcohols with ammonia.

The above catalytic reactions are carried out at relatively low temperatures. First of all since the thermodynamic equilibrium calls for a low temperature and secondly in view of the stability of the compounds to be processed. One of the most important reactions with nickel catalysts, however, is performed at a very elevated temperature, viz. the hydrocarbon-steam reforming process. This process provides hydrogen for the desulphurisation of crude oil fractions, for the production of ammonia, and hydrogen and carbon monoxide for the production of methanol. Accordingly, the steam-reforming is carried out on a very large scale.

It is obvious that the demands nickel catalysts have to meet are widely divergent in the various processes. Nickel catalysts of strongly differing structure and thermal stability are thus used. With liquid-phase hydrogenations, which usually are carried out at temperatures at 100°C to 200°C, the demands upon the structure and thermal stability of the nickel catalyst are completely different from those made upon a steam-reforming catalyst, which must withstand temperatures of about 850°C, or even as high as 1,100°C in the secondary reformer for prolonged periods of time.

With low-temperature, liquid-phase reactions the bulk density of the catalyst is important, since the rate of settling of the catalyst can determine its performance in batch processes. As the catalysts are being used at low temperatures, a high thermostability is not required. Consequently, a catalyst that has to be reduced at elevated temperatures to provide the catalytically active metallic nickel is not favorable. As a result, Raney nickel exhibiting a high density and, thus, a high rate of settling and not calling for reduction at high temperatures is generally used, in spite of its relatively high price.

In some liquid-phase processes where the pore-size distribution of the catalyst is important, e.g., because of the selectivity, Raney nickel, containing fairly narrow pores may be less suitable. Transport through the pores of the catalysts can strongly affect the selectivity of catalytic reactions. An instance is the hydrogenation of fatty oils as will be dealt with later.

The various processes, in which nickel catalysts, either supported or unsupported find application, are carried out in a large variety of reactor types, viz, slurry phase reactors, fixed bed reactors including trickle flow reactors, moving bed and fluid bed reactors. Generally, the ultimate choice of the reactor type is governed by the specific reaction conditions with respect to optimal catalyst activity and selectivity, on the one hand, and by the economy and the ease of control of the process, on the other hand. The optimal catalyst formulation, in turn, results from a careful tuning of the different steps constituting the catalytic process, viz.:

1. Diffusion of the reactants to the catalyst particle (extrapellet transport)
2. Diffusion of the reactants through the pores of the catalyst particle (intrapellet transport)
3. Adsorption of at least one of the reactants on the catalyst surface
4. Reaction of the adsorbed intermediate to the desired product(s)
5. Diffusion of the product(s) through the pores of the catalyst particle
6. Diffusion of the product(s) away from the catalyst particle.

In continuous, fixed bed, gas-phase processes, the nickel catalysts must be present as bodies of at least about 0.5 mm to prevent the pressure drop over the catalyst bed being too large. In almost all nickel-catalyzed gas-flow processes supported catalysts are used. Pure nickel catalysts sinter rapidly at temperatures of about 300°C, which leads to a loss of active surface area. To reduce the surface of pure nickel catalysts, which may be oxidized during processing to bodies of the desired dimensions, temperatures of at least 200°C are required. However, at 200°C sintering already proceeds, which results in a decrease of the active surface area and a strong deterioration of the pore structure. Consequently, only when a support of a surface sufficiently inert with the reactants and reaction products involved cannot be obtained, pure nickel catalysts are preferably used.

Nickel is generally applied onto silica or alumina as a support. Supported catalysts are usually thermostable up to temperatures of about 500°C. The pore size distribution of supported catalysts can be reasonably well controlled. The production of bodies of the required shape and dimensions does not present significant problems. Catalysts to be used at more elevated temperatures must meet with more heavy demands.

Although basically the overall reaction rate is determined by one or more of the steps mentioned above, there are other factors that qualify the catalyst on the long run. It is frequently observed that the catalytic activity tends to decrease with time on stream. The loss of activity of nickel catalysts can often be ascribed to either of the following causes, or a combination thereof:

1. Thermal aging, comprising sintering and phase transformations
2. Deposition of carbon
3. Structural collapse, possibly as a consequence of (1) or (2)
4. Chemical poisoning by, e.g., sulphur or halogen compounds.

Apart from the latter, the above factors inducing catalyst deactivation can be considerably opposed by adapting the structure of the catalyst.

Especially for steam-reforming catalysts the requirements are severe. In steam-reforming, the primary reformer is being operated at a maximum temperature of about 850°C and steam pressures of 20 bar or more. Under these conditions silica cannot be used as a support. The silica volatilizes as $Si(OH)_4$, from which subsequently SiO_2 is being deposited at sites where the temperature is lower. In steam-reforming deposition of silica can be expected to proceed mainly in the waste-heat boiler, which would decrease the thermal efficiency of the plant considerably. Alumina, therefore, is the support of choice for steam-reforming catalysts. However, it is not easy to render an alumina-supported nickel catalysts sufficiently thermostable, especially at high nickel loadings. The loading of the primary reformer catalyst is therefore only about 15 wt%. The secondary reforming catalyst has to operate at temperatures still more elevated, viz. about 1,100°C. In this temperature range nickel-on-alumina catalysts are only thermostable provided the nickel loading is of the order of about 5 wt%.

An additional requirement of steam-reforming catalysts, which is not often dealt with in the literature, is the thermal conductivity. As mentioned, the steam-reforming reaction is strongly endothermic. Consequently, thermal energy must be supplied at a high rate to the catalyst, which calls for a good thermal conductivity.

Supported nickel catalysts to be used in fixed-bed, gas-flow reactions are being produced in a large variety. As previously dealt with, problems arise when the catalysts have to be operated at temperatures of about 800°C or higher together with high steam pressures, and when the thermal conductivity of the catalysts should be high.

In this chapter, we first discuss the production of nickel catalysts. Both unsupported and supported catalysts are reviewed. Next, the reduction of nickel precursors applied on supports are discussed. Subsequently, the characterization of (supported) nickel catalysts are dealt with, and finally the use of nickel catalysts in technical reactions.

Two reactor types are discussed and the specific catalyst requirements in several reactions are evaluated. First of all, we focus on nickel catalysts used in fixed bed reactors for the methanation and steam-reforming reaction of methane. The importance of thermostability and resistance to deactivation are considered. Subsequently, the use of nickel catalysts in slurry reactors is dealt with. The effects of pore structure, specific surface area, and surface poisoning on the activity, and selectivity in the hydrogenation of fats and oils and of fatty nitrils are discussed.

PRODUCTION OF NICKEL CATALYSTS

Raney nickel catalysts are produced by melting nickel and aluminum in a weight ratio from 40 to 50 mole% Ni [2]. It is important that the considerable difference in electronegativity creates nickel-aluminum alloys that are brittle. Consequently, fracturing the melt into small lumps can be done readily. Subsequently, the aluminum is leached by reaction with alkali. The nickel remains as very small particles. The nickel particles are generally agglomerated. It is possible that some alumina not dissolved into the alkaline solution is present as a support for the nickel particles.

Since the leaching of aluminum leads to evolution of hydrogen, carrying out leaching on a large scale is not easy. To prevent formation of much foam, it has been proposed to mix the lumps of the alloy with solid sodium hydroxide. Subsequent addition of small amounts of water leads to a slow evolution of hydrogen. After reaction of a substantial fraction of the aluminum, more water is added.

It has been found that large quantities of hydrogen evolve out of Raney nickel. Initially it was assumed that the hydrogen was present inside the small nickel particles. Desorption of the dissolved hydrogen should lead to nickel particles containing a large amount of vacancies. Later work indicated that the evolution of hydrogen is due to reaction of residual aluminum with water. The presence of residual aluminum in Raney nickel is important. A reason for the protective effect of alumina is its less noble character compared with nickel. As long as alumina is present will be oxidized first. Since aluminum grows a protective oxide layer, provided the pH values is not extremely high or low, neither of the metals will be completely oxidized. Consequently, Raney nickel can be stored in an active state under water for very prolonged periods of time. Thermodynamically, water can oxidize nickel surfaces only at very low partial pressures of hydrogen. It has been found that water can oxidize nickel surfaces only if the partial pressure of hydrogen is very low. The slow evolution of hydrogen from residual aluminum might also protect the nickel surface from oxidation and thus from deactivation. The fact that Raney nickel is used very much in batch reactions is undoubtedly connected with the above protection against deactivation. A tedious thermal treatment to produce active nickel catalysts is not required with Raney nickel.

Another advantage of Raney nickel is the rapid settling of Raney nickel catalysts. Separation of the catalyst from the reaction products can be effected very readily, which is another reason for the frequent use of Raney nickel in batch liquid-phase conversions of organic products. In the patent literature many modifications of Raney nickel have been mentioned that are difficult to rationalize. Often a small fraction of another metal, e.g., chromium, is added to the nickel-aluminum melt. The addition of chromium renders the catalyst more stable in the hydrogenation of, e.g., nitro compounds.

A drawback of Raney nickel is that the production using electrical energy to produce the nickel-aluminum melt is rather expensive. Moreover, poisoned Raney nickel catalysts cannot readily be regenerated. Remelting the nickel with aluminum and leaching of the aluminum is costly.

The production of very small, not strongly agglomerated nickel particles is also being carried out. To this end nickel formate is suspended into an organic liquid of a thermal stability sufficient to withstand temperatures of about 200°C. Instead of nickel formate, nickel oxalate can be used. Subsequently, the nickel formate or the nickel oxalate is thermally decomposed at 200°C to metallic nickel containing some carbon. The problem with nickel catalysts thus produced is the difficult separation of the extremely small particles from the reaction products.

Production of supported nickel catalysts can be done according to two essentially different procedures. In the first procedure the support and the nickel precursor are coprecipitated. Selective removal of water and the oxygen of the nickel oxide present in the dried catalyst leads to a generally highly porous catalyst. The other procedure starts from a support produced in a separate process, onto which a nickel precursor is applied. When a large nickel surface area per unit volume of catalyst is required, the support must be highly loaded. With separately produced supports, it is difficult to apply a high loading of a nickel precursor so as to obtain after thermal treatment a dense, homogeneous distribution of small nickel particles over the support. Consequently, nickel catalysts of an appreciable loading are usually produced by coprecipitation. Nickel catalysts of a lower loading, thus exposing a smaller nickel surface area per unit volume, are usually produced by impregnation of separately produced carriers.

Impregnation of a carrier by a solution of a nickel precursor and drying is a relatively easy procedure, also on an industrial scale. Since bodies of silica and alumina supports of the required mechanical strength in a range of different shapes and dimensions are marketed, impregnation and drying is one of the most obvious procedure to develop industrial catalysts. Nickel nitrate is an attractive precursor to impregnate carriers. During thermal treatment the nitrate decomposes relatively readily and no components that can poison the nickel are left. With nickel sulphate, for instance, some sulphur can remain in the catalyst after thermal treatment, which poisons the nickel.

Generally it is favorable to evacuate the support prior to the impregnation with the solution of the nickel precursor. Impregnation can be done with a volume of the solution of the precursor appreciably larger than the pore volume of the support. Gradual evaporation of the water finally leads to crystallization of the nickel precursor mostly on the bodies of the impregnated carrier. However, much of the precursor has to be transported from the large volume of the solution of the precursor which is out of the pore system of the carrier into the carrier during the evaporation of the liquid. Consequently, a large fraction of the impregnated precursor can be deposited at the outermost surface of the bodies of the support. If a relatively high, thermostable nickel surface area is aimed at, deposition mainly at the outermost edge of the support bodies is not attractive.

An inhomogeneous distribution of the nickel over the support results less readily when the impregnation is done with an amount of liquid about equal to the pore volume of the support. This procedure is known as incipient wetness impregnation. For a homogeneous distribution of the nickel throughout the carrier, it is essential that the liquid breaks up into small volumes due to capillary forces of the narrow pores in the carrier. Otherwise, most of the nickel is again deposited at the outermost layer of the carrier, where the evaporation of the liquid proceeds. The small volumes of the solution remaining after evaporation of the main part of the liquid lead to crystallization of relatively small particles of the precursor. Since usual supports contain a fairly wide distribution of pore sizes, a rather broad distribution of nickel particles sizes results after thermal treatment of impregnated supports. Especially electron microscopy has demonstrated clearly the broad particle size distribution resulting from impregnating and drying procedures.

The thermal treatment of impregnated carriers must be controlled in detail, as is evident from a controversy in the literature [3]. In a study of the infrared spectra of molecular nitrogen adsorbed on supported nickel particles prepared by impregnation of fumed silica supports with nickel nitrate, different groups got initially radically different results. It emerged that the difference was due to one group reducing the impregnated silica carrier after drying at about 120°C, whereas the other group first calcined the dried impregnated carrier at 550°C in air to remove water and to decompose the nickel nitrate. Since calcination at high temperatures leads to melting of the nickel nitrate prior to decomposition, calcination followed by reduction leads to appreciably larger nickel particles. Reduction of the merely dried impregnated support leads to a very broad particle size distribution of nickel particles comprising also a significant fraction of very small nickel particles.

Nickel catalysts to be used in steam-reforming have to be highly thermostable. Steam-reforming catalysts are therefore produced by impregnation of alfa-alumina, a highly thermostable support. Nickel oxide and alumina can react to nickel aluminate; it is almost impossible to reduce the nickel in the aluminate to metallic nickel, the active component. Therefore, the use of a spinel, magnesium aluminate, as a support for steam-reforming catalysts has been proposed. A spinel should be much less liable to reaction with nickel aluminate. For steam-reforming at elevated temperatures, the activity of the catalyst is of minor importance as compared to the thermal stability and thermal conductivity. In spite of the low surface area of alpha-alumina, being generally less than 1 m^2/g, most steam-reforming catalysts are being produced by impregnation of alpha-alumina. Since powdered alpha-alumina cannot easily be processed to mechanically strong bodies, bodies of alpha-alumina are produced by conversion of preshaped gamma-alumina into alpha-alumina. The reaction to alpha-alumina is done by keeping the gamma-alumina at temperatures above about 1,000°C. It is obvious that impregnation of preshaped bodies of alpha-alumina is the only viable procedure to produce industrially nickel-on-alumina steam-reforming catalysts.

With supports of a higher specific surface area, the distribution of the nickel over the (internal) surface of the support must be highly uniform and dense. Consequently, impregnation and drying is not an attractive procedure to prepare steam-reforming catalysts of a large surface area to be applied at about 500°C for the reforming of higher hydrocarbons to methane. Catalysts for the latter application, which due to the relatively moderate temperature used should possess a large surface area, are produced by coprecipitation of nickel and a precursor of the support. Since silica cannot be used in steam-reforming processes for the reason discussed, alumina is the most obvious support for these catalysts. Many details about the production of coprecipitated steam-reforming catalysts have not been published. In this review, therefore, only the main items of the coprecipitation procedure as evident from the (patent) literature will be dealt with. Two essentially different methods can be distinguished. The first procedure comprises raising the pH of a solution of aluminum and nickel from a level of about 2 up to about 7 or higher. The second method involves introduction of a solution of nickel and aluminum into a liquid, the pH of which is kept at a constant level of about 7 by simultaneous introduction of an alkaline solution.

The solubility of hydrated aluminum oxides, such as gibbsite and bayerite, is much lower than that of nickel hydroxide. As a result, raising the pH of a solution of nickel and aluminum from a level of about 2 will result in initial precipitation of only hydrated aluminum oxide. At more elevated pH levels, nickel hydroxide or basic nickel salts will precipitate. Coprecipitates of nickel and aluminum prepared by raising the pH from about 2 are exhibiting only X-ray diffraction patterns of aluminum hydroxides. The precipitated nickel species apparently is badly crystallized. It can be expected that the mixing of nickel and aluminum prepared by raising the pH is less intimate than with precipitates prepared at a constant pH level.

The latter precipitates can be expected to exhibit a hydrotalcite structure. This structure is derived from that of $Mg(OH)_2$, brucite. In this structure a layer of magnesium ions is covered at both sides with hydroxyl ions. The hydroxyl ions of neighboring layers are hydrogen bonded. In the hydrotalcite structure a fraction of trivalent aluminum ions has been accommodated. The excess of positive charge thus present is compensated for by the presence of additional anions, such as carbonate, or nitrate, in between the layers. The chemical composition of hydrotalcite, viz. $M(II)_6M(III)_2(OH)_{16}CO_3$, reflects its structure. Most probably, the trivalent metal ions are present in the layer of bivalent metal ions. Some authors, however, state that (part of) the trivalent ions are present in between the layers.

The formation of a hydrotalcite structure leads to a much more intimate mixing of nickel and aluminum ions than obtained with raising the pH of a nickel and aluminum solution. The evidence for formation of a hydrotalcite structure is mainly from the chemical composition. An amount of anions, such as carbonate or nitrate, appears to be present in the thoroughly washed precipitates. However, an X-ray diffraction pattern pointing to a hydrotalcite structure is exhibited only after the precipitates have been hydrothermally treated.

With coprecipitated catalysts, it is difficult to control the porous structure. Electron microscopic investigation of coprecipitated nickel on alumina catalysts produced at a constant pH level shows that the nickel particles present in the reduced catalysts are intimately mixed with small alumina particles. The resulting catalysts can be expected to display a high thermostability. It is, however, difficult to prevent diffusion limitation with these coprecipitated nickel-on-alumina catalysts.

Coprecipitation has also been used to prepare nickel-on-silica catalysts. Van Eijk-van Voorthuijzen and Franzen [5] prepared these catalysts by adding a sodium silicate solution to a nickel nitrate solution. As a result, mainly nickel hydrosilicate precipitates. The nickel hydrosilicate particles are rather large, which brings about that in the pretreated catalyst a large part of the nickel ions is occluded in the silica and thus cannot be reduced, nor can display any catalytic activity.

Since the porous structure of coprecipitated nickel catalysts is difficult to control, precipitation of nickel species onto a powdered, separately prepared support has also been done. When a precipitant is added to a suspension of a powdered support in a nickel solution, the precipitant is entering the solution outside the porous system of the support. If the nucleation of the precipitate proceeds rapidly, which is desirable in order to produce small particles, precipitation will proceed mainly outside the pores of the carrier. As a result, the distribution of the nickel precursor over the support can be expected to be rather bad with precipitated supported catalysts.

To improve the production of precipitated supported catalysts, deposition-precipitation was developed [5]. According to this procedure, the precipitation is conducted so as to have nucleation of a precipitated nickel precursor exclusively on the surface of the support. First of all this calls for a significant interaction between nuclei of the nickel precursor to be precipitated and the surface of the support. Moreover, the solution must be kept homogeneous, in order to prevent locally high concentrations that would cause nucleation of nickel precursors without interaction with the support.

Two different general procedures can be used to effect the above precipitation from a homogeneous solution onto a suspended support, viz. reaction of a dissolved compound to a precipitating agent and injection of a precipitating agent into the suspension of the support. With the first procedure the reacting compound is dissolved into a suspension of the support in a solution of the active precursor at a temperature sufficiently low to render the rate of the reaction insignificant. Raising the temperature after the suspension has been homogenized brings about an increase in the concentration of the species to be precipitated completely uniformly throughout the solution. The second procedure uses injection of a precipitating agent below the surface of a suspension of the support in a solution of an active precursor. Since below the surface of the suspension sufficiently high shear stresses can be established, a rapid distribution of the precipitating agent can be affected owing to which the concentration increases homogeneously too.

Both of the above procedures have their limitations. By reaction of a previously dissolved compound a decrease of the pH value, for instance, is difficult to achieve. Moreover, the procedure calls for a precipitation time of about 20 hours. In spite of the fact that the catalysts produced often are used for more than about two years, a precipitation time of 20 hours or more lowers the capacity of the plant where the catalysts are produced too much. Though hydrolysis of urea at temperatures above 100°C at elevated pressures has been proposed, this procedure calls for expensive equipment and, hence, is not favorable. Finally, precipitating agents as urea and ammonium cynanate release ammonia. Ammonia can lead to soluble ammonia complexes and to waste water, which is difficult to deal with. Nevertheless, scaling up does not present problems and the procedure can provide excellent catalysts. Though the injection procedure can be used more universally, it must be carried out carefully and requires a vigorous agitation of the suspension. Scaling up is more difficult with the injection method. Circulation of a large volume of the suspension of the support from a large vessel through a small vigorously agitated vessel where the injection is done has provided good results.

The above limitations have led to development of an electrochemically controlled deposition-precipitation procedure. With the production of supported nickel catalysts, nickel can be anodically oxidized in an electrochemical cell. Cathodic reduction of water results in the production of hydroxyl ions and gaseous hydrogen and brings about an increase in the pH-value and supplies the hydroxyl to react with nickel ions. This method was recently elaborated at our laboratory and leads to highly dispersed supported nickel catalysts [6]. Nickel alloy catalysts can also be produced easily by this method.

REDUCTION OF NICKEL CATALYST PRECURSORS

The reduction procedure for nickel catalyst precursors is essential with respect to the ultimate catalyst structure and performance. Generally, reduction at low temperatures is favored in view of the high costs of reduction at elevated temperature. Moreover, reduction at high temperatures may cause sintering of the nickel particles. To discuss the parameters determining the reduction process, we have to survey the reduction kinetics of NiO. Furthermore, we have to consider the production techniques used.

When a calcination step is used, the nickel compound is converted to nickel oxide at high temperatures in an oxidizing atmosphere. To remove the physically and chemically bonded water before reduction, the carriers loaded with the nickel precursor are usually calcined. Since much water evolving during the reduction can lead to sintering of the nickel particles and to flooding of downstream sections of a catalyst bed to be reduced, it is favorable to remove as much of the water as possible before the reduction.

Dealing with catalyst precursors prepared by impregnation techniques, calcination leads to the impregnated nickel compound being decomposed and converted to nickel oxide. With deposition-precipitation and coprecipitation, the nickel compound is (partially) decomposed as well. The calcining step of a mixed precipitate containing nickel ions and support ions results in a nickel oxide phase and a layer of unconverted precursor, present between the nickel oxide and the support. The thermostability is positively affected by the presence of this layer. This was demonstrated unambiguously for Ni/SiO_2 catalysts prepared by deposition-precipitation from a homogeneous solution [7].

When no calcining step is taken, the decomposition and reduction may proceed simultaneously. In this case not only the reduction kinetics of nickel oxide, but also that of the nickel precursor should be accounted for.

The reduction of nickel oxide has been extensively studied. Ostyn and Carter [8] assume the surface of nickel oxide to become supersaturated with respect to metal formation in the early stages of the reduction of nickel oxide by reaction with hydrogen or carbon monoxide. Once the metal nuclei have been formed, growth will occur by a solid state reaction at the metal-oxide interface [8]. Generally, volume changes can introduce large strain at the interface.

Labohm [9] studied the reduction of Ni (100) surfaces oxidized by exposure to oxygen. The onset of reduction was observed at about 150°C, a temperature not significantly different from the onset of reduction of bulk nickel oxide. Consequently, nucleation of metallic nickel is not likely to be involved in the rate-limiting step. In Labohm's experiments a very thin oxide layer was present on a metallic nickle single crystal. Dissociation of molecular hydrogen may limit the rate of the reduction. Initially hydrogen dissociates only on some defects at the surface; the resulting hydrogen atoms are highly reactive and are reacting very rapidly with the oxygen ions. When a bare nickel surface has been produced, dissociation proceeds much more frequently on the nickel surface. As a result, the reduction proceeds at a rate sharply increasing during the initial stage of the reduction. The importance of the dissociation of hydrogen atoms was evident from the fact that atomization of molecular hydrogen by a heated filament caused the reduction to proceed already at room temperature. The importance of the surface defect density can be derived from the fact that annealing the Ni (100) surface being covered with oxygen overnight led to a much lower rate of reduction.

From careful analysis of the kinetics of the reduction process, Labohm arrived at the conclusion that desorption of water is the rate-limiting step in the reduction.

Labohm's conclusion that desorption of water is the rate-limiting step agrees with the results of Kuypers [7]. This author studying a nickel-on-silica catalyst prepared by homogeneous deposition-precipitation, observed reaction of oxide ions with molecular hydrogen to water already at temperatures as low as 22°C. The catalyst had been previously reduced at 450°C and reoxidized at 440°C. The appearance in the infrared spectrum of bands due to bridged OH-groups and/or physisorbed water, demonstrated the reaction to hydroxyl ions and water. He assumed the reaction of hydrogen and oxygen ions to take place at defect sites. In contrast to the oxidized nickel single crystal surfaces discussed above, supported nickel particles have much more surface defects. Therefore the reaction between hydrogen and oxygen ions exhibits a significant rate already at a temperature as low as 22°C. With the small supported nickel oxide particles, the desorption of water also appeared to be the rate-limiting step.

If the reduction of the nickel oxide within supported nickel catalysts should result in small nickel particles, it is essential to limit the coalescence of the individual nuclei after completion of the reduction procedure. Coalescence of the metallic nickel particles resulting from the reduction leads to large nickel crystallites and a broad nickel particle size distribution. The reduction conditions must be adjusted so as to prevent coalescence.

However, it is mainly the structure of the catalyst precursor that determines the reduction procedure to be applied. If the nickel oxide particles do not exhibit any interaction with the support, the reduction conditions required to reduce the nickel oxide are very close to those causing migration and coalescence of nickel particles. Therefore, to obtain small nickel crystallites and a narrow size distribution, interaction with the support is a prerequisite.

Roman and Delmon [10] have studied the reduction of nickel-on-silica. They reported the reduction process to proceed in two stages. In the first stage the so called "initiable" fraction of the nickel ions was reduced. It was established that the onset of the reduction of this fraction could be affected by addition of a promotor. Reduction of the initiable fraction was followed by the "spontaneous" reduction of a second fraction. The extent of this fraction was found to increase steeply with the nickel content. Roman and Delmon's results again indicate that desorption of water resulting from a relatively rapid reaction of hydrogen and oxide ions at defect sites is the rate-determining step in the initial stage of the reduction process. At defects molecular hydrogen reacts relatively fast with oxide ions to hydroxyl groups and water. The formation of a free metallic nickel surface is, however, impeded by the desorption of water and hydroxyl groups formed initially. Either the formed water molecules and hydroxyl groups are blocking the defect sites for further dissociative adsorption of molecular hydrogen, or migration of hydrogen atoms generated at the defect sites to the undisturbed nickel oxide surface is hampered. The supply of hydrogen atoms to the surface of nickel oxide is, hence, limited during the first stage of the reduction. The oxide ions present at the defect sites lead to the "initiable" fraction of the nickel ions, that are the nickel ions being rapidly reduced during the initial stage.

If a promotor, such as copper or paladium or platinum is added, the dissociation of hydrogen proceeds at the promotor. Migration of the more numerous hydrogen atoms generated at the promotor to the oxide ions of nickel oxide and subsequently reaction can now proceed more easily. Accordingly, platinum and copper ions homogeneously distributed over the surface of a nickel-on-silica catalyst were found to facilitate the reduction of nickel oxide and nickel hydrosilicate [13].

Finally, it was observed by Roman and Delmon that a part of the nickel ions could not be reduced at all. Especially at low nickel loadings this fraction was relatively important. It is obvious to attribute the fraction of nickel that could not or much more difficult be reduced to nickel having reacted to nickel hydrosilicate. Since at low loading a larger fraction of the nickel ions contacts the silica support, the fraction of nickel that is difficult to reduce increases at lower loadings.

The calcination temperature is not only important with respect to the decomposition of the nickel precipitate into nickel oxide, but also affects the kinetics of the reduction of nickel oxide. Too high a temperature results in the disappearance of defects in the nickel oxide as observed by Noskova et al. [12]. Nickel oxide calcined at 300°C can be reduced more easily and at a lower temperature than nickel oxide calcined at 1,000°C. Moreover, for supported nickel oxide, the activation energy of reduction is raised from 19.5 to 23–34 Kcal/mole. Interestingly, Labohm measured an activation energy of 23 Kcal/mole for the reduction of oxygen layer present on a Ni (100) surface. Therefore, to facilitate the reduction of a nickel compound, the calcination temperature must be high enough to decompose the precursor, on the one hand and should be kept as low as possible on the other hand. This experimental evidence clearly indicates the importance of the density of surface defects in the reduction of nickel oxide.

The influence of water, present in the hydrogen flow, on the reduction behavior must also be considered. Previously we argued already that especially in the initial stage of the reduction, desorption of water is involved in the rate-determining step. Accordingly, it was concluded by Coenen [11] that water vapor has a retarding effect on the reduction of both supported and unsupported nickel oxide. A thermodynamic effect on the reduction is not likely but the experimental evidence points to an effect of water on the kinetics of the reduction. Kuypers [7] observed by infrared spectroscopy that even at temperatures as high as 440°C the water cannot be completely removed. With silica supported copper-nickel catalyst precursors, we observed in situ formation of hydrosilicate by the presence of water (set free by the reduction of copper with hydrogen) [13]. This was concluded from temperature-programmed reduction experiments, in which a part of the nickel was found to be reduced at higher temperature than needed for the reduction of an unpromoted nickel-on-silica catalyst.

THE CHARACTERIZATION OF NICKEL CATALYSTS

Since nickel catalysts are very important in catalysis, much attention has been paid to the characterization of nickel catalysts and catalyst precursors. Parameters such as the pore structure, the active nickel surface area, and its accessibility of it are determining the rate of the catalytic reaction. Particle size as well as size distribution of the loaded support may have a large effect on activity and selectivity. Furthermore, the stability of the catalyst is important. The stability is determined by mechanical strength and attrition resistance on the one hand, and by the resistance to deactivation by sintering or surface poisoning on the other hand.

We will describe some characterization techniques that can be used to evaluate the parameters mentioned. The pore structure and the BET surface can be determined by nitrogen physisorption and Hg-porosimetry. The free nickel surface area and possible surface poisoning can be measured by chemisorption techniques in combination with magnetic measurements. Infrared spectroscopy can also be used to assess surface poisoning. The structure and mean crystallite size of the nickel particles can be determined by X-ray diffraction. To establish the particle size, size distribution, and possible sintering of the active nickel phase we can use electron microscopy or magnetic measurements. Information on mechanical strength and attrition resistance can be obtained by measuring the maximum pressure that can be applied onto the sample, and by measuring the weight loss as a function of time in a fluidized catalyst bed, respectively.

Pore Structure and BET Surface

For the accessibility of the active surface, the pore structure of the catalyst is very important. To determine the porous structure, *nitrogen physisorption* and *Hg-porosimetry* are very useful to provide the BET surface, the shape of the pores, and the pore size distribution.

Nitrogen physisorption experiments can yield information about the shape of the pores and the pore size distribution, and also about the BET surface. When nitrogen is admitted to a sample previously pretreated and evacuated at 77 K, adsorption and filling of the pores will occur dependent on the partial pressure of the nitrogen. Based upon an extensive literature study, Lowell et al. [14] give five typical adsorption isotherms. The shape of the adsorption isotherm indicates where completion of a monolayer and capillary condensation in the pores proceed.

If multilayer adsorption is possible, the surface area of a sample can be determined with the method developed by Brunauer, Emmet, and Teller [16]. They derived Equation 1 as the mathematical representation of the adsorption isotherms. The volume v_m corresponds with a monolayer adsorbed on the surface and from the known surface area of an adsorbed nitrogen molecule (16.2 A^2) the so called BET surface can be calculated [16].

$$\frac{P}{v(P_0 - P)} = \frac{1}{v_m c} + \frac{(c-1)P}{v_m c\ P^0} \qquad (1)$$

With this method, relative pressures about 0.03 and 0.3 are applied.

Broekhoff [15] described the analysis of nitrogen adsorption isotherms at pressures up to 1 bar. He considered several pore shapes i.e. cylindrical pores, spheroidal cacities, and slit-shaped pores. The pore shape and pore size distribution determine the shape of the adsorption-desorption hysteresis loop. Assuming, for example, slit-shaped pores open at both ends, the following equation can be applied to the desorption branch only

$$V_k = \sum_{D_k - 2t_k}^{D_k} [k^c - (t_{k-1} - t_k) * S_k^{cum}] \qquad (2)$$

where V_k = pore volume of the pores of mean pore diameter D_k
S_k = total surface area of these pores;
t_k = thickness of the adsorbed layer at the relative pressure x_k;
c = constant;
$V_k^c = V_k^c - V_{k-1}^c$;

$$S_k^{cum} = \sum_{i=1}^{k-1} S_i;$$

and S_k is related to V_k by

$$S_k = 2V_k/D_k$$

In the Figures 1 and 2 the results of some nitrogen physisorption experiments are given. In Figure 1 the adsorption-desorption curve of a porous silica (Aerosil, Degussa 380V), used as a support for nickel, is given. The BET surface area is 226 m^2/g. Only very few narrow pores are present and the silica has a relatively large surface area. If nickel is applied onto this silica using deposition-precipitation of nickel ions by hydrolysis of urea [17], the surface area increases to 284 m^2/g despite the larger density of the material. The nickel loading, of the reduced catalyst was 40 wt%. Electron micrographs of the dried precipitate indicate the formation of small platelike nickel hydrosilicate particles. After calcination and reduction a porous material results. The adsorption-desorption isotherms and the corresponding pore size distribution of the nickel-on-silica catalyst are represented in Figure 2.

In agreement with the electron microscopic observations, analysis of the shape of the adsorption-desorption hysteresis loop according to Broekhoff [15] indicates the presence of slit-shaped pores. The pore-size distribution was calculated using the simple procedure of Brunauer, Halenda, and Joyner. Broekhoff has shown that this procedure is basically incorrect. However, the pore size distributions of Figures 1 and 2 clearly indicate the profound effect of the application of nickel on the porous structure.

Another technique to determine the pore size distribution is Hg-porosimetry [25]. The pores of a sample are previously evacuated and assumed to be filled with mercury dependent on the mercury

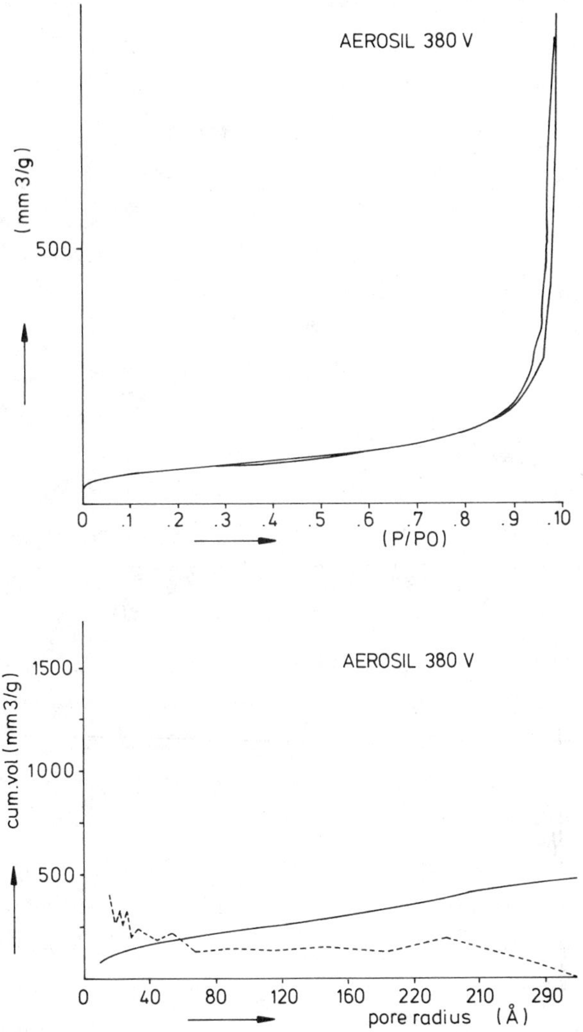

Figure 1. The adsorption-desorption isotherms and the pore size distribution of silica measured by nitrogen physisorption.

pressure applied. The higher the pressure, the smaller the size of the pores that can be filled. Equation 3 gives the Washburn equation relating the applied pressure and the size of the pores that can be filled at this pressure.

$$P * r = -2 * \nu * \cos \Theta \quad (3)$$

where P = mercury pressure
r = pore radius filled with mercury at a pressure P;
ν = surface tension of mercury (480 Dynes/cm^2);
Θ = contact angle of the mercury (assumed to be 141.3°);

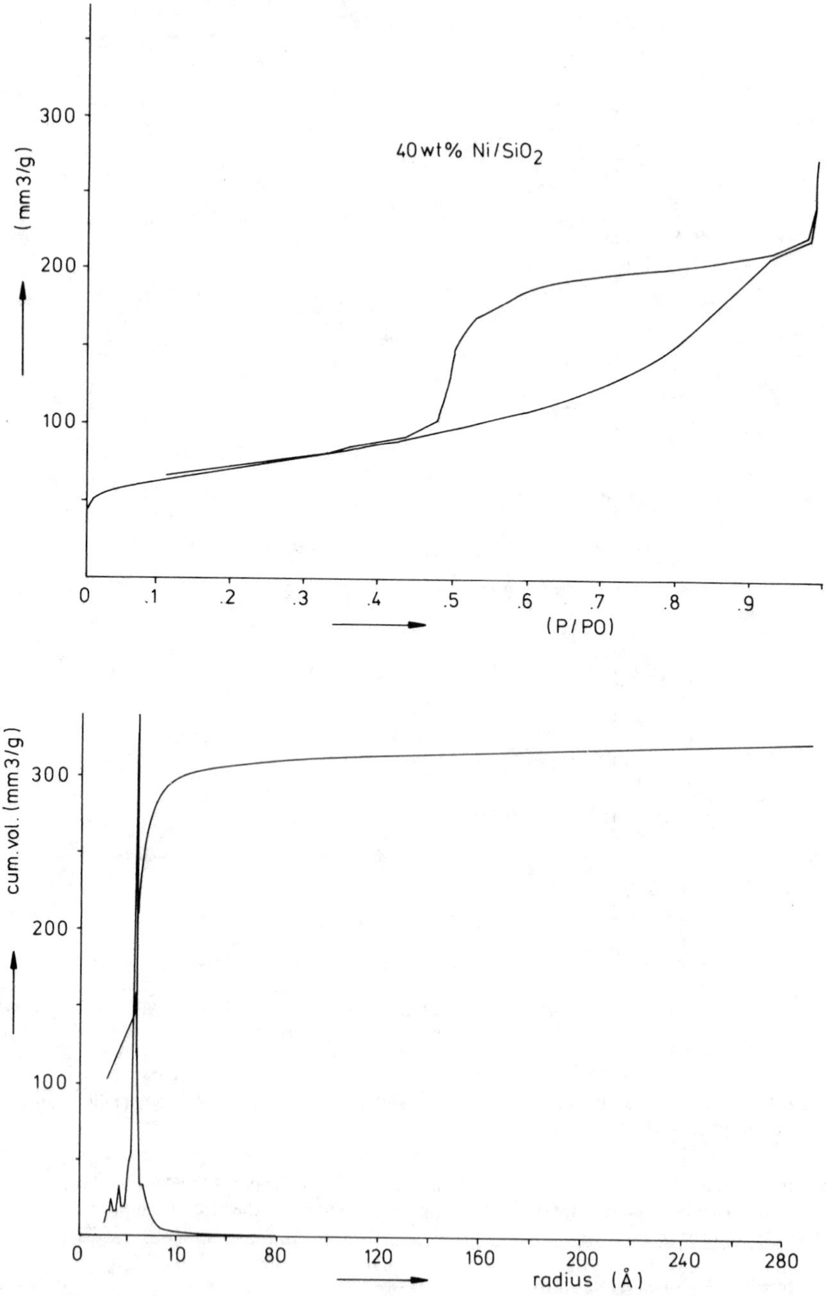

Figure 2. The adsorption-desorption isotherms and the pore size distribution of a nickel-on-silica catalyst measured by nitrogen physisorption.

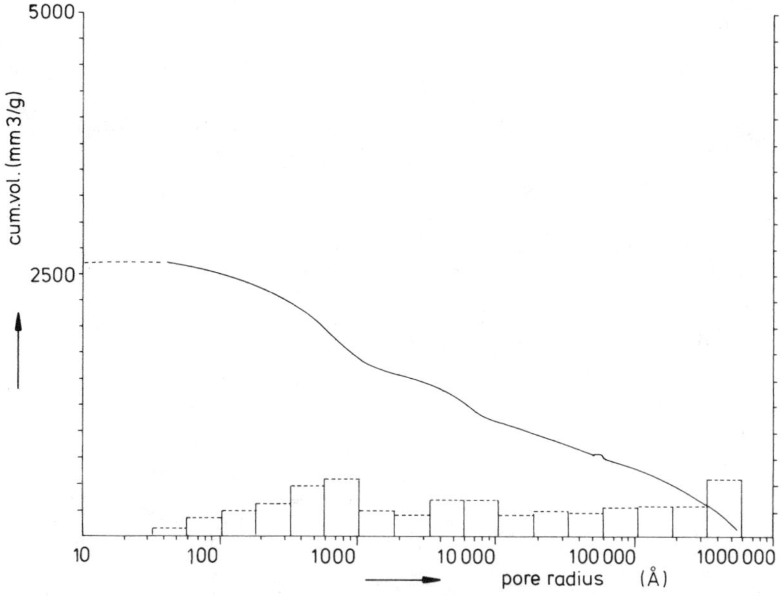

Figure 3. The pore size distribution of the Ni/SiO_2 sample measured with Hg-porosimetry.

The pores are assumed to be cylindrical. In Figure 3 the results are given of the sample measured by Hg-porosimetry.

Due to the limited pressure that can be applied, in our apparatus about 1,990 bar, the larger part of the pores, i.e., those of about 2.0 nm present in the sample, cannot be measured by Hg-porosimetry. Another problem can be the compression of the sample causing lowering of the pore volume and the mean pore size. Sudden changes of the volume adsorbed are indicative for this phenomenon.

On using —Al_2O_3 prepared by decomposition of alum [18] we obtain better results. In Figures 4 and 5 the pore size distributions are given. The results of the nitrogen physisorption measurements agree with those of the Hg-porosimetry. The largest pores measured with Hg-porosimetry are of the size of the interparticle space. This filling of the interparticle spaces with mercury should not be considered if only information about the pore structure is required.

In conclusion, the application of nitrogen physisorption and Hg-porosimetry is very useful to characterize pore structure and total surface area and can be indicative to characterize diffusion processes.

Chemisorption

Chemisorption techniques for determining active surface areas are well studied. Mostly static chemisorption is used [19, 20], but there are also some investigations into the applicability of dynamic chemisorption [21, 22].

With the static chemisorption procedure, the sample is previously pretreated and evacuated to desorb all molecules or atoms present on the surface. Calibrated pulses of a probe molecule are dosed and the equilibrium pressure is measured. From the calibrated volumes of the dosing and catalyst cells, the amount of chemisorbed molecules is calculated from which the active surface area can be obtained. This method is described by several authors. For nickel O_2, and N_2O are being used as probe molecules.

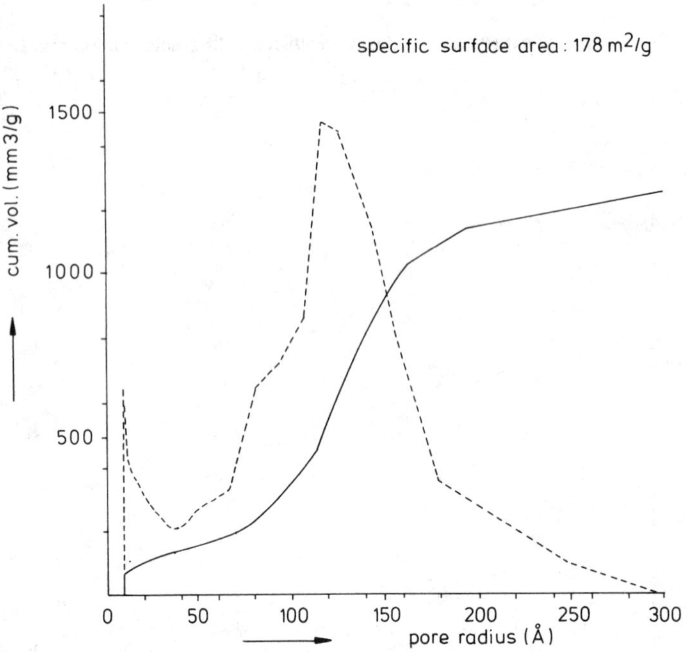

Figure 4. The pore size distribution of the alumina sample measured with nitrogen physisorption.

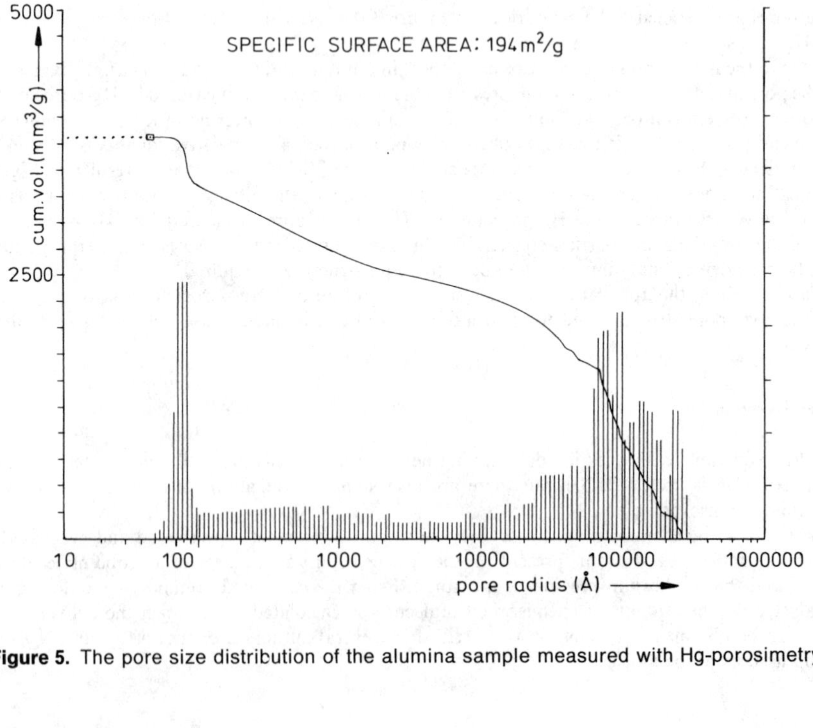

Figure 5. The pore size distribution of the alumina sample measured with Hg-porosimetry.

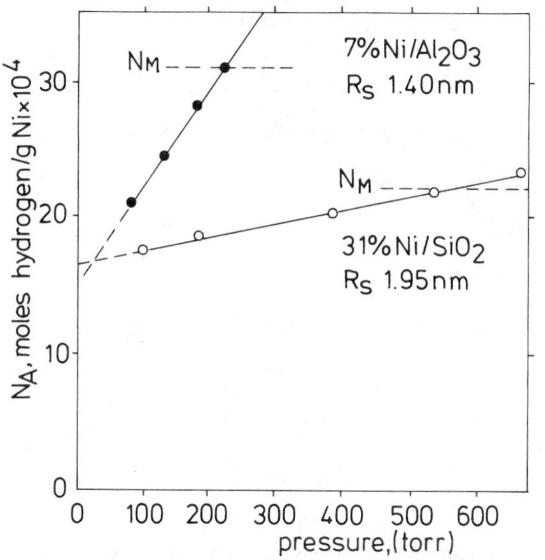

Figure 6. Hydrogen chemisorption on nickel supported by alumina or silica.

The establishment of the exact monolayer coverage, however, is very difficult. With hydrogen chemisorption, for example, it is not known at what equilibrium pressure the monolayer adsorption is accomplished. Some authors [7] assume monolayer adsorption at an equilibrium pressure of 30 torr, whereas other authors [23] extrapolate the adsorption isotherm experimentally measured to zero pressure. Another problem is the determination of the dispersion from the measured surface area due to the fact that the shape of the particles is governed by the extent of interaction between the nickel particles and the support. With silica, the metal support interaction generally results in hemispherical nickel particles. Using support materials exhibiting less interaction, such as alumina, spherical particles may be formed during reduction. The preparation technique, the loading, and the pretreatment also determine the extent of interaction. Accordingly, different amounts of hydrogen are chemisorbed at the same nickel particle size. The ratio of adsorbed hydrogen atoms to surface nickel atoms usually is assumed to be unity. In Figure 6 [23] the dependence of the hydrogen uptake by nickel on the nature of the support is given. The surface averaged particle sizes indicated in the figure were determined by magnetic methods a description of which will be given below. The monolayer adsorption is represented by N_m. It can be seen that there is only a small difference in crystallite size, the particle radii being 1.4 and 1.95 nm, respectively. The difference in the metal loading was a factor 4.5, approximately. From this it can be calculated that the alumina sample chemisorbs about twice as much hydrogen as the silica sample per surface atom of nickel, assuming spherical particles.

Chemisorption of N_2O or O_2 will lead to oxidation of the surface layer. The O/Ni ratio will be unity at monolayer coverage. However, with O_2 and, to a less extent, with N_2O, oxidation of the bulk of the nickel will occur. With N_2O the rate of bulk oxidation is much lower than the rate of surface oxygen chemisorption.

In Figure 7, the adsorption isotherms of H_2 and N_2O on a Ni/SiO_2 sample are given [7]. The take up of a large amount of hydrogen at very low equilibrium pressure is obvious. The slope of the N_2O isotherm can be seen to decrease drastically when surface oxidation ceases and bulk oxidation starts.

X-ray Diffraction

A relative simple characterization technique to determine the structure and the nickel crystallite size is *X-ray diffraction.* If nickel metal is present, the X-ray diffraction pattern of the pure nickel

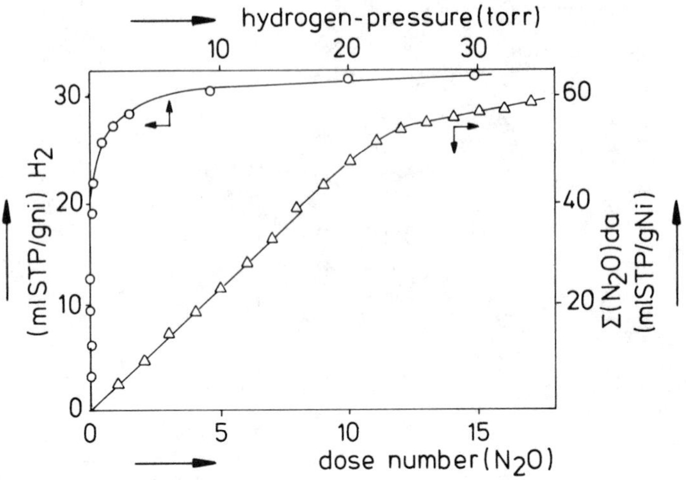

Figure 7. A comparison of the integral amount of dissociatively chemisorbed N_2O and the amount of adsorbed H_2, both at 303 K on the same sample of Ni/SiO_2.

is found. If amounts of other metals are present, a shift of the d-values can be observed dependent on the concentration of the second metal. For Raney-nickel, the aluminum can cause a shift in d-value.

If small nickel metal particles are present on a carrier material, the broadening of the nickel diffraction peaks can be used to estimate the mean size of the crystallites. For X-ray diffraction, the angle of diffraction is found by

$$n\lambda = 2d \sin \Theta \tag{4}$$

where n = order of diffraction
λ = wave length (A)
d = lattice parameter
Θ = angle of diffraction

For crystallites smaller than about 20.0 nm in size a line broadening is found, characterized by

$$D = \frac{K\lambda}{B \cos \Theta} \tag{5}$$

where K = shape factor (1.0747 for spherical particles) [25]
B = line broadening, taken at 50% of the peak maximum.

The line broadening caused by the tiny dimensions of the crystallites has to be distinguished from the instrumental line broadening also present. Equation 6 gives a frequently applied relation to account for this additional line broadening [14]:

$$B_t^2 = B_p^2 + B_i^2 \tag{6}$$

where B_t^2 = total line broadening
B_p^2 = particle line broadening
B_i^2 = instrumental line broadening

The instrumental line broadening can be measured either by using a calibrated sample with large particles that give a negligible line broadening by themselves or by adding a small amount of a material that causes no line broadening and has diffraction patterns at d-values not interfering with those of the structure to be characterized. Using this technique to determine the mean particle size of a 40 wt% nickel-on-silica catalyst, we found a mean radius (which is proportional to r^4/r^3) of 2.23 nm, assuming hemispherical particles. The diffraction pattern was obtained from a Guinier-Johansson camera [26].

Magnetic Behavior

The ferromagnetic behavior of nickel can also be used to characterize nickel catalysts.

One of the techniques for bulk ferromagnetic materials is the measurement of its magnetic susceptibility. For nickel much work has been carried out with high field techniques [27–31]. Parameters such as degree of reduction, saturation magnetization, and particle size distribution can be measured. The particle size distribution has to be calculated from experimental data. The calculation techniques are rather complicated and might give erroneous results [31]. To reliably use these magnetic methods the magnetization to be measured should follow the Langevin function, and therefore the nickel particles present should have radii between about 1 nm and 7.5 nm. Nickel particles of these sizes are single domain and behave superparamagnetically, two conditions necessary to obey to the Langevin equation. To find out whether an unknown size distribution consists of particles of the appropriate size, usually a check on superparamagnetism is performed. The magnetization is measured at two different temperatures and plotted as a function of H/T. If the particles behave superparamagnetically, the curves should match.

The measurement of particle size distributions is important for several reasons. With structure-sensitive reactions, it is important to know the fraction of the particles of the size that exhibits a maximum activity and/or selectivity. Secondly, when sintering occurs, determination of the particle size distribution at several stages is a powerful tool to investigate the mechanism of sintering [13]. The rate of sintering can be dependent on the initial metal particle size distribution. Since two samples having the same mean particle size need not have the same size distribution, they may sinter at different rates.

As previously stated, the experimental data for superparamagnetic particles of a uniform size follow the Langevin equation [32]:

$$M/M_s = \coth(m_p * H/k * T) - k * T/m_p * H \tag{7}$$

where m_p = magnetic moment of the particle
M = magnetization
M_s = saturation magnetization
H = strength of the applied field
k = Boltzmann constant
T = temperature,

and $$m_p = M_{sp} * v \tag{8}$$

where M_{sp} = spontaneous magnetization of the particle
v = volume of the particle

If only particles of one size are present, the radius can be calculated from the values of M/M_s at several values of H/T. If the value of $m_p * H/k * T$ is very small (at low field strengths) the value of M/M_s can be approximated by

$$M/M_s \approx m_p * H/3 * k * T \tag{9}$$

i.e., the low field approximation. If, on the other hand at high field strength, the value of $m_p * H/k * T$ is very large, Equation 7 simplifies to:

$$M/M_s \approx 1 - k * T/m_p * H \tag{10}$$

Theoretically, the high-field and the low-field approximation should result in the same value of v.

When particles displaying a distribution of various radii are present, the assumption of M_{sp} being independent of v leads to the total magnetization given by

$$M = V * M_{sp} * \int_0^\infty [\coth(M_{sp} * v * H/k * T) - k * T/M_{sp} * v * H]\, f(v)\,dv \tag{11}$$

where f(v) = function representing the particle volume distribution
V = total volume of the magnetic particles

The volume distribution is also represented by Equation 12.

$$\int_0^\infty f(v)\, dv = V \tag{12}$$

If an unknown distribution of radii is present, several methods can be used to estimate the particle size distribution. If only a mean size is needed, both the high-field and the low-field approximations give an average particle size, although the average is different [32]. At low field strengths the mean size is given by

$$\frac{\int_0^\infty v^2 * f(v, t)\, dv}{\int_0^\infty v * f(v, t)\, dv} \tag{13}$$

and in the high-field approximation

$$\frac{\int_0^\infty v * f(v, t)\, dv}{\int_0^\infty f(v, t)\, dv} \tag{14}$$

In Figure 8 the calculated size distribution of a magnetization curve calculated from an imaginary size distribution [13] is given at the top. At the bottom, the calculated size distribution is represented. It can be seen that the two distributions match satisfactorily. Other results with different calculation procedures are reviewed by Richardson and Desai [30].

Results of measurements of a nickel-on-silica sample are given in Figures 9 and 10. In Figure 9 the magnetization curves are given at two temperatures, viz. 77 K and 298 K.
The overlap characteristic for the absence of multidomain particles is evident. The measured curves at two different temperatures match quite closely.

In Figure 10 the results of the calculation of the particle size distribution are given. The real size distribution was also determined by electron microscopy and will be dealt with later.

When we use the low-field approximation and measure the effect of chemisorption on the magnetization at low magnetic field strengths, we can deduce the surface coverage and/or the surface reaction. When chemisorption occurs, the interaction of the chemisorbed molecules or atoms affect on the d-band electrons of the surface nickel atoms. The effects of chemisorption on the ferromagnetic moments of small nickel particles can be explained most easily by a destroy of the ferromagnetic coupling of the moments of the nickel surface atoms involved in the adsorption from the ferromagnetic moment of the nickel particle. Hydrogen adsorption presumably leads to a disappearance of the magnetic moments of the nickel surface atoms binding hydrogen. An example of the effect of chemisorption on nickel is given in Figure 11.

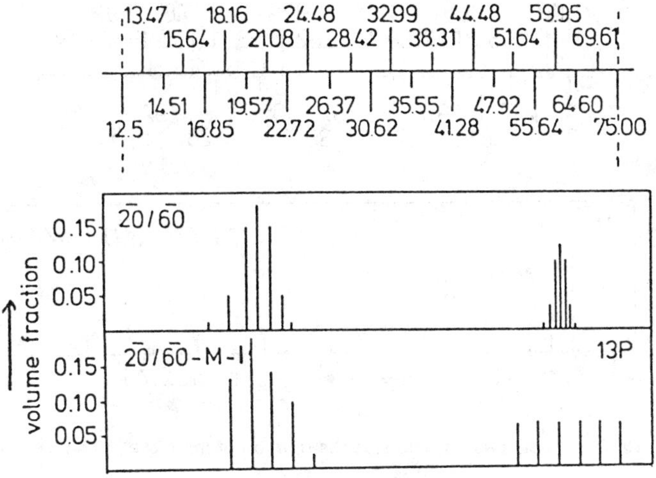

Figure 8. An imaginary size distribution (top) and the calculated size distribution obtained from the magnetization curve corresponding with the imaginary size distribution.

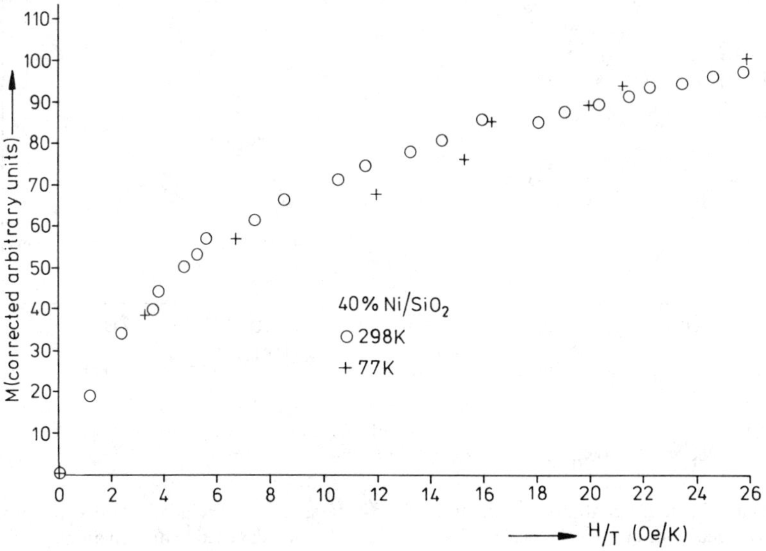

Figure 9. The magnetization curves of the nickel catalyst at 293 K and 77 K.

The measurements were performed with a low field apparatus as described by Selwood [32]. From the hydrogen adsorption curve, it can be seen that at the monolayer coverage, corresponding with a hydrogen uptake slightly above 20 ml STP/g Ni, the magnetization has decreased to about 80% of the initial magnetization. The same value is attained after chemisorption of about 5 ml STP/g Ni

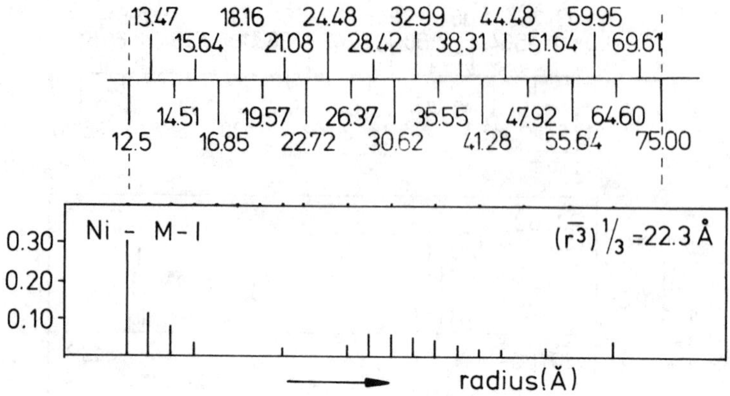

Figure 10. The calculated particle size distribution of the nickel-on-silica sample.

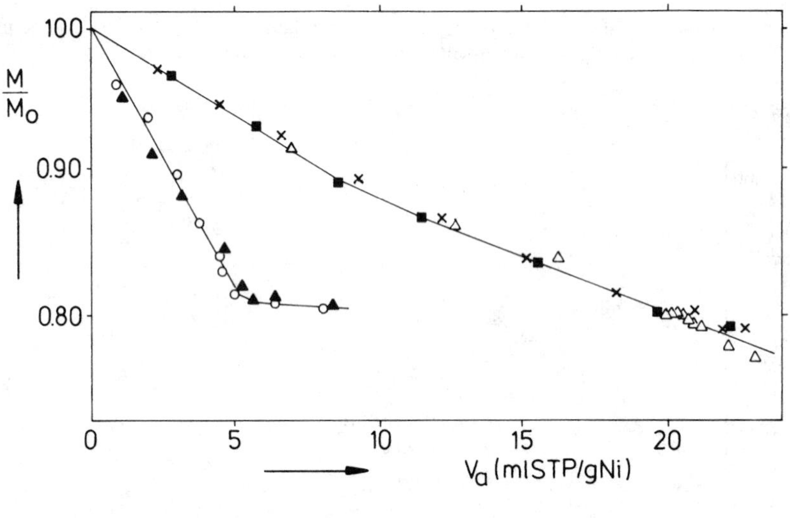

Figure 11. The relative magnetization of a Ni/SiO_2 catalyst as a function of the adsorbed volume of hydrogen (the lower curve) and methane (the upper curve).

of methane. From a quantitative evaluation of these data, it was concluded [7] that methane apparently reacts with the nickel surface to a surface carbide and adsorbed hydrogen atoms, according to Equation 15.

$$CH_4 + 7\,Ni \longrightarrow Ni_3C + 4\,Ni{-}H \qquad (15)$$

Electron Microscopy

An alternative method for the measurement of the particle size distribution, viz. electron microscopy, is represented in Figure 12.

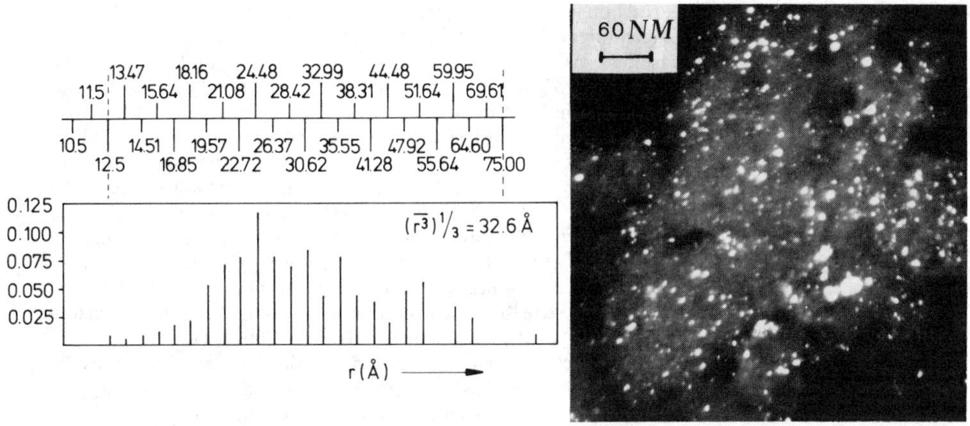

Figure 12. The measured particle size distribution from electron micrographs and a representative electron micrograph of the Ni/SiO_2 sample.

It is difficult to assess the real size distribution from electronmicrographs. Approximations are very easily to be made, but to measure the exact distribution, many particles have to be considered. Especially if some larger particles are present, i.e., particles at least twice as large as the mean size, the ratio of the number of these larger particles to the number of the remainder of the particles must be known or carefully estimated to establish the surface or volume averaged size distribution. If this is taken into account, electron microscopy is an appropriate method to determine the size of the particles present, or to obtain information about sintering effects.

For studying the deactivation of nickel catalysts by carbon deposition, electron microscopy is very useful too. Especially filamentous carbon can be clearly observed with this technique. In Figures 13 and 14 electronmicrographs of nickel catalysts deactivated by filamentous carbon are given.

USES OF NICKEL CATALYSTS

In this part of the chapter we focus on the application of nickel catalysts in fixed bed and slurry reactors. The first category is illustrated with a discussion of the catalysts used for the steam-reforming of natural gas and for the methanation reaction. As in both processes besides the thermostability of the catalyst, its resistance to carbon deposition is extremely important, a special paragraph is devoted to this subject. The application of nickel catalysts in slurry reactors will be elaborated for the hydrogenation of fats and oils and for the production of primary and secondary amines from fatty nitriles.

Nickel Catalysts in Fixed Bed Reactors

General Description of Some Applications

Several industrially extremely important reactions are conducted in fixed bed reactors using nickel catalysts. Of particular interest are the steam reforming of natural gas, and the hydrogenation of carbon monoxide, both reactions being essential steps in the production of hydrogen as a feedstock, e.g., ammonia. Whereas the methane steam-reforming is strongly endothermic, its reverse reaction, the methanation of CO, of course, is equally exothermic. Thermodynamically, the formation of CO and H_2 is favored at high temperatures:

$$CH_4 + H_2O \longrightarrow CO + 3\,H_2 \qquad \Delta H^\circ_{298} = 206\ \text{kJ/mol} \tag{16}$$

Consequently, the reforming reaction generally is carried out at temperatures of 800°C and above. The use of these very high temperatures calls for high thermal and mechanical stability of the nickel catalysts used. High thermostability is also a requirement to the nickel catalysts used for the purification of hydrogen flows by hydrogenation of the residual amounts of CO (<1 vol%) not converted in the up-stream CO-shift unit(s). Although the CO conversion is favored at low temperatures, the catalyst should not be damaged by a sudden occurrence of high temperatures, which may easily arise as a result of temporary malfunctioning of the CO-shift unit. When the CO content of the feed to the methanator increases considerably, also the adiabatic temperatures rise in the methanation reactor will raise steeply. On the other hand, the temperature at which the reaction over nickel catalyst is being conducted should not be too low, as at low temperatures the formation of nickel carbonyl proceeds. Transport of nickel via gaseous nickel carbonyl, $Ni(CO)_4$, is known [13] to bring about Ostwald ripening and, hence, considerable growth of the nickel crystallites with consequent loss of activity. For these reasons the operation temperature of adiabatic reactors for the methanation of gases of low CO content generally is in between 250 and 450°C [33].

The hydrogenation of benzene to cyclohexane is another example of a very exothermic hydrogenation reaction ($\Delta H^\circ_{298} = -207$ kJ/mol), which is conducted in a fixed bed. Thermodynamically, the reaction is limited at high temperatures, so again the reactor temperature should be carefully controlled. A frequently applied method to maintain the temperature at an acceptable low level is to cool and to recycle a part of the cyclohexane produced. Alternatively, or additionally, one can use a catalyst displaying a smaller activity per unit volume so as to spread out the reaction zone through a large part of the catalyst bed. Nevertheless, as with methanation and steam reforming, the stability of the catalyst, rather than its initial activity is of prime concern to the industrial manufacturers of cyclohexane.

A special configuration of a catalytic fixed bed is found in a so-called "trickle-flow" reactor. In the trickle flow reactor a liquid phase and a gas phase are passed through a fixed bed of catalyst particles, usually in a cocurrent flow. Since each catalyst particle is wetted by a thin layer of the liquid, the reactant gas has to diffuse through this layer to the catalyst surface. As also the catalyst pores will be filled with the liquid, the internal transport will proceed in the liquid phase, too. The physical transport phenomena in the trickle bed are therefore more or less comparable to those observed in the slurry reactor, which is the most widespread three-phase (gas-liquid-solid) reactor type. The greatest advantage of the trickle flow reactor as compared to the slurry reactor lies, of course, in the much easier separation of the catalyst from the reaction products. The trickle flow reactor is used mainly when the volatility of the liquid reactant is that low, that complete gasification is not practical. The gaseous reactant is mostly hydrogen. An example of a nickel catalysed reaction conducted in a trickle-flow is the conversion of a technical grade "white oil" to a pharmaceutical grade by hydrogenation of small, residual amounts of aromatics. The white oil thus obtained finds application in, e.g., pharmaceutical industries and the food industry.

Nickel Catalysts for Steam-Reforming and Methanation

Steam-reforming. In a typical reformer the nickel catalyst is contained in 40 to 400 reactor tubes of an internal diameter varying from 70 to 160 mm [34]. As the tubes are heated by firing in a furnace, they have to be constructed of high quality material. Generally, an expensive, alloy nickel chromium steel is used for this purpose. Since the life of the tubes is very sensitive to small variations in the maximum tube wall temperature, as well as to the number of shut-downs, the catalyst should allow stable operation of the reactor. In a recent review Rostrup-Nielsen summarizes the various requirements to the reformer, and the implications of these demands with respect to the catalyst [34]. Characteristic for a well-functioning reformer are:

1. Full conversion, i.e. close approach to equilibrium at the reformer exit
2. Low tube wall temperatures to ensure long life
3. Constant pressure drop, which, moreover, is equal for all tubes to ensure an evenly distributed flow in order to prevent "hot spots" or "hot bands."

To meet the requirements (1) and (2) the catalyst should be sufficiently active. A lack of catalyst activity will cause overheating of the tube wall, as well of the gas and the catalyst contained by the tube. Overheating may also result from an unequal distribution of the flow over the tubes due to differences in pressure drop, the tubes exhibiting the largest pressure drop becoming too hot. When the temperature exceeds a critical limit, the rate of (pyrolytic) carbon deposition rises considerably, which, in turn, causes a decrease of the catalyst activity, an increase of the pressure drop and, consequently, a further rise of the temperature. To secure a constant and equal pressure drop over all tubes, the catalyst should not degradate, neither under process conditions, nor during upsets or start-up and shut-down of the plant. The catalyst should, therefore, be chemically and physically stable and be resistant to carbon deposition. Moreover, to keep the radial temperature gradient in the reactor tubes as small as possible, a high thermal conductivity of the catalyst is preferred.

The most suitable catalyst formulations have been reviewed recently by Rostrup-Nielsen [34] and particularly by Ross [35]. Here we will confine ourselves to presenting the main characteristics.

For the steam reforming of natural gas, ultrastable, ceramic supports are preferred over porous supports, because the former are less liable to deterioration and, moreover, possess a higher thermal conductivity. The most frequently applied ceramic support is α-alumina, but also magnesium aluminum spinel, magnesia, and zirconia thermally heated at very high temperatures are sometimes used. The nickel loading of the ceramic support is relatively small, usually about 15 wt%. Under reaction conditions part of this nickel may react with the support to a nonactive compound. Even when an α-alumina support of very low reactivity is applied, the formation of nickel aluminate of low reducibility can proceed. When magnesia is used as the support, a solid solution, $(Ni_xMg_{1-x})O$, is produced, which again is difficult to reduce. As dealt with in an earlier paragraph, the strong interaction thus obtained between the nickel and the carrier material (α-alumina, magnesia) will stabilize the dispersion to some extent and, hence, the specific catalytic activity of the nickel in the working catalyst. Nevertheless, the nickel surface area of typical steam reforming catalysts is quite small, usually in the range of 1 to 5 m^2/g.

An interesting catalyst preparation procedure was reported by Ross [35]. It was established that an outstanding steam reforming catalyst is obtained by using a method based on the technique of deposition-precipitation from a homogeneous solution. According to this method preshaped α-alumina bodies, e.g., "Raschig" rings, are impregnated with a solution containing urea and the components that are to be precipitated. The impregnated rings are heated in an oven at 100°C, which brings about hydrolysis of the urea and precipitation of the catalyst precursor. Optionally this procedure is repeated once or several times after intermediate heating at higher temperatures to expell the water. It has been found that especially a coprecipitation of $Ni(NO_3)_2$, $Al(NO_3)_3$, and $La(NO_3)_3$ gives excellent results. It should be noted that in catalysts of this type the -alumina does not act as a support for the nickel, but rather as a host, in the pores of which coprecipitation proceeds.

Methanation. Just like the catalysts used in steam reforming, also those applied in the extremely exothermic methanation reaction have to be very thermostable. Compared with the previously mentioned methanation of traces of CO in the ammonia synthesis gas, the demands upon thermostability are even more severe for catalysts used for the production of substitute natural gas (SNG) from coal- or oil-derived synthesis gas. For each percent of CO in the feed the adiabatic temperature rise in the methanator amounts to about 80°C. To cope with the high temperatures that are inevitable in the methanation of feedstocks of high CO content, nickel catalysts prepared by impregnation techniques using porous support are not suitable. In addition, also the previously discussed catalysts for the steam reforming of natural gas have displayed a poor performance. Their activity is too small because of the low porosity and the limited specific nickel surface area.

The most proper catalyst unitl now has been prepared by coprecipitation of $Ni(NO_3)_2$ and $Al(NO_3)_3$, as discussed earlier. In the literature a number of different promotors added to catalysts of this type, e.g., lanthanum, cerium, and chromium can be found [35]. The coprecipitated catalysts are claimed to be stable up to temperatures of 600 to 700°C. They find also application in the production of SNG from light hydrocarbons, e.g., naphtha, by reaction with steam in the endothermic "low temperature steam reforming," often referred to as the catalytic rich gas (CRG) Process.

The overall reaction in CRG-type processes, which are carried out in the temperature range of 350 to 550°C, can be approximated by:

$$C_nH_{2n+x} + (n-1)/2\ H_2O \longrightarrow (3n+1)/4\ CH_4 + (n-1)/4\ CO_2 \quad (17)$$

The nickel catalysts used in the processes dealt with in this paragraph, i.e., steam-reforming of CH_4, methanation and CRG-type processes, all suffer from gradual deactivation, even after thorough purification (desulfurization) of the feed. The activity loss is caused by the formation of carbonaceous deposits. Recently, a number of patents has appeared, which claim a markedly enhanced stability with respect to carbon deposition of catalysts prepared according to the method of deposition-precipitation from a homogeneous solution [36, 37]. The next paragraph elaborates the ideas that led to these patents.

The Development of "Carbon-Resistant" Nickel Catalysts

In nickel-catalyzed processed involving CO and/or hydrocarbons, fouling of the catalyst by the deposition of carbon may occur. The first step in the carbon formation process is the dissociative chemisorption of either CO or the hydrocarbon involved, or both, according to:

$$CO \longrightarrow C^* + O^* \quad (18)$$

$$C_nH_m \longrightarrow xC^* + yH^* + C_{n-x}H^*_{m-y} \quad (19)$$

* = adsorbed

As far as the chemisorbed carbon atoms do not react further, e.g., with H_2 or H_2O, they may give rise to two different types of carbonaceous deposits, i.e., encapsulating carbon and/or filamentous (or whisker) carbon, to be discussed later. A third carbon type, pyrolytic carbon, is formed homogeneously in the gas phase at extremely high temperatures due to thermal cracking reactions. This type of carbon tends to be deposited not only on the catalyst particles, but also as a dense layer on the reactor wall. Like encapsulating carbon it brings about a progressive deactivation of the catalyst. Moreover, the deposition of pyrolytic carbon causes a steadily increasing pressure drop over the reactor (tube), as does filamentous carbon. Being unfavorable in general, a large pressure drop is particularly disadvantageous in the steam reforming of natural gas, since it may give rise to the occurrence of overheated ractor tubes, as discussed earlier. Within the scope of this chapter we will no longer dwell on pyrolytic carbon, since its formation is hardly affected by the catalyst, although in the very endothermic steam reforming process a high catalyst activity may accomplish that the high temperature level favoring the formation of pyrolytic carbon is not attained.

Encapsulation of the active nickel particles is caused by "polymerization" of the carbon atoms (or hydrocarbon fragments), that are adsorbed on the nickel surface according to Reactions 18 and 19. This phenomenon is observed most abundantly at moderate temperatures ($<500°C$) as prevailing in CRG-type processes [35]. The deposition of encapsulating carbon also depends on the nature of the feed, aromatics exhibiting the largest rate of formation.

The growth of carbon filaments in nickel catalysts has been known for quite a long time [38]. It was established that many filaments contain a nickel particle, still exposed to the gasphase, at the free end [e.g., 39]. This is nicely illustrated in Figure 13. Recently, De Bockx et al. [40], Kock et al. [41], and Boellaard et al. [42] reported on the basic aspects of the growth mechanism of the filaments. These authors found that surface carbon atoms resulting from Reactions 18 and 19 dissolve into the nickel to constitute a carbidic phase, which in the steady state of the process is substoichiometric. Subsequently, at crystallographic planes strongly interacting with graphite usually present at the interface between the nickel carbide and the support carbon is excreted. The interaction with graphite is mainly determined by the fit of the basal graphite plane on the metal surface. The fit of graphite on the (0001) surface of nickel carbide is very good. The continuous migration of carbon from the gas-metal interface to excreting planes generally present at the metal-

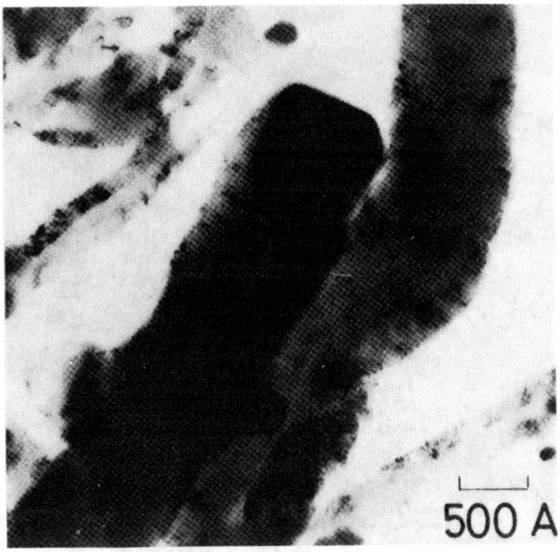

Figure 13. Electron micrograph showing a facetted nickel particle at the head of a carbon filament.

support interface results in the growth of a graphitic carbon filament. Since the filament grows out exclusively at two planes of the nickel particle usually present at the metal support interface, the nickel particle is lifted from the support at the top of the continuously elongating filament. In this way a network of filaments is created, which ultimately leads to disintegration of the catalyst pellets and to reactor plugging [39]. Figure 14 shows electron micrographs of a heavily carbon fouled catalyst.

It is common practice to obstruct the formation of filamentous carbon, as well as of encapsulating carbon, by enhancing the rate of reaction between the surface carbon atoms and the reactant, either hydrogen (methanation, other hydrogenations) and/or steam (steam reforming, other reactions). To this end the partial pressure of the hydrogen and/or steam is raised to a high level, where also from a thermodynamic point of view the deposition of carbon is less favourable, either by separately carrying out the water-gas shift reaction in a preceeding unit, or by simply adding steam. However, since both solutions are expensive, other answers to the carbon problem have to be envisaged.

As previously discussed, a characteristic aspect of the mechanism of filamentous carbon growth is the formation of crystallographic planes where graphite layers can be excreted at the interface with the support on the nickel particles catalysing the formation of the filaments. Consequently, a strong bond between the nickel particles and the support can be expected to oppose the production of carbon filaments. From the literature [43], it is known that a chemical bond between a metal particle and an ionic substrate can be achieved by partial oxidation of the metal at the interface with the substrate. Accordingly, it seems attractive to use partially reduced nickel catalysts in order to prevent the formation of filamentous carbon. However, as dealt with earlier, in almost all procedures known to prepare an active nickel catalyst initially a precursor is formed, which consists of small, supported particles of nickel (hydr-) oxide. The reduction of these particles, once started, tends to proceed to completeness. The adhesion of the resulting metal particles to the support is due to Van der Waals forces only and, hence, not sufficiently strong to inhibit the formation of crystal planes where graphite layers and thus carbon filaments can be excreted. However, the reduction behavior of catalysts prepared according to the method of deposition-precipitation from a homogeneous solution is different. Generally, a partly reduced catalyst results, in which the metallic

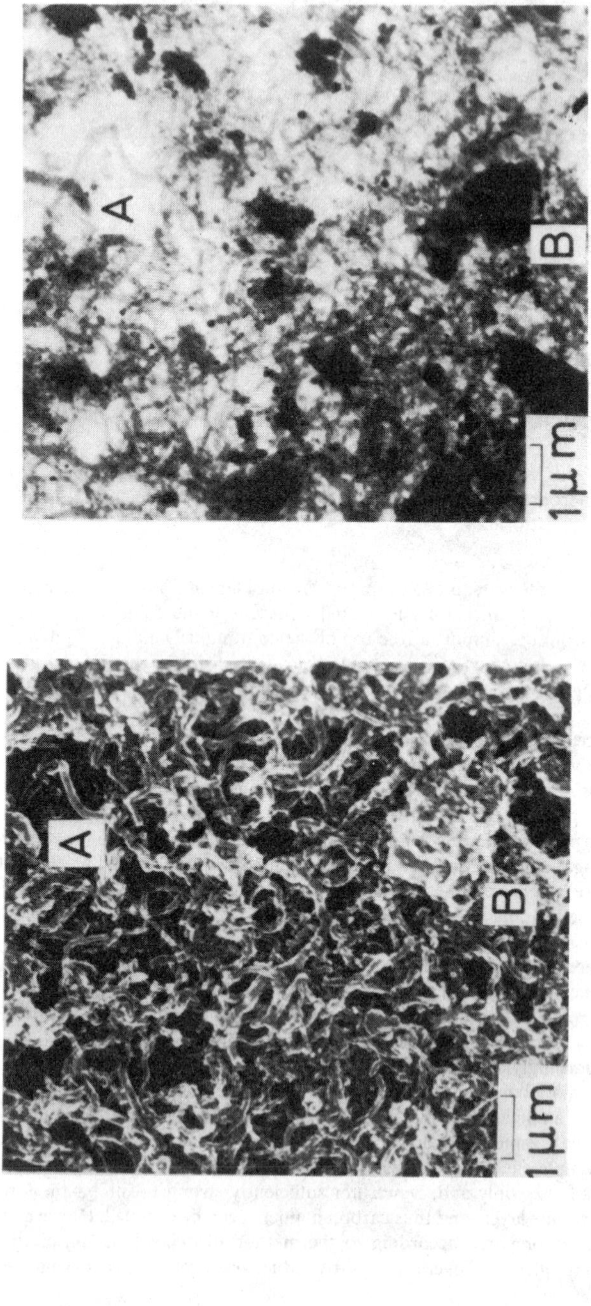

Figure 14. Electron micrograph showing a network of carbon filaments deposited during methanation of a CO-rich gas using a conventional nickel catalyst.

nickel particles are anchored to the silica support by a stable interfacial layer of nickel hydrosilicate. Since the interfacial layer acts as a "glue layer" between the nickel and the silica, the nucleation and subsequent growth of carbon filaments is markedly restrained.

Reportedly, catalysts of this type are very suitable for the production of methane from [36, 37]:

1. Light hydrocarbons, naphtha. On bench-scale the catalysts have proven to exhibit a stable activity in CRG-type processes, even at very small H_2O/C ratios (down to $H_2O:C = 1:1$). Although at small H_2O/C ratios and at low catalyst temperatures, encapsulating carbon may be deposited, regeneration of the catalyst by a burn-off procedure in air is readily accomplished, because the thermostable nature of the catalysts can easily cope with the locally high temperatures occuring during burn-off.
2. Methanol. This is disproportionated directly without any steam added according to:

$$4\,CH_3OH \longrightarrow 3\,CH_4 + CO_2 + 2\,H_2O \tag{20}$$

3. Synthesis gas. Gas of low H_2/CO ratios, as derived from a coal (or oil) gasifiers, can be directly methanated after desulphurization without a preceding water-gas shift step. Only at H_2/CO ratios below unity the synthesis gas must contain some H_2O in order to achieve full CO-conversion. (Of course, in many cases steam will already be present as a coolant).
4. Carbon monoxide. Even pure CO is converted by a stoichiometric amount of steam according to:

$$4\,CO + 2\,H_2O \longrightarrow CH_4 + 3\,CO_2 \tag{21}$$

Despite the outstanding results for methane production, the applicability of the discussed catalysts for a steam reforming of natural gas is poor. At the high temperatures of above 800°C that prevail in the steam reforming process, the silica support tends to volatilize due to the reaction with high pressure steam to $Si(OH)_4$. Consequently, the silica would be slowly removed from the catalyst bed and deposited in colder parts down-steam of the reactor, such as boilers, heat exchangers and subsequent catalytic reactors. Unfortunately, similarly prepared catalysts with alumina or titania as the support did not display as large a carbon-resistence as their silica-supported counterparts [44].

Nickel Catalysts in Slurry Phase Reactors

The Hydrogenation of Fats and Oils

Traditionally, many hydrogenation reactions are carried out in batch operation using slurry phase reactors. This holds true also for the selective hydrogenation of natural (poly-) unsaturated fats and oils to desirable products, such as margarines and edible oils, on the one hand, and fats useful in very diverse applications, e.g., in soap manufacturing, on the other hand.

The fats and oils under consideration, i.e., as derived from either vegetables or from fish and marine animals, are, like all fats, composed of numerous different triglycerides. Each triglyceride molecule consists of a glycerol molecule combined with three either identical or different fatty acid molecules. The fatty acid molecules may differ in chain length and in the degree of unsaturation. Many fatty acids contain 16 or 18 carbon atoms although in triglycerides derived from fish very long chains of up to 30 carbon atoms are most common. Generally, the dimensions of a triglyceride molecule are in the range of 1.5–2.0 nm.

The length of the fatty acid chains is an important parameter, which has a marked effect on the melting behavior of the fat. While the melting point is found to increase with larger chain lengths, it is also controlled by the degree of unsaturation of the chains, poly-unsaturated fats exhibiting lower melting points. Other significant parameters in this respect are the distribution of the double (or even triple) bonds along the chain, and the configuration of the hydrogen atoms, either *cis* or *trans*, at the double bond. As a rule, the *cis*-isomers, which are almost exclusively found in nature, exhibit a broader melting traject at a lower temperature level.

Not only the melting behavior, but also the stability of fats against oxidation is related to the number of double bonds present. The higher the degree of unsaturation, the lower the stability against oxidation; *cis*-isomers being more reactive than *trans*-isomers.

It is a general purpose in the fat hardening industry to manufacture a stable product that displays a melting behavior that has been adapted to its particular application. Besides, a special selectivity is required in the manufacturing of some diet margarines. It has been known for some time that the proportion of polyunsaturates in the food should not be too low, since they are believed to contribute to the lowering of the cholesterol level in the human blood. A high cholesterol level is a well-known risk factor in obtaining heart diseases. In the preparation of diet margarines, therefore, a ratio of 1.5 to 1 of polyunsaturates to saturates is aimed at. The polyunsaturated fatty acid that is most abundantly present as a triglyceride constituent in natural oils is linoleic acid containing two double bonds. It is the task of the diet margarine manufacturer to conduct the oil hardening step under such conditions that the linoleic acid groups are left unreacted as much as possible, whereas more unsaturated groups (such as linolenic acid) are hydrogenated (to preferably linoleic acid) to improve the oxidative stability and, hence, the keeping qualities of the product.

The previous example concerning the production of diet margarines illustrates that the hydrogenation of fats and oils is a very complicated process in which high demands are made especially upon the selectivity of the applied catalyst. To understand the factors controlling the selectivity we will consider in some detail the hardening process. For a more thorough discussion of the subject the reader is referred to an excellent review by Patterson [45].

The hydrogen consumed in the hydrogenation process has to surmount many transport resistances. In the autoclave, gaseous hydrogen is forced to dissolve into the oil by continuously dispersing it as fine bubbles through the liquid using a stirrer. The solubility of the hydrogen is a function of the nature of the oil to be hydrogenated, as well as of the temperature and the H_2 pressure applied. Generally, at higher temperatures and higher H_2-pressures the solubility rises.

Once dissolved, the hydrogen has to diffuse through the stationary layer, which surrounds the gas bubble, to the bulk of the oil. From there it travels to the stationary layer enveloping the catalyst particle. After having crossed this boundary layer too, a part of the hydrogen which does not absorb on the nickel at the outer surface of the catalyst particle, diffuses through the catalyst pores to the interior parts of the particle, where it is finally adsorbed. Just like the hydrogen, the triglycerides to be hydrogenated have to pass through the diffusion layer surrounding the particle and have, at least partly, to diffuse through the pores to the active nickel surface. Once arrived there, polyunsaturated molecules are adsorbed more strongly than monounsaturates, which is important in view of the selectivity of the process. After adsorption and subsequent reaction the products desorb and migrate back to the pore mouths. Finally, they cross the diffusion layer around the particle and reach the bulk of the oil.

With respect to catalytic activity, it was established by Coenen [cited in 45], who did a great deal of the pioneering work on this subject, that the activity of nickel-based hydrogenation catalysts is proportional to the extent of the "easily accessible" nickel surface area. The concept "easily accessible" was defined by Coenen as being that part of the nickel surface area that is present in short pores of a width larger than 2.5 nm. An excellent correlation was obtained when the activity of a number of catalysts for the hydrogenation of an uncontaminated oil was plotted as a function of SA"/D, wherein SA" stands for the nickel surface area present in pores wider than 2.5 nm and D is the average particle size. The result of Coenen clearly demonstrates that the hydrogation activity of a technical catalyst is not merely determined by the rate of the chemical hydrogenation step, but also by the rate of transport of the reactant molecules to the catalytically active surface. Nickel crystallites present in pores of a width below 2 nm, which roughly corresponds to the dimensions of the triglyceride molecules, are completely unattainable and consequently, inactive.

While the physical parameters of the catalyst, such as particle size and porosity, were shown to be important parameters with respect to catalytic activity, they have a more dramatic effect on the selectivity of the catalyst. In the present context it is sufficient to define "selectivity" as the rate at which polyunsaturated molecules are hydrogenated to monounsaturates, as compared to the rate at which monounsaturates are converted to saturated molecules. As with many hydrogenation reactions, there is a delicate balance on the active nickel surface between hydrogenation and isomerization. The higher the surface coverage of hydrogen, the faster the hydrogenation reaction, while the extent of isomerization decreases. Of course, besides hydrogenation and isomerization, there is always the possibility that the triglyceride molecule desorbs from the surface virtually unchanged. The hydrogen surface coverage is controlled mainly by the process conditions chosen, such as temperature, hydrogen pressure, and stirring intensity, since, as we have seen, above, under practical operating conditions the rate of hydrogen supply is usually restricted by transport limitations.

In addition to the hydrogen surface coverage, particularly the diameter of the catalyst pores is of crucial importance with respect to the selectivity of the process. Take, for instance, a catalyst containing narrow pores, which are only slightly wider than the dimensions of the triglyceride molecule. Inevitably, triglycerides present in such pores are subject to successive adsorptions on the active nickel particles, which causes them to leave the pores as highly saturated molecules. As a consequence, the eventual product will be a mixture of overhardened and underhardened material with only a minor fraction of *trans*-isomers. The situation is quite different when a catalyst is used, which consists of very small particles of a very open pore structure. In that case, most of the triglycerides will contact the nickel surface only once, which results in a product containing relatively large proportions of *mono*- and *di*-unsaturates as well as *trans*-isomers, and relatively small amounts of polyunsaturates and saturates. Hence, both activity and selectivity are improved by a high faction of easily accessible nickel surface area.

It was previously stated that at low hydrogen surface coverages isomerization is favored over hydrogenation. Sometimes the isomerization capability of a catalyst is intentionally enlarged by deliberately poisoning the catalyst. Sulfur is almost exclusively used as the poisoning agent. On the sulphur-poisoned nickel surface the adsorption of hydrogen is strongly diminished. Evidently, the promotion of *trans*-isomer formation thus achieved is accompanied by a drop in catalytic activity. Another consequence of the poisoning of the nickel surface is that the formation of fully saturated triglycerides is suppressed, thus enhancing the selectivity of the catalyst. Of course, the latter effect is noticeable only with catalysts that in the unpoisoned state exhibit poor selectivity due to pore transport limitations.

Although at first sight the effect of poisoning on catalytic behavior might look quite straightforward, the subject is much more complex. Above, a more or less even distribution of the poison (sulfur) over the nickel was assumed. However, the results are completely different when oils are hydrogenated that contain considerable amounts of poisons, e.g., inorganic acids, that instantaneously react with the nickel surface. Such poisons will irreversibly accumulate on the nickel crystallites first encountered, which are located at the outermost surface of the catalyst particles and at the pore mouths. The hydrogenation reaction is, thus, forced to proceed in the less accessible parts of the catalyst. As a result, not only the activity, but also the selectivity of the catalyst will drop appreciably, while also the formation of *trans*-isomers will be reduced.

In the previous discussion we have seen the dimensions and the porosity of the catalyst particles to be important parameters with respect to the activity and selectivity in fat hydrogenation. As the catalyst has to be removed from the product, the particle size is also of importance with regard to the ease at which the catalyst can be separated by filtration. Generally, a rather broad size distribution of small particles leads to a poor filterability of the catalyst, which is economically unfeasible. Hence, the design of suitable catalysts also addresses their filterability.

The first section of this chapter dealt with the preparation of fat hardening catalysts. As discussed by Patterson [45], catalysts that meet the different demands most satisfactorily are usually prepared either by precipitation of a nickel precursor onto a Kieselguhr support, or by coprecipitation of the nickel with sodium silicate. The dimensions of the catalyst particles thus produced, which are in the 10-m range, allow a fairly rapid filtration of the catalyst. The mechanical properties of such catalysts permit repeated filtration and, therefore, repeated use, provided the physical and chemical properties of the catalyst have not changed too drastically in the previous hydrogenation runs.

The Hydrogenation of Fatty Nitriles

In the previous paragraph the hydrogenation of fats and oils was argued to call for a very selective catalyst. The same applies to the preparation of primary or secondary amines from fatty nitriles.

Like fat hardening, the production of amines is usually carried out in a slurry phase reactor. The hydrogenation of fatty nitriles is industrially important, since fatty amines are used for the manufacturing of numerous useful products, such as corrosion inhibitors, surface active agents, non-ionic surfactants, shampoos and many more.

To gain insight into the factors governing the selectivity of the nitrile hydrogenation process, we first focus on the reaction mechanism. In elaborating this subject use has been made of a recent review by Volf and Pasek [46].

The hydrogenation of a (saturated) fatty nitrile has been found to proceed in two consecutive steps. First the nitrile is converted to an aldimine, which subsequently is hydrogenated to the amine:

$$RC \equiv N + H_2 \longrightarrow RHC = NH \tag{22}$$

$$RHC = NH + H_2 \longrightarrow RH_2CNH_2 \tag{23}$$

Alternatively, after some primary amine has been formed, this may react partly with the aldimine according to:

$$RHC = NH + RH_2CNH_2 \longrightarrow \underset{\displaystyle NH_2}{\underset{|}{RC}}HNHCH_2R \tag{24}$$

Subsequently, the 1-aminodialkylamine thus formed can loose ammonia to yield an alkylidene-alkylamine, which finally is hydrogenated to a secondary amine:

$$\underset{\displaystyle NH_2}{\underset{|}{RC}}HNHCH_2R \longrightarrow RHC = NCH_2R + NH_3 \tag{25}$$

$$RHC = NCH_2R + H_2 \longrightarrow RH_2CNHCH_2R \tag{26}$$

Similarly, starting with the aldimine and the secondary amine, tertiary amines are produced. Hence, a mixture of primary, secondary and tertiary amines may be formed, the final composition being determined by both the catalyst characteristics and the reaction conditions. The selectivity problem is even more pronounced, when less expensive, unsaturated fatty nitriles are used for the production of amines. In that case not only the nitrile group, but also the alkyl chain tends to be hydrogenated.

A close examination of the reaction mechanism reveals that it is composed of two essentially different reaction types. Some steps, Reactions 22, 23, and 26, are typically hydrogenations, whereas other steps, e.g., Reaction 24, are often referred to as "condensation" reactions of an acid-base character. The hydrogenation reactions, as well as the condensation reactions are deemed to proceed on the metal parts of the catalyst. The chemical nature of the support, the acid-base properties of which might be considered to affect the rate of the condensation reactions, does not seem to influence the selectivity. However, with respect to the role of the support the evidence is not unambiguous. Reportedly, catalysts based on "basic" zinc oxide display a high selectivity for the preparation of primary amines. Perhaps this observation has some relation to industrial practice, where in nickel-catalyzed nitrile hydrogenations sometimes caustic soda is added to the autoclave in order to enhance primary amine selectivity. Anyway, much of the details on catalytic selectivity have not been elucidated as yet. According to the scarcely available literature, the best approach is often to consider the relative rates of the hydrogenation and the condensation reactions. Whereas on nickel, the respective rates are comparable, other metals, such as platinum and palladium, display a substantially higher rate of condensation yielding a high proportion of tertiary amines. On the other hand, copper-based catalysts usually exhibit a low hydrogenation activity, which results in a high secondary amine content in the product.

Dealing with nickel catalysts, the concept of "competitive" reactions, viz. hydrogenation versus condensation, can be used to explain the effect of various operating parameters, such as temperature. H_2-pressure and the addition of ammonia, on the selectivity. Generally, it is observed that at higher temperature the formation of secondary amines is increased. This has been ascribed to the apparent activation energy of the condensation reaction yielding the alkylidenealkylamine to be higher than that of the hydrogenation steps. Similarly, an enhanced proportion of secondary amines in the product can be predicted, when the hydrogen pressure is reduced, which, of course, slows down the rate of hydrogenation. Indeed this has been observed for, e.g., the hydrogenation of valeronitril on a rhodium catalyst, but, on the other hand, the selectivity of the hydrogenation of stearonitril over nickel catalysts was reported by Volf and Pasek not to be affected at all by the hydrogen pressure applied. Hence, concerning the effect of hydrogen pressure on the selectivity many details remain obscure.

The suppressive effect of ammonia on the formation of secondary amines is ascribed to a reversible reaction proceeding between the ammonia and the intermediate aldimine, the concentration of which is consequently reduced. Due to the lower aldimine concentration Step 24 of the previous reaction scheme, by which eventually secondary amines are produced, is retarded. It can be argued, however, that as a consequence of the aldimine-ammonia interaction also the rate of primary amine formation is adversely affected (Step 23). This, indeed, is what is observed experimentally, but usually the effect on Step 24 exceeds that on Step 23. The restraining effect of ammonia on the hydrogenation activity of the catalyst is disadvantageous especially, when, besides the nitrile group, also the alkyl chain must be hydrogenated. Therefore, various procedures exist for the production of saturated fatty primary amines from unsaturated fatty nitriles. They all have in common that the hydrogenation of the nitrile group on the one hand, and of the alkyl chain on the other, are conducted in more or less separate process steps. A procedure proposed by a large catalyst manufacturer [47] is as follows. First the nitrile is hydrogenated ($P_{H2} = 30$ bar) at 140°C in the presence of ammonia ($P_{NH3} = 24$ bar). Also some water (0.5 wt%) is added to the reactants to reinforce the effect of the ammonia by enlarging its solubility. After completion of the nitrile hydrogenation the hydrogenation of the alkyl chain is accelerated by venting off the ammonia and, subsequently, by increasing the hydrogen partial pressure ($P_{H2} = 54$ bar) and raising the temperature to 175°C. Unfortunately, the latter reaction conditions give rise to some selectivity loss due to the formation of secondary (and tertiary) amines.

REFERENCES

1. Sebatier, P., and Senderens, J. B., C.R. Acad, Sci. 134 (1902) 514.
2. Anderson, J. R., *Structure of metallic catalysts*, Academic Press, London (1975).
3. Eischens, R. P., and Jacknow, J., in 3rd *ICC*, (W. M. H. Sachtler and P. Zwietering, eds.) North-Holl. Publ. Co. A'dam (1965) 627.
4. van Eyk van Voorthuijsen, J. J. B., and Franzen, P., *Prec. Trav. Chim.* 69 (1960) 666.
5. Hermans, L. A. M., and Geus, J. W., *Prec. Prep. Cat.* II, (P. Grange, P. A. Jacobs, and G. Poncelet, eds.), (1978) B2.
6. van Stiphout, P. C. M., Donker, H., Bayense, C. R., Geus, J. W., and Versluis, F., in *Prep. Cat* IV, (B. Delmon, P. Grange, P. A. Jacobs, and G. Poncelet, eds.) Elsevier (1987) 55.
7. Kuypers, E. G. M., Thesis, State University of Utrecht (1982).
8. Ostyn, K. M., and Carter, C. B., *Surf. Sci.* 121 (1982) 360.
9. Labohm F., Thesis, State University of Utrecht (1985).
10. Roman, A., and Delmon, B., *J. Cat.* 30 (1983) 333.
11. Coenen, J. W. E., in *Prep. Cat* II, (P. Grange, P. A. Jacobs, and G. Poncelet, eds.) Elsevier Sci. Publ. (1979) 89.
12. Noskova, S. P., Boriskova, M. S., Dzis'ko, V. A., Khisamieva, S. G., and Alabuzhev, Y. A., *Kin. Cat.* 15 no. 3 (1974) 527.
13. van Stiphout, P. C. M., Thesis, State University of Utrecht (1987).
14. Lowell, S. and Shields, J. E. *Powder Surface Area and Porosimetry*, 2nd Ed., Chapman and Hall, London (1984).
15. Broekhoff, J. C. P., Thesis, University of technology Delft 1969.
16. Maron, S. H., and Lando, J. B., *Fundamentals of Physical Chemistry*, Macmillan Publ. Inc. New York (1974).
17. Geus, J. W. *Prep. Cat* III, (P. Grange, P. A. Jacobs, and G. Poncelet, eds.) Elseviers Science Publ., Amsterdam (1983).

18. Tyburg, I., private communication.
19. Ponec, V., Knor, Z., and Cerny, S., *Adsorption on Solids*, Butterworth and Co. (1974).
20. Anderson, J. R., *Chemisorption and Reactions on Metallic Films*, Academic Press, London (1971) Vol 1, 2.
21. Freel, J., *J. Cat. 25* (1972) 139.
22. Sarkany, J., and Gonzales, R. D., *J. Cat. 76* (1982) 75.
23. Richardson, J. T., and Cale, T. S., *J. Cat. 102* (1986) 419.
24. Coenen, J. W. E., Thesis, University of Technology, Delft, 1958.
25. Lipson, H., and Steeple, H., *Interpretation of X-ray Powder Diffraction Patterns*, Macmillan, London, (1970).
26. *Powder Diffraction File Search Manual*, Joint Committee on Powder Diffraction Standards, Pennsylvania, 1976.
27. Foner, S., *Rev. Sci. Instr. 30* 7, (1959), 548.
28. De Montgolfier, P., Martin, G. A., and Delmon, J. A., *J. Phys. Chem. solids 34*, (1973), 801.
29. Heukelom, W. Broeder, J. J., and van Reyen, L. L., *J. Chim. phys. 51*, (1954), 474.
30. Richardson, J., and Desai, P., *J. Cat. 42*, (1976), 294.
31. Dreyer, H., *Z. anorg. allg.* Chem. *362*, (1968), 233.
32. Selwood, P. W., *Chemisorption and Magnetization*, Academic Press, New York, (1975).
33. Thomas, C. L., in *Catalytic Processes and Proven Catalysts*, Academic Press, New York and London, (1970).
34. Rostrup-Nielsen, J. R., in *Catalysis, Science and Technology* (J. R. Anderson and M. Boudart, eds.), Vol. 5, Springer-Verlag, Berlin, Heidelberg, New York, Tokyo, (1984), pp. 1–118.
35. Ross, J. R. H., in *Catalysis*, Vol. 7, The Royal Society of Chemistry, Alden Press, Oxford, (1985), pp. 1–46.
36. European Patent Application 0135 729 A1.
37. European Patent Specification 0 086 538 B1.
38. Baker, R. T. K., *Catal. Rev. Sci. Eng. 19* (1979) 161.
39. Kuypers, E. G. M., Tjepkema, R. B., and Geus, J. W., *J. Molec. Catal. 25* (1984) 241.
40. de Bockx, P. K., Kock, A. J. H. M., Klop, W., Boellaard, E., and Geus, J. W., *J. Catal. 96* (1985) 454.
41. Kock, A. J. H. M., de Bockx, P. K., Boellaard, E., Klop, W., and Geus, J. W., *J. Catal. 96* (1985) 468.
42. Boellaard, E., Kock, A. J. H. M., de Bockx, P. K., and Geus, J. W., *J. Catal. 96* (1985) 481.
43. Geus, J. W., in *Chemisorption and Reactions on Metallic Films* (J. R. Anderson, ed.), Academic Press, London, (1971) p. 129.
44. de Bockx, P. K., Thesis, State University of Utrecht (1985).
45. Patterson, H. B. W., in *Hydrogenation of Fats and Oils*, Applied Science Publishers, London and New York, (1983).
46. Volf, J., and Pasek, J., in *Studies in Surface Science and Catalysis*, Vol. 27, *Catalytic Hydrogenation* (L. Cervenij, ed.), Elsevier, Amsterdam, (1986) pp. 105–144.
47. Brochure, "Harshaw Catalysts", Harshaw Chemie, B. V., De Meern, The Netherlands.

CHAPTER 4

OPTIMIZATION OF CATALYTIC ACTIVITY DISTRIBUTIONS IN POROUS PELLETS

Costas G. Vayenas and Xenophon E. Verykios

Institute of Chemical Engineering and High Temperature Chemical Processes
Department of Chemical Engineering
University of Patras
Patras, Greece

CONTENTS

INTRODUCTION

The importance of uniformity in the distribution of catalytically active material within a three-dimensional carrier has long been appreciated by practitioners of the catalytic art. As a result, in most theoretical and experimental studies, activity distribution within catalyst particles and pellets has been assumed to be uniform. An extensive literature exists dealing with the methodology of preparation of such catalysts [1, 2] and with interactions between chemical and physical transport phenomena within the porous structure of these solids [3, 4]. The effects of intraparticle mass and heat diffusional resistances in catalysts exhibiting uniform activity distributions have been extensively studied in terms of point and overall effectiveness, selectivity, yield, and stability of catalyst particles and chemical reactors.

The implications of nonuniform distribution of active ingredients within the porous structure of supports has also received considerable attention in recent years. It has been demonstrated, both theoretically and experimentally, that nonuniformly activated catalysts can offer increased yield and selectivity, decreased thermal sensitivity, improved poisoning and deactivation characteristics, and increased attrition resistance in certain cases of industrial importance. Such catalysts have been shown to offer significant yield advantage over uniformly activated pellets under SO_2 oxidation, increased selectivity to phthalic anhydride from naphthalene and to ethylene oxide from ethylene, and increased activity for carbon monoxide oxidation.

Nonuniformly active catalysts arise via complex interactions of phenomena related to intrapellet flow, diffusion, adsorption, and reaction. Generally, partial impregnation of a porous support will result in activity profiles decreasing toward the pellet center. On the other hand, catalysts partially poisoned by impurities in chemical feedstocks will exhibit oppositely shaped activity distributions. More complicated activity distributions can be achieved by proper selection of method and conditions of impregnation. This usually involves the addition of inactive species which adsorb on the support, preferentially blocking sites near the center or the outer area of the pellet.

The art of catalyst preparation is slowly evolving into a science as more insight into the phenomena involved in catalyst preparation is obtained and the effects of these phenomena on physicochemical properties of catalysts are better understood and more clearly related to the performance of the catalysts. As efforts to custom-design catalysts for particular applications intensify, it is almost certain that catalysts with nonuniform activity distribution will be utilized in industrial applications. Currently, such catalytic configurations are only known to be employed in automotive exhaust catalysis.

ACTIVITY DISTRIBUTIONS AND EFFECTIVENESS FACTOR

The effects of nonuniform activity distributions can be accounted for by appropriate modification of reaction rate constants. The activity profile can be incorporated into the reaction rate constant, which then becomes a function of position inside the catalyst particle. A common form of such functionality is the one described by

$$k = k^* u(y) \tag{1}$$

where u(y) is an activity distribution function and k* is the volume-averaged rate constant, defined by

$$k^* = \frac{1}{V_p} \int_{V_p} k(y)\, dV \tag{2}$$

Instead of the volume-averaged rate constant, the maximum value of the rate constant, usually pertaining to its value at surface conditions has been used in some earlier cases [5]. The most common activity expressions which have been used are the following:

$$u(y) = (y/R)^{\alpha} \tag{3a}$$

$$u(y) = (1 - y/R)^{\alpha'} \tag{3b}$$

$$u(y) = \alpha_0 + \alpha_1 (y/R)^2 + \alpha_2 (y/R)^4 + \cdots \tag{3c}$$

To insure meaningful comparisons of catalytic performance of pellets with different activity distributions, it is necessary to normalize the profile under the restriction of equal amounts of catalytically active material in all cases. If we define a dimensionless spatial variable $z = y/R$ and let n be the geometric parameter of the system (n = 0 for slabs, n = 1 for cylinders, n = 2 for spheres), then the constraint becomes

$$(n + 1) \int_0^1 u(z) z^n\, dz = 1 \tag{4}$$

A more extensive analysis, relating the intrinsic rate constant to particular activity profiles, was performed by Cervello et al. [6] who also accounted for the fact that agglomeration of active ingredient in certain areas of the pellet would decrease the specific active area. Thus, catalytic activity or reaction rate constant, is not directly proportional to the concentration of active material. This factor is accounted for with the introduction of a diminution coefficient. This added complexity has not been used by other authors.

For the purpose of reactor design, the most important performance aspect is usually the effectiveness factor. For this reason, considerable efforts have been made to develop consistent and manageable expressions for η for different reacting systems (7–15) Kasaoka and Sakata (7) developed analytical expressions for η for a single, first-order reaction occurring in an isothermal slab. The intrinsic rate constant and effective diffusivity were assumed to vary with position in the slab, either linearly or hyperbolically. The resulting expressions for η involved standard Bessel functions. In order to facilitate comparisons between uniformly and nonuniformly activated catalysts, a modified Thiele modulus was defined by:

$$\phi^* = L(k^0/D_e^0)^{1/2} \int_0^1 u(z)\, dz \tag{5}$$

which handled the normalization very well.

The same type of reaction was investigated by Nystrom [8] in spherical geometry, assuming an activity profile of the form

$$k = k^0[(z - z^*)/(1 - z^*)]^{\alpha}(1 - w) + w \tag{6}$$

where z^* and w are arbitrary constants whose values are bounded between 0 and 1. A series solution for the effectiveness factor was obtained in this case,

$$\eta = 3/\phi^2 \left\{ \left[\sum_{m=1}^{\infty} m\beta_m/(1 - z^*) \sum_{m=1}^{\infty} \beta_m \right] - 1 \right\} \tag{7}$$

where β_m are the series coefficients in the solution of the modified state equation. Similarly, Wang and Varma [16] derived analytical expressions for η for a first-order isothermal reaction occurring in catalysts with a step function distribution of activity, in both rectangular and spherical geometries. The effects of external mass transfer resistances were also considered. Because step function activity distributions have been found in many cases to result in near-optimum catalyst performance, the results obtained in this study are given in detail in Table 1. Figure 1 provides an explanation of the spacial variables involved. In Cases 2 and 3 (Table 1), plots of ln ϕ approach asymptotic slopes of -1 and -2, respectively, a result similar to the asymptotic behavior of uniformly activated catalysts.

The asymptotic behavior of catalysts with nonuniform activity distributions has also been studied by Lee [10] and Yortsos and Tsotsis [14, 15]. In the region of strong diffusional limitations ($\phi > 3$), Lee [10] derived an expression for η for an isothermal particle of rectangular geometry under a reaction of arbitrary kinetics:

$$\eta = \frac{\left\{ 2D_e u^0 \int_0^{C_s} r(C)\, dC \right\}^{1/2}}{L\, r(C^0) \int_0^1 u(z)\, dz} \tag{8}$$

where r refers to the rate of reaction and u_s to the surface activity of the pellet. For a first-order reaction and an activity distribution of the form $u = (\alpha + 1)z^{\alpha}$, Equation 8 reduces to

$$\eta = (1/L)[D_e/k^0(1 + \alpha)]^{1/2} = 1/\phi \tag{9}$$

The asymptotic values of η were also investigated by Yortsos and Tsotsis [11] for first-order isothermal reaction and arbitrary geometry using the Liouville-Green approximation. Shape and activity normalization was shown to be possible if there are no points within the catalyst or at its surface where the activity assumes a zero value. For large values of ϕ and for any geometry, η can be obtained by

$$\eta = \frac{1}{\phi V_p} \iint_S u^{1/2}\, dS \tag{10}$$

Table 1
Effectiveness Factors for Step Distribution Profiles [9]

Case 1: $z_1 + z_2 < 1$	
Slab:	$\eta = \dfrac{\rho}{\phi^2 z_2} \dfrac{\tanh(\phi z_2)}{(\rho/\phi) + \{1 - (z_1 + z_2)\} \tanh(\phi z_2)}$
Sphere:	$\eta = \dfrac{3\rho(z_1 + z_2)}{\phi^2\{(z_1 + z_2) - z_1^3\}} \dfrac{X}{\{1 - (z_1 + z_2)\}X + \rho\{w + \tanh(v - w)\}}$
Case 2: $z_1 + z_2 = 1$ no external mass transfer	
Slab:	$\eta = \dfrac{\tanh \bar{\psi}}{\bar{\psi}}$
Sphere:	$\eta = \dfrac{3}{\phi(1 - z_1^3)} \dfrac{\bar{\psi} + (\phi^2 z_1 - 1) \tanh \bar{\psi}}{\phi\{\phi z_1 + \tanh \bar{\psi}\}}$
Case 3: $z_1 + z_2 = 1$ external mass transfer is not negligible	
Slab:	$\eta = \dfrac{\tanh \bar{\psi}}{\bar{\psi}\{1 + (\phi/Bi) \tanh \bar{\psi}\}}$
Sphere:	$\eta = \dfrac{3}{\phi^2(1 - z_1^3)} \dfrac{\bar{\psi} + (\phi^2 z - 1) \tanh \bar{\psi}}{\{\phi z_1 + \tanh \bar{\psi}\} + (1/Bi)\{\bar{\psi} + (\phi^2 z - 1) \tanh \bar{\psi}\}}$
$\rho = D_e(3)/D_e(2)$; $w = \phi z$; $v = \phi(z_1 + z_2)$; $X = (wv - 1) \tanh(v - w) + (v - w)$; $\bar{\psi} = \phi(1 - z_1)$	

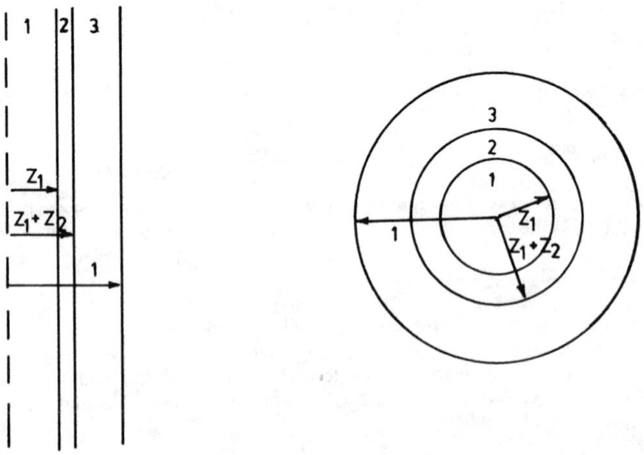

Figure 1. Step distribution activity profiles in plane and spherical geometry.

For power law rate expressions having reaction orders greater than 0.5, Gottifredi et al. [12, 13] developed analytical expressions for asymptotic values of η as $\phi \to 0$ or $\phi \to \infty$. These expressions were then combined to provide suitable approximations of η for all values of ϕ. The strength of this development is the simplicity of its application, thus making it ideal for design purposes.

Finally, if external mass transfer is considered, the effectiveness factor for the Robin problem, η_R, can be easily found if η_D, the effectiveness factor for the Dirichlet problem, is known. η_D can be obtained either by one of the methods of approximation discussed in this section or by direct integration of the state equations and subsequent quadrature [14, 15]. For arbitrary kinetics as well as for isothermal or nonisothermal rate expressions, if Equation 2 is satisfied,

$$1/\eta_R = (\phi_R/\phi_D)^2(1/\eta_D) + \phi_R^2/[\mathrm{Bi}(1 + n)] \tag{11}$$

where Bi is the standard Biot number and n is the geometric order.

It is often desirable to express the Thiele modulus and effectiveness factor in generalized terms so as to account for different geometries. Wang and Varma [9] proposed a method to shape-normalize Thiele moduli for simple profiles for which analytical Bessel function solutions are known:

$$u(z) = mz^{\alpha}; \qquad m > 0, \alpha > 0 \tag{12a}$$

$$u(z) = mz + b; \qquad m < 0, m + b > 0 \tag{12b}$$

Integration of the first-order system equations and subsequent comparison of results obtained under different geometries yields a modified Thiele modulus of the form

$$\phi_m = (V_p/Au^0)(k^*u^0/D_e)^{1/2} \tag{13}$$

where A is the pellet surface area. However, this normalization was not deemed possible for pellets having zero surface activity. The result of this normalization is shown in Figure 2 for the activity profile given by Equation 12a.

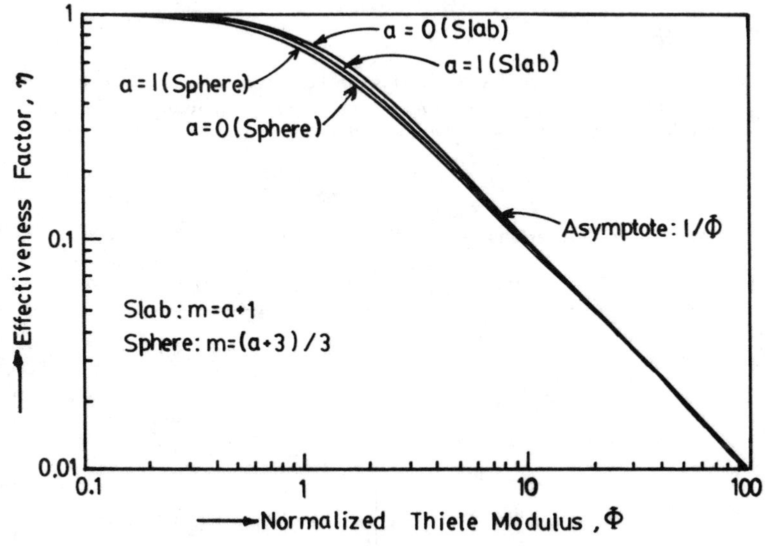

Figure 2. Effectiveness factor vs normalized Thiele modulus for the activity profile $u(z) = mz^{\alpha}$. (Reprinted with permission from Ref. [16].)

Morbidelli and Varma [17] considered pellets of arbitrary geometry, divided into three zones as shown in Figure 1, in which only the middle zone is catalytically active. This allows for analysis of step function distributions as well as any general profile by proper choice of z_1 and z_2. The authors developed a modified Thiele modulus and modified Biot number to account for external mass transfer:

$$\phi_m = (V_p/A_{\bar{z}}u(z))(k^*u(\bar{z})/D_{e|\bar{z}})^{1/2} \tag{14}$$

$$Bi_m = (V_p/A_{\bar{z}}u(z))(k_m/D_{e|\bar{z}}) \tag{15}$$

where $\bar{z} = z_1 + z_2$ (see Figure 1) and the quantity $V_p/A|_z\, u(\bar{z})$ is the normalized distance parameter, R. If $z_1 + z_2 = 1$, Equation 15 reduces to Equation 13. In addition, an internal Biot number was also defined as

$$Bi_{int} = \int_{y=z/R}^{y=1/R} (D_e(2)/D_e(3))(A_{|\bar{z}}/A(y))\, dy \tag{16}$$

The effectiveness factor in the presence of external mass transfer is given by:

$$1/\eta_R = 1/\eta_D + A_{|\bar{z}}\phi_m^2/ABi_m + \phi_m^2/Bi_{int} \tag{17}$$

It must be noted that both Bi_m and Bi_{int} must approach ∞ for the regular Biot number to approach infinity. In the case that $\phi_m \rightarrow 0$, $\eta_R \rightarrow \eta_D$ and $\eta_D \rightarrow 1$ for all geometries and activity profiles. If $\phi_m \rightarrow \infty$, four specific cases arise and are given in Table 2. If $u(z) = 0$, shape normalization is possible only if Bi_m and Bi_{int} are infinite. This represents a relaxation of the criteria developed by Wang and Varma [16].

More recently, Vayenas and Pavlou [18] derived analytical effectiveness factor expressions for the case where the catalyst is deposited in a very thin shell inside the pellet. In this case the catalyst distribution function u(z) can be approximated by:

$$u(z) = \delta(z - z_c)/(n + 1)z^n \tag{18}$$

where z_c denotes the location of the catalyst zone. This can be considered a special case of the problem treated by Wang and Varma [16] when $z_1 = z_c$ and $z_2 \rightarrow 0$. The resulting effectiveness factor expression is valid for arbitrary kinetics with or without external heat and mass transfer

Table 2
Asymptotic Expressions for the Effectiveness Factor [17]

Bi_m	Bi_{int}	η
∞	∞	$\dfrac{1}{\Phi_m}$ if $u(Z_2) \neq 0$
finite	∞	$\dfrac{A_s}{A_{s\|Z_2}} \cdot \dfrac{Bi_m}{\Phi_m^2}$
∞	finite	$\dfrac{Bi_{int}}{\Phi_m^2}$
finite	finite	$\dfrac{A_{s\|Z_2}}{A_s} \cdot \dfrac{\Phi_m^2}{Bi_m} + \dfrac{\Phi_m^2}{Bi_{int}}$

resistances:

$$\eta = (1 - x_c)/\phi_B^2; \qquad x_c \text{ root of } F_1/(1 - x_c) = 1/\phi_B^2 \tag{19}$$

where ϕ_B is a generalized shape normalizing Thiele modulus defined as

$$\phi_B = \phi(1/Bi + \int_{zc}^{1} z^{-n}\, dz)^{1/2} \tag{20}$$

and F_1 is a dimensionless generalized rate expression [18]. Since Dirac type distributions have been recently shown to be optimal for effectiveness factor maximization, the subject is treated in more detail later.

SINGLE AND MULTIPLE REACTIONS UNDER ISOTHERMAL CONDITIONS

The effects of nonuniform activity distributions on the performance of heterogeneous catalysts have mostly been demonstrated under the assumption of isothermal pellets [7, 19–30]. In the absence of poisoning, for first-order reactions, it can easily be seen that a thin layer of active material deposited in the periphery of the catalyst particle results in optimum catalyst performance. Since, in this case, diffusional effects are minimized, reaction proceeds using a higher reactant concentration than in the case in which the same amount of active material has been distributed uniformly throughout the catalyst pellet. A thin layer of catalytically active ingredient in the periphery of the pellet remains more vulnerable to poisoning and attrition, however.

Nonlinear rate expressions offer added complexity in the solution of mass balance equations. Do and Bailey [22] developed a method to handle power law, Michaelis-Menten, and other non-linear rate expressions, introducing a new integral transform technique that reduces the nonlinear differential equation to a nonlinear algebraic equation, easily solved using the Newton-Raphson or other numerical techniques.

For single first-order reactions of the type $A \rightarrow B$, analytical expressions for the effectiveness factor for various activity profiles were derived by Kasaoka and Sakata [7]. Logarithmic plots of η versus ϕ resulted in asymptotes whose slope was invariably -1. As diffusional resistances increase ($\phi \rightarrow \infty$), most or all of the reaction occurs at the periphery of the catalyst. Thus, at the limit of $\phi \rightarrow \infty$, catalysts with the same surface activity result in the same effectiveness, and the form of the activity profile is immaterial.

The results discussed above do not apply in the case in which the reaction proceeds with a negative-order dependence on reactant concentration. Negative-order rate expressions usually result from strong adsorption of the reactant on the catalyst surface. The oxidation of CO over Pt or Pd is a prime example of negative-order rate expressions following Langmuir-Hinshelwood kinetics. In the presence of excess oxygen, the rate of reaction is given by

$$r = kC_{CO}/(1 + KC_{CO})^2 \tag{21}$$

Since CO adsorbs strongly on the catalyst, the parameter KC_{CO} is usually much larger than unity, rendering the reaction order negative. This reaction has been studied both theoretically [23–26] and experimentally [27–29]. The latter studies will be discussed later.

The oxidation of CO over Pt has been analyzed by Becker and Wei [24] for four different activity profile configurations in rectangular geometries, and with symmetric boundary conditions. Results of their investigations are summarized in Figure 3. The outer shell type catalyst is the most effective one for high values of the Thiele modulus. The core catalyst is the most effective for small values of ϕ while the middle impregnated catalyst is the most effective for the narrow range $1 < \phi < 2$. For moderate CO conversions, the core catalyst operates under the lowest temperatures, but if a conversion higher than 82% is required, the middle layered catalyst is the most effective.

The same reaction was investigated by Villadsen [26] under activity profiles of the form

$$k = k_{|z=0}(1 - z)^n \tag{22}$$

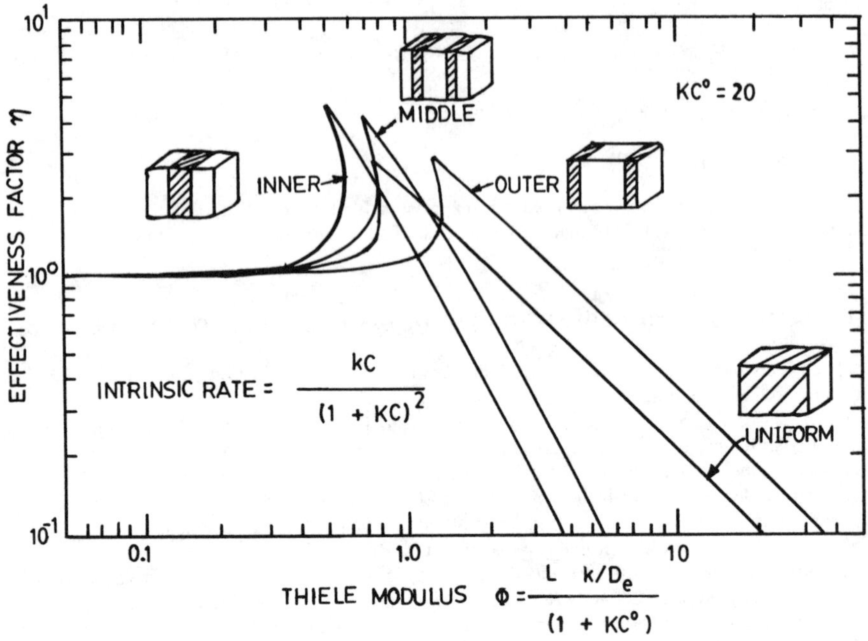

Figure 3. Isothermal effectiveness factors for bimolecular Langmuir kinetics in Cartesian geometry for $KC_{CO} = 20$. (Reprinted with permission from Ref. [24].)

He observed that as η increased, the maximum effectiveness factor also increased while maximum η occurred at decreasing values of ϕ. These conclusions can be generalized to any reaction exhibiting negative-order kinetics. For such cases, concentration gradients inside catalyst particles can prove beneficial, and effectiveness can easily exceed unity. Effectiveness can be improved by appropriate activity distribution inside the catalyst particle.

Catalytic effectiveness for first-order parallel reactions occurring isothermally follows the same pattern as for single reactions. Maximum effectiveness is obtained when the active material is distributed at the outer layer of the pellet. The activity profile has no effect on selectivity, which is defined exclusively in terms of kinetic parameters. When the two reactions are of different order, however, selectivity can be significantly affected by activity distribution. Since the reaction exhibiting higher order kinetics is favored by higher reactant concentrations, catalytic activity may be distributed in such a way as to be exposed to high or low reactant concentration, depending on the relative orders of the desired and undesired reactions. Such schemes can influence particle selectivity.

Consecutive reactions of the form $A \rightarrow B \rightarrow C$ in which B is the desired product, have been studied in detail. Expressions for effectiveness factor and selectivity may be obtained from their defining relationships,

$$\eta = [3/(1 + \zeta)] \int_0^1 uz^2(x_1 + \alpha x_2)\, dz \tag{23}$$

$$S^{-1} = [3/\eta(1 + \zeta)] \int_0^1 uz^2 x_1\, dz \tag{24}$$

where $\zeta = k_2^0 C_B^0 / k_1^0 C_A^0$

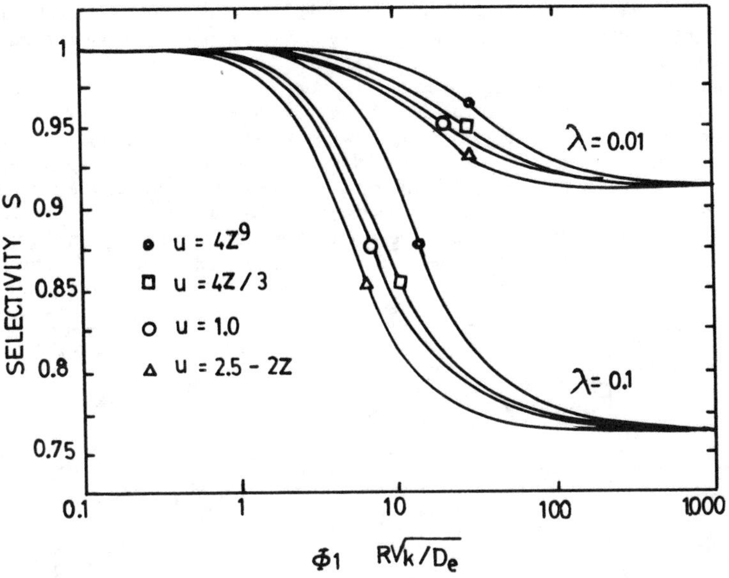

Figure 4. Effect of activity profiles on selectivity for a first order isothermal consecutive reaction system with $\xi/x_2^0 \to \infty$. (Reprinted with permission from Ref. [19].)

It has been observed [19] that, for activity distributions with nonzero surface value, as ϕ_1 becomes very large, selectivity approaches an asymptotic value independent of the activity profile, as shown in Figure 4. The parameters that dictate the particular asymptotic value are ξ/x_2^0 and λ, where $\xi = D_{e1}/D_{e2}$, $x_2^0 = C_2^0/C_1^0$, and $\lambda = \phi_2^2/\phi_1^2$. As λ decreases, ϕ_1 becomes much larger than ϕ_2 and the first reaction is promoted considerably more than the second reaction, resulting in improved selectivity. Likewise, as ξ/x_2^0 increases, the relative concentration driving force of the first reaction becomes stronger than that of the second, again resulting in increased selectivity. Since asymptotic values of selectivity are reached for both limiting cases, the shape of the activity profile affects selectivity only at intermediate values of ϕ_1. For these intermediate values of ϕ_1, the steepest activity distribution (egg shell type) yields highest selectivity, as Figure 4 indicates.

These considerations have also been extended to enzyme reactions of the form $S + E \rightleftharpoons ES \rightarrow P + E$, following Michaelis-Menten kinetics. Such systems were examined by Horvath and Engasser (20) on pellicular catalysts, consisting of a layer of active material extending from the surface of the pellet to a depth d. Two cases were studied: fixed enzyme concentration regardless of d and fixed amount of enzyme in the pellet. It was shown that enzyme distributions of this form result in significantly improved effectiveness. The case of substrate-inhibited enzymatic reactions was investigated by Morbidelli et al. [31] who showed that, in immobilized enzyme systems, an optimal distribution of the enzyme exists and it is a Dirac delta function located at the point where the reaction rate exhibits its maximum value.

SINGLE AND MULTIPLE REACTIONS UNDER NONISOTHERMAL CONDITIONS

Although isothermal operation of a catalyst pellet may be justified in many cases, if the reactions involved are sufficiently endothermic or exothermic, significant intraparticle temperature gradients can develop. In such cases, in addition to concentration profiles inside catalyst particles, temperature profiles affect local activity and selectivity, and their interplay with activity profiles becomes stronger than in the case of isothermal operation. In mathematical terms, in addition to mass balance equations, the energy balance must be satisfied, resulting in a system of highly nonlinear simultaneous differential equations.

For single reactions of the form A → B, the variation of η as a function of the Thiele modulus, heat of reaction parameter, and activity distributions of uniform, concave, and convex forms were investigated by Juang and Weng [32]. As Figure 5 shows, concave profiles yield highest activity for low values of ϕ. However, for higher values of ϕ, the convex profile offers highest effectiveness. Multiple steady states were observed for sufficiently high values of β. Furthermore, the multiplicity criterion developed by Aris [4] for uniformly activated catalysts was shown to also apply for non-uniformly activated ones. The range of Thiele moduli in which multiple steady states are observed is very small, occurring at small to intermediate values of ϕ and is independent of the activity profile.

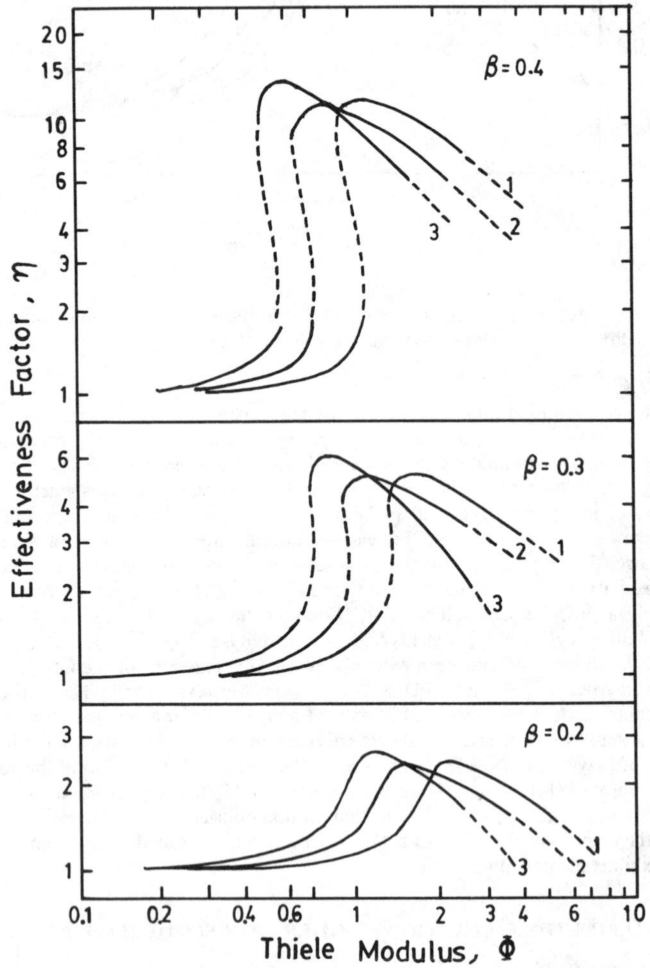

Figure 5. Effects of ϕ_1 on effectiveness factor for a non-isothermal first order reaction with $\gamma = 20$: (1) convex; (2) uniform; (3) concave. (Reprinted with permission from Ref. [32].)

For consecutive reactions of the form A → B → C, expressions for the effectiveness factor and selectivity can be derived from their defining relationships:

$$\eta = [3/(1+\zeta)] \int_0^1 uz^2\{x_1 \exp[\gamma_1(1-1/\theta)] - \zeta x_2 \exp[\gamma_2(1-1/\theta)]\}\, dz \tag{25}$$

$$S^{-1} = [3/\eta(1+\zeta)] \int_0^1 uz^2 x_1 \exp[\gamma_1(1-1/\theta)]\, dz \tag{26}$$

Under the assumptions that $\beta_1 = \beta_2$ and $\phi_1 = \phi_2$, [32] effectiveness factors for uniform, concave and convex distributions follow the same trends as those observed in the single reaction case. Selectivity was found to be approximately unity for all three activity profiles for values of ϕ_1 up to approximately 0.7. A rapid decrease in selectivity was observed at higher values of ϕ_1, approaching an asymptotic value that was nearly independent of the activity profile. The only region in which the activity profile was found to affect selectivity significantly was at ϕ_1 values between 0.7 and 2, which is also the region of rapid decline of selectivity. With increasing values of ϕ_1, selectivity was found to decrease first when a concave activity profile was assumed, followed by a uniform and then a convex profile. Thus, the convex profile is the most desirable since it offers higher selectivity over a larger range of values of ϕ_1 (see Figure 6). The values of γ_1 and γ_2 were found to affect that asymptotic value of selectivity but had no observable influence on the point of declension.

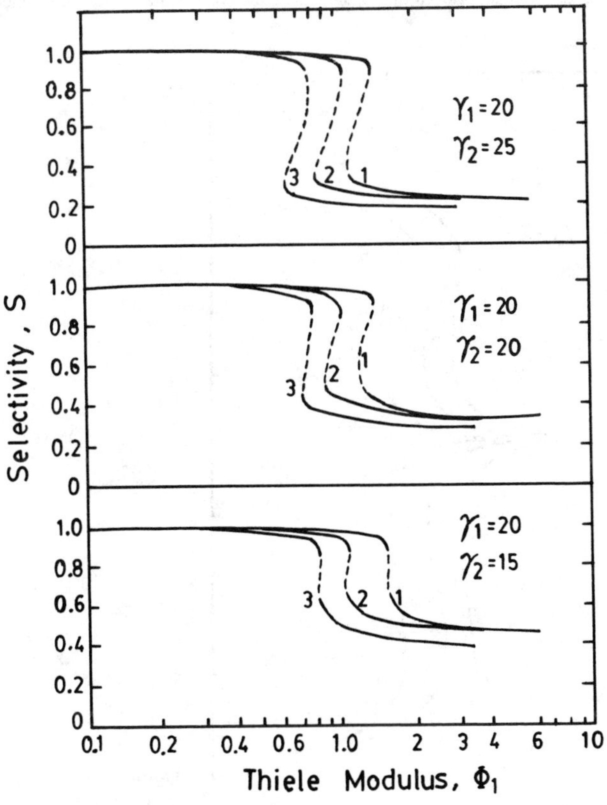

Figure 6. Effects of ϕ_1 on selectivity for a non-isothermal first order series reaction system for $\beta_1 = \beta_2 = 0.2$, $\xi/x_2^0 = 0.5$. (Reprinted with permission from Ref. [32].)

From work on uniformly activated catalysts, several insights concerning the behavior of non-uniformly activated pellets can be obtained. The second reaction has a strong influence in dictating overall system behavior. If the reaction is net exothermic in nature, the isothermal catalyst yields better selectivity under all activity profiles. For net endothermic reaction networks, selectivity enhancement is possible, to a small degree, for nonisothermal pellets. If a combination of heat effects exists, the value of ϕ_2 dictates whether the system behaves in a net exothermic or net endothermic manner. The larger the value of ϕ_2, the greater the dominance of the second reaction.

For a wide range of conditions, adequate selectivity is obtained only when the rate of the second reaction is inhibited from a low intraparticle concentration of intermediate. But improved selectivity results in lower catalyst activity due to reduced reaction rates, and thus the yield is often unreasonably small. The egg shell type catalyst varies in its effectiveness depending upon the relative activation energies of each reaction. If $\gamma_1 > \gamma_2$, the small temperature gradient resulting from this profile would significantly reduce selectivity for an exothermic system but could increase selectivity for an endothermic system. On the other hand, if $\gamma_1 < \gamma_2$, selectivity for an exothermic system increases over that of an isothermal system since internal temperature gradients are beneficial.

First order parallel reactions under the assumption that $\beta_1 = \beta_2$ were studied by Juang and Weng [32] and their results are summarized in Figure 7. If $\gamma_1 < \gamma_2$, selectivity approaches asymptotic values as $\phi_1 \rightarrow 0$ and as $\phi_1 \rightarrow \infty$. For exothermic systems, selectivity decreases rapidly at intermediate values of ϕ_1. The asymptotic values of selectivity are nearly independent of the activity profile. However, at intermediate values of ϕ_1 the concave profile is the least selective while the

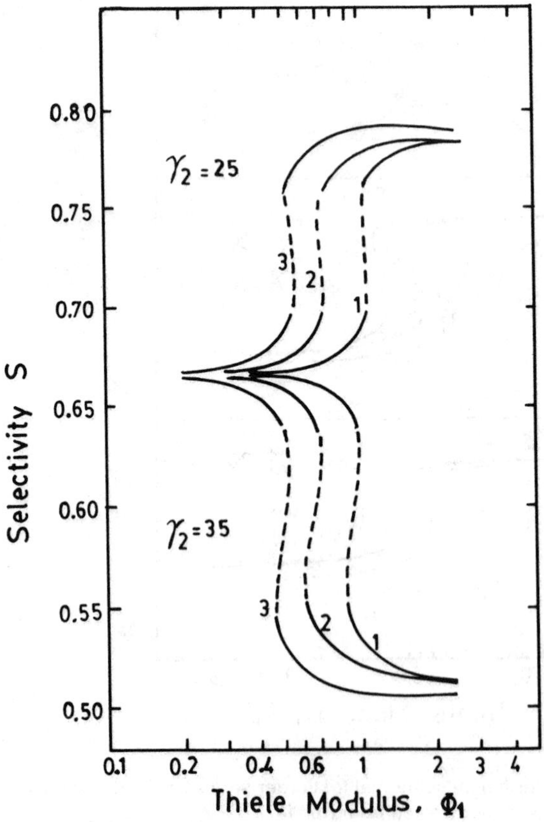

Figure 7. Effects of ϕ_1 on selectivity for a non-isothermal first order parallel reaction system for $\beta = 0.2$, $k = 0.5$, $\gamma_1 = 30$. (Reprinted with permission from Ref. [32].)

convex one is the most selective. In the case of $\gamma_1 > \gamma_2$, selectivity assumes the same asymptotic values as $\phi_1 \to 0$, independent of γ_1 or γ_2, increases rapidly at moderate values of ϕ_1 and approaches another asymptote as $\phi_1 \to \infty$. At the intermediate values of ϕ_1, the concave profile is the most selective while the convex one is the least selective. It should be noted that if $\gamma_1 = \gamma_2$, selectivity is unaffected by the particular profile assumed.

Johnson and Verykios [33] studied the second-order parallel reaction network as well as the ethylene oxidation scheme [34] under experimentally determined Langmuir-Hinshelwood kinetic rate expressions. Activity profiles of the form: $k = k^0 z^\alpha$, $\alpha \geq 0$, were assumed, with the activation energy of the desired reaction lower than the activation energy of the undesired one. The effectiveness factor was shown to approach an asymptotic value as $\phi_1 \to 0$ for all activity distributions. At higher values of ϕ_1, however, η was found to increase with increasing nonuniformity of the activity distribution, but the opposite was noted for small values of ϕ_1. Nonuniform activity distributions were shown to enhance selectivity for all values of ϕ_1, with more dramatic enhancement at intermediate values of ϕ_1. The variation of activity with respect to ϕ_1 for various activity distributions is shown in Figure 8. Obviously then, catalysts approaching the egg shell configuration are both more active and more selective under a large range of values of the Thiele modulus.

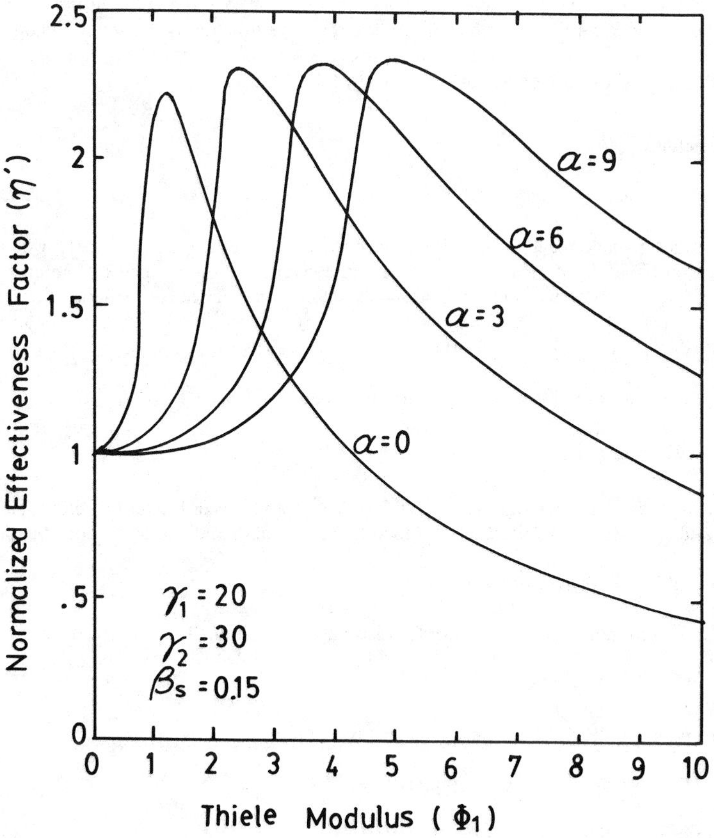

Figure 8. Effects of ϕ_1 on effectiveness for a second-order parallel reaction network for the activity profile $u(z) = z^\alpha$. (Reprinted with permission from Ref. [34].)

If a reaction system results in intraparticle temperature gradients, it is often beneficial to use nonuniform activity distributions. Generally, if ϕ_1 is large, a pellet having a large portion of its active material concentrated in the outer periphery of the catalyst yields higher activity and selectivity. If ϕ_1 is small, an egg yolk catalyst exhibits the best activity.

OPTIMIZATION OF ACTIVITY DISTRIBUTIONS

The factors that influence the definition of optimal activity distribution within a catalyst pellet include effectiveness, selectivity, and durability. In cases where catalyst poisoning can be assumed to be insignificant, the definition of the optimization problem and of the corresponding objective function is straightforward. Thus, in the case of a single reaction the optimal activity distribution is the one which maximizes the effectiveness factor or minimizes the total amount of catalyst needed to achieve a given global reaction rate. In the case of networks of parallel or consecutive reactions, the optimal catalyst distribution is usually defined as the one which maximizes selectivity to a desired product, but other objective functions such as the global rate of production of the desired product can also be used. Most of the problems related to optimal catalyst activity distribution in pellets without poisoning have been solved rigorously in recent years for Langmuir-Hinshelwood [35, 36] and arbitrary kinetics [18, 37–40], and the solutions are presented in this section. When catalyst poisoning is significant, the choice of the objective function is less unambiguous. Furthermore, in most cases no rigorous analytical expressions have been found yet for the optimal activity profile. Progress in this area is summarized in the following section.

Single Reactions

Problem Formulation

We consider a single reaction A → B with arbitrary but known kinetics, f(C, T), where C is the concentration of species A. The reaction occurs in a symmetric porous pellet of volume V_p which contains G_m grams of active catalyst. The steady-state mass balance can be written as

$$D_e(1/y^n)\, d/dy[y^n\, dC/dy] = f(C, T)g(y) \tag{27}$$

where g(y) is the local active catalyst density such that

$$\int_{V_p} g(y)\, dV = G_m = g_0 V_p \tag{28}$$

with g_0 being the volume averaged active catalyst density and n = 0, 1, 2 for the infinite slab, infinite cylinder and sphere respectively. The corresponding boundary conditions (BCs) of Equation 27 are:

$$\text{At } y = 0,\ dC/dy = 0; \qquad \text{At } y = R,\ C = C^0 \tag{29}$$

For the case of finite external mass transfer resistance the second BC is replaced by

$$\text{At } y = R, \qquad D_e\, dC/dy = K_g(C^0 - C) \tag{29a}$$

The corresponding steady-state energy balance is

$$K_e(1/y^n)\, d/dy[y^n\, dT/dy] = f(C, T)g(y)(\Delta H) \tag{30}$$

with boundary conditions,

$$\text{At } y = 0,\ dT/dy = 0; \qquad \text{At } y = R,\ T = T^0 \tag{31}$$

When the external heat transfer resistance is finite, the second BC is replaced by

$$\text{At } y = R, \qquad K_e\, dT/dy = h(T^0 - T) \tag{31a}$$

Introducing the dimensionless active catalyst density $u(y) = g(y)/g_0$ and the following dimensionless quantities

$$z = y/R; \quad x = C/C^0; \quad \theta = T/T^0; \quad \chi(x, \theta) = f(C, T)/f(C^0, T^0); \quad Bi = K_g R/D_e;$$

$$Bi_{th} = hR/K_e; \quad \beta = (-\Delta H)C^0 D_e/K_e T^0; \quad \phi^2 = g_0 R^2 f(C^0, T^0)/(n + 1)D_e C^0$$

the mass balance equation can be written in the form

$$L[x] = (n + 1)\phi^2 \chi(x, \theta)u(z) \tag{32}$$

with boundary conditions

$$\text{At } z = 0,\ dx/dz = 0; \qquad \text{At } z = 1,\ x = 1 \tag{33}$$

$$\text{or,} \quad \text{At } z = 1,\ dx/dz = Bi(1 - x) \tag{33a}$$

and the energy balance equation in the form

$$L[\theta] = -(n + 1)\beta\phi^2 \chi(x, \theta)u(z) \tag{34}$$

with boundary conditions,

$$\text{At } z = 0,\ d\theta/dz = 0; \qquad \text{At } z = 1,\ \theta = 1 \tag{35}$$

$$\text{or,} \quad \text{At } z = 1,\ d\theta/dz = Bi_{th}(1 - \theta) \tag{35a}$$

where

$$L[\ ] = (1/z^n)\, d/dz[z^n d[\ ]/dz] \tag{36}$$

From its definition, the dimensionless catalyst concentration u(z) satisfies Equation 4, i.e.

$$\int_0^1 u(z)z^n\, dz = 1/(n + 1) \tag{4}$$

From the definition of the effectiveness factor η it follows that

$$\eta = \int_0^1 \chi(x, \theta)u(z)z^n\, dz \Big/ \int_0^1 u(z)z^n\, dz \tag{37}$$

Using Equations 4, 35, and 36, one obtains

$$\eta = (n + 1) \int_0^1 \chi(x, \theta)u(z)z^n\, dz = (1/\phi^2)[dx/dz]_{z=1} \tag{38}$$

The optimal active catalyst density function u(z) is the one that maximizes the effectiveness factor η (Equation 37) under the constraint set by Equation 4, while x(z) and $\theta(z)$ can be computed for a particular u(z) through Equations 32 to 35. An alternative formulation of the optimization problem is the minimization of the mass of active catalyst, G, required to achieve a given global reaction rate r_p in a pellet of volume V_p. In this case,

$$r = \eta f(C^0, T^0)(G/V_p) = (n+1)\left[\int_0^1 \chi(x, \theta)u(z)z^n\,dz\right]f(C^0, T^0)g_0 \tag{39}$$

and the objective function to be minimized is

$$g_0 = r_p \Big/ \left[f(C^0, T^0)(n+1)\int_0^1 \chi(x, \theta)a(z)z^n\,dz\right] \tag{40}$$

where u(z) must again satisfy Constraint 4.

Optimal Catalyst Distribution

It has been shown by Vayenas and Pavlou [18, 39] and by Chemburkar et al. [38] that the optimal catalyst distribution for effectiveness factor maximization is given by

$$u(z) = [1/(n+1)z^n]\,\delta(z - z_{opt}) \tag{41}$$

where

$$z_{opt} = 1 - \Omega \qquad \text{for slab } (n = 0) \tag{41a}$$

$$z_{opt} = \exp(-\Omega) \qquad \text{for cylinder } (n = 1) \tag{41b}$$

$$z_{opt} = 1/(1 + \Omega) \qquad \text{for sphere } (n = 2) \tag{41c}$$

and

$$\Omega = [(1 - x_{opt})/\phi^2\eta_{max}] - 1/Bi \tag{41d}$$

The meaning of x_{opt} and η_{max} in the above expressions is the following: For isothermal pellets $\chi(x, \theta) = \chi(x)$ and x_{opt} is defined as the x value that maximizes the kinetic expression $\chi(x)$ in the interval $[x_{min}, x_{max}]$ for $n = 0$ and $[0, x_{max}]$ for $n = 1, 2$. The corresponding maximum χ value is η_{max}, i.e. $\eta_{max} = \chi(x_{opt})$. The parameters x_{min}, x_{max} [0, 1] are defined respectively as the minimum roots of

$$(1 - x)/\chi(x) = \phi^2(1 + 1/Bi) \tag{42}$$

$$(1 - x)/\chi(x) = \phi^2/Bi \tag{43}$$

By choosing x_{opt} in the above intervals it is automatically ensured (18) that physically meaningful values, i.e., $0 \le z_{opt} \le 1$ are obtained for the optimal catalyst location, Equation 41. The geometric meaning of x_{min}, x_{max} and x_{opt} is shown in Figure 9 for an arbitrary kinetic expression $\chi(x)$.

For nonisothermal pellets one distinguishes two cases depending on whether $Bi = Bi_{th}$ or $Bi \neq Bi_{th}$. In the former case the equation,

$$\theta = 1 + \beta(1 - x) \tag{44}$$

is valid through the pellet and consequently,

$$\chi(x, \theta) = \chi(x, 1 + \beta(1 - x)) = \chi_1(x) \tag{45}$$

Accordingly, x_{opt} in Equation 41 is the x value that maximizes $\chi_1(x)$ in the interval $[x_{min}, 1]$ for $n = 0$ and [0, 1] for $n = 1, 2$, where x_{min} is defined again from Equation 42 with $\chi(x)$ replaced by $\chi_1(x)$. The corresponding maximum χ_1 value is η_{max}, i.e. $\eta_{max} = \chi_1(x_{opt})$.

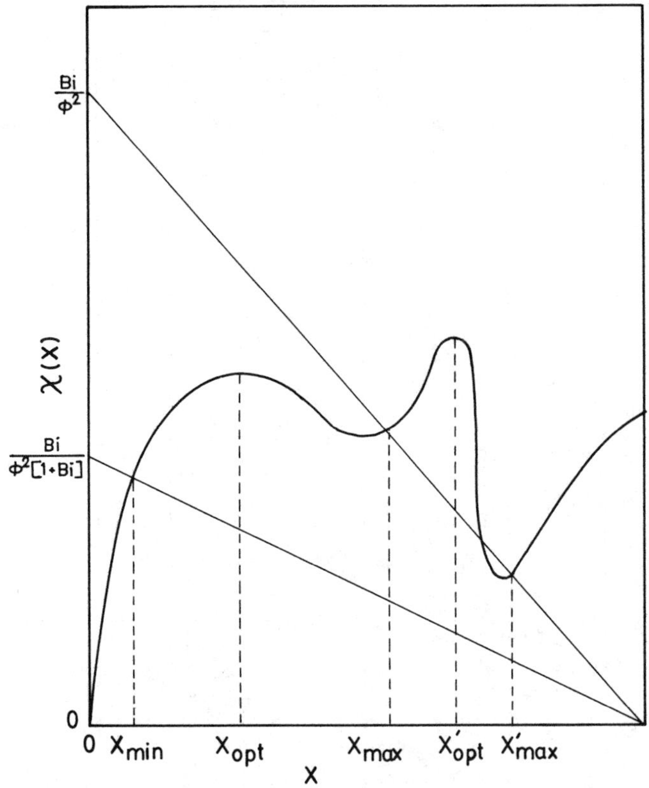

Figure 9. Graphical determination of x_{min}, x_{max}, and x_{opt}. It follows from the definition of x_{max} and x_{opt} that the values denoted x'_{max} and x'_{opt} are not permissible. (Reprinted with permission from Ref. [18].)

In the general case of a nonisothermal pellet with external temperature gradients and $Bi \neq Bi_{th}$, x_{opt} and η_{max} are defined as follows: First, a generally multivalued function F(x) is defined by computing for each x [0, 1] all the positive roots of the algebraic equation:

$$F = \chi[x, 1 + \beta(1 - x) + \beta(\rho - 1)(\phi^2/Bi)F] \tag{46}$$

with $\rho = Bi/Bi_{th}$. It has been shown [18] that this equation has at least one positive root for every fixed x [0, 1]. The maximum effectiveness factor, η_{max}, in Equation 41d is then the maximum value of F that satisfies

$$(1 - x)/F \leq \phi^2(1 + 1/Bi), \qquad \text{for } n = 0 \tag{47}$$

and

$$(1 - x)/F \geq \phi^2/Bi, \qquad \text{for } n = 1, 2 \tag{48}$$

The corresponding value of x is equal to x_{opt}.

TABLE 3
Definition of x_{opt}, η_{max}, x^*_{opt} and η for the Optimal Catalyst Distribution Expressions (Equations 41, 49, and 50)

		$\beta = 0, 1/Bi = 0$	$\beta = 0, 1/Bi > 0$	$\beta \neq 0, Bi = Bi_{th}$	$\beta \neq 0, Bi \neq Bi_{th}$
Effectiveness Maximization	x_{opt} constraints	$x_{min} \leqq x_{opt}$ (n = 0)	$x_{min} \leqq x_{opt} \leqq x_{max}$ (n = 0) $x_{opt} \leqq x_{max}$ (n = 1, 2)	$x_{min} \leqq x_{opt}$ (n = 0)	
	$x_{min} \in [0, 1]$	minimum root of $1 - x = \Phi^2(1 + 1/Bi)\chi(x)$		minimum root of $1 - x = \Phi^2(1 + 1/Bi)\chi_1(x)$	
	$x_{max} \in [0, 1]$	minimum root of $1 - x = (\Phi^2/Bi)\chi(x)$		minimum root of $1 - x = (\Phi^2/Bi)\chi_1(x)$	
	η_{max}	$\chi(x_{opt})$		$\chi_1(x_{opt})$	maximum root of $F = \chi(x, 1 + \beta(1 - x) + \beta(\rho - 1)(\Phi^2/Bi)F)$ with $1 - x \leqq \Phi^2(1 + 1/Bi)F$ $1 - x \geqq (\Phi^2/Bi)\ F$
Catalyst Mass Minimization	x^*_{opt} constraints	$x^*_{min} \leqq x^*_{opt}$ (n = 0)	$x^*_{min} \leqq x^*_{opt} \leqq x^*_{max}$ (n = 0) $x^*_{opt} \leqq x^*_{max}$ (n = 1, 2)	$x^*_{min} \leqq x^*_{opt}$ (n = 0)	$x^*_{min} \leqq x^*_{opt} \leqq x^*_{max}$ (n = 0) $x^*_{opt} \leqq x^*_{max}$ (n = 1, 2)
	x^*_{min}	0 ; $1 - (1 + 1/Bi)\psi$;		$(1 + 1/Bi)\psi \geqq 1$ $(1 + 1/Bi)\psi \leqq 1$	$\psi = rR^2/(n + 1)D_eC^0$
	x^*_{max}	0 ; $1 - \psi/Bi$;		$\psi/Bi \geqq 1$ $\psi/Bi \leqq 1$	x^*_{opt} : x value maximizing F(x) $F(x) = \chi(x, 1 + \beta(1 - x) + \beta(\rho - 1)\psi/Bi)$
	η	$\chi(x^*_{opt})$		$\chi_1(x^*_{opt})$	$F(x^*_{opt})$

The above definitions are summarized in Table 3. Figures 10 and 11 show the dependence of the optimal catalyst location z_{opt} on the Thiele modulus for the cases of bimolecular Langmuir-Hinshelwood kinetics in isothermal pellets and linear kinetics in nonisothermal pellets with no external temperature gradients.

Equations 41a-d have also been shown [18] to provide the solution to the dual optimization problem of catalyst mass minimization to obtain a given global reaction rate with Ω replaced by

$$\Omega^* = [(n+1)D_eC^0(1 - x^*_{opt})/rR^2] - 1/Bi \tag{49}$$

and x^*_{opt} defined in Table 3. The minimum mass $G_{m,min}$ of active catalyst required to achieve the desired global reaction rate, r_p, is given by

$$G_{m,min} = r_pV_p/f(C^0, T^0)\eta \tag{50}$$

where the effectiveness factor η equals $\chi(x^*_{opt})$ for isothermal pellets, $\chi_1(x^*_{opt})$ for nonisothermal pellets with $Bi = Bi_{th}$ and $F(x^*_{opt})$ for nonisothermal pellets with $Bi \neq Bi_{th}$.

The fact that the optimal catalyst activity distribution for single reactions is an appropriately chosen Dirac-type function poses some important practical questions. In order to maximize the

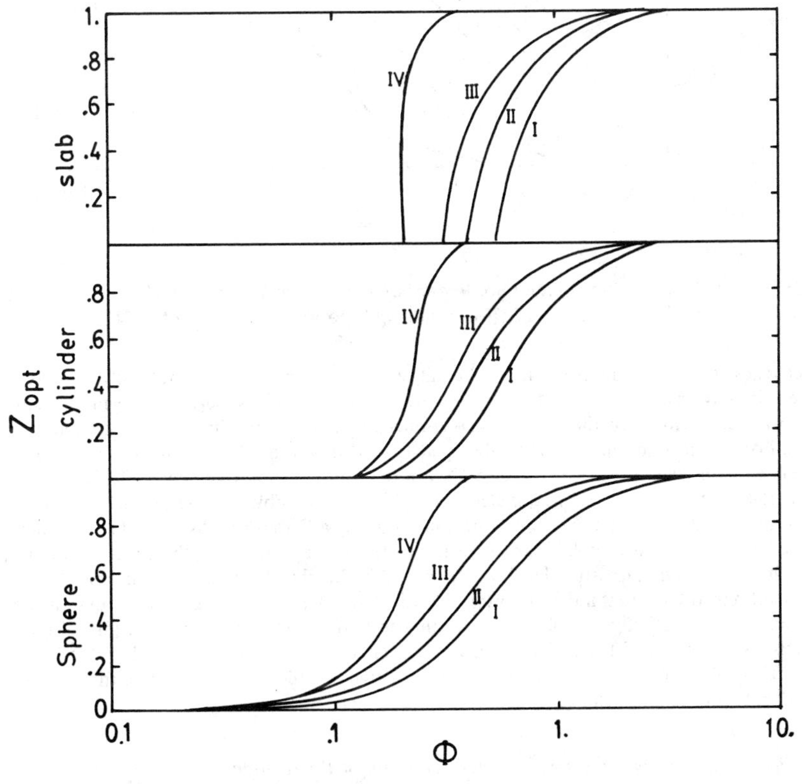

Figure 10. Optimal catalyst location for bimolecular Langmuir-Hinshelwood kinetics $\chi(x) = (1+\sigma)^2x/(1+\sigma x)^2$ in isothermal pellets; (I) $\sigma = 10$, Bi = 100, (II) $\sigma = 20$, Bi = 100, (III) $\sigma = 40$, Bi = 100, (IV) $\sigma = 40$, Bi = 1. (Reprinted with permission from Ref. [18].)

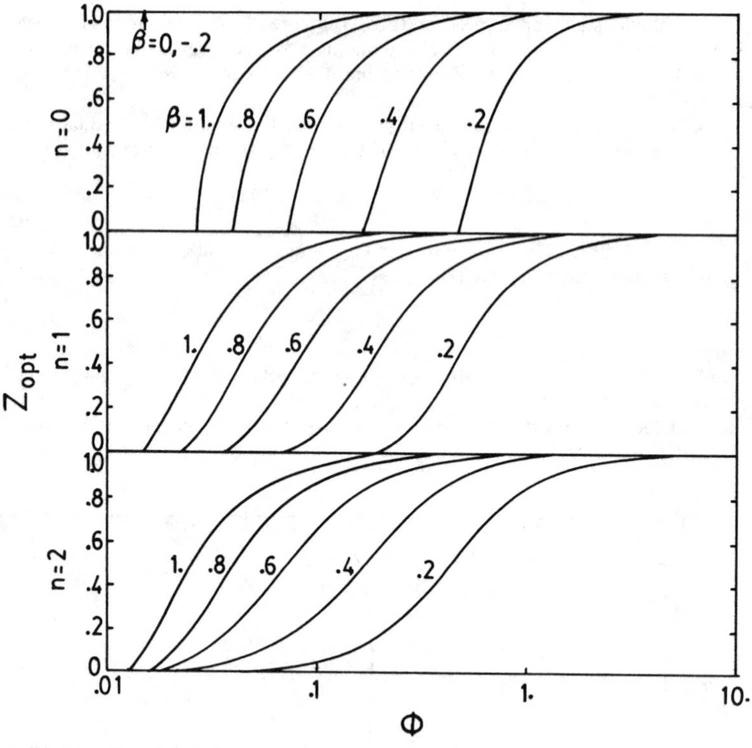

Figure 11. Optimal catalyst location for linear kinetics in nonisothermal slabs (n = 0), cylinders (n = 1) and spheres (n = 2); $\gamma = 20$. (Reprinted with permission from Ref. [18].)

effectiveness factor or minimize the total catalyst mass, one must concentrate all the active component in a precise location in the particle, e.g., on a very thin spherical zone in the case of a spherical pellet. However, the minimum zone thickness is, of course, limited by practical consideration. For example, in the case of catalyst pellets used in automotive exhaust catalytic converters the active components Pt, Rh, Pd, and Ce are deposited in approximately 100-μm-wide bands located near or below the external pellet surface [27, 28]. An obvious question is how closely one can approximate such a catalyst concentration profile by a Dirac-type distribution. A second question of equal importance is how sensitive the pellet performance is to the exact location of the catalyst zone. The first question has been addressed by Morbidelli et al. [35]. They used numerical computations to show that if the catalyst is deposited in a step manner, centered around the optimal location, then the effectiveness factor is insignificantly decreased provided the width of the active zone is less than 4% of the pellet dimensions. Such widths are easily realized in the laboratory (41, 42). The question of catalyst performance sensitivity to the exact location of the catalyst zone is addressed in the following section.

Effectiveness Factors of Pellets with Dirac-Type Catalyst Distribution

It was shown in the previous section that the optimal catalyst activity profile for effectiveness factor maximization corresponds to an appropriately chosen Dirac-type distribution. Analytical expressions were presented for the optimal catalyst location. Once such a pellet has been fabricated it is important to know how its performance will change if the ambient conditions change so that the catalyst location is not the optimal anymore. This consideration is of great importance in any industrial catalytic reactor where reactant concentration and temperature will inevitably change along the length of the reactor.

For pellets with the catalyst located at a specific position z_c, a simple analytical shape normalizing effectiveness factor expression has been obtained by Vayenas and Pavlou [18] by introducing the following generalized Thiele modulus:

$$\phi_B = \phi\left[(1/Bi) + \int_{Z_c}^{1} z^{-n}\,dz\right]^{1/2}$$
$$= \left[\{g_0 R^2 f(C^0, T^0)/(n+1)D_e C^0\}(1/Bi + \int_{Z_c}^{1} z^{-n}\,dz)\right]^{1/2} \quad (51)$$

Once the catalyst location z_c is specified, ϕ_B can be readily computed and the effectiveness factor is obtained from:

$$\eta = (1 - x_c)/\phi_B^2 \quad (52)$$

where x_c is the root of

$$F_1/(1 - x_c) = 1/\phi_B^2 \quad (53)$$

and designates the reactant concentration at the catalyst location.

The function $F_1(x_c)$ is generally defined from

$$\phi(x_c, \theta_c) = \phi[x_c, 1 + \beta(1 - x_c)(1 + 1/Bi_{th}\mu)/(1 + 1/Bi\mu)] = F_1(x_c) \quad (54)$$

where

$$\mu = \int_{Z_c}^{1} z^{-n}\,dz \quad (55)$$

When $Bi = Bi_{th}$ then $F_1(x_c) = \phi_1(x_c)$. Furthermore, in the case of isothermal pellets ($\beta = 0$), then $F_1(x_c)$ simply reduces to $\phi(x_c)$. Figure 12 shows the dependence of η on the shape normalizing modulus ϕ_B for the case of a first order reaction in a pellet with both internal and external gradients for various values of β, Bi and Bi_{th}. Note that Bi and Bi_{th} are expressed as multiples of $1/\mu$. This is because this catalyst location parameter, Bi and Bi_{th} appear in Equation 54 only as the products $Bi\mu$ and $Bi_{th}\mu$.

It should be noticed that η always approaches $1/\phi_B^2$ for large ϕ_B values (Figure 12). This is true for any type of kinetics and is a direct consequence of Equation 52. It can also be noticed from Equation 54 that if one defines a modified Prater number β^* according to:

$$\beta^* = \beta[\mu + 1/Bi]/[\mu + 1/Bi_{th}] \quad (56)$$

then the dependence of η on ϕ_B is identical to the one obtained in pellets with no external temperature gradients or $Bi = Bi_{th}$ with β replaced by β^*.

As shown in Figure 12 steady state multiplicities appear over a rather wide range of parameters. It has been shown rigorously [18] that steady state multiplicities appear when the uniqueness criterion,

$$(1 - x)F_1'(x) + F_1(x) \geq 0 \quad (57)$$

is violated. In this case the optimum catalyst location z_{opt} may additionally correspond to other steady states with lower η values. Which of these steady states prevails, obviously depends on the previous history of the pellet.

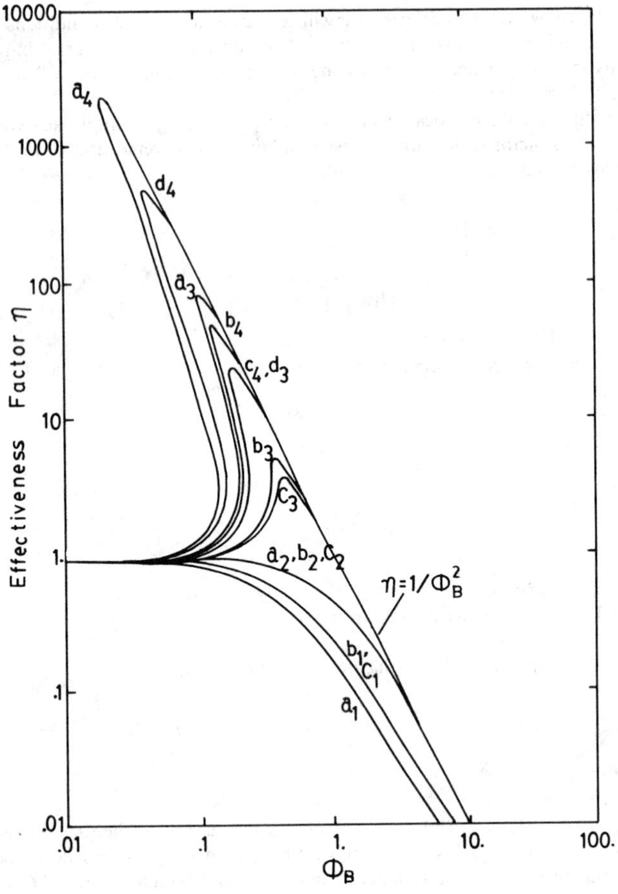

Figure 12. Effectiveness factor η vs the generalized shape normalizing modulus ϕ_B for linear kinetics with $\gamma = 20$: (a) $Bi = 10/\mu$, $Bi_{th} = 0.5/\mu$; (b) $Bi = 100/\mu$, $Bi_{th} = 5/\mu$; (c) $Bi = 1{,}000/\mu$, $Bi_{th} = 50/\mu$; (d) $Bi = 1{,}000/\mu$, $Bi_{th} = 1/\mu$; subscripts 1, 2, 3, 4 denote $\beta = -0.2, 0, 0.2, 0.4$, respectively. (Reprinted with permission from Ref. [18].)

Parallel Reactions

In the case of parallel reactions, $A - f_1 \rightarrow B$, $A - f_2 \rightarrow C$, of arbitrary kinetics $f_1(C_1)$ and $f_2(C_1)$ the dimensionless steady state mass balances of A and of the desired product B are:

$$(1/z^n)\, d/dz[z^n\, dx_1/dz] = (n + 1)[\phi_1^2\chi_1(x_1, \theta) + \phi_2^2\chi_2(x_1, \theta)/\xi]u(z) \tag{58}$$

$$(1/z^n)\, d/dz[z^n\, dx_2/dz] = -(n + 1)\xi\phi_1^2\chi_1(x, \theta)u(z) \tag{59}$$

with boundary conditions

$$\text{At } z = 0,\ dx_1/dz = dx_2/dz = 0; \qquad \text{At } z = 1,\ x_1 = 1,\ x_2 = x_2^0 \tag{60}$$

where $\xi = D_{e,1}/D_{e,2}$. The steady state dimensionless energy balance is

$$(1/z^n)\,d/dz[z^n\,d\theta/dz] = (n+1)[\beta_1\phi_1^2\chi_1(x_1,\theta) + \beta_2\phi_2^2\chi_2(x_1,\theta)/\xi]u(z) \tag{61}$$

The global pellet selectivity, S, (moles B produced/moles A reacted) is defined by:

$$S = \frac{\int_0^1 \xi\phi_1^2\chi_1(x_1,\theta)u(z)z^n\,dz}{\int_0^1 [\xi\phi_1^2\chi_1(x_1,\theta) + \phi_2^2\chi_2(x_1,\theta)]u(z)z^n\,dz} \tag{62}$$

For the isothermal case it has been shown by Vayenas and Pavlou [39] that the optimal catalyst distribution is an appropriate Dirac-type distribution. Defining as $x_{1,opt}$ the x_1 value that maximizes the function

$$S(x_1) = \xi\chi_1(x_1)/[\xi\chi_1(x_1) + \lambda\chi_2(x_1)] \tag{63}$$

where $\lambda = \phi_2^2/\phi_1^2$ and defining Ω^* according to:

$$\Omega^* = 1 - x_{1,opt}/[\phi_1^2\chi_1(x_{1,opt}) + \phi_2^2\chi_2(x_{1,opt})]/\xi] \tag{64}$$

it was shown that the optimal catalyst distribution is given by

$$u(z)_{opt} = \delta(z - z_{opt})/(n+1)z^n \tag{65}$$

with

$$z_{opt} = 1 - \Omega^* \qquad \text{for } n = 0 \text{ (slab)} \tag{65a}$$

$$z_{opt} = \exp(-\Omega^*) \qquad \text{for } n = 1 \text{ (cylinder)} \tag{65b}$$

$$z_{opt} = 1/(1 + \Omega^*) \qquad \text{for } n = 2 \text{ (sphere)} \tag{65c}$$

or, in a more compact form

$$\int_{z_{opt}}^1 z^{-n}\,dz = \Omega^* \tag{66}$$

The maximum global selectivity S_{max} is defined by:

$$S_{max} = \frac{\xi\chi_1(x_{1,opt})}{\xi\chi_1(x_{1,opt}) + \lambda\chi_2(x_{1,opt})} \tag{67}$$

In the case of slab geometry it is necessary to ensure that $\Omega^* \leq 1$. This introduces a minimum active density, $g_{0,min}^*$, which is required to obtain S_{max}:

$$g_{0,min}^* = \frac{D_{e,1}(C_1^0, -C_{1,opt})}{R^2[f_1(C_{1,opt}) + f_2(C_{1,opt})]} \tag{68}$$

It follows from Equation 64 that in the case of power law kinetics $\chi_1(u_1) = u_1^{p_1}$, $\chi_2(u_1) = u_1^{p_2}$, $z_{opt} = 1$ for $p_1 > p_2$ and $z_{opt} = 0$ for $p_1 < p_2$, i.e. the external shell distribution is optimal when the order of the desired reaction is higher than the order of the undesirable one.

Figure 13 shows the dependence of z_{opt} and S_{max} on the ratio of kinetic constants λ for the case of parallel reactions with bimolecular and monomolecular Langmuir kinetics and different adsorption sites for the two reactions. Increasing λ naturally decreases the maximum obtainable global

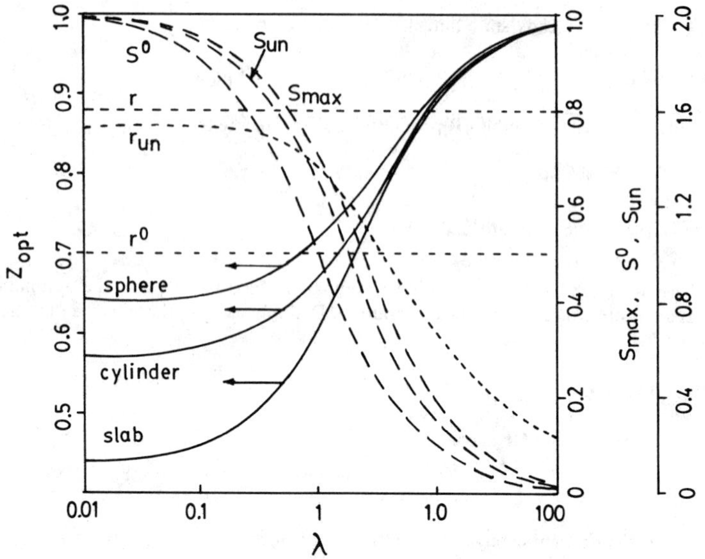

Figure 13. Effect of the ratio λ of kinetic constants on the optimal catalyst location (solid lines), global selectivity (dashed lines) and dimensionless rate of production of B (dotted lines) for the optimal distribution (S_{max}, $\hat{r}$), uniform distribution for slab geometry (S_{un}, r_{un}) and external shell distribution (S^0, r^0). Parallel reactions: $\chi_1(x_1) = (1 + \sigma_1)^2 x_1/(1 + \sigma_1 x_1)^2$; $\chi_2(x_1) = (1 + \sigma_2)x_1/(1 + \sigma_2 x_1)$; $\sigma_1 = 5$; $\sigma_2 = 20$; $\phi_1 = 1$; $\xi = 1$. (Reprinted with permission from Ref. [39].)

selectivity S_{max}, while the corresponding z_{opt} decreases. This is because when the undesirable reaction becomes very fast the catalyst must be located near the pellet surface in order for the reactant concentration to remain at the value of $u_{1,opt}$, which is not affected by λ. The same figure compares S_{max} with the global selectivities obtained with uniform (S_{un}) and external shell (S^0) catalyst distributions. It can be seen that the differences between S_{max}, S_{un} and S^0 are significant when λ is of order one, i.e. when the two reactions have comparable rates.

The optimum catalyst distribution not only maximizes the global selectivity but also maintains a high net rate of production of the desired product. This is shown in Figure 13 where the dimensionless production rate r of the desired product B is plotted versus λ for the optimum ($\hat{r}$), uniform (r_{un}) and external shell (r^0) catalyst distributions. It can be seen that $\hat{r}$ is consistently higher than r_{un} and r^0 for all values of λ. It is worth noting that $\hat{r}$ and r^0 are not affected by λ, since ϕ_1 remains constant and the reactant concentration remains at $u_{1,opt}$ and 1, respectively. However, r_{un} is affected since increasing λ causes a decrease in reactant concentration throughout the pellet.

Figure 14 shows the effect of catalyst location z_c on the global selectivity, S, for the same type of kinetics and parameter values used in Figure 13 and compares S with S_{un} obtained with uniform catalyst distribution in flat, cylindrical and spherical pellets. It can be seen that for all pellet geometries there exist wide ranges of catalyst location z_c for which S exceeds S_{un} and S^0. The latter, as shown in the figure, is equal to 0.5. On the basis of Figure 14 one can draw two practical qualitative conclusions for this reaction system. First that pellets in which the active catalyst is deposited in a zone of thickness of order 5% of the dimensions of the pellet and centered at z_{opt} will exhibit global selectivities very near S_{max}. Second that even if reaction conditions change so that z_{opt} increases significantly, a pellet with a near Dirac-type distribution will still exhibit substantially higher selectivity than a pellet with uniform catalyst distribution.

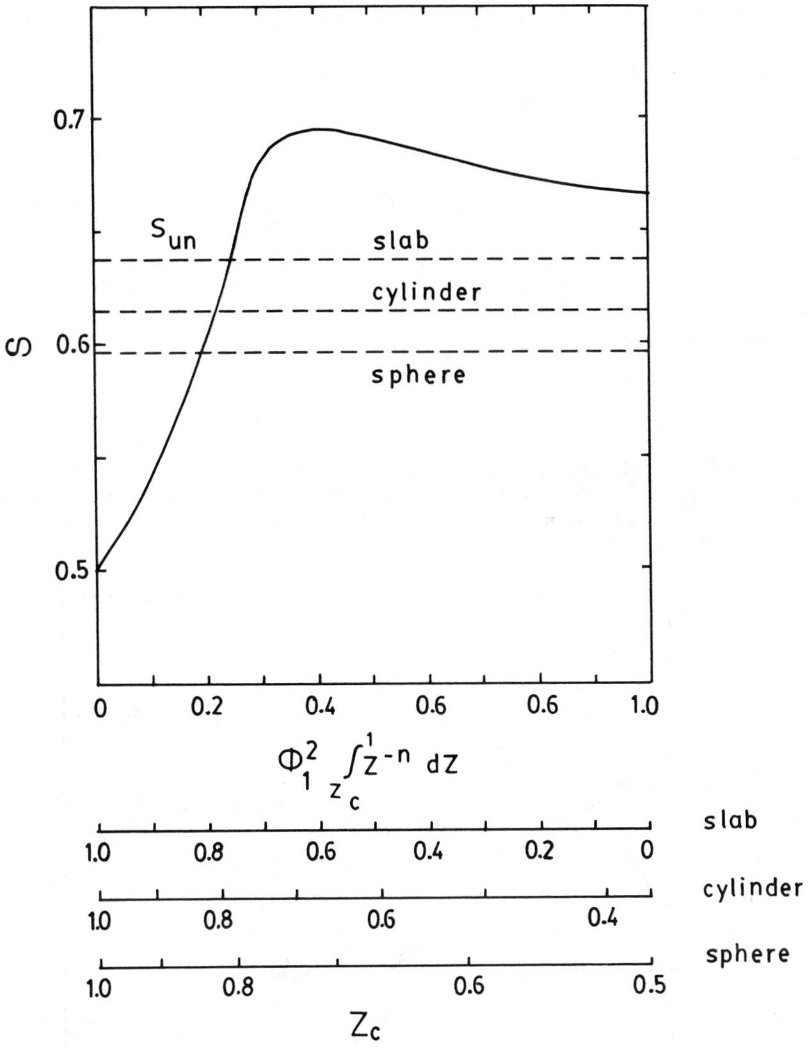

Figure 14. Dependence of the global selectivity for a Dirac-type distribution on the catalyst location z_c. The horizontal lines correspond to uniform catalyst distribution global selectivity. Parallel reactions: $\chi_1(x_1) = (1 + \sigma_1)^2 x_1/(1 + \sigma_1 x_1)^2$; $\chi_2(x_1) = (1 + \sigma_2)x_1/(1 + \sigma_2 x_1)$; $\sigma_1 = 5$; $\sigma_2 = 20$; $\phi_1 = 1$; $\phi_2 = 1$; $\xi = 1$. (Reprinted with permission from Ref. [39].)

In the case of nonisothermal pellets it has been shown recently by Vayenas and Pavlou [43] that Equations 64–66 again provide the optimal catalyst activity distribution. However, in this case $x_{1,opt}$ must be defined in a different manner.

Considering kinetic expressions of the form

$$\chi_i(x_1, \theta) = \chi_i^*(x_1)\exp[\gamma_i(1 - 1/\theta)] \qquad (i = 1, 2) \tag{69}$$

with $\chi_1(0, \theta) = 0$ one defines a function $G(x_1)$ from the following equation

$$\frac{G - x_2^0}{1 - x_1} = \frac{\chi_1^*(x_1)}{\varepsilon} \tag{70}$$

where

$$\varepsilon = \chi_i^*(x_1) + \lambda\chi_2^*(x_1)\exp\left[(\gamma_2 - \gamma_1)\left(\frac{(\beta_1 - \beta_2)(G - x_2^0) + \beta_2(1 - x_1)}{1 + (\beta_1 - \beta_2)(G - x_2^0) + \beta_2(1 - x_1)}\right)\right] \tag{70a}$$

If Equation 70 has more than one roots for a given x_1, then $G(x_1)$ is defined as the largest of all roots. Then $x_{1,opt}$ is defined as the x_1 value which maximizes the two sides of Equation 70. The corresponding maximum selectivity S_{max} is then given by:

$$S_{max} = \frac{G(x_{1,opt}) - x_2^0}{1 - x_{1,opt}} \tag{71}$$

As shown in Figure 15 there also exists a simple geometric method to determine x_{opt}. One considers the graph of $G(x_1)$, which always contains the point $(1, x_2^0)$ and draws from this point the tangent to the graph of $G(x_1)$ with the minimum slope. The point of tangency defines $x_{1,opt}$ and the slope of the tangent is $-S_{max}$.

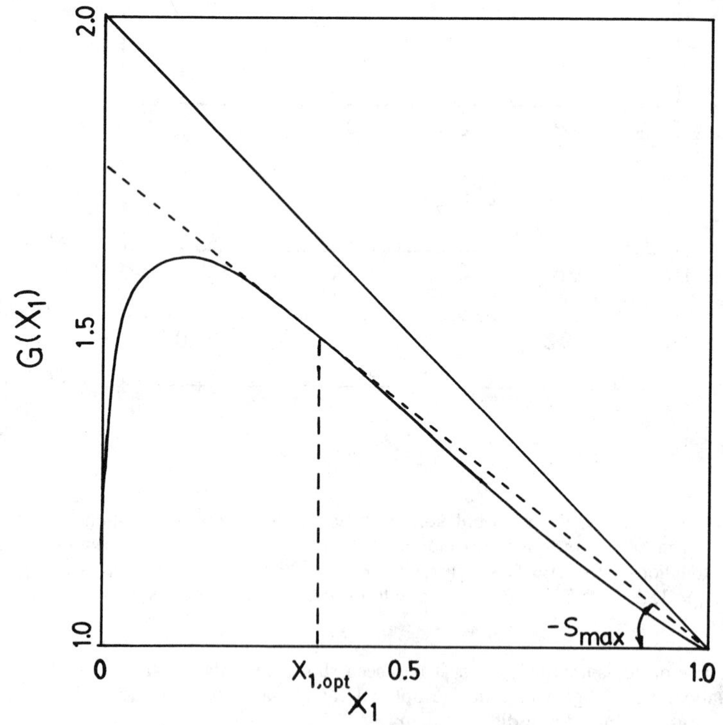

Figure 15. Graph of G (x_1) and geometric determination of $x_{1,opt}$ and S_{max} for the case of parallel reactions in a nonisothermal pellet: $\chi_1^*(x_1) = x_1^2$; $\chi_2^*(x_1) = x_1$; $\lambda = 1$; $x_2^0 = 1$; $\beta_1 = 0.2$; $\beta_2 = 0.4$; $\gamma_1 = 20$; $\gamma_2 = 4$. (Reprinted with permission from Ref. [43].)

Figure 16 shows the dependence of z_{opt} and S_{max} on the ratio of kinetic constants λ for the case of linear and second order parallel exothermic reactions. The same figure compares S_{max} with the global selectivity obtained with uniform (S_{un}) and external shell (S^0) catalyst distributions.

Consecutive Reactions

The problem of finding the optimal catalyst distribution for selectivity maximization in consecutive reaction systems has been solved recently for isothermal pellets under the restriction of positive order kinetics of the undesirable reaction [39]. Considering the consecutive reactions

$$A - f_1 \rightarrow B - f_2 \rightarrow C$$

with arbitrary kinetics $f_1(C_1)$ for the first reaction and positive order kinetics $f_2(C_2)[f'_2(C_2) > 0]$ for the undesirable reaction, one can write the dimensionless mass balance equations for A and B in the form

$$(1/z^n)\, d/dz[z^n\, dx_1/dz] = (n+1)\phi_1^2\chi_1(x_1)u(z) \tag{72}$$

$$(1/z^n)\, d/dz[z^n\, dx_2/dz] = (n+1)[\phi_2^2\chi_2(x_2) - \xi\phi_1^2\chi_1(x_1)]u(z) \tag{73}$$

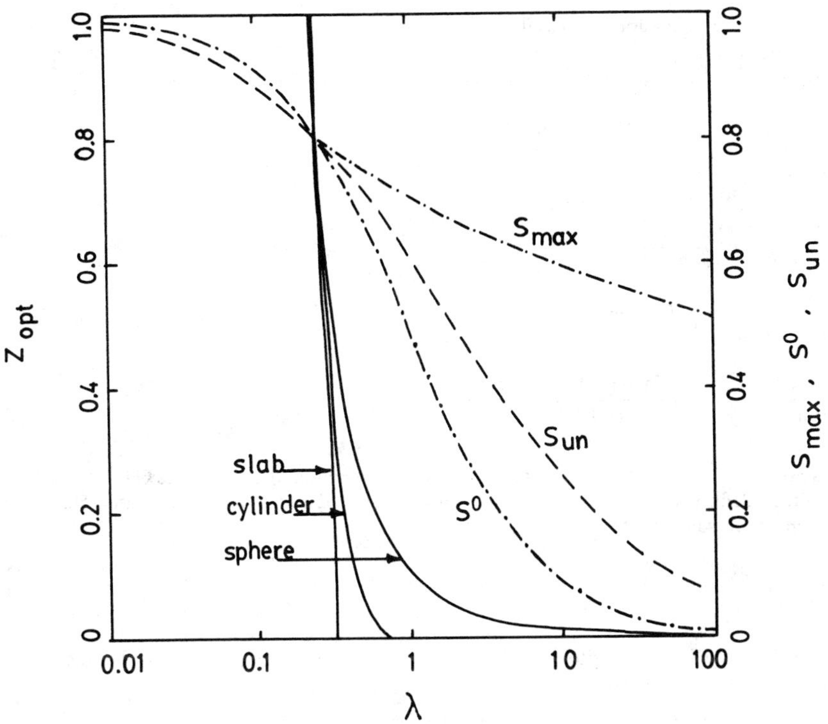

Figure 16. Effect of the ratio λ of the kinetic constants evaluated at surface conditions on the optimal catalyst location (solid lines) and global selectivity (dashed lines) for the optimal (S_{max}), uniform (S_{un}) and external shell distribution (S^0). Parallel reactions: $\chi_1^*(x_1) = x_1^2$; $\chi_2^*(x_1) = x_1$; $\phi_1 = 1$; $\beta_1 = 0.1$; $\beta_2 = -0.7$; $\gamma_1 = 5$; $\gamma_2 = 25$. (Reprinted with permission from Ref. [43].)

with boundary conditions,

$$\text{At } z = 0,\ dx_1/dz = dx_2/dz = 0; \qquad \text{At } z = 1,\ x_1 = 1,\ x_2 = x_2^0 \tag{74}$$

The global selectivity, S, is the ratio of the rate of net production of B divided by the rate of consumption of A and can be written as

$$S = 1 - (\lambda/\xi)\frac{\int_0^1 \chi_2(x_2)u(z)z^n\,dz}{\int_0^1 \chi_1(x_1)u(z)z^n\,dz}$$

$$= -(1/\xi)(dx_2/dx_1) \tag{75}$$

with $\lambda = \phi_2^2/\phi_1^2 = \xi f_2(C_1^0)/f_1(C_1^0)$ (76)

It has been shown [39] that the optimal catalyst distribution function u(z) is again an appropriately chosen Dirac δ-function of the type

$$u(z) = \delta(z - z_{opt})/(n + 1)z^n \tag{77}$$

with

$$z_{opt} = 1 - \Omega \qquad \text{for } n = 0 \text{ (slab)} \tag{78a}$$

$$z_{opt} = \exp(-\Omega) \qquad \text{for } n = 1 \text{ (cylinder)} \tag{78b}$$

$$z_{opt} = 1/(1 + \Omega) \qquad \text{for } n = 2 \text{ (sphere)} \tag{78c}$$

where

$$\Omega = \frac{1 - x_{1,opt}}{\phi_1^2\chi_1(x_{1,opt})} \tag{79}$$

To define $x_{1,opt}$ in Equation 79 and consequently the optimal catalyst location, z_{opt}, a function $G(x_1)$ is defined by:

$$\frac{G(x_1) - x_2^0}{1 - x_1} = \xi - \frac{\lambda\chi_2(G(x_1))}{\chi_1(x_1)} \tag{80}$$

Since $\phi_2' > 0$ one can easily show that $G(x_1)$ is a true function. It also satisfies $G(0) = 0$, $G(1) = x_2^0$. One then defines $x_{1,opt}$ the value of x_1 which maximizes the two sides of Equation 80. The corresponding maximum selectivity, S_{max}, is then given by:

$$S_{max} = \frac{G(x_{1,opt}) - x_2^0}{1 - x_{1,opt}} \tag{81}$$

For the special case of positive order kinetics ($\phi_1' > 0$) it has been proven [39] that the following four propositions are valid:

1. For positive order kinetics, $z_{opt} = 1$ and $S_{max} = S^0 = 1 - \lambda\chi_2(x_2^0)/\xi$, provided that $S^0 \geq 0$, i.e., provided that the selectivity in the absence of diffusional limitations is nonnegative.
2. For positive order power law kinetics with $0 > S^0 > -x_2^0/\xi$, $z_{opt} = 1$ and $S_{max} = 1 - \lambda\chi_2(x_2^0)/\xi$, provided that the order of the first reaction is higher than or equal to the order of the undesirable reaction.

3. For positive order power law kinetics with $S^0 < -x_2^0/\xi$, $z_{opt} = 0$ and $S_{max} = -x_2^0/\xi$, provided that the order of the first reaction is higher than or equal to the order of the undesirable reaction.
4. For linear kinetics, $z_{opt} = 1$ and $S_{max} = 1 - \lambda x_2^0/\xi$ for $\xi - (\lambda - 1)x_2^0 \geq 0$, while for $\xi - (\lambda - 1)x_2^0 \leq 0$, $z_{opt} = 0$ and $S_{max} = -x_2^0/\xi$. In the special case of $\xi - (\lambda - 1)x_2^0 = 0$, all Dirac-type distributions give the same global selectivity $S_d = -x_2^0/\xi$.

The maximum global selectivity, S_{max}, can be dramatically higher than the global selectivity obtained with other catalyst distributions, such as uniform ($u(z) = 1$) or external shell distribution ($u(z) = \delta(z - 1)/(n + 1)$). This is illustrated in Figure 17 for the case of bimolecular Langmuir kinetics for the desirable reaction and linear kinetics for the undesirable one. The global pellet selectivity for uniform catalyst distribution S_{un} shown in Figure 17 corresponds to the slab geometry and was obtained by solving numerically the conservation equations (72 and 73) together with BCs (74) with $u(z) = 1$. Figure 17 compares the maximum global selectivity S_{max} with the uniform distribution global selectivity S_{un} and with the global selectivity for the external shell distribution S^0

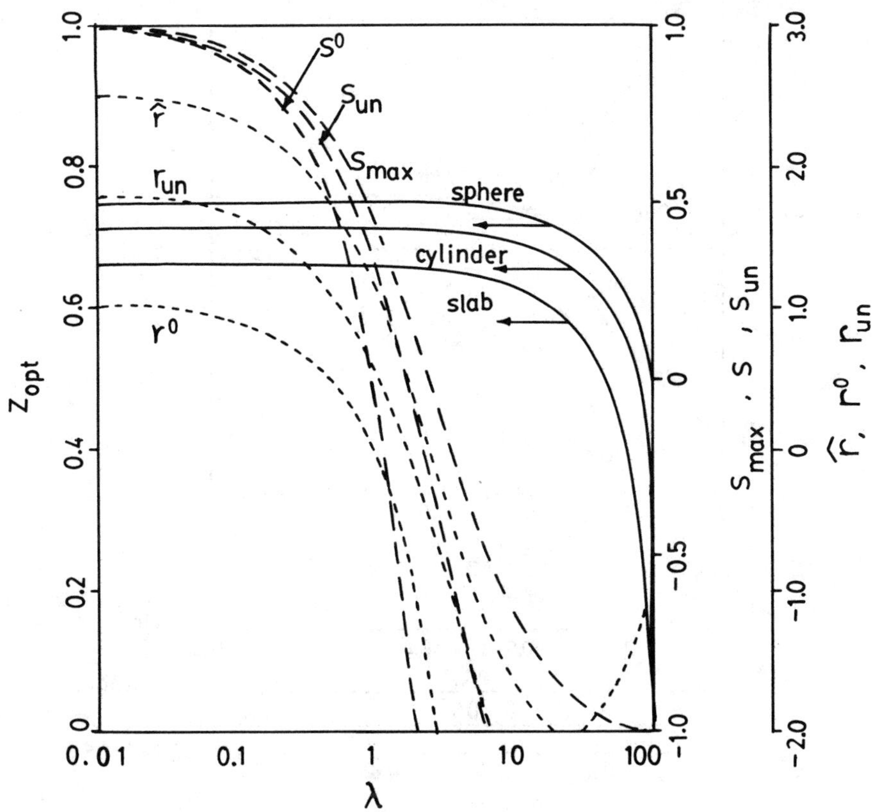

Figure 17. Effect of the ratio λ of kinetic constants on the optimal catalyst location (solid lines), global selectivity (dashed lines) and dimensionless rate of production of B (dotted lines) for the optimal distribution (S_{max}, $\hat{r}$), uniform distribution for slab geometry (S_{un}, r_{un}) and external shell distribution (S^0, r^0). Consecutive reactions: $\chi_1(x_1) = (1 + \sigma)^2 x_1/(1 + \sigma x_1)^2$; $\chi_2(x_2) = x_2$; $\sigma = 8$; $\phi_1 = 1$; $\xi = 1$; $x_2^0 = 1$. (Reprinted with permission from Ref. [39].)

as functions of the ratio of kinetic constants λ of the undesirable and desirable reactions. When λ is reasonably large, i.e., when the undesirable reaction is relatively fast, then the differences between S_{max}, S_{un} and S^0 become very important. Thus for $\lambda = 0.9$ one obtains $S_{max} = 48.7\%$, $S_{un} = 36.7\%$ and $S^0 = 8.8\%$, while for $\lambda = 1.9$, $S_{max} = 14.9\%$, $S_{un} = -6.2\%$ and $S^0 = -90.5\%$. The latter means that under these conditions a uniform or external shell catalyst distribution would lead to a net *consumption* of the desired product B while the optimum catalyst distribution leads to a net *production* of B. Physically this is because the optimum catalyst distribution exposes the catalyst to reactant concentrations which maximize the ratio of the rates of the desired and undesired reactions.

As shown in Figure 17 the difference between S_{max}, S_{un}, and S^0 increase with increasing λ. For the parameter values shown in this figure, S_{un} always exceeds S^0, but this is obviously not a general conclusion. An important advantageous feature of the optimal catalyst distribution is that it not

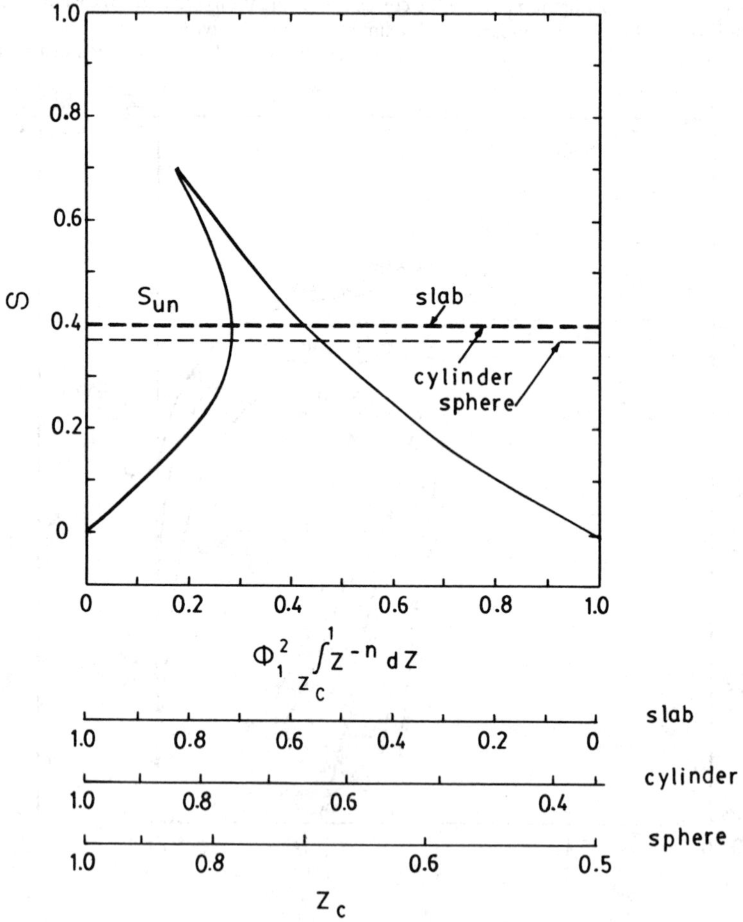

Figure 18. Dependence of the global selectivity for a Dirac-type distribution on the catalyst location z_c. The horizontal lines correspond to uniform catalyst distribution global selectivity. Consecutive reactions: $\chi_1(x_1) = (1 + \sigma)^2 x_1/(1 + \sigma x_1)^2$; $\chi_2(x_2) = x_2$; $\sigma = 20$; $\phi_1 = 1$; $\phi_2 = 1$, $\xi = 1$; $x_2^0 = 1$. (Reprinted with permission from Ref. [39].)

only maximizes the global pellet selectivity, but also gives high rates of production of the desired product. This is also shown in Figure 17 where the dimensionless rate of production r of the desired product B is plotted versus λ for the optimum (r), uniform (r_{un}) and external shell (r^0) catalyst distributions. It can be seen that r is consistently higher than r_{un} and r^0 for all λ values. This is again because the optimum catalyst distribution exposes the catalyst to reactant concentrations which give high values for the net rate of production of B. However, it should be noted that the optimum catalyst distribution for selectivity maximization does not strictly maximize the dimensionless rate of production r of the desired product.

The optimum catalyst location z_{opt} is also depicted in Figure 17 as a function of λ for the slab, cylinder and sphere geometries. For λ values below 10 the optimum catalyst location is rather insensitive to changes in λ, but for λ approaching 100 the optimum catalyst location moves rapidly towards the center of the pellet. For such high λ values there is inevitably a net consumption of the desired product, thus the optimum policy is to place the catalyst near the pellet center in order to limit the rate of the very fast undesirable reaction.

Figure 18 shows the influence of catalyst location z_c on the global selectivity S for the same type of kinetics used in Figure 17 and compares S with S_{un}. It can be seen that for all three pellet geometries there exist reasonably wide ranges of catalyst location z_c for which S exceeds substantially the uniform catalyst distribution selectivity S_{un}. The left part of these regions however, near z_{opt}, are characterized by steady state multiplicities. Of the three steady states which exist in this region the intermediate one is unstable. Which of the other two steady states prevails depends obviously on the previous history of the pellet. It is therefore clear that the optimum catalyst distribution may generally correspond to other, undesirable, steady states as well. From a practical viewpoint Figure 18 shows that the exact catalyst loaction or the width of the catalyst zone may not be very crucial, but that reactor start-up can be important in order to obtain a desired high selectivity steady state.

EFFECTS OF POISONING

Issues discussed in previous sections apply in cases in which catalysts do not experience any deactivation. In practice, however, catalysts often lose part of their activity with time on stream as a result of their participation in the catalytic process. The most common form of deactivation is poisoning. The susceptibility of catalyst particles to poisoning adds a new dimension to the issue of nonuniform activity distributions since, in addition to effectiveness and selectivity, poisoning characteristics must be considered. Alternatively, effectiveness and possibly selectivity become functions of time on stream and the effects of nonuniform distributions on these parameters must be integrated over the active life of the catalyst.

Under conditions of first-order reaction and shell progressive poisoning, Varghese and Wolf [30] showed that diluting catalytic activity and producing less severe activity profiles is beneficial in terms of activity. Becker and Wei [25] reached to essentially the same conclusion examining CO oxidation under shell progressive poisoning and showed that the "egg yolk" catalyst is more effective in all ranges of ϕ, the middle layered catalyst in somewhat effective while the "egg shell" catalyst is barely functional. Nevertheless, if poisoning occurs in a uniform manner, all types of catalysts exhibit the same poisoning characteristics and the form of the activity profile is immaterial. Their main conclusions are summarized on Figure 19.

The effect of poisoning on the consecutive reaction scheme were investigated by Shadman-Yazdi and Petersen [5] and Corbett and Luss [19]. The former considered the case of self-deactivation and the latter examined independent poisoning in addition to the self-fouling case. In the case of poisoning due to chemical impurities in the feedstock, the rate expression for the accumulation of poison is given by [19]

$$dp/dt = -k_p p^n(z, t) \tag{82}$$

where p represents the ratio of unpoisoned sites at any time. For the case of uniform poisoning, if $n < 1$, poisoning increases the relative nonuniformity of the activity distribution or the steepness

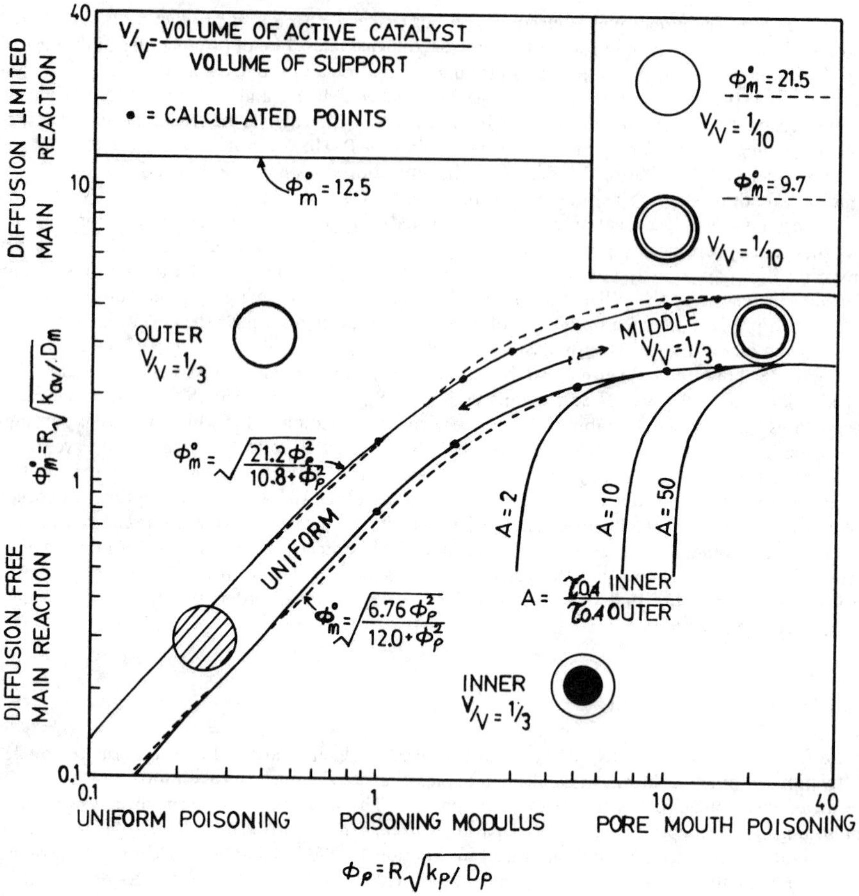

Figure 19. Catalyst selection chart for four catalyst designs based on a criterion of longest useful life. (Reprinted with permission from Ref. [25].)

of the activity profile, while the opposite occurs if $n > 1$, and the uniformity of the catalyst is not affected if $n = 1$ [19].

The analysis of shell progressive poisoning is considerably more complicated since it results in nonuniform deactivation. Under low diffusional resistances, a catalyst with active material distributed near its periphery (egg shell) exhibits highest selectivity but incurs very rapid decrease in activity. On the other hand, under large diffusional resistances, sites near the periphery of the catalyst are more active than those distributed in the interior. Thus, selectivity and effectiveness are higher at all times.

A rigorous approach to the problem of determining the optimal activity profile for the case of linear kinetics and uniform poisoning was followed by DeLancey [44]. He chose the following objective function, E:

$$E = \begin{bmatrix} \text{average reaction rate} \\ \text{over operating time} \end{bmatrix} - q \begin{bmatrix} \text{quantity of} \\ \text{active catalyst} \end{bmatrix} \tag{83}$$

where q is an adjustable parameter. He used Pontryagin's continuous maximum principle to show that the optimal catalyst distribution profile corresponds to uniform activity to a depth d from the surface, followed by a totally inert core. The optimal impregnation depth was found to be

$$d = (1/\phi_\theta) \cosh^{-1}(1/q_\theta)^{1/2} \tag{84}$$

with

$$q_\theta = q(\theta/\tau_p)/(1 - e^{-\theta/\tau_p}) \tag{85}$$

$$\phi_\theta = \phi\{(\theta/\tau_p)/(1 - e^{-\theta/\tau_p})\}^{1/2} \tag{86}$$

where θ is the total operating time and τ_p the poisoning time constant.

For the case of shell progressive poisoning, the situation is qualitatively different and the optimal catalyst distribution profile problem has been solved rigorously for small values of ϕ only [45]. Considering linear kinetics in isothermal flat, cylindrical or spherical pellets and invoking the quasi-steady-state hypothesis the dimensionless steady state mass balance of the reactant can be written as

$$(1/z^n)\, d/dz(z^n\, dx/dz) = (n + 1)\phi^2 x u(x) \tag{87}$$

with boundary conditions

$$\text{At } z = 0,\ dx/dz = 0 \tag{88}$$

$$(1 - x_p)/(1 - z_p) \qquad \text{for } n = 0 \tag{88a}$$

$$\text{At } z = z_p,\ dx/dz = (x_p - 1)/z_p \ln z_p \qquad \text{for } n = 1 \tag{88b}$$

$$(1 - x_p)/z_p(1 - z_p) \qquad \text{for } n = 2 \tag{88c}$$

where z_p is the location of the deactivation front and x_p is the reactant concentration at this point. The position of the deactivation front changes with time and thus the solution of Equation 87 with BCs of Equations 88 yields the concentration profile in the pellet at a given time instant. Hence, x in the pellet depends both on z and on z_p. The effectiveness factor of the pellet, defined as the global reaction rate divided by the global rate obtainable with a fresh catalyst for $\phi = 0$, is then given by:

$$\eta(z_p) = (n + 1) \int_0^{z_p} \chi(z, z_p) u(z) z^n\, dz \tag{89}$$

Bacaros et al. [45] assumed a linear relationship between z_p and time, i.e.

$$1 - z_p = \tau = t/t_0 \tag{90}$$

where t_0 is the time for complete deactivation, and chose as the objective function the total dimensionless reactant conversion until complete deactivation, H:

$$H = \int_0^1 \eta(\tau)\, d\tau = (n + 1) \int_0^1 \int_0^{z_p} \chi(z, z_p) u(z) z^n\, dz\, dz_p \tag{91}$$

It was found that when ϕ is less than 0.5, strictly when $\phi \to 0$, then the optimal catalyst distribution is a Dirac delta function of the type

$$u(z) = \delta(z - z_c)/(n + 1)z^n \tag{92}$$

Table 4
Catalyst Location and Reactant Conversion Corresponding to the Optimal Dirac Delta Function Type Distribution [45]

n	z_c	H
0	0	$1/(1 + \Phi^2)$
1	root of $\Phi^2 z_c \ln z_c - (\Phi^2 + 1)z_c + \Phi^2 = 0$	$\frac{1 - z_c}{1 + \Phi^2 \ln z_c}$
2	$\frac{\Phi}{(1 + \Phi)}$	$\frac{1}{(1 + \Phi)^2}$

where z_c and the corresponding H values are given in Table 4. However, as shown in Figure 20. for $\phi > 1$ a Dirac type distribution is not optimal and the uniform catalyst distribution appears not to be significantly inferior to any other activity distribution [45].

In summary, while for unpoisoned pellets no case is known where the optimal catalyst distribution is not a Dirac type distribution, this conclusion does not generally hold for poisoned pellets either in the case of uniform or in the case of shell progressive poisoning.

REACTOR PERFORMANCE CONSIDERATIONS

Relatively little work has been done on the subject of design or analysis of heterogeneous reactors employing catalysts with nonuniform activity distributions. The main reason is that an analytical expression for the pellet effectiveness factor is a prerequisite for minimizing computer time. Thus, employment of complex distributions and reaction networks tends to complicate reactor models significantly. A step distribution, one in which the catalyst is impregnated with a constant concentration of active material from its surface to a specific depth, is one of the few profiles yielding a manageable expression for η.

Certain approximations, however, can be applied to make the mathematical analysis of the reactor model more tractable. Aris [46] showed that the effectiveness factor for a spherical pellet in which the active material has been deposited in the outer periphery may be approximated by the infinite plate formula,

$$\eta = \tanh \phi/\phi \tag{93}$$

It was also shown [47] that effectiveness factors for other particle shapes may be expressed in this manner. For an n-th order reactor, ϕ can be obtained from the expression developed by Petersen [47]:

$$\phi = (n + 1/2)(V_i/S_x)(k/D_e) \tag{94}$$

where V_i is the volume of the catalyst particle that is impregnated and k is the rate constant in the same region. If the active profile in any particular geometry is equated to an equivalent profile in rectangular geometry by requiring equivalence of their volume-averaged rate constants, η can be obtained. Using such transformations, Smith [48] studied the effects of nonuniform activity distributions on yield of intermediate in the first-order consecutive reaction scheme.

Smith and Carberry [49, 50] analyzed the performance of nonisothermal, nonadiabatic fixed-bed reactors employing nonuniformly activated catalysts for the production of phthalic anhydride from naphthalene, and also studied the effects of varying the fraction of pellet radius that was catalytically active and the total amount of catalytic activity of the pellet. It was shown that partial impregnation

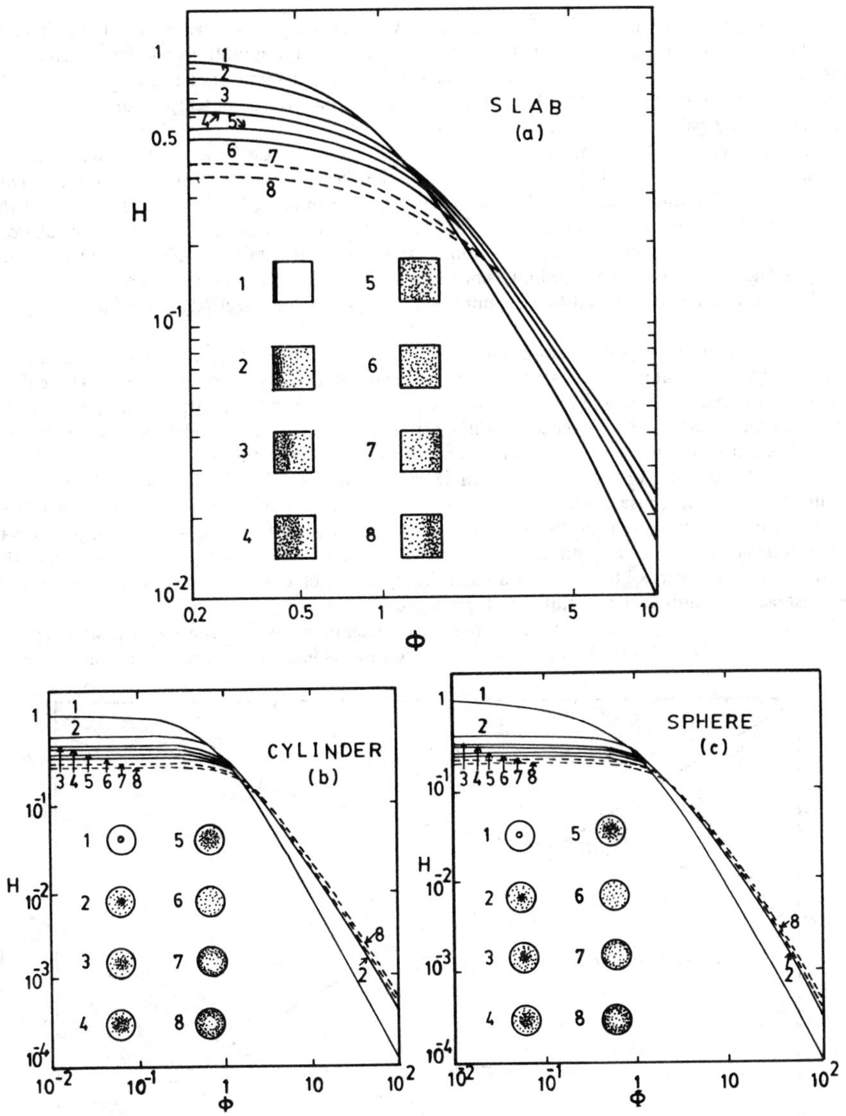

Figure 20. Shell progressive poisoning: Dependence of total dimensionless conversion H on Thiele modulus ϕ for various activity distributions. Numbers denote: (1)—Optimal for $\phi \rightarrow 0$ (Table 4) Dirac distribution; (2, 3, 4, 5)—$u_2(z) = A_{2n}/(z + \alpha_2)^2$ with $\alpha_2 = 0.1$ (2), 0.5 (3), 0.9 (4), 3.0 (5); (6)—uniform distribution; (7, 8)—$u_1(z) = A_{1n}z^{\alpha_1}$ with $\alpha_1 = 0.5$ (7), 0.9 (8). A_{1n}, A_{2n} are geometry dependent normalizing constants. (Reprinted with permission from Ref. [45].)

results in improved yields of phthalic anhydride. A catalytically active pellet core is detrimental to yield because it is inaccessible to naphtahalene due to diffusion limitations and fast reaction, but it is accessible to phthalic anhydride due to the slower rate of its conversion to maleic anhydride. Since the activation energies of both reactions are approximately equal, temperature gradients inside the catalyst pellets do not affect yield.

Cukierman et al. [51] extended their pellet model of the van deVusse reaction over catalysts with nonuniform activity distributions and obtained the effects of system parameters on the activity distribution which offers optimum integral reactor yield. Similarly, Verykios et al. [52] used the ethylene oxidation model developed earlier [34] to analyze the performance of nonisothermal, nonadiabatic fixed-bed reactors employing nonuniformly activated catalysts. They showed that such catalysts offer improved reactor stability since runaway conditions developing with uniformly activated catalysts are avoided, and there is improved overall reactor selectivity and yield of ethylene oxide.

Morbidelli et al. [53] performed an analysis of isothermal, fixed-bed reactors in the plug flow regime in which the catalyst pellets were assumed to have an activity distribution of the Dirac delta function form. All pellets in the reactor were considered to have the catalytic activity placed at the same position z. Later work by the same authors [54] resulted in the optimization of z for the case in which z is a function of reactor position, and for the case where z is assumed constant over the reactor length. Because of the particular activity distribution employed, analytical solutions were obtained for the bulk phase reactant concentration as a function of distance. It was shown that three steady-state solutions can occur, two of which are stable. The reactor steady-state multiplicity was found to be solely due to that induced by the performance of the catalyst pellet. In particular, the steady-state multiplicity of the pellet located at the reactor inlet. Criteria were developed to predict the existence of multiple steady states and ignition conditions.

An example of the rigorously optimized reactor is given in Figure 21 where z_c is plotted against reactor length. It was observed that z_c is dependent on the Thiele modulus while the concentration

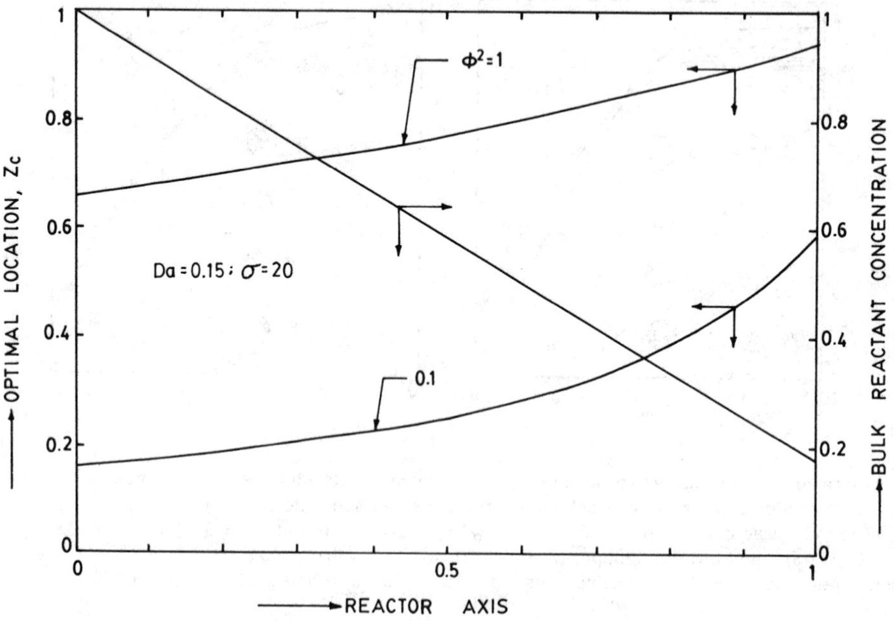

Figure 21. Position of activity, z_c, versus reactor length for a rigorously optimized reactor. (Reprinted with permission from Ref. [53].)

profile in the reactor is not. The optimal reactor performance, on the other hand, depends solely on the Damkohler number (Da) and the dimensionless adsorption constant, σ.

IMPREGNATION MODELS AND EXPERIMENTAL STUDIES

Many theoretical studies of the effects of nonuniform activity distributions on effectiveness, selectivity, yield, and poison resistance of the catalysts have appeared in the literature, as discussed in the previous sections. However, very few investigators have attempted to verify their models experimentally. Such attempts would require fundamental studies involving preparation of catalysts with desired activity distributions, determination of the activity profile, detailed characterization of the catalyst, and performance evaluations in studies with probe reactions and properly designed reactors. One can appreciate the difficulties encountered in such studies.

The process of impregnation of support materials with solutions containing a precursor of the active ingredient has been modeled by various investigators [41, 55, 56]. Harriott [55] solved numerically the transient diffusion equations to predict the distribution of active ingredient inside the support. He also verified his model experimentally by impregnating α-alumina pellets with silver nitrate. The distribution of silver inside the support, after reduction, was determined using autoradiography. The resulting activity distributions agreed well with model predictions in cases in which the solute in the impregnating solution was strongly adsorbed on the surface of the support. The process of transport and deposition of material during impregnation of a porous solid was idealized by Vincent and Merrill [56] to that of a single cylindrical pore. Plug flow and constant pressure drop in the pore was assumed. Both cases, mass transfer across the liquid-solid interface and adsorption kinetics controlling, were examined and shown to yield similar impregnation profiles in systems in which saturation occurs.

A mathematical model for a competitive multicomponent adsorption process was developed by Hegedus et al. [41]. Such a model can describe simultaneous impregnation by two or more active components or when site-blocking agents are used to manipulate intrapellet distribution of the active ingredient. Impregnation of Al_2O_3 with Rh in the presence of HF was used to compare model predictions with experimental results. Figure 22 shows computed Rh profiles at impregnation times of 5 and 10 min. The predicted peak locations are in reasonable agreement with those obtained experimentally using ion microprobe mass analysis. Good agreement between model predictions and experimental results was also observed in the amount of Rh taken up by the pellets. The authors also showed that the Rh peak can be flexibly positioned at desired locations within the pellet by an appropriate choice of initial HF concentration.

Preparation of catalysts with nonuniform distribution of the active ingredient has mostly been empirically investigated. Becker and Nutal [57] showed that site-blocking agents can be used to achieve impregnated sections near the outer surface of the pellet, below the outer surface, or in a core at its center. Chen and Anderson [58] revealed various impregnation techniques leading to nonuniform profiles of Cr in Al_2O_3 spheres while Shyr and Ernst [42] investigated the possibility of using chemical additives in impregnating solutions as a means of controlling the distribution of Pt within Al_2O_3 particles. The latter authors examined a large number of acids and salts as coingredients with H_2PtCl_6 and obtained the profiles shown in Figure 23. Similarly, preparation methods resulting in catalysts with nonuniform distribution of activity were investigated by Becker and Nuttall [57] for Pt/Al_2O_3. Alumina was impregnated with H_2PtCl_6 in the presence of citric acid, resulting in subsurface layers of Pt of controlled depth and width as thin as 50 μm. The critical variables were found to be impregnation time, severity of reduction and immobilization, and drying sequence. Thus, the Pt band was found to be deposited deeper toward the center of the pellet with increasing citric acid concentration while the severity of nonuniformity was found to decrease with increasing impregnation time. The distribution of Pt within the support was determined by the use of a scanning electron microprobe.

The effects of nonuniform activity distribution on effectiveness and poison resistance characteristics of noble metal/Al_2O_3 automobile exhaust catalysts were experimentally investigated by Hegedus and co-workers [27–29]. In cases in which poisons, such as lead and phosphorus, react with both the active component and the support, the impregnation depth was shown to affect the poison characteristics of the catalyst significantly. When bimetallic Pt and Pd catalysts were used,

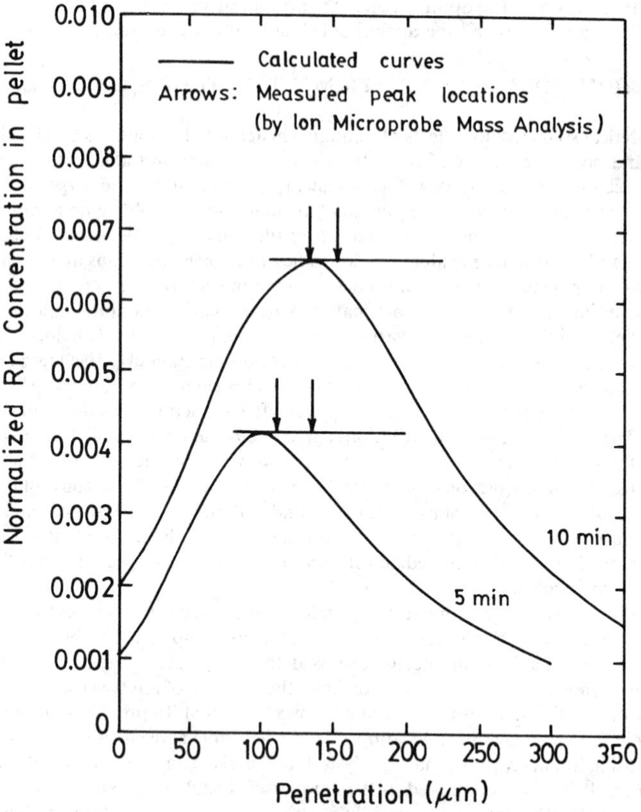

Figure 22. Rh distribution in the catalyst pellets in an experiment with HF + Rh: comparison of theory with measurements. (Reprinted with permission from Ref. [41].)

the relative location of each of the metals inside the support was found to influence performance characteristics significantly. Thus, a catalyst consisting of a Pt exterior band followed by a Pd interior band showed higher initial hydrocarbon and CO oxidation activity as well as superior Pb and P poison resistance. When rhodium was also included in the catalyst for nitrogen oxide emission control, a pellet configuration consisting of an external shell of Pt followed by Rh and Pd rings was found to exhibit improved poison resistance characteristics.

The influence of nonuniform activity distribution on selectivity has been studied experimentally by Kotter and Riekert [59, 60] for the case of propene partial oxidation to acrolein. They prepared three pellets having the same amount of CuO catalyst but different catalyst concentration profiles: uniform, outer shell and inner core. A cross-section of these catalysts, showing the distribution of the active ingredient is shown on Figure 24. The authors found that selectivity to acrolein obtained with uniformly active pellets is higher than the value obtained with the inner core distribution but lower than that obtained with the external shell distribution, in good agreement with theoretical predictions for parallel-consecutive reaction networks.

In a recent study Kunimori et al. [61] compared experimentally the performance of "egg-white" and "egg-shell" type Pt/Al_2O_3 catalysts used for CO oxidation. They found that the "egg-white" type catalyst was more active in agreement with theory and with the catalytic converter practice.

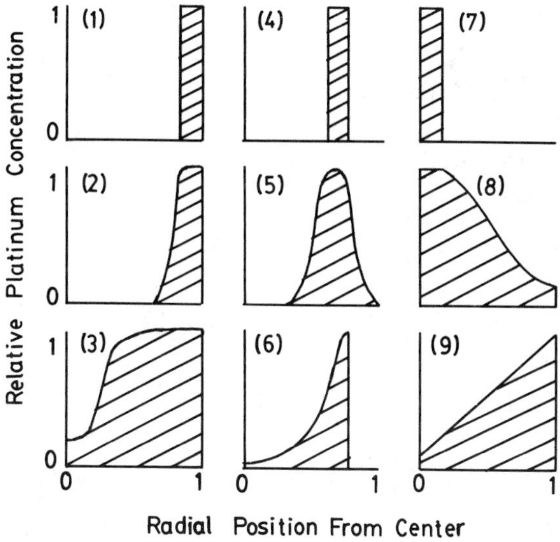

Figure 23. Types of Pt profiles obtained in co-impregnation experiments. (Reprinted with permission from Ref. [42].)

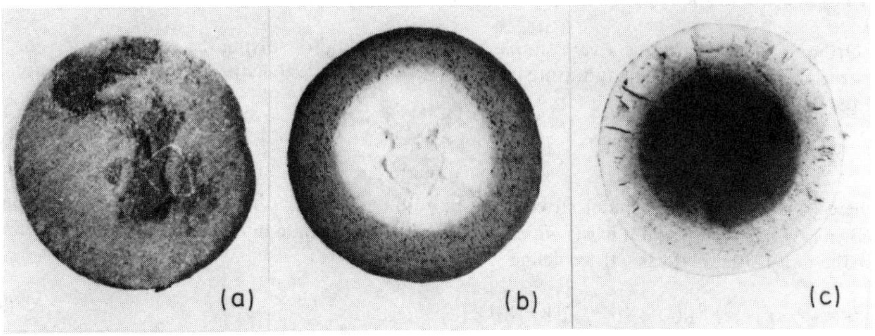

Figure 24. Photographs of cross sections of $CuO/\alpha{-}Al_2O_3$ pellets with (a) uniform, (b) external shell, and (c) inner core CuO catalyst distribution. (Reprinted with permission from Ref. [59].)

It is obvious that considerably more experimental work is required in order to verify the beneficial effects of nonuniformly activated catalysts that have been theoretically predicted.

APPENDIX—NUMERICAL SOLUTION TECHNIQUES

In this section, general methods are presented to solve the isothermal and non-isothermal balance equations. To illustrate each solution method, where necessary, the first order consecutive reaction scheme $A \rightarrow B \rightarrow C$ is used in spherical geometry. Reiterating the isothermal and non-isothermal balance equations,

Isothermal
$$\frac{1}{z^2}\frac{d}{dz}\left(z^2\frac{dx_1}{dz}\right) - \phi_1^2 u x_1 = 0 \tag{95a}$$

$$\frac{1}{z^2}\frac{d}{dz}\left(z^2\frac{dx_2}{dz}\right) - u(\phi_2^2 x_2 - \psi\phi_1^2 x_1) = 0 \tag{95b}$$

Non-Isothermal

$$\frac{1}{z^2}\frac{d}{dz}\left(z^2\frac{dx_1}{dz}\right) - \phi_1^2 u x_1 \exp(\gamma_1[1 - 1/\theta]) = 0 \tag{96a}$$

$$\frac{1}{z^2}\frac{d}{dz}\left(z^2\frac{dx_2}{dz}\right) - u[\phi_2^2 x_2 \exp(\gamma_2[1 - 1/\theta]) - \psi\phi_1^2 x_1 \exp(\gamma_1[1 - 1/\theta])] = 0 \tag{96b}$$

$$\frac{1}{z^2}\frac{d}{dz}\left(z^2\frac{d\phi}{dz}\right) + u[\beta_1\phi_1^2 x_1 \exp(\gamma_1[1 - 1/\theta]) + \beta_2\phi_2^2 x_2 \exp(\gamma_2[1 - 1/\theta])] = 0 \tag{96c}$$

where $\psi = D_{e_A}C_A^0/D_{e_B}C_A^0$

with the boundary conditions that the state variables equal unity at the pellet surface and their derivatives are zero at the pellet center.

Orthogonal Collocation

Orthogonal collocation is a very simple and quick method of solving the state equations of the system. In order to use the quandrature formulas, however, the activity profile must be a polynomial of the form:

$$u(z) = a_0 + a_1 z^2 + \cdots a_N z^{2N} \tag{97}$$

where N is the number of internal collocation points used. For this particular system, we have shown (37) that a univariant exists which can be used to eliminate one of the differential equations for the non-isothermal case. If we define

$$\theta = 1 + (\beta_1 + \psi\beta_2)(1 - x_1) + \beta_2(1 - x_2) \tag{98}$$

and the following variables for the isothermal and non-isothermal reactions,

$$f_1 = x_1 \quad \text{or} \quad x_1 \exp[\gamma_1(1 - 1/\theta(x_1, x_2))] \tag{99a}$$

$$f_2 = x_2 \quad \text{or} \quad x_2 \exp[\gamma_2(1 - 1/\theta(x_1, x_2))] \tag{99b}$$

the algebraic equations resulting from the method of orthogonal collocation may be generalized in the following form:

$$\sum_{j=1}^{N} B_{ij}x_{1j} + B_{N+1} - \phi_1^2 u_i f_{1_i} = 0 \tag{100a}$$

$$\sum_{j=1}^{N} B_{ij}x_{2j} + B_{N+1} - u_i\phi_2^2 f_{2_i} - \psi\phi_1^2 = 0 \tag{100b}$$

The 2N non-linear algebraic equations may then be solved using a conventional secant method. The effectiveness factor and selectivity may be found using the quadrature formulas:

$$\eta = \frac{3}{1+\bar{\alpha}}\left\{\sum_{i=1}^{N} W_i u_i [f_{1_i} - \bar{\alpha} f_{2_i}] + u_{N+1}\cdot(1+\bar{\alpha})\right\} \tag{101}$$

$$S^{-1} = \frac{3}{\eta(1+\bar{\alpha})}\left\{\sum_{i=1}^{N} W_i u_i f_{1_i} + u_{N+1}\right\} \tag{102}$$

It must be noted that since the integration of the state equations depends only on discrete values of u, Equations 100a and 100b hold for any activity distribution. But in order to employ the quadrature formulas, u must be of the form given by Equation 97, otherwise the results of Equations 101 and 102 are not valid.

Shooting Method

In either case, isothermal or nonisothermal, there are two second order differential equations to be solved. Expanding these into four first order differential equations,

$$\dot{x}_1 = x_3 \tag{103a}$$

$$\dot{x}_2 = x_4 \tag{103b}$$

$$\dot{x}_3 = -\frac{2}{z} x_3 + \phi_1^2 u f_1 \tag{103c}$$

$$\dot{x}_4 = -\frac{2}{z} x_4 + u(\phi_2^2 f_2 - \psi \phi_1^2 f_1) \tag{103d}$$

with the boundary conditions,

$$x_1(1) = x_2(1) = 1; \qquad x_3(0) = x_4(0) = 0 \tag{103e}$$

We choose either the surface of the catalyst or its center from which to start the integration. The choice is based upon the stability analysis of the system. The catalyst center as a starting point will be used to illustrate the method. The method objective is to choose values of $x_1(0)$ and $x_2(0)$ that will satisfy the boundary conditions at the pellet surface. The essence of the shooting method lies in the technique of employing a Newton-Raphson method to obtain the values of $x_1(0)$ and $x_2(0)$ quickly. We shoot or solve the differential equations for initial guesses for $x_1(0)$ and $x_2(0)$ as well as for each initial condition plus an incremental amount, δ, while holding the other conditions constant. The partial derivatives below may then be calculated and the Jacobian specified.

$$\frac{\partial x_i(1)}{\partial x_k(D)} = \frac{x_i(1)|_{x_k+\delta} - x_i(1)|_{x_k}}{\delta} \qquad i = 1, 2, k = 1, 2 \tag{104}$$

The values of $x_1(0)$ and $x_2(0)$ for the next iteration, j + 1, are given by:

$$\vec{x}^{j+1}(0) = \vec{x}^{j}(0) - J^{-1}\left[\frac{\vec{x}(1)}{\vec{x}(0)}\right]\vec{x}(1) \tag{105}$$

where $J\left[\frac{\vec{x}(1)}{\vec{x}(0)}\right]$ is the Jacobian.

Finite Differences—Isothermal Case

The first and second derivatives in the state equations may be expressed in finite difference forms:

$$\left.\frac{dx_k}{dz}\right|_{z_i} = \frac{x_{k_{i+1}} - x_i}{\Delta z}$$
$$\left.\frac{d^2x_k}{dz^2}\right|_{z_i} = \frac{x_{k_{i+1}} - 2x_{k_i} + x_{k_{i-1}}}{(\Delta z)^2} \tag{106}$$

The mass balance equations after substitution are given by:

$$\left[\frac{z_i + 2\,\Delta z}{z_i(\Delta z)^2}\right] x_{1_{i+1}} + \left[\frac{-2(z_i + \Delta z)}{z_i(\Delta z)^2} - \Phi_1^2 u_i\right] x_{1_i} + \frac{1}{(\Delta z)^2} x_{1_{i-1}} = 0 \tag{107a}$$

$$\left[\frac{z_i + 2\,\Delta z}{z_i(\Delta z)^2}\right] x_{2_{i+1}} + \left[\frac{-2(z_i + \Delta z)}{z_i(\Delta z)^2} - \Phi_2^2 u_i\right] x_{2_i} + \frac{1}{(\Delta z)^2} x_{2_{i-1}} + \psi\Phi_1^2 u_i x_{1_i} = 0 \tag{107b}$$

which may be written as:

$$a_{2_i} x_{1_{i+1}} + a_{1_i} x_{1_i} + c x_{1_{i-1}} = 0 \tag{108a}$$

$$a_{5_i} x_{2_{i+1}} + a_{4_i} x_{2_i} + c x_{2_{i-1}} + a_{3_i} x_{1_i} = 0 \tag{108b}$$

The boundary conditions must also be incorporated into this scheme.

At $i = 2$, $x_{1_1} = x_{2_1} = 1$

$$a_{2_2} x_{1_3} + a_{1_2} x_{1_2} = -c \tag{108c}$$

$$a_{5_2} x_{2_3} + a_{4_2} x_{2_2} + a_{3_2} x_{1_2} = -c \tag{108d}$$

At $i = n$, $x_{i_n} = x_{i_{n+1}}$

$$(a_{2_n} + a_{1_n}) x_{1_n} + c x_{1_{n-1}} = 0 \tag{108e}$$

$$(a_{5_n} + a_{4_n}) x_{2_n} + c x_{2_{n-1}} + a_{3_n} x_{1_n} = 0 \tag{108f}$$

The system of equations may then be written in matrix form and solved by traditional methods. The dimension of the matrix is $(n - 1) \times (n - 1)$:

$$\begin{bmatrix}
a_{12} & 0 & a_{22} & 0 & & & & & & & \\
a_{32} & a_{42} & 0 & a_{52} & & & & & & & \\
c & 0 & a_{13} & 0 & a_{23} & 0 & & & & & \\
0 & c & a_{33} & a_{43} & 0 & a_{53} & & & & & \\
 & c & 0 & a_{14} & 0 & a_{24} & 0 & & & & \\
 & 0 & c & a_{34} & a_{44} & 0 & a_{54} & & & & \\
 & & & & & & & \ddots & & & \\
 & & & & & & & c & 0 & a_{1n} + a_{2n} & 0 \\
 & & & & & & & 0 & c & 0 & a_{4n} + a_{5n}
\end{bmatrix}
\begin{bmatrix} x_{12} \\ x_{22} \\ x_{13} \\ x_{23} \\ x_{14} \\ x_{24} \\ \vdots \\ x_{1n} \\ x_{2n} \end{bmatrix}
\begin{bmatrix} -c \\ -c \\ 0 \\ 0 \\ 0 \\ 0 \\ \vdots \\ 0 \\ 0 \end{bmatrix}$$

Quasilinearization—Non-Isothermal Case

If the system rate expression is non-linear or the pellet is not isothermal, an iterative approach using finite differences can be used. Initially, a trial solution $x_1^1(z)$, $x_2^1(z)$ is chosen to form a basis for the first iteration. The non-linearities in the rate expression are then represented in a truncated Taylor series expansion based on the j − 1 iteration.

$$f(x_1^j, x_2^j) \cong f(x_1^{j-1}, x_2^{j-1}) + \left.\frac{\partial f}{\partial x_1}\right|_{x_1^{j-1}} (x_1^j - x_1^{j-1}) + \left.\frac{\partial f}{\partial x_2}\right|_{x_2^{j-1}} (x_2^j - x_2^{j-1}) \tag{109}$$

The linearized form of the state equations may be expressed in terms of finite differences, placed in the form $Ax = b$, and solved by the method explained in the previous section. The new solution then forms the basis for the next iteration. To help stability, the previous two iterations are usually averaged so that

$$x^j = \frac{1}{2}(x^{j-1} + x^{j-2}) \tag{110}$$

The effectiveness factor and selectivity are easily found by standard quadrature methods.

NOTATION

A	surface area
A_{ln}, A_{zn}	normalizing activity distribution parameters
Bi	standard Biot number, K_mL/D_e
Bi_{int}	internal Biot number, defined by Equation 16
Bi_m	modified Biot number, defined by Equation 15
Bi_{th}	thermal Biot number, hL/K_e
C	concentration
C^0	surface or bulk concentration
D_e	effective diffusivity
Da	Damkohler number, $KL(1-\epsilon)/[V(1+\sigma)^2]$
E	activation energy
$F(x), F_1(x)$	dimensionless rate expressions defined by Equations 46 and 54, respectively
$f(C, T)$	dimensional rate expression
$G(x)$	Function characteristic of Dirac type catalyst distribution defined by Equations 70 and 80 for parallel and consecutive reactions, respectively
$g(y)$	dimensional active catalyst distribution
g_0	volume averaged active catalyst density
K	adsorption equilibrium constant
k	reaction rate constant
k^*	volume-averaged rate constant
L	slab half-width or reactor length
$L[\ ]$	operator defined by Equation 36
n	geometric order ($n = 0$ slab, $n = 1$ cylinder, $n = 2$ sphere)
P	ratio of unpoisoned sites
p	order of a reaction for power law kinetics
R	pellet radius
r	dimensionless reaction rate, $(du/dz)_1$
$\hat{r}$	dimensionless reaction rate obtained with the optimal catalyst distribution
r^0	dimensionless reaction rate obtained with external shell catalyst distribution
r_p	global dimensional reaction rate
r_{un}	uniform distribution dimensionless reaction rate
S	global selectivity
T	temperature
T^0	surface or bulk temperature
$u(z)$	dimensionless activity distribution function
V_i	volume of impregnated portion of pellet
V_p	volume of pellet
x	dimensionless concentration, C/C_0
y	dimensional spatial coordinate
z	dimensionless spatial coordinate
z_c	catalyst location in Dirac-type distribution
z_{opt}	optimal catalyst location

Greek Letters

α	constants in Equation 3
β	heat of reaction parameter, $(-\Delta H)C^0D_e/K_eT^0$
β^*	modified heat of reaction parameter defined by Equation 56
γ	Arrhenius parameter, E/RT_0
δ	Dirac delta function
ζ	dimensionless parameter, $k_2^0C_B^0/k_1^0C_A^0$
η	effectiveness factor
θ	dimensionless temperature, T/T^0
κ	dimensionless parameter k_2^0/k_1^0
λ	ratio of Thiele moduli, ϕ_2^2/ϕ_1^2
μ	defined by Equation 55
ξ	$D_{e,1}/D_{e,2}$
ρ	Bi/Bi_{th}
ρ_p	catalyst pellet density
σ	dimensionless adsorption equilibrium constant, KC^0
τ_p	poisoning time constant
ϕ	Thiele modulus
ϕ^*	modified Thiele modulus defined by Equation 5
ϕ_m	modified Thiele modulus defined by Equations 13, 14
ϕ_B	generalized shape normalizing Thiele modulus defined by Equation 51
$\chi(x, \theta)$	dimensionless rate expression, $f(C, T)/f(C^0, T^0)$
ψ	dimensionless parameter $r_pR^2/(n + 1)D_eC^0$
Ω, Ω^*	dimensionless optimal catalyst location parameters defined by Equations 41d, 79, and 49, 64, respectively

Subscripts

1, 2	first, second reaction in series schemes; desired, undesired in parallel scheme

Superscripts

0	conditions at the surface of the pellet
′	derivative with respect to the argument of the function
un	uniform catalyst distribution

REFERENCES

1. Thomas, C. L., *Catalytic Processes and Proven Catalysts*, Academic Press, N.Y., 1970.
2. Trimm, D. L., *Design of Industrial Catalysts*, Elsevier, N.Y. 1980.
3. Satterfield, C. N., *Mass Transfer in Heterogeneous Catalysis*, MIT Press, Boston, 1970.
4. Aris, R., *The Mathematical Theory of Diffusion and Reaction in Permeable Catalysts*, Oxford University Press, Oxford, 1975.
5. Shadman-Yazdi, F., and Petersen, E. E., "Changing Catalyst by Varying the Distribution of Active Catalyst within Porous Support," *Chem. Eng. Sci., 27*, 227 (1972).
6. Cervello, J., Melendo, J. F. J., and Hermana, E., "Effect of Variable Specific Rate Constant in Non-Uniform Catalysts," *Chem. Eng. Sci., 32*, 155 (1977).
7. Kasaoka, S., and Sakata, Y., "Effectiveness Factors for Non-Uniform Catalyst Pellets," *J. Chem. Eng. Jpn., 1*, 138 (1968).
8. Nystrom, M., "Effectiveness Factors for Non-Uniform Catalytic Activity of a Spherical Pellet," *Chem. Eng. Sci., 33*, 379 (1978).
9. Wang, J. B., and Varma, A., "Effectiveness Factors for Pellets with Step-Distribution of Catalyst," *Chem. Eng. Sci., 33*, 1549 (1978).

10. Lee, W. H., Generalized Effectiveness Factor for Pellets with Nonuniform Activity Distribution: Asymptotic Region of Strong Diffusion Effects, *Chem. Eng. Sci.*, *36*, 1921 (1981).
11. Yortsos, Y. C., and Tsotsis, T. T., "Asymptotic Behavior of the Effectiveness Factor for Variable Activity Catalysts," *Chem. Eng. Sci.*, *37*, 237 (1982).
12. Gottifredi, J. C., Gonzo, E. E., and Quiroga, O. D., "Isothermal Effectiveness Factor-I. Analytical Expression for Single Reaction with Arbitrary Kinetics. Slab Geometry," *Chem. Eng. Sci.*, *36*, 705 (1981).
13. Gottifredi, J. C., Gonzo, E. E., and Quiroga, O. D., "Isothermal Effectiveness Factor-II. Analytical Expression for Single Reaction with Arbitrary Kinetics. Geometry and Activity Distribution," *Chem. Eng. Sci.*, *36*, 713 (1981).
14. Yortsos, Y. C., and Tsotsis, T. T., "On the Relationship Between the Effectiveness Factors for the Robin and Dirichlet Problem for a Catalyst with Variable Catalytic Activity," *Chem. Eng. Sci.*, *36*, 1734 (1981).
15. Yortsos, Y. C., and Tsotsis, T. T., "On the Relationship Between the Effectiveness Factors for the Robin and Dirichlet Problem for a Catalyst with Nonuniform Catalytic Activity. The Case of Generalized Isothermal and Nonisothermal Kinetics," *Chem. Eng. Sci.*, *37*, 1436 (1982).
16. Wang, J. B., and Varma, A., "On Shape Normalization for Non-Uniformly Active Catalyst Pellets," *Chem. Eng. Sci.*, *35*, 613 (1980).
17. Morbidelli, M., and Varma, A., "On Shape Normalization for Non-Uniformly Active Catalyst Pellets-II," *Chem. Eng. Sci.*, *38*, 297 (1983).
18. Vayenas, C. G., and Pavlou, S., "Optimal Catalyst Activity Distribution and Generalized Effectiveness Factors in Pellets. Single Reactions with Arbitrary Kinetics," *Chem. Eng. Sci.*, *42*, 2633 (1987).
19. Corbett, W. E., and Luss, D., "The Influence of Non-Uniform Catalytic Activity on the Performance of a Single Spherical Pellet." *Chem. Eng. Sci.*, *29*, 1473 (1974).
20. Horvath, C., and Engasser, J., "Pellicular Heterogeneous Catalysts. A Theoretical Study of the Advantages of Shell Structured Immobilized Enzyme Particles," *Ind. Eng. Chem., Fundam.*, *12*, 229 (1973).
21. Ernst, W. R., and Daugherty, D. J., "A Method for the Study of Performance of a Single Spherical Particle with Nonuniform Catalytic Activity," *AIChE J.*, *24*, 935 (1978).
22. Do, D. D., and Bailey, J. E., "Approximate Analytical Solutions for Porous Catalysts with Nonuniform Activity," *Chem. Eng. Sci.*, *37*, 545 (1982).
23. Wei, J., and Becker, E. R., "The Optimum Distribution of Catalytic Material on Support Layers in Automotive Catalysts," *Adv. Chem. Ser.*, No. 143, 116, (1974).
24. Becker, E. R., and Wei, J., "Nonuniform Distribution of Catalysts on Supports, I. Bimolecular Langmuir Reactions," *J. Catal.*, *46*, 365 (1977).
25. Becker, E. R., and Wei, J., "Nonuniform Distribution of Catalysts on Supports II. First order Reactions with Poisoning," *J. Catal.*, *46*, 372 (1977).
26. Villadsen, J., "The Effectiveness Factor for an Isothermal Pellet with Decreasing Activity Towards the Pellet Surface," *Chem. Eng. Sci.*, *31*, 1212 (1976).
27. Hegedus, L. L., and Summers, J. C., "Improving the Poison Resistance of Supported Catalysts," *J. Catal.*, *48*, 345 (1977).
28. Summers, J. C., and Hegedus, L. L., "Effects of Platinum and Palladium Impregnation on the Performance and Durability of Automobile Exhaust Oxidizing Catalysts," *J. Catal.*, *51*, 185 (1978).
29. Hegedus, L. L., Summers, J. C., Schlatter, J. C., and Baron, K., "Poison-Resistant Catalysts for the Simultaneous Control of Hydrocarbon, Carbon Monoxide, and Nitrogen oxide Emissions," *J. Catal.*, *56*, 321 (1979).
30. Varghese, P., and Wolf, E. E., "Effectiveness and Deactivation of a Diluted Catalyst Pellet," *AIChE J.*, *26*, 55 (1980).
31. Morbidelli, M., Servida, A., and Varma, A., "Optimal Distribution of Immobilized Enzymes in a Pellet for a Substrate-Inhibited Reaction," *Biotechnol. Bioeng.*, *26*, 1508 (1984).
32. Juang, H. D., and Weng, H. S., "Performance of Catalysts with Nonuniform Activity Profiles. 2. Theoretical Analysis for Nonisothermal Reactions," *Ind. Eng. Chem., Fundam.*, *22*, 224 (1983).

33. Johnson, D. L., and Verykios, X. E., "Effects of Radially Nonuniform Distributions of Catalytic Activity on Performance of Spherical Catalyst Pellets," *AIChE J.*, *30*, 44 (1984).
34. Johnson, D. L., and Verykios, X. E., "Selectivity Enhancement in Ethylene Oxidation Employing Partially Impregnated Catalysts," *J. Catal.*, *79*, 156 (1983).
35. Morbidelli, M., Servida, A., and Varma, A., "Optimal Catalyst Activity Profiles in Pellets 1. The Case of Negligible External Mass Transfer Resistance," *Ind. Eng. Chem., Fundam.*, *21*, 278 (1982).
36. Morbidelli, M., and Varma, A., "Optimal Catalyst Activity Profiles in Pellets. 2. The Influence of External Mass Transfer Resistance," *Ind. Eng. Chem., Fundam.*, *21*, 284 (1982).
37. Dougherty, R. C., and Verykios, X. E., "Optimization of Catalytic Activity Distributions in Series and Parallel Reaction Schemes," *AIChE J.*, *32*, 1858 (1986).
38. Chemburkar, R., Morbidelli, M., and Varma, A., "Optimal Catalyst Activity Profiles in Pellets. 7. The Case of Arbitrary Reaction Kinetics with Finite External Heat and Mass Transport Resistances," *Chem. Eng. Sci.*, in press, (1987).
39. Vayenas, C. G., and Pavlou, S., "Optimal Catalyst Distribution for Selectivity Maximization in Pellets: Parallel and Consecutive Reactions," *Chem. Eng. Sci.*, *42*, 1655, (1987).
40. Morbidelli, M., Servida, A., Carra, A., and Varma, A., "Optimal Catalyst Activity Profiles in Pellets 3. The Nonisothermal Case with Negligible External Transport Limitations," *Ind. Eng. Chem. Fundam.*, *24*, 116 (1985).
41. Hegedus, L. L., Chou, T. S., Summers, J. C., and Potter, N. M., in *Preparation of Catalysts II: Proceedings of the Second International Symposium on Scientific Bases for the Preparation of Heterogeneous Catalysts* (B. Delmon et al., eds.), Elsevier, Amsterdam, 1979 p. 171.
42. Shyr, Y. S., and Ernst, W. R., "Preparation of Nonuniformly Active Catalysts," *J. Catal.*, *63*, 425 (1980).
43. Vayenas, C. G., and Pavlou, S., "Optimal Catalyst Activity Distribution for Parallel Reaction Selectivity Maximization in Nonisothermal Pellets," *Chem. Eng. Sci.*, in press (1988).
44. DeLancey, G. B., "An Optimal Catalyst Activation Policy for Poisoning Problems," *Chem. Eng. Sci.*, *28*, 105 (1973).
45. Bacaros, T., Bebelis, S., Pavlou, S., and Vayenas, C. G., "Optimal Catalyst Distribution in Poisoned Pellets: The Case of Linear Kinetics and Shell-Progressive Poisoning in *Catalyst Deactivation* (B. Delmon and G. F. Froment, eds.) Elsevier, Amsterdam, 1987 p. 459.
46. Aris, R., "On Shape Factors for Irregular Particles," *Chem. Eng. Sci.*, *6*, 262 (1957).
47. Petersen, E. E., *Chemical Reaction Analysis*, Prentice-Hall, Englewood Cliffs, New Jersey, 1965.
48. Smith, T. G., "Design Considerations for Fixed-Bed Reactors using Pellets of Nonuniform Catalytic Activity," *Ind. Eng. Chem., Process Des. Dev.*, *15*, 388 (1976).
49. Smith, T. G., and Carberry, J. J., "Optimization of a Non-Isothermal, Non-Adiabatic Fixed-Bed Catalytic Reactor Model," *Adv. Chem. Ser.*, No. 133, 362 (1974).
50. Smith, T. G., and Carberry, J. J., "On the Use of Partially Impregnated Catalysts for Yield Enhancement in Non-Isothermal, Non-Adiabatic Fixed Bed Reactors," *Can. J. Chem. Eng.*, *53*, 347 (1975).
51. Cukierman, A. L., Laborde, M. A., and Lemcoff, N. O., "Optimum Activity Distribution in a Catalyst Pellet for a Complex Reaction," *Chem. Eng. Sci.*, *38*, 1977 (1983).
52. Verykios, X. E., Kluck, R. W., and Johnson, D. L., "Fixed-Bed Reactor Simulation with Nonuniformly Activated Catalyst Pellets," in *Modeling and Simulation in Engineering* (W. F. Ames, ed.), North-Holland, Amsterdam, 1983, p. 3.
53. Morbidelli, M., Servida, A., Carra, S., and Varma, A., "Optimal Catalyst Activity Profiles in Pellets 5. Optimization of the Isothermal Fixed-Bed Reactor," *Ind. Eng. Chem., Fundam.*, *25*, 313 (1986).
54. Morbidelli, M., Servida, A., and Varma, A., "Optimal Catalyst Activity Profiles in Pellets 4. Analytical Evaluation of the Isothermal Fixed-Bed Reactor," *Ind. Eng. Chem. Fundam.*, *25*, 307 (1986).
55. Harriott, P., "Diffusion Effects in the Preparation of Impregnated Catalysts," *J. Catal.*, *14*, 43 (1969).
56. Vincent, R. C., and Merrill, R. P., "Concentration Profiles in Impregnation of Porous Catalysts," *J. Catal.*, *35*, 206 (1974).

57. Becker, E. R., and Nutal, T. A., in *Preparation of Catalysts I: Proceedings of the Second International Symposium on Scientific Bases for the Preparation of Heterogeneous Catalysts* (B. Delmon et al., eds.), Elsevier, Amsterdam, 1979, p. 159.
58. Chen, H. C., and Anderson, R. B., "Concentration Profiles in Impregnated Chromium and Copper on Alumina," *J. Catal.*, *43*, 200 (1976).
59. Kotter, M., and Riekert, L., "Impregnation-Type Catalysts with Nonuniform Distribution of the Active Component Part I: Influence of the Accessibility of the Active Component on Activity and Selectivity," *Chem. Eng. Fundam.*, *2*, 19 (1983).
60. Kotter, M., and Riekert, L., "Impregnation-Type Catalysts with Nonuniform Distribution of the Active Component Part II: Preparation and Properties of Catalysts with Different Distribution of the Active Component on Inert Carriers," *Chem. Eng. Fundam.*, *2*, 21 (1982).
61. Kunimori, K., Kawasaki, E., Nakajima, I., and Uchijima, T., "Catalytic Performance of Egg-White Type Pt/Al_2O_3 Catalyst: Multiple Steady States in the Oxidation of CO," *Appl. Catal.*, *22*, 115 (1986).

CHAPTER 5

CATALYTIC CRACKING OF HEAVY VACUUM GAS OILS

Jan-Erik A. Otterstedt

Department of Engineering Chemistry
Chalmers University of Technology
Gothenburg, Sweden

and

Lawrence L. Upson

Katalistiks b.v.
Leiderdorp, The Netherlands

CONTENTS

INTRODUCTION

Beginning with the establishment of the OPEC crude oil price controls in 1973, there has been an ever-intensified effort on the part of refiners throughout the world to process heavier and heavier crudes and convert bottom-of-the-barrel-material into gasoline, diesel, and light cycle oil ranges.

Profit margins have shrunk dramatically over this period and refiners without flexibility of converting these feedstocks into predominantly transportation fuels have suffered competitively or terminated their operations. Today, when crude oil prices are unexpectedly low the economic incentive for cracking heavy oils is not as strong as it was about five years ago, but as the supply of light crudes dwindle the need and incentive to refine heavy oils remains.

The chief primary conversion unit in most refineries, the fluid catalytic cracking, unit, is well designed to handle a variety of the feedstocks which can be converted to appropriate liquid products. The first section of this chapter defines and characterizes such oils, and the next describes the problems related to catalytic cracking of heavy oils. The third section deals with catalysts especially designed for cracking heavy oils and is followed by a description of special techniques such as metal passivation, emission control, and promoted combustion, which are valuable aids to the refiner. In the last section, changes in reactor and regenerator design and performance required in heavy oil operations are discussed.

DEFINITION AND CHARACTERIZATION OF HEAVY OILS

On the time scale of man, petroleum oils are stable substances. They do not react with the rock formations that contain them, nor do they separate or precipitate with measurable rate. This pseudo-stable condition of petroleum oils implies that there are only a limited number of functionalities defined in terms of chemical bonds and hetero-atoms in oil molecules. Furthermore, the distribution of functionalities, but not the type of functionalities, in an oil fraction varies with the boiling point of the fraction. Hence, the same compound types are present in a low boiling fraction as in a high boiling fraction of vacuum gas oil and indeed also in the asphaltene fraction [1]. The increasing portion of large molecules containing hetero-atoms and metal contaminants in fractions of increasing boiling point accounts for the difficulties in processing of heavy oils [2, 3]. Although the same type of functionalities are present in the asphaltene fraction as in for instance vacuum gas oil, the degree of association due to the sheer size of the molecules and due to the presence of several functionalities in the same molecule is much higher in the asphaltene fraction. A major reason for the difficulties in catalytic cracking of heavy feeds has, therefore, to do with the low volatility of the large molecules and molecular clusters of the asphaltene and resin fractions. This causes them to be present on or in the catalyst as liquids and be carried over into the regenerator where they will make coke and deposit metals onto the catalyst. The term "heavy oil" may be defined as follows:

- Specifically, atmospheric tower bottoms, also known as reduced or topped crudes
- More generally, crude oil components boiling above 900°F and including heavy gas oil, vacuum gas oil and vacuum resid fractions containing molecules with carbon numbers over 20 and containing relatively small quantities of normal and iso-paraffins and relatively large portions of naphthenes, mono- and polynuclear aromatics, and resins and asphaltenes boiling above, 1,000°F.

The possibility of converting the heavy molecules of atmospheric tower bottoms into liquid range products by straightforward catalytic cracking is so remote that it is not a serious consideration, but the incentive for converting any part is sufficient to justify substantial effort.

Feed Characterization

The characterization of heavy vacuum gas oils, atmospheric and vacuum resids will enable the refiner to estimate product distributions and yields obtained by cracking such heavy feeds. In addition, if properly done, such evaluations will indicate how to avoid compatibility problems when preparing heavy feeds for the catalytic cracker by blending vacuum gas oils and resids.

Density and specific gravity (ASTM D-287, D-1298, D-941, D-1217, and D-1555). The density used to be the principal specification for feedstocks and refinery products but it is now largely replaced by specific gravity which approximates closely to density or by API gravity (4). It is easy to measure and gives a rough approximation of the aromatic content of the feed.

Viscosity (ASTM D-445, D-88, D-2161, D-341, and D-2270). The viscosity is usually expressed as "stokes" or "poises" (poises = stokes × specific gravity) and the viscosity of crude oils may vary from several stokes for the lighter crude oils to several thousand stokes for the heavier crude oils and even to several million stokes for residua.

Carbon residue (ASTM-189 and D-524). The carbon residue of a crude oil is a property that can be correlated with the API gravity of the oil; it is roughly inversely related to the API-gravity. The carbon residue gives indication of the coke forming tendency of an oil and is directly proportional to the sulphur content, nitrogen content, viscosity and proportion of asphaltenes in the oil. There are two methods for determining the carbon residue: the Conradson method and the Ramsbottom method and both are equally applicable.

Metals content (ASTM D-4821). The metals content of a feedstock is usually determined as the inorganic ashes remaining after ignition and burning off of the organic material. Individual metals may thus be determined by subjecting the ashes to a spectrographic analysis.

Distillation characteristics (ASTM D-86, D-216, D-285, D-477, and D-2892). The distillation characteristics of crude oils give an indication of the relative proportions of the various fractions—products present. For a residuum, not much information will be gained from an examination of the distillation characteristics, while for instance, an asphaltic crude oil might be able to yield some of the lower boiling petroleum products.

Gas chromatography can also be used to determine distillation characteristics for oil fractions boiling below 550°C by simulated distillation; ASTM D-2887-73.

Pour point (ASTM D-97, and Anilin point, ASTM D-611). The pour point of a crude oil is the lowest temperature at which the oil will pour or flow under prescribed conditions and is a rough indication of the relative paraffinity and aromaticity of the oil. For heavy oils and residua, the pour points are usually above 0°C.

The aniline point of a crude oil or crude oil products is the temperature at which equal parts of aniline and the oil are completely miscible. The aniline point increases with paraffinicity and is mostly used to estimate the aromaticity of light crudes and distillates. The aniline point is only infrequently used to characterize heavy oils and residua because of their complex compositions.

Correlations Between Feedstock Properties and Processability

Depending on who does it, the purpose of feedstock characterization can be to predict product yields and quality or to guide for developing fluid cracking catalysts with improved selectivity.

An ultimate goal of characterization of FCC-feedstocks is to relate the feed quality to product yields and qualities for a particular set of operating conditions. Many methods have been suggested in the literature for characterization of petroleum feedstocks. One such method is the UOP K-factor. Ardern et al. [5] correlated gasoline yields as a function of coke make with the K-factor. In general, as K increased, gasoline decreased at constant coke make, Figure 1. The UOP K-factor is, however, not adequate to characterize complex FCC feedstocks, Hinds [6], e.g., found that two FCC feedstocks with the same API pour point, Conradson carbon and K-factor gave significantly different gasoline, gas and coke yields. Decroocq [7] has investigated the effect of the feed composition on performance in catalytic cracking. When the paraffinic content decreased (and the aromatic content increased), from an aniline point of 110°C to an aniline point of 63°C the conversion dropped from 93% to 70%. Decroocq [7] and Ginzel [8] studied the effect of hydrotreatment on composition and crackability of feedstocks. Hydrotreatment at 48 bars increased the conversion from 48.5 to 61.0 whereas the paraffinic content, as expressed by the UOP K-factor, increased from 11.6 to 11.7. These results further suggest that the K-factor is a very insensitive characterization of feedstocks.

n-d-M

The n-d-M method uses such physical properties of the feedstock as density, refractive index and average molecular weight to predict the paraffinic, naphthenic and aromatic contents of FCC feedstocks [9]. The aromatic content (C_A) calculated by this method has been found to be quite effective

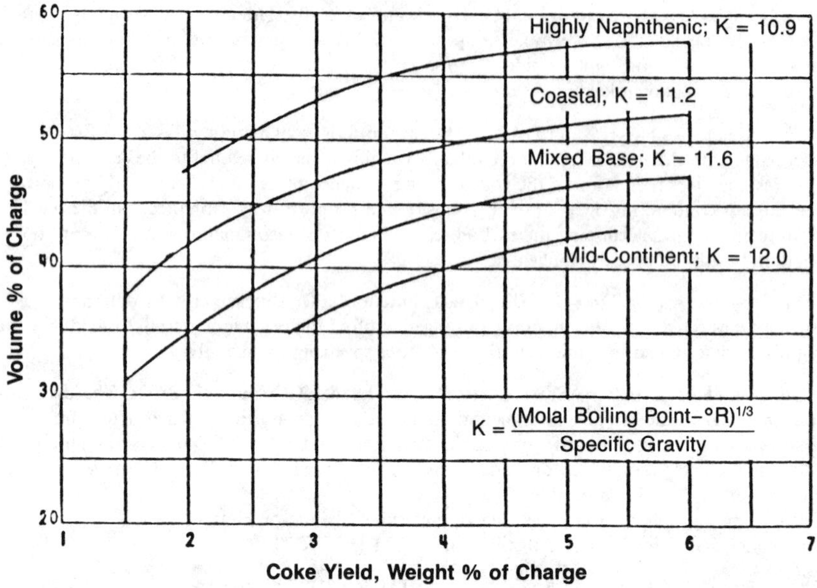

Figure 1. Effect of type of charge on gasoline yield; once-through cracking of distillate gas oils [5].

in predicting conversion [10], whereas the ratio of naphthene to paraffins (C_N/C_p) has been found to be very useful in predicting selectivity and octane effects [11].

Hydrogen Content

The hydrogen content of an FCC feedstock can also be used to characterize the crackability of the feedstock as described by Valeri [12]. Valeri also shows how a comparison of the total H_2 in the FCC products with the H_2 in the feed (a H_2 balance) provides a valuable check upon the FCC yield data reliability.

New Correlations

Dhulesia [13] has recently developed new correlations that are claimed to accurately predict the important FCC feedstock characterization parameters: aromatic carbon content, hydrogen content and molecular weight. The characterization method used in his model requires the following usual laboratory tests carried out in a refinery on a daily basis:

1. Specific gravity at 15°C
2. Refractive index and the temperature at which it is measured
3. Sulfur content
4. Basic nitrogen content
5. Conradson carbon content
6. Metals content (nickel and vanadium)
7. Viscosity at 37.8 and 98.9°C
8. ASTM D-1160 distillation

There is not yet any information in the literature that reports on how closely Dhulesia's new correlations are able to predict product yield and quality of a wide range of FCC feedstocks. The methods used to characterize FCC feedstocks previously described above are based on estimating average properties such as the paraffinic, naphthenic, and aromatic contents of FCC feedstocks by using easily determined physical properties such as specific gravity, refractive index, viscosity, etc. The fact that they can satisfactorily predict product yields and qualities of many types of FCC feedstocks in combination with their ease of use, they can easily be carried out on a day to day routine basis, make them quite useful to refiners.

If, however, more detailed information is required, for instance to determine the response of a certain feedstock to a new catalyst or to modifications in established catalysts, then improved methods are needed. Fu and Schaffer [14] studied the individual effect of about 30 different nitrogen compounds on cracking catalysts and could demonstrate that not all nitrogen compounds are equally harmful for catalytic cracking. The results of their study clearly emphasized that it is not sufficient to use the total nitrogen (or even basic nitrogen) concentration to predict the poisoning effect of nitrogen in an FCC feed. They concluded that quantitative predictions of the effects of nitrogen will require a better understanding of both the specific structures of the nitrogen compounds in the feed and the acidic property of the cracking catalysts. Allen et al. [15] separated a Mexican crude atmospheric tower bottom (ATB), a Canadian tar sand ATB, the heavy distillate of a hydroliquefied bituminus coal, and the heavy distillate of a Colorado shale oil by solubility and ion exchange chromatography into 9 fractions. The objective of their work was to provide detailed structural characterizations of the whole and fractionated heavy oils. The structural profiles were obtained principally from proton NMR and elemental analysis data with some additional data from mass spectrometry, infrared spectrometry and carbon-13 NMR. The characterizations along with processability studies of the separated fractions provided an improved fundamental understanding of heavy fuel fractions, which may lead to improvements of current processing technology.

Blending of FCC feedstock with higher aromatic materials such as lube oil extracts, deasphalted oils, or coker gas oils frequently produces results which are not anticipated based upon the analytical properties of the blended feed materials [16]. In the situation reported, a correlation between UOP K value and FCCU conversion was found to be generally reliable for normal VGO feeds. However, when lube oil extracts were included in the feed, conversions were consistently lower than predicted. It may be possible to use the new correlations of Dhulesia to predict conversion and selectivity of blended FCC feedstocks provided that the components of the blends have been used in the calibration of the correlations. Pazos et al. [17] have demonstrated the inability of conventional characterization methods to predict the response of crude oils from the Bachaquero and Boscan fields in Venezuela to hydroprocessing. A more careful characterization revealed that 14% of the metals in Bachaquero crude exists as porphyrins as compared to 25% for a Boscan crude. Metals, which are present in well defined structures, for instance porphyrin type molecules, are more reactive than non-porphyrin metals. The American Petroleum Institute research project 6D was initiated with the objective to develop new methods for characterizing heavy oils [18]. Heavy distillates were separated into the seven classes of molecular types shown in Figure 2, using liquid chromatography. Table 1 is an example of data on two distillates from 4 crude oils. The Wilmington distillates are high in heteroatom (S, O, N)-containing hydrocarbons, whereas the Swan Hills distillates are low in such hydrocarbons. Swan Hills is high in saturated hydrocarbons, whereas the Wilmington hydrocarbons are about equally divided between saturates and aromatics. The higher boiling distillates from all four oils contain considerably more non-hydrocarbon compounds than do the lower boiling distillates. This increase is accompanied by a decrease in saturates, but the total aromatic content remains about the same.

Definition of quantitative effects of feedstock structure on product yields quality, particularly in the heavy oil category of molecular structure, is being sought in many laboratories. The inherently better performance of a zeolite catalyst cracking a predominately paraffinic or naphthenic feedstock has been described many times. This strongly suggests that the higher H/C ratio of such materials aids in preventing coke formation which, in turn, allows higher conversion levels and the formation of relatively larger numbers of gasoline molecules compared with an aromatic feedstock [19]. Studies have shown that hydrotreated feedstocks give yield patterns nearly identical to un-hydrotreated feeds of the same H/C ratio [20]. This observation further strengthens the notion that H/C ratio can play an important, if not decisive, role in predicting the quality of an FCC feed. This is illustrated by the resid feeds from two widely different sources shown in Table 2 [21]. The dissimilarity of the two, even with virtually identical UOP K-factors, can be brought into sharp focus by considering

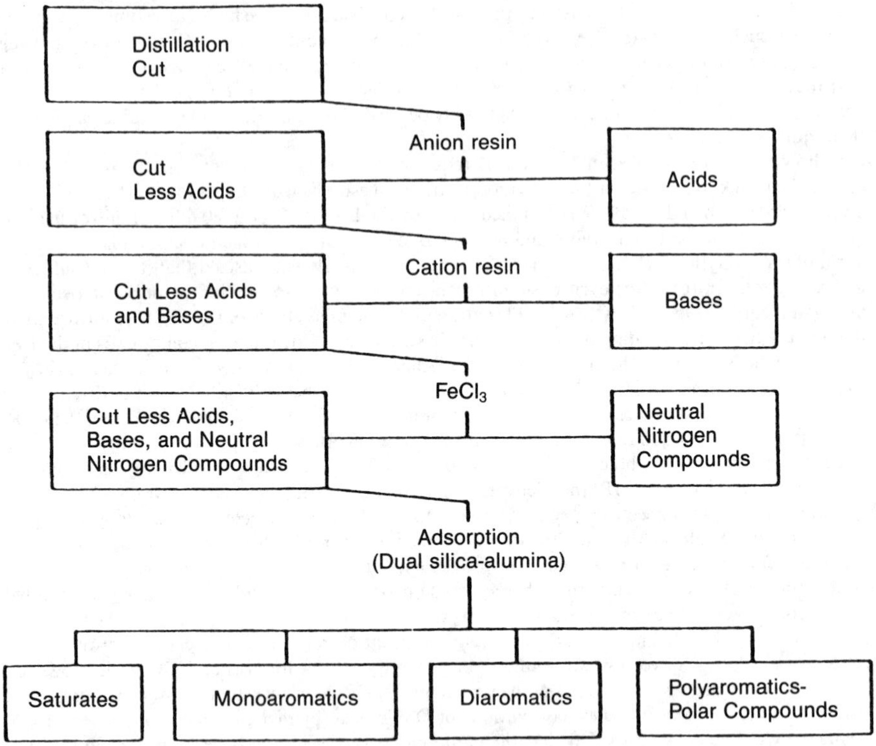

Figure 2. Outline of separation scheme for high-boiling petroleum cuts [18].

the relative amounts of high H/C ratio, high molecular weight components in the two feeds compared with the relative amounts of relatively lower H/C ratio, high molecular weight entities. Within the table the former are identified in the 650°F–1,025°F boiling range as type A materials while the latter (including thiophenes and unknowns) are identified as type B components. The ratio A/B is a measure of the magnitude of high H/C feedstock components whose size is in the range to geometrically affect cracking rates in zeolite catalysts, compared to low H/C ratio components with similar size related characteristics. Thus, the Escravos feedstock shown ($A/B = 3.06$) is projected to be more readily "crackable" than the Abu Bu Khoosh feedstock ($A/B = 1.92$). The Escravos feedstock also shows a substantially higher percentage of easy-to-crack saturates and a lower percentage of aromatic and polar compounds, (and particularly asphaltenic materials) than the Abu Bu Khoosh.

PROBLEMS RELATED TO CRACKING HEAVY OIL FRACTIONS

Molecular size and shape have long been known to play an important role in determining catalyst activity and coke forming tendencies particularly in zeolite cracking catalysts [20, 22]. Nace, for example, reported in 1970 the significant reduction in rate constants observed with zeolite catalysts when the naphthene feed was changed from 2–3 to 3–4 rings, but that no such decrease was observed with considerably larger pore synthetic silica/alumina catalyst. Similarly, two-ring aromatics from cycle oils with dimensions close to the 8 Å entry ports of faujasite appeared to assure coke formation and possible diffusional problems since some coke would invariably deposit at those locations. Partially hydrogenated rings of aromatics and aromatic ring segments of high boiling compounds

Table 1
Example of Characterization Data from Initial Separation [15]

Crude Oil	Boiling Range, °C	Weight-Percent of Distillate							
		Acids	Bases	Neutral Compounds	Saturates	Aromatic Compounds			Recovery
						Mono-	Di-	Poly-	
Wilmington	370–535	5.6	6.8	4.2	36.9	16.8	12.4	17.3	100.0
	535–675	9.3	12.7	21.3	20.8	11.8	8.9	15.3	100.1
Gach Saran	370–535	1.7	2.1	2.3	48.5	16.8	11.7	18.0	101.1
	535–675	5.4	8.7	8.9	31.6	12.2	8.2	25.0	100.0
Swan Hills	370–535	1.8	2.2	1.9	65.9	12.6	6.3	10.8	101.5
	535–675	3.5	4.5	[1]5.6	[1]39.2	9.7	5.0	14.2	99.9
Recluse	370–535	1.4	1.1	.9	74.1	11.3	5.1	6.1	100.0
	535–675	2.9	3.3	[1]3.0	[1]68.8	8.1	3.7	10.1	99.9

[1] *Values corrected from wax-free distillate to whole distillate basis. Waxes considered entirely saturate and essentially free of nitrogen and sulfur.*

Table 2
Resid Feedstock Crackability Criteria As a Function of Molecular Composition [21]

650–1,025°F Feedstock	UOP K Factor	← A → Cy Para. Vol%	Benzi Ar. Vol%	A	← B → PHA Vol%	Thlophene + Unknown, Vol%	B	A/B
Abu Bu Khoosh	11.83	31	19	60	16	10	26	1.92
Escravos	11.85	43	9	62	14	3	17	3.06

650–1,025°F Feedstock	← Facile Cracking → Saturates, Vol 650–1,025°F	1,025°F+	B	← Difficult Cracking → Aromatics + Polar Molecules, 1,025°F+, Vol%	Asphaltenes Vol%	Carbon Residue, 1,025°F+, Vol%
Abu Bu Khoosh	26	9.4	35.4	70.1	20.6	21.6
Escravos	31	27	58	66.7	6.6	11.8

can be cracked into the gasoline range, resulting in higher octane gasoline from the catalytic cracking, but naphthalenes, phenanthrene, pyrene, etc. invariably go to coke [23]. To further complicate the situation, resins and asphaltenes as major components of the Conradson carbon residue can be counted on, if given no pretreatment (such as catalytic hydrogen addition), to be converted to coke some place on the catalyst surface. This "place" is likely to be the locus of acidity, activity, and high surface area; i.e. the zeolite. The expected and observed severe activity losses caused by such "molecular" entities must be avoided or minimized in commercial operations.

Otterstedt et al. [24] have recently reviewed catalytic cracking of heavy oil fractions and illuminated the following problems:

Metals

The metal content is considerably higher in heavy oil than in regular vacuum gas oil. Nickel and vanadium are particularly important since they can be present in high concentrations and will have detrimental effects on the cracking performance of the catalyst. Nickel deposited on the catalyst causes non-selective cracking, leading to high hydrogen and C_1–C_4 gas production and high coke formation on the catalyst. Vanadium will penetrate into the zeolite and react destructively with it. Figure 3 shows the change in specific surface of a catalyst when contaminated with metals and sub-

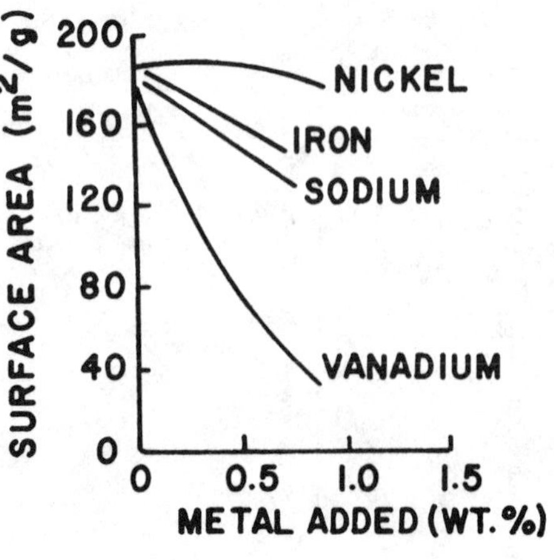

Figure 3. Surface area as a function of metal impregnated in FCC catalyst [21].

jected to a steaming test at 788°C for 5 hours. Nickel and vanadium are usually present in porphyrin-like molecules and as naphthenates. Sodium is often present in resids as a result of poor desalting. Sodium neutralizes the acid sites which are vital for the cracking activity of the catalyst, it also leads to collapse of the crystalline structure of molecular sieves at high temperatures.

Sulfur

Sulfur is present as mercaptans, sulfides, thiophenes, and other organo-sulfur compounds. The catalytic cracking of the heavy feeds increases the SO_x content in the stack gas from the catalytic cracker. For cracking unhydrotreated gas oils, as a rule of thumb, 5% of the total S is transferred into the coke on the catalyst and this appears as SO_2 in the stack gas of a FCC unit; in other words, one wt% S in the feed gives about 1,000 ppm SO_2 in the regenerator stack. For resid cracking, the proportion of SO_2 in the stack gas can be much higher than these values. Emissions have to be reduced below 60 kg S per 1,000 barrels of feed in California by January 1, 1987. Similar restrictions are being imposed or contemplated in many other countries also.

Sulfur compounds in the feed strongly affect FCCU reactor performance. Sulfur acts as a temporary catalyst poison with resulting loss in conversion and also results in a decrease in gasoline selectivity [25]. In the reported case, an increase in feed sulfur of 1% decreased gasoline selectivity from 70 wt% to 68 wt%. In addition, a significant amount (20–30%) of the feed sulfur is converted to H_2S in the reactor, which can result in a substantial increase in the load to the gas compressor and to the gas plant.

Nitrogen and Oxygen

The content of nitrogen is higher in heavier feeds than in regular vacuum gas oil. Basic nitrogen compounds such as pyridines and quinolines are strongly adsorbed at the acid sites of the catalyst resulting in reduced activity and higher rate of coke formation. Neutral types of nitrogen compounds such as carbazoles, indoles, and pyroles are not as strongly adsorbed on the acid sites of the catalyst. Hence they do not affect the cracking performance of the catalyst very much.

As in the case of nitrogen and sulfur, the content of oxygen also increases with the boiling point of an oil fraction but relatively little attention has been paid to the effect of oxygen on the performance of cracking catalysts.

Asphaltenes

Asphaltenes are aggregates of molecules containing polycyclic aromatics and functionalities of several types. The size of asphaltenes vary in the range 25–300 Å. Since the pores of the zeolites are too small to accept asphaltenes, catalysts with much larger pore structure than zeolites are required to crack asphaltenes. Alternatively, asphaltenes can be cracked on a matrix in which the regular zeolites used in cracking catalysts are embedded. There are also commercial processes available for separating out asphaltenes from crude oils.

The H/C ratio

Figure 4 shows that the H/C atomic ratio for normal petroleum feedstocks varies from 1.5 to 1.9, and for resids from 1.4 to 1.8. For all useable premium transportation fuels this ratio should be in the range 1.8 to 2.1. Catalytic cracking can be considered to be a process that produces products with H/C ratio in the desired range from heavy oils and where some of the hydrogen needed for raising the H/C ratio of the products has been supplied by the heavier components of the oil that are converted to coke. Coke formation is a mixed blessing in that coke causes rapid catalyst deactivation, but also provides a source of heat for the endothermic cracking reactions by coke combustion, and is a source of hydrogen for stabilizing valuable lower molecular weight products.

Coke that is formed in a catalytic cracker can be considered to come from three distinctly different sources. One source is catalytic coke, which is produced from the cracking of hydrocarbon molecules. The catalytic coke can be subdivided into two classes (a) coke produced from the catalytic

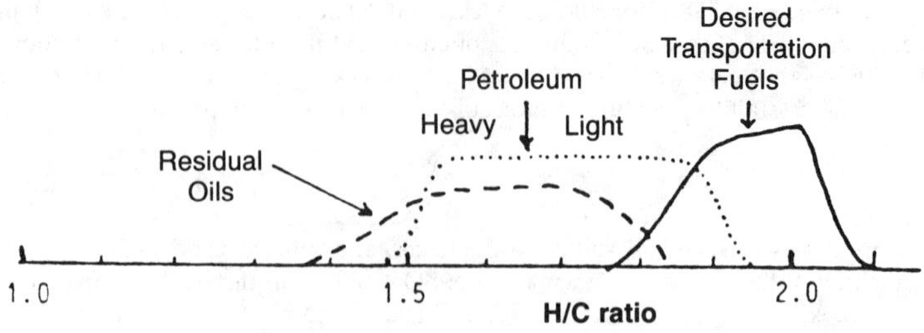

Figure 4. H/C ratio for heavy and light petroleum feedstocks, residual oils, and the desired end products [24].

activity of the catalyst itself and (b) coke produced from the catalytic action of the metals deposited upon the catalyst. This latter form is frequently referred to as "contaminant" coke. Contaminant coke is associated with heavy oils through the metals content, in particular nickel and vanadium, present in such oils.

A small portion of the feed is believed to deposit a coke-like material on the catalyst regardless of the degree of conversion. This second type of coke, so called Conradson carbon, comes from the very heavy, high molecular weight, polycyclic compounds in the feed that deposit on the hot catalyst surface on contact and are too high boiling in nature to be vaporized or steam stripped from the catalyst. This type of coke increases with the "heaviness" of the oil.

The final coke component, called catalyst circulation coke, is not really coke but is possibly a hydrocarbon in the cycle oil boiling range that has not been stripped from the catalyst when the catalyst leaves the reactor. The amount of this material burned in the regenerator depends upon the stripping efficiency and the catalyst circulation rate. This type of coke depends only indirectly on the "heaviness" of the feed oil in that stripping may be less efficient when a heavy oil is used as a cracker feed.

The problems discussed in this section are invariably associated with the components of the feedstock: metals, nitrogen, sulfur, and molecular structure as it affects crackability and strippability. The solution to these problems will come through improved catalytic materials, (the next section) and equipment design ("Reactor and Regenerator Design for Heavy Oil Processing").

CATALYTIC MATERIALS FOR CRACKING HEAVY OILS

Efficient catalytic cracking of heavy oils to useful liquid products requires specially designed catalysts that minimize heavy bottom yields (compounds boiling above 640°F) and minimize catalytic coke formation. This section first discusses the design of a catalyst for heavy oils cracking and then reviews some recent investigations on cracking of heavy oils.

Design of Catalysts for Heavy Oil Cracking

Catalysts for heavy oils, "resid" or "bottom of the barrel" catalysts all contain zeolites incorporated into a matrix. Our discussion of the design of catalysts for heavy oil cracking will therefore begin with a review of zeolites and matrix materials.

Zeolites

The zeolite component must possess:

1. High activity. Activity of the pure zeolite is proportional to its framework tetrahedral Al-content.

2. Resistance to deactivation by coking or poisoning by metals or hetero-atoms (S, N).
3. Hydrothermal and thermal stability in order to withstand the regeneration conditions. Stability increases for decreasing structural Al-content and depends on the nature and extent of ion exchange.

A zeolite consists essentially of SiO_4 and AlO_4 tetrahedra linked to each other by common oxygen atoms. The fourfold coordination of the alumina atoms with oxygen in the structure results in a net negative charge, which for electrical neutrality accommodates a cation. These cationic and anionic sites give rise to the active sites.

The ratio between the silica and the alumina tetrahedra is a very important parameter to characterize the zeolite structure. Generally, the molecular ratio of SiO_2 and Al_2O_3 is called the silica to alumina ratio (SAR). The unit cell is the elementary building block of a specific zeolite structure. One unit cell in for instance the Y-zeolite crystal contains 192 tetrahedra. A zeolite Y with a SAR of 5 will consequently contain 55 alumina tetrahedra or potentially acid sites per unit cell. Figure 5 shows the relation between the number of aluminum ions per unit cell, APC, and SAR in the SAR range 5–50 [25].

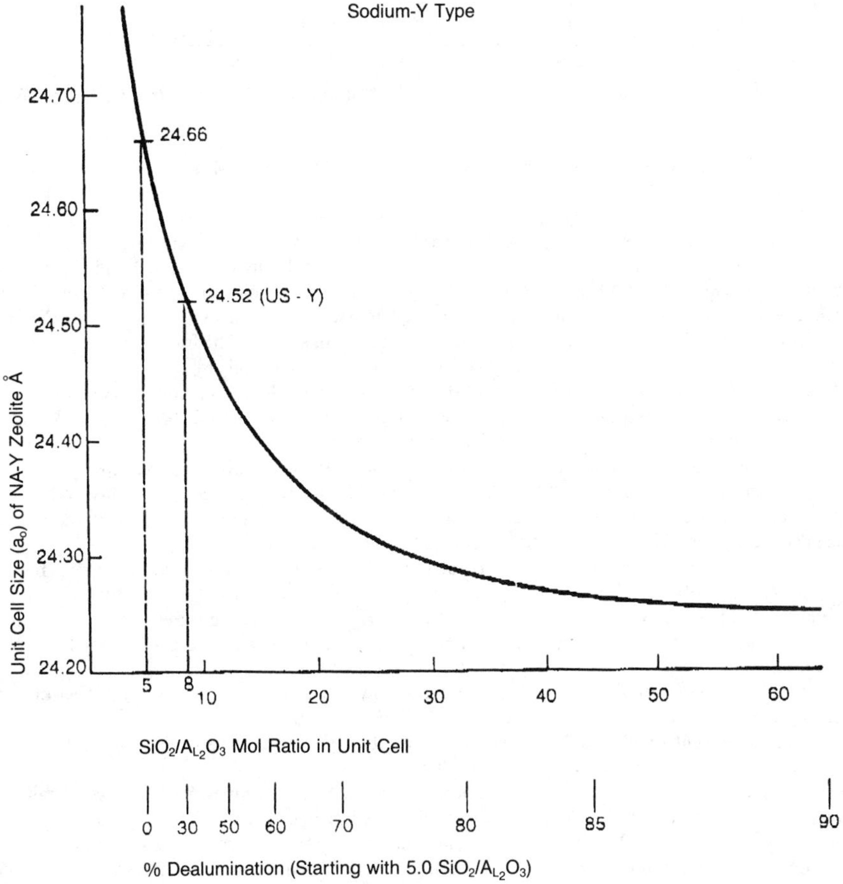

Figure 5. Relationship between cell size and cell $SiO_2/A_{L_2}O_3$ ratio [26].

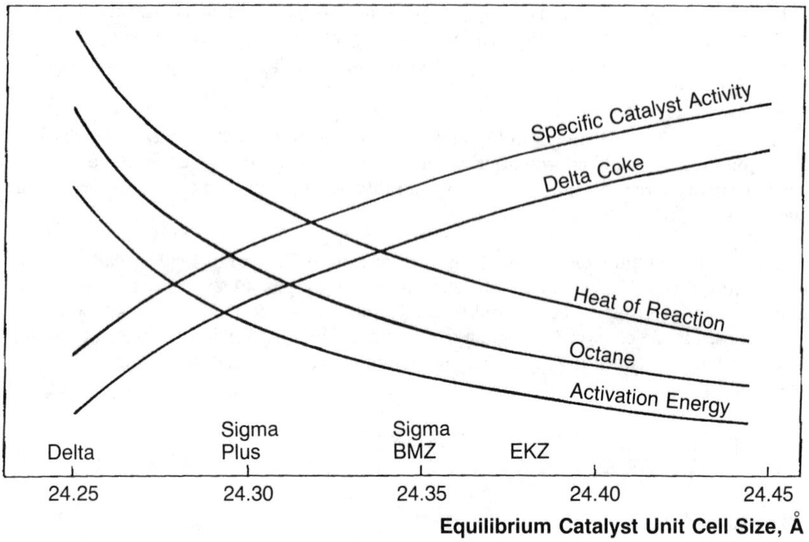

Figure 6. The effect of lower equilibrium catalyst unit cell size [27].

After the crystallization step in a zeolite production process a zeolite will undergo significant changes in chemical composition and in structure when it is subjected to thermal and steam treatments in the catalyst plant and later in the FCC-unit. In the presence of steam a thermal dealumination can occur that essentially involves a high temperature hydrolysis of Si—O—Al bonds and leads to the formation of neutral and cationic aluminum species. The frame work sites vacated by aluminum can be occupied by silicon, which is rendered more mobile by the removal of adjacent aluminum. This structural rearrangement of the zeolite leads to a highly silicious, very stable framework. During the thermal dealumination process aluminum released from the framework will be transferred to non-framework positions. This non-framework aluminum can exhibit acidic properties and may have a significant influence on the zeolite site accessibility and selectivity.

Hydrogen transfer reactions are extremely important for catalyst activity, selectivity and performance characteristics such as heat of cracking. Figure 6 shows these effects as equilibrated unit cell size decreases from 24.45 (high H_2 transfer) to 24.25 (low H_2 transfer).

The acid site distribution and strength is related to the number of aluminum in the next nearest neighbor as described by Pine [28]. Figure 7 shows this acid site distribution as a function of unit cell size. In this figure O-NNN is a site that has no aluminum atoms on any of the next nearest neighbor sites. According to Pine, the strength of these sites decrease as: O-NNN > 1-NNN > 2-NNN, etc.

Figure 8 shows the influence of unit cell size gas on yield, and Figure 9 shows the effect of APC on the research octane number RON-O, and MAT conversion.

Alumina deficient zeolite can be prepared in a number of ways and Table 3 shows various ways to modify the aluminum content of zeolites [30].

The preferred technique to remove alumina from the zeolite framework involves chemically treating the Y-zeolite with ammonium fluorosilicate according to a recent patent by Breck and Skeels [31]. In this procedure aluminum is removed and silicon is reinserted into the framework at the site where the aluminum atom was removed. The silicon reinsertion eliminates the void spaces in the crystal structure when aluminum is removed, which occur in other aluminum removal processes such as hydrothermal removal (ultrastable-Y process) and other chemical removal processes (EDTA etc.). With this procedure, perfect sieve crystalline structures with silica/alumina ratios from 6–20 can be readily produced. This sieve structure has been designated as the LZ-210 type sieve.

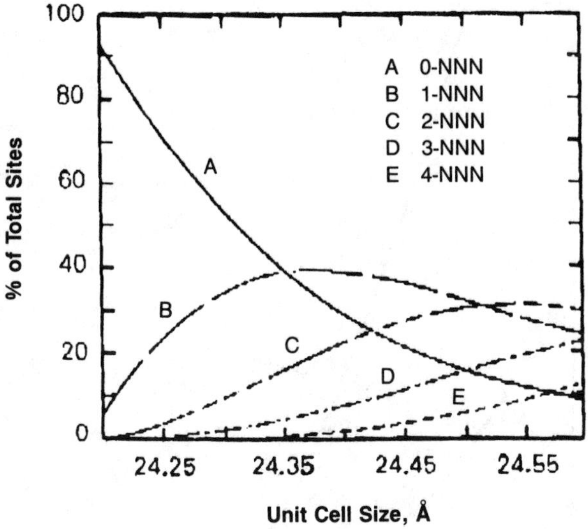

Figure 7. Acid site distribution is a function of zeolite unit cell size [28].

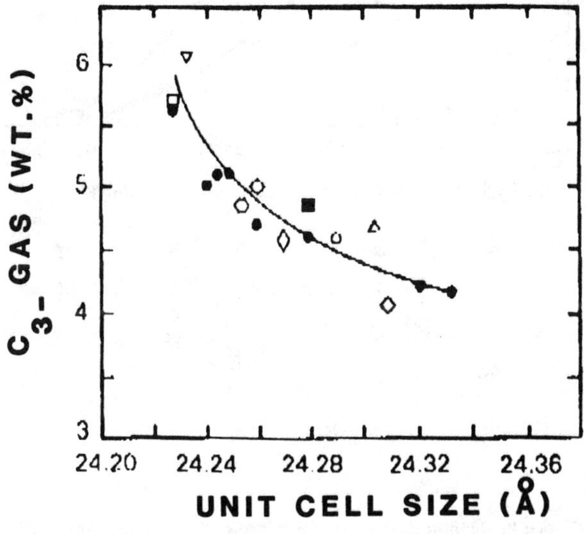

Figure 8. Dependence of light gas yield on zeolite unit cell size [28].

An additional feature of the LZ-210 sieve is that the aluminum taken from the framework is totally removed from the sieve by the chemical solution. This contrasts to framework aluminum removal in the USY process where the removed aluminum remains in the sieve and has non-selective catalytic activity, catalysing gas and coke formation.

New zeolites in cracking catalyst formulations and their catalytic potentials are shown in Table 4 [30]. The potential of pillared clays as cracking catalysts for heavy oils will be demonstrated below.

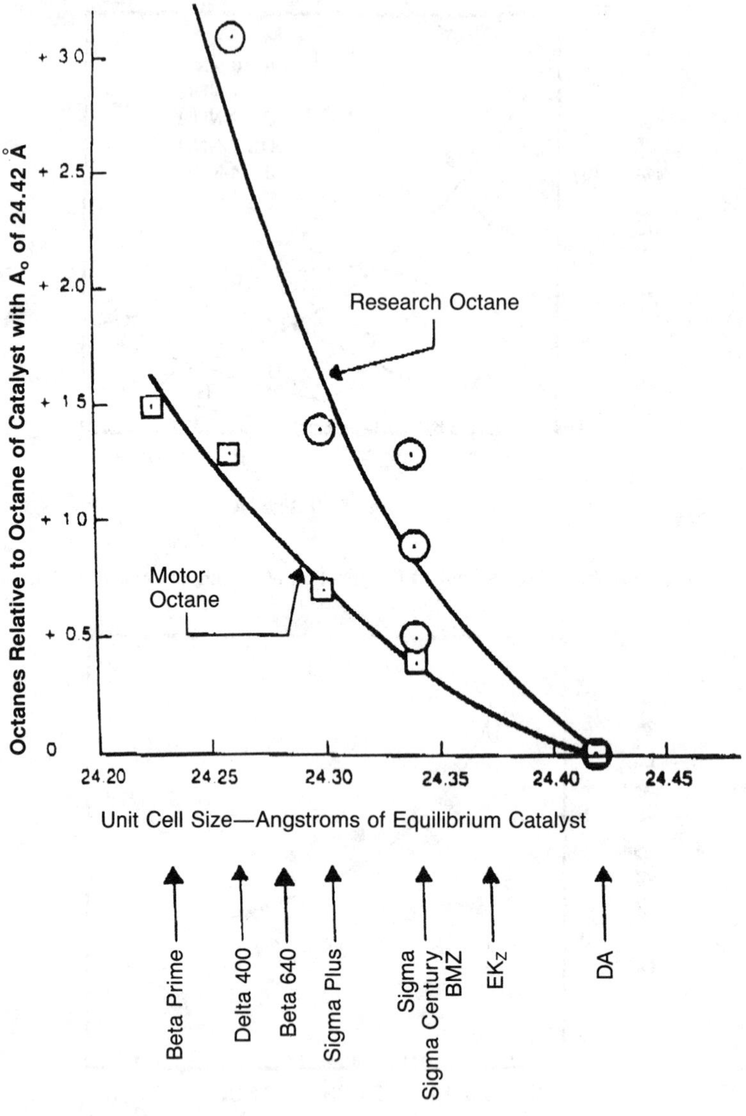

Figure 9. Octane data from commercial FCCU operations [29].

Matrix Materials

The active component of modern cracking catalysts is a zeolite, usually of type Y in the rare earth or hydrogen form, which is incorporated into a matrix. Zeolites are too active to be used alone as cracking catalysts. One role of the matrix is therefore to "dilute" the activity of zeolites to a level that can be handled in catalytic cracking units. Fluid catalytic cracking catalysts are spherical

Table 3
Modification of the Aluminum Content of Zeolites [30]

1. Dealumination methods [4]
a. Hydrothermal treatments: steaming of the ammonium form of mordenite or Y zeolites (preparation of ultrastable (USY). Al remains in the cage and channels.
b. Chemical treatments in solution of steamed zeolites, e.g. USY, with acids, bases, salts (KF, $CrCl_3$, $(NH_4)_2SiF_6$(31), or chelating agents.
c. Chemical treatments of non-steamed zeolites:
– in solution: see 1-B
– by gaseous reagents: $SiCl_4$, SiF_4, BCl_3(32), F_2, . . .

2. Alumination methods
a. Chemical treatments by gaseous reagents: Al halides (27–29).
b. Alumina binder activation (30).
c. Chemical treatments in solution: Na aluminate (33), $(NH_4)_3AlF_6$(29, 34).

Table 4
New Zeolites in Cracking Catalysts Formulations [30]

Catalyst Type	Catalytic Potential	Remarks and References
Zeolite mixtures (large pore + molecular shape selective)	Boost in octane number. Bulky molecules conversion in large pore component; M-forming type reactions in shape-selective additive.	Addition of 5% ZSM 5 to a standard RE-Y catalyst boosts the octane number by about 3 units, at the expense however of gasoline yield (5% decrease) [38] [56].
High silica large pore zeolites	Improved thermal and hydro thermal stability for operation in severe conditions. Treatment of heavy feeds, higher isomerization activity.	Materials prepared by direct synthesis or by improved chemical dealumination of known zeolites [31]. Zeolites of potential interest are Y, type L, Beta, and ZSM-12 [14, 15].
Novel molecular sieves	Limited information currently available.	Frameworks containing tetrahedrally coordinated Si, Al, and P atoms should possess acid properties [39–41].
Amorphous catalysts	Processing of heavy feedstocks. Reduced diffusion limitations.	Submicrocrystalline zeolites [42] and controlled pore size silica aluminas [43].
Pillared clays	Potential to be defined. Thermal stability needs improvements.	Possess interlayer acidity [44, 45].

particles with average particle size of about 70 micrometers which are exposed to severe mechanical and thermal strains in the cracking process. The matrix, therefore, must have high mechanical strength, attrition, resistance, and pore structure which does not collapse or limit access of reactant molecules to the zeolite component of the catalyst. The increasing interest in cracking heavy oils during the last 10 years has brought out further demands on matrix performance. As we have already explained, heavy oils contain molecules that are too large to readily enter the pore structure of zeolites. Matrices with a certain degree of cracking activity will therefore be needed for cracking large molecules or aggregates of molecules into fragments which can undergo subsequent cracking inside the zeolite. Furthermore, heavy oils contain metals that react destructively with zeolite, for instance vanadium, or behave as non-selective catalysts, for instance, nickel. Metal tolerant catalysts will therefore require materials that can passivate, bury, or by other means reduce the effects of metals to manageable levels. Sodium ions, which are always present even in deeply ion exchanged zeolites, will cause degradation of zeolite under severe thermal or hydrothermal conditions. Some matrices may act as "sodium sinks," allowing solid-solid ion exchange, thus improving the thermal stability of the zeolite crystals which is of particular importance in heavy oil cracking where regenerator temperatures may be very high [32, 33, 34]. The matrix will also act as heat carrier or "sink," facilitating heat transfer during regeneration and cracking.

Materials commonly used for matrices in fluid cracking catalysts are silica-alumina, alumina, different clays, silica-magnesia, and combinations of such materials.

Design of Catalysts for Heavy Oils

In one approach to catalysts for conversion of large molecules a zeolite is incorporated into an active matrix. Figure 10 shows that the first step in the conversion will involve precracking of the large molecules on the matrix surface or on the surface of the zeolite crystals [35]. The precracked molecules can undergo further cracking in the zeolite to desirable products or on the matrix surface to products that may or may not be desirable depending on the nature of the matrix surface. With the right combination of external surface of zeolite crystals and properties of the matrix surface, for instance total acidity and ratio between Lewis to Bronsted acid sites, an optimum selectivity in the precracking step can be achieved. Figure 11 shows that an optimum pore size distribution in the matrix is required in order to crack large molecules [35]. The pores designated "A" in Figure 11 are not accessible to large molecules. "B" have a pore size 2–6 times the size of the large molecules and are therefore accessible in addition to giving a large contribution to the surface area of the

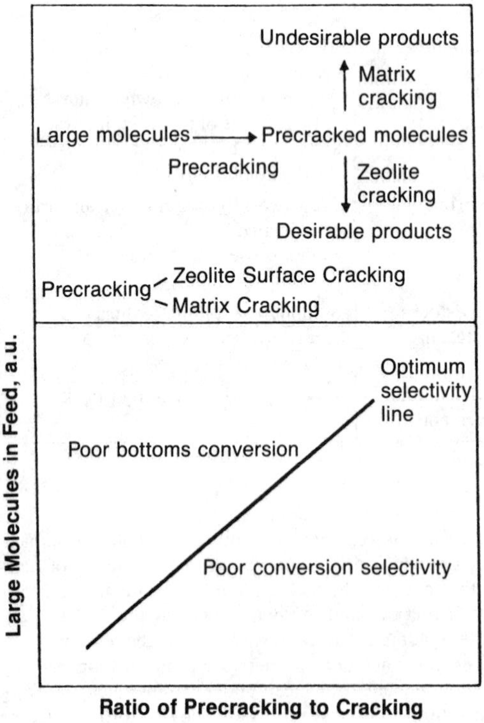

Figure 10. Simplified model for optimization of precracking [35].

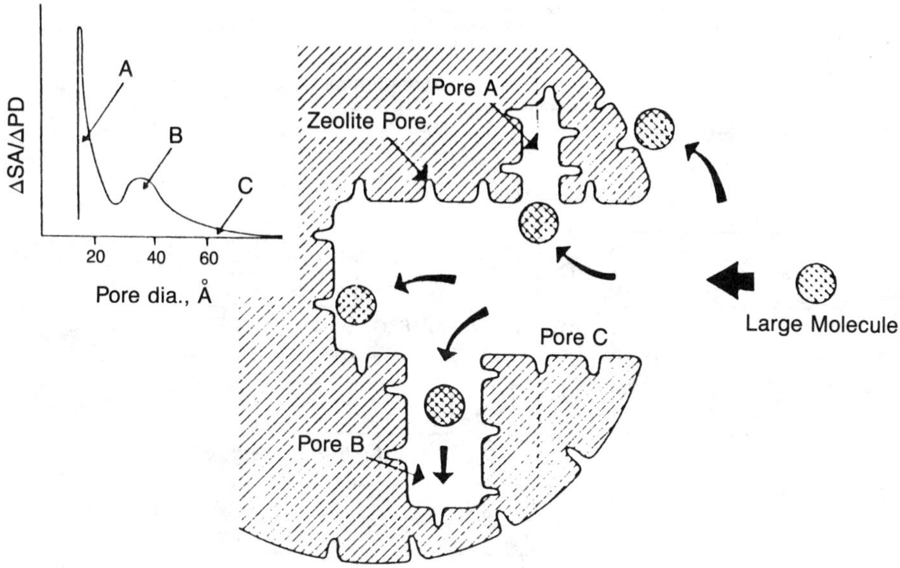

Figure 11. Effect of pore size distribution on bottoms conversion [35].

matrix. "C" pores are many times larger than the large molecules and are therefore readily accessible but they contribute only little to the surface area of the matrix. Matrices suitable for precracking large molecules must therefore have most of their surface area in pores of type "B." The zeolite incorporated into such matrix should be a low sodium dealuminized zeolite Y in the hydrogen form or partially exchanged with rare earth ions, or a deeply ion exchanged zeolite Y in the rare earth form, a so called calcined rare earth Y, CREY. Catalysts of this type will be further discussed a bit later.

In another approach to designing catalysts for heavy oils, materials with regular pore structures having pore sizes larger than those of zeolite Y are being used. One type of such materials is cross-linked smectites, which are discussed in more detail later.

Where Do Large Molecules Crack to What?

Nilsson et al. have investigated the contributions from zeolite, matrix, and thermal cracking to the conversion of large molecules over EKZ-4, a commercial cracking catalyst containing rare earth zeolite Y in a clay-binder matrix [36]. The feeds were prepared by fractionating a crude oil from Wilmington, California, USA according to the distillation scheme shown in Figure 12. A heavy vacuum gas oil (HVGO), used as MAT-standard feed, was included in their investigation. The boiling point ranges of the different feeds are shown in Figure 13 and the feedstock analysis in Table 5. The fractions were cracked at 560° and also at 500°C, with the exception of fraction 7, which did not vaporize completely at the lower temperature. The contributions of thermal and matrix cracking to the product yield were determined by cracking over alpha-alumina and matrix, respectively.

Figure 14 shows that the total conversion for the different fractions is roughly constant whereas the contribution from thermal cracking increases for the heavier fractions. In Figure 15 the overall conversion is separated into the contributions due to zeolite cracking, matrix cracking and thermal cracking. The cracking activity of zeolite decreases, which presumably reflects the difficulty of larger molecules to penetrate the pore structure of the zeolite.

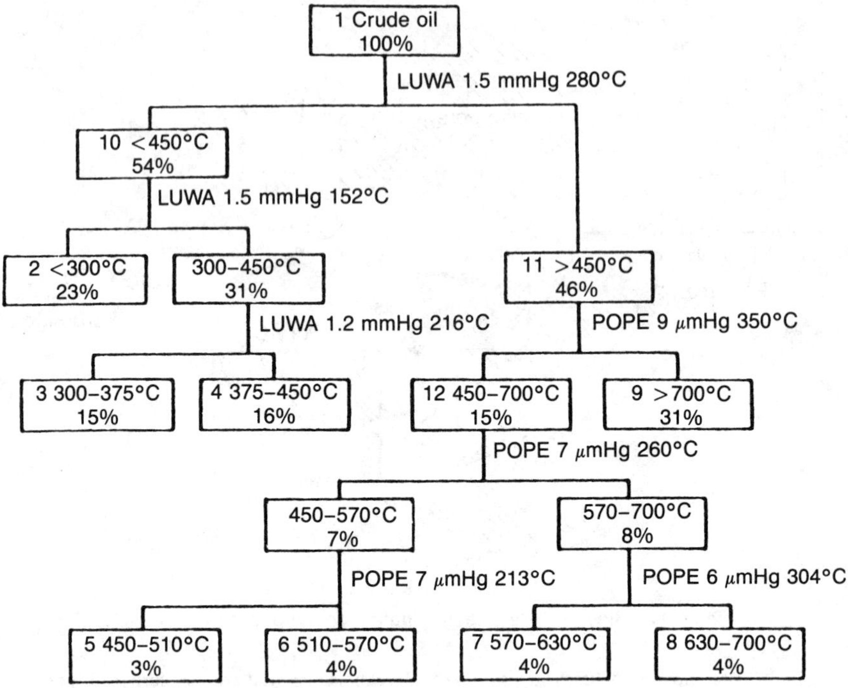

Figure 12. Distillation scheme. Yields given as volume % of crude oil [36].

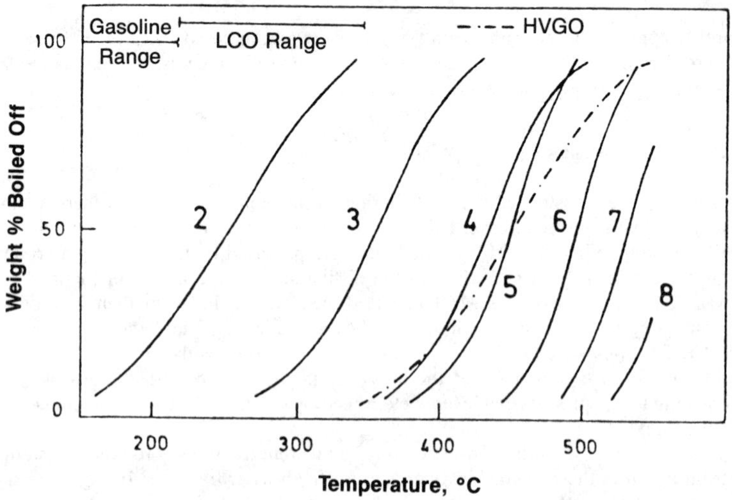

Figure 13. Boiling point ranges of the different oil fractions [35].

Table 5
Feedstock Analysis [36]

Analysis	Oil Fractions 4	5	6	7	8	HVGO
Simulated distillation[a] (5% off–95% off)	360–502	381–496	445–541	483–73% off at 548°C	519–28% off at 548%	346–544
Elementary analysis: (weight %)						
Carbon	84.4	84.6	84.3	84.8	84.4	87.0
Hydrogen	11.5	11.1	11.1	11.2	11.1	12.5
Nitrogen	0.53	0.64	0.75	0.84	0.87	0.10
Sulfur	1.64	1.75	2.05	2.27	2.40	0.40
Oxygen	0.64	0.61	0.65	0.80	1.02	0.33
Metals (ppm):						
Nickel	—	—	2	3	19	0.2
Vanadium	—	—	—	—	9	—
Sodium	—	—	0.6	0.7	7.6	—
Density (g/cm^3)[b]	.9510	.9703	.9750	.9789	.9852	.9058
Viscosity (cst, 50°C)[c]	97	236	972	2468	7725	34
Ramsbottom carbon[d] (weight %)	0.4	0.4	0.9	1.7	3.6	0.4

[a] *ASTM D 2887-73*, [b] *ASTM D 1298*, [c] *ASTM D 445*, [d] *ASTM D 524.*

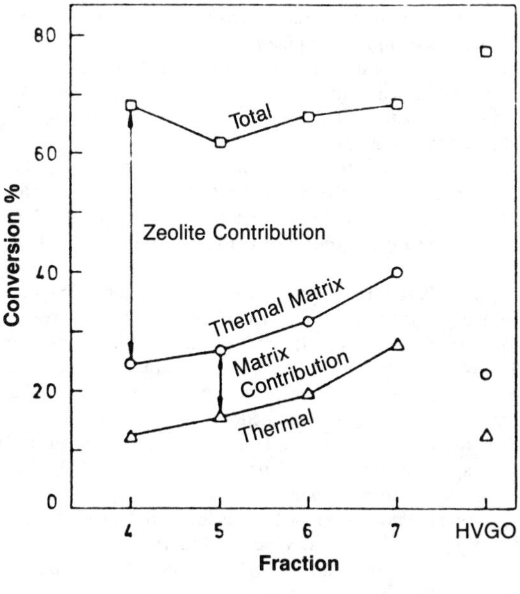

Figure 14. Conversion at 560°C as a function of feed and bed material. Cracking catalyst, EKZ 4 (□) Catalyst matrix, spraydried kaolin (○), thermal cracking, α-alumina (△) [36].

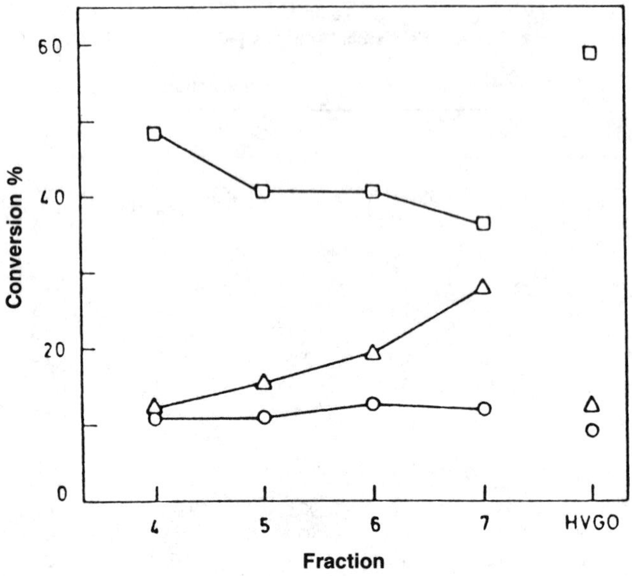

Figure 15. Conversion at 560°C separated into contributions from the zeolite and the matrix. Zeolite cracking (□), matrix cracking (○), thermal cracking (△) [36].

Table 6 shows the product yields for catalytic, matrix and thermal cracking for the different feeds. The coke yields increase for the different cracking processes with increasing boiling point of the fractions. The coke yield from different oil fractions on alpha-alumina increases as the Ramsbottom carbon of the cut, whereas the coke on the zeolite, as the difference between the total coke and the coke on the matrix and from the thermal cracking, is nearly the same for the different fractions. The conversion of the HVGO is about 10% higher than that of the Wilmington cuts but the zeolite coke yield is somewhat lower, reflecting differences in compositions between the feeds.

The amount of gas formed in catalytic cracking is fairly constant when comparing the yields from the different fractions. The yields from cracking on the matrix and the alpha-alumina increase with boiling point of the feed. The gas yield from the heavy vacuum gas oil is higher than from the Wilmington fractions indicating that the former oil more readily overcracked at high temperatures.

The overall gasoline yield is constant for the different fractions, whereas the gasoline formed by matrix and thermal cracking increases, implying that the gasoline formed on the zeolite decreases with increasing boiling point of the fractions. The investigators determined the gasoline formed on the zeolite and the matrix and Figure 16 shows that the zeolite contribution to the gasoline yield decreases while it is almost constant on the matrix. The HVGO yields more gasoline on the zeolite, whereas the gasoline yield on the matrix is the same for all oils studied.

The yields of light cycle oil on the catalyst and the matrix decrease for the first two fractions but increase for the heaviest cuts. This effect is especially pronounced for the matrix, indicating that the moderate activity of this material minimizes further cracking of formed light cycle oil into lighter materials. Furthermore, under given cracking conditions, a heavier feed will generally yield products in a higher boiling point range than a lighter feed. The yield from thermal cracking also shows a sharp increase for the heavier cuts, which indicates that the high amount of LCO from the matrix is at least partly a result of contributions from thermal reactions.

The results of this investigation show that the catalyst matrix plays a more important role when cracking the high boiling fractions, whereas the efficiency of the zeolite is reduced due to diffusional

Table 6
Yields of Coke, Gas, Gasoline, and Light Cycle Oil (LCO) at 560°C [36]

	Yields from Different Feeds/Weight % of feed														
	4			5			6			7			HVGO		
	A	B	C	A	B	C	A	B	C	A	B	C	A	B	C
Coke	6.9	1.1	.2	7.7	1.4	.2	9.0	2.6	.3	10.0	3.8	.7	5.9	.8	.3
Gas	21	9	5	18	8	7	19	9	7	21	13	10	25	8	6
Gasoline	40	15	8	36	17	8	38	20	12	37	23	17	46	14	6
Conversion	68	25	13	62	26	15	66	32	19	68	40	28	77	23	12
LCO	18	14	7	15	13	7	16	18	8	18	23	14	14	14	9
Uncracked (HCO)	14	61	80	23	61	78	18	50	73	14	37	58	9	63	79

A—Catalytic cracking (EKZ 4)
B—Matrix cracking (spray dried kaolin)
C—Thermal cracking (χ-alumina)

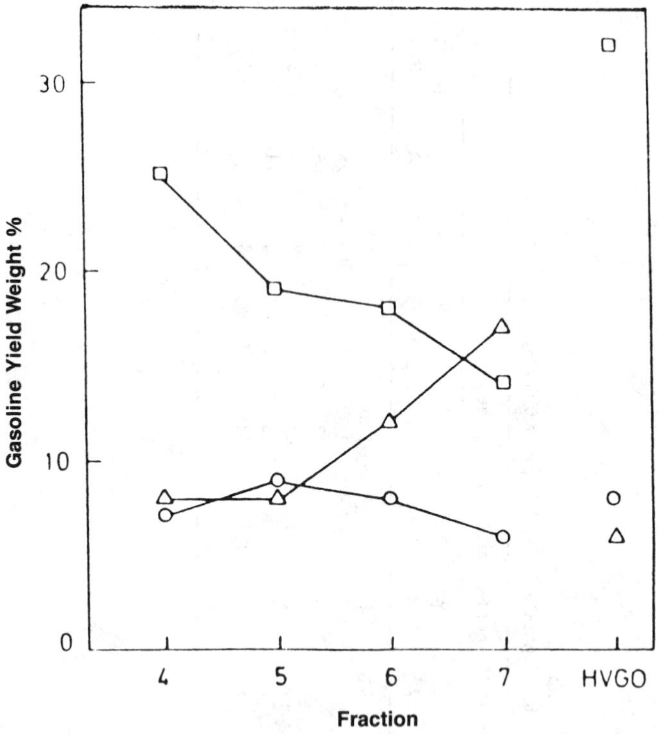

Figure 16. Gasoline yields at 560°C separated into the contributions from the zeolite and the matrix. Zeolite cracking, (□), matrix cracking, (○), thermal cracking, (△) [36].

barriers for the larger molecules in these cuts. The moderate activity of the matrix gives it a high selectivity for light cycle oils, whereas the higher activity of the cracking catalyst, due to the zeolite, tends to crack this products further into lighter compounds.

The investigators also point out the importance of characterizing the chemical composition of a feed for catalytic cracking. Although fractions 4 and 5 have very similar boiling point ranges and chemical and physical properties, they show quite different behavior in the cracking tests. The boiling point range of the HVGO is somewhere between fractions 5 and 6 but the cracking tests show that this oil is more readily converted by the cracking catalyst. Nilsson and Otterstedt (37) have characterized fractions 4 through 7 by nuclear magnetic resonance spectrometry, gel permeation chromatography, and bonded phase liquid chromatography before and after catalytic cracking. Figure 17 shows that the molecular weights of the different feed stocks increase with boiling point. The molecular weights calculated from the response of the UV detector are lower compared to those obtained from the refractive index, RI, detector since aromatic rings, due to their more condensed structure, occupy a smaller volume and has a larger retention volume compared to a straight hydrocarbon chain of the same molecular weight. Fractions 4 and 5 have the same molecular weights, as calculated from the refractive index detector response, which is supported by the great similarities in their boiling point curves; see Figure 13. The molecular weight as determined from the UV response, however, shows a steady increase with boiling point. The similarity in the refractive index response is probably an effect of a change in composition of the saturate fraction, not detected by the UV detector, towards more naphthenic compounds, which, due to their more condensed structure, will elute at the same time as straight-chain paraffins with lower molecular weights.

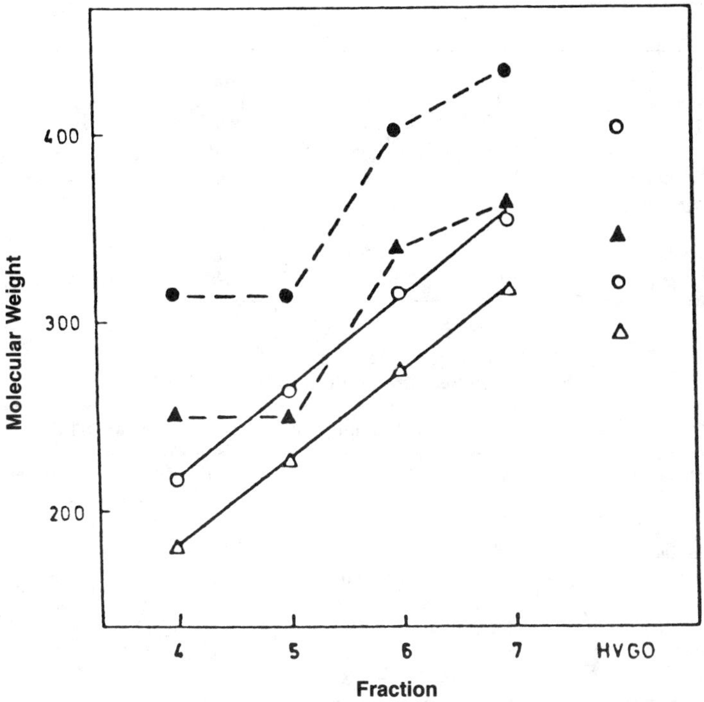

Figure 17. Molecular weights of the different feedstocks determined by gel permeation chromatography. Weight average molecular weight, (M_w), refractive index detector (RI) (●); number average molecular weight (M_n), (RI) (▲), UV detector (○); (M_n), UV (△) [37].

Tables 7 and 8 show that the distribution of molecular types in the liquid products after cracking at 500 and 600°C shifts towards more aromatics, particularly monoaromatics, and polars with increasing boiling point range of the feed. The yields of monoaromatic increase at the higher temperature at the expense of polynuclear aromatics and polars. The conversion of polars decreases with increasing boiling point of the feed at 500°C but increases with the boiling point at 560°C, indicating that polars are readily converted by thermal reactions to products in the gasoline range.

Table 6 shows that fraction 5 gave a significantly lower conversion than fraction 4, indicating a basic difference in composition between the two fractions. The amount of polars in fractions 4 and 5 are almost equal but more of these compounds from fraction 4 are converted. Fraction 5 is the light end of four step-wise distillations, see Figure 12, whereas fraction four is the heavy end from three distillation steps at lower cutpoints. Obviously, the heavy end of fraction 4 contains compounds susceptible to thermal decomposition that has been separated from fraction 5 in the distillation process. This fraction has a lower content of polars than expected and the contribution to the overall conversion from the decomposition of these molecules is low compared to the other fractions. A more detailed analysis of the polar fractions is, however, necessary to reveal the structures that readily decompose into light products of the gasoline boiling point range.

Otterstedt et al. have studied fluid catalytic cracking of mixtures of atmospheric resids with heavy vacuum gas oil in a pilot scale continuously circulating fluid catalytic cracking unit with 0, 15, and 30 wt% resid at reactor temperatures 482, 510, and 538°C [38]. The catalyst was an equilibrium EKZ-3, made by Katalistiks BV, obtained from a commercial FCC-unit. The properties of the feedstocks are shown in Table 9. The resid lowered the conversion (case 1) or the yields of the gasoline

Table 7
Product Distribution from Catalytic Cracking at 560°C in Weight % [37]

	4	5	6	7	HVGO
Saturates	55.8	53.9	37.9	31.0	66.7
Monoaromatics	32.8	32.4	45.4	52.1	23.3
Diaromatics	4.5	3.8	4.4	4.8	5.1
Fluorene	.37	.35	.35	.36	.34
3-ring compounds	1.7	1.8	1.8	1.9	1.9
4-ring compounds	1.4	1.5	1.8	1.8	1.2
Polars	3.2	5.9	8.7	8.2	1.6
Polars in feedstock	10.3	11.5	20.1	26.6	4.4
difference	−7.1	−5.6	−11.4	−17.8	−2.8

Table 8
Effect of Temperature on Product Distribution [37]

	Weight % at 560°C–Weight % at 500°C				
	4	5	6	7	HVGO
Saturates	—	—	—	—	—
Monoaromatics	8.6	8.3	14.8	—	2.9
Diaromatics	−3.6	−4.6	−3.6	—	−1.0
Fluorene	−.19	−.26	−.19	—	−.10
3-ring compounds	−1.0	−1.4	−.50	—	−.44
4-ring compounds	−1.1	−.74	−1.5	—	−.53
Polars	−2.9	−1.8	−9.2	—	−.70

Table 9
Analysis of Feedstocks [38]

	HVGO	Atmospheric Resid
Origin	North sea	60% North sea 40% Nigeria
Density at 15°C, g/cm³	0.9058	0.9468
°API	24.6	17.9
Viscosity at 50°C, cst	34	190
Conradson carbon residue, wt%	0.4	6.4
Hydrogen, wt%	12.5	11.6
Carbon, wt%	87.0	86.8
Nitrogen, wt%	0.1	0.3
Sulphur, wt%	0.4	1.3
Nickel, ppm	0.2	14
Vanadium, ppm	0.1	28
Simulated distillation, °C IBP	256	230
10 wt%	361	339
30 wt%	412	410
50 wt%	445	467
70 wt%	478	556
90 wt%	523	—
FBP	600	—

Erdöl und Kohle—Erdgas—Petrochemie vereinigt mit Brennstoff-Chemie

Table 10
Conversion and Product Yield of Resid [38]

	AVGO Base Case	15% Atmospheric Resid + 85% AVGO		
		Case 1	Case 2	Case 3
Reactor conditions				
Temperature, °C	482	482	523	482
WHSV, h^{-1}	39	39	39	20
C/O, wt/wt	4	4	4	4
Conversion, wt%	70	41.1	70	70
Yields				
Coke, wt%	1.4	2.1	4.8	6.0
Gas, wt%	15.0	17.8	54.8	29.5
Gasoline, wt%	53.8	21.2	10.3	34.2
LCO, wt%	14.0	18.5	7.5	18.1
ACO, wt%	16.0	40.4	22.6	12.1

and light cycle oils (case 2), whereas those of coke and gases increased. Table 10 shows the conversion and product yields when heavy gas oil containing 15 wt% resid is cracked at three different sets of operating conditions. The base case corresponds to cracking a 100% heavy vacuum gas oil. Case 1 shows that resid undergoes 41% conversion when heavy vacuum gas oil containing 15 wt% resid is cracked under the same conditions as in the base case. The conversion of resid can be increased to 70% by raising the reactor temperature to 523°C as is shown in case 2, or, as is shown in case 3, by reducing the space velocity from 39 to 20. The response of the feed stock to an increase in temperature is less favorable than those of Wilmington fractions 6 and 7, see Tables 6–8, which probably is due to severe overcracking of the HVGO, masking the beneficial effect of increased reaction temperature on the cracking of the resid fraction.

Effect of Zeolite and Matrix Type on Cracking Heavy Oils

Otterstedt et al. [39] have done a systematic study on the effects of alumina addition to the matrix of cracking catalysts, containing different types of zeolite Y, on the cracking performance of these catalysts when cracking HVGO and Wilmington fraction number 6; see Table 5. Catalysts containing REY, CREY, USY and REUSY in kaolin-binder and in kaolin-alumina-binder matrices were prepared and investigated for catalytic cracking using an MAT-unit. After deactivation at 790°C for 18 hours in 100% steam.

Figure 18 shows the dependence of conversion upon catalyst to oil ratio when cracking Wilmington oil number 6 over the different catalysts containing zeolites in active and in active matrices. At a given catalyst to oil ratio, the catalysts containing active matrices result in higher conversions showing that the matrix indeed does contribute to the conversion. As the contribution of zeolite component to the conversion decreases, due to degradation in the deactivation procedure, the contribution from the matrix becomes increasingly important.

Figures 19 and 20 show that the gasoline and LCO yields are higher over catalysts containing an active matrix. Furthermore, the authors found that the coke and gas yields also were higher over catalysts with an active matrix.

Mott [40] has developed a new method for interpreting MAT-results which he calls "dynamic activity" and which is claimed to more directly correspond to the activity which the catalyst would give in a commercial FCCU. A plot of second conversion, that is conversion (wt%)/(100 − conversion (wt%)) versus coke yield results in a straight line with an intercept with the abscissa representing the Conradson of the feed oil and a slope giving the dynamic activity of the catalyst. A steeper slope, that is a higher dynamic activity, indicates a better ability for the catalyst to

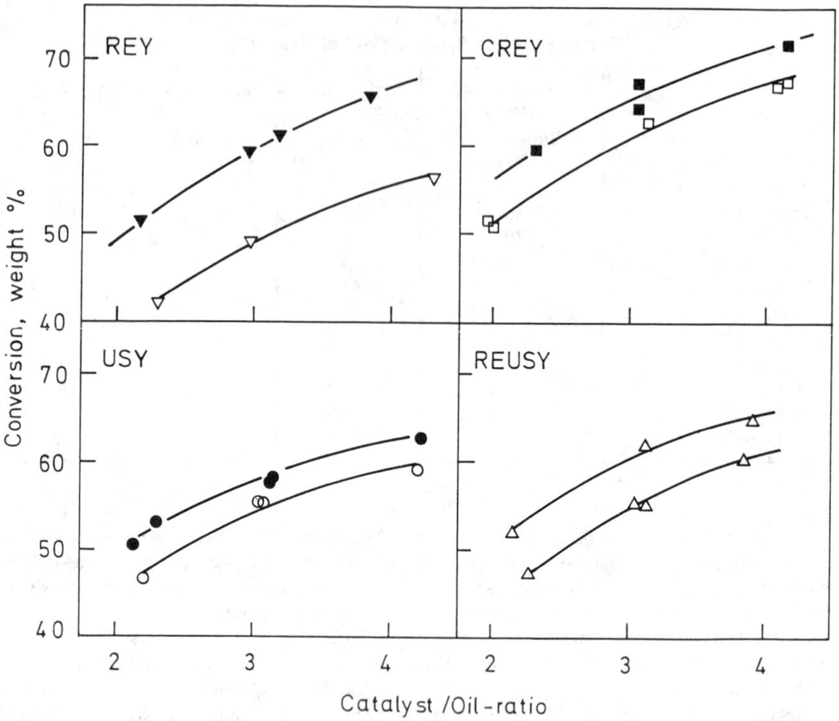

Figure 18. Dependence of MAT-conversion on catalyst to oil ratio when cracking oil no. 6 over catalysts containing different zeolites in active (solid symbols) and inactive (open symbols) matrices [39].

convert the feed commercially. This concept was used by the authors for evaluating the FCCU cracking performance of the catalyst studied in their investigation. Figure 21 shows the second order conversion versus coke yield when cracking HVGO and oil number 6 over the different catalysts containing zeolites in active and inactive matrices. From these plots it is clear, that for all types of zeolites and both oil feeds, the catalysts having inactive matrices would perform better in a commercial FCCU compared with those containing active matrices in spite of the fact that the latter type of catalyst is more active according to the standard MAT evaluation.

The surface of boehmite that has been exposed to temperatures of a regenerator, typically 700–800°C, will contain predominantly Lewis acid sites (41). Such sites are catalytically active with a preponderance for coke making in processes like catalytic cracking [42]. The high surface area alumina component of the active matrix is therefore responsible for the non-selective cracking behavior, that is high coke and gas yield characteristic of such a matrix. Alumina as an active component of the catalyst is one example of the approach to cracking heavy oils involving incorporation of various types of zeolite Y in active matrices. With the right contributions of external surface of zeolite crystals and properties of the matrix surface, for instance total acidity and the ratio between Lewis and Bronstedt acid sites, an optimum selectivity in the precracking step on the matrix surface can be achieved. The results of the reported study indicate that the properties of the alumina surface do not lead to an optimum selectivity for desired products.

In another approach, more reliance is put on the ability of the zeolite component to crack heavy molecules, although it is well known that the pore opening of such zeolites, about 8 Å, are too

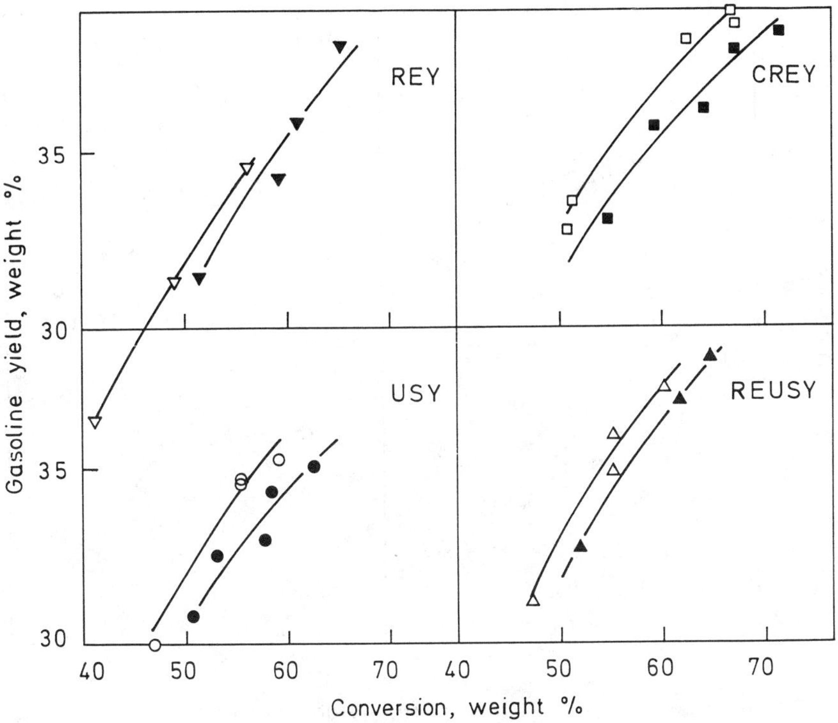

Figure 19. Dependence of MAT gasoline yields on conversion when cracking oil no. 6 over catalysts containing different zeolites in active (solid symbols) and inactive (open symbols) matrices [39].

small to admit the large molecules present in heavy oils. Nevertheless, it has been reported that cracking catalysts containing USY are more efficient "bottoms" catalysts than those containing REY [43]. Moreover, Rabo [44] has recently discovered that significant changes occur in the crystal structure of USY and dealuminated-silicon-enriched zeolites of the type LZ-210 (Union Carbide) upon hydrothermal treatment. During the steam treatment aluminum ions are removed from the framework sites and replaced by silicon ions. The effect of the redistribution of framework silicon ions is to reduce the high concentration of defect sites (Al-vacancies) ultimately, this steam-induced recrystallization results in the formation of near defect-free silicon-rich lattice segments, and 20–300 Å size intracrystalline cavities, that is a secondary pore structure, throughout the zeolite crystals. The debris, consisting of amorphous alumina or alumina-silica, is deposited in the secondary pores where it can effect cracking of large molecules, typical of the heavy cycle oil (HCO) fraction (defined as: wt% HCO = 100 – wt% LCO). The higher LCO- and thus lower HCO- yields observed for the USY and REUSY catalysts when compared with REY and CREY catalysts at the same conversion, see Figure 20, indeed indicate a better ability for catalysts containing ultrastable zeolite Y to crack heavy feeds to desirable products.

Cross-Linked Smectites as Catalysts for Cracking Heavy Oils

Since smectites, pillared or cross-linked with inorganic polycations, were first reported in the late seventies, a major objective has been to prepare materials of this type suitable as catalysts for

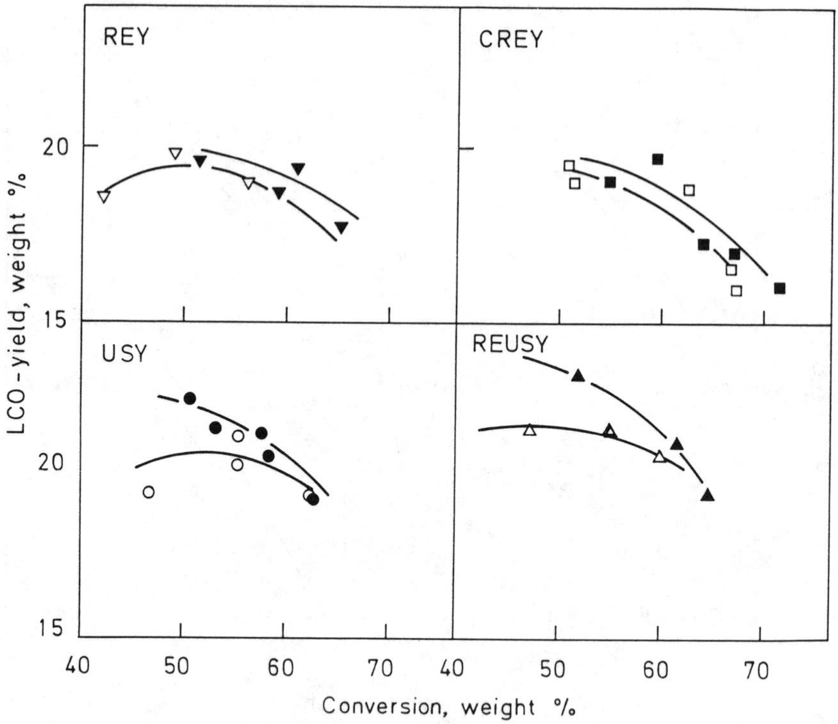

Figure 20. Dependence of MAT LCO yields on conversion when cracking oil no. 6 over catalysts containing different zeolites in active (solid symbols) and inactive (open symbols) matrices [39].

catalytic cracking of heavy oil fractions. These materials are particularly interesting for this application as they can be prepared with pore openings larger than those in zeolite Y. The use of previously reported pillared smectites for this purpose, is however, limited by their lack of thermal and hydro-thermal stability. At the thermal and hydro-thermal conditions in the regenerator of a fluid catalytic cracker, these materials rapidly lose most of their surface area and their catalytic activity.

The potential of these materials as catalysts for cracking was first demonstrated by Vaughan et al. [45] by cracking a gas oil over a sample of aluminum oxide pillared montmorillonite. The sample was exposed to a temperature of 530°C for 3 hrs. prior to the test, which is considerably less severe than the conditions in a typical regenerator, and it showed a micro activity test (MAT) conversion of 77.3%. By hydrothermal treatment of the basic aluminum chloride solution used in the preparation and by co-polymerizing with silica Vaughan et al. [46] succeeded in preparing a pillared smectite with an MAT-activity, after steam treatment at 677°C for 8 hrs., comparable to that of a commercial REY catalyst treated in the same manner. Occelli and Tindwa [47] studied the thermal effects on the surface area and catalytic cracking activity of aluminum oxide pillared montmorillonite. They found that the activity of samples activated at temperatures of up to 540°C was similar to that of a commercial clay based cracking catalyst containing 15 wt% zeolite. At higher temperatures, a progressive collapse of the pillared structures occured with a corresponding decrease in surface area and in cracking activity.

The product distribution when cracking a gas oil over pillared smectites was further investigated by Occelli [48]. After mild hydro-thermal deactivation the pillared clay was found to be as active

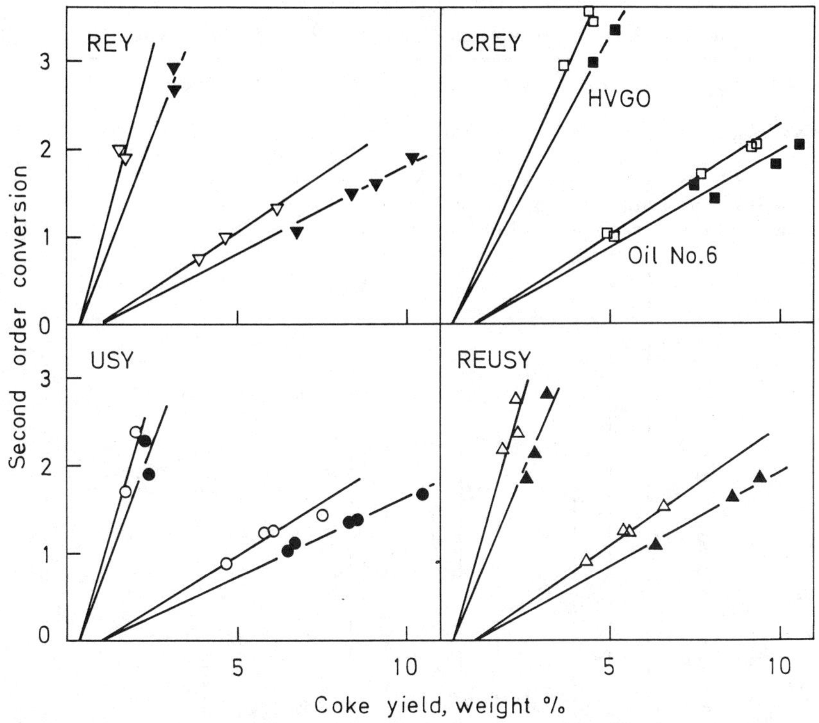

Figure 21. Relationship between second order conversion and coke yield when cracking HVGO and oil no. 6 over catalysts containing different zeolites in active (solid symbols) and inactive (closed symbols) matrices [39].

as certain commercial FCC catalysts and showed a greater light cycle oil (LCO) selectivity and greater carbon, hydrogen and light gas make.

Sterte and Otterstedt [49] reported on the preparation and properties of alumina-montmorillonite complexes prepared by interacting montmorillonite with positively charged, fibrillar boehmite particles. In another study [50], some physical and chemical properties including thermal and hydrothermal stability, of these materials were reported. Sterte and Otterstedt [51] have studied the catalytic cracking of Wilmington fractions 4 and 6 and HVGO, over alumina-montmorillonite complexes prepared from aluminum chlorohydrate solutions hydrothermally treated at temperatures of 120 and 140°C. The study also included the cracking over these materials when used as matrices in admixtures with rare earth exchanged zeolite Y.

Surface areas and pore volumes of catalysts used in their investigation are shown in Table 11 where M1 is a reference catalyst containing 20% rare earth exchanged zeolite Y (REY) in a kaolin-binder matrix. M2, M3 and M4 are catalysts prepared from untreated aluminum chlorohydrate (ACH) solution and from ACH-solutions hydrothermally treated at 120° and 140°C respectively. Z2, Z3, and Z4 are the corresponding montmorillonite catalysts containing 20% REY. Z1 is a reference catalyst similar to M1. Figure 22 shows the result of acidity measurements, using pyridine adsorption, for the fresh and deactivated alumina-montmorillonites and for the reference catalyst [50]. The fresh sample, prepared from the untreated ACH solution, shows a very high pyridine adsorption, whereas the adsorption of the fresh samples prepared from ACH-solutions treated at 120° and 140°C is somewhat lower. For the steam deactivated samples, the reverse situation is observed. Whereas the sample prepared from the untreated ACH-solution retains very little of its

Table 11
Surface Areas and Pore Volumes of Catalysts Used in this Study [51]

Catalyst[a]	M1	M2	M3	M4	Z1	Z2	Z3	Z4
Surface area, m^2/g^b	115	61	113	143	92	176	139	214
Pore volume, cm^3/g^b	0.11	0.11	0.17	0.26	0.14	0.18	0.21	0.31

[a] *All samples were steam treated at 750°C for 18 hr. prior to measurements.*
[b] *Surface areas and pore volumes measured by nitrogen adsorption.*

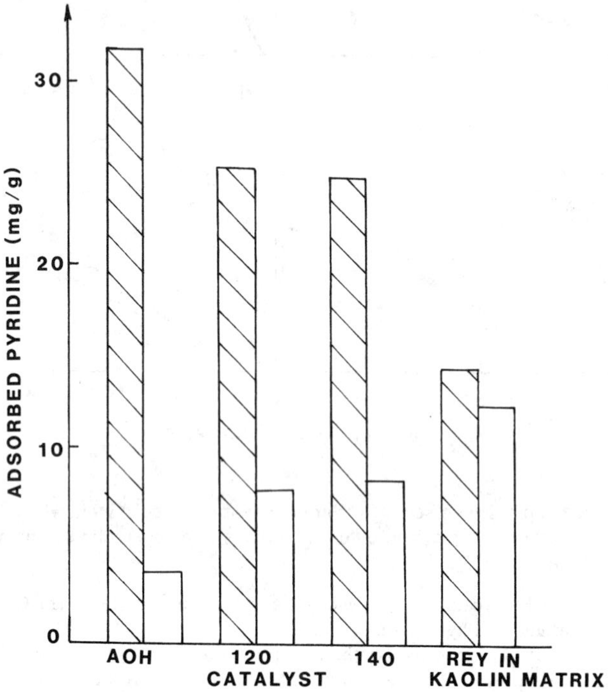

Figure 22. Adsorption of pyridine by fresh (solid staples) and steam treated (open staples) alumina-montmorillonites [50].

original acidity, the samples prepared from the solutions treated at 120°C and 140°C show a much higher acidity retention. The acidity of the reference catalyst decreases only slightly upon steaming at 750°C for 18 hrs.

Table 12 shows the MAT-cracking results of cracking Wilmington oils number 4 (at 500°C) and number 6 (at 560°C) over the different alumina-montmorillonite complexes and over the reference catalyst M1. The conversions of the cross-linked montmorillonites follow the same order as the surface areas shown in Table 11 with the exception of oil number 6 at 500°C, which is probably due to poor volatilization of this oil at 500°C. Catalyst M4 converts oil number 6 at 560°C more efficiently than the reference catalyst M1.

At the same conversion level, the cross-linked montmorillonites appear to produce more coke and less gas than the reference catalyst while the gasoline yields are essentially the same or somewhat higher than those over the reference catalyst (exception: oil number 4 over M1 at 500°C).

Table 12
MAT-Cracking Results for Alumina-Montmorillonite Complexes [51]

Catalyst Designation	Oil No.	Conversion Wt%	Gasoline Wt%	Coke Wt%	Gas Wt%	LCO Wt%	t °C
M1	4	56.0	31.8	10.2	14.0	13.4	500
M2	4	21.3	12.6	4.2	4.5	11.6	500
M3	4	42.9	24.2	9.8	9.0	17.1	500
M4	4	50.0	28.9	10.7	11.0	19.3	500
M1	6	47.6	22.6	12.7	11.7	9.3	500
M2	6	23.3	13.2	5.4	4.7	8.9	500
M3	6	46.4	24.6	12.6	9.2	16.4	500
M4	6	51.1	25.5	15.3	10.3	17.1	500
M1	6	52.9	23.3	13.2	16.5	12.4	560
M2	6	33.4	17.9	6.5	9.0	15.0	560
M3	6	54.5	24.7	15.0	14.8	18.2	560
M4	6	61.3	26.3	19.2	15.8	18.6	560

The alumina-montmorillonite complexes showed a much higher selectivity for light cycle oil (LCO) compared with the reference zeolite catalyst. This was also observed by Occelli in a study of conventional alumina pillared montmorillonite [48]. The investigators found, as Nilsson et al. [36], that heavy oils such as Wilmington oil number 6 are more efficiently converted at higher temperatures. At 560°C, the gasoline + LCO yields are 44.9% and 35.7% for the alumina-montmorillonite catalyst M4 and the reference catalyst M1, respectively, whereas at 500°C the combined yields are 42.6% and 31.9%.

Table 13 shows the distribution of molecular types in the liquid products from the cracking reactions, as measured by bonded phase chromatography. At 500°C, the responses of the different molecular types to cracking over the alumina-montmorillonite catalysts, as exemplified by catalyst M4 and the reference catalyst M1, are the same. At 560°C, the alumina-montmorillonite catalyst M4 converts polar hydrocarbons more efficiently into liquid products than the reference M1, as was also found by Nilsson and Otterstedt [37]. At both temperatures, but particularly so at the higher temperature, the content of monoaromatics increases significantly.

Table 14 shows the results of cracking oil number 4 (at 500°C), HVGO (at 500°C), and oil number 6 (at 560°C) over the different alumina-montmorillonites in admixture with zeolite Y and the reference catalyst Z1. All the alumina-montmorillonite catalysts showed higher conversion than the reference catalyst. Z4, containing montmorillonite complexed with ACH hydrothermally treated at 140°C, had higher gasoline yields than the reference catalyst at all conditions studied.

The large difference in conversion between the reference catalyst and the zeolite containing alumina-montmorillonites made a conclusive comparison of selectivity patterns for the different

Table 13
Hydrocarbon Distribution in Liquid Cracking Products Using Alumina-Montmorillonite Complexes/wt% [51]

Catalyst designation	M1	M2	M3	M4	oil no. 4	M1	M2	M3	M4	oil no. 6
Feed oil, no.	4	4	4	4	—	6	6	6	6	—
Reactor temperature, °C	500	500	500	500	—	560	560	560	560	—
Linear hydrocarbons, wt%	45.8	49.9	42.1	45.1	55.2	24.5	27.2	26.5	23.3	46.5
Monoaromatics, wt%	37.0	34.9	40.6	37.7	27.1	52.0	50.2	54.2	55.9	26.1
Diaromatics, wt%	5.9	3.9	5.1	5.2	3.5	4.3	2.8	3.5	5.2	2.6
Triaromatics, wt%	1.9	1.0	1.9	2.0	1.0	0.8	0.5	0.9	1.3	0.6
Polar hydrocarbons, wt%	9.2	10.3	10.2	10.0	13.2	18.3	19.1	14.9	14.4	24.1

Table 14
MAT-Cracking Results for REY Containing Alumina-Montmorillonites [51]

Catalyst Designation	Oil No.	Conversion Wt%	Gasoline Wt%	Coke Wt%	Gas Wt%	LCO Wt%	t °C
Z1	4	52.7	32.5	8.4	11.8	15.7	500
Z2	4	64.7	36.9	11.6	16.2	11.1	500
Z3	4	63.8	35.1	12.0	16.7	11.8	500
Z4	4	74.0	41.6	14.5	17.9	13.3	500
Z1	6	57.2	27.6	12.7	17.0	15.1	560
Z2	6	62.3	26.6	15.3	20.4	9.9	560
Z3	6	63.1	27.9	15.6	19.6	11.1	560
Z4	6	72.1	30.4	19.6	22.1	12.7	560
Z1	HVGO	73.3	47.1	8.6	17.6	14.5	500
Z2	HVGO	78.2	46.5	9.9	21.8	10.7	500
Z3	HVGO	79.7	46.8	10.4	22.5	11.3	500
Z4	HVGO	83.7	49.5	12.6	21.6	10.4	500

Table 15
Gasoline, Gas, Coke and LCO Yields of Catalysts Z1–Z4 When Cracking Oil No. 4 at a MAT-Conversion of 64.0 wt%/wt% [51]

Catalyst Designation	Gasoline Wt%	Gas Wt%	Coke Wt%	LCO Wt%
Z1	36.4	16.2	11.4	14.8
Z2	36.7	16.0	11.4	11.2
Z3	35.2	16.7	12.0	11.8
Z4	37.5	15.2	11.2	14.8

catalysts difficult. The investigators therefore determined the conversion as a function of catalyst to oil ratio and obtained the results shown in Table 15. The alumina-montmorillonite catalysts have nearly the same gasoline, gas and coke yields as the reference catalysts. Possibly, Z4 has a somewhat better selectivity for gasoline than the reference catalyst.

Sterte's and Otterstedt's results indicate that the hydrothermal stability of montmorillonite pillared with hydrothermally treated aluminum chlorohydrate solutions has been improved to a level where they begin to look as interesting candidates for "bottom of the barrel" catalysts. The pore structure of these materials is such that large molecules present in heavy oils readily can enter the structure and there undergo efficient cracking. The surface area of the material can be provided with an acidity which makes the activity and selectivity quite similar to zeolitic cracking catalysts.

SPECIAL TECHNIQUES IN CRACKING OF HEAVY OILS

As mentioned earlier, heavy oils inherently contain high contents of contaminant metals, particularly vanadium and nickel, high contents of sulfur and nitrogen and high levels of coke-forming hydrocarbons (high carbon residue). Each of these characteristics create problems within the FCCU, which require special techniques to minimize the difficulties that they create.

Metals Control Techniques

The deposition of contaminant metals upon cracking catalysts causes a variety of problems. Vanadium has been shown [19, 23, 52] to cause a significant loss of catalyst activity. It is believed

[23] to deactivate the catalyst by migrating over the matrix surface to a molecular sieve site where it forms a eutectic compound with the sieve. The eutectic then fluxes at temperatures of 630°C or higher (a temperature achieved in nearly all FCCU regenerators) and destroys the sieve.

Nickel on the other hand does not seem to have a major effect upon catalyst deactivation. It has been found [53, 54], however, to strongly catalyze non-selective cracking reactions producing large amounts of coke and hydrogen.

Vanadium

Techniques to protect the catalyst against vanadium attack have largely been directed towards matrix modifications. This has been achieved by incorporating into the catalyst matrix system, components that can trap the vanadium away from the molecular sieve [55, 56, 57]. One of the most commonly used techniques is to use a high surface area, active component in the matrix such as active alumina. Figure 23 illustrates this type of protection against vanadium for three REY catalysts containing various amounts of matrix surface area. The moderate and high matrix surface area containing catalysts have clearly better vanadium tolerance over the catalyst with a low matrix surface area.

Other compounds containing calcium [58] and magnesium [59] and, more recently, barium titanate [60] have been found in laboratory tests to have vanadium trapping capabilities. Difficulties

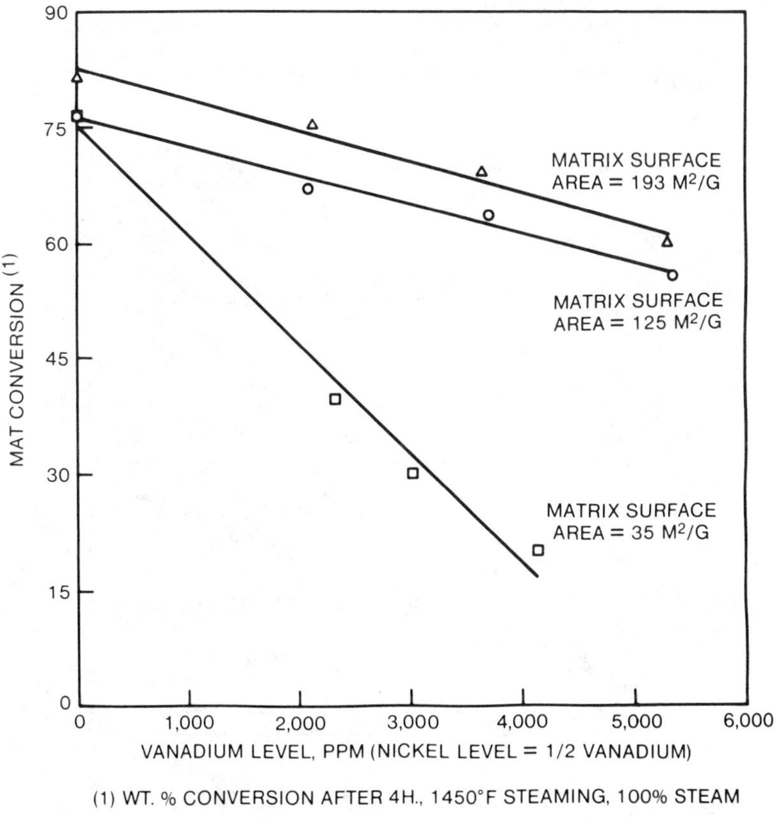

Figure 23. High matrix surface area catalysts resist vanadium poisoning [55].

with some of these materials have been experienced in actual commercial use due to the susceptibility of these materials to sulfur poisoning.

Chemical treatment via the continuous addition of a vanadium passivating additive to the FCCU feed has also been proposed [61]. Figure 24 illustrates the results of a commercial test run using such an additive. As seen, the use of such an additive was accompanied by an increase in equilibrium catalyst microactivity from 64 to 67 even though the vanadium on catalyst increased from 2,250 ppm to 2,550 ppm.

Some catalyst work has also shown that the type of sieve used in the catalyst can also effect vanadium resistance. Specifically, catalysts containing the new LZ-210 sieves have been shown (62) to have improved vanadium resistance.

Nickel

The most commonly used approach to control the non-selective catalytic effect of nickel has been through the use of an antimony containing additive. Philips Petroleum [63] first introduced this technology in 1976, and it has gained wide acceptance since then. In this procedure antimony is deposited on the circulating FCC equilibrium catalyst by injecting a proprietary antimony containing liquid continuously into the feed to the cat cracker. The injected material effectively reduces the undesired H2 producing activity of nickel without deactivating the FCC catalyst. Some commercial data reported by Phillips [63] is shown in Table 16. As shown there, the use of their metals passivation technique reduced H2 production by an average of 44% for the 9 different commercial applications reported. The use of antimony has also been said to reduce the effect of nickel upon catalytic coke formation. This, however, has been more difficult to document.

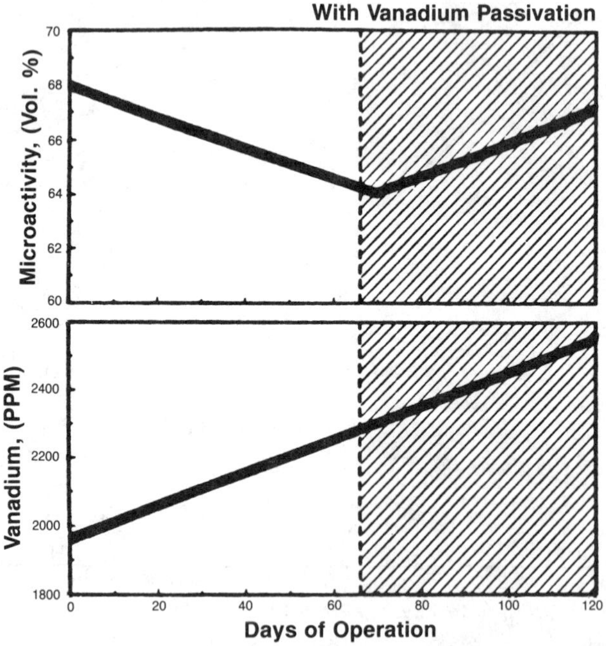

Figure 24. Effect of vanadium on equilibrium catalyst activity with/without continuous vanadium passivation [61).

Table 16
Hydrogen Yield Decrease Experienced by Phillips Licensees Using Metals Passivation [63]

Licensee	Catalyst 4 Ni + V ppm	Hydrogen Yield SCF/B FF Unpassivated	Passivated	% Change
1	3,600	92	58	37
2	16,200	202	104	49
3	6,540	64	21	67
4	10,820	126	62	51
5	8,800	87	55	37
6	6,140	161	103	36
7	8,300	105	85	19
8	10,800	71	19	73
9	9,300	159	109	31
				44 (Average)

The amount of antimony deposited upon equilibrium catalyst is usually adjusted so that the antimony content on the catalyst is in the range of 15–20% of the nickel on the catalyst. The use of antimony is most effective when the catalyst nickel content is over 1,500 ppmw.

The effect of nickel can also be strongly influenced by sieve characteristics. For example the new LZ-210, reduced framework alumina sieves have been found to be less sensitive to the effect of contaminant metals than other sieve systems. This is seen in Figures 25 and 26 [64] where two Katalistiks' catalysts containing the same maxtix component, very similar rare earth exchanged levels, and the same amount of sieve are compared. Beta 640, which contains the LZ-210 sieve, is

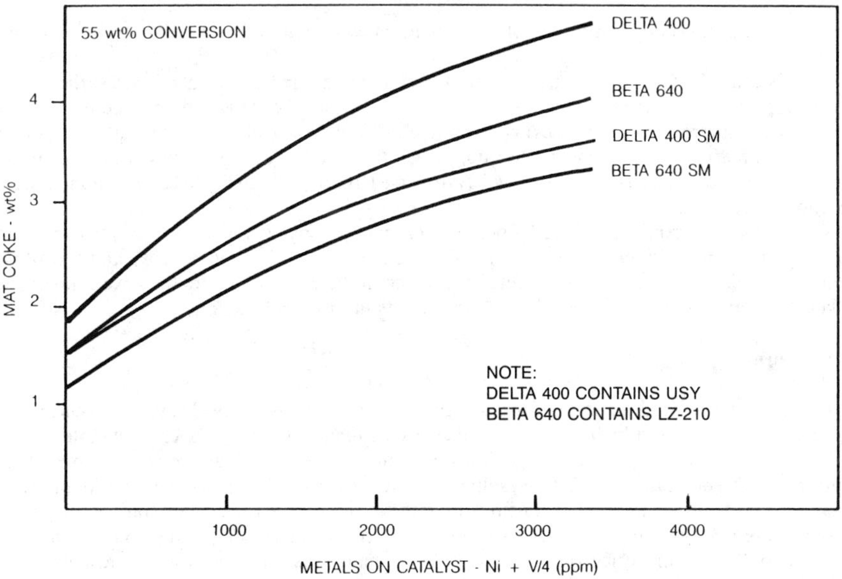

Figure 25. MAT coke yield vs. metals loading [64].

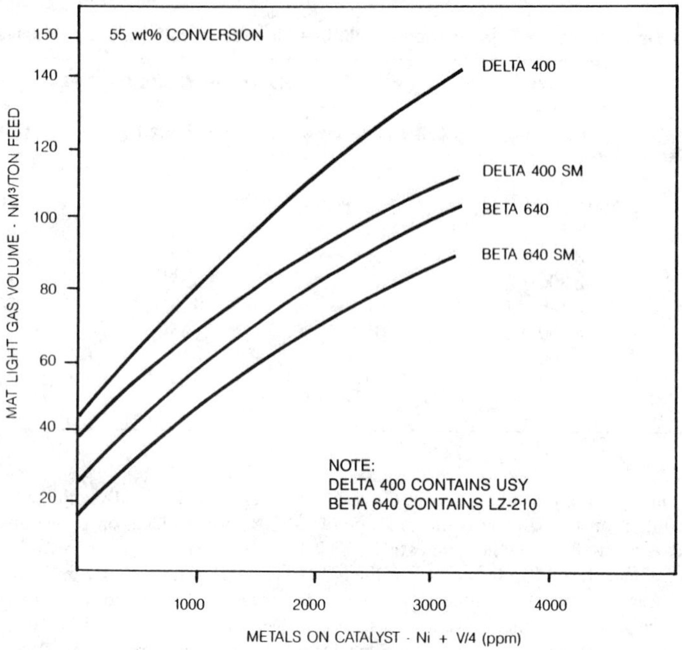

Figure 26. Light gas production vs. metals loading [64].

seen to have significantly improved coke and light gas selectivity over Delta 400 which contains USY sieve.

Likewise, the matrix also influences the effect of contaminant metals. As mentioned earlier, active alumina is frequently added to the matrix to improve the resistance to vanadium deactivation. It is also added to improve bottoms cracking. From the point of view of nickel contamination, however, these active matrices are detrimental to catalyst performance [56]. By providing increased surface area, over which the nickel can be more widely dispersed, the nickel's ability to catalyze non-selective reactions is enhanced.

Katalistiks has recently introduced a proprietary matrix system (designated "SM") that provides improved bottoms cracking but at the same time reduces the metals catalyzed coke and gas formation. This is also shown in Figures 25 and 26. As seen in these figures, where the sieve components is kept constant, switching to the "SM" matrix results in lower coke and gas.

SO_x Control

The technology to reduce SO_x emissions present in FCCU regenerator flue gas has centered on three main areas: (1) feed hydrotreating, (2) flue gas scrubbing, and (3) FCC catalyst systems.

Feed hydrotreating can substantially reduce SO_x emmissions as well as provide improved FCC conversion. The decrease in FCCU feed sulfur, however, generally does not achieve a proportionate decrease in SO_x emissions since it most readily removes non-thiophenic sulfur compounds, which normally are converted to H2S and leave with the reactor products [65]. They do not contribute strongly to coke sulfur, which is the source of SO_x emmissions. The highly aromatic sulfur compounds that do predominately go to coke are much more difficult to remove via hydrotreating.

Hydrotreating involves substantial investment. It has been estimated [66] that a 50,000 bpd unit for 90% sulfur removal would cost up to $100 million. Operating costs are also high, estimated for this 50,000 bpd unit to be $2/bbl.

Flue gas scrubbing using a dual alkali-citrate system is a more cost effective means for reducing regenerator SO_x levels, where SO_x reduction is the main reason for the investment. However, costs are still high. Current investment cost estimates [66] range from $50–$70 million with operating costs at $1/bbl. This does not eliminate the environmental problem, but merely transfers it from the regenerator flue gas to an external liquid and/or solid stream that must be disposed of.

The most promising and cost effective system is through the use of a catalytic additive. No investment cost is required by the refiner with operating costs well below that of a flue gas scrubber [67].

In this concept a metal oxide, under proper regenerator oxidizing conditions reacts with SO_x in the regenerator to form a stable compound (presumably a sulfate). The sulfur is then released from the metal oxide by reducing it to H_2S in the reactor-stripper section. The sulfur can ultimately be recovered from the product gas by a sulfur plant. The SO_x reduction additive is then recycled with the circulating FCC catalyst back to the regenerator to start the cycle again.

For maximum operating efficiency, these catalytic SO_x reduction systems require the FCCU to operate with excess O_2 in the full CO combustion mode. The effectiveness of these SO_x catalysts is improved when operating in conjunction with a noble metal CO oxidation promoter, while the presence of carbon on the regenerated FCC catalyst above 0.2% reduces their effectiveness [67].

The early SO_x reduction catalysts required large addition rates to be effective (3–5% of the circulating inventory), which detracts from the performance of the bulk cracking catalyst. This can result in a yield debit that has been estimated [68] at $0.03/bbl for every 1% of SO_x agent in the FCCU inventory.

Very recently, significant advances have been made towards increasing the activity of the SO_x agent. It is now possible to use a sufficiently active agent so that the amount added is small enough that it does not adversely affect FCC performance. The improvement that has been achieved is illustrated in Figure 27 which shows the evaluation of a proprietary SO_x agent DESOX. The early version of this catalyst (DESOX 276) required a concentration in the FCC inventory of 4% to achieve >80% reduction in SO_x emissions. This catalyst then evolved through technological advances to DESOX 280, which required a concentration of <0.5% in the FCC inventory to achieve the same reduction in SO_x emissions [68].

NO_x Control

Much less attention has been paid to NO_x control than to SO_x control. However, for resid and heavy feed processing, it is inevitable that FCC feed nitrogen contents will rise to levels that could cause NO_x pollution problems.

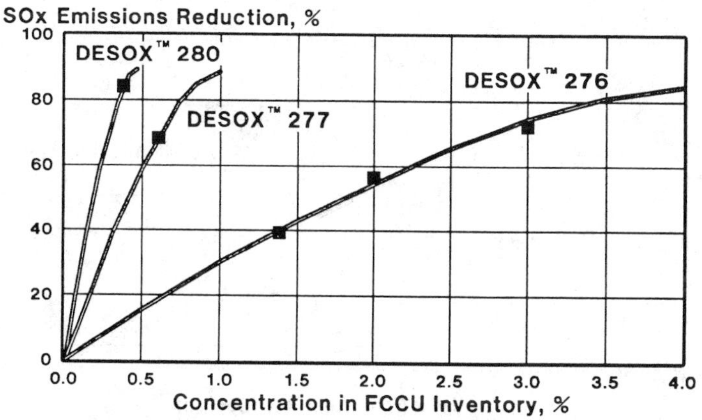

Figure 27. Relative performances of DESOX™ 276, DESOX™ 277, and DESOX™ 280 [68].

Also it has been observed in the past [66] that catalytic solutions to reduce SO_x frequently result in increased NO_x emissions. Some commercial data showing this effect is seen in Figure 28 where it is seen that NO_x emissions rose 100% when SO_x emissions were reduced from 70 kg/1,000 bbls to 50/kg bbls.

Catalyst makers are now looking into systems where SO_x reduction can be achieved without a NO_x penalty or preferably where a NO_x improvement can be simultaneously achieved. This work is in its infancy.

Promoted Combustion

Resid and heavy feed operations inherently means processing feeds with high coke making tendencies. This in turn means that regenerator temperature will most probably be a problem.

When processing standard VGO feed, it has been found [69] that the technique of burning all the CO in the regenerator to CO_2, usually thru the aid of a CO combustion catalyst, substantially improves FCCU profitability. However, this technique also results in a significant increase in regenerator temperature as seen in Figure 29 [70].

With resid processing, this temperature increase could be unacceptable. In such a case, the best procedure would be to reduce the amount of CO burned to CO_2 until the regenerator temperature was decreased to the desired level. This normally would be the regenerator metallurgical temperature limit, where FCCU economics are generally optimal.

This type of partial CO combustion control can only be achieved when a CO combustion promoter is used [70]. With a CO combustion promoter, CO contents in the regenerator flue can be controlled between 0 and 10%, as required to achieve the desired regenerator temperature. Control is achieved by varying the air rate. Control can also be achieved, to some extent by varying the amount of combustion promoter in the circulating catalyst inventory. This is illustrated in Figure 30 where it can be seen that a partially promoted system will operate at a lower coke on regenerated catalyst (CRC) level than will a fully promoted system at the same flue gas CO content. Generally, it is desirable to operate at lower CRC levels since this reduces catalyst addition requirements

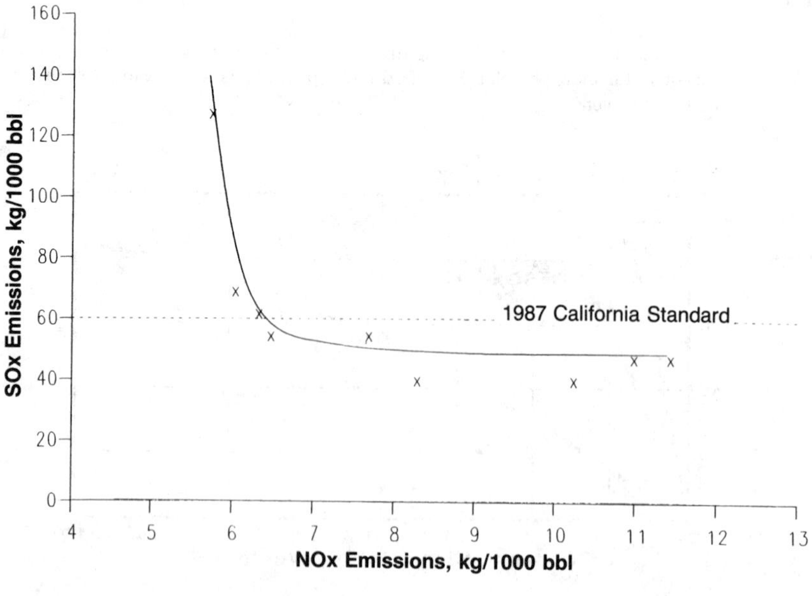

Figure 28. SO_x vs. No_x emissions commercial data [66].

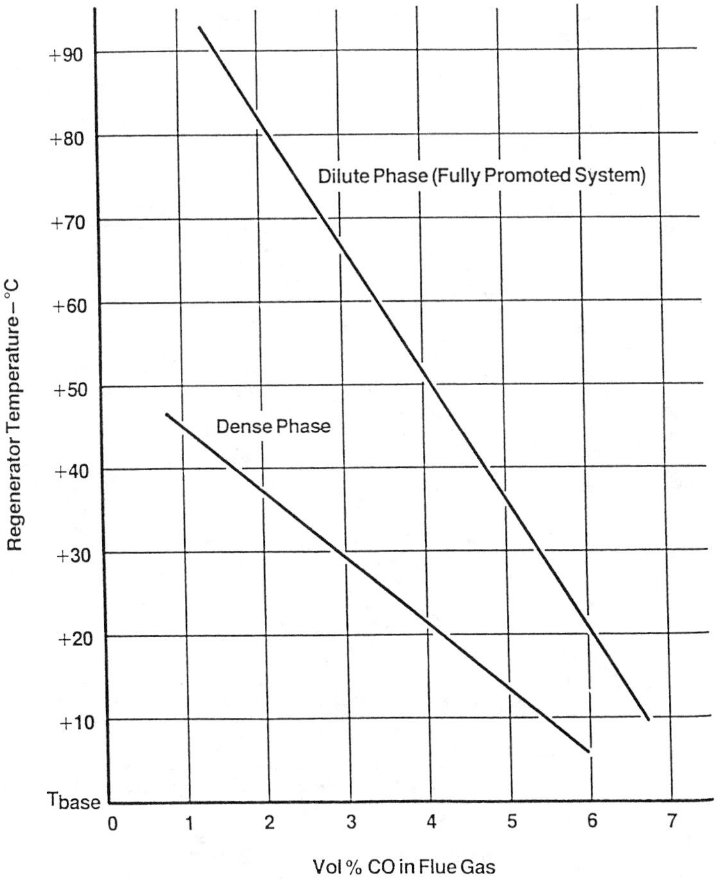

Figure 29. Effect of CO burning on regenerator temperatures [70].

(catalyst cost) and possibly improves cracking selectivity. In this illustration a fully promoted system would imply a catalyst system containing ~2 ppm platinum while partially promoted would imply <1 ppm.

With high metals levels on the equilibrium catalyst, as is typical with heavy oil processing, some CO combustion promotion will be achieved by the metals themselves. However better control of the regenerator is achieved if some promoter is also added.

REACTOR AND REGENERATOR DESIGN FOR HEAVY OIL PROCESSING

Catalyst manufacturers are not the only ones who have been active in recent years improving and adapting their products to make them suitable for processing heavy oils. FCC equipment designers and process licensors have also been busy adapting the FCCU hardware to meet the special needs required when heavy oils and resids are processed.

In general these design and hardware changes have taken the form of improved feed distribution and feed management systems in the riser area and heat removal and improved heat management systems on the regenerator side.

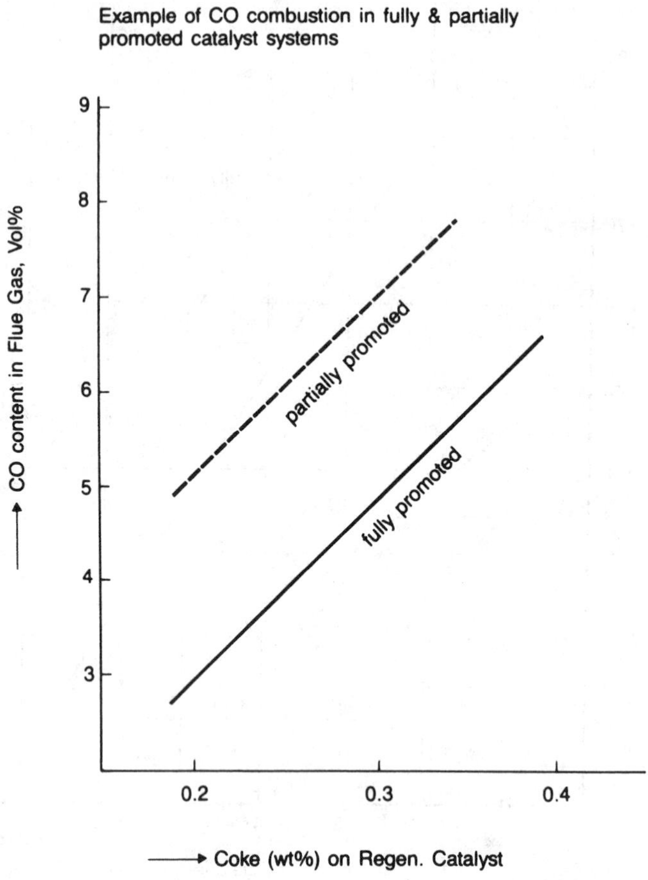

Figure 30. CRC vs. CO in flue gas [70].

Feed Management

Good FCC operation requires that the hot regenerated catalyst be well mixed with the hydrocarbon feed when these two components come together in the riser reactor. Coke deposition on the catalyst can occur at this contact point if feed vaporization is slow and/or incomplete. Heat transfer at this contact point should thus be as rapid as possible to minimize this unwanted coke formation. This is particularly important with heavy oils and residual feeds that contain highly aromatic, high boiling compounds that are more prone to form coke than are conventional VGO feeds.

In the past, FCCUs that processed conventional VGO type feeds achieved feed and catalyst mixing by injecting the feed into the upflowing catalyst stream in the riser thru a simple bayonet type, centrally located, end of riser feed injection nozzle. With this design, large feed droplets are produced at the nozzle exit (typically 100 microns or larger) and poor feed dispersion is obtained within the stream of regenerated catalyst and considerable back mixing occurs [71]. This condition is normally acceptable when cracking conventional VGO. With feed preheat temperatures in the range of 300–350°C, the majority of the VGO feed is vaporized (up to 75%) [72] with the remainder vaporizing quickly after contacting the hot catalyst.

However, with heavy oils and resids, this simple bayonet feed nozzle design creates problems. With such feeds the liquid phase can exist for a sufficiently long time to thermally crack [73] resulting in high gas yields and large amounts of thermal coke which deactivate the catalyst.

To provide better feed dispersion, particularly for heavy oil processing, multiple nozzle, high energy point input (high pressure drop) feed injection systems have been developed recently. In these systems up to 10–12 feed spray nozzles are located around the bottom circumference of the riser. To assist in feed vaporization and improve dispersion, steam is usually injected into the feed line upstream of the spray nozzles at rates typically equal to 1–5 wt% of the feed. When properly designed these systems (71, 73) produce a feed spray having liquid droplets equal to or smaller in size than the average catalyst particle (<70 microns). This greatly improves heat transfer rate and reduces thermal cracking. Reducing the oil droplet size from 100 microns to 30 microns has been shown by Mauleon et al. [71] to reduce the vaporization time by 60%.

Changing to a high energy, multi-nozzle system from the older style simple bayonet nozzle has also produced impressive improvements in feed conversion and product selectivity [73, 74]. Data reported by Johnson [73] illustrate this:

	Before Multi-Nozzle System	After Multi-Nozzle System
Conversion—vol%	69.9	78.4
Gasoline (C5-220°C)—vol%	54.4	59.5
C3 + C4—vol%	21.0	27.6
Fuel Gas—wt%	4.8	3.9
Coke—wt%	6.8	6.8

Other feed to riser techniques have also been developed recently to achieve even further improvements. One such development by UOP [75] designated the "lift-gas riser" design has reduced riser back mixing. In a conventionally designed riser, regenerated catalyst enters the feed mixing zone as a relatively slow moving dense bed. The catalyst is then accelerated up the riser as a rapidly moving dilute bed due to the influence of the vaporizing and cracking hydrocarbons and the dispersion steam. Severe back mixing occurs during the transition from dense to dilute phase flow, which promotes non-selective cracking.

In the "lift-gas riser" system, the hot regenerated catalyst is first accelerated up the riser by an inert diluent gas, such as fuel gas. The hydrocarbon feed is then injected further up the riser using an efficient nozzle dispersion system. By the time the catalyst reaches the point in the riser where feed is injected, it is travelling at equilibrium slip velocity in a well distributed dilute phase zone, thus nearly eliminating all back mixing. This system is shown in Figure 31. UOP has also found [76] that contacting the freshly regenerated catalyst with a light hydrocarbon such as fuel gas partially passivates the oxidized contaminent metals and thus reduces their non-selective catalytic activity. Data from Cabrera et al. [76] from a commercial operation feeding a deep cut VGO illustrate the lift gas advantage:

	Left Gas Riser System	Conventional Riser System
Feed Rate	Base + 15%	Base
Reactor Temp °C	530	530
Preheat Temp °C	264	242
Regen. Temp °C	718	734
Conversion—vol%	70.2	71.0
Gasoline—vol%	53.0	51.5
C3 + C4—vol%	15.1	16.8
Dry Gas wt%	4.1	4.7
Coke wt%	4.6	4.7

Total [77] has developed a variation on this procedure in which light gas is injected at the bottom of the riser, feed is injected into the riser downstream of the lift gas, and a quench recycle

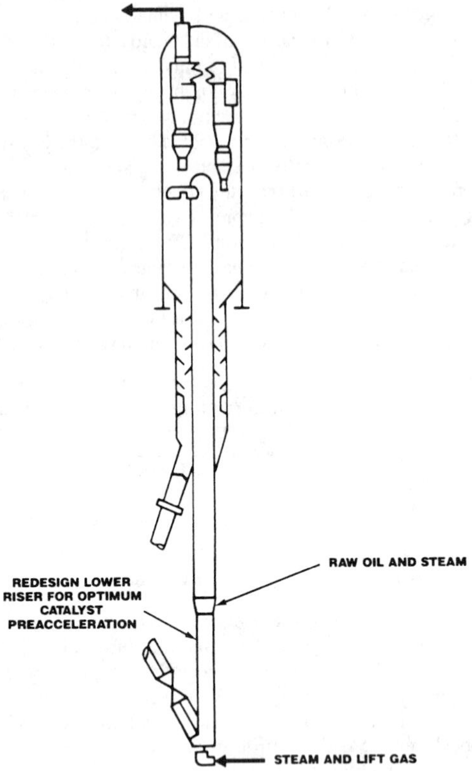

Figure 31. Revamp of lower riser section and new feed distributors [76].

steam is injected still further downstream. The advantage of this system is that it allows the catalytic and feed mixing temperature to be adjusted independently of the reactor temperature and can be considerably higher than would otherwise be possible. In conventional systems, the mix temperature is not an independant variable. Total says that the higher mix temperature improves FCCU operations through: (1) more rapid feed vaporization, (2) less coke desposition on the catalyst in the lower portion of the riser, (3) higher catalyst circulation rates, and (4) higher conversion and better bottoms cracking.

Regenerator Design

Processing heavy feeds can result in regenerator conditions that are severely damaging to catalyst performance. Various approaches have been taken recently by FCC process designers to solve this problem.

Two-Stage Regeneration

One approach has been to divide the regeneration process into two stages [75, 77, 78, 79]. In the first stage where steam partial pressure is high, regenerator temperatures are kept low. In the second stage, where steam partial pressure is low, high temperatures are used to burn the catalyst free of coke. This staging process thus avoids the combination of high steam partial pressure and high temperature, which is so damaging to catalyst activity.

First-stage regeneration is carried out in an oxygen limited environment. Temperatures are controlled around 700°C. As a result about 75% of the hydrogen and 50% of the carbon is burned from the catalyst. Consequently, nearly all of the steam produced from the combustion of hydrogen is formed at relatively mild conditions. Not only is hydrothermal deactivation minimized by low temperature control of the first stage but the risk of hot spots is also minimized. This risk is particularly great for highly coked fresh catalyst particles when they first enter the generator.

Second-stage burning is done with excess oxygen at higher temperatures. The absence of steam minimizes catalyst deactivation damage.

Regenerator Temperature Control

Most residual feeds, if not properly controlled, will produce regenerator temperatures that will exceed the maximum allowable regenerator temperature. For 304-H type stainless steel (an alloy frequently used in modern FCCUs) this maximum temperature would be 770°C (80).

Catalyst coolers have been used in some recent designs and FCCU revamps. Early catalyst designs [81] used internal bed heat transfer coils located near the wall of the regenerator in the dense phase. Heat removal is achieved by circulating boiler feed water through the tubes and generating steam. These type units have very little flexibility to process feeds that vary widely in feed quality.

External catalyst coolers provide more flexibility and are now advocated by several process licensors [82, 83, 84]. By varying the amount of catalyst that circulates through the cooler, the amount of heat removal can be adjusted. For good quality (low coking) feeds, it is possible to take the external cooler completely out of service. This was not possible with the internal bed coils [83]. An illustration of a regenerator with an external catalyst cooler is shown in Figure 32.

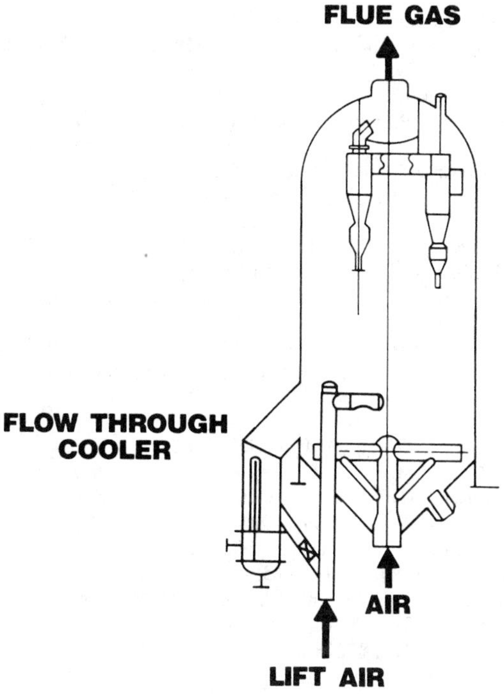

Figure 32. Flow-through catalyst cooler [76].

In the Total design [73, 80], a completely different approach is taken. Catalyst cooling is not used and the regenerator temperature is allowed to rise to its natural heat balance level, which could be well above 800°C. To achieve this, the temperature sensitive internals (cyclones and cyclone hangers) are taken out of the dilute phase and located outside of the regenerator. Refractory lining protects the regenerator itself. This design is combined with the two-stage regenerator concept. The maximum temperatures are reached only in the second stage where the atmosphere is essentially moisture free, and thus less damaging to the catalyst.

REFERENCES

1. Venuto, P. B., and Habib, E. T., *Rev. Sci. Eng.*, 18, 1 (1978).
2. Elvin, F. J., and Krikorian, K. V., *Katalistiks 4th Annual FCC Symposium*, Amsterdam, 1983, pp. 12:1–12:3.
3. Magee, J. S., and Griffith, S. D., *Katalistiks 4th Annual FCC Symposium*, Amsterdam, May 18–19, 1983, pp. 3:1–3:27.
4. Speight, J. G., *The Desulfurization of Heavy Oils and Residua*, Marcel Dekker Inc., New York, 1981, p. 38.
5. Ardern, D. B., Dart, J. C., and Lassiat, R. C., *Adv. Chem. Series*, 5, 13 (1951).
6. Hinds, G. P., *Proc. Am. Petroleum Institute*, Div. of Refining, 49, 147 (1969).
7. Decroocq, D., *Catalytic Cracking of Heavy Petroleum Fractions*, Institute Francaise de Petrole, Paris, 1984, p. 53.
8. Ginzel, W., *Katalistiks 6th Annual FCC Symposium*, Munich, 1985, pp. 8:1–8:18.
9. van Nes, K., and van Westen, H. A., *Aspects of the Constitution of Mineral Oils*, Elsevier Publishing Company, New York, 1951, p. 335.
10. Yen, L. C., and Wrench, R. E., *Katalistiks 5th Annual FCC Symposium*, Vienna, May 23–24, 1984, pp. 4:1–4:32.
11. Andreasson, H. U., and Upson, L. L., *Oil and Gas Journal*, Aug. 5, 1985, p. 91.
12. Valeri, F., *Katalistiks 8th Annual FCC Symposium*, Budapest, June 1–4, 1987, to be published.
13. Dhulesia, H., *Oil and Gas Journal*, Jan. 13, 51 (1986).
14. Fu, C. M., and Schaffer, A. M., *Ind. Eng. Prod. Res. Dev.*, 24, 68 (1985).
15. Allen, D. T., Grandy, D. W., Jeong, K. M., and Petrakis, L., *Ind. Eng. Chem. Process Des. Div.*, 24, 737 (1985).
16. van der Zwan, H., *Katalistiks Internal Communication*, 26, Nov. 1985.
17. Pazos, J. M., Gonzales, J. C., and Salazar, Guillon, A. J., *Ind. Eng. Chem. Process Des. Dev.*, 22, 653 (1983).
18. Haines, W. E., and Thompson, C. J., *Separating and Characterizing High Boiling Petroleum Distillates: The US BM-API Procedure*, U.S. EDRA; LERC-75/5, BERC-75/2.
19. Ritter, R. E., Rheaume, L., Welch, W. A., and Magee, J. S., *NPRA Annual Meeting*, AM-81-44, 1 (1981).
20. Owen, H., Suyder, P. W., and Venuto, P. B., *Proc. Sixth Intern. Cong. Catal.*, 2, 1073 (1977).
21. Zandona, O. J., Busch, L. E., and Hettinger, W. P., Jr., *NPRA Annual Meeting*, AM-82-61, 11 (1982).
22. Nace, D. M., *Ind. Eng. Chem. Prod. Res. Dev.*, 9, 203 (1970).
23. Upson, L. L., and Jaras, S. G., *NPRA Annual Meeting*, AM-82-49, 3 (1982).
24. Otterstedt, J. E., Gevert, S. B., Jaras, S. G., and Menon, P. G., *Applied Catalysis*, 22, 159 (1986).
25. Upson, L. L., *Katalistiks 1st Annual FCC Symposium*, Bordeaux, Oct. 28–29, 1980, pp. 4:1–4:13.
26. Upson, L. L., *Katalistiks Symposium on Octane*, Amsterdam/Madrid, Jan. 28/30, 1986.
27. Magnusson, J. E., *Katalistiks Symposium on Octane*, Amsterdam/Madrid, Jan. 28/30, 1986.
28. Pine, L. A., Maher, P. J., and Wachter, W. A., *J. of Catalysis*, 85, 466 (1984).
29. Upson, L. L., *Katalistiks 8th Annual FCC Symposium*, Budapest, June 1–4, 1987, to be published.
30. Derouane, E. G., *Ketjen Catalysts Symposium*, Scheveningen, 1986, p. G-3.
31. Skeels, G. W., and Breck, D. W., *U.S. Patent 4,610,856*, September 9, 1986.

32. Venuto, P. B., and Habib, E. T., *Fluid Catalytic Cracking with Zeolite Catalysts*, Marcel Dekker Inc., New York, 1979, p. 43.
33. Oblad, A. G., *Oil and Gas Journal*, 70(13), 84 (1972).
34. Eastwood, S. C., Plank, C. J., and Weisz, P. B., *Proc. Sixth Int. Cmgr. Catal.*, 2, 1071 (1971).
35. Takatsuka, T., "*Bottoms Cracking Capacity of Resid FCC Catalysts*", Translation of Japanese publication, November 1984.
36. Nilsson, P., Massoth, F. E., and Otterstedt, J-E, *Applied Catalysis*, 26, 175 (1986).
37. Nilsson, P., and Otterstedt, J-E, accepted for publication in *Applied Catalysis.*
38. Otterstedt, J-E, Mattsson, M., and Röj, A., *Erdöl und Kohle*, 39(2), 69 (1986).
39. Otterstedt, J-E, Sterte, J., and Zhu, Y-M, paper submitted for publication in *Applied Catalysis.*
40. Mott, R. W., *Oil & Gas Journal*, 85(4), 73 (1984).
41. Linsen, B. G., and Steggerda, J. J., *Physical and Chemical Aspects of Adsorbents and Catalysts.* B. G. Linsen (ed.), Academic Press, London and New York, 1970, p. 207.
42. Hall, W. K., Lutinsky, F. E., and Gerberich, H. R., *J. Catal.*, 3, 512 (1964).
43. Ritter, R. E., Creighton, J. E., Robiere, T. G., Chin, D. S., and Wear, C. C., Paper AM-86-45, *NPRA Annual Meeting*, San Antonio, March 23–25, 1984.
44. Rabo, J. A., Pellet, R. G., Risch, A. P., and Blockwell, C. S., Paper presented at the *Katalistiks 8th Catalytic Symposium*, Budapest, June 1–4, 1987.
45. Vaughan, D. E. W., Lussier, R. J., and Magee, J. S., *U.S. Patent No. 4,176,090* (1979).
46. Vaughan, D. E. W., Lussier, R. J., and Magee, J. S., *U.S. Patent No. 4,248,739* (1981).
47. Occelli, M. L., and Tindwa, R. M., *Clay & Clay Minerals*, 31, 22 (1983).
48. Occelli, M. L., *I & EC Prod. Rev. Dev. Journal.* 22, 553 (1983).
49. Sterte, J., and Otterstedt, J-E, in "*Scientific Bases for the Preparation of Heterogenous Catalysts*", preprints, paper G1, Louvain-la-Neuve. Belgium, Sept. 1–4, 1986.
50. Sterte, J., Otterstedt, J-E, Thulin, H., and Massoth, F. E., paper submitted for publication in *Applied Catalysis.*
51. Sterte, J., and Otterstedt, J-E, paper submitted for publication in *Applied Catalysis.*
52. Campagna, R. J., Krisna, A. S., and Yanik, S. J., *Oil and Gas Journal*, Oct. 31, 1983, pp. 128–134.
53. Jaras, S. G., *Applied Catalysis*, 2, 1982, pp. 207–218.
54. Cimbalo, S. G., Foster, R. L., and Wachtel, S. J., *Oil and Gas Journal*, May 15, 1972, pp. 112–122.
55. Silverman, L. D., Winkler, S., Tiethof, J. A., and Witoshkin, A., Paper AM-86-62, presented at the 1986 NPRA Annual Meeting, Los Angeles, California, March 1986.
56. Upson, L. L., Paper AM-84-58, presented at the 1984 NPRA Annual Meeting, San Antonio, Texas, March 1984.
57. Groenenboom, C. J., van Houtert, F. W., and van Maare, J., *Ketjen Catalysts Symposium '84*, pp. 55–64.
58. Mitchell, B., and Vogel, R., U.S. Patent 4,451,355 (1984).
59. Occelli, M., and Kennedy, J. V., U.S. Patent 4,465,588 (1984).
60. Groenenboom, C. J., European Patent Office Publication Number 0-194-536 (1986).
61. Barlow, R. C., Paper AM-86-57, presented at the 1986 NPRA Annual Meeting, Los Angeles, California, March 1986.
62. Magee, J. S., Mitchell, B. R., and Moore, J. W., *Katalistiks 7th Annual FCC Symposium*, Venice, May 12–13, 1986, pp. 3:1–3:15.
63. McCarthy, W. C., Hutson, T., and Mann, J. W., *Katalistiks 3rd Annual FCC Symposium*, Amsterdam, May 26–27, 1982, pp. 13:1–13:16.
64. Upson, L. L., *Katalistiks 8th Annual FCC Symposium*, Budapest, June 2–4, 1987, pp. 18.1–18.11.
65. Wollaston, E. G., Forsythe, W. L., and Vasalos, I. A., *Oil and Gas Journal*, Aug. 2, 1971, pp. 64–69.
66. Aitken, E. J., Baron, K., McArthur, D. P., and Mester, Z. C., *Katalistiks 6th Annual FCC Symposium*, Munich, May 22–23, 1985, pp. 6:1–6:15.
67. Habib, E. T., *Oil and Gas Journal*, Aug. 8, 1983, pp. 111–113.
68. Powell, J. W., *Katalistiks 7th Annual FCC Symposium*, Venice, May 12–13, 1986, pp. 11:1–11:4.
69. Upson, L. L., Paper AM-79-39, presented at the 1979 NPRA Annual Meeting, San Antonio, Texas, March 1979.

70. Upson, L. L., and van der Zwan, H., *Katalistiks 7th Annual FCC Symposium*, Venice, May 12–13, 1986, pp. 9:1–9:15.
71. Mauleon, J. L., and Courcelle, J. C., *Katalistiks 7th Annual FCC Symposium*, Munich, May 22–23, pp. 9:1–9:18.
72. Venuto, P. B., and Habib, E. T., *Fluid Catalytic Cracking with Zeolite Catalysts*, Marcel Dekker, Inc., New York, 1979, p. 60.
73. Johnson, A. R., Paper 86-AM-42, presented at the 1986 NPRA Annual Meeting, March 23–25, 1986, Los Angeles.
74. Farrar, G. L., (ed.), *Questions and Answers on Refinery Technology*, G. L. Farrar and Assoc., Tulsa, 1979, p. 62.
75. Hammershaimb, H. V., and Lomas, D. A., *Katalistiks 6th Annual FCC Symposium*, Munich, May 22–23, 1976, pp. 11:1–11:12.
76. Cabrera, C. A., Hemler, C. L., and Davis, S. P., *Katalistiks 8th Annual FCC Symposium*, Budapest, June 1–4, 1987, pp. 14.1–14.15.
77. Mauleon, J. L., and Sigaud, J. B., *Oil and Gas Journal*, Feb. 23, 1987, p. 52.
78. Barger, D. W., *Katalistiks 5th Annual FCC Symposium*, Vienna, May 23–24, 1984, pp. 8:1–8:16.
79. Dean, R., Mauleon, J. L., and Letzsch, W. S., *Oil and Gas Journal*, Oct. 11, 1982.
80. Mauleon, J. L., Sigaud, J. B., and Henrich, G., Paper given at the Japan Petroleum Institute Conference, Tokyo, Oct. 11, 1982.
81. Rush, J. B., *Chem. Engineering Progress*, Dec. 1981, pp. 29–32.
82. Yen, L. C., Wrench, R. E., and Kuo, C. M., *Katalistiks 6th Annual FCC Symposium*, Munich, May 22–23, pp. 10:1–10:13.
83. Murphy, J. R., Paper presented at Japan Petroleum Institute Conference, Tokyo, Oct. 27–28, 1986.
84. Cabrera, C. A., and Hemler, C. L., Paper AM-86-60, presented at the 1986 NPRA Annual Meeting, Los Angeles, March 1986.

CHAPTER 6

REGENERATION OF HYDROTREATING CATALYSTS

E. Furimsky

Energy Research Laboratories
Canada Centre for Mineral and Energy Technology (CANMET)
Energy, Mines and Resources
Ottawa, Ontario, Canada,

and

Yuji Yoshimura

National Chemical Laboratory for Industry
Tsukuba, Ibaraki, Japan

CONTENTS

INTRODUCTION

The catalyst inventory accounts for a significant portion of the overall cost of catalytic operations thus a careful maintenance of this inventory is necessary to decrease operational costs. The aim is to use the catalyst for as long as possible. During operation the catalyst activity gradually declines. The decline may be offset by a change of processing parameters such as temperature, pressure and residence time. At a certain stage a complete replacement of the catalyst might be necessary. In systems where the catalyst is continuously fed to and withdrawn from the reactor the activity may be maintained by periodically withdrawing the portion of spent catalyst and replacing it by the fresh catalyst. The spent catalyst may be regenerated and returned back to the operation.

The catalyst activity decline may be attributed to several factors [1–3]. With respect to oxidative regeneration the formation of carbonaceous deposits (coke) is of the main interest. This represents a reversible form of deactivation. The regeneration of the fluid catalytic cracking (FCC) catalysts has been widely investigated. The available information forms a base for the research on regeneration of hydrotreating catalysts.

The lifetime of FCC and hydrotreating catalysts differs markedly. Because of high temperatures and low H_2 pressures applied during cracking operations the deactivation of FCC catalysts is rapid. This requires an immediate catalyst regeneration in order to avoid the use of large amounts of catalyst. Thus, in case of commercial FCC units the catalyst regeneration is part of the continuous operation. This suggests that the regeneration of FCC catalysts such as silica-aluminas and zeolites is among the most advanced regeneration processes.

Hydrotreatment of petroleum fractions is usually performed in fixed bed reactors. For light fractions the catalyst lifetime is rather long. Thus, once the hydrotreating reactor is loaded with catalyst it can operate satisfactorily for at least one year. In such cases the need for regenerator that would be used only sporadically cannot be justified. The spent catalyst may however be reclaimed by the operators of regeneration units who can resell the regenerated catalyst to refiners.

Hydrotreatment of light, middle and gas oil fractions is carried out to remove undesirable species such as sulfur and nitrogen in order to meet specifications of commercial products. This sometimes requires hydrogenation of olefins and aromatics. The objective of hydroprocessing operations is the conversion of heavy feeds, e.g., vacuum residues, bitumen, solvent refined coals, etc, to primary products which may require additional hydrotreatment. The primary upgrading technologies such as LC-Fining and HRI processes employ catalysts which are similar in chemical composition to those used for hydrotreatment. However, because of the nature of feedstocks the catalyst lifetime is very short. The upgrading of such heavy feedstocks using a fixed bed catalyst reactor appears to be impractical. Therefore, these processes employ either continuous or periodic additions of fresh catalyst and the withdrawal of spent catalysts. For large upgrading units the amount of spent catalyst produced per day may be large enough to justify the regeneration on site in order to decrease the cost of catalyst inventory. It is therefore anticipated that regenerator units will represent an important part of large scale plants producing synthetic fuels.

HYDROTREATING CATALYSTS

For the purpose of this review the hydrotreating catalysts are identified as molybdate and/or tungstate catalysts promoted by Ni and/or Co and supported on gamma alumina. The chemical composition and properties of some well known catalysts are shown in Table 1. In refining practice the catalysts are used in the form of pellets or extrudates of varying shapes and sizes. Commercial applications of these catalysts have been known for decades. They include treatment under high H_2 pressure of a wide boiling range liquid as well as slurries of organic solids with various solvents. Different aspects of these catalysts, i.e., properties, preparation, use, etc., have been periodically reviewed [4–6]. Therefore, only a brief reference is made to structure and stability of these catalysts.

The most common method of preparation of hydrotreating catalysts is based on impregnation of supports with the solution of compounds, which on calcining yield MoO_3 and/or WO_3 for active ingredients and CoO and/or NiO for promoters. The active metal oxides are spread on the support surface in a monolayer-like form. The promoters, when introduced to the support simultaneously

Table 1
Properties of Some Commercial Hydrotreating Catalysts

	Nalco NT-550	AKZO 153S	Ketjen 124	Cyanamid HDS-2A
MoO_3	—	15.0	12.0	15.4
WO_3	22.0	—	—	—
CoO	—	—	4.0	3.2
NiO	5.1	3.0	—	—
surf. ar. m^2/g	250	130	176	310
pore vol. ml/g	0.50	0.48	0.53	0.75

with active metals will interact with the monolayer. The gamma alumina appear to be the most frequently used support material.

Conditions applied during catalyst preparation influence its surface structure. Parameters such as surface area, pore diameter, pore volume and size distribution influence the use of active surface and the access of reactant molecules to active sites. Surface parameter requirements depend on type of hydrotreated feedstock. The prolonged tempering at high temperatures may affect the surface structure of the catalyst. It is therefore essential that the temperature applied during calcining and utilization is not much in excess of 500°C. Otherwise the catalyst activity may be decreased because of sintering and association of active metals and promoters with the support. The crystal growth involving active metal containing species may cause the activity decrease as well.

In most of the industrial applications the hydrotreating catalysts are in a sulfided form, which is more active and stable than the oxidic form. The sulfided form can be obtained either by reacting the oxidic catalyst with a sulfiding agent, e.g., H_2S, CS_2, thiophene, etc., prior to its use or via an in situ sulfidation during initial stages of hydrotreatment. In the latter case the sulfiding occurs with the participation of S-containing compounds present in the feedstock. During sulfidation the oxides of Mo and/or W are converted to MoS_2 and/or WS_2. At certain concentrations, the promoters are associated with the sulfides in a non-sulfided form. It appears that the excess of promoting metals is converted to Co_aS_8 and/or Ni_3S_2. The alumina support remains intact during sulfidation [7].

The higher activity of the sulfided form compared with oxidic form of hydrotreating catalysts may be explained using the dual hypothesis of active sites [8]. This hypothesis assumes an anion vacancy adjacent to Mo and/or W ions as the site for heteroring adsorption. The other requirement is the presence of active hydrogen which is attached to sulfur in the vicinity of the vacancy as shown in Figure 1. The active hydrogen transfer to reactant molecule from the S—H group is more favorable than that from the O—H group because of the higher bond strength of the latter. The forms of adsorption other than the one shown in Figure 1 cannot be ruled out. Thus, a flat adsorption or an adsorption involving a C—C or X—C (X-heteroatom) bonds may also occur particularly when the concentration of active surface hydrogen is high.

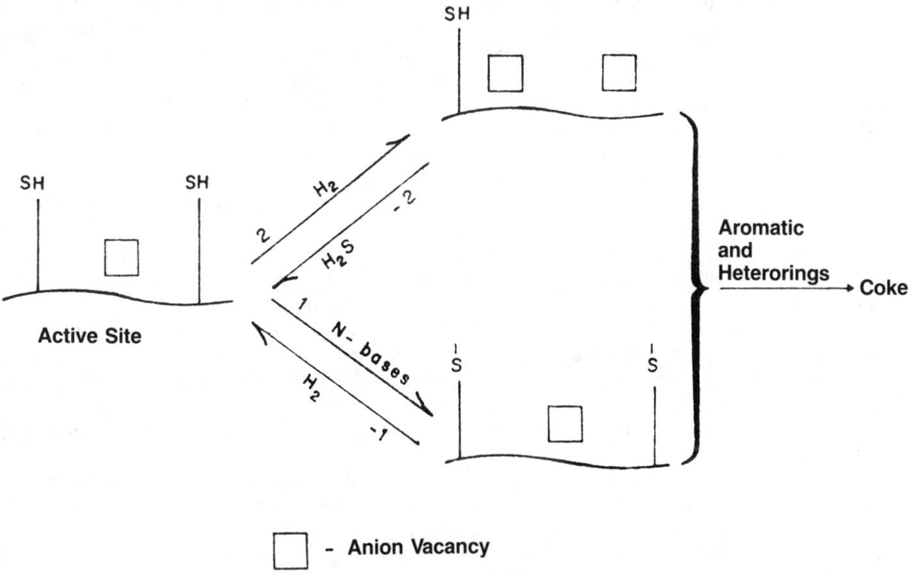

Figure 1. Tentative routes for deactivation of active site.

The performance of hydrotreating catalysts may be also influenced by some process parameters. In a fixed bed, the size of reactor, space velocity, temperature and H_2 pressure are among important parameters. With respect to catalyst regeneration the procedure applied during draining the reactor at the end of the operation is crucial. For an ebulated bed such as that used for upgrading heavy feedstocks, the form and dimensions of catalyst particles are important. For example, the LC-Fining process employs extradates of a very small diameter to achieve sufficient contact times.

DEACTIVATION OF HYDROTREATING CATALYSTS

Many studies that appeared in the scientific literature identify the formation of carbonaceous deposits, i.e., fouling as the main cause of activity decline. The rate of fouling depends on the properties of the feedstocks and increases with the average molecular weight of the feedstock. To a certain extent the fouling represents a physical contact of large molecules with catalyst surface which results in blocking active sites and plugging the catalyst pores. Poisoning differs from fouling in that it represents a chemical interaction of feedstock molecules with catalyst surface. Chemisorption extends the lifetime of adsorbed species and as such increases the chance of their polymerization to large coke molecules. Fouling and poisoning are reversible forms of catalyst deactivation, i.e., their effects can be reversed on regeneration. On the other hand, the loss of catalyst activity caused by crystal growth and sintering represents an irreversible form of deactivation.

The N-containing heterocyclic compounds are generally identified as severe poisons of hydrotreating catalysts. This results from their basic character given by the presence of unpaired electron on N heteroatom on one side and the presence of Lewis acids on catalyst surface capable of accepting the unpaired electrons on the other. Properties of catalyst support determine the concentration of Lewis acids. It has been established that the concentration of Lewis acids in silica containing supports is much higher than that in pure alumina. This may be the main reason that the alumina is the most widely used support for the preparation of hydrotreating catalysts. On the basis of a high content of N in coke deposits the N-containing compounds of the feedstock were assumed to be the important precursors to coke formation [9].

The destruction of Bronstadt acidity may be another reason for the loss of catalyst activity. It was proposed that Bronstadt acids participate in active hydrogen transfer from catalyst surface to reactant molecules [8]. In case that the proton acceptor is in a proximity, the Bronstadt acid can release the proton. It was also confirmed that aromatic structures can readily accept proton and as such can be converted to stable carbonium ions [10]. Such ions tend to couple particularly in the presence of metals [11]. Multiplication of coupling steps may lead to two dimensional deposit formation. Also, the N-containing heterorings are known proton acceptors [12]. Such species are believed to be the origin of mesophase formation, which from a crystallinity point of view, is an important part of coke. When supply of active hydrogen becomes limited even olefinic structures, if present in the feed, may contribute to coke formation. Such situations may occur during the last stages of catalyst utilization.

It appears that the interaction of N-containing compounds with Lewis acids and the associated coke formation may occur on the support surface uncovered by active ingredients. On the other hand the destruction of Bronstadt acids may block active sites when the dual definition of the site is assumed as shown in Figure 1. This means that a proper orientation of reactant molecules at active sites previously stripped of active hydrogen may lead to direct coke formation at the site. Under active hydrogen deficient conditions compounds other than N-containing bases may become the precursors for coke formation at the site.

The effects of chemical composition of feedstocks on catalyst deactivation are illustrated in Table 2. The three feedstocks differ markedly in properties as shown by the average molecular weight values and aromaticity. These feedstocks were hydrotreated in the presence of a presulfided cobalt-molybdate catalyst under similar conditions, i.e., a series of experiments was performed from 380° to 420°C at 13.9 MPa of H_2 [9]. The spent catalyst was extracted by pentane to remove carryovers. This was followed by benzene extraction to isolate the benzene soluble portion of carbonaceous deposits. The chemical composition of the extract and the coke remaining on the catalyst surface after the extraction is also shown in Table 2. Surprisingly, the amount of coke deposited on the catalyst surface during hydrotreatment of the coal-derived liquid was larger than that for heavy gas oil despite the former was much lighter. This is attributed to a higher aromaticity of the coal-derived

Table 2
Chemical Composition of Feedstocks, Benzene Extracts and Carbonaceous Deposits

Property	Coal Derived Liquid	Heavy Gas Oil	Bitumen
Feedstock			
average mol. weight	140	350	800
carbon, total	85.3	84.5	83.0
carbon arom. + olef %	52.7	27.4	30.6
carbon alif %	47.3	72.6	69.4
C/N	200	225	225
C/O	21	254	138
C/S	*	63	47
C/H	0.74	0.68	0.66
Benzene Extract			
C/N	43	60	119
C/O	14	40	97
C/S	*	53	46
C/H	0.94	0.92	0.92
Carbonaceous Deposits			
carbon, wt%	7.0	4.6	13.9
nitrogen, wt%	0.4	0.48	0.29
C/N	20	11	56

liquid rather than to a markedly higher C/O ratio. Thus, most of the oxygen in the liquid was of a phenolic type [11]. The C/N ratio of the extracts and coke after benzene extraction confirms that N-containing compounds contributed significantly to coke formation especially during hydrotreatment of the heavy gas oil, e.g., the C/N ratio decreased by factors of 10 and 20 for the coal-derived liquid and heavy gas oil, respectively. For bitumen the C/N ratio decreased only by a factor of 4 suggesting that for this feedstock the physical interaction of large asphaltene molecules with catalyst surface may be the main cause of deactivation. A small difference in C/S ratio between feedstocks and benzene extracts suggests that the contribution of S-containing compounds present in feedstocks to deposit formation is markedly lower than that of N-containing compounds. It appears that the participation of O-containing compounds in coke forming reactions varies among feedstocks. Thus, for the heavy gas oil the O-containing species may play an important role in coke forming reactions whereas for bitumen and coal-derived liquid their role may not be significant. It was assumed that for the heavy gas oil the furanic rings account for most of the O-containing compounds [13].

Besides support properties other factors such as type and amount of active metals and promoters, effectiveness of their distribution on the support, surface structure, shape and size of pellets or extrudates, etc., influence the structure of coke and its rate of formation. The catalyst structure must ensure an efficient supply of active hydrogen to reactant molecules adsorbed on the catalyst surface to prevent their conversion to coke. Full use of available active surface is another important requirement. In this regard the pore volume and pore size distribution are important especially when heavy feedstocks are hydrotreated. The published information on these aspects of hydrotreating catalysts was recently reviewed by Thakur and Thomas [2].

The average molecular weight and boiling range of feedstock determine radial distribution of coke in catalyst particles. Thus, for heavy feedstocks the pore diameter must be large enough to ensure the penetration of large asphaltene molecules into the particle interior to achieve an efficient use of active surface. It appears that the pore diameter of 10 to 15 nm is an optimum for hydrodesulfurization and asphaltene conversion. Increasing the pore diameter above the optimum improves the penetration of large molecules even more but it results in a decrease of active surface. When pores are not large enough the diffusion of large molecules will be restricted. This will result in a preferential deposit formation on the outer parts of catalyst particles. This was confirmed by large deposits of vanadium on the exterior of pellets [14, 15], i.e., vanadium is known to be present in petroleum in the form of large vanadyl porphirin molecules. At the same time the organometallic compounds containing Ni tend to be distributed more evenly across the pellet. This suggests that the coke structure across the pellet will be non-uniform. For light and middle distillates optimal pore diameter is not as critical because compared with asphaltenes much smaller molecules can penetrate the catalyst pellet interior. This ensures a more complete use of active surface and a more uniform distribution and structure of coke. This may be illustrated on the results published by Saint Just who contacted a series of hydrotreating catalysts with a toluene solution of asphaltenes [16]. For catalysts having a small pore diameter a formation of a "skin" on the outer parts of the catalyst particles was observed whereas toluene could penetrate rapidly into the particle interior.

MECHANISM OF BURNOFF

The type of reactions that occur during burnoff of spent hydrotreating catalysts depends on the oxidizing agent. The O_2 (air or diluted air) are the most frequently used. The complexity of the mechanism compared with FCC catalysts is indicated by chemical changes incurred during burnoff by both the coke and catalyst material. The complexity increases if steam and/or CO_2 are added to the oxidizing gas.

The first contact of O_2 with the coke leads to the formation of surface complexes that are believed to be the precursors to formation of burnoff products. The surface complexes are stable until a certain temperature is reached. Figure 2 shows that for the spent nickel-molybdate catalyst a rapid complex decomposition occurs at about 280°C [17]. The temperature of complex decomposition depends on the amount and structure of coke deposited on the catalyst. These changes may be described by the following tentative mechanism in which [CHNSO] denotes the coke and [CHNSO—O_2] denotes the surface complex:

$$[\mathrm{CHNSO}] \xrightarrow{O_2} [\mathrm{CHNSO{-}O_2}]$$

$$[\mathrm{CHNSO{-}O_2}] \xrightarrow{O_2} \text{resids} + \text{products } (\mathrm{CO_2, CO, H_2O, SO_2} \text{ and } \mathrm{NO_x})$$

$$\text{resid}_1 + \text{resid}_2 \longrightarrow \text{resid}_1 - \text{resid}_2$$

$$\text{resids} \xrightarrow{O_2} [\text{resids} - O_2]$$

$$\text{resid}_1 - \text{resid}_2 \xrightarrow{O_2} [\text{resid}_1 - \text{resid}_2 - O_2]$$

$$[\text{resids} - O_2] \xrightarrow{O_2} \text{products}$$

$$[\text{resid}_1 - \text{resid}_2 - O_2] \xrightarrow{O_2} \text{products}$$

The decomposition products indicate the oxidation of organic S and N in addition to that of C and H. It is believed that organic O will end up in products as CO or CO_2. Then the complete set of organic elements oxidation reactions should contain:

$$H + \tfrac{1}{4}O_2 \longrightarrow \tfrac{1}{2}H_2O$$

$$C + \tfrac{1}{2}O_2 \longrightarrow CO$$

$$C + O_2 \longrightarrow CO_2$$

$$\text{S org} + O_2 \longrightarrow SO_2$$

$$\text{N org} + \frac{x}{2}O_2 \longrightarrow NO_x$$

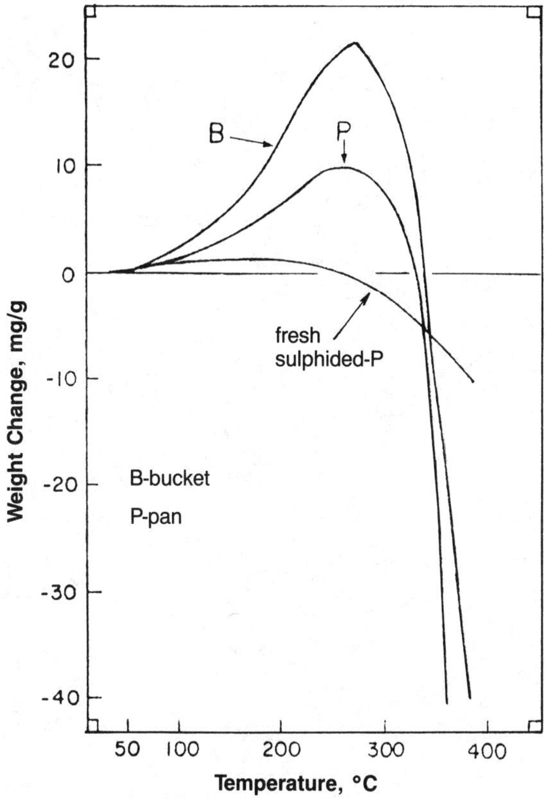

Figure 2. Weight change during temperature programmed oxidation in air.

If steam and/or CO_2 are added to the oxidizing gas the $C + H_2O$ and $C + CO_2$ reactions should be also considered. However, their contribution to the overall coke removal at temperatures usually applied during coke burnoff may not be important because of a markedly larger driving force for $C + O_2$ reactions [18].

The mechanism of intimate actions of O_2 with coke molecules is not well understood and it may involve a complex set of autoxidation reactions. The speculative mechanism shown in Figure 3 was developed on the basis of extensive information in the scientific literature on autoxidation of hydrocarbons. In this scheme tentative reactions leading to formation of coke molecules are also shown. This includes hydrocracking of asphaltene molecule, i.e., the cleavage of weak bonds yielding volatile hydrocarbons and leaving behind unstable residual species which may combine to give a large coke molecule. For this purpose the asphaltene model developed by Suzuki et al. was used [19]. On exposure to air the chemisorption of O_2 by coke will occur. Initially the most reactive sites of coke molecules such as benzylic and hydroaromatic groups will be attacked preferentially [17]. This results in the formation of peroxides and hydrogen peroxide groups as well as carbon centered peroxyradicals. Thermal decomposition of these groups and radicals leads to formation of CO_2, CO and H_2O. The last step in Figure 3 depicts the decomposition in the absence of O_2. In the presence of O_2 the formation of additional O-containing groups and radicals would follow the decomposition. It is believed that mobility of the newly formed O-containing groups will be lower than that of the groups formed initially. A non-radical and non-chain association of O_2 with coke may exist as well. For example, 9,10-substituted anthracene is known to react with O_2 to give 9,10 endo-peroxides [20].

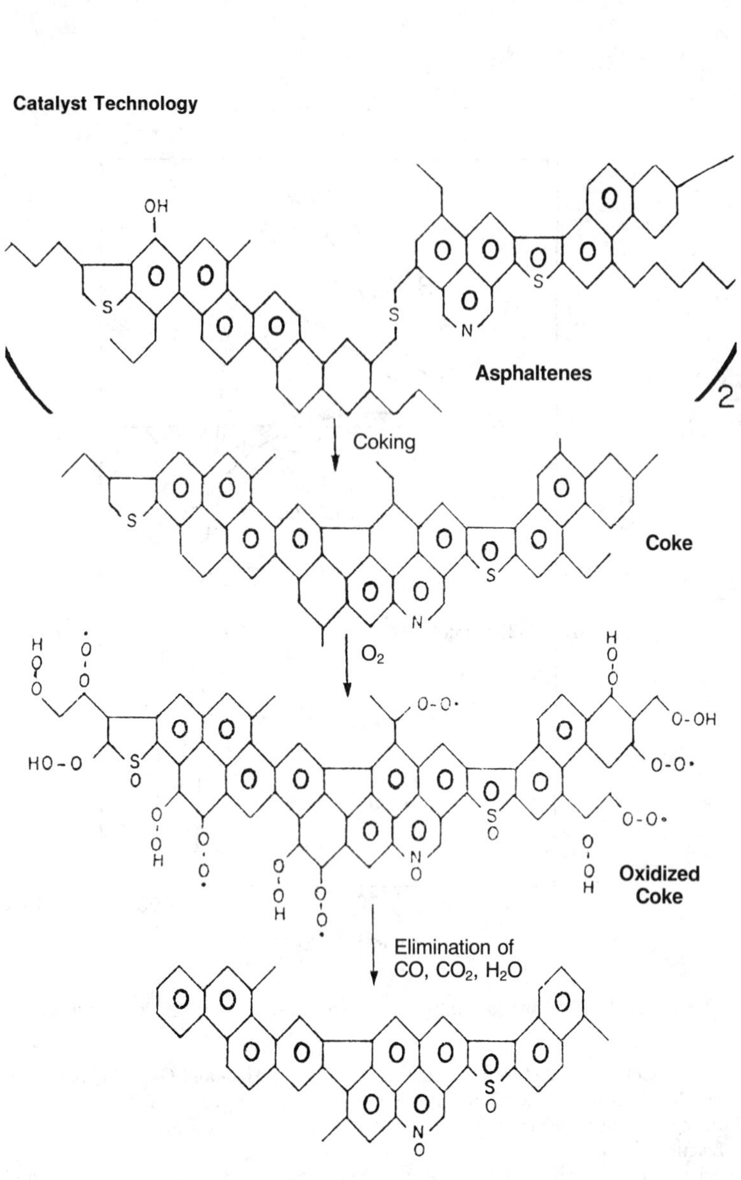

Figure 3. Mechanism of complex formation during autoxidation of coke molecules.

The O_2 chemisorption leads to a change in the chemical structure of coke molecules as the result of a gradual removal of carbon. This begins with the most reactive groups followed by removal of groups with decreasing reactivity. The extent of structural changes depends on temperature. Thus, below 250°C only the most reactive species are removed. The continuous removal of reactive groups is accompanied by a gradual decrease in reactivity of residual species left on the surface. This suggests that the last part of the coke molecule must be of a rather low reactivity. This clarifies the assumption of two types of coke, one very reactive and the other non-reactive, which are frequently mentioned in the scientific literature. It is believed that the non-reactive "hard" coke was formed during oxidation of the "soft" coke as the result of removing reactive groups from coke molecules. Further, the non-reactive residual species formed during decomposition of oxidized coke molecules shown in the last step in Figure 3 may combine on the catalyst surface giving a larger molecule of lower reactivity. Besides the two dimensional growth a three dimensional growth (graphitization) cannot be ruled out. Thus, coke molecules that are the most resistant to oxidation may not have been present in the original coke but may have been formed during oxidation.

During operation a large portion of active metals and promoters of hydrotreating catalysts are in a sulfided form. During burnoff the sulfides are converted to their oxides giving SO_2 as the main volatile product. The following approximate reactions are believed to occur during oxidation:

$$MoS_2(WS_2) \xrightarrow{-O_2} MoO_3(WO_3) + 2\,SO_2$$

$$\tfrac{1}{9}\,Co_9S_8(\tfrac{1}{3}\,Ni_3S_2) \xrightarrow{-O_2} CoO(NiO) + \tfrac{8}{9}\,SO_2(\tfrac{2}{3}\,SO_2)$$

The SO_2 maximum at about 250°C (Figure 4) was attributed to the sulfides oxidation whereas that at about 460°C to oxidation of organic sulfur (21). Some evidence was obtained that organic O may

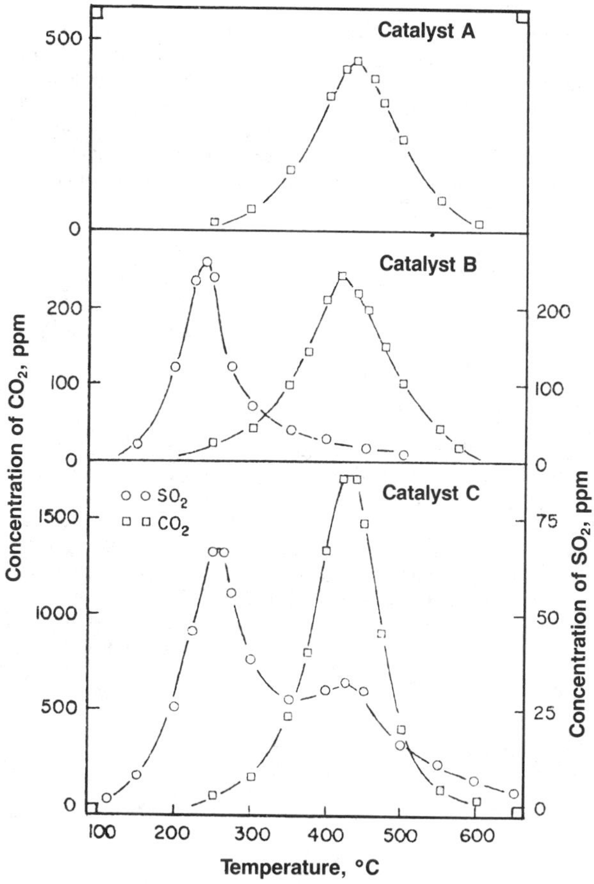

Figure 4. Product distribution from temperature programmed burnoff of catalysts in air: OSO_2; □ CO_2 (A-oxidic Co—MO/Al_2O_3 catalyst used for HDO of a phenol solution, B-sulfided Co—Mo/Al_2O_3 catalyst used for HDO of phenol solution, C-oxidic Co—Mo/Al_2O_3 catalyst used to hydrotreat Athabasca bitumen).

also take part in SO_2 forming reactions particularly under O_2 deficient conditions at higher temperatures. Also, MoO_3 and/or WO_3 if present or formed during early stages of burnoff will later engage in sulfides oxidation.

A spent nickel-molybdate catalyst was studied by Wukasch and Rase using a differential thermal analysis technique [22]. In static air two exothermic (at about 295 and 400°C) and one endothermic (at about 100°C) peaks were observed. The two exothermic peaks are attributed to oxidation of metal sulfides and coke, respectively, whereas the endothermic peak reflects the moisture removal. In qualitative terms these results agree with those shown in Figure 4. A cobalt-molybdate catalyst used to liquefy a coal exhibited Raman absorption typical for carbon and MoS_2 [23]. The disappearance of this adsorption after burnoff in air would again support the results in Figure 4.

Transition metals such as V, Ni, Ti and Fe that accumulate in coke during hydrotreatment of heavy feedstocks are converted during burnoff to corresponding oxides, e.g., V_2O_5, NiO, TiO_2, and Fe_2O_3, respectively. These transformations are of crucial importance because they cause an irreversible change of catalyst surface due to interaction of these oxides with active metals, promoters, and catalyst support.

The above discussion of coke burnoff reactions assumes a direct interaction of O_2 with coke molecules. Also the sulfide oxidation assumed participation of gaseous O_2. An indirect interaction, i.e., O transfer with the aid of metal ions must also be considered. It is generally known that some metal ions are quite active O transfer agents. This kind of reaction is believed to be a part of catalytic burnoff. The removal of the most reactive groups during early stages of burnoff may be non-catalytic. However, with progress of burnoff the catalytic reactions may contribute significantly to the overall coke removal. The participation of Mo oxides in carbon oxidation may be illustrated on the following set of reactions:

$$MoO_3 + C \longrightarrow MoO_2 + CO$$

$$2\,MoO_3 + C \longrightarrow 2MoO_2 + CO_2$$

$$MoO_3 + CO \longrightarrow MoO_2 + CO_2$$

$$MoO_2 + \tfrac{1}{2}\,O_2 \longrightarrow MoO_3$$

This series of reactions represents a catalytic cycle in which the active species is consumed and subsequently recovered. It was shown that all these reactions are thermodynamically favorable [24]. Such catalytic cycle may be established for other transition metals which are part of hydrotreating catalysts or part of the coke deposited on the catalyst surface during hydrotreating operations.

The trends in CO formation during regeneration of a nickel-molybdate catalyst in pure CO_2 are shown in Figure 5. The rapid CO buildup on CO_2 admission was attributed to the presence of active species such as metal carbides and metallic forms of active metals, promoters and transition metals which are part of the coke [25]. Such species may be formed during heating the spent catalyst under N_2 prior to CO_2 admission. The following reactions were shown to be thermodynamically favorable:

$$Mo + 2\,CO_2 \longrightarrow MoO_2 + 2\,CO$$

$$2\,Mo + C \longrightarrow Mo_2C$$

$$Mo + C \longrightarrow MoC$$

whereas the driving force of carbide reactions with CO_2 such as:

$$Mo_2C + CO_2 \longrightarrow 2\,Mo + 2\,CO$$

$$MoC + CO_2 \longrightarrow Mo + 2\,CO$$

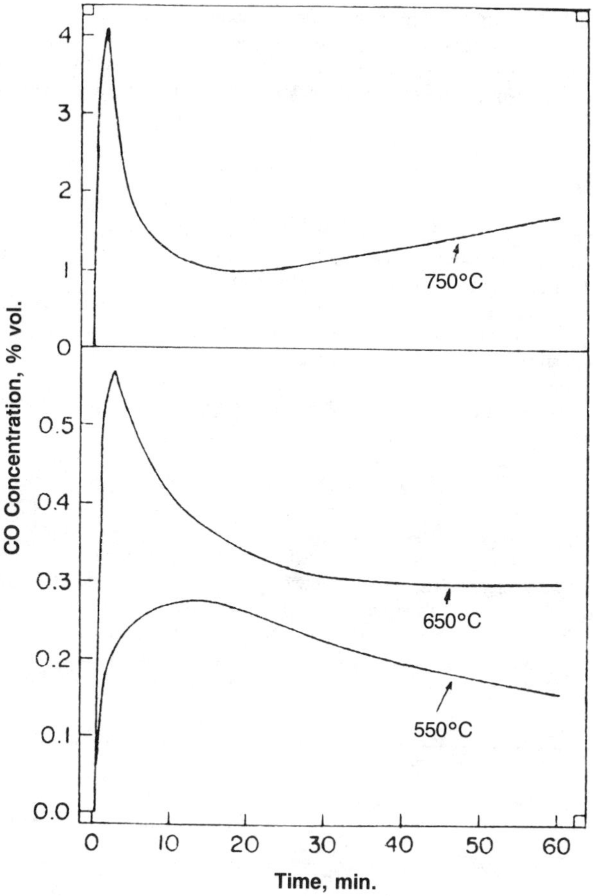

Figure 5. CO formation during isothermal gasification of Ni—Mo/Al_2O_3 catalyst in pure CO_2.

exhibit a steep increase with temperature. The participation of carbides of Ni and Co is also probable. This set of reactions may indicate an irreversible removal of active Mo if its reaction with CO_2 giving MoO_2 and CO is the most predominant. This may explain the rapid CO buildup followed by a sudden decrease in rate as shown in Figure 5. It is believed that reduced forms of active metals and promoters as well as their carbides play an important role during regeneration in the presence of H_2O.

In summary of this part of the chapter the complexity of the oxidative regeneration mechanism of spent hydrotreating catalysts is emphasized. This involves a simultaneous change in the inorganic part of the spent catalyst and coke deposits during burnoff. Moreover, the oxidized form of catalyst may chemically interact with coke. These changes depend on temperature. Thus, the removal of H from coke is the most rapid and it occurs at temperatures where C removal is insignificant [26]. On the other hand the highest rate of removal of organic S occurs at a similar temperature as that of organic C as indicated in Figure 4. In view of a higher stability of N- and O-containing structures [27] the maximum of the conversion of these elements to volatile products may occur at higher temperatures than required for oxidation of C and S. It is indeed believed that the accumulation of organic N and O in "hard" coke formed in the course of polymerization during burnoff will be more extensive than that of organic S. The extent of chemical change incurred during burnoff by mineral and organic components is also temperature dependent. Thus, an extensive oxidation of metal sulfides occurs at temperatures where the destruction of organic components of spent catalyst is insignificant.

KINETICS OF BURNOFF

The burnoff mechanism indicated the importance of the chemical structure of coke as well as the state of active metals and promoters in spent catalysts on the burnoff rate. The access of oxidizing agent molecules to coke molecules is also important. This depends on physical properties such as pore volume and size distribution, surface area, etc. The diffusion effects of oxidizing agents (O_2, CO_2 and H_2O) into catalyst particles and that of oxidation products (e.g., CO, CO_2, SO_2, and NO_x) out of particles are significant especially at the later stages of burnoff. These effects may explain slow burnoff rates at later stages as shown in Figure 6 using results obtained at 500°C. The estimate of kinetic parameters during very early stages of burnoff is of crucial importance because high burnoff rates may cause catalyst overheating.

Kinetic data estimates are usually based on measurement of absolute yields of products such as shown in Figure 6 for the sum of CO and CO_2 and/or the measurement of weight loss during the burnoff. The latter is less reliable because it involves the oxidation of both coke and metal sulfides. It is rather difficult to apply a correction to account for the effect of sulfides oxidation on the overall weight decrease [24]. For product yields that are used for kinetic data estimates a quantitative analysis of burnoff products within a few seconds of air admission is required.

A temperature increase on air admission to the spent catalyst appears to be a common observation during regeneration. The results in Figure 7 show that the increase is caused by the heat evolved during oxidation of both the coke and metal sulfides. This may affect kinetic measurements particularly those of initial rate constants. It was shown by Massoth that the temperature increase may

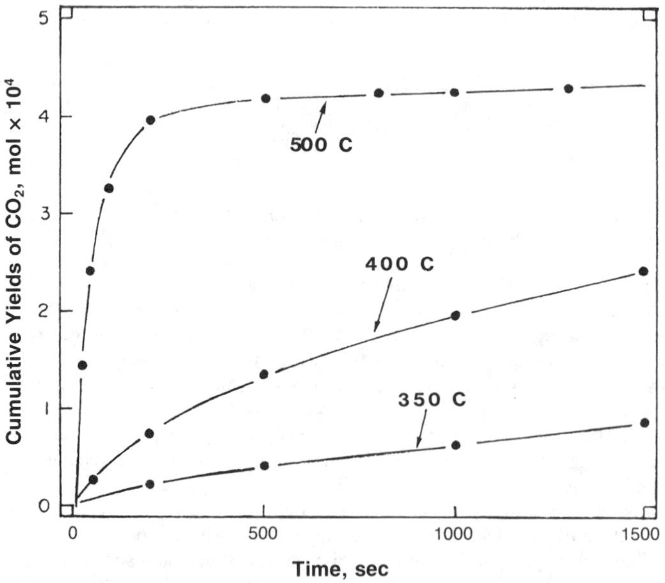

Figure 6. Cumulative yields of CO_2 from isothermal burnoff of spent catalyst in air.

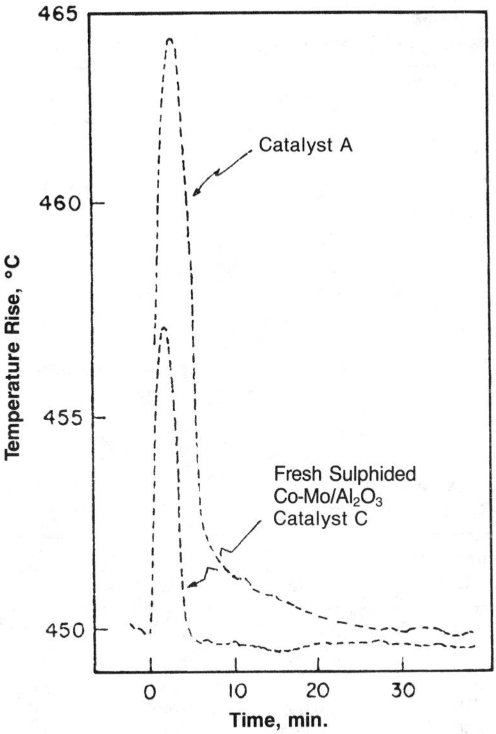

Figure 7. Temperature rise during early stages of burnoff in a thermogravimetric reactor at 450°C in air (A—Co—Mo/Al_2O_3 catalyst used to hydrotreat Athabasca bitumen, C-fresh sulfided Co—Mo/Al_2O_3 catalyst).

be diminished by mixing catalyst particles with a non-reactive alumina [28]. A modification of this technique was used to measure the rate constants of hydrotreating catalysts [24]. In this work the temperature increase on air admission to a spent molybdate catalyst held at 500°C was less than 4°C. For catalyst particles that were not diluted with inert particles the temperatures increase as high as 35°C was recorded. In the work published by Sanford a large amount of spent nickel-molybdate catalyst was exposed to air in an oven [29]. Here, the temperature increase on air admission was as high as 130°C.

A group of spent hydrotreating catalysts was used to estimate initial rate constants to burnoff. Some properties of these catalysts are shown in Table 3 whereas the rate constants are summarized in Table 4. For these calculations the first order kinetics with respect to carbon and the O_2 partial pressure was assumed. The constants were calculated from the following formula:

$$k = r/C_0 \cdot Po_2$$

where r is the rate estimated from initial slope such as shown in Figure 6, C_0 initial concentration of carbon and P partial pressure of O_2. The rate constants in CO_2 were estimated from CO yields such as shown in Figure 8 using the following formula:

$$k = \tfrac{1}{2}r/C_0 \cdot Pco_2$$

The constants were obtained in pure CO_2 in order to avoid the order uncertainties. The constants obtained in CO_2 are several orders of magnitude smaller than those in air and they indicate that the regeneration in CO_2 may require temperatures in excess of 750°C to achieve the rates which are comparable to those in air at 350°C. For catalyst A the rate constants in air were also estimated

Table 3
Properties of Spent Catalysts

	Catalyst		
	A	B	C
MoO_3, wt%	15.0	16.0	16.0
CoO	—	4.0	4.0
NiO	4.0	—	—
carbon	18.8	11.4	2.8
hydrogen	1.5	2.1	—
sulphur	7.1	4.4	6.1
nitrogen	0.5	0.5	0
N_2BET s.a., M^2/g	26	65	126
upgraded feed	solv. ref. coal	bitumen	phenol + hexadecane

Note: Oxides contents are for fresh catalysts

Table 4
Initial Rate Constants (1/min. atm)

Method	Ox. Agent	Temperature °C	Catalyst A	B	C
fixed bed	air	350	—	0.12	0
		400	—	0.39	3.1
		500	—	5.37	18.9
	CO_2	550	0.002	0.007	—
		650	0.003	0.018	0.009
		750	0.021	0.025	0.025
TGA	air	350	—	0.01	—
		400	—	0.26	—
		450	—	0.61	—
		500	—	0.63	—

at 50% carbon conversion. The values at 350°, 400° and 500°C were 0.02, 0.07 and 1.72 l/min. atm, respectively. Activation energies estimated from initial rate constants and those obtained at 50% carbon conversions were 102.6 and 119 kJ/mol respectively. For catalyst A the rate constants were obtained in both fixed bed and TGA reactors. The results indicate the effect of experimental techniques on rate constant values.

Rate constants for regeneration of spent hydrotreating catalysts in steam are not availabe. It is however believed that their values should be in the range of rate constants in CO_2 rather than those in air. Of particular interest are the rate constants obtained in the mixture of air + CO_2 and air + steam. Thus, a brief information indicates the existence of a process for regeneration of hydrotreating catalysts using a mixture of O_2 and steam [30]. In this regard the presence of steam and/or CO_2 may prevent catalyst overheating because the excess heat is consumed in their endothermic reactions with carbon.

Published information on kinetic parameters of burnoff of spent hydrotreating catalysts is limited. The kinetics of burnoff of nickel-molybdate catalyst used for upgrading a solvent refined coal was reported by Nalitham et al. [31]. The initial rate constants in air estimated at 350°, 400° and 450°C (e.g., 0.027, 0.235 and 1.26 l/min) are in the same range as those for catalyst A (Table 4). The activation energy (142.5 kJ/mol) agrees well with that reported by Massoth (133.8 kJ/mol) for regeneration of molybdate catalyst used for coal liquefaction [32]. The higher activation energies reported by

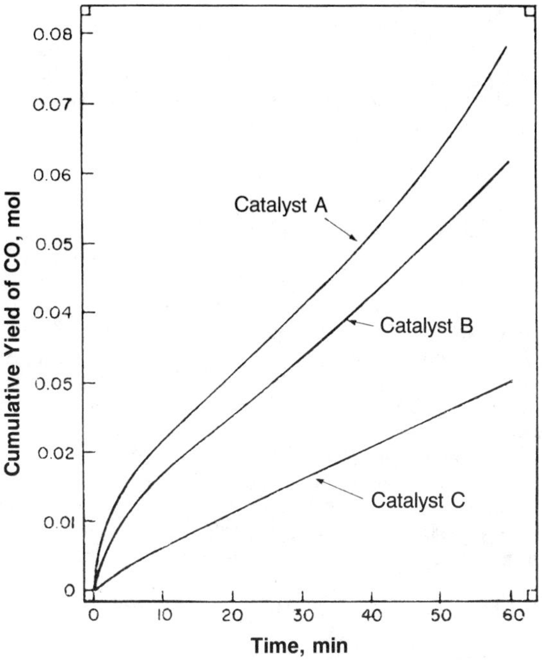

Figure 8. Cumulative yields of CO from gasification of catalysts A, B, and C at 750°C in pore CO_2.

these authors compared with that for catalyst A are attributed to a markedly higher hydrogen content in the latter. Alvarez et al. reported the activation energy of 156.4 kJ/mol for burnoff of a molybdate catalyst containing 4.1 wt% V and 36 wt% coke [33].

Although air appears to be the most convenient oxidizing agent great care must be taken during regeneration to prevent uncontrolled burnoff especially in the presence of large amounts of reactive species in coke. In most of the regeneration studies published in the scientific literature the spent catalyst was pretreated (tempering in inert atmosphere or vacuum, solvent extraction, etc.) to remove trapped gases and carryovers which are not part of coke molecules. Such pretreatment may not be practical in industrial regeneration processes performed in situ. In this case the use of a diluted air may avoid an uncontrolled temperature rise. Thus, the first order kinetics in carbon and O_2 concentration suggests that the air dilution will decrease proportionally the burnoff rate. After most of the reactive species were removed the O_2 concentration may be increased.

Information on burnoff of spent hydrotreating catalysts in pellet form is also limited. As expected the temperature profile during burnoff of coke loaded pellets will be markedly different than that of a powder form of spent catalysts. The presence of hot spots during the pellet burnoff was observed by Alvarez et al. [33]. Diffusion effects during burnoff of a pellet are also believed to be much more significant compared with that of fine particles. This will alter the chemical composition of coke relative to that of catalyst material. This suggests that powder data may have a limited use for practical regeneration processes. The need for kinetic parameters on burnoff of pellets and/or extrudates of spent hydrotreating catalysts is, therefore emphasized.

DEVELOPMENT OF BURNOFF MODELS

The information on mechanism and kinetics of burnoff is a base for development of mathematical models to predict regeneration conditions. For spent FCC catalysts numerous attempts have been made to predict the conditions by fitting experimentally predetermined parameters into equations derived theoretically. For spent hydrotreating catalysts the model development is still in the stage of infancy. This is given by the complexity of mechanism and kinetics of burnoff of hydrotreating catalysts compared with that of FCC catalysts. This may be illustrated by a discussion of basic assumptions used to formulate model equations for FCC catalysts and their applicability for model development of burnoff of spent hydrotreating catalysts.

Model for Burnoff of FCC Catalysts

The published information on different phases of development of burnoff models of spent FCC catalysts was recently reviewed in detail by Hughes [34]. Some of the observations and conclusions made for FCC catalysts are related to regeneration of other types of deactivated catalysts. For example, two distinct types of burnoff, i.e., chemically and diffusion controlled, observed by Weisz and Goodwin appear to have a general application [35]. The former, occurring at lower temperatures ($\approx 300°C$), represents a radially uniform burnoff. In this case the O_2 has sufficient time to penetrate whole particles before it is consumed. In other words the burnoff rate will be equal at all points of particle radius. At higher temperatures ($\approx 500°C$) the burnoff is rapid and most of the O_2 is consumed before it can penetrate deeply into the particle. This will result in a diffusion controlled burnoff. In the intermediate region both chemically and diffusion controlled burnoff will contribute to the overall rate of regeneration. These authors further observed the first order burnoff kinetics with respect to coke at concentrations lower than 6 wt% for the catalyst, having in the fresh state the surface area of about 250 m^2/g [36]. Thus, they concluded that in this concentration range the coke is evenly distributed on the surface in a monolayer like form.

The reactions to be considered for development of mathematical equations must include the oxidation of both carbon (to CO and CO_2) and hydrogen (to H_2O) where organic sulfur and nitrogen contents are not important.

Earlier work considered oxidation of carbon only. The complexity in deriving mathematical equations was shown by Sampath and Hughes who proposed a homogeneous, sharp interface and finite thickness unreacted core models [37] to account for three cases described by Weisz and Goodwin [35]. Some important assumptions that were used for the model development are:

1. Coke burnoff was non-catalytic.
2. Catalyst particles were spherical, had a homogeneous structure and were large enough to allow internal mass and temperature gradients.
3. Size of particles did not change appreciably during burnoff.
4. Radial distribution of coke was uniform.
5. Burnoff was irreversible.
6. Reactant gas concentration changed little during burnoff.
7. Parameters such as activation energy, heat of reaction, density and specific heat of solid, diffusivity of gas in solid, mass and heat coefficient of gas and of solid remained invariant during the burnoff.
8. Carbon was the only component of coke.
9. For the sharp interface and finite thickness unreacted core models the unreacted core was stationary relative to reactant diffusion in product layer.

Several predictions could be made from mathematical equations derived using these assumptions [38], e.g., decreasing temperature rise with increasing particle size and with increasing thermal conductivity of particle solids. Also, increasing the flow of reactant gas and/or its diffusivity into particles resulted in lowering the temperature rise.

It was shown by Massoth that hydrogen must be considered as an important component of coke as carbon [28]. Therefore, the heat of combustion of both hydrogen and carbon must be included in models predicting the temperature profile of coke burnoff. The hydrogen oxidation reaction was included by Hughes et al. to advance the models discussed above [39]. Using a higher burnoff rate of hydrogen compared with carbon these authors identified two zones of burnoff, i.e., the inner zone having the original composition of coke and the outer zone containing carbon only. The removal of hydrogen occurred at the sharp interface between these two zones whereas that of carbon occurred between the surface and the sharp interface. The increased temperature rise with increasing H/C ratio of coke as well as that with increasing coke loading could be predicted from the advanced model. Also, rather good predictions of temperature profile in a wider temperature range of burnoff could be made compared with models which included carbon as the only component of coke.

The model developed by Hughes et al. [39], was further refined by Hashimoto et al. who assumed a continuous change of carbon concentration in the outer zone of particle in addition to other assumptions usually applied during model development [40]. The refined model was used to predict conversion of carbon, hydrogen and total conversion with time. An excellent agreement of theoretical data with experimental results from burnoff of silica alumina catalyst performed in a thermogravimetric reactor was obtained. The first order kinetics for the burnoff of hydrogen and carbon was also confirmed with calculated activation energies of 140.3 kJ/mol and 156.2 kJ/mol, respectively. These authors advanced their models by including intrapellet diffusion effects [26]. This resulted in a rather accurate prediction of effects of H/C ratio and the amount of coke on temperature rise in comparison with experimental results. The increase of initial temperature rise with increasing partial pressure of O_2 in oxidizing medium could be predicted as well.

Model for Burnoff of Hydrotreating Catalysts

The complexity of the burnoff mechanism for hydrotreating catalysts has been identified as the main reason for the lack of effort in developing mathematical models to predict temperature profile. Thus, some assumptions used to develop burnoff models for FCC catalysts cannot be used for that of hydrotreating catalysts. First, the chemical composition of catalysts at the beginning and at the end of burnoff may differ markedly. This is demonstrated by the oxidation reaction of metal sulfides to their oxides during burnoff. The sulfide oxidation reactions were observed to compete successfully for O_2 with combustion reactions. Low temperature coefficients of the former indicate their importance relative to combustion reactions with decreasing temperature. Although these changes occur in a monolayer of catalyst they will inevitably alter its chemical composition. This must lead to a change in some physical parameters of the catalyst, e.g. density, specific heat, heat conductivity, etc. The changes may influence the gas diffusion into and from the particles. These changes suggest that the assumption of the invariability of the chemical structure of catalyst material during burnoff that applied to model formulation of FCC catalysts does not apply to hydrotreating catalysts.

The oxides of metals which are either active ingredients or promoters of hydrotreating catalysts are established catalysts for oxidation of carbon [41]. It was shown earlier that these oxides may play an important role in overall coke removal. The catalytic removal of carbon requires a coke molecule to be in proximity to metal oxide. For example, coke molecules formed during interaction of feedstock molecules, e.g., N-containing bases and/or condensed aromatic structures, with Lewis acidity of the support will be further from the oxides than those formed as the result of destruction of Bronstadt acidity depicted S—H groups attached to Mo and/or W [12].

The involvement of oxides of other metals, e.g., V, Ti, Fe, etc., in carbon oxidation reactions cannot be ruled out. At the end of burnoff these oxides remain on the catalyst surface. Repeating utilization regeneration cycles will lead to build up of the metals on the surface. This suggests that each regeneration cycle would require a modification to the burnoff model.

The heat of reaction is an essential parameter of mathematical models for predicting temperature rise on air admission. For catalysts used to hydrotreat heavy feeds, the heat evolved during oxidation of both organic and inorganic sulfur must be included in the overall heat released during burnoff. It appears that the oxidation of organic N is a thermally neutral reaction. If transition metals are part of the coke, the heat associated with their conversion to oxides has to be considered as well. Thus, the overall burnoff heat of spent hydrotreating catalysts represents a combination of several reactions besides the oxidation of carbon and hydrogen that are the only oxidation reactions considered for model formulation of FCC catalysts.

A uniform radial distribution of coke assumed for FCC catalysts may not apply to spent hydrotreating catalysts especially when the latter are used to hydrotreat heavy feedstocks. This is demonstrated by the preferential adsorption of large asphaltene molecules on outer parts of catalyst particles as discussed earlier. Also, the V-containing species tend to accumulate on outer parts compared with Ni- and Ti-containing species which are distributed more evenly throughout particles. Thus, the overall burnoff as well as the participation of the metals in the burnoff will not be uniform. This may add to the complexity in developing mathematical models for burnoff of spent hydrotreating catalysts.

Few attempts to develop a burnoff model of spent hydrotreating catalysts include the work published by Klusacek et al. (42). These authors used a cobalt-molybdate catalyst used to hydrotreat a light fraction derived from a conventional crude. The selection of this feedstock ensured the absence of transition metals in the coke. Also, the state of a uniform distribution of coke throughout the catalyst pellet may have been approached. These authors developed a set of mathematical equations assuming C and S as the only elements undergoing oxidation during burnoff. They attempted to predict temperature rise of the gas exiting the fixed bed of catalyst pellets compared with the temperature of the gas entering the reactor. A good agreement between experimentally measured and theoretically calculated temperatures was obtained. However, temperature changes occurring in a single pellet were not measured. In fact the temperature was measured at the bottom and on the top of catalyst bed only.

Nalitham et al. formulated a kinetic model which was used to predict burnoff profile of a nickel-molybdate catalyst used for upgrading a solvent refined coal [31]. The model was derived on the basis of parameters such as carbon conversion at different stages of burnoff, predetermined experimentally. These authors indicated a need for two kinds of models to account for burnoff of reactive and non-reactive coke in early and late stages of burnoff, respectively.

It appears that no other studies are available in the scientific literature attempting to formulate a model for burnoff of spent hydrotreating catalysts. The two attempts discussed above represent a preliminary stage compared with a complex mathematical models derived for FCC catalysts. Nalitham et al. described several differences between spent FCC and hydrotreating catalysts which make the predictions of some burnoff parameters difficult if not impossible [31].

PROPERTIES AND STRUCTURE OF REGENERATED CATALYSTS

The activity of regenerated catalysts is the main parameter of interest. The objective is to maintain the original activity after many successive utilization-regeneration cycles. Published results on change of catalyst activity during regeneration vary. Thus, some studies show that the activity after regeneration may increase whereas others indicate an activity loss after the first utilization-regeneration cycle. The different observations may be attributed to different conditions applied during hydrotreatment and subsequent regeneration. In this regard the type of hydrotreated feed may have pronounced effects. Repeating the cycles will lead to a gradual change of catalyst structure. A general consent is that the change is more pronounced for catalysts used to hydrotreat heavy feeds containing asphaltenic molecules and organonetallic compounds. The results published by Inoguchi et al. show that for a catalyst deactivated by coke only, almost all activity was recovered compared with an activity loss for a catalyst deactivated by metals [43].

The work published by Artega et al. represents the first attempt to find a more direct relation between deactivation and regeneration [44]. In this work the properties of a cobalt-molybdate catalyst from an accelerated aging were investigated. The aging was performed at 450°C in a stream of either butadiene or methylcyclopentane. The hydrodesulfurization and hydrogenation activity was determined after each of the three deactivation-regeneration cycles. After the first cycle the catalyst activity increased compared with the fresh catalyst and the increased activity was maintained even after the third cycle. The same observation was made for the blank catalyst treated similarly. These authors carried out extensive evaluations of regenerated catalysts using spectroscopic techniques such as XPS, IR and UV. The results indicate a considerable increase in surface concentration of Mo species after the first cycle. After two subsequent cycles the Mo concentration decreased presumably due to the formation of molybdenum aluminates. The Co surface concentration increased during regeneration. The confirmation of the presence of sulphate ions in the regenerated catalyst appears to be an important observation made by these authors. The amount of this ion gradually increased with the number of cycles. It is believed that this species may

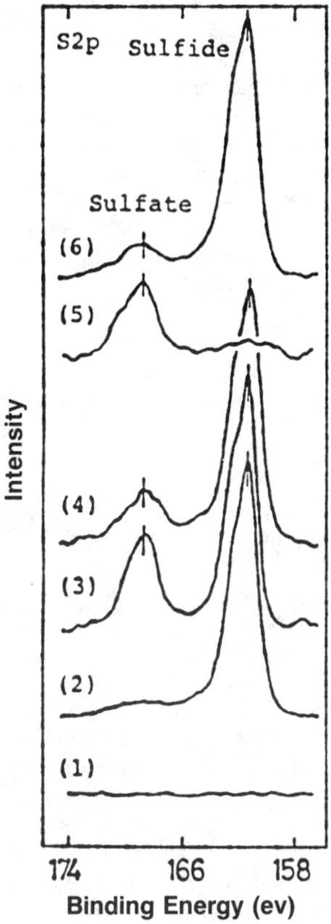

Figure 9. The XPS spectra of S2p for the fresh and spent catalysts: 1—oxidic, 2—presulfided, 3—spent, 4—spent-degassed, 5—spent-degassed-regenerated, 6—spent-degassed-regenerated-presulfided.

contribute to an irreversible loss of catalyst activity. The presence of sulphate ion was confirmed even in the spent catalyst prior to its exposure to O_2 [45]. As the results in Figure 9 show the concentration of this ion increased significantly during regeneration.

The loss of catalyst activity on regeneration of a hydrotreating catalyst was reported by Hiemenz [46]. Thus, the temperatures of hydrotreating would have to be increased by about 20°C after each utilization regeneration cycle in order to maintain the same conversions as achieved in the presence of the fresh catalyst. The results published by Sakabe and Yagi suggest that a cobalt-molybdate catalyst used for hydrodesulfurization of a residue lost some of its activity on regeneration [47]. However, its activity for hydrocracking of a residue slightly improved. This observation may result in economic benefits if hydrodesulfurization and hydrocracking units are in the same location.

The measurement of surface structure is a common way to determine effects of regeneration on catalyst properties. During regeneration of catalysts used to hydrotreat a coker and virgin gas oil the surface area was completely restored whereas a surface area loss was observed for catalysts used to hydrotreat a heavy feedstock containing organometallic compounds [48]. For six investigated catalysts (two nickel-molybdate, three cobalt-molybdate and one nickel-tungstate) the surface area loss ranged from 3 to 30% of the original value. Also, the pore volume distribution skewed to larger pore sizes. A similar observation was made by Curtis et al. during regeneration of a nickel-molybdate catalyst used to hydrotreat feedstocks of varying solvent refined coal/solvent ratio [49]. The loss of surface area was more pronounced for the high ratio feedstocks. It also appears that the restoration of surface area is favored by lower regeneration temperatures. The greater percentage loss of surface area than that of pore volume observed by Wukasch and Rase was attributed to coke deposition in small pores [22]. Similar observation was made by Stephens and Stohl [50].

The surface area may not be a proper parameter to measure the activity change during utilization-regeneration cycles. This was confirmed by the different activity of regenerated catalysts even in cases where the original surface area was completely restored [48, 51]. In this respect the most consistent results were published by Hertan et al. [52]. These authors observed a correlation between surface acidity as measured by pyridine adsorption and hydrogenation activity of regenerated nickel-molybdate catalyst used for upgrading liquid products from coal liquefaction. A similar correlation between surface area and activity was not established. The loss of activity while maintaining a similar surface area may be reconciled by assuming an agglomeration of active ingredients during regeneration as observed by Bogdanor and Rase [53] and Artega et al. [44].

Diffusivity measurements performed on fresh, spent and regenerated cobalt-molybdate catalysts were used to study effects of deactivation and regeneration on catalyst properties [54]. The diffusivity was determined by measuring the residual coronene concentration in cyclohexane solution which was in contact with the catalysts. The increased diffusivity on regeneration confirmed that the coke deposited in pores was the cause of catalyst deactivation.

The activity of regenerated catalysts depends also on conditions applied during regeneration. The work published by Matyas and Potts can be used as an example to illustrate these effects [55]. These authors studied the activity of regenerated nickel-molybdate catalysts used for upgrading a solvent refined coal. The spent catalyst was regenerated by two different laboratories. The activity of regenerated catalysts for naphthalene hydrogenation exhibited different patterns.

Migration of metals occurring during heat treatment of hydrotreating catalysts is a generally established phenomenon. These effects occurring during regeneration of a nickel-molybdate catalyst in air were investigated by Bogdanor and Rase [53]. At 380°C both Mo and Ni migrated towards the centre of the pellet. This was attributed to a thermal gradient resulting from the burnoff on the exterior of pellets. At 560°C the Mo and Ni moved towards the exterior. Also this observation was attributed to thermal gradient resulting from burnoff of the last portion of coke at the centre of pellets. The sulfiding temperature of the regenerated catalyst had a pronounced effect on the metals distribution. For example, temperature increase from 232° to 371°C shifted the maximum of Mo/Ni intraparticle ratio from the centre to the edge of the particles. Apparently, a proper temperature control can lead to any derived profile. The regeneration followed by sulfiding had little effect on profiles of V and Fe. These authors used the XPS technique to determine the type of compounds formed during regeneration and sulfidation. Thus, during the former the MoS_2 was converted to MoO_3 whereas on sulfidation the MoO_3 was converted back to MoS_2. However, the MoS_2 crystallites of the sulfided catalyst were larger than those of the sulfided fresh catalyst indicating some crystal growth. The presence of sulfate ion in the regenerated catalyst was also confirmed by these authors, whereas the results were inconclusive regarding the fate of MoO_2. The change of surface concentration of metals occurring during regeneration of a nickel-molybdate catalyst used to hydrotreat a coal derived liquid [45] is shown in Table 5.

Table 5
The XPS Surface Composition of Fresh, Spent and Regenerated Catalysts

	Al	C	S	Ni	Mo	Ni/Mo
Fresh-oxidic	1	0.65	0	0.08	0.09	0.93
Fresh-presulph	1	0.30	0.20	0.06	0.09	0.72
Fresh-degas	1	0.62	0.18	0.06	0.08	0.71
Fresh-degas-regen	1	0.41	0.04	0.07	0.09	0.84
Fresh-degas-regen-presul	1	0.38	0.18	0.07	0.08	0.81
Spent	1	1.05	0.17	0.05	0.09	0.59
Spent-degas	1	1.40	0.16	0.06	0.10	0.61
Spent-degas-regen	1	0.52	0.03	0.08	0.08	0.91
Spent-degas-regen-presul	1	0.60	0.18	0.06	0.09	0.75

INDUSTRIAL REGENERATION

In spite of a limited information published in the scientific literature the spent hydrotreating and hydroprocessing catalysts have been regenerated industrially. A detailed description of regeneration procedures, i.e., in-site and off-site, was published by Tamayama [56]. The reported experimental conditions reflect the precautions which must be taken to avoid catalyst overheating.

The in situ regeneration is carried out in the hydrotreating reactor when the catalyst activity loss cannot be further offset by adjusting processing parameters. Prior to the admission of O_2 containing gas the fixed bed of spent catalyst is deoiled in the recycle gas that is later replaced by N_2. The burnoff begins by adding 0.5 vol% of O_2 at the reactor temperature of about 330°C. Later the O_2 concentration is increased to about 0.65 vol% and the burnoff is completed in $N_2 + O_2$ mixture containing about 1.0 vol% O_2. For the in situ regeneration in the reactive gas containing both O_2 and steam the deoiling begins in the mixture of recycle gas and steam and is completed in the flow of steam only. The burnoff begins by adding 0.5 vol% O_2 at about 400°C and is completed in O_2 + steam mixture containing about 1.5 vol% of O_2.

For the off-site regeneration the spent catalyst is withdrawn from hydrotreating reactor and transferred to regeneration unit. Different types of regenerators have been used, e.g., trays, rotary kilns and conveyors. Catalyst Recovery Int., employs a conveyor method where the tunnel consists of a deoiling and regeneration zone. For an efficient regeneration the careful control of experimental parameters such as catalyst depth, residence time, temperature, the O_2 concentration during and after burnoff, is being emphasized.

CONCLUSIONS

The complexity of mechanism may be the reason for limited information on regeneration of hydrotreating catalysts compared with other types of industrial catalysts, e.g., FCC catalysts. For the former, the compounds of active metals and promoters undergo chemical change in addition to complex reactions occurring during burnoff of carbonaceous deposits. The results of burnoff of a fresh sulfided catalyst as well as that of corresponding spent sulfided catalysts may aid the elucidation of the overall regeneration mechanism. The approach based on controlled deactivation using a set of well defined model reactions followed by regeneration may yield valuable information.

The burnoff experiments performed on spent catalysts in crushed form should be expanded to include pellets and/or extrudates. Temperature profiles determined on unpretreated spent catalysts may differ from those determined on pretreated (extraction, tempering under vacuum, etc.) catalysts. Thus, trapped gases, products and feedstock carried over with spent catalysts may add to the complexity of the regeneration mechanism.

For heavy oil upgrading processes employing molybdate or tungstate catalysts, an on-site regeneration system may be required in order to lower the cost of catalyst inventory. The regeneration of catalysts used in such processes represents a challenging research project.

REFERENCES

1. Bartholomew, C. H., "Catalyst Deactivation," *Chem. Eng.* Nov. 12, 96 (1984).
2. Thakur, D. S., and Thomas, M. G., "Catalyst Deactivation in Heavy Petroleum and Synthetic Crude Processing," *Appl. Catal., 15*, 197 (1985).
3. Furimsky, E., "Deactivation and Regeneration of Refinary Catalyst," *Erdoel und Kohle, 32*, 383 (1979).
4. Massoth, F. E., "Characterization of Molybdena Catalysts," *Adv. Catal., 27*, 265 (1978).
5. Grange, P., "Catalytic Hydrodesulphurization," *Catal. Rev. Sci. Eng., 21*, 135 (1980).
6. Gates, B. C., Katzer, J. R., and Schuit, G. C. A., "Chemistry of Catalytic Processes," McGraw-Hill series in Chem. Eng., 1979.
7. Furimsky, E., "Role of MoS_2 and WS_2 in Hydrodesulphurization," *Catal. Rev. Sci. Eng., 22*, 371 (1980).

8. Lipsch, J. M. T. G., Schuit, G. C. A., "The CoO—MoO_3—Al_2O_3 Catalyst," *J. Catal., 15*, 179 (1969).
9. Furimsky, E., "Chemical Origin of Coke Deposited on Catalyst Surface," *Ind. Eng. Chem., Prod. Res. Dev.*, 17, 329 (1978).
10. Flockhart, B. D., Sesay, I. M., and Pink, R. C., "Nature of Radical Formed from Perylene on Alumina Surface," *J. Chem. Soc. Chem. Comm.*, 735 (1980).
11. Furimsky, E., "Characterization of Deposits Formed on Catalyst Surface During Hydrotreatment of Coal Derived Liquids," *Fuel. Proc. Technol., 6*, 1 (1982).
12. Furimsky, E., "Deactivation of Molybdate Catalysts by Nitrogen Bases," *Erdoel und Kohle, 35*, 455 (1982).
13. Furimsky, E., "Catalytic Deoxygenation of Heavy Gas Oil," *Fuel, 57*, 494 (1978).
14. Tam, P. W., Harnsberger, H. F., and Bridge, A. G., "Effect of Feed Metals on Catalyst Aging in Hydroprocessing Residuum," *Ind. Eng. Chem, Proc. Des. Dev., 20*, 262 (1981).
15. Stanulonis, J. J., Gates, B. C., and Olson, J. H., "Catalyst Aging in a Process for Liquefaction and Hydrodesulphurization of Coal," *AICHE J, 22*, 576 (1976).
16. Saint-Just, J., "Catalyst Characterization by Adsorption of Petroleum Asphaltenes in Solution," *Ind. Eng. Chem., Prod. Res. Dev., 19*, 71 (1980).
17. Furimsky, E., Duguay, D. G., and Houle, J., "Chemisorption of Oxygen by Coke Deposited on Catalyst Surface," *Fuel, 67*, 182 (1988).
18. Barin, I., and Knacke, O., "Thermochemical Properties of Inorganic Substances," Springer-Verlag, Berlin, New York, 1973.
19. Suzuki, T., Itoh, M., Takegami, Y., and Watanabe, Y., "Chemical Structure of Tar Sands Bitumen by ^{13}C and ^{1}H.N.M.R. Spectroscopic Methods," *Fuel, 61*, 402 (1982).
20. Howard, J. A., "Homogeneous Liquid Phase Autoxidations," *Adv. Free Rad. Chem., 14*, 72 (1973).
21. Yoshimura, Y., and Furimsky, E., "Oxidative Regeneration of Hydrotreating Catalysts," *App., Catal., 23*, 157 (1986).
22. Wukasch, J. E., and Rase, J. F. "Some Characteristics of Deposits on a Commercially Aged, Gas-Oil Hydrotreating Catalyst," *Ind. Eng. Chem., Prod. Res. Dev., 21*, 558 (1982).
23. Brown, F. R., Makovsky, L. E., and Rhee, R. H., "Roman Specta of Supported Molybdena Catalysts: *J. Catal., 50*, 385 (1977).
24. Furimsky, E., and Yoshimura, Y., "Mechanism of Oxidative Regeneration of Molybdate Catalysts," *Ind. Eng. Chem., Res., 26*, 657 (1987).
25. Furimsky, E., Houle, J., and Yoshimura, Y., "Use of Boudart Reaction for Regeneration of Hydrotreating Catalysts," *Appl. Catal., 33*, 97 (1987).
26. Hashimoto, K., Takatani, K., and Masuda, T., "Transient Changes in the Temperature and Conversion of a Singled Coked Catalyst Pellet During Regeneration," *Chem. Eng. J., 29*, 85 (1984).
27. Furimsky, E., "Thermochemical and Mechanistic Aspect of Removal of Sulphur, Nitrogen and Oxygen from Petroleum," *Erdoel und Kohle*, 36, 518 (1983).
28. Massoth, F. E., "Oxidation of Coked Silica-Alumina Catalyst," *Ind. Eng. Chem., Proc. Des. Dev., 6*, 200 (1967).
29. Sanford, E. C., "Regeneration of Catalyst from Hydrotreating Bitumen Derived Coker Gas Oil," Proc. 6th Can. Symp. on Catalysis, Kingston, Ontario, 1986.
30. Aalund, L. R., "Pemex Studies Catalyst Regeneration," *Oil and Gas J.*, Aug. 30, 114 (1982).
31. Nalitham, R. V., Tarrer, A. R., Guin, J. A., and Curtis, C. W., "Kinetics of Coke Oxidation from Solvent Refined Conf Hydrotreating Catalysts," *Ind. Eng. Chem., Proc. Des. Dev., 24*, 160 (1985).
32. Massoth, F. E., "Characterization of Coke on Coal Catalysts by an Oxidation Technique," *Fuel Proc. Technol., 4*, 63 (1981).
33. Alvarez, D., Galiasso, R., and Andrea, P., "Studies of Poisoning and Regeneration of Hydro-desulphurization and Hydrodemetallization Catalyst During Treatment of Venezuelan Crude Oil," *J. Japan Petrol. Inst., 22*, 4,234 (1979).
34. Hughes, R., "Deactivation of Catalysts," Acad. Press, New York, London, 1984.

35. Weisz, P. B., and Goodwin, R. D., "Combustion of Carbonaceous Deposits within Porous Catalyst Particles 1. Diffusion Controlled Kinetics," *J. Catal.*, *2*, 397 (1963).
36. Weisz, P. B., and Goodwin, R. D., "Combustion of Carbonaceous Deposits within Porous Catalyst Particles II Intrinsic Burning Rate," *J. Catal.*, *6*, 227 (1966).
37. Sampath, B. S., and Hughes, R., "A Review of Mathematical Models in Single Particle Gas-Solid Non-Catalytic Reactions," *Chem. Eng.*, *10*, 485 (1973).
38. Sampath, B. S., Ramachandran, P. A., and Hughes, R., "Modelling of Non-Catalytic Gas-Solid Reactions, I. Transient Analysis of the Particle Pellet Model" *Chem. Eng. Sci.*, *30*, 125 (1975).
39. Ramachandran, P. A., Rachid, M. H., and Hughes, R., "Model for Coke Oxidation from Catalyst Pellets in the Initial Burning Period," *Chem. Eng. Sci.*, *30*, 1391 (1975).
40. Hashimoto, K., Takatani, K., Iwasa, H., and Masuda, T., "A Multiple Reaction Model for Burning Regeneration of Coked Catalysts," *Chem. Eng. J.*, *27*, 177 (1985).
41. Che, M., and Bond, G. C., "Adsorption and Catalysis on Oxide Surfaces," Elsevier, Amsterdam, 1985.
42. Klusacek, K., Davidova, H., Fott, P., and Schneider, P., "HDS Catalyst Regeneration; Coke Burnoff in Air in a Shallow Bed," *Chem. Eng. Sci.*, *9*, 1717 (1985).
43. Inoguchi, M., Sakurada, S., Satomi, Y., Inaba, K., Kagaya, H., Tate, K., Mizutori, T., Nishiyama, R., Nagai, T., and Onishi, S., "Studies of Hydrodesulphurization Catalysts (Part 7), Regeneration of Used Catalysts," *Bull. Tap. Petrol. Inst.*, *14*, 2, 153 (1972).
44. Artega, A., Fierro, J. L. G., Dalannay, F., and Delmon, B., "Simulated Deactivation and Regeneration of an Industrial CoMo/g-Al_2O_3 Hydrodesulphurization Catalyst," *Appl. Catal.*, *26*, 227 (1986).
45. Yoshimura, Y., Furimsky, E., Sato, T., Shimada, H., Matsubayashi, N., and Nishijima, A., "Oxidative Regeneration of Ni—Mo—Al_2O_3 Catalysts Used for Hydrotreatment of Coal-Derived Oil," Proc. 23rd Coal Science and Fuel Soc. Japan, Tokyo, Oct. 1986. p. 333.
46. Hiemenz, W., "Reaction Mechanism and Rates in Residue Hydrodesulphurization," Proc. World Petrol. Congr. Sect. III, pap. 20, p. 307, 1963.
47. Sakabe, T., and Yagi, T., "Crack Residues with Spent HDS Catalyst," *Hydrocarb. Proc.*, *12*, 103 (1979).
48. Ocampo, A., Schrodt, J. T., and Kovach, S. H., "Deactivation of HDS Catalysts under Coal Liquids. I Loss of Hydrogenation Activity Due to Carbonaceous Deposits," *Ind. Eng. Chem. Prod. Res. Dev.*, *17*, 57 (1978).
49. Curtis, C. W., Guin, J. A., Nalitham, J., Mohsin, A., Tarrer, A. R., Potts, J. D., and Hastings, K. E., "A Study of Deactivation and Regeneration of Catalysts Used in the LC-Fining of Solvent Refined Coal," *Am. Chem. Soc. Div. Fuel. Chem. Preprints*, *29*, 79 (1984).
50. Stephens, H. P., and Stohl, F. V., "Determination of Intrinsic Activity and Effective Diffusivity of Aged Coal Liquefaction Catalysts," *Am. Chem. Soc. Div. Fuel. Chem. Preprints*, *29*, 79 (1984).
51. Ihnatowicz, M., Pawlak, S., Pawlowski, M., and Sadowski, W., "Changes in Chemical Composition and Porous Texture of Nickel-Molybdate Catalyst Used in Coal Hydrogenation," *Koks, Smola, Gas*, *29*, 254 (1984).
52. Hertan, P. A., Larkins, F. P., and Jackson, W., "Regeneration Studies on Nickel-Molybdate Catalysts Used for the Upgrading of Coal-Derived Liquids," *Fuel Proc. Technol.*, *10*, 121 (1985).
53. Bogdanor, J. M., and Rase, H. F., "Characteristics of a Commercially Aged Ni—Mo/Al_2O_3 Hydrotreating Catalysts: Component Distribution, Coke Characteristics and Effects of Regeneration," *Ind. Eng. Chem., Prod. Res. Dev.*, *25*, 220 (1986).
54. Johnson, B. G., Massoth, F. E., and Bartholdy, J., "Diffusion and Catalytic Activity Studies on Resid Deactivated HDS Catalysts," *AICHE J.*, *32*, 1980 (1986).
55. Matyas, R. S., and Potts, J. D., "Advanced Research Program for Expanded Bed Hydroprocessing of Coal Extract," DE-86003571, DOE/PC/50021 Report Vol. 3, 1985.
56. Tamayama, M., "Regeneration of Commercial Catalysts," *Kagaku Kogaku*, *50*, 9,624 (1986).

CHAPTER 7

ACTIVITY, SELECTIVITY, AND DEACTIVATION OF COAL HYDROLIQUEFACTION CATALYSTS: PORE DIFFUSION EFFECTS

B. D. Adkins, D. R. Milburn, and B. H. Davis

Kentucky Energy Cabinet Laboratory
Lexington, Kentucky, USA

CONTENTS

INTRODUCTION

The hydroliquefaction of coal using heterogeneous catalysts may be strongly influenced by diffusion of coal components into the pores of the catalyst, and the problem is compounded when the catalyst is in pellet form. This is not surprising, when the size of the molecules and/or micellar-type structures is considered. For example, a range of 15 to 50 Å diameter has been estimated for a moeity having molecular weight of 1,000 amu [1], with the actual size depending on configuration. Catalyst pore structure is an important variable in the optimization of three important catalyst performance parameters: conversion, selectivity, and deactivation. These parameters are related to one another from the viewpoint of the chemical reaction(s) that occur in the catalyst and thus share a common dependence upon pore diffusion effects.

Hence, it is not surprising that pore structure has received attention as a catalyst design parameter. Of particular interest is the development and use of "bimodal" catalysts that contain significant volumes of both mesopores and macropores. For convenience, mesopores may be classified as pores having diameters less than 1,000 Å and macropores as those having diameters greater than 1,000 Å. These stand in contrast to catalysts having little or no macroporosity, which are called "unimodal." Bimodal and unimodal catalysts of various pore sizes have been compared extensively in the development of coal liquefaction catalysts. It is important to realize that, although catalyst "pore size" is often used as a property correlatable with diffusivity, other parameters such as the size distribution, shape and surface topography, and interconnectivity of the pores will also affect the diffusivity.

Theoretical relationships between diffusivities and pore structures are numerous [e.g., 2–5]. Gregg and Sing [6], for example, review methods commonly used for measuring pore structures (gas adsorption and mercury porosimetry). An alternate approach is to measure pore structures and diffusivities experimentally. Transport diffusivities can be measured with the Wicke-Kallenbach [7], kinetic, and chromatographic methods; self-diffusivities can be measured with isotopic tracer and NMR methods. Dogu [5] and Ruthven [8] have reviewed these methods.

MATHEMATICAL RELATIONSHIPS BETWEEN CONVERSION, SELECTIVITY AND DEACTIVATION IN THE PRESENCE OF DIFFUSIONAL LIMITATIONS

It is possible to describe, in mathematical terms, how activity, selectivity, and deactivation are all affected by presence of diffusion gradients in the catalyst pellet. However, a precise mathematical model requires knowledge of the reactants, products, reaction mechanisms, and parameters such as diffusion constants and rate constants. Such detailed information is seldom known for coal hydroprocessing. In spite of this, it is useful to develop the following mathematical formalism so that models involving varying degrees of approximation may be compared.

For an isothermal catalyst pellet operating under negligible boundary layer transport resistance and containing species (both reactants and products) in concentrations C_i, $i = 1 \ldots \underline{I}$, each of which can interreact to form any other species, there are $\underline{I}$ conservation equations of the form:

$$\frac{\partial C_i}{\partial t} = \nabla D_i \nabla C_i - \sum_{\substack{j=1 \\ j \neq i}}^{I} \{\psi_{ij}(k_{ij}, \Gamma_i) - \psi_{ji}(k_{ji}, \Gamma_j)\} \qquad i = 1 \ldots, I \tag{1}$$

where D_i is the effective diffusivity of the ith species and ψ_{ij} is a function describing the rate at which species i converts.to species j. The ψ_{ij} function includes the single site rate constant k_{ij} as well as the surface concentration of adsorbed ith species, Γ_i. The surface concentrations are usually modeled by site balances incorporating the concentrations (C) and adsorption equilibrium constants (K) of all species that adsorb on the active sites as well as the total concentration $\mathfrak{z}_{ij}$ of active sites, e.g., LHHW (Langmuir-Hinshelwood-Hougen-Watson) kinetic rate expressions:

$$\frac{\partial C_i}{\partial t} = \nabla D_i \nabla C_i - \sum_{\substack{j=1 \\ j \neq i}}^{I} \begin{bmatrix} \psi'_{ij}\{k_{ij}, (C_m, K_m, m = 1 \ldots I), \mathfrak{z}_{ij}\} \\ -\psi'_{ji}\{k'_{ji}, (C_m, K_m, m = 1 \ldots I), \mathfrak{z}_{ji}\} \end{bmatrix} \tag{2}$$

With time, active sites for each reaction will be blocked by the products of secondary reactions. If we assume that sites are lost through mechanisms related to the chemical reactions, and not by physical changes such as sintering, the site concentrations must be written in terms of the concentrations, Q_n, $n = 1 \ldots N$, of N types of contaminants. Thus:

$$\mathfrak{z}_{ij} = \mathfrak{z}_{ij}(Q_n, n = 1 \ldots N) \qquad \begin{matrix} i = 1 \ldots I \\ j = 1 \ldots I \end{matrix} \quad j \neq i \tag{3}$$

Likewise, the size of the catalyst pores, and hence the diffusivities, D_i, will be affected by the contaminating species:

$$D_i = D_i(Q_n, n = 1 \ldots N) \qquad i = 1 \ldots I \tag{4}$$

Finally, N conservation equations are required for the N contaminants. Assuming that the contaminants are formed by irreversible secondary reactions or adsorption processes, and thus do not diffuse throughout the catalyst once formed:

$$\frac{\partial Q_n}{\partial t} = \sum_{j=1}^{I} \Omega_{nj}\{k_{nj},(C_m, K_m, m = 1 \ldots I), \mathfrak{z}_{nj}\} \qquad n = 1 \ldots N \tag{5}$$

where Ω_{nj} is another rate function. With the exception of the diffusion flux term, Equations 2 and 5 are completely analogous. Terms for the rates of contaminant formation (secondary side reactions) do not appear in Equation 2; the main reactions are assumed to be much faster than the side reactions.

In principle, Equations 2 through 5 are sufficient to model the activity, selectivity, and deactivation of porous heterogeneous catalysts. Being gradient equations, they hold at discrete points in the spacetime occupied by a single catalyst pellet and usually require integration subject to appropriate boundary conditions.

Reactor-scale continuity equations may also have to be written and provisions made for homogeneous thermal reactions occurring outside the catalyst pellets . But even in the absence of these complications, Equations 2–5 are much too general to be used directly. There are far too many reactants, products, and contaminants in a coal liquefaction chemical environment to allow the construction of this detailed type of model. Instead, kinetic "lumps" must be constructed, and the accuracy with which the lumps model the overall characteristics of the detailed mechanism is always a valid question.

Other problems exist in addition to lumping. Assume for the moment that deactivation can be neglected. The solution to the partial differential equations in Equation 2 describes a path through composition space that the reacting mixture follows from a starting composition to a final composition (not necessarily equilibrium). This path also represents the solution to a system of parametric equations relating the quantities of various components to one another, in which time has been eliminated. Following the suggestions of Sylvestri and Prater [9], this path defines the selectivity of the reaction mechanism. Thus, selectivity can be defined as the particular sequence of compositions that can be produced from a given starting composition, or even as the underlying system of parametric equations that determine this sequence; for a given mechanism, this selectivity depends on the starting composition, on the rate constants, and on the diffusion constants. Selectivity, so defined, does not depend upon time to the extent that time has been parametrically eliminated. Another extension of the parametric treatment is that the eliminated relation between time and composition defines the conversion-time relationship; conversion, as defined, must also depend on the starting composition, rate constants, and diffusion constants, as well as on time.

For a particular starting composition and catalyst, kinetic data can be obtained to elucidate the selectivity curve and the conversion-time relationship. In practice, the definition of selectivity is more likely to be based on the yield of some specific product; in this case it will be time-dependent. Conversion will probably be defined as the disappearance of the starting material. However, in the absence of a detailed mathematical model and its solution, it is not possible to calculate the rate and diffusion constants from the conversion-selectivity measurements. Additionally, the assumption of a specific model does not guarantee that a mathematically tractable data analysis scheme will present itself.

This problem has been treated in successive stages in a series of classic papers by Wei and Prater [10], Wei [11, 12], and Sylvestri and Prater [9] for the case of a non-deactivating catalyst. Equation 2, assuming first-order reactions and the absence of gradient terms, is the basis of the Wei-Prater paper. The Wei and Prater model thus consists of $\underline{I}$ ordinary first-order differential equations in the following matrix form:

$$\frac{\partial \bar{C}}{\partial t} = -\mathbf{k}\bar{C} \tag{6}$$

where **k** is the square rate constant matrix:

$$\mathbf{k} = \begin{bmatrix} \sum_{j=2}^{I} k_{1j}3_{1j} & -k_{21}3_{21} & \cdots & -k_{I1}3_{I1} \\ -k_{12}3_{12} & \sum_{\substack{j=1 \\ j\neq 2}}^{I} k_{2j}3_{2j} & \cdots & -k_{I2}3_{I2} \\ \vdots & \vdots & & \vdots \\ -k_{1I}3_{1I} & -k_{2I}3_{2I} & \cdots & \sum_{j=1}^{I-1} k_{Ij}3_{Ij} \end{bmatrix}$$

This matrix possesses $\underline{I}$ eigenvalues, $\lambda_1, \lambda_2 \ldots \lambda_I$. These eigenvalues define a new set of differential equations with solutions:

$$\beta_i = \beta_{i0}e^{-\lambda_i t} \qquad i = 1 \ldots I \tag{7}$$

and the β's represent the concentration of $\underline{I}$ fictitious pseudocomponents. These pseudocomponents are linear combinations of the real components and have the important property of being uncoupled from one another. One of these pseudocomponents (β_1) is the final composition, and its eigenvalue (λ_1) is zero. The Wei and Prater paper develops a method for experimentally determining the rate constants, $k_{ij}3_{ij}$, in which experimental reaction paths in composition space are measured and the pseudocomponents are obtained from these and straight-line reaction paths.

In a follow-up study, Wei [11, 12] found that the effect of diffusion gradients is to change Equation 6 to:

$$\frac{\partial \bar{C}}{\partial t} = \bar{D}\nabla^2\bar{C} - \mathbf{k}\bar{C} \tag{8}$$

where it is assumed that the diffusivity vector $\bar{D}$ is independent of position and time, a valid assumption for non-deactivating catalysts. Otherwise, Equation 8 is identical to Equation 2 for a first-order reaction scheme. The eigenvalue solution given in Equation 7 is no longer valid for Equation 8, but Wei showed some important comparisons between Equation 6 and 8. If only the steady-state version of Equation 8 is considered, i.e.

$$-\bar{D}\nabla^2\bar{C} = -\mathbf{k}\bar{C} \tag{9}$$

then Wei showed that Equation 9 can be transformed similar to the transformation of Equation 6 from Equation 7. Wei labeled the matrix obtained in this transformation, $\mathbf{k}'$, the "diffusion-disguised rate constant matrix," where each element $k_{ij}3_{ij}$ is a function of the rate constant matrix **k**, the diffusivity vector $\bar{D}$, and the particle geometry. For the fully unsteady-state Equation 8, the analysis is more difficult.

Wei's results are illustrated graphically for a three-component system in Figures 1A and 1B. The curved solid lines show a typical set of paths given by the solution to Equation 6, and the straight-line paths correspond to the pure pseudocomponents in Equation 7. Figure 1A shows the new paths (dashed lines) that satisfy Equation 9 if the diffusivities are equal ($\bar{D}$ is a scalar); for this case, all paths except the straight-line paths will be altered. For unequal diffusivities (Figure 1B), even the straight-line paths may be shifted. One of Wei's conclusions is that intraparticle diffusion gradients cause the selectivity paths emanating from different starting compositions to become reaction paths between the reaction components. The example given by Wei [12] is for the consecutive reaction

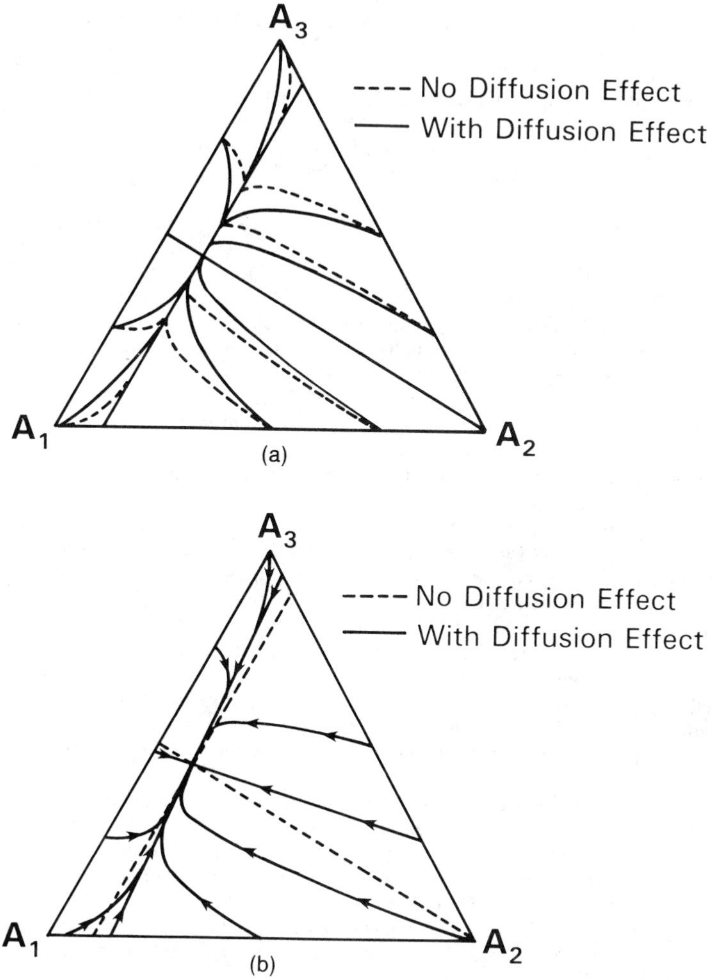

Figure 1. Effect of diffusivity on selectivity paths for a three component system as demonstrated by Wei: (a) $D_{A1} = D_{A2} = D_{A3}$; (b) $D_{A1} \neq D_{A2} \neq D_{A3}$. (Reprinted with permission from Ref. [10].)

mechanism, $A_1 \rightarrow A_2 \rightarrow A_3$; with diffusion-gradient conditions this becomes equivalent to a parallel mechanism having the additional reaction path between A_1 and A_3.

EXPERIMENTAL ASSESSMENT OF PORE DIFFUSION EFFECTS

Theoretically, it is possible to observe experimental differences in selectivity and conversion in catalysts having different pore structures and, by comparing the effective rate constants for different catalysts, to obtain a quantitative measure of the diffusional limitations for each reactant lump.

Wei developed a mathematical model involving square matrices of Thiele moduli (ϕ_{ij}, i = 1, . . . , I, j = 1, . . . , I, i ≠ j) and effectiveness factors η_{ij}, for the I^2-I independent reactions. These effectiveness factors directly point to diffusion-limited reactions. The Thiele modulus-effectiveness factor concept is reviewed in a number of places, e.g., [2, 3, 5, 13]. For catalyst design purposes, however, the precise effectiveness factors may not be required; rather, a qualitative assessment of these factors may suffice. A reasonable experimental approach would be to measure a reaction selectivity curve, change some catalyst-dependent parameters that are included in the Thiele moduli, and remeasure the selectivity curve.

The Thiele modulus for species i reacting in first-order fashion to species j is $\phi_{ij} = L(k_{ij}\mathfrak{z}_{ij}/D_i)^{1/2}$, where L is a characteristic diffusion length associated with the pellet. The most easily changed parameter is L, the particle size. Since generalizations of L and the phi-eta relationship have been developed [14, 15], this approach can be used with virtually any catalyst particle shape. Another variable is the pore structure, which may change D_i. This approach has also been used extensively.

However, there are several potential pitfalls of both experimental and theoretical nature associated with the methodology. Changes in particle size may cause differences in reactor mixing and/or boundary layer properties. This introduces variables not relevant to the pore diffusion problem. While the altered-pore-structure approach can circumvent this, it suffers from the possibility that larger-pore catalysts will have lower specific surface area, and that the effects of enhanced diffusion rates will be mitigated. Also, distribution and dispersion of the active phase may depend upon the pore structure.

Because of these problems, and others, much literature on the influence of pore diffusion on activity, selectivity and deactivation of porous catalysts stops short of a complete mathematical model. More commonly, key points are addressed. For example, some papers contain experimental determinations and/or theoretical models relating the diffusivities of "representative" compounds to pore structure. Similarly, experimental or theoretical descriptions of the changes in these diffusivities due to accumulation of various contaminants may be found. Other studies deal more with catalytic reaction mechanisms and the catalytically active sites in either nondeactivating or fully deactivated catalysts. Another key point is the construction of meaningful "lumps" of reactants, products, and reaction pathways, where the goal, of course, is to develop a phenomenological model of the chemical process using the minimum number of "lumps" required to attain the desired accuracy.

In the material that follows, several qualitative and quantitative studies are reviewed. The common factor in these studies is that they address a possible link between the catalyst pore structure and catalyst activity, selectivity, or deactivation in a coal hydroliquefaction environment. These studies are grouped according to whether the primary emphasis has been on the kinetics of the main reactions, i.e., from the viewpoint of Equation 2 ("liquefaction" or "upgrading" models), or on the contaminant-producing side reactions, from the viewpoint of Equation 5 ("deactivation" models). In theory, the formalism of Equations 2–5 encompasses both viewpoints, even though it is rare to find both incorporated into a single model.

LIQUEFACTION AND UPGRADING

The role of catalysts in the formation of liquid products during coal hydroliquefaction has been widely studied. Pore structure effects have been a prominent target of many of these studies. However, no consensus exists even for the exact role of the catalyst.

One major function of the catalyst in liquefaction is believed to be hydrogenation of donor solvent molecules which, in turn, donate hydrogen to stabilize coal fragments produced by thermal bond rupture. This catalyst function is often indicated as the major role of the catalyst in the initial stages of coal dissolution [16–20]. For porous catalysts, a common rationale for this is that the interior catalyst surface is inaccessible to large coal molecules but is accessible to the donor solvent. Catalytic hydrogenation of solvent is fundamental to the Exxon Donor Solvent (EDS) process [21] and is an important feature of the second-stage catalytic reactors in two-stage (thermal-catalytic) type processes, such as the Wilsonville, AL [22, 23] Integrated Two-Stage Liquefaction (ITSL) process.

An interesting coal liquefaction model based on solvent hydrogenation is that developed by Klunder et al. [24]. This model is similar to one suggested earlier by Reuther [25] in which the catalyst simply fixes the ratio between hydrogenated and dehydrogenated donor species. Klunder's and Reuther's models provide ample demonstration that coal liquefaction kinetics are inherently complicated, even in the absence of transport phenomena such as intraparticle diffusion gradients. In addition to predicting a nonlinear relationship between coal dissolution rate and catalyst mass in a given reactor, these models also predict mulitple steady-state modes of isothermal reaction operation (for example, in terms of distillate production). At the heart of these predictions is an autocatalysis-type effect in which one of the products of hydrogen-donor "catalyzed" coal dissolution serves as additional hydrogen donor precursor molecules.

However, liquefaction catalysts may do more than hydrogenate donor solvent [26–33]. For example, catalytic hydrocracking may occur in primary liquefaction, depending of course on the accessibility of the catalyst surface to large molecules. Also, hydrodenitrogenation (HDN), hydrodeoxygenation (HDO), and hydrodesulfurization (HDS) are well-known catalyst functions that have a complicated dependence on hydrogenation and hydrogenolysis activities. In short, there is no clear ranking of catalytic functions in either primary liquefaction or upgrading. It also follows that catalytic chemistry cannot be divorced from process design, and catalysts are often designed with specific processes in mind. Shah [34] provides a good review of process designs investigated in the years prior to 1981, and the catalytic chemistry associated with those processes. Numerous other reviews of catalytic mechanisms and kinetics are available e.g., [35–37]. In this work, only those studies addressing the pore diffusion problem are considered in further detail.

COAL LIQUEFACTION AND RESID CONVERSION

Lumpability Studies

One major theoretical difficulty is choosing the appropriate kinetic lumps. Almost invariably, these lumps are based upon a solubility classification similar to the following: coal (**C**), the starting material; preasphaltene (**P**), the heaviest, most coal-like dissolution product, soluble in THF, pyridine or cresol but is insoluble in benzene or toluene; asphaltene (**A**), an intermediate material that is soluble in benzene or toluene but insoluble in pentane or hexane; oil (**O**), a pentane or hexane-soluble material, essentially all distillable; and gases (**G**) and water (**W**). The thermal stability of these lumps is usually ranked as **C** < **P** < **A** < **O**. Resid is commonly defined as a mixture of **P**, **A**, and **O** but not including **C**.

A "lumpability" analysis of this system, based on an underlying cracking mechanism, has been published by Prasad et al. [38]. In this chapter, the authors considered a kinetic scheme where the composition of the coal-derived material is described in terms of a continuous mixture instead of some number of individual components. This model is based on a theoretical treatment of reactions in continuous mixtures originally developed by Aris and Gavalas [39] in 1966, and applied to coal liquefaction by Syamlal and Wittman [40] in 1985. The treatment assumes a continuous distribution of molecules having the chemical formula $C_{x_1}O_{x_2}$, with $0 \le x_1 \le u$ and $0 \le x_2 \le v$, where u and v are the number of carbon and oxygen atoms in a hypothetical starting molecule, and can theoretically be obtained from coal analysis. The generalized reaction scheme is written as:

$$C_{x_1}O_{x_2} \longrightarrow C_{x_1'}O_{x_2'} + C_{x_1-x_1'}O_{x_2-x_2'},$$

which represents a first-order cracking of any molecule to a stoichiometric number (ν) of two types of smaller molecules. Based on this kinetic scheme, Prasad and co-workers obtained the following equation:

$$\frac{\partial\xi(y_1, y_2, \theta)}{\partial\theta} = -k(y_1, y_2)\xi(y_1, y_2, \theta) + uv \int_{y_1'}^{1} \int_{y_2'}^{1} k(y_1, y_2)\nu(y_1, y_2, y_1', y_2')\xi(y_1', y_2', \theta)\, dy_2'\, dy_1' \tag{10}$$

This can give the instantaneous state of the reaction mixture at any dimensionless time $\theta = k(u, v)t$, where $y_1 = x_1/u$, $y_2 = x_2/v$, $\xi(y_1, y_2, \theta)$ is the normalized number distribution of molecules at time θ, $\nu(y_1, y_2, y_1', y_2')$ is the stoichiometric number for production of molecules $y_1'y_2'$ from y_1y_2, and $k(y_1, y_2)$ is the rate constant function for the above cracking scheme. Prasad et al. solved Equation 10 numerically for a number of test cases.

Equation 10 can be obtained from Equation 2, given two conditions: the absence of diffusion gradients, $\nabla D_i \nabla C_i = 0$, and $I \to \infty$. One problem with Equation 10 is that experimental verification requires determination of the molecular distribution $\xi(y_1, y_2\theta)$ at different times, as well as extensive analysis to determine the rate and stoichiometric distribution functions. Prasad et al., explored a lumping scheme based upon solubility in which lumping functions are used of the form $M = \gamma/(12_{x_1} + 16_{x_2})$, implying that as molecular weight increases, solubility in any given solvent decreases; γ represents a solvation-strength constant. To compare the modeling results with published coal liquefaction studies, they use two solubility functions M_1 and M_2:

$$\text{Oil, gas, water (\textbf{OGW}):} \quad \mathbf{OGW} = \int_0^1 \int_0^1 M_1 \xi(y_1, y_2, \theta)\, \partial y_2\, \partial y_1$$

$$\text{Asphaltenes (\textbf{A}):} \quad \mathbf{A} = \int_0^1 \int_0^1 (M_2 - M_1)\xi(y_1, y_2, \theta)\, \partial y_2\, \partial y_1 \tag{11}$$

$$\text{Preasphaltenes (\textbf{P}):} \quad \mathbf{P} = \int_0^1 \int_0^1 (1 - M_2)\xi(y_1, y_2, \theta)\, \partial y_2\, \partial y_1$$

Using their numerical solutions to Equation 10, they simulated coal liquefaction data based on coal molecules of molecular weight between 2,000 and 4,000, a rate constant function that decreases with number of carbon atoms from the maximum rate constant k(u, v), an assumed stoichiometric function, and with $\gamma_1 = 200$ and $\gamma_2 = 400$. One such simulation is shown in Figure 2. From the simulations they concluded that: (a) the lumped product distribution is relatively insensitive to u and v since C and O are weighted only by mass in the lumping functions: (b) the often-reported maximum in preasphaltenes is easily obtained; and (c) the starting molecular weight has an important influence on the lumped product distribution.

Prasad et al. [41] applied their model to published data for the catalyzed and uncatalyzed liquefaction of brown coals. In doing so, they used estimates for initial molecular weight in terms of both u and v, based on coal analysis, and obtained good agreement with the lumped data. They concluded that the effect of the catalyst was to increase the entire rate function uniformly such that only conversion, not selectivity, changed; it appeared the scaling of their solutions using different values of k(u, v) was all that was necessary in order to fit both catalytic and noncatalytic data. The authors suggested that the dimensionless time be used as a "severity index" analogous to that defined by Petrakis [42] which could adequately represent both thermal and catalytic coal liquefaction kinetics.

It is tempting to think that because the conversion, and not selectivity, appeared to change in going from thermal to catalytic reactions, that the reacting species were not diffusion-limited. Recall the Wei model [11, 12] which shows that selectivity (path through composition space) can be changed significantly by strong diffusion limitations. However, Prasad et al's., findings are not amenable to this interpretation for several reasons. First, the Prasad et al. model is strongly dependent on an assumed mechanism, which tends to reduce the discriminating power of the model. Second, the Wei analysis shows that strong diffusional limitations decrease selectivity in the sense that apparent rate constants are more similar than the true rate constants. It is possible that the catalytic reactions could be much more selective, as in the sense of having widely differing cracking rate constants for different molecular sizes, than the thermal reactions, but diffusional limitations in the catalyst could actually smooth these out. The only way to provide for this possibility is to change the diffusivities without changing the "true" rate constants; i.e., a comparison of catalysts with different pore structures.

Likewise, it is difficult to use the Prasad et al. model to form a conclusion about the "lumpability" of coal liquefaction products, due to the number of assumptions required of the underlying catalytic mechanisms and yet, by necessity, these underlying mechanisms are oversimplified. In particular, omission of the hydrogen-donating role of the solvent, and the effect of the catalyst on this solvent,

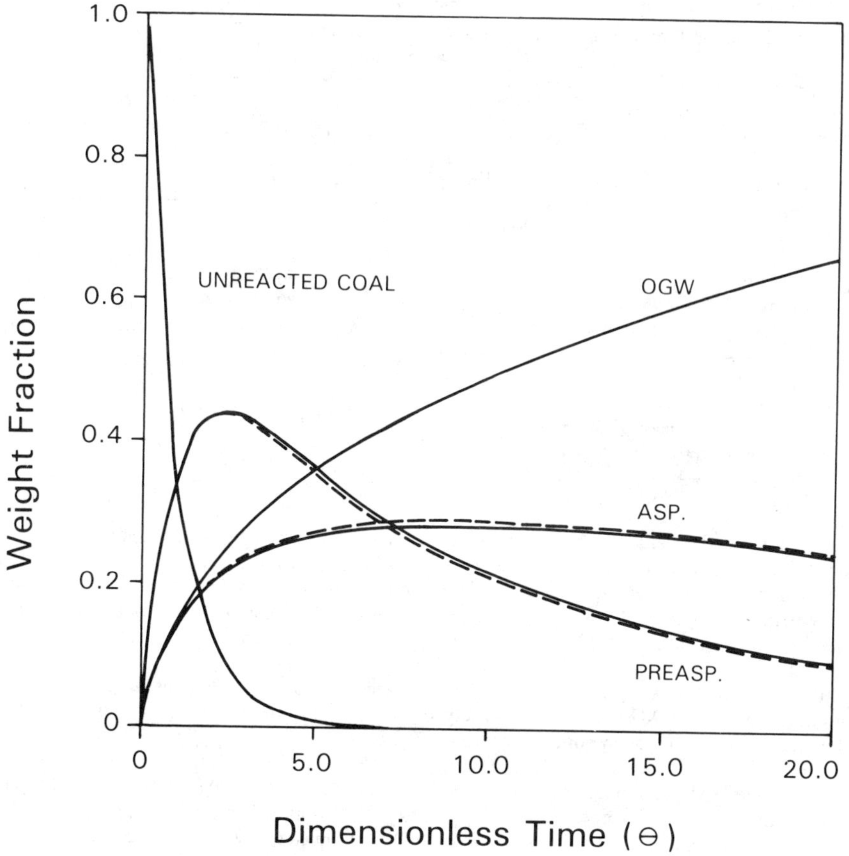

Figure 2. Simulated coal liquefaction data from Prasad, et al.'s [41] reaction continuum model (Equations 10 and 11) including appropriate lumping assumptions. (Reproduced by permission of the American Institute of Chemical Engineers.)

is significant. It is obvious that the lumpability of coal liquefaction is not nearly as well understood as that of catalytic cracking [43–46].

Lumped Kinetic Studies

Numerous investigators have considered the formation of primary product lumps—preasphaltenes, asphaltenes, oils and gases—from the viewpoint of catalyst selectivity. Several of these have specific mathematic or experimental provisions for pore diffusion effects. A simplified reaction scheme for the lumps is **C** (+**O**) → **P** → **A** → **O**; specific mechanisms can be found in several reviews [34, 35, 47]. Thomas [19] suggested that "typical" coal liquefaction catalysts can provide the following enhancements over thermal liquefaction alone: **C** → **P**, **A**: 10–20%; **P** → **A**, **O**; up to 200%; **A** → **O**: up to 400%. Kang [48] has also postulated that the catalyzed conversion of coal (**C** → **P**, **A**) is often severely limited by pore diffusion; thus many catalysts offer little improvement in this step. This suggests a rough ranking of pore diffusion limitations in "typical" catalysts of **C** > **P** > **A**.

Table 1
Catalysts Used by Workers at Amoco in a Catalytic Liquefaction Study Using Hydrogenated Anthracene Oil

Catalyst	Ave. Pore Diameter, Å	Surface Area, m^2/g	Pore Volume, cc/g	Major Pores, Å	1000 Å+ Pores, Vol. %[(2)]	Bulking Density, g/cc
HDS-1442A	58	323	.64	20–140	28	0.57
Grace-70BP*[(1)]	69	203	.57	30–130	39	0.63
Kaiser 100UP	105	195	.70	50–250	4	0.59
Grace-120B	111	162	.62	70–200	17	0.68
Grace-200B	183	91	.53	105–350	18	0.73

(1) *$\frac{1}{8}''$ sphere; others are $\frac{1}{16}''$ extrudates.*
(2) *By mercury porosimetry.*
* *B = biomodal, U = unimodal, P = phosphoric acid impregnating aid.*
Reprinted with permission from Ref. 50.

One of the earliest studies aimed specifically at the pore diffusion effect was reported by Yen et al. [49] in 1976. They compared coal conversion in the presence of identical masses of catalysts having unimodal pore size distributions with peak pore diameters of 220 Å and 120 Å. Their results showed the large-pore (220 Å) catalyst gave better overall conversion of the coal; this occurred even though the small-pore (120 Å) catalyst had a larger specific surface area than the large-pore catalyst.

Bertolacini and co-authors at Amoco [50], prepared several catalysts consisting of Co or Ni promoter and either Mo or W on a variety of W. R. Grace aluminum oxide supports. These aluminas varied in major mesopore size from 60 Å to 200 Å; all but one had bimodal pore-size distributions. Of particular interest is a series of 0.16 cm ($\frac{1}{16}$ inch) diameter Co—Mo catalyst pellets (Table 1). Production of asphaltenes and oils from Illinois #6 coal (−400 mesh), in a CSTR using hydrogenated anthracene oil at 427°C and 12.9 MPa (137 atm) increased as the mean mesopore size increased from 60 to 120 Å (Figure 3A); this trend continued over the entire life of the catalysts. The exception to this trend is the Grace-200B based catalyst. It appears that above 120 Å pore diameter, further increases in the production of asphaltenes and oils does not occur. Also, the performance of the single unimodal-pore catalyst was worse than any of the bimodal catalysts. The Amoco investigators took this data as evidence that pore diffusion effects in mesopores impacts the production of asphaltenes and oils from preasphaltenes, with mesopores between 100 and 200 Å representing an optimum size. They also concluded that macropores serve as "feeder" pores and help overcome the diffusion limitations behavior in mesopores.

However, the Amoco workers recognized that these findings are clouded somewhat by complications external to pore diffusion effects. First, the experiments were performed with a constant catalyst mass and not with constant active surface area; likewise, the pore volume in the reactor varied from one catalyst to the next. Also, Co and Mo levels were not adjusted to maintain constant coverage. Finally, only one residence time was used in these experiments, so that a comparison of "conversion-selectivity" curves for the different catalysts is not possible. Instead, the Amoco data follows a path (Figure 3B) for deactivating catalysts at essentially constant reaction spacetime. Thus, a deactivation model is required to analyze this data systematically. In the following paragraphs, we develop a simple deactivation model using Equations 2, 3, and 5.

The first simplification comes from the Amoco workers' observation that the amount of unconverted coal in the products is identical for both thermal and catalytic reactions. Furthermore, the unconverted coal is very low (<10%), so the coal dissolution reaction can be depicted as going to completion. Because the thermal reaction produced asphaltenes and oils in abundance, the simplest way of incorporating the observed catalyst effects is to combine the thermal production

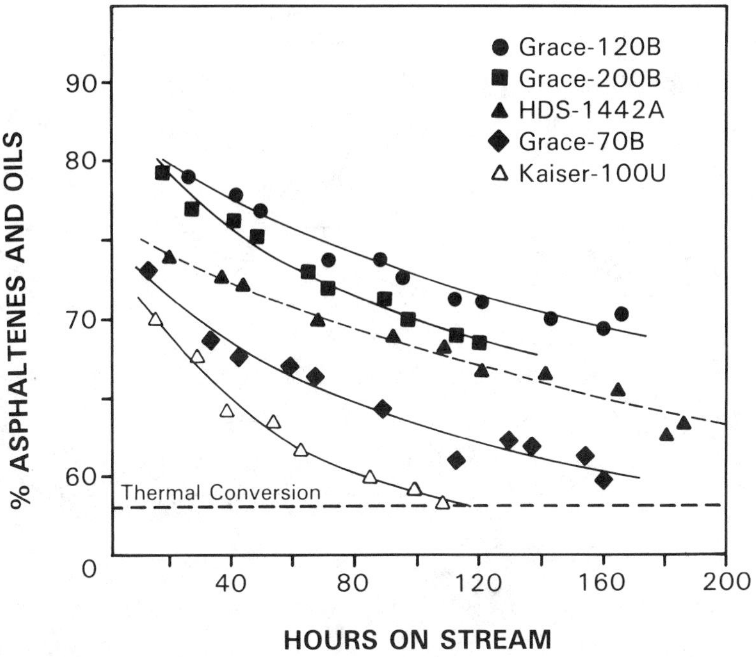

Figure 3A. Amoco Oil Co. data showing relative yields of asphaltenes and oils from coal, employing five different Co—Mo catalysts with different pore structures, shown in Table 1. (From Electric Power Research Institute EPRI report AF-1084, "Catalyst Development for Coal Liquefaction," © 1979. Reprinted with permission.)

of **P**, **A**, and **O** from coal with catalytic production of **A** and **O** from **P**. Thus the Amoco workers postulated the following mechanism:

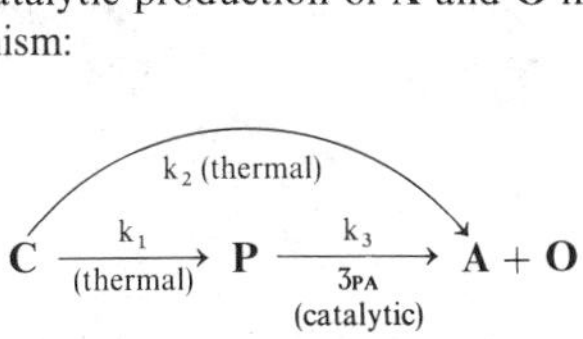

This mechanism may be used for both liquefaction and resid conversion kinetics. A second simplification comes from assuming that the thermal reaction is sufficiently rapid to be essentially separable (in time) from the catalytic reaction. The condition that allows this is $k_1 \gg k_3\eta_{PA}$. It is often reported that, at temperatures above 400°C, the disappearance of coal is very rapid compared to the disappearance of preasphaltene [35, 41, 47, 57]. Assuming that thermal reactions go to completion rapidly in comparison to the catalytic reactions, Equation 2 can be written as:

$$\frac{\partial C_P}{\partial t} = -k_3 C_P \eta_{PA} \tag{12}$$

where it has also been assumed that gradientless conditions hold inside the pellet. The initial condition is $C_P(t = 0) = C_{PO}$, where C_{PO} is the preasphaltene concentration resulting from rapid

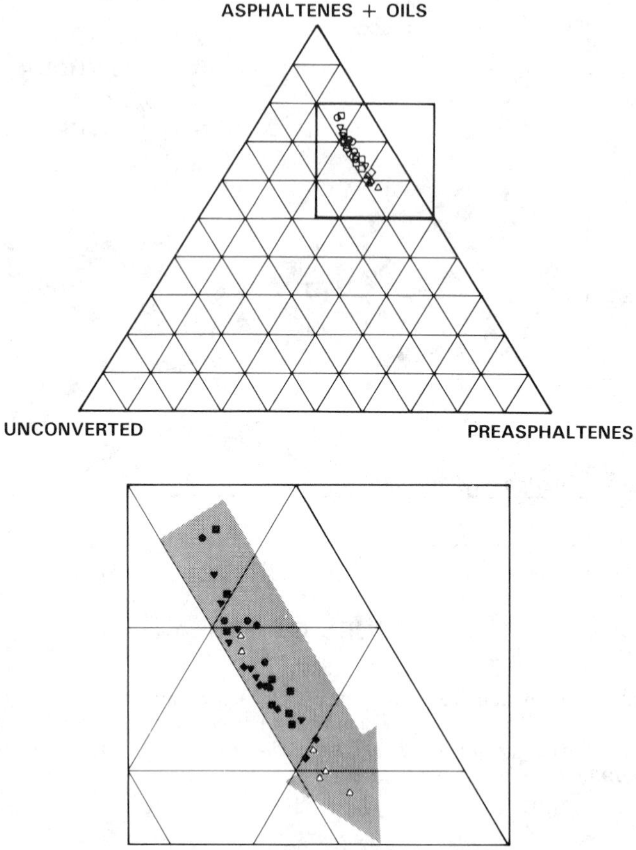

Figure 3B. Data from Figure 3A replotted as a selectivity curve. Deactivation with time is shown.

thermal dissolution. C_{PO} can be estimated from the thermal conversion data; it is not equal to the amount of coal converted since the mechanism includes the thermal production of asphaltenes and oils.

Finally, in their simplest form, Equations 3 and 5 correspond to the "independent" deactivation mechanism:

$$\text{site} \xrightarrow{k_d} \text{deactivated site}$$

in which the rate of loss of sites depends only upon the site concentration, and the site deactivation rate constant, k_d:

$$\frac{\partial \mathfrak{z}_{PA}}{\partial t} = -k_j \mathfrak{z}_{PA} \tag{13}$$

Since gradientless conditions within the pellet are assumed, we need not consider Equation 4. For a gradientless CSTR reactor, Equations 12 and 13 can be solved to obtain:

$$\ln\left(\frac{C_{PO}}{C_P} - 1\right) = \ln(k_3\tau) - k_d t \tag{14}$$

where τ is an integration constant related to the residence time.

The Amoco data are now replotted in Figure 4A according to Equation 14, and the values of $\ln(k_3\tau)$ and k_d obtained by regression analysis are plotted in Figures 4B and 4C against the catalyst mesopore volume and surface area in the reactor, respectively. Several important points can be gained from this analysis. First, Equation 14 fits the data very well; this is somewhat surprising considering the three major assumptions in this simplest-case model: (a) purely catalytic production of asphaltenes and oils from preasphaltenes at an effectiveness factor of unity; (b) separability of thermal and catalytic reactions; and (c) independent deactivation. Second, the rate constant k_3 (Figure 4C) correlates very well with catalytic surface area in the reactor for the three Amoco bimodal catalysts (since τ is the same for all catalysts); both the American Cyanamid 1442A catalyst and the unimodal-pore catalyst fall well below this correlation line. Third, the deactivation rate

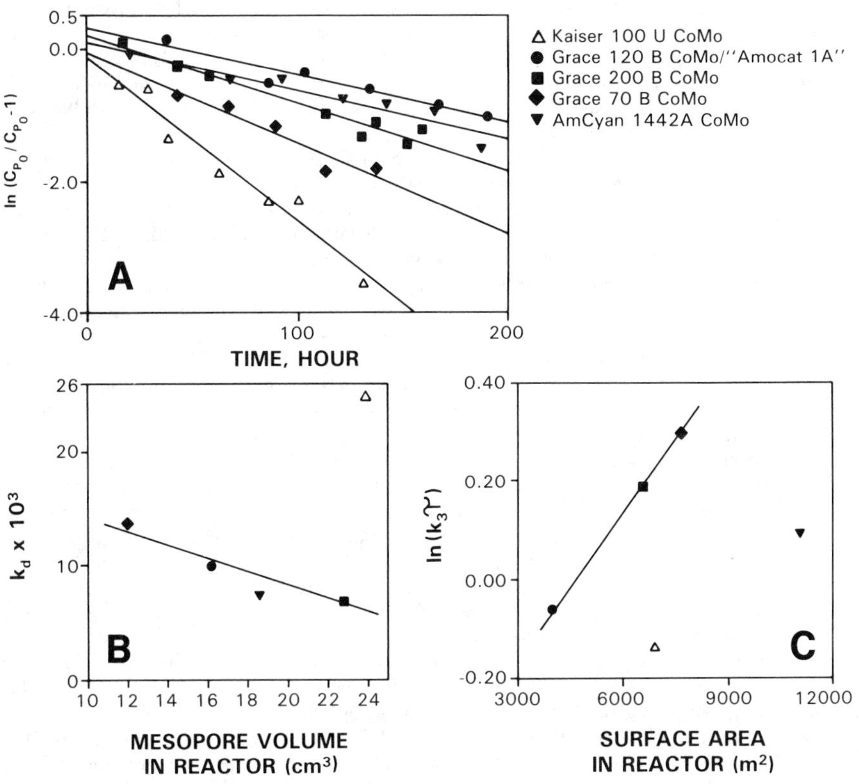

Figure 4. (A) Amoco worker's data from Figure 3 plotted according to Equation 14. (B) Deactivation rate constant (k_d), and (C) initial rate activity ($\ln k_3\tau$) from (A).

constant k_d (Figure 4B) correlates with mesopore volume in the reactor for all four bimodal catalysts; the single unimodal catalyst point is much higher than this correlation line.

Taken together, these results show that the differences in production of asphaltenes and oils, as reported in the Amoco work, can be explained with a simplest-case model based on the Amoco proposed mechanism wherein pore diffusion limitations are not required. Instead, this model requires only that: (a) activity is proportional to the total catalyst surface area in the reactor; (b) deactivation resistance depends mainly upon the amount of mesopore volume available for storing contaminants; (c) the rate of contaminant accumulation depends only upon the extent of deactivation; and (d) the effect of macropores is either through a more uniform distribution of contaminants or simply more pore volume, and thus increase deactivation resistance. Certainly these statements cannot be interpreted as literal conclusions; for example, other investigations cast doubt on the likelihood of a preasphaltene conversion effectiveness factor of unity. However, Equation 14 is a much better discriminator of the deactivation mechanism than of the main reaction kinetics; the effectiveness factor may not be important in this model. Thus, the effect of macroporosity on initial activity (Figure 4C) may not be paradoxical. This analysis points out the difficulties inherent in assigning the results of kinetic measurements to pore diffusion effects when other variables are present, especially for deactivating catalysts.

Because of the magnitude of the catalyst testing program, the Amoco study is a very important contribution to the coal liquefaction catalyst design literature. To date, few studies have matched the quantity of data produced in this study. The findings in this project led to the development of the Amocat 1A, 1B and 1C liquefaction catalysts; these are Co—Mo, Mo, and Ni—Mo, respectively, supported on W. R. Grace's 120 Å bimodal alumina. The preparation of this bimodal alumina is described in U.S. Patent No. 4,154,812 [51]. In 1982, the investigators at Amoco completed a second assessment of catalyst performance in coal liquefaction [52]. This work encompassed both laboratory-scale experiments as well as experimental runs in the Hydrocarbon Research Inc. (HRI) 3 ton/day process development unit, and in the Catlettsburg, KY H-Coal pilot plant (run 10). These Amoco 1A, 1B and 1C catalysts were compared with a unimodal, small-pore (50–60 Å mean pore diameter) American Cyanamid HDS-1442A Co—Mo catalyst. The Amocat catalysts were claimed to perform better at all levels of testing, and this has been confirmed in later work at American Cyanamid [53]. However, just as in the original Amoco work, it is difficult to assign the enhanced conversion only to pore diffusion effects, since many other factors were involved.

In the American Cyanamid study, the conversion of coal resids (containing preasphaltenes, asphaltenes and oils by solubility classification) to asphaltenes and oils was studied in a 1-liter CSTR at 425°C, 14 MPa (2,000 psi) and 1,600 rpm. Both solvent and coal resid were obtained from the Wilsonville pilot plant. However, unlike the Amoco work, unconverted coal was not present. Eleven Co—Mo and Ni—Mo catalysts, both unimodal- and bimodal-pore, were compared. Four of their catalytic runs are amenable to a comparative analysis using Equation 14, which does not invoke catalytic conversion of coal. The results of this analysis are shown in Figure 5. These results agree with Amoco's in that the initial activity (rate constant k_3) is higher for bimodal catalysts than for unimodal catalysts and it increases with surface area. However, the deactivation rate constant k_d does not reflect the same trend shown in the Amoco study since deactivation resistance is not noticeably improved by providing more mesopore volume. However, liquefaction runs in the Cyanamid study provided only two bimodal and two unimodal catalysts that could be compared at the same temperature and coal feed rate; three were Ni—Mo and one was Co—Mo (Amocat 1A). Furthermore, the unimodal catalysts were of an experimental bead design, whereas the bimodal catalysts were conventional pellets.

The comparison of catalysts under conditions of constant surface area in the reactor and constant dispersion of active ingredient were realized in a study published in 1981 by Ho and Weller [1]. Ho and Weller performed the hydroliquefaction of a high-volatile A bituminous West Virginia coal in the presence of unimodal-pore Co—Mo catalysts with mean pore diameters of 90 Å, 180 Å, 530 Å and 850 Å. These catalysts were prepared by aqueous impregnation of molybdenum and cobalt onto 40–60 mesh Corning "controlled pore size" aluminas. Ho and Weller adjusted the Mo loading to maintain 1×10^{-3} g MoO_3 per square meter of alumina surface area and they also based the catalyst-to-coal mass ratio on the amount of MoO_3 and CoO, and not total catalyst. Their liquefaction runs, conducted in a 1-liter CSTR at 400°C, 8.4 MPa (1,200 psi), and stirred at

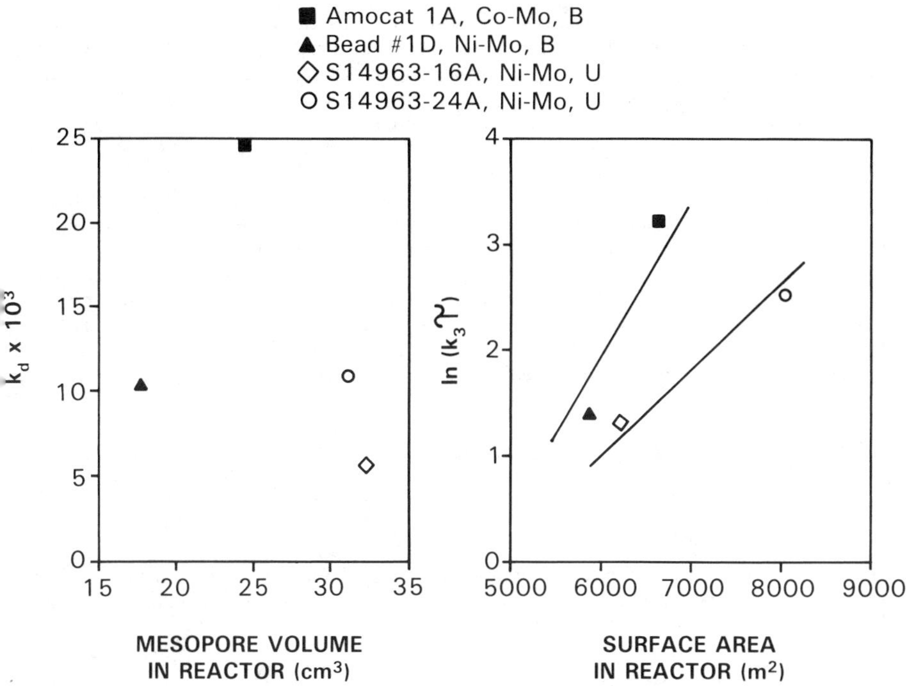

Figure 5. Analysis of the American Cyanamid coal liquefaction data for two unimodal and two bimodal catalysts using Equation 14.

950 rpm, revealed several things. In contrast to an earlier finding at Amoco that suggested that alumina supports might catalyze some coal liquefaction reactions, their aluminas caused little enhancement in either total coal conversion or oil production, indicating that catalytic activity is correctly assigned to Mo and Co. Modest increases in total coal conversion and oil production were seen with presulfided rather than with unsulfided (assumedly oxide) catalysts; both catalysts provided significant improvements in total conversion over thermal runs. The most significant results, however, were a trend showing total coal conversion increasing with catalyst pore size. Asphaltene concentration in the product increased even more than total conversion as the pore size increased; oil concentration either decreased or remained constant. Ho and Weller suggested that the production of asphaltenes is diffusion-limited in the small pore (90 Å and 180 Å diameter) catalysts, even in these small particles (0.42–0.25 mm). Apparently, the production of oils is not diffusion limited to the same extent, so that as pore size increases, the net result is an apparent enhanced selectivity to asphaltenes.

While not quantitative, the findings of Ho and Weller represent the best attempt up to that time to separate external variables (surface area, catalyst dispersion) from true pore diffusion effects. A similar study to that of Ho and Weller was conducted by Ahmed and Crynes [54], using Co—Mo catalysts. Unfortuntely, three commercial HDS unimodal-pore catalysts having mean mesopore diameters between 50 and 66 Å were chosen. This small difference means that unaccounted differences in other catalyst properties must be equally suspect in their results. More recently, Shimada et al. [55] compared five Mo—Al_2O_3 catalysts for production of asphaltenes and oils. The five catalysts were prepared by aqueous impregnation of Mo on 1.5 mm spherical beads of Al_2O_3; however, the impregnations were not adjusted to maintain constant coverage of the alumina. Three of the alumina supports were of unimodal pore size distribution, with mean pore diameters of ca. 60, 100, or 350 Å; the remaining two were bimodal, with mesopores of ca. 40 and 100 Å diameter respectively, and macropores of 10,000 Å diameter. A subbituminous Taiheyo coal was liquefied at 400°C and 9.8 MPa (1,400 psi) hydrogen pressure for a period of 2 hours. In terms of production of asphaltenes plus oils, their results showed that production of asphaltenes and oils increased with increasing mesopore diameter up to 100 Å but, above that, little increase was seen. They also show that macroporosity can enhance overall conversion; the measured effect is similar to that reported by Amoco.

Perhaps the most quantitative attempt to examine the role of pore diffusion in coal liquefaction were recently published by workers at Auburn University [56, 57]. In this study the authors obtained catalyst effectiveness factors with a model having parallel thermal and catalytic kinetics and a non-deactivating catalyst. Gradient terms were included. The mechanism used in the Auburn model differs from Amoco's in several ways. The Auburn workers provided for a hydrogen-donor pathway that involves a reaction between coal and a "reactive fraction" (α) of a hydrogen-donating oil; in addition they provided for a thermal reaction step between preasphaltenes and asphaltenes. Also, they included gas production in their model.

$$\mathbf{C} + \alpha\mathbf{O} \xrightarrow[\text{(thermal)}]{k_1} \mathbf{P} \xrightarrow[\text{(thermal)}]{k_2} \mathbf{A} \xrightarrow[\text{(thermal)}]{k_3} \mathbf{O}$$

with k_4 (thermal) giving $\mathbf{G}$, and $\mathbf{P} \xrightarrow[\text{(catalytic)}]{k_2'} \mathbf{A} \xrightarrow[\text{(catalytic)}]{k_3'} \mathbf{O}$

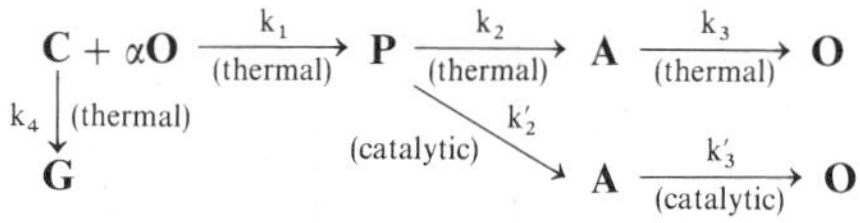

where primed rate constants refer to catalytic steps and unprimed constants to thermal steps. Assuming first order behavior, this mechanism gives the following kinetic equations of the form of Equation 2:

$$\partial C_{c,s}/\partial t = k_1 C_{c,s} C_{0,s} - k_4 C_{c,s}$$

$$\partial C_{p,s}/\partial t = k_1 C_{c,s} C_{0,s} - D_p \, \partial C_p/\partial s|_{s=L}\omega$$

$$\partial C_{A,s}/\partial t = k_2 C_{p,s} - k_3 C_{A,s} - D_A \, \partial C_A/\partial s|_{s=L}\omega \tag{15}$$

$$\partial C_{0,s}/\partial t = -k_1 \alpha C_{c,s} C_{0,s} + k_3 C_{A,s} - D_0 \, \partial C_0/\partial s|_{s=L}\omega$$

$$\partial C_{G,s}/\partial t = k_4 C_{c,s}$$

The s-subscripted concentrations refer to concentration in the reactor solution (assuming well-mixed behavior), ω is the external catalyst surface area per volume of reactant liquid, and the mass fluxes are specified at the surface of the catalyst pellets. Equation 15 holds for the reactor as a whole; the mass fluxes must be obtained from similar equations written for the catalyst pellets. If thermal reactions inside the catalyst pellet are negligible compared to catalytic reactions:

$$0 = D_p \, \partial^2 C_p/\partial s^2 - k_2' C_p \mathfrak{z}$$

$$0 = D_A \, \partial^2 C_A/\partial s^2 + k_2' C_p \mathfrak{z} - k_3' C_A \mathfrak{z} \tag{16}$$

$$0 = D_0 \, \partial^2 C_0/\partial s^2 + k_3' C_A \mathfrak{z}$$

where it is assumed that only one type of catalytic site of concentration $\mathfrak{z}$ is present. Concentrations not s-subscripted specify conditions inside the catalyst pellet, which is assumed to be a slab of half thickness L, and z is the distance along the coordinate axis oriented from the center-plane of the slab to the surface. The boundary conditions are $C_p(s = L) = C_{p,s}$, $C_A(s = L) = C_{A,s}$, $C_0(s = L) = C_{0,s}$, $\partial C_p/\partial s(s = 0) = 0$, $\partial C_0/\partial s(s = 0) = 0$, where zero boundary layer transport resistance has been assumed. The solution to the first part of Equation(s) 16 was given by Thiele [58] in 1939; Gollakota et al. [57] used this solution to solve the remaining two equations.

Combined with Equation 15, the result was:

$$\partial C_{ps}/\partial t = k_1 C_{c,s} C_{0,s} + (k_2 + k_{2e}) C_{p,s}$$

$$\partial C_{As}/\partial t = \{k_2 + k_{2e}(1 - \delta)\} C_{p,s} - (k_3 + k_{3e}) C_{A,s} \tag{17}$$

$$\partial C_{0s}/\partial t = -k_1 \alpha C_{cs} C_{0s} + (k_3 + k_{3e}) C_{As} + k_{2e} \delta C_{p,s}$$

where $k_{2e}\varepsilon = \dfrac{k'_2 \mu \varepsilon}{\rho \eta_1}$, $\quad k_{3e} = \dfrac{k'_3 \mu \varepsilon}{\rho \eta_2}$, $\quad \delta = \left(1 - \dfrac{\eta_1}{\eta_2}\right) \Big/ \left(\dfrac{1 - \phi_1^2}{1 - \phi_2^2}\right)$

using the well-known effectiveness factor approach. The dimensionless groupings ϕ_1 and ϕ_2 are the Thiele moduli for the reactions **P** → **A** and **A** → **O**, respectively:

$$\phi_1 = L\left(\frac{k'_2 \varepsilon}{D_p}\right)^{1/2}, \qquad \phi_2 = L\left(\frac{k'_3 \varepsilon}{D_A}\right)^{1/2}$$

The catalyst mass density is ρ, and the mass of catalyst per unit volume of reactor is μ.

Equation(s) 17 can be fitted to experimental data to obtain η_1 and η_2, which are the catalytic effectiveness factors for the reactions **P** → **A** and **A** → **O**, respectively. However, a provision must be made for the fraction of oil which is thermally reactive, α. This model was applied by Gollakota et al. to three sets of coal liquefaction data (Figure 6): thermal alone, thermal plus pelleted catalyst, and thermal plus powdered catalyst. The catalyst, Harshaw 0402T Co—Mo—Al_2O_3 in 0.48 cm ($\frac{3}{16}$ inch) pellets, was exposed to carbon disulfide and coal-derived solvent at 365°C for 72 hours prior to use. For the powdered catalyst studies, the preexposed catalyst was crushed and sized to −200 mesh. The coal was a bituminous Elkhorn No. 3, and the solvent was coal-derived SRC II; the coal was sized to −200 mesh and dried before use. Coal conversion was accomplished in tubing bomb microreactors at 450°C and 850 cpm; details of the product separation and classification are given by Curtis et al. [59]. The algorithm to fit the conversion data to the model is developed by Song [60] and is based on techniques developed by previous authors [61, 62]. The value for α was determined by minimizing the error norm for all three data sets; for the results shown in Figure 6, the value was calculated to be 0.2.

The results obtained from the analysis of the data in Figure 6 are shown in Table 2. From these results, and assuming that η_1 and η_2 are essentially unity for the powdered catalyst, the Auburn investigators concluded that η_1 was essentially zero and η_2 was about 0.66 for the 0.48 cm pellets of Harshaw 0402T catalyst. These results are qualitatively significant and suggest that pore diffusion

Table 2
First-Order Rate Constants (min^{-1})

Thermal	Pellet	Powder
$k_1 = 0.18 \pm 0.03$	$k_1 = 0.23 \pm 0.05$	$k_1 = 0.17 \pm 0.02$
$k_2 = 0.068 \pm 0.008$	$k_2 + k_{2e} = 0.058 \pm 0.01$	$k_2 + k_{2e} = 0.21 \pm 0.05$
	$k_2 + k_{2e}(1 - \epsilon) = 0.065 \pm 0.01$	
$k_3 = 0.0094 \pm 0.01$	$k_3 + k_{3e} = 0.025 \pm 0.006$	$k_3 + k_{3e} = 0.033 \pm 0.001$
$k_4 = 0.0195 \pm 0.004$	$k_4 = 0.024 \pm 0.009$	$k_4 = 0.023 \pm 0.004$

thermal $\quad \text{coal} \xrightarrow{k_1} \text{preasphaltenes} \xrightarrow{k_2} \text{asphaltenes} \xrightarrow{k_3} \text{oils}$

$\quad \text{coal} \xrightarrow{k_4} \text{gases}$

catalytic $\quad \text{preasphaltenes} \xrightarrow{k'_2} \text{asphaltenes} \xrightarrow{k'_3} \text{oils}$

Reprinted with permission from Ref. 57.

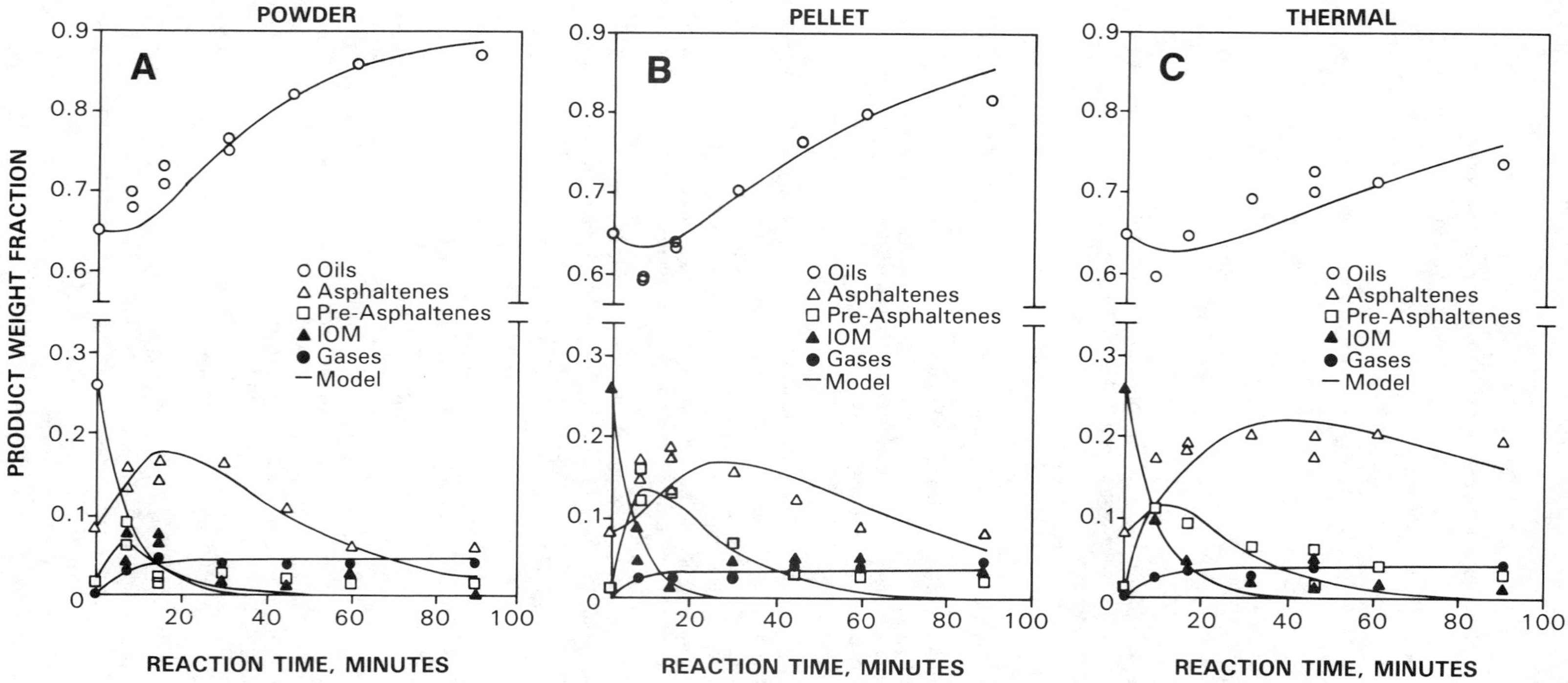

Figure 6. Coal liquefaction data using Harshaw 0402T Co—Mo—Al_2O_3 catalyst as measured at Auburn University using the model described in Equation 17. (A) Powdered catalyst; (B) 3/16 inch catalyst pellets; (C) No catalyst present. (Reprinted with permission from Ref. [57], © 1985 American Chemical Society.

essentially bars the catalyst from participating in the reaction **P** → **A**. It is interesting to contrast this finding with the results shown in Figures 4 and 5 which are based on an analysis of the Amoco and American Cyanamid data using Equation 14, which implicitly assumes an effectiveness factor of unity for the reaction **P** → **A** + **O**. The correlations between the results in Figures 4 and 5 with catalyst variables (surface area and pore volume) suggest that, even if the effectiveness factor for this reaction is not actually unity, neither is it zero. A possible explanation for this discrepancy is that the deactivation model, Equation 14, is more sensitive to the effectiveness factor for contaminant accumulation process leading to deactivation than for the effectiveness factor for the main reaction.

The Gollakota et al. model has not been used at this writing to compare catalysts of different pore sizes. Such a comparison would provide additional credibility to the conclusions concerning effectiveness factors; nevertheless, it is probably the best model yet published for pore diffusion effects in coal liquefaction.

COAL LIQUIDS UPGRADING

To some extent, coal liquid upgrading is similar to the upgrading of heavy petroleum residua. The primary goal of upgrading is to decrease the levels of N, S, and O in the oil (**O**) fraction, and to do some additional molecular weight reduction as well. Hydrogenation functions are important here. The kinetics of HDN, HDS, and hydrocracking have been discussed extensively in the petroleum literature; for coal-derived materials, numerous references are also available [63–66, 28, 34, 36, 37]. A general review of these bodies of literature is beyond the scope of this chapter; only those studies dealing with pore diffusion effects will be considered.

Sooter [66] considered the influence of catalyst pore size on the hydrodesulfurization of coal-derived liquids. He desulfurized an anthracene oil having 0.43% sulfur at various temperatures, pressures, and space rates in a trickle-bed downflow reactor, and used the same three unimodal-pore Co—Mo catalysts (having average pore diameters between 50 and 66 Å) later used in the Ahmed and Crynes [54] liquefaction study. Sooter's kinetic data suggested a mechanism that was overall second-order in terms of total sulfur. He explained this as the additive effect of two distinctly different and independent sulfur-containing lumps that were desulfurized at different rates. One lump, consisting of low-boiling sulfur compounds, was much more easily desulfurized than a second lump consisting of higher molecular weight compounds. Such lumps are commonly used in modeling petroleum HDS kinetics [67].

At this point Sooter employed a trial-and-error method using rate measurements obtained with different particle sizes of the same catalyst to estimate the catalyst effectiveness factors for desulfurizing the "refractory" lump. This method was essentially the analytical equivalent of the graphical "triangle method" developed by Weisz and Prater [68]. Effectiveness factors between 0.8 and 1.0 were indicated for each catalyst for particles ranging between 0.32 cm ($\frac{1}{8}$ inch) pellets, and 48-mesh powders, in the temperature range of 315 to 343°C. Sooter concluded that pore diffusion was not rate-controlling in any of his measurements; however, he noted that desulfurization rates decreased as the mean pore size decreased. His explanation for this apparent contradiction between the indicated pore size effects and the high effectiveness factors was that the large molecules must be adsorbed in the correct orientation; this becomes more difficult in the small-pore catalysts.

One important consequence of Sooter's work was the suggestion that much of the existing knowledge about petroleum HDS should be directly applicable to the HDS of coal-derived oils, for example, specific compound rates [69], "two-lump" kinetics [70, 71], patent data for pore-structure catalysts [72], and so on. From this starting point a model based on a petroleum "literature consensus" could be modified for coal-derived oils; this was later developed at Oklahoma State [73]. In a trickle bed reactor the resulting equation gave the HDS rate for the refractory-type sulfur lump, which the authors assumed to be represented by dibenzothiophene:

$$C_s = C_{s,0} - \frac{(1 + K_pC_s)\ln(C_s - C_{s0})}{2(K_p - K_s)} - \frac{(K_p - K_s)(C_R^2 - C_{R0}^2)}{4(1 + K_pC_s)} - \frac{k\,K_{H_2}K_sC_{H2}\eta\mu}{2(1 + K_pC_s)(K_s - K_p)(LHSV)\rho(1 + K_{H2}C_{H2})} \tag{18}$$

where ρ = catalyst density
μ = weight of catalyst per volume reactor
K_p, K_s, K_{H2} = Langmuir adsorption equilibrium constants for product, sulfur compound, and hydrogen, respectively
C_{H2} = the concentration of dissolved hydrogen in the liquid
C_s = sulfur content in the reactor effluent
C_{s0} = sulfur in the feed

In this model it is assumed that: (a) a Langmuir-Hinshelwood type mechanism is operative in the wetted catalyst, (b) relationships between vapor and liquid phase composition, and lumped catalytic reaction mechanism, could be taken from existing literature for petroleum trickle-bed desulfurization reactors [74, 75]; (c) liquid properties would, however, be estimated from correlations [76] developed for SRC recycle solvents; (d) H_2 and H_2S are not diffusion-limited, but organic sulfur compounds may be; and (e) the effectiveness factor for HDS does not change with position in the reactor. Strictly speaking, the latter assumption is valid only for low coverages of sulfur compounds compared to product, which results in a LHHW rate equation that is overall first order in sulfur compounds, and hence, a Thiele modulus which is independent of sulfur concentration.

Unfortunately, the utility of Equation 18 remains unknown. The Oklahoma State workers did not attempt to estimate the effectiveness factor η or other parameters in Equation 18 by fitting it to experimental data. Theoretically, the effectiveness factor for a bimolecular Langmuir-Hinshelwood reaction can be calculated *a priori* [77]. However, experimental determination of η using a model such as Equation 18 is preferred to *a priori* calculations, even though the experimental approach is also uncertain. The reason for this view is the number of assumptions required to construct the quantitative model. Not only is the complex hydrodynamic and thermal behavior of multiphase reactors a problem, but the reaction mechanism itself is difficult to describe with a single rate law. Nowhere is this more evident than in the literature on the HDN mechanism. For example, a literature consensus suggests that aromatic nitrogen-containing rings must be saturated before C—N bond scission occurs. Along this line, one finds empirical equations, such as the following one developed by Mobil investigators [79] to relate the fraction of aromatics (f_a) to the nitrogen content (C_N), HDN rate constant k_f, and hydrogenation rate constant k_r, for an SRC recycle solvent:

$$f_a = \left[\frac{k_r}{k_r + k_f C_N}\right] + \left[f_0 - \frac{k_r}{k_r + k_f C_N}\right] e^{[-k_f C_N + k_r/\text{LHSV}]} \tag{19}$$

where f_0 is the fractional initial aromaticity. This coupling of the HDN reaction rate to aromaticity of the total liquid, whether done with empirical equations such as Equation 19 or with detailed rate equations, is difficult. Also, evidence exists to support the view [28, 78] that desorption of certain nitrogen-containing molecules is sufficiently slow relative to the C—N bond-breaking rate, that the adsorption-desorption equilibrium of these compounds, is not achieved. From a kinetic viewpoint, the catalyst's HDN performance may actually lie somewhere between that of a pure adsorbent [78] and a Langmuir-Hinshelwood type catalyst. The most strongly adsorbed nitrogen compounds are the most basic [80–82]; presumably these are adsorbed irreversibly on acid sites. These basic nitrogen compounds may be intermediates formed during the hydrogenation of other, less basic, nitrogen compounds [83], and are almost certainly involved in catalyst coking [82–86]. Finally, at least two authors [87, 88] report that several basic nitrogen compounds have *increased*, not decreased, the rate of HDS of dibenzothiophenes. These authors interpret this as evidence that even though the nitrogens are strongly adsorbed on some sites, they liberate other sites that are more important in the HDS mechanism from strongly adsorbed HDS products such as H_2S. Clearly, the adsorption-reaction behavior of molybdenum-based catalysts in a simultaneous HDS, HDO and HDN environment does not lead readily to a single comprehensive rate law expression. An example of this complexity is evident in a summary of kinetic results for the HDS of thiophene and dibenzothiophene (89). A variety of rate expressions produce activation energies for the HDS of the thiophene reaction ranging from 3 to 21.6 kcal/mole (Table 3) and from 14 to 39 kcal/mole for dibenzothiophene (Table 4). As progressively more complex reaction mixtures are used, problems encountered with their kinetic measurements will increase. It also appears that the

Table 3
Kinetic Equations for Thiophene Hydrodesulphurization.

Reference	Date	Solvent Temp./K Press./atm	Catalyst Used	Ea/kcal mol^{-1}	Rate Expression $r = r_{HDS}$ r° = initial rate
Satterfield	1968	— 508–538 1	Co—Mo/Al_2O_3	3.7	$r = k \frac{K_T P_T}{(1 + K_T P_T + K_S P_S)^2} P_H$
Ozimek	1975	— 580–673 1	Co—Mo/Al_2O_3	21.6	$r^\circ = k \frac{K_T P_T^\circ}{(1 + K_T P_T^\circ)^2} P_H^\circ$
Massoth	1977	— 673 1	Mo/Al_2O_3	—	$r = k \frac{K_T P_T}{(1 + K_T P_T + K_S P_S)^n} P_H^m$
Morooka	1977	benzene 523–623 1	Co—Mo/Al_2O_3	20	$r = k \frac{K_T P_T}{(1 + K_T P_T + K_S P_S)^2} P_H$
Chakraborty	1978	naphtha 510–563 1	Ni—Mo/Al_2O_3	3	$r = k \frac{K_T P_T}{(1 + K_S P_S)^2} P_H$
Kawaguchi	1978	*n*-hexane 543–623 1	Ni—Mo/Al_2O_3	16	$r = k \frac{K_T P_T}{(1 + K_T P_T + K_S P_S)} \cdot \frac{K_H P_H}{(1 + \sqrt{K_H P_H})^2}$
Vyskocil	1979	— 623 1	Co—Mo/Al_2O_3	—	$r^\circ = k \frac{K_T P_T^\circ}{(1 + K_T P_T^\circ)^2} P_H^\circ$
Lee	1977	— 523–586 1	Co—Mo/Al_2O_3	—	$r = k \frac{K_T P_T K_H P_H}{(1 + K_T P_T + K_S P_S)} \left\{ \frac{1}{1 + K_H P_H} + k'' \right\}$

Reprinted with permission from Ref. 89.

Table 4
Kinetic Equations for Dibenzothiophene Hydrodesulfurization (subscript D refers to DBT)

Reference	Date	Solvent Temp./K Press./atm	Catalyst Used	Ea/kcal mol^{-1}	Rate Expression ($r = r_{HDS}$)
Frye	1967	oil 533–643 6–27	$Co—Mo/Al_2O_3$	30.8	$r = k\frac{K_DP_D}{(1 + K_DP_D + K_SP_S)^2}P_H$
Galiasso	1970	cetane 583–648 10–80	$Co—Mo/Al_2O_3$	17	$r = k\frac{K_DP_D}{(1 + K_DP_D + K_SP_S + \sum K_iP_i}P_H$
Mahoney	1978	oil 540–570 21.4	Pt/Al_2O_3	28	$r = k\frac{K_DP_D}{(1 + K_DP_D + K_SP_S)^n}P_H \quad n = 1 \text{ or } 2$
Dhainaut	1979	— 513 0.06 to 1	$Co—Mo/Al_2O_3$	16.3	$r = k\frac{K_DP_D}{(1 + K_DP_D + K_SP_S)}\cdot\frac{(K_HP_H)^m}{1 + (K_HP_H)^m} \quad m = 0.5 \text{ or } 1$
Aguilar	1979	— 473–523 1	$Co—Mo/Al_2O_3$	13.5	$r = k\frac{K_DP_D}{(1 + K_DP_D + K_SP_S)}\cdot P_H$
Broderick	1981	*n*-hexadecane 548–598 34 to 160	$Co—Mo/Al_2O_3$	30	$r = k\frac{K_DP_D}{(1 + K_DP_D + K_SP_S)^2}\cdot\frac{K_HP_H}{(1 + K_HP_H)}$
Singhal	1981	tetralin 558–623 7–26	$Co—Mo/Al_2O_3$	39	$r = k\frac{K_DP_D}{(1 + K_DP_D + K_PP_P)}\cdot\frac{K_HP_H}{1 + K_HP_H}$
Vrinat	1982	— 473–513 1–50	$Co—Mo/Al_2O_3$	23	$r = k\frac{K_DP_D}{(1 + K_DP_D + K_SP_S)}\cdot\frac{K_HP_H}{1 + K_HP_H}$

Reprinted with permission from Ref. 89.

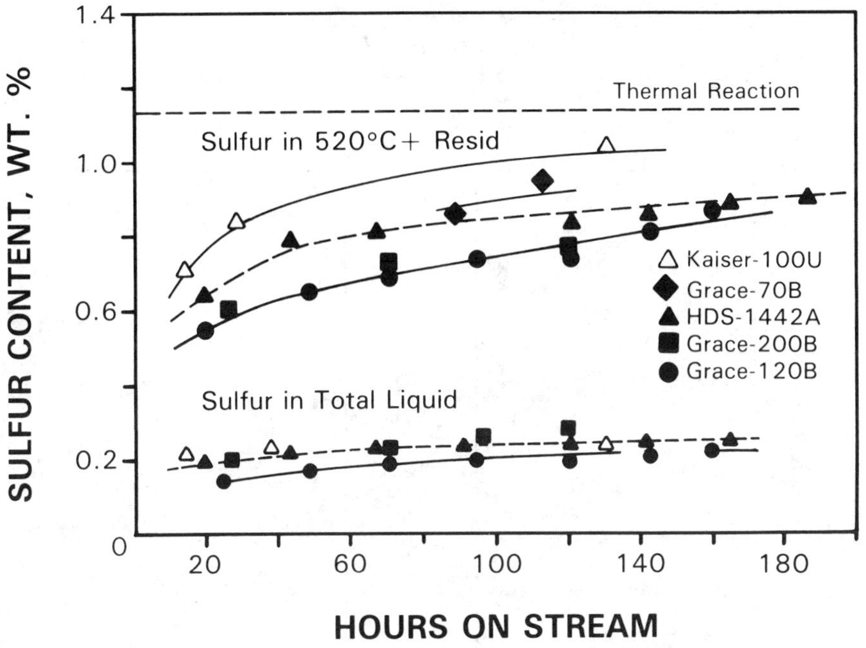

Figure 7. Sulfur content of total products and of 520 C+ resid as measured by Amoco investigators using five different CoMo catalysts listed in Table 1 [50].

calculated kinetic parameters are very sensitive to slight changes in the rate expression. The data in Tables 3 and 4 serve to emphasize that, although a review of coal liquefaction data may point to deficiencies in some studies, we should remain respectful of the accomplishments in view of the complexity of the process.

In 1979, the Amoco EPRI project [50] published correlations between coal liquid desulfurization rate and pore size. Sulfur removal was measured simultaneously with the liquefaction conversion data. The liquefaction results (Figure 3) and experimental conditions obtained with five catalysts were discussed previously. The total sulfur in the distillate product, and sulfur content of the "520+ resid," a non-distillate coal liquefaction product, with time on stream are shown for these catalysts in Figure 7. Interestingly, the ranking of these catalysts is virtually identical to the ranking for liquefaction activity, as shown in Figure 3. This result suggests that we apply the simple deactivation model, developed in Equation 14, to the 520+ resid data. Once again, Equation 14 is valid only if the sulfur in the 520+ resid sulfur lump (the "refractory" lump) is produced very rapidly during coal thermal dissolution, and is then followed by a first-order catalytic desulfurization mechanism. Plotting Amoco's data according to Equation 14 produces the initial reaction rate constants $\ln(k_3\tau)$ and deactivation rate constants k_d shown in Figure 8. These results are very similar to those for preasphaltene conversion shown in Figure 4, again suggesting that surface area in the reactor, presence of macropores, and differences in catalyst are important factors in determining an initial catalyst activity, while mesopore volume in the reactor and presence of macropores are important factors in deactivation resistance. Diffusion gradient effects are not strongly indicated in either case.

A similar conclusion, based on a total nitrogen removal, was reached in a study performed at Filtrol [90] since the authors concluded that "the most active catalysts for HDN had the greatest SA and PV values". In a later study, workers at PETC [91] compared the HDN performance of

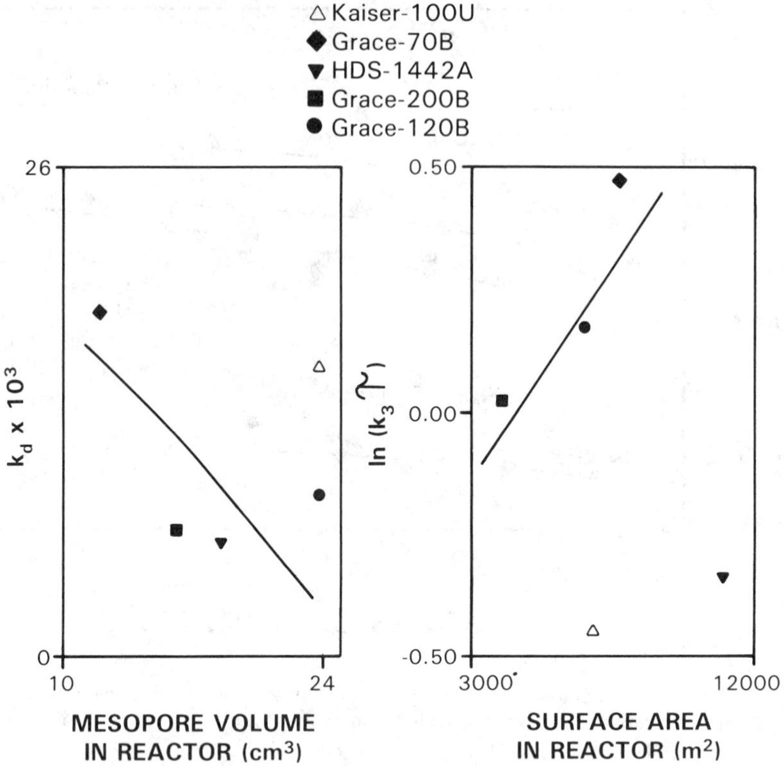

Figure 8. Deactivation rate constant (k_d) and initial reaction rate constant (ln $k_3\tau$) calculated from data in Figure 7 using Equation 14.

two unimodal and two bimodal Ni—Mo catalysts, with average mesopore diameters ranging from 70 to 120 Å. Although the mesopore volume in the reactor was kept fairly constant, the surface area varied over a factor of two in this group of catalysts, and the dispersions of Ni and Mo were likewise varied. Thus the effect of pore size and bimodality *vs.* unimodality are clouded somewhat. However, the loss in pore volume, shown in Figure 9, reveals a clear separation of bimodal-pore and unimodal-pore catalysts, but almost no differences due to average pore size or surface area. This supports other studies that suggest that the major effect of bimodality is to improve the distribution, and thus sorption capacity, of contaminants. However, the PETC data do not correlate HDN activity with loss of pore volume, suggesting that site deactivation also occurs.

From the viewpoint of restoration of original pore volume, bimodal catalysts should be less regenerable than unimodal catalysts, simply because the pellet interior has been made more accessible to non-removable metal deposits. Regeneration experiments reported in the PETC study support this view.

Another study of sulfur and nitrogen removal rates using coal liquefaction catalysts was reported by workers at American Cyanamid [53]. Again, due to external variables, their findings are difficult to correlate with pore size for the seven different catalysts examined. Both the PETC and American Cynamid studies reported that Shell 324M catalyst was the best HDN catalyst tested. In the PETC study, the authors claimed that the higher HDN activity of the unimodal-pore Shell 324M catalyst was due to a high loading of Ni and Mo, and that the bimodality of the other catalysts

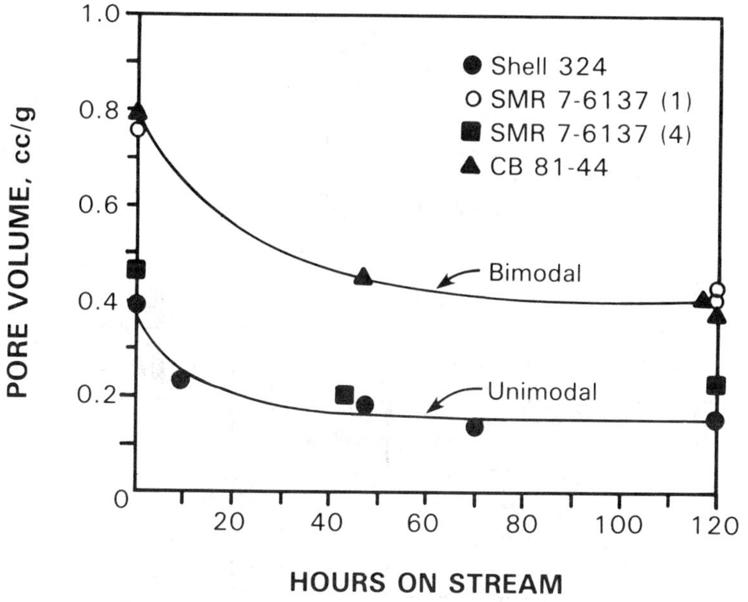

Figure 9. Pore volume trends with age for bimodal and unimodal catalysts used in a PETC hydrodenitrogenation study [91].

helped offset an even lower activity due to much lower loadings. The American Cyanamid authors concluded that the "bead design" allowed an almost comparable HDN activity to be achieved with a catalyst containing less Mo and Ni. Both conclusions suggest diffusion-limited reactions but are not definitive. "Bead design," e.g. surface-to-volume ratio, can change rates only when the reaction is diffusion-limited.

Finally, some recent results were published by the PETC workers [94] in which Ni—Mo unimodal-pore catalysts having mean pore sizes between 49 to 270 Å were used to hydrotreat three coal-derived residua in a CSTR. Activities were reported on a unit surface area basis, so the results are inherently less ambiguous than those reported in previous studies. The PETC workers found that HDN, HDS and hydrogenation activity increased with increasing pore diameter, and that HDN and hydrogenation activities were more sensitive to surface area and pore volume than HDS activity.

DEACTIVATION OF COAL LIQUEFACTION CATALYSTS

Numerous studies of the deactivation kinetics of coal liquefaction catalysts have been published. While the mathematical emphasis is usually on the kinetics of the deactivation process itself, the final goal is to predict activity or optimize catalyst lifetime. Experimentally, a deactivation model is easier to verify than a pure activity model, because the deactivation process results in more directly measurable features such as the spatial distribution of the contaminants inside the pellet, the distribution of contaminants in the pores, and so on. These measurables are frequently used advantageously in deactivation modeling.

If the dominant cause of catalyst deactivation is the accumulation of contaminants, with subsequent blocking of catalyst active sites, then Equations 2–5 are sufficient for modeling. Many models have been developed for catalyst deactivation that fit this framework; see, for example, the review by Hughes [92]. However, Equations 3, 4, and 5 will not be adequate when catalyst

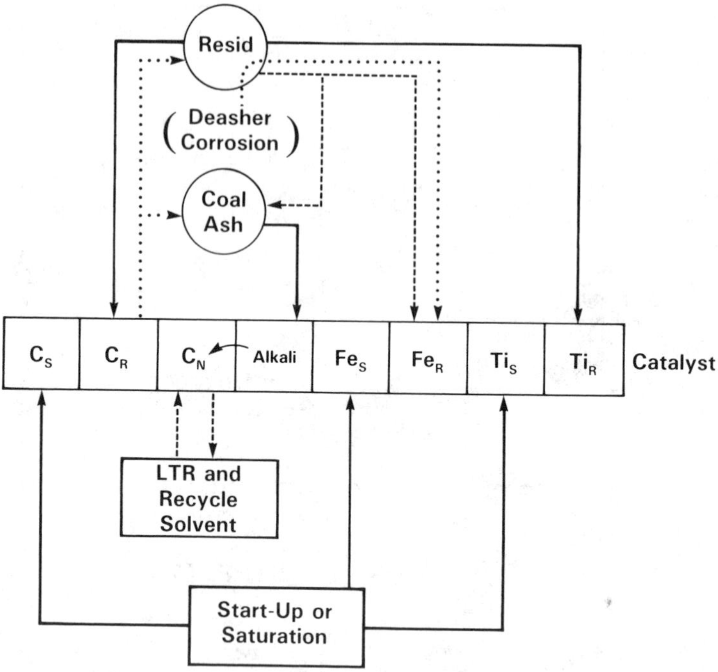

Figure 10. Phenomenological model of contaminant deposition on a hydrotreating catalyst from the Wilsonville two-stage coal liquefaction pilot plant.

deactivation occurs as a result of processes independent of the accumulation of contaminants as, for example, sintering or loss of dispersion of active phase, or sintering of the porous support. Loss of dispersion of Co in Co-Mo catalysts [93] and Mo in Ni-Mo catalysts [94], used in the H—Coal process: a similar loss of dispersion has not been reported for Ni—Mo coal liquefaction catalysts. Thus it is important to remember that contamination-based deactivation models may be oversimplified for coal liquefaction catalysts.

Three major types of contaminants accumulate in coal liquefaction catalysts: coke, trace metals, and alkali. The nature of these contaminants is a major research concern, as is the complex interaction between these contaminants and the process. A reasonably detailed phenomenological picture of these interactions is a virtual prerequisite to detailed kinetic modeling. As an example, a phenomenological model (Figure 10) involving three types of "coke" (basic nitrogen, resid-associated, and generic "fast" coke), two types each of Fe and Ti deposits ("fast" and resid- associated), alkali metals, coal ash, and thermal resid (non- vacuum-distillable material) has been reported by Adkins et al. [82, 138]. This model fits the accumulation patterns for at least six Wilsonville, AL pilot plant runs; these include four configurations of the pilot plant which differ in the way that thermal resid and coal ash are handled. Models such as this are important aids in understanding the global characteristics of the catalyst deactivation phenomenon and help illustrate the important contaminants. Much research has been concerned with specific contaminants in coal liquefaction catalysts; examples include basic nitrogen compounds as poisons [78, 80–83, 119], the nature of Fe and Ti contaminants [114, 126, 128–131], and the adsorption of alkali metals [82, 114, 124].

In the following section, some of the current knowledge of the effects of pore diffusion on the deposition of carbon and trace metals in coal liquefaction catalysts are reviewed. Before proceeding, it is helpful to review contaminant accumulation modeling in a broader sense.

DEVELOPMENT OF GENERAL CONTAMINANT ACCUMULATION MODELS

Published mathematical models for contaminant deposition differ widely. Fortunately most fit the framework of Equations 2–5 and can be schematically indicated on the diagram shown in Figure 11. For a single reactant, i, which converts to a product, j, on a single catalytic site this diagram plots the site concentration $\mathfrak{z}_{ij}$ against the effective diffusivity D_i. At any time $\mathfrak{z}_{ij}$ will be related to the amount of contaminant present through Equation 3, and D_i will be related to the amount present through Equation 4. Note that this diagram shows the effect of time but not of position in the catalyst.

The type of model that must be constructed depends upon the path taken by the contamination process in Figure 11. This path can be described most simply in terms of a time-dependent Thiele modulus, which for a first-order reaction is $L(k_{ij}\mathfrak{z}_{ij}/D_i)^{1/2}$, where k_{ij} is the single-site reaction rate constant. The shaded region labeled "poisoning" represents a special type of decreasing-ϕ contamination. In the poisoning region, active sites are deactivated by small amounts of contaminant; thus $\mathfrak{z}_{ij}$ decreases but D_i remains constant. This allows Equation 4 to be omitted in poisoning models. Power-law functions are most often used for Equation 3, with an exponent (b) being equal to the number of active sites deactivated per molecule of poison. In the simple linear case (b = 1), this reduces to Wheeler's [95] uniform deactivation model; higher exponents have also been proposed [96–98]. More complex poisoning models have been developed, such as the one by Masamune and Smith [99], where different mechanistic paths are envisioned for the poisoning

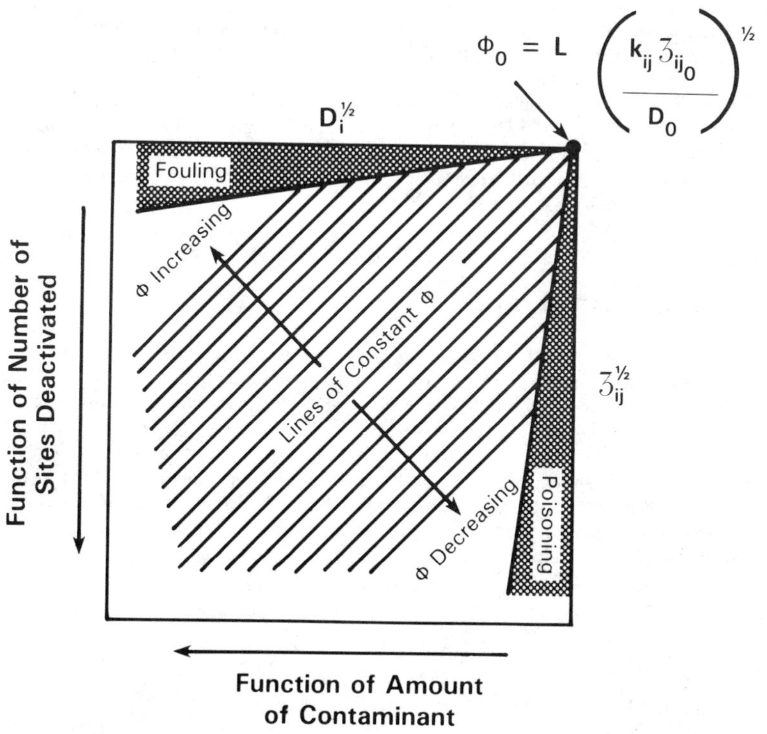

Figure 11. Schematic diagram showing the two most important parameters in modeling contaminant deposition.

reaction. Also of interest is the model of Murakami et al. [100], where unsteady-state effects and "fast poisoning" reactions are included. A model developed by Kam et al. [101] adds the complexity of Langmuir-Hinshelwood kinetics.

Conversely, the path may follow the direction of increasing ϕ. The simplest of these paths lie in the region labeled "fouling," where $\mathfrak{z}_{ij}$ remains constant while D decreases. Conceptually, this corresponds to deposition of material that does not deactivate a significant fraction of active sites but accumulates in quantities sufficient to reduce D_i. In this case, fouling models can omit Equation 3. For large ϕ_0, the fouling phenomenon has been called "pore plugging" or "pore blocking." Hiemenz [102] was among the first to postulate pore blocking as a catalyst deactivation mechanism. Newson [103] used algebraic approximations, valid for large ϕ_0, to the differential equations of continuity and assumed a first-order irreversible adsorption of foulant. Rajagopalan and Luss [104] constructed a more elaborate first order model in which the effect of pore size distributions under restricted diffusion conditions is considered. A more recent fouling model by Oyekunle and Hughes [105] includes unsteady-state terms in the continuity equations and assumes a second order fouling reaction.

The region between poisoning and fouling is simply a mixed contamination region. This is the most complex region for model development since both $\mathfrak{z}_{ij}$ and D_i may be functions of the amount of contaminants. One example of such a model was developed by Tsotsis [106]; he assumed a parallel reaction scheme, first order reaction, and $b = 1$. Another example is the model of Ahn and Smith [107] that is based on a moving boundary of deactivated surface as a result of both rapid poisoning of active sites and the subsequent heavy fouling of the poisoned areas. Modeling in this region is further complicated when intricate mechanistic pathways and complex reaction rate laws are used.

The important insight to be gained from Figure 11 is that if catalyst characterization can be used to identify (approximately) the path followed by the deactivation process in question, considerable modeling simplifications will result. Of particular interest are the measurements of the spatial distribution of the foulant at different times, as well as pore structure determinations and/or model compound diffusivity measurements on spent catalysts. Since catalyst characterization is the best way to obtain evidence about catalyst deactivation, including pore diffusion effects, it is not surprising that many characterization studies have been reported for spent coal liquefaction catalysts [17, 50, 52, 53, 80–82, 91, 108–138].

COKING IN COAL LIQUEFACTION CATALYSTS

Several detailed kinetic models for coke deposition in coal liquefaction have been constructed. For the most part, these models follow either the mixed contamination or fouling guidelines and the mathematics tend to be complicated. However, as is frequently the case, the most difficult aspect of modeling coke accumulation is not the numerical or mathematical difficulties, but the experimental discrimination of key modeling assumptions using catalyst characterization and kinetic data. Experimental model discrimination is the biggest problem facing engineers working in this area.

A good example of this problem can be found in the rather ambitious mixed contamination model derived by Crynes and Seapan [132] and their students. The Crynes and Seapan model assumes a simple parallel fouling mechanism of the form:

$$\mathrm{A} \longrightarrow \mathrm{Product}$$

$$\mathrm{A} \longrightarrow \mathrm{Coke}$$

where "A" and "product" can refer to any lumped first-order reaction groups (for example, products and reactants in a lumped HDS or HDN reaction). Note that the parallel coke formation path assumes that only one reactant lump (the one being modeled kinetically) is responsible for coking. Next, the Crynes and Seapan model assumes a single type of catalytic site and a power-law site-blocking mechanism for Equation 3. This site equation, combined with Equation 2, yields, for the reactant

$$\varepsilon \frac{\partial C_A}{\partial t} = \frac{1}{R^2}\frac{\partial}{\partial R}\left(R^2 D_A \frac{\partial C_A}{\partial R}\right) - \rho k_a(1 - Q/Q_{max})^a C_A \quad (20^*)$$

and for the coke, Equation 5 becomes:

$$\frac{\partial Q}{\partial t} = k_c(1 - Q/Q_{max})^b C_A \quad (21^*)$$

where k_c, k_a = intrinsic rate constants for the coking and main reactions, respectively
a, b = site-blocking exponents for the main and coking reactions
Q_{max} = value of Q at complete deactivation

Note that the gradient term in Equation 20* is written for a spherical catalyst pellet of radius R_0.

The diffusivity relationship, Equation 4, is included in the Crynes and Seapan model in the following equation:

$$D_A = D_{A0}\left\{\frac{\varepsilon_0 - \dfrac{Q\rho}{\rho_c}}{\varepsilon_0}\right\} e^{-4.6(\sigma/r_{p0}\sqrt{\varepsilon/\varepsilon_0})} \quad (22^*)$$

which assumes that (a) parallel, noninteracting cylindrical pores have a local radius that is changed from initial pore radius, r_{p0}, by the square root of the local fraction porosity remaining and ε_0 is an initial porosity that is uniform throughout the catalyst; (b) local porosity is equal to original porosity minus the fraction porosity occupied by carbon, given by Q times the coke density, ρ, divided by catalyst density, ρ_c; and (c) that the effective diffusivity of reactant A depends on the local pore radius through the Satterfield [139] correlation. In Equation 22*, D is the effective diffusivity in the fresh catalyst, and σ is the critical molecular diameter of reactant A. Next, Seapan and Crynes added two more equations based on Equations 2 and 5 to provide for axial gradient conditions in a fixed-bed reactor under ideal radial mixing conditions:

$$\varepsilon_b \frac{\partial C_{As}}{\partial t} = -\frac{F}{S}\frac{\partial C_{A,s}}{\partial z} - \mu k_a C_{A,s}\left[\frac{\int_0^{R_0} 3k_a(1 - Q/Q_{max}{}^a C_A\,\partial R}{R_0 k_a C_{As}}\right] \quad (23^*)$$

$$\frac{\partial Q_s}{\partial t} = k_c C_{A,s}\left[\frac{\int_0^{R_0} 3k_c(1 - Q/Q_{max})^b C_A\,\partial R}{R_0 k_c C_{A,s}}\right] \quad (24^*)$$

where ε_b = bed porosity
F = oil feed rate
z = distance from reactor entrance
s = reactor cross-section
μ = catalyst bed density

The two terms in square brackets on the right-hand sides of Equations 23* and 24* are effectiveness factors for the main and coking reactions; these must be computed with the aid of Equations 20*–22*. Preliminary measurements of this reactor coke profile obtained in hydroprocessing tests of an SRC feedstock showed that coke deposition decreased with distance in the reactor; this is

* Equations indicated with an asterisk have been rewritten by the authors to conform to the notation used in this chapter; in some cases this may require an interpretation by the present authors.

consistent with a parallel-type fouling mechanism. In a parallel mechanism, coking rate is coupled to concentration of reactant, which decreases axially in a plug flow reactor.

The Crynes and Seapan model was nondimensionalized and solved numerically; details are given in the thesis by Chang [140]. The numerical solutions were compared to measurements of the rate of hydrogenation and hydrodenitrogenation of SRC and EDS feedstocks in a plug flow reactor at 400°C, as well as axial measurements of the coke profile and other factors. From this regression, the authors suggest that the following parameters were fitted:

$$k_a = 1.13 \times 10^{-6}\ m^3\,s^{-1}\,kg^{-1}, \qquad k_c = 0.95 \times 10^{-9}\ m^3\,s^{-1}\,kg^{-1}\ \text{(hydrogenation reaction)},$$

$$k_c = 3.7 \times 10^{-9}\ m^3\,s^{-1}\,kg^{-1}\ \text{(HDN reaction)}, \qquad a = \tfrac{1}{2},\ b = 2, \qquad \sigma = 1.65\ \text{nm},$$

$$D_{A0} = 0.19 \times 10^{-5}\ cm^2\,s^{-1}, \qquad \phi_A = 11.4, \qquad \eta_A = 0.25$$

However, a critical evaluation of these results is difficult for several reasons. First, details of the criteria used in the regression analysis are not presented. Problems associated with regressing data to multiple parameters are well known, and in some cases can lead to entirely artificial parameter values; this is a major concern. More importantly, while the comparison of model and data may be able to provide a discrimination of gross modeling features (such as the overall parallel fouling mechanism, based on the reactor coke profile, or the average rate of coking across the bed), the discrimination of fine modeling features is not possible.

For example, the authors use the fitted parameters to calculate the coke profile inside the catalyst pellet at various positions in the reactor; they then superimpose data points obtained at various positions within a catalyst pellet using scanning Auger spectroscopy. Typical results are shown in Figure 12; the catalyst coke profile measurements do not satisfactorily support the model, defined by the best fitted parameters. The model predicts a rather severely diffusion-limited coke pattern, while the limited data presented are consistent with either a uniform or mildly diffusion-limited interparticle coke distribution. Numerous investigators have used extensive electron microprobe analysis and reported coke deposition profiles that are uniform or appear mildly diffusion-limited [50, 80, 81, 112, 114, 133, 134] while few measurements of severely diffusion-limited coke profiles have been reported. Likewise, the predicted major pore size (Figure 13) do not agree with measured data obtained using mercury porosimetry.

Attempts to precisely model accumulation kinetics must make the best possible use of experimental data. Otherwise, there is no advantage gained in constructing detailed models; less detailed, more empirical models are equally verifiable. Along this line of reasoning, a model was constructed by Sandia Laboratory investigators [116, 117]. The combined effects of carbon and metals contamination in a mixed- contamination type model incorporated three additional characterization features: (a) coke, measured by microprobe analysis, is often distributed uniformly in the catalyst pellet; (b) metal deposits often tend to approximate the "shell-progressive" pattern; and (c) the pore volume losses due to carbon are much greater than those due to metals because the metals accumulate in much lower amounts and are denser deposits. The Sandia workers made the following simplifying assumptions: (a) that coking follows Wheeler's [95] "uniform poisoning" model with a site-blocking exponent of unity; (b) that metal deposits follow Wheeler's other extreme, the "pore mouth poisoning" case, in which metal deposits move progressively inwards in a shell-progressive mode; and (c) that the effective diffusivity changes with time but, since the pore volume losses are mainly due to uniformly distributed carbon, not with catalyst position. The Sandia workers then constructed the following model:

$$\frac{\eta}{\eta_0} = \sqrt{\frac{\rho D}{\rho_0 D_0}}\ \frac{\tanh\left\{\sqrt{\frac{\rho D_0}{\rho_0 D}}\,\phi_0\left(\frac{3_m}{3_{m0}}\right)\sqrt{\frac{3_c}{3_{c0}}}\right\}}{\tanh \phi_0}$$
$$\times \left[\frac{1}{1+\sqrt{\frac{\rho D_0}{\rho_0 D}}\left(1-\frac{3_m}{3_{m0}}\right)\sqrt{\frac{3_c}{3_{c0}}}\tanh\left\{\sqrt{\frac{\rho D_0}{\rho_0 D}}\,\phi_0\left(\frac{3_m}{3_{m0}}\right)\sqrt{\frac{3_c}{3_{c0}}}\right\}}\right]\sqrt{\frac{3_c}{3_{c0}}} \qquad (25^*)$$

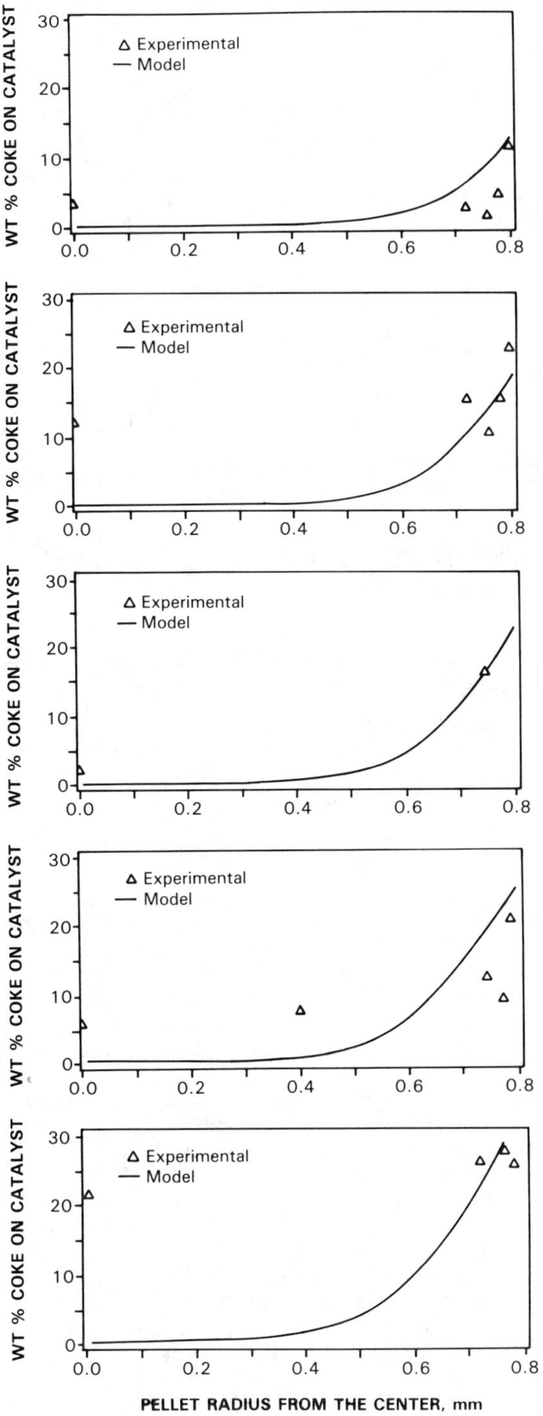

Figure 12. Comparison of coke deposition profiles calculated using the Crynes and Seapan model with experimental coke concentration measured by scanning Auger spectroscopy [132].

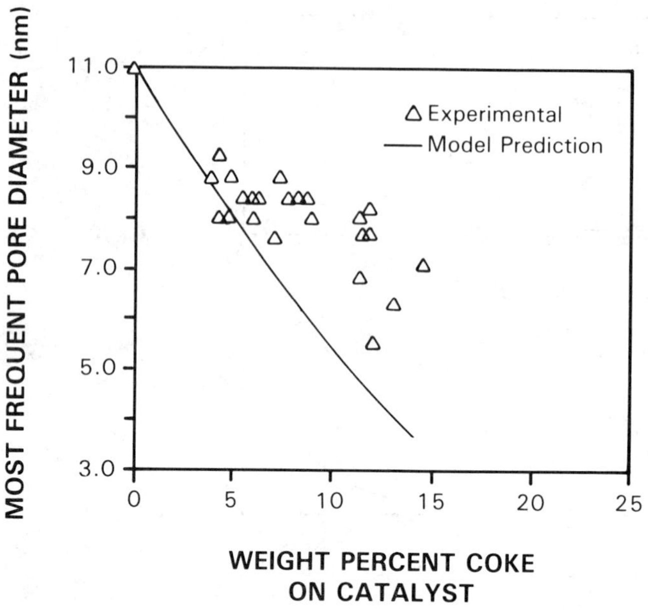

Figure 13. Comparison of major pore size predicted by the Crynes and Seapan model (Equations 20–24) and that measured by Hg porosimetry [132].

where $\mathfrak{z}_c$ = coking sites
$\mathfrak{z}_m$ = metals accumulation sites
$\mathfrak{z}_c + \mathfrak{z}_m = \mathfrak{z}$, $\mathfrak{z}_{co} + \mathfrak{z}_{mo} = \mathfrak{z}_0$, η_0 and ϕ_0 are the effectiveness factor and Thiele modulus for the fresh catalyst

The Sandia workers reasoned that by crushing the spent catalysts and measuring the rate of a model compound reaction, the hydrogenation of pyrene at 300°C in a microreactor, relative to the rate data for fresh catalysts, the fraction of intrinsic activity remaining (the $\mathfrak{z}/\mathfrak{z}_0$'s) could be measured. Likewise, the fractional global activity η/η_0 could be obtained directly by measuring the rate on whole spent catalysts. From these measurements, the Sandia workers calculated the effective diffusivities of pyrene in spent Ni—Mo catalysts obtained from the Wilsonville pilot plant. Furthermore, by plotting $\eta/\eta_0\sqrt{\rho_0 D_0/\rho D}$ vs $\mathfrak{z}$ for the spent catalysts (Figure 14A), they concluded that the dominant deactivation effect is uniform poisoning due to carbon, because the upwards concavity of the plot is associated with the uniform-poisoning term in Equation 25*. For catalysts in which the carbon had been combusted away, the downward concavity, which would be expected for shell-progressive poisoning due to the remaining metals deposits, could be seen (Figure 14B).

Workers at Auburn University [125] attempted to measure the loss of effective diffusivity in spent catalysts from Wilsonville process using a more direct approach. The method chosen by the Auburn workers was to measure the rate of uptake of octane from an octane-decane solution in the fresh and aged catalysts. The model used to calculate the effective diffusivity was similar to that derived by Ma and Evans [141] and assumes, like the Sandia model, that the effective diffusivity does not change with position in the catalyst pellet. It is interesting that the effective diffusivities measured for catalysts from the same Wilsonville run using the two methods, the Sandia reaction model and the Auburn diffusion model, compare favorably with one another, as shown in Figure 15. Both sets of measurements indicate that the greatest loss in effective diffusivity occurs early in the run when carbon accumulation is rapid.

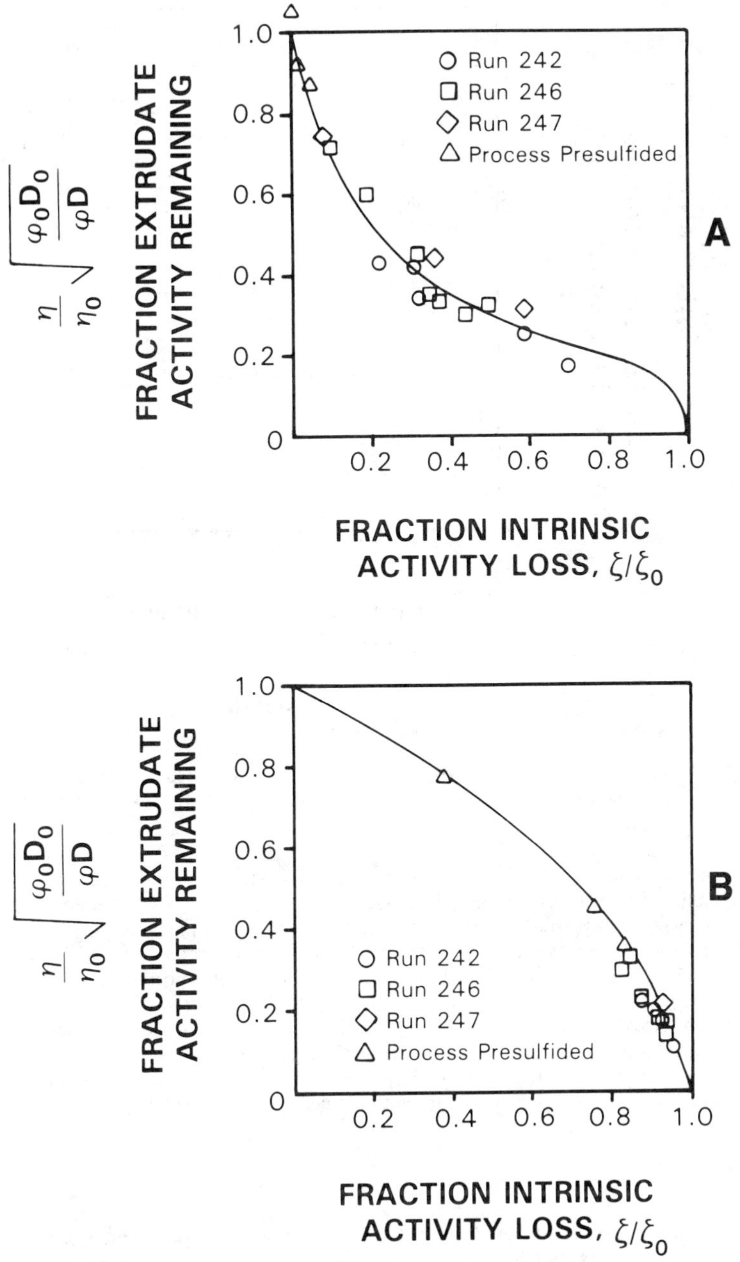

Figure 14. Fraction extrudate activity remaining versus fraction intrinsic activity loss measured for pyrene hydrogenation on spent catalysts from the Wilsonville liquefaction pilot plant by workers at Sandia [117].

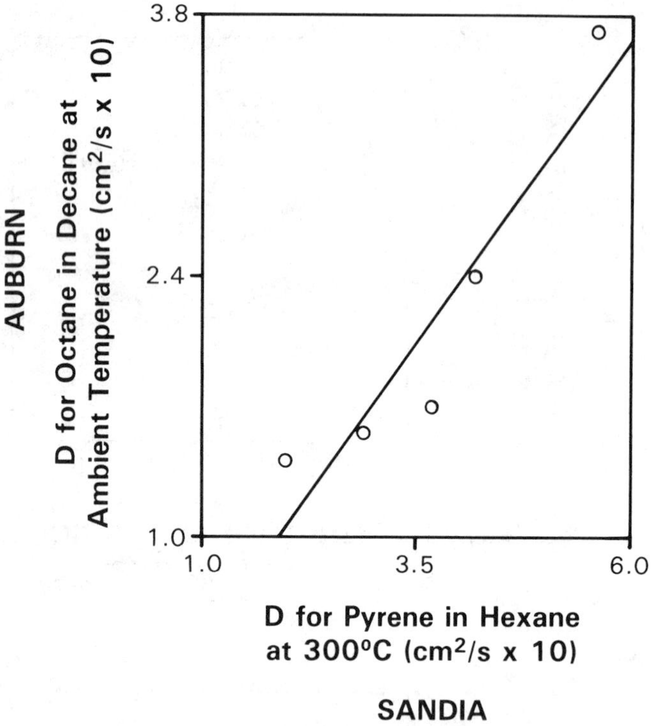

Figure 15. Effective diffusivities for identical spent catalyst samples measured indirectly by Sandia workers (using modeling Equation 25), and measured directly by Auburn workers [125].

Finally, a very different type of study of coke deposition kinetics in coal liquefaction catalysts has been published by Adkins et al. [134]. It is based entirely on the pore size distributions calculated from gas adsorption isotherms. The concept is based in part upon previous work by Prasher et al., [143] and is similar to recent work applied to the problem of carbon combustion from porous catalysts by Chang and Perlmutter [144]. In this model, the rate of deposition of carbon in a pore under steady-state conditions is equal to the rate of diffusion, which is the diffusion flux $D\nabla^2 C$ times the pore cross-sectional area, A, where C is the concentration of coke precursor. The rate of deposition is also equal to $\rho p\, dr_p/dt$, where ρ is the molar density, p is the pore perimeter and r_p is the hydraulic radius (equal to 2A/P; since the pores are assumed to be of constant cross-sectional area along the pore length but are not restricted to right circular cylinders). Thus:

$$\frac{\partial r_p}{\partial t} = \frac{r_p}{2}\frac{D}{\rho}\nabla^2 C \tag{26}$$

An assumption is made that the gradient term can be represented approximately as a power-law function of the pore size r_p, so that:

$$\frac{\partial r_p}{\partial t} = \frac{1}{2}\frac{D}{\rho} r_p^e r_p \tag{27}$$

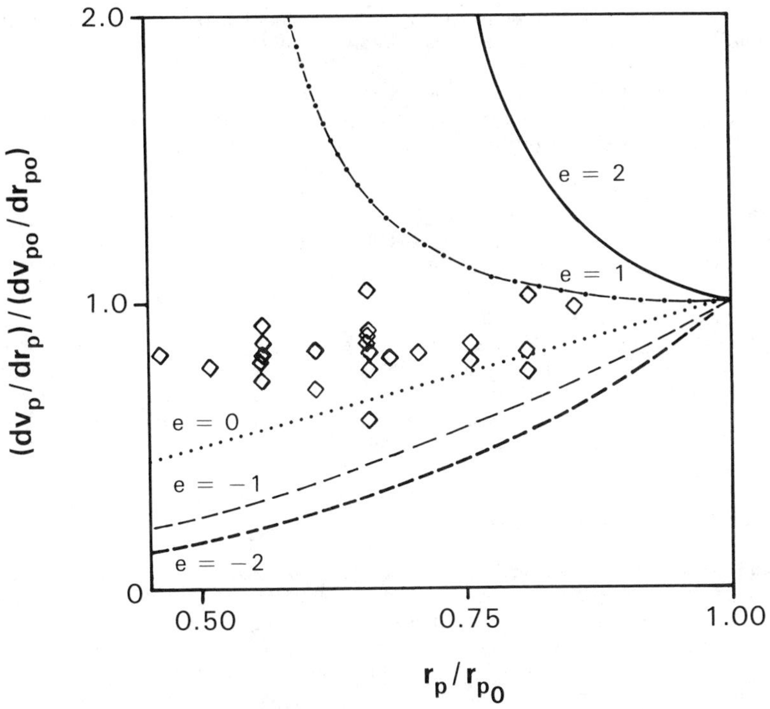

Figure 16. Analysis of a comparison of pore size distributions for spent catalysts with that of the fresh catalyst using Equation 29. Catalysts were obtained from various Wilsonville coal liquefaction runs.

For sufficiently small changes in pore size, we can replace r_p on the right-hand side of Equation 27 with r_{po}, which is the initial pore size, so that:

$$\frac{\partial r_p}{\partial t} = \frac{1}{2} D r_{po}^{e+1} \tag{28}$$

Pore volume relationships can now be added to enable pore size distributions of fresh and spent catalysts to be related to one another via a "continuous unique mapping" function:

$$\frac{\partial V_p/\partial r_p}{\partial V_{po}/\partial r_{po}} = \frac{(r_p/r_{po})^2}{1-(e+1)(1-r_p/r_{po})} \tag{29}$$

where dV_p/dr_p is the pore volume-pore size derivative obtained from the adsorption measurements for spent catalysts, and dV_{po}/dr_{po} is that of the fresh catalyst.

An analysis of experimental data obtained on unimodal-pore Ni—Mo catalysts aged in the Wilsonville process using this equation is shown in Figure 16. The pore size distributions were calculated using several different thermodynamic models [142] with essentially identical results. For simplicity, only the peak maxima are plotted against each other in Figure 16. The power-law exponent e that fits the data in Figure 16 is zero; this indicates that the diffusion term in the model does not vary with pore size. For comparison, an electron microprobe analysis did not reveal globally diffusion-limited carbon deposition patterns; since this catalyst (Shell 324 Ni—Mo) has essentially no macroporosity, the consensus is that carbon deposition in this catalyst is not diffusion limited.

It is not possible at this time to completely understand the formation of coke in coal liquefaction catalysts, although portions of this process can be discerned. Coke formation is, to a large extent, a rapid self-deactivating process which, even for catalysts without macroporosity, is probably not diffusion limited. If the effectiveness factor for preasphaltene conversion is low, as the Auburn workers [56, 57] and Ho and Weller [1] reported, coke formation is only weakly dependent on preasphaltene concentration and more strongly dependent on oil production. This is supported by Adkins, et al.'s [138] phenomenological model. The majority of the coke on the catalyst comprises two rapidly accumulated types of coke, "fast" coke and basic nitrogen coke. These are not affected by the presence or absence of a high preasphaltene content thermal resid feed stream and therefore, must be associated with the oil stream. The third type of coke is associated with the thermal resid and is accumulated very slowly, suggesting that it may be diffusion limited. The Crynes and Seapan [132] work supports a "parallel" coking scheme where coke decreases with distance from the entrance to the reactor, which is expected for conversion of coke precursors. However, a simple adsorption mechanism also explains this phenomena. Clearly much work remains to completely develop the engineering implications of coke formation.

MODELS FOR METALS ACCUMULATION

Fe and Ti are frequently reported to be the major metals deposited on coal liquefaction catalysts, although alkali metals are often observed at similar levels. Numerous investigators have measured penetration profiles for Fe and Ti in coal liquefaction catalysts and found them to be indicative of intermediate to strong diffusion limitations [50, 53, 114, 115, 117–120, 137]. Equally debated is the source of these contaminants, i.e., whether they are associated with organometallics (e.g. porphyrins) or inorganic particles. For Ti, as an example, some authors favor organometallics [114, 118, 124, 126, 128] while others argue for inorganic origins [129, 130]; neither viewpoint has been proven conclusively.

Few models have been constructed to describe the kinetics of these accumulation processes. In 1978 [114, 145] it was reported that the penetration profiles of Fe and Ti could be fitted to an error function profile, but no model was presented to explain this result. An extensive analysis of these profiles was advanced recently by Adkins et al. [137] for Ni—Mo catalysts used in the Wilsonville process. A detailed model was developed subsequent to the development of a phenomenological model [82, 138]. As shown in Figure 10, this pointed to the existence of two types each of Fe and Ti: a rapidly saturating "start-up" or "fast" species apparently associated with reactor start-up or catalyst presulfidation, and a slowly accumulating resid-associated species. Furthermore, SEM microprobe measurements indicated that the start-up species were distributed uniformly; this could be seen quite easily in catalysts for which the resid stream had been diverted from the hydrotreating reactor. The resid-associated species were responsible for the diffusion-limited deposition patterns.

The model developed by Adkins et al. took advantage of several simplifications. First, the Wilsonville hydrotreating reactor was operated with essentially a single catalyst charge, so that the time spent in the reactor by any catalyst sample is well known. This allows a direct comparison of the model with characterized samples. Furthermore, the bed was continuously ebullated so that well-mixed reactor conditions were present. The size of the reactor and the amount of catalyst, ca. 228 kg (500 lbs), are both sufficiently large to make the results practical.

Secondly, the accumulation pathways for Fe and Ti (Figure 11) probably lie in the poisoning region. The evidence for this is: (a) the level of metal accumulation is much lower (no more than 1–2% by weight) than that of carbon (up to 14 wt%); (b) carbon fouling occurs rapidly and remains essentially constant throughout the metals accumulation period; (c) measurements of the pore size distributions show significant initial changes due to carbon fouling but during the metals accumulation period the pore structures show little change; (d) along the same lines, the workers both at Sandia [116, 117] and Auburn [125] show that the major reductions in effective diffusivity for

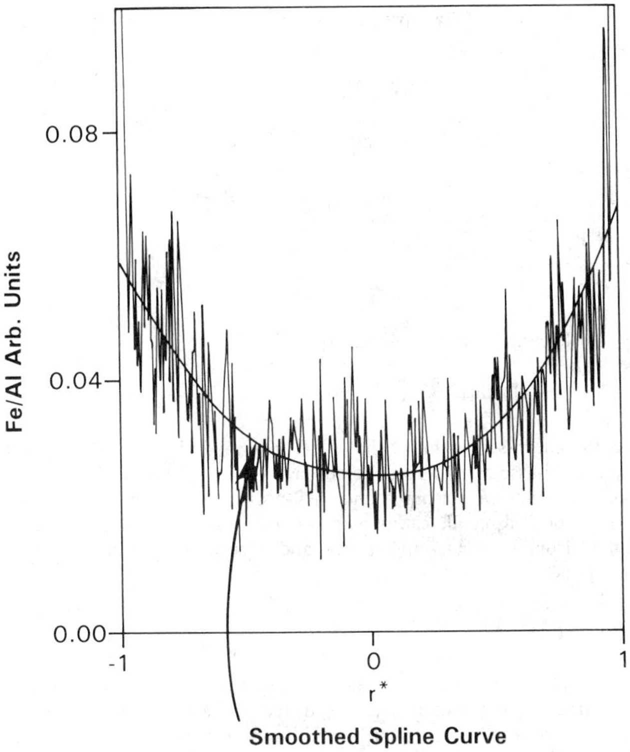

Figure 17. A typical Fe profile for spent Wilsonville hydrotreating catalysts as measured by scanning electron microscopy.

model compounds occurred early in the catalyst life before any significant metals accumulation; (e) the SEM and pore size distribution analysis (Reference 133 and previously discussed) show that carbon is deposited uniformly throughout the interior and throughout the catalyst mesopores; and finally (f) poisoning behavior suggested in the measurements made at several laboratories [110, 117, 135, 136] shows that the rate of metals uptake diminished as the metals accumulated. Thus, a poisoning model was constructed for the deposition of the resid-associated Fe and Ti as follows:

$$\frac{\partial C}{\partial t} = D\frac{1}{R}\frac{\partial}{\partial r}\left(R\frac{\partial C}{\partial R}\right) - k_0(1 - Q/Q_0)^b C^a \quad (30)$$

$$\frac{\partial Q}{\partial t} = k_0(1 - Q/Q_0)^b \frac{C^a}{a} \quad (31)$$

where C is the concentration of adsorbed metal precursor and Q is that of the adsorbed metal. The details of the numerical solution techniques are given elsewhere [137]; simulated metals deposition profiles were compared to hundreds of metals deposition profiles like the one shown in Figure 17. These profiles were measured on at least three pellets from each of more than 50 catalyst samples from several runs. From this analysis, the following simplified version of the model in

Equation 30 was shown to be fully representative of the measured deposition patterns:

$$0 = \frac{1}{R^*}\frac{\partial}{dR^*}\left(R^*\frac{\partial C^*}{\partial R^*}\right) - \phi_0^2(1 - Q^*)C^* \tag{32}$$

$$\frac{\partial Q^*}{\partial \theta} = \frac{\phi_0^2}{\chi}(1 - Q^*)C^* \tag{33}$$

where $R^* = R/R_0$
$C^* = C/C_0$
$Q^* = Q/Q_{max}$
$\theta = De\, t/R_0$
ϕ = Thiele modulus for metals adsorption
$\phi_0 = R_0(k_0/D)^{1/2}$
χ = "poison tolerance" (Q_{max}/C_0)

Furthermore, the authors determined that the Thiele moduli for the deposition of both resid-associated Ti and resid-associated Fe was somewhere between 3 and 7, this corresponds to a case intermediate between uniform poisoning and shell-progressive poisoning. The actual metals deposition pattern in the Wilsonville catalysts is apparently a combination of a rapidly saturating uniform poisoning from the "start-up" species and a slow intermediate poisoning due to the resid-associated species.

COMBINED EFFECTS

Currently, the Sandia model is the most detailed attempt to combine the effects of carbon and metals in deactivating coal liquefaction catalysts, including losses in diffusivity due to early fouling. With the exception of considering metals deposition to be a shell progressive mechanism instead of a combination of uniform and intermediate poisoning mechanisms, it is in good agreement with most of the characterization and detailed modeling efforts. It also has the advantage of straightforward algebraic equations instead of differential equations. It does not, however, predict the kinetics of the coking or metals deposition processes and must be combined with other models in order to be used in, for example, reactor optimization studies. Overall, the applicability of the Sandia model is good, as compared, for example, to the Crynes and Seapan model [132], or with another existing model [108, 109], derived as a means of optimizing the choice of catalyst particle size from the viewpoint of deactivation resistance, that incorporates only a shell-progressive poisoning mechanism.

SUMMARY

A great deal of evidence supporting pore diffusion effects in heterogeneous coal liquefaction catalysts exists. Although much has been learned, the overall picture remains fragmentary. Part of the problem lies in constructing an accurate mechanistic picture of the catalytic reaction chemistry involved. A related difficulty is a demonstration of the difference in two selectivity paths in a manner consistent with Wei's [12] theoretical treatment of selectivity and pore diffusion. In fact, the "selectivity" is likely to be blurred by product lumping. This understanding is additionally confused by contaminant accumulation reactions (deactivation) that must be considered. Another problem is purely experimental: findings in a comparison of surface areas, pore volumes, and other catalyst properties that change simultaneously with pore size cannot be assigned unambiguously to pore diffusion effects. This problem is seen, for example, in the extensive work done at Amoco and American Cyanamid.

However, in designing catalysts, it is not of paramount importance that the nature of improved performance be precisely identified. The improved performance itself is, to a large extent, the final product. Even though few pore diffusion effects have been demonstrated conclusively, some tentative conclusions can be made. These include:

1. For "typical" coal liquefaction catalysts, coal dissolution is rapidly achieved thermally, under appropriate conditions, and the only likely role of the catalyst is indirect, through the donor solvent hydrogenation. Oil production almost certainly occurs at a higher effectiveness factor than preasphaltene conversion (production of asphaltenes and oils).
2. Pore structure bimodality has an effect on catalyst performance and catalyst deactivation resistance. There is, however, no single explanation for the observed effects. Both activity and deactivation resistance are improved in many cases by bimodal pore structures.
3. Mesopore size has been demonstrated to affect catalyst performance. For the most part, the observed effects are associated with diffusional restrictions combined with trade-offs involving catalyst surface area and catalyst pore volume.
4. Coke formation in coal liquefaction catalysts is more likely associated with oil production or upgrading than with preasphaltene conversion. Adsorption phenomena may play an important role in coke formation; strongly adsorbed compounds such as basic nitrogen compounds are especially suspect. In keeping with the link to oil production, coke formation is probably not diffusion limited in the majority of cases.
5. Conversely, metals accumulation is subject to diffusion limits ranging from intermediate (for example, corresponding to a Thiele modulus of 3) to very strong. Metals can often be correlated with process streams concentrated in preasphaltenes, but ash components may also be involved. Not surprisingly, catalysts with bimodal pore structures often show significantly higher rates of metals adsorption.
6. Currently no adequate simple model exists for incorporating carbon and metals accumulation into predictions of catalyst deactivation.

It is clear that there are many unanswered questions involving the engineering implications of pore diffusion effects. The area most in need of research is not the development of more sophisticated mathematical models, but rather applied research that can provide shortcuts and the all-important model verification.

NOTATION

A	asphaltene
A	pore cross sectional area
a	reaction rate order
b	deactivation rate order
C	coal
C	concentration
$\bar{C}$	concentration vector
D	effective diffusivity, $cm^2\ s^{-1}$
$\bar{D}$	diffusivity vector
e	exponent in Equations 27–29
F	feed rate
f	fraction
G	gas
i, j, m, n	indicial variables
K	adsorption equilibrium constant
k	reaction rate constant
k	rate constant matrix
k_d	site deactivation rate constant
LHSV	liquid hourly space velocity
M	lumping function
O	oil
P	preasphaltene
p	perimeter
P	pressure
Q	concentration of adsorbed contaminants
R	radial distance
R_0	radius of particle
r_p	pore radius
S	reactor cross-sectional area
s	distance from center of slab of half-thickness L
t	time
u, v	initial numbers C_uO_v in Prasad model
V_p	pore volume
W	weight of catalyst
x_1, x_2	numbers C_x, O_{x2} in Prasad model of coal molecule
y_1, y_2	dimensionless numbers $y_1 = x_1/u_1y_2 = x_2/v$
z	distance along reactor bed

Greek

α	reactive oil fraction
τ	space time
γ	lumping constant
ω	external catalyst area per volume of reactor
ε	porosity
ρ	mass or molar density
δ	ratio in Equation 17
μ	mass of catalyst per unit of volume of reactor
σ	radius of solute molecule
ψ, ψ', Ω	rate functions
Γ	surface concentration
$\mathfrak{z}$	concentration of catalyst sites
ϕ	Thiele modulus
η	effectiveness factor
ξ	normalized distribution of molecules in Prasad model
θ	dimensionless time
ν	stoichiometric number

REFERENCES

1. Ho, P. N., and Weller, S. W., "Effects of Pore Diameter and Catalyst Loading in Hydroliquefaction of Coal with $CoO/MoO_3/Al_2O_3$ Catalysts," *Fuel Proc. Tech.*, 4, 21 (1981).
2. Froment, G. F., and Bischoff, K. B., *Chemical Reactor Analysis and Design*, John Wiley and Sons, New York, 1979, p. 178.
3. Satterfield, C. N., *Mass Transfer in Heterogeneous Catalysis*, MIT Press, Cambridge, MA, 1970, p. 33.
4. Jackson, R., *Transport in Porous Catalysts*, Elsevier Publishing, Amsterdam, 1977.
5. Dogu, G., *Handbook of Heat and Mass Transfer, Vol. 2*, (N. P. Cheremisinoff, ed.), Gulf Publishing, Houston, 1986, p. 433.
6. Gregg, S. J., and Sing, K. S. W., *Adsorption, Surface Area and Porosity, 2nd ed.*, Academic Press, London, 1982.
7. Wicke, E., and Kallenbach, R., "Die Oberflachendiffusion von Kohlendioxyd in activen Kohlen," *Kolloid Z.* 97, 135 (1941).
8. Ruthven, D. M., *Principles of Adsorption and Adsorption Processes*, John Wiley and Sons, New York, 1984.
9. Sylvestri, A. J., and Prater, C. D., "Kinetic Studies of the Selectivity of Xylene Isomerization over Silica-Alumina Catalyst," *J. Phys. Chem.*, 68, 3268 (1964).
10. Wei, J., and Prater, C. D., *Advances in Catalysis, Vol. 13*, Academic Press, New York, 1962.
11. Wei, J., "Intraparticle Diffusion Effects in Complex Systems of First Order Reactions. I. The Effects in Single Particles" *J. Catal.*, 1, 526 (1962).
12. Wei, J., "Intraparticle Diffusion Effects in Complex Systems of First Order Reactions. II. The Influence of Diffusion on the Performance of Chemical Reactors," *J. Catal.*, 1, 538 (1962).
13. Bird, R. B., Stewart, W. E., and Lightfoot, E. N., *Transport Phenomena*, John Wiley and Sons, New York, 1960, p. 542.
14. R. Aris, "On Shape Factors for Irregular Particles-I. The Steady State Problem. Diffusion and Reaction," *Chem. Eng. Sci.*, 6, 262 (1957).
15. Miller, D. J., and Lee, L. H., "Shape Normalization of Catalyst Pellet," *Chem. Eng. Sci.*, 38, 363 (1983).
16. Patzer, J. F., and Montagna, A. A., "Coal Liquefaction Catalysts," *Ind. Eng. Chem. Proc. Des. Dev.*, 19, 382 (1980).
17. Thakur, D. S., and Thomas, M. G., "Catalyst Deactivation During Direct Coal Liquefaction, A Review" *Ind. Eng. Chem. Prod. Res. Dev.*, 23, 349 (1984).
18. Shah, Y. T., Cronauer, D. C., McIlvreid, H. G., and Paraskos, J. A., "Kinetics of Catalytic Liquefaction of Big Horn Coal in a Segmented Bed Reactor," *Ind. Eng. Chem. Proc. Des. Dev.*, 17, 288 (1978).
19. Thomas, M. G., "Catalyst Behavior in Direct Coal Liquefaction," Proceedings of the Sixth Annual EPRI Contractor's Conference on Coal Liquefaction, Palo Alto, CA, EPRI AP-2079-LD (Oct 1981).

20. Miller, R. L., Silver, H. F., and Hurtubise, R. J., "Upgrading of Recycle Solvent Used in the Direct Liquefaction of Wyodak Coal," *Ind. Eng. Chem. Proc. Des. Dev.*, 21, 170 (1982).
21. Epperly, W. R., Wade, D. T., and Plumlee, K. W., "Synfuels Processing: Donor Solvent Coal Liquefaction," *Chem. Eng. Prog.*, 77, 73 (1981).
22. Rao, A. K., Moniz, M. J., Lee, J. M., and Pillai, R. S., "Advances in Integrated Two-Stage Coal Liquefaction," *Chem. Eng. Prog.*, 33, November 1984.
23. Lamb, C. W., Nalitham, R. V., and Johnson, T. W., "Process Development Studies of Two-Stage Liquefaction at Wilsonville," *ACS Div. Fuel Chem. Prepr.*, 31, 240 (1986).
24. Klunder, E. B., Krastman, D., and Mima, J. A., "Iron-Catalyzed Coal Liquefaction: Evidence for Isothermal Multiplicity," DOE Project Report DOE/PETC/TR-86/4 (March, 1986).
25. Reuther, J. A., "Kinetics of Heterogeneously Catalyzed Coal Hydroliquefaction," *Ind. Eng. Chem. Proc. Des. Dev.*, 16, 249 (1977).
26. Whitehurst, D. D., Mitchell, T. O., Farcusia, M., and Dickert, J. J., Jr., Mobil Oil Co., Princeton, NJ, "Exploratory Studies in Catalytic Coal Liquefaction," EPRI Project Report AF-1184 (September 1979).
27. Derbyshire, F. J., Odoerfer, G. A., and Varghese, P., Mobil Oil Co., Princeton, NJ, "Fundamental Studies in the Conversion of Coals of Fuels of Increased Hydrogen Content. The Chemistry and Mechanism of Coal Conversion to Clean Fuel," EPRI Project Report AP-2912 (March 1983).
28. Wiser, W. H., Massoth, F. E., and Shabtai, J., University of Utah, Salt Lake City, UT, "Chemistry and Catalysis of Coal Liquefaction: Catalytic and Thermal Upgrading of Coal Liquids: and Hydrogenation of CO to Produce Fuels," DOE Project Report DOE/ET/14700-T1, Vol. 2 (June 1985).
29. Wiser, W. H., Shabtai, J., and Oblad, A. G., University of Utah, Salt Lake City, UT, "Chemistry and Catalysis of Coal Liquefaction: Catalytic and Thermal Upgrading of Coal Liquids: and Hydrogenation of CO to Produce Fuels," DOE Project Report DOE/ET/14700-T1, Vol. 4 (June 1985).
30. Schwager, I., and Stamires, D. N., Filtrol Corp., Los Angeles, CA, "Development of New Catalysts for Coal Liquids Refining," DOE Project Report DOE/ET/12103-T4 (June 1981).
31. Sullivan, R. F., O'Rear, D. J., and Frumkin, H. A., Chevron Research Co., Richmond, CA, "Refining and Upgrading of Synfuels from Coal and Oil Shales by Advanced Catalytic Processes," DOE Project Report DOE/ET/10532-T3 (September 1985).
32. Katzer, J. R., Stiles, A. B., and Kwart, H., University of Delaware, Newark, DE, "Development of Unique Catalysts for Hydrodenitrogenation of Coal-Derived Liquids," DOE Report FE-3297-5 (February 1980).
33. Laine, R. M., Hirshon, A. S., and Wilson, R. B., Jr., SRI International, Menlo Park, CA, "Novel Catalytic Methods for Heteroatom Removal in Coal Liquids Upgrading," DOE Report DOE/PC/60781-3 (June 1984).
34. Shah, Y. T., *Reaction Engineering in Direct Coal Liquefaction*, Addison-Wesley, 1981.
35. Gertenbach, D. D., Baldwin, R. M., and Bain, R. L., "Modeling of Bench-Scale Coal Liquefaction Systems," *Ind. Eng. Chem. Process Des. Dev.*, 21, 490 (1982).
36. Oblad, A. G., "Catalytic Liquefaction of Coal and Refining of Product," *Catal. Rev. Sci. Eng.*, 14, 83 (1976).
37. Mills, G. A., "Catalytic Aspects of Synthetic Fuels from Coal," *Catal. Rev. Sci. Eng.*, 14, 69 (1976).
38. Prasad, G. N., Wittman, C. V., Agnew, J. B., and Shridar, T., "Modeling of Coal Liquefaction Kinetics Based on Reactions in Continuous Mixtures, Part I: Theory," *AIChE J.*, 32, 1277 (1986).
39. Aris, R., and Gavalas, G. R., "On the Theory of Reactions in Continuous Mixtures," *Phil. Trans. Roy. Soc. Lond.*, 260, 351 (1966).
40. Syamlal, M., and Wittman, C. V., "Continuous Reaction Mixture Models for Coal Liquefaction Kinetics," *Ind. Eng. Chem. Fund.*, 24, 82 (1985).
41. Prasad, G. N., Agnew, J. B., and Sridhar, T., "Modeling of Coal Liquefaction Kinetics Based on Reactions in Continuous Mixtures. Part II: Comparison with Experiments on Catalyzed and Uncatalyzed Liquefaction of Coals of Different Rank," *AIChE J.*, 32, 128 (1986).

42. Petrakis, L. W., Jones, G. L., Grandy, D. W., and King, A. B., "Freed Radicals in Coal and Coal Conversions. 10. Kinetics and Reaction Pathways in Hydroliquefaction," *Fuel*, 62, 681 (1983).
43. Nace, D. M., Voltz, S. E., and Weekman, V. W., "Application of a Kinetic Model for Catalytic Cracking. Effects of Charge Stocks," *Ind. Eng. Chem. Proc. Des. Dev.*, 10, 530 (1971).
44. Nace, D. M., Voltz, S. E., and Weekman, V. W., "Application of a Kinetic Model for Catalytic Cracking. Some Correlations of Rate Constants," *Ind. Eng. Chem. Proc. Des. Dev.*, 10, 538 (1971).
45. Jacob, S. M., Gross, B., Voltz, S. E., and Weekman, V. W., "A Lumping and Reaction Scheme for Catalytic Cracking," *AIChE J.*, 22, 701 (1976).
46. Anderson, J. D., and Lamb, D. E., "Naphthalene via Hydrodealkylation," *Ind. Eng. Chem. Proc. Des. Dev.*, 3, 177 (1964).
47. Shalabi, M. A., Baldwin, R. M., Bain, R. L., Gary, J. H., and Golden, J. O., "Noncatalytic Coal Liquefaction in a Donor Solvent. Rate of Formation of Oil, Asphaltenes, and Preasphaltenes," *Ind. Eng. Chem. Proc. Des. Dev.*, 18, 474 (1979).
48. Kang, C. C., Paper presented at Proceedings of the International Conference on Coal Science, Pittsburgh, 1983, p. 75.
49. Yen, Y. K., Furlani, D. E., and Weller, S. W., "Batch Autoclave Studies of Catalytic Hydrodesulfurization of Coal," *Ind. Eng. Chem. Prod. Res. Dev.*, 15, 24 (1976).
50. Kim, D. K., Bertolacini, R. J., Gutberlet, L. C., Forgac, J. J. M., and Robinson, K. K., Amoco Oil Co., Napierville, IL, and McDaniel, C. V., W. R. Grace & Co., Columbia MD, "Catalyst Development for Coal Liquefaction," Final Report, EPRI AF-1233, EPRI Project 408-1 (November 1979).
51. Sanchez, M. G., and Laine, N. R., U.S. Patent No. 4,154, 812, W. R. Grace & Co., New York (1977).
52. "Coal Liquefaction Catalyst Development," DOE/ET/14803-T8, Final Report DOE Project DE-AC22-79ET-14803, Amoco Oil, Napierville, IL. (Aug 1982).
53. Sinna, V. T., Kutzenco, P. D., Preston, W. J., Ungar, J. K., Brinen, J. S., Muchnick, T. L., and Hyman, D., American Cyanamid Co., Stamford, CT, "Development of Significantly Improved Catalysts for Coal Liquefaction and Upgrading of Coal Extracts," Final Report DOE/PC/40091-T15 (Feb 1985).
54. Ahmed, M. M., and Crynes, B. L., "Coal Liquids Hydrotreatment-Catalyst Pore Size Effects" *Am. Chem. Soc. Div. Petr. Chem. Prepr.*, 23, 137 (Sept. 1978).
55. Shimada, H. Kurita, M., Sato, T., Yoshimura, Y., Kawakami, T., Yoshitomi, S., and Nishijima, A., "Effect of Pore-Size Distribution on the Catalytic Performance for Coal Liquefaction," *Bull. Chem Soc. Jpm.*, 57, 2000 (1984).
56. Tarrer, A. R., Guin, J. A., and Curtis, C. W., "Studies in Coal Liquefaction with Application to the SRC and Related Processes," DOE report DOE/ET/13397-18, Feb–Apr 1983.
57. Gollakota, S. V., Guin J. A., and Curtis, C. W., "Parallel Thermal and Catalytic Kinetics in Direct Coal Liquefaction," *Ind. Eng. Chem. Proc. Des. Dev.*, 24, 1148–54 (1985).
58. Thiele, E. W., "Relation between Catalytic Activity and Size of Particle," *Ind. Eng. Chem.*, 31, 916 (1939).
59. Curtis, C. W., Guin, J. A., Tarrer, A. R., and Huang, W. J., "Two-Stage Coal Liquefaction Using Sequential Mineral and Hydrotreating Catalysts," *Fuel Proc. Tech.*, 7, 277 (1983).
60. Song, S. K., Ph.D. Dissertation, Auburn University, 1983.
61. Seinfeld, J. H., Gavalas, G. R., "Analysis of Kinetic Parameters from Batch and Integral Reaction Experiments," *AIChE J.*, 16, 645 (1970).
62. Ralston, M. L., Jennrich, R. I., "Dud, A Derivative-Free Algorithm for Nonlinear Least Squares," *Technometrics*, 20, 7 (1978).
63. Katzer, J. R., and Sivasubramanian, R., "Process and Catalyst Needs for Hydrodenitrogenation," *Catal. Rev. Sci. Eng.*, 20, 155 (1978).
64. Shah, Y. T., and Cronauer, D. C., "Oxygen, Nitrogen, and Sulfur Removal Reactions in Donor Solvent Coal Liquefaction," *Catal. Rev. Sci. Eng.*, 20, 209 (1979).
65. Baldwin, R. M., Colorado School of Mines, Golden, Co, "Clean Solid and Liquid Fuels from Coal," DOE Report DOE/ET/10600-T1 (December 1981).

66. Sooter, M., "Effect of Catalyst Pore Size on Hydrodesulfurization of Coal Derived Liquids" Ph.D. Dissertation, Oklahoma State University, 1974.
67. Speight, J. G., *The Chemistry and Technology of Petroleum*, M. Dekker, New York, 1980.
68. Weisz, P. B., and Prater, D. B., *Advances in Catalysis, Vol. 6*, Academic Press, New York, p. 143 (1954).
69. Rall, H. T., Thompson, C. J., Coleman, H. J., and Hopkins, R. L., U.S. Bureau of Mines, Separation and Identification Section, RP48A (1970).
70. Van Zoonen, D., and Douwes, C. Th., *J. Inst. Petrol. 49*, 383 (1963).
71. Schmid, B. K., and Beuther, H., Proceedings of the Sixth World Petroleum Congress, Section VII, 233 (1963).
72. Beuther, H., and Schmid, B. K., U.S. Patent No. 3,383,301, Gulf Research and Development Co. (1967).
73. Seapan, M., Crynes, B. L., Dale, S., Gokhale, A., Pendergast, T., El-Bishtawi, R., Milam, V., and Collier, T., "Kinetics of Hydrogenation of Alternative Crude Oils," Oklahoma State University, Stillwater, OK, DOE Report DOE/BC/10306-10 (July 1982).
74. Frye, C. G., and Mosby, J. F., "Kinetics of Hydrodesulfurization," *Chem. Eng. Prog.*, 63, 66 (1967).
75. Froment, G. F., and Bischoff, K. B., *Chemical Reactor Analysis and Design*, John Wiley and Sons, 1979, p. 141.
76. Prather, J. W., Ahanger, A. M., Pitts, W. S., Henley, J. P., Tarrer, A. R., and Guin, J. A., *Ind. Eng. Chem. Proc. Des. Dev. 16*, 267 (1977).
77. Roberts, G. W., and Satterfield, C. N., "Effectiveness Factor for Porous Catalysts," *Ind. Eng. Chem Fund.*, 4, 288 (1965); 5, 317 (1966); 5, 325 (1966).
78. Berg, L., and McCandless, F. P., Montana State University, Bozeman, MT, "Catalytic Hydrogenation of Coal Derived Liquids," DOE Report FE-2034-27 (December 1980).
79. Stein, T. R., Bendoraitis, J. G., Cabal, A. V., Callen, R. B., Dabkowski, M. J., Heck, R. H., Ireland H. R., and Simpson, C. A., Mobil Research Co., Princeton, NJ, EPRI Report AF-444 (1977).
80. Yoshimura, Y., Hayamizu, K., Sato, T., Shimada, H., and Nishijima, A., "The Effect of Toluene-Insoluble Fraction of Coal on Catalytic Activities of a Ni—Mo— —Al_2O_3 Catalyst in the Hydrotreating of Coal Liquids," *Fuel Proc. Tech.*, 16, 55 (1987).
81. Yoshimura, Y., Sato, T., Shimada, H., and Nishijima, A., "Effect of Ni—Mo Catalyst Mesopore Diameter on Catalytic Activities in Hydrotreating of Coal Liquid," *Fuel Sci. Tech. Intl.*, 4, 621 (1986).
82. Adkins, B. D., Adkins, S. R., Davis, B. H., and Milburn, D. R., "A model for Accumulation of C, Fe, and Ti Foulants in Coal Liquefaction Catalysts," *Proc. Fourth Int. Symp. Cat. Deact.* (in press) 1987.
83. Furimsky, E., "Deactivation of Molybdate Catalysts of Nitrogen Bases," *Erdol und Kohle*, 35, 455 (1982).
84. Satterfield, C. N., Modell, M., Hites, R. A., and Declerk, C. J., "Intermediate Reactions in the Catalytic Hydrodenitrogenation of Quinoline," *Ind. Eng. Chem. Process Des. Dev.*, 17, 2 (1978).
85. Parry, E. P., "An Infared Study of Pyridine Adsorbed on Acidic Solids. Characterization of Surface Acidity," *J. Catal.*, 2, 371 (1963).
86. Flinn, R. R., Larson, O. A., and Beuther, H., "How Easy is Hydrodenitrogenation?" *Hydroc. Process. Petr. Refin.*, 42, 129 (1963).
87. Nagai, M., "High Activity and Selectivity of a 'Poisoned' $NiMo/Al_2O_3$ Catalyst for a Desulfurization Reaction," *Ind. Eng. Chem. Prod. Res. Dev.*, 24, 489 (1985).
88. Lavopa, M., and Satterfield, C. N., Paper Presented at the Tenth North American Catalysis Society Meeting, San Deigo, CA, May 1987.
89. Vrinat, M. L., "The Kinetics of the Hydrodesulfurization Process—A Review," *Appl. Catal.*, 6, 137 (1983).
90. Schwager, I., and Stamires, D. N., Filtrol Co., Los Angeles, CA, "Development of New Catalysts for Coal Liquids Refining," DOE Report DOE/ET/12103-T4 (April 1981).
91. Steigel, G. J., Tischer, R. E., and Polinski, L. M., PETC, Pittsburgh, PA, "Hydroprocessing of Solvent Refined Coal: Catalyst Screening Results," DOE Report DOE/PETC/TR-82/7 (March 1982).

92. Hughes, R., *Deactivation of Catalysts*, Academic Press, London, 1984.
93. Freeman, G. B., Heink, J., Long, N. J., and Davis, B. H., "Coal Liquefaction Catalysts. The Growth of Cobalt Sulfide Particles During Use at 450°C," *Appl. Catal.*, 23, 309 (1986).
94. Cillo, D. L., Steigel, G. J., Tischer, R. E., and Krastman, D. US DOE PETC, Pittsburgh, PA, "Hydroprocessing of Coal-Derived Residuum: Part 1, Effect of Unimodal Catalyst Pore Size Distribution," DOE Report DOE/PETC/TR-87/8 (May, 1987).
95. Wheeler, A., "Reaction Rates and Selectivity in Catalyst Pores," *Adv. Catal*, 3, 250 (1951).
96. Fuentes, G. A., "Catalyst Deactivation and Steady-State Activity: A Generalized Power-Law Equation Model," *Appl. Catal.*, 15, 33 (1985).
97. Fuentes, S., and Figueras, F., "Kinetics of Self-Poisoning of Pd/Al_2O_3 Catalysts in the Hydrogenolysis of Cyclopentane: Influence of the Dispersion of Palladium and Sulfate Poisoning," *J. Catal.*, 54, 347 (1978).
98. Levenspiel, O., "Experimental Search for a Simple Rate Equation to Describe Deactivating Porous Catalyst Particles," *J. Catal.*, 25, 265 (1972).
99. Masamune, S., and Smith, J. M., "Performance of Fouled Catalyst Pellets," *AIChE J.*, 12, 384 (1966).
100. Murakami, Y., Kobayashi, T., Hattori, T., and Masuda, M., "Effect of Intraparticle Diffusion on Catalyst Fouling," *Ind. Eng. Chem. Fund.*, 7, 599 (1968).
101. Kam, E. K. T., Ramachandran, P. A., and Hughes, R., "The Effect of Film Resistances on the Fouling of Catalyst Pellets-I. Pseudo-Steady State Analysis," *Chem. Eng. Sci.*, 32, 1307 (1977).
102. Heimenz, W., Discussion Section 3, paper 20, Sixth World Petroleum Congress, Frankfurt, June 21 (1963).
103. Newson, E., "Catalyst Deactivation due to Pore Plugging by Reaction Products," *Ind. Eng. Chem. Proc. Des. Dev.*, 14, 27 (1975).
104. Rajagopalan, K., and Luss, D., "Influence of Catalyst Pore Size on Demetallation Rate," *Ind. Eng. Chem. Proc. Res. Dev.*, 18, 459 (1979).
105. Oyekunle, L. O., and Hughes, R., "Metal Deposition in Residuum Hydrodesulphurisation Catalysts," *Chem. Eng. Res. Des.*, 62, 339 (1984).
106. Tsotsis, T. T., University of California, Berkeley, CA, "Novel Approaches Concerning Catalyst Deactivation," DOE Report DOE/PC/41263-T1 (1982).
107. Ahn, B. J., and Smith, J. M., "Deactivation of Hydrodesulfurization Catalysts by Metals Deposition," *AIChE J.*, 30, 739 (1984).
108. Polinski, L. M., Steigel, G. J., and Tischer, R. E., "1980 Status Review-Hydroliquefaction of Coal with Supported Catalysts" PETC, Pittsburgh, PA, DOE Report DOE/PETC/TR81-2 (1981).
109. Polinski, L. M., Steigel, G. J., and Saroff, L., "Use of Fundamental Concepts in Catalyst Aging to Increase Catalyst Utilization during Coal Liquefaction, Steam Reforming and Other Carbon-Forming Reactions," *Ind. Eng. Chem. Proc. Des. Dev.*, 20, 470 (1985).
110. Steigel, G. J., Tischer, R. E., Cillo, D. L., and Narain, N. K., "Catalyst Deactivation in Two-Stage Coal Liquefaction," *Ind. Eng. Chem. Prod. Res. Dev.*, 24, 206 (1985).
111. Shimada, H., Kurita, M., Sato, T., Yoshimura, Y., Kabayashi, Y., and Nishijima, A., "Effect of Pore-Size Distribution on the Catalytic Performance for Coal Liquefaction. II. Carbonaceous and Metallic Deposition on the Catalyst," *Bull. Chem. Bull. Soc. Jpn.*, 59, 2885 (1986).
112. Yoshimura, Y., Shimada, H., Sato, T., Kubota, M., and Nishijima, A., "Initial Catalyst Deactivation in the Hydrotreatment of Coal Liquid Over Ni—Mo and Co—Mo— —Al_2O_3 Catalysts," *Appl. Catal.*, 29, 125 (1987).
113. Mochida, I., Sakanishim, K., Korai, Y., and Fujitsu, H., "Two-stage Catalytic Up-grading of Vacuum Residue of a Wandoan Coal Liquid" *Fuel*, 65, 1090 (1986).
114. Holloway, P. N., Sandia National Laboratories, "Chemical Studies of the SYNTHOIL Process: Catalyst Deactivation," Sandia Report SAND78-0056 (1978).
115. Cable, T. L., Massoth, F. E., and Thomas, M. G., "Studies of an Aged H-Coal Catalyst," *Fuel Proc. Tech.*, 4, 265 (1981).
116. Stephens, H. P., and Stohl, F. V., "Determination of the Intrinsic Activity and Effective Diffusivity of Aged Coal Liquefaction Catalysts," *ACS Div. Fuel Chem. Prepr.*, 29, 79 (1985).

117. Stohl, F. V., and Stephens, H. P., "Catalyst Deactivation in Direct Coal Liquefaction: A Comparative Study of Wilsonville Runs," Sandia Report SAND85-0852 (1985).
118. Lynch, A. W., "Titanium Deposition on Coal Liquefaction Catalysts," *Appl. Catal.*, 24, 227 (1986).
119. Stohl, F. V., and Stephens, H. P., "The Impact of the Chemical Constituents of Hydrotreater Feed on Catalyst Activity," *ACS Div. Fuel Chem. Prepr.*, 31, 251 (1986).
120. Stohl, F. V., Qader, Q. A., Massoth, F. E., and Thakur, D. S., "Studies of Catalyst Samples from a Two-Stage Direct Coal Liquefaction Run," *Ind. Eng. Chem. Res.*, 26, 840 (1987).
121. Ternan, M., and Brown, J. R., "Hydrotreating a Distillate Liquid Derived from Subbituminous Coal Using a Sulphided CoO—MoO —Al_2O_3 Catalyst," *Fuel*, 61, 1110 (1982).
122. Furimsky, E., "Characterization of Deposits Formed on Catalyst Surfaces During Hydrotreatment of Coal-Derived Liquids," *Fuel Proc. Tech.*, 6, 1 (1982).
123. Ocampo, A., Schrodt, J. T., and Kovach, S. M., "Deactivation of Hydrodesulfurization Catalysts under Coal Liquids. 1. Loss of Hydrogenation Activity Due to Carbonaceous Deposits," *Ind. Eng. Chem. Prod. Res. Dev.*, 17, 56 (1978).
124. Kovach, S. M., Castle, L. J., Bennett, J. V., and Schrodt, J. T., "Deactivation of Hydrodesulfurization Catalysts under Coal Liquids. 2. Loss of Hydrogenation Activity Due to Adsorption of Metallics," *Ind. Eng. Chem. Prod. Res. Dev.*, 17, 62 (1978).
125. Guin, J. A., Tsai, K. J., and Curtis, C. W., "Intraparticle Diffusivity Reduction during Hydrotreatment of Coal-Derived Liquids," *Ind. Eng. Chem. Proc. Des. Dev.*, 25, 515 (1986).
126. Garg, D., and Givens, E. N., "Catalyst Performance in Hydroprocessing Solvent-Refined Coal" *Fuel Proc. Tech.*, 9, 29 (1984).
127. Bhan, O. K., and Crynes, B. L., "Temperature-Zoned Reactors For Coal Liquids Hydrotreatment," *Chem. Eng. Prog.*, 48 (November 1984).
128. Treblow, M., Spitler, C. A., and Brown, F. R., "Hydrogenation Reactions of Model Titanium Compounds under Coal Liquefaction Conditions" *AIChE J.*, 29, 1011 (1983).
129. Coates, D. J., Evans, J. W., and Pollack, S. J., "Identification of the Origin of TiO_2 Deposits Surrounding a Used Hydrodesulphurization Catalyst," *Fuel*, 61, 1245 (1982).
130. Robbat, A., Finseth, D. H., and Let, R. G., "Organic Titanium Coal and the Deposition of Titanium on Direct Liquefaction Catalysts. An Alternative View," *Fuel*, 63, 1710 (1984).
131. Hertan, P. A., Larkins, F. P., and Jackson, W. R., "Effect of an Iron Contaminant on the Performance of a Coal Hydroliquefaction Nickel Molybdenum Catalyst," *Appl. Catal.*, 11, 139 (1984).
132. Crynes, B. L., and Seapan, M., Oklahoma State University, Stillwater, OK, "Catalysts for Upgrading Coal-Derived Liquids," DOE Project Report DOE/ET/14876-12 (June 1983).
133. Adkins, B. D., Milburn, D. R., Adkins, S. R., and Davis, B. H., "Deactivation in Hydrotreater Catalysts: The Distribution of Fouling Components," *Proc. Tenth EPRI Contr. Conf. Clean Liq. Sol. Fuels*, (April 1985).
134. Adkins, B. D., and Davis, B. H., "Coking and Porosity in a Two-Stage Coal Liquefaction Catalyst," *ACS Div. Pet. Chem. Prepr.*, 330, 479 (1985).
135. Freeman, G., Adkins, B. D., Moniz, M., and Davis, B. H., "Coal Liquefaction Catalysis. Characterization of a Series of Aged Catalysts," *Appl. Catal.*, 15, 49 (1985).
136. Adkins, B. D., Cisler, K., and Davis, B. H., "Coal Liquefaction Catalysis: Metals Deposition in the Presence or Absence of Coal Ash," *Appl. Catal.*, 23, 111 (1986).
137. Adkins, B. D., Milburn, D. R., and Davis, B. H., "A Model for Diffusion Limited Accumulation of Fe and Ti in Coal Liquefaction Catalysts," *Ind. Eng. Chem. Res.*, submitted.
138. Adkins, B. D., Milburn, D. R., Goodman, J. P., and Davis, B. H., "A Mechanism for Coking of Coal Liquefaction Catalysts Involving Basic Nitrogen Compounds, Sodium, and Catalyst Acid Sites", *Appl. Catal.*, (in press) 1988.
139. Satterfield, C. M., Colton, C. K., and Pitcher, W. H., Jr., "Restricted Diffusion in Liquids within Fine Pores," *AIChE J.*, 19, 628, (1973).
140. Chang, H. J., Ph.D. Thesis, Oklahoma State University, Stillwater, OK, (1982).
141. Ma, Y. H., and Evans, L. B., "Transient Diffusion from a Well-Stirred Reservoir to a Body of Arbitrary Shape," *AIChE J.*, 14, 956 (1968).

142. Adkins, B. D., and Davis, B. H., "Particle Packings and the Computation of Pore Size Distributions from Capillary Condensation Hysteresis," *J. Phys. Chem.*, 90, 4866 (1986).
143. Prasher, B. D., Gabriel, G. A., and Ma, Y. H., "Catalyst Deactivation by Pore Structure Changes. The Effect of Coke and Metal Depositions on Diffusion Parameters," *Ind. Eng. Chem. Process Des. Dev.*, 17, 3 (1978).
144. Chang, Y., and Perlmutter, D. D., "Effect of Pore-Distributed Coke on Catalyst Regeneration Kinetics," *AIChE J.*, 33, 940 (1987).
145. Mullendore, A. W., and Lieberman, M. L., Ed., "Chemical Studies on SYNTHOIL Process, Third Quarterly Rpt.," Sandia Report SAND76-0335 (June, 1976).
146. Stiegel, G. J., Polinski, L. M., Tischer, R. E., "Catalyst Deactivation during Coal Liquefaction. The Effect of Catalyst Diameter," *Ind. Eng. Chem. Process Des. Dev.*, 21, 477 1982.

CHAPTER 8

TEMPERATURE PROGRAMMED DESORPTION TECHNIQUE

Pio Forzatti, Enrico Tronconi, and Luca Lietti

Dipartimento di Chimica Industriale ed Ingegneria
Chimica "G. Natta" del Politecnico
Milano, Italy

CONTENTS

INTRODUCTION

The so-called desorption methods provide a suitable tool for studying the interaction of the reactants with the catalyst surface in heterogeneous catalytic reactions. Such methods induce desorption of previously chemisorbed species, typically by addition of energy. Thus, the nature of the desorbing species, and its rate of desorption, can be determined.

As opposite to all other desorption methods, Temperature Programmed Desorption (TPD) can be used under conditions approximating practical reaction conditions in so far as it does not require vacuum. Because of this it has been widely employed to study the desorption of adsorbed molecules from real catalysts since it was proposed by Cvetanovic and Amenomiya [1]. During TPD the catalyst sample is subjected to a linear increase in temperature with time; the adsorbed species desorb into a stream of inert carrier gas, and their concentration is recorded as a function of time (or temperature). A TPD spectrum is therefore a record of the concentration of the desorbed molecule as a function of temperature. The shape of the curve and the positions of its peaks are related to the kinetic parameters of the desorption process; accordingly, they convey information on how the molecule is adsorbed on the catalyst.

When the desorbed species are not produced by simple desorption of the initially adsorbed molecule but originate from surface-catalyzed decomposition of the adsorbate, reaction of the adsorbate with a reagent present in the carrier gas stream, or reaction between coadsorbates the technique is referred to as Temperature Programmed Surface Reaction (TPSR) or Temperature Programmed Reaction (TPR). In this case several products may be obtained, and suitable analytical facilities are required for their identification. Valuable information on surface reaction mechanism and kinetics can be obtained, since intermediate species can in principle be detected as soon as they form, due to the unsteady nature of the technique.

EXPERIMENTAL

Apparatus

The apparatus used in our laboratory for TPD experiments is schematically shown in Figure 1. An inert carrier gas from a cylinder, such as high purity He or N_2, is passed through a Cu deoxo unit and a molecular sieve trap cooled with liquid nitrogen to remove traces of oxygen and water respectively. The carrier gas stream is then split into two, one going directly to the reference arm of the detector, the other passing first through the reactor and then to the detector. The flow of each stream is accurately measured and rapidly controlled by a Brooks Model 5850-TR Mass Flow meter/controller. A narrow cylindrical quartz reactor (i.d. = 5 mm), with the design reported by Falconer and Schwarz [2] and with quartz wool to sustain the catalyst, is employed, which ensures small radial temperature gradients in the catalyst bed as well as negligible reagent uptake from the reactor wall. The reactor is inserted in an electric furnace controlled by a proportional-integrative-derivative temperature programmer providing a linear temperature rise up to 1,073 K, and the quartz tube is wound with a wire net to increase its thermal capacity. The reactor and the furnace are provided with a proper cooling device. The temperature of the catalyst is measured by a stainless-steel, shielded 0.5 mm diameter, chromel-alumel thermocouple directly immersed in the catalyst bed, which eventually results in negligible temperature lags.

The catalyst is saturated by means of either gas sampling valve GSV1 (through a dedicated line) or a syringe (through an injection point IP placed at the top of the reactor) when gas or liquid reagents are used, respectively. The apparatus is also provided with a vacuum line to remove from the catalyst the species condensed inside the pores or weakly physisorbed on the surface. The quartz reactor is directly connected to the GC detector, from which TPD traces are obtained. Both TCD and FID, possibly in a series arrangement, can be used. All tubes and connections downstream from the reactor are heated to prevent condensation of the desorbed species.

The apparatus in Figure 1 is also provided with a dedicated line for catalyst pretreatment and with special devices for the analysis and identification of the desorbed compounds.

Accordingly, the carrier gas line can be modified so as to bypass the GC, and samples of the carrier gas containing the desorbed species can be periodically analyzed in the course of a replicated TPD experiment using gas sampling valve GSV2, four-way valve FWV and a separation column inserted in the GC. Besides, the desorbing products can be condensed in a trap inserted immediately downstream of the reactor, cooled at the liquid nitrogen temperature, and then analyzed typically by GC, GC-MS or GC-FTIR. The two different but complementary analytical procedures enable the detection and identification of both light and heavy products in complex mixtures.

The apparatuses reported in the literature may differ from that shown in Figure 1 for a number of noticeable features, including the obtainement of TPD traces in vacuo as opposite to in flowing of an inert carrier gas, the use of a static system for adsorption measurements, the detection of the desorbed species and their identification by on-line MS.

Procedure

A typical TPD experiment consists of the following steps: 1) catalyst pretreatment; 2) adsorption of the adsorbate; 3) evacuation to remove the weakly physisorbed species; 4) desorption of

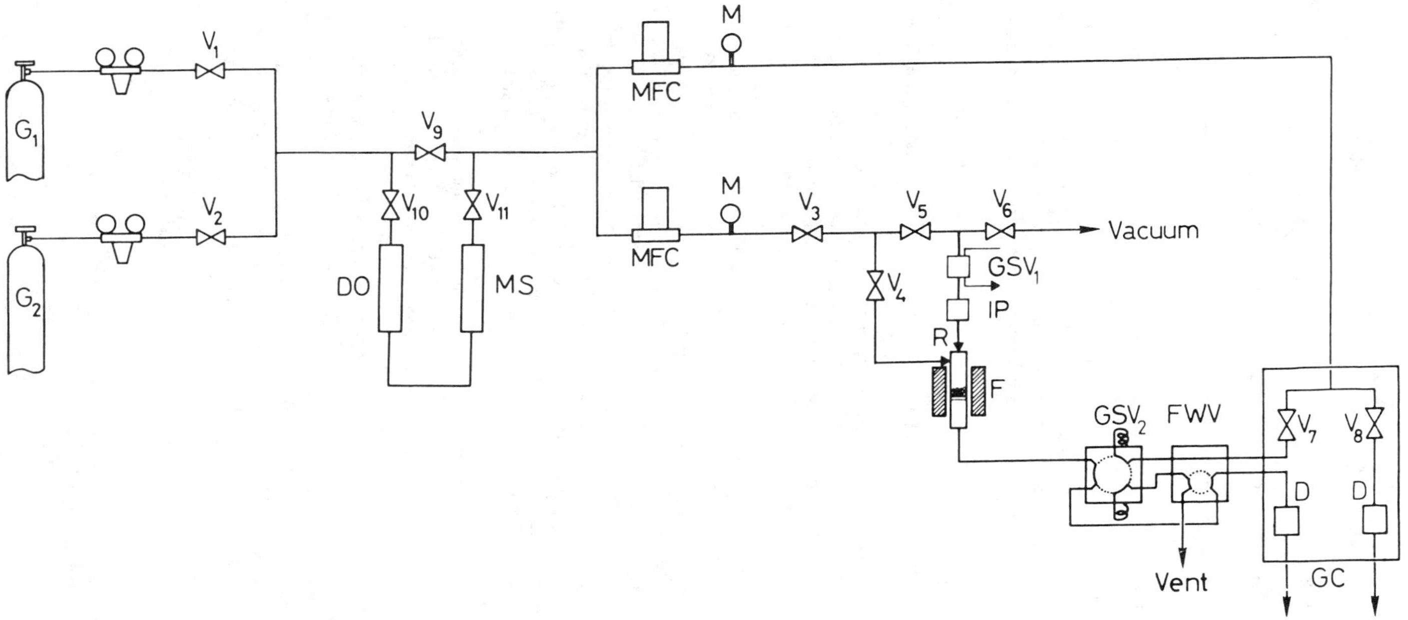

Figure 1. Schematic diagram of the TPD apparatus: G_1 and G_2, gas cylinders; V, valves; MFC, mass flow controller; M. manometer; DO, Cu deoxo unit; MS, molecular sieve trap; IP, injection point; R, reactor; F, furnace; GSV, gas sampling valves, FWV, four-way valve; GC, gas-chromatograph; D, detector.

Table 1
Typical Catalyst Parameters and Operating Conditions

Mass of catalyst bed, W_c	$0.03 \div 0.2$ g
Average particle radius, R_p	$10^{-2} \div 10^{-3}$ cm
Carrier gas flow rate, Q	$1 \div 5$ cm^3/s
Heating rate, β	$5 \div 30$°C/min

the adsorbed species into the stream of the carrier gas; 5) detection and analysis of the desorbed gas to establish its concentration and nature.

Typical catalyst parameters and operating conditions are listed in Table 1. The small catalyst load results in a bed depth that one hopes is smaller than the length of a perfect mixer, which eventually validates a CSTR treatment of the data. Also, appropriately small average catalyst particle radius and reasonably high gas flow rates ensure the absence of intraparticle and interphase diffusion limitations respectively.

The catalyst is usually pretreated in situ at the higher temperature reached during the TPD runs and under flow of the inert carrier in order to prevent, in the course of the measurement, any modification of the catalyst surface characteristics induced by temperature rise. Specific pretreatment, such as prereduction, may be required depending on the type of reagent-surface interaction one is interested in. Then a few pulses of reagent are passed over the catalyst at a given temperature until saturation is achieved. The adsorption of the reagent can be performed at different temperatures, which results in different initial surface coverages, and it can be measured also manometrically in a static system. The weakly physisorbed species are removed by evacuating the reactor, and are possibly collected in a trap. After evacuation the carrier gas is allowed to flow over the catalyst bed for several minutes until the recorder line becomes stabilized. Precooling of the reactor down to ≈ 273 K is required to obtain a linear temperature rise already from room temperature. Then the temperature of the catalyst is increased linearly by the programming controller. The heating rate β can be changed only in a reasonably narrow range of values, considering that it is very hard to realize large variations of β without involving large differences in the temperature distribution inside the catalyst bed, that is to say without violating the usual hypothesis of isothermal bed conditions. As the catalyst is heated, the adsorbed molecule desorbs and is carried to the detector where a signal proportional to its concentration in the carrier gas is obtained. The desorption increases with temperature, initially at an exponential rate. The surface is progressively depleted of the adsorbed molecule and the rate of desorption goes through a maximum and finally falls to zero. The recorder trace appears as a peak, with the abscissa representing the time or the catalyst temperature. Figure 2 gives a simple conceptual picture of the catalyst temperature, the surface coverage of the adsorbate, and its gas-phase concentration as function of time. In general, if different adsorption states of the same adsorbate are present or different molecules are adsorbed on the catalyst, more than one peak will appear at different temperatures.

After completion of the run the TPD experiment is possibly repeated with a fresh catalyst sample. In this case the carrier gas line is modified so as to bypass the GC, and samples are removed at regular times and injected by means of a gas sampling valve into the GC column to assess the nature and the relative amount of the desorbing species. Condensation of the products in a trap, followed by GC, GC-MS or GC-FTIR analyses may also be required. The TPD spectra are processed to determine the kinetic parameters of the desorption process, according to a number of analysis techniques described in a later section.

THEORY

The TPD technique can provide valuable information on the interactions between a molecule and the catalyst surface. Such information is best exploited in studies of catalyst activity/selectivity and/or reaction mechanism.

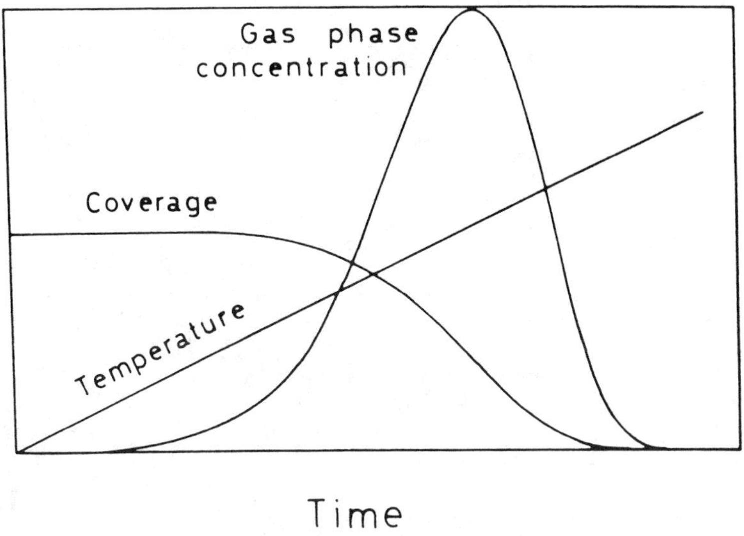

Figure 2. Temperature, gas-phase concentration of adsorbate and surface coverage versus time during a TPD run.

For these purposes, however, it is required that the experimental conditions be carefully designed, and the quantitative analysis of the TPD trace be performed with caution. In fact, only recently it has been pointed out that the physical processes may play an important role in the course of TPD experiments. Such effects may include mass transfer both within the catalyst particles and at the gas-catalyst interface, as well as the corresponding effects of heat transfer. Furthermore, if the catalyst is arranged in the form of a packed bed, dispersion of mass and heat in both the axial and radial directions should in principle be considered.

In the following we will discuss how the TPD system can be modeled, and how the analysis of the general conservation equations enables the identification of the appropriate operating conditions for TPD experiments. Thus spurious intrusions due to physical effects can be minimized. This eventually allows the estimation of the true kinetic parameters for desorption (and possibly readsorption) during TPD experiments.

General Conservation Equations

We will consider here the case of a single molecule, the adsorbate, desorbing into an inert carrier gas. It is here assumed that both the catalyst pellets and the reactor are isothermal, so that a unique value of temperature can be used in describing the system. Notice that typically very small amounts of catalyst are used in TPD runs, so that thermal effects are indeed negligible. Also, we will assume that interphase mass transfer is fast, based on the high flow rates of carrier gas typically adopted. Finally, perfect radial mixing in the reactor will be assumed.

Under the above hypotheses, description of a TPD experiment requires consideration of the time-dependent mass balances over the single catalyst particle for the surface and the fluid-phase concentrations of the adsorbate, along with an overall mass balance for the adsorbate in the catalyst bed. These are given below for catalyst particles with a spherical geometry, as shown in Figure 3. Notice that no specific assumption is made here on the adsorption-desorption kinetics.

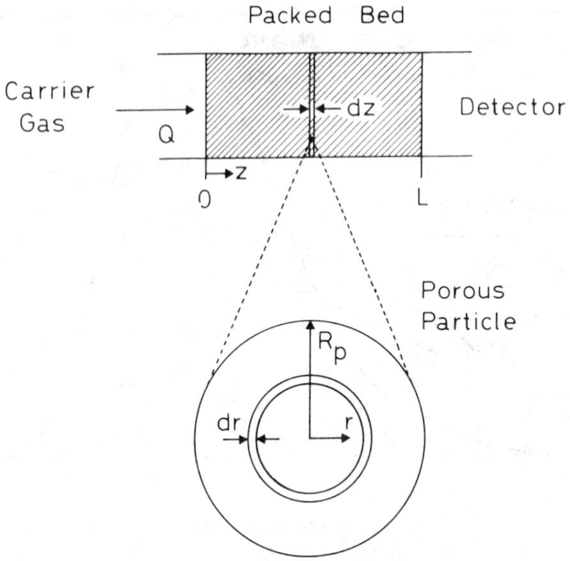

Figure 3. Schematic picture of catalyst bed and porous catalyst particle in a TPD experiment from a packed bed.

Adsorbate mass balance on the surface of a catalyst particle and associated initial condition.

$$-\frac{\partial \theta}{\partial t} = r_d - r_a \qquad \text{at } t = 0 \quad \theta = 1 \tag{1}$$

where θ = fractional surface coverage
t = run time
r_d, r_a = absolute rates of desorption and readsorption, respectively

Adsorbate mass balance in the gas phase inside the catalyst pores and associated initial and boundary conditions.

$$\varepsilon_p \frac{\partial C}{\partial t} = D_p \frac{1}{r^2} \frac{\partial}{\partial r}\left(r^2 \frac{\partial C}{\partial r}\right) - v_m \frac{\partial \theta}{\partial t}$$

$$r = 0 \qquad \frac{\partial C}{\partial r} = 0 \qquad \forall t \tag{2}$$

$$r = R_p \qquad C = C^0(z) \qquad \forall t$$

$$t = 0 \qquad C = 0 \qquad \forall r$$

where C = gas-phase concentration of the adsorbate within the catalyst particle
ε_p = particle void fraction
D_p = adsorbate diffusivity in the pores
r = the radial coordinate ($0 \leq r \leq R_p$ = particle radius)
v_m = the initial number of adsorbed molecules for unit catalyst volume
C^0 = gas-phase concentration of the adsorbate in the reactor, which varies in general along the axial coordinate z

Adsorbate mass balance in the catalyst bed and associated initial and boundary conditions.

$$\varepsilon_b \frac{\partial C^0}{\partial t} = -u \frac{\partial C^0}{\partial z} + D_b \frac{\partial^2 C^0}{\partial z^2} + \frac{3}{R_p}(1 - \varepsilon_b)D_p \frac{\partial C}{\partial r}\bigg|_{r=R_p}$$

$$t = 0 \qquad C^0 = 0 \qquad \forall z$$

$$z = 0 \qquad uC^0 = D_b \frac{\partial C^0}{\partial z} \qquad \forall t \tag{3}$$

$$z = L \qquad \frac{\partial C^0}{\partial z} = 0 \qquad \forall t$$

where ε_b = bed void fraction
      u = interstitial gas velocity
      D_b = adsorbate diffusivity in the bed

Equation 3 is written for the general case of intermediate axial backmixing. Two well known limiting cases are worth considering,

<u>P</u>lug <u>F</u>low <u>R</u>eactor ($D_b = 0$) → <u>no backmixing</u>

$$\varepsilon_b \frac{\partial C^0}{\partial t} = -u \frac{\partial C^0}{\partial z} + \frac{3}{R_p}(1 - \varepsilon_b)D_p \frac{\partial C}{\partial r}\bigg|_{r=R_p} \tag{3a}$$

<u>C</u>ontinuous <u>S</u>tirred <u>T</u>ank <u>R</u>eactor → <u>perfect backmixing</u>

$$\varepsilon_b \frac{\partial C^0}{\partial t} = (1 - \varepsilon_b)\frac{-\rho_c Q C^0}{W_c} + \frac{3}{R_p}(1 - \varepsilon_b)D_p \frac{-\partial C}{\partial r}\bigg|_{r=R_p} \tag{3b}$$

The CSTR limit, Equation 3b, is suitably applied in the case of shallow beds, where the concentration of adsorbate in the gas phase can be taken as approximately uniform throughout the catalyst bed. Since this is very often the case in TPD experiments, we will consider only Equation 3b in the following treatment. The PFR limit has been discussed by Demmin and Gorte [3]. Rieck and Bell [4] have proposed a criterion to determine the equivalent number of CSTR's in series for the TPD catalyst bed.

Dimensional Analysis

Let us define the dimensionless variables:

$$\rho = \frac{r}{R_p} \qquad \tau = \frac{\beta t}{\Delta T} \qquad \gamma = \frac{Q \, \Delta T \, \rho_c C}{3 v_m \beta W_c}$$

where β = heating rate
      ΔT = temperature range of the TPD run
      ρ_c = density of the catalyst pellet

Then, Equation 2 can be rearranged in nondimensional form as

$$\varepsilon_p \frac{\beta R_p^2}{D_p \, \Delta T} \frac{\partial \gamma}{\partial \tau} = \frac{1}{\rho^2} \frac{\partial}{\partial \rho}\left(\rho^2 \frac{\partial \gamma}{\partial \rho}\right) - \frac{Q \rho_c R_p^2}{3 W_c D_p} \frac{\partial \theta}{\partial \tau} \tag{4}$$

Likewise, Equation 3b becomes

$$\frac{\varepsilon_b}{1-\varepsilon_b}\frac{\beta W_c}{\Delta T\, Q\rho_c}\frac{\partial \gamma^0}{\partial t} = -\gamma^0 + \frac{3W_cD_p}{Q\rho_cR_p^2}\left.\frac{-\partial\gamma}{\partial\rho}\right|_{\rho=1} \tag{5}$$

Thus, the following dimensionless groups of parameters governing the TPD process are identified:

$\psi_1 = (\beta R_p^2/D_p\,\Delta T)$, representing the ratio of the characteristic time for internal diffusion ($=R_p^2/D_p$) to the characteristic time of the TPD experiment ($=\Delta T/\beta$).

$\psi_2 = (\beta W_c/\Delta T\, Q\rho_c)$, representing the ratio of the characteristic time for convective removal of the desorbed species ($=W_c/Q\rho_c$) to the time of the TPD run.

$\Phi_1 = (\rho_cQR_p^2/3W_cD_p)$ ratio of the characteristic time for internal diffusion to the characteristic time for convective removal of the desorbed species.

Under typical TPD operating conditions the heating rate β is of the order of 10°C/min, while ΔT may be of several hundred degrees. Hence, the duration of a TPD experiment is at least of several minutes. On the other hand, both the time for intraparticle diffusion and the residence time will be much shorter, even in the worst conditions. Accordingly, $\psi_1 \ll 1$ and $\psi_2 \ll 1$, which implies that there is no build up of adsorbate either inside the catalyst pores or in the TPD reactor. If so, the following pseudo steady-state form of the above equations with associated initial and boundary conditions can be regarded as appropriate:

$$-\frac{\partial\theta}{\partial\tau} = \frac{r_d - r_a}{\beta/\Delta T} \qquad \tau = 0 \rightarrow \theta = 1 \tag{6}$$

$$\frac{1}{\rho^2}\frac{d}{d\rho}\left(\rho^2\frac{d\gamma}{d\rho}\right) - \Phi_1\frac{\partial\theta}{\partial\tau} = 0$$

$$\rho = 0, \tau > 0 \qquad \frac{d\gamma}{d\rho} = 0 \tag{7}$$

$$\rho = 1, \tau > 0 \qquad \gamma = \gamma^0$$

$$\Phi_1\gamma^0 = \left.\frac{-d\gamma}{d\rho}\right|_{\rho=1} \tag{8}$$

This set of equations appears to provide a reasonable model for diffusion affected TPD from a bed of spherical porous particles. The effects of internal diffusion are controlled by the parameter Φ_1: the greater Φ_1, the greater the intraparticle gas-phase concentration gradients.

For TPD of physisorbed methanol from γ-Al_2O_3 with particles of different sizes, Tronconi & Forzatti [5] plotted the observed peak temperatures T_M and values of the measured desorption rate constant at fixed T, k_{eff}, versus Φ_1. The original plot, reported in Figure 4, shows that no effect of Φ_1 is apparent as long as $\Phi_1 < 1$, whereas T_M shifts to higher temperatures and k_{eff} drops when Φ_1 exceeds unity, due to the onset of internal concentration gradients. It is worth noticing here that the observed reduction of the desorption rate with growing Φ_1 is not simply the result of the slowing down of intraparticle diffusion, but is due to a faster rate of readsorption of the desorbed molecules induced by the strong internal concentration gradients, which determine high gas-phase concentrations within the pores. This point is further discussed later.

If internal diffusion of the desorbing species is not rate controlling, then the rate of diffusion is much greater than the space velocity, and $\Phi_1 \ll 1$. In this case the adsorbate gas concentration is uniform both outside and inside the catalyst particles, and the TPD model equations in dimen-

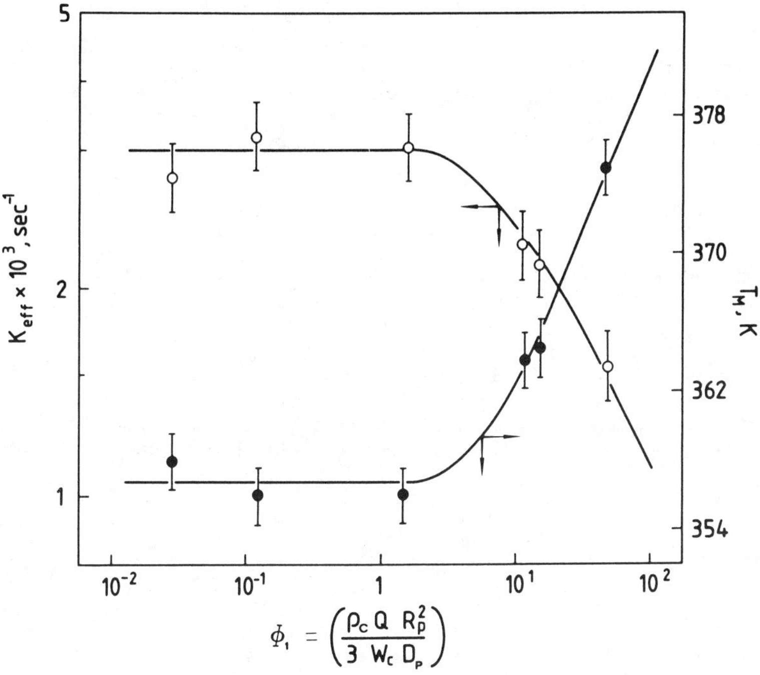

Figure 4. Plot of effective desorption rate constante, k_{eff} (open circles) and peak temperature, T_M (solid circles) versus $\Phi_1 = (\rho_c Q R_p^2/3W_c D_p)$. (Reprinted with permission from Ref. [5].)

sional form reduce to

$$\frac{-d\theta}{dt} = r_d - r_a \qquad t = 0 \rightarrow \theta = 1 \tag{9}$$

$$QC^0 = \frac{v_m W_c}{\rho_c} \frac{-d\theta}{dt} \tag{10}$$

i.e., the well-known mass balances for the solid and the gas phase originally proposed by Cvetanovic and Amenomiya [1]. In this form, the previous equations provide the basis for determining the adsorption and desorption kinetics of the adsorbate.

Kinetic Expressions

The expression for the rate of desorption is generally written as

$$r_d = k_d^0 \exp\left(\frac{-E_d}{RT}\right)\theta^n$$

where an Arrhenius temperature dependence has been assumed for the desorption rate constant k_d. In principle, both k_d^0 and the activation energy of desorption, E_d, can be a function of the surface coverage θ.

In the following we discuss first the case of homogeneous surfaces, with constant k_d^0 and E_d. The order n reflects the number of species originally present onto the catalyst surface from which the desorbing molecule is formed. Thus, n = 1 for nondissociative adsorption, n = 2 if dissociative adsorption occurs and two (unlike) species recombine upon desorption.

The rate of adsorption (or "readsorption", as often used in TPD) can be represented by a Langmuir form

$$r_a = k_a^0 \exp\left(\frac{-E_a}{RT}\right) C^0(1-\theta)^m$$

where m is the number of species into which the adsorbed molecule has decomposed. For overall reversible systems, m = n. Consider now the case of:

1. First-order kinetics (n = m = 1)
2. Linear heating schedule, $T = T^0 + \beta t$

Then, the mass balance of the adsorbate, Equation 1 of the previous section, can be combined with the kinetic expressions to yield, for the general case where both desorption and readsorption occur,

$$-\beta\frac{d\theta}{dT} = k_d\theta - k_a C^0(1-\theta) \tag{11}$$

and

$$QC^0 = -\frac{v_m W_c}{\rho_c}\beta\frac{d\theta}{dT} \tag{12}$$

or

$$C^0 = \frac{\dfrac{v_m W_c}{\rho_c}k_d\theta}{Q + \dfrac{v_m W_c}{\rho_c}k_a(1-\theta)} \tag{13}$$

It is most convenient to treat separately the two limiting cases of no readsorption and equilibrated readsorption.

Readsorption Is Negligible

$$Q \gg \frac{v_m W_c}{\rho_c}k_a(1-\theta)$$

The carrier gas flow rate is so high that the desorbing species is not allowed sufficient time to readsorb. Then, the above equations reduce to

$$C^0 = \frac{v_m W_c}{\rho_c Q}k_d^0 \exp\left(\frac{-E_d}{RT}\right)\theta \tag{14}$$

$$-\frac{d\theta}{dT} = \frac{k_d^0}{\beta}\exp\left(\frac{-E_d}{RT}\right)\theta \tag{15}$$

A useful relationship can be derived by considering the condition for the maximum concentration

$$\frac{dC^0}{dT} = 0 \qquad \text{at } T = T_M$$

which results in

$$(k_d)_M = \beta \frac{E_d}{RT_M^2} \tag{16}$$

Equation 16 is the basis for some methods of analysis of TPD curves, as discussed in a later section.

Desorption-Readsorption Equilibrium Is Established

$$Q \ll \frac{v_m W_c}{\rho_c} k_a(1 - \theta)$$

In this limit of low flow rates,

$$C^0 = K \frac{\theta}{1 - \theta} \tag{17}$$

where $K = k_d/k_a$, the equilibrium constant of desorption
$K = K^0 \exp(-\Delta H/RT)$
$\Delta H = E_d - E_a$
$K^0 = \exp(\Delta S/R)$

At the peak maximum of the TPD curve,

$$(K)_M = \frac{v_m \beta W_c}{\rho_c Q}(1 - \theta_M)^2 \frac{\Delta H}{RT_M^2} \tag{18}$$

Effects of Readsorption

It is of the utmost importance to assess whether readsorption is relevant in a TPD experiment. In fact, should readsorption occur freely, only adsorption equilibrium constants and heats of adsorption can be determined, but not the individual adsorption and desorption kinetic parameters.

The observable effects of readsorption on TPD curves have been reproduced by numerical simulations and analyzed. It has been observed that TPD peaks tend to broaden and shift to higher temperatures with growing readsorption rates. This has suggested the use of a "Shape Index" suitable for discriminating among different situations. The shape index S has been defined as the slope of the TPD curve at the inflection points (Figure 5). Ibok and Ollis [6] showed that S assumes typical, different values for 1st- and 2nd-order kinetics, depending whether there is no readsorption or equilibrated readsorption. The feasibility of this approach, however, has been questioned for a number of reasons [7]: (a) the typical values of S for 1st order desorption and 2nd order desorption with readsorption are close and hardly distinguishable in practice; (b) S is actually a function of E_d/RT; (c) accurate estimates of the slopes of the TPD curve are hard to obtain. Accordingly, the unambiguous determination of the relevance of readsorption from a single TPD curve appears to be difficult

An alternative approach is based on the analysis of a series of TPD curves obtained at different carrier gas flow rates. Inspection of Equations 16 and 18 shows that the temperature T_M of the

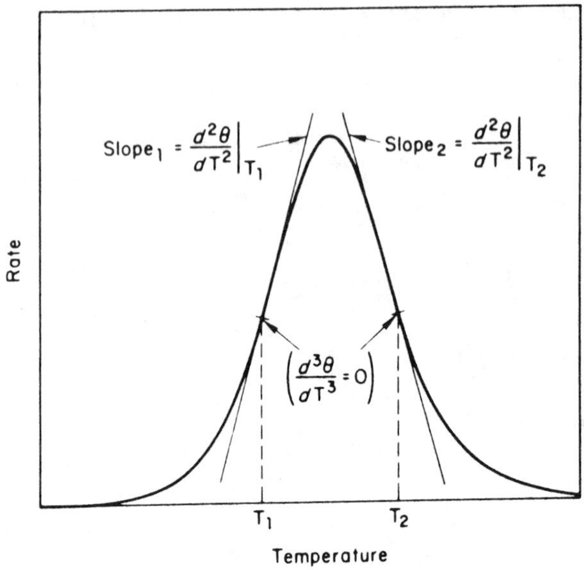

Figure 5. Determination of shape index for a TPD curve. (Reprinted with permission from Ref. [2].)

peak maximum is not a function of the flow rate Q if readsorption is negligible, the opposite is true when equilibrated readsorption occurs. Hence readsorption can be excluded if the position of the TPD peak is not affected by variations in the carrier gas flow.

In practice, large Q-changes may be required to determine significant shifts of the TPD peak. Furthermore, it has been stressed [8] that in the presence of strong internal diffusional limitations the peak temperature becomes independent of gas flow rate even if readsorption is important. Therefore a regime analysis should be performed before hand in order to exclude the presence of diffusional intrusions; only after that, the significance of readsorption could possibly be established.

An analysis has been published that determines the kinetic constants for desorption and readsorption as functions of T, without necessarily assuming the limiting cases of no readsorption and of equilibrated readsorption [9]. This analysis is here presented in its original form, based on linear 1st-order kinetics, but it can easily be extended to other cases.

Consider the mass balances for the gas and solid phases,

$$QC^0 = \frac{v_m W_c}{\rho_c} \frac{-d\theta}{dt} \tag{19}$$

$$\frac{-d\theta}{dt} = k_d\theta - k_a C^0 \tag{20}$$

By eliminating $(-d\theta/dt)$ and rearranging, one obtains the following linear form

$$\frac{\theta}{C^0} = \frac{1}{k_d} \frac{\rho_c Q}{v_m W_c} + \frac{k_a}{k_d} \tag{21}$$

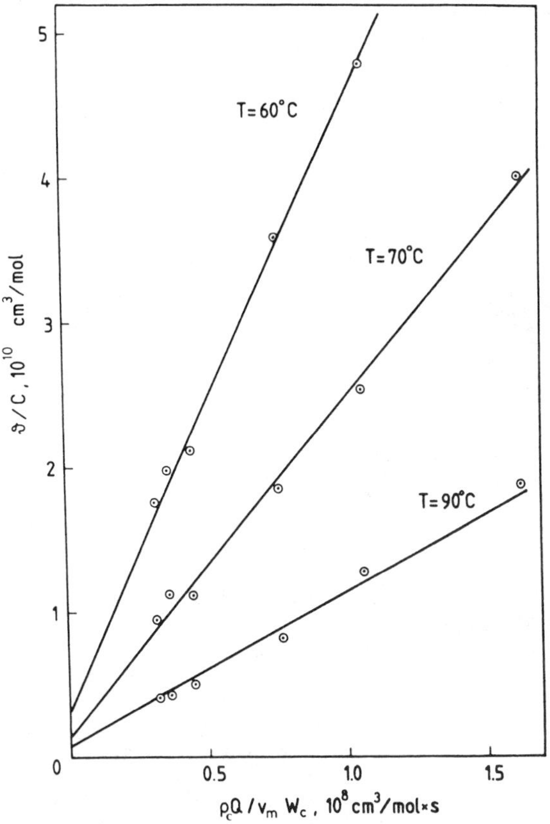

Figure 6. Isothermal characteristic plots for determining the rate constants for adsorption and desorption (Eq. 21). Application to methanol desorption from γ-Al_2O_3. (Reprinted with permission from Ref. [9].)

Hence, isothermal characteristic linear plots of (θ/C^0) versus $(\rho_c Q/v_m W_c)$ can be constructed from TPD curves recorded at different flow rates and/or with different catalyst loads. For each temperature, the slope of the corresponding plot is inversely proportional to k_d, while the intercept yields the adsorption equilibrium constant, i.e. k_a/k_d. The limiting behaviors corresponding to negligible readsorption ($k_a/k_d \approx 0$) and to equilibrated readsorption ($\theta/C^0 \approx k_a/k_d$) would result in lines passing through the origin and in horizontal lines, respectively. The feasibility of this approach has been demonstrated for TPD of methanol from γ-Al_2O_3 (see Figure 6).

Coupled Effects of Internal Diffusion and Readsorption

As already mentioned, the diffusional intrusions that may affect TPD from porous catalysts actually originate from an articulate coupling between diffusion and readsorption. This is best illustrated by considering the TPD model of Equations 6–8 with simple linear kinetics assumed for both desorption and readsorption. In nondimensional form,

$$\frac{1}{\rho^2}\frac{d}{d\rho}\left(\rho^2\frac{d\gamma}{d\rho}\right)-\Phi_1\frac{\partial\theta}{\partial\tau}=0 \tag{22}$$

$$\frac{\partial\theta}{\partial\tau}=3\Phi_2\gamma-\left(k_d\frac{\Delta T}{\beta}\right)\theta \tag{23}$$

$$\Phi_1\gamma^0=\left.\frac{-d\gamma}{d\rho}\right|_{\rho=1} \tag{24}$$

with initial and boundary conditions

$$\begin{aligned} &\tau=0, && 0\le\rho\le 1 && \theta=1\\ &\rho=0, && \tau\ge 0 && \frac{d\gamma}{d\rho}=0\\ &\rho=1, && \tau\ge 0 && \gamma=\gamma^0 \end{aligned} \tag{25}$$

The parameter $\Phi_2 = (v_m W_c k_a/\rho_c Q)$ represents the ratio of the characteristic time for convective removal of desorbed species to time for readsorption ($=1/(v_m k_a)$): high Φ_2-values correspond to relevant readsorption effects.

This model was shown by Tronconi & Forzatti [9] to simulate effectively the growth of T_M and the drop in k_{eff} observed on increasing the catalyst particle size beyond a critical value during TPD of methanol from γ-Al_2O_3, as reported in Table 2. The kinetic parameters for adsorption and desorption were secured by running TPD experiments with different carrier gas rates and catalyst loads in the diffusion-free regime, according to the procedure described earlier. Once validated, the model lends itself nicely to demonstrate how intraparticle and readsorption interact in causing a reduction of the net observed desorption rate. Solutions of Equations 22–24 covering a wide range of values for the governing parameters Φ_1 and Φ_2 are plotted in Figure 7 as k_{eff}/k_d versus Φ_1, with Φ_2 as a parameter. Figure 7 summarizes several possible limiting cases as well as the intermediate situations.

1. When Φ_1 is small (i.e. no gradients exist in the gas phase), the rate of desorption is controlled by readsorption, and $k_{eff} = k_d/(1 + \Phi_2)$ [1].
2. As Φ_1 increases, diffusional limitations become manifest and k_{eff}/k_d decreases with growing Φ_1 [8].
3. The extent of variation of k_{eff}/k_d when Φ_1 is large depends on Φ_2: it is nil when $\Phi_2 = 0$, and is more apparent for large values of Φ_2. Figure 8 shows calculated intraparticle gas-phase

Table 2

Methanol TPD from γ-Al_2O_3. Comparison of Computed and Experimental Values for Peak Temperature, T_M, and Effective Desorption Rate Constant, k_{eff}, at 70°C and 90°C.

	T_M, °C		k_{eff}(70°C), s^{-1}		k_{eff}(90°C), s^{-1}	
R_p, cm	exp	calc	exp	calc	exp	calc
$3.5 \cdot 10^{-3}$	85	83	$3.0 \cdot 10^{-3}$	$3.6 \cdot 10^{-3}$	$8.3 \cdot 10^{-3}$	$8.2 \cdot 10^{-3}$
$7.1 \cdot 10^{-3}$	83	83	$3.4 \cdot 10^{-3}$	$3.6 \cdot 10^{-3}$	$8.1 \cdot 10^{-3}$	$8.2 \cdot 10^{-3}$
$2.3 \cdot 10^{-2}$	83	84	$3.3 \cdot 10^{-3}$	$3.5 \cdot 10^{-3}$	$7.2 \cdot 10^{-3}$	$7.7 \cdot 10^{-3}$
$6.5 \cdot 10^{-2}$	91	89	$2.5 \cdot 10^{-3}$	$2.7 \cdot 10^{-3}$	$6.5 \cdot 10^{-3}$	$6.1 \cdot 10^{-3}$
$7.4 \cdot 10^{-2}$	91.5	90	$2.3 \cdot 10^{-3}$	$2.6 \cdot 10^{-3}$	$5.2 \cdot 10^{-3}$	$5.6 \cdot 10^{-3}$
$1.5 \cdot 10^{-1}$	102	100	$1.7 \cdot 10^{-3}$	$1.6 \cdot 10^{-3}$	$3.5 \cdot 10^{-3}$	$3.4 \cdot 10^{-3}$

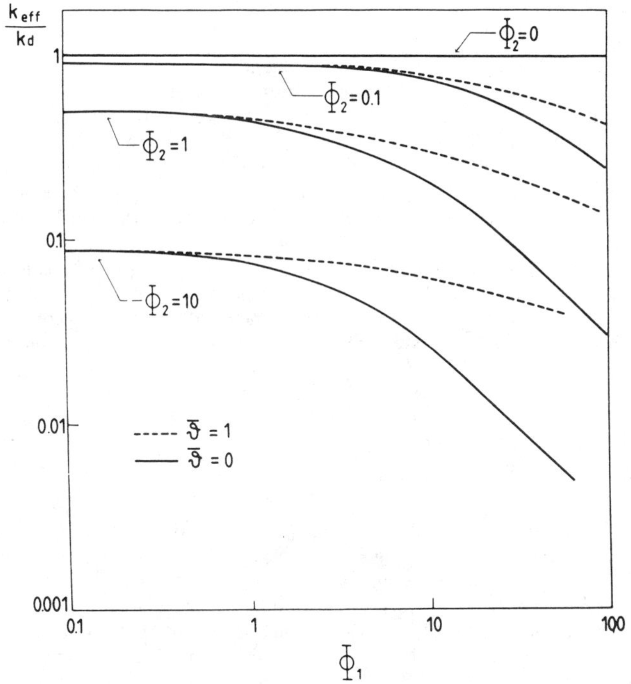

Figure 7. Coupled effects of internal diffusion and readsorption k_{eff}/k_d versus Φ_1 with Φ_2 as a parameter, for $\bar{\theta} = 1$ and $\bar{\theta} = 0$ (Equations 22–25). (Reprinted with permission from Ref. [9].)

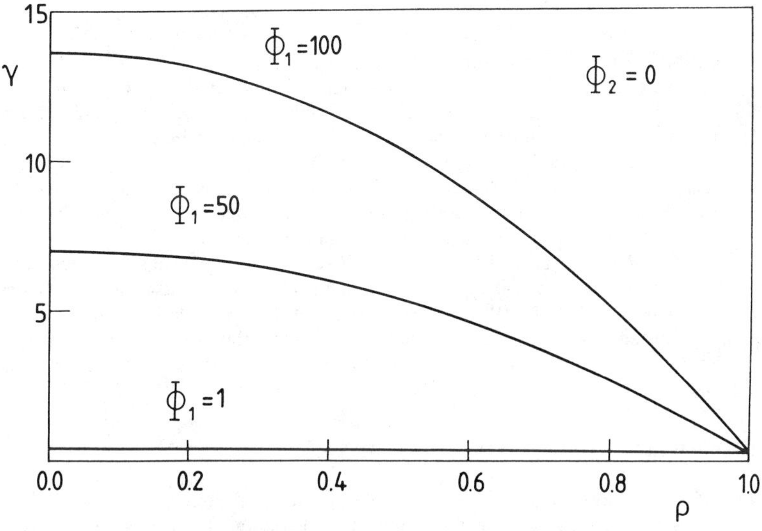

Figure 8. Calculated intraparticle radial profiles of γ, dimensionless gas-phase concentration. Case of no readsorption ($\tau = 0.4$; $E_d/RT = 30$; $k_d^0\, \Delta T/\beta = 6 \cdot 10^{10}$; $\Delta T/T^\circ = 1$. (Reprinted with permission from Ref. [9].)

concentration profiles for $\Phi_2 = 0$. While a strong gradient develops as Φ_1 increases, the concentration at the catalyst edge, which is proportional to the net rate of desorption, remains the same, so that no modification in the shape of the TPD curve occurs. This indicates that the existence of strong C-gradients inside the particles ($\Phi_1 > 1$) is only a necessary condition (not a sufficient one) for the TPD experiments to be affected by diffusional intrusions. C-gradients only indirectly slow down desorption by causing a buildup of adsorbate within the pores, which enhances the local rate of readsorption. Such a mechanism can be active only when $\Phi_2 > 0$.

4. Figure 7 shows that, for fixed Φ_1 and Φ_2, k_{eff}/k_d is also a function of $\bar{\theta}$ in the diffusion-controlled regime: k_{eff}/k_d changes during the TPD run, and tends to a minimum when complete depletion of the desorbing surface is approached. Different functional dependencies corresponding to the limiting cases of $\bar{\theta} = 1$ and $\bar{\theta} = 0$ are apparent, which originate from distinct physical situations. At the beginning of the TPD run ($\theta \equiv \bar{\theta} = 1$), there is a uniform initial coverage of the catalyst surface. An analytical solution is possible in this case,

$$\frac{k_{eff}}{k_d} = \left[\Phi_2\left(1 + \frac{\Phi_1}{\sqrt{3\Phi_1\Phi_2}\coth\sqrt{3\Phi_1\Phi_2} - 1}\right)\right]^{-1}$$

On the other hand, as $\bar{\theta} \to 0$, k_{eff}/k_d becomes asymptotically dependent on $(\Phi_1\Phi_2)^{-1} = 3D_p/v_m k_a R_p^2$ in the region of strong limitations, which agrees with the results of Gorte's approximate analysis for a slab geometry [8].

Thus, it is apparent that high values of Φ_1 result in the formation of significant concentration gradients in the pores, but this does not necessarily affect the TPD curve unless readsorption is fast. Also, the ratio k_{eff}/k_d changes during the TPD run, the "worse" situation corresponding to the end of the experiment. It has also been shown that the same results of Figure 7 hold in the case of heterogeneous surfaces with a linear θ-dependence of the desorption energy [10].

Design of Experimental Conditions

Inspection of the groups of variables identified by dimensional analysis provides guidance for the optimal choice of the TPD operating conditions.

In order to avoid accumulation of the adsorbate either in the catalyst pores or in the catalyst bed, both ψ_1 and ψ_2 should be made as small as possible. In practice, sufficiently slow heating rates shall be adopted. This secures also the isothermality of the desorbing bed.

Internal concentrations gradients are controlled by $\Phi_1 = (\rho_c Q R_p^2/3W_c D_p)$. Gorte [8] proposed that concentration gradients are negligible when $\Phi_1 < 0.1$, while diffusion becomes rate controlling as Φ_1 exceeds 20. In order to avoid diffusional intrusions, then, one wants to make Φ_1 small. This can be accomplished by reducing Q and R_p, and by increasing W_c. However, a great catalyst load may prevent a CSTR treatment of the TPD data, whereas a low flow rate slows down interphase transport. Furthermore, both increasing W_c and reducing Q favors the readsorption of the desorbed species, as reflected by greater Φ_2 values. It seems then that the size of the catalyst particles should be minimized. Consider that, due to the very limited bed depth, this does not result in a significant pressure drop anyway. The parameters governing the design of the TPD experiments are summarized in Table 3.

METHODS OF ANALYSIS OF THE TPD CURVES

Several techniques have been developed to secure kinetic parameters from the analysis of TPD spectra. Such parameters include the pre-exponential factor and the activation energy (or the enthalpy change) of desorption, as well as the order of desorption (and possibly of readsorption).

A TPD spectrum contains a great amount of information, concerning the effects of both the surface coverage and of temperature. The problem is typically to decouple such effects since coverage- and T-changes occur simultaneously during a TPD run.

Table 3
Main Dimensionless Groups Governing the Design of TPD Experiments from Porous Catalysts

Group	Physical Interpretation	Effect
$\psi_1 = \left(\frac{\beta R_p^2}{D_p \Delta T}\right)$	Ratio of time for intraparticle diffusion to run time	If $\psi_1 \ll 1$, no buildup in the particle
$\psi_2 = \left(\frac{W_c \beta}{\rho_c Q \Delta T}\right)$	Ratio of residence time to run time	If $\psi_2 \ll 1$, no buildup in the reactor
$\Phi_1 = \left(\frac{\rho_c Q R_p^2}{3 W_c D_p}\right)$	Ratio of time for intraparticle diffusion to residence time	If $\Phi_1 \ll 1$, negligible internal C-gradients
$\Phi_2 = \left(\frac{v_m W_c k_a}{\rho_c Q}\right)$	Ratio of time for readsorption to residence time	If $\Phi_2 \ll 1$, readsorption is negligible

Basically, the approaches proposed in the literature for this purpose fall into one of the following categories:

1. Methods using only the peak maximum of several TPD curves.
2. Methods using desorption rate isotherms from several TPD curves.
3. Methods based on TPD curve fitting.
4. Methods based on single curve analysis.

Such methods are briefly reviewed in the following for the case of homogeneous surfaces. The extension to the case of heterogeneous surfaces, where E_d (or ΔH) and possibly the pre-exponential factor are functions of the surface coverage, is subsequently discussed.

Homogeneous Surfaces

Methods that Exploit Only the Point Maximum of the TPD Curves (heating rate variations)

This class of methods takes advantage of the condition

$$\frac{dC^0}{dT} = 0 \qquad \text{at } T = T_M$$

If readsorption is negligible, for generic nth-order desorption kinetics this results in

$$(k_d)_M = \frac{1}{n\theta_M^{n-1}}\beta\frac{E_d}{RT_M^2} = k_d^0 \exp\left(\frac{-E_d}{RT_M}\right) \tag{26}$$

By taking the logarithms of both sides, and rearranging,

$$\ln\frac{\beta}{T_M^2} = \ln\frac{Rk_d^0 n\theta_M^{n-1}}{E_d} - \frac{E_d}{R}\frac{1}{T_M} \tag{27}$$

With increasing heating rates, TPD peaks shift to higher temperatures. Hence, if a number of TPD spectra are recorded for a range of heating rates β, a plot of $\ln(\beta/T_M^2)$ versus $(1/T_M)$ will be linear, with slope equal to $(-E_d/R)$, and intercept $\ln[(Rk_d^0 n\theta_M^{n-1})/E_d]$.

Notice that the desorption order n cannot be estimated independently of the pre-exponential factor k_d^0, so that it has to be either assumed, or determined otherwise, e.g., by the methods discussed in the following sections.

Similar equations can be easily derived for the limiting case of free readsorption. Thus,

$$\ln\frac{\beta}{T_M^2} = \ln\frac{RK^0\rho_c Qn\theta_M^{n-1}}{\Delta H v_m W_c(1-\theta_M)^{n+1}} - \frac{\Delta H}{R}\frac{1}{T_M} \quad 28$$

and again a linear plot of $\ln(\beta/T_M^2)$ versus $1/T_M$ yields $(-\Delta H/R)$ as the slope.

It deserves to be stressed that β should be varied over at least two orders of magnitude in order to achieve significant changes in $\ln(\beta/T_M^2)$. However, it is hard to realize such large variations of β, without involving significant disuniformities in the temperature distribution inside the catalyst bed; indeed, the hypothesis of isothermal bed conditions might not hold any longer. Also, it has been reported that this method is sensitive to even small experimental errors in T_M [11].

Methods Based on Desorption Rate Isotherms

These methods use desorption rate isotherms extracted from a family of TPD traces with different initial surface coverages. Different heating rates can be also used. Isotherms are constructed by considering points corresponding to the same temperature taken from the different TPD curves (see Figure 9). Each point provides data on desorption rate and surface coverage as a function of temperature, $C^0(T)$ and $\theta(T)$. Thus, in principle, the whole TPD curve is exploited rather than just its point maximum. If readsorption is negligible, the basic TPD equations can be rearranged as

$$\ln C^0 = \ln\frac{v_m W_c k_d^0}{\rho_c Q} - \frac{E_d}{RT} + n\ln\theta \quad (29)$$

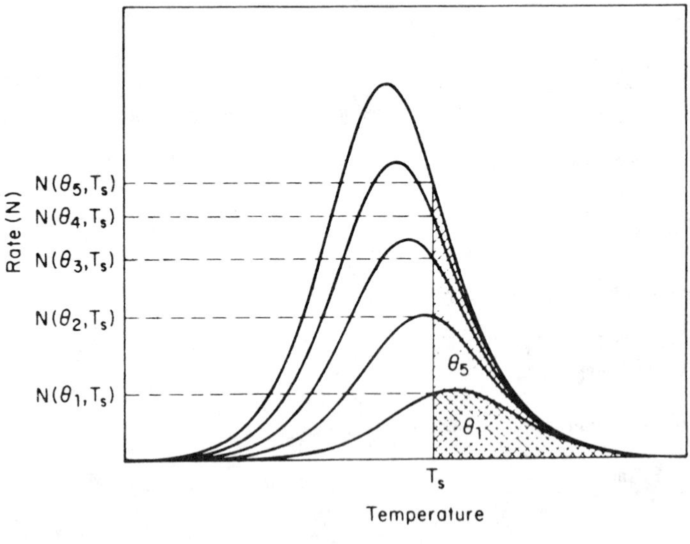

Figure 9. Method of desorption rate isotherms applied to five curves with different initial coverages. (Reprinted with permission from Ref. [2].)

and

$$\ln C^0 = \ln \frac{v_m W_c k_d^0 \theta^n}{\rho_c Q} - \frac{E_d}{R}\frac{1}{T} \tag{30}$$

The procedure is applied in two steps. Equation 29 is first applied to the treatment of isothermal data, and provides a characteristic plot whose slope is the order of desorption. Once n is determined, plots of ln C^0 versus 1/T at fixed coverages (Equation 30) are used to evaluate the activation energy.

A merit of this technique is to enable one to identify situations where the kinetic parameters are coverage dependent. In fact one finds in such cases that the desorption order, calculated from the slopes of the isothermal plots, apparently varies with coverage [12].

Accuracy is improved by large variations of θ at fixed temperature. This is more easily achieved by varying the heating rate β rather than the initial surface coverage, as pointed out by Taylor and Weinberg [12]. Also, linearity of the heating schedule is unimportant here, since C^0, θ, and T values are evaluated independently.

This technique is easily modified for the case of equilibrated readsorption.

Curve Fitting

In principle, standard nonlinear regression techniques applied to a single TPD trace can be used to determine all the kinetic parameters, e.g. by minimizing the sum of squares of differences between experimental and calculated curves. However, strong correlations among the parameters estimates are expected, so that the physicochemical significance of such estimates may be questionable. Furthermore, ambiguities may arise because different models provide equally good fits of the same TPD data.

Single Curve Methods

While the methods previously discussed are most commonly adopted in the analysis of TPD curves, there have been also attempts at deriving approaches suitable for the estimation of all the kinetic parameters from a single TPD trace. As already noted, this is possible in principle, since each TPD run provides information on the dependence of the desorption rate on both θ and T. Hence, desorption order, n, and activation energy, E_d, should be possibly estimated.

Developing the ideas of previous authors, Chan et al. [13] proposed to calculate E_d from the half width $W_{1/2}$, i.e. the peak width at half of the maximum amplitude (see Figure 10). They presented the following equations for first-order and second-order desorption, respectively,

$$\frac{E_d}{RT_M} = -1 + \left(1 + \frac{5.832 T_M^2}{W_{1/2}^2}\right)^{0.5} \tag{31}$$

$$\frac{E_d}{RT_M} = 2\left[-1 + \left(1 + \frac{3.117\, T_M^2}{W_{1/2}^2}\right)^{0.5}\right] \tag{32}$$

These equations were derived from an approximate treatment of the TPD equations. Similar formulas are available also for three-quarter widths, $W_{3/4}$.

Two similar approaches have been developed to determine the desorption order n.

The Shape Index Analysis technique considers the index S, defined as the ratio of the slopes of the TPD curve at the inflection point. Based on a single TPD curve, estimation of S enables prediction of the desorption order as well as the presence of readsorption. However, as already noted in a previous section this method suffers from both practical and theoretical difficulties.

As an alternative approach, Chan et al. [13] have proposed to determine the desorption order by a "skewness parameter," i.e. an index of TPD peak asymmetry.

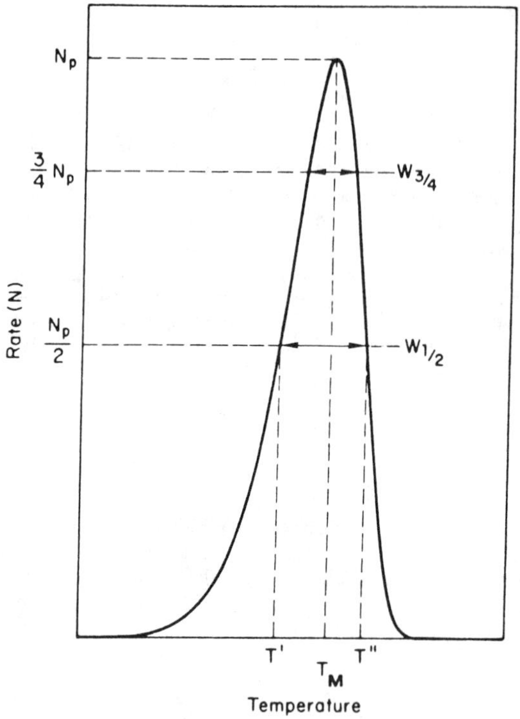

Figure 10. Method of half-widths: location of $W_{1/2}$ and $W_{3/4}$. (Reprinted with permission from Ref. [2].)

A complete method of analysis of a single TPD curve has been given by Forzatti et al. [14]. Based on the normalization of the curve with respect to its point of maximum, and exploiting the necessary condition $(dC^0/dT)_M = 0$, they arrive at the following expression for the activation energy of desorption (case of no readsorption):

$$\frac{E_d}{RT_M} = \frac{n}{\theta_M S_n} \qquad (33)$$

where $S_n = \int_0^{+\infty} \frac{C^0}{C_M} \frac{dT}{T_M}$

represents the area of the normalized TPD curve. It is worth mentioning that the equations proposed by Chan et al. for E_d/RT_M by peak width analysis (Equations 31 and 32) appear to be approximations of the above more general, yet simple relationship. The desorption order can be obtained from

$$n = \frac{\ln(C^0/C_M)}{\ln\left(\frac{\theta}{\theta_M}\right) + \frac{1 - T_M/T}{\theta_M S_n}} \qquad (34)$$

When Equation 34 is applied to several points of the TPD curve, it can also serve to detect whether the kinetic parameters are coverage dependent. In this case, in fact, different values of n would be estimated, depending on the corresponding θ-value. Equation 33 appears to have some inherent merits. It is easy to use, is not particularly sensitive to errors in the determination of T_M, θ_M or C_M^0, and makes use of integral data (S_n) rather than differential data (e.g., slopes of the TPD curve), so that a higher degree of accuracy is expected from its application.

Heterogeneous Surfaces

As suggested by both the theory of activated complexes and by the collision theory of reaction rates, the rate parameters for desorption are in reality functions of coverage. This has been confirmed by experiments in many instances, but relatively little work has been done so far on the analysis of thermal desorption from heterogeneous surfaces. In a first attempt to deal with the coverage dependence of the desorption rate parameters, Carter [15] and Tokoro et al. [16] proposed methods of analysis belonging to the "curve fitting" family, where the constant pre-exponential factor and the distribution of the activation energy are obtained by least-squares techniques. The most useful methods presented so far to obtain the coverage dependence of the desorption rate parameters are essentially developments of the methods based on the desorption rate isotherms previously discussed for the homogeneous case. Thus, King's method [17] makes use of a family of desorption traces corresponding to different initial coverages to construct suitable Arrhenius plots at fixed coverages, whose slopes yield $E_d(\theta)$. If the pre-exponential factor is coverage independent, the kinetic order can also be calculated by the same method. Otherwise, the order is assumed, and $k_d^0(\theta)$ is estimated.

Taylor and Weinberg [12] questioned the accuracy of King's procedure, owing to the weak temperature variations resulting from different initial surface coverages, and proposed instead to obtain a family of desorption traces by varying the heating rate β. As outlined by the authors, this implies a more extended range of surface temperatures, so that the accuracy of the Arrhenius plots is improved.

A different approach has been presented recently, which belongs to the class of "single curve" methods [14, 18]. It relies on a parabolic approximation of the unknown profile of activation energy, $E_d(\theta)$, in the neighborhood of the point maximum. Points from the TPD curve in the neighborhood of the peak maximum can then be arranged in a suitable characteristic plot, whose slope yields $E_d(\theta_M)/RT_M$. From this, the entire $E_d(\theta)$ profile can be constructed based on the values of T, C, and θ taken from the TPD curve. The method handles also situations with coverage dependent preexponential factors, on assuming that k_d^0 varies with θ in accordance with the activation energy ("compensation effect"), i.e.,

$$k_d^0(\theta) = \exp\frac{E_d(\theta)}{RT_s} \qquad (35)$$

In Equation 35 T_s is an adjustable parameter called "isokinetic temperature". The feasibility of this method has been demonstrated by analyzing one by one the TPD curves with different β presented by Taylor and Weinberg. The results were found in good agreement with $E_d(\theta)$ and $k_d^0(\theta)$ profiles given in the original publication, and obtained from the simultaneous analysis of ten spectra with heating rates varied from 4.5 to 212 K/s (see Figure 11).

EXAMPLES

TPD of CO from Ir (110)

In a classical piece of work Taylor and Weinberg [12] illustrated a method of data analysis particularly suitable for assessing the coverage dependence of desorption rate parameters. TPD runs were performed on a sample of Ir (110), using CO as the adsorbate. The concentration of desorbing CO was monitored by a quadrupole mass spectrometer connected with a PDP11-10

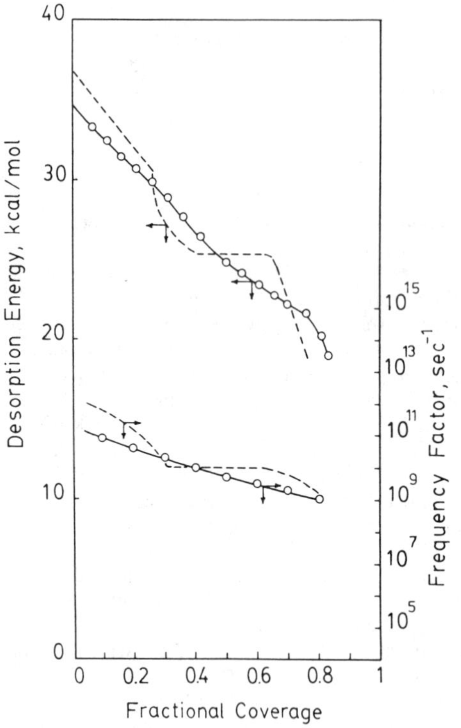

Figure 11. $E_d(\theta)$ and $k_d^0(\theta)$ profile obtained from analysis of curves a, b, and c shown in Figure 4 of Ref. [12]. Full lines: results from method of Ref. [14]. Dashed lines: results from method of Ref. 12. (Reprinted with permission from Ref. [14].)

computer, which recorded also the temperature of the sample as a function of time. Both variables could be sampled at a frequency of 60 Hz. For the data analysis, the method based on changes in the initial surface coverage was first attempted. For each spectrum θ^0 was varied by altering the gas exposure to the sample. The resulting TPD curves are shown in Figure 12. Order plots, ln C^0 as a function of ln θ for fixed temperatures, were then constructed. The desorption order, determined from the slopes of the plots, was found to be one only at low coverages, where the desorption rate parameters are weak functions of θ. At high coverages, however, desorption orders up to eight were estimated. Such scarcely plausible results could be explained by the authors as due to a strong coverage dependence of the rate parameters. In fact, they obtained an additional set of ten TPD spectra in which the heating rate was varied between 4.5 and 212 K/s. Arrhenius plots for points of constant coverage were constructed from the data, which yielded directly accurate estimates of the coverages. Since the pre-exponential factor is known to vary with coverage, too, the order of the desorption process, appearing in the intercept of the Arrhenius plot, must be assigned a priori. Based on the order plots at low coverage, and on independent evidence pointing to a molecular adsorption of CO, Taylor and Weinberg assumed first order desorption kinetics. The computed estimates for the desorption energy and for the preexponential factor are reported in Figure 11 as a function of coverage. Figure 11 demonstrates that both rate parameters vary significantly with coverage, and displays the occurrence of the "compensation effect", i.e., the desorption energy and the preexponential factor vary sympathetically with coverage.

In addition to the feasibility of determining coverage-dependent rate parameters, the method of analysis proposed by Taylor and Weinberg exhibits another advantage. As stressed in the original paper, the heating rate variation appears superior to the variation of initial surface coverage in determining large changes in T at fixed coverages. Accordingly desorption energies can be calculated with intrinsically greater accuracy.

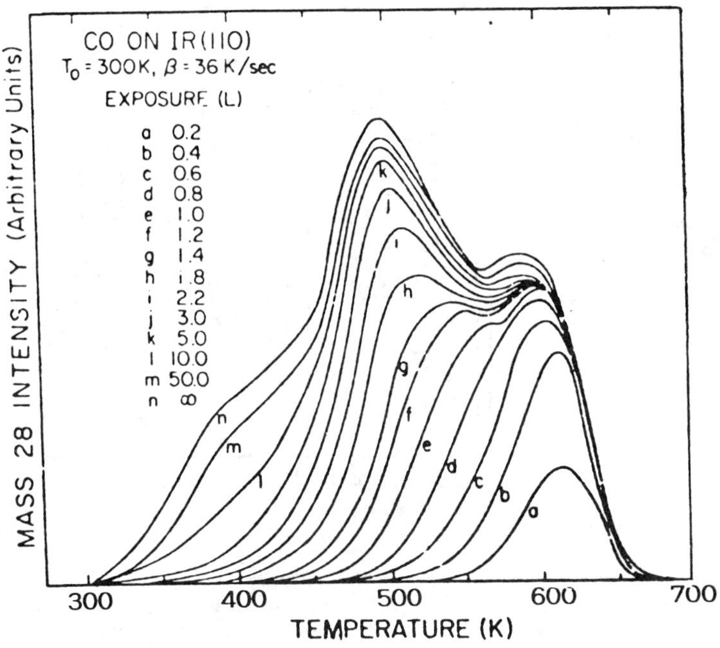

Figure 12. TPD curves of CO from Ir(100) corresponding to different initial coverages. (Reprinted with permission from Ref. [12].)

Combined FT-IR and TPD Investigation on the Interaction of Methanol with TiO_2 Anatase

During TPD experiments the interest is concentrated basically in the detection and identification of the desorbed species. More direct and complementary information on the chemical nature of the adsorbed species can be provided by additional techniques, typically by FT-IR. Thus combined FT-IR and TPD investigations are particularly suitable to study gas-surface interactions in heterogeneous catalysis.

The following example illustrates the combined use of FT-IR and TPD in the study of the interaction of methanol with the surface of TiO_2 anatase [19].

Figure 13 shows the FT-IR spectra of TiO_2 (Degussa P-25) after contact with methanol at low pressure. The presence of an undissociated form of CH_3OH interacting with a Lewis acid center and of adsorbed methoxy groups (species a and b in Figure 14) are revealed by the appearance of νOH and δOH bands (3,470 and 1,365 cm^{-1}), along with the higher frequency component of the two νCH doublets (2,953 and 2,849 cm^{-1}), and by the bands still present after evacuation, respectively. Formate ions are progressively formed on increasing the temperature up to 523 K (ν_{as}COO, δCH and ν_sCOO bands at 1,560, 1,378 and 1,360 cm^{-1} in curve d of Figure 13); further heating at 723 K results in a lower intensity of the bands of both formate and methoxy groups, which are however still present. Figures 15 and 16 show the FT-IR spectra of TiO_2 after contact with methanol at high pressure and subsequent evacuation at increasing temperature. Upon admission of CH_3OH at 10 Torr the bands associated with surface OH groups of TiO_2 anatase disappear and the νOH and δOH bands of species a are perturbed. Thus, the presence of H-bonded methanol species d and e can be inferred. Also the presence of a CH_3OH adsorbed species acting as a protor donor in hydrogen bonding with the basic sites of the surface (species c in Figure 14) is revealed by the disappearance upon prolonged evacuation at r.t. of νOH and νCO bands at 3,150 and 1,032 cm^{-1},

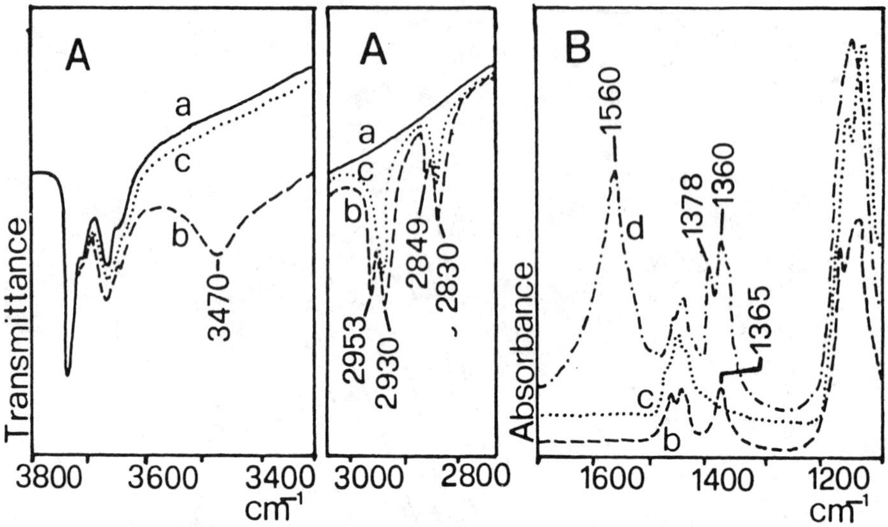

Figure 13. (A) Transmittance FT-IR spectra (3,800–2,700 cm^{-1}) of an activated TiO_2 disc (a), in contact with methanol vapor (up to 0.1 Torr) (b), and after evacuation at 473 K (c). (B) Absorbance FT-IR spectra (1,700–1,000 cm^{-1}) of the species formed on TiO_2 anatase: b and c, same as above; d, after evacuation at 523 K. Spectra of B are plotted in absorbance after subtracting the spectrum of the starting sample in order to point out the bands near the cut-off due to bulk Ti—O vibrations. (Reprinted with permission from Ref. [19].)

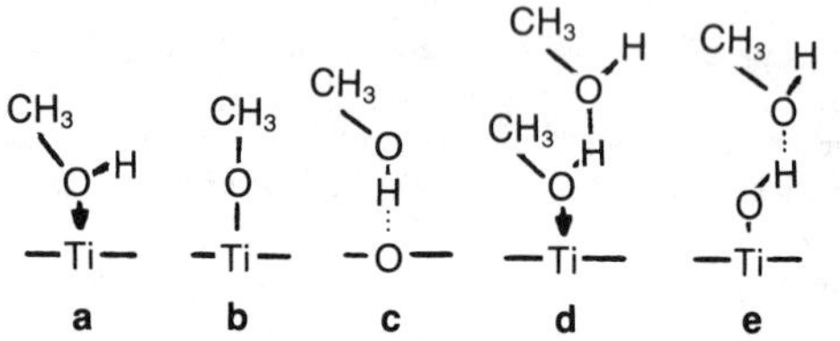

Figure 14. Proposed structures of adsorbed methanol forms on TiO_2 anatase. (Reprinted with permission from Ref. [19].)

along with the decrease of δOH band at 1,460 cm^{-1}. Under the same conditions the δOH band of species a at 1,035 cm^{-1} is restored, which indicates that species d decomposes through methanol desorption. On rising the evacuation temperature up to 473 K νOH and νCO bands at 3,420 and 1,060 cm^{-1}, originating from species d and e, progressively disappear and only the bands due to methoxy groups are detected, whereas bands due to surface OH groups are not restored. This eventually indicates that species a transforms into methoxy groups.

The previous data were used to interpret TPD of CH_3OH from TiO_2 anatase. Actually the full line TPD curve given in Figure 17 has been decomposed into four single TPD peaks, based on the FT-IR investigation and the on-line GC analysis: peak I, associated with the evolution of weakly adsorbed methanol species c; peak II, associated with the evolution of methanol from species d and e; peak III, associated with the decomposition of methoxy groups followed by CH_2O evolution; peak IV, associated with methanol evolution resulting from a surface Cannizzaro-type disproportionation reaction of dioxomethylene species leading to methoxy and formate species. Indeed, this reaction has been detected spectroscopically on pure TiO_2, as well as on other TiO_2 based catalysts. Also the decrease of formate ions, after evacuation up to 723 K, results in the evolution

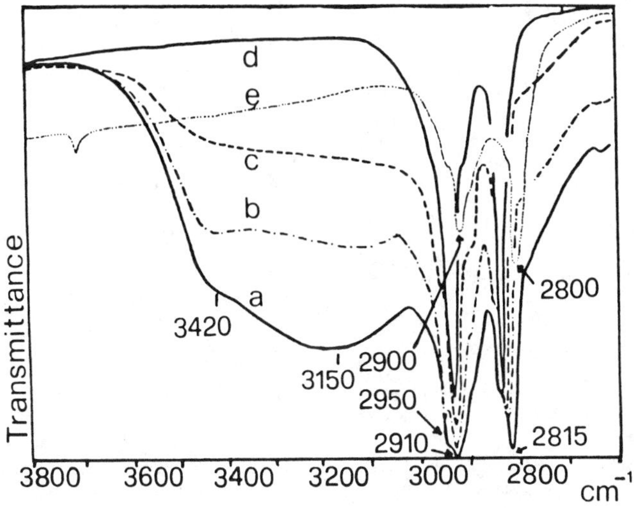

Figure 15. Transmittance FT-IR spectra (3,800–2,600 cm^{-1}) of TiO_2 disc after contact with methanol vapor (10 Torr) at r.t. (b); evacuation at 373 K (c); and evacuation at 473 K (d); TiO_2 + 2% K^+ after contact with methanol vapor at 10 Torr and evacuation at 573 K (e). (Reprinted with permission from Ref. [19].)

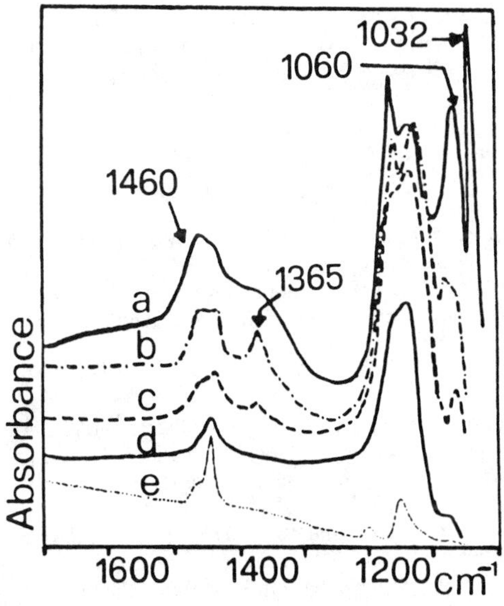

Figure 16. Absorbance FT-IR spectra (1,700–1,000 cm^{-1}) of the species formed on the surface of anatase after the same treatments as in Figure 15. (Reprinted with permission from Ref. [19].)

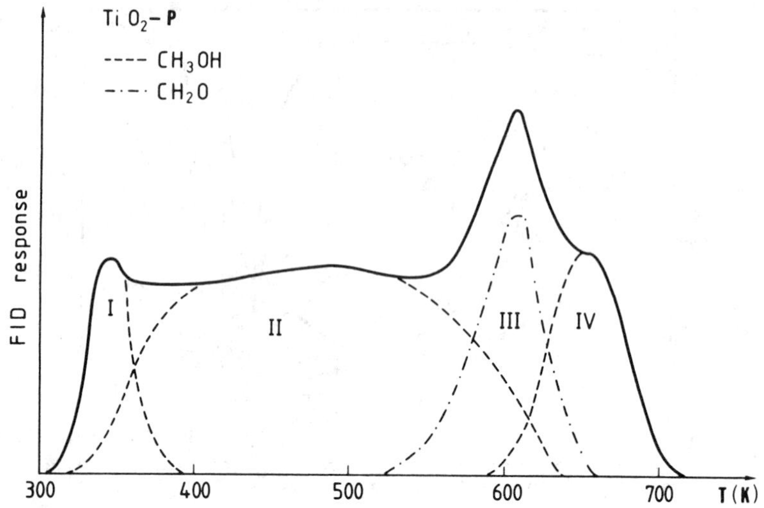

Figure 17. TPD curve of methanol TiO_2—P. (Reprinted with permission from Ref. [19].)

of CO which could not be detected by FID, but was confirmed by TCD in replicated experiments. The decomposition of the full line curve in Figure 17 has been made assuming that curves I and IV are symmetrical. Curves I, III, and IV have been analyzed on the basis of a homogeneous surface model and first order desorption kinetics. The following energies of desorption were calculated: curve I, $E_d = 10$ Kcal/mol; curve III, $E_d = 27$ Kcal/mol; curve IV, $E_d = 32$ Kcal/mol. The analysis of curve II was not attempted, nor in the framework of a heterogeneous surface model because FT-IR results proved that the requirement of a single adsorption state is not fulfilled.

Experimental Study on the Separability of Reaction-Deactivation Kinetics by TPD of Alcohols from γ-Al_2O_3

The following example illustrates the use of TPD during an experimental study designed to gain fundamental insight into the separability of reaction-deactivation kinetics [20].

The kinetic analysis of catalyst deactivation phenomena is commonly developed under the assumption that the deactivation rate may be separated from the rate of the main reaction:

$$r = r_0(C_i, T)a \tag{36}$$

where r_0 is the reaction rate for the fresh catalyst and for fixed values of the process variables C_i and T, and a is a scaled variable ($0 \le a \le 1$) which fully accounts for deactivation effects. This approach, although employed successfully for many different reaction and catalytic systems, does not seem entirely appropriate particularly for deactivation by poisoning.

This problem has been addressed experimentally in [20] by using the TPD method. The desorption of alcohols from γ-Al_2O_3 was chosen as the experimental reaction-catalyst system, and poisoning was simulated by impregnating the catalyst samples with NaOH solutions. Hence the following equation

$$r = v_m \frac{-d\theta}{dt} = v_m k_d \theta \tag{37}$$

provides the rate expression for the model reaction. The energetic description of the non-ideal catalytic surface, which is required to handle the problem as indicated by Butt et al. [21], is given by the $E_d(\theta)$ profile resulting from the analysis of the TPD traces. The non separable and separable forms of the overall rate of desorption can be specified as follows,

$$(r_T)_{NS,i} = \int_{E_{d_1}}^{E_{d_2}} a_i(E_d) r_0(E_d) \frac{dE_d}{(E_{d_2} - E_{d_1})} \tag{38}$$

$$(r_T)_{S,i} = \frac{\bar{a}_i}{(E_{d_2} - E_{d_1})} \int_{E_{d_1}}^{E_{d_2}} r_0(E_d)\, dE_d \tag{39}$$

$a_i(E_d)$ is a local activity factor corresponding to a desorption energy E_d on a catalyst with a level of poison i, and $\bar{a}_i$ is an average activity:

$$a_i(E_d) = \frac{r_i(E_d)}{r_0(E_d)} = \frac{v_{m,i} k_d(E_d) \theta_i(E_d)}{v_{m,0} k_d(E_d) \theta_0(E_d)} \tag{40}$$

$$\bar{a}_i = \int_{E_{d_1}}^{E_{d_2}} a_i(E_d) \frac{dE_d}{(E_{d_2} - E_{d_1})} \tag{41}$$

The comparison between separable and non separable rate forms was performed in terms of the ratio $(r_T)_{NS,i}/(r_T)_{S,i}$, the deviation of this ratio from unity implying that the separable rate form is not appropriate.

The thermal desorption spectra of methanol from fresh and Na poisoned γ-Al_2O_3 are shown in Figure 18. The complex shape of the TPD trace with two peaks and peak asymmetry is related to the heterogeneity of the γ-Al_2O_3 surface with sites of different acidic strength. Poisoning by Na

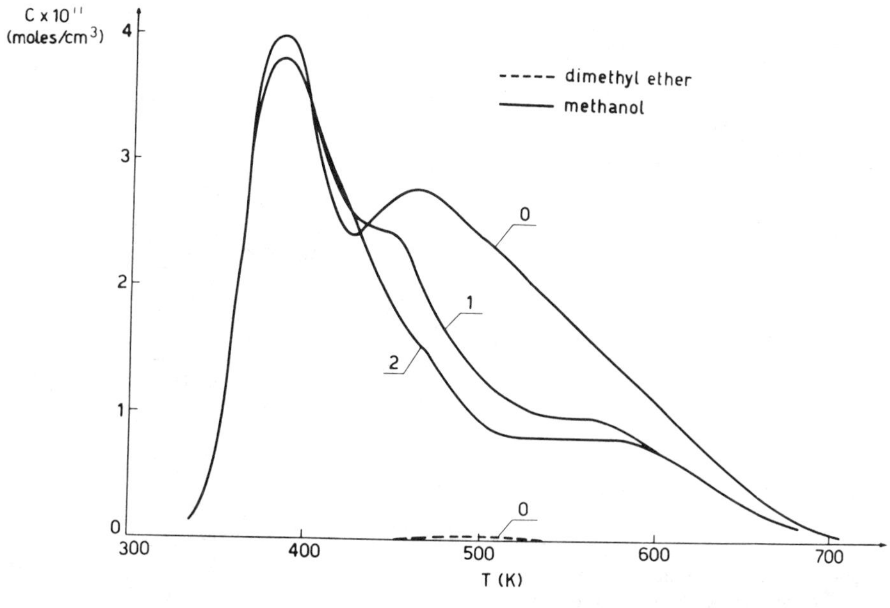

Figure 18. Thermal desorption curves of methanol from γ-Al_2O_3. Poison level 0 = 0% Na; level 1 = 0.8% Na; level 2 = 1.5% Na. (Reprinted with permission from Ref. [20].)

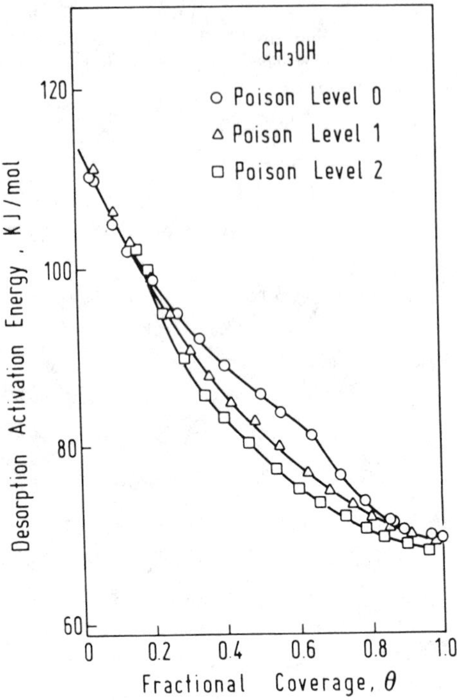

Figure 19. Calculated distribution profiles of activation energy for methanol desorption from fresh and Na-poisoned γ-Al_2O_3. Poison level 0 = 0% Na; level 1 = 0.8% Na; level 2 = 1.5% Na. (Reprinted with permission from Ref. [20].)

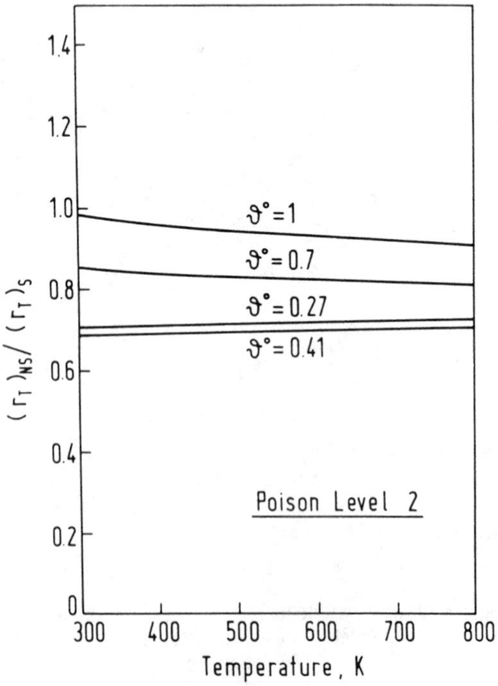

Figure 20. Methanol desorption from 1.5% Na-poisoned γ-Al_2O_3. Plots of calculated $(r_T)_{NS}/(r_T)_S$ versus temperature initial coverage θ^0 as a parameter. (Reprinted with permission from Ref. [20].)

reduces the amount of methanol desorbed at temperatures above 420 K, which indicates a preferential poisoning of the active sites with higher energy of activation.

The results of the TPD analysis are presented in Figure 19 in terms of $E_d(\theta)$ vs θ for the three levels of poison considered. The calculated values of the ratio $(r_T)_{NS,i}/(r_T)_{S,i}$ (Figure 20) is significantly lower than 1, which indicates that the separable rate form tends to overestimate the rate of the desorption reaction. This agrees with the observation that the most active sites are those preferentially poisoned. Accordingly local activities corresponding to higher E_d values are much smaller than the average activity appearing in the separable rate expression. The effect of θ^0 can be explained considering that initial coverages corresponding to the region where the gap between the energy profiles is wider emphasize the effect of non uniform poisoning, so that larger deviations of $(r_T)_{NS,i}/(r_T)_{S,i}$ from unity are derived. For very small initial surface coverages, however, it becomes more and more difficult to distinguish betweeen the poisoned and unpoisoned samples and $(r_T)_{NS,i}/(r_T)_{S,i}$ tends to 1 as θ^0 approaches zero.

In conclusion the assumption of separability turned out to be critical for the model reaction of methanol desorption from γ-Al_2O_3 because of the occurrence of a selective form of poisoning, which eventually led the separable rate form to overestimate the catalyst activity as a result of an incorrect averaging process. Also, a uniform poisoning was found superimposed on a selective poisoning in the case of ethanol desorption. In such a case, separability of the kinetics depends on the relative weight of the two contributions, the separable representation becoming less critical when the uniform poisoning process is more relevant. Finally, in the case of ethanol desorption it was observed that Na acts as a poison for ethanol evolution, but it promotes the formation of more sites for ethylene desorption. Hence, changes in selectivity do not appear to provide conclusive evidence of non separable kinetics, contrary to what frequently stated in the literature.

As a last comment it is worth pointing out that TPD proved to be a suitable experimental tool for investigating the separability of reaction-deactivation kinetics because it was able to provide a complete energetic and kinetic description of non ideal, heterogeneous catalytic surfaces.

TPSR of n-Butanal over a Zn—Cr—O Catalyst

This example demonstrates the application of the Temperature Programmed Surface Reaction technique to investigate the functionalities of a Zn—Cr—O catalyst [22].

The TPSR trace of n-butanal upon adsorption at 35°C after catalyst pretreatment under reducing atmosphere is shown in Figure 21. Two maxima, with $T_M = 89$°C and 383°C, and shoulders at

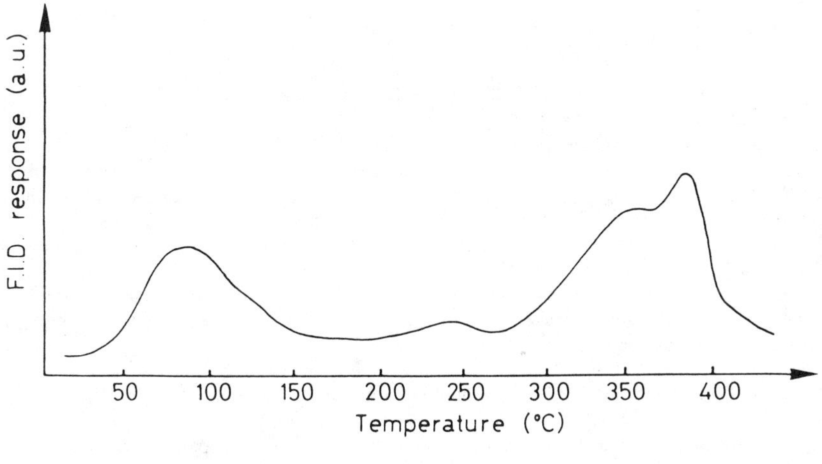

Figure 21. TPSR trace of n-butanal from the Zn—Cr—O sample.

Table 4
Quantitative Analysis of the TPSR Products Desorbed in the Range 30–200°C

Products	Relative Amount*
n-butanal	17%
1-butanol	12%
4-heptanone	5%
2-ethyl-2-hexenal	60%
isomer of 2-ethyl-2-hexenal	3%
doubly unsaturated C_{12} aldehyde	3%

* *on the basis of GC analysis*

Table 5
Quantitative Analysis of the TPSR Products Desorbed in the Range 250–450°C

Products	Relative Amount*
Propylene	39.4%
C_7 linear olefins	21.7%
Butenes	9.4%
C_5 hydrocarbons	5.8%
Ethylene	5.2%
4-heptanone	4.0%
C_8 dienes	3.8%
C_9–C_{16} unsaturated hydrocarbons (aromatics)	3.0%
C_7 dienes	2.0%
C_8 saturated ketone	1.3%
C_8 unsaturated ketone	1.3%
C_5–C_6 ketones	1.6%
toluene	1.0%
2-ethyl-2-hexenal	0.5%

* *on the basis of GC analysis*

about 130°C and 350°C, are manifest, together with a weak maximum at 250°C. The compounds desorbed into the carrier gas stream have been both analyzed on-line by GC, and condensed into a CS_2 trap at −196°C, and analyzed by GC, GC-FTIR, GC-MS. Tables 4 and 5 report the results of the analyses. Only small amounts of n-butanal desorb intact in the low-temperature region. The other identified compounds originate from surface catalyzed decomposition either of the initially adsorbed molecules or of adsorbed species produced upon adsorbate-gas phase reagent interaction. Most of the products can be explained by invoking the presence of two classes of intermediate surface species represented in Figures 22 and 23, and resulting from the adsorption of n-butanal (species A) and from a surface aldol-like condensation of two aldehyde molecules (species B), respectively. Indeed, the observed products have been explained starting from the above surface intermediates on assuming the following catalyst functionalities:

1. Aldol-like condensation for 2-ethyl-2-hexenal and a doubly unsaturated C_{12} aldehyde.
2. Hydrogenation, mainly for 1-butanol (along with hydrolysis).
3. Dehydrogenation for dienes, trienes and aromatics from the corresponding olefins.
4. Decarboxylation for propylene, 4-heptanone, and for C_7 linear olefins.
5. Dehydration for butenes, and C_8 dienes

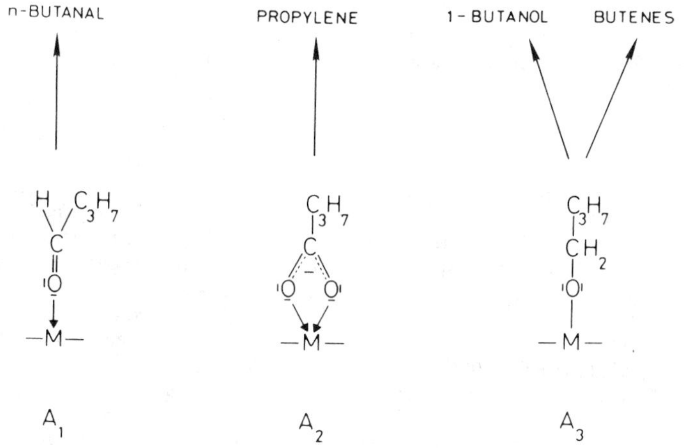

Figure 22. Intermediate surface species originating from the adsorption of n-butanal, and products desorbed thereof.

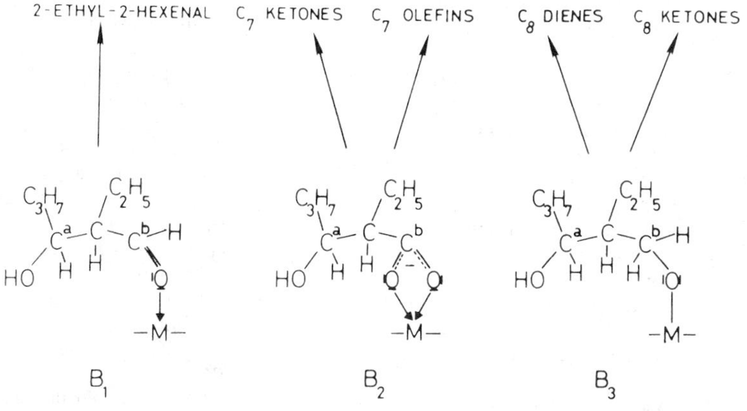

Figure 23. Intermediate surface species originating from the aldol-like condensation of two n-butanal molecules, and products desorbed thereof.

6. Isomerization of the C=C double bond for both hydrocarbon and oxygenated unsaturated compounds.
7. Cracking, for a number of light products.

The different functionalities are associated with different ranges of temperature, and have been discussed with respect to their relevance to the direct synthesis of methanol and higher alcohols from CO and H_2.

It is worth mentioning that the complex product mixture could be properly analyzed only by means of advanced techniques, such as GC-MS and GC-FTIR. As a matter of fact, the complete detection and identification of the products in a TPD or TPSR investigation appears to be a critical issue, and should never be overlooked.

Acknowledgments

The financial support of Ministero della Pubblica Istruzione (Roma) is gratefully acknowledged.

NOTATION

a	activity factor in a separable rate expression (s^{-1})
$a_i(E_d)$	activity of a homogeneous surface subunit for a level of poison i
$\bar{a}_i$	averaged activity for the level of poison i
C	gas phase concentration of desorbed species within the pellet (mol/cm^3)
C^0	gas phase concentration of the desorbed species in the reactor (mol/cm^3)
C_i	process variable i
D_b	effective bed diffusivity (cm^2/s)
D_p	effective particle diffusivity (cm^2/s)
E_a	activation energy for adsorption (Kcal/mol)
E_d	activation energy for desorption (Kcal/mol)
k_a	adsorption rate constant (cm^3/mol s)
k_a^0	preexponential factor for adsorption (cm^3/mol s)
k_d	desorption rate constant (s^{-1})
k_d^0	preexponential factor for desorption (s^{-1})
k_{eff}	effective desorption rate constant (s^{-1})
K	equilibrium constant for desorption
K^0	preexponential factor for desorption equilibrium constant
i	level of catalyst poison
m	order of readsorption
n	order of desorption
Q	flow rate of carrier gas (cm^3/s)
r	radial coordinate (cm) or rate of reaction (mol/cm^3 s)
r_0	rate of reaction on fresh catalyst (mol/cm^3 s)
r_i	rate of reaction on catalyst with level of poison i (mol/cm^3 s)
r_a	rate of readsorption
r_d	rate of desorption
$(r_T)_{NS}$	overall rate of reaction for non separable kinetics (mol/cm^3 s)
$(r_T)_S$	overall rate of reaction for separable kinetics (mol/cm^3 s)
R	gas constant (Kcal/mol k)
R_p	average particle radius (cm)
t	time (s)
T	temperature (K)
T^0	initial temperature of TPD run (K)
T_M	temperature of the TPD peak maximum
T_s	isokinetic temperature (K)
u	interstitial gas velocity (cm/s)
v_m	initial concentration of adsorbate on the catalyst (mol/cm^3)
$W_{1/2}$	half width of the TPD peak
$W_{3/4}$	three-quarter width of the TPD peak
W_c	catalyst mass (g)
z	reactor axial coordinate (z)
β	heating rate (K/s)
γ	dimensionless gas-phase concentration within the pellet
γ^0	dimensionless gas-phase concentration in the reactor
ΔE_d	range of activation energies (Kcal/mol)
ΔH	enthalpy of adsorption (Kcal/mol)
ΔS	entropy of adsorption (Kcal/mol K)
ΔT	temperature range of TPD run (K)
ε_B	void fraction of catalyst bed
ε_p	void fraction of catalyst particle
θ	surface concentration of adsorbate
θ^0	initial surface concentration of adsorbate
$\rho = (r/R_p)$	dimensionless radial coordinate
ρ_c	density of catalyst pellet (g/cm^3)
$\tau = (\beta t/\Delta T)$	dimensionless run time
Φ_1	modulus for diffusion effects
Φ_2	modulus for readsorption effects
ψ_1	modulus for accumulation in the pellet
ψ_2	modulus for accumulation in the bed

REFERENCES

1. Cvetanovic, R. J., and Amenomiya, Y., "Application of a Temperature-Programmed Desorption Technique to Catalyst Studies," *Adv. Catal*: 17, 103 (1967).
2. Falconer, J. L., and Schwarz, J. A., "Temperature-Programmed Desorption and Reaction: Application to Supported Catalysts," *Catal. Rev.-Sci. Eng.*: 25, 141 (1983).
3. Demmin, R. A., and Gorte, R. J., "Design Parameter for Temperature-Programmed Desorption from a Packed Bed," *J. Catal.*: 90, 32 (1984).
4. Rieck, J. S., and Bell, A. T., "Influence of Adsorption and Mass Transfer Effects on Temperature-Programmed Desorption from Porous Catalysts," *J. Catal.*: 85, 143 (1984).
5. Tronconi, E., and Forzatti, P., "Experimental Criteria for Diffusional Limitations during Temperature-Programmed Desorption from Porous Catalysts," *J. Catal.*: 93, 197 (1985).
6. Ibok, E. E., and Ollis, D. F., "Temperature-Programmed Desorption from Porous Catalysts: Shape Index Analysis," *J. Catal.*: 66, 391 (1980).
7. Criado, J. M., Malet, P., Munuera, G., and Rives-Arnau, V., "Remarks on "Temperature-Programmed Desorption from Porous Catalysts: Shape Index Analysis," *J. Catal.*: 75, 428 (1982).
8. Gorte, R. J., "Design Parameters for Temperature-Programmed Desorption from Porous Catalysts" *J. Catal.*: 75, 164 (1982).
9. Tronconi, E., and Forzatti, P., "Modelling and Experimental Verification of TPD from Porous Catalysts," *Chem. Eng. Sci.*: 41, 2541 (1986).
10. Tronconi, E., and Forzatti, P., "Diffusion-Limited Temperature Programmed Desorption from Heterogeneous Catalytic Surfaces," *Chem. Eng. Sci.*: 42, 2779 (1987).
11. Brenner, A., and Hucul, D. A., "Experimental Errors in the Application of Temperature-Programmed Desorption to Practical Catalysts," *J. Catal.*: 56, 134 (1979).
12. Taylor, J. L., and Weinberg, W. H., "A Method for Assessing the Coverage Dependence of Kinetic Parameters: Application to Carbon Monoxide Desorption from Iridium (110)," *Surface Sci.*: 78, 259 (1978).
13. Chan, C. M., Aris, R., and Weinberg, W. H., "An Analysis of Thermal Desorption Mass Spectra," *Appl. Surface Sci.*: 4, 234 (1980).
14. Forzatti, P., Borghesi, M., Pasquon, I., and Tronconi, E., "Thermal Desorption from Heterogeneous Surfaces: Normalized Curve Treatment," *Surface Sci.*: 137, 595 (1984).
15. Carter, G., "Thermal Resolution of Desorption Energy Spectra," *Vacuum*: 12, 245 (1962).
16. Tokoro, Y., Uchijima, T., and Yoneda, Y., "Analysis of Thermal Desorption Curves for Heterogeneous Surfaces. II. Nonlinear Variations of Activation Energy of Desorption," *J. Catal.*: 56, 110 (1979).
17. King, D. A., "Thermal Desorption from Metal Surfaces: a Review," *Surface Sci.*: 47, 384 (1975).
18. Forzatti, P., Borghesi, M., Pasquon, I., and Tronconi, E., "A Novel Analysis of TPD from Heterogeneous Catalytic Surfaces: a Normalized Single Curve Approach to the Case of Free Readsorption," *Proceedings 9th Iberoamerican Symposium on Catalysis*: 1, 281 (1984).
19. Busca, G., Forzatti, P., Lavalley, J. C., and Tronconi, E., "A TPD, FT-IR and Catalytic Study of the Interaction of Methanol with Pure and KOH Doped TiO_2 Anatase," *Catalysis by Acids and Bases* (B. Imelik et al., eds.), Elsevier, Amsterdam, 1985, p. 15.
20. Forzatti, P., Borghesi, M., Pasquon, I., and Tronconi, E., "Experimental Study on the Separability of Reaction-Deactivation Kinetics: Thermal Desorption of Alcohols from γ—Al_2O_3," *AIChE Journal*: 32, 87 (1986).
21. Butt, J. B., Watcher, C. K., and Billimoria, R. M., "On the Separability of Catalytic Deactivation Kinetics," *Chem. Eng. Sci.*: 33, 1321 (1978).
22. Lietti, L., Botta, D., Forzatti, P., Mantica, E., Pasquon, I., and Tronconi, E., "Synthesis of Alcohols from Carbon Oxides and Hydrogen. VIII. A Temperature Programmed Reaction Study of n-Butanal on a Zn—Cr—O Catalyst.," J. Catal.: 111, 000 (1988).

SECTION II

MULTIPHASE REACTOR OPERATIONS

CONTENTS

CHAPTER 9

DYNAMICS OF AGITATED MULTIPHASE CATALYTIC REACTORS AND ADSORBERS

B. J. McCoy, M. A. Galan, and J. M. Smith

Department of Chemical Engineering
University of California
Davis, California, USA

CONTENTS

INTRODUCTION

Well-stirred multiphase reactors are significant in chemical reaction engineering both as processing equipment and as apparatus for experimental investigations of kinetics and mass transfer phenomena [1]. As processing equipment, such reactors are operated as batch or continuous-flow systems (Figure 1). The batch reactor is inherently dynamic, i.e., always in an unsteady-state mode evolving to chemical equilibrium. The continuous-flow reactor, in response to a change in inlet condition, will pass through a transient before steady-state is reached. For start-up and control, and for measuring parameters for transient processes of this kind, mathematical models quantifying the dynamic response are desirable. The steady-state reactors are reviewed by Chaudhari and Ramachandran [2] and Shah [3]. In this review we are principally concerned with dynamic, linear systems.

Transient experiments provide an attractive method for measuring transport, chemical kinetic, and equilibrium parameters of reaction systems. Dynamic responses to imposed conditions are related by mathematical models to these parameters. At steady state all mass transport and reaction processes in a chemical reactor occur at the same rate, whereas under dynamic conditions the individual processes can take place at different rates at the same time. For example, in heterogeneous catalysis the rate of adsorption of a reactant on the solid, catalytic surface can be different from the subsequent rate of reaction on the surface. Because of the resulting change in adsorbed concentration with time, it is possible, in principle, to evaluate both adsorption and surface reaction rates by dynamic experiments.

Several investigators have studied dynamic fluid-solid catalytic reactions [e.g., Bell and Hegedus, [4], Tamaru, [5], Kobayashi and Kobayashi, [6]. Bennett [7, 8] and Suzuki and Smith [9] discussed methods for using dynamic data to avoid the assumption that one step in a heterogeneous

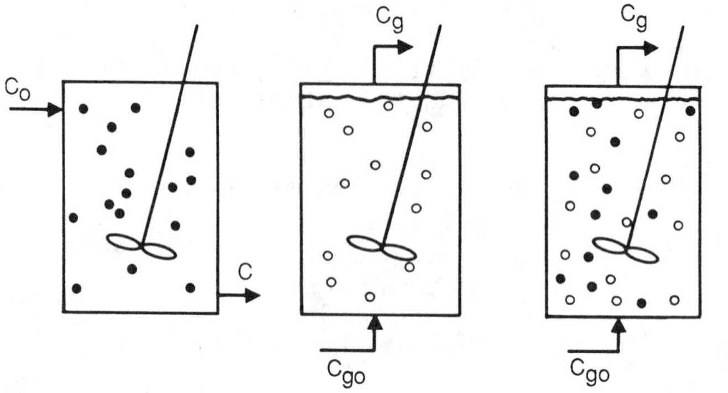

Figure 1. Schematic drawings of agitated multiphase catalytic reactors and adsorbers: continuous-flowing stirred liquid with suspended particles, continuously-flowing gas in stirred liquid, and continuously-flowing gas in stirred liquid with suspended particles.

catalytic reaction controls the overall rate, an assumption that is usually invoked in interpreting steady state information.

Gaseous reactants or adsorbates are usually dissolved by bubbling the gas into the stirred liquid. A dissolved reactant may adsorb onto a solid catalyst surface and react, or may react due to a homogeneous, soluble catalyst. In general, adsorption will precede heterogeneously-catalyzed reaction, as a two-step process. Reversible or irreversible adsorption are special cases of the two-step reaction. In two-phase gas-liquid reactions, after reactant gas in the bubbles dissolves, a two-step mechanism may occur: reversible association of reactant with the homogeneous catalyst followed by an irreversible reaction.

Liquid-solid reactors may be operated with reactant fed to the well-stirred vessel in the continuous-flow mode (Figure 1). Such two-phase reactors, in general, may involve a two-step reaction, i.e., reversible adsorption preceding irreversible reaction. The special cases, e.g., the continuous-flow stirred-tank with reversible or irreversible adsorption only (no reaction), are also of interest.

Analysis of the response to input disturbances has long been used to determine mixing characteristics, or residence time distributions, of industrial processing equipment, e.g., for absorbers, heat exchangers, fixed-bed reactors, etc. In the last two decades input-response methods have been applied in laboratory chemical reactors with known mixing characteristics to evaluate rate parameters. Thus, for fixed-bed adsorbers, the rate parameters have been explicitly related [10] to the moments of the response curve for an impulse input by using a model describing the overall adsorption in terms of longitudinal dispersion, fluid-to-particle mass transfer, intraparticle diffusion, and adsorption rate at a catalytic site. For rate parameters independent of equipment size, e.g., intraparticle diffusion, and adsorption and surface-reaction rate coefficients, dynamic measurements can be carried out in the laboratory, and the parameter values then used for design of commercial equipment. In principle, pulse, step, and periodic input disturbances can be used. Only the first two experimental procedures have proven popular.

According to the Langmuir-Hinshelwood concept of heterogeneous reactions, the dissolved reactants adsorb onto the solid surface before reacting. The rarely-observed Eley-Rideal mechanism postulates that molecules from the fluid phase react directly at the solid surface. For linear kinetics the Langmuir-Hinshelwood model allows first-order reversible adsorption followed by irreversible first-order surface reaction. The Eley-Rideal model, on the other hand, admits a single first-order fluid-phase reaction. Ahn and Smith [11] explained that, in general, these two approaches are equivalent only at steady state, and for dynamic systems the one-step mechanism is not an accurate substitute for the correct two-step mechanism. McCoy [12] used a moment theory to develop a criterion for kinetic parameters, i.e., to determine under what conditions the one-step mechanism can be an adequate approximation. The necessary and sufficient condition for this approximation to be valid is that the adsorbed species concentration is unchanging with time, i.e., a pseudo-steady state.

As the zero moment describes the character of a steady-state process, in the treatment that follows, a composite rate coefficient, $k_0 = (1/k_a + 1/Kk_r)^{-1}$, appears in the expressions for the zero moment. For higher moments, however, the separate adsorption rate coefficient, k_a, the adsorption equilibrium coefficient, K, and the surface reaction rate coefficient, k_r, appear. This allows the evaluation of each rate constant, k_a and k_r, from transient experiments, but not from steady-state experiments.

The objective of this chapter is to review work, particularly that done in our laboratory, on experiments and mathematical modeling of transient, agitated, multiphase, catalytic reactors, and adsorbers. Three-phase (gas-liquid-suspended solid particles) and two-phase (fluid-solid and gas-liquid) continuous-flow reactors are discussed. Similarities in the governing differential equations for these systems are evident. Much of our research effort has been directed toward the separate measurement of adsorption and reaction rate coefficients for catalytic reactions, possible only by dynamic experiments. The theoretical developments and experimental procedures needed for this analysis are featured prominently in what follows.

MOMENT THEORY

In flow systems, responses to transients due to impulse (delta function) or step inputs are conveniently represented as temporal moments at the outlet [13, 14]. From these moments the concentration as a function of time at the outlet can be reconstructed as an expansion in Hermite or Laguerre polynomials [15]. The impulse response is most important, because all other responses (for linear systems) can be represented as a superposition, i.e., an integration of the impulse response multiplied by the actual input [16]. In particular, the step response is simply the time integral of the impulse response.

The temporal moments are conveniently calculated from the Laplace transform $\bar{C}$ of the time-dependent concentration, C(t),

$$\bar{C} = \int_0^\infty C(t)e^{-st}\, dt \tag{1}$$

by applying the identity

$$m_n = (1/C_0) \lim_{s\to 0} d^n\bar{C}/ds^n = (1/C_0) \int_0^\infty t^n C(t)\, dt \tag{2}$$

where C_0 is a concentration characteristic of the input pulse. The zero moment is proportional to the total mass of reactant in the pulse, since

$$C_0 Q m_0 = \int_0^\infty QC(t)\, dt \tag{3}$$

in terms of the (constant) volumetric flow rate, Q. Figure 2 shows this as the area of the pulse, $C(t)/C_0$ vs. t. The normalized first moment,

$$\mu_1 = m_1/m_0 \tag{4}$$

represents the average time (center of mass) of the exiting pulse (Figure 2). The normalized second central moment, or variance,

$$\mu_2' = (1/m_0) \int_0^\infty (t - \mu_1)^2 (C/C_0)\, dt \tag{5}$$

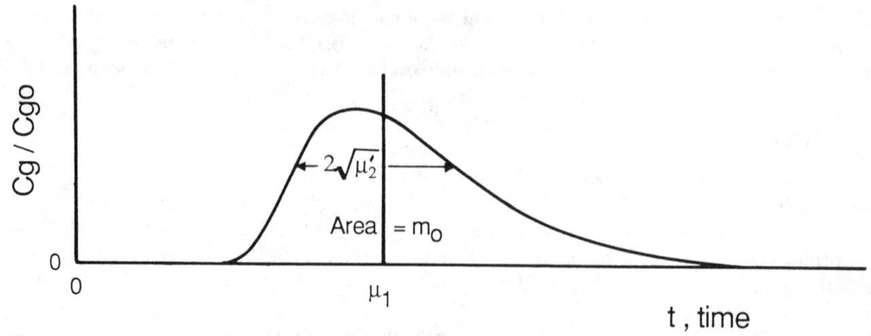

Figure 2. Sketch of a concentration pulse response showing m_0, the zero moment, as the area under the concentration history curve; μ_1, the normalized first moment as the average of the pulse; and μ_2', the variance representing the square of the width of the pulse.

is a measure of the width of the pulse. Higher moments provide other shape characteristics of the shape of the pulse.

As the integral of the impulse response is the step function response, conversely, the derivative of the step response is the impulse response. This relationship allows the determination of moments from step-response (breakthrough curve) data. The zero moment for the step response is simply the unconverted fraction of the reactant in the outlet (Figure 3) after the response has come to steady state; that is

$$m_0 = \frac{C_q}{C_{q0}} \tag{6}$$

where C_0 is the inlet concentration. The first moment can be shown to be

$$m_1 = \int_0^\infty (1 - C/C_0)\, dt \tag{7}$$

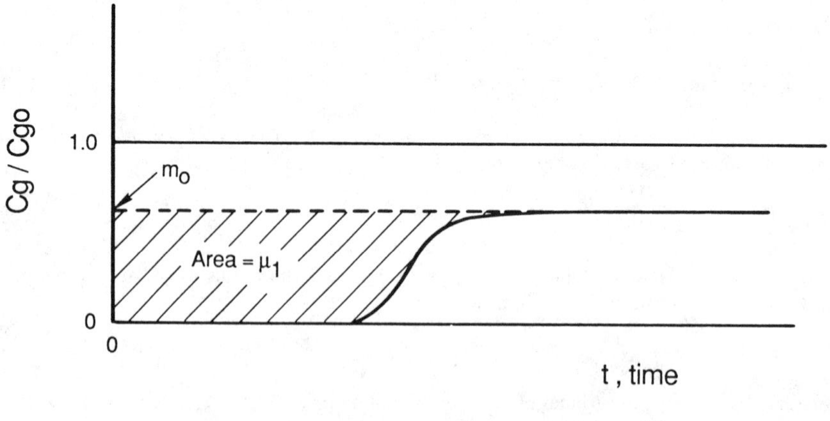

Figure 3. Sketch of a unit concentration step response showing m_0, the zero moment as the steady-state unconverted fraction, and μ_1, the normalized first moment as the area between the steady-state asymptote and the concentration history curve.

which is the area between $C(t)/C_0$ and the value of m_0 (Figure 3). The second moment for the response to the step input is given by

$$m_2 = 2\int_0^{\infty} (1 - C/C_0)t\,dt \tag{8}$$

Experimental moments can be applied to determine parameters for a system if a mathematical model is available. Likewise, if the parameters are known, then the moments can be calculated and the shape of the transient response predicted.

The strategy of the moment approach to analyzing dynamic systems is, first, to construct the governing differential equations, with initial and boundary conditions, second, to solve the equations in Laplace transform space, and third, to use the derivatives and limits of Equation 2 to determine moment expressions in terms of the transport and kinetic parameters of the system. Then experimental data for moments from dynamic experiments can be compared with the derived expressions to determine values of parameters. Alternatively, if these parameters are known or can be estimated, the moments can be predicted, and the transient constructed.

AGITATED LIQUID-SOLID SLURRY REACTORS

In these systems no gas phase is present and the reactant or adsorbate is introduced in the liquid feed to the reactor [17–19]. The basic equations are similar to those for the three-phase systems. We present here the development for reversible first-order adsorption followed by irreversible first-order reaction on the solid catalyst particle, and for the special case of adsorption alone.

Reaction

Mass balances for the reactant in the bulk liquid, liquid-filled pores, and the catalyst site are

$$dC_L/dt = (C_0 - C_L)/\tau - k_s a_s (C_L - C_i(r = R)) \tag{9}$$

$$\beta\,\partial C_i/\partial t = D_e \frac{1}{r^2}\frac{\partial}{\partial r}\left(r\frac{\partial C_i}{\partial r}\right) - \rho_p k_a (C_i - n/K) \tag{10}$$

$$\partial n/\partial t = k_a(C_i - n/K) - k_r n \tag{11}$$

Boundary and initial conditions are

$$k_s(C_L - C_i(r = R)) = D_e(\partial C_i/\partial r)_{r=R} \tag{12}$$

$$(\partial C_i/\partial r)_{r=R} = 0 \tag{13}$$

$$C_L(t = 0) = C_i(t = 0) = 0 \tag{14}$$

In Equation 9, a_s, the mass transfer area per unit particle-free fluid, can be written for spherical particles in terms of the particle density, ρ_p, the total mass of particles per unit particle-free fluid, m_s, and the surface area per sphere volume, $3/R$,

$$a_s = (3/R)m_s/\rho_p \tag{15}$$

As discussed earlier, the zero moment is the steady-state unconverted fraction of reactant in the exit stream obtained either by setting the time derivatives in Equations 9 and 10 equal to zero and solving for C/C_0, or by evaluating the $s = 0$ limit of the Laplace transform of the exit concentration, the resultant zero moment expression is

$$m_0 = C_L/C_0 = 1/[1 + \tau a_s k_s/(1 + Bi/3\phi^2\eta)] \tag{16}$$

in terms of the vessel holding time,

$$\tau = V_L/Q_L \tag{17}$$

the Biot number,

$$Bi = Rk_s/D_e \tag{18}$$

the reaction-diffusion (Thiele) modulus,

$$\phi^2 = \rho_p k_0 R^2/9D_e \tag{19}$$

and the effectiveness factor,

$$\eta = (3/R)D_e(\partial C_i/\partial r)_{r=R}/\rho_p k_0 (C_i)_{r=R} = [-1 + 3\phi/\tanh(3\phi)]/3\phi^2 \tag{20}$$

The global effectiveness factor, η_G, is defined as in Equation 20, but with the bulk concentration C replacing $C_i(r = R)$. The relationship between the two effectiveness factors is

$$1/\eta_G = 1/\eta + 3\phi^2/Bi \tag{21}$$

which simplifies Equation 16 to

$$m_0 = C_L/C_0 = 1/[1 + \tau a_s k_s 3\phi^2 \eta_G/Bi] = 1/[1 + \tau m_s \eta_G k_0] \tag{22}$$

For small particles, intraparticle diffusion is unimportant in the slurry reactor and C_i does not depend on r. Under this condition Equation 10 is replaced by

$$\beta\, \partial C_i/\partial t = k_s(3/R)(C - C_i) - \rho_p k_a(C_i - n/K) \tag{23}$$

For this case Equations 9, 23, and 11 can be solved for the moments, which are functions of the two kinetic rate constants k_a and k_r, as well as k_s. For example, the zero moment expression is

$$m_0 = 1/[(1 + \tau a_s k_s)/(1 + Bi/3\phi^2)] \tag{24}$$

since $\eta \simeq 1$

For completely reversible processes the normalized zero moment m_0 is unity since all the reactant fed to the reactor ultimately appears in the exit stream. The normalized first moment $\mu_1 = m_1/m_0$ is a function of K, the equilibrium uptake capacity of the system. When the reaction or adsorption steps are irreversible, however, both the zero and first moment expressions contain the rate constants.

Adsorption

For reversible adsorption, the governing equations are Equations 9, 10, and 11 with $k_r = 0$. Results for the first and second moments [19] are

$$\mu_1 = \tau(1 + m_s K)/H + \tau \tag{25}$$

$$\mu_2' = \tau^2(1 + m_s K)^2 + 2m_s K^2/k_a + 2\tau(R^2/2D_e + R/k_s)[(\beta + \rho_p k)^2 m_s/\rho_p] \tag{26}$$

Note that the zero moment, m_0, is unity and the first moment is a function only of the capacity of the system. For reversible adsorption, the second moment depends upon all the parameters in the governing differential equations.

For irreversible adsorption Equation 11 becomes

$$\partial n/\partial t = k_a C_i \tag{27}$$

The desorption rate constant vanishes, i.e., $k_a/K = 0$, so that k_0 is replaced with k_a in Equations 19 and 20, which are otherwise unchanged. In this case the only rate parameters affecting the moments are k_s, D_e, and k_a. Furusawa and Smith [19] found that for benzaldehyde in aqueous slurries of activated carbon, adsorption was irreversible in the time interval of the experiments. Also, they employed small particles so that there was no retardation of the rate due to intraparticle diffusion. Then the zero, first, and second equations involve only k_s and k_a. The resultant expressions are

$$m_0 = [1 + \tau/(1/k_s a_s + 1/k_a m_s)]^{-1} \tag{28}$$

$$\mu_1 = [1/\tau + 1/(1/k_s a_s + 1/k_a m_s)]^{-1} \tag{29}$$

$$\mu_2' = [1/\tau + 1/(1/k_s a_s + 1/k_a m_s)]^{-2} \tag{30}$$

These equations may be used to determine mass transfer and adsorption rate constants from experimental measurements of moments for irreversible adsorption.

AGITATED GAS-LIQUID BUBBLE REACTORS

In gas-liquid reactions where the gaseous reactant is bubbled through a well-stirred liquid the location of the reaction depends primarily upon the reaction kinetics. For very fast kinetics the reaction can occur entirely in the thin film of liquid surrounding the gas bubble. For slow kinetics the reaction is predominantly in the bulk liquid. Also, intermediate cases are possible. An analysis of this problem has been presented by Levenspiel and Godfrey [20], and others [21, 22] for steady-state operation, but there appears to be no analysis for dynamic operation. Our first objective is to develop the theory for the dynamic behavior of a well-stirred bubble reactor, accounting for reaction in both the thin film and bulk liquid. Under dynamic conditions it is possible in principle to evaluate rate constants for the individual transport and reaction steps involved in the overall reaction.

Model

The dynamic model is for an overall first-order reaction in a two-phase, stirred reactor that includes association and reaction in the agitated bulk liquid, as well as diffusion and association and reaction within the liquid film surrounding each gas bubble. The assumptions are:

1. The reaction system is isothermal.
2. The liquid is well mixed and the discrete gas bubbles have a residence time distribution corresponding to complete mixing.
3. Mass transfer resistance in the gas phase is negligible relative to resistance in the liquid phase.
4. Film theory is adequate to describe the mass transfer of dissolved gas reactant between the gas bubble and the agitated liquid.
5. The overall reaction is irreversible and first-order with respect to catalyst and dissolved gas concentrations.
6. The two-step reaction mechanism consists of a first-order reversible association of dissolved gas with catalyst, followed by a first-order irreversible reaction.

Based on these assumptions, the mass balance equation for the gas concentration, $C_g(t)$, with diffusion into the gas-liquid film is

$$V_B V_L\, dC_g/dt = Q(C_{g0} - C_g) + V_L a_B D(\partial C_f/\partial x)_{x=0} \tag{31}$$

The mass balance equations, which include association and reaction in the film, for the dissolved reactant concentration in the film, $C_f(t, x)$, are

$$\partial C_f/\partial t = D(\partial^2 C_f/\partial x^2) - \sigma k_a(C_f - N_f/K) \tag{32}$$

$$dN_f/dt = k_a(C_f - N_f/K) - k_r N_f \tag{33}$$

where $N_f(t)$ is the concentration of the reactant-catalyst complex in the film, and σ is the catalyst concentration. The boundary conditions for C_f are

$$C_f(x = 0) = C_g/H \tag{34}$$

$$C_f(x = d) = C_L \tag{35}$$

in terms of the film thickness, $d = D/k_L$.

The diffusion of the complex in the stagnant film is neglected in Equation 33. This assumption has been justified under most conditions by comparison of reactant concentration profiles in the film at steady-state with and without complex diffusion.

The mass balance equations for dissolved reactant gas and the reactant-catalyst complex in the bulk liquid are

$$dC_L/dt = -a_B D(\partial C_f/\partial x)_{x=d} - \sigma k_a(C_L - N_L/K) \tag{36}$$

$$dN_L/dt = k_a(C_L - N_L/K) - k_r N_L \tag{37}$$

The initial conditions require that all concentrations are initially zero:

$$C_g(t = 0) = C_f(x, t = 0) = C_L(t = 0) = N_f(t = 0) = N_L(t = 0) = 0 \tag{38}$$

and the input to the system for our experiments is an impulse,

$$C_{g0} = C_0\, \delta(t) \tag{39}$$

Moment Expressions

The five differential equations, Equations 31–33, 36, and 37 are readily solved in the Laplace domain. The normalized, zero temporal moment, m_0, calculated as the limit when the Laplace parameter vanishes, is equivalent to the unreacted fraction in steady-state operation,

$$m_0 = 1/[1 + K_L Ha(Ha + \phi' \coth Ha)/(\phi' + Ha \coth Ha)] \tag{40}$$

in terms of the dimensionless group K_L and ϕ' and the Hatta number Ha. The mass transfer group K_L is defined by

$$K_L = \frac{k_L a_B V_L}{Q_g H} = \frac{k_L a_B L}{H v_B V_B} \tag{41}$$

The first moment, m_1, calculated as the limit of the first derivative of the Laplace transform solution, is

$$m_1 = (V_B V_L/Q)(1 + \pi)/[1 + K_L Ha(Ha + \phi' \coth Ha)/(\phi' + Ha \coth Ha)]^2 \tag{42}$$

where

$$\pi = \frac{(1+\xi)\mathrm{Ha}}{\mathrm{HV_B}[\phi' + \mathrm{Ha}\coth(\mathrm{Ha})]^2}\left[\frac{\phi'\coth(\mathrm{Ha})}{2} + \left(1 - \frac{\phi'}{2}\right)\mathrm{csch}^2(\mathrm{Ha}) + 1\right]\mathrm{Ha}^2 + \frac{\coth(\mathrm{Ha})}{2\phi'}\mathrm{Ha}^3 + \frac{\mathrm{csch}^3(\mathrm{Ha})}{2\phi'}\mathrm{Ha}^4 \quad (43)$$

The square of the dimensionless group, Ha, is the ratio of the maximum possible conversion of oxygen in the film to the maximum diffusion transport of oxygen through the film, and can be written as follows:

$$\mathrm{Ha}^2 = [(k_h\sigma C_g/H)/(DC_g/H)] = k_h\sigma D/k_L^2 \quad (44)$$

The group ϕ' is the ratio of the maximum possible reaction rate of oxygen in the bulk liquid to the maximum mass transfer rate of oxygen to the bulk,

$$\phi' = \sigma k_h/k_L a_B \quad (45)$$

Thus, Ha provides a condition to determine if the reaction in the film is negligible (Ha $\ll$ 1) or not (Ha $\gg$ 1), and ϕ' determines if the whole process is mass transfer controlled ($\phi' \gg 1$) or reaction controlled ($\phi' \ll 1$).

The Hatta number, Ha, is defined in terms of the combined rate coefficient, k_h, which is given by

$$1/k_h = 1/k_a + 1/Kk_r \quad (46)$$

The zero moment, Equation 40, contains k_h only, and thus provides information available from steady-state data. Appearing in the quantity π [via ξ, see Equation 49] in the first moment, Equation 42, however, is the ratio, k_h/k_r. This allows the separate determination of k_r, and hence k_a, when k_h is known from dynamic response data.

In the fast reaction regime, for which the reaction occurs exclusively in the film, we have Ha $\gg$ 1, and Equation 40 reduces to

$$1/(1 - m_0) = 1 + 1/K_L\mathrm{Ha} = 1 + QH/a_B V_L(D\sigma k_h)^{1/2} \quad (47)$$

This result is identical to the analysis based on a penetration-diffusion model with infinite film thickness. The dimensionless group K_L is independent of Q since a_B is proportional to Q [17]. Hence, according to Equation 47, conversion in the fast reaction regime will not be affected by a change in gas flow rate. This condition can be used for the experimental determination of mass transfer area for the fast reaction case, when the reaction rate is known. The first moment equation in this reaction regime, reduced from Equation 42, can be written as

$$m_1 = m_0^2[V_B + \mathrm{Ha}(1+\xi)/2H\phi']V_L/Q \quad (48)$$

where

$$\xi = k_h^3/Kk_r^2 \quad (49)$$

In the slow reaction regime, where the reaction takes place only in the bulk liquid, we have Ha $\ll$ 1, and Equation 40 reduces to

$$1/(1 - m_0) = 1 + 1/K_L + 1/(K_L\phi') = 1 + 1/K_L + QH/V_L k_h\sigma \quad (50)$$

Equation 50 is identical to the result obtained from the model of Fu and McCoy [23]. Under these conditions the conversion is a function of gas flow rate. By plotting$1/(1 - m_0)$ versus QH/V_L, quantities that are known experimentally, a straight line should be obtained. The overall reaction rate coefficient, k_h, and the dimensionless mass transfer coefficient, K_L, can be extracted from the slope and intercept, respectively.

Next we consider the conditions under which the reaction in the bulk is sufficiently fast to reduce the bulk concentration of dissolved gas to zero. The reaction rate is controlled by the rate at which oxygen can be transferred to the bulk liquid (i.e., film mass transfer is controlling, and $\phi' \gg 1$), while at the same time the reaction is still in the slow reaction regime. Under these circumstances, Equation 50 reduces to

$$1/(1 - m_0) = 1 + 1/K_L \tag{51}$$

and the conditions to be fulfilled are

$$(D\sigma k_h)^{1/2}/k_L \ll 1 \ll \sigma k_h/k_L a_B \tag{52}$$

The sulfite oxidation reaction has been utilized to measure $k_L a_B$ according to Equations 20, 21, and 22.

Sketches of the concentration profiles represented by the various reaction regimes are shown in Figure 4, where reaction causes the profile in the film to deviate from linearity.

The conversion, $(1 - m_0)$, predicted by Equations 40, 47, and 50, is plotted versus Ha for different values of ϕ' and two values of K_L in Figure 5. The graphs show the transition from fast to slow reaction for different rates of mass transfer. For large ϕ', i.e., $k_h \gg k_L a_B$, the transition region between the two asymptotes is very small, and the entire range of Hatta number can be represented well by the asymptotic relations, Equations 47 and 50. As ϕ' becomes small, however, according to Figure 2, the transition region becomes more significant. The relationships for m_0, Equations 40, 47, and 50, and their graphs in Figure 2 should be useful in analysis and design for gas-liquid, first-order reactions in stirred vessels.

To measure separately k_a and k_r requires the first moment from dynamic response experiments. In the slow reaction regime, for $Ha \ll 1$, Equation 42 becomes

$$m_1 = m_0^2[V_B + (1 + \xi)/H(1 + \phi')^2]V_L/Q \tag{53}$$

As the measured first moment includes the effect of the dead volume, we write the observed re-

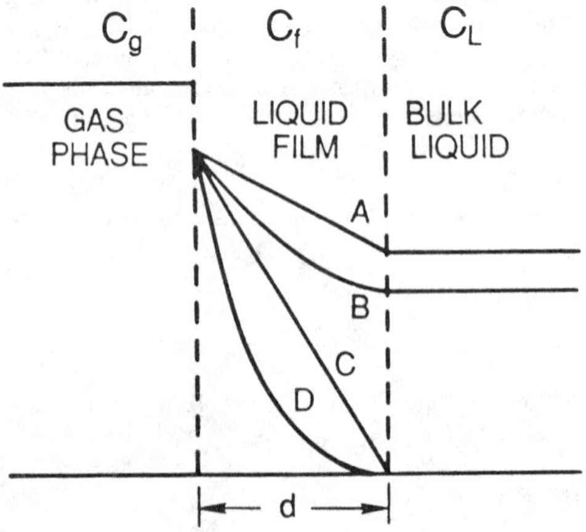

Figure 4. Concentration profiles for the homogeneously catalyzed reaction of dissolved gas in a stirred, gas-liquid bubble reactor: A, slow reaction, no reaction in the film; B, reaction in both film and bulk liquid; C, mass-transfer controlled slow reaction; D, fast reaction

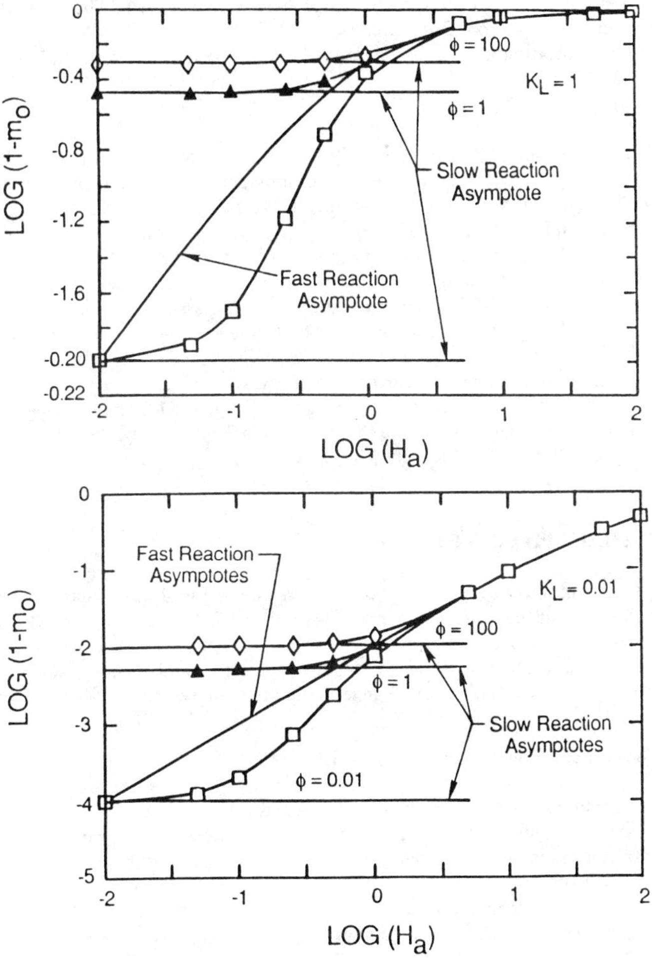

Figure 5. Dimensionless plot of conversion, $1 - m_0$, versus Hatta number, Ha, for different values of mass transfer groups, ϕ and K_L.

duced first moment μ_1^0 as

$$\mu_1^0 = m_1/m_0 + (V_0 - V_B V_L)/Q \tag{54}$$

from which is obtained, with Equation 50, the following relation useful for analyzing experimental data:

$$\mu_1^0(Q/V_L) + V_B(1 - m_0) = H(Q/\sigma V_L)^2(1 - m_0)^2/m_0[(1/k_h)^2 + \sigma/Kk_r^2] + V_0/V_L \tag{55}$$

Due to the small gas holdup V_B, the term $V_B(1 - m_0)$ can be neglected. A straight line is expected if the left side of Equation 55 is plotted versus $H(Q/\sigma V_L)^2(1 - m_0)^2/m_0$. Since k_h is already available, the slope gives σ/Kk_r^2, from which k_r can be evaluated if K is known. The value of k_a can then be determined, in principle, from Equation 46.

For reversible association alone (no reaction), Equation 55 reduces to the following expression:

$$\mu_1^0 = [(1 + \sigma K)/H + V_0/V_L]V_L/Q \tag{56}$$

showing that the slope of a plot of μ_1^0 versus V_L/Q yields a value of K when H and V_0 are known.

This discussion on the dynamic analysis of the homogeneous reaction of a dissolved gas in a gas-liquid bubble reactor is applicable to reactions that are first-order in the dissolved gas reactant. The zero-moment results are represented in terms of the conversion, $1 - m_0$, and show how the various regimes are affected by reaction and mass transfer rates for steady-state systems. The first-moment results are specific to a system following the mechanism of reversible association and irreversible reaction, or, one of its special cases (e.g., reversible association alone, or irreversible reaction alone). Aside from providing equations for analyzing experimental data, the moment theory presented here can also be used to predict reactor behavior, if estimates of the reaction and mass transfer parameters are available. The zero moment gives, for either steady-state or transient systems, the conversion in terms of the system parameters. While the first moment yields only partial information about the transient response of the system, it is the most important piece of information, namely, the response time of the transient.

AGITATED THREE-PHASE REACTORS

The derivation of moment equations for the dynamic behavior of three-phase slurry systems has been presented by Ramachandran and Smith [24] and by Weng and Smith [25], and Ahn, et al [11]. In the first work the accumulation term in the gas bubbles was neglected. The argument for this assumption is based upon the small residence time for the bubbles in the slurry and probably is valid in most cases. However, the more general equations developed in [11] are presented here.

Basic Equations for Reaction Case

The more important restrictions in the derivation are: (a) plug flow of discrete gas bubbles (this assumption does not significantly affect our results, as seen later); (b) Uniform catalyst-particle and liquid concentrations throughout the slurry; and (c) first-order and reversible adsorption of gaseous reactant, and first-order and irreversible surface reaction on the catalyst sites. Then the four mass-conservation equations for reactant in the gas bubbles, in the slurry liquid, in the liquid-filled pores of the carbon particles, and at a reaction site are:

$$V_B \frac{\partial C_g}{\partial t} = -v_B V_B \frac{\partial C_g}{\partial z} - k_L a_B (C_g/H - C_L) = 0 \tag{57}$$

$$\left(1 - \frac{\beta m_s}{\rho_p}\right)\frac{dC_L}{dt} = \frac{k_L a_B}{L}\int_0^L (C_g/H - C_L)\,dz - k_s a_s[C_L - (C_i)_{r=R}] \tag{58}$$

$$\beta \frac{\partial C_i}{\partial t} = D_e \frac{1}{r^2}\frac{\partial}{\partial r}\left(r^2 \frac{\partial C_i}{\partial r}\right) - \rho_p k_a (C_i - n/K) \tag{59}$$

$$\frac{\partial n}{dt} = k_a(C_i - n/K) - k_r n \tag{60}$$

It is Equation 60 for reversible adsorption and irreversible surface reaction that applies in its complete form for dynamic studies and makes it possible to evaluate k_a and k_r separately.

For a step input of reactant the initial and boundary conditions are

$$C_g = C_{g0} \text{ for } t \geq 0 \text{ at } z = 0 \tag{61}$$

$$C_L = C_i = n = 0 \text{ for } t = 0 \tag{62}$$

$$\left(\frac{\partial C_i}{\partial r}\right)_{r=0} = 0 \text{ for all t and z} \tag{63}$$

$$k_s[C_L - (C_i)_{r=R}] = D_e\left(\frac{\partial C_i}{\partial r}\right)_{r=R} \text{ for all t and z} \tag{64}$$

By solving these equations in the Laplace domain, and taking the limit of C_g and dC_g/ds as the Laplace variable s approaches zero, the expressions for the zero and first moments are:

$$m_0 = \exp(-K_L) + \frac{1 - \exp(-K_L)}{1 + \dfrac{K_L B_0}{1 - \exp(-K_L)}} \tag{65}$$

$$m_1 = \tau_g\left[1 - \frac{2}{1 + \dfrac{K_L B_0}{1 - \exp(-K_L)}}\right]\exp(-K_L) + \frac{\tau_g[1 + \exp(-K_L) + 2B_0] + K_L(B_s + \epsilon)}{\left[1 + \dfrac{K_L B_0}{1 - \exp(-K_L)}\right]^2} \tag{66}$$

The dimensional groups are defined as

$$B_s = \frac{Ra_s}{2k_L a_B}\left[\frac{\rho_p K}{\left(1 + \dfrac{k_r}{k_a/K}\right)^2} + \beta\right]\frac{\coth\phi - \phi\,\mathrm{csch}^2\,\phi}{\phi\left(1 + \dfrac{\phi\coth\phi - 1}{Bi}\right)^2} \tag{67}$$

$$\epsilon = \left(1 - \frac{m_s\beta}{\rho_p}\right)\Big/ k_L a_B \tag{68}$$

$$\tau_g = \frac{L}{v_B} = V_B V_L/Q \tag{69}$$

The dimensionless groups are:

$$B_0 = \frac{k_s a_s}{k_L a_B}\left(1 - \frac{Bi}{Bi + \phi\coth\phi - 1}\right) = \frac{k_s a_s}{k_L a_B} 3\eta_G\phi^2/Bi \tag{70}$$

$$\phi^2 = \frac{\rho_p R^2}{D_e}\left[\frac{1}{K}\left(\frac{1}{k_a/K} + \frac{1}{k_r}\right)\right]^{-1} \tag{71}$$

The moments can be evaluated from the measured response curves, for a step-function input, from the equations

$$m_0 = C_g/C_{g,0} \tag{72}$$

$$m_1 = \int_0^\infty (C_{g\infty} - C_g)/C_{g,0}\, dt \tag{73}$$

Modified Equations for Evaluating Rate Constants

Equation 65 for the zero moment can be rearranged to the form:

$$\frac{1}{1 - m_0} = \frac{1}{K_L B_0} + \frac{1}{1 - \exp(-K_L)} \tag{74}$$

For spherical particles, the outer surface area of the particles per unit volume of liquid, is given by Equation 15. Next, Equation 15 and the second equality of Equation 69 can be used to express v_B in terms of V_L. Then the expressions for B_0 (Equation 70) and K_L (Equation 41) can be simplified and substituted in Equation 74 to obtain

$$\frac{1}{1 - m_0} = \left\{\frac{3m_s k_s}{HR\rho_p}\left(1 - \frac{Bi}{Bi + \phi \coth \phi - 1)}\right)\right\}^{-1} \frac{Q}{V_L} + \frac{1}{1 - \exp(-K_L)} \tag{75}$$

where the right side second term refers to mass-transfer and the first to overall rate in the catalyst particle at steady state. In terms of an effectiveness factor η, the rate is given by

$$r_v = m_s \eta k_0 (C_i)_{r=R} \tag{76}$$

with

$$\eta = \frac{3}{\phi}(\coth \phi - 1/\phi) \tag{77}$$

Equation 76 can be written

$$\frac{1}{1 - m_0} = \frac{1}{1 - \exp(-K_L)} + \frac{HR\rho_p}{3m_s k_s}(1 + 3Bi/\eta\phi^2)(Q/V_L) \tag{78}$$

The group K_L, Equation 41, is independent of Q since a_B and V_B are both proportional to Q. For reaction runs at fixed m_s and agitation speed, by varying the gas flow rate we expect a straight line when plotting $1/(1 - m_0)$ vs Q/V_L. The intercept gives K_L, which is related to the gas-to-liquid mass transfer coefficient $k_L a_B$ by Equation 41. The slope gives $\eta\phi^2$ if k_s and Bi are known, and then we can calculate k_0 given D_e.

Experimentally measured first moments include the residence time in the dead volume V_d between the valve and the dispersion tube and between the upper surface of the slurry and the sample injection valve of the chromatograph. Thus the observed, reduced first moment μ_1^0 can be expressed as

$$\mu_1^0 = \frac{m_1}{m_0} + V_d/Q \tag{79}$$

Since $V_d = V_0 - V_B V_L$, Equation 66 for m_1 and Equation 65 for m_0 can be used with Equations 67 and 15 to write Equation 79 as

$$\begin{aligned} \mu_1^0\left(\frac{Q}{V_L}\right) m_0 \left(\frac{K_L B_0}{1 - m_0}\right)^2 + V_B K_L B_0 \left(\frac{2}{1 - \exp(-K_L)} - \frac{2}{K_L} - 1\right) \\ = \left(\frac{V_0}{V_L}\right) m_0 \left(\frac{K_L B_0}{1 - m_0}\right)^2 \\ + \frac{1}{H}\left[\frac{3m_s}{2}\left\{\frac{\beta}{\rho_p} + \frac{K}{[1 + k_r/(k_a/K)]^2}\right\} \frac{\coth \phi - \phi \operatorname{csch}^2 \phi}{\phi\left(1 + \dfrac{\phi \coth \phi - 1}{Bi}\right)^2} + \left(1 - \frac{m_s \beta}{\rho_p}\right)\right] \end{aligned} \tag{80}$$

where V_0 is the dead volume without gas flow through the slurry. V_0 is related to known quantities by the expression:

$$V_T - V_L - V_{particles} = V_0 = V_T - V_L - \frac{m_s V_L(1-\beta)}{\rho_p} \tag{81}$$

The magnitude of the second term on the left side of Equation 80 is limited to $\pm V_B K_L B_0$. In our experiments this term is very small. This is because H for oxygen is large and the residence of the gas bubbles is small so that K_L from Equation 41 becomes small. A straight line is expected if the left side of Equation 80 is plotted vs. $m_0[K_L B_0/(1-m_0)]^2$. The intercept of such a line yields a value of the ratio $k_r/(k_a/K)$, provided K is known. The other quantities such as $K_L B_0$, and ϕ are known from the zero-moment results through Equation 74. The slope of the line yields V_0/V_L. The resulting value can be checked by comparing it with V_0 estimated via Equation 81.

In summary, from zero and first moment data, k_s, and D_e, Equations 75 and 80 can be used to obtain separate values of k_a and k_r, provided K is known.

Evaluation of K from Inert Tracer Runs

When step functions of inert tracer are fed to the slurry, Equation 66 reduces to

$$m_1 = \tau_g + \left(\frac{m_s K + 1}{H}\right)\frac{V_L}{Q} \tag{82}$$

with the residence time in the dead volume, the reduced first moment is

$$\mu_1^0 = \left(\frac{m_s K + 1}{H} + \frac{V_0}{V_L}\right)\frac{V_L}{Q} \tag{83}$$

Equation 83 shows that the slope of a plot of μ_1^0 vs. V_L/Q yields a value of K provided that Henry's law constant for the reactant and V_0 are known. The zero moment for reversible adsorption is unity.

Equations for Well-Mixed Gas Bubbles

Equations 57 and 58 are based upon plug flow of gas bubbles. At the other extreme, the residence time distribution of the bubbles would vary from zero to infinity with a distribution corresponding to that of fluid in a well-stirred vessel. For this case Equations 57 and 58 are replaced by

$$V_B V_L \frac{dC_g}{dt} = Q(C_{g0} - C_g) - k_L a_B V_L\left(\frac{C_g}{H} - C_L\right) \tag{84}$$

$$\left(1 - \frac{\beta m_s}{\rho_p}\right)\frac{dC_L}{dt} = k_L a_B\left(\frac{C_g}{H} - C_L\right) - k_s a_s[C_L - (C_i)_{r=R}] \tag{85}$$

Solving Equations 84, 85, 59, and 60, with the boundary and initial conditions, leads to the following expressions for the moments:

$$m_0 = \left(1 + K_L - \frac{K_L}{1 + B_0}\right)^{-1} \tag{86}$$

$$m_1 = \frac{\tau_g(1+B_0)^2 + K_L(B_s + \epsilon)}{(1 + B_0 + K_L B_0)^2} \tag{87}$$

As was done for the plug flow of gas bubbles, Equations 86 and 87 can be rearranged to suggest the proper functions for obtaining linear plots of the zero and first moment data. These forms, analogous to Equations 75 and 80, are

$$\frac{1}{1-m_0} = \left[\frac{3m_s k_s}{HR\rho_p}\left(1 - \frac{Bi}{Bi + \phi\coth\phi - 1}\right)\right]^{-1}\frac{Q}{V_L} + \frac{1}{K_L} + 1 \tag{88}$$

$$\left[\mu^0\frac{Q}{V_L} + V_B(1-m_0)\right]\frac{m_0 K_L^2}{(m_0 + K_L m_0 - 1)^2} = \frac{V_0 m_0 K_L^2}{V_L(m_0 + K_L m_0 - 1)^2} + \frac{1}{H}\left[\frac{3m_s}{2}\left\{\frac{\beta}{\rho_p} + \frac{K}{[1 + k_r/(k_s/K)]^2}\right\}\frac{\coth\phi - \operatorname{csch}^2\phi}{\phi\left(1 + \dfrac{\phi\coth\phi - 1}{Bi}\right)^2} + \left(1 - \frac{m_s\beta}{\rho_p}\right)\right] \tag{89}$$

Equations 75 and 80 for plug-flow bubbles and Equations 88 and 89 for well-mixed bubbles differ only in their functions of K_L, the dimensionless group concerned with mass transfer from gas bubble to liquid [see Equation 41]. When K_L approaches zero, which corresponds to a slightly soluble gas (H is very large), the two sets of equations give the same values for the moments.

If data were sufficiently accurate the second central moment could be used for parameter estimation. From the second derivative of the Laplace-transformed gas concentration (well-mixed bubble model), the expression for the second moment can be derived:

$$\mu_2' = \mu_1^2 + 2m_0 K_L(B_s + \epsilon)^2/(1 + B_0)^3 + \frac{m_0 K_L}{(Bi + \phi\coth\phi - 1)(1 + B_0)^2}\cdot\left(2B_s A_0 + \frac{M_r Bi A_1}{Bi + \phi\coth\phi - 1}\right) \tag{90}$$

where the dimensional groups are defined as

$$\mu_1 = m_0\left\{\tau_g + \frac{K_L(B_s + \epsilon)}{(1 + B_0)^2}\right\} \tag{91}$$

$$\tau_g' = V_g V_L/Q \tag{92}$$

$$A_0 = \frac{R^2}{2D_e}\frac{\rho_p K}{\left(1 + \dfrac{k_r}{k_s/K}\right)^2} + \beta\left[\frac{\coth\phi}{\phi} - \operatorname{csch}^2\phi\right] \tag{93}$$

$$A_1 = \frac{R^2}{D_e}\frac{\rho_p K^2/k_s}{\left(1 + \dfrac{k_r}{k_s/K}\right)^3}\left[\frac{\coth\phi}{\phi} - \operatorname{csch}^2\phi\right] + \left(\frac{R^2}{2D_s}\right)\left[\frac{\rho_p K}{\left(1 + \dfrac{k_r}{k_a/K}\right)^2}\right] + \beta^2\frac{\coth\phi}{\phi^3} + \frac{\operatorname{csch}^2\phi}{\phi^2} - 2\frac{\coth\phi}{\phi}\operatorname{csch}^2\phi \tag{94}$$

$$M_r = \frac{k_s a_s}{k_L a_s} \tag{95}$$

In the absence of reaction, Equation 90 for the second moment reduces to the simple adsorption case given by Niiyama and Smith [17] for plug-flow bubbles and negligible τ_g'. Although present data are insufficiently accurate to estimate reliable values of second moments, future improved experimental methods may allow application of these expressions.

Adsorption Case

For the case of reversible adsorption with reaction we have $k_r = 0$ in Equations 60, and 57–64 are applicable. Resultant equations for the first and second moments (the zero moment m_0 is unity) are [17]

$$\mu_1 = \frac{m_1}{m_0} = \frac{m_s K + 1}{H}\left(\frac{V_L}{Q_g}\right) \tag{96}$$

$$\mu_2 = \frac{m_2}{m_1} = \frac{2}{H}\left[\left(\frac{1}{5}\frac{R}{D_e a_s} + \frac{1}{k_s a_s}\right)\left(m_s\frac{\beta}{\rho_p} + m_s K\right)^2 + \frac{m_s K^2}{k_a}\right]\frac{V_L}{Q} \tag{97}$$

$$+\left(\frac{m_s K + 1}{H}\right)^2 \frac{1 + e^{-K_L}}{1 - e^{-K_L}}\left(\frac{V_L}{Q}\right)^2 \tag{98}$$

EXPERIMENTAL RESULTS

The moment equations given earlier have been employed with experimental data, from several operating modes of agitated reactors, to evaluate rate and equilibrium parameters. Results of some of these investigations are presented here to demonstrate the potential of dynamic techniques in studying agitated reactors and adsorbers. First, a cautionary note is in order about accuracy. In principle, values of several parameters can be extracted by using moments from a single experiment. Higher moments, however, are unlikely to be accurate due to the effect of the tail of the response curve. Second moments normally are the highest order for which reliable values can be obtained. Hence, for evaluating parameters it is necessary to carry out multiple experiments by changing the operating condition having the greatest effect on the parameter to be evaluated. For example, the contribution of intraparticle diffusion to the moments in a slurry reactor is most influenced by the size of the catalyst particle. Therefore, if intraparticle diffusivity is to be determined, data should be taken for different particle sizes. If reaction rate parameters are to be evaluated, and separated from mass transfer coefficients, experiments would be carried out at different temperatures.

It is important to correct for retention time and dispersion (first and second moments) in dead volumes. These are the volumes of the connecting lines between point of injection and entrance to the reactor and between exit of the reactor and the detector. Such corrections can be determined by geometric measurements, by injecting an inert tracer, or by bypassing the reactor.

Equilibrium Parameters

Solubility of gases in liquids can readily be measured in gas-liquid agitated vessels under appropriate conditions. Henry's constant H is directly related to the corrected first moment of the response to an impulse by the equation

$$\mu_1 = V_L/Q \tag{99}$$

This expression has been applied [17, 26] for evaluating solubilities of H_2S, O_2, and propane in water and other solvents. To use this method the solubility capacity must be a significant contribution compared to the dead volume effect.

For three-phase adsorbers, first moments can be used along with the previously determined solubility, to obtain adsorption equilibrium constants, K. The appropriate expression is

$$\mu_1 = (m_s K + 1)V_L/HQ \tag{100}$$

In theory it is possible to evaluate adsorption equilibrium constants as well as rate parameters by using higher moments. This approach is seldom used, however, because of the inaccuracies mentioned earlier.

Rates of Adsorption

Second-moment data for three-phase adsorbers provide information about mass transfer from gas-bubble to bulk liquid, from bulk liquid to outer surface of the adsorbent particle, intraparticle diffusion, and the rate constant for reversible adsorption at an interior catalyst site. For linear systems (a requirement for moment analysis) each of these four steps in the overall process is an additive contribution to the second moment. Niiyama and Smith [17] have used the equations presented in the section on three-phase reactors (adsorption case) to evaluate these parameters for adsorption and adsorption of nitric oxide in aqueous slurries of activated carbon. Figures 6 and 7 show typical results for first and second moments.

For reversible adsorption the first moment for two or three-phase reactors is a function only of the equilibrium properties of the system, and the zero moment is unity. The second moment is needed to provide information about rate parameters. For irreversible adsorption both the zero and first moment are influenced by the rate processes. This is illustrated by the equations given in the liquid-solid reactor section.

Intraparticle Diffusion

In agitated slurries of relatively large adsorbent particles, intraparticle mass transport may retard the overall rate of adsorption. This is because diffusivities in liquid-filled pores are as much as three orders of magnitude less than diffusivities in gases. Komiyama and Smith [18] determined intra-

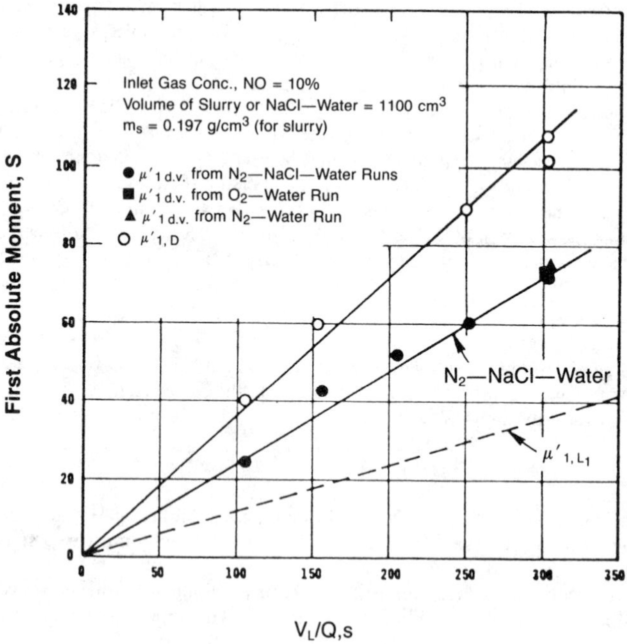

Figure 6. First moment data for adsorption of NO in aqueous slurries of activated carbon. The moments are defined as follows: $\mu'_{\text{d.v.}}$ is the first absolute moment in the dead volume, $\mu'_{1,D}$ is the first absolute moment at the detector, and $\mu'_{1,L1}$ is the first absolute moment in the slurry, or for the liquid when no particles are present. [Reprinted with permission from Ref. [17].]

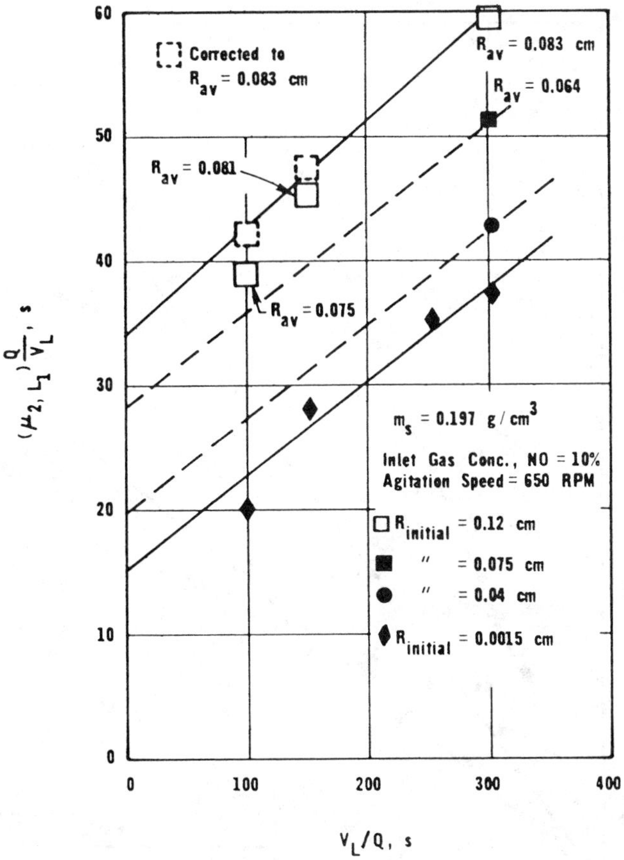

Figure 7. Second moment data for the nitric oxide-water-carbon system; R denotes carbon particle size. [Reprinted with permission from Ref. [17].]

particle diffusivities and effectiveness factors from dynamic experiments in an agitated liquid-solid adsorber. Information about surface versus pore-volume diffusion can be obtained by varying the solvent in which the tracer is dissolved. For example, for the adsorption of benzaldehyde on Amberlite particles in a methanol slurry, intraparticle diffusion was the primary resistance in the liquid-filled pores. In contrast, when aqueous slurries were employed, intraparticle transport was principally by surface migration of adsorbed benzaldehyde.

Gas-Liquid Bubble Reactor

The zero and first moment equations developed for bubble reactors have been applied to investigate the oxidation of sulfite by cobalt ion catalyst by introducing pulses of oxygen into an agitated aqueous sulfite solution [23]. The results of these studies suggested that a two-step mechanism is applicable; reversible association of dissolved reactant gas with the homogeneous catalyst followed by an irreversible decomposition to product. These first-order (in dissolved reactant gas) processes are amenable to treatment by the moment theory. Specific values could not be obtained for the

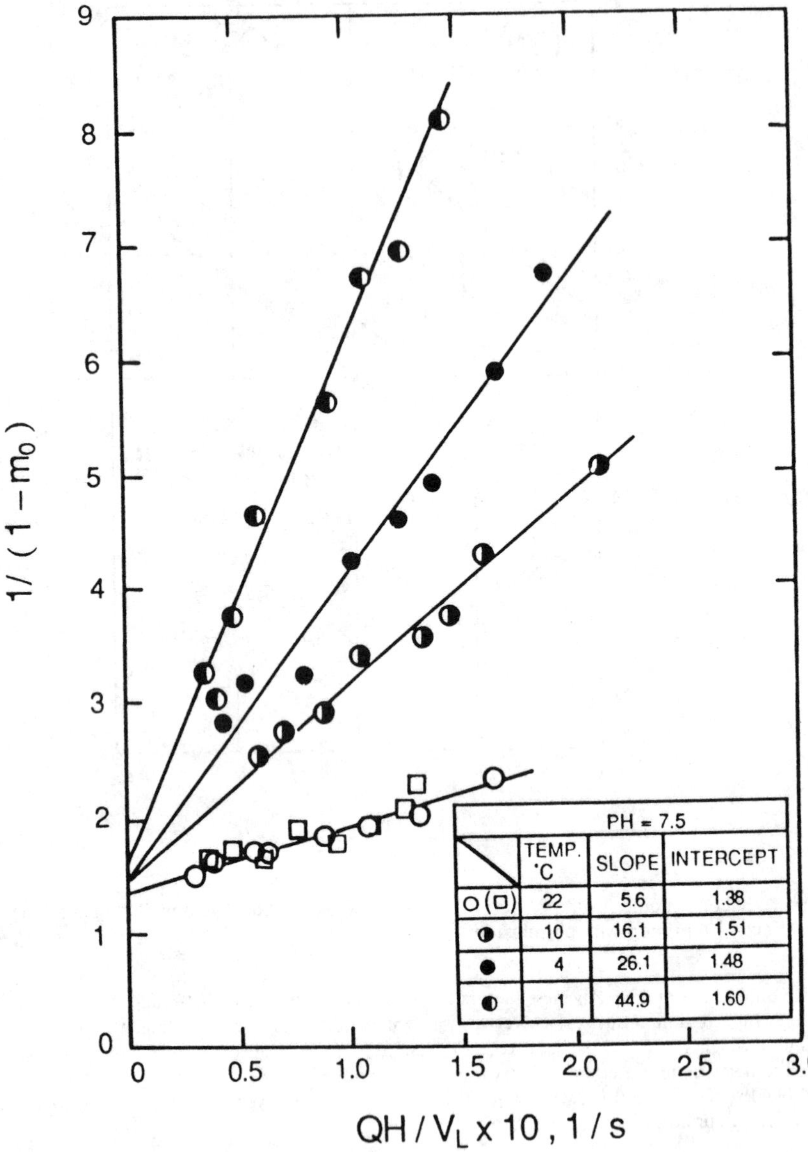

Figure 8. Zero moment plots for reactions at pH = 7.5 for oxidation of sulfite solutions in a bubble reactor.

rate constants for each step, because the necessary equilibrium constant for the association step alone could not be measured in the absence of reaction. Analysis of the results, however, did provide limiting values for rate constants for both steps. Figures 8 and 9 show illustrative moments determined from the response curves to impulse inputs. Note the increased scatter of the data for the first moments compared to the zero moments.

Agitated Three-Phase Reactors

Ahn, et al. [11, 27] have applied the moment method to studying adsorption and surface reaction rates for the catalytic oxidation of sulfur dioxide in aqueous slurries of activated carbon and for the hydrogenation of a-methyl styrene in a slurry reactor with Pd/Al_2O_3 catalyst particles. These two reactions are examples of reversible adsorption followed by an irreversible surface reaction. Therefore, the equations developed for the zero and first moments, (Equations 65 and 66), are applicable. The results of these studies indicated that neither the adsorption nor the subsequent surface reaction controlled the overall rate. A further study by Recasens, et al. [28] of the effect of temperature on the relative importance of the adsorption and reaction steps for SO_2 oxidation showed that as the temperature was increased, from 1.5 to 26°C, the surface reaction step more nearly controlled the overall rate.

Dynamic experiments can be employed to study the effects of other variables than temperature on adsorption and surface reaction rates in heterogeneous catalysis. In an investigation of poisoning

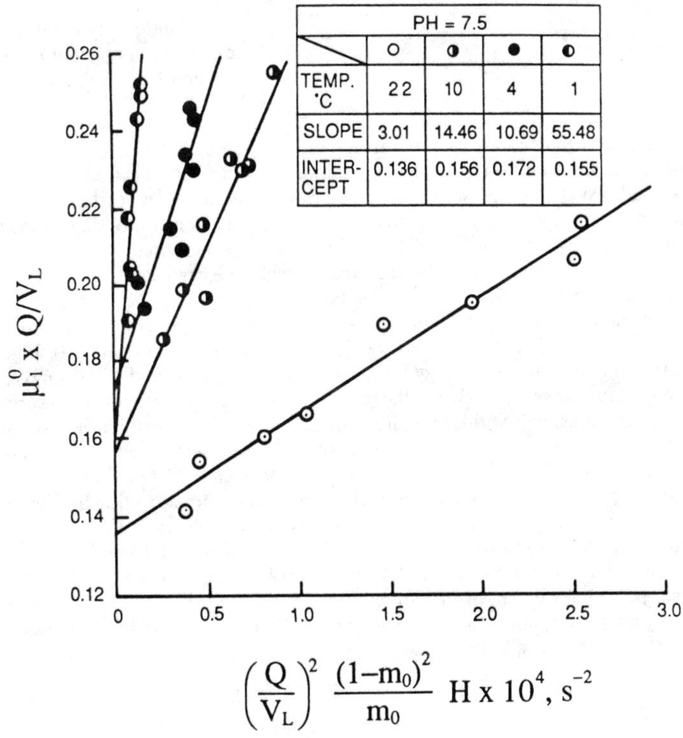

Figure 9. First moment plots for reactions at pH = 7.5 for oxidation of sulfite solutions in a bubble reactor.

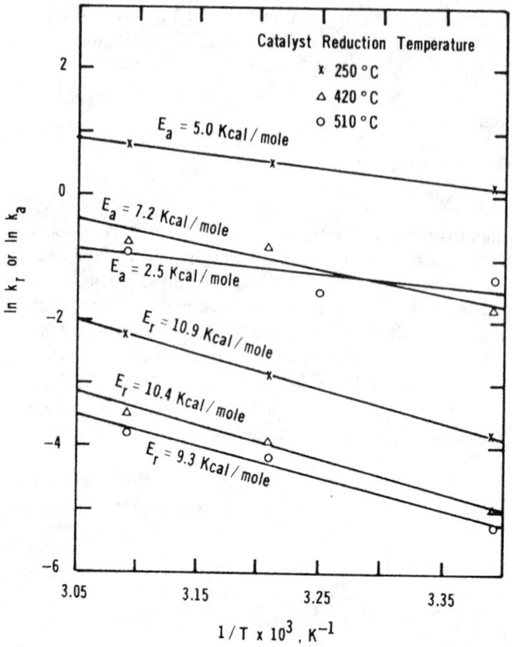

Figure 10. Temperature dependence of adsorption and reaction rate coefficients for hydrogenation of a-methyl styrene on Pd/Al_2O_3 catalyst in an agitated gas-liquid-solid reactor. The energies of activation, E_a for the adsorption rate constant k_a, and E_r for the surface reaction rate constant, k_r, were measured at three different catalyst reduction temperatures. [Reprinted with permission from Ref. [30].]

by carbon disulfide of the active sites for hydrogenation of methyl styrene, Chen, et al. [29] found that adsorption occurred on both poisoned and unpoisoned sites, but reaction occurred only when hydrogen was adsorbed on unpoisoned sites. The rate constant for the surface reaction per unit mass of catalyst was directly proportional to the fraction of unpoisoned sites, suggesting that partial poisoning did not change the activity of the remaining unpoisoned sites.

Further studies by Chen, et al. [30] for the same system were carried out to determine the effect of increasing the temperature for reducing the $PdCl_2$ to Pd in H_2. The results showed that the dispersion (% metal exposed) of palladium decreased and caused a reduction in equilibrium adsorption and adsorption rate and surface rate coefficients (per unit mass of catalyst), Figure 10. The heat of adsorption and activation energy for the surface reaction, 3.8 and 10 kcal/mole, were independent of reduction temperature. Hence, the relative importance of adsorption and surface reaction was unaffected. In agreement with the earlier work [27] neither adsorption nor surface reaction controlled the overall hydrogenation rate. Approximately, for every seven molecules of hydrogen that were adsorbed, five desorbed and two reacted with styrene to form cumene.

Chen, et al. [31] also studied the effect of palladium content on adsorption and surface reaction rates at different temperatures. By estimating the number of active sites by CS_2 poisoning, information was obtained about the dispersion and rate constants per active catalyst site. A nine-fold increase of palladium content on the catalyst (0.05 to 0.45%) showed but a three-fold increase in rate constants per site for either adsorption or surface reaction. All of these results were obtained by impulse-response studies in an agitated slurry reactor, demonstrating the usefulness of dynamic techniques for research on multiphase reactions.

CONCLUSION

The continuous-flow, well-stirred reactor is a utilitarian apparatus for investigating fundamental questions of kinetics and chemical reaction engineering. The main advantage is that very small particles can be suspended in the liquid, thus reducing the intraparticle diffusion resistance. The agitation ensures homogeneity in the liquid, thus further simplifying the system and its mathematical description.

For the three types of agitated multiphase reactors and adsorbers considered here, i.e., liquid-solid, gas-liquid, and gas-liquid-solid, the mass balance equations have common features. Mass transfer from gas bubble to liquid and from liquid to particle surface are treated in a similar manner for all the reactors. Intraparticle diffusion is the same process, whether the particles are in the two- or three-phase system. This leads to an expression for the effectiveness factor for the first-order reaction that simplifies equations for steady-state results, i.e., the zero moment expressions.

In this review we have focused on a catalytic reaction, for either homogeneous or heterogeneous catalysts, that can be described by a two-step mechanism. For the fluid-solid surface, this mechanism is based on the Langmuir-Hinshelwood model, here linearized for surfaces with unlimited active sites or low surface coverage of adsorbed species. This approach allows mathematical reductions from general expressions that include both adsorption (or association to form a homogeneous complex) and irreversible reaction. Thus, purely reversible adsorption is a special case that applies when $k_r = 0$. The case of irreversible adsorption applies when the equilibrium coefficient becomes very large.

Only with dynamic experiments is it possible to measure the separate values for adsorption and reaction rates. The governing mass balance equations, when they are linear, are conveniently treated with the moment technique. The moment analysis provides basic information about the shape of the concentration response, higher moments yielding more detailed information. For example the zero moment characterizes totally the steady state, and the first moment places the average time of the response. The second central moment specifies the width of the response, the third central moment its asymmetry, and so on through the hierarchy. Other methods of treating dynamic data are discussed by Wakao and Kaguei [32].

The moment approach not only allows analysis of data, but furthermore suggests an experimental program. We have seen in this article how plotting moments versus process variables leads to linear relationships, thus guiding the experimenter in deciding what operating parameters to vary. This procedure has obvious advantages for testing hypothesized models and measuring parameters.

Acknowledgment

This work was supported by the US-Spain Joint Committee for Scientific and Technological Cooperation, Grant CCB-8509/002.

NOTATION

a_B	specific area of gas bubbles per unit of bubble- and particle-free liquid, cm^{-1}
a_s	specific external area of particles per unit bubble- and particle-free liquid, cm^{-1}
Bi	Biot number ($Bi = Rk_s/D_e$)
B_0	dimensionless quantity defined by Equation 70
B_s	quantity defined by Equation 67, s
C_f	concentration in the film, Equation 32, mol cm^{-3}
C_g	concentration in gas phase, mol cm^{-3}; C_{g0} = concentration in feed gas; $C_{g\infty}$ = steady state concentration in exit gas
C_i	concentration in pore liquid, mol cm^{-3}
C_L	concentration in bulk liquid, mol cm^{-3}
$\tilde{C}$	Laplace transform of C(t), s mol cm^{-3}
D	molecular diffusivity, $cm^2\ s^{-1}$
D_e	effective diffusivity in liquid-filled pores of catalyst sphere, $cm^2\ s^{-1}$
d	film thickness, cm
d_p	diameter of the spherical particle, cm
E	energy of activation, cal mol^{-1}
Ha	Hatta number, $(k_h\sigma D)^{1/2}/k_L$
H	Henry's law constant defined as $H = C_g/C_L$ at equilibrium
k_a	adsorption rate constant, $cm^3\ (g\ s)^{-1}$
k_h	combined rate constant, defined by Equation 46, $cm^3/(g\ s)^{-1}$
k_L	gas-to-liquid mass-transfer coefficient, cm s^{-1}
k_0	$(1/k_a + 1/k_rK)^{-1}$, overall reaction rate constant in the particle $cm^3\ (g\ s)^{-1}$

k_r surface reaction rate constant, s^{-1}
k_s liquid-to-solid mass-transfer coefficient, $cm\ s^{-1}$
K adsorption equilibrium constant, $cm^3\ g^{-1}$
K_L dimensionless mass transfer quantity define by Equation 41
L depth of slurry, cm
m_0 zero-order moment
m_1 first-order moment, s
m_n m-th order moment, s^m
m_s catalyst loading or mass of carbon per unit volume of bubble- and particle-free liquid, $g\ cm^{-3}$
n adsorbed concentration, $mol\ g^{-1}$
Q_L liquid flow rate to reactor, $cm^3\ s^{-1}$
Q gas flow rate to reactor, $cm^3\ s^{-1}$
r radial coordinate from center of catalyst sphere, cm
r_v rate of reaction based on unit volume of free liquid, $mol\ (cm^3\ s)^{-1}$
N_f concentration of reactant-catalyst complex in the film, $mol\ cm^{-3}$
N_L concentration of reactant-catalyst complex in the bulk liquid, $mol\ cm^{-3}$
s Laplace variable, s^{-1}
R radius of spherical particle, cm
t time, s
v_B vertical component of bubble velocity, $cm\ s^{-1}$
V_B bubble holdup of slurry, i.e. bubble volume per unit particle- and bubble-free liquid
V_d dead volume including gas space over slurry, tubing and trap, during operation, from four-way valve to gas chromatograph, cm^3
V_L volume of liquid, cm^3
V_0 dead volume at zero gas flow, cm^3
V_T total volume of system, from four-way valve to gas chromatograph, cm^3
x coördinate in the film, cm
z vertical coordinate from gas disperser, cm

Greek Symbols

β internal porosity of particles
δ Dirac delta function
ϵ quantity defined by Equation 68, s
μ_1 m_1/m_0, normalized first moment, s
μ_1^0 observed first moment [Equation 53]
μ_2 m_2/m_0, normalized second moment, s^2
μ' normalized second central moment, s^2
π dimensionless group defined by Equation 43
ϕ Thiele modulus, Equations 19 or 71
ϕ' dimensionless group defined by Equation 45
σ catalyst concentration, $mol\ cm^{-3}$
ρ_p liquid-free particle density, $g\ cm^{-3}$
η effectiveness factor, Equation 20
τ average residence time of liquid, V_L/Q_L
τ_g average residence time of gas bubbles ($\tau_g = L/v_B$)
τ'_g defined by Equation 92
η_G global effectiveness factor defined by Equation 21

REFERENCES

1. Smith, J. M., *Chemical Engineering Kinetics*, Third Ed., Chap. 10 and 13, McGraw-Hill, New York, 1981.
2. Shah, Y. T., *Gas-Liquid-Solid Reactor Design*, McGraw-Hill, New York, 1979.
3. Ramachandran, P. A., and Chaudhari, R. V., *Three Phase Catalytic Reactors*, Gordon and Breach, New York, 1983.
4. Bell, A. T., Hegedus, L. L., (eds.) *Catalysis Under Transient Conditions*, ACS Symp. Ser. 178 (1982).
5. Tamaru, K., *Dynamic Heterogeneous Catalysis*, Academic Press New York, (1978)
6. Kobayashi, H., and Kobayashi, M., *Cat. Revs. Sci. Eng.* 10, 139 (1974).
7. Bennett, C. O., *AIChE J.* 13, 890 (1967).
8. Bennett, C. O., *Cat. Revs. Sci. Eng.* 13, 2 (1976).
9. Suzuki, M., and Smith, J. M., *Chem. Eng. Sci.* 26, 221 (1971).
10. Schneider, P., and Smith, J. M., *AIChE J.*, 14, 762 (1968).

11. Ahn, B.-J., McCoy, B. J., and Smith, J. M., *AIChE J.* 31, 541 (1985).
12. McCoy, B. J., *Chem. Eng. Sci.* 39, 1524 (1984).
13. Furusawa, T., Suzuki, M., Smith, J. M., *Catalysis Reviews—Sci. Eng.* 13, 43 (1976).
14. Suzuki, M., Smith, J. M., *Advances in Chromatography*, 13, 213 (1975).
15. McCoy, B. J., *Chem. Eng. Commun.* 52, 93 (1987).
16. Razavi, M. S., McCoy, B. J., Carbonell, R. G., *The Chem. Eng. J.* 16, 211 (1978).
17. Niiyama, N., and Smith, J. M., *AIChE J.* 22, 961 (1976).
18. Komiyama, H., and Smith, J. M., *AIChE J.* 21, 1110 (1974); 21, 728 (1974); 20, 88 (1973).
19. Furusawa, T., Smith, J. M., *IEC Funds.* 12, 197, 360 (1973).
20. Levenspiel, O., Godfrey, J. H., *Chem. Eng. Sci.* 29, 1723 (1974).
21. Danckwerts, P. V., *Gas-Liquid Reactions*, McGraw-Hill, New York, 1970.
22. Astarita, G., *Mass Transfer with Chemical Reaction*, Elsevier, New York, 1967.
23. Fu, C.-C., Smith, J. M., McCoy, B. J., "Dynamic Study of Homogeneous Reactions in a Stirred Bubble Reactor: Oxidation of Sulfite," submitted (1987).
24. Ramachandran, P. A., Smith, J. M., *Chem. Eng. Sci.* 32, 873 (1977).
25. Weng, H. S., Smith, J. M., *Chem. Eng. J.* 28, 115 (1984).
26. Yow, J., and Smith, J. M., *Latin Amer. J. of Chem. Eng. and Applied Engr.* 13, 132 (1983).
27. Ahn, B.-J., McCoy, B. J., and Smith, J. M., *AIChE J.* 32, 566 (1986).
28. Recasens, F., Smith, J. M., McCoy, B. J., *Chem. Eng. Sci.* 39, 1469 (1984).
29. Chen, S.-Y., McCoy, B. J., Smith, J. M., *AIChE J.* 32, 2056 (1986).
30. Chen, S.-Y., Smith, J. M., McCoy, B. J., *Chem. Eng. Sci.* 42, 293 (1987).
31. Chen, S.-Y., Smith, J. M., McCoy, B. J., *J. Catalysis* 102, 365 (1986).
32. Wakao, N., Kaguei, S., *Heat and Mass Transfer in Packed Beds*, Chap. 1, Gordon and Breach, New York (1982).

CHAPTER 10

HEAT TRANSFER IN CATALYTIC PACKED BED REACTORS

Stephen Whitaker

Department of Chemical Engineering
University of California
DAVIS, CA California, USA

CONTENTS

INTRODUCTION

In this chapter we consider a line of analysis that leads from the axioms of continuum mechanics for multicomponent systems to the thermal analysis of packed bed catalytic reactors. We begin with the axioms for mass, momentum, and energy and from these we obtain an equation for the temperature in a multicomponent system. Jump conditions at phase interfaces are constructed that can be used, along with the governing equation for the temperature, to determine the temperature field when chemical reactions are taking place.

Since most reactor design problems involve multiphase systems with interfacial regions that can only be determined in an average or statistical sense, a detailed knowledge of the temperature field is not possible. This situation naturally leads to a search for average temperatures and the governing differential equations for averaged quantities. Use of the method of volume averaging provides a precise route from the point equation for the temperature to the thermal design equations for a packed bed catalytic reactor.

After a presentation of the axioms for multicomponent, reacting systems, we direct our attention to the heat conduction problem in a porous catalyst pellet. The constraint of *local thermal equilibrium* is imposed in order to obtain a one-equation model for the heat conduction process. Then the form of the temperature dependence for the area-averaged rate of reaction is discussed, and a general approach to heat conduction in microporous media is presented. After completing the analysis of heat conduction in porous catalysts, we move on to study the fluid-phase heat transport process. An equation for the volume-averaged temperature is derived, and the assumptions that must be made in order to obtain the traditional model are identified. The general closure problem for the combined fluid and solid-phase heat transport process is then developed, and the general form of the two-equation model for heat transfer in catalytic packed bed reactors is presented. The non-traditional convective and conductive transport mechanisms are discussed and the route to non-isothermal effectiveness factors is outlined in terms of the method of volume averaging.

The design of packed bed catalytic reactors can be thought of as a model chemical engineering problem, since it involves so much of what we think of as chemical engineering. For example, in the typical design one encounters: fluid mechanics, heat transfer, mass transfer, chemical kinetics, process dynamics, and control, adsorption, and thermodynamics. The generality of the problem is illustrated in Figure 1, and in this chapter we will consider only the thermal aspects of packed bed catalytic reactor design. While the scope of this presentation might appear to be rather limited within the broad domain of reactor design, we will follow a route that has wide applications.

In a simplistic sense, our objective in catalytic reactor design is the determination of the rate of reaction per unit volume. Since reaction rate coefficients are highly temperature dependent, reactor design requires a knowledge of the temperature and the prediction of that temperature is the objective of this chapter. The development presented here is meant to compliment a previous study of transport processes with heterogeneous reaction [1]. That study dealt exclusively with the mass transfer process that takes place in catalytic packed bed reactors with a special emphasis on diffusion in porous catalysts. The axioms associated with mass transport in multi-component systems can be expressed in terms of the species body illustrated in Figure 2 and are given by

$$\frac{d}{dt}\int_{\mathcal{V}_A(t)} \rho_A \, dV = \int_{\mathcal{V}_A(t)} r_A \, dV \tag{1}$$

$$\sum_{A=1}^{A=N} r_A = 0 \tag{2}$$

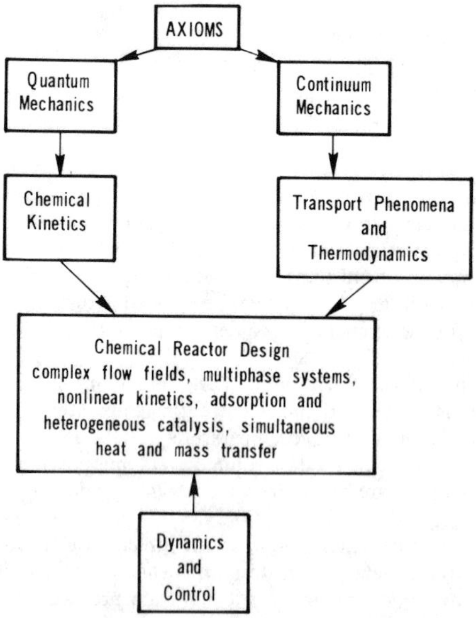

Figure 1. Foundations of chemical reactor design.

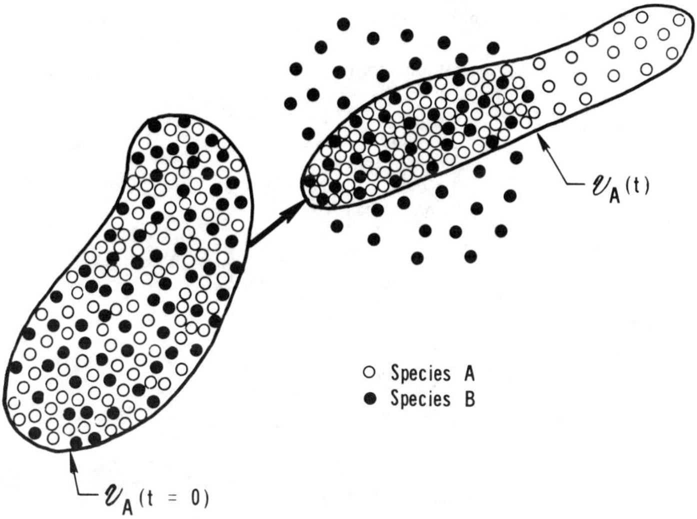

Figure 2. Motion of a species body.

Here $V_A(t)$ represents the volume of the species A body illustrated in Fig. 2, ρ_A represents the species mass density, and r_A represents the mass rate of production of species A owing to homogeneous chemical reaction.

The species continuity equation can easily be extracted from Equation 1 and it takes the form

$$\frac{\partial \rho_A}{\partial t} + \nabla \cdot (\rho_A \mathbf{v}_A) = r_A \tag{3}$$

Here $\mathbf{v}_A$ represents the species velocity and it is this velocity that describes the motion of the species body illustrated in Figure 1. If we define the total density ρ and the mass average velocity $\mathbf{v}$ according to

$$\rho = \sum_{A=1}^{A=N} \rho_A, \qquad \rho \mathbf{v} = \sum_{A=1}^{A=N} \rho_A \mathbf{v}_A \tag{4}$$

we can sum Equation 3 over all N components in the system to obtain

$$\frac{\partial \rho}{\partial t} + \nabla \cdot (\rho \mathbf{v}) = 0 \tag{5}$$

Both the species continuity equation and the total continuity equation will be of use to us in the thermal analysis of a packed bed reactor. In thinking about these two continuity equations, we must remember that ρ_A is the *dependent variable* in Equation 3 while ρ plays the same role in Equation 5. To solve Equation 5 and thus determine ρ as a function of time and space, we need to know the mass average velocity $\mathbf{v}$, which will be determined by the laws of mechanics. In the design of a chemical reactor it is more important to determine ρ_A as a function of time and space, and to do this we need to know the species velocity $\mathbf{v}_A$ and the mass rate of production of species A per unit volume, r_A. The former is determined by the laws of mechanics for multicomponent systems while the latter is determined by quantum mechanical considerations as suggested in Figure 1.

The laws of mechanics for multicomponent, reacting systems are stated in terms of the species body shown in Figure 2 and we list them as

1. Linear Momentum

$$\frac{d}{dt}\int_{V_A(t)} \rho_A \underset{\sim}{v}_A \, dV = \int_{V_A(t)} \rho_A \underset{\sim}{b}_A \, dV + \int_{A_A(t)} \underset{\sim}{t}_A \, dA + \int_{V_A(t)} \sum_{B=1}^{B=N} \underset{\sim}{P}_{AB} \, dV + \int_{V_A(t)} r_A \underset{\sim}{v}_A^* \, dV \tag{6}$$

2. Angular Momentum

$$\frac{d}{dt}\int_{V_A(t)} \underset{\sim}{r} \times \rho_A \underset{\sim}{v}_A \, dV = \int_{V_A(t)} \underset{\sim}{r} \times \rho_A \underset{\sim}{b}_A \, dV + \int_{A_A(t)} \underset{\sim}{r} \times \underset{\sim}{t}_A \, dA + \int_{V_A(t)} \underset{\sim}{r} \times \sum_{B=1}^{B=N} \underset{\sim}{P}_{AB} \, dV + \int_{V_A(t)} \underset{\sim}{r} \times (r_A \underset{\sim}{v}_A^*) \, dV \tag{7}$$

3. Diffusive Source of Momentum

$$\sum_{A=1}^{A=N} \sum_{B=1}^{B=N} \underset{\sim}{P}_{AB} = 0 \tag{8}$$

4. Chemical Reaction Momentum Source

$$\sum_{A=1}^{A=N} r_A \underset{\sim}{v}_A^* = 0 \tag{9}$$

The linear momentum equation for a species body is based on the concept that the time rate of change of linear momentum of the body is equal to the force acting on the body plus the source of momentum owing to chemical reaction. In Equation 6 we note that $\rho_A \underset{\sim}{v}_A$ represents the species A linear momentum, while $\rho_A \underset{\sim}{b}_A$ and $\underset{\sim}{t}_A$ represent the body force and surface force respectively that act upon the species A body. In the absence of electric fields $\rho_A \underset{\sim}{b}_A$ can be replaced by $\rho_A \underset{\sim}{g}$ where $\underset{\sim}{g}$ is the gravitational vector; however, if one is concerned with the motion of ionic species the body force $\rho_A \underset{\sim}{b}_A$ takes on a crucial role.

The velocity of species A produced by chemical reaction has been designated by $\underset{\sim}{v}_A^*$ with the thought that it need not be equal to the continuum velocity $\underset{\sim}{v}_A$. In Equation 6, the term $\underset{\sim}{P}_{AB}$ represents the force per unit volume that species B exerts on species A and we expect that this force will be important when species A and B are moving at different velocities, i.e., $\underset{\sim}{P}_{AB}$ is intimately related to the process of diffusion. It is of some interest to note that the source of linear momentum, $r_A \underset{\sim}{v}_A^*$, is not invariant to a Galilean transformation; however, the time rate of change of momentum on the left side of Equation 6 also fails to be invariant but combines with the momentum source owing to chemical reaction in order to produce a result which is invariant to a Galilean transformation.

In writing the angular momentum axiom given by Equation 7 we have assumed that all torques are the moments of forces [3] so that the effect of intrinsic angular momentum has been neglected. The influence of intrinsic angular momentum on the mass average angular momentum principle has been discussed by Aris [4], and it may be of some interest to explore the influence of this effect on the species angular momentum principle.

Axioms 3 and 4 simply indicate that there can be no source of mass average momentum as a result of the diffusive force $\underset{\sim}{P}_{AB}$, and that linear momentum is conserved in the course of chemical reactions.

The derivation of the species stress equations of motion parallels that for single component systems [5] and leads to

$$\rho_A\left(\frac{\partial \mathbf{v}_A}{\partial t} + \mathbf{v}_A \cdot \nabla \mathbf{v}_A\right) = \rho_A \mathbf{b}_A + \nabla \cdot \mathbf{T}_A + \sum_{B=1}^{B=N} \mathbf{P}_{AB} + r_A(\mathbf{v}_A^* - \mathbf{v}_A) \tag{10}$$

while the angular momentum principle given by Equation 7 yields the expected symmetry condition given by

$$\mathbf{T}_A = \mathbf{T}_A^T \tag{11}$$

It is shown elsewhere [1, 6] that Equation 10 is the origin of the Stefan-Maxwell equations and thus Fick's law for binary systems.

If we define the following mass average quantities

$$\rho = \sum_{A=1}^{A=N} \rho_A \tag{12}$$

$$\mathbf{v} = \sum_{A=1}^{A=N} (\rho_A/\rho)\mathbf{v}_A \tag{13}$$

$$\mathbf{T} = \sum_{A=1}^{A=N} (\mathbf{T}_A - \rho_A \mathbf{u}_A \mathbf{u}_A) \tag{14}$$

$$\mathbf{b} = \sum_{A=1}^{A=N} (\rho_A/\rho)\mathbf{b}_A \tag{15}$$

in which $\mathbf{u}_A$ is the mass diffusion velocity given by

$$\mathbf{u}_A = \mathbf{v}_A - \mathbf{v} \tag{16}$$

we can sum Equations 10 and 11 to obtain the traditional results given by

$$\rho\left(\frac{\partial \mathbf{v}}{\partial t} + \mathbf{v} \cdot \nabla \mathbf{v}\right) = \rho \mathbf{b} + \nabla \cdot \mathbf{T} \tag{17}$$

$$\mathbf{T} = \mathbf{T}^T \tag{18}$$

Here we have used Equations 8 and 9 to eliminate the diffusive source of momentum resulting from the force $\mathbf{P}_{AB}$ and the chemical reaction momentum source which is coupled to the mass source term in Equation 3. If one decomposes the total stress tensor according to

$$\mathbf{T} = -p\mathbf{I} + \boldsymbol{\tau} \tag{19}$$

one can express Equation 17 as the viscous stress equations of motion.

$$\rho\left(\frac{\partial \mathbf{v}}{\partial t} + \mathbf{v} \cdot \nabla \mathbf{v}\right) = -\nabla p + \rho \mathbf{b} + \nabla \cdot \boldsymbol{\tau} \tag{20}$$

$$\boldsymbol{\tau} = \boldsymbol{\tau}^T \tag{21}$$

When the viscous stress is given by Newton's law of viscosity, the Navier-Stokes equations result.

$$\rho\left(\frac{\partial \mathbf{v}}{\partial t} + \mathbf{v} \cdot \nabla \mathbf{v}\right) = -\nabla p + \rho \mathbf{b} + \mu \nabla^2 \mathbf{v} \tag{22}$$

Here we have assumed that the viscosity μ is constant, and this result confirms the idea that the Navier-Stokes equations represent the governing equations for the mass average velocity.

ENERGY

In the previous paragraphs we have briefly considered the axioms of mass and mechanics for multicomponent, reacting systems, and we are now in a position to consider the axioms for the energy of such systems. The structure of the axioms for mass and mechanics was that of balance equations containing source terms and constraints on the source terms. The axioms for energy are similar in form, and for the species A body shown in Figure 2 we express the axioms as

$$1.\ \frac{d}{dt}\int_{V_{A(t)}}\left(\rho_A e_A + \frac{1}{2}\rho_A v_A^2\right) dV = -\int_{A_{A(t)}} (\underset{\sim}{q}_A + \underset{\sim}{q}_A^R)\cdot \underset{\sim}{n}\, dA + \int_{V_{A(t)}} \sum_{B=1}^{B=N} Q_{AB}\, dV + \int_{A_{A(t)}} \underset{\sim}{t}_A \cdot \underset{\sim}{v}_A\, dA + \int_{V_{A(t)}} \rho_A \underset{\sim}{b}_A \cdot \underset{\sim}{v}_A\, dV + \int_{V_{A(t)}} \sum_{B=1}^{B=N} \underset{\sim}{P}_{AB}\cdot \underset{\sim}{v}_A\, dV + \int_{V_{A(t)}} r_A\left(e_A^* + \frac{1}{2} v_A^{*2}\right) dV \tag{23}$$

$$2.\ \sum_{A=1}^{A=N} r_A\left(e_A^* + \frac{1}{2}v_A^{*2}\right) = 0 \tag{24}$$

$$3.\ \sum_{A=1}^{A=N}\sum_{B=1}^{B=N} Q_{AB} = 0 \tag{25}$$

4. e_A is a state function (26)

Here we have used e_A to represent the internal energy per unit mass for species A, while $\underset{\sim}{q}_A$ represents the conductive heat flux vector and $\underset{\sim}{q}_A^R$ represents the radiative heat flux vector. One must think of $\underset{\sim}{q}_A^R$ as a measure of the rate of exchange of photons between species A and the surroundings [7], while the term Q_{AB} represents the rate of thermal energy exchange between species B and species A. For example, if a region in space is subject to a flux of photons that are absorbed only by species B, the energy of species A will increase owing to the exchange term, Q_{AB}. In axiom 1 we have suggested, in keeping with Equations 6 and 7, that the species A produced by chemical reaction need not have the same internal or kinetic energy per unit mass as the continuum values designated by e_A and $\frac{1}{2}v_A^2$.

The nature of the first axiom given by Equation 23 is that the rate of increase of internal and kinetic energy of species A is equal to the rate of supply of non-mechanical energy (the first two terms on the right side of Equation 23), the rate of supply of mechanical energy (the third, fourth, and fifth terms on the right side), and the source of internal and kinetic energy owing to chemical reaction. The second axiom is analogous to Equations 2 and 9 while the third axiom is the thermal analogue of Equation 8. The fourth axiom is the central theme of thermodynamics and states that the internal energy is a function of the thermodynamic state of the system.

The differential equation associated with Equation 23 is given by

$$\frac{\partial}{\partial t}\left(\rho_A e_A + \frac{1}{2}\rho_A v_A^2\right) + \underset{\sim}{\nabla}\cdot\left[\left(\rho_A e_A + \frac{1}{2}\rho_A v_A^2\right)\underset{\sim}{v}_A\right] = -\underset{\sim}{\nabla}\cdot(\underset{\sim}{q}_A + \underset{\sim}{q}_A^R) + \sum_{B=1}^{B=N} Q_{AB} + \underset{\sim}{\nabla}\cdot(\underset{\sim}{T}_A\cdot\underset{\sim}{v}_A) + \rho_A\underset{\sim}{b}_A\cdot\underset{\sim}{v}_A + \sum_{B=1}^{B=N}\underset{\sim}{P}_{AB}\cdot\underset{\sim}{v}_A + r_A\left(e_A^* + \frac{1}{2}v_A^{*2}\right) \tag{27}$$

In our studies of mass we were interested in ρ_A and this, in turn, required knowledge of the species velocity, $\underset{\sim}{v}_A$. In our study of the energy of multicomponent systems, we are primarily interested in developing an equation for the temperature and we have a secondary interest in an equation for the enthalpy. In order to develop these equations from Equation 27 it will be useful to eliminate the mechanical terms by means of the species mechanical energy equation. This is derived by forming the scalar product of Equation 10 with the species velocity $\underset{\sim}{v}_A$ in order to obtain

$$\frac{\partial}{\partial t}\left(\frac{1}{2}\rho_A v_A^2\right) + \underset{\sim}{\nabla}\cdot\left[\left(\frac{1}{2}\rho_A v_A^2\right)\underset{\sim}{v}_A\right] + r_A\left(\frac{1}{2}v_A^2\right)$$

$$= \underset{\sim}{\nabla}\cdot(\underset{\approx}{T}_A\cdot\underset{\sim}{v}_A) - \underset{\approx}{T}_A:\underset{\sim}{\nabla}\underset{\sim}{v}_A + \rho_A\underset{\sim}{b}_A\cdot\underset{\sim}{v}_A + \sum_{B=1}^{B=N}\underset{\sim}{P}_{AB}\cdot\underset{\sim}{v}_A + r_A(\underset{\sim}{v}_A^*\cdot\underset{\sim}{v}_A) \tag{28}$$

Considerable manipulation is required to obtain this result and the species continuity equation given by Equation 3 is used as part of the development. For single component systems this result reduces to the traditional form of the mechanical energy equation [8] that is so useful in the analysis of incompressible flow processes. In our case, we wish only to subtract Equation 28 from Equation 27 in order to obtain the species thermal energy equation given by

$$\frac{\partial}{\partial t}(\rho_A e_A) + \underset{\sim}{\nabla}\cdot(\rho_A e_A\underset{\sim}{v}_A) = -\underset{\sim}{\nabla}\cdot(\underset{\sim}{q}_A + \underset{\sim}{q}_A^R) + \sum_{B=1}^{B=N} Q_{AB} + \underset{\approx}{T}_A:\underset{\sim}{\nabla}\underset{\sim}{v}_A$$

$$+ r_A\left(e_A^* + \frac{1}{2}v_A^{*2} - \underset{\sim}{v}_A^*\cdot\underset{\sim}{v}_A + \frac{1}{2}v_A^2\right) \tag{29}$$

This result will be more useful to us when expressed in terms of enthalpy, thus we define the species enthalpy per unit mass h_A according to the relation

$$\rho_A h_A = \rho_A e_A + p_A \tag{30}$$

Here p_A represents the partial pressure of species A, and when this result is used in Equation 29 we obtain

$$\frac{\partial}{\partial t}(\rho_A h_A) + \underset{\sim}{\nabla}\cdot(\rho_A h_A\underset{\sim}{v}_A) = -\underset{\sim}{\nabla}\cdot(\underset{\sim}{q}_A + \underset{\sim}{q}_A^R) + \sum_{B=1}^{B=N} Q_{AB} + \underset{\approx}{T}_A:\underset{\sim}{\nabla}\underset{\sim}{v}_A + \frac{\partial p_A}{\partial t} + \underset{\sim}{\nabla}\cdot(p_A\underset{\sim}{v}_A)$$

$$+ r_A\left(e_A^* + \frac{1}{2}v_A^{*2} - \underset{\sim}{v}_A^*\cdot\underset{\sim}{v}_A + \frac{1}{2}v_A^2\right) \tag{31}$$

About the partial pressure for species A, we should note that it is defined by

$$p_A = \rho_A^2\left(\frac{\partial e_A}{\partial \rho_A}\right)_{s,\rho_B,\rho_C,\ldots} \tag{32}$$

where s represents the entropy per unit mass. We define the total pressure as

$$p = \sum_{A=1}^{A=N} p_A \tag{33}$$

and one can prove as a theorem that

$$p = -\left(\frac{\partial U}{\partial V}\right)_{S,m_A,m_B,\ldots} \tag{34}$$

Here we have used the classic thermostatics nomenclature in which U is the total internal energy, S is the total entropy and m_A, m_B, etc. represent the mass of species A, B, etc. Strictly speaking, Equation 34 is only applicable for systems at equilibrium whereas Equations 32 and 33 are restricted only by the constraint of local thermodynamic equilibrium. This means that a single temperature can be used to characterize the internal energy of all the species, and it is not the species enthalpy equation given by Equation 31 that we need but instead the total enthalpy equation. This is obtained by summing Equation 31 over all N species leading to

$$\frac{\partial}{\partial t}\sum_{A=1}^{A=N}\rho_A h_A + \nabla\cdot\sum_{A=1}^{A=N}\rho_A h_A \mathbf{v}_A = -\nabla\cdot(\mathbf{q}+\mathbf{q}^R) + \sum_{A=1}^{A=N}\mathbf{T}_A:\nabla\mathbf{v}_A + \sum_{A=1}^{A=N}\left[\frac{\partial p_A}{\partial t} + \nabla\cdot(p_A\mathbf{v}_A)\right]$$
$$- \sum_{A=1}^{A=N} r_A\left(\mathbf{v}_A^*\cdot\mathbf{v}_A - \frac{1}{2}v_A^2\right) \tag{35}$$

Here the two total heat flux vectors are defined by

$$\mathbf{q} = \sum_{A=1}^{A=N}\mathbf{q}_A, \qquad \mathbf{q}^R = \sum_{A=1}^{A=N}\mathbf{q}_A^R \tag{36}$$

In addition, we have used axiom 3 to eliminate the term involving Q_{AB} and axiom 2 to eliminate the term involving $e_A^* + \frac{1}{2}v_A^{*2}$. One of our objectives is the derivation of an equation for the total enthalpy per unit mass which is identified as h and defined by

$$\rho h = \sum_{A=1}^{A=N}\rho_A h_A \tag{37}$$

To achieve this we need to use the decomposition indicated by Equation 16, and in addition we will decompose the species stress tensor according to

$$\mathbf{T}_A = -p_A\mathbf{I} + \boldsymbol{\tau}_A \tag{38}$$

in which p_A is defined by Equation 32. If we focus our attention on the right side of Equation 35 and use Equations 16 and 38 we can obtain, after some algebraic manipulation, the following result

$$\frac{\partial}{\partial t}\sum_{A=1}^{A=N}\rho_A h_A + \nabla\cdot\sum_{A=1}^{A=N}\rho_A h_A \mathbf{v}_A = -\nabla\cdot(\mathbf{q}+\mathbf{q}^R) + \boldsymbol{\tau}:\nabla\mathbf{v} + \frac{\partial p}{\partial t}$$
$$+ \mathbf{v}\cdot\nabla p + \sum_{A=1}^{A=N}(\boldsymbol{\tau}_A:\nabla\mathbf{u}_A + \mathbf{u}_A\cdot\nabla p_A)$$
$$- \sum_{A=1}^{A=N} r_A\left[\mathbf{v}_A^*\cdot\mathbf{v} + \mathbf{v}_A^*\cdot\mathbf{u}_A - \frac{1}{2}(v^2 + 2\mathbf{v}\cdot\mathbf{u}_A + u_A^2)\right] \tag{39}$$

Here we have defined the total viscous stress tensor by

$$\boldsymbol{\tau} = \sum_{A=1}^{A=N}\boldsymbol{\tau}_A \tag{40}$$

One can now use the second axiom for mass to obtain

$$\sum_{A=1}^{A=N} r_A\left(\frac{1}{2}v^2\right) = 0 \tag{41}$$

and use of the fourth axiom for the mechanics of multicomponent systems yields

$$\sum_{A=1}^{A=N} r_A \mathbf{v}_A^* \cdot \mathbf{v} = 0 \tag{42}$$

With these simplifications we can express the enthalpy equation as

$$\frac{\partial}{\partial t} \sum_{A=1}^{A=N} \rho_A h_A + \nabla \cdot \sum_{A=1}^{A=N} \rho_A h_A \mathbf{v}_A = -\nabla \cdot (\mathbf{q} + \mathbf{q}^R) + \boldsymbol{\tau} : \nabla \mathbf{v} + \frac{Dp}{Dt} + \sum_{A=1}^{A=N} (\boldsymbol{\tau}_A : \nabla \mathbf{u}_A + \mathbf{u}_A \cdot \nabla p_A)$$
$$- \sum_{A=1}^{A=N} r_A \left(\mathbf{v}_A^* \cdot \mathbf{u}_A - \mathbf{v} \cdot \mathbf{u}_A - \frac{1}{2} u_A^2 \right) \tag{43}$$

It is important to note that the last term in this result represents a source of kinetic energy owing to chemical reaction and it can be expressed as

$$\sum_{A=1}^{A=N} r_A \left(\mathbf{v}_A^* \cdot \mathbf{u}_A - \mathbf{v} \cdot \mathbf{u}_A - \frac{1}{2} u_A^2 \right) = \mathbf{O}\left\{ \sum_{A=1}^{A=N} r_A \left(\frac{1}{2} u_A^2 \right) \right\} \tag{44}$$

From this we can see that the last two terms in Equation 43 represent a diffusive rate of work and a diffusive kinetic energy source owing to chemical reactions. One can put forth convincing arguments that these terms are negligible in the total enthalpy equation, thus we express Equation 43 as

$$\frac{\partial}{\partial t} \sum_{A=1}^{A=N} \rho_A h_A + \nabla \cdot \sum_{A=1}^{A=N} \rho_A h_A \mathbf{v}_A = -\nabla \cdot (\mathbf{q} + \mathbf{q}^R) + \boldsymbol{\tau} : \nabla \mathbf{v} + \frac{Dp}{Dt} \tag{45}$$

The enthalpy of species A per unit volume can also be represented in terms of the molar concentration c_A and the partial molar enthalpy H_A according to

$$\rho_A h_A = c_A H_A \tag{46}$$

This allows us to write Equation 45 as

$$\frac{\partial}{\partial t} \sum_{A=1}^{A=N} c_A H_A + \nabla \cdot \sum_{A=1}^{A=N} c_A H_A \mathbf{v}_A = -\nabla \cdot (\mathbf{q} + \mathbf{q}^R) + \boldsymbol{\tau} : \nabla \mathbf{v} + \frac{Dp}{Dt} \tag{47}$$

which is essentially the form given by Bird, Stewart and Lightfoot [9]. Equations 45 and 47 are particularly useful relations for the development of jump conditions at phase interfaces where we are concerned with enthalpy changes associated with adsorption and chemical reaction.

There are a variety of routes that one can follow to obtain an equation for the temperature from Equation 45. In this development we will use Equation 37 along with the decomposition indicated by Equation 16 in order to obtain a total enthalpy equation given by

$$\frac{\partial}{\partial t} (\rho h) + \nabla \cdot (\rho h \mathbf{v}) = -\nabla \cdot (\mathbf{q} + \mathbf{q}^R) - \nabla \cdot \sum_{A=1}^{A=N} \rho_A h_A \mathbf{u}_A + \boldsymbol{\tau} : \nabla \mathbf{v} + \frac{Dp}{Dt} \tag{48}$$

This is a convenient starting point for the development of a macroscopic enthalpy balance; however, for our purposes we wish to simplify the left hand side of this result using the total continuity equation given by Equation 5. This leads to

$$\frac{\partial}{\partial t} (\rho h) + \nabla \cdot (\rho h \mathbf{v}) = \rho \frac{\partial h}{\partial t} + \rho \mathbf{v} \cdot \nabla h \tag{49}$$

By axiom 4 given earlier as Equation 26 we know that h is a function of the state of the system, and we can identify the state of the system in terms of the temperature, pressure and the N-1 independent mass fractions. This means that the enthalpy per unit mass can be represented by

$$h = h(T, p, \omega_A, \omega_B \cdots \omega_{N-1}) \tag{50}$$

The partial derivative with respect to time takes the form

$$\frac{\partial h}{\partial t} = \left(\frac{\partial h}{\partial T}\right)_{p,\omega}\left(\frac{\partial T}{\partial t}\right) + \left(\frac{\partial h}{\partial p}\right)_{T,\omega}\left(\frac{\partial p}{\partial t}\right) + \sum_{A=1}^{A=N-1}\left(\frac{\partial h}{\partial \omega_A}\right)_{T,p,\omega_B}\left(\frac{\partial \omega_A}{\partial t}\right) \tag{51}$$

Here we have used a subscript ω to indicate that all $N - 1$ independent mass fractions are held constant, and we have used a subscript ω_B to indicate that all independent mass fractions except ω_A are held constant. The constant pressure heat capacity for a mixture is defined by

$$c_p = \left(\frac{\partial h}{\partial T}\right)_{p,\omega} \tag{52}$$

and the derivative of the enthalpy per unit mass with respect to the total pressure is related to the coefficient of thermal expansion for a mixture according to

$$\left(\frac{\partial h}{\partial p}\right)_{T,\omega} = \frac{1}{\rho}(1 - T\beta) \tag{53}$$

Here β can be represented as

$$\beta = -\frac{1}{\rho}\left(\frac{\partial \rho}{\partial T}\right)_{p,\omega} \tag{54}$$

Use of these relations in Equation 51 leads to

$$\frac{\partial h}{\partial t} = c_p\left(\frac{\partial T}{\partial t}\right) + \frac{1}{\rho}(1 - T\beta)\left(\frac{\partial p}{\partial t}\right) + \sum_{A=1}^{A=N-1}\left(\frac{\partial h}{\partial \omega_A}\right)_{T,p,\omega_B}\left(\frac{\partial \omega_A}{\partial t}\right) \tag{55}$$

and by analogy we can express the gradient of the enthalpy as

$$\underset{\sim}{\nabla} h = c_p \underset{\sim}{\nabla} T + \frac{1}{\rho}(1 - T\beta)\underset{\sim}{\nabla} p + \sum_{A=1}^{A=N-1}\left(\frac{\partial h}{\partial \omega_A}\right)_{T,p,\omega_B}\underset{\sim}{\nabla}\omega_A \tag{56}$$

Substitution of these two results into Equation 49 allows us to express that equation as

$$\frac{\partial}{\partial t}(\rho h) + \underset{\sim}{\nabla}\cdot(\rho h \underset{\sim}{v}) = \rho c_p \frac{DT}{Dt} + (1 - T\beta)\frac{Dp}{Dt} + \sum_{A=1}^{A=N-1}\left(\frac{\partial h}{\partial \omega_A}\right)_{T,p,\omega_B}\rho\left(\frac{\partial \omega_A}{\partial t} + \underset{\sim}{v}\cdot\underset{\sim}{\nabla}\omega_A\right) \tag{57}$$

in which the material derivatives are given by

$$\frac{DT}{Dt} = \frac{\partial T}{\partial t} + \underset{\sim}{v}\cdot\underset{\sim}{\nabla} T, \qquad \frac{Dp}{Dt} = \frac{\partial p}{\partial t} + \underset{\sim}{v}\cdot\underset{\sim}{\nabla} p \tag{58}$$

A bit of manipulation with the total continuity equation leads to

$$\rho\left(\frac{\partial \omega_A}{\partial t} + \underset{\sim}{v}\cdot\underset{\sim}{\nabla}\omega_A\right) = \frac{\partial \rho_A}{\partial t} + \underset{\sim}{\nabla}\cdot(\rho_A \underset{\sim}{v}_A) - \underset{\sim}{\nabla}\cdot(\rho_A \underset{\sim}{u}_A) \tag{59}$$

and use of the species continuity equation given by Equation 3 allows us to express this as

$$\rho\left(\frac{\partial \omega_A}{\partial t} + \underset{\sim}{v} \cdot \underset{\sim}{\nabla} \omega_A\right) = r_A - \underset{\sim}{\nabla} \cdot (\rho_A \underset{\sim}{u}_A) \tag{60}$$

Use of this result in Equation 57 and substitution of the latter into Equation 48 yields an equation for the temperature given by

$$\rho c_p \frac{DT}{Dt} = -\underset{\sim}{\nabla} \cdot (\underset{\sim}{q} + \underset{\sim}{q}^R) - \underset{\sim}{\nabla} \cdot \sum_{A=1}^{A=N} \rho_A h_A \underset{\sim}{u}_A + \underset{\approx}{\tau} : \underset{\sim}{\nabla} \underset{\sim}{v} + T\beta \frac{Dp}{Dt}$$
$$- \sum_{A=1}^{A=N-1} \left(\frac{\partial h}{\partial \omega_A}\right)_{T,p,\omega_B} r_A + \sum_{A=1}^{A=N-1} \left(\frac{\partial h}{\partial \omega_A}\right)_{T,p,\omega_B} \underset{\sim}{\nabla} \cdot (\rho_A \underset{\sim}{u}_A) \tag{61}$$

One can follow the developments in Slattery [5] to show that

$$\left(\frac{\partial h}{\partial \omega_A}\right)_{T,p,\omega_B} = h_A - h_N \tag{62}$$

This result can be used to express the reaction rate term in Equation 61 as

$$\sum_{A=1}^{A=N-1} \left(\frac{\partial h}{\partial \omega_A}\right)_{T,p,\omega_B} r_A = \sum_{A=1}^{A=N-1} h_A r_A - h_N \sum_{A=1}^{A=N-1} r_A \tag{63}$$

To the right side of this result we can add and subtract $h_N r_N$ and then use Equation 2 to obtain

$$\sum_{A=1}^{A=N-1} \left(\frac{\partial h}{\partial \omega_A}\right)_{T,p,\omega_B} r_A = \sum_{A=1}^{A=N} h_A r_A \tag{64}$$

Because the diffusive mass fluxes are constained by

$$\sum_{A=1}^{A=N} \rho_A \underset{\sim}{u}_A = 0 \tag{65}$$

we can repeat this same procedure to obtain

$$\sum_{A=1}^{A=N-1} \left(\frac{\partial h}{\partial \omega_A}\right)_{T,p,\omega_B} \underset{\sim}{\nabla} \cdot (\rho_A \underset{\sim}{u}_A) = \sum_{A=1}^{A=N} h_A \underset{\sim}{\nabla} \cdot (\rho_A \underset{\sim}{u}_A) \tag{66}$$

Substitution of Equations 64 and 66 into Equation 61 leads to a greatly simplified form given by

$$\rho c_p \frac{DT}{Dt} = -\underset{\sim}{\nabla} \cdot (\underset{\sim}{q} + \underset{\sim}{q}^R) - \sum_{A=1}^{A=N} \rho_A \underset{\sim}{u}_A \cdot \underset{\sim}{\nabla} h_A + \underset{\approx}{\tau} : \underset{\sim}{\nabla} \underset{\sim}{v} + T\beta \frac{Dp}{Dt} - \sum_{A=1}^{A=N} h_A r_A \tag{67}$$

In general, one wants to express the source term owing to chemical reactions in terms of partial molar enthalpies and molar rates of production per unit volume. Because of this, we express the last term in Equation 67 as

$$\sum_{A=1}^{A=N} h_A r_A = \sum_{A=1}^{A=N} H_A R_A \tag{68}$$

in which R_A is the molar rate of production of species A owing to chemical reaction. Use of

Equation 68 in Equation 67 allows us to write the temperature equation as

$$\rho c_p\left(\frac{\partial T}{\partial t} + \mathbf{v}\cdot\nabla T\right) = -\nabla\cdot(\mathbf{q} + \mathbf{q}^R) - \sum_{A=1}^{A=N} \rho_A \mathbf{u}_A \cdot \nabla h_A + \boldsymbol{\tau}:\nabla\mathbf{v} + T\beta\frac{Dp}{Dt} - \sum_{A=1}^{A=N} H_A R_A \tag{69}$$

This result is equivalent to that given by Bird, Stewart and Lightfoot [9]; however, one must be careful to note the difference in the interpretation of $\mathbf{q}$. In this approach $\mathbf{q}$ represents only the heat flux resulting from conduction, and it is expressed by Fourier's law as

$$\mathbf{q} = -k\nabla T \tag{70}$$

for isotropic media.

JUMP CONDITIONS

In this development we will ignore all tangential interfacial transport in the construction of jump conditions at phase interfaces. This means that surface diffusion will be ignored, and we will consider only the transport of mass and energy normal to the γ-κ interface shown in Figure 3. The interface moves with a velocity $\mathbf{w}$ as indicated in Figure 3, and we would like to develop the jump condition for some generic transport process described by

$$\frac{\partial\psi}{\partial t} + \nabla\cdot(\psi\mathbf{u}) = \nabla\cdot\boldsymbol{\pi} + \sigma \tag{71}$$

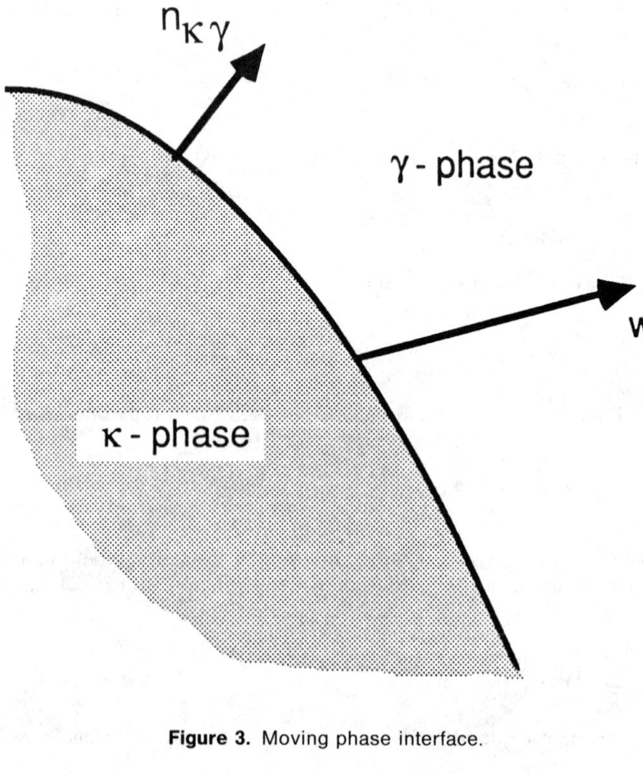

Figure 3. Moving phase interface.

Here ψ represents some quantity per unit volume and the convective flux, diffusive flux and source of this quantity are represented by $\psi \underset{\sim}{u}$, π and σ respectively. It is important to keep in mind that in this presentation $\psi \underset{\sim}{u}$ and π have no tangential components. Given this restriction, one can follow developments in Slattery [5], to arrive at the jump condition given by

$$\frac{\partial \hat{\psi}}{\partial t} = [\psi_\kappa(\underset{\sim}{u}_\kappa - \underset{\sim}{w}) - \psi_\gamma(\underset{\sim}{u}_\gamma - \underset{\sim}{w}) - (\underset{\sim}{\pi}_\kappa - \underset{\sim}{\pi}_\gamma)] \cdot \underset{\sim}{n}_{\kappa\gamma} + \hat{\sigma} \tag{72}$$

here $\hat{\psi}$ represents the quantity per unit area and $\hat{\sigma}$ represents the source of this quantity per unit area.

In most reactor design applications one uses the molar form of the species continuity equation, thus Equation 3 is expressed as

$$\frac{\partial c_A}{\partial t} + \underset{\sim}{\nabla} \cdot (c_A \underset{\sim}{v}_A) = R_A \tag{73}$$

and the jump condition is given by

$$\frac{\partial \hat{c}_A}{\partial t} = [c_{A\kappa}(\underset{\sim}{v}_{A\kappa} - \underset{\sim}{w}) - c_{A\gamma}(\underset{\sim}{v}_{A\gamma} - \underset{\sim}{w})] \cdot \underset{\sim}{n}_{\kappa\gamma} + \hat{R}_A \tag{74}$$

In this representation $\hat{c}_A$ is the surface concentration (moles/m^2) and $\hat{R}_A$ is the heterogeneous molar rate of production of species A (moles/sm^2). In general, it is convenient to use the molar form of the enthalpy equation in order to develop the thermal jump condition. Thus we make use of Equation 47 and neglect interfacial mechanical work terms in order to obtain

$$\frac{\partial}{\partial t} \sum_{A=1}^{A=N} \hat{c}_A \hat{H}_A = \left[\sum_{A=1}^{A-N} c_{A\kappa} H_{A\kappa}(\underset{\sim}{v}_{A\kappa} - \underset{\sim}{w}) - \sum_{A=1}^{A=N} c_{A\gamma} H_{A\gamma}(\underset{\sim}{v}_{A\gamma} - \underset{\sim}{w}) + (\underset{\sim}{q}_\kappa + \underset{\sim}{q}_\kappa^R) - (\underset{\sim}{q}_\gamma + \underset{\sim}{q}_\gamma^R) \right] \cdot \underset{\sim}{n}_{\kappa\gamma} \tag{75}$$

Here $\hat{H}_A$ represents the partial molar enthalpy of the adsorbed species, and this quantity will be important whenever the heat of adsorption is significant.

HEAT TRANSPORT IN POROUS CATALYSTS

In Figure 4 we have illustrated a fluid-solid system in which the σ-phase represents porous catalyst pellets. Our first objective is to analyze the heat transport process that occurs in the catalyst pellets and we will then move on to the analysis of the fluid phase shown in Figure 4. Our treatment of both processes will be based on Equation 69 which we list here as

$$\rho c_p \left(\frac{\partial T}{\partial t} + \underset{\sim}{v} \cdot \underset{\sim}{\nabla} T \right) = -\underset{\sim}{\nabla} \cdot (\underset{\sim}{q} + \underset{\sim}{q}^R) - \sum_{A=1}^{A=N} \rho_A \underset{\sim}{u}_A \cdot \underset{\sim}{\nabla} h_A + \underset{\approx}{\tau} : \underset{\sim}{\nabla} \underset{\sim}{v} + T\beta \frac{Dp}{Dt} - \sum_{A=1}^{A=N} H_A R_A \tag{76}$$

For a single reaction, the individual reaction rates can be expressed in terms of the stoichiometric coefficients ν_A and the overall reaction rate according to

$$R_A = \nu_A R, \qquad A = 1, 2, \ldots, N \tag{77}$$

This allows us to express the source term in Equation 76 as

$$\sum_{A=1}^{A=N} H_A R_A = \left(\sum_{A=1}^{A=N} \nu_A H_A \right) R = \Delta H_r R \tag{78}$$

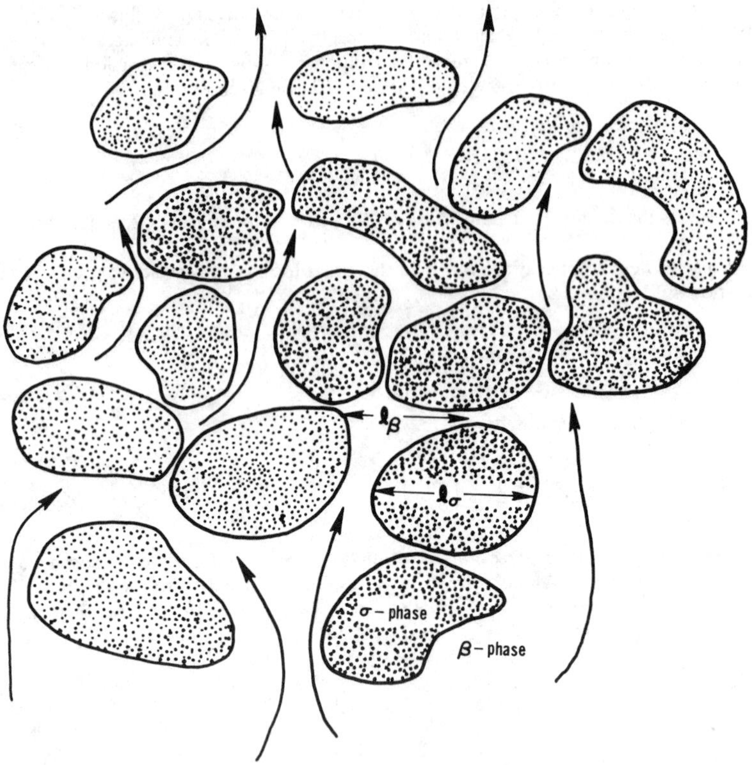

Figure 4. Heat transfer in a fluid-solid system.

Here ΔH_r represents the heat of reaction that is negative for exothermic reactions and positive for endothermic reactions.

In our study of heat transport in porous catalysts, we can neglect the effect of homogeneous reactions, the mechanical energy source terms, and the convective and diffusive fluxes of energy. This leads to an energy equation of the form

$$\rho c_p \frac{\partial T}{\partial t} = -\nabla \cdot (\mathbf{q} + \mathbf{q}^R) \tag{79}$$

The importance of radiant energy transport depends on both the absolute temperature and the path length for radiant energy transport. At room temperature, radiation is an important mechanism of energy transport in fiber glass insulation [10, 11]; however, for the typical porous catalyst the path length for radiant energy transport is small enough so that this mechanism can be ignored for the typical reactor design problem. This allows us to write our energy transport equation as

$$\rho c_p \frac{\partial T}{\partial t} = \nabla \cdot (k \nabla T) \tag{80}$$

We are interested in developing the volume-averaged form of this equation for the catalyst pellet illustrated in Figure 5. The macroscopic length scale is identified as L and one should think of

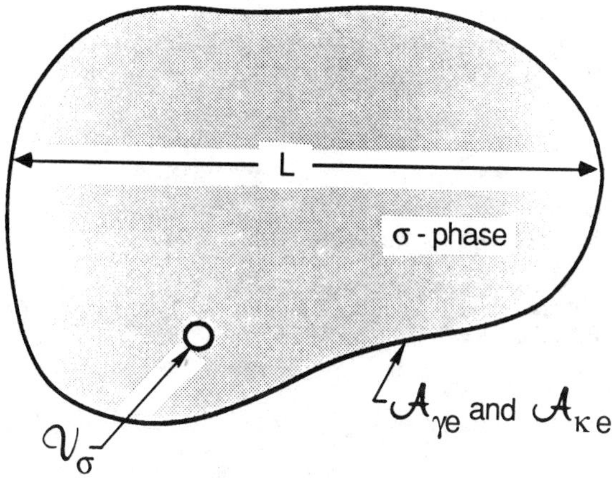

Figure 5. Porous catalyst pellet.

this as the effective particle diameter, d_p. It is impossible to solve Equation 80 for both the fluid and solid phases that make up the porous catalyst, and we seek instead to develop an equation for the average temperature in the region identified by V_σ. The details of this region are shown in Figure 6 where the solid phase has been identified as the κ-phase and the fluid phase as the γ-phase. One should keep in mind that the γ-phase and the β-phase are the same fluid phase; however, it is convenient to refer to the fluid phase that is inside the porous catalyst as the γ-phase.

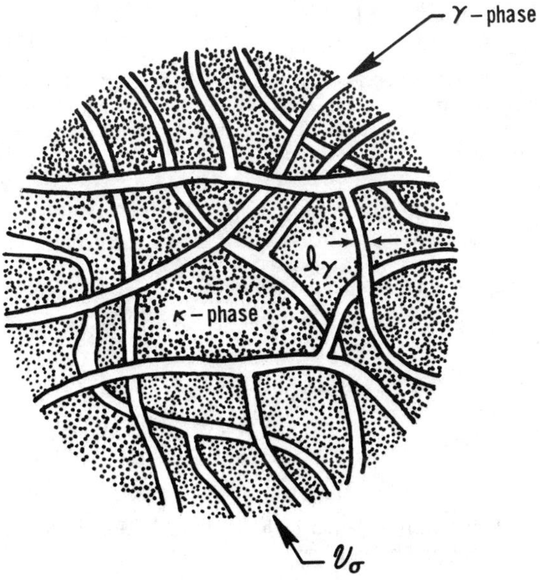

Figure 6. Averaging volume within a porous catalyst.

At the κ-γ interface there will be a source or a sink of thermal energy owing to heterogeneous chemical reactions. In order to identify the conditions at the catalytic surface, we assume that the κ-phase is impermeable and write the mass and energy jump conditions as

$$\frac{\partial \hat{c}_A}{\partial t} = c_{A\gamma}(\underset{\sim}{v}_{A\gamma} - \underset{\sim}{w}) \cdot \underset{\sim}{n}_{\gamma\kappa} + \hat{R}_A \tag{81}$$

$$\frac{\partial}{\partial t} \sum_{A=1}^{A=N} \hat{c}_A \hat{H}_A = \sum_{A=1}^{A=N} c_{A\gamma} H_{A\gamma}(\underset{\sim}{v}_{A\gamma} - \underset{\sim}{w}) \cdot \underset{\sim}{n}_{\gamma\kappa} + (\underset{\sim}{q}_\gamma - \underset{\sim}{q}_\kappa) \cdot \underset{\sim}{n}_{\gamma\kappa} \tag{82}$$

These relations are obtained directly from Equations 74 and 75 using the convention that $\underset{\sim}{n}_{\gamma\kappa} = -\underset{\sim}{n}_{\kappa\gamma}$. One can use Equation 81 in Equation 82 and arrange the latter in the form

$$\sum_{A=1}^{A=N} (\hat{H}_A - H_{A\gamma}) \frac{\partial \hat{c}_A}{\partial t} + \sum_{A=1}^{A=N} \hat{c}_A \left(\frac{\partial \hat{H}_A}{\partial t} \right) = -\sum_{A=1}^{A=N} H_{A\gamma} \hat{R}_A + (\underset{\sim}{q}_\gamma - \underset{\sim}{q}_\kappa) \cdot \underset{\sim}{n}_{\gamma\kappa} \tag{83}$$

Once again we will restrict our discussion to the case of a single reaction so that the individual rates of heterogeneous reaction can be expressed as

$$\hat{R}_A = \nu_A \hat{R}, \qquad A = 1, 2, \ldots, N \tag{84}$$

The heat of reaction is defined in a manner analogous to Equation 78

$$\Delta H_r = \sum_{A=1}^{A=N} \nu_A H_{A\gamma} \tag{85}$$

and this allows us to express the thermal jump condition as

$$\sum_{A=1}^{A=N} (\hat{H}_A - H_{A\gamma}) \frac{\partial \hat{c}_A}{\partial t} + \sum_{A=1}^{A=N} \hat{c}_A \left(\frac{\partial \hat{H}_A}{\partial t} \right) = -\Delta H_r \hat{R} + (\underset{\sim}{q}_\gamma - \underset{\sim}{q}_\kappa) \cdot \underset{\sim}{n}_{\gamma\kappa} \tag{86}$$

In reactor design calculations, it appears that the left side of this result is universally neglected. Since the catalytic surface can often be treated as quasi-steady from the point of view of mass transfer [12, 13], it is attractive to impose a comparable constraint for the heat transfer process. This quasi-steady constraint can be expressed as

$$\sum_{A=1}^{A=N} (\hat{H}_A - H_{A\gamma}) \frac{\partial \hat{c}_A}{\partial t} + \sum_{A=1}^{A=N} \hat{c}_A \left(\frac{\partial \hat{H}_A}{\partial t} \right) \ll \Delta H_r \hat{R} \tag{87}$$

and this allows us to write the thermal jump condition as

$$(\underset{\sim}{q}_\gamma - \underset{\sim}{q}_\kappa) \cdot \underset{\sim}{n}_{\gamma\kappa} = \Delta H_r \hat{R} \tag{88}$$

At this point we are ready to use the method of volume averaging [14–17] to develop equations for the average temperature in the region V_σ shown in Figure 5.

Volume Averaging

The detailed problem under investigation is the heat conduction process associated with the system illustrated in Figure 6 and it can be described as

$$(\rho c_p)_\kappa \frac{\partial T_\kappa}{\partial t} = \underset{\sim}{\nabla} \cdot (k_\kappa \underset{\sim}{\nabla} T_\kappa), \qquad \text{in the } \kappa\text{-phase} \tag{89}$$

Boundary Condition 1:

$$T_\kappa = T_\gamma, \qquad \text{at the } \kappa\text{-}\gamma \text{ interface} \tag{90a}$$

Boundary Condition 2:

$$\underset{\sim}{n}_{\gamma\kappa} \cdot k_\kappa \underset{\sim}{\nabla} T_\kappa = \underset{\sim}{n}_{\gamma\kappa} \cdot k_\gamma \underset{\sim}{\nabla} T_\gamma + \Delta H_r \hat{R}, \qquad \text{at the } \kappa\text{-}\gamma \text{ interface} \tag{90b}$$

$$(\rho c_p)_\gamma \frac{\partial T_\gamma}{\partial t} = \underset{\sim}{\nabla} \cdot (k_\gamma \underset{\sim}{\nabla} T_\gamma), \qquad \text{in the } \gamma\text{-phase} \tag{91}$$

Boundary Condition 3:

$$T_\kappa = G(t), \qquad \text{at } A_{\kappa e} \tag{92a}$$

Boundary Condition 4:

$$T_\gamma = F(t), \qquad \text{at } A_{\gamma e} \tag{92b}$$

Here $A_{\kappa e}$ and $A_{\gamma e}$ represent the entrances and exits of the κ and γ-phases at the surface of the porous catalyst illustrated in Figure 5. In general, the boundary conditions at the interface between the catalyst pellet and the surrounding fluid are known only in terms of average temperatures; however, the boundary conditions given by Equations 92 need to be stated as a matter of completeness. With the exception of the source term in Equation 90b, this problem is identical to that studied by Nozad et al. [18] among many others.

Our first objective is to derive equations for the local volume-averaged temperatures in the κ and γ-phases. The κ-phase superficial average temperature is defined by

$$\langle T_\kappa \rangle = \frac{1}{V_\sigma} \int_{V_\kappa} T_\kappa \, dV \tag{93}$$

where V_κ is the volume of the κ-phase contained within the averaging volume V_σ. The volume fraction of the κ-phase is given by

$$\epsilon_\kappa = V_\kappa / V_\sigma \tag{94}$$

and the volume fractions for the κ and γ-phases are naturally constrained by

$$\epsilon_\kappa + \epsilon_\gamma = 1 \tag{95}$$

To obtain an equation for $\langle T_\kappa \rangle$ we associate an averaging volume with every point in space and form the integral of Equation 89 to obtain

$$(\rho c_p)_\kappa \frac{1}{V_\sigma} \int_{V_\kappa} \left(\frac{\partial T_\kappa}{\partial t} \right) dV = \frac{1}{V_\sigma} \int_{V_\kappa} \underset{\sim}{\nabla} \cdot (k_\kappa \underset{\sim}{\nabla} T_\kappa) \, dV \tag{96}$$

It is important to note at this point that we have not assumed that $(\rho c_p)_\kappa$ is constant, but rather we have neglected variations in this quantity within the averaging volume V_σ. Since the κ-phase is assumed to be rigid, we can interchange integration and differentiation on the left hand side of Equation 96 to obtain

$$(\rho c_p)_\kappa \frac{\partial \langle T_\kappa \rangle}{\partial t} = \langle \underset{\sim}{\nabla} \cdot k_\kappa \underset{\sim}{\nabla} T_\kappa \rangle \tag{97}$$

Use of the spatial averaging theorem [19] allows us to interchange integration and differentiation on the right hand side of Equation 96 or Equation 97. This yields

$$(\rho c_p)_\kappa \frac{\partial \langle T_\kappa \rangle}{\partial t} = \underset{\sim}{\nabla} \cdot \langle k_\kappa \underset{\sim}{\nabla} T_\kappa \rangle + \frac{1}{V_\sigma} \int_{A_{\kappa\gamma}} \underset{\sim}{n}_{\kappa\gamma} \cdot k_\kappa \underset{\sim}{\nabla} T_\kappa \, dA \tag{98}$$

in which $A_{\kappa\gamma}$ represents the interfacial area contained within the averaging volume.

It is consistent with the assumption made concerning $(\rho c_p)_\kappa$ to neglect variations of k_κ within the averaging volume. This allows us to write

$$\langle k_\kappa \underset{\sim}{\nabla} T_\kappa \rangle = k_\kappa \langle \underset{\sim}{\nabla} T_\kappa \rangle = k_\kappa \left[\underset{\sim}{\nabla} \langle T_\kappa \rangle + \frac{1}{V_\sigma} \int_{A_{\kappa\gamma}} \underset{\sim}{n}_{\kappa\gamma} T_\kappa \, dA \right] \tag{99}$$

so that Equation 98 takes the form

$$(\rho c_p)_\kappa \frac{\partial \langle T_\kappa \rangle}{\partial t} = \underset{\sim}{\nabla} \cdot \left\{ k_\kappa \left[\nabla \langle T_\kappa \rangle + \frac{1}{V_\sigma} \int \underset{\sim}{n}_{\kappa\gamma} T_\kappa \right] \right\} + \frac{1}{V_\sigma} \int_{A_{\kappa\gamma}} \underset{\sim}{n}_{\kappa\gamma} \cdot k_\kappa \underset{\sim}{\nabla} T_\kappa \, dA \tag{100}$$

In general we would like to work with the κ-phase intrinsic average temperature which is defined by

$$\langle T_\kappa \rangle^\kappa = \frac{1}{V_\kappa} \int_{V_\kappa} T_\kappa \, dV \tag{101}$$

and this average temperature is related to the superficial average by

$$\langle T_\kappa \rangle = \epsilon_\kappa \langle T_\kappa \rangle^\kappa \tag{102}$$

We can use this representation in Equation 100 to obtain

$$\epsilon_\kappa (\rho c_p)_\kappa \frac{\partial \langle T_\kappa \rangle^\kappa}{\partial t} = \underset{\sim}{\nabla} \cdot \left\{ k_\kappa \left[\epsilon_\kappa \underset{\sim}{\nabla} \langle T_\kappa \rangle^\kappa + \langle T_\kappa \rangle^\kappa \underset{\sim}{\nabla} \epsilon_\kappa + \frac{1}{V_\sigma} \int_{A_{\kappa\gamma}} \underset{\sim}{n}_{\kappa\gamma} T_\kappa \, dA \right] \right\}$$

$$+ \frac{1}{V_\sigma} \int_{A_{\kappa\gamma}} \underset{\sim}{n}_{\kappa\gamma} \cdot k_\kappa \underset{\sim}{\nabla} T_\kappa \, dA \tag{103}$$

At this point we are confronted with two problems: the area integral of $\underset{\sim}{n}_{\kappa\gamma} T_\kappa$ and the interfacial flux term. The former problem can be simplified by the use of Gray's decomposition [20]

$$T_\kappa = \langle T_\kappa \rangle^\kappa + \tilde{T}_\kappa \tag{104a}$$

$$T_\gamma = \langle T_\gamma \rangle^\gamma + \tilde{T}_\gamma \tag{104b}$$

in order to obtain

$$\frac{1}{V_\sigma} \int_{A_{\kappa\gamma}} \underset{\sim}{n}_{\kappa\gamma} T_\kappa \, dA = \frac{1}{V_\sigma} \int_{A_{\kappa\gamma}} \underset{\sim}{n}_{\kappa\gamma} \langle T_\kappa \rangle^\kappa \, dA + \frac{1}{V_\sigma} \int_{A_{\kappa\gamma}} \underset{\sim}{n}_{\kappa\gamma} \tilde{T}_\kappa \, dA \tag{105}$$

It has been shown by Carbonell and Whitaker [21] that this relation can be simplified to

$$\frac{1}{V_\sigma} \int_{A_{\kappa\gamma}} \underset{\sim}{n}_{\kappa\gamma} T_\kappa \, dA = \frac{1}{V_\sigma} \int_{A_{\kappa\gamma}} \underset{\sim}{n}_{\kappa\gamma} \, dA \langle T_\kappa \rangle^\kappa + \frac{1}{V_\sigma} \int_{A_{\kappa\gamma}} \underset{\sim}{n}_{\kappa\gamma} \tilde{T}_\kappa \, dA \tag{106}$$

provided the macroscopic length scale illustrated in Figure 5 is large compared to the radius of the averaging volume, V_σ. The averaging theorem can now be used to develop the geometrical relation

$$\frac{1}{V_\sigma}\int_{A_{\kappa\gamma}} \underset{\sim}{n}_{\kappa\gamma}\, dA = -\underset{\sim}{\nabla}\epsilon_\kappa \tag{107}$$

so that Equation 106 takes the form

$$\frac{1}{V_\sigma}\int_{A_{\kappa\gamma}} \underset{\sim}{n}_{\kappa\gamma} T_\kappa\, dA = -\langle T_\kappa\rangle^\kappa \underset{\sim}{\nabla}\epsilon_\kappa + \frac{1}{V_\sigma}\int_{A_{\kappa\gamma}} \underset{\sim}{n}_{\kappa\gamma}\tilde{T}_\kappa\, dA \tag{108}$$

When this result is substituted into Equation 103 we obtain the governing equation for $\langle T_\kappa\rangle^\kappa$.

$$\epsilon_\kappa(\rho c_p)_\kappa \frac{\partial\langle T_\kappa\rangle^\kappa}{\partial t} = \underset{\sim}{\nabla}\cdot\left\{\epsilon_\kappa k_\kappa\left[\underset{\sim}{\nabla}\langle T_\kappa\rangle^\kappa + \frac{1}{V_\kappa}\int_{A_{\kappa\gamma}} \underset{\sim}{n}_{\kappa\gamma}\tilde{T}_\kappa\, dA\right]\right\} + \frac{1}{V_\sigma}\int_{A_{\gamma\kappa}} \underset{\sim}{n}_\kappa\cdot k_\kappa \underset{\sim}{\nabla} T_\kappa\, dA \tag{109}$$

The analysis of the γ-phase heat conduction process is identical to that just given and leads to

$$\epsilon_\gamma(\rho c_p)_\gamma \frac{\partial\langle T_\gamma\rangle^\gamma}{\partial t} = \underset{\sim}{\nabla}\cdot\left\{\epsilon_\kappa k_\gamma\left[\underset{\sim}{\nabla}\langle T_\gamma\rangle^\gamma + \frac{1}{V_\gamma}\int_{A_{\kappa\gamma}} \underset{\sim}{n}_{\gamma\kappa}\tilde{T}_\gamma\, dA\right]\right\} + \frac{1}{V_\sigma}\int_{A_{\gamma\kappa}} \underset{\sim}{n}_\kappa\cdot k_\kappa \underset{\sim}{\nabla} T_\kappa\, dA \tag{110}$$

If we were interested in developing a two-equation model of heat conduction in porous catalysts, we would need to utilize the decomposition given by Equation 104 for both T_κ and T_γ in the flux terms in Equations 109 and 110 and then develop a closure scheme for $\tilde{T}_\kappa$ and $\tilde{T}_\gamma$. This type of approach has been explored for the process of diffusion in a micropore-macropore model of a porous catalyst [22]; however, it is not needed here because the constraints associated with local thermal equilibrium are generally satisfied.

One-Equation Model

The one-equation model is based on the assumption that the energy transport process can be characterized by a single temperature. This assumption is valid when the system is in a state of local thermal equilibrium [23–25] and this condition appears to prevail for almost all practical problems of heat conduction in porous media. It seems intuitively appealing that the spatial average temperature, given by

$$\langle T\rangle = \frac{1}{V_\sigma}\int_{V_\sigma} T\, dV = \epsilon_\kappa\langle T_\kappa\rangle^\kappa + \epsilon_\gamma\langle T_\gamma\rangle^\beta \tag{111}$$

would be the proper single temperature to characterize the heat conduction process. One can proceed on firm ground by representing the κ and γ-phase temperatures by

$$\langle T_\kappa\rangle^\kappa = \langle T\rangle + \hat{T}_\kappa \tag{112a}$$

$$\langle T_\gamma\rangle^\gamma = \langle T\rangle + \hat{T}_\gamma \tag{112b}$$

where $\hat{T}_\kappa$ and $\hat{T}_\gamma$ represent large scale spatial deviations as opposed to the small scale deviations $\tilde{T}_\kappa$ and $\tilde{T}_\gamma$. When Equations 112 are used in Equations 109 and 110 and the latter two equations are added, we obtain

$$[\epsilon_\kappa(\rho c_p)_\kappa + \epsilon_\gamma(\rho c_p)_\gamma]\frac{\partial\langle T\rangle}{\partial t} = \nabla\cdot\left\{\epsilon_\kappa k_\kappa\left[\nabla\langle T\rangle + \frac{1}{V_\kappa}\int_{A_{\kappa\gamma}} n_{\kappa\gamma}\tilde{T}_\kappa\, dA\right]\right.$$
$$\left. + \epsilon_\gamma k_\gamma\left[\nabla\langle T\rangle + \frac{1}{V_\gamma}\int_{A_{\gamma\kappa}} n_{\gamma\kappa}\tilde{T}_\gamma\, dA\right]\right\} + \frac{1}{V_\sigma}\int_{A_{\kappa\gamma}} n_{\kappa\gamma}$$
$$\cdot [k_\kappa\nabla T_\kappa - k_\gamma\nabla T_\gamma]\, dA - \left\{\epsilon_\kappa(\rho c_p)_\kappa\frac{\partial\hat{T}_\kappa}{\partial t} + \epsilon_\gamma(\rho c_p)_\gamma\frac{\partial\hat{T}_\gamma}{\partial t}\right.$$
$$\left. - \nabla\cdot(\epsilon_\kappa k_\kappa\nabla\hat{T}_\kappa) - \nabla\cdot(\epsilon_\gamma k_\gamma\nabla\hat{T}_\gamma)\right\} \tag{113}$$

Local thermal equilibrium requires that the following constraints be satisfied

$$\frac{\partial\hat{T}_\kappa}{\partial t} \ll \frac{\partial\langle T\rangle}{\partial t}, \qquad \frac{\partial\hat{T}_\gamma}{\partial t} \ll \frac{\partial\langle T\rangle}{\partial t}, \qquad \nabla\hat{T}_\kappa \ll \nabla\langle T\rangle, \qquad \nabla\hat{T}_\gamma \ll \nabla\langle T\rangle \tag{114}$$

and when these conditions prevail, we can discard the last four terms in Equation 113 and use the boundary condition given by Equation 90b to arrive at

$$\langle\rho\rangle c_p\frac{\partial\langle T\rangle}{\partial t} = \nabla\cdot\left\{\epsilon_\kappa k_\kappa\left[\nabla\langle T\rangle + \frac{1}{V_\kappa}\int_{A_{\kappa\gamma}} n_{\kappa\gamma}\tilde{T}_\kappa\, dA\right]\right.$$
$$\left. + \epsilon_\gamma k_\gamma\left[\nabla\langle T\rangle + \frac{1}{V_\gamma}\int_{A_{\gamma\kappa}} n_{\gamma\kappa}\tilde{T}_\gamma\, dA\right]\right\} - \frac{1}{V_\sigma}\int_{A_{\kappa\gamma}} \Delta H_r\hat{R}\, dA \tag{115}$$

Here $\langle\rho\rangle$ is the spatial average density defined in the manner suggested by Equation 111 and C_p is the mass fraction weighted heat capacity defined by

$$\langle\rho\rangle C_p = \epsilon_\kappa(\rho c_p)_\kappa + \epsilon_\gamma(\rho c_p)_\gamma \tag{116}$$

In order to be confident about neglecting the last four terms in Equation 114, one needs estimates of $\hat{T}_\kappa$ and $\hat{T}_\gamma$ so that the magnitude of the terms involving these large scale deviations can be determined. The route to these estimates is not obvious; however, a place to start is with Equations 111 and 112, which can be used to express $\hat{T}_\kappa$ and $\hat{T}_\gamma$ as

$$\hat{T}_\kappa = \langle T_\kappa\rangle^\kappa - \langle T\rangle = \epsilon_\gamma(\langle T_\kappa\rangle^\kappa - \langle T_\gamma\rangle^\gamma) \tag{117a}$$

$$\hat{T}_\gamma = \langle T_\gamma\rangle^\gamma - \langle T\rangle = \epsilon_\kappa(\langle T_\gamma\rangle^\gamma - \langle T_\kappa\rangle^\kappa) \tag{117b}$$

Here it becomes clear that we need an estimate of $\langle T_\kappa\rangle^\kappa - \langle T_\gamma\rangle^\gamma$ if we are to be able to determine under what circumstances local thermal equilibrium is valid. The first development of an estimate of $\langle T_\kappa\rangle^\kappa - \langle T_\gamma\rangle^\gamma$ was given in a study of drying porous media [24] and was subsequently extended to packed bed catalytic reactor design [25]. The crux of the estimation scheme is associated with the interfacial flux terms in Equations 109 and 110, and for the case under investigation these estimates take the form

$$\frac{1}{V_\sigma}\int_{A_{\kappa\gamma}} n_{\kappa\gamma}\cdot k_\kappa\nabla T_\kappa\, dA = 0\left[\frac{a_{\kappa\gamma}k_\kappa(\langle T_\kappa\rangle^\kappa - \langle T_i\rangle_{\kappa\gamma})}{\ell_\kappa}\right] \tag{118a}$$

$$\frac{1}{V_\sigma}\int_{A_{\gamma\kappa}} n_{\gamma\kappa}\cdot k_\gamma\nabla T_\gamma\, dA = 0\left[\frac{a_{\kappa\gamma}(\langle T_\gamma\rangle^\gamma - \langle T_i\rangle_{\kappa\gamma})}{\ell_\gamma}\right] \tag{118b}$$

Here ℓ_κ and ℓ_γ are the characteristic lengths illustrated in Figure 6, and $a_{\kappa\gamma}$ is the interfacial area per unit volume that can be written explicitly as

$$a_{\kappa\gamma} = A_{\kappa\gamma}/V_\sigma \tag{119}$$

In obtaining these estimates of the interfacial flux we have used $\langle T_i \rangle_{\kappa\gamma}$ to represent the area-averaged temperature at the κ-γ interface and this average is expressed as

$$\langle T_i \rangle_{\kappa\gamma} = \frac{1}{A_{\kappa\gamma}} \int_{A_{\kappa\gamma}} T_i \, dA \tag{120}$$

Here T_i is equal to T_κ and T_γ according to the boundary condition given by Equation 90a. We can eliminate $\langle T_i \rangle_{\kappa\gamma}$ from Equations 118a and b by means of the flux boundary condition given by Equation 90b, and this allows us to estimate the interfacial fluxes given by Equations 118a and b as

$$\frac{1}{V_\sigma} \int_{A_{\kappa\gamma}} \underset{\sim}{n}_{\kappa\gamma} \cdot k_\kappa \underset{\sim}{\nabla} T_\kappa \, dA = \underset{\sim}{0} \left\{ \frac{a_{\kappa\gamma}(\langle T_\gamma \rangle^\gamma - \langle T_\kappa \rangle^\kappa)}{\dfrac{\ell_\kappa}{k_\kappa} + \dfrac{\ell_\gamma}{k_\gamma}} \right\} + \underset{\sim}{0} \left\{ \frac{a_{\kappa\gamma} \langle \Delta H_r \hat{R} \rangle_{\kappa\gamma}}{1 + \dfrac{\ell_\kappa k_\gamma}{\ell_\gamma k_\kappa}} \right\} \tag{121a}$$

$$\frac{1}{V_\sigma} \int_{A_{\gamma\kappa}} \underset{\sim}{n}_{\gamma\kappa} \cdot k_\gamma \underset{\sim}{\nabla} T_\gamma \, dA = \underset{\sim}{0} \left\{ \frac{a_{\kappa\gamma}(\langle T_\kappa \rangle^\kappa - \langle T_\gamma \rangle^\gamma)}{\dfrac{\ell_\kappa}{k_\kappa} + \dfrac{\ell_\gamma}{k_\gamma}} \right\} + \underset{\sim}{0} \left\{ \frac{a_{\kappa\gamma} \langle \Delta H_r \hat{R} \rangle_{\kappa\gamma}}{1 + \dfrac{\ell_\kappa k_\gamma}{\ell_\gamma k_\kappa}} \right\} \tag{121b}$$

Use of Equations 121a and 117a in Equation 109 allows us to obtain estimates of $\hat{T}_\kappa$ in terms of the derivatives of $\langle T_\kappa \rangle^\kappa$ that appear in Equation 109. These estimates of $\hat{T}_\kappa$ can then be used in Equation 114 to determine under what circumstances Equation 115 is a valid representation of the heat transfer process. The analysis is very long and algebraically complex and the results for the packed bed heat transfer problem have been presented elsewhere [25]. Following that previous development, we can express the constraints associated with local thermal equilibrium as

$$\epsilon_\eta \left(\frac{\ell_\eta}{\alpha_\eta a_{\eta\omega} t} \right) \left(1 + \frac{\ell_\omega k_\eta}{\ell_\eta k_\omega} \right) < 1 \tag{122a}$$

$$\epsilon_\eta \left(\frac{\ell_\eta}{L^2 a_{\eta\omega}} \right) \left(1 + \frac{\ell_\omega k_\eta}{\ell_\eta k_\omega} \right) < 1 \tag{122b}$$

$$\frac{K^\sigma_{eff}}{k_\omega} \left(\frac{\ell_\omega}{\alpha_{eff} a_{\eta\omega} t} \right) < 1 \tag{123a}$$

$$\left(\frac{K^\sigma_{eff}}{k_\omega} \right) \left(\frac{\ell_\omega}{L^2 a_{\eta\omega}} \right) < 1 \tag{123b}$$

Here we have used the convention that

$$\omega = \kappa, \gamma; \qquad \eta = \kappa, \gamma; \qquad \omega \neq \eta$$

and we have used α to represent the thermal diffusivity according to

$$\alpha_\eta = k_\eta/(\rho c_p)_\eta; \qquad \alpha_{eff} = K^\sigma_{eff}/\langle \rho \rangle c_p \tag{124}$$

where K^σ_{eff} is the effective thermal conductivity.

The constraints given by Equation 122 result from the direct comparison of transient and conductive terms in Equation 113. For example, Equation 122a results from the constraints

$$\frac{\partial \hat{T}_\kappa}{\partial t} \ll \frac{\partial \langle T \rangle}{\partial t}, \qquad \frac{\partial \hat{T}_\gamma}{\partial t} \ll \frac{\partial \langle T \rangle}{\partial t} \tag{125}$$

while Equation 122b is derived from comparable constraints concerning the conductive terms. The constraints given by Equation 123 are obtained by requiring that the large scale deviation terms in Equation 113 are small compared to the interfacial flux term in that equation. These constraints involve the term $\Delta H_r \hat{R}$ as indicated by the form of Equation 115. It is shown elsewhere [25] how this heterogeneous thermal source is eliminated from the analysis in order to arrive at Equations 123.

If we use as an approximation

$$a_{\eta\omega} \sim \ell_\eta^{-1} \tag{126}$$

we can replace the constraints given by Equations 122 and 123 with

$$\left(\frac{\ell_\eta^2}{\alpha_\eta t}\right) < 1 \tag{127a}$$

$$\left(\frac{\ell_\eta^2}{L^2}\right) < 1 \tag{127b}$$

provided $(\ell_\eta k_\omega / \ell_\omega k_\eta)$ and $K_{eff}^\sigma / k_\omega$ do not differ greatly from unity. For porous catalysts ℓ_η is usually extremely small compared to $\sqrt{\alpha_\eta t}$ and L, thus the condition of local thermal equilibrium is generally valid. This means that we can return to Equation 115 and direct our attention to the development of reliable expressions for $\tilde{T}_\kappa$ and $\tilde{T}_\gamma$.

Closure

When local thermal equilibrium is applicable we can use a single temperature to describe the heat transfer process, and that single temperature is governed by Equation 115 which we express as

$$\langle \rho \rangle C_p \frac{\partial \langle T \rangle}{\partial t} = \nabla \cdot \left\{ \epsilon_\kappa k_\kappa \left[\nabla \langle T \rangle + \frac{1}{V_\kappa} \int_{A_{\kappa\gamma}} \mathbf{n}_{\kappa\gamma} \tilde{T}_\kappa \, dA \right] + \epsilon_\gamma k_\gamma \left[\nabla \langle T \rangle + \frac{1}{V_\gamma} \int_{A_{\gamma\kappa}} \mathbf{n}_{\gamma\kappa} \tilde{T}_\gamma \, dA \right] \right\} - a_{\kappa\gamma} \langle \Delta H_r \hat{R} \rangle_{\kappa\gamma} \tag{128}$$

To obtain a closed form of this result we must be able to represent $\tilde{T}_\kappa$ and $\tilde{T}_\gamma$ as functions of the dependent variable. The most reliable source of information concerning these fields rests with the governing differential equations for $\tilde{T}_\kappa$ and $\tilde{T}_\gamma$. These can be derived following the method of Crapiste et al. [26] which we will illustrate in the following paragraphs.

We begin our development with Equation 89 and use the decomposition given by Equation 104a to arrive at

$$(\rho c_p)_\kappa \frac{\partial \tilde{T}_\kappa}{\partial t} - \nabla \cdot (k_\kappa \nabla \tilde{T}_\kappa) = -\left[(\rho c_p)_\kappa \frac{\partial \langle T_\kappa \rangle^\kappa}{\partial t} - \nabla \cdot (k_\kappa \nabla \langle T_\kappa \rangle^\kappa) \right] \tag{129}$$

The intrinsic phase average of this result is given by

$$\frac{1}{V_\kappa} \int_{V_\kappa} \left[(\rho c_p)_\kappa \frac{\partial \tilde{T}_\kappa}{\partial t} - \nabla \cdot (k_\kappa \nabla \tilde{T}_\kappa) \right] dV = -\frac{1}{V_\kappa} \int_{V_\kappa} \left[(\rho c_p)_\kappa \frac{\partial \langle T_\kappa \rangle^\kappa}{\partial t} - \nabla \cdot (k_\kappa \nabla \langle T_\kappa \rangle^\kappa) \right] dV \tag{130}$$

At this point we use the same idea that led from Equation 105 to Equation 106 and assume that averaged quantities can be treated as constants within the averaging volume. This means that Equation 130 takes the form

$$\frac{1}{V_\kappa}\int_{V_\kappa}\left[(\rho c_p)_\kappa \frac{\partial \tilde{T}_\kappa}{\partial t} - \nabla \cdot (k_\kappa \nabla \tilde{T}_\kappa)\right] dV = -\left[(\rho c_p)_\kappa \frac{\partial \langle T_\kappa \rangle^\kappa}{\partial t} - \nabla \cdot (k_\kappa \nabla \langle T_\kappa \rangle^\kappa)\right] \tag{131}$$

and we can use this result in Equation 129 to obtain an integral-differential equation for $\tilde{T}_\kappa$ given by

$$(\rho c_p)_\kappa \frac{\partial \tilde{T}_\kappa}{\partial t} - \nabla \cdot (k_\kappa \nabla \tilde{T}_\kappa) = \frac{1}{V_\kappa}\int_{V_\kappa}\left[(\rho c_p)_\kappa \frac{\partial \tilde{T}}{\partial t} - \nabla \cdot (k_\kappa \nabla \tilde{T}_\kappa)\right] dV \tag{132}$$

While this governing equation for $\tilde{T}_\kappa$ appears to be more complex than the governing equation for T_κ, it is susceptible to several simplifications that lead to a relatively simple boundary value problem for $\tilde{T}_\kappa$ and also for $\tilde{T}_\gamma$. To begin with, we can express Equation 127a as

$$\frac{\ell_\kappa^2}{\alpha_\kappa t} < 1 \tag{133}$$

and note that when this constraint is satisfied the $\tilde{T}_\kappa$-field is quasi-steady. Since we have already imposed this constraint in the development of the one-equation model, it is appropriate to impose it at this point and expression Equation 132 as

$$\nabla \cdot (k_\kappa \nabla \tilde{T}_\kappa) = \frac{1}{V_\kappa}\int_{V_\kappa} \nabla \cdot (k_\kappa \nabla \tilde{T}_\kappa)\, dV \tag{134}$$

In some cases one may wish to take into account the spatial variations of the effective thermal conductivity over an entire catalyst pellet. However, the closure problem for $\tilde{T}_\kappa$ is a local problem and in the domain of this local problem it is quite acceptable to impose the constraint

$$k_\kappa \nabla^2 \tilde{T}_\kappa \gg \nabla k_\kappa \cdot \nabla \tilde{T}_\kappa \tag{135}$$

This allows us to express Equation 134 as

$$\nabla^2 \tilde{T}_\kappa = \frac{1}{V_\kappa}\int_{V_\kappa} \nabla^2 \tilde{T}_\kappa\, dV \tag{136}$$

with a similar result for $\tilde{T}_\gamma$.

In order to develop the boundary conditions for $\tilde{T}_\kappa$ and $\tilde{T}_\gamma$ we return to the boundary condition given by Equation 90a and make use of the decompositions given by Equation 104 and 112 to obtain

Boundary Condition 1:

$$\tilde{T}_\kappa + \langle T \rangle + \hat{T}_\kappa = \tilde{T}_\gamma + \langle T \rangle + \hat{T}_\gamma, \qquad \text{at the } \kappa\text{-}\gamma \text{ interface} \tag{137}$$

Clearly this reduces to

Boundary Condition 1:

$$\tilde{T}_\kappa + \hat{T}_\kappa = \tilde{T}_\gamma + \hat{T}_\gamma, \qquad \text{at the } \kappa\text{-}\gamma \text{ interface} \tag{138}$$

and further simplification requires some knowledge of the magnitude of the large scale deviations,

$\hat{T}_\kappa$ and $\hat{T}_\gamma$, relative to the magnitude of the small scale deviations, $\tilde{T}_\kappa$ and $\tilde{T}_\gamma$. Since $\hat{T}_\kappa$ is the difference between two average temperatures

$$\hat{T}_\kappa = \langle T_\kappa \rangle^\kappa - \langle T \rangle \tag{139}$$

while $\tilde{T}_\kappa$ is the difference between a point temperature and an average temperature

$$\tilde{T}_\kappa = T_\kappa - \langle T_\kappa \rangle^\kappa \tag{140}$$

we should expect that $\hat{T}_\kappa \ll \tilde{T}_\kappa$. Estimates of $\hat{T}_\kappa$ and $\hat{T}_\gamma$ are available [24, 25] and they were used to produce the constraints given by Equations 122 and 123 associated with the one-equation model. On the basis of the closure problem for $\tilde{T}_\kappa$ and $\tilde{T}_\gamma$, Nozad et al. [18] have produced estimates of $\tilde{T}_\kappa$ and $\tilde{T}_\gamma$. When these estimates are used with the constraints

$$\hat{T}_\kappa \ll \tilde{T}_\kappa, \qquad \hat{T}_\gamma \ll \tilde{T}_\gamma \tag{141}$$

one finds a more severe set of constraints than those given by Equations 122 and 123. We list the constraints associated with Equation 141 as

$$\epsilon_\eta \left(\frac{\ell_\eta}{\alpha_\eta a_{\eta\omega} t} \right) \left(1 + \frac{\ell_\omega k_\eta}{\ell_\eta k_\omega} \right) < \left(\frac{\ell_\eta}{L} \right) \tag{142a}$$

$$\epsilon_\eta \left(\frac{\ell_\eta}{L^2 a_{\eta\omega}} \right) \left(1 + \frac{\ell_\omega k_\eta}{\ell_\eta k_\omega} \right) < \left(\frac{\ell_\eta}{L} \right) \tag{142b}$$

and note that the first of these will always be satisfied at sufficiently long times while the second will always be satisfied at sufficiently large values of the macroscopic length scale. One should keep in mind that the constraints given by Equations 122, 123, and 142 are all based on order of magnitude analysis, and this means that they provide nothing more than indications about when the assumptions will succeed or fail. A precise delineation between the one-equation model given by Equation 115 and the two-equation model represented by Equations 109 and 110 requires a comparison of results from both models for a wide range of parameters. This will undoubtedly be done in the future, but for the present we must rely on Equations 142 in order to express Equation 138 as

Boundary Condition 1:

$$\tilde{T}_\kappa = \tilde{T}_\gamma, \qquad \text{at the } \kappa\text{-}\gamma \text{ interface} \tag{143}$$

We are now in a position to consider the flux boundary condition given by Equation 91. The representations for T_κ and T_γ illustrated in Equation 137 are used in Equation 90b to obtain

Boundary Condition 2:

$$\underline{n}_{\gamma\kappa} \cdot k_\kappa \underline{\nabla} \tilde{T}_\kappa = \underline{n}_{\gamma\kappa} \cdot k_\gamma \underline{\nabla} \tilde{T}_\gamma + \underline{n}_{\gamma\kappa} \cdot k_\gamma \underline{\nabla} \langle T \rangle$$
$$+ \underline{n}_{\gamma\kappa} \cdot k_\gamma \underline{\nabla} \hat{T}_\gamma - \underline{n}_{\gamma\kappa} \cdot k_\kappa \underline{\nabla} \langle T \rangle - \underline{n}_{\gamma\kappa} \cdot k_\kappa \underline{\nabla} \hat{T}_\kappa + \Delta H_r \hat{R} \tag{144}$$

In developing the one-equation model given by Equation 115 from Equation 113 we have imposed constraints of the type

$$\underline{\nabla} \hat{T}_\kappa \ll \underline{\nabla} \langle T \rangle, \qquad \underline{\nabla} \hat{T}_\gamma \ll \underline{\nabla} \langle T \rangle \tag{145}$$

Because of this, the constraints given by Equations 122 and 123 allow us to neglect the terms in Equation 144 that involve $\underline{\nabla} \hat{T}_\kappa$ and $\underline{\nabla} \hat{T}_\gamma$.

At this point we can summarize our boundary value problem for $\tilde{T}_\kappa$ and $\tilde{T}_\gamma$ as

$$\nabla^2\tilde{T}_\kappa = \frac{1}{V_\kappa} \int_{V_\kappa} \nabla^2\tilde{T}_\kappa \, dV \tag{146}$$

Boundary Condition 1:

$$\tilde{T}_\kappa = \tilde{T}_\gamma, \quad \text{at the } \kappa\text{-}\gamma \text{ interface} \tag{147a}$$

Boundary Condition 2:

$$\underline{n}_{\gamma\kappa} \cdot k_\kappa \underline{\nabla}\tilde{T}_\kappa = \underline{n}_{\gamma\kappa} \cdot k_\gamma \underline{\nabla}\tilde{T}_\gamma + \underline{n}_{\gamma\kappa} \cdot (k_\gamma - k_\kappa)\underline{\nabla}\langle T\rangle + \Delta H_r\hat{R}, \quad \text{at the } \kappa\text{-}\gamma \text{ interface} \tag{147b}$$

$$\nabla^2\tilde{T}_\gamma = \frac{1}{V_\gamma} \int_{V_\gamma} \nabla^2\tilde{T}_\gamma \, dV \tag{148}$$

Boundary Condition 3:

$$\tilde{T}_\kappa = g(t), \quad \text{at } A_{\kappa e} \tag{149a}$$

Boundary Condition 4:

$$\tilde{T}_\gamma = f(t), \quad \text{at } A_{\gamma e} \tag{149b}$$

The latter two boundary conditions are associated with the boundary conditions given by Equations 92, and while $\tilde{T}_\kappa$ and $\tilde{T}_\gamma$ are generally unknown at the surface of the catalyst pellet illustrated in Figure 5 we need to include Equations 149 to have a well-posed boundary value problem. In reality, the boundary conditions at $A_{\kappa e}$ and $A_{\gamma e}$ are listed more as a remainder of what we do not know rather than what we do know about $\tilde{T}_\kappa$ and $\tilde{T}_\gamma$. In addition to the governing equations and boundary conditions given by Equations 146 through 149, we note that Equations 104 require that

$$\langle\tilde{T}_\kappa\rangle^\kappa = 0, \quad \langle\tilde{T}_\gamma\rangle^\gamma = 0 \tag{150}$$

These conditions are based on the idea that $\langle T_\kappa\rangle^\kappa$ and $\langle T_\gamma\rangle^\gamma$ can be treated as constants within an averaging volume.

If we ignore the influence of the boundary conditions at $A_{\kappa e}$ and $A_{\gamma e}$, we can see that there are only two terms that are the sources of the $\tilde{T}_\kappa$ and $\tilde{T}_\gamma$-fields. Thus if $\underline{\nabla}\langle T\rangle$ and $\Delta H_r\hat{R}$ are zero, a solution to Equations 146 through 148 is $\tilde{T}_\kappa = \tilde{T}_\gamma = 0$. Given the potential importance of $\Delta H_r\hat{R}$ on $\tilde{T}_\kappa$ and $\tilde{T}_\gamma$, we need to consider this term carefully. The heat of reaction will be a function of the temperature at the κ-γ interface, and on the basis of Equation 90a we can express this idea as

$$\Delta H_r = \Delta H_r(T_\kappa) \tag{151}$$

The functional dependence of the heterogeneous rate of reaction is more complex since it depends on both temperature and the surface concentration of the reacting species. If the catalytic surface can be treated as *quasi-steady* (12), the reaction rate can be expressed in terms of the bulk concentrations and we express this idea as

$$\hat{R} = \hat{R}(T_\kappa, c_A, c_B, \ldots) \tag{152}$$

In terms of the one-equation model given by Equation 128, it is only the area-average of ΔH_r that is required. Since the closure problem must lead to a representation of $\tilde{T}_\kappa$ and $\tilde{T}_\gamma$ in terms of $\langle T\rangle$ and perhaps $\langle\Delta H_r\hat{R}\rangle_{\kappa\gamma}$, we need to decompose $\Delta H_r\hat{R}$ according to

$$\Delta H_r\hat{R} = \langle\Delta H_r\hat{R}\rangle_{\kappa\gamma} + \widetilde{\Delta H_r\hat{R}} \tag{153}$$

At this point we make an important simplification and assume that the deviation, $\widetilde{\Delta H_r \hat{R}}$, can be neglected relative to the area average. This means that Equation 147a takes the form

$$\mathbf{n}_{\gamma\kappa} \cdot k_\kappa \nabla \tilde{T}_\kappa = \mathbf{n}_{\gamma\kappa} \cdot k_\gamma \nabla \tilde{T}_\gamma + \mathbf{n}_{\gamma\kappa} \cdot (k_\gamma - k_\kappa) \nabla \langle T \rangle + \langle \Delta H_r \hat{R} \rangle_{\kappa\gamma}, \qquad \text{at the } \kappa\text{-}\gamma \text{ interface} \tag{154}$$

With this simplification we eliminate the possibility of interaction between the temperature deviations, $\tilde{T}_\kappa$ and $\tilde{T}_\gamma$, and the concentration deviations, $\tilde{c}_A$ and $\tilde{c}_B$, etc. It would seem plausible that the influence of $\tilde{c}_A$, $\tilde{c}_B$, etc. on $\tilde{T}_\kappa$ and $\tilde{T}_\gamma$ would be small compared to the influence of $\langle c_A \rangle^\gamma$, $\langle c_B \rangle^\gamma$, etc. via $\langle \Delta H_r \hat{R} \rangle_{\kappa\gamma}$; however, a detailed analysis remains to be done and we will encounter this problem again.

If one accepts the use of Equation 154 in place of Equation 147b, the analysis follows the earlier work of Ryan et al. [27, 28], Nozad et al. [18] and Ochoa et al. [29]. We begin by representing $\tilde{T}_\kappa$ and $\tilde{T}_\gamma$ by the following expressions

$$\tilde{T}_\kappa = \mathbf{g} \cdot \nabla \langle T \rangle + r \langle \Delta H_r \hat{R} \rangle_{\kappa\gamma} + \psi \tag{155a}$$

$$\tilde{T}_\gamma = \mathbf{f} \cdot \nabla \langle T \rangle + s \langle \Delta H_r \hat{R} \rangle_{\kappa\gamma} + \xi \tag{155b}$$

in which ψ and ξ are completely arbitrary functions. Because ψ and ξ are arbitrary, we can specify the functions $\mathbf{g}$, $\mathbf{f}$, r and s according to the following boundary value problems.

Problem I

$$\nabla^2 \mathbf{g} = \frac{1}{V_\kappa} \int_{V_\kappa} \nabla^2 \mathbf{g} \, dV \tag{156}$$

Boundary Condition 1:

$$\mathbf{g} = \mathbf{f}, \qquad \text{at the } \kappa\text{-}\gamma \text{ interface} \tag{157a}$$

Boundary Condition 2:

$$\mathbf{n}_{\gamma\kappa} \cdot k_\kappa \nabla \mathbf{g} = \mathbf{n}_{\gamma\kappa} \cdot k_\gamma \nabla \mathbf{f} + \mathbf{n}_{\gamma\kappa}(k_\gamma - k_\kappa), \qquad \text{at the } \kappa\text{-}\gamma \text{ interface} \tag{157b}$$

$$\nabla^2 \mathbf{f} = \frac{1}{V_\gamma} \int_{V_\gamma} \nabla^2 \mathbf{f} \, dV \tag{158}$$

Boundary Condition 3:

$$\mathbf{g} = \mathbf{g}(t), \qquad \text{at } A_{\kappa e} \tag{159a}$$

Boundary Condition 4:

$$\mathbf{f} = \mathbf{f}(t), \qquad \text{at } A_{\gamma e} \tag{159b}$$

$$\langle \mathbf{g} \rangle^\kappa = 0, \qquad \langle \mathbf{f} \rangle^\gamma = 0 \tag{160}$$

Problem II

$$\nabla^2 r = \frac{1}{V_\kappa} \int_{V_\kappa} \nabla^2 r \, dV \tag{161}$$

Boundary Condition 1:

$$r = s, \qquad \text{at the } \kappa\text{-}\gamma \text{ interface} \tag{162a}$$

Boundary Condition 2:

$$\underset{\sim}{n}_{\gamma\kappa} \cdot k_\kappa \underset{\sim}{\nabla} r = \underset{\sim}{n}_{\gamma\kappa} \cdot k_\gamma \underset{\sim}{\nabla} s + 1, \qquad \text{at the } \kappa\text{-}\gamma \text{ interface} \tag{162b}$$

$$\nabla^2 s = \frac{1}{V_\gamma} \int_{V_\gamma} \nabla^2 s \, dV \tag{163}$$

Boundary Condition 3:

$$r = r(t), \qquad \text{at } A_{\kappa e} \tag{164a}$$

Boundary Condition 4:

$$s = s(t), \qquad \text{at } A_{\gamma e} \tag{164b}$$

$$\langle r \rangle^\kappa = 0, \qquad \langle s \rangle^\gamma = 0 \tag{165}$$

When g, $\underset{\sim}{f}$, r, and s are specified in this manner, one can follow the analysis of Nozad et al. [18] or Whitaker [30, 31] to show that ψ and ξ make negligible contributions to $\tilde{T}_\kappa$ and $\tilde{T}_\gamma$ respectively.

It should be clear at this point that the closure problem is nearly as complex as the original problem stated by Equations 89 through 92. However, it should be intuitively appealing that $\tilde{T}_\kappa$ and $\tilde{T}_\gamma$ are not influenced by the boundary conditions imposed at $A_{\kappa e}$ and $A_{\gamma e}$. The same holds true for the fields $\underset{\sim}{g}$, $\underset{\sim}{f}$, r and s, and this means that it should be sufficient to solve for these functions in some representative region such as that shown in Figure 7. The results can then be used to evaluate $\tilde{T}_\kappa$

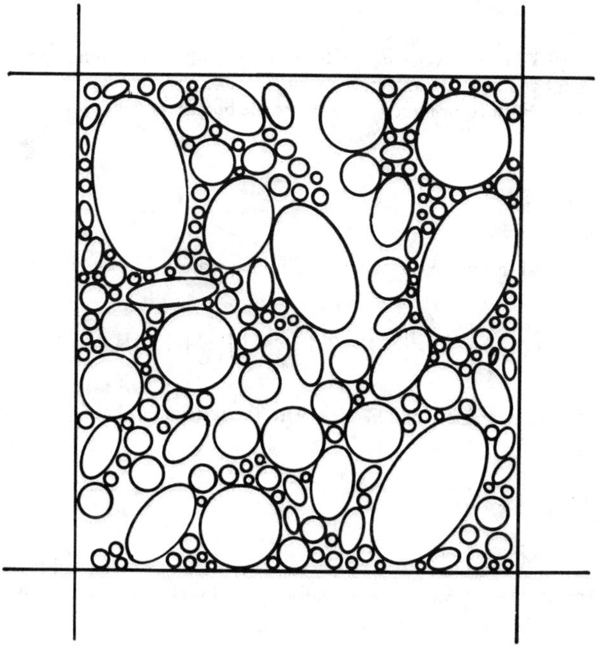

Figure 7. Unit cell in a spatially periodic porous medium.

and $\tilde{T}_\gamma$ which are given by

$$\tilde{T}_\kappa = \underset{\sim}{g} \cdot \nabla\langle T\rangle + r\langle \Delta H_r \hat{R}\rangle_{\kappa\gamma} \tag{166a}$$

$$\tilde{T}_\gamma = \underset{\sim}{f} \cdot \nabla\langle T\rangle + s\langle \Delta H_r \hat{R}\rangle_{\kappa\gamma} \tag{166b}$$

If we want to solve for $\underset{\sim}{g}$, $\underset{\sim}{f}$, r and s in the region illustrated in Fig. 7, we must be willing to abandon the boundary conditions given by Equations 159 and 164. This leaves us without any long range variables in the closure boundary value problems and the region shown in Figure 7 automatically becomes a unit cell in a spatially periodic porous medium. Under these circumstances the boundary conditions given by Equations 159 and 164 can be replaced with the following periodicity conditions

$$\underset{\sim}{g}(\underset{\sim}{r} + \underset{\sim}{\ell}_i) = \underset{\sim}{g}(\underset{\sim}{r}), \qquad r(\underset{\sim}{r} + \underset{\sim}{\ell}_i) = r(\underset{\sim}{r}), \qquad i = 1, 2, 3 \tag{167a}$$

$$\underset{\sim}{f}(\underset{\sim}{r} + \underset{\sim}{\ell}_i) = \underset{\sim}{f}(\underset{\sim}{r}), \qquad s(\underset{\sim}{r} + \underset{\sim}{\ell}_i) = s(\underset{\sim}{r}), \qquad i = 1, 2, 3 \tag{167b}$$

Here $\underset{\sim}{\ell}_i$ represents the three non-unique lattice vectors needed to construct a spatially periodic porous medium. Many of the details concerning spatially periodic porous media are given by Brenner [32].

We now return to Equation 128 and make use of Equations 157, 162, and 166 in order to express our one-equation model for the temperature as

$$\langle\rho\rangle c_p \frac{\partial\langle T\rangle}{\partial t} = \nabla \cdot \left\{ \left[(\epsilon_\kappa k_\kappa + \epsilon_\gamma k_\gamma)\underset{\approx}{I} + \frac{k_\kappa - k_\gamma}{V_\sigma} \int_{A_{\kappa\gamma}} \underset{\sim}{n}_{\kappa\gamma}\underset{\sim}{g}\, dA \right] \cdot \nabla\langle T\rangle \right\}$$
$$+ \nabla \cdot \left\{ \left[\frac{k_\kappa - k_\gamma}{V_\sigma} \int_{V_\kappa} \underset{\sim}{n}_{\kappa\gamma} r\, dA \right] \langle \Delta H_r \hat{R}\rangle_{\kappa\gamma} \right\} - a_{\kappa\gamma}\langle \Delta H_r \hat{R}\rangle_{\kappa\gamma} \tag{168}$$

Here we have treated $\nabla\langle T\rangle$ and $\langle \Delta H_r \hat{R}\rangle_{\kappa\gamma}$ are constants within the averaging volume, thus these terms have been removed from the integrals over the interfacial area, $A_{\kappa\gamma}$.

Without solving Problem II for r and s, we can use the boundary conditions to estimate the magnitude of r as

$$r = \underset{\sim}{0}\begin{Bmatrix} \ell_\kappa / k_\kappa \\ \ell_\gamma / k_\gamma \end{Bmatrix} \tag{169}$$

When this result is used in the next to the last term in Equation 168 we obtain

$$\nabla \cdot \left\{ \left[\frac{k_\kappa - k_\gamma}{V_\sigma} \int_{A_{\kappa\gamma}} \underset{\sim}{n}_{\kappa\gamma} r\, dA \right] \langle \Delta H_r \hat{R}\rangle_{\kappa\gamma} \right\} = \underset{\sim}{0}\left[\left(\frac{k_\omega}{k_\eta} - 1 \right) \left(\frac{\ell_\eta}{L} \right) a_{\kappa\gamma}\langle \Delta H_r \hat{R}\rangle_{\kappa\gamma} \right] \tag{170}$$

Here we have again used $\omega = \kappa, \gamma$ and $\eta = \kappa, \gamma$ with the restriction that $\omega \neq \eta$. The constraint

$$\left(\frac{k_\omega}{k_\eta} - 1 \right) \left(\frac{\ell_\eta}{L} \right) \ll 1 \tag{171}$$

is similar in nature to that given by Equation 122b at it allows us to discard the term represented in Equation 170 relative to the last term in Equation 168. This allows us to express the one-equation model for the temperature as

$$\langle\rho\rangle C_p \frac{\partial\langle T\rangle}{\partial t} = \nabla \cdot (\underset{\approx}{K}_{eff} \cdot \nabla\langle T\rangle) - a_{\kappa\gamma}\langle \Delta H_r \hat{R}\rangle_{\kappa\gamma} \tag{172}$$

Here $\underset{\approx}{K}_{eff}$ represents the effective thermal conductivity tensor, which is defined by

$$\underset{\approx}{K}_{eff} = (\epsilon_\kappa k_\kappa + \epsilon_\gamma k_\gamma)\underset{\approx}{I} + \frac{k_\kappa - k_\gamma}{V_\sigma} \int_{A_{\kappa\gamma}} \underset{\sim}{n}_{\kappa\gamma}\underset{\sim}{g}\, dA \tag{173}$$

Since $\underset{\approx}{K}_{eff}$ is a rather weak function of the temperature, one finds that Equation 172 is generally written as

$$\langle\rho\rangle C_p \frac{\partial\langle T\rangle}{\partial t} = \underset{\approx}{K}_{eff}:\underset{\sim}{\nabla}\underset{\sim}{\nabla}\langle T\rangle - a_{\kappa\gamma}\langle \Delta H_r \hat{R}\rangle_{\kappa\gamma} \tag{174}$$

Under these circumstances the skew-symmetric part of $\underset{\approx}{K}_{eff}$ makes no contribution to the heat flux and it is appropriate to represent the thermal conductivity tensor as

$$\underset{\approx}{K}_{eff} = (\epsilon_\kappa k_\kappa + \epsilon_\gamma k_\gamma)\underset{\approx}{I} + \frac{k_\kappa - k_\gamma}{V_\sigma} \int_{A_{\kappa\gamma}} \frac{1}{2}(\underset{\sim}{n}_{\kappa\gamma}\underset{\sim}{g} + \underset{\sim}{g}\underset{\sim}{n}_{\kappa\gamma})\, dA \tag{175}$$

At this point we are confronted with two problems: (1) determination of the effective thermal conductivity for the porous catalyst, and (2) evaluation of the heterogeneous thermal source.

Heterogeneous Thermal Source

The heat of reaction, ΔH_r, will depend on the temperature at the $\kappa - \gamma$ interface, and on the basis of Equation 90a we can express this idea as

$$\Delta H_r = \Delta H_r(T_\kappa) \tag{176}$$

The functional dependence of $\hat{R}$ will be more complex since it depends on the temperature of the surface and the surface concentrations of the various reacting species. However, in many cases a catalytic surface can be treated as quasi-steady [12] and under those circumstances the functional dependence of can be expressed as

$$\hat{R} = \hat{R}(T_\kappa, c_A, c_B, \ldots) \tag{177}$$

Without offering any specific constraints, we assume that the average of products that makes up the heterogeneous thermal source can be expressed as the products of averages. We express this idea as

$$\langle \Delta H_r \hat{R}\rangle_{\kappa\gamma} = \langle \Delta H_r\rangle_{\kappa\gamma}\langle \hat{R}\rangle_{\kappa\gamma} \tag{178}$$

Given the temperature dependence of the heat of reaction indicated by Equation 176, one can wonder how the area average of ΔH_r depends on $\langle T\rangle$. This question has been explored elsewhere [33] and that study indicates that $\langle \Delta H_r\rangle_{\kappa\gamma}$ can be expressed as

$$\langle \Delta H_r\rangle_{\kappa\gamma} = \Delta H_r(\langle T\rangle) + \frac{1}{2}\langle \underset{\sim}{y}\underset{\sim}{y}\rangle_{\kappa\gamma}:\underset{\sim}{\nabla}\langle T\rangle\underset{\sim}{\nabla}\langle T\rangle\left(\frac{\partial^2 \Delta H_r}{\partial T_\kappa^2}\right) \tag{179}$$

in which $\underset{\sim}{y}$ is the position vector relative to the centroid of the averaging volume. Whenever the following constraint is satisfied

$$\frac{1}{2}\langle \underset{\sim}{y}\underset{\sim}{y}\rangle_{\kappa\gamma}:\underset{\sim}{\nabla}\langle T\rangle\underset{\sim}{\nabla}\langle T\rangle\left(\frac{\partial^2 \Delta H_r}{\partial T_\kappa^2}\right) \ll \Delta H_r(\langle T\rangle) \tag{180}$$

one can simplify equation 179 to

$$\langle \Delta H_r\rangle_{\kappa\gamma} = \Delta H_r(\langle T\rangle) \tag{181}$$

Similar constraints can be developed for the functional dependence of $\langle \hat{R} \rangle_{\kappa\gamma}$ on $\langle T \rangle$, $\langle c_A \rangle^\gamma$, $\langle c_B \rangle^\gamma$, etc., and when these constraints are satisfied one can express Equation 178 as

$$\langle \Delta H_r \hat{R} \rangle_{\kappa\gamma} = \Delta H_r \hat{R} \tag{182}$$

Here it is understood that ΔH_r and $\hat{R}$ depend on the volume-average quantities $\langle T \rangle$, $\langle c_A \rangle^\gamma$, $\langle c_B \rangle^\gamma$, etc., in the same manner as they depend on T_κ, c_A, c_B, etc., as indicated in Equations 176 and 177. It would appear that the form indicated by Equation 182 has been universally used by those who study the nonisothermal catalyst pellet problem; however, the validity of that relation certainly needs to be examined for cases of practical importance. Use of Equation 182 in Equation 174 leads to the following form of our one-equation model

$$\langle \rho \rangle C_p \frac{\partial \langle T \rangle}{\partial t} = \underset{\approx}{K}_{eff} : \underset{\sim}{\nabla}\underset{\sim}{\nabla} \langle T \rangle - a_{\kappa\gamma} \Delta H_r \hat{R} \tag{183}$$

In accepting this simplified form one must keep in mind that $\hat{R}$ will be an exponential function of the temperature and the constraint comparable to that given by Equation 180 may be violated in the presence of high temperature gradients.

Effective Thermal Conductivity

From Equation 175 and closure Problem I (Equations 156–160) we see that the effective thermal conductivity tensor depends only on k_κ, and k_γ and the geometry of the system under consideration. Even though the heterogeneous thermal source term $\langle \Delta H_r \hat{R} \rangle_{\kappa\gamma}$ appears in the general closure problem for $\tilde{T}_\kappa$ and $\tilde{T}_\gamma$, we have been able to show that it gives rise to a source term of negligible importance in the governing equation for $\langle T \rangle$. This means that the effective thermal conductivity can be measured in passive systems (without chemical reactions) and used in the analysis of active systems (with chemical reactions). In addition this means that Problem II of the closure problem given by Equations 156 through 165 need not be solved. Problem I of the closure problem can be simplified by repeating a proof given by Ochoa et al. [29] which allows one to show that the Laplacians of $\underset{\sim}{g}$ and $\underset{\sim}{f}$ are zero. This leads to a closure problem given by

Closure Problem

$$\nabla^2 \underset{\sim}{g} = 0, \quad \text{in the } \kappa\text{-phase} \tag{184}$$

$$\underset{\sim}{g} = \underset{\sim}{f}, \quad \text{at the } \kappa\text{-}\gamma \text{ interface} \tag{185a}$$

$$\underset{\sim}{n}_{\gamma\kappa} \cdot k_\kappa \underset{\sim}{\nabla} \underset{\sim}{g} = \underset{\sim}{n}_{\gamma\kappa} \cdot k_\gamma \underset{\sim}{\nabla} \underset{\sim}{f} + \underset{\sim}{n}_{\gamma\kappa}(k_\gamma - k_\kappa), \quad \text{at the } \kappa\text{-}\gamma \text{ interface} \tag{185b}$$

$$\nabla^2 \underset{\sim}{f} = 0, \quad \text{in the } \gamma\text{-phase} \tag{186}$$

$$\underset{\sim}{g}(\underset{\sim}{r} + \underset{\sim}{\ell}_i) = \underset{\sim}{g}(\underset{\sim}{r}), \quad \underset{\sim}{f}(\underset{\sim}{r} + \underset{\sim}{\ell}_i) = \underset{\sim}{f}(r), \quad i = 1, 2, 3 \tag{187}$$

$$\langle \underset{\sim}{g} \rangle^\kappa = 0, \quad \langle \underset{\sim}{f} \rangle^\gamma = 0 \tag{188}$$

The proof given by Ochoa et al. [29] relies upon the spatial periodicity of $\underset{\sim}{g}$ and $\underset{\sim}{f}$, but aside from that restriction it is quite general and has other applications within the method of volume averaging.

There are numerous experimental results for the effective thermal conductivity of unconsolidated porous media, and these have been considered from the theoretical point of view by Nozad et al. [18]. The theoretical results are based on the solution of Equations 184–188 and the spatially periodic model of a porous medium illustrated in Figure 8. Unhappily, the parameter c/a is adjustable and without a detailed understanding of the solid mechanics of unconsolidated media we can only search for a value of c/a that provides good agreement between theory and experiment. In Figure

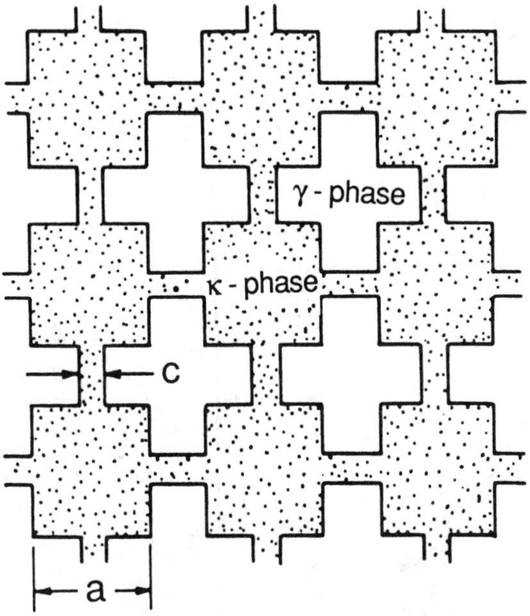

Figure 8. Model for particle–particle contact.

9 we have shown a comparison between theory and experiment for $c/a = 0.01$ and a wide variety of experimental data. Much of the scatter results from the fact that the volume fraction for the experimental data ranges from $\epsilon_\gamma = 0.31$ to $\epsilon_\gamma = 0.52$ while the theoretical calculations are based on $\epsilon_\gamma = 0.36$. The geometrical model shown in Figure 8 represents an isotropic system with regard to the heat conduction process, and it is the single distinct component of $\underset{\approx}{K}_{eff}$ defined by Equation 175 that is shown in Figure 9. Because of the wide range of experimental studies presented in Figure 9 and the reasonably good agreement with the single theoretical results for $c/a = 0.01$, one is tempted to think of the theoretical result as a universal curve for unconsolidated porous media. *This would most certainly be a mistake.* In an unpublished study by Wu [34], the experimental system of Nozad [35] was re-used to measure the effective thermal conductivity for the systems consisting of spheres of urea formaldehyde, stainless steel, bronze, glass, and aluminum with air being the continuous fluid phase. All experimental values for the effective thermal conductivity were in excellent agreement with those obtained by Nozad *except for* the aluminum-air system. The porous medium made from the 1 mm-diameter aluminum spheres used by Nozad produced an effective thermal conductivity that was four times larger than that measured by Nozad. An inspection of the spheres indicated that they had been deformed by use in other experiments performed in our laboratory and therefore produced a porous medium with a higher effective contact area. When Wu repeated the experiments with new aluminum spheres, the original results of Nozad were reproduced without difficulty. The conclusion here should be obvious: The effective thermal conductivity is very sensitive to the nature of the particle-particle contact, especially for large values of the ratio, k_κ/k_γ. A dramatic example of this fact is contained in the theoretical study of Batchelor and O'Brien [36]. They considered a regular array of spheres that were in contact at *single points* as illustrated in Figure 10. Their system is similar to that shown in Figure 8 with the squares replaced by spheres and the contact area tending toward zero, i.e., $c/a \rightarrow 0$. Batchelor and O'Brien used the method of matched asymptotic expansions to solve the point-contact heat conduction problem; however, they obtained only the first term of the inner expansion. This left them with an adjustable coefficient in their expression for the effective thermal conductivity, but their analysis did provide the correct form for K_{eff} at larger values of k_κ/k_γ. At large values of k_κ/k_γ. Nozad et al. [18] were able to use a regular perturbation expansion to show that K_{eff} was a linear function of k_κ/k_γ for a finite contact area; however, for point-contact between

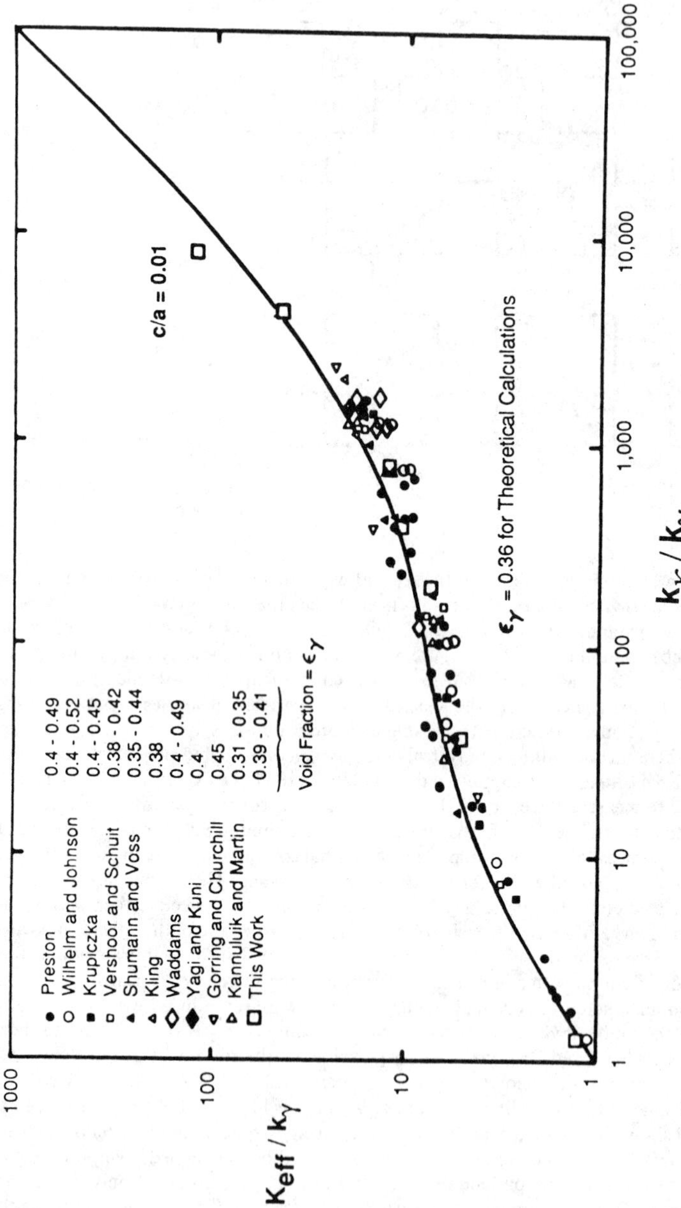

Figure 9. Theoretical and experimental values of the effective thermal conductivity.

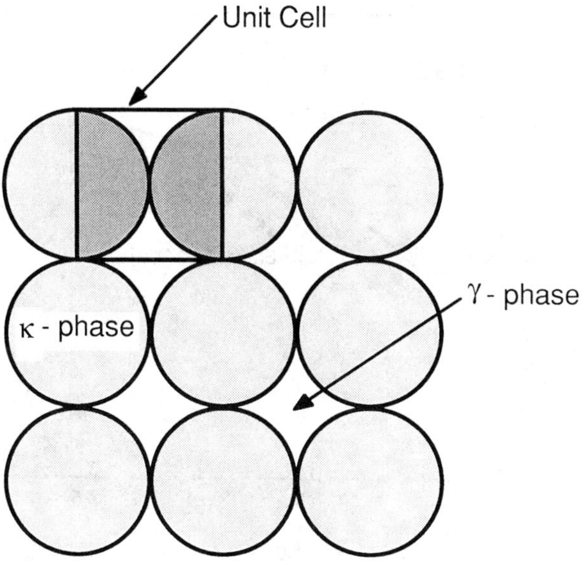

Figure 10. Model for point–contact heat transfer.

particles Batchelor and O'Brien [36] were able to show that K_{eff} was a logarithmic function of k_κ/k_γ. In Figure 11 we have presented the theoretical result for Batchelor and O'Brien along with the experimental data of Swift [37] and some recent results of Shonnard [38]. Swift's data were obtained using metal powders with the particle diameter being on the order of 100 microns, while Shonnard's results were obtained using metal hemispheres having diameters on the order of 5 centimeters. Shonnard's experiments were carried out with a unit cell, such as the one illustrated in Figure 10, with the intention of testing the Batchelor and O'Brien theory. The theoretical line in Figure 11 is given by

$$\frac{K_{eff}}{k_\gamma} = 4 \ln(k_\kappa/k_\gamma) - 11 \tag{189}$$

in which the number eleven is an adjustable parameter chosen by Batchelor and O'Brien. Certainly the theory is in reasonable good agreement with the experimental data of Shonnard and it predicts quite well the trend of the data obtained by Swift. It is not clear why the packed metal powders used by Swift exhibit point-contact heat conduction characteristics, but they certainly do just that.

In addition to experimental values of the effective thermal conductivity that are significantly lower than those illustrated in Figure 9, there are values that are significantly higher. The data of Hadley [39] are an example for which compressed metal powder gave rise to values of K_{eff} considerable greater than those illustrated in Figure 9. The higher values resulted from both a reduced value of the void fraction ϵ_γ, and from an increase in the particle-particle contact area. Oppio [40] has extended the calculations of Nozad and her results are shown in Figure 12. While Hadley's results contain information about the void fraction, and Oppio's results contain information about the particle-particle contact, there is not sufficient information from either study to make a meaningful comparison between theory and experiment.

It should be clear from the experimental and theoretical results shown in Figures 9, 11, and 12, that the effective thermal conductivity of two-phase systems is a strong function of the ratio of conductivities, k_κ/k_γ, and the topology of the two phases. Obviously, the theoretical prediction of K_{eff}

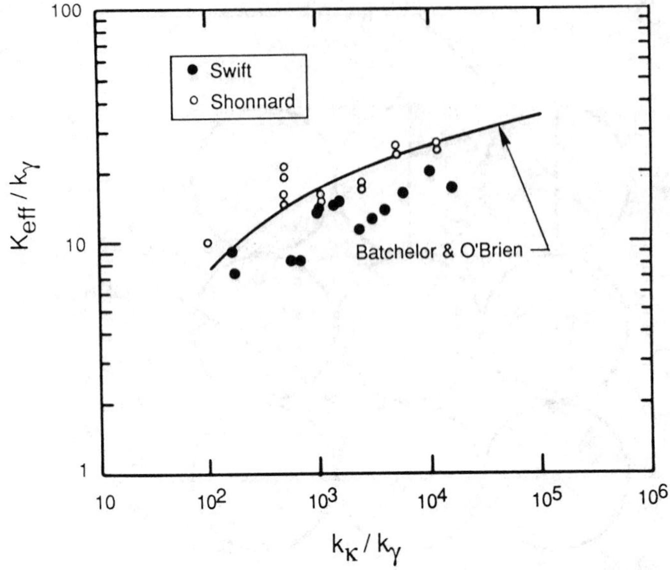

Figure 11. Comparison of theory and experiment for point–contact heat conduction.

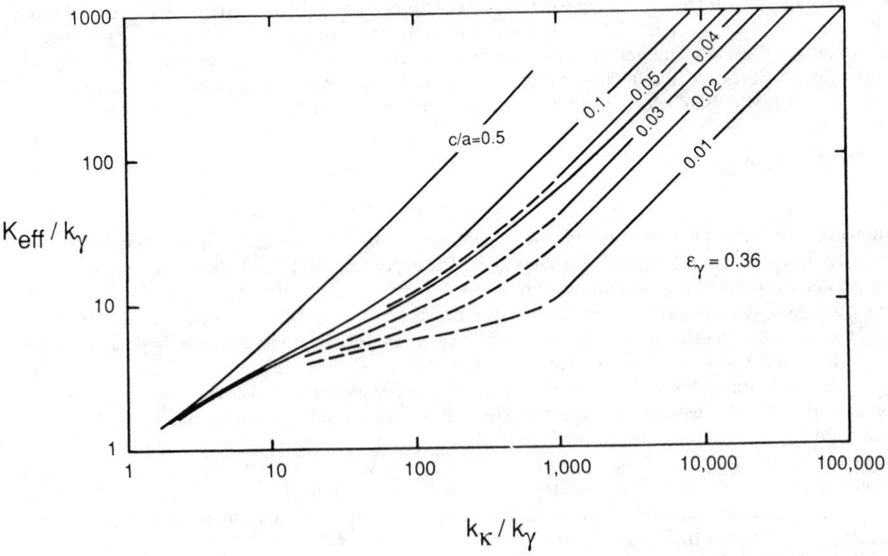

Figure 12. Influence of the particle–particle contact area in the effective thermal conductivity.

requires a knowledge of k_κ and k_γ and the geometrical structure of the porous medium under consideration.

While the problem of unconsolidated porous media illustrates some successes and some unsolved problems, the matter of porous catalyst pellets remains in an empirical-experimental state. The geometrical structure is often explored by means of mercury porosimetry and Dullien [41] has pointed out that this experimental technique provides unreliable information concerning the pore-size distribution. Regardless of whether pore-size distributions can be accurately measured or not, we know that there is a distribution of pore-sizes in any porous catalyst pellet and that a significant portion of the pores will be small enough so that free-molecule flow will be the dominant mechanism of mass and energy transport. Because of this we need to consider the micropore-macropore analysis of heat conduction.

Micropore-Macropore Systems

In our initial study of heat conduction and reaction in a κ-γ system, we assumed that the thermal conductivity of the γ-phase underwent negligible variations within the averaging volume. In a system having micropores in which free-molecule flow takes place, the thermal conductivity of the γ-phase will depend on the pore diameter, thus the approximation of negligible variations in k_γ is no longer valid.

The micropore-macropore system that we wish to analyze is illustrated in Figure 13 and it is similar to the system shown in Figure 6. However, in this case we are confronted with a variety of pore sizes

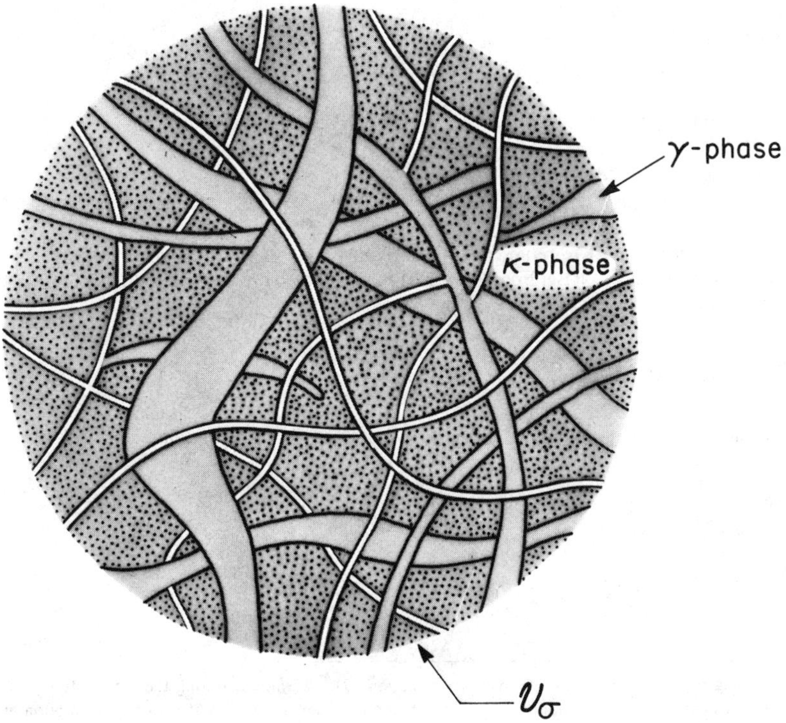

Figure 13. Micropore–macropore system.

and in Figure 13 we have highlighted one set of pores that we intend to treat as a single phase. To be specific we consider this to be the j-phase which has an average pore diameter d_j. The entire γ-phase is to be represented in terms of M phases with M-1 of these being micropore phases while the Mth phase is the macropore phase. The number of phases required to accurately model the system will obviously depend on the pore-size distribution. We assume that each individual micropore phase can be described by a density, a heat capacity, and a thermal conductivity so that the original problem posed by Equation 89–92 can be replaced by*

$$(\rho c_p)_\kappa \frac{\partial T_\kappa}{\partial t} = \underset{\sim}{\nabla} \cdot (k_\kappa \underset{\sim}{\nabla} T_\kappa) \tag{190}$$

Boundary Condition 1:

$$T_\kappa = T_\mu, \qquad \text{at } A_{\kappa\mu},\ \mu = 1, 2, \ldots, M \tag{191a}$$

Boundary Condition 2:

$$\underset{\sim}{n}_{\mu\kappa} \cdot k_\kappa \underset{\sim}{\nabla} T_\kappa = \underset{\sim}{n}_{\mu\kappa} \cdot k_\mu \underset{\sim}{\nabla} T_\mu + \Delta H_r \hat{R}_\mu, \qquad \text{at } A_{\kappa\mu},\ \mu = 1, 2, \ldots, M \tag{191b}$$

$$(\rho c_p)_\mu \frac{\partial T_\mu}{\partial t} = \underset{\sim}{\nabla} \cdot (k_\mu \underset{\sim}{\nabla} T_\mu), \qquad \mu = 1, 2, \ldots, M \tag{192}$$

Boundary Condition 1′:

$$T_\mu = T_\nu, \qquad \text{at } A_{\mu\nu},\ \mu = 1, 2, \ldots, M \quad \mu \neq \nu \tag{193a}$$

Boundary Condition 2′:

$$\underset{\sim}{n}_{\mu\nu} \cdot k_\mu \underset{\sim}{\nabla} T_\mu = \underset{\sim}{n}_{\mu\nu} \cdot k_\nu \underset{\sim}{\nabla} T_\nu, \qquad \text{at } A_{\mu\nu},\ \mu = 1, 2, \ldots, M \quad \mu \neq \nu \tag{193b}$$

Here we have used μ and ν to represent the M distinct γ-phases with the idea in mind that $\mu = M$ represents the macropore phase. For a system of this type the volume averaging theorem for the κ-phase takes the form

$$\langle \underset{\sim}{\nabla} \psi_\kappa \rangle = \underset{\sim}{\nabla} \langle \psi_\kappa \rangle + \sum_{\mu=1}^{\mu=M} \frac{1}{V_\sigma} \int_{A_{\kappa\mu}} \underset{\sim}{n}_{\kappa\mu} \psi_\kappa \, dA \tag{194}$$

and one can repeat the development given by Equations 93–109 to obtain

$$\epsilon_\kappa (\rho c_p)_\kappa \frac{\partial \langle T_\kappa \rangle^\kappa}{\partial t} = \underset{\sim}{\nabla} \cdot \left\{ \epsilon_\kappa k_\kappa \left[\underset{\sim}{\nabla} \langle T_\kappa \rangle^\kappa + \sum_{\mu=1}^{\mu=M} \frac{1}{V_\kappa} \int_{A_{\kappa\mu}} \underset{\sim}{n}_{\kappa\mu} \tilde{T}_\kappa \, dA \right] \right\} + \sum_{\mu=1}^{\mu=M} \frac{1}{V_\sigma} \int_{A_{\kappa\mu}} \underset{\sim}{n}_{\kappa\mu} \cdot k_\kappa \underset{\sim}{\nabla} T_\kappa \, dA \tag{195}$$

---

* In proposing the boundary condition given by Equation 191a, we are neglecting the temperature jump that occurs at gas-solid surfaces. Continuity of the temperature is, of course, consistent with the assumption of local thermal equilibrium and because of the small length scales associated with micropores this assumption should be satisfactory. On the other hand, this intuitive line of thinking needs to be replaced with a rigorous analysis that will be done at some later date.

The analysis leading to Equation 110 can be repeated for one of the γ-phases that we identify as the μ-phase in order to obtain

$$\epsilon_\mu(\rho c_p)_\mu \frac{\partial\langle T_\mu\rangle^\mu}{\partial t} = \nabla \cdot \left\{\epsilon_\mu k_\mu\left[\nabla\langle T_\mu\rangle^\mu + \frac{1}{V_\mu}\int_{A_{\mu\kappa}} \mathbf{n}_{\mu\kappa}\tilde{T}_\mu \, dA + \sum_{\substack{\nu=1\\ \nu\neq\mu}}^{\nu=M} \frac{1}{V_\mu}\int_{A_{\mu\nu}} \mathbf{n}_{\mu\nu}\tilde{T}_\mu \, dA\right]\right\}$$
$$+ \sum_{\substack{\nu=1\\ \nu\neq\mu}}^{\nu=M} \frac{1}{V_\sigma}\int_{A_{\mu\nu}} \mathbf{n}_{\mu\nu}\cdot k_\mu\nabla T_\mu \, dA + \frac{1}{V_\sigma}\int_{A_{\mu\kappa}} \mathbf{n}_{\mu\kappa}\cdot k_\mu \nabla T_\mu \, dA \qquad (196)$$

This result can be summed over all the micropore phases and the single macropore phase to obtain

$$\sum_{\mu=1}^{\mu=M} \epsilon_\mu(\rho c_p)_\mu \frac{\partial\langle T_\mu\rangle^\mu}{\partial t} = \nabla \cdot \left\{\sum_{\mu=1}^{\mu=M} \epsilon_\mu k_\mu\left[\nabla\langle T_\mu\rangle^\mu + \frac{1}{V_\mu}\int_{A_{\mu\kappa}} \mathbf{n}_{\mu\kappa}\tilde{T}_\mu \, dA\right]\right\}$$
$$+ \sum_{\mu=1}^{\mu=M} \frac{1}{V_\sigma}\int_{A_{\mu\kappa}} \mathbf{n}_{\mu\kappa}\cdot k_\mu\nabla T_\mu \, dA \qquad (197)$$

When the constraint of *local thermal equilibrium* is imposed, we can add Equations 195 and 197 to obtain

$$\left[\epsilon_\kappa(\rho c_p)_\kappa + \sum_{\mu=1}^{\mu=M} \epsilon_\mu(\rho c_p)_\mu\right]\frac{\partial\langle T\rangle}{\partial t} = \nabla \cdot \left\{\epsilon_\kappa k_\kappa\left[\nabla\langle T\rangle + \sum_{\mu=1}^{\mu=M} \frac{1}{V_\kappa}\int_{A_{\kappa\mu}} \mathbf{n}_{\kappa\mu}\tilde{T}_\kappa \, dA\right]\right.$$
$$\left. + \sum_{\mu=1}^{\mu=M} \epsilon_\mu k_\mu\left[\nabla\langle T\rangle + \frac{1}{V_\mu}\int_{A_{\mu\kappa}} \mathbf{n}_{\mu\kappa}\tilde{T}_\mu \, dA\right]\right\}$$
$$- \sum_{\mu=1}^{\mu=M} \frac{1}{V_\sigma}\int_{A_{\kappa\mu}} \Delta H_r \hat{R}_\mu \, dA \qquad (198)$$

For simplicity one might extend the definitions given by Equations 116, 115, and 128 to write

$$\langle\rho\rangle C_p = \epsilon_\kappa(\rho c_p)_\kappa + \sum_{\mu=1}^{\mu=M} \epsilon_\mu(\rho c_p)_\mu \qquad (199a)$$

$$a_{\kappa\gamma}\langle\Delta H_r \hat{R}_\mu\rangle_{\kappa\gamma} = \sum_{\mu=1}^{\mu=M} \frac{1}{V_0}\int_{A_{\kappa\mu}} \Delta H_r \hat{R}_\mu \, dA \qquad (199b)$$

so that Equation 198 can be written as

$$\langle\rho\rangle C_p \frac{\partial\langle T\rangle}{\partial t} = \nabla \cdot \left\{\epsilon_\kappa k_\kappa\left[\nabla\langle T\rangle + \sum_{\mu=1}^{\mu=M} \frac{1}{V_\kappa}\int_{A_{\kappa\mu}} \mathbf{n}_{\kappa\mu}\tilde{T}_\kappa \, dA\right]\right.$$
$$\left. + \sum_{\mu=1}^{\mu=M} \epsilon_\mu k_\mu\left[\nabla\langle T\rangle + \frac{1}{V_\mu}\int_{A_{\mu\kappa}} \mathbf{n}_{\mu\kappa}\tilde{T}_\mu \, dA\right]\right\} - a_{\kappa\gamma}\langle\Delta H_r \hat{R}_\mu\rangle_{\kappa\gamma} \qquad (200)$$

The closure problem for the micropore-macropore problem follows the development given by Equations 129–167. Without going through the details, we note that the spatial deviation temperatures can be represented as

$$\tilde{T}_\kappa = \mathbf{g}\cdot\nabla\langle T\rangle, \qquad \tilde{T}_\mu = \mathbf{f}_\mu\cdot\nabla\langle T\rangle, \qquad \mu = 1, 2, \ldots, M \qquad (201)$$

and the one-equation model represented by Equation 200 takes the form

$$\langle\rho\rangle C_p \frac{\partial\langle T\rangle}{\partial t} = \nabla \cdot \left\{ \left[\left(\epsilon_\kappa k_\kappa + \sum_{\mu=1}^{\mu=M} \epsilon_\mu k_\mu \right) \underset{\approx}{I} + \left(\sum_{\mu=1}^{\mu=M} \frac{k_\kappa - k_\mu}{V_\sigma} \int_{A_{\kappa\mu}} \underset{\sim}{n}_{\kappa\mu} \underset{\sim}{g}\, dA \right) \right] \cdot \nabla\langle T\rangle \right\} - a_{\kappa\gamma}\langle \Delta H_r \hat{R}_\mu \rangle_{\kappa\gamma} \tag{202}$$

Here we have used the boundary condition given by Equation 191a along with arguments presented earlier in Equations 137–143 in order to obtain

Boundary Condition 1:

$$\underset{\sim}{g} = \underset{\sim}{f}_\mu, \quad \text{at } A_{\kappa\mu},\ \mu = 1, 2, \ldots, M \tag{203}$$

The arguments leading from Equation 174 to Equation 183 need to be examined in detail for the micropore-macropore system illustrated in Figure 13. If they were valid for that more complex system, one could simply make use of Equation 183 with the effective thermal conductivity defined by

$$\underset{\approx}{K}_{eff} = \left(\epsilon_\kappa k_\kappa + \sum_{\mu=1}^{\mu=M} \epsilon_\mu k_\mu \right) \underset{\approx}{I} + \sum_{\mu=1}^{\mu=M} \frac{k_\kappa - k_\mu}{V_\sigma} \int_{A_{\kappa\mu}} \frac{1}{2} (\underset{\sim}{n}_{\kappa\mu} \underset{\sim}{g} + \underset{\sim}{g} \underset{\sim}{n}_{\kappa\mu})\, dA \tag{204}$$

About the ϵ_μ we should remember that

$$\epsilon_\gamma = \sum_{\mu=1}^{\mu=M} \epsilon_\mu \tag{205}$$

and about the k_μ we should remember

$$k_M = k_\gamma \tag{206}$$

The problem of evaluating the k_μ for $\mu = 1, 2, \ldots, M - 1$ is not completely resolved; however, some insight is given by Prakouras et al. [42].

The closure problem that must be solved in order to evaluate the terms in Equation 204 is given by a variation of Equations 184–188, and without discussion we simply list the result as

Closure Problem for Micropore-Macropore System

$$\nabla^2 \underset{\sim}{g} = 0, \quad \text{in the } \kappa\text{-phase} \tag{207}$$

Boundary Condition 1:

$$\underset{\sim}{g} = \underset{\sim}{f}_\mu, \quad \text{at } A_{\kappa\mu},\ \mu = 1, 2, \ldots, M \tag{208a}$$

Boundary Condition 2:

$$\underset{\sim}{n}_{\mu\kappa} \cdot k_\kappa \nabla \underset{\sim}{g} = \underset{\sim}{n}_{\mu\kappa} \cdot k_\mu \nabla \underset{\sim}{f}_\mu + \underset{\sim}{n}_{\mu\kappa}(k_\mu - k_\kappa), \quad \text{at } A_{\kappa\mu},\ \mu = 1, 2, \ldots, M \tag{208b}$$

$$\nabla^2 \underset{\sim}{f}_\mu = 0, \quad \text{in the } \mu\text{-phase},\ \mu = 1, 2, \ldots, M \tag{209}$$

Boundary Condition 1′:

$$\underset{\sim}{f}_\mu = \underset{\sim}{f}_\nu, \quad \text{at } A_{\mu\nu},\ \mu = 1, 2, \ldots, M,\ \mu \neq \nu \tag{210a}$$

Boundary Condition 2′:

$$\mathbf{n}_{\mu\nu} \cdot k_\mu \nabla \mathbf{f}_\mu = \mathbf{n}_{\mu\nu} \cdot k_\nu \nabla \mathbf{f}_\nu + \mathbf{n}_{\mu\nu}(k_\nu - k_\mu), \qquad \text{at } A_{\mu\nu},\ \mu = 1, 2, \ldots, M,\ \mu \neq \nu \tag{210b}$$

$$\mathbf{g}(\mathbf{r} + \ell_i) = \mathbf{g}(\mathbf{r}), \qquad \mathbf{f}_\mu(\mathbf{r} + \ell_i) = \mathbf{f}_\mu(\mathbf{r}), \qquad i = 1, 2, 3,\ \mu = 1, 2, \ldots, M \tag{211}$$

$$\langle \mathbf{g} \rangle^\kappa = 0, \qquad \langle \mathbf{f}_\mu \rangle^\mu = 0, \qquad \mu = 1, 2, \ldots, M \tag{212}$$

With the solution of this closure problem may appear to be excessively complex, it is comparable in difficulty to a random capillary model [43] and indeed that particular geometrical model can be solved within the framework of Equations 207–212. One must keep in mind, however, that random capillary tube models are generally used to predict mass transport and in that case the detailed structure of the κ-phase is not particularly important. For the case of heat conduction, we know that the details of the geometrical structure of the κ-phase are very important. Thus accurate prediction of the effective thermal conductivity of porous catalysts pellets requires more knowledge of the topological details than is currently available.

FLUID PHASE HEAT TRANSPORT

In the previous section we analyzed the heat transfer process in a porous catalyst phase in order to obtain a local volume-averaged equation for the temperature given by

$$\langle \rho \rangle C_p \frac{\partial \langle T \rangle}{\partial t} = \nabla \cdot (\mathbf{K}_{\text{eff}} \cdot \nabla \langle T \rangle) - a_{\kappa\gamma} \langle \Delta H_r \hat{R}_\mu \rangle_{\kappa\gamma} \tag{213}$$

The principle of local thermal equilibrium was used in order to obtain a one-equation model for κ-γ system illustrated in Figure 6, and the temperature $\langle T \rangle$ is the single temperature that describes the thermal state of the κ-γ system. We now turn our attention to the β-phase illustrated in Figure 4, and in order to simplify the nomenclature for this analysis we are going to express Equation 213 as

$$(\rho c_p)_\sigma \frac{\partial T_\sigma}{\partial t} = \nabla \cdot (k_\sigma \nabla T_\sigma) + \phi_\sigma \tag{214}$$

Here we have assumed that the heat transfer process in a porous catalyst is isotropic, and we have used nomenclature that is consistent with Figure 4 and previous studies of heat transfer in two-phase systems [21, 25, 44]. The boundary conditions at the β-σ interface can be expressed as

Boundary Condition 1:

$$T_\beta = T_\sigma, \qquad \text{at the } \beta\text{-}\sigma \text{ interface} \tag{215}$$

$$\mathbf{n}_{\beta\sigma} \cdot k_\beta \nabla T_\beta = \mathbf{n}_{\beta\sigma} \cdot k_\sigma \nabla T_\sigma, \qquad \text{at the } \beta\text{-}\sigma \text{ interface} \tag{216}$$

and the thermal energy equation for the β-phase can be expressed as [7]

$$(\rho c_p)_\beta \left(\frac{\partial T_\beta}{\partial t} + \mathbf{v}_\beta \cdot \nabla T_\beta \right) = \nabla \cdot (k_\beta \nabla T_\beta) \tag{217}$$

When thinking about these equations one should remember that the system under consideration contains one solid phase and one fluid phase. The solid phase is identified in Figure 6 as the κ-phase while the fluid is indicated as the γ-phase. The combination of these two phases is referred to as the σ-phase as illustrated in both Figures 4 and 5, and the fluid phase that is exterior to the κ-γ system is identified as the β-phase.

The boundary conditions given by Equations 215 and 216 are based on the idea that the volume-averaged temperature in the σ-phase can be treated as a point temperature in terms of its relation to the temperature in the β-phase. This idea has been used in the analogous mass transfer problem [22], and in order to indicate the nature of the approximation, we express a more precise form of Equation 215 as

Boundary Condition 1a:

$$T_\beta = T_\kappa, \qquad \text{at } A_{\kappa\beta} \text{ on the } \beta\text{-}\sigma \text{ interface} \tag{218a}$$

Boundary Condition 1b:

$$T_\beta = T_\gamma, \qquad \text{at } A_{\gamma\beta} \text{ on the } \beta\text{-}\sigma \text{ interface} \tag{218b}$$

These boundary conditions should be interpreted in terms of Figure 14, which illustrates an interface between a porous catalyst and a surrounding fluid phase. From Equations 104 and 112 we know that the boundary conditions can be written as

Boundary Condition 1a:

$$T_\beta = \langle T \rangle + \hat{T}_\kappa + \tilde{T}_\kappa, \qquad \text{at } A_{\kappa\beta} \tag{219a}$$

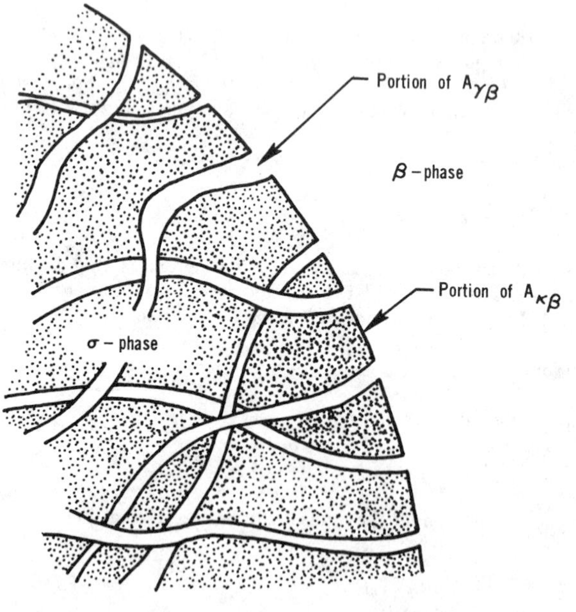

Figure 14. Interface between a porous catalyst and a continuous fluid phase.

Boundary Condition 1b:

$$T_\beta = \langle T \rangle + \hat{T}_\gamma + \tilde{T}_\gamma, \qquad \text{at } A_{\gamma\beta} \tag{219b}$$

Since the heat transfer process in the porous catalyst pellet is restricted by Equation 141, we can express the idea of continuity of temperature as

Boundary Condition 1a:

$$T_\beta = \langle T \rangle + \tilde{T}_\kappa, \qquad \text{at } A_{\kappa\beta} \tag{220}$$

Boundary Condition 1b:

$$T_\beta = \langle T \rangle + \tilde{T}_\gamma, \qquad \text{at } A_{\gamma\beta} \tag{221}$$

The closure problem described earlier led us to the results

$$\tilde{T}_\kappa = \mathbf{g} \cdot \nabla \langle T \rangle, \qquad \tilde{T}_\gamma = \mathbf{f} \cdot \nabla \langle T \rangle \tag{222}$$

and these can be used to express the boundary condition as

Boundary Condition 1a:

$$T_\beta = T_\sigma + \mathbf{g} \cdot \nabla T_\sigma, \qquad \text{at } A_{\kappa\beta} \tag{223a}$$

Boundary Condition 1b:

$$T_\beta = T_\sigma + \mathbf{f} \cdot \nabla T_\sigma, \qquad \text{at } A_{\gamma\beta} \tag{223b}$$

Here we have adopted the nomenclature associated with the transition from Equation 213 to Equation 214. From the closure problem for $\mathbf{g}$ and $\mathbf{f}$ we know that the order of magnitudes of these two vector fields are on the order of the length scales ℓ_γ and ℓ_κ where ℓ_γ is illustrated in Figure 6. We express this idea as

$$\mathbf{g}, \mathbf{f} = \mathbf{O}(\ell_\kappa, \ell_\gamma) \tag{224}$$

and note that if ℓ_κ and ℓ_γ are sufficiently small we should be able to replace Equation 223 with Equation 215. Obviously the magnitude of $\nabla_3 T_\sigma$ has something to do with this simplification and we will comment on the boundary conditions given by Equation 215 and 223 later in the analysis. The flux condition given by Equation 216 can be reconsidered from the same point of view and the results that are analogous to Equations 223 are

Boundary Condition 2a:

$$\mathbf{n}_{\beta\sigma} \cdot k_\beta \nabla T_\beta = \mathbf{n}_{\beta\sigma} \cdot k_\kappa [\nabla T_\sigma + \nabla(\mathbf{g} \cdot \nabla T_\sigma)], \qquad \text{at } A_{\kappa\beta} \tag{225a}$$

Boundary Condition 2b:

$$\mathbf{n}_{\beta\sigma} \cdot k_\beta \nabla T_\beta = \mathbf{n}_{\beta\sigma} \cdot k_\gamma [\nabla T_\sigma + \nabla(\mathbf{f} \cdot \nabla T_\sigma)], \qquad \text{at } A_{\gamma\beta} \tag{225b}$$

Justifying the reduction of these flux expressions to that given by Equation 216 will be more difficult than the simplifications of Equations 223 to Equation 216; however, we will delay commenting on this problem until some later time.

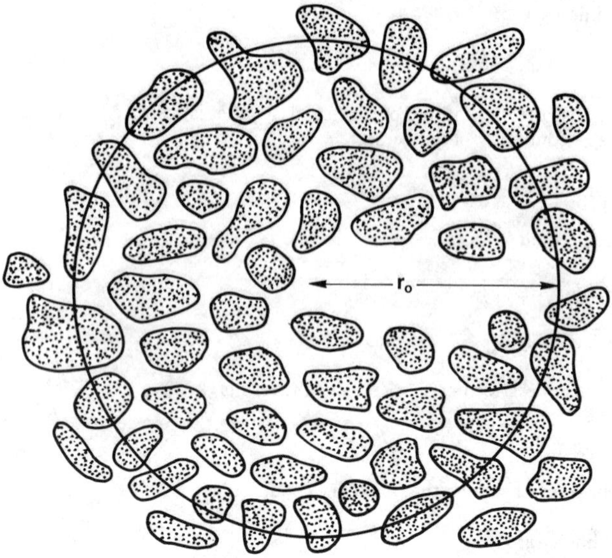

Figure 15. Averaging volume for a packed bed.

Volume Averaging

At this point we accept Equations 214–217 as a reasonable representation of the heat transport process under consideration and direct our attention to the volume average form of the governing equations. The averaging volume to be used is illustrated in Figure 15, and we designate this averaging volume as $\mathscr{V}$.

The average of Equation 214 can be expressed as

$$\frac{1}{V}\int_{V_\sigma}(\rho c_p)_\sigma \frac{\partial T_\sigma}{\partial t}\, dV = \frac{1}{V}\int_{V_\sigma} \underset{\sim}{\nabla}\cdot(k_\sigma \underset{\sim}{\nabla} T_\sigma)\, dV + \epsilon_\sigma\langle\phi_\sigma\rangle^\sigma \tag{226}$$

in which ϵ_σ is the volume fraction of the σ-phase. This is given explicitly by

$$\epsilon_\sigma = V_\sigma/V \tag{227}$$

It is plausible to neglect variations of $(\rho c_p)_\sigma$ within the averaging volume so that Equation 226 takes the form

$$\epsilon_\sigma(\rho c_p)_\sigma \frac{\partial\langle T_\sigma\rangle^\sigma}{\partial t} = \frac{1}{V}\int_{V_\sigma} \underset{\sim}{\nabla}\cdot(k_\sigma \underset{\sim}{\nabla} T_\sigma)\, dV + \epsilon_\sigma\langle\phi_\sigma\rangle^\sigma \tag{228}$$

Our treatment of the conductive term in this equation follows Equations 97–109 and leads to

$$\epsilon_\sigma(\rho c_p)_\sigma \frac{\partial\langle T_\sigma\rangle^\sigma}{\partial t} = \underset{\sim}{\nabla}\cdot\left\{\epsilon_\sigma k_\sigma\left[\underset{\sim}{\nabla}\langle T_\sigma\rangle^\sigma + \frac{1}{V_\sigma}\int \underset{\sim}{n}_{\sigma\beta}\tilde{T}_\sigma\, dA\right]\right\} + \frac{1}{V}\int_{A_{\sigma\beta}} \underset{\sim}{n}_{\sigma\beta}\cdot k_\sigma \underset{\sim}{\nabla} T_\sigma\, dA + \epsilon_\sigma\langle\phi_\sigma\rangle^\sigma \tag{229}$$

There is an alternate form of Equation 228 that will be useful to us, and it can be obtained simply by use of the divergence theorem. This leads to

$$\epsilon_\sigma(\rho c_p)_\sigma \frac{\partial \langle T_\sigma \rangle^\sigma}{\partial t} = \frac{1}{V}\int_{A_{\sigma e}} \underset{\sim}{n}_{\sigma e} \cdot k_\sigma \underset{\sim}{\nabla} T_\sigma \, dA$$

$$+ \frac{1}{V}\int_{A_{\sigma\beta}} \underset{\sim}{n}_{\sigma\beta} \cdot k_\sigma \underset{\sim}{\nabla} T_\sigma \, dA + \epsilon_\sigma \langle \phi_\sigma \rangle^\sigma \tag{230}$$

in which $A_{\sigma e}$ represents the area of entrances and exists of the σ-phase contained within the averaging volume shown in Figure 15. This result will be useful in a subsequent discussion of the traditional model of heat transfer in packed bed catalytic reactors. In addition, it provides an interesting physical interpretation of the conductive term in Equation 229, since comparison of Equations 229 and 230 reveals that

$$\underset{\sim}{\nabla} \cdot \left\{ \epsilon_\sigma k_\sigma \left[\underset{\sim}{\nabla} \langle T_\sigma \rangle^\sigma + \frac{1}{V_\sigma}\int_{A_{\sigma\beta}} \underset{\sim}{n}_{\sigma\beta} \tilde{T}_\sigma \, dA \right] \right\} = \frac{1}{V}\int_{A_{\sigma e}} \underset{\sim}{n}_{\sigma e} \cdot k_\sigma \underset{\sim}{\nabla} T_\sigma \Delta \tag{231}$$

In our treatment of the β-phase we will assume that the flow is incompressible so that Equation 217 takes the form

$$(\rho c_p)_\beta \left[\frac{\partial T_\beta}{\partial t} + \underset{\sim}{\nabla} \cdot (\underset{\sim}{v}_\beta T_\beta) \right] = \underset{\sim}{\nabla} \cdot (k_\beta \underset{\sim}{\nabla} T_\beta) \tag{232}$$

The volume-averaged version of this result is given by

$$\epsilon_\beta(\rho c_p)_\beta \frac{\partial \langle T_\beta \rangle^\beta}{\partial t} + (\rho c_p)_\beta \left[\underset{\sim}{\nabla} \cdot \langle \underset{\sim}{v}_\beta T_\beta \rangle + \frac{1}{V}\int_{A_{\beta\sigma}} \underset{\sim}{n}_{\beta\sigma} \cdot \underset{\sim}{v}_\beta T_\beta \, dA \right]$$

$$= \underset{\sim}{\nabla} \cdot \left\{ \epsilon_\beta k_\beta \left[\underset{\sim}{\nabla} \langle T_\beta \rangle^\beta + \frac{1}{V_\beta}\int_{A_{\beta\sigma}} \underset{\sim}{n}_{\beta\sigma} \tilde{T}_\beta \, dA \right] \right\} + \frac{1}{V}\int_{A_{\beta\sigma}} \underset{\sim}{n}_{\beta\sigma} \cdot k_\beta \underset{\sim}{\nabla} T_\beta \, dA \tag{233}$$

One can impose the restriction

$$(\rho c_p)_\beta \frac{1}{V}\int_{A_{\beta\sigma}} \underset{\sim}{n}_{\beta\sigma} \cdot \underset{\sim}{v}_\beta T_\beta \, dA \ll \frac{1}{V}\int_{A_{\beta\sigma}} \underset{\sim}{n}_{\beta\sigma} \cdot k_\beta \underset{\sim}{\nabla} T_\beta \, dA \tag{234}$$

and follow the analysis of Carbonell and Whitaker [21] in order to express Equation 233 as

$$\epsilon_\beta(\rho c_p)_\beta \frac{\partial \langle T_\beta \rangle^\beta}{\partial t} + (\rho c_p)_\beta \underset{\sim}{\nabla} \cdot (\epsilon_\beta \langle v_\beta \rangle^\beta \langle T_\beta \rangle^\beta) + (\rho c_p)_\beta \underset{\sim}{\nabla} \cdot \langle \tilde{v}_\beta \tilde{T}_\beta \rangle$$

$$= \underset{\sim}{\nabla} \cdot \left\{ \epsilon_\beta k_\beta \left[\underset{\sim}{\nabla} \langle T_\beta \rangle^\beta + \frac{1}{V_\beta}\int_{A_{\beta\sigma}} \underset{\sim}{n}_{\beta\sigma} \tilde{T}_\beta \, dA \right] \right\} + \frac{1}{V}\int_{A_{\beta\sigma}} \underset{\sim}{n}_{\beta\sigma} \cdot k_\beta \underset{\sim}{\nabla} T_\beta \, dA \tag{235}$$

Here the term $(\rho c_p)_\beta \underset{\sim}{\nabla} \cdot \langle \tilde{\underset{\sim}{v}}_\beta \tilde{T}_\beta \rangle$ represents the dispersive transport, and a representation for $\tilde{T}_\beta$ is required in order to specify even the form of this term. Before exploring this problem in detail, we want to indicate what must be done to extract the traditional model of packed bed heat transfer from the development presented thus far.

Traditional Model

If one is willing to accept the following postulate concerning the temperature deviation in the β-phase

$$\tilde{T}_\beta = \underset{\sim}{F}_\beta \cdot \underset{\sim}{\nabla} \langle T_\beta \rangle^\beta \tag{236}$$

and the following definition of a film heat transfer coefficient

$$\frac{1}{V}\int_{A_{\beta\sigma}} \mathbf{n}_{\beta\sigma}\cdot k_\beta \nabla T_\beta \, dA = a_{\beta\sigma} h(\langle T_\beta\rangle_{\beta\sigma} - \langle T_\beta\rangle^\beta) \tag{237}$$

the fluid-phase thermal energy equation takes the form

$$\epsilon_\beta(\rho c_p)_\beta\left[\frac{\partial\langle T_\beta\rangle^\beta}{\partial t} + \langle \mathbf{v}_\beta\rangle^\beta\cdot\nabla\langle T_\beta\rangle^\beta\right]$$
$$= \nabla\cdot[(\mathbf{K}^\beta_{eff} + \mathbf{K}_D)\cdot\nabla\langle T_\beta\rangle^\beta] - a_{\beta\sigma}h(\langle T_\beta\rangle^\beta - \langle T_\beta\rangle_{\beta\sigma}) \tag{238}$$

Here we have used the incompressible form of the continuity equation

$$\nabla\cdot(\epsilon_\beta\langle \mathbf{v}_\beta\rangle^\beta) = 0 \tag{239}$$

in order to simplify the volume-averaged convective transport term, and we have used the definitions

$$\mathbf{K}^\beta_{eff} = \epsilon_\beta k_\beta\left(\mathbf{I} + \frac{1}{V_\beta}\int_{A_{\beta\sigma}} \mathbf{n}_{\beta\sigma}\mathbf{f}_\beta \, dA\right) \tag{240}$$

$$\mathbf{K}_D = \epsilon_\beta(\rho c_p)_\beta\left(\frac{1}{V_\beta}\int_{V_\beta} \tilde{\mathbf{v}}_\beta \mathbf{f}_\beta \, dV\right)$$

where $\mathbf{K}_D$ should be referred to as the fluid-phase thermal dispersion tensor.

We have referred to Equation 236 as a postulate since it is easy to show that the representation given by Equation 236 is incomplete. About Equation 237 we should note that $\langle T_\beta\rangle_{\beta\sigma}$ represents an area-average defined by

$$\langle T_\beta\rangle_{\beta\sigma} = \frac{1}{A_{\beta\sigma}}\int_{A_{\beta\sigma}} T_\beta \, dA \tag{241}$$

and on the basis of the boundary condition given by Equation 215 we have

$$\langle T_\beta\rangle_{\beta\sigma} = \langle T_\sigma\rangle_{\beta\sigma} \tag{242}$$

At this point we could return to the more precise version of Equation 215 that is given by Equation 233, and note that the area-average of T_β is actually given by

$$\langle T_\beta\rangle_{\beta\sigma} = \langle T_\sigma\rangle_{\beta\sigma} + \frac{1}{A_{\kappa\beta}}\int_{A_{\kappa\beta}} \mathbf{g}\cdot\nabla T_\sigma \, dA + \frac{1}{A_{\gamma\beta}}\int_{A_{\gamma\beta}} \mathbf{f}\cdot\nabla T_\sigma \, dA \tag{243}$$

Given the constraints imposed on $\mathbf{g}$ and $\mathbf{f}$ by Equation 160, it seems plausible that the last two terms in Equation 243 can be neglected. The precise motivation for this would be stated by the restriction

$$\frac{1}{A_{\kappa\beta}}\int \mathbf{g}\cdot\nabla T_\sigma \, dA + \frac{1}{A_{\gamma\beta}}\int \mathbf{f}\cdot\nabla T_\sigma \, dA \ll (\langle T_\beta\rangle^\beta - \langle T_\beta\rangle_{\beta\sigma}) \tag{244}$$

It is important to recognize that while Equation 237 can stand as a definition of the film heat transfer coefficient, it forces a commitment to a symmetric representation of the heat conduction process in the σ-phase. We summarize this traditional model as

Fluid-Phase Transport

$$\epsilon_\beta(\rho c_p)_\beta\left[\frac{\partial\langle T_\beta\rangle^\beta}{\partial t} + \langle \underset{\sim}{v}_\beta\rangle^\beta \cdot \underset{\sim}{\nabla}\langle T_\beta\rangle^\beta\right]$$
$$= \underset{\sim}{\nabla}\cdot[(\underset{\approx}{K}^\beta_{eff} + \underset{\approx}{K}_D)\cdot\underset{\sim}{\nabla}\langle T_\beta\rangle^\beta] - a_{\beta\sigma}h(\langle T_\beta\rangle^\beta - \langle T_\beta\rangle_{\beta\sigma}) \tag{245}$$

Boundary Conditions

Boundary Condition 1:

$$\langle T_\beta\rangle_{\beta\sigma} = \langle T_\sigma\rangle_{\beta\sigma}, \qquad \text{at } A_{\beta\sigma} \tag{246}$$

Boundary Condition 2:

$$-\underset{\sim}{n}_{\sigma\beta}\cdot k_\sigma\underset{\sim}{\nabla}T_\sigma = h(\langle T_\sigma\rangle_{\beta\sigma} - \langle T_\beta\rangle^\beta), \qquad \text{at } A_{\beta\sigma} \tag{247}$$

Porous Catalyst Phase

$$(\rho c_p)_\sigma\frac{\partial T_\sigma}{\partial t} = \underset{\sim}{\nabla}\cdot(k_\sigma\underset{\sim}{\nabla}T_\sigma) + \phi_\sigma \tag{248}$$

In this approach one must model the porous catalyst phase as spherical pellets, infinitely long cylindrical pellets, or flat slabs of porous catalyst that are of infinite extent. With this type of model one is forced to neglect particle-to-particle transport and the nature of this restriction can be made more precise by referring to Equation 230. The neglect of particle-to-particle heat conduction is comparable to

$$\frac{1}{V}\int_{A_{\sigma e}}\underset{\sim}{n}_{\sigma e}\cdot k_\sigma\underset{\sim}{\nabla}T_\sigma\, dA \ll \frac{1}{V}\int_{A_{\sigma\beta}}\underset{\sim}{n}_{\sigma\beta}\cdot k_\sigma\underset{\sim}{\nabla}T_\sigma\, dA \tag{249}$$

and this allows us to combine Equations 216, 230 and 237 to obtain

$$-a_{\beta\sigma}h(\langle T_\beta\rangle^\beta - \langle T_\beta\rangle_{\beta\sigma}) = \epsilon_\sigma\langle\phi_\sigma\rangle^\sigma - \epsilon_\sigma(\rho c_p)_\sigma\frac{\partial\langle T_\sigma\rangle^\sigma}{\partial t} \tag{250}$$

If the heat transfer process in the porous catalyst phase can be treated as quasi-steady, i.e.

$$\epsilon_\sigma(\rho c_p)_\sigma\frac{\partial\langle T_\sigma\rangle^\sigma}{\partial t} \ll \epsilon_\sigma\langle\phi_\sigma\rangle^\sigma \tag{251}$$

we can use Equation 250 in Equation 245 to obtain

Fluid-Phase Transport

$$\epsilon_\beta(\rho c_p)_\beta\left[\frac{\partial\langle T_\beta\rangle^\beta}{\partial t} + \langle \underset{\sim}{v}_\beta\rangle^\beta \cdot \underset{\sim}{\nabla}\langle T_\beta\rangle^\beta\right] = \underset{\sim}{\nabla}\cdot(\underset{\approx}{K}^T_{eff}\cdot\underset{\sim}{\nabla}\langle T_\beta\rangle^\beta) + \epsilon_\sigma\langle\phi_\sigma\rangle^\sigma \tag{252}$$

where

$$\underset{\approx}{K}^T_{eff} = \underset{\approx}{K}^\beta_{eff} + \underset{\approx}{K}_D \tag{253}$$

This representation is found often in texts on reactor design; however, the nature of the restrictions is not always made clear. In order to be more precise than the representation of the heat transfer problem given by Equations 245–248, we need to avoid the ad hoc expression for $\tilde{T}_\beta$ given by Equation 236 and this requires the development of a closure scheme.

Closure

In order to obtain a reliable expression for $\tilde{T}_\beta$ we make use of the decompositions

$$T_\beta = \langle T_\beta \rangle^\beta + \tilde{T}_\beta \tag{254a}$$

$$\underline{v}_\beta = \langle \underline{v}_\beta \rangle^\beta + \tilde{\underline{v}}_\beta \tag{254b}$$

in Equation 217 and arrange the result as

$$(\rho c_p)_\beta \left[\frac{\partial \tilde{T}_\beta}{\partial t} + \underline{v}_\beta \cdot \underline{\nabla}\tilde{T}_\beta + \tilde{\underline{v}}_\beta \cdot \underline{\nabla}\langle T_\beta \rangle^\beta \right] - \underline{\nabla} \cdot (k_\beta \underline{\nabla}\tilde{T}_\beta)$$

$$= - \left[(\rho c_p)_\beta \left(\frac{\partial \langle T_\beta \rangle^\beta}{\partial t} + \langle \underline{v}_\beta \rangle^\beta \cdot \underline{\nabla}\langle T_\beta \rangle^\beta \right) - \underline{\nabla} \cdot (k_\beta \underline{\nabla}\langle T_\beta \rangle^\beta) \right] \tag{255}$$

At this point we follow the method of Crapiste et al. [26] which is illustrated by Equations 129–132. With Equation 255, this approach leads to

$$(\rho c_p)_\beta \left[\frac{\partial \tilde{T}_\beta}{\partial t} + \underline{v}_\beta \cdot \underline{\nabla}\tilde{T}_\beta + \tilde{\underline{v}}_\beta \cdot \underline{\nabla}\langle T_\beta \rangle^\beta \right] - \underline{\nabla} \cdot (k_\beta \underline{\nabla}\tilde{T}_\beta)$$

$$= \frac{1}{V_\beta} \int_{V_\beta} \left\{ (\rho c_p)_\beta \left[\frac{\partial \tilde{T}_\beta}{\partial t} + \underline{v}_\beta \cdot \underline{\nabla}\tilde{T}_\beta + \tilde{\underline{v}}_\beta \cdot \underline{\nabla}\langle T_\beta \rangle^\beta \right] - \underline{\nabla} \cdot (k_\beta \underline{\nabla}\tilde{T}_\beta) \right\} dV \tag{256}$$

and from Equation 214 we can follow the same approach to obtain a governing equation for $\tilde{T}_\sigma$. This is given by

$$(\rho c_p)_\sigma \frac{\partial \tilde{T}_\sigma}{\partial t} - \underline{\nabla} \cdot (k_\sigma \underline{\nabla}\tilde{T}_\sigma) - \tilde{\phi}_\sigma = \frac{1}{V_\sigma} \int_{V_\sigma} \left[(\rho c_p)_\sigma \frac{\partial \tilde{T}_\sigma}{\partial t} - \underline{\nabla} \cdot (k_\sigma \underline{\nabla}\tilde{T}_\sigma) - \tilde{\phi}_\sigma \right] dV \tag{257}$$

Here we have used the decomposition

$$T_\sigma = \langle T_\sigma \rangle^\sigma + \tilde{T}_\sigma \tag{258}$$

in Equation 214 in order to arrive at Equation 257, and when Equations 254a and 258 are used in the boundary conditions given by Equations 215 and 216 we obtain

Boundary Condition 1:

$$\tilde{T}_\beta = \tilde{T}_\sigma + (\langle T_\sigma \rangle^\sigma - \langle T_\beta \rangle^\beta), \quad \text{at } A_{\beta\sigma} \tag{259}$$

Boundary Condition 2:

$$\underline{n}_{\beta\sigma} \cdot k_\beta \underline{\nabla}\tilde{T}_\beta = \underline{n}_{\beta\sigma} \cdot k_\sigma \underline{\nabla}\tilde{T}_\sigma + \underline{n}_{\beta\sigma} \cdot k_\sigma \underline{\nabla}\langle T_\sigma \rangle^\sigma - \underline{n}_{\beta\sigma} \cdot k_\beta \underline{\nabla}\langle T_\beta \rangle^\beta, \quad \text{at } A_{\beta\sigma} \tag{260}$$

At this point it should be clear that $\tilde{T}_\beta$ depends on $\underline{\nabla}\langle T_\beta \rangle^\beta$ because of the volume source term, $\tilde{\underline{v}}_\beta \cdot \underline{\nabla}\langle T_\beta \rangle^\beta$, in Equation 255 and because of the surface source term $\underline{n}_{\beta\sigma} \cdot k_\beta \underline{\nabla}\langle T_\beta \rangle^\beta$ in Equation 260. However, it should also be clear that $\tilde{T}_\beta$ depends on other quantities and that the functional dependence given by Equation 236 may be a serious over-simplification. Under many circumstances one can treat the closure problem as quasi-steady on the basis of the constraints

$$\frac{k_\beta t^*}{(\rho c_p)_\beta l_\beta^2} \gg 1, \qquad \frac{k_\sigma t^*}{(\rho c_p)_\sigma l_\sigma^2} \gg 1 \tag{261}$$

where l_β and l_σ are the characteristic lengths illustrated in Figure 4 and t^* is a characteristic process time. Since the closure problem is a local problem, one can neglect the variations of k_β and k_σ in the solution for $\tilde{T}_\sigma$ and $\tilde{T}_\beta$. Because of this, and because of the constraints given by Equation 261, we can express Equations 256 and 257 as

$$(\rho c_p)_\beta(\mathbf{v}_\beta \cdot \nabla\tilde{T}_\beta + \tilde{\mathbf{v}}_\beta \cdot \nabla\langle T_\beta\rangle^\beta) - k_\beta\nabla^2\tilde{T}_\beta = \frac{1}{V_\beta}\int_{V_\beta}\left[(\rho c_p)_\beta(\mathbf{v}_\beta \cdot \nabla\tilde{T}_\beta + \tilde{\mathbf{v}}_\beta \cdot \nabla\langle T_\beta\rangle^\beta - k_\beta\nabla^2\tilde{T}_\beta)\right]dV \tag{262}$$

$$k_\sigma\nabla^2\tilde{T}_\sigma + \tilde{\phi}_\sigma = \frac{1}{V_\sigma}\int_{V_\sigma}(k_\sigma\nabla^2\tilde{T}_\sigma + \tilde{\phi}_\sigma)\,dV \tag{263}$$

If we are willing to solve the closure problem for a unit cell, such as the one illustrated in Figure 7, then $\tilde{T}_\beta$ and $\tilde{T}_\sigma$ are spatially periodic, i.e.

$$\tilde{T}_\beta(\mathbf{r} + \mathbf{l}_i) = \tilde{T}_\beta(\mathbf{r}), \qquad \tilde{T}_\sigma(\mathbf{r} + \mathbf{l}_i) = \tilde{T}_\sigma(\mathbf{r}), \qquad i = 1, 2, 3 \tag{264}$$

Under these circumstances one can follow the proof of Ochoa et al. [29] to show that Equations 262 and 263 take on a simplified form leading to the following closure problem.

$$(\rho c_p)_\beta(\mathbf{v}_\beta \cdot \nabla\tilde{T}_\beta + \tilde{\mathbf{v}}_\beta \cdot \nabla\langle T_\beta\rangle^\beta) = k_\beta\nabla^2\tilde{T}_\beta \tag{265}$$

Boundary Condition 1:

$$\tilde{T}_\beta = \tilde{T}_\sigma + (\langle T_\sigma\rangle^\sigma - \langle T_\beta\rangle^\beta), \qquad \text{at } A_{\beta\sigma} \tag{266}$$

Boundary Condition 2:

$$\mathbf{n}_{\beta\sigma} \cdot k_\beta\nabla\tilde{T}_\beta = \mathbf{n}_{\beta\sigma} \cdot k_\sigma\nabla\tilde{T}_\sigma + \mathbf{n}_{\beta\sigma} \cdot k_\sigma\nabla\langle T_\sigma\rangle^\sigma - \mathbf{n}_{\beta\sigma} \cdot k_\beta\nabla\langle T_\beta\rangle^\beta, \qquad \text{at } A_{\beta\sigma} \tag{267}$$

$$0 = k_\sigma\nabla^2\tilde{T}_\sigma + \tilde{\phi}_\sigma \tag{268}$$

$$\langle\tilde{T}_\beta\rangle^\beta = 0, \qquad \langle\tilde{T}_\sigma\rangle^\sigma = 0 \tag{269}$$

In order to complete our statement of the closure problem, we need to express $\tilde{\phi}_\sigma$ in some useful form. By definition we have

$$\tilde{\phi}_\sigma = \phi_\sigma - \langle\phi_\sigma\rangle^\sigma \tag{270}$$

and in a previous study by the author [33] it has been shown that

$$\langle\phi_\sigma\rangle^\sigma = \phi_\sigma(\langle T_\sigma\rangle^\sigma) + \frac{1}{2}\langle\mathbf{y}_\sigma\mathbf{y}_\sigma\rangle^\sigma : \nabla\langle T_\sigma\rangle^\sigma\nabla\langle T_\sigma\rangle^\sigma\left(\frac{\partial^2\phi_\sigma}{\partial T_\sigma^2}\right) \tag{271}$$

provided the spatial deviation defined by Equation 258 can be represented as

$$\tilde{T}_\sigma = \mathbf{G}_\sigma \cdot \nabla\langle T_\sigma\rangle^\sigma \tag{272}$$

In Equation 272 $\mathbf{y}_r$ is the position vector relative to the centroid of $\mathscr{V}_\sigma$.

Since Equations 265–268 indicate a more complex functional dependence for $\tilde{T}_\sigma$ we must think of Equation 271 as an approximation. With this statement as a precaution, we follow the development given by Equations 179–181 and impose the restriction

$$\frac{1}{2}\langle \underset{\sim}{y}_\sigma \underset{\sim}{y}_\sigma \rangle^\sigma : \nabla\langle T_\sigma\rangle^\sigma \nabla\langle T_\sigma\rangle^\sigma \left(\frac{\partial^2 \phi_\sigma}{\partial T_\sigma^2}\right) \ll \phi_\sigma(\langle T_\sigma\rangle^\sigma) \tag{273}$$

so that Equation 270 takes the form

$$\tilde{\phi}_\sigma = \phi_\sigma(T_\sigma) - \phi_\sigma(\langle T_\sigma\rangle^\sigma) \tag{274}$$

Use of Equation 258 allows us to write this result as

$$\tilde{\phi}_\sigma = \phi_\sigma(\langle T_\sigma\rangle^\sigma + \tilde{T}_\sigma) - \phi_\sigma(\langle T_\sigma\rangle^\sigma) \tag{275}$$

and a Taylor series expansion leads to

$$\tilde{\phi}_\sigma = \left(\frac{\partial \phi_\sigma}{\partial T_\sigma}\right)\tilde{T}_\sigma + \frac{1}{2}\left(\frac{\partial^2 \phi_\sigma}{\partial T_\sigma^2}\right)\tilde{T}_\sigma\tilde{T}_\sigma + \cdots \tag{276}$$

Here all derivatives are evaluated at the reference temperature, $\langle T_\sigma\rangle^\sigma$. One can limit the analysis by

$$\frac{1}{2}\left(\frac{\partial^2 \phi_\sigma}{\partial T^2}\right)\tilde{T}_\sigma\tilde{T}_\sigma \ll \left(\frac{\partial \phi_\sigma}{\partial T_\sigma}\right)\tilde{T}_\sigma \tag{277}$$

so that Equation 276 takes the linearized form which we write as

$$\tilde{\phi}_\sigma = \left(\frac{\partial \phi_\sigma}{\partial T_\sigma}\right)\tilde{T}_\sigma \tag{278}$$

This representation for $\tilde{\phi}_\sigma$ would be satisfactory if ϕ_σ were a function of only the temperature T_σ; however, ϕ_σ will depend on the temperature *and* the concentration of the reacting species as we indicated in Equation 177. If we limit our discussion to the classic case of a first order, irreversible reaction, the functional dependence of ϕ_σ can be expressed as

$$\phi_\sigma = \phi_\sigma(T_\sigma, c_\sigma) \tag{279}$$

Here we have used c_σ to represent the intrinsic phase average concentration of the reacting species, and we could be more explicit by writing

$$c_\sigma = \langle c_A\rangle^\gamma, \qquad \text{reacting species} \tag{280}$$

It is not too difficult to show that the more general representation of $\tilde{\phi}_\sigma$ is given by

$$\tilde{\phi}_\sigma = \left(\frac{\partial \phi_\sigma}{\partial T_\sigma}\right)\tilde{T}_\sigma + \left(\frac{\partial \phi_\sigma}{\partial c_\sigma}\right)\tilde{c}_\sigma \tag{281}$$

so that Equation 268 takes the form

$$0 = k_\sigma \nabla^2 \tilde{T}_\sigma + \left(\frac{\partial \phi_\sigma}{\partial T_\sigma}\right)\tilde{T}_\sigma + \left(\frac{\partial \phi_\sigma}{\partial c_\sigma}\right)\tilde{c}_\sigma \tag{282}$$

Referring to Equations 265–268, with the latter taking the form given by Equation 282, we can see that the closure problem represents a situation in which $\tilde{T}_\beta$, $\tilde{T}_\sigma$, and $\tilde{c}_\sigma$ must all be determined simultaneously. A little thought will indicate that $\tilde{c}_\sigma$ will be coupled to the concentration deviation in the β-phase, thus the closure problem is quite complex for the general case.

In order to illustrate the nature of the closure problem and the structure of the volume-averaged transport equations, we will avoid the coupled heat and mass transfer closure problem by imposing the restriction

$$\left(\frac{\partial \phi_\sigma}{\partial c_\sigma}\right)\tilde{c}_\sigma \ll \left(\frac{\partial \phi_\sigma}{\partial T_\sigma}\right)\tilde{T}_\sigma \tag{283}$$

This is a severe limitation since *just the opposite* is true for many practical reactor design problems, and the need for a more thorough analysis should be obvious.

The decoupled closure problem can now be summarized as

$$(\rho c_p)_\beta(\mathbf{v}_\beta \cdot \nabla\tilde{T}_\beta + \tilde{\mathbf{v}}_\beta \cdot \nabla\langle T_\beta\rangle^\beta) = k_\beta \nabla^2 \tilde{T}_\beta \tag{284}$$

Boundary Condition 1:

$$\tilde{T}_\beta = \tilde{T}_\sigma + (\langle T_\sigma\rangle^\sigma - \langle T_\beta\rangle^\beta), \qquad \text{at } A_{\beta\sigma} \tag{285}$$

Boundary Condition 2:

$$\mathbf{n}_{\beta\sigma} \cdot k_\beta \nabla\tilde{T}_\beta = \mathbf{n}_{\beta\sigma} \cdot k_\sigma \nabla\tilde{T}_\sigma + \mathbf{n}_{\beta\sigma} \cdot k_\sigma \nabla\langle T_\sigma\rangle^\sigma - \mathbf{n}_{\beta\sigma} \cdot k_\beta \nabla\langle T_\beta\rangle^\beta, \qquad \text{at } A_{\beta\sigma} \tag{286}$$

$$0 = k_\sigma \nabla^2 \tilde{T}_\sigma + \left(\frac{\partial \phi_\sigma}{\partial T_\sigma}\right)\tilde{T}_\sigma \tag{287}$$

At this point one can follow the closure analysis of Ochoa et al. [29], Whitaker [31], or the earlier work of Zanotti and Carbonell [45], and express $\tilde{T}_\beta$ and $\tilde{T}_\sigma$ as

$$\tilde{T}_\beta = \mathbf{F}_\beta \cdot \nabla\langle T_\beta\rangle^\beta + \mathbf{G}_\beta \cdot \nabla\langle T_\sigma\rangle^\sigma + R_\beta(\langle T_\sigma\rangle^\sigma - \langle T_\beta\rangle^\beta) \tag{288a}$$

$$\tilde{T}_\sigma = \mathbf{F}_\sigma \cdot \nabla\langle T_\beta\rangle^\beta + \mathbf{G}_\sigma \cdot \nabla\langle T_\sigma\rangle^\sigma + \mathbf{R}_\sigma(\langle T_\sigma\rangle^\sigma - \langle T_\beta\rangle^\beta) \tag{288b}$$

The new functions $\mathbf{F}_\sigma$, $\mathbf{G}_\beta$, etc., are determined by a set of boundary value problems that can be expressed as

<u>*Problem I*</u>

$$(\rho c_p)_\beta(\mathbf{v}_\beta \cdot \nabla\mathbf{F}_\beta + \tilde{\mathbf{v}}_\beta) = k_\beta \nabla^2 \mathbf{F}_\beta \tag{289a}$$

Boundary Condition 1:

$$\mathbf{F}_\beta = \mathbf{F}_\sigma, \qquad \text{at } A_{\beta\sigma} \tag{289b}$$

Boundary Condition 2:

$$\mathbf{n}_{\beta\sigma} \cdot k_\beta \nabla\mathbf{F}_\beta = \mathbf{n}_{\beta\sigma} \cdot k_\sigma \nabla\mathbf{F}_\sigma - \mathbf{n}_{\beta\sigma} k_\beta, \qquad \text{at } A_{\beta\sigma} \tag{289c}$$

$$0 = k_\sigma \nabla^2 \mathbf{F}_\sigma + \left(\frac{\partial \phi_\sigma}{\partial T_\sigma}\right)\mathbf{F}_\sigma \tag{289d}$$

$$\mathbf{F}_\sigma(\mathbf{r} + \ell_i) = \mathbf{F}_\beta(\mathbf{r}), \qquad \mathbf{F}_\sigma(\mathbf{r} + \ell_i) = \mathbf{F}_\sigma(\mathbf{r}), \qquad i = 1, 2, 3 \tag{289e}$$

$$\langle \mathbf{F}_\beta\rangle^\beta = 0, \qquad \langle \mathbf{F}_\sigma\rangle^\sigma = 0 \tag{289f}$$

Problem II

$$(\rho c_p)_\beta \mathbf{v}_\beta \cdot \nabla \mathbf{G}_\beta = k_\beta \nabla^2 \mathbf{G}_\beta \tag{290a}$$

Boundary Condition 1:

$$\mathbf{G}_\beta = \mathbf{G}_\sigma, \qquad \text{at } A_{\beta\sigma} \tag{290b}$$

Boundary Condition 2:

$$\mathbf{n}_{\beta\sigma} \cdot k_\beta \nabla \mathbf{G}_\beta = \mathbf{n}_{\beta\sigma} \cdot k_\sigma \nabla \mathbf{G}_\sigma + \mathbf{n}_{\beta\sigma} k_\sigma, \qquad \text{at } A_{\beta\sigma} \tag{290c}$$

$$0 = k_\sigma \nabla^2 \mathbf{G}_\sigma + \left(\frac{\partial \phi_\sigma}{\partial T_\sigma}\right) \mathbf{G}_\sigma \tag{290d}$$

$$\mathbf{G}_\beta(\mathbf{r} + \mathbf{l}_i) = \mathbf{G}_\beta(\mathbf{r}), \qquad \mathbf{G}_\sigma(\mathbf{r} + \boldsymbol{\ell}_i) = \mathbf{G}_\sigma(\mathbf{r}), \qquad i = 1, 2, 3 \tag{290e}$$

$$\langle \mathbf{G}_\beta \rangle^\beta = 0, \qquad \langle \mathbf{G}_\sigma \rangle^\sigma = 0 \tag{290f}$$

Problem III

$$(\rho c_p)_\beta \mathbf{v}_\beta \cdot \nabla R_\beta = k_\beta \nabla^2 R_\beta \tag{291a}$$

Boundary Condition 1:

$$R_\beta = R_\sigma + 1, \qquad \text{at } A_{\beta\sigma} \tag{291b}$$

Boundary Condition 2:

$$\mathbf{n}_{\beta\sigma} \cdot k_\beta \nabla R_\beta = \mathbf{n}_{\beta\sigma} \cdot k_\sigma \nabla R_\sigma, \qquad \text{at } A_{\beta\sigma} \tag{291c}$$

$$0 = k_\sigma \nabla^2 R_\sigma + \left(\frac{\partial \phi_\sigma}{\partial T_\sigma}\right) R_\sigma \tag{291d}$$

$$R_\beta(\mathbf{r} + \boldsymbol{\ell}_j) = R_\beta(\mathbf{r}), \qquad R_\sigma(\mathbf{r} + \boldsymbol{\ell}_j) = R_\sigma(\mathbf{r}), \qquad i = 1, 2, 3 \tag{291e}$$

$$\langle R_\beta \rangle^\beta = 0, \qquad \langle R_\sigma \rangle^\sigma = 0 \tag{291f}$$

Although only a portion of Problem I has been explored in detail [46], some results for flow in capillary tubes have been produced by Zanatti and Carbonell [45] for the case of heat transfer in two-phase systems.

A general theory of heat transfer in catalytic packed bed reactors is obtained by substitution of Equations 288 into Equations 229 and 235; however, before doing so we need to use the decompositions for T_β and T_σ in order to express the local volume averaged equations as

Solid Phase

$$\epsilon_\sigma (\rho c_p)_\sigma \frac{\partial \langle T_\sigma \rangle^\sigma}{\partial t} = \nabla \cdot \left\{ \epsilon_\sigma k_\sigma \left[\nabla \langle T_\sigma \rangle^\sigma + \frac{1}{V_\sigma} \int_{A_{\sigma\beta}} \mathbf{n}_{\sigma\beta} \tilde{T}_\sigma \, dA \right] \right\}$$
$$- \nabla \epsilon_\sigma \cdot k_\sigma \nabla \langle T_\sigma \rangle^\sigma + \frac{1}{V} \int_{A_{\sigma\beta}} \mathbf{n}_{\sigma\beta} \cdot k_\sigma \nabla \tilde{T}_\sigma \, dA + \epsilon_\sigma \langle \phi_\sigma \rangle^\sigma \tag{292}$$

Fluid Phase

$$\epsilon_\beta(\rho c_p p)_\beta\left[\frac{\partial\langle T_\beta\rangle^\beta}{\partial t}+\langle \underset{\sim}{v}_\beta\rangle^\beta\cdot\underset{\sim}{\nabla}\langle T_\beta\rangle^\beta\right]$$
$$=\underset{\sim}{\nabla}\cdot\left\{\epsilon_\beta k_\beta\left[\underset{\sim}{\nabla}\langle T_\beta\rangle^\beta+\frac{1}{V_\beta}\int_{A_{\beta\sigma}}\underset{\sim}{n}_{\beta\sigma}\tilde{T}_\beta\,dA\right]-(\rho c_p)_\beta\langle\tilde{\underset{\sim}{v}}_\beta\tilde{T}_\beta\rangle\right\}$$
$$-\underset{\sim}{\nabla}\epsilon_\beta\cdot k_\beta\underset{\sim}{\nabla}\langle T_\beta\rangle^\beta+\frac{1}{V}\int_{A_{\beta\sigma}}\cdot k_\beta\underset{\sim}{\nabla}\tilde{T}_\beta\,dA \tag{293}$$

Here we see "convective-like" terms in both Equations 292 and 293 that result from the interfacial flux terms according to

$$\frac{1}{V}\int_{A_{\beta\sigma}}\underset{\sim}{n}_{\beta\sigma}\cdot k_\beta\underset{\sim}{\nabla}\langle T_\beta\rangle^\beta\,dA=\left\{\frac{1}{V}\int_{A_{\beta\sigma}}\underset{\sim}{n}_{\beta\sigma}\,dA\right\}\cdot k_\beta\underset{\sim}{\nabla}\langle T_\beta\rangle^\beta$$
$$=-\underset{\sim}{\nabla}\epsilon_\beta\cdot k_\beta\underset{\sim}{\nabla}\langle T_\beta\rangle^\beta \tag{294}$$

In general, these terms will be small except near the wall of a packed bed, non-adiabatic reactor; however, the length scale constraints upon which Equations 292 and 293 are based, tend to fail near the wall, thus it may be misleading to retain these terms when a more thorough analysis would generate other comparable terms in the wall region. We will leave this problem unanswered for the present, and turn out attention to the use of Equations 288 in Equation 292 and 293.

When Equation 288b is used in the local volume-averaged transport equation for the porous solid temperature, we obtain

$$\epsilon_\sigma(\rho c_p)_\sigma\frac{\partial\langle T_\sigma\rangle^\sigma}{\partial t}+\underset{\sim}{u}_{\sigma\sigma}\cdot\underset{\sim}{\nabla}\langle T_\sigma\rangle^\sigma+\underset{\sim}{u}_{\sigma\beta}\cdot\underset{\sim}{\nabla}\langle T_\beta\rangle^\beta$$
$$=\underset{\sim}{\nabla}\cdot(\underset{\approx}{K}_{eff}\cdot\underset{\sim}{\nabla}\langle T_\sigma\rangle^\sigma)+\epsilon_\sigma\langle\phi_\sigma\rangle^\sigma-a_{\beta\sigma}h_{\sigma\beta}(\langle T_\sigma\rangle^\sigma-\langle T_\beta\rangle^\beta)+\underset{\sim}{\nabla}\cdot(\underset{\approx}{K}_{\sigma\beta}\cdot\underset{\sim}{\nabla}\langle T_\beta\rangle^\beta) \tag{295}$$

In this result, the first term on the left side and the first three terms on the right side are similar in form to what one might develop on an intuitive basis. However, the remaining terms are all the result of rigorous analysis and cannot be ignored. The coefficients that appear in Equation 295 are defined by

$$\underset{\sim}{u}_{\sigma\sigma}=k_\sigma\left[\underset{\sim}{\nabla}\epsilon_\sigma-\frac{1}{V}\int_{A_{\sigma\beta}}\underset{\sim}{n}_{\sigma\beta}\cdot(\underset{\approx}{I}R_\sigma+\underset{\sim}{\nabla}\underset{\sim}{G}_\sigma)\,dA\right] \tag{296a}$$

$$u_{\sigma\beta}=k_\sigma\left[\frac{1}{V}\int_{A_{\sigma\beta}}\underset{\sim}{n}_{\sigma\beta}\cdot(\underset{\approx}{I}R_\sigma-\underset{\sim}{\nabla}\underset{\sim}{F}_\sigma)\,dA\right] \tag{296b}$$

$$\underset{\approx}{K}^\sigma_{eff}=\epsilon_\sigma k_\sigma\left[\underset{\approx}{I}+\frac{1}{V_\sigma}\int_{A_{\sigma\beta}}\underset{\sim}{n}_{\sigma\beta}\underset{\sim}{G}_\sigma\,dA\right] \tag{296c}$$

$$\underset{\approx}{K}_{\sigma\beta}=\frac{k_\sigma}{V}\int_{A_{\sigma\beta}}\underset{\sim}{n}_{\sigma\beta}\underset{\sim}{F}_\sigma\,dA \tag{296d}$$

$$a_{\beta\sigma}h_{\sigma\beta}=-\frac{k_\sigma}{V}\int_{A_{\sigma\beta}}\underset{\sim}{n}_{\sigma\beta}\cdot\underset{\sim}{\nabla}R_\sigma\,dA \tag{296e}$$

In writing Equation 295 we have ignored variations in the coefficients defined by Equations 296 in order to gain some degree of simplification. Although the general closure problem leading to the determination of the coefficients in Equations 296 has never been solved, we have some experience with various parts of the closure problem [18, 21, 22, 27, 28, 29, 35, 45, 46]. On the basis of that experience, we can make the following crude estimates

$$\underset{\sim}{F}_\beta = \underset{\sim}{O}(\underset{\sim}{F}_\sigma) = \underset{\sim}{O}(\ell_\sigma), \qquad \underset{\sim}{G}_\beta = \underset{\sim}{O}(\underset{\sim}{G}_\sigma) = \underset{\sim}{O}(\ell_\sigma) \qquad R_\beta = \underset{\sim}{O}(R_\sigma) = \underset{\sim}{O}(1) \tag{297}$$

In addition, we can estimate gradients as

$$\underset{\sim}{\nabla}\psi_\sigma = \underset{\sim}{O}(\psi_\sigma/\ell_\sigma), \qquad \underset{\sim}{\nabla}\psi_\beta = \underset{\sim}{O}(\psi_\beta/\delta_\beta) \tag{298}$$

where the β-phase length scale can be estimated

$$\delta_\beta = \begin{cases} \ell_\sigma, & \text{Re} < 1 \\ \ell_\sigma/\sqrt{\text{Re}}, & \text{Re} > 1 \end{cases} \tag{299}$$

In Equations 298 we have used ψ_σ to represent some quantity associated with the σ-phase, while ψ_β has a similar meaning for the β-phase. On the basis of the results given by Equations 297 we can estimate the coefficients in Equations 296 as

$$\underset{\sim}{u}_{\sigma\sigma} = \underset{\sim}{O}(k_\sigma a_{\beta\sigma}) \tag{300a}$$

$$\underset{\sim}{u}_{\sigma\beta} = \underset{\sim}{O}(k_\sigma a_{\beta\sigma}) \tag{300b}$$

$$\underset{\approx}{K}^\sigma_{\text{eff}} = \underset{\sim}{O}(\epsilon_\sigma k_\sigma) \tag{300c}$$

$$\underset{\approx}{K}_{\sigma\beta} = \underset{\sim}{O}(\epsilon_\sigma k_\sigma) \tag{300e}$$

$$h_{\sigma\beta} = \underset{\sim}{O}(k_\sigma/l_\sigma) \tag{300d}$$

This suggests that *none* of the terms in Equation 295 can be discarded; however, one should remember that estimates are just that. If one models a porous medium as a bundle of capillary tubes [45], it is not too difficult to show that

$$\underset{\sim}{u}_{\sigma\sigma} = \underset{\approx}{K}_{\sigma\beta} = 0, \qquad \text{bundle of capillary tubes} \tag{301a}$$

Because of this, there is motivation for discarding the non-traditional or the non-intuitive terms in Equation 295, but this should be avoided until detailed calculations have been completed. In fact, we now have sufficient information to suggest that the term involving $\underset{\approx}{K}_{\sigma\beta}$ *should not be neglected.* Once again we note that for a bundle of capillary tubes [21], one can arrive at

$$\frac{1}{V}\int_{A_{\sigma\beta}} \underset{\sim}{n}_{\sigma\beta}\underset{\sim}{F}_\sigma \, dA = 0, \qquad \text{bundle of capillary tubes} \tag{302}$$

while for more general porous media there is a great deal of theoretical and experimental evidence indicating that

$$\frac{1}{V_\sigma}\int_{A_{\sigma\beta}} \underset{\sim}{n}_{\sigma\beta}\underset{\sim}{G}_\sigma \, dA = \underset{\sim}{O}(1) \tag{303}$$

Given the similarity between the boundary value problems for $\underset{\sim}{F}_\sigma$ and $\underset{\sim}{G}_\sigma$, the estimates represented by Equations 300c and 300d seem quite plausible, and this suggests that the term in Equation 295 involving $\underset{\approx}{K}_{\sigma\beta}$ should not be discarded on an intuitive basis.

We now turn our attention to the fluid phase and make use of Equation 288a in Equation 293 in order to obtain

$$\epsilon_\beta(\rho c_p)_\beta\left[\frac{\partial\langle T_\beta\rangle^\beta}{\partial t} + \langle \mathbf{v}_\beta\rangle^\beta \cdot \nabla\langle T_\beta\rangle^\beta\right] + \mathbf{u}_{\beta\beta}\cdot\nabla\langle T_\beta\rangle^\beta + \mathbf{u}_{\beta\sigma}\cdot\nabla\langle T_\sigma\rangle^\sigma$$
$$= \nabla\cdot(\mathbf{K}_{\text{eff}}^{T}\cdot\nabla\langle T_\beta\rangle^\beta) + a_{\beta\sigma}h_{\beta\sigma}(\langle T_\sigma\rangle^\sigma - \langle T_\beta\rangle^\beta) + \nabla\cdot(\mathbf{K}_{\beta\sigma}\cdot\nabla\langle T_\sigma\rangle^\sigma) \tag{304}$$

Once again we encounter some non-traditional convective and conductive transport mechanisms. The five coefficients in Equation 304 that need to be determined by a solution of the closure problem are given by

$$\mathbf{u}_{\beta\beta} = k_\beta\nabla\epsilon_\beta + \frac{k_\beta}{V}\int_{A_{\beta\sigma}} \mathbf{n}_{\beta\sigma}(\mathbf{I}R_\beta - \nabla\mathbf{F}_\beta)\,dA - \frac{(\rho c_p)_\beta}{V}\int_{V_\beta}\tilde{\mathbf{v}}_\beta R_\beta\,dV \tag{305a}$$

$$\mathbf{u}_{\beta\sigma} = -\frac{k_\beta}{V}\int_{A_{\beta\sigma}} \mathbf{n}_{\beta\sigma}\cdot(\mathbf{I}R_\beta + \nabla\mathbf{G}_\beta)\,dA + \frac{(\rho c_p)_\beta}{V}\int_{V_\beta}\tilde{\mathbf{v}}_\beta R_\beta\,dV \tag{305b}$$

$$\mathbf{K}_{\text{eff}}^{T} = \epsilon_\beta k_\beta\left[\mathbf{I} + \frac{1}{V_\beta}\int_{A_{\beta\sigma}} \mathbf{n}_{\beta\sigma}\mathbf{F}_\beta\,dA\right] - \frac{(\rho c_p)_\beta}{V}\int_{V_\beta}\tilde{\mathbf{v}}_\beta\mathbf{F}_\beta\,dV \tag{305c}$$

$$\mathbf{K}_{\beta\sigma}^{T} = \frac{k_\beta}{V}\int_{A_{\beta\sigma}} \mathbf{n}_{\beta\sigma}\mathbf{G}_\beta\,dA - \frac{(\rho c_p)_\beta}{V}\int_{V_\beta}\tilde{\mathbf{v}}_\beta\mathbf{G}_\beta\,dV \tag{305d}$$

$$a_{\beta\sigma}h_{\beta\sigma} = \frac{k_\beta}{V}\int_{A_{\beta\sigma}} \mathbf{n}_{\beta\sigma}\cdot\nabla R_\beta\,dA \tag{305e}$$

One can repeat the order of magnitude analysis that led to Equations 300 in order to obtain the following representations

$$\mathbf{u}_{\beta\beta} = \mathbf{O}(k_\beta a_{\beta\sigma}) + \mathbf{O}[(\rho c_p)_\beta\langle\mathbf{v}_\beta\rangle^\beta] \tag{306a}$$

$$\mathbf{u}_{\beta\sigma} = \mathbf{O}(k_\beta a_{\beta\sigma}) + \mathbf{O}[(\rho c_p)_\beta\langle\mathbf{v}_\beta\rangle^\beta] \tag{306b}$$

$$\mathbf{K}_{\text{eff}}^{T} = \mathbf{O}(\epsilon_\beta k_\beta) + \mathbf{O}[\epsilon_\beta(\rho c_p)_\beta\ell_\sigma\langle\mathbf{v}_\beta\rangle^\beta] \tag{306c}$$

$$\mathbf{K}_{\beta\sigma}^{T} = \mathbf{O}(\epsilon_\beta k_\beta) + \mathbf{O}[\epsilon_\beta(\rho c_p)_\beta\ell_\sigma\langle\mathbf{v}_\beta\rangle^\beta] \tag{306d}$$

$$h_{\beta\sigma} = 0\quad\begin{cases} k_\beta/\ell_\sigma, & Re < 1\\ k_\beta\sqrt{Re}/\ell_\sigma, & Re > 1\end{cases} \tag{306e}$$

Once again our order of magnitude estimates suggest that none of the non-traditional terms in Equation 304 can be discarded unless a detailed solution of the closure problem indicates that they are indeed negligible.

CONCLUSION

In this chapter we have illustrated a rigorous approach to heat transfer and reaction in porous catalysts that leads to a traditional result given by Equation 183. The closure problem associated with Equation 183 was *de-coupled* from the mass transport closure problem by means of the simplification indicated in Equation 154. The thermal closure problem that led to Equation 183 allows one to determine, on a strictly theoretical basis, the effective thermal conductivity for the κ-γ system. In our study of heat transfer in the fluid phase of packed bed catalytic reactors, we have illustrated how the method of volume averaging can be used to arrive at the traditional model given by Equations 245–248. In doing so, we have used an overly-simplistic representation for $\tilde{T}_\beta$ (compare Equation 236 with Equation 288) and an expression for the interfacial heat flux (see Equation 237) that perhaps does not adequately represent the physics of the process under consideration. For example, use of Equation 288a leads to

$$\frac{1}{V}\int_{A_{\beta\sigma}} \underset{\sim}{n}_{\beta\sigma} \cdot k_\beta \underset{\sim}{\nabla} T_\beta \, dA = a_{\beta\sigma} h_{\beta\sigma}(\langle T_\sigma \rangle^\sigma - \langle T_\beta \rangle^\beta) + k_\beta\left[\frac{1}{V}\int_{A_{\beta\sigma}} \underset{\sim}{n}_{\beta\sigma} \cdot \underset{\sim}{\nabla} \underset{\sim}{F}_\beta \, dA - \underset{\sim}{\nabla}\epsilon_\beta\right] \cdot \underset{\sim}{\nabla}\langle T_\beta\rangle^\beta + k_\beta\left[\frac{1}{V}\int_{A_{\beta\sigma}} \underset{\sim}{n}_{\beta\sigma} \cdot \underset{\sim}{\nabla} \underset{\sim}{G}_\sigma \, dA\right] \cdot \underset{\sim}{\nabla}\langle T_\sigma\rangle^\sigma \quad (307)$$

rather than the traditional representation given by Equation 237. The advantage of the traditional model rests largely with the ability to calculate non-isothermal effectiveness factors by means of the simultaneous solution of Equation 248 and the associated diffusion-reaction transport equation [1]. In the method of volume averaging the coupling between heat and mass transport takes place at two levels:

1. Between the volume averaged transport equations.
2. Between the transport equations for the spatial deviations that must be determined to complete the closure.

In this development we have ignored the coupling at the spatial deviation level. This is apparent in the simplification that takes place between Equations 177 and 183 with the latter being the accepted form of the "point equation" in the porous catalyst. In the second level of averaging, we have ignored the coupling in the closure problem by the imposition of the restriction given by Equation 283. Under these circumstances, one has lost the opportunity of calculating a non-isothermal effectiveness factor, thus the closure problem obviously needs to be extended. In the traditional model the difficulty is removed by operating in a mixed mode: a volume averaged transport equation is used for the fluid phase while a "point equation" is used for the solid phase. The validity of this approach needs to be carefully considered and further work is obviously in order.

Acknowledgement

This work was supported by NSF Grant CBT 8611610.

NOTATION

- $A_{\eta\omega}$ area of the η-ω interface contained within an averaging volume, m^2
- $A_{\eta e}$ macroscopic area of entrances and exits for the η-phase, m^2
- $a_{\eta\omega}$ $A_{\eta\omega}/V$ or $A_{\eta\omega}/V_\sigma$, interfacial area per unit volume, m^{-1}
- $\underset{\sim}{b}_A$ species A body force per unit mass, N/kg
- $\underset{\sim}{b}$ total body force per unit mass, N/kg
- c_A concentration of species A, $kgmoles/m^3$
- $\hat{c}_A$ surface concentration of species A, $kgmoles/m^2$
- $\langle c_A \rangle^\omega$ intrinsic phase average concentration of species A in the ω-phase, $kgmoles/m^3$
- c_p constant pressure heat capacity, kcal/kgK
- C_p mass fraction weighted constant pressure heat capacity, kcal/kgK
- e_A species A internal energy per unit mass, kcal/kg

e_A^* internal energy of species A generated or consumed by chemical reaction, kcal/kg

$\underline{f}$ vector field that maps $\underline{\nabla}\langle T_\gamma\rangle^\gamma$ onto $\tilde{T}_\gamma$, m

$\underline{F}_\beta$ vector field that maps $\underline{\nabla}\langle T_\beta\rangle^\beta$ onto $\tilde{T}_\beta$, m

$\underline{F}_\sigma$ vector field that maps $\underline{\nabla}\langle T_\sigma\rangle^\sigma$ onto $\tilde{T}_\sigma$, m

$\underline{g}$ vector field that maps $\underline{\nabla}\langle T_\kappa\rangle^\kappa$ onto $\tilde{T}_\kappa$, m

$\underline{G}_\beta$ vector field that maps $\underline{\nabla}\langle T_\beta\rangle^\beta$ onto $\tilde{T}_\beta$, m

$\underline{G}_\sigma$ vector field that maps $\underline{\nabla}\langle T_\sigma\rangle^\sigma$ onto $\tilde{T}_\sigma$, m

h_A species A partial mass enthalpy, kcal/kg

h total enthalpy per unit mass, kcal/kg; film heat transfer coefficient in the traditional model, kcal/m²K

$h_{\sigma\beta}$ σ-phase film heat transfer coefficient for the volume-averaged thermal energy equations ($h_{\alpha\beta} \neq h_{\beta\alpha}$), kcal/m²K

$h_{\beta\sigma}$ β-phase film heat transfer coefficient for the volume-averaged thermal energy equations ($h_{\beta\sigma} \neq h_{\sigma\beta}$). kcal/m²K

H_A species A partial molar enthalpy, kcal/kg-mole

$\hat{H}_A$ adsorbed species A partial molar enthalpy, kcal/kg-mole

$\underset{\approx}{I}$ unit tensor

k_η thermal conductivity of the η-phase, kcal/m K

$\underset{\approx}{K}_{eff}^\omega$ effective thermal conductivity tensor for the ω-phase, kcal/m K

$\underset{\approx}{K}_D$ thermal dispersion tensor for the β-phase, kcal/m K

$\underset{\approx}{K}_{eff}^T$ sum of the effective thermal conductivity tensor and the thermal dispersion tensor, kcal/m K

L macroscopic characteristic length scale, m

ℓ_ω microscopic characteristic length scale for the ω-phase, m

ℓ_i $i = 1, 2, 3$ lattice vectors for a spatially periodic porous media, m

$\underline{n}_{\omega\eta}$ unit normal vector pointing from the ω-phase to the η-phase

$\underline{n}_{\omega e}$ outwardly directed unit normal vector at the entrances and exits of the ω-phase

p_A partial pressure of species A, N/m²

p total pressure, N/m²

$\underline{P}_{AB}$ force per unit volume exerted by species B on species A

$\underline{q}_A$ species A heat flux vector, kcal/m K

$\underline{q}_A^R$ species A radiant energy flux vector, kcal/m K

$\underline{q}$ total heat flux vector, kcal/m K

$\underline{q}^R$ total radiant energy flux vector, kcal/m K

$\underline{q}_\omega$ total heat flux vector for the ω-phase, kcal/m K

Q_{AB} rate of thermal energy exchange between species B and species A, kcal/m³s

r_A mass rate of production of species A per unit volume, kg/m³s

R_A molar rate of production of species A per unit volume, kg-mole/m³s

$\hat{R}_A$ molar rate of production of species A per unit area, kg-mole/m²s

R overall homogeneous reaction rate, kg-mole/m³s

$\hat{R}$ overall heterogeneous reaction rate, kg-mole/m²s

$\hat{R}_\mu$ overall heterogeneous reaction rate in the μ-subphase of the γ-phase, kg-mole/m²s

Re Reynolds number

$\underline{r}$ position vector, m

s entropy per unit mass, kcal/kg K

t time, s

T_ω temperature in the ω-phase, K

$\langle T_\omega\rangle^\omega$ intrinsic phase average temperature in the ω-phase, K

$\tilde{T}_\omega$ $T_\omega - \langle T_\omega\rangle^\omega$, local spatial deviation temperature, K

$\langle T\rangle$ spatial average temperature, K

$\hat{T}_\omega$ $\langle T_\omega\rangle^\omega - \langle T\rangle$, large-scale spatial deviation temperature, K

$\underline{t}_A$ species A stress vector, N/m²

$\underset{\approx}{T}_A$ species A stress tensor, N/m²

$\underset{\approx}{T}$ total stress tensor, N/m²

$\underline{u}_A$ $\underline{v}_A - \underline{v}$, species A mass diffusion velocity, m/s

$\underline{v}_A$ species A velocity, m/s

$\underline{v}$ mass average velocity, m/s

$\underline{v}_A^*$ velocity of species A generated or consumed by chemical reaction, m/s

$\underline{v}_\beta$ mass average velocity in the β-phase, m/s

$\langle\underline{v}_\beta\rangle^\beta$ intrinsic phase average velocity in the β-phase, m/s

$\tilde{\underline{v}}_\beta$ $\underline{v}_\beta - \langle\underline{v}_\beta\rangle^\beta$, local spatial deviation velocity, m/s

V averaging volume for the β-σ system, m³

V_σ averaging volume for the κ-γ system, m³

V_ω volume of the ω-phase contained within either V or V_σ, m^3
$V_A(t)$ volume of a species A body, m^3
$\underset{\sim}{w}$ velocity of a moving interface, m/s
$\underset{\sim}{y}$ position vector relative to the centroid of the averaging volume, m.

Greek Letters

α $k/\rho c_p$, thermal diffusivity, m^2/s
α_{eff} $K^\sigma_{eff}/\langle\rho\rangle C_p$, thermal diffusivity for the porous catalyst phase, m^2/s
ΔH_r molar heat of reaction, kcal/kg-mole
ϵ_η volume fraction of the η-phase given by V_η/V or V_η/V_σ
κ k_κ/k_γ, ratio of conductivities
ν_A stoichiometric coefficient for species A
ρ_A species A mass density, kg/m^3
ρ total mass density, kg/m^3
$\langle\rho\rangle$ spatial average mass density, kg/m^3
$\underset{\approx}{\tau}_A$ species A viscous stress tensor, N/m^2
$\underset{\approx}{\tau}$ total viscous stress tensor, N/m^2
ϕ_σ thermal source in the porous catalyst phase, $kcal/m^3s$
ω_A ρ_A/ρ, species A mass fraction

REFERENCES

1. Whitaker, S., "Transport Processes with Heterogeneous Reaction," in *Concepts and Design of Chemical Reactors*, edited by S. Whitaker and A. E. Cassano, Gordon and Breach, New York (1986).
2. Truesdell, C., and Toupin, R., "The Classical Field Theories," in *Handbuch der Physik*, Vol. III, Part 1, edited by S. Flügge, Springer-Verlag, New York (1960).
3. Truesdell, C., *Essays in the History of Mechanics*, Springer-Verlag, New York (1968).
4. Aris, R., *Vectors, Tensors and the Basic Equations of Fluid Mechanics*, Prentice-Hall, Inc., Englewood Cliffs, New Jersey (1962).
5. Slattery, J. C., *Momentum, Energy and Mass Transfer in Continua*, R. E. Krieger Pub. Co., Malabar, Florida (1981).
6. Whitaker, S., "Mass Transport in Porous Catalyst Pellets," *Transport in Porous Media*, 2, 269–299 (1987).
7. Whitaker, S., *Fundamental Principles of Heat Transfer*, R. E. Krieger Pub. Co., Malabar, Florida (1983).
8. Whitaker, S., *Introduction to Fluid Mechanics*, R. E. Krieger Pub. Co., Malabar, Florida (1981).
9. Bird, R. B., Stewart, W. E., and Lightfoot, E. N., *Transport Phenomena*, John Wiley and Sons, Inc., New York (1960).
10. Glandt, E. D., "Simultaneous Conduction and Radiation in Porous and Composite Materials: Effective Thermal Conductivity," *Ind. Eng. Chem. Fundam.*, 22, 276–282 (1983).
11. Whitaker, S., "Radiant Energy Transport in Porous Media," *Ind. Eng. Chem. Fundam.*, 19, 210–218 (1980).
12. Carbonell, R. G., and Whitaker, S., "Adsorption and Reaction at a Catalytic Surface: The Quasi-Steady Condition," *Chem. Eng. Sci.*, 39, 1319–1321 (1984).
13. Whitaker, S., "Transient Diffusion, Adsorption and Reaction in Porous Catalysts: The Reaction Controlled, Quasi-Steady Catalytic Surface," *Chem. Eng. Sci.*, 41, 3015–3022 (1986).
14. Anderson, T. B., and Jackson, R., "A Fluid Mechanical Description of Fluidized Beds," *Ind. Eng. Chem. Fundam.*, 6, 527–538 (1967).
15. Marle, C. M., "Ecoulements Monophasiques en Milieu Poreux," *Rev. Inst. Francais du Pètrole*, 22, 1471–1509 (1967).
16. Slattery, J. C., "Flow of Viscoelastic Fluids Through Porous Media," *AIChE Journal*, 13, 1066–1071 (1967).
17. Whitaker, S., "Diffusion and Dispersion in Porous Media," *AIChE Journal*, 13, 420–427 (1967).
18. Nozad, I., Carbonell, R. G., and Whitaker, S., "Heat Conduction in Multiphase Systems I: Theory and Experiment for Two-Phase Systems," *Chem. Eng. Sci.*, 40, 843–855 (1985).
19. Whitaker, S., "A Simple Geometrical Derivation of the Spatial Averaging Theorem," *Chem. Engr. Ed., Winter*, 18–21 and 50–52 (1985).

20. Gray, W. G., "A Derivation of the Equations for Multiphase Transport," *Chem. Eng. Sci.*, 30, 229–233 (1975).
21. Carbonell, R. G., and Whitaker, S., "Heat and Mass Transfer in Porous Media," pages 123–198 in *Fundamentals of Transport in Porous Media*, edited by J. Bear and M. Y. Corapcioglu, Martinus Nijhoff Publishers, Dordrecht, The Netherlands (1984).
22. Whitaker, S., "Diffusion and Reaction in a Micropore-Macropore Model of a Porous Medium," *Latin Amer. J. Chem. Engr. Appl. Chem.*, 13, 143–183 (1983).
23. Whitaker, S., "Simultaneous Heat, Mass and Momentum Transfer in Porous Media: A Theory of Drying," pages 119–203 in *Advances in Heat Transfer*, Vol. 13, Academic Press, New York (1977).
24. Whitaker, S., "Heat and Mass Transfer in Granular Porous Media," pages 23–61 in *Advances in Drying*, Vol. 1. Hemisphere Publishing Corp., New York (1980).
25. Whitaker, S., "Local Thermal Equilibrium: An Application to Packed Bed Catalytic Reactor Design," *Chem. Eng. Sci.*, 41, 2029–2039 (1986).
26. Crapiste, G. H., Rotstein, E., and Whitaker, S., "A General Closure Scheme for the Method of Volume Averaging," *Chem. Eng. Sci.*, 41, 227–235 (1986).
27. Ryan, D., Carbonell, R. G., and Whitaker, S., "Effective Diffusivities for Catalyst Pellets under Reactive Conditions," *Chem. Eng. Sci.*, 35, 10–16 (1980).
28. Ryan, D., Carbonell, R. G., and Whitaker, S., "A Theory of Diffusion and Reaction in Porous Media," *AIChE Symposium Series*, #202, Vol. 71, 46–62 (1981).
29. Ochoa, J. A., Stroeve, P., and Whitaker, S., "Diffusion and Reaction in Cellular Media," *Chem. Eng. Sci.*, 41, 2999–3013 (1986).
30. Whitaker, S., "Flow in Porous Media I: A Theoretical Derivation of Darcy's Law," *Transport in Porous Media*, 1, 3–25 (1986).
31. Whitaker, S., "Flow in Porous Media II: The Governing Equations for Immiscible, Two-Phase Flow," *Transport in Porous Media*, 1, 105–125 (1986).
32. Brenner, H., "Dispersion Resulting From Flow Through Spatially Periodic Porous Media," *Trans. Roy. Soc.* (*London*), 297, 81–133 (1980).
33. Whitaker, S., "The Role of the Volume-Averaged Temperature in the Analysis of Nonisothermal, Multiphase Transport Phenomena," Chem. Engr. Comm.
34. Wu, L. C., *Unpublished Experimental Results*, Department of Chemical Engineering," University of California at Davis (1984).
35. Nozad, I., *Ph.D. thesis*, Department of Chemical Engineering, University of California at Davis, (1983).
36. Batchelor, G. K., and O'Brien, R. W., *Proc. Roy. Soc.* (*London*), A355, 313–328 (1977).
37. Swift, D. L., "The Thermal Conductivity of Spherical Metal Powders Including the Effect of an Oxide Coating," *Int. J. Heat Mass Transfer*, 9, 1061–1073 (1966).
38. Shonnard, D. R., "Experimental Determination of Unit Cell Effective Thermal Conductivities for Point Contact," *M.S. Thesis*, Department of Chemical Engineering, University of California at Davis (1985).
39. Hadley, G. R., "Thermal Conductivity of Packed Metal Powders," *Int. J. Heat Mass Transfer*, 29, 909–920 (1986).
40. Oppio, J., personal communication (1984).
41. Dullien, F. A. L., *Porous Media: Fluid Transport and Pore Structure*, Academic Press, New York (1979).
42. Prakowras, A. G., Vachow, R. I., Crane, R. A., and Khader, M. S., "Thermal Conductivity of Heterogeneous Mixtures," *Int. J. Heat Mass Transfer*, 21, 1157–1166 (1978).
43. Gavalas, G. R., "A Random Capillary Model with Application to Char Gasification at Chemically Controlled Rates," *AIChE J.* 26, 577–598 (1980).
44. Whitaker, S., "Heat Conduction in Porous Media with Homogeneous and Heterogeneous Thermal Sources," *Proceedings Euromech*, 194, 39–44, Nancy, France (1985).
45. Zanotti, F., and Carbonell, R. G., "Development of Transport Equations for Multiphase Systems III: Application to Heat Transfer in Packed Beds," *Chem. Eng. Sci.*, 39, 299–311 (1984).
46. Eidsath, A., Carbonell, R. G., Whitaker, S., and Herrmann, L. R., "Dispersion in Pulsed Systems III: Comparison between Theory and Experiments for Packed Beds," *Chem. Eng. Sci.*, 38, 1803–1816 (1983).

CHAPTER 11

A GENERAL PRESENTATION OF MODELING OF CATALYTIC FLUIDIZED BED REACTORS

C. Laguérie and H. Angélino

Laboratoire de Genie Chimique
ENSIGC
Toulouse Cedex, France

CONTENTS

INTRODUCTION

In the past three decades, several studies have been performed to a better understanding of phenomena involved in fluidized bed reactors. Many of them have generated models whose success has been very often restricted to specific conditions. Most of these models rest on the two-phase theory of fluidization, but their assumptions may differ considerably leading to strong discrepancies between their predictions. However, few comparative studies have been reported in the literature. Furthermore, most of them concern simple first-order reaction at mild conditions. Therefore, choosing between several models for reactor design or scaling-up purposes is still an uncertain exercise.

This chapter aims at giving a general scope of fluidized bed reactor modeling resting on a classification of models according to their basic concepts. Assumptions regarding the nature of the phases, the interphase gas-exchange, and the behavior of the emulsion gas are especially considered.

Particular attention will be paid to the studies of discrimination between models, and finally, an example of simulation of the unsteady state operation of a catalytic fluidized bed reactor is described.

GENERAL PRESENTATION OF FLUIDIZED BED REACTOR MODELING

Most of the fluidized bed reactor models of the literature can be ranked in two main categories [1–5]: simple two-phase models and bubbling-bed models. The models of the former group consider a fluidized bed reactor as consisting of two parallel phases with crossflow between them, i.e., an upward dilute phase corresponding to the bubbles and allowed to include a certain amount of associated solids, and a dense phase flowing either upward or downward according to the operating conditions. The models belonging to the latter group are based on the properties of rising bubbles. They use results from independent theoretical and experimental studies relative to physics and hydrodynamics of fluidized beds.

However this simplified classification does not cover all the types of models perfectly. Thus another group derived from either one or the other above category but considering a multiple-zone division of the bed can be discerned. Furthermore a stochastic approach begins to be developed.

Simple Two-Phase Models

This type of models is schematically represented in Figure 1. They involve six independent parameters to be either fixed or adjusted:

1. Volume of the dense phase, V_e.
2. Gas flow rate through the dense phase, Q_e or superficial velocity of gas through the dense phase, U_e.
3. Fraction of all solids asssociated to the dilute (upward) phase, γ_b.
4. Rate of cross-flow between the two phases, X.
5. Axial mixing dispersion coefficient of gas in the dense phase, D_e.
6. Axial mixing dispersion coefficient of gas in the dilute phase, D_b.

Usually gas of the dilute phase is assumed to rise in plug flow so that $D_b = 0$. Therefore, these models range from one-parameter models to five-parameter models. Some of these parameters can indeed be evaluated from empirical correlations obtained with small-scale equipment. The different assumptions, which have been variously combined by the authors, concern the phase division,

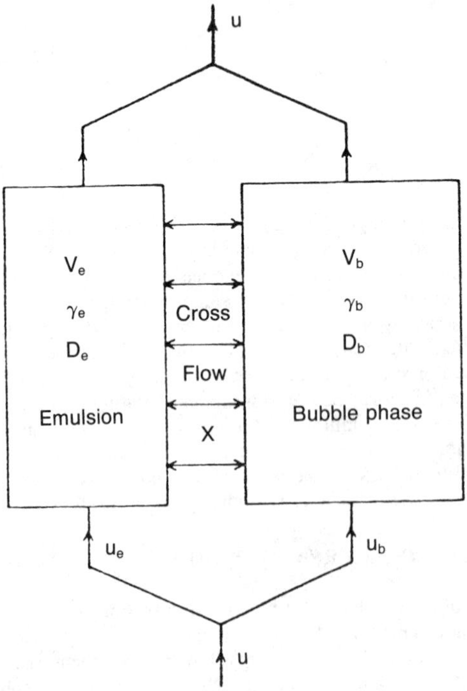

Figure 1. Simple two-phase model.

bubble flow, type of flow through the emulsion, and the interphase mass transfer:

Phase division—

- Dense phase + bubble phase devoid of solids [6–10, 12, 15, 16, 18–20]
- Dense phase + bubble phase containing some solids [11, 13, 14, 17]

Flow of gas through the bubble phase—

- Visible flow of gas assumed to be in excess of that required at incipient fluidization [6, 9, 12, 13, 15–18]
- Entire flow of gas [10, 11, 17]
- Not specified flow (model parameter) [7, 8, 14, 19, 20]

Behavior of the emulsion gas—

- Plug flow [8, 11–13, 17]
- Perfect mixing [10–12, 17]
- Axial dispersion model [6, 7, 9, 18–20]
- Tanks-in-series model [16]
- Downflow allowed [7, 8, 11, 19, 20]

Interphase mass transfer—

- Measured by gas mixing or kept as correlating parameter [6–10, 17, 18]
- Calculated on the basis of chemical reaction data [11–13, 15, 16, 18]
- Derived from mechanistic equations [9, 14, 19, 20].

It can be noted that the dilute phase may be considered completely free of solids or containing a certain amount of solids belonging to the clouds and wakes of the bubbles and that all assumptions from plug flow to complete mixing have been quoted for the emulsion gas. However, finite gas backmixing represented by either axial dispersion, tanks-in-series models, or counter-current flow are often chosen to give a more realistic picture.

Most of the simple two-phase models are derived from those of May [6] and Van Deemter [7, 8]. The model of Van Deemter assumes the formation and disintegration of aggregates of particles in a dynamic equilibrium. Large aggregates fall down through the bed entraining gas with them until they are broken up into small fragments and single particles, which are then carried upward by the gas stream until they coalesce with other aggregates and begin again to fall. Thus, a fluidized bed consists of two phases: the dispersed (dilute) phase in which gas rises at high vertical velocities with only small aggregates and single particles carried up with it and the dense phase which contains the solids and intersticial gas of the large aggregates. The volume of the dense and dilute phase may be evaluated from the overall bed expansion. When the superficial gas velocity is not too small, most of the gas passes through the bed in the dilute phase. There exists a continuous exhange of gas and particles between the two phases. The gas exchange is characterized by a number of interphase transfer units n_K. The random motions in the gas are described with the aid of an eddy diffusivity, E. They are assumed to occur in the dense phase only. In the mathematical formulation of the model, this gas eddy diffusion is rendered by means of a number of eddy diffusion units, n_E, which may be related to a number of backmixing units, n_B, for experimental determinations. By assuming that chemical reaction proceeds mainly in the dense phase, it can be characterized by another dimensionless parameter, the number of reaction units, n_R. The values of the model parameters can be obtained from a given program of experiments involving bed expansion measurements as well as tracer experiments to give the residence time distribution of gas, and studies of the catalyst activity in fixed bed reactors. This model has been successfully used by the Shell company for designing a catalytic reactor for the air oxidation of hydrogen chloride to chlorine. However, as underlined by Yates [2, 3], the main drawback of this method is the cost involved in carrying out an extensive experimental program, needing the use of several reactors, to establish the necessary correlations although once they have been established, it is possible to easily design a similar reactor using similar catalyst particles.

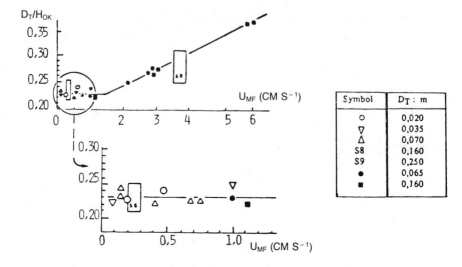

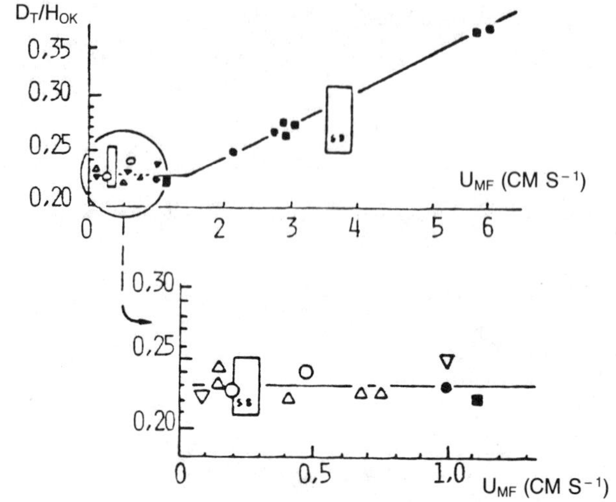

Symbol	D_T : m
○	0,020
▽	0,035
△	0,070
S8	0,160
S9	0,250
●	0,065
■	0,160

Figure 2. Effect of the bed diameter and the minimum fluidization velocity on the height of transfer unit between dilute and dense phase [21, 22].

Therefore Botton et al. [9, 21, 22], resting on the Van Deemter model, have shown that the scaling-up of a deep catalytic reactor is possible from chemical and specifically physical laboratory experiments only, without needing a pilot plant stage. This mainly stands for cases where the conversion is limited by the interphase gas exchange. It is assumed that the bubbles are practically devoid of catalyst and that axial dispersion occurs in the dense phase. The authors have correlated the height of transfer unit between the two phases on the one hand and the bed diameter and the incipient fluidization velocity of the catalyst under its normal operating conditions on the other hand (Figure 2). Furthermore, from tracer experiments, they have observed that the ratio n_K/n_E remains between 0.5 and 1. They have concluded from their work that the scaling up can be approached from reaction runs performed in a bench reactor as small as 2 cm in diameter for catalyst particles not coarser than 100 μm.

There is also a very interesting approach developed by Werther [10] by which the catalytic reaction occurring in a fluidized bed reactor is described as an absorption from the bubble phase with a subsequent pseudo-homogeneous reaction in the catalytic suspension surrounding the bubbles. Empirical correlations have been given for the interphase mass transfer, the specific interfacial area, and the bubble gas holdup. These correlations take into account the influence of the reactor geometry. The practical application of the model has been illustrated by testing its predictions with data of the literature [11, 12, 19, 20].

Bubbling Bed Reactor Models

Some models of this category are schematically represented in Figures 3 and 4. They take into account the physical picture of the fluidized bed with bubble dynamics. The bubble diameter, bubble rise velocity, cloud extent, bubble wake fraction, throughflow of gas in bubbles, and gas exchange coefficients are explicit model parameters that may be evaluated from experimental or theoretical correlations.

However, the following assumptions must be made regarding the distinction between the phases, the flow of gas passing through the bed as bubbles that percolate through the emulsion phase and the type of gas flow in this phase:

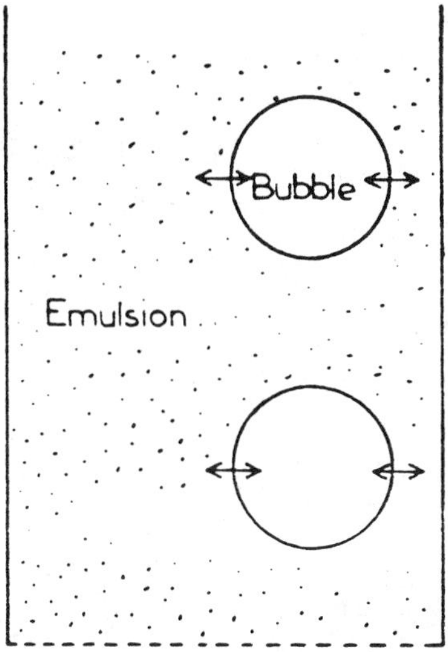

Figure 3. Davidson and Harrison model.

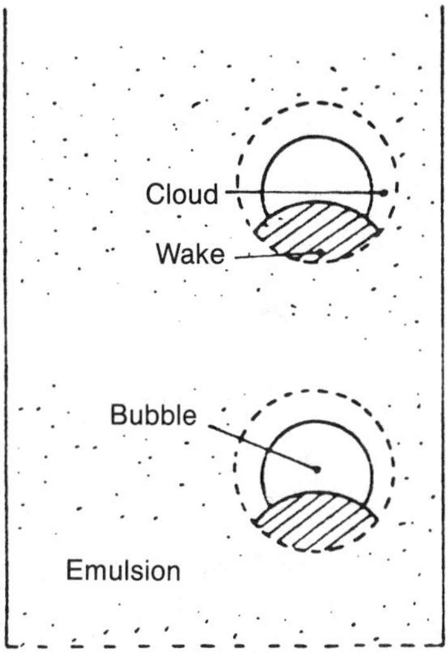

Figure 4. Kunii and Levenspiel bubbling bed reactor model.

Phases chosen—

- Two phases: emulsion phase + bubbles devoid of solids [25, 29]
- Two phases: emulsion phase + bubbles-clouds-wakes [27, 30–35]
- Three phases: emulsion phase + bubbles + clouds-wakes [36–39]

Flow of gas as bubbles—

- Visible flow assumed to be in excess of that required at incipient fluidization [25–34, 36, 37]
- Entire flow of gas [35, 36]

Behavior of the emulsion gas—

- Plug flow [25–34]
- Perfect mixing [25–29, 37, 38, 41]
- Axial dispersion model
- Tanks-in-series model [35, 39]
- Reversal flow of emulsion phase [36–39]

Interphase mass transfer—

- Transfer rate obtained experimentally [35, 40]
- Transfer rate calculated from chemical reaction [34]
- No resistance to bubble-to-cloud transfer [31, 33–35]
- Bubble-to-cloud transfer by diffusion and/or throughflow [25–30, 32, 36–39]
- No resistance to cloud-to-emulsion transfer [25–27, 30]
- Cloud-to-emulsion transfer by diffusion [27, 28, 33, 36–39]
- No cloud-to-emulsion transfer [27, 31, 32]

Bubble size—

- Considered as constant [25, 26, 31–33, 36, 42]
- Varying with height [27, 34, 35, 37, 42, 43]
- Plugs [28, 29, 38]

Cloud size—

- Calculated from Davidson-Harrison [26] analysis [27, 31, 32, 35–38]
- Calculated from Murray [44] or corrected Murray [45] analysis [33, 34–39]
- Not taken into account [25, 26, 42, 43]

Flow within bubbles—

- Streamlines [32]
- Complete mixing [21–31, 33–43]

Flow within clouds—

- Streamlines [27, 32]
- Complete mixing [31, 33–41]

Wake—

- Included with cloud [31, 33, 34, 36–41]
- Ignored [25, 26, 28, 30, 42, 43]
- Treated as a part of emulsion [32, 35]

It can be noted that the emulsion phase may either include the bubble clouds or not, that the bubble wakes are often attached to the clouds and that they may be considered as an individual third phase. Likewise overall resistance to interphase gas exchange may be assumed as resulting from one or two steps. It goes without saying that, even though assumptions may be variously combined, they are not quite independent from each other. For instance, assuming clouds to constitute an intrinsic phase means that there must exist finite bubble-to-cloud and cloud-to-emulsion mass transfer resistances.

The main practical advantage of the bubbling bed reactor models should be to render possible design of fluidized bed reactors without carrying out any experiments unless kinetic data must be determined, by only using existing hydrodynamic or tranfer data. But serious deficiences are encountered mainly due to an insufficient knowledge of the behavior of free bubbles. Most of the studies relative to bubbles deal with single or isolated bubbles rising through a bed under incipient fluidization conditions and the models consider implicitely that a bubble assemblage in a vigorously fluidized bed acts as if bubbles were independent on each other. In fact when bubbles are moving freely, their interactions result in shape changes, velocity changes, interpenetration of their clouds and coalescence. These interactions are rarely taken into account though they have drastic consequences especially on gas-solid contact and interphase gas exchange. It is clear that despite high degrees of sophistication that have been models, the complex behavior of the reactor cannot be exactly reflected. Therefore, the quality of the predictions may fail strongly under conditions where the assumptions used do not give a quite good picture of the bed.

The basis of these models are now to be considered further.

Analysis of the Main Assumptions of Bubbling Bed Reactor Models

Division of gas between phases. Many of the bubbling-bed-reactor models are based on the two-phase theory of fluidization [46], which states that all gas in excess of that just required at incipient fluidization passes through the bed as bubbles. However, in recent years, many experimental works have clearly demonstrated that, in freely bubbling bed, the two-phase theory overestimates the visible bubble flow [47–56]. Two features can explain the deficiency of the two-phase theory: the dense phase of a fluidized bed can increase its voidage beyond that corresponding to the incipient fluidization [48–51], and the dense-phase gas velocity may be several times higher than the incipient fluidization values [52–56].

A recent experimental work by Yates and Newton [56] has shown that increasing the fraction of fine particles in the bed results in a considerable increase in the flow rate of the interstitial gas with respect to that predicted by the two-phase theory.

The consequences of using the two-phase theory for reactor modeling is to predict underestimated conversions. But, at the present time, it is quite impossible to estimate a priori the division of inlet gas between the different phases. However, for very high fluidization velocities, gas-flow through the emulsion can be considered as negligibly small [35–37].

Division of solids between phases. Analysis of bubble motion is of the first importance to obtain a description of the flow pattern for gas as well as for solids. Several theoretical studies by the methods of fluid mechanics can be found in the literature [26, 44, 57–61], nevertheless that formulated by Davidson and Harrison [26], despite its simplicity, is usually considered as correct enough for reactor modeling. It predicts a flow of gas through the bubble, entering it as its base and leaving at the top. The form of the streamlines depends on the ratio of bubble velocity to intersticial gas velocity, α. When $\alpha < 1$, a common situation in beds of coarse particles, gas uses the bubble as a low resistance short circuit in its percolation through the dense phase [3]. When $\alpha > 1$, a normal situation in beds of small particles, gas leaving at the top of the bubble is dragged back and re-enters the bubble at its base. The recirculation of gas is confined within a region surrounding the bubble cavity, called the cloud region the extent of which depends on the α-value. Bubble gas can only contact the particles in the cloud. In addition to the Davidson theory, more rigorous analysis [44, 57] as well as experimental studies [45, 62] have demonstrated that bubbles are not spherical as postulated by Davidson and Harrison, but they exhibit identations caused by a wake of particles carried up with them and occupying as much as one third of the bubble volume [45]. Presence of solids in the clouds and the wakes that are directly related to bubble motion has led to a variety of assumptions concerning the division of solids between the phases, but these assumptions are not quite independent of the treatment of the interphase mass transfer. Furthermore, according to Clift [55], the significance of the cloud in freely bubbling bed is somewhat questionable. Analysis predicting the existence and size of clouds consider the dense phase as a continuum and derive the cloud boundary from a closed gas streamline, which is only valid when the cloud thickness exceeds largely the particle diameter. For fluidized beds of fine particules, as those used usually as catalysts, the estimated thickness of the bubble clouds is less than ten particle diameters. In fact it becomes very difficult to distinguish the cloud from the adjacent dense phase. Besides, the clouds are submitted to severe perturbations as bubbles coalesce and their identity is strongly affected.

Interphase gas exchange. Because the bubbles and the emulsion are in contact over a large surface area, there exists a gas exchange between the two phases. This exchange is of importance on gas solids contacting and in turn on the performance of fluidized bed reactors, but it is very complex and it has given rise to large distinctions between the models. In the case of a single bubble rising in a fluidized bed, two consecutive resistances to bubble-to-emulsion transfer can be distinguished (Figure 5): the bubble-to-surrounding cloud-wake region transfer on one hand, and the cloud-wake-to-emulsion transfer on the other hand. Various combinations of these resistances have been assumed:

1. Direct bubble-to-emulsion transfer (no resistance to cloud-to-emulsion transfer). This was first postulated by Davidson et al. [25, 26, 28] and by Zenz and Othmer [63]. Davidson assumed the gas transfer from bubble to emulsion to be resulting from two super-imposed mechanisms:

   The convective throughflow of gas derived from the Davidson theory:

$$q = \frac{3\pi}{4} u_{mf} d_b^2 \quad (1)$$

   The convective diffusion at the bubble-emulsion interface, evaluated by analogy with film-controlled diffusion between a spherical-cap shape bubble and a liquid through which it is rising:

$$k_{be} = 0.975 D_G^{1/2} d_b^{-1/4} g^{1/4} \quad (2)$$

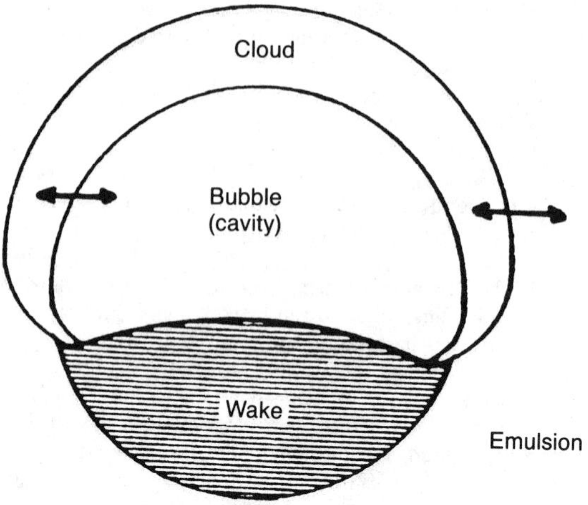

Figure 5. Interphase mass transfer.

The overall exchange rate per unit bubble volume is then:

$$K_{be} = 4.5(u_{mf}/d_b) + 5.85(D_G^{1/2}g^{1/4}/d_b^{5/4}) \quad (3)$$

Hovmand and Davidson [28], from a work performed in a two-dimensional bed, have observed that this overall exchange rate is less than the sum of the two mechanisms considered individually and that there exists some interaction between them, which can be taken into account by correcting each individual contribution by means of interaction coefficients.

2. Bubble-cloud-to-emulsion transfer (no resistance to bubble to-cloud transfer). By considering the cloud surrounding the bubble as constituting with it a single phase, assumed to be completely mixed, and by doing an analogy with transfer from a drop of an immiscible liquid rising through another, Partridge and Rowe [33, 45] proposed to derive the mass transfer coefficient from the following correlations:

$$Sh_c = 2 + 0.69Sc^{1/3}Re_c^{1/2} \quad (4)$$

where Re_c is the Reynolds number defined with respect to the cloud diameter and the relative velocity between rising cloud and emulsion.

The cloud-to-emulsion exchange rate per unit volume of bubble-cloud space is then:

$$K_{bce} = 3.9\varepsilon D_G Sh_c/V_{bc}^{2/3} \quad (5)$$

Gupalo et al. [64] have proposed another correlation to evaluate the mass transfer coefficient:

$$Sh_c = (1 + \frac{2}{\pi} Pe)^{1/2} \quad (6)$$

where Pe is the Peclet number for the cloud.

3. Bubble-to-cloud-to-emulsion transfer. Kunii and Levenspiel [36, 65] have taken into account the two stages of gas exchange between the bubbles and the emulsion phase. They have considered that the bubble-to-cloud-and-wake transfer can be evaluated as proposed by Davidson and Harrison [26] whereas the cloud-and-wake-to-emulsion transfer rate is given by an ex-

pression derived from the Higbie penetration theory:

$$K_{ce} = 6.78(\varepsilon_{mf} D_G U_b / d_b^3)^{1/2} \tag{7}$$

The overall transfer rate per unit bubble volume is then calculated from:

$$\frac{1}{K_{be}} = \frac{1}{K_{bc}} + \frac{1}{K_{ce}} \tag{8}$$

A very useful empirical expression for the overall transfer rate has been given by Kobayashi et al. [66]:

$$K_{be} = \frac{0.11}{d_b} \tag{9}$$

This correlation has been recommended by several authors [5, 35, 67].

In the general case of multiple bubbles, splitting, coalescence, wake shedding, etc. . . . render the interphase mass transfer more complicated to be analyzed [55]. Sit and Grace [68], who have measured the transfer of ozone between bubbles and emulsion in a two-dimensional bed with different sizes of particles, have shown that the overall transfer rate, corrected for bubble growth, increases with particle diameter and depends on the bubble shape, and that there exists some enhancement of transfer due to bubble interactions. In a more recent work [69] they have postulated that coalescence leads to an increase in the throughflow of gas that can affect the gas transfer. They have suggested to apply an enhancement factor of 1.8 to the throughflow term for 40% of the bubbles in the bed. This corresponds to an overall enhancement of 32% of the transfer due to coalescence.

Another important factor able to enhance the interphase mass transfer is the gas adsorption on the particles [3, 20, 34, 40, 70–74]. This phenomenon has been confirmed by experimental studies [3, 40, 74, 74]. A theoretical expression has been derived by Chiba and Kobayashi [34] for the ratio of interphase mass transfer coefficients in the presence and absence of adsorption effect. The main parameters are the adsorption equilibrium constant and the ratio of bubble velocity to interstitial gas velocity. Another expression has been proposed by Gupalo et al. [73]. It also depends on the adsorption equilibrium constant and on the emulsion voidage. As it has been noted by Yates [3], the importance of the adsorption effect for fluidized bed reactor modeling is obvious since enhancement of mass transfer leads to improve gas-solid contact and in turn reactant conversion, but a compensated effect caused by mixing in the emulsion phase should be considered. Likewise, Morooka et al. [75] have found that adsorptivity had a smaller effect than predicted.

Behavior of emulsion gas. It is reasonably admitted that the gas percolates between the particles closely to plug flow at velocities near to the minimum fluidization velocity. On the contrary, at very high gas velocities mixing of emulsion gas becomes intense and it can be assumed completely mixed. Between these two limiting cases, axial mixing occurs and the degree of backmixing is increased with the gas velocity. Many authors [6, 7, 20, 35, 36, 39, 76–82] have investigated backmixing of emulsion gas. The best physical description of the phenomenon has been given by Kunii and Levenspiel [36]. Each bubble carries solid particles upward in its wake as it rises. To compensate for upflow of particles with bubbles, there must be a downflow of solids in the emulsion so that the mean dense phase velocity is negative. Assuming that the relative velocity between solids and interstitial gas of emulsion remains equal to the interstitial minimum fluidization velocity, it can be shown that emulsion gas can flow downward when the ratio of superficial gas velocity to minimum fluidization velocity is greater than a critical value usually comprised between 6 and 11 [36].

This type of backmixing can be taken into account for modeling by considering the flow reversal [20, 36, 37, 39], by introducing an axial dispersion coefficient [20, 27], or by assuming the bed as an assemblage of vertical compartments consisting of the bubble phase and the emulsion phase, with complete mixing of the gas flowing through each of the two phases [35, 39]. For fine-particle systems such as FCC, Mao, and Potter [20] have shown that a dense phase diffusion model and a counter-current backmixing model predict quite close conversions even though there may be observable differences between the predicted concentration profiles. However, agreement deteriorates as particles size becomes larger. They conclude that the countercurrent backmixing model is possibly the best one although more work is needed to firm up this result.

Multiple-Zone Models

Rather recent experimental works [67, 83–87] have underlined the need to consider regions other than the bubbling zone in modeling fluidized bed reactors. The very high reaction rate near the distributor has been observed by a lot of authors. In this part of the reactor where bubbles are being formed, interphase gas transfer appears to be very fast and gas-solid contact very good. Similarly, due to the presence of solids in the freeboard, reaction can proceed to some extent. Thus three zones can be distinguished in a fluidized bed reactor: the grid region, the fully bubbling bed, and the freeboard.

Behie and Kehoe [88] modeled the grid jet entry zone at the bottom of fluidized beds. Their model consists in an extent of the Davidson-Harrison model to this zone. They considered mass transfer between the emulsion phase and turbulent gas jets, which were assumed to break up after a certain distance into bubbles.

This model has been extended by Errazu and de Lasa [89, 90] to a non-isothermal heterogeneous reaction and by Grace and de Lasa [91] to more realistic grid jet models. More recently, Bauer and Werther [86, 87] have applied the original two-phase model of Werther [10] by considering the dilute phase as consisting of both the grid jets at the bottom of the bed and the bubbles rising above the entry zone. All the parameters have been evaluated from results of investigations into fluidized bed hydrodynamics. The model has been verified using RTD measurement techniques and by conversion measurements for the catalytic decomposition of ozone carried out in two fluidized bed reactors 0.2 m and 1.0 m in diameter.

Nevertheless, the existence of grid jets has been brought into doubt by the work of Rowe et al. [92] who concluded that permanent jets could be formed only if particles were locally defluidized or if a surface was available near the orifice on which a jet could stabilize. When these conditions are not achieved, the gas streams breaks down into a succession of recognizable bubbles. Nevertheless, regardless of how jets are defined, reliable measurements of mass transfer between phases are still lacking [55, 93].

Models for the freeboard region have been proposed by Miyauchi, Furusaki et al. [94, 95] and Yates and Rowe [96]. They showed that the axial distribution of reactivity possibly plays an important role on the selectivity or the stability and should carefully be considered in the design of fluidized catalyst beds [97, 98]. The model of Miyauchi [94, 95] requires experimental determination of the concentration profile of dilute phase solids and makes no allowance for recycling of entrained particles. Yates and Rowe [96] have assumed that the freeboard contains perfectly mixed, equally dispersed particules derived from bubble wakes. The reaction of wake particles ejected is a model parameter. They have estimated particle hold up in the freeboard by assuming that particles reach the teminal fall velocity immediately after ejection, which limits their model to particles leaving the bed. De Lasa and Grace [99] have developed a model where conversion in the freeboard is obtained based on particle trajectories predicted from the work of George and Grace [100] who derived a mechanistic model for entrainment resting on ejection of particles by bubbles bursting at the bed surface. All particles can be treated independently of their terminal fall velocities and thermal gradient can be computed.

Beyond conversion predictions, all these works have also pratical implication for the placement of cyclones to return particles that are carried over from fluidized beds [99].

Stochastic Modeling of Fluidized Bed Reactors

Fluidized beds exhibit fluctuating characteristics. The flow pattern of gas and solids in and around the dense and dilute phases fluctuate constantly and the various components in the dense phase are intermittenly exposed to bubbles whose gas composition is different. Therefore probabilistic approaches have been developped for modeling fluidized bed reactors [101–103]. Based on a previous work [104] Too et al. [103] have derived a stochastic compartmental model for treatment of dispersive mixing and chemical reactions simultanously. Their model describes a fluidized bed reactor as a series of ideally stirred tanks of various sizes corresponding to bubble cloud, and emulsion phases. It takes into account both flow reversal and the height of entering jets in addition to all other phenomena contained in usual deterministic models. Complex reactions have been simulated and the axial concentration profiles have been predicted. Conclusions of their work have revealed that flow reversal conditions are rather uncommon, slugging occurring generally before onset of flow reversal. On the contrary, they have shown that inclusion of the jet height as a parameter in determining the size of the first compartment has a significant effect on the number of compartments necessary at rather low superficial gas velocities. For high gas velocities, the bubble size increases and becomes the dominating parameter. They conclude that the use of the stochastic approach reduces computational efforts for formulating and solving the model equations. Moreover, the stochastic formulation offers additional information such as the variance of the concentrations. However, further investigations need to be carried out.

COMPARISON OF SOME FLUIDIZED BED REACTOR MODELS

Despite the number of models and the variety of their assumptions, it is surprising to find so few comparative studies in the literature [5, 22, 67, 93, 105–108]. The simplest way of evaluating fluidized bed reactor models is to perform experimental work by measuring the inlet and outlet gas stream composition. The evaluation and discrimination techniques used by Chavarie and Grace [67] are much more demanding on the models since the authors have measured separately concentrations in the individual phases at various levels in the bed. Thus, they were concerned with the degree of correspondence between predicted and observed reactant concentration profiles. The reaction chosen was the catalytic decomposition of ozone. Bubble phase ozone concentrations were determined by absorption of U.V. light by the bubble through pairs of quartz windows situated in fifty-four points of the walls. Reactant concentrations in the emulsion phase were measured by withdrawal of gas samples from a number of sampling points along the bed. Visible bubble properties were determined by means of cinephotography. It was pointed out that the visible bubble flow rate is lower than expected from the two-phase theory, but it increases with height above the distributor. This result leads to some difficulties since the models tested were based on the two-phase theory.

A limitation of this study is that the reactor is a two-dimensional bed and hence the quantitative information obtained could not be directly applicable to large-scale reactors. Nevertheless, very interesting conclusions were drawn. Four among the most important bubbling bed reactor models were evaluated and discriminated between them: Davidson and Harrison [26], Partridge and Rowe [33], Kunii and Levenspiel [36] and Kato and Wen [35]. These models are based on some common assumptions such as the operation of the reactor under isothermal conditions, the voidage of the emulsion phase equal to that of the bed at incipient fluidization conditions, and the perfect mixing of gas within each bubble and each cloud if especially considered. Other assumptions underline the specificity of each model. The presentation of these is synoptically given in Table 1. Chavarie and Grace showed that purely on a statistical ground, none of these models could give an accurate representation of the experimental data obtained in their work even though the interphase gas transfer was used as an adjustable parameter.

The Davidson and Harrison model with the assumption of perfect mixing of the dense phase gas (DPPM) (Figure 6a) underestimates seriously the overall conversion. By assuming plug flow in the dense phase (DPPF), it gave better predictions of the overall conversion but the predicted concentrations in the individual phases did not agree with the observed profiles.

An incompatibility between predicted cloud areas and the total bed cross-sectional area due to overestimation of the visible bubble flow by the two-phase theory prevented direct application of the Partridge and Rowe model.

The bubbling bed model of Kunii and Levenspiel (Figure 6b) provided the best overall predictions of the experimental data and the dense phase concentration profiles were in reasonable agreement with those observed.

Table 1
Specific Assumption of the Models Tested by Chavarie and Grace [67] and by Stergiou and Laguerie [5, 107]

Model	Phase Chosen	Bubble Size	Flow of Gas Through the Phases	Type of Gas Flow Through Emulsion Phase	Transfer of Gas Between Phases
Davidson and Harrison [26]	Two phases: Bubble phase completely free of solids Emulsion phase	Constant	All the gas flow in excess of that required for incipient fluidization passes through the bed as bubbles (Toomey's theory)	Two limiting cases are considered: Perfect mixing Plug flow giving two different models	No resistance to transfer across cloud/emulsion interface
Partridge and Rowe [33]	Two phases: Void units consisting of bubbles and their associated clouds Emulsion phase	Function of the level in the bed	Visible gas flow is estimated from Toomey's theory and experimental data	Plug flow	No resistance to transfer across bubble/cloud interface
Kunii and Levenspiel [36]	Three phases: Bubble phase Cloud-wake phase Emulsion phase	Constant	Glas flow in the emulsion phase is neglected	Downflow of emulsion gas	Two resistances to be considered across: Bubble/cloud-wake interface Cloud-wake/emulsion interface
Kato and Wen [35]	The fluidized bed is represented by a number of compartments in series consisting of two phases: Bubbles and their associated clouds Emulsion	Function of the level in the bed	Gas flow in the emulsion phase is neglected	Perfect mixing in the emulsion phase within each compartment	No resistance to transfer across bubble/cloud interface

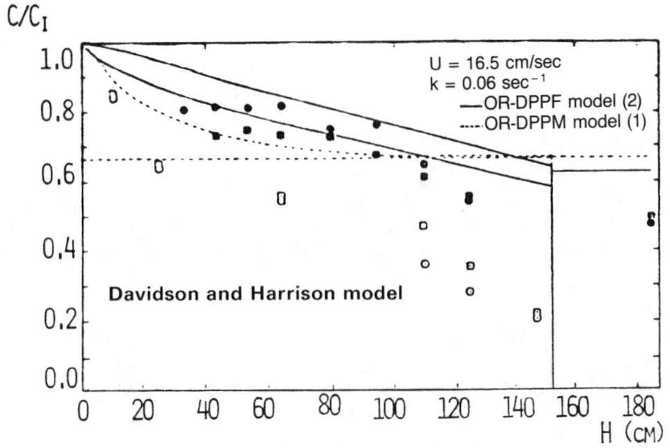

A

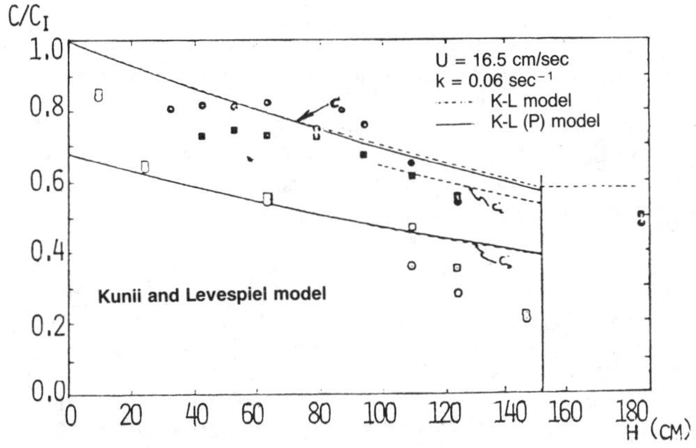

B

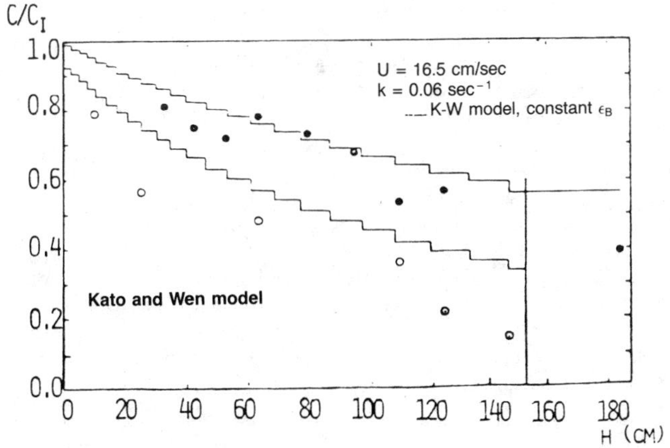

C

Figure 6A. Ozone concentration profiles [67].
Figure 6B. Ozone concentration profiles [67].
Figure 6C. Ozone concentration profiles [67].

The Kato and Wen bubble assemblage model (Figure 6c) led to the best predictions of the bubble concentration profiles, but the dense phase profiles and the overall conversions were seriously overpredicted.

However, multiple reactions rather than single first-order reactions are more useful for evaluation of models. A reliable model must be able to predict product selectivity as well as conversion over a wide range of operating conditions [93]. With this purpose, Stergiou et al. [5, 107] have undertaken a study consisting of discriminating between these four models by comparing their predictions with data obtained by carrying out experiments on the catalytic ammoxidation of propylene to acrylonitrile. This is a rather complex and highly exothermic reaction leading to several side products such as carbon oxides, acrolein, acetonitrile, allylalcohol and hydrogen cyanide. Experiments were performed in a 165 mm dia. reactor filled up to 6 kg of a commercial catalyst and fitted with a perforated plate distributor. They were designed to test the models as selectively as possible under conditions in which bubble coalescence occurs. The models were treated by estimating the visible bubble properties from the same relations of the literature in order to avoid any risks of discrepancy arising from the use of different sources of evaluation. Bubble size was determined by choosing the correlation of Rowe [109], but the Kato and Wen model was aslo treated by using the Kobayaski's correlation as proposed by the authors [35]. The ratio of the wake volume to the bubble volume was considered equal to 0.25 [45]. The bubble velocity was çalculated by the correlation of Davidson and Harrison [26] and the bed expansion from the continuity equation based on the two-phase theory. Cloud volume, gas flow through the individual phases, and interphase gas exchange were calculated as recommended by the authors. The experiments provided the overall conversions of propylene and selectivities of acrylonitrile. All the models were found to give a rather good agreement between calculated and experimental selectivities. The reason is undoubtedly that this variable is mainly governed by kinetic considerations. Therefore, it could not be taken as a significant criterion for discrimination. As for the conversions of propylene, conclusions derived are close to those of the study of Chavarie and Grace. However, the model of Davidson and Harrison has been found to overestimate the conversions, whatever the assumption regarding the type of gas flow through the emulsion it refers to (Figure 7a and b). Obviously, the lack of fit of the "dense-phase-in-plug flow" model was greater. This lack of agreement led to suspect that the model fails in the interphase gas exchange estimate. It does not deal with a resistance between the cloud and the emulsion phases.

Values of the mass transfer coefficient per unit bubble volume for a bubble diameter up to 44 mm were found to be three times higher than those calculated from the other models under the same conditions [5, 107]. These only differed from each other by less than 35%, the model of Kunii and Levenspiel leading to the lowest values.

The model of Partridge and Rowe (Figure 7c) offered a rather good prediction of conversion for the lowest values of the gas flow rate ($u/u_{mf} < 5$). However, it gave strongly underestimated conversion for higher values. Similar deficiencies of the model as those underlined by Chavarie and Grace were clearly observed. In the cited study, the visible bubble flow rate would have to be decreased by 20% to predict more accurate values of the conversion.

Agreement between experimental and theoretical values of propylene conversions given by the Kunii and Levenspiel model was very good (Figure 7d) for high gas flow rates ($u/u_{mf} > 7$), but the model was not statistically acceptable for lower flow rates. This is not surprising since it mainly rests on the assumption that a reversed flow of gas through the emulsion phase what was found to occur for $u/u_{mf} > 6$.

The Kato and Wen model predicted a better overall agreement (Figure 7e) but F-test revealed that the model was only valid for the highest values of the mass of catalyst. Using the Kobayashi's correlation to predict the bubble diameter led to strongly underestimated conversions. This undoubtedly results from an over-estimation of the diameter. It was shown indeed that the bubble size calculated by the relation of Kobayashi is on average twice as great as that evaluated by the Rowe correlation.

The model sensitivity to changes in the values of some factors was investigated by the authors. It was shown that a 50% change in the bubble diameter resulted in a conversion change between 20 and 40% according to the conditions used while a 50% change in the gas interchange affected the conversion by no more than 15% whatever the model was. The bubble size appeared to be a

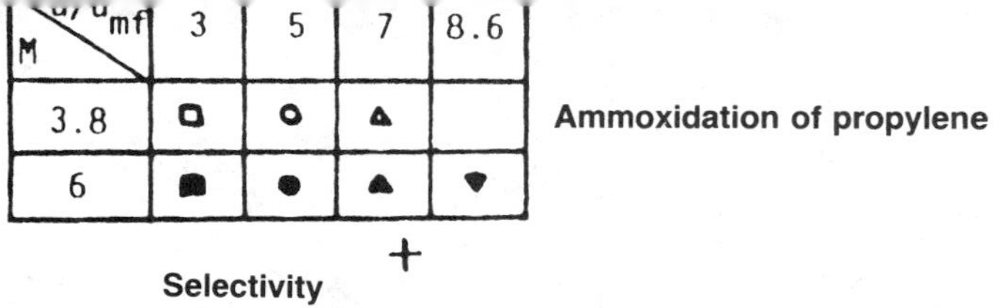

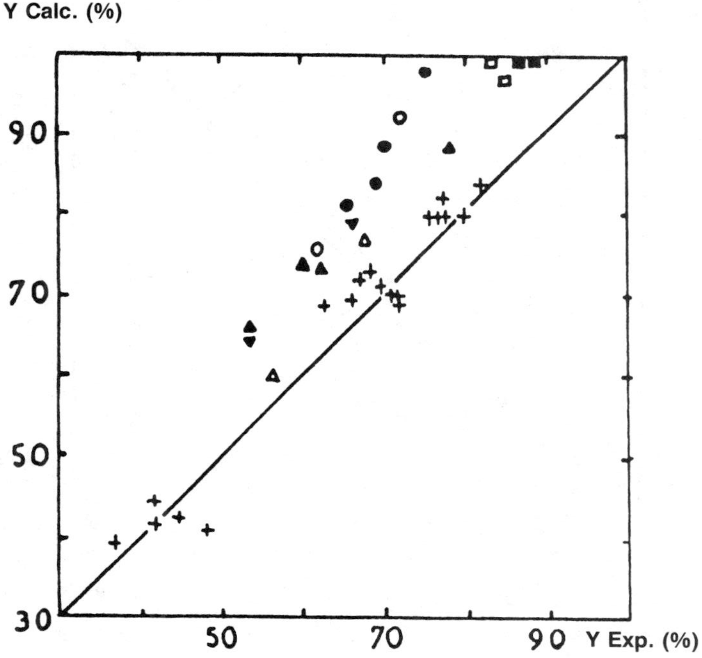

Figure 7A. Davidson and Harrison model—plug flow of emulsion gas [5].

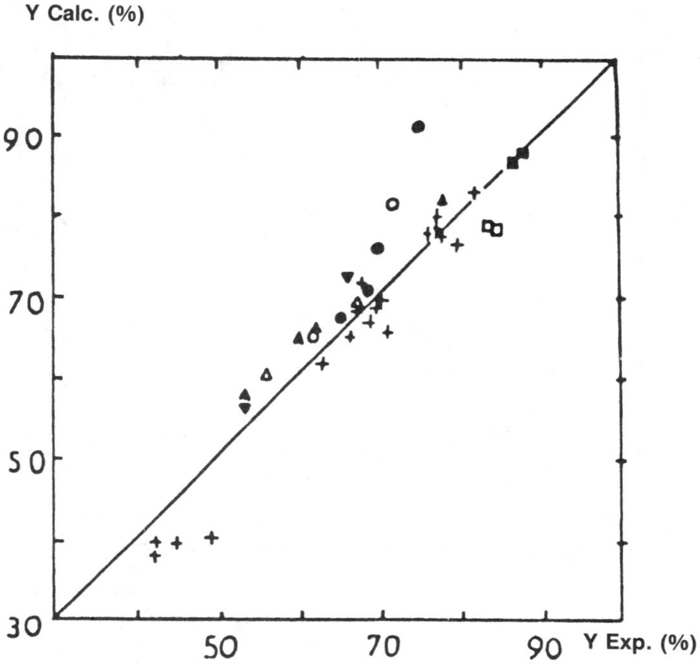

Figure 7B. Davidson and Harrison model—perfect mixing of emulsion gas [5].

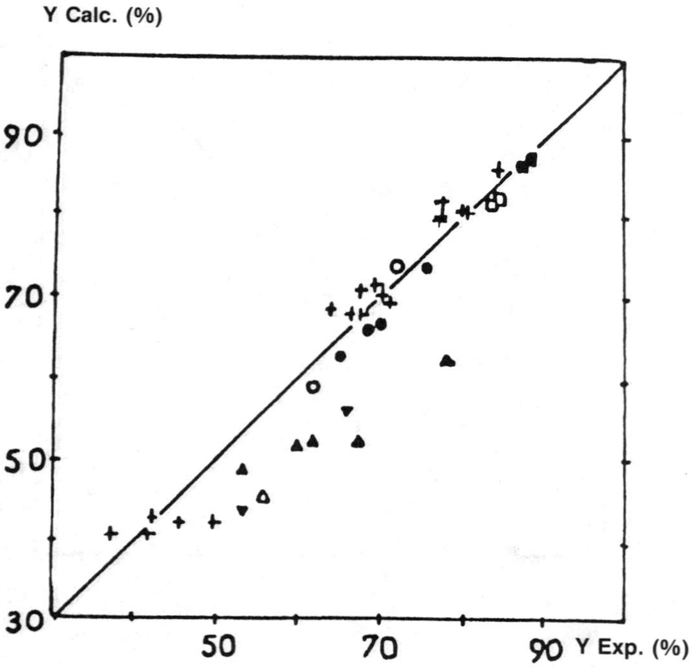

Figure 7C. Partridge and Rowe model [5].

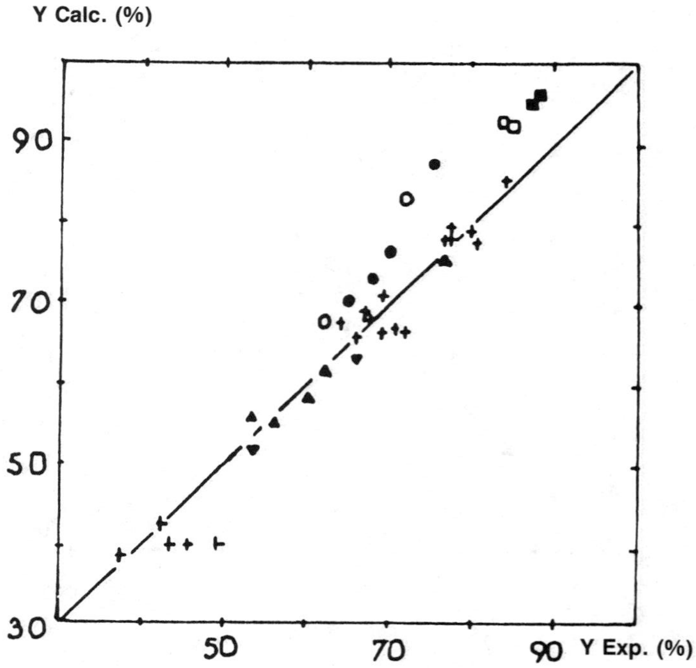

Figure 7D. Kunii and Levenspiel model [5].

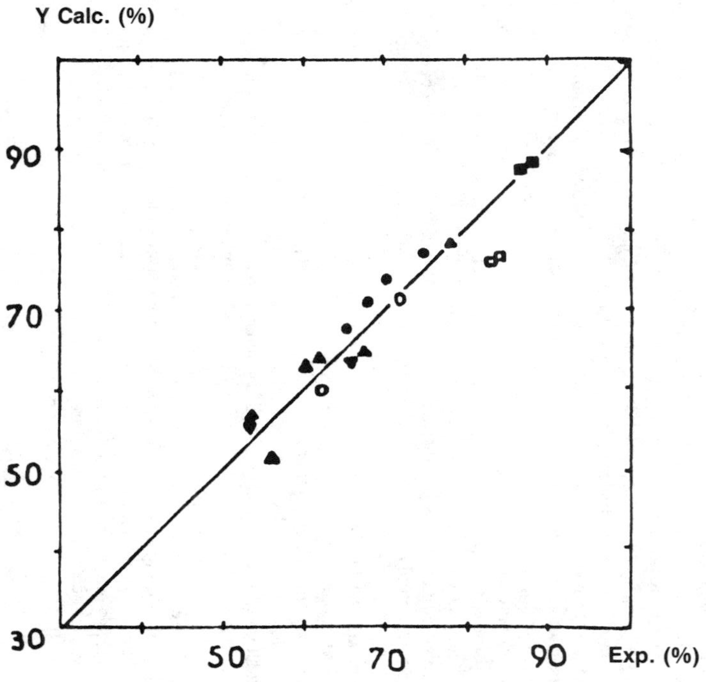

Figure 7E. Kato and Wen model, wake included with cloud [5].

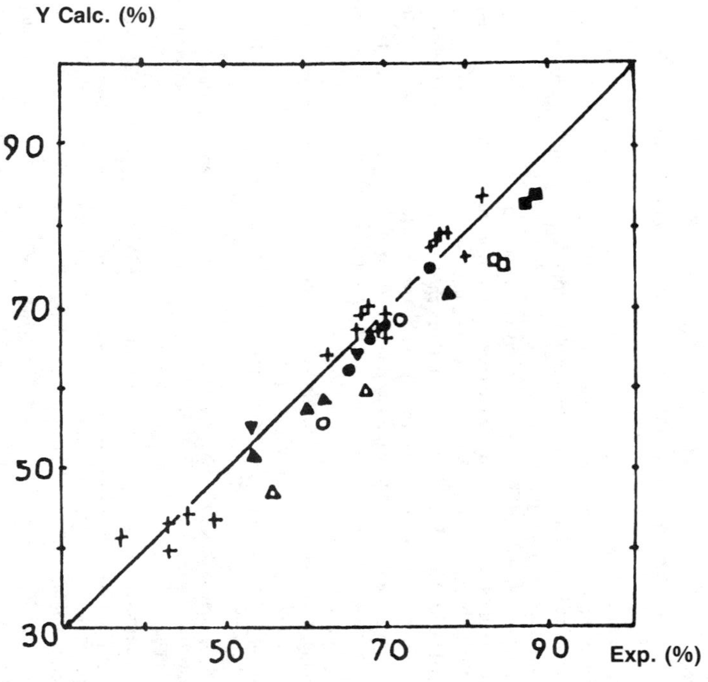

Figure 7F. Kato and Wen model, Rowe's correlation for bubble diameter [5].

very sensitive factor, more especially as the expanded bed is relatively shallow. This reflects the need of studying the grid region in industrial reactors as recognized also by Chavarie and Grace.

Some modifications of the model of Kato and Wen were explored by Stergiou et al. [5, 107]. They found that including the wake with the cloud of the bubbles results in a sensible improvement of the conversion predictions and makes the model acceptable on a statistical ground under the whole conditions of the study (Figure 7f).

The same modification was previously proposed by Chavarie and Grace [67], but the conclusion was that if the modified model gives reasonable predictions for the bubble phase concentrations, it overpredicts dense phase concentration and underestimates overall conversion of ozone in their two-dimensional bed reactor. Besides the latter authors showed that, in spite of efforts to improve the description of the flow distribution between the phases and the interphase mass transfer, the Partridge and Rowe model fails to give a good representation of the experimental data. As for the Kunii and Levenspiel model, it could be simplified by assuming perfect mixing between bubbles and cloud-wake regions, without loosing too much accuracy.

Another comparative study was carried out by Shaw et al. [108] using a 20-cm dia. fluidized bed reactor for the catalytic hydrogenolysis of butane. Most of the models tested showed good agreement with their experimental data though the authors have adjusted empirically the interphase gas exchange. However, their study is not very useful for discriminating.

More recently, Yue and Birk [93] have evaluated three models representing a wide range of complexity, by comparing their predictions with data obtained for the dehydration of ethanol over a zeolite catalyst. The simplest of these model was of the well mixed single phase type. The other two models were of compartmental types: one by Kato and Wen [35] and the other by Peters et al. [39]. Concentration profiles given by the well mixed single phase model were well above the experimental ones. This suggests that only part of the catalyst in the reactor is effectively utilized. This part is less than 25%. The same tendency could be observed, but at a lesser extent, with the other two models. Attempts were made to modify them. The conclusion was that the upper region of the reactor was inefficiently used due to possible bubble channeling or slugging, gas by passing and gas-solid interphase transfer limitation.

Carrying out the same reaction as above, Sitzmann et al. [110] found an accurate description of the fluidized bed measurements by using a comparatively simple two-phase model. However, there is a need to determine suitable kinetics by utilizing exactly the same catalyst that must be used in the fluidized bed and at the correct level of activity.

Another important aspect to be considered when evaluating fluidized bed reactor models is the effect of volume change on conversions. Reactions involving a strong decrease in number of moles are typified by oxychlorination of ethylene, methane synthesis, or Fisher-Tropoch synthesis, but numerous complex reactions involve volume changes that may affect not only the bulk flow but also the bubble emulsion-gas interchange. Balance of flow between the bubble phase and the emulsion phase can be successfully introduced in model equations [111–113].

In the particular case of slugging-bed reactor, Yates and Gregoire [105] have compared results of experiments on the catalytic oxidation of o-xylene with the prediction of two theoretical models:

1. The Hovmand and Davidson model [29], which is basically an extension of the Davidson and Harrison model [25, 26].
2. The more recent model of Raghuraman and Potter [38], which assumes that the inter-slug region is divided in two phases: a well mixed particulate phase traveling as a wake behind the rising slugs and the properly so called emulsion phase, and that gas exchange occurs in two stages, between slug and wake and between wake and emulsion phase.

As shown in Figure 8, predictions of the original two models (HD for Hovmand and Davidson model and RP for Raghuraman and Potter model) considerably differ from the experimental data. This can be explained by the fact that none of these models takes account of reaction in the region of the bed immediately above the distributor where the bed is operating in the freely-bubbling mode and slugs have not yet been formed. Therefore, the two models have been corrected to take account of the reaction in the pre-slugging zone by applying the Kunii and Levenspiel model (KL) to this

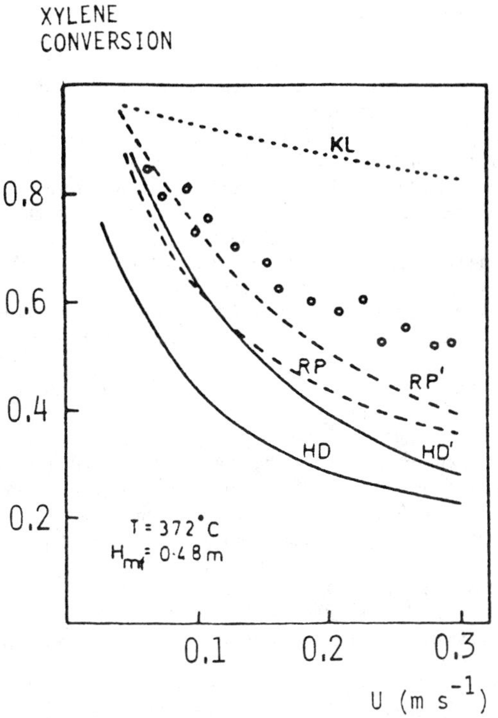

Figure 8. Comparison between predictions of the models and experimental data [105].

region. This has the effect of increasing the predicted conversion (HD′ and RP′ in Figure 8) since contact between gas and catalyst in the part close to the distributor is better than predicted by the slugging-bed models. Nevertheless, it is appearent that the predictions of the two models remain underestimated even though the corrected Raghuraman-Potter model was found to give the better agreement. It can also be noted that the concentrations profiles predicted by the Kunii and Levenspiel model applied to the bed as a whole led to strong overestimation, but the bubble diameter taken as a quarter of the bed diameter has been perhaps underevaluated.

These comparative studies show clearly that none of the models proposed in the literature can be confidently taken under any operating conditions. The Kunii and Levenspiel model gives rather good predictions for high fluidization velocities. The Kato and Wen model corrected by including wakes with clouds and by using more adequate correlations for bubble diameter estimates can offer useful predictions, but no general conclusion can be drawn. Moreover, importance of the grid region and the freeboard is difficult to evaluate. Besides, suitable kinetics must be used and flow balance between the bubble and emulsion phase should be introduced to compensate for the volume change accompanying numerous complex reactions.

MULTIPLICITY OF STEADY-STATES AND TRANSIENT BEHAVIOR SIMULATION OF FLUIDIZED BED REACTORS

Under normal operating conditions, a reactor is subject to numerous and various perturbations that can lead to variations of its operation between more or less steady states. This behavior is the more pronounced as marked temperature differences exist between the bubble and emulsion phases or between the solid particles and the gas phase as it is for highly exothermic reactions. Besides, the system can exhibit multiple steady states for given ranges of operating and kinetic variables. Several studies have demonstrated this possibility for simple as well complex reactions [42, 114–121].

Bukur and Amundson [114–116] derived a three-phase model consisting of a dilute phase (bubble phase), an intersticial gas phase, and a solid phase and based on the two-phase theory for the division of gas flow, for a non-isothermal gas fluidized-bed catalytic reactor with continuous circulation of catalyst particles. In their model, the dilute phase was assumed to be in plug flow, the interstitial gas to be either completely mixed or in plug flow, and the particles to be both perfectly mixed and uniform. They showed that the conversion and the steady state profiles of temperature and concentration in the reactor are the same irrespectively of the assumption relative to the flow pattern of the emulsion gas. Numerical results confirmed that the dense phase is uniform in temperature and concentration of a reacting species and at least a single steady state solution was obtained. But it was shown that multiple steady states can be obtained for adiabatic reactors or for highly exothermic reactions carried out in a reactor with a cooling surface. Exact uniquiness and multiplicity criteria could be derived and the transient behavior of the system was simulated on a numerical ground leading to the conclusion that the initial temperature of the catalyst particles is a predominant factor in determining which steady state is to be approached. Following a previous work performed by El Nashaie and Yates [117], Bukur [116] investigated uniqueness and multiplicity of the steady states in an isothermal batch fluidized bed reactor. The model of Davidson and Harrison and that of Partridge and Rowe were chosen. He showed that material balance equations for the two models can be transformed into a single equation, which is in the same form as for an isothermal continuous stirred tank reactor; and he derived exact criteria for unique and multiple steady states. He noted that multiple solutions may exist for some values of model parameters.

In their study, Sheplev and Luss [118] introduced the axial conductivity-model with the corresponding Danckwerts boundary conditions. Their model predicted that up to five steady-state solutions may exist and that two of them are stable. Moreover, their work indicated that steady-state multiplicity may occur for parameter values encountered in industrial applications. Temperature gradients were found to be possible in the reactor.

Another interesting study was carried out by Kulkarni, Ramachandran, and Doraiswamy [120] for a non-isothermal first order reaction. They represented the behavior of the fluidized bed reactor in a compact form including two groups of parameters and they derived the necessary and sufficient criteria for the existence of multiple steady states in terms of these two parameters. Their results have been presented in a convenient graphical form.

Beside the studies relative to the multiplicity of steady states, some works have been devoted to the analysis of the transient behavior of fluidized bed reactors [122–130]. Fan et al. [122] presented a transient axial dispersion model for isothermal catalytic fluidized bed reactors. This model takes into account the significant variations of physical properties along the axial coordinate and the axial dispersion in the three phases (bubble, cloud + wake and emulsion phases) and considers a non-linear chemical reaction. The authors evaluated the length of the transient period for different values of the main parameters. Their numerical results have been favorably compared with data of the literature.

Yang et al. [124] operated a pilot scale fluidized bed reactor carrying highly exothermic butane hydrogenolysis reactions to investigate the computer control of temperature, conversion, and selectivities. The non-linear behavior of the reactor was analyzed and it was shown that by adequately matching the process response characteristics and by choosing self-tuning adaptive controllers, the unstable oscillatory behavior of the cascade control system could be overcome and acceptable performance could be achieved over a wide range of operating conditions. These conclusions are in good agreement with those of McFarlane et al. [125].

Jaffres et al. [126] used a two-stage simulation of the operating procedure followed by Kizer [131, 132] for the oxidation of benzene to maleic anhydride in a 20-cm dia. fluidized bed reactor mounted directly on a fluidized bed preheater. First, they performed a thermal simulation with no reaction, by doing some simplifications. Then, using the Davidson and Harrison model, they simulated the transient operation of the reactor. The time required to reach the steady state operation was found in a reasonable agreement with the observed experimentally. In another work, Jaffres et al. [106, 127] developed a pseudo steady state simulation of the response of benzene and maleic

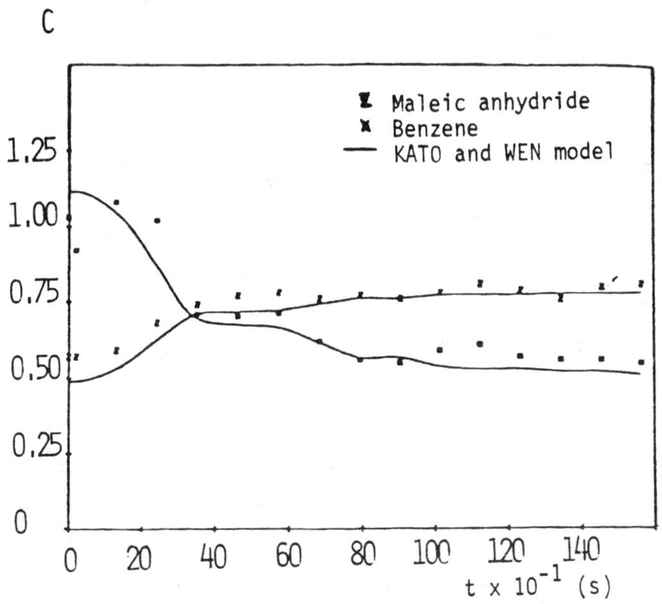

Figure 9. Simulation of the transient response of a fluidized bed reactor [128].

anhydride concentrations during transition between steady states experiments, from the Kato and Wen model (Figure 9).

In a follow up of the previous study of Stergiou et al. [5, 107] concerning the steady state simulation of a fluidized bed reactor for the catalytic ammoxidation of propylene to acrylonitrile, Koutchoukali et al. [128, 129] used the corrected Kato and Wen model for simulating the unsteady state operation of the reactor. Experiments were performed by maintaining the reaction temperature constant by blowing air at ambient temperature outside the reactor. The speed revolution of the ventilator was regulated according to an electrical signal delivered up by an Apple II microcomputer. Adaptive control of the temperature was chosen [130] and the maximum fluctuation offered by the control circuit did not exceed $\pm 3°C$ thus satisfying an isothermal model. The main conclusions of the work were the following ones:

1. The transient regime following a change in reactant concentration is very rapid (Figure 10), but the time laps required to attain a new stable steady state is slightly underpredicted by the simulation model. This can result from some gas mixing in the preheater of the reactants as well as in the freeboard of the reactor resulting in a dispersion of residence time which is not taken into account in the model.
2. A discrepancy of less than 5% exists between the theoretical and experimental concentrations, which can be explained from differences between experimental and theoretical initial conditions. It can also be noted that sudden variations in reactant concentrations modify the reaction kinetics that were determined under steady state conditions.

However, the study of Jaffres as well as that of Koutchoukali confirm that the bubble assemblage model of Kato and Wen, with slight modifications, can describe well enough the transient behavior of a fluidized bed reactor. But more works not limited to quasi isothermal reactions would be useful to provide arms to an optimal control of fluidized bed reactors.

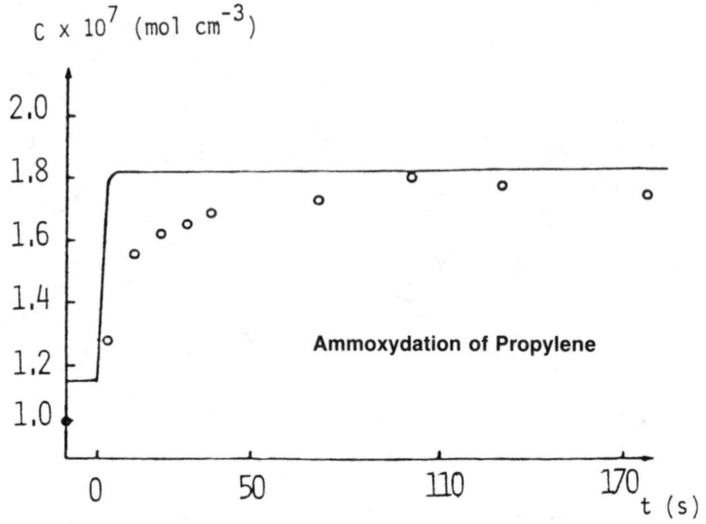

Figure 10. Simulation of the transient response of a fluidized bed reactor [130].

CONCLUSION

It can be said that modeling fluidized bed reactor has now reached a high level on a theoretical ground. But there is a drastic lack in comparative studies based on tests of predictions with data obtained under available conditions of reactor operation. Moreover, effects of entrance region at and near the distributor and those of the disengaging zone above bed surface on the conversion would have to be carefully considered by reference to large-scale reactors. It requires the allowance for commercial data as complete as possible. This is the price for making useful tools for scaling up.

NOTATION

C	concentration of reactant
d_b	bubble diameter
d_c	cloud diameter
D_b, D_e	axial mixing dispersion coefficient of gas resp. in bubble phase, in emulsion phase
D_G	diffusivity of gas
E	eddy diffusivity
g	acceleration of gravity
h	height
H_{ok}	height of transfer unit between the dense and dilute phases
k	mass transfer coefficient
K	mass transfer coefficient per unit bubble volume
n_B, n_E, n_K, n_R	number of backmixing, eddy diffusion, transfer, reaction units
q	convective through flow of gas in bubbles
Q_e	gas flow rate through the dense phase
t	time
T	temperature
u	fluidisation velocity
u_b	bubble velocity
u_e	velocity of emulsion gas
u_f	intersticial gas velocity
u_{mf}	minimum fluidization velocity
V_e	volume of dense phase
X	interphase gas exchange

Greek Letters

α ratio of bubble velocity to interstitial gas velocity

γ_b fraction of solids associated with bubble

ε emulsion phase voidage

ε_{mf} bed voidage at incipient fluidization

μ viscosity of gas

ρ density of gas

Dimensionless Numbers

Re_c $\frac{(u_b - u_e)\, d_c}{\mu}$, Reynolds number of cloud

Sc $\frac{\mu}{\rho D_G}$, Schmidt number

Sh_c $\frac{k_{ce} d_c}{D_G}$, Sherwood number of cloud

Subscripts

b bubble

c cloud

e emulsion

REFERENCES

1. Grace, J. R., "An evaluation of Models for Fluidized-Bed Reactors," *A.I.Ch.E. Symp. Ser.*, 67(116), pp. 159–167, (1971).
2. Yates, J. G., "Fluidized Bed Reactors," *Chem. Eng.*, 53, pp. 671–677, (1985).
3. Yates, J. G., "*Fundamental of Fluidized-Bed Chemical Processes*," Butterworth, London (1983).
4. Laguerie, C., "Bases de la Modelizacion de los Reactores Cataliticos de Lecho Fluidizado," *Ingenieria Quimica*, pp. 77–88, (1983).
5. Stergiou, L., Laguerie, C., and Gilot, B., "A discrimination Between Some Fluidized Bed Reactor Models for Ammoxidation of Propylene to Acrylonitrile," *Chem. Eng. Sci.*, 39, pp. 713–730, (1984).
6. May, W. G., "Fluidized Bed Reactor Studies," *Chem. Eng. Prog.*, 55(12), pp. 49–56, (1959).
7. Van Deemter, J. J., "Mixing and Contacting in Gas-Solid Fluidized Beds," *Chem. Eng. Sci.*, 13, pp. 143–154, (1960).
8. Van Deemter, J. J., "The Counter-Current Flow Model of a Gas-Solid Fluidized Bed," *Proc. Int. Symp. Fluidization*, Eindhoven, Netherlands, University Press, pp. 334–347, (1967).
9. Botton, R., and Vergnes, F., "Catalytic Fluidized Reactor Scale-Up. An Approach Chemical and Specifically Physical Laboratory Data Without the Need of a Pilot Plant Stage," *Chem. Ing. Tech.*, 53(6), pp. 481–502, (1981).
10. Werther, J., "Modeling and Scale-up of Industrial Fluidized Bed Reactors," *Chem. Eng. Sci.*, 35, pp. 372–377, (1980).
11. Lewis, W. K., Gilliland, E. R., and Glass, W., "Solid-Catalyzed Reaction in a Fluidized Bed," *A.I.Ch.E. Jl.*, 5, pp. 419—425, (1959).
12. Shen, C. Y., and Johnstone, H. F., "Gas-Solid Contact in Fluidized Beds," *A.I.Ch.E. Jl.*, 1, pp. 349–354, (1955).
13. Mathis, J. F., and Watson, C. C., "Effect of Fluidization on Catalytic Cumene Dealkylation," *A.I.Ch.E. Jl.*, 2, pp. 518–524, (1956).
14. Lanneau, K. P., "Gas Solids Contacting in Fluidized Beds," *Chem. Engrs.*, 38, pp. 125–143, (1960).
15. Gomezplata, A., and Shuster, W. W., "Effect of Uniformity of Fluidization on Catalytic Cracking of Cumene," *A.I.Ch.E. Jl.*, 6, pp. 454–459, (1960).

16. Mamuro, T., and Muchi, I., "A Mathematical Model for a Fluidized Bed Catalytic Bed Reactor," *Int. Chem. Eng.*, 5, pp. 732–736, (1965).
17. Kobayashi, H., Arai, F., and Chiba, T., "Estimation of Catalytic Conversion in Gas Fluidized Beds by Means of a Two Phase Model," "Effect of Bed Diameter," *Kagaku Kogaku*, 33, pp. 274–280, (1969).
18. Mireur, J. P., and Bischoff, K. B., "Mixing and Contacting Models for Fluidized Beds," *A.I.Ch.E. Jl.*, 13, pp. 839–845, (1967).
19. Mao, Q. M., and Potter, O. E., "Modeling Fluidized Bed Reactors," *Winning Compet. World, 12th Aust. Chem. Eng. Conf.*, 2, pp. 855–861, (1984).
20. Mao, Q. M., and Potter, O. E., *Modeling Fluidized Bed Reactors* in *Frontiers in Chemical Reaction Engineering*, Wiley International, New Delhi, pp. 195–215, (1984).
21. Botton, R., Cosserat, D., Vergnes, F., and Charpentier, J. C., "Conception, Extrapolation et Amélioration Potentielle de Certains Réacteurs de L'industrie Chimique. Une Analyse Générale et Quelques Exemples Vécus," *Entropie*, 109, pp. 4–20, (1983).
22. Laguerie, C., Vergnes, F., and Botton, R., "Comparaison de Quelques Modèles de Réacteurs à Lit Fluidisé en vue de leur Extrapolation," *Bull. Soc. Chim. France*, 6, pp. 1041–1046, (1985).
23. Massimilla, L., and Johnstone, H. F., "Reaction Kinetics in Fluidized Beds," *Chem. Eng. Sci.*, 16, pp. 105–112, (1961).
24. Heidel, K., Schugerl, K., Fetting, F., and Schiemann, G., "Einflub von Mischungsvorgängen auf den Umsatz Bein der Athylenhydrierung in Fliebbetten," *Chem. Eng. Sci.*, 20, pp. 557–585, (1965).
25. Orcutt, J. C., Davidson, J. F., and Pigford, R. L., "Reaction Time Distributions in Fluidized Catalytic Reactors," *Chem. Eng. Prog. Symp. Ser.*, 58 (38), pp. 1–15, (1962).
26. Davidson, J. F., and Harrison, D., *Fluidized particles*, Cambridge Univ., Press, Cambridge, (1963).
27. Toor, F. D., and Calderbank, P. H., "Reaction Kinetics in Gas-Fluidized Catalyst Beds—Mathematical Models," *Proc. Int. Symp. Fluidization*, Eindhoven, Netherlands Univ. Press, pp. 373–390, (1967).
28. Hovmand, S., and Davidson, J. F., "Chemical Conversion in a Slugging Fluidized Bed," *Trans. I. Chem. Engrs.*, 46, pp. 190–198, (1968).
29. Hovmand, S., and Davidson, J. F., "Pilot Plant and Laboratory Scale Fluidized Reactors at High Gas Velocities; the Relevance of Slug Flow," in *Fluidization*, Academic Press, London, Ch. 5, pp. 193–260, (1971).
30. Calderbank, P. H., and Toor, F. D., "Fluidized Bed as Catalytic Reactors," in *Fluidization*, Academic Press, London, Ch. 8, pp. 383–420, (1971).
31. Rowe, P. N., "Gas Solid Reaction in a Fluidised Bed," *Chem. Eng. Prog.* 60(3), pp. 75–82, (1964).
32. Pyle, D. L., and Jones, B. R. E., "A Theoretical Study of Complex Reactions in Fluidised Catalytic Reactors," *Chem. Eng. Sci.*, 25, pp. 859–865, (1970).
33. Partridge, B. A., and Rowe, P. N., "Chemical Reaction in a Bubbling Gas Fluidised Bed," *Trans. I. Chem. Engrs.*, 44, pp. 335–348, (1966).
34. Chiba, T., and Kobayashi, H., "Modeling of Catalytic Fluidized Bed Reactors," *Proc. Int. Conf. on Fluidization and its Applications*, Cepadues, Toulouse, pp. 368–480, (1973).
35. Kato, K., and Wen, C. Y., "Bubble Assemblage Model for Fluidized Bed Catalytic Reactors," *Chem. Eng. Sci.*, 24, pp. 1351–1369, (1969).
36. Kunii, D., and Levenspiel, O., *Fluidization Engineering*, Wiley, New York, (1969).
37. Fryer, C. C., and Potter, O. E., "Countercurrent Backmixing Model for Fluidized Bed Catalytic Reactors. Applicability of Simplified Solutions," *Ind. Eng. Chem. Fundam.*, 11, pp. 338–344, (1972).
38. Raghuramam, J., and Potter, O. E., "Countercurrent Backmixing Model for Slugging Fluidized-Bed Reactors," *A.I.Ch.E.*, 24, pp. 698–704, (1978).
39. Peters, M. H., Fan, L. S., and Sweeney, T. L., "Reactant Dynamics in Catalytic Fluidized Bed Reactors with Flow Reversal of Gas in the Emulsion Phase," *Chem. Eng. Sci.*, 37, pp. 553–563, (1982).

40. Nozaki, Y., Furusaki, S., and Miyauchi, T., "Determination of the Parameters of a Fluidized Bed of Fine Catalyst Particles by Gas Absorption," *Int. Chem. Eng.*, 25, pp. 499–506, (1985).
41. Dogu, G., and Sozen, Z., "Kinetics of Catalytic Oxidation of Ethylene: Fixed Bed and Fluidized Bed Studies," *Chem. Eng. Jl.*, 31, pp. 145–151, (1985).
42. Bukur, D. B., and Nasif, N., "The Effect of Bubble Size Variation on the Performance of Fluidized Bed Reactors," *Chem. Eng. Sci.*, 40, pp. 1925–1933, (1985).
43. Chang, C. C., Fan, L. T., and Rong, S. X., "Modelling of Shallow Fluidized Bed Reactors. Analytic Solution of Simplified Model," *Can. Jl. Chem. Eng.*, 60, pp. 272–281, (1982).
44. Murray, D., "On the Mathematics of Fluidisation. Part 2: Steady Motion of Full Developed Bubbles," *J. Fluid Mech.*, 22, pp. 57–80, (1965).
45. Rowe, P. N., and Partridge, B. A., "An X-Ray Study of Bubbles in Fluidized Beds," *Trans. I. Chem. Engrs.* 43, pp. 157–175, (1965).
46. Toomey, R. D., and Johnstone, H. P., "Gaseous Fluidisation of Solid Particles," *Chem. Eng. Prog.*, 48, pp. 220–226, (1952).
47. Grace, J. R., and Clift, R., "On the Two-Phase Theory of Fluidization," *Chem. Eng. Sci.*, 29, pp. 327–334, (1974).
48. Yacono, C. X. R., "An X-Ray Study of Bubbles in Gas Fluidized Beds of Small Particles," *Ph. D. Thesis*, University College, London, (1975).
49. Rowe, P. N., and Yacono, C. X. R., "The Bubbling Behaviour of Fine Powders When Fluidised," *Chem. Eng. Sci.*, 31, pp. 1179–1192, (1976).
50. Rowe, P. N., and Everett, D. J., "Fluidised Bed Bubbles Viewed by X-Rays. Part 3: Bubbles Size and Number When Unrestrained Three Dimensional Growth Occurs," *Trans. I. Chem. Engrs*, 50, pp. 55–60, (1972).
51. Rowe, P. N., Santoro L., and Yates, J. G., "The Division of Gas Between Bubble and Interstitial Phases in Fluidized Bed of Fine Powders," *Chem. Eng. Sci.*, 33, pp. 133–140, (1978).
52. Grace, J. R., and Harrison, D., "The Behaviour of Freely Bubbling Fluidised Beds," *Chem. Eng. Sci.*, 24, pp. 497–508, (1969).
53. Pyle, D. L., and Harrison, D., "An Experimental Investigation of the Two-Phase Theory of Fluidization," *Chem. Eng. Sci.*, 22, pp. 199–1207, (1967).
54. Godard, K. E., and Richardson, J. F., "Distribution of Gas Flow in a Fluidized Bed," *Chem. Eng. Sci.*, 23, pp. 660–667, (1968).
55. Clift, R., "Physical Aspects of Chemical Reactors: An Occamist View of Fluidized Bed Reactors Modelling," *Chem. Eng.*, 388, pp. 29–33, (1983).
56. Yates, J. G., and Newton, D., "Fine Particle Effects in a Fluidized Bed Reactor," *Chem. Eng. Sci.*, 41, pp. 801–806, (1986).
57. Jackson, R., "The Mechanics of Fluidised Beds: Part 1: the Stability of the State of Uniform Fluidisation," *Trans. I. Chem. Engrs.*, 41, pp. 13–18, (1963).
58. Weiland, R. H., "A Low-Reynolds Number Model for Gas Bubbles in Fluidized Beds," in *Fluidization Technology, Hemisphere Publishing Co.*, Washington, 1, pp. 3–7, (1976).
59. Martin-Gautier, A. L., and Pyle, D. L., "The Fluid Mechanics of Single Bubbles," in *Fluidization Technology Hemisphere Publishing Co.*, Washington, 1, 21–25, (1976).
60. Reuter, H., "Pressure Distribution Around Bubbles in the Gas Solid Fluidized Bed," *Chem. Ing. Tech.*, 35, pp. 98–103, (1963).
61. Collins, R., "The Effect of Some Insteady Motions on Gas Flow Patterns Around a Fluidization Bubble," in *Fluidization, Plenum Press*, New York, 75, (1980).
62. Rowe, P. N., and Widmer, A. J., "Variation in Shape with Size of Bubbles in Fluidized Beds," *Chem. Eng. Sci.*, 28, pp. 980–981, (1973).
63. Zenz, F. A., and Othmer, D. F., "Fluidization and Fluid-Particle Systems," Reinhold, New York, (1960).
64. Gupalo, Y. P., Ryazantsev, Y. S., and Sergeev, Y. S; "Mass Transfer from a Bubble to the Dense Phase in a Fluidized Bed Reactor," *Proc. 4th International/6th Europ. Symp. on Chem. Reaction Engng*, 1, pp. 162–167, (1976).
65. Kunii, D., and Levenspiel, O., "Bubbling Bed Model," *Ind. Eng. Chem. Fund.*, 7 (3), pp. 446–452, (1968).

66. Kobayashi, H., Arai, F., Tzawa, N., and Miya, T., "Performance of Gas Solid Fluidized Bed Catalytic Reactor," *Kagaku Kogaku*, 30 (7), pp. 656–662, (1966).
67. Chavarie, C., and Grace, J. R., "Performance Analysis of a Fluidized Bed Reactor—I—Visible Flow Behaviour," "Performance Analysis of a Fluidized Bed Reactor—II—Observed Reactor Behaviour Compared with Simple Two-Phase Models," "Performance Analysis of a Fluidized Bed Reactor—III—Modification and Extension of Conventional Two-Phase Models," *Ind. Eng. Chem. Fund.*, 14, 75 (1975), 14, 79 (1975) and 14, 86 (1975).
68. Sit, S. P., and Grace, J. R., "Interphase Mass Transfer in an Aggregative Fluidized Bed," *Chem. Eng. Sci.*, 33, pp. 1115–1122, (1978).
69. Sit, S. P., and Grace, J. R., "Effect of Bubble Interaction on Interphase Mass Transfer in Gas Fluidized Beds," *Chem. Eng. Sci.*, 36, pp. 327–335, (1981).
70. Drinkenburg, A. A. H., and Rietema, K., "Gas Transfer From Bubbles in a Fluidized Bed to the Dense Phase—II Experiments," *Chem. Eng. Sci.*, 28, pp. 259–273, (1973).
71. Yates, J. G., and Constans, J. A. P., "Residence Time Distributions in a Fluidised Bed in Which Gas Adsorption Occurs Stimulus—Response Experiments," *Chem. Eng. Sci.*, 28, pp. 1341–1348, (1973).
72. Nguyen, H. V., and Potter, O. E., "Adsorption Effects on Mixing," in *Fluidization Technology, Hemisphere Publishing*, Washington, pp. 290–294, (1976).
73. Gupalo, Y. P., Ryazentsev, Y. S., and Sergeev, Y. A., "Unsteady Mass Exchange Between a Bubble and the Dense Phase in a Fluidized Bed," in *Fluidization, Cambridge Univ. Press*, pp. 162–166, (1978).
74. Bohle, H., and Van Swaaij, W. P. M., "The Influence of Gas Adsorption on Mass Transfer and Gas Mixing in a Fluidized Bed," in *Fluidization, Cambridge Univ. Press*, pp. 167–172, (1978).
75. Morooka, S., Nishinaka, M., and Kato, Y., "Overall Mass Transfer Coefficient Between the Bubble Phase and the Emulsion Phase in Free and Eight-Stage Fluidized Beds," *Int. Chem. Eng.*, 17, pp. 254–260, (1977).
76. De Grott, J. H., "Scaling-Up of Gas-Fluidized Bed Reactors," *Proc. Int. Symp. on Fluidization*, Eindhoven (Netherlands) Univ. Press, Amsterdam, pp. 348–358, (1967).
77. Calderbank, P. H., Toor, F. D., and Lancaster, F. M., "Reaction Kinetics in Gas-Fluidized Catalyst Beds," *Proc. Int. Symp. on Fluidization*, Eindhoven (Netherlands) Univ. Press, Amsterdam, pp. 652–663.
78. Van Deemter, J. J., "Mixing and Contacting in Gas Solid Fluidized Beds," *Chem. Eng. Sci.*, 13, pp. 143–154, (1960).
79. Latham, R., Hamilton, C., and Potter, O. E., "Back-Mixing and Chemical Reaction in Fluidized Bed," *Brit. Chem. Engng.*, 13, pp. 666–671, (1968).
80. Potter, O. E., "Mixing," in *Fluidization, Academic Press London*, Ch. 7, pp. 293–382, (1971).
81. Schugerl, K; Comments in ref. (77).
82. Botton, R., "Gas-Solid Contacting in Fluidized Beds," *Chem. Eng. Prog. Symp. Series*, 66 (101), pp. 8–18, (1970).
83. Furusaki, S., Kikuchi, T; and Miyauchi, T., "Axial Distribution of Reactivity Inside a Fluid-Bed Contactor," *A.I.Ch.E. Jl.*, 22, pp. 354–361, (1976).
84. Ford, W., Reineman, R. C., Vasalos, I. A., and Fahrig, R. J., "Operating Cat Crackers for Maximum Profit," *Chem. Eng. Prog.*, 73 (4), pp. 92–96, (1977).
85. Pereira, FJ., and Beer, J. M., "A Mathematical Model of NO Formation and Destruction in Fluidized Combustion of Coal," in *Fluidization, Cambridge Univ. Press*, pp. 401–407, (1978).
86. Bauer, W., Werther, J., and Emig, G., "Influence of Gas Distributeur on the Performance of Fluidized Bed Reactor," *Ger. Chem. Eng.*, 4, pp. 291–298, (1981).
87. Bauer, W., and Werther, J., "The Role of Gas Distribution in Fluidized Bed Chemical Reactor Design," *Chem. Eng. Commun.*, 18, pp. 137–146, (1982).
88. Behie, L. A., and Kehoe, P., "The Grid Region in a Fluidised Bed Reactor," *A.I.Ch.E. Jl.*, 19, pp. 1070–1073, (1973).
89. Errazu, A. F., De Lasa, H. I., and Sarti, F., "A Fluidized Bed Catalytic Cracking Regenerator Model: Grid Effects," *Can. Jl. Chem. Eng.*, 57, pp. 191–201, (1979).

90. De Lasa, H. I., Errazu, A., Barreiro, E., and Solioz, S., "Analysis of Fluidized Bed Catalytic Regenerator Models in an Industrial Scale Unit," *Can. Jl. Chem. Eng.*, 59, pp. 549–553, (1981).
91. Grace, J. R., and De Lasa, H. I., "Reaction Near the Grid in Fluidized Beds," *A.I.Ch.E. Jl.*, 24, pp. 364–366, (1978).
92. Rowe, P. N., Mac Gillivray, H. J., and Cheesman, D. J., "Gas Discharge from an Orifice into a Gas Fluidised Bed," *Trans. I. Chem. Engrs.*, 57, pp. 194–199, (1979).
93. Yue, P. L., and Birk, R. H., "Fluidised Bed Studies of the Dehydration of Ethanol over a Zeolite Catalyst," *Chem. Eng. Res. Des.*, 63, pp. 250–257, (1985).
94. Miyauchi, T., "Concept of Successive Contact Mechanism for Catalytic Reaction in Fluid Beds," *Chem. Eng. Japan*, 7, pp. 201–207, (1974).
95. Miyauchi, T., and Fursaki, S., "Relative Contribution of Variables Affecting the Reaction in Fluid Bed Contactors," *A.I.Ch.E. Jl.*, 20, pp. 1087–1096, (1974).
96. Yates, J. G., and Rowe, P. N., "A Model for Chemical Reaction in the Freeboard Region Above a Fluidized Bed," *Trans. I. Chem. Eng.*, 55, pp. 137–148, (1977).
97. Miyauchi, T., Furusaki, S., Yamada, K., and Matsumura, M., "Experimental Determinations of the Vertical Distribution of Contact Efficiency Inside a Fluidized Catalyst Bed," in *Fluidization, Plenum Press*, New York, pp. 571–580, (1980).
98. Furusaki, S., Takahashi, M., and Miyauchi, T., "Stability of Chemical Reaction in Fluid Catalytic Reaction," *J. Chem. Eng. Japan*, 11, pp. 309–318, (1978).
99. De Lasa, H. I., and Grace, J. R., "The Influence of the Freeboard Region in a Fluidized Bed Catalytic Cracking Regenerator," *A.I.Ch.E. Jl.*, 25, pp. 984–991, (1979).
100. George, S. Z., and Grace, J. R., "Entrainment of Particles from Aggregative Fluidized Beds," *A.I.Ch.E. Symp. Series*, 74 (176), pp. 67–74, (1978).
101. Krambeck, F. J., Katz, S., and Shinnar, R., "A Stochastic Model for Fluidized Beds," *Chem. Eng. Sci.*, 24, pp. 497–504, (1969).
102. Ligon, J. R., and Amundson, N. R., "Modelling of Fluidized Bed Reactors—VI(a) An Isothermal Bed with Stochastic Bubbles," *Chem. Eng. Sci.*, 36, pp. 653–701, (1981).
103. Too, J. R., Fux, R. O., Fan, L. T., and Nassar, R., "Stochastic Modeling of a Fluidized Bed Reactor," *A.I.Ch.E. Jl.*, 31, pp. 992–998, (1985).
104. Fan, L. T., Too, J. R., and Nassar, R., "Stochastic Flow Reactor Modellin—A General Continuous Time Compartment Model With First-Order Reactions, Residence Time Distribution Theory," in *Chemical Engineering, Ed. by PETHO, A. and NOBLE, R.D.*, Verlag Chemie, Weinheim, West Germany, (1982).
105. Yates, J. G., and Gregoire, J. Y., "An Experimental Test of Slugging-Bed Reactor Models," in *Fluidization, Plenum Press New York*, pp. 581–588, (1980).
106. Jaffres, J. L., Chavarie, C., Patterson, I., Perrier, M., Casalegno, L., and Laguerie, C., "Conversion and Selectivity Modeling of the Oxidation of Benzene to Maleic Anhydride in a Fluidized Bed Reactor," in *Fluidization, United Engineering Trusties*, Tokyo, pp. 565–574, (1983).
107. Stergiou, L., and Laguerie, C., "An Experimental Evaluation of Fluidized Bed Reactor Models," in *Fluidization, United Engineering Trusties*, Tokyo, pp. 557–564, (1983).
108. Shaw, I. D., Hoffman, T. W., and Reilly, P. M., "Experimental Evaluation of Two-Phase Models Describing Catalytic Fluidized Bed Reactors," *A.I.Ch.E. Symp. Series*, 70 (141), pp. 41–52, (1974).
109. Rowe, P. N., "Prediction of Bubble Size in a Gas Fluidised Bed," *Chem. Eng. Sci.*, 31, pp. 285–288, (1976).
110. Sitzmann, W., Werther, J., Bock, W., and Emig, G., "Modelling of Fluidized Beds—Determination of Suitable Kinetics for Complex Reactions," *Ger. Chem. Eng.*, 8, pp. 301–307, (1985).
111. Kai, T., and Furusaki, S., "Effect of Volume Change on Conversions in Fluidized Catalyst Beds," *Chem. Eng. Sci.*, 39, pp. 1317–1319, (1984).
112. Kai, T., Furusaki, S., and Yamamoto, K., "Methanisation of Carbon Monoxide by a Fluidized Catalyst Bed," *Jl. Chem. Eng. Japan*, 17, pp. 280–285, (1984).

113. Kai, T., and Furusaki, S., "Methanation of Carbon Dioxide and Fluidization Quality in a Fluid Bed Reactor—The Influence of a Decrease in Gas Volume," *Chem. Eng. Sci.*, 42, pp. 335–339, (1987).
114. Bukur, D. B., Wittmann, C. Y., and Amundson, N. R., "Analysis of a Model for a Nonisothermal Continuous Fluidized Bed Catalytic Reactor," *Chem. Eng. Sci.*, 29, pp. 1173–1192, (1974).
115. Bukur, D. B., and Amundson, N. R., "Mathematical Modelling of Fluidized Bed Reactors—III. Axial Dispersion Model," *Chem. Eng. Sci.*, 30, pp. 1159–1167, (1975).
116. Bukur, D. B., "Multiplicity of Steady States in an Isothermal Batch Fluidized Bed Reactor," *Chem. Eng. Sci.*, 33, pp. 1055–1060, (1978).
117. Elnashaie, S., and Yates, J. G., "Multiplicity of the Steady State in Fluidised Bed Reactors—I. Steady State Considerations," *Chem. Eng. Sci.*, 28, pp. 515–520, (1973).
118. Sheplev, V. S., and Luss, D., "Steady State Multiplicity of Fluidized Bed Reactors—The Solid Circulation Model," *Chem. Eng. Sci.*, 34, pp. 515–520, (1979).
119. Kulkarni, B. D., Ramachandran, P. A., and Doraiswamy, L. K., "Criteria for Steady State Multiplicity in Fluidized Bed Reactors," in *Fluidization, Plenum Press New York*, pp. 589–598, (1980).
120. Volin, Y. M., Kolobashkin, V. S., Makhlin, V. A., and Ostrovskii, G. M., "Optimization of Heterogeneous Catalytic Processes in Fluidized Bed," *Chem. Eng. Commun.*, 29, pp. 271–281, (1984).
121. Elshishini, S. S., Elnashaie, S. S., and Erifaie, M. A., "Multiplicity of the Steady State in Fluidized Bed Reactors—VIII Partial Oxidation of O-Xylene," *Comput. Chem. Engng*, 11, pp. 101–110, (1987).
122. Fan, L. S., and Fan, L. T., "Transient and Steady State Characteristics of a Gaseous Reactant in Catalytic Fluidized Bed Reactors," *A.I.Ch.E. Jl.*, 26, pp. 139–144, (1980).
123. Tojo, K., Chang, C. C., and Fan, L. T., "Modeling of Dynamic and Steady-State Shallow Fluidised Bed Coal Combustors—Effects of Feeder Distribution," *Ind. Eng. Chem. Process Des. Dev.*, 20, pp. 411–416, (1981).
124. Yang, S. M., McGregor, J. F., Taylor, P. A., and Hoffman, T. W., "Control of a Pilot Plant Fluidized Bed Reactor," *Proc. 2nd Workd Cong. Chem. Engng*, Monréal, 5, pp. 381–385, (1981).
125. McFarlane, R. C., Hoffman, T. W., Taylor, P. A., and McGregor, J. G., "Control of Fluidized Bed Reactors," *Ind. Eng. Chem. Proc. Des. Dev.*, 22, pp. 22–28, (1983).
126. Jaffres, J. L., Chavarie, C., Patterson, W. I., and Laguerie, C., "Simulation of a Fluidized Bed Reactor for the Production of Maleic Anhydride," *A.I.Ch.E. Meeting*, San Francisco (1980).
127. Jaffres, J. L., "Modélisation et Contrôle par Miniordinateur d'un Réacteur à lit Fluidisé," *Ph. D. Thesis*, University of Montréal (June 1982).
128. Koutchoukali, M.S., Laguerie, C., and Najim, K., "A Study of the Unsteady State Operation of a Catalytic Fluidized Bed Reactor for Ammoxidation of Propylene to Acrylonitrile," in *Frontiers in Chemical Reaction Engineering*, Wiley International, New Delhi, pp. 442–450, (1984).
129. Koutchoukali, M. S., Laguerie, C., and Najim, K., "Modelling of the Transient and Steady State Operation of a Fluidized Bed Reactor with Adaptive Control of Temperature," *Chem. Eng. Comm.*, 44, pp. 197–207, (1986).
130. Koutchoukali, M. S., Laguerie, C., and Najim, K., "Model Reference Adaptive Control System of a Catalytic," *Fluidized Bed Reactor*, Automatica, 22, pp. 101–104, (1986).
131. Kizer, O., Laguerie, C., and Angelino, H., "Etude Expérimentale de L'oxydation Catalytique du Benzène en Anhydride Maléïque en Couche Fluidisée," *Chem. Eng. Jl.*, 14, p. 205, (1977).
132. Kizer, O., Chavarie, C., Laguerie, C., and Cassimatis, D., "Quadratic Model of the Behaviour of a Fluidized Bed Reactor: Catalytic Oxidation of Benzene to Maleic Anhydride," *Can. Jl. Chem. Eng.*, 56, p. 716, (1978).

CHAPTER 12

CATALYTIC GASIFICATION OF CARBONACEOUS MATERIALS

Deepak Kunzru

Department of Chemical Engineering
Indian Institute of Technology
Kanpur, India

CONTENTS

INTRODUCTION

Although the technology for catalytic gasification of coal is more than a hundred years old, there has been a renewed interest in the catalytic gasification of carbonaceous materials due to its application in several areas such as conversion of coal to synthetic natural gas or synthesis gas [1, 2]; removal of coke deposits from solid catalysts [3]; and the inhibition of coke formation during pyrolysis of hydrocarbons [4]. Carbon is also used as a support or a catalyst in several reactions [5, 6] and it is important to know the catalytic effect of various substances on the rate of gasification.

Most of the studies on carbon gasification have been conducted with either hydrogen, oxygen, carbon dioxide, or steam as the gasifying agents. The main reactions with these gases are:

$$C + 2\,H_2 \rightleftharpoons CH_4; \qquad \Delta H(1{,}000\ K) = -89.9\ kJ/mol \tag{1}$$

$$C + O_2 \rightleftharpoons CO_2; \qquad \Delta H(1{,}000\ K) = -394.9\ kJ/mol \tag{2}$$

$$C + CO_2 \rightleftharpoons 2\,CO; \qquad \Delta H(1{,}000\ K) = 170.7\ kJ/mol \tag{3}$$

$$C + H_2O \rightleftharpoons CO + H_2; \qquad \Delta H(1{,}000\ K) = 136.0\ kJ/mol \tag{4}$$

(The heats of reaction have been obtained from Reference 7.) Due to the recent interest in coal gasification, technologically the most important reaction is the steam gasification of carbon to form carbon monoxide and hydrogen (Reaction 4). This chapter covers the carbon-steam and carbon-carbon dioxide reactions.

Need for Catalysts

The main gas-solid reactions occurring during coal gasification are Reactions 1, 3, and 4. In addition to these heterogeneous reactions, the water-gas shift reaction,

$$CO + H_2O \rightleftharpoons CO_2 + H_2 \tag{5}$$

also occurs in the gas phase. Reactions 3 and 4 are highly endothermic whereas Reaction 1 is exothermic. In most gasifiers, the heat of reaction is supplied by burning a fraction of the coal feed with air or oxygen [2, 8]. Due to kinetic constraints on the carbon-steam and carbon-carbon dioxide reactions, the gasifiers are generally operated above 1,300 K. At these temperatures, the exothermic carbon-hydrogen reaction is limited by thermodynamic constraints [7]. To supply some or all of the heat of reaction by the hydrogasification reaction, the gasifiers have to be operated at a lower temperature. The heat changes associated with the equilibration of the C—H—O system are shown in Figure 1 for a starting mixture of pure C and H_2O ($H/O = 2$). As can be seen from this figure, for a sufficiently low operating temperature, it is possible to make the system autothermic. However, reducing the operating temperature reduces the rate of Reactions 3 and 4, and to maintain reasonable rates of reactions at the reduced temperature, catalysts are necessary.

In a large number of catalytic reactions, the catalyst deactivates due to coke deposition and has to be periodically regenerated with air and/or steam. Incorporation of suitable gasification catalysts can reduce the regeneration time, or, if steam is being used as a reactant or inert in the system, can help in reducing the coke deposition on the catalyst [9, 10].

Another potential application for gasification catalysts is in reducing the coke deposition during pyrolysis of naphtha and other hydrocarbon feedstocks used in the manufacture of light olefins. Under normal pyrolysis conditions (1,100 K; 101.3 kPa), steam, which is used as a diluent, does not react with the coke deposited on the reactor walls. Coating the reactor walls with a gasification catalyst to enhance the carbon-stream reaction can significantly reduce the coke deposition and thus increase the on-stream time [4].

CATALYSTS

Many minerals, metals, and inorganic salts have been investigated as possible gasification catalysts and this vast body of research has shown that the most active catalysts for steam and CO_2 gasification are alkali and alkaline earth metal salts and transition metals such as nickel, cobalt, and iron [11–13]. Recent research has concentrated mainly on these catalysts with most of the studies dealing with alkali metal salts [14–16]. It has been shown that not only is the nature of the

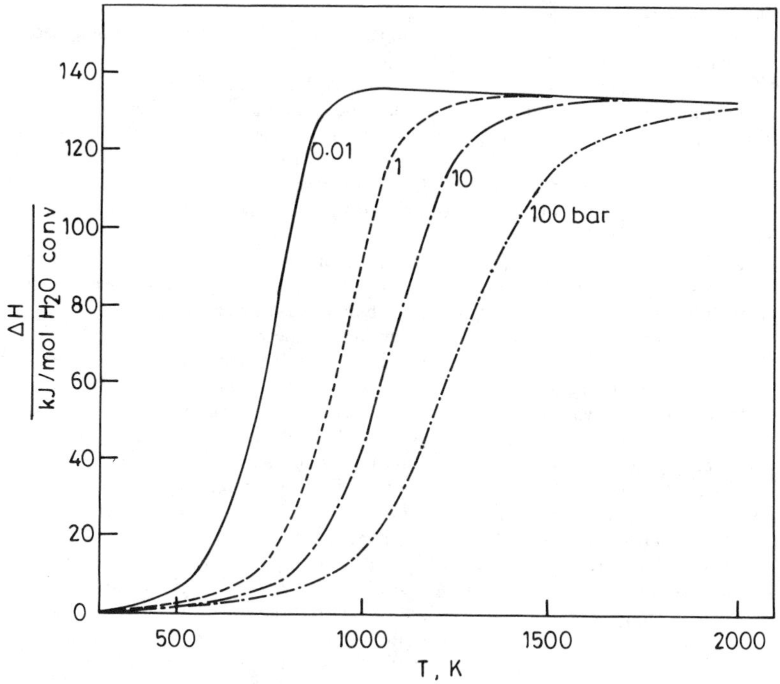

Figure 1. Enthalpy changes associated with the equilibration of the allothermic H—O—C system. (Reprinted with permission from Ref. [7].)

active metal important but the associated anion can also affect the activity [17]. In addition, the catalyst activity also depends on the kind of carbonaceous material and its pretreatment [18, 19], and may or may not depend on the method of catalyst loading [20]. In contrast to the large number of publications on carbon and coal gasification, only a limited number of studies have been reported on the gasification of coke deposited on catalysts [3, 21].

Effect of Cation on Activity

Most of the investigations made to determine the activity of different alkali metals have employed metal carbonates. Although the gasification rate depends on the nature of the carbonaceous material, it has been generally found that, on coals and chars, the reactivity of the metal increases with atomic weight [13]:

Cs > Rb > K > Na > Li

For instance, for an activated carbon feed and an atomic carbon to metal ratio of 51.8, the catalytic gasification rate/uncatalyzed rate for CO_2 gasification at 1,000 K was 11.4, 24.2, 36.1 and 47.7 for Na_2CO_3, K_2CO_3, Rb_2CO_3 and Cs_2CO_3, respectively [22]. Similarly, for the steam gasification of Illinois coal char, catalytic activity increased with atomic number, and for weak-acid salts, activity approximately doubled between lithium and cesium [17]. However, the nature of the carbonaceous material and the pretreatment conditions are important and can change the above sequence. Thus, for the gasification of graphite by CO_2 or steam, Li_2CO_3 has been reported to be the most active alkali metal carbonate [23, 24]. It has been suggested that the difference in the catalyst activity between graphitic and non-graphitic carbon is most likely due to the absence of heteroatoms and bound hydrogen on the graphite surface [24].

The alkaline earth metals also exhibit catalytic activity for the gasification of carbon. However, they form complexes with carbon less readily than the alkali metals and, therefore, are generally less effective than the alkali metals [17]. Contradictory results have been reported for the variation of the activity with the atomic weight of the alkaline earth metal. For CO_2 gasification, McKee [25] and Spiro et al. [24] found the catalytic activity to increase with molecular weight. In contrast, Kapteijn et al. [26] reported the activity of the earth alkaline elements to increase in the order: $Ca > Sr \approx Ba > Mg \approx Be \approx$ Activated carbon. Kapteijn et al. [26] argued that the char or graphite used in the earlier studies [24, 25] had a low surface area, which could result in a poor catalyst dispersion, thus masking the intrinsic activity of the metal. The lower activity of Sr and Ba was attributed to the higher stability of the carbonate phase, whereas the lower activity of Mg and Be was attributed to the unfavorable equilibrium of the reaction of MO with CO_2 to give $MO \cdot O$ and CO, which was suggested as one of the steps in the mechanism. A problem associated with use of alkaline earth metals is catalyst deactivation due to sintering.

Several investigators have studied the catalytic effect of platinum-group metals, iron and nickel [19, 27–31]. These metals are generally less effective than alkali and alkali earth metals although for one particular coal the nickel catalyzed gasification rate was reported to be much higher than the potassium catalyzed rate [30]. No explanation was given for this anomalous behavior but it is most likely due to better catalyst dispersion. For steam gasification of carbon, Rewick et al. [31] determined the catalytic activity sequence for different metals as $Pt > Ru > Ni > Co > Fe$ and their results are shown in Table 1. Kasaoka et al. [19] reported the activity sequence for the transition metals to be $Co > Ni > Fe$. In their study, the rate of steam gasification in the presence of Fe (Fe_3O_4) was even lower than the uncatalysed gasification rate. Fe in a more reduced state (FeO or metallic Fe) gave much improved results. It has been generally observed that transition metals are effective catalysts only in the elemental state and the presence of hydrogen is helpful in keeping the catalysts in a reduced form [28, 32, 33].

Gasification of coke deposited on industrial catalysts is usually carried out by using oxygen and/or steam. Rates of gasification not only depend on the metal component but also on the structure of the deposited coke [3]. Generally, highly crystalline carbons are more difficult to gasify [10]. Gasification of coke deposits from four different types of refinery catalysts was studied by Figueiredo [3]. His results show that gasification of coke on a silica-alumina catalyst was not catalyzed whereas gasification of coke from Pt/Al_2O_3 and Ni/Al_2O_3 catalysts was catalysed significantly. Decoking of coke from catalysts may occur in two stages. In the beginning, due to the coke deposits the metal may not affect the gasification whereas, as the gasification proceeds the

Table 1
Effect of Different Metal Catalysts on Steam Gasification of Sterling FT Carbon

Catalyst	Loading Wt%	Net Gas Formation Rate* (cm^3/(min) (g carbon)) 975 K	1,025 K	1,075 K	1,125 K	1,175 K
None	—	0	0.20	0.22	0.65	1.9
Pt	5.0	—	—	4.6	18	38
Pt	0.8	0.37	1.1	2.8	7.0	15
Ru	0.8	0.41	0.80	2.1	5.3	11
Ni	0.8	0.10	0.43	1.1	2.2	3.1
Co	0.8	—	—	0.22	0.97	1.6
Fe	0.8	—	—	0	0.09	0.26

* *The rate data are expressed in terms of net CO or H_2 formation.*
Reprinted with permission from Ref. 31.

encapsulating coke layer is removed and the gasification may become catalyzed. As in coal gasification, a reducing atmosphere may be necessary to keep the metals in the reduced state.

Several investigations have been conducted on gasification catalysts composed of two or more components and a cooperative effective has been reported [17, 27, 34–37]. Depending on the system, various reasons have been suggested for the observed synergism. A mixture of potassium sulfate and iron sulfate was found to have a higher activity compared to the pure sulfates or metals. The higher activity was attributed to the formation of a low melting phase that improved the wettability of the carbon surface [36]. Chemical activation has been suggested as a reason for the higher activity of a mixture of K_2SO_4 and Na_2CO_3 or NaCl, whereas the improved activity of a mixture of K_2SO_4 and $Ca(OH)_2$ was explained by a mechanism where the sulfate anion is effectively immobilized by the calcium to liberate the potassium to act as a catalyst [17]. A possible mechanism, in which the calcium effects the nickel- carbon interaction, has been suggested for the enhancement of the catalytic effect of nickel by calcium [27].

Effect of Anion on Activity

The effect of the anion on the activity of the gasification reaction has been studied mainly for alkali metals [14, 17, 38]. In general, the alkali salts of weak acids such as hydroxides and carbonates are more effective catalysts than the alkali salts of strong acids such as sulfates and chlorides [17, 39, 40]. There is strong evidence to suggest that chlorides do not possess any catalytic activity as demonstrated by Mims and Pabst [41]. In their experiments, the catalytic activity of K_2CO_3 was destroyed when it was converted to KCl by reaction with HCl. Although chlorides as such are poor catalysts, hydrolysis of the salt can improve the activity [11].

The data reported by Lang [17] for various alkali salts for the steam gasification of a coal char is shown in Figure 2. He explained these results by postulating that the strong-acid ions such as

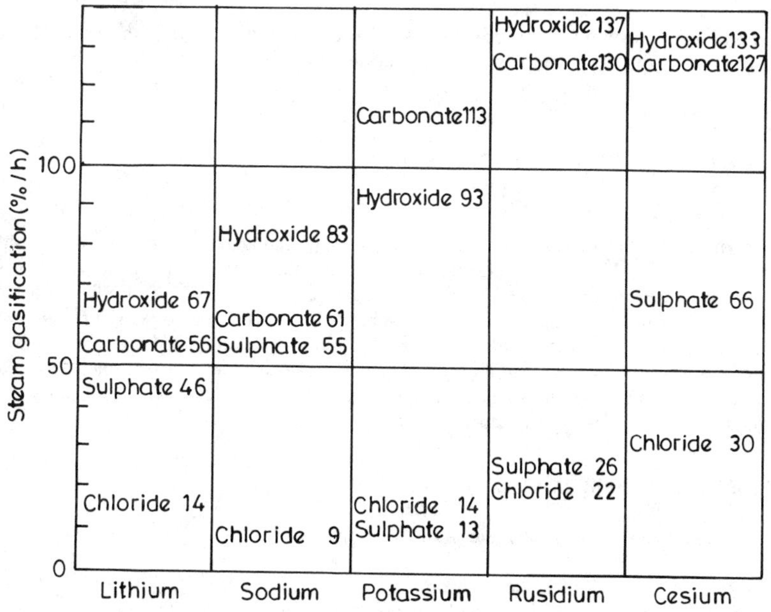

Figure 2. Gasification rates for Illinois coal char catalyzed with alkali metal salts. Catalyst loading equivalent to 15 wt% K_2CO_3 on coal. (Reprinted with permission from Ref. [17].)

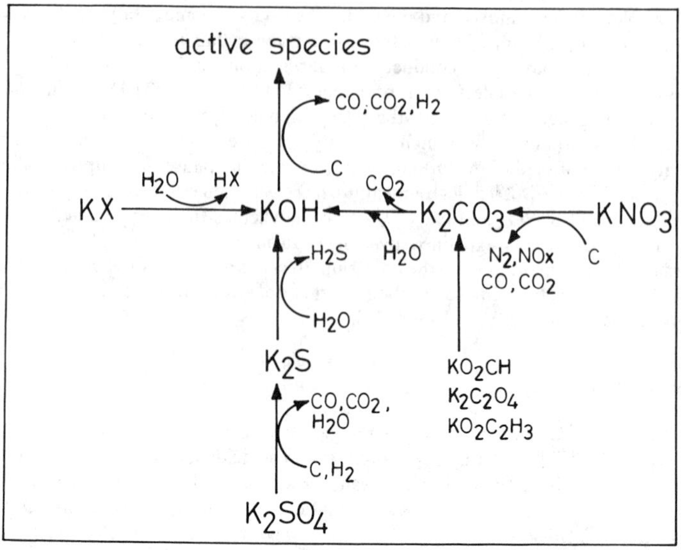

Figure 3. Reaction scheme for the activation reactions of various potassium salts. (Reprinted with permission from Ref. [40].)

sulfates and chlorides inhibit the formation of the metal-carbon complex, the precursor for the active gasification sites, by competing for the cation. Hüttinger and Minges [14, 40] studied the water vapor gasification of carbon and coal by different potassium salts and the sequence of catalytic activity was found to be:

$$KOH \approx K_2CO_3(\approx KO_2CH \approx K_2C_2O_4 \approx KO_2C_2H_3)$$
$$\approx KNO_3 > K_2SO_4 > KCl$$

This activity sequence was exactly as predicted from fundamental thermodynamic equilibrium considerations. They postulated that, regardless of the potassium salt used, the active species is formed from potassium hydroxide. Their results suggested that all the salts are first converted to potassium hydroxide which then forms the active potassium-carbon complex. The reaction scheme suggested by them for the activation reactions is shown in Figure 3. This reaction scheme could adequately explain their experimental results. There is evidence to suggest that once liberated from the inhibiting effect of the anion, all the alkali metals have the same activity for gasification although the number of active sites formed depends on the nature of the cation [17, 22, 42].

EXPERIMENTAL OBSERVATIONS

Effect of Metal Loading on Gasification Rate

For alkali metals, the initial rate of carbon gasification with either CO_2 or steam increases with metal/carbon molar ratio until a saturation point of approximately 0.1 [24, 38, 41, 43]. Below saturation, the dependence is usually linear and a typical variation for the initial rate of CO_2 gasification with K/C atomic ratio for a bituminous coal char is shown in Figure 4. A similar linear relationship was also reported for the steam gasification by sodium salts [38]. This linear variation

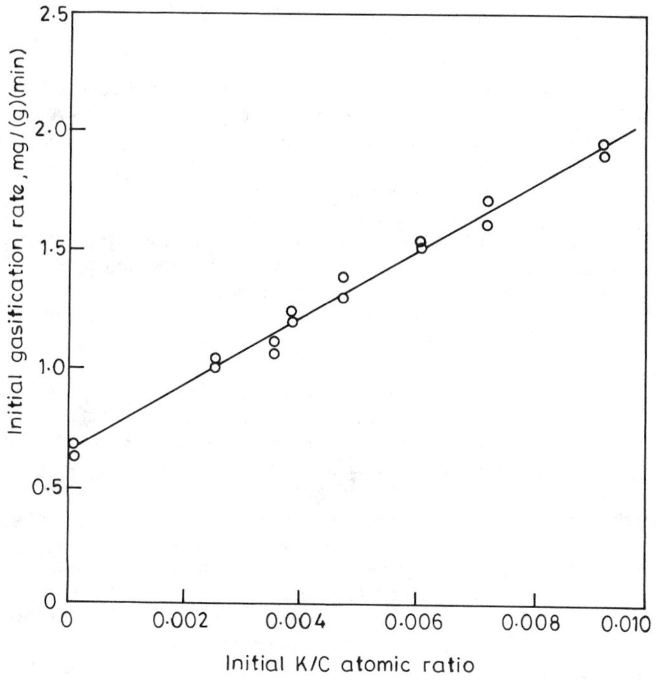

Figure 4. Dependence of initial gasification rate on initial catalyst loading. (Reprinted with permission from Ref. [43].)

implies that at low metal/carbon ratio, the number of carbon sites activated is directly proportional to the metal/carbon ratio, whereas at higher loadings, the catalytic activity is limited by the number of carbon sites available for activation. The number of sites available for activation depends on the type of char or carbon and its pretreatment [41, 44]. In some cases, the rate at high metal loadings can decrease possibly due to the plugging of the pores of the substrate [45, 46].

The effect of catalyst concentration of alkaline earth metals on gasification activity has been studied by several investigators [24–26]. Generally, the rate of gasification increases with catalyst concentration, although for a low surface area coal char, above a calcium loading of 5 wt%, the activity was found to be independent of catalyst loading [24], probably as a result of the poor catalyst dispersion. The rate of gasification not only depends on the initial metal/carbon ratio but for a fixed catalyst loading, the gasification rate varies with carbon conversion. The variation of gasification rate with conversion is a complex phenomena and depends on the initial char properties, the change in surface area with conversion, the change in the metal/carbon ratio as the reaction proceeds, and on the catalyst loss due to devolatilization and deactivation. The rate of gasification at low conversions can decrease, increase or remain fairly constant [38, 39].

Yuh and Wolf [38] found the gasification rates with 10% Na to be nearly constant with time up to a conversion of 50–60%, whereas with 5% Na, the gasification rate initially increased with conversion and then decreased. These trends were explained on the basis that at high metal loadings, the sodium/carbon molar ratio was near the saturation value (0.12), so that the release of any sodium due to carbon conversion did not change the concentration of active sites. In contrast, for metal loadings below the saturation value, initially all the potential sites are not activated and the sodium released due to carbon conversion was available to activate additional sites on the carbon surface. Hamilton et al. [43] observed the gasification rate to initially decrease, followed by an increase and then a further decrease with increasing conversion. The specific surface area showed a maxima with conversion as also reported by Wigmans et al. [47]. The increase in surface area at low conversions is most likely caused by the catalyst mobility and unplugging of the pores, whereas the loss in area at high conversions is due to the collapse of the carbon pore structure. The results were explained on the basis of a model that accounted for the loss in active sites and the change in surface area during gasification.

The methods most commonly used for loading the catalyst on char, coal, or carbon are ion exchange, impregnation by incipient wetness or from excess aqueous solutions, or mechanical mixing of the catalyst and carbonaceous substrate. Generally, for alkali metal catalysts, the contacting method does not affect the catalyst activity under gasification conditions [11, 38, 41]. Experimental evidence conclusively shows that under gasification conditions, the alkali metal salts melt to form a liquid film that is very mobile and redistributes itself over the carbon surface [15, 48]. Thus, the initial method of catalyst loading has no effect on the gasification rate. In contrast to this, since the formation of a mobile film is less likely, the gasification activity for alkaline earth metals strongly depends on the preparation method [20, 24, 26].

Very limited data are available on the effect of metal loading on the gasification rate catalyzed by transition metals and Pt-group metals. The effectiveness of the catalyst is influenced not only by the pretreatment of the carbonaceous material but also by the method of catalyst loading, kind of starting salt and the reducing conditions used. At low metal loadings, the rate generally increases with the metal content on the carbon; however, the increase is not directly proportional to the metal content, i.e., the rate enhancement per unit weight of catalyst decreases [19, 27, 31]. For instance, in the nickel catalysed steam gasification of a bituminous coal, the initial gasification rate at 1,023 K was approximately 0.2, 0.4, 0.5, 0.6, 0.7, 1.2, 1.5, and 1.7 $kg\,h^{-1}\,kg^{-1}$ for nickel loadings of 0, 0.2, 0.5, 1.1, 1.8, 5.2, 8.3, and 9.1 wt%, respectively [49]. The dispersion of the catalyst significantly affects the activity and higher metal loadings result in poorer dispersion and less use of the catalyst. Consequently, the rate is not directly proportional to the catalyst content on the carbon.

Not much information is available on the effect of metal content on the gasification rate of coke deposited on catalysts. Most of the studies have been conducted on nickel and iron foils [3, 50]. Various kinds of coke can be formed and the rate of gasification depends on the nature of the coke deposit [3]. With nickel and iron foils, filamentous carbon growth, in which the metal is incorporated on top of the growing carbon chain, is usually observed. During filament growth, the metals are detached from the foil surface and the metal-carbon system acts as a supported metal catalyst. Since the foil acts as an infinite source of metal, the concentration of the metal in the coke is proportional to the coke deposited. For filamentary carbon growth on foils, the rate of gasification has been observed to be constant over a large range of carbon conversion and proportional to the initial amount of coke deposited.

Effect of Carbonaceous Substrate

During gasification, the carbon acts as a catalyst support as well as the reactant and the nature of the carbonaceous material can affect the gasification rate by either changing the state of dispersion of the catalyst or by influencing the intrinsic activity of the active sites. High surface area chars or carbons result in better dispersion of the catalyst. For alkali metal catalysts, with high surface area char or carbon the reactivity remains constant over a broad conversion range due to better dispersion of the catalyst [22]. For nickel catalysts, the chars with a larger surface area had a higher reactivity, although the reactivity was not directly proportional to the surface area [27].

The enhancement in gasification rate has also been correlated with the crystallinity of the substrate for alkali metals as well as nickel [27, 51]. The increase in the rate was more for carbons with higher crystallinity and graphite exhibited the largest increase in the gasification rate. It should be emphasized that the uncatalyzed gasification rate decreases with increasing crystallinity. Although the exact reason for this dependency is still not clear, this variation in rate with crystallinity may be, among other reasons, due to the distribution of hetero-atoms on the carbon surface and the variation of metal ion concentrations in the coal char. Nickel catalysts were found to be better dispersed over low rank coal chars possibly due to the presence of oxygen containing groups that can act as cation exchange sites for nickel atoms resulting in better dispersion.

The rate of gasification of coke deposits from catalysts also depends on the crystallinity of the deposit. Depending upon the process leading to coke deposition, the coke may consist of condensed high molecular weight aromatic compounds as well as carbons of different structures [3, 10]. Metal catalysts generally lead to the formation of highly crystalline carbons that are difficult to gasify. The surface area of the coke deposit is also an important parameter and higher the surface area, higher is the rate of gasification. Generally, the rate of gasification depends on the gas-coke-catalyst surface area.

Although the intrinsic activity varies with the nature of the substrate, all evidence indicates that the different carbonaceous materials react by a common mechanism.

Effect of Gaseous Environment

In the absence of product gases, the carbon conversion during steam or carbon dioxide gasification initially increases with the partial pressure of the reactant and then levels off at approximately a pressure of 15 bars due to the saturation of the active inner surface with adsorbed H_2O or CO_2 molecule [52]. As shown in Reactions 3 and 4, the main reaction products are carbon monoxide in CO_2 gasification and carbon monoxide and hydrogen in steam gasification. During CO_2 or steam gasification, the reaction products retard the rate of gasification, presumably by competing for the active sites. Carbon monoxide has been reported to inhibit the CO_2 gasification of various carbonaceous materials [22, 43]. For steam gasification, Mims and Pabst [53] found the gasification rate to depend on the p_{H_2O}/p_{H_2} ratio, whereas Lang [17] reported the inhibiting effect of CO_2 and attributed this to the destruction of the active alkali-carbon complex. Lewis et al. [54] observed the steam gasification rate to decrease with CO_2, H_2 and CO. The effect of rate inhibition by CO was explained by the formation of CO_2 and H_2 through the water-gas shift reaction, which was at equilibrium for their experimental conditions.

Hüttinger and Minges [14] postulated that the inhibition of hydrogen in water vapor gasification was due to the blocking of the active sites on the carbon surface by the hydrogen molecule and also due to the lowering of the water vapor partial pressure in the pores as a result of a molecular sieve effect. High hydrogen pressures can also change the product gas composition by increasing the methanation of carbon monoxide, which is generally negligible at atmospheric pressure [7]. With nickel and iron catalysts, presence of hydrogen helps to keep the metal in the reduced state, thus improving the stability of the catalyst [19, 28]. A similar effect is observed during gasification of coke deposits from nickel and iron foils [3].

Carbon-Catalyst Interaction

Many studies have been conducted to investigate the interaction between the catalyst and the carbonaceous substrate under both reducing and oxidizing conditions. Most have concentrated on alkali metal catalysts with particular emphasis on potassium carbonate. The experimental techniques used have included temperature-programmed desorption (TPD), temperature-programmed reduction (TPR), thermogravimetric analysis (TGA), Fourier Transform-infra red (FT-i.r.) spectroscopy, Knudsen Cell mass spectroscopy, nuclear magnetic resonance (NMR) etc.

A common technique to study the carbon-catalyst interactions has been TPD in which the catalysed sample is heated, using a linear rate of heating, in a flow of inert gas and the evolved gases are measured as a function of temperature. A typical concentration profile, obtained by Sams and Shadman [55] on heating a graphitized carbon containing 10.7 wt% K_2CO_3, is shown in Figure 5. Although there is general agreement that the major gases formed are CO and CO_2, the reported results of different investigators are at variance on the temperature at which these gases are formed, the relative amounts and the origin of the CO and CO_2. For instance, Wood et al. [15] also observed a CO_2 peak below 500 K, but, in contrast to the CO_2 profile shown in Figure 5, both CO and CO_2 were detected above 900 K. Kapteijn et al. [18] reported CO_2 evolution

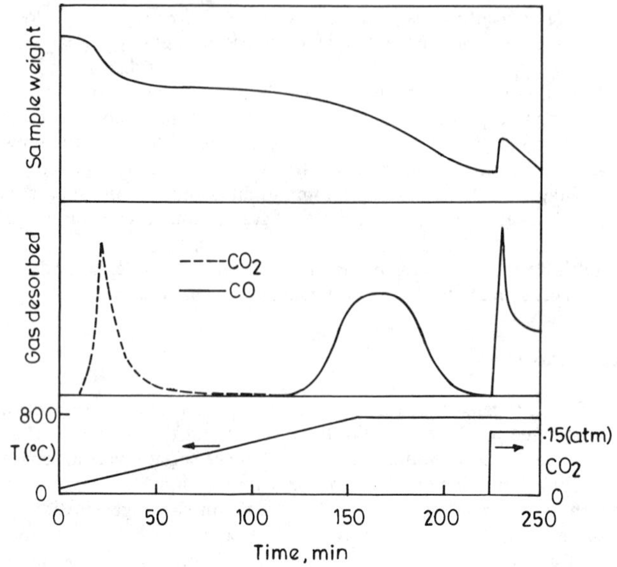

Figure 5. Typical profiles of sample weight and CO, CO_2, concentrations during TPD experiments. (Reprinted with permission from Ref. [55].)

between 500 and 1,000 K; Saber et al. [56] detected CO_2 only above 900 K, whereas McKee and Chatterjee [16, 23] did not observe any significant CO_2 in the evolved gases. In all these studies, the major product, above 900 K, was carbon monoxide.

There is some controversy regarding the origin of the CO_2 produced in the initial stages of heating. In the study of Sam and Shadman [55], the molar amounts of CO_2 and H_2O evolved below 500 K were proportional to the initial K/C atomic ratio and for every mole of initial carbonate, one mole each of CO_2 and H_2O was formed. They proposed that the initial carbonate was converted to bicarbonate (as also confirmed by powder X'ray diffraction) and the evolved CO_2 and H_2O were formed due to the bicarbonate decomposition as follows:

$$2\,KHCO_3 \longrightarrow K_2CO_3 + CO_2 + H_2O \tag{6}$$

The formation of potassium bicarbonate has also been proposed by Cerfontain and Moulijn [57] who studied the catalyst-carbon interaction using in situ F.T.-i.r. A similar behavior was observed with cesium carbonate. On the other hand, Moulijn and Kapteijn [13] proposed that the CO_2 evolution between 500 and 1,000 K was due to the decomposition of K_2CO_3 to form potassium oxide of undetermined structure. Similar results were obtained by Freriks et al. [58] using TPD combined with IR. Using isotope labeling, Yokoyama et al. [59] deduced tha the CO_2 evolution was exclusively due to the carbonate decomposition. In complete contrast to the above studies, Saber et al. [60], using isotopically labeled potassium carbonate, found that the evolution of CO_2 was not due to the decomposition of the carbonate but by the decomposition of surface oxides on the carbon. They proposed that the evolved CO_2 was labeled due to an exchange reaction. It seems that the amount and nature of the oxygen, either chemisorbed or inherently present in the carbon substrate, is important and could be the reason for the different results obtained by various investigators [40].

As the temperature is progressively increased, the catalyst undergoes reduction due to contact with the carbon and this is the source of the carbon monoxide obtained at high temperatures in all TPD studies. Many investigators have reported that 3 moles of CO are evolved for each mole of metal carbon initially present [16, 23, 38, 55]. This implies complete reduction of the carbonate to the metal, most probably by a carbothermal reaction:

$$M_2CO_3 + 2\,C \longrightarrow 2\,M + 3\,CO \tag{7}$$

In contrast, the presence of CO_2 above 1,000 K, has been attributed to a two-step reduction process [61]

$$M_2CO_3 \longrightarrow M_2O + CO_2 \tag{8}$$

$$M_2O \longrightarrow 2\,M + CO \tag{9}$$

Mims and Pabst [53, 62], using a technique involving surface methylation and ^{13}C-NMR, confirmed the presence of oxygen containing groups on the carbon surface. They postulated phenolate-like structures and correlated the gasification rate to the concentration of these surface groups. These complexes are stable at gasification temperatures and are most likely the active intermediates during gasification. The presence of partially reduced surface groups has also been reported by Saber et al. [60]. In their study, the ratio of potassium atoms remaining on the carbon surface to the remaining surface oxygen atoms was approximately two, irrespective of the amount of surface oxygen originally present. Kapteijn et al. [18] studied the outgasing patterns for all alkali metals to be quite similar indicating identical surface groups to be involved. Their results suggested the presence of two types of oxidic species; surface bonded-OM species of high stability and oxidic species having a lower interaction with the carbon. Similarly, Wigmans et al. [63] postulated the existence of three types of surface complexes including metal intercalated in the carbon. Wood et al. [15] studied the alkali metal carbonate/carbon interaction using Knudsen cell mass spectrometry and observed that alkali metal atoms were the main gaseous species in equilibrium with mixtures of the carbonate and coal or char. The measured vapor pressure of the metal was lower than the expected value for a carbothermic reaction. Although the exact structure of the solid phase was not determined, their results indicated that oxygen was present in the solid phase. They postulated that at high temperatures, the alkali metal carbonates, in the presence of carbon, are converted to a non-stoichiometric oxide containing an excess of the metal, and this oxide melts to form a liquid film that spreads over the carbon surface. Further evidence for the presence of a surface salt structure for various sodium and potassium catalysts is provided by Yuh and Wolf [38, 64]. For sodium impregnated coal, all devolatilized and partially gasified samples showed three i.r. absorption bands at 1,675, 1,450, and 880 cm^{-1} when treated with salts that were catalytically active. In contrast, these bands were not observed with NaCl, which did not act as a catalyst for the gasification reaction. They interpreted their results based on the formation of Coal-C—Na and Coal-O—Na surface complexes.

The existence of alkali metal intercalation compounds under gasification conditions has been a matter of controversy. Wen [12] proposed that the metal intercalates are the active species for gasification; however, recent evidence indicates that intercalation compounds are unstable at high temperatures and are unlikely to be the intermediates during gasification [11, 65]. The results of these investigations suggest that a metal-oxygen aromatic carbon complex is formed during reduction of an alkali metal salt with carbon. The following reduction scheme, which can explain most of the reported results, has been proposed for the reduction of K_2CO_3 by carbon [55].

$$K_2CO_3 \xrightarrow{C} (\text{—}CO_2K) + (\text{—}COK) \tag{10}$$

$$(\text{—}CO_2K) + C \longrightarrow (\text{—}CK) + CO_2 \tag{11}$$

$$(\text{—}CO_2K) + C \longrightarrow (\text{—}COK) + CO \tag{12}$$

$$(\text{—}COK) + C \longrightarrow (\text{—}CK) + CO \tag{13}$$

$$(\text{—}CK)_{(s)} \longrightarrow K_{(g)} \tag{14}$$

In this scheme, —CO_2K, —COK, and —CK represent the surface groups. The surface oxides were postulated to have carboxylic ($-C{\overset{\displaystyle O}{\diagup\!\!\diagup}}\diagdown OK$) and phenolic (—C—OK) goups as reported in i.r. studies. They postulated that the relative rates of Reactions 11 to 13 depends on the nature of the carbon, explaining the presence or absence of CO_2 at high temperatures. The available data indicates that Reaction 11 is negligible for highly crystalline carbons such as graphite. Reaction 14 has been included to explain the presence of metal atoms in the gas phase and is in agreement with the observation that metal loss due to vaporization occurs readily only for reduced samples.

REACTION MECHANISM

Alkali Metal Catalysts

The mechanism of carbon gasification by alkali metals has been extensively studied and an excellent critical review by Wood and Sancier [11] summarizes the various proposed mechanisms and reaction intermediates. Other reviews [12, 13] have also been published on this subject. The various mechanisms can be broadly classified as either oxygen transfer mechanism, free radical mechanism or mechanisms involving intermediates such as charge transfer complexes, electron donor complexes or intercalation compounds. The mechanisms proposed by various investigators have been elegantly compared by Moulijn and Kapteijn [13].

Based on the available information, there does not seem to be too much support for the participation of metal intercalation compounds or charge transfer complexes as intermediates for the gasification reaction. Moreover, although the existence of free radicals during catalytic gasification has been confirmed by electron spin resonance (ESR), their exact role is still not clear [66, 67]. There seems to be a general agreement that an oxygen transfer mechanism can satisfactorily explain the experimental results.

Oxygen transfer mechanism basically involves a redox cycle in which the catalyst is first reduced by the carbon and then oxidized by the reactant (CO_2 or H_2O) to complete the cycle. The various postulated oxygen transfer mechanisms essentially differ in the proposed nature of the reactive intermediate and the detailed elementary chemical steps. An oxygen transfer mechanism was proposed as early as 1931 [68] and later extended by McKee and Chatterjee [23], who postulated a carbothermic reduction of the carbonate to explain the catalytic activity of K_2CO_3 for CO_2 gasification. Their kinetic scheme, consisting of three elementary steps, is as follows:

$$K_2CO_3 + 2\,C \longrightarrow 2\,K + 3\,CO \tag{15}$$

$$2\,K + 3\,CO_2 \longrightarrow K_2O + CO \tag{16}$$

$$K_2O + CO_2 \longrightarrow K_2CO_3 \tag{17}$$

A similar scheme was proposed by Veraa and Bell [39] for carbon gasification by steam:

$$K_2CO_3 + 2\,C \longrightarrow 2\,K + 3\,CO \qquad (15)$$

$$2\,K + 2\,H_2O \longrightarrow 2\,KOH + H_2 \tag{18}$$

$$CO + H_2O \longrightarrow CO_2 + H_2 \tag{19}$$

$$2\,KOH + CO_2 \longrightarrow K_2CO_3 + H_2O \tag{20}$$

However, Hüttinger and Minges [40], using free energy change calculations for the possible reactions, have argued that Reaction 15 is thermodynamically not favored. They postulate that during gasification of graphite or coal, the active species are formed from KOH, as shown in Figure 3.

According to their mechanism, during graphite gasification, the KOH is formed by the hydrolysis of K_2CO_3, whereas during the gasification of coal, K_2CO_3 first decomposes on the carbon surface to yield K_2O and CO_2; the K_2O is then subsequently hydrolyzed to KOH.

Spiro et al. [69] also postulated KOH as a reaction intermediate. In their mechanism, in addition to Reactions 15 to 17, the following cycle is also included:

$$KOH + C \longrightarrow KH + CO \tag{21}$$

$$KH + CO_2 \longrightarrow KOH + CO \tag{22}$$

Recent investigations have conclusively shown that oxide groups, rather than alkali metals, are the intermediates during catalytic gasification by CO_2 or steam. Mims and Pabst [53, 62] suggested the existence of surface groups of potassium phenolate type, formed due to the interaction of the carbonate with the carbon substrate. From their data they concluded that approximately 4–5 potassiums ions were associated with each active site. Their proposed mechanism includes a slow reduction step and a fast CO_2 dissociation equilibrium.

A number of investigators [55, 60, 70] have used step-response experiments to determine the stoichiometry of the surface oxides. A typical variation of the sample weight and CO concentration with time is shown in Figure 5 and the main features are a weight gain and a CO overshoot on introduction of the oxidizing reactant (CO_2 or H_2O). The weight gain has been attributed to a rapid oxygen uptake by the sample due to the oxidation of the reduced catalyst intermediate resulting in the CO overshoot. However, some CO may also be produced due to the oxidation of the carbon. Kepteijn and Moulijn [70] proposed the following elementary steps:

$$K_xO_y + CO_2 \longrightarrow K_xO_{y+1} + CO \tag{23}$$

$$K_xO_{y+1} + C \longrightarrow K_xO_y + CO \tag{24}$$

Reaction 24 was assumed to be rate controlling and the rate was observed to be proportional to the concentration of K_xO_{y+1} species. They also determined that x/y was greater than 0.5. In contrast, Saber et al. [60] determined the surface K:O ratio under oxidizing conditions to be approximately one. Sams and Shadman [55], using both the CO overshoot and the weight gain data to calculate the oxygen uptake during oxidation, determined the potassium to oxygen ratio in the fully oxidized from of the surface complex to be approximately 0.5. Although the results of the different investigators are in qualitative agreeement, the reason for the discrepancy between the K/O values for the oxidized surface complex could be either the different nature of the carbon or that the catalyst losses during gasification have not been properly accounted for. Sams and Shadman [55] argued that the completely reduced surface complex is not likely under oxidizing conditions and proposed the following scheme for the catalytic gasification.

$$(\text{—}CO_2K) + C \longrightarrow (\text{—}COK) + CO \tag{25}$$

$$(\text{—}COK) + CO_2 \longrightarrow (\text{—}CO_2K) + CO \tag{26}$$

where Reaction 25 is rate controlling.

Wood et al. [15] using their data and the results of other investigators on surface area changes, increase in electrical conductivity etc., proposed that at subgasification temperatures the catalyst is transformed into a liquid layer of non-stoichiometric oxide which spreads and wets the carbon surface. Using their data on Knudsen cell mass spectrometry, they concluded that the oxide melt contains an excess of the metal, both as ions and in a dissolved state. They postulated a dynamic balance between the reducing process at the carbon-catalyst interface and an oxidizing step at the gas-catalyst surface.

From the previous discussion, it is evident that catalytic gasification due to alkali metals can be explained by a number of oxygen transfer mechanisms, each differing in the details regarding the precise steps and intermediates. Moulijn and Kapteijn [13] have shown that most of the proposed mechanisms explain the catalytic effect by postulating that one of the following three basic steps are affected:

$$K_xO_y + CO_2 \longrightarrow K_xO_{y+1} + CO \tag{23}$$

$$K_xO_{y+1} + C \longrightarrow K_xO_{y+1} + C(O) \tag{27}$$

$$C(O) \longrightarrow CO \tag{28}$$

where C(O) is a surface complex. In addition another reaction,

$$C(O) + CO \longrightarrow CO_2 + C \tag{29}$$

is necessary to explain the observation, that, although carbon monoxide enhances the exchange reaction (Reaction 16), it inhibits the gasification reaction. The reaction scheme, consisting of Reaction 23, 27, to 29, can explain all the observed experimental results. Similar steps can be proposed for steam gasification. However, it should be emphasized that there is still no consensus regarding the precise chemical steps by which the oxygen transfer occurs [11].

Alkaline Earth Metal Catalysts

For alkaline earth metal catalysts, the nature of the active species is still a matter of discussion. McKee [25] proposed pathways similar to that for alkali metals to explain the catalytic effect of alkaline earth metals. He proposed the following mechanism for CO_2 gasification:

$$MCO_3 + C \longrightarrow MO + 2\,CO \tag{30}$$

$$MO + CO_2 \longrightarrow MCO_3 \tag{31}$$

Tentative results suggest that for alkaline earth metals also, the active species is the oxide [26]. It has been observed that on heating in an inert atmosphere, the calcium decomposes to yield calcium oxide and CO_2. The following mechanism has been proposed by Sears et al. [71] to explain the catalytic effect of calcium carbonate:

$$CaCO_3 \rightleftharpoons CaO + CO_2 \tag{32}$$

$$CaO + CO_2 \longrightarrow CaO \cdot O + CO \tag{33}$$

$$CaO \cdot O + C \longrightarrow CaO + C(O) \tag{34}$$

$$C(O) \longrightarrow CO \tag{35}$$

where CaO · O is a surface peroxide and the rate determining step is the release of CO from the carbon structure. Increasing the partial pressure of CO_2 decreases the rate of gasification indicating that the oxide is the active species. More work is needed to precisely determine the nature of the active species during alkaline earth metal catalyzed gasification of carbon.

Transition Metal Catalysts

Just as for alkali metals, various mechanisms have been suggested for the catalytic gasification in the presence of transition metals. The postulated mechanisms include electron transfer mechanisms, oxygen transfer mechanism, and a dissolution/precipitation mechanism. It seems that the oxygen transfer mechanism can explain most of the experimental results [28], and for steam gasifi-

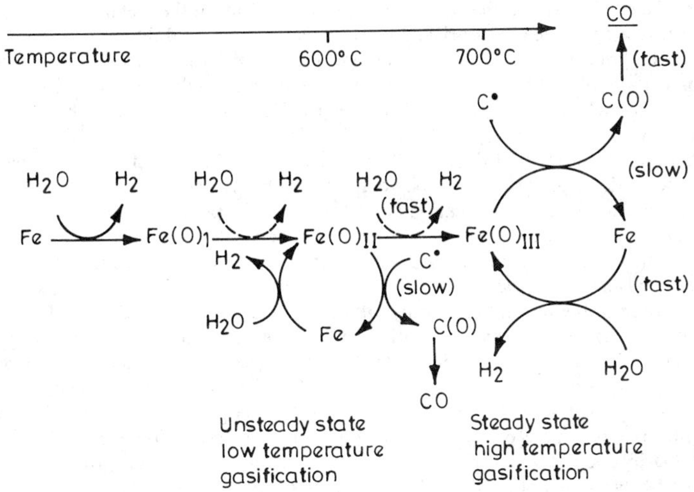

Figure 6. Oxygen transfer mechanism for iron-catalyzed water vapor gasification of coal or char. (Reprinted with permission from Ref. [28].)

cation may be represented as:

$$M + H_2O \longrightarrow MO + H_2 \quad (36)$$

$$MO + C \longrightarrow C(O) + M \quad (37)$$

$$C(O) \longrightarrow CO \quad (38)$$

Hermann and Hüttinger [28] studied the iron-catalyzed water vapor gasification of polyvinylchloride cokes using TPD of carbon monoxide from frozen in carbon-oxygen surface complexes. Their results confirmed the oxygen transfer mechanism. They observed the existence of three iron-oxygen surface complexes of different stability and attributed the most stable complex to be the reaction intermediate for steady state gasification. The reaction scheme proposed by them is shown in Figure 6. Reaction 37 was found to be the rate controlling step in the previous scheme.

Baker and Sherwood [50] investigated the steam gasification of graphite by nickel using controlled atmosphere electron microscopy and determined the gasification rate to be proportional to (nickel particle size)$^{-1/2}$, which implies that the mechanism is controlled by diffusion. They suggested the possibility of two steps occurring simultaneously: a step involving the dissociation of the water molecule on the metal surface (Reaction 36) and another step involving the diffusion of carbon through the catalyst particle. The relative rates of these steps would depend on the properties of the carbon-catalyst system. Nishiyama [27] has also suggested the possibility of dissolution of carbon into nickel particles.

Gasification of Coke from Transition Metals

Removal of coke deposited on catalysts is complicated by the fact that several different types of carbon deposits can form on transition metals such as iron and nickel [3, 9, 10, 72, 73]. As many as seven different types of carbon have been identified on nickel catalysts. Depending on the actual mechanism of coke deposition, the coke may either be present on the metal surface such that the metal is encapsulated or the chemisorbed molecules may dissolve and diffuse through the metal to dislocations and grain boundaries where they precipitate out forming filamentous carbon. These filamentous carbons may be formed from metal carbide intermediates. In filamentous carbons, since the metal particles are attached on top of the growing carbon chain, the coke deposition does not significantly reduce the catalytic activity although it can lead to catalyst deterioration. The filaments continue to grow until the metal is deactivated by formation of encapsulating coke.

Most of the work on gasification of coke deposits has been conducted on filamentous carbons. Studies of gasification of coke on nickel catalysts indicate that pore diffusional resistances are important at high temperatures, whereas the reaction is chemically controlled at low temperatures. For steam gasification, mass transfer control has been observed above 1,120 K [74]. The generally accepted mechanism for the gasification of filamentous carbon on nickel and iron involves the dissolution of carbon in the metal, followed by diffusion of carbon through the metal particle to the metal gas interface and subsequent gasification with the adsorbed species. The diffusion of carbon through nickel or iron is most likely the controlling step since the experimentally observed activation energy for nickel catalyzed gasification (134.4 ± 8.4 kJ/mole) is in agreement with the value of 139 kJ/mole reported for the diffusion of carbon in nickel [9]. Similar results have also been obtained with nickel/alumina catalysts, although the observed activation energy (76 kJ/mole) was lower [21]. Gasification of bulk carbon from transition metal catalysts may also be affected by the spillover of adsorbed reactant (CO_2 or H_2O) from the metal to the support [10].

In brief, gasification of coke from transition metals depends on the nature and morphology of the carbon deposit, the concentration of metal in the coke, the presence of encapsulating coke, the importance of dissolution/diffusion effects and the possibility of spillover effects.

REACTION KINETICS

Compared to the literature on other aspects of coal gasification, relatively few studies have been conducted on determining the kinetics of catalytic gasification of carbonaceous materials. Most of the kinetic studies deal with alkali metal catalysts and a recent review on the kinetics of alkali metal catalysed gasification is available [7]. In general, the rate of gasification depends on the concentration of the gaseous reactants and products, type of carbon, catalyst concentration, temperature, carbon conversion, and the instantaneous specific surface area of the carbon. In addition, the mineral constituents of the ash can affect the gasification rate by reacting with the catalyst to form inactive species.

The rate of gasification can be expressed as

$$r_n = N_T f(T, p_i) \tag{39}$$

where r_n = rate of gasification, $\dfrac{\text{kmol carbon gasified}}{\text{(kmol initial carbon)(h)}}$

N_T = concentration of active sites, $\dfrac{\text{kmol}}{\text{(kmol initial carbon)}}$

Depending on the initial catalyst concentration and surface area of the carbonaceous substrate, N_T and therefore r_n, may change or remain constant with carbon conversion. If the surface area of the carbon is large or the initial catalyst concentration is low, then N_T depends only on the initial catalyst concentration and does not change with conversion. On the other hand, for a low surface area carbon or high catalyst loading, the carbon surface will be saturated with active sites and N_T will depend on the carbon conversion. Generally, the variation in N_T with conversion has been modeled in terms of changes in the specific surface area, as discussed later. Several other factors, such as sintering, poisoning and evaporation losses of the catalyst, can also affect N_T and result in the variation of r_n with conversion.

Alkali Metal Catalysts

Constant Active Site Concentration

Carbon dioxide gasification. Most of the kinetic studies on CO_2 gasification catalyzed by alkali metals have assumed a simplified model to correlate the kinetic data [22, 42, 70]. This model is consistent with the accepted oxygen transfer mechanism and similar to the scheme proposed for uncatalyzed carbon gasification. The model can be represented as [22]:

$$\text{Step 1:}\quad \sigma + CO_2 \underset{k_{-1}}{\overset{k_1}{\rightleftharpoons}} \sigma\cdot O + CO \tag{40}$$

$$\text{Step 2:}\quad \sigma\cdot O + C \xrightarrow{k_2} \sigma + CO \tag{41}$$

where σ is a catalytically active site. In this scheme, the second step is assumed to be rate-controlling and first step is assumed to be at quasi-equilibrium. Then,

$$r_n = k_2[\sigma\cdot O] \tag{42}$$

In Equation 42, the reverse reaction in Step 2 has been neglected. Applying the steady state assumption to $[\sigma\cdot O]$, we have,

$$\frac{-d[\sigma\cdot O]}{dt} = k_2[\sigma\cdot O] - k_1\sigma p_{CO_2} + k_{-1}[\sigma\cdot O]p_{CO}$$

$$= 0 \tag{43}$$

Moreover, since the total number of active sites on the catalyst is assumed to be constant, we have

$$N_T = \sigma + \sigma\cdot O = \text{constant} \tag{44}$$

Combining Equations 42 to 44, yields

$$r_n = \frac{N_T k_1 k_2 p_{CO_2}}{k_2 + k_1 p_{CO_2} + k_{-1}p_{CO}} \tag{45}$$

As a simplification, it is generally assumed that $k_2 \ll k_{-1}p_{CO}$ (valid for low CO partial pressure). With this assumption, the expression for the gasification rate can be written as

$$r_n = \frac{k_2 N_T}{1 + \dfrac{p_{CO}}{K_1 p_{CO_2}}} \tag{46}$$

where $K_1 = k_1/k_{-1}$

is the equilibrium constant for Step 1 (Reaction 40).

The rate data for carbon gasification catalysed by metals such as Na, K, Rb, Cs and Ca have been very satisfactorily correlated using this model [22, 42, 70]. Kapteijn et al. [22] studied the kinetics of Na, K, Rb, and Cs catalyzed gasification and their results for the variation of (k_2N_T) and K_1 with temperature are shown in Figures 7 and 8, respectively. The parameter values of Equation 46 were determined using standard non-linear parameter estimation techniques. As can

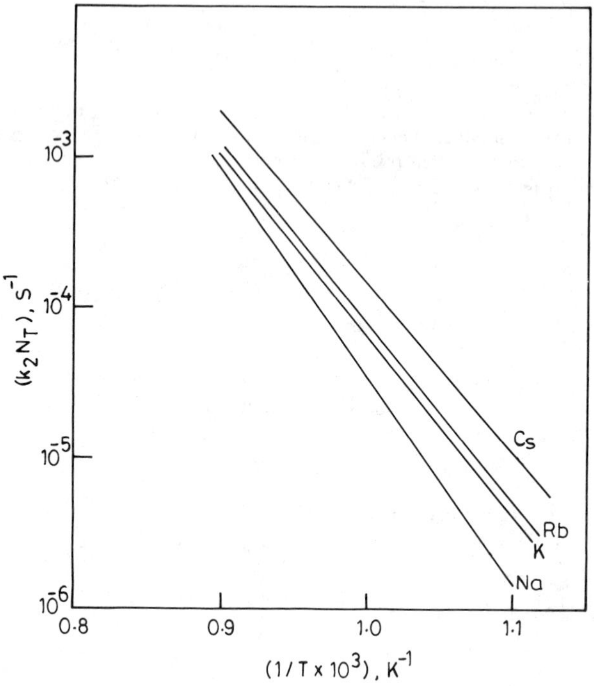

Figure 7. Variation of $(k_2 N_T)$ with temperature for different alkali metals (data from Ref. [22]).

be seen from these figures, the equilibrium constant for the first step (K_1) is approximately the same for the different alkali elements and is within a factor of two of the value determined from Ergun's correlation [75] for uncatalyzed carbon gasification, which is within the accuracy of this correlation. This implies that the presence of the catalyst does not affect the oxidation of the active sites. Similar results for K_1 were obtained by Freund [42] for gasification of different carbons catalyzed by potassium and calcium. Freund also determined that the activation energy for the decomposition of the surface complex, E_2, was essentially the same (244 ± 13 kJ/mol) for uncatalyzed and catalyzed gasification. He suggested that the catalyst only affects the active site density of the material (i.e., N_T) but does not appreciably influence the desorption process. Similar conclusions were made by Kapteijn et al. [22]. However, in their study, E_2 although similar for the different alkali metals (Figure 7), was lower by 20–30 kJ/mol than the uncatalyzed reaction. They suggested the possibility that either the catalyst has a minor effect on the desorption step or that the energy barrier for the release of CO from the carbon is dependent on the oxygen coverage.

This method of analyzing the rate data only yields the combined value of k_2N_T. To determine k_2 and N_T separately, transient experiments are necessary. Considering the two-step kinetic model (Equations 40 and 41), we see that, if the steady state gasification is disturbed by suddenly switching the reactant flow to an inert gas, the $[\sigma \cdot O]$ species will no longer be produced and only decay with time as follows:

$$\frac{-d[\sigma \cdot O]}{dt} = k_2[\sigma \cdot O] + k_{-1}[\sigma \cdot O]p_{CO} \tag{47}$$

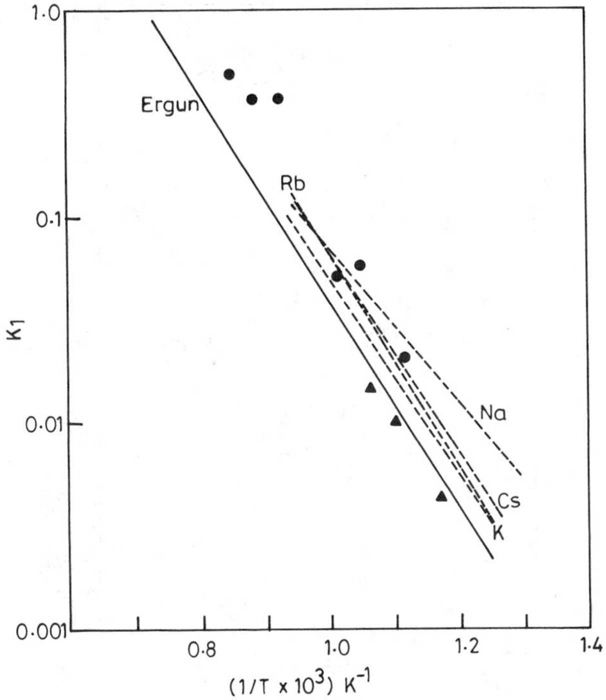

Figure 8. Variation of K_1 with temperature for different alkali metals. Upper three symbols are from Ref. [40]. (Reprinted with permission from Ref. [22].)

For low partial pressures of carbon monoxide, the second term on the r.h.s. of Equation 47 can be neglected, and

$$\frac{-d[\sigma \cdot O]}{dt} = k_2[\sigma \cdot O] \tag{48}$$

Thus, the concentration of $[\sigma \cdot O]$ will decay as follows:

$$[\sigma \cdot O] = [\sigma \cdot O]_{ss} \exp(-k_2 t) \tag{49}$$

This analysis assumes that there are no other pathways for the decomposition of the surface complexes. Therefore, in a transient experiment, the yield of carbon monoxide will decrease with time and, from Equation 41, can be used to calculate the concentration of $[\sigma \cdot O]$ at any time. Freund [76] used transient experiments to determine k_2 and N_T for the gasification of an uncatalyzed carbon and calcium-catalyzed carbon, and his results are shown in Figure 9. His results show that although the uncatalyzed and catalyzed rates differed by a factor of 100, k_2 was the same in both cases. These findings give strong support to the contention that the alkali metals and alkaline earth metals catalyze the gasification by increasing the effective number of active sites. The rate constant, k, obtained by Freund [76] could be expressed as

$$k_2 = 10^{11.6 \pm 2.3} \exp[-(225{,}000 \pm 39{,}000)/RT], \ \text{min}^{-1}$$

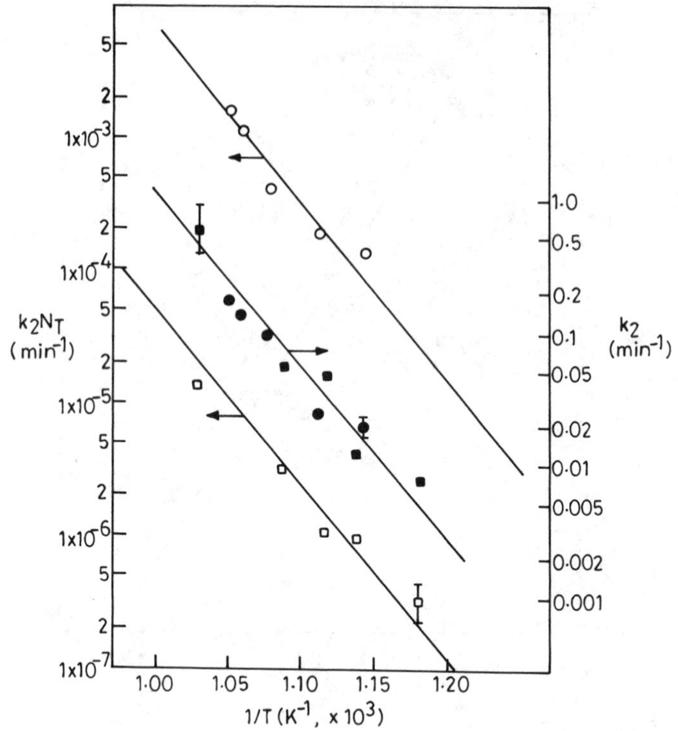

Figure 9. Arrhenius plot of (k_2 N_T) and k_2: ○ and ●, Ca-catalyzed carbon; □ and ■, uncatalyzed carbon. (Reprinted with permission from Ref. [76].)

Moreover, N_T was more or less constant with temperature and was 5.9×10^{-3} mol/mol of carbon for a calcium content of 1.5 at. %. Similar transient experiments were conducted by Cerfontain et al. [77] who obtained a value of 1.4×10^{-2} for N_T for a 10 wt% K_2CO_3 containing activated carbon, corresponding to about 70% of the potassium being active.

It should be emphasized that although the transient kinetic experiments convincingly show the effect of the catalyst on N_T, some questions remain unanswered. For instance, in some other calcium-carbon systems no decay of $[\sigma \cdot O]$ was observed [76]. A possible reason for this could be the different carbon used. Furthermore, transient experiments indicate that the oxygen exchange step (Equation 40) is more complex than the one-step assumed in such models [7].

Steam gasification. The available limited data indicates that a two-step model can be used to describe the kinetics of catalytic steam gasification also [53, 78]. For steam gasification, the two-step model can be written as:

$$\text{Step 1:} \quad \sigma + H_2O \underset{k_{-3}}{\overset{k_3}{\rightleftharpoons}} \sigma \cdot O + H_2 \tag{50}$$

$$\text{Step 2:} \quad C + \sigma \cdot O \underset{k_{-4}}{\overset{k_4}{\rightleftharpoons}} \sigma + CO \tag{51}$$

where Reaction 51 is the rate controlling step. For the general case,

$$r_n = \frac{k_3k_4N_T\left[p_{H_2O} - \dfrac{p_{CO}p_{H_2}}{K_3}\right]}{k_4 + k_{-3}p_{H_2} + k_3p_{H_2O} + k_{-4}p_{CO}} \tag{52}$$

Equation 52 takes into account the rate inhibition by the products and is applicable for any conversion level. The gasification kinetics in gasifiers is further complicated by the presence of CO_2, which is produced due to the water gas shift reaction. This CO_2 can further gasify the coal and modify the kinetics.

Neglecting the reverse reaction in the second step and assuming the $k_4 \ll k_3p_{H_2O}$, the gasification kinetics at low conversion can be expressed as

$$r_n = \frac{k_4N_T}{1 + p_{H_2}/K_3p_{H_2O}} \tag{53}$$

where $K_3 = k_3/k_{-3}$ is the equilibrium constant for Step 1 (Reaction 50). This expression is identical to the expression for r_n obtained for CO_2 gasification (Equation 46).

Kapteijn and Moulijn [7] demonstrated that the data of Mims and Pabst [53] could be satisfactorily modeled using a linearized form of Equation 53. The equilibrium constant, K_3, was 0.1 at 977 K, which corrected for the water gas shift reaction was in good agreement with the value of 0.06 obtained for CO_2 gasification. This implies that the steps in CO_2 and H_2O gasification are similar. The observed activation energy in steam gasification usually varies between140–180 kJ/mol.

Variable Active Site Concentration

As mentioned earlier, the main factors contributing to the variation of the gasification rate with conversion are the changes in catalyst dispersion due to reaction and the variation in the specific surface area of the substrate as the reaction proceeds.

Various models have been proposed to model the pore structure in porous solids [79–81]. The random pore model proposed by Bhatia and Perlmutter [81] can explain both the decrease as well as the maxima in specific surface area as conversion progresses. Both trends have been experimentally observed and this model has been used with some success to account for surface area changes during uncatalyzed gasification. Using the random pore model, the specific surface area can be related to the conversion, as:

$$S_v = S_{vo}(1 - x)[1 - \psi \ln(1 - x)]^{0.5} \tag{54}$$

where ψ is a "initial pore structure" parameter. For $0 < \psi < 2$, S_v shows a monotonic decrease with conversion, whereas for $\psi \geq 2$, S_v goes through a maxima with increasing conversion. Assuming that the catalyst-solid contact area is proportional to the solid area and that sufficient catalyst is available for dispersion over the whole carbon surface, the variation in the active site concentration can be expressed as:

$$N_T = N_{To}(1 - x)[1 - \psi \ln(1 - x)]^{0.5} \tag{55}$$

Depending on the nature of the variation, Equation 55 can be simplified as,

$$N_T = N_{To}(1 - x)^m \tag{56}$$

or

$$r_n = N_{To}(1 - x)^m f(T, p_i) \tag{57}$$

The spherical shrinking core model and the grain model (spherical particles) are special cases of Equation 57 with m = 2/3. It should be mentioned that the random pore model approaches the grain model for $\psi = 1$. Guzman and Wolf [46] used the grain model to correlate the variation of gasification rate with conversion for K_2CO_3-catalysed steam gasification. The grain model could be used to fit the data in the complete range of operating variables studied (temperature: 970–1,070 K; 33.4 wt% K_2CO_3; carbon conversion: 0–70%). The activation energy was independent of conversion, and was 244 and 260 kJ/mol for coal and char, respectively. Depending on the system, different values of m have been reported for modeling the gasification kinetics [7].

Hamilton et al. [43] modeled the variation in the gasification rate with conversion by combining the catalyst loss and the change in catalyst/carbon ratio resulting due to reaction. The loss in active sites was assumed to be first order. Their model contains two adjustable parameters. Depending on the model parameters, an increasing or a decreasing trend of the rate at low conversions could be explained. At higher conversions, the variation in the gasification rate could be modeled solely in terms of the changes in surface area.

Transition Metal Catalysts

The data available on kinetics of carbon gasification catalysed by transition metals indicates that expressions similar to Equation 57 can also be used to model the gasification kinetics. For instance, in the temperature range of 1,050–1,110 K, Miura et al. [82] determined the value of m to be 2/3 for nickel-catalyzed gasification and attributed the decrease in the rate with conversion to the agglomeration of nickel particles due to sintering. In contrast, the value of m was unity for iron-catalyzed gasification. The activation energy for nickel-catalyzed gasification is usually in the range 135–180 kJ/mol [50].

The kinetic data on gasification of coke from transition metal foils and catalysts is very limited. For CO_2 gasification of coke on iron foils, the gasification rate was found to be independent of the partial pressure of CO_2 and most probably controlled by solid state diffusion [3]. Similarly, for steam gasification of coke on nickel foils, the rate was independent of the reactant partial pressure and controlled by diffusion of carbon through the nickel. The observed activation energy was (134.4 ± 8.4) kJ/mole and the gasification rate was proportional to the initial weight of carbon [21]. For steam gasification of coke from Ni/Al_2O_3 catalyst, the activation energy was (76 ± 4) kJ/mole and the gasification rate was independent of the initial weight of carbon. In contrast to foils, the amount of nickel available is limited, and this indicates that most of the nickel present in the catalyst is initially transferred to the coke so that the rate does not depend on the coke content. Further work is required to determine the effect of initial metal loading and coke content on the gasification kinetics.

Gasification of Coke during Pyrolysis

Rates of coke formation and gasification during steam cracking of n-hexane were investigated in a jet-stirred reactor for potassium carbonate coated stainless steel surfaces in the temperature range of 993–1,113 K [4]. The rate of coke gasification during pyrolysis increased with an increase in K_2CO_3 concentration, temperature, coke concentration, and steam partial pressure. The rate of coke deposition as well as coke gasification approached a constant asymptotic value after approximately 3h. For a fixed K_2CO_3 concentration, the asymptotic rate of coke gasification could be expressed as

$$r_{ga} = A_g \exp\left(-\frac{E_g}{RT}\right) C_c^c C_{H_2O}^h \tag{58}$$

where C_c, the coke concentration on the surface, was calculated from the total coke deposited until the time the asymptotic coking rate was first attained. The parameters of Equation 58 were estimated by minimizing the residual sum of squares between the calculated and experimental rates of catalytic gasification using nonlinear regression. The parameter values are shown in Table 2.

Table 2
Parameter Estimates for Rate of Catalytic Gasification of Coke during n-Hexane Pyrolysis

Parameter	95% Confidence Limits
A_g	$(3.13 \pm 0.74) \times 10^{12}$[kg coke/h][$(m^2$/kg of coke$)^{0.72}$][$(m^3$/kmol$)^{2.7}$]
E_g	154 ± 32 kJ/mol
c	0.72 ± 0.20
h	2.7 ± 0.8

The value of 154 ± 32 kJ/mol obtained for the activation energy is in good agreement with the value of 146 ± 21 kJ/mol reported by Mims et al. [83] for the K_2CO_3-catalyzed graphite-steam reaction. Similar results have been reported for the catalytic gasification of coke during naphtha pyrolysis [84].

GASIFICATION REACTORS AND MODELS

Although many studies have been conducted on the fundamental aspects of catalytic coal gasification, very few studies have reported on catalytic gasification in large scale reactors. The only process that seems to be ready for commercial exploitation is the Exxon Catalytic Coal Gasification Process [1, 85]. Extensive pilot plant runs have been successfully demonstrated. A simplified flow sheet of this process is shown in Figure 10. In this process, the coal impregnated with K_2CO_3 catalyst is dried and fed via a lockhopper system to the fluidized bed reactor where it is gasified

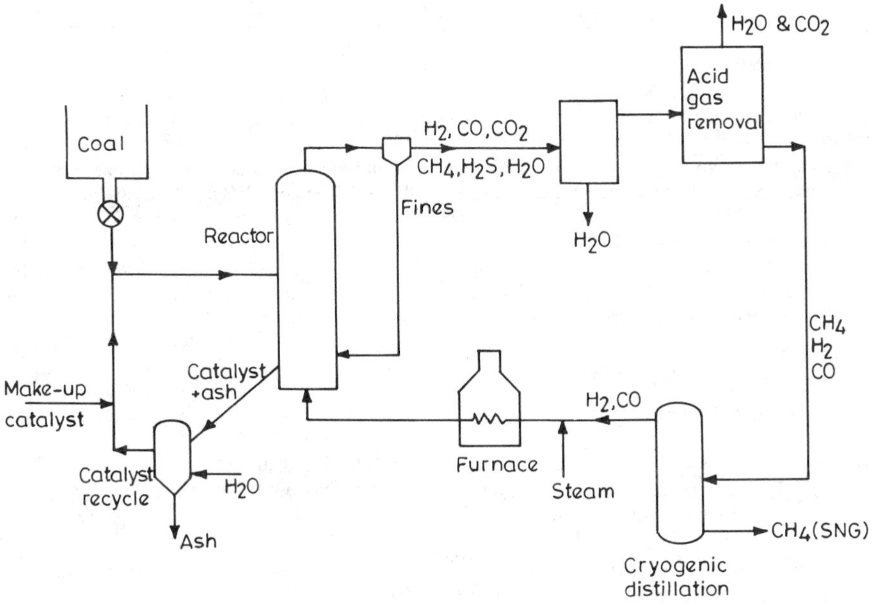

Figure 10. A simplified flowsheet for the Exxon Cataytic Gasification Process.

with steam at approximately 970 K and moderate pressure (3.5 MPa). Syngas ($CO + H_2$) is separated from the product CH_4 and recycled. Except for small quantities of H_2S and NH_3, the main products are CO_2 and CH_4. No tars or oils are produced. Although the reactor operates autothermally, heat is required to preheat the coal. The disadvantage of the process is the large amount of K_2CO_3 required, which requires very efficient catalyst recovery systems.

Tomita et al. [86] studied the nickel-catalyzed gasification of brown coal in a bench-scale continuous fluidized bed reactor at atmospheric pressure and a temperature range of 773–973 K. The nickel loading on the coal varied from 12–14 wt% and the coal particle size ranged from 0.25–0.5 mm. Compared to a conversion of 58% at 973 K for uncatalyzed gasification, the carbon conversion for catalyzed gasification was 80%. Moreover, unlike uncatalyzed gasification, there was no agglomeration of coal particles in the presence of nickel and the fluidization was smooth. Another advantage of catalytic gasification was the absence of any tar or soot. These were most probably adsorbed on the catalyst and then gasified. From their data, they concluded that the product gas composition was controlled by the gas phase equilibrium of the following reactions:

$$CO + H_2O \rightleftharpoons CO_2 + H_2 \tag{59}$$

$$CO + 3\,H_2 \rightleftharpoons CH_4 + H_2O \tag{60}$$

The product gas phase concentration calculated assuming equilibrium of the above two reaction was in good agreement with the experimentally measured values. For example, at 873 K and 0.1 MPa, the calculated values were: H_2, 67.4; CO, 5.3; CO_2, 26.9; and CH_4, 0.4 mol%. In comparison, the observed values were: H_2, 63; CO, 10; CO_2, 24 and CH_4, 3 mol% No H_2S was detected in the product gases. Most likely it reacts with the catalyst causing partial deactivation. The nickel recovery from the residue was accomplished using the ammonia leaching method and a recovery of 90 wt% of the nickel was achieved. The process looks promising but it has, as yet, not been demonstrated on a pilot plant scale. Further work is required to study the effect of catalyst deactivation and the economics of the process.

Reactor Modeling

Modeling of catalytic gasification reactors can be carried out using models similar to those developed for uncatalysed coal gasification reactors. Coal gasification can be conducted either in fluidized bed, moving-bed, or entrained bed reactors, and various models for such reactors have been developed for uncatalyzed coal gasification [8, 87–91]. These models can be used for catalytic reactors also, with the uncatalyzed intrinsic gasification rate replaced by the corresponding catalytic gasification rate.

Eakman et al. [85] developed a model for the Exxon Catalytic Gasification Process based on the two-phase theory of fluidization. The intrinsic gasification kinetics, developed from independent laboratory data, was expressed as

$$r_G = \frac{C_K k_G [p_{H_2O} - p_{CO} p_{H_2}/a_c K_G]}{p_{H_2} + b_1 p_{CO} p_{H_2} + b_2 p_{H_2O}} \tag{61}$$

where C_K = moles of catalytically active K per unit volume of emulsion
K_G = carbon-steam reaction equilibrium constant (based on β-graphite)
a_c = carbon activity relative to β-graphite (asumed = 2)

$$k_G = 6.8 \times 10^7 \exp\left(\frac{-15{,}100}{T}\right) \frac{\text{k moles}}{\text{(h)(k mole K)}}$$

$b_1 = 0.207 \times 10^{-5}\ Pa^{-1} (0.210\ atm^{-1})$
$b_2 = 0.595$

Similar intrinsic reaction rate expressions were developed for the methanation reaction and the water-gas shift reaction. These intrinsic rate expressions were then combined with the mass balance equations in the emulsion and bubble phases to obtain the product gas concentration profiles. The calculated values were in good agreement with the values measured in a pilot plant reactor.

Modeling of catalytic gasification reactors has not received too much attention, and although the basic reactor models are well developed, more work is needed to confirm the results of these models with experimental data.

CONCLUSIONS

The cited studies show that the most effective catalysts for carbon gasification are alkali and alkaline earth metals and transition metals such as nickel and iron. These studies demonstrate that not only is the nature of the cation important, but the anion can also affect the activity of the catalyst, especially for alkali and alkaline earth metals. There is a consensus that an oxygen transfer mechanism can explain the experimental results although the precise chemical steps are still a matter of controversy. Gasification of coke from transition metals is most likely controlled by the diffusion of carbon through the metal crystallite.

The kinetics of alkali metal and alkaline earth metals catalyzed gasification can be satisfactorily represented by a two-step kinetic model consistent with the oxygen transfer mechanism. The available evidence suggests that these catalysts do not affect the oxidation of the active sites or the desorption of the oxidized intermediate, but increase the rate by increasing the active site concentration. Various structural models can be used to model the variation of gasification rate with conversion. Reactor modeling of catalytic gasifiers has hardly been studied but it should be possible to modify the models developed for uncatalyzed coal gasifier to account for the presence of the catalyst.

There are some areas in which further work is required and these include kinetics of coke gasification from transition metal catalyst; kinetics of catalyzed steam gasification, and modeling of catalytic gasification reactors.

NOTATION

A_G	frequency factor for rate of coke gasification during pyrolysis, defined in Equation 58
a_c	carbon activity relative to β-graphite
b_1, b_2	constants in Equation 61
C_c	coke concentration, kg/m^2
C_{H_2O}	steam concentration, kg/m^3
C_K	moles of active catalyst per unit volume of emulsion, $kmol/m^3$
c	reaction order, defined in Equation 58
E_2	activation energy for the desorption step in the two-step kinetic model, kJ/mol
E_g	activation energy for coke gasification during pyrolysis, kJ/mol
ΔH	heat of reaction, kJ/mol
h	reaction order, defined in Equation 58
K_1	equilibrium constant for the oxygen exchange reaction between CO_2 and an active site, k_1/k_{-1}
K_3	equilibrium constant for the oxygen exchange reaction between steam and an active site, k_3/k_{-3}
K_G	equilibrium constant for carbon-steam reaction
k_1, k_2, k_3, k_4	forward rate constants
$k_{-1}, k_{-2}, k_{-3}, k_{-4}$	reverse rate constants
m	reaction order, defined in Equation 56
N_T	concentration of active sites, k mol/(k mol of initial carbon)
p_i	partial pressure of component i, Pa

r_G rate of gasification, k moles of carbon/(h) (m^3 of emulsion)
r_n rate of gasification, k moles of carbon/(h) (k mol of initial carbon)
S_v specific surface area of carbon, m^2/kg
T temperature, K
t time, h
X carbon conversion

Greek Letter

ψ initial pore structure parameter in the random pore model

Subscripts

0 initial condition

REFERENCES

1. Nahas, N. C., "Exxon Catalytic Coal Gasification Process," Fuel, *62*, 239 (1983).
2. Massey, L. G., Coal Gasification for High and Low Btu Fuels, *Coal Conversion Technology* (C. Y. Wen and E. S. Lee, eds), Addison-Wesley, Reading, 1979, pp. 362–392.
3. Figueiredo, J. L., "Gasification of Carbon Deposits on Catalysts and Metal Surfaces," *Fuel, 65*, 1377 (1986).
4. Mandal, T. K., and Kunzru, D., "Catalytic Gasification of Coke during the Pyrolysis of n-Hexane," *Ind. Eng. Chem. Proc. Des. Dev., 25*, 794 (1986).
5. Thomas, C. L., *Catalytic Processes and Proven Catalysts*, Academic Press, New York, 1970.
6. Butterworth, S. L., and Scaroni, A. L., "Carbon-coated Alumina as a Catalyst Support 1. Preparation via Liquid and Vapor Phase Pyrolysis," *Appl. Cat., 16*, 375 (1985).
7. Kapteijn, F., and Moulijn, J. A., Kinetics of catalysed and uncatalysed coal gasification, *Carbon and Coal Gasification Science and Technology* (J. L. Figueiredo and J. A. Moulijn, eds), NATO ASI Ser., Ser. E. 1986, 105, pp 291–360.
8. Yoon, H., Wei, J., and Denn, M. M., "A Model for Moving Bed Coal Gasification Reactors," *AIChE J., 24*, 885 (1978).
9. Trimm, D. L., "The Formation and Removal of Coke from Nickel Catalyst," *Catal. Rev.-Sci. Eng., 16*, 155 (1977).
10. Trimm, D. L., Poisoning of Metallic Catalysts, *Deactivation and Poisoning of Catalysts* (J. Oudar and H. Wise, eds.), Marcel Dekker, New York, 1985, pp. 173–79.
11. Wood, B. J., and Sancier, K. M., "The Mechanism of the Catalytic Gasification of Coal Char: A Critical Review," *Catal. Rev.-Sci. Eng., 26*, 233 (1984).
12. Yen, W. Y., "Mechanisms of Alkali Metal Catalysis in the Gasification of Coal, Char or Graphite," *Catal. Rev.-Sci. Eng., 22*, 1 (1980).
13. Moulijn, J. A., and Kapteijn, F., Catalytic gasification, *Carbon and Coal Gasification. Science and Technology* (J. L. Figueiredo and J. A. Moulijn, eds), NATO ASI Ser., Ser. E. 1986, 105, pp. 181–195.
14. Hüttinger, K. J., and Minges, R., "The Influence of the Catalyst Precursor Anion in Catalysis of Water Vapour Gasification of Carbon by Potassium 2. Catalytic Activity as influenced by Activation and Deactivation Reaction," *Fuel, 65*, 1122 (1986).
15. Wood, B. J., Fleming, R. H., and Wise, H., "Reactive Intermediate in the Alkali-carbonate-catalysed Gasification of Coal Char," *Fuel, 63*, 1600 (1984).
16. McKee, D. W., and Chatterjee, D., "The Catalysed Reaction of Graphite with Water Vapor," *Carbon, 16*, 53 (1978).
17. Lang, R. J., "Anion Effects in Alkali-catalysed Steam Gasification," *Fuel, 65*, 1324 (1986).

18. Kapteijn, F., Abbel, G., and Moulijn, J. A., "CO_2 Gasification of Carbon Catalysed by Alkali Metals. Reactivity and Mechanism," *Fuel, 63*, 1036 (1984).
19. Kasaoka, S., Sakata, Y., Yamashita, H., and Nishino, T., "Effects of Catalysis and Composition of Inlet Gas on Gasification of Carbon and Coal," *Int. Chem. Eng., 21*, 419 (1981).
20. Liu, Z., and Zhu, H., "Steam Gasification of Coal Char using Alkali and Alkaline-earth Metal Catalysts," *Fuel, 65*, 1334 (1986).
21. Figueiredo, J. L., and Trimm, D. L., "Gasification of Carbon Deposits on Nickel Catalysts", *J. Catal., 40*, 154 (1975).
22. Kapteijn, F., Peer, O., and Moulijn, J. A., "Kinetics of Alkali Carbonate Catalysed Gasification of Carbon 1. CO_2 Gasification," *Fuel, 65*, 1371 (1986).
23. McKee, D. W., and Chatterjee, D., "The Catalytic Behaviour of Alkali Metal Carbonates and Oxides in Graphite Oxidation Reaction," *Carbon, 13*, 381 (1975).
24. Spiro, C. L., McKee, D. W., Kosky, P. G., Lamby, E. J., and Maylotte, D. H., "Significant Parameters in the Catalysed CO_2 Gasification of Coal Chars," *Fuel, 62*, 323 (1983).
25. McKee, D. W., "Catalytic Effects of Alkaline Earth Carbonates in the Carbon-Carbon Dioxide Reaction," *Fuel, 59*, 308 (1980).
26. Kapteijn, F., Porre, H., and Moulijn, J. A., "CO_2 Gasification of Activated Carbon Catalysed by Earth Alkaline Elements", *AIChE J., 32*, 691 (1986).
27. Nishiyama, Y., "Catalytic Behaviour of Iron and Nickel in Coal Gasification," *Fuel, 65*, 1404 (1986).
28. Hermann, G., and Hüttinger, K. J., "Mechanisms of Non-Catalysed and Iron-catalysed Water Vapour Gasification of Carbon," *Fuel, 65*, 1410 (1986).
29. Tomita, A., Higashiyama, K., and Tamai, Y., "Scanning Electron Microscopic Study on the Catalytic Gasification of Coke," *Fuel, 60*, 103 (1981).
30. Tomita, A., and Tamai, Y., "Low Temperature Gasification of Yallourn Coal Catalysed by Nickel," *Fuel, 60*, 992 (1981).
31. Rewick, R. T., Wentreck, P. R., and Wise, H., "Carbon Gasification in the Presence of Metal Catalysts," *Fuel, 53*, 274 (1974).
32. Walker, P. L., Jr., Matsumoto, S., Hanzawa, T., Muira, T., and Ismail, I. M. K., "Catalysis of Gasification of Coal Derived Cokes and Chars," *Fuel, 62*, 140 (1983).
33. Yamada, T., Tomita, A., Tamai, Y., and Homa, T., "Catalytic Activity of Physically-mixed Nickel Compounds on the CO_2 Gasification of Phenolformaldehyde Resin Char," *Fuel, 62*, 246 (1983).
34. Baker, R. T. K., Dudash, N. S., Lund, C. R. F., and Chludzinski, J. J., Jr., "Comparison of the Catalytic Influence of Nickel and Cu-Ni Alloys on the Graphite-steam Reaction," *Fuel, 64*, 1151 (1985).
35. Rao, V. U. S., Szirmae, A., and Fisher, R. M., "Studies of Auger Electron Spectroscopy and Characteristic-Energy-Loss Spectra of Alloy Catalysts for the Gasification of Graphite in Water Vapor and Hydrogen," *J. Catal, 62*, 44 (1980).
36. Adler, J., and Hüttinger, K. J., "Mixtures of Potassium Sulphate and Iron Sulphate as Catalysts for Water Vapour Gasification of Carbon 1, Kinetic Studies," *Fuel, 63*, 1393 (1984).
37. Lund, C. R. F., Chludzinski, J. J., Jr., and Baker, R. T. K., "Platinum, Barium and Platinum-barium Catalysed Gasification of Graphite in Steam and CO_2," *Fuel, 64*, 789 (1985).
38. Yuh, S. J., and Wolf, E. E., "Kinetics and F.T.-i.r. Studies of the Sodium Catalysed Steam Gasification of Coal Chars," *Fuel, 63*, 1604 (1984).
39. Veraa, M. J., and Bell, A. T., "Effect of Alkali Metal Catalysts on Gasification of Coal Char," *Fuel, 57*, 194 (1978).
40. Hüttinger, K. J., and Minges, R., "Influence of Catalyst Precursor Anion in Catalysis of Water Vapour Gasification of Carbon by Potassium 1. Activation of the Catalyst Precursors," *Fuel, 65*, 1112 (1986).
41. Mims, C. A., and Pabst, J. K., "Alkali-Catalysed Carbon Gasification. I. Nature of the Catalytic Sites," *Am. Chem. Soc., Fuel Chem. Div. Prepr., 25*, 258 (1980).
42. Freund, H., "Kinetics of Carbon Gasification by CO_2," *Fuel, 64*, 657 (1985).
43. Hamilton, R. T., Sams, D. A., and Shadman, F., "Variation of Rate During Potassium-catalysed CO_2 Gasification of Coal Char," *Fuel, 63*, 1008 (1984).

44. Mahajan, O. P., Komatsu, M., and Walker, P. L., Jr., "Low-temperature Air Oxidation of Caking Coals. 1. Effect on Subsequent Reactivity of Chars Produced," *Fuel*, *59*, 3 (1980).
45. Sams, D. A., and Shadman, F., "Catalytic Effect of Potassium on the Rate of Char-CO_2 Gasification," *Fuel*, *62*, 880 (1983).
46. Guzman, G. L., and Wolf, E. E., "Kinetics of the K_2CO_3-Catalysed Steam Gasification of Carbon and Coal," *Ind. Eng. Chem. Proc. Des. Dev.*, *21*, 25 (1982).
47. Wigmans, T., Goebel, J. C., and Moulijn, J. A., "The Influence of Pretreatment Condition on the Activity and Stability of Sodium and Potassium Catalysts in Carbon-Steam Reactions," *Carbon*, *21*, 13 (1983).
48. Marsh, H., and Mochida, I., "Catalytic Gasification of Metallurgical Coke by Carbon Dioxide using Potassium Salts," *Fuel*, *60*, 231 (1981).
49. Higashiyama, K., Tomita, A., and Tamai, Y., "Action of Nickel Catalyst during Steam Gasification of Bituminous and Brown Coals," *Fuel*, *64*, 1157 (1985).
50. Baker, R. T. K., and Sherwood, R. D., "Catalytic Gasification of Graphite by Nickel in Various Gaseous Environments," *J. Catal.*, *70*, 198 (1981).
51. McKee, D. W., Spiro, C. L., Kosky, P. G., and Lamby, E. J., "Catalysis of Coal Char Gasification by Alkali Metal Salts," *Fuel*, *62*, 217 (1983).
52. Schumacher, W., Mühlen, H. J., Van Heck, K. H., and Jüntgen, H., "Kinetics of K-catalysed steam and CO_2 Gasification in the Presence of Product Gases," *Fuel*, *65*, 1360 (1986).
53. Mims, C. A., and Pabst, J. K., "Role of Surface Salt Complexes in Alkali-Catalysed Carbon Gasification," *Fuel*, *62*, 176 (1983).
54. Lewis, W. K., Gilliland, E. R., and Hipkin, H., "Carbon-Steam Reaction at Low Temperatures," *Ind. Eng. Chem.*, *45*, 1697 (1953).
55. Sams, D. A., and Shadman, F., "Mechanism of Potassium-Catalysed Carbon/CO_2 Reaction," *AIChE J.*, *32*, 1132 (1986).
56. Saber, J. M., Falconer, J. L., and Brown, L. F., "Carbon Dioxide Gasification of Carbon Black: Isotope Study of Carbonate Catalysis," *J. Catal.*, *90*, 65 (1984).
57. Cerfontain, M. B., and Moulijn, J. A., "The Interaction of CO_2 and CO with an Alkali Carbonate Carbon System Studied by in Situ Fourier Transform Infrared Spectroscopy," *Fuel*, *65*, 1349 (1986).
58. Freriks, I. C. L., Van Wecham, H. M. H., Stuiver, J. C. M., and Bouwman, R., "Potassium-Catalysed Gasification of Carbon with Steam: A Temperature-Programmed Desorption and Fourier Transform Infrared Study," *Fuel*, *60*, 463 (1981).
59. Yokoyama, S., Tanaka, K., Toyoshima, I., Miyahara, K., Yoshida, K., and Tashiro, J., "X-Ray Photoelectron Spectroscopic Study of the Surface of Carbon doped with Potassium Carbonate," *Chem. Letters* p. 599 (1980).
60. Saber, J. M., Falconer, J. L., and Brown, L. F., "Interaction of Potassium Carbonate with Surface Oxides of Carbon," *Fuel*, *65*, 1356 (1986).
61. Cerfontain, M. B., and Moulijn, J. A., "Alkali-Catalysed Gasification Reactions Studied by in Situ FTIR Spectroscopy," *Fuel*, *62*, 256 (1983).
62. Mims, C. A., and Pabst, J. K., "Chemical Characterization of Active Sites in Alkali-Catalysed Gasification," *Proc. Int. Conf. Coal. Sci.*, Dusseldorf, W. Germany, 1981.
63. Wigmans, T., van Doorn, J., and Moulijn, J. A., "Temperature-Programmed Desorption Study of Na_2CO_3-containing Activated Carbon," *Fuel*, *62*, 190 (1983).
64. Yuh, S. J., and Wolf, E. E., "FTIR Studies of Potassium Catalyst-treated Gasified Coal Chars and Carbons," *Fuel*, *62*, 252 (1983).
65. Ferguson, E., Schlogl, R., and Jones, W., "Gasification of Potassium-Intercalated and Impregnated Natural Graphites," *Fuel*, *63*, 1048 (1984).
66. Sancier, K. M., "Effects of Catalysts and Steam Gasification on the e.s.r. of Carbon Black," *Fuel*, *62*, 331 (1983).
67. Sancier, K. M., "Effects of Catalysts and CO_2 Gasification on the e.s.r. of Carbon Black," *Fuel*, *63*, 679 (1984).
68. Fox, D. A., and White, A. H., "Effect of Sodium Carbonate upon Gasification of Carbon and Production of Producer Gas," *Ind. Eng. Chem.*, *23*, 259 (1931).

69. Spiro, C. L., McKee, D. W., Kosky, P. J., and Lamby, E. J., "Catalytic CO_2 Gasification of Graphite versus Coal Char," *Fuel, 62,* 180 (1983).
70. Kapteijn, F., and Moulijn, J. A., "Kinetics of the Potassium Carbonate-Catalysed CO_2 Gasification of Activated Carbon," *Fuel, 62,* 221 (1983).
71. Sears, J. T., Muralidhara, H. S., and Wen, C. Y., "Reactivity Correlations for the Coal Char-CO_2 Reaction," *Ind. Eng. Chem. Proc. Des. Dev., 19,* 358 (1980).
72. Bokx, P. K., Kock, A. J. H. M., Boellaard, E., Klop, W., and Geus, J. W., "The Formation of Filamentous Carbon on Iron and Nickel Catalysts 1. Thermodynamics," *J. Catal., 96,* 454 (1985).
73. McCarty, J. G., and Wise, H., "Hydrogenation of Surface Carbon on Alumina Supported Nickel," *J. Catal., 57,* 406 (1979).
74. Bernardo, C. A., and Trimm, D. L., "The Kinetics of Gasification of Carbon Deposited on Nickel Catalysts," *Carbon, 17,* 115 (1979).
75. Ergun, S., "Kinetics of the Reaction of Carbon Dioxide with Carbon," *J. Phy. Chem., 60,* 480 (1956).
76. Freund, H., "Gasification of Carbon by CO_2: a Transient Kinetics Experiment," *Fuel, 65,* 63 (1986).
77. Cerfontain, H. B., Kapteijn, F., and Moulijn, J. A., "The Mechanism of the Potassium-Catalysed Carbon Gasification: a Study by Transient Techniques," *Int. Cong. Catal.* (*Proc.*) 8th, 1984 (pub. 1985) 3, III. 593-III. 603.
78. Holstein, W. L., and Boudart, M., "Transition Metal and Metal Oxide Catalysed Gasification of Carbon by Oxygen, Water and Carbon Dioxide," *Fuel, 62,* 162 (1983).
79. Doraiswamy, L. K., and Sharma, M. M., *Heterogeneous Reactions: Analysis, Examples and Reactor Design, Vol. I,* John Wiley, New York, 1984, pp. 462–476.
80. Szekely, J., and Evans, J. W., "A Structural Model for Gas-Solid Reactions with a Moving Boundary," *Chem. Eng. Sci., 25,* 1091 (1970).
81. Bhatia, S. K., and Perlmutter, D. D., "A Random Pore Model for Fluid-Solid Reactions: I. Isothermal, Kinetic Control," *AIChE J., 26,* 379 (1980).
82. Miura, K., Aimi, M., Naito, T., and Hashimoto, K., "Steam Gasification of Carbon. Effect of Several Variables on the Rate of Gasification and the Rates of CO and CO_2 Formation," *Fuel, 65,* 407 (1986).
83. Mims, C. A., Chludzinski, J. J., Jr., Pabst, J. K., and Baker, R. T. K., "Potassium-Catalysed Gasification of Graphite in Oxygen and Steam," *J. Catal., 88,* 97 (1984).
84. Kunzru, D., Bahadur, N. P., and Sahu, D., "Reduction of Coke Formation During Naphtha Pyrolysis," Proceedings of 4th APCChE Congress, Singapore, 1987, p. 89.
85. Eakman, J. M., Wesselhoft, R. D., Dunkleman, J. J., and Vadovic, C. J., "Gasifier Operation and Modeling in the Exxon Catalytic Coal Gasification Process," *Coal Processing Technology Vol. VI,* AIChE, 1980, pp. 146–158.
86. Tomita, A., Watanabe, Y., Takarada, T., Ohtsuka, Y., and Tamai, Y., "Nickel-Catalysed Gasification of Brown Coal in a Fluidised Bed Reactor at Atmospheric Pressure," *Fuel, 64,* 795 (1985).
87. Caram, H. S., and Amundson, N. R., "Fluidized Bed Gasification Reactor Modeling. 1. Model Description and Numerical Results for a Single Bed," *Ind. Eng. Chem. Proc. Des. Dev., 18,* 80 (1979).
88. Wen, C. Y., and Chaung, T. Z., "Entrainment Coal Gasification Modeling," *Ind. Eng. Chem. Proc. Des. Dev., 18,* 684 (1979).
89. Amundson, N. R., and Arri, L. E., "Char Gasification in a Countercurrent Reactor," *AIChE J., 24,* 87 (1978).
90. Caram, H. S., and Fuentes, C., "Simplified Model for a Countercurrent Char Gasifier," *Ind. Eng. Chem. Fundam., 21,* 464 (1982).
91. Sprouse, K. M., "Modeling Pulverized Coal Conversion in Entrained Flows," *AIChE J., 26,* 964 (1980).

CHAPTER 13

PRINCIPLES OF LIQUID PHASE CATALYTIC HYDROGENATION

R. A. Rajadhyaksha and S. L. Karwa

Department of Chemical Technology
University of Bombay
Matunga, Bombay, India

CONTENTS

INTRODUCTION

Reduction of unsaturated functional groups is one of the important chemical reactions in the manufacture of organic chemicals. The various reductions commonly carried out in industrial practice are listed in Table 1. These reductions can be carried out using several chemical reductants. The reductants used industrially include

1. Metal (zinc or iron) in acidic or basic solution.
2. Sodium sulfide and polysulfides.
3. Complex metal hydrides such as sodium borohydride and lithium aluminium hydride.

The principal alternative to chemical reduction is hydrogenation using heterogeneous catalysts. This option offers several advantages over chemical reduction.

1. The cost of hydrogen is lower as compared to that of most other reducing agents.
2. The products can be easily separated at the end of the reaction and the loss of product during recovery is minimum.
3. Chemical reductions lead to formation of by-products (such as metal sludge), which pose problems of waste disposal. No such by-products are formed in catalytic hydrogenation.
4. The catalytic hydrogenation can often be more selective.

Table 1
Major Reductions Carried Out in Industrial Practice

Reaction	Industrial Application
$-CH{=}CH- \longrightarrow -CH_2{-}CH_2-$	Vegetable oils
$-C{\equiv}C- \longrightarrow -CH{=}CH-$	1,4-*cis*-Butenediol
$-CHO \longrightarrow -CH_2OH$	Sorbitol
$-\overset{\overset{O}{\|}}{C}- \longrightarrow -\overset{\overset{OH}{\mid}}{C}H-$	Manitol, Benzhydrol
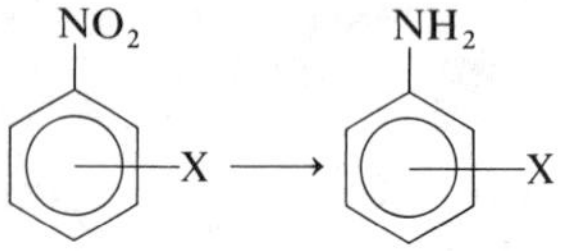	Aniline, Toluenediamine
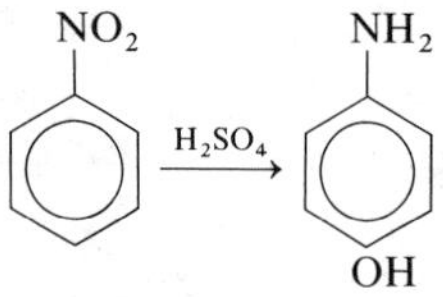	*p*-Aminophenol
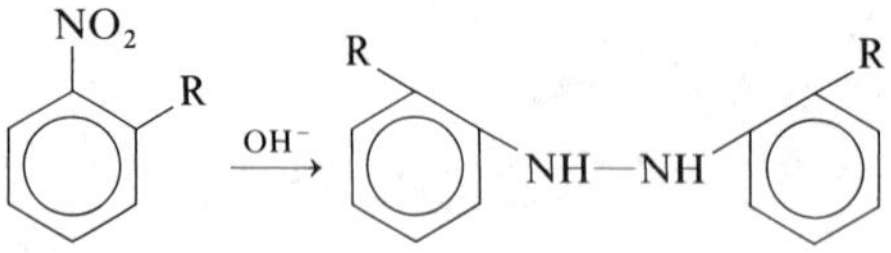	Hydrazobenzene
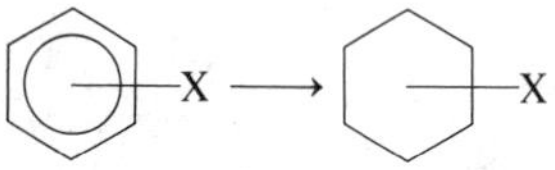	Cyclohexylamine
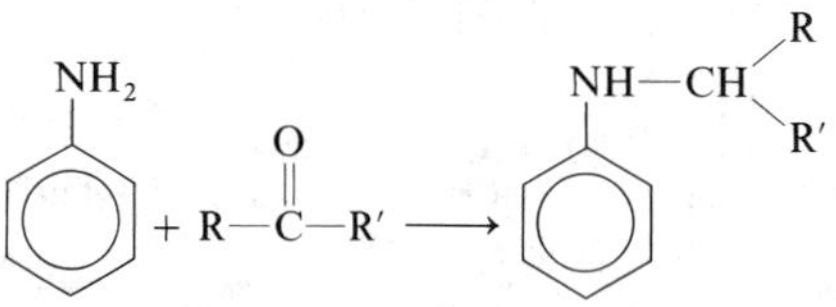	Ephidrine, Alkyl toludines
$R{-}C{\equiv}N \longrightarrow RCH_2NH_2$	Fatty amines Hexamethylene diamine
$R{-}C({=}O)Cl \longrightarrow RCHO$	Trimethoxybenzaldehyde
$R{-}C({=}O)OR' \longrightarrow RCH_2OH + R'OH$	Fatty alcohols

It is needless to emphasize the importance of these factors in industrial practice. Hence, catalytic hydrogenation has found overwhelming preference over chemical reduction, and is practiced extensively.

Sabatier [1] demonstrated in 1897 that organic compounds can be reduced with hydrogen gas in the presence of finely divided nickel. The pioneering contributions of Adams, Adkins, Ipatieff, and Raney followed in the next forty years [2–6]. Several catalysts discovered during this period find industrial use even today. Due to the obvious relevance of this class of reaction to synthesis of organic chemicals, extensive work has been done in this area over the last ninety years. The objective of this chapter, however, is not to present a review of the massive amount of information that now exists in the literature. An important outcome of the research carried out in this area is that it clearly identifies the factors that influence the rate and selectivity of hydrogenation reactions. Some guidelines have also emerged for selection of these important parameters for optimal operation. This chapter presents a review of such guiding principles. Although these principles do not permit a priori selection of process parameters, they considerably reduce the size of the parameter space that may be required to be searched to arrive at the optimum.

The principal parameters that influence rate and selectivity of hydrogenation reactions are the catalyst (active component), support, solvent, and additives. The first section of this chapter discusses the principles that govern the selection of the catalyst, support, and solvent. Although the effect of additives has been studied for a large number of reactions, the mode of action of additives is not understood adequately, and there appear to be no general trends that would help to choose the additive for a given reaction. The discussion on additives is, therefore, restricted to a few examples that demonstrate the dramatic influence of additives on rate and selectivity. The second section discusses a few industrially important hydrogenation reactions. The emphasis is on the considerations involved in selection of process parameters. Thus, the discussion on these reactions also serves as application of the principles discussed in the first section to specific systems.

The third section is devoted to a brief discussion on asymmetric hydrogenation using heterogeneous catalysts. Asymmetric synthesis is, at present, one of frontier areas in synthetic chemistry. The principal relevance of this area is to the synthesis of drugs where only one of the enantiomers is often observed to exhibit the desired therapeutic activity. Liquid phase hydrogenation is involved extensively in the synthesis of drugs. It was, therefore, considered worthwhile to present a review of the existing knowledge in the area.

GENERAL PRINCIPLES

Choice of Catalytic Metal

The transition metals of Group VIIIB of the periodic table represent the most active class of catalysts for hydrogenation. The most commonly used metals are nickel, palladium, and platinum. Rhodium and ruthenum also exhibit high catalytic activity, but their use is restricted to a few specific reactions. The catalytic activity of noble metals, in general, has been observed to be 100 to 1,000 times greater than base metals for most reactions. Hence, in spite of the higher cost they compete with the base metals for industrial applications. Reduction of a given functional group can be carried out at a lower temperature using an appropriate noble metal catalyst when compared with the base metal catalysts. Use of noble metal catalysts is usually preferred for more expensive products where higher catalyst costs can be tolerated to achieve higher selectivity to the desired product. For lower value products a large number of recycles of the catalyst become necessary if the use of noble metal catalyst has to become economic. For use of noble metals it is also necessary that the raw material is available in highly pure form and is free from catalyst poisons. Irreversible poisoning of noble metals makes their use very expensive. Apart from the metals, a mixed oxide of copper and chromium (copperchromite) is also used for liquid phase hydrogenation. This catalyst exhibits much lower activity as compared to metals and requires relatively higher temperature and pressure. The order of activity of different catalysts varies for the different functional groups. Further, several hydrogenation reactions can lead to formation of multiple products. The selectivity for such reductions also differs significantly from one metal to another.

Thus, apart from the few factors mentioned, the considerations of activity and selectivity play an important role in selection of the catalyst for a given reaction. Considerable information already exists regarding the relative activities and selectivities of different metals for reduction of different functional groups. It is extensively reviewed in the authoritative books by Rylander [7] and Freifelder [8]. A brief account of these principles follows.

Olefins

Hydrogenation of double bonds, which are not hindered sterically, is most facile as compared to that of other reducible functional groups. Nickel among the base metals and palladium among the noble metals exhibit the highest activity and are most commonly used for hydrogenation of simple olefins. However, in several systems, considerations other than activity can play an important role in the choice of the catalyst. The catalysts active for hydrogenation also catalyze double bond migration and *cis-trans* isomerization of olefins. For a simple olefin, the effect of double bond migration will not be noticed when it is followed by hydrogenation. However, in a olefin with a complex structure, the double bond can migrate to a sterically hindered location, which can result in a considerable decrease in the rate of hydrogenation. In compounds containing hydroxyl groups, migration of double bond towards the carbon bearing the hydroxyl group can result in formation of keto compounds by internal hydrogen transfer. The keto compounds thus produced may not get hydrogenated under the conditions employed and appear as by-products. In the case of asymmetric substrates, double bond migration can result in loss of asymmetry. Similarly, *cis-trans* isomerization prior to hydrogenation can result in the formation of products of undesirable steric configuration. Preventing the isomerization reactions can, thus, become important in several systems. The order of activity of different metals for double bond migration is found to be Pd > Ni ≫ Rh ∼ Ru > O_s ∼ Ir ∼ Pt [9]. The order of activity among the noble metals for *cis-trans* isomerization has also been found to be similar. Thus, the metals that are most active for hydrogenation are the undesirable ones from the above consideration. Platinum is usually preferred when isomerization reactions must be suppressed.

Selective hydrogenation of double bond in the presence of other reducible function can usually be achieved without difficulty. Only when the double bond is sterically hindered selective hydrogenation may become difficult. For selective hydrogenation of unsaturated aliphatic ketones, palladium is found to be more selective than nickel [7].

Acetylenes

The importance of hydrogenation of acetylenic compounds in industrial practice lies in the selective synthesis of *cis*-olefins. The hydrogenation of acetylenes, thus, involves two types of selectivities viz. selective partial hydrogenation of the acetylene to the olefin with minimum formation of alkane and selective addition of hydrogen to form the *cis* product. Bond and Wells [10] observed the following order of selectivity for the formation of olefin: Pd > Pt > Rh > Ir. Palladium has also been observed to give highest selectivity towards *cis* addition [10, 11]. Hence, palladium emerges to be the most attractive catalyst for hydrogenation of acetylenes and is, indeed, used extensively in practice. The selectivity of palladium for formation of olefins is reported to be enhanced by addition of a variety of modifiers [7]. Among these, the Lindlar catalyst, which is made up of palladium supported on calcium carbonate and modified by compounds of lead, has been found to be very effective [12, 13, 14].

Carbonyl Compounds

For aliphatic aldehydes not containing any other reducible group, nickel and ruthenium have been found to be the most suitable catalysts. Among the two, ruthenium has greater poison resistance. It is nonpyrophoric and is also resistant to corrosive reaction media. Nickel offers the advantage of lower cost. Several catalysts have been investigated for selective hydrogenation of unsaturated aldehydes to unsaturated alcohols. Good yields of unsaturated alcohols could be obtained using platinum or platinum oxide modified with zinc, iron, cobalt or nickel [7]. Raney cobalt has also been shown to exhibit good selectivity for unsaturated alcohols [15].

For reduction of aromatic aldehydes, palladium has been found to be superior to other metals. The accompanying side reaction is the further conversion of the alcohol to hydrocarbon. Generally, over palladium, the aromatic alcohols can be obtained in high selectivity. The selectivity can be further improved by addition of basic additives like alkali and tertiary amines. If the aromatic ring also bears a halogen atom, palladium would catalyze dehalogenation to a significant extent. In such a system, platinum may be preferred to palladium [16, 17].

For hydrogenation of aliphatic ketones, nickel and ruthenium are again the favored catalysts from the point of view of cost and activity. For aromatic ketones palladium exhibits the highest activity and, hence, is used commonly. Hydrogenolysis of the carbinols to hydrocarbons is a major side reaction in hydrogenation of aromatic ketones. Palladium exhibits high catalytic activity for this reaction as well. The activity for hydrogenolysis can be suppressed effectively by addition of alkali or organic bases [18, 19].

Aromatic Nitrocompounds

Hydrogenation of nitroaromatics is most commonly carried out using nickel, palladium, and platinum catalysts. Ruthenium is much less active as compared to palladium and platinum. Rhodium does exhibit high activity, but is not favored in practice due to its high cost. For the same reason platinum is less frequently used as compared to nickel and palladium. With proper choice of process conditions, quantitative yields of aromatic amines can be obtained. Partial reduction of nitroaromatics to the corresponding hydroxyl amines is of industrial interest since hydroxyl amines can be rearranged to a variety of useful products in different reaction media. Platinum has been found to be the most selective catalyst for the partial hydrogenation [20, 21]. The selectivity for phenyl hydroxyl amine can be further enhanced by addition of various additives [21]. Hydrogenation of halonitroaromatics also requires special type of catalysts since considerable dehalogenation occurs on nickel and palladium catalysts. Platinum exhibits lower activity for dehalogenation. Poisoned platinum catalysts can give quantitative conversion of halonitroaromatics to the corresponding haloanilines [22].

Carbocyclic Aromatics

Hydrogenation of carbocyclic aromatics is one of the difficult hydrogenations. Rhodium and ruthenium are the most active catalysts for this reaction. Greenfield [23] observed the following order of activity for hydrogenation of benzene and isobutylbenzene: Rh > Ru ≫ Pt ≫ Pd ≫ Ni > Co. The ring hydrogenation of most aromatic compounds can be carried out under mild conditions (ambient temperature) using rhodium. All other catalysts require elevated temperatures (>150°C) and pressures. Hydrogenolysis of the substituents and condensation of the reactant to form bi-cyclic products (in the case of anilines) are the important side reactions. Rhodium and ruthenium exhibit the lowest activity for these reactions and, hence, are the preferred catalysts from the consideration of both activity and selectivity. Addition of water has been observed to have very favorable effect on the activity of ruthenium catalysts [7]. Palladium has been found to be the most selective catalyst for partial hydrogenation of phenols to cyclohexanones [7]. Palladium is also used industrially for hydrogenation of benzoic acid to cyclohexane carboxylic acid [24].

Nitriles

Hydrogenation of nitriles can produce primary, secondary, and tertiary amines. The selectivity depends markedly on additives, solvent, support, and process conditions. The low molecular aliphatic nitriles have a greater tendency to form coupled products while the long chain nitriles produce primary amines more selectively. The noble metal catalysts have been observed to give predominantly secondary and tertiary amines while nickel has been found to be more selective towards primary amine [7]. Most common systems of industrial importance involve selective reduction of nitriles to primary amines. Hence, nickel is the most commonly used catalyst.

Choice of Support

The metallic catalysts normally employed in industrial practice contain metal dispersed in the form of small crystallites on a high surface area support. The primary function of the support is to increase the surface area of the active metal. In a slurry phase hydrogenation, the minimum particle size that can be handled without difficulty is about 5 microns. If a metallic catalyst is employed as spheres of this diameter, the metal surface area will be less than 0.5 m^2/g, while for noble metals supported on carbon or alumina, the metal surface area can be as high as 100 m^2/g of metal. Thus, the efficiency of the metal catalyst is greatly enhanced by using a support. The support also imparts stability to the metal surface area by reducing the rate of sintering. An additional function often performed by the support is that it serves as a sink for the adsorption of catalyst poisons.

The materials normally employed as support include kieselguhr, activated carbon, alumina, calcium carbonate, and barium sulphate. Approximate surface areas of these materials are given in Table 2. For nickel and cobalt catalysts, kieselguhr is the normally employed support. The catalysts normally have a metal content of 50 to 80% w/w. The optimal metal content of a catalyst is decided on the consideration of cost. As the metal content is decreased the metal surface area (per gram of metal) increases, however the quantity of support required for a given quantity of metal also increases. The optimum represents a compromise between the two factors. Since for base metals the optimum metal content is high, use of expensive high surface area supports is not justified.

Activated carbon is the most extensively used support for noble metal catalysts. The optimum metal content lies between 1 to 5%. Activated carbon offers very high surface areas as compared to other support materials. An important reason for the preference for carbon is the ease of recovery of noble metal from the spent catalyst. The noble metal can be separated from the support simply by controlled ignition of the carbon. A disadvantage in using carbon, however, is that it is believed to promote intermolecular condensation reactions of reactants and products. Rylander and coworkers [25, 26] observed that in hydrogenation of nitriles, oximes, and anilines formation of condensation products was somewhat higher on carbon as compared to alumina. In such systems, alumina supported catalysts may be preferred.

Although in slurry phase hydrogenation, the catalyst is employed in the form of fine particles of 5–50 micron diameter, pore diffusion within the particle can still play an important role. Such pore diffusion limitation can adversely affect the selectivity in the systems where the required product can undergo further reaction to give unwanted products. Hence, nonporous supports are to be preferred for such systems. Common examples of this type include hydrogenation of acetylenic compounds to olefins and reduction of acid chlorides to aldehydes. Calcium carbonate and barium sulphate are commonly employed as supports in such systems. Calcium carbonate should be prefered wherever possible since it can be readily dissolved in acid while recovering the noble metal. However, when acidic compounds are present in the reaction medium, barium sulphate has to be used.

Catalyst Structure

After having selected the metal and the support, it is essential to ensure that the catalyst has the desirable structure. The important structural parameters from the consideration of activity and

Table 2
Supports Used for Liquid Phase Hydrogenation Catalysts

Support	Surface Area, m^2/g
Carbon	800–1000
Alumina	150–300
Kieselguhr	15–40
Barium sulphate	1–10
Calcium carbonate	1–10

selectivity are textural properties of the support; metal crystallite size; and distribution of the metal within the support particles. Pore diffusional limitations adversely influence the activity and selectivity in most systems. Hence, supports with wider pores are generally desirable. However, with increase in the mean pore diameter, the surface area decreases. Supports like carbon, silica, and alumina are available with widely different textural properties. Selection of the support with optimum textural properties requires screening of catalysts made from the different support materials. The catalytic activity for hydrogenation reactions usually increases linearly with metal surface area. Hence, to achieve maximum efficiency, it would be necessary that the metal crystallite size is as small as possible. This is achieved by optimizing the procedure for impregnation of the metal precursor and the subsequent reduction. Usually, liquid phase hydrogenations are carried out using the standard catalysts offered by the catalyst manufacturers. The optimization required in the selection of the support and for maximizing the metal surface area is carried out by the catalyst manufacturers, and the user can spare himself from carrying out this arduous exercise.

The choice of distribution of metal on the support particles requires some careful consideration from the user. At one extreme the metal can be uniformly distributed throughout the support particle, another extreme would be to have the metal deposited on the external surface of the particle only and the core completely devoid of metal. The activity, selectivity, resistance to sintering and poisons can be very different for these two types of catalysts. This is very elegantly demonstrated in the study reported by Acres and co-workers [27, 28]. Some of their findings are discussed below to emphasize the importance of this factor.

Acres and co-workers [27] used three catalysts with similar composition but different types of distribution of palladium on the carbon particles.

Type 1—All the metal located on the external surface of the particles.

Type 2—Exponentially decreasing concentration of the metal from the surface to the interior.

Type 3—Uniformly distributed metal in the carbon particles.

Figure 1 shows the variation of metal surface area with the metal loading for the three types of

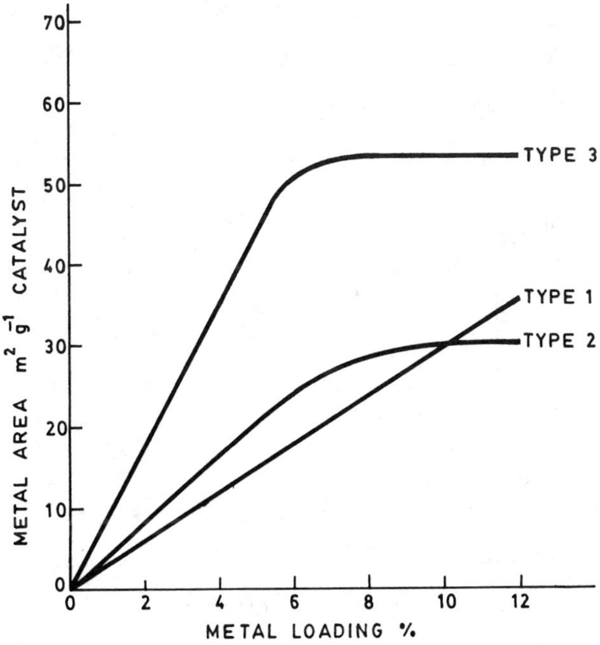

Figure 1. Variation of metal surface area with metal content. (Reprinted with permission from Ref. [27].)

catalysts. The metal area is maximum for the catalyst where metal is distributed over the whole surface area of the support. Figure 2 shows the variation of catalytic activity for hydrogenation of nitrobenzene with metal loading for the three types of catalysts. For each type of catalyst, the activity varies linearly with metal surface area. However, comparison of the activity of the three types of catalysts shows an inverse relationship with metal surface area. Hydrogenation of soya bean oil was also investigated on these catalysts. In this case as well, the Type 1 catalyst showed the highest activity while Type 3 was the least active (Table 3). To investigate the dependence of catalytic activity on distribution of the metal, the catalysts were examined by ESCA. The palladium signal observed by ESCA will be proportional to the amount of metal available on the external surface of the catalyst particles. Figure 3 shows the variation of Pd_{3d} signal with metal content for the three types of catalysts. A clear linear relationship between the Pd_{3d} signal and the catalytic activity is evident. The study clearly demonstrates that the metal deposited on the external surface is more effective than that located inside the support particle. Such behavior should arise due to the diffusional resistance that the reactant molecules must overcome to reach the metal located within.

However, the catalyst with metal predominantly on the external surface is not always desirable. Since in such a catalyst most of the support area is unused, the catalyst is prone to sintering. When Acres and co-workers studied hydrogenation of benzoic acid on the above catalyst, they observed that the Type 1 catalyst was the least efficient since it sintered easily at the higher temperature (373 K) required for this reaction. Thus, for reactions carried out at higher temperatures, it may be preferable to employ a catalyst where the metal is distributed over larger surface area.

Solvents

Solvents must be employed in liquid phase hydrogenation for a variety of reasons such as to dissolve solid reactants and products; to control the temperature rise by absorbing the heat generated

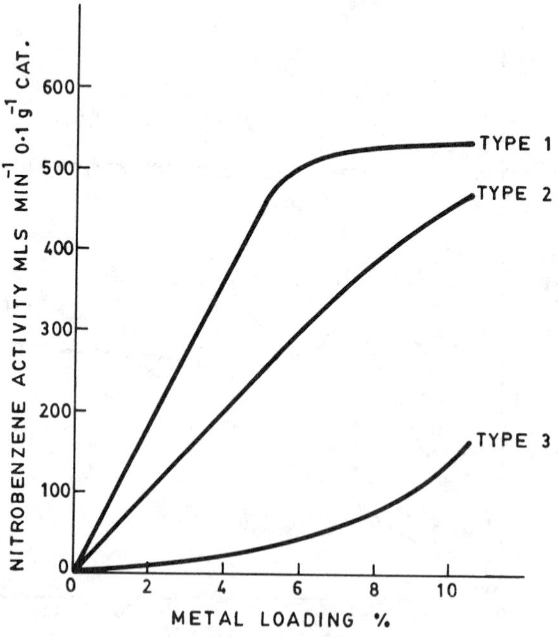

Figure 2. Variation of catalytic activity for hydrogenation of nitrobenzene with metal content. (Reprinted with permission from Ref. [27].)

Table 3
Effect of Catalyst Structure on Activity [27]

Catalyst	Palladium Content, %	Metal Area, m^2/g	Catalytic Activity (arbitrary units) Nitrobenzene	Soya Bean Oil	Pd_{3d} ESCA Counts, $\times 10^4$
Type 1	5.1	15	469	625	20.0
Type 2	4.91	23	243	328	8.0
Type 3	4.97	49	25	165	4.0

in highly exothermic reactions; and to increase life of the catalyst dissolving the carbonaceous residues formed on the catalyst surface. Although solvents are primarily employed for such reasons, they are also observed to have pronounced effect on the rate and selectivity of the reaction. Thus, the choice of solvent is an important factor in optimizing the process conditions and one can indeed tune the selectivity of a reaction by choosing an appropriate solvent.

Several factors can govern the effect of solvent on the rate of reactions. Some of the factors which are commonly recognised include:

1. Solubility of hydrogen in the reaction medium.
2. Competitive adsorption of solvent and reactants on the catalyst.
3. Agglomeration of catalyst in some solvents.
4. Intermolecular interaction between the reactant and solvent molecules.

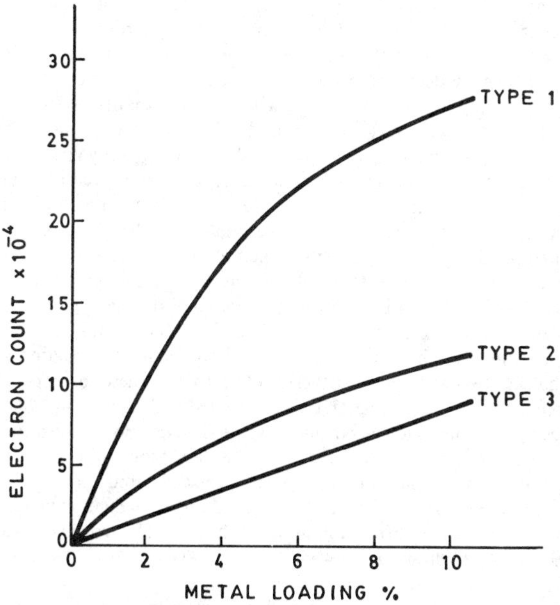

Figure 3. Variation of Pd_{3d} ESCA signal with metal content. (Reprinted with permission from Ref. [27].)

Table 4
Activity Coefficients of Acetone in Different Solvents [30]

Solvent	Activity Coefficient at 0.1 Mol Fraction and 298 K
i-Propanol	1.98
Methanol	2.25
n-Octane	4.43
i-Octane	4.43
n-Hexane	4.54
Cyclohexane	4.70

(Reprinted with permission from Ref. 30)

In order to make a rational choice of the solvent, it would be desirable that the relative importance of these factors is understood. This, however, presents some difficulties. It is difficult to investigate competitive adsorption of reactants and solvent experimentally. In the case of noble metal catalysts, in particular, it is difficult to discriminate between adsorption on the metal and that on the support. The problem of agglomeration is relevant mainly to the carbon supported catalysts. The agglomeration properties of carbon supported catalysts are indeed different in different solvents. But it is difficult to study the state of agglomeration under agitation. This factor, however, is likely to be unimportant at low concentration of catalysts normally employed in industrial practice. The solubility of hydrogen can be readily measured. The effect of intermolecular interaction can also be correlated with the various molecular properties of the reactants and the solvent and, thus, is amenable to investigation. Several researchers have, indeed, investigated the role of these factors. The findings of these studies are briefly reviewed below.

Kishida and Teranishi [29] studied hydrogenation of acetone over Raney nickel and observed that the rate decreased in different solvents in the following order: *n*-hexane > cyclohexane > methanol > *i*-propanol. They correlated the kinetic data by a Langmuir-Hinshelwood kinetic expression and showed that the decrease in the reaction rate is due to the increased contribution of the solvent adsorption term in the denominator, which implies that the solvent effect arises due to competitive adsorption. However, while correlating the kinetic data, they assumed that the surface reaction rate constant is the same in all the solvents. Recently, Rajadhyaksha and Karwa [30] estimated activity coefficients of acetone in various solvents which are given in Table 4. It is apparent that the order of variation of the reaction rate in different solvents observed by Kishida and Teranishi is the same as that of the activity coefficient of acetone. Thus, the observed variation of reaction rate can also be attributed to intermolecular interaction between acetone and the solvent.

Lemcoff [31] also studied hydrogenation of acetone over Raney nickel and observed that the rate decreased in different solvents in the following order: *i*-octane > *n*-octane > *i*-propanol. He showed that the variation of rate correlates with that of solubility parameters as well as dielectric constants of the solvents, thus implying that the thermodynamic interaction probably plays an important role. The variation of activity coefficient of acetone in these solvents (Table 4) also agrees with the variation of reaction rate. Caga et al. [32] studied hydrogenation of 1-octyne and phenyl acetylene on reduced palladium oxide in various solvents. The reaction rate was observed to decrease in the following order: methanol (23.9) > ethanol (16.8) > *n*-propanol (13.1) > *n*-butanol (11.3) > *n*-alkanes ($\sim$1.9). Values in the parentheses indicate dielectric constants of the solvents. A clear correlation between the reaction rate and dielectric constant is evident, which again implies a role of thermodynamic interactions. A correlation between the rate of hydrogenation and intermolecular interactions has also been emphasized by Iwamato et al. [33], Baltzly [34], Abe et al. [35], and Lo and Paulaitis [36].

Rajadhyaksha and Karwa [30] recently studied hydrogenation of *o*-nitrotoluene on palladium-on-carbon in various solvents. They also measured solubility of hydrogen in reaction medium under the reaction conditions. To investigate the role of thermodynamic interaction, activity coefficients of the reactant were estimated. Their results are summarized in Table 5. In agreement with the

Table 5
Hydrogenation of *o*-Nitrotoluene in Different Solvents

Solvent	H_2 Solubility in Reaction Mixture at 333 K, 1,380 kPa (ml of Hydrogen*/ml of Solution)	Activity Coefficient of *o*-Nitrotoluene at 333 K and 30% w/w	Specific Reaction Rate at 333 K ($\times 10^4$, gmol/gs)	Activation Energy, (kJ/gmol)
Methanol	0.809	5.1	2.14	34.36
i-Propanol	0.825	3.6	1.34	45.52
i-Butanol	0.844	3.3	1.31	50.08
Cyclohexanol	0.325	2.6	0.51	60.48
Hexane	1.981	3.7	1.29	66.21
Benzene	0.571	1.085	0.77	67.93
Methanol + DMSO (4%)	—	—	0.66	27.25

* *Volume as measured at 303 K and 101 kPa pressure.*

(Reprinted with permission from Ref. 30)

Table 6
Effect of Addition of Water on Hydrogenation of Nitrobenzene

Solvent	Activity Coefficient of *o*-Nitrotoluene in Reaction Medium	Rate of Hydrogenation at 333 K, gmol g^{-1} s^{-1}
Methanol	3.65	3.58
Methanol containing 18% w/w water	7.45	5.67

(Reprinted with permission from Ref. 30)

several previous studies, a correlation between the activity coefficient and reaction rate is evident. The authors further considered the mode in which the intermolecular interactions can influence the rate. The higher activity coefficient of the reactant in the solution phase (i.e., repulsive interaction between the solvent and the reactant) should result in higher concentration of the reactant in the sorbed phase on the surface of the catalyst. This should, in turn, result in increase in reaction rate. However, the hydrogenation of *o*-nitrotoluene over palladium-on-carbon was observed to be zero order in all the solvents. This implied that the catalyst was probably saturated with the nitro compound and, hence, variation of the sorbed phase concentration is not likely to be the cause of the variation in rate. The authors, therefore, measured the activation energies in different solvents, which are also given in Table 5. A decrease in activation energy with increase in activity coefficient is evident. This observation suggests that the solvent molecules can interact with the adsorbed reactant molecules on the catalyst surface and influence the energetics of the catalytic reaction and, thus, influence the rate. To demonstrate the effect of intermolecular interactions further, authors carried out hydrogenation of nitrobenzene on palladium-on-carbon in methanol and methanol-water mixture. The results are given in Table 6. Addition of water causes a dramatic increase in the value of activity coefficient and results in equally significant increase in the rate of reaction.

Thus, the results of the several reported studies indicate that thermodynamic interaction between the reactant and the solvent probably is an important factor governing the effect of solvent. Activity coefficient is a convenient measure of the intermolecular interaction, although it does not seem possible to arrive at a quantitative relationship between the rate and activity coefficient. A simple rule that emerges out these studies is that a polar solvent for a non-polar reactant and non-polar solvent for a polar reactant will give higher reaction rate.

Results of Rajadhyaksha and Karwa [30] show no correlation between the rate and solubility of hydrogen in the medium. It appears possible that the solubility of hydrogen may not have a significant effect on reaction rate. In a hydrogenation reaction, equilibrium exists between the adsorbed hydrogen on the catalyst and the dissolved hydrogen in the solution which, in turn, is in equilibrium with the hydrogen in the gas phase. In the experiments carried out with different solvents, the hydrogen pressure in the gas phase was the same and, hence, the hydrogen concentration in the sorbed phase could have remained the same in spite of significant variation in the solubility of hydrogen in the reaction medium. More experimental studies seem necessary to investigate the relevance of solubility of hydrogen.

Solvents can also influence the selectivity of hydrogenation reactions. The mechanism by which the solvents influence selectivity varies from system to system and no generalization seems possible in this regard. Improvement in selectivity could perhaps be more important to an industrial chemist since it can avoid recurring loss of a valuable reactant and minimize the separation problems. A few examples will be considered to demonstrate this effect.

Muth et al. [37] studied hydrogenation of 2-nitro-2-carbamoylbiphenyl, A, over platinum catalyst. When the reaction was carried out in tetrahydrofuran, N-hydroxyphenanthridone, B, was obtained in 70% yield. However, in ethanol, phenanthridone, C, was obtained in 91% yield. This marked difference in selectivity was attributed to the strong hydrogen bonding between the intermediate hydroxyl amine function with ethanol which prevents the cyclisation reaction.

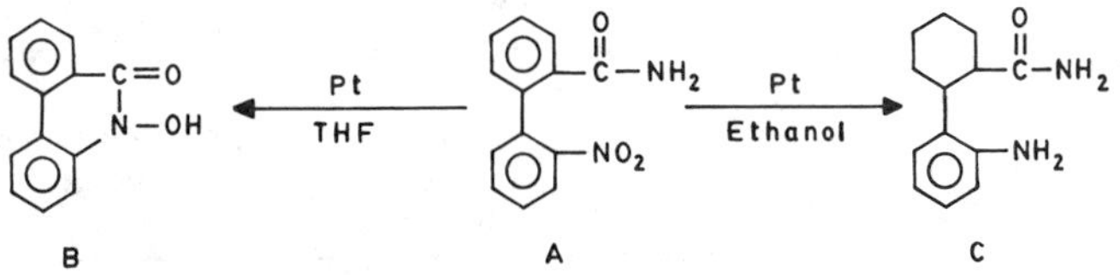

Karwa and Rajadhyaksha [38] studied partial hydrogenation of nitrobenzene over platinum on carbon catalyst in different solvents. Table 7 shows the maximum selectivity for phenyl hydroxyl amine observed in different solvents. The rate of reaction as well as selectivity show a marked variation and show a correlation with the dielectric constant of the solvent. With increase in dielectric constant the interaction between the solvent and phenyl hydroxyl amine becomes increasingly favorable. It was, therefore, proposed that more polar solvents aid the desorption of phenyl hydroxyl amine, thus, preventing its further hydrogenation to aniline.

Solvents can also influence stereoselectivity of hydrogeneration reactions. Augustine and co-workers [39, 40] studied hydrogenation of β-octalone over palladium in various solvents. Table 8

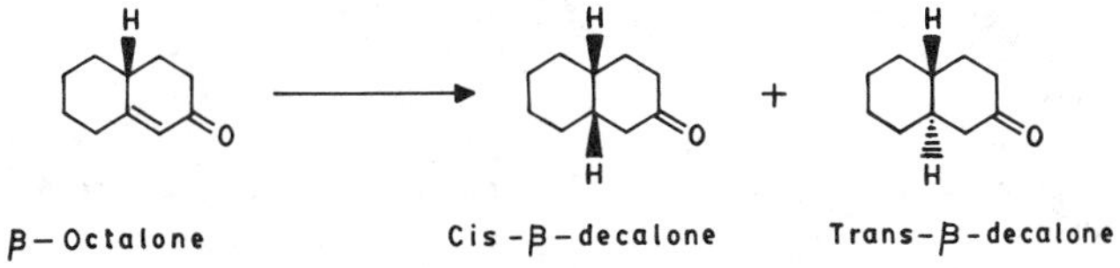

shows the yields of *cis-* and *trans-β*-decalone in different solvents. When all the solvents were considered together no correlation between the stereoselectivity and the properties of the solvent could be seen. However, when protic and aprotic solvents were separated a correlation between the stereoselectivity and the dielectric constant could be seen in each group. It is noteworthy that in protic solvents the percentage of *cis-β*-decalone decreases with increase in dielectric constant while in aprotic solvents it increases with increase in dielectric constant.

The studies considered in this section vividly demonstrate that the choice of solvent can be crucial in hydrogenation reactions. There is clearly more than one way in which solvents can influence the rate and selectivity. An important point that emerges from the reported studies is that solvent molecules probably directly interact with adsorbed reacting species and, hence, can modify the course of events occurring on the catalyst surface. Variation of activation energy and stereoselectivity of reactions with change in solvent are some of the observations that support the above view. In this light, the solvents ought to be considered as co-catalysts or promotors. It is rather fortuitous

Table 7
Partial Hydrogenation of Nitrobenzene to Phenyl Hydroxyl Amine in Different Solvents [42]

Solvent	Dielectric Constant	Maximum Selectivity to PHA, mol%	Time Required to Reach Maximum Concentration of PHA, secs
No solvent	—	15.6	9600
Benzene	2.23	11.5	11100
Ethyl acetate	6.00	22.0	9720
i-Butanol	18.7	67.0	6300
Methanol	32.6	70.0	2700
18% w/w water in methanol	—	76.0	2280

Table 8
Effect of Solvent on Stereoselectivity

Solvent	Dielectric Constant	*cis*-β-Decalone in Product, %
Aprotic solvents		
N,*N*-Dimethyl formamide	38.0	79
Acetone	21.0	63
Ethylacetate	6.0	57
Diethyl ether	4.3	58
Dioxane	2.2	52
Cyclohexane	2.1	51
n-Hexane	1.9	48
Hydroxylic solvents		
Methanol	33.6	41
i-Propanol	26.0	49
Ethanol	25.1	55
n-Propanol	21.8	68
sec-Butanol	18.7	70
n-Butanol	17.8	71
t-Butanol	10.9	91

(Reprinted with permission from Ref. 40)

that although the present understanding regarding the molecular interactions on catalyst surface is quite inadequate, it is still possible in many cases to correlate the rate and selectivity with the molecular properties of the solvents.

Additives

Addition of small quantities of various substances is known to have pronounced effects on the course of hydrogenation reactions. The additives can influence the rate and selectivity in various ways. Some of the mechanisms are given below.

1. Additives can block selectively the sites on the catalyst surface which are responsible for the undesirable reaction.
2. The additive can have the strength of adsorption intermediate between that of the reactant and product, so that it can be easily displaced from the catalyst surface by the reactant but it prevents adsorption of the product. The further reaction of the product can, thus, be prevented.
3. The additive can modify the electronic properties of the catalyst by adsorption.
4. The additive can act as a spacer on the catalyst surface by irreversible adsorption. This would prevent the intermolecular reactions of the reacting species.
5. The additive can act as a scavenger for catalyst poisons or harmful side products.

There is a large number of reported studies that demonstrate effect of additives. These are extensively reviewed in the book by Freifelder [8]. Additives are also commonly employed in industrial practice. The discussion here is restricted to a few examples to bring out the importance of this factor.

Hydrogenation of Nitrobenzene to Phenylhydroxylamine (PHA)

Selective hydrogenation of nitrobenzene to PHA can be carried out on platinum catalyst. The principal side reaction is the formation of aniline. It is observed that several additives like amines and sulfur compounds can improve selectivity to PHA but most of them greatly posion the catalyst. Rylander et al. [41] reported use of dimethyl sulfoxide (DMSO), which improved the selectivity markedly without any significant decline in rate. Karwa and Rajadhyaksha [38] observed that addition of as low as 1–2% (w/w) of DMSO improved the selectivity to PHA from 26% to 70%. The decrease in reaction rate was by a factor of 1.5. They observed that in the early part of the reaction PHA and aniline are formed simultaneously from nitrobenzene. Hydrogenation of PHA to aniline is probably poisoned in the presence of nitrobenzene and it occurs only when nitrobenzene is fully converted. Thus, there appear to be two types of sites on the catalyst surface: (a) sites where desorption of PHA is not possible and, hence, nitrobenzene is converted to aniline, and (b) sites where PHA can desorb without further reaction. DMSO probably blocks the former sites selectively, thus, improving the selectivity to PHA. Figure 4 shows the effect of DMSO concentration on the reaction rate and selectivity [42].

Resenmund Reduction

The Rosenmund reduction involves hydrogenation of acid chloride to aldehyde. The undesirable reactions are the subsequent conversion of aldehyde to alcohol and alkane.

$$R.COCl \xrightarrow{Pd/BaSO_4} RCHO + HCl \longrightarrow RCH_2OH \longrightarrow RCH_3 + H_2O$$

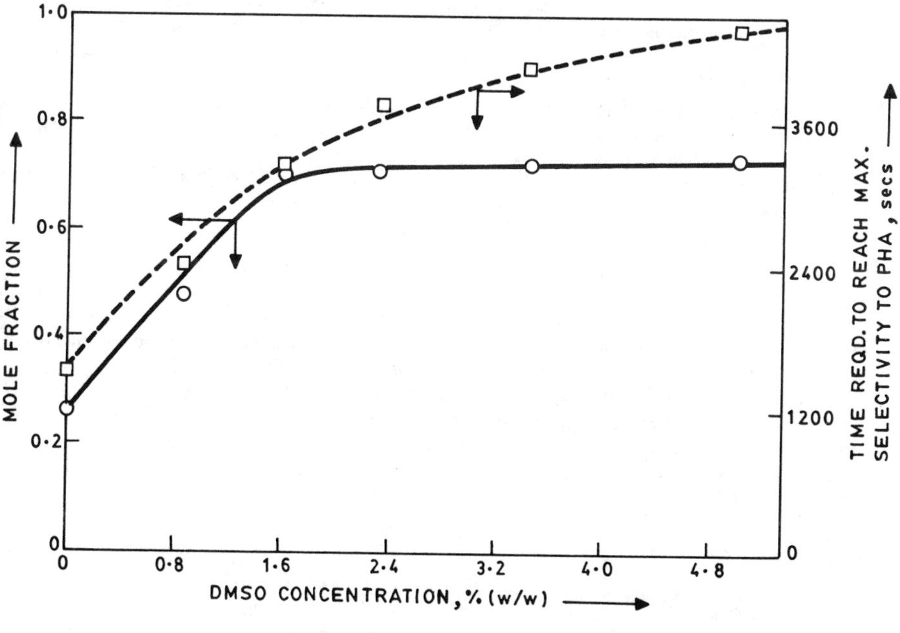

Figure 4. Effect of concentration of dimethyl sulfoxide on the rate and selectivity of partial hydrogenation of nitrobenzene to PHA.

Table 9
Effect of Additives on Hydrogenation of *o*-Nitrochlorobenzen [22]

Catalyst	Inhibitor	Hydrogenation time, min	Product	
			Aniline	2-Chloronitrobenzene
Pd-on-C*	—	75	52.4	44.9
Pd-on-C (sulfided)	—	110	5.4	93.4
Pd-on-C	Dicyandiamide 1%	115	2	96.8
Pt-on-C*	—	85	23.6	73.5
Pt-on-C (sulfided)	—	105	<0.2	>99.8
Pt-on-C	Dicyandiamide 1%	105	<0.2	>99.8
Nickel** (113 W)	—	20	52.4	
Nickel	Dicyandiamide 1.7 g	27	0.3	98.8

Reaction conditions:
* *157 g 2-chloronitrobenzene in 80 ml methanol, 0.2 g catalyst, pressure—1 MPa, temperature—398 K*
** *62.8 g 2-chloronitrobenzene in 180 ml methanol, 1.6 g nickel, pressure—1 MPa, temperature—393 K*

Formation of alcohol and water further reduce the yield since they react with the acid chloride. The reaction is commonly carried out using palladium catalyst. Refluxing temperature is employed to flush out the hydrochloric acid formed.

Additives like quinoline-S, thiourea, and thiophene have been shown to improve the selectivity for the aldehyde [43]. It was proposed that hydrogenation of aldehyde requires multiple sites on the catalyst surface and the additives reduce the probability of such ensembles of sites being available on the catalyst surface. It is also possible that the additives prevent the adsorption of aldehyde but not of the acid chloride.

Peters and Van Bekkum [44] employed ethyl diisopropylamine, both as additive and acid acceptor. Refluxing temperatures were not necessary since the acid was scavanged by the amine. The amine also prevented subsequent reduction of aldehyde. The reaction could be carried at room temperature and with high selectivity; the over-reduction was always less than 1% and almost no decarbonylation could be detected.

Reduction of Halonitroaromatics

In the reduction of halonitroaromatics, significant dehalogenation occurs on palladium and nickel catalysts. Better selectivity is achieved on platinum catalysts. The dehalogenation can be effectively suppressed on all the three catalysts by employing appropriate additives. Strätz [22] has reported data on the effect of additives on a variety of commercial catalysts offered by Degussa. The data are summarised in Table 9. Sulfided platinum catalyst give high selectivity without the addition of inhibitor. Dicyandiamide is shown to be a very effective additive. Other additives, which have also been employed successfully, include morpholine, triethylphosphite, phosphorous acid, and tetraethylene pentamine.

Hydrogenation of Acetophenone

In hydrogenation of acetophenone, hydrogenolysis of the phenyl ethanol to ethyl benzene is the undesirable side reaction. The hydrogenolysis is known to be favored by acids and suppressed by bases. Table 10 shows the maximum yield of phenylethanol obtained in the presence of acidic and basic additives [45] over 5% palladium-on-carbon catalyst in methanol.

Table 10
Effect of Additives on Hydrogenation of Acetophenone

Additive	Mol Per Mol of Acetophenone	Maximum Yield of Phenylethanol, %
None	—	90
Acetic acid	0.20	60
Hydrochloric acid	0.014	76
Sodium hydroxide	0.008	100

(Reprinted from Ref. 45 with permission)

Hydrogenation of Glucose

Hydrogenation of glucose to sorbitol is commonly carried out using Raney nickel catalyst. Shetkar and Rajadhyaksha [46] studied the effect of adding molybdic acid and chromic acid on the rate of reaction. Table 11 shows that addition to the extent of 0.01 to 0.02% w/w on glucose resulted in almost two fold increase in reaction rate. Use of such additives can give considerable reduction of catalyst cost.

INDUSTRIAL LIQUID PHASE HYDROGENATION PROCESSES

Hydrogenation of Vegetable Oils

The naturally produced vegetable oils consist of a complex mixture of triglycerides of saturated, monoenic, and polyunsaturated fatty acids. Most of the oils contain triglycerides of C_{16} and C_{18} fatty acids, although some containing as high as C_{30} acids have also been identified (e.g., fish oils). The common fatty acids include stearic acid, palmitic acid (both saturated), oleic acid (one double bond), linoleic acid (two double bonds), and linolenic acid (three double bonds). The saturated acids are unsuitable for human consumption and have high melting point. The polyunsaturated acids have poor stability against oxidation and polymerization. Oxidation of oils results in rancidity and loss of flavor. Thus, the saturated as well as polyunsaturated acids are undesirable and it is necessary to maximize the content of mono- and di-unsaturated acids. The *cis* isomers of unsaturated acids are more easily assimilated in the human body and have high nutritious value. The *trans* acids are not assimilated in the body. The oleic, linoleic, and linolenic acids present in natural oils have the desired *cis* configuration at all the double bonds.

The hydrogenation of oils is carried out primarily to hydrogenate the polyunsaturated acids so that the oil has high stability against oxidation during storage and also at high temperatures

Table 11
Effect of Additives on Hydrogenation of Glucose

Catalyst	Additive	Conversion of Glucose to Sorbitol in 3,600 secs, %
Raney nickel	—	41.6
Raney nickel	0.02% molybdic acid	78.5
Raney nickel	0.01% chromic acid	78.6

Reaction conditions: 30% glucose (w/w) in water, 2.1% Raney nickel (w/w on glucose), temperature—513 K, pressure—5.5 MPa

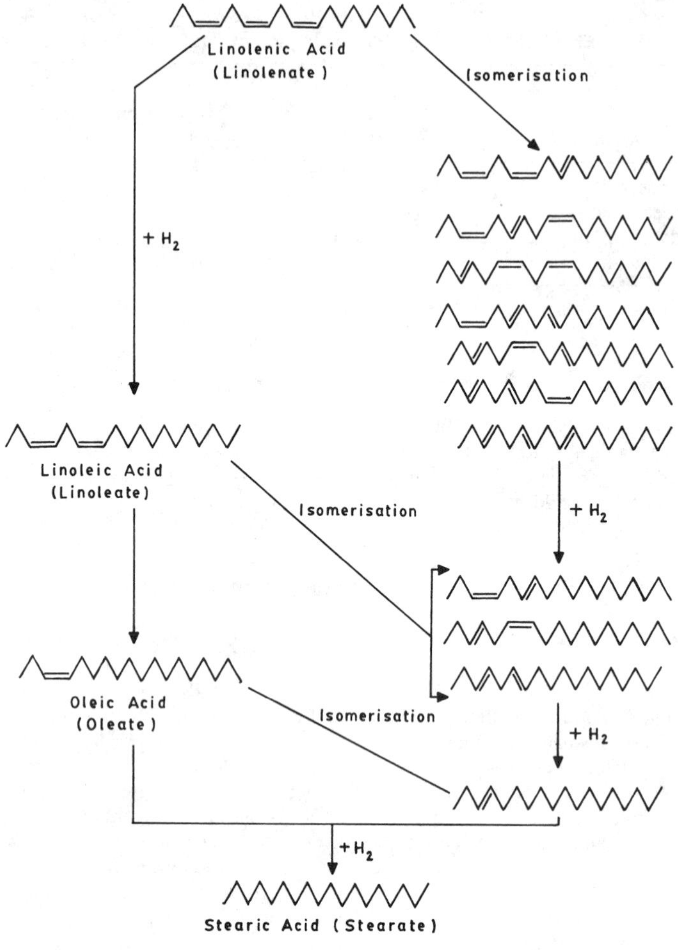

Figure 5. Schematic diagram of the reactions involved in hydrogenation of vegetable oils.

employed while frying. The hydrogenation, however, is accompanied by *cis-trans* isomerization and double bond migration. The typical transformations taking place during hydrogenation are schematically shown in Figure 5 [28]. The hydrogenation is to be achieved with minimum formation of saturated acids so that the oil remains liquid up to $-5°C$ and no turbidity arises due to crystallization of saturated triglycerides. Further, it is also essential to minimize formation of *trans* acids due to their lower nutritious value. Thus, hydrogenation of oils involves several selectivities [47]:

Selectivity I (S_I): Measures the preferential hydrogenation of linoleic acid as compared to oleic acid.

Selectivity II (S_{II}): Measures the preferential hydrogenation of linolenic acid over linoleic acid. This selectivity is very important since it is desirable to hydrogenate polyunsaturated acids without hydrogenating linoleic acid, which has high nutritional value.

Selectivity of isomerization (S_i): Defined as number of *trans* double bonds formed per double bond hydrogenated.

Triglyceride selectivity (S_T): Measures the extent to which the three fatty acid components of a triglyceride molecule are hydrogenated independently. If all the three fatty acid residues of a given triglyceride molecule are fully saturated, the resultant tristearin has low solubility in oil and its presence in relatively small amounts raises the melting point very significantly. Thus, it is preferable that the fully saturated fatty acid residues are randomly distributed in all the triglyceride molecules. If the catalyst has tendency to adsorb the triglyceride molecule in such a way that once it is adsorbed, all the three fatty acid residues get hydrogenated before the molecule desorbs, the catalyst would have very poor triglyceride selectivity.

A good catalyst for oil hydrogenation should have high S_I, S_{II}, and S_T, and low S_i. The efficiency of various metals has been investigated for hydrogenation of oils. Nickel exhibits high activity for the reaction, however, has low values of S_I and S_{II}. It also leads to the formation of *trans* acids in significant amount. Nickel, however, exhibits good resistance to poisons that are always present in vegetable oils in trace amounts [48]. Copper catalysts exhibit very high values of S_I and S_{II} [49, 50]. However, copper catalysts have considerably lower activity as compared to nickel and they are sensitive to poisons, which does not allow their reuse. The overall consumption of copper catalysts is, thus, 5–10 times that of nickel catalysts, which makes them unsuitable for industrial use [48]. Further, small traces of copper in the end product catalyse oxidation of oil.

Rylander [51] has discussed application of noble metals to hydrogenation of oils. The noble metal catalysts show the following order of activity:

$$\text{Pd} > \text{Rh} > \text{Pt} \gg \text{Ir} > \text{O}_s$$

The order of activity for *cis-trans* isomerization is

$$\text{Pd} > \text{Rh} > \text{Ru} > \text{Ir} > \text{Pt}$$

Thus, although palladium has high activity for hydrogenation, it also catalyzes *cis-trans* isomerization to the highest extent. In this respect palladium is inferior to nickel. However, palladium exhibits high S_I and S_{II} as compared to nickel. Further, palladium does not form soap with free fatty acids. Soap formation indeed occurs with nickel and copper. Palladium is 80–100 times more active than nickel. The main reason that has so far prevented use of palladium in industrial practice is its sensitivity to poisons. Palladium is required to be employed in much smaller quantities as compared to nickel, and hence, is more susceptible to poisoning.

Thus, although nickel exhibits poor S_I and S_{II}, considerations of cost compel its use in industrial practice. Nickel is almost exclusively used for hydrogenation of oils. The commercial catalyst contains about 60–70% nickel supported on kieselguhr. Since the catalyst is pyrophoric after reduction, it is often coated with saturated oil and supplied in the form of flakes. The structure of support is indeed very important. Coenen et al. [47] studied the effect of the pore structure of support on selectivity. The activity as well as selectivity was observed to be superior on supports with wider pores due to absence of pore diffusional limitations.

The selectivities S_I and S_{II} are also influenced by process conditions. The catalyst has a preference for hydrogenation of polyunsaturates since they have higher strength of adsorption. Hence, high selectivity can be achieved by plentiful supply of polyunsaturates to the catalyst surface. Thus, in order to achieve high selectivity, it is necessary to ensure absence of concentration gradients in the liquid phase so that the concentration of polyunsaturates at the catalyst surface is equal to their concentration in the bulk. This requires the reaction rates at the catalyst surface to be carefully controlled. Further, it is observed that high S_I and S_{II} can be achieved if hydrogen concentration on the catalyst surface is low. Thus, the reaction ought to be carried out at a lower pressure and at a lower degree of agitation so that hydrogen concentration in the liquid phase as well as on the catalyst surface is lowered due to gas-liquid diffusional limitation. The hydrogenation is typically carried out between 450–525 K and at 200–300 kPa pressure of hydrogen.

Most oil hydrogenations are carried out in batch reactors. The oil hydrogenation plants are often required to switch from one feed stock to another depending on the availability of oils and also are required to tailor the properties of the product. Batch reactors offer the flexibility necessary to suit their requirement. Although continuous plants offer better heat economy, they are inflexible in this respect. A change over of a feedstock requires about three times the residence time of the system to produce a product of required characteristics and during this period off-standard product will be obtained. However, if a regular supply of a particular feedstock is available, the continuous operation yields a product of more consistent quality than batch operation [48].

Fixed-bed reactors have been found unsuitable for hydrogenation of oils for a variety of reasons. The principal reason is the pore diffusional limitations that arise due to use of pelleted catalyst. This influences the selectivities S_I and S_{II} very adversely. Further, poisoning of the catalyst can result in short catalyst life, which is also unsuitable for fixed-bed operation. Continuous stirred tank reactors also give poor selectivities due to spread of residence time. Due to a wide residence time distribution, some of the oil gets over hydrogenated while some escapes with little or no hydrogenation. The former results in poor melting point characteristics while the latter gives poor oxidation stability. To narrow the residence time distribution, five to six stirred tanks in series are employed in practice [48]. A BUSS system for oil hydrogenations consists of 4–6 loop reactors in series. The reactors have a common hydrogen headspace and the oil flows from one compartment to another [52].

Hydrogenation of Glucose

Sorbitol finds several applications in the pharmaceutical, food, and resin industries. It is employed as a sweetener in several medical preparations and is an intermediate for the manufacture of Vitamin C. Sorbitol is also employed in manufacture of resins along with other polyols. It is manufactured by hydrogenation of aqueous solution of glucose or as a mixture with manitol by hydrogenation of fructose. Glucose is obtained by hydrolysis of starchy material in the form of syrup. The syrup contains traces of natural materials like proteins that act as poisons for the catalyst employed for hydrogenation. The syrup is, therefore, required to be purified by ion exchange or crystallization of glucose followed by redissolution in demineralized water. The principal side reactions in the hydrogenation are caramelization, Cannizaro reaction to produce gluconic acid, and isomerization leading to formation of manitol. The reaction is preferably carried out below 413 K to prevent caramelization. To minimize the Cannizaro reaction, the reaction is carried out in mildly acidic solution. The gluconic acid formed is often removed by treating the product solution in an ion-exchanger.

$$
\begin{array}{ccc}
\text{CHO} & & \text{CH}_2\text{OH} \\
| & & | \\
\text{H}-\text{C}-\text{OH} & & \text{H}-\text{C}-\text{OH} \\
| & & | \\
\text{HO}-\text{C}-\text{H} & \xrightarrow{\text{H}_2} & \text{HO}-\text{C}-\text{H} \\
| & & | \\
\text{H}-\text{C}-\text{OH} & & \text{H}-\text{C}-\text{OH} \\
| & & | \\
\text{H}-\text{C}-\text{OH} & & \text{H}-\text{C}-\text{OH} \\
| & & | \\
\text{CH}_2\text{OH} & & \text{CH}_2\text{OH}
\end{array}
$$

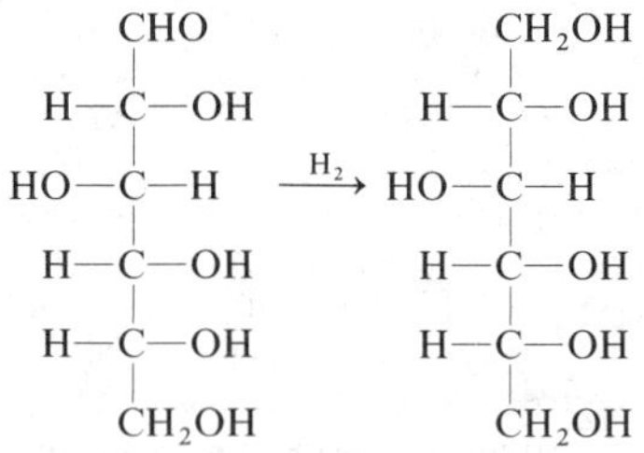

About 80% of world production of sorbitol is carried out employing Raney nickel catalyst [53]. The hydrogenation is carried out using 35–50% aqueous solution of glucose at 393–423 K and 7–10 MPa pressure. The choice of Raney nickel appears to be due to its lower cost as compared to the supported catalyst. Degussa has developed a molybdenum doped catalyst [53], that is reported to have a higher resistance to poisons and able to reduce formation of gluconic acid and manitol. Noble metal catalysts have been extensively investigated for this reaction. Ruthenium based catalyst are found to be most promising [53–56]. Recently, Cora Engineering Company has announced a process based on a noble metal catalyst [57]. The principal advantages of the process are claimed to be:

1. Low pressure and low temperature operation (3 MPa and 393 K).
2. Glucose syrup can be used as such since the catalyst is resistant to poisons.
3. The catalyst is resistant to acidic conditions.
4. Plant capital cost is reduced by 20%.

The possibility of employing highly acidic conditions with ruthenium also permits polyols to be obtained directly from cellulosic materials by simultaneous hydrolysis and hydrogenation [54, 55].

Most of the plants in the world involve batch operation. The continuous processes commonly employ two or three bubble column slurry reactors in series. To ensure adequate turbulence for suspension of the catalyst and high mass transfer coefficients, high L/D (>20) and high gas velocities (10 moles of hydrogen per mole of glucose) are employed. The selectivity in continuous process is reported to be lower than that in batch reactor [58]. Although there are many patents on fixed bed process, very few plants are known to employ this in practice. The plant of VEB in Germany employs a trickle bed reactor using supported copper oxide and nickel oxide as catalyst. The reaction is carried out at 408 K and 20 MPa pressure [59]. Trickle bed reactor offers several advantages for this system. Since long contact times can be provided, the reaction can be carried out at lower temperature, which minimizes side reactions. Low liquid hold-up also suppresses homogeneous side reactions. If supported ruthenium catalyst is to be employed, the additional advantage will be reduction in loss of the expensive catalyst due to the reduced handling.

Hydrogenation of Aromatic Nitro Compounds

A variety of aromatic nitro compounds are hydrogenated to corresponding amines in large quantities. The principal amines to be produced by this route are aniline and toluene-diamine. The major outlet for these amines is for the manufacture of polyurethanes. Aniline also finds application in the manufacture of rubber chemicals, dyes, and agricultural products. Other nitro compounds to be hydrogenated include nitrotoluenes, nitroanisoles, nitrophenols, nitroanilines, and *m*-dinitrobenzene. The aromatic amines produced from these compounds are mainly used in the manufacture of dyestuffs. The reduction of the nitrocompounds can be carried out in quantitative yields.

A variety of products of industrial importance can be produced by hydrogenation of nitrocompounds in basic or acidic media. A generally accepted reaction mechanism for formation of various products from nitrobenzene is shown in Figure 6. Reduction of nitrobenzene in acidic medium can result in rearrangement of the intermediate phenyl hydroxyl amine (PHA) to form a variety of disubstituted anilines depending on the reaction medium. A major industrial product manufactured by this route is *p*-aminophenol. In basic media, the partially hydrogenated products of nitro compound react to form azoxybenzene. This can undergo further hydrogenation to form hydroazobenzene, which is an important industrial intermediate. Reduction of halonitroaromatics and partial reduction of dinitroaromatics pose problems of selectivity. Special catalysts have been developed for hydrogenation of these compounds, which give selectivities acceptable for industrial operation. The principles of these hydrogenation processes are briefly discussed in the following section.

Reduction of Aromatic Nitro Compounds to Amines

Aniline is mostly produced by vapor phase hydrogenation in either fixed-bed or fluidized-bed reactors. However, several liquid phase processes are also being practiced [22]. Due to the high volume of production, the hydrogenation is carried out mostly in continuous mode. The reaction is typically carried out at 353–393 K employing palladium-on-carbon or nickel-on-silica catalysts. Yield of aniline is reported to be over 99%.

Toluenediamine is exclusively produced in liquid phase mainly due to excessively high heat of reaction. The different processes differ in the choice of catalyst, solvent, reaction conditions, and the type of reactor. Strätz [22] has described the principal features of the various processes. The Du Pont process employs a continuous stirred tank reactor with external filter. Palladium-on-carbon is used as catalyst and the reaction is carried out at 343–353 K and 0.5–0.7 MPa pressure. The product itself serves as the solvent and the concentration of the reactant is kept as low as 0.5%. The yields are reported to be over 99%. The process of Olin Mathieson employs a continuous stirred tank reactor with an internal filter. The reaction is carried out using nickel catalyst (supported or Raney type) at 383–413 K and 2.5–3.5 MPa pressure using methanol as solvent.

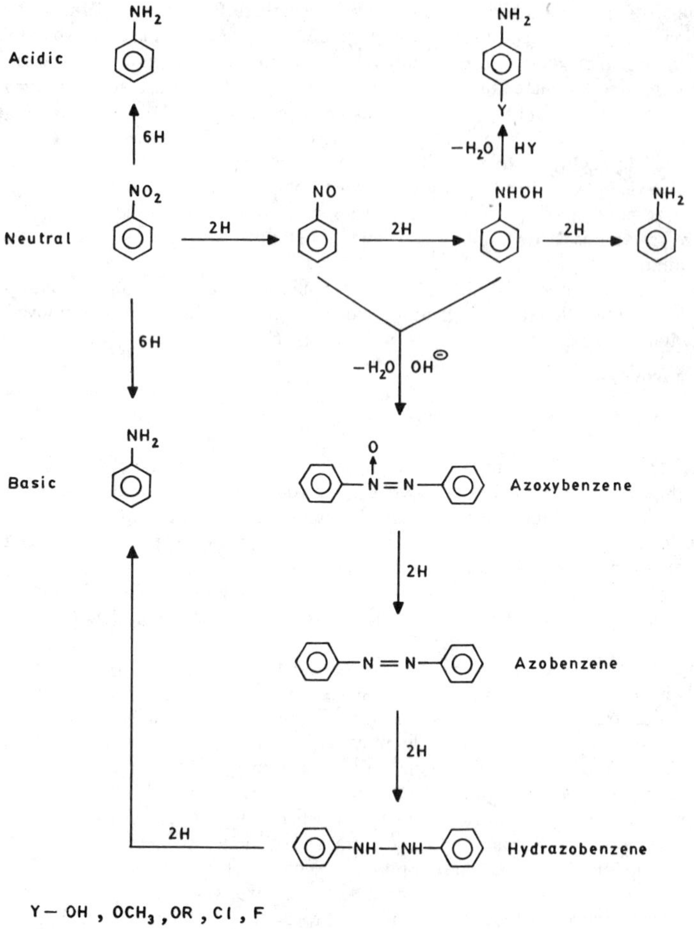

Figure 6. Network of reactions involved in hydrogenation of nitroaromatics.

The Bayer/Mobay process employs four bubble column slurry reactors in series. The product solution containing 33% toluenediamine, 19% water, and rest methanol is recycled as the solvent. About half of the feed is added to the first reactor and one quarter each to the second and the third reactor. The reaction is carried out below 373 K at 15–20 MPa pressure using nickel based catalyst. Yield of toluenediamine is over 98%.

Reductions of most other nitrocompounds to amines is carried out in batch reactors using nickel or palladium catalysts.

Selective Hydrogenation to Phenyl Hydroxyl Amine (PHA) and Its Rearrangements

Selective hydrogenation of nitrobenzene to PHA has been studied by several workers [38, 41, 60, 61]. Rylander and co-workers [60] showed that platinum-on-carbon is the most selective catalyst for the reaction. The selectivity to PHA could be improved considerably by addition of

Table 12
Effect of Substituents on Partial Reduction of Nitroaromatics [42]

Nitroaromatic	Maximum Selectivity to Hydroxyl Amine, mol%	Time Required to Reach the Maximum Concentration of Hydroxyl Amine, secs
Nitrobenzene	70	2700
2-Nitrochlorobenzene	59	3720
2-Nitrotoluene	45	4800
2-Nitroanisole	38	6300

Reaction conditions: 30% w/w nitroaromatic in methanol, catalyst loading—5% Pt-on-C, 0.3% w/w on substrate, DMSO concentration—1.6% w/w on substrate, temperature—333 K, pressure—1.5 MPa

dimethyl sulphoxide (DMSO). Karwa and Rajadhyaksha [38] studied the reaction under wide variety of conditions on platinum-on-carbon catalyst using DMSO as additive. The reaction was investigated in the temperature range 303–333 K. The selectivity to PHA was observed to be higher at lower temperatures. The selectivity was unaffected by variation of pressure from 0.7 to 2.1 MPa. Aniline was found to be the major product on palladium-on-carbon catalyst.

The additional substituents were observed to have significant effect on the rate and selectivity. Table 12 shows that both the rate and the selectivity decrease with increase in the electron-releasing tendency of the substituent.

PHA undergoes Bamberger's rearrangement in acidic medium to yield para substituted aniline with some ortho isomer. The rearranged products can be obtained in one step by hydrogenating the nitrocompound in acidic medium, so that the hydroxyl amine undergoes rearrangement as soon as it is formed. The rearrangement is believed to occur in the following manner:

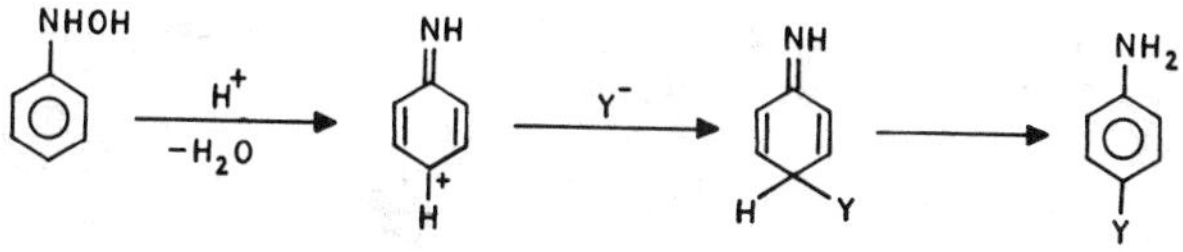

The substituent incorporated during the rearrangement depends on the reaction medium. In aqueous sulphuric acid, *p*-amino-phenol is the predominant product while in methanolic sulphuric acid, *p*-anisidine is the major product. If anhydrous hydrochloric acid or hydrofluoric acid is used *p*-chloroaniline and *p*-fluoroaniline are obtained as principal products [62].

The industrial product produced by this route is *p*-amino phenol. Hydrogenation of nitrobenzene is carried out over platinum catalyst in dilute sulfuric acid. The major by-products are aniline and *o*-aminophenol. Yields of *p*-aminophenol have been reported in the range of 75–85% [22].

Reduction of Nitrocompounds in Basic Media

Azoxy, azo, and hydrazo compounds can be obtained by catalytic hydrogenation of the appropriate nitro compound in alkaline medium. Most of the information about this reaction is in the form of patents. Recently, Karwa and Rajadhyaksha [63] investigated this reaction on platinum and palladium catalysts. The reactions were carried in methanolic solution in the temperature range 353–383 K, pressure range 1.5–3.5 MPa and alkali concentration 3–10%. Platinum-on-carbon catalyst was found to give higher selectivity than the palladium catalyst. Figure 7 shows typical variation of product composition with time. Aniline, azobenzene, and azoxybenzene are formed simultaneously as nitrobenzene is consumed. Further hydrogenation of azo and azoxybenzene is

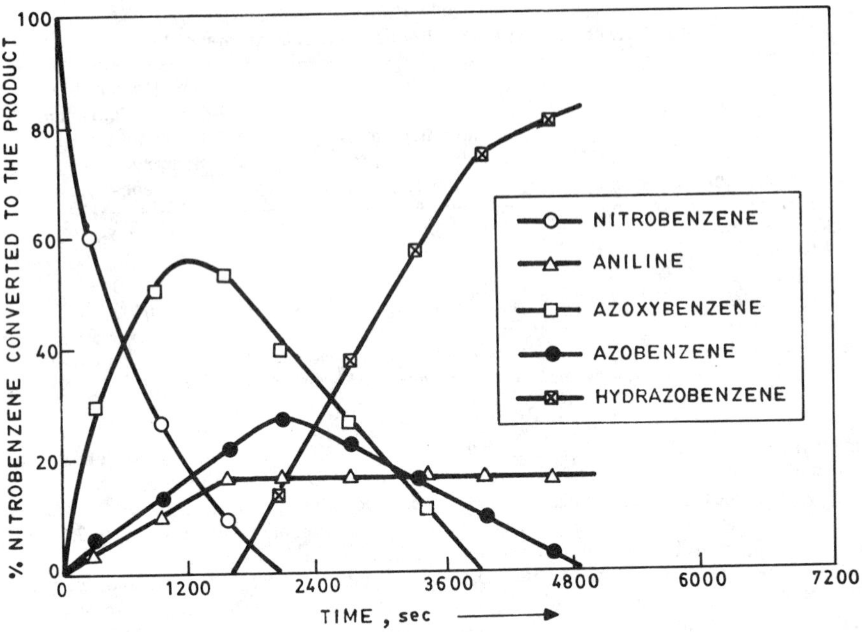

Figure 7. Typical variation of product composition in hydrogenation of nitrobenzene in basic medium.

poisoned in the presence of nitrobenzene. After all the nitrobenzene is converted, azo and azoxybenzene are quantitatively hydrogenated to hydrazobenzene. The maximum yield of hydrazobenzene was observed to be 85%. The yield could be further improved by addition of DMSO. However, the rate of reaction was significantly reduced by the addition. In the case of substituted nitrobenzenes, the rate and selectivity was observed to decrease when electron-releasing substituents were present.

Hydrogenation of Halonitro and Polynitro Aromatics

The catalysts commonly employed for hydrogenation of nitrocompounds catalyze dehalogenation and, hence, are unsuitable for reduction of halonitro aromatics. Over the last twenty years, a variety of catalyst inhibitors that suppress dehalogenation selectively have been discovered [22]. Sulfided palladium and platinum catalysts also permit synthesis of haloamines in high yields. Selectivities obtainable with the modified catalysts are already given in Table 9.

In the reduction of dinitro compounds, selective reduction of only one nitro group is often required. The conventional route to achieve this selective reduction is by using sodium sulfide or polysulfide as reductant in alkaline medium. This method often gives unacceptable yields and can present pollution problems. Attempts have been made to develop selective catalysts for such reductions. Jones et al. [64] studied hydrogenation of dinitro compounds of wide variety of catalysts. Raney copper proved to be uniquely selective for the hydrogenation of 2,4-dinitroalkyl benzenes. 2,4-dinitropropyl benzene could be reduced to 4-amino-2-nitropropyl benzene with 80–92% yields. Selectivity for reduction in para position increased with the steric hindrance of the alkyl group. The selectivity decreased when more electron-releasing substituents were present on the ring. Raney copper may prove to be attractive for industrial use for specific systems.

Hydrogenation of Adiponitrile

Hexamethylenediamine (HMDA), which is one of the principal raw materials for the manufacture of nylon-66, is almost exclusively manufactured by hydrogenation of adiponitrile. Only a small fraction is made by ammonolysis of hexamethylenediol. Hydrogenation is necessarily carried out in liquid phase since HMDA is unstable at the boiling point of adiponitrile. The principal problem in the hydrogenation is the coupling reaction of the intermediates in the reaction. Since noble metals catalyze formation of secondary and tertiary amines, they are not suitable for the reaction. Most industrial processes employ nickel or cobalt based catalysts [65]. Adiponitrile can also undergo cyclization to form 1,2-diaminocyclohexane. Cobalt has a lower tendency to catalyze this reaction as compared to nickel [20]. The formation of side products is suppressed by adding large excess of ammonia. Several patents claim that incorporation of promotors such as manganese, copper, aluminium improve activity of cobalt catalysts [20].

Several processes for the manufacture of HMDA has been described in the literature [66, 67]. With cobalt catalyst, temperatures above 373 K and pressures of 60–65 MPa are employed. With nickel catalyst, the reaction is carried out at 348 K and 3 MPa pressure. The selectivity obtained with cobalt catalysts is reported to be superior. A Du Pont process employs iron oxide catalyst at temperatures in the range 373–453 K and pressures of 30–35 MPa. Selectivity of 90–95% can be obtained when cobalt or iron catalysts are employed. Fixed-bed reactors are preferred due to high pressures employed for the reaction. While with nickel catalyst, which catalyze the reaction at lower pressure, slurry reactors are commonly employed.

Manufacture of Hydrogen Peroxide

Hydrogen peroxide is produced by a cyclic process where an alkyl anthraquinone is hydrogenated to the corresponding hydroquinone, and then the hydroquinone is oxidized by air to produce hydrogen peroxide and the original anthraquinone. The hydrogen peroxide dissolved in organic phase is stripped into water by counter-current extraction in a packed column. The organic phase is then treated to remove side products and is recycled.

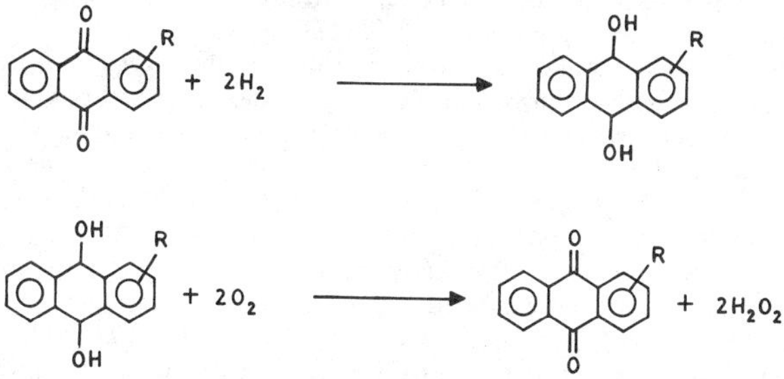

Pistor [68] has reviewed various processes employed for the manufacture of hydrogen peroxide. Several processes employ a mixture of alkyl anthraquinone and alkyl tetrahydroquinone. The most commonly used pair is 2-ethylanthraquinone (EAQ) and 2-ethyltetrahydroquinone (THEAQ) [69]. To increase the solubility of the anthraquinone and the hydroquinone in the organic solvent, other substituents like *t*-butyl and 2-amyl have also been employed [20]. The solvent is always a mixture of a aromatic hydrocarbon like benzene or xylene and C_7–C_{11} alcohols. The solubility of the anthraquinone and the hydroquinone and the need to minimize loss of solvent during extraction of hydrogen peroxide are the principal considerations in selection of the solvent system.

Raney nickel and supported palladium catalysts have been used in industrial practice for this reaction [65]. Palladium catalyst offers several advantages over nickel [70]. It exhibits high activity for hydrogenation of aromatic ketones; and is nonpyrophoric, and hence, is not affected by the unextracted hydrogen peroxide or the dissolved oxygen present in the recycled organic phase. Further, the principal side reactions in the hydrogenation are saturation of the aromatic ring and hydrogenolysis of the hydroxyl function. Palladium catalysts have been observed to be satisfactory in minimizing these side reactions. The life of palladium catalysts has also been observed to be longer as compared to nickel. In view of this, palladium catalysts are widely preferred in practice. The reaction is typically carried out at 303–309 K and 200 kPa pressure. Fixed-bed as well as slurry reactors have been used [20].

ASYMMETRIC HYDROGENATION

In the manufacture of several drugs, synthesis of a specific optical isomer is often required. The conventional synthetic methods lead to formation of racemic mixtures of the enantiomers, which are required to be resolved by rather tedious separation techniques. The undesirable enantiomer often has a limited use and represents loss of valuable raw materials. Asymmetric synthesis, in which the desired optical isomer is obtained selectively or in large excess, has, therefore, been a subject of considerable interest in recent years. Success has been achieved in developing homogeneous enantioselective catalyst for some hydrogenations. A catalyst of this type is being used for commercial manufacture of L-dopa (3,4-dihydroxy phenyl alanine) [71]. A limited enantioselectivity has also been achieved using heterogeneous catalysts. However, their use in industrial practice is not known. An overview of the research carried out using heterogeneous catalysts is presented in this section.

For a compound containing one asymmetric carbon atom, two optical isomers are possible. They are mirror images of each other and are called enantiomers. For a compound with two centers of asymmetry, four optical isomers are possible. The isomeric structures that are not mirror images are called distereomers. The asymmetric synthesis can be divided into enantioselective and distereoselective synthesis. Most of the reported work on asymmetric hydrogenation involves enantioselective synthesis.

When a compound with one center of asymmetry is synthesised from a compound without an asymmetric carbon atom (prochiral compound), the two enantiomers should normally be formed in equal amounts since their transition states have identical free energies. In order to achieve selective synthesis of one of the enantiomers, the catalyst must contain an optically active component. The reactant should first form an adduct with the optically active component. When the adduct undergoes hydrogenation, the resultant product will contain two centers of asymmetry and, hence, will have two distereomers. Since these are not mirror images, their transition states can have different free energies. Hence, selective formation of one of the distereomer will be possible. After having formed a specific distereomer, when the adduct breaks up, a specific enantiomer of the hydrogenated reactant can be obtained. This has been the underlying principle of most of the attempts made to achieve enantioselective hydrogenation. The different approaches differ in the manner in which the optically active component is incorporated in the catalyst.

The first attempt to prepare an enantioselective catalyst was carried out as early as in 1934 by Schwab et al. who studied reactions catalyzed by nickel supported on the asymmetric surfaces of quartz [72]. The selectivity was found to be very poor. Akabory et al. [73] studied hydrogenation of oximes and oxabones on palladium supported on natural silk. Maximum optical yield* of 36% could be obtained. A useful approach was developed by Isoda et al. [74], who employed Raney nickel catalyst modified by preadsorption of optically active compounds like amino acids. This approach was extensively investigated further by Izumi and co-workers [75]. Most of their studies were devoted to hydrogenation of methyl acetoacetate to methyl 3-hydroxy butyrate and related reactions using Raney nickel catalyst. A variety of reaction conditions and catalyst modifiers were investigated. Tartaric acid was found to be the most suitable modifiers. Optical yields in the range of 10 to 78% could be achieved. Sachtler and co-workers [76–78] studied hydrogenation using nickel-on-silica catalyst modified by tartaric acid.

Role of tartaric acid in modifying the selectivity has been extensively discussed. It was expected that the presence of tartaric acid will result in difference in activation energy for the formation of

---

* The "optical yield" of an isomer is defined as the optical rotation of the product mixture expressed as percentage of the optical rotation of the pure isomer.

the two enantiomers. However, it was observed that in the hydrogenation of methyl acetoacetate, the activation energies were the same regardless of the reaction rate and optical yield [75]. Hence, it was proposed by Izumi and co-workers that enantio differentiation probably does not occur during reaction. Tartaric acid interacts with the reactant leading to adsorption in a specific orientation and hydrogenation then occurs on the catalyst surface. An alternate view has been expressed by Sachtler [79]. A substantial part of the metal surface is expected to be covered by the modifier. If the metal surface was the locus of catalytic reaction, the rate of hydrogenation should be much lower on the modified catalyst. The experimental observations, however, show that the rate of hydrogenation was of the same order on the modified and unmodified catalysts. This implies that the active site on the modified catalyst may not be the metal surface. Investigation of the metal surface by infrared spectroscopy suggests that chemisorption of tartaric acid and methyl acetoacetate on the catalyst surface is "corrosive." In the complexes formed due to chemisorption, nickel is probably in the ionic state and is detached from the metal surface. The chemisorbed hydrogen can be present in the dissociated form on the metal surface or the hydrogen atoms can occupy vacant legand positions in the nickel tartarate complex. According to Sachtler and co-workers, the hydrogenation could be occurring on the nickel tartarate complex. Efforts to carry out hydrogenation using supported nickel tartarate, however, were unsuccessful. It was, therefore, proposed that the metal surface is necessary to produce dissociated hydrogen, which then spills over to the nickel tartarate complex, where enantioselective hydrogenation could occur.

In 1978, Harada and Izumi reported further improvement in the optical yield by using sodium bromide as the second modifier [80, 81]. When Raney nickel modified by tartaric acid and sodium bromide was employed, optical yield of 89% could be achieved in hydrogenation of methylacetoacetate. It was observed that the rate decreased with increased doping of sodium bromide. It was, therefore, proposed that sodium bromide poisons enantioselective as well as nonselective sites, but the nonselective sites are poisoned preferentially resulting in improved optical yield. Sachtler [79], however, observed that the rate of hydrogenation was unchanged after addition of sodium bromide. Bostclaar and Sachtler [82] studied the effect of various alkali halides as modifiers. The adsorption of alkali halides was observed to be reversible. Sodium bromide, sodium iodide, and potasium iodide were found to be the most effective modifiers.

Izumi and co-workers [74] have extensively investigated the effect of various variables in the catalyst preparation on the enantio differentiating ability of the catalyst. Temperature and the pH during pretreatment of the catalyst with tartaric acid have been shown to have pronounced effect on the enantioselectivity of the catalyst. Pretreatment of the catalyst with compounds like acetone, methyl ethyl ketone, cyclohexanone, or methylacetoacetate prior to treatment with tartaric acid also influence the selectivity of the catalyst. Presence of residual aluminium in the Raney nickel can have marked influence on the enantioselectivity. In the hydrogenation of methylacetoacetate, the optical yield was observed to increase from 35% to 76% by reducing the aluminium content of the Raney nickel from 6% by weight to trace amounts. Thus, in order to obtain a highly selective catalyst, the preparation parameters must be carefully optimized. A careful control on the preparation conditions is also essential to prepare catalyst of reproducible properties.

The research on asymmetric hydrogenation using heterogeneous catalyst is certainly in its early stages, since most of the work has been restricted to hydrogenation of prochiral carbonyl compounds using nickel catalysts. However, the fact that optical yield as high as 89% could be obtained using a cheap catalyst like Raney nickel, ought to be considered very promising. The heterogeneous catalysts are, as such, cost effective as compared to homogeneous catalyst due to ease of their recovery and reuse. More intense research activity would certainly be witnessed in this area in the coming years.

CONCLUSION

This chapter reviewed the principles of liquid phase catalytic hydrogenations. It emphasized that the rate and selectivity of hydrogenation reactions is amenable to considerable manipulation. The profound influence of the key parameters on the rate and selectivity was demonstrated through numerous examples. Unlike other catalytic processes, where each reaction requires a specific catalyst, a wide variety of liquid phase hydrogenations are carried out using a relatively small number of standard catalysts. Hence process optimization through appropriate choice of the discussed parameters is of primary importance to this class of reactions. It would be apparent from this chapter, however, that the principles that govern the choice of these parameters are largely empirical. There seem to be very few studies concerning the substrate-catalyst interaction and the mechanism of promotion and inhibition. Hence the understanding of the surface chemistry of this class of reactions is still very limited. Fundamental studies devoted to these aspects may help considerably to rationalize the concepts in this area.

REFERENCES

1. Sabatier, P., and Senderens, J. B., *Compt. Rend.*, 124, 1358 (1897).
2. Vorhees, V., and Adams, R., *J. Ame. Chem. Soc.*, 44, 1397 (1922).
3. Adams, R., and Shriner, R. L., *J. Ame. Chem. Soc.*, 45, 2171 (1923).
4. Ipatieff, V., *Catalytic Reactions at High Pressures and Temperatures*, McMillan and Co., New York, 1932.
5. Raney, M., U.S. Patents 1,563,587 (1927); 1,628,190 (1927); 1,915,473 (1933).
6. Adkins, H., *Reactions of Hydrogen with Organic Compounds over Copper Chromium Oxide and Nickel Catalysts*, Wisconsin University Press, Madison, 1937.
7. Rylander, P. N., *Catalytic Hydrogenation in Organic Synthesis*, Academic Press, New York, 1979.
8. Freifelder, M., *Practical Catalytic Hydrogenation—Techniques and Applications*, Wiley-Interscience, New York, 1971.
9. Gostunskaya, I. V., Petrova, V. S.. Leonava, A. I., Mironava, V. A., Abubaker, M., and Kazanskii, B. A., *Neftekhimiya*, 7(1), 3 (1967).
10. Bond, G. C., and Wells, P. B., *J. Catalysis*, 5, 419 (1966).
11. Yoshida, N., and Hirota, K., *Bull. Chem. Soc. Jap.*, 48, 184 (1975).
12. Lindlar, H., and Dubuis, R., *Organic Synthesis*, 46, 89 (1966).
13. Gutmann, H., and Lindlar, H., in *Chemistry of Acetylenes* (H. G. Viehe, ed.) Dekker, New York, 1969; p. 355.
14. Henrick, C. A., *Tetrahedron*, 33, 1845 (1977).
15. Hotta, K., and Kubomatsu, T., *Bull. Chem. Soc. Jap.*, 42, 1447 (1969).
16. Carothers, W. H., and Adams, R., *J. Ame. Chem. Soc.*, 46, 1675 (1924).
17. Gardener, J. H., and McDonnell, T. F., *J. Ame. Chem. Soc.*, 63, 2279 (1941).
18. Hiskey, R. G., and Northrop, R. C., *J. Ame. Chem. Soc.*, 83, 4798 (1961).
19. Cohen, S., Thom, E., and Bendich, A., *J. Org. Chem.*, 28, 1379 (1963).
20. Rylander, P. N., in *Catalysis: Science and Technology* Vol. 4, (J. R. Anderson and M. Boudart, eds.), Springer Verlag, New York, 1983.
21. Karwa, S. L., and Rajadhyaksha, R. A., *Ind. Eng. Chem.* Res., 26, 1746 (1987).
22. Strätz, A. M., in *Catalysis of Organic Reactions* (J. R. Kosak, ed.), Marcel Dekker, New York, 1984; p. 335.
23. Greenfield, H., Ann. N.Y. *Acad. Sci.*, 214, 233 (1973).
24. Taverna, M., and Chiti, M., *Hydrocarbon Processing*, 49 (Nov.), 137 (1970).
25. Rylander, P. N., Hasbrouck, L., and Karpenko, I., Ann. N.Y. *Acad. Sci.*, 214, 100 (1973).
26. Rylander, P. N., *Chem. Eng. Progr.*, 76(6), 35 (1980).
27. Acres, G. J. K., Bird, A. J., King, F., and Jenkins, J. W., in *Catalysis of Organic Reaction*, (J. R. Kosak, ed.), Marcel Dekker, New York, 1984.
28. Acres, G. J. K., Bird, A. J., Jenkins, J. W., and Kind, F., in *Characterisation of Catalyst*, (J. M. Thomas and R. M. Lambert, eds.), John Wiley, New York, 1980; p. 55.
29. Kishida, S., and Teranishi, S., *J. Catalysis*, 12, 90 (1968).
30. Rajadhyaksha, R. A., and Karwa, S. L., *Chem. Eng. Sci.*, 41, 1765 (1986).
31. Lemcoff, N. O., *J. Catalysis*, 46, 356 (1977).
32. Caga, I. T., Shutt, E., and Winterbottom, J. M., *J. Catalysis*, 44, 271 (1976).

33. Iwamoto, I., Aonuma, T., and Keil, T., *Int. Chem. Eng.*, 11, 573 (1971).
34. Baltzy, R., *J. Org. Chem.*, 41, 920 (1976).
35. Abe, I., Hayashi, K., and Kitagawa, M., *Kagaku to Kogyo* (Osaka), 53(7), 274 (1979); (Chem. Abstr. 91-199408).
36. Lo, H. S., and Paulaitis, M. E., *AIChE J.*, 27, 842 (1981).
37. Muth, C. W., Elkins, J. R., DeMatte, M. L., and Chiang, S. T., *J. Org. Chem.*, 32, 1106 (1967).
38. Karwa, S. L., and Rajadhyaksha, R. A., *Ind. Eng. Chem. Res.*, in press (1987).
39. Augustine, R. L., Migliorini, D. C., Foscante, R. E., Sodano, C. S., and Sisbarro, M. J., *J. Org. Chem.*, 34, 1075 (1969).
40. Augustine, R. L., *Adv. Catal.*, 25, 56 (1976).
41. Rylander, P. N., Korpenko, I. M., and Pond, G. R., Ann. N.Y. *Acad. Sci.*, 172, 266 (1970).
42. Karwa, S. L., Ph.D. Thesis, University of Bombay, 1987.
43. Affrossman, S., and Thompson, S. J., *J. Chem. Soc.*, 2024 (1962).
44. Peters, J. A., and van Bekkum, H., *Red. Trav. Chim. Pays-Bas*, 100, 21 (1981).
45. Rylander, P. N., in *Catalysis of Organic Reactions*, (W. H. Jones, ed.), Academic Press, New York, 1980; p. 155.
46. Shetkar, U. R., and Rajadhyaksha, R. A., unpublished work (1987).
47. Coenen, J. W. E., Boerma, H., Linsen, B. G., and DeVries, B., in *Proceedings of 3rd Int. Congr. on Catalysis*, (W. M. H. Sachtler, G. C. A. Schuit and P. Zwitering, eds.), North Holland, Amsterdam, 1965; p. 1387.
48. Coenen, J. W. E., *J. Ame. Oil. Chem. Soc.*, 53, 382 (1976).
49. Hilditch, T. P., and Moor, C. W., *J. Soc. Chem. Ind.* London, 42, 15T (1923).
50. Okkerse, C., de Jorge, A., Coenen, J. W. E., and Razendaal, A., *J. Ame. Chem. Soc.*, 44, 1520 (1966).
51. Rylander, P. N., *J. Ame. Oil. Chem. Soc.*, 47, 482 (1970).
52. Patterson, H. B. W., *Hydrogenation of Fats and Oils*, Applied Science Publishers, London, 1983; p. 72.
53. Albert, R., Strätz, A., and Vollneim, G., *Chem. Ing. Tech.*, 52, 582 (1980).
54. Wisniak, J., and Simon, R., *Ind. Eng. Chem. Prod. Res. Dev.*, 18(1), 50 (1979).
55. Sharkov, V. I., *Angew. Chem. (Int. Ed.)*, 2(8), 405 (1963).
56. Wright, L. W., *Chem. Tech.*, 2, 43 (1974).
57. Cora Engineering Company, *Chem. Eng. News*, April 30, 19 (1984).
58. Germain, A., L'Homme, G., and Legebure, A., in *Chemical Engineering of Gas-Liquid-Solid Catalytic Reactions*, (G. A. L'Homme, ed.) CEBEDOC, Liege, 1979; p. 265.
59. Haidegger, E., Peter, T., Gems, I., and Karoliji, J., *Ind. Eng. Chem. Prod. Res. Dev.*, 7, 107 (1968).
60. Sagimori, A., *Bull. Chem. Soc. Japn.*, 33, 1599 (1960).
61. Toya, K., *J. Chem. Soc. (Chem. Comm.)*, 464 (1966).
62. Fidler, D. A., Logan, J. S., and Boudakian, M. M., *J. Org. Chem.*, 26, 4014 (1961).
63. Karwa, S. L., and Rajadhyaksha, R. A., *Ind. Eng. Chem. Res.*, in press (1987).
64. Jones, W. H., Benning, W. F., Mulvey, D. M., Pallack, P. I., Schaeffer, J. C., Tull, R., and Weinstock, L. M., Ann. N.Y. *Acad. Sci.*, 158, 471 (1969).
65. Kirk-Othmer *Encyclopedia of Chemical Technology*, 3rd edition, John Wiley and Sons, New York, 1981.
66. "1977 Petrochemical Handbook Issue," *Hydrocarbon Processing*, 56 (Nov.), 169 (1977).
67. Hatch, F., and Matar, S., *Hydrocarbon Processing*, 57 (Aug.), 163 (1978).
68. Pistor, H., in Winnacker-Kiichler *Chemische Technologie*, Bd. I, Carl Hanser Verlag, 1978; p. 513.
69. Berglin, J., and Schöön, N., *Ind. Eng. Chem. Proc. Des. Dev.*, 20, 615 (1981).
70. Schumb, W. C., Satterfield, C. N., and Wenterworth, R. L., *Hydrogen Peroxide*, Reinhold Publishing Corpn., New York, 1955.
71. Koenig, K. E., in *Catalysis of Organic Reactions*, (J. R. Kosak, ed.), Marcel Dekker, New York, 1984; p. 63.
72. Schwab, G. M., Rost, F., and Rudolph, L., *Kolloid-Zeitschrift*, 68, 174 (1934).
73. Akabori, S., Izumi, Y., Fuji, Y., and Sakurai, S., *Nature*, 178, 323 (1956).
74. Isoda, T., Ichikawa, A., and Shimamoto, T., *J. Sci. Res. Inst.* (*Riklen hokoku*), 34, 134 (1958).

75. Izuki, Y., *Adv. Catal.* 32, 215 (1983).
76. Hoek, A., and Sachtler, W. M. H., *J. Catalysis*, 58, 276 (1979).
77. Hoek, A., Woerde, H. M., and Sachtler, W. M. H., *Proc. 7th Int. Congr. Catalysis*, (T. Seiyama and T. Tanabe, eds.), Elsevier, Amsterdam, 1981, p. 376.
78. Woerde, H. M., Bostelaar, L. J., Hock, A., and Sachtler, W. M. H., *J. Catalysis*, 76, 316 (1982).
79. Sachtler, W. M. H., in *Catalysis of Organic Reactions*, (R. L. Augustine, ed.), Marcel Dekker, New York, 1986; p. 189.
80. Harada, T., and Izumi, Y., *Chem. Lett.*, 1195, (1978).
81. Harada, T., Yamamoto, H., Onaka, S., Imaida, M., Ozaki, H., Tai, A., and Izumi, Y., *Bull. Chem. Soc. Jap.*, 54, 2323 (1981).
82. Bostelaar, L. J., and Sachtler, W. M. H., *J. Mol. Cat.*, 27, 387 (1984).

CHAPTER 14

PRINCIPLES OF SLURRY POLYMERIZATION

Yasuo Hatate

Department of Chemical Engineering
Kagoshima University
Kagoshima, Japan

CONTENTS

INTRODUCTION

"Slurry polymerization" is used in this chapter to describe polymerization in slurry conditions at ordinary temperatures. Strictly speaking, "heterogeneous polymerization" may also be used because the chapter also discusses two-phase separation polymerization. In that polymerization, the system separates into two phases, and the polymer produced does not precipitate alone to form a polymer-rich phase swollen with monomer and/or solvent. This chapter does not cover popcorn polymerization because it does not produce a useful polymer material, although it is regarded as a typical heterogeneous polymerization. Suspension polymerization is also omitted due to the perfect homogeneous polymerization in the mechanism. However, it seems to be a useful polymerization process to prepare microspheres [1–4].

Polymerizations discussed here are as follows:

1. Precipitation polymerization, such as acrylonitrile bulk polymerization.
2. Two-phase separation polymerization, such as vinyl chloride bulk polymerization and styrene polymerization in isooctane solvent, in which the polymerization suspended in water would avoid the cohesive trouble caused by the polymer-rich phase.
3. Emulsion polymerization.
4. Dispersion polymerization, which is a precipitation polymerization in organic media.

PRECIPITATION POLYMERIZATION

In homogeneous polymerization, the polymerization behavior in the early stage could be desribed by simple kinetics until the autoaccelerating effect would be predominant at high conversions. However, various complicated features are kinetically found even at the beginning of reaction for heterogeneous polymerization. Now, we will start from acrylonitrile bulk polymerization of a representative monomer in this category.

Acrylonitrile

Bulk polymerization of acrylonitrile is a typical example of precipitation polymerizations widely studied so far [5–11]. Polyacrylonitrile dissolves in only limited solvents such as dimethylformamide and dimethylsulfoxide. It is, of course, perfectly insoluble in its own monomer. Hence, the polyacrylonitrile produced will precipitate in the medium to form a slurry solution. The following characteristics of this polymerization were reported by Bamford et al. [5, 12–14]. Autoacceleration is always observed in this system. This is believed to come from the precipitated polymer. Free radicals occluded in the precipitated polymer exhibit no reactive behavior and have a extremely long life at low temperatures. So, if the reaction temperature rises up to 60°C, an extremely fast reaction will occur in which approximately 10% of the available monomer is consumed in about two minutes, and after this initial fast reaction the reaction rate will fall to a normal one. This comes from the dependency of the activity of occluded radicals on temperature.

Even in the precipitation polymerization, the reaction mechanisms would be consistant with those in homogeneous polymerization, involving initiation propagation, and termination reactions, in which the overall reaction rate is proportional to the radical concentration. One distinguished feature of precipitation polymerization is the occlusion of radicals, which will reduce every elementary reaction rate, but most seriously bimolecular termination. Since the rate of polymerization mainly depends on the relative rates of propagation and termination, the overall effect of occlusion is expected to an increase in polymerization rate and an increase in the contribution of chain transfer relative to bimolecular termination.

In summary, moderate degrees of occlusion result in an increase in rate of polymerization and polymer molecular weight. Extreme degrees of occlusion cause complete trapping of radicals to the point where chain propagation is inhibited.

Since the polymerization behavior is very dependent upon physical factors that control the degree of occlusion, it is not surprising that quantitative kinetic analysis is difficult.

Lewis et al. [10] made a kinetic study of the polymerization at 50°C of acrylonitrile and acrylonitrile-benzene mixtures catalyzed by azobisisobutyronitrile. A plot of rate vs. catalyst concentration, I, on logarithmic scales is a curve, the rate varying as $I^{0.89}$ at $I = 10^{-4}$ mol/l, but as $I^{0.33}$ at $I = 10^{-2}$ mol/l. They discussed the following three loci of polymerization:

1. *The solution phase.* Radicals are generated in the monomer-rich liquid phase, and hence polymer chains must be initiated in this phase.
2. *The surface phase.* While this may not be a separate phase in the thermodynamic sense, adsorption of a growing radical on the particle surface would confine the reaction to this locus throughout much of the life of the chain.
3. *The interior phase.* Precipitated polymer chains are expected to be tightly coiled. A coiled radical would have reduced reactivity since there is a high probability that the radical end will be occluded within the coil. Trapped radicals are presumed to be deeply buried in the interior phase.

Although occlusion of growing radicals within the precipitated polymer has been emphasized by Bamford et al. to play an important role in the acrylonitrile precipitation polymerization, they concluded that the kinetic results can be accounted for by considering surface polymerization only. It was concluded from the facts that (a) the precipitated phase contains about 5% monomer, having a glass temperature of about 80°C and does not polymerize appreciably below 80°C; and (b) the large surface of particles constitutes an efficient radical trap that maintains the concentration of radicals in the solution phase at a very low level due to the extreme insolubility of radicals in the solution. Radicals arrive at the surface at a rate determined by the decomposition of the initiator and efficiency of initiator. Propagation occurs on the surface at a rate determined by the activity of monomer at the surface. The propagation rate constant is presumably influenced somewhat by the presence of the solid surface. The principal difference from homogeneous polymerization is that the rate constant for bimolecular termination should be greatly reduced since the growing chains are an integral part of a solid particle. Termination of growing chains by initiator radicals can become an important reaction. Under conditions where diffusion is restricted, the twin chains initiated by two radicals from the same initiator molecule may remain close together for a time, so that termination has a higher probability than in the case of random distribution of radicals [15]. It results in a rate expression formally equivalent to a reaction first order in radical concentration, with half-life τ.

The following reactions summarize the scheme:

Initiation

$$I \longrightarrow 2R \qquad dR/dt = 2fk_dI \tag{1}$$

$$R + M \longrightarrow P_1\cdot \qquad -dR/dt = dP_1\cdot/dt = k_iMR \tag{2}$$

Propagation

$$P_n\cdot + M \longrightarrow P_{n+1}\cdot \qquad -dM/dt = R_p = k_pMP\cdot \tag{3}$$

Termination

$$P_n\cdot + P_m\cdot \longrightarrow P_{n+m} \qquad -dP\cdot/dt = 2k_tP^2\cdot + 2P\cdot/\tau_h \tag{4}$$

$$P_n\cdot + R \longrightarrow P_n \qquad -dP\cdot/dt = -dR/dt = k_t'PR \tag{5}$$

Dissipation of initiator radicals by coupling reaction

$$2R \longrightarrow \text{products} \qquad -dR/dt = 2k_t''R^2 \tag{6}$$

Assuming steady-state conditions in all radicals in all radical species, we can write

$$dR/dt = 0 = 2fk_dI - k_iMR - k_t'P\cdot R - 2k_t''R^2 \tag{7}$$

and,

$$dP\cdot/dt = 0 = k_iRM - 2k_tP^2\cdot - 2P\cdot k_h - k_t'P\cdot R \tag{8}$$

Hence,

$$P\cdot = (2fk_dI - k_iRM - 2k_t''R^2)/k_t'R \tag{9}$$

and,

$$R = (2k_tP^2\cdot + 2P\cdot/\tau_h)/(k_iM - k_t'P\cdot) \tag{10}$$

where $P\cdot = \sum_{n=1}^{\infty} P_n\cdot$

Using Equation 3 we can combine the above expressions for P· and R to obtain an expression only in R_p as follows;

$$\frac{\beta_4(1-4\beta_3)}{M^3}R_p^4+\frac{(1-8\beta_3)}{M^2}R_p^3-\left(\frac{4\beta_3}{M\beta_4}+\frac{M\beta_4}{\beta_1^2}-\frac{k_dI}{M\beta_2}\right)R_p^2-\left(\frac{M^2}{\beta_1^2}-\frac{2Mk_dI}{\beta_1\beta_2}\right)R_p+\frac{M^3k_dI}{\beta_1^2\beta_2}=0 \tag{11}$$

where $\beta_1 = k_t'/(k_ik_p)$
$\beta_2 = 1/(f\tau k_p)$
$\beta_3 = k_tk_t''/k_t'^2$
$\beta_4 = k_t\tau/k_p$

Thus, the system is basically a four-parameter one. Four parameters in Equation 11 were determined from a least square method using many experimental data of M, I and R_p. Once values of the β_s' were obtained, the relations between R_p and I at a constant monomer concentration M would be calculated from Equation 11. In Figure 1, predicted results from Equation 11 were compared with observed data for bulk polymerization ($M_0 = 14.79$ mol/l). However, this treatment could not prevail inspite of its precious quantitative aspect due to the oversimplication in the kinetic mechanism and the obscure physical meaning of parameters obtained.

Sugimori et al. [11, 16, 17] carried out the precipitation polymerization of acrylonitrile in aqueous solution initiated by $Na_2S_2O_5/NaNO_2$ redox catalyst system over a wide range of conversion. Their works seem worthwhile to be outlined.

Experimental procedure. After ten minutes reaction of $Na_2S_2O_5$ and $NaNO_2$ at pH = 2.5 using sulfuric acid and a given temperature, a given amount of acrylonitrile was charged in forty minutes to start the polymerization in an atmosphere of nitrogen. Adopting such a semi-batch operation, almost spherical particles of about several 10 μm in diameter could be obtained in the particles concentration ranges of 10^5–10^8 particles/cc.

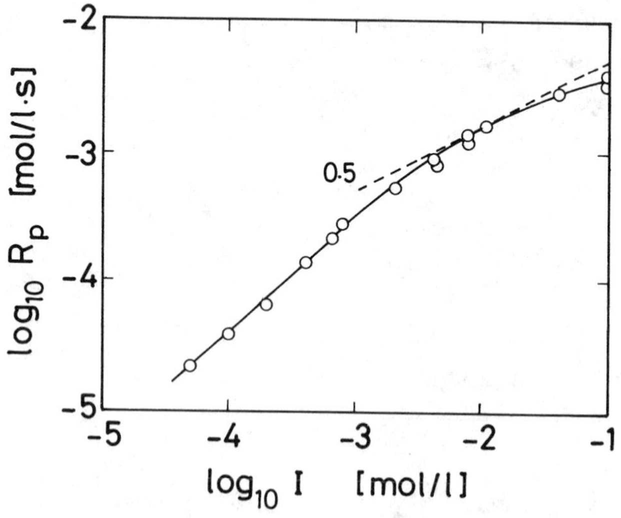

Figure 1. Rate of bulk polymerization of acrylonitrile at 50°C as a function of AIBN concentration [10].

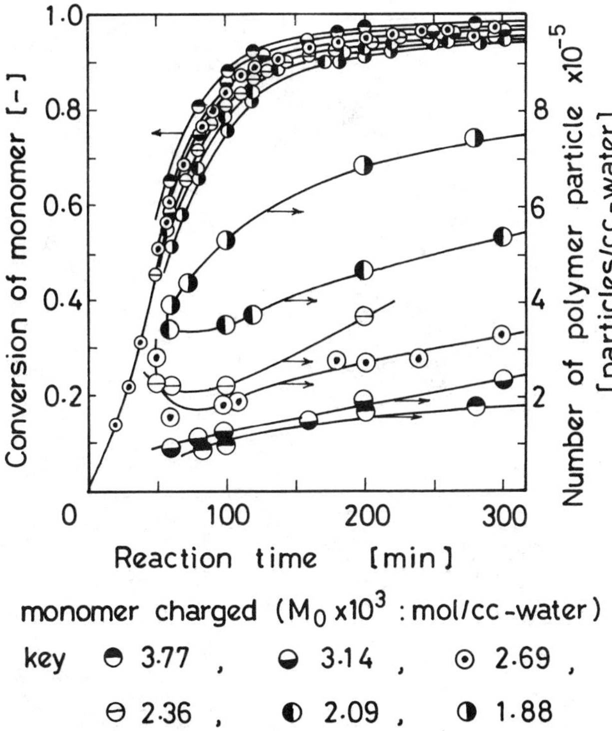

Figure 2. Effect of monomer charged on conversion and number of polymer particles in the course of polymerization (55°C, pH = 2.5, concentration of $Na_2S_2O_5 = 3.76 \times 10^{-5}$ mol/cc-water, concentration of $NaNO_2 = 1.04 \times 10^{-5}$ mol/cc-water) [16].

Results. In Figure 2, monomer conversion and polymer particles number were plotted against reaction time for various amounts of monomer charged. Monomer conversion rates and time dependencies of number average degrees of polymerization of polymer samples obtained were also shown in Figures 3 and 4, respectively, for various A, B, M_0, and reaction temperatures. Monomer concentrations adsorbed in polymer phase M_{pa} and monomer concentrations in aqueous phase M_1 were measured during the polymerization for various conditions to obtain the following correlation:

$$M_{pa} = 73.6\, M_1^{1.4} \tag{12}$$

Discussion and conclusion. Since Mickley et al.'s conclusion [18] was confirmed from observed values of R_p, M_1, and M_p, they concluded that polymerization occurs individually, both in the aqueous solution phase and in the polymer phase formed by the precipitation. Assumed elementary reaction processes are shown in Table 1, in which the reaction in the monomer phase is not considered due to the minor effect on the overall reaction. A schematic diagram of elementary reactions and phase transfer process is shown in Figure 5, the assigned numbers in which represent the elementary processes to be described for rate expressions: (1) initiation (liquid phase), $2fk_dI$; (2) propagation (liquid phase), $k_pP_n \cdot M$; (3) invasion of radicals from liquid to precipitation phase, $\mathbf{k}_{in}P \cdot N_p$; 4 propagation (polymer phase), $N_pk'_pP^*_nM_p$; 5 chain transfer to monomer (polymer phase), $N_pK'_{fm}P^*_nM_p$; (5)′ reinitiation from active monomer (polymer phase), $N_pK'_{im}M^*M_p$; (6) es-

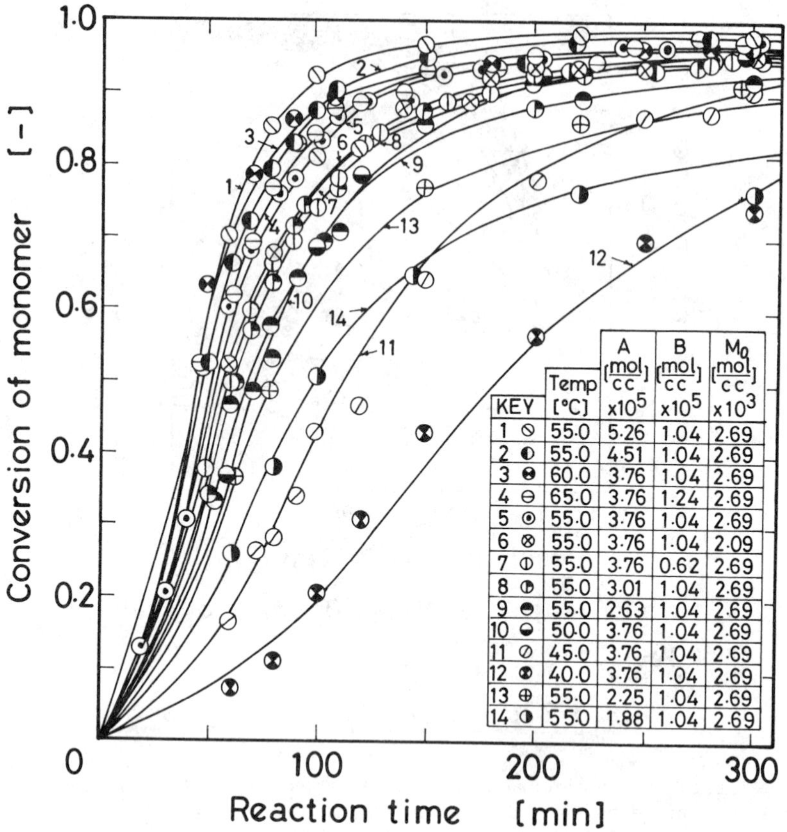

Figure 3. Changes of conversion in the course of polymerization [16].

cape of active monomer from precipitation phase to liquid, $N_pk_fM^*/v_p$; (7) reinitiation from active monomer (liquid phase): $k_{im}M\cdot M_1$; (7)′ chain transfer to monomer (liquid phase), $k_{fm}P_n\cdot M_1$; (8) termination (liquid phase), $k_{tc}P_n\cdot P_m\cdot v_1$, $k_{td}P_n\cdot P_m\cdot v_1$; (9) precipitation or coalescence; and (10) termination (polymer phase), $N_pk'_{tc}P^*_nP^*_mv_p$, $N_pk'_{td}P^*_nP^*_mv_p$. Assuming a stationary state in radical concentration, the following equations are obtained:

$$v_1dM\cdot/dt = k_mP\cdot M_1 - k_{pm}M\cdot M_1 + N_pk_fM^*/v_p = 0 \tag{13}$$

$$N_pdM^*/dt = N_p[k'_mP^*M_p - k'_{pm}M^*M_p - k_fM^*/v_p] = 0 \tag{14}$$

$$v_1dP\cdot/dt = 2fk_dI - (k_{tc} + k_{td})P^2\cdot v_1 + N_pk_fM^*/v_p - N_pk_{in}P\cdot = 0 \tag{15}$$

$$N_pdP^*/dt = N_p[k_{in}P\cdot - (k'_{tc} + k'_{td})P^{2*}/v_p - k_fM^*/v_p] = 0 \tag{16}$$

where $P\cdot = \sum_{n=1}^{\infty} P_n\cdot$

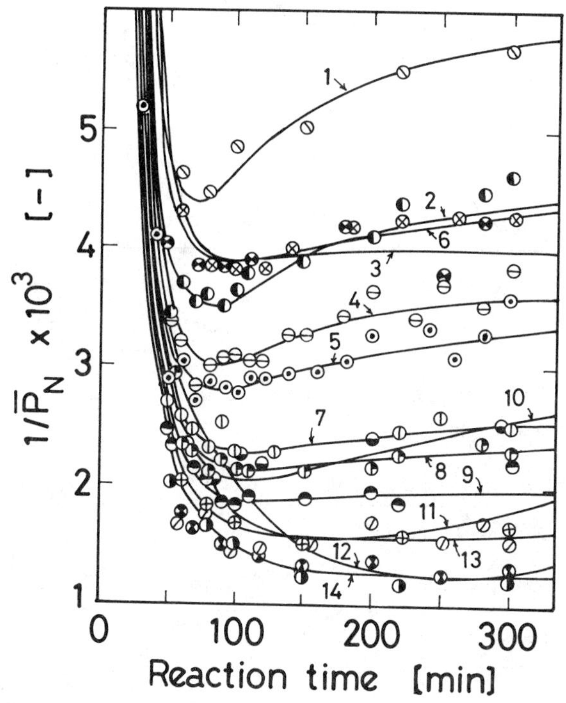

Figure 4. Changes of degree of polymerization in the course of polymerization (all keys are the same as in Figure 4) [16].

Active monomer in the polymer phase would be almost consumed by the reinitiation reaction with M_p, so $k'_{pm}M^*M_p \gg k_f M^*/v_p$. Termination reaction rate in the polymer phase could be neglected. Hence, the following equation can be obtained using Equations (14) and (16).

$$P^*/v_p = (k_{in}k'_{im}/k_f k'_{fm})P\cdot \tag{17}$$

From Equations 15, 16, and 17,

$$P\cdot = \left\{\frac{2fk_dI}{(k_{tc}+k_{td})(v_1+K_t v_p N_p)}\right\}^{1/2} \tag{18}$$

where

$$K_t = [(k'_{tc}+k'_{td})/(k_{tc}+k_{td})](k_{in}k'_{im}/k_f k'_{fm})^2 \tag{19}$$

Since monomer would be substantially consumed by the propagation reaction, the overall monomer consumption rate is written as follows:

$$R_p = k_p P\cdot M_1 + k'_p P^* M_p N_p$$
$$= k_p \left\{\frac{2fk_dI}{(k_{tc}+k_{td})(v_1+K_t v_p N_n)}\right\}^{1/2} (M_1 + Kv_pN_pM_p) \tag{20}$$

Table 1
Reaction Scheme

Liquid Phase	Polymer Phase
Initiation	
$A + B \underset{}{\overset{K_e}{\rightleftarrows}} I$	
$I \xrightarrow{k_d} 2R\cdot$	
$R\cdot + M_1 \xrightarrow{k_i} P_1\cdot$	
Propagation	
$P_{n-1}\cdot + M_1 \xrightarrow{k_p} P_n\cdot$	$P^*_{n-1} + M_p \xrightarrow{k'_p} P^*_n$
Termination	
Combination	
$P_n\cdot + P_m\cdot \xrightarrow{k_{tc}} P_{n+m}$	$P^*_n + P^*_m \xrightarrow{k'_{tc}} P_{n+m}$
Disproportionation	
$P_n\cdot + P_m\cdot \xrightarrow{k_{td}} P_n + P_m$	$P^*_n + P^*_m \xrightarrow{k'_{td}} P_n + P_m$
Transfer to monomer	
$P_n\cdot + M_1 \xrightarrow{k_{fm}} P_n + M_1\cdot$	$P^*_n + M_p \xrightarrow{k'_{fm}} P_n + M^*$
$M_1\cdot + M_1 \xrightarrow{k_{im}} P_1\cdot$	$M^* + M_p \xrightarrow{k'_{im}} P^*_1$

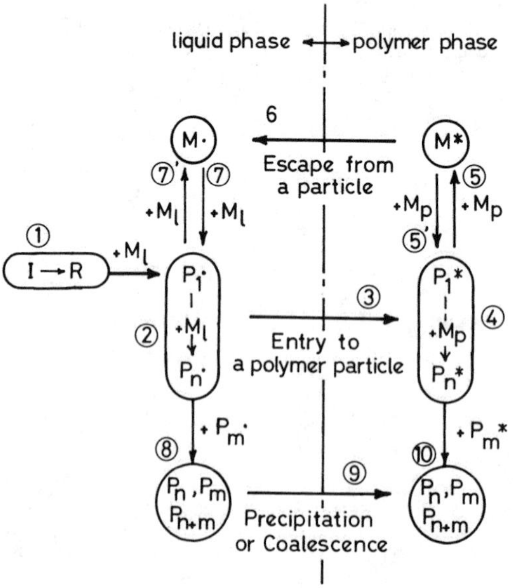

Figure 5. Schematic diagram of radical transfer processes [16].

where

$$K = k'_p k_{in} k'_{im} / k_p k_f k'_{fm} \tag{21}$$

Assuming $k_{fm}/k'_{fm} = k_p/k'_p$ and $k_{tc}/k_{td} = k'_{tc}/k'_{td}$,

$$\frac{dP}{dt} = \left\{\frac{2fk_d I}{(k_{tc} + k_{td})(v_1 + K_t v_p N_p)}\right\}^{1/2} \left\{k_{fm}(M_1 + K v_p N_p M_p) + \left(\frac{k_{tc}}{2} + k_{td}\right)\left(\frac{2fk_d I}{k_{tc} + k_{td}}\right)^{1/2} (v_1 + K_t v_p N_p)^{1/2} + k_{fs} S v_1\right\} \tag{22}$$

Hence,

$$\frac{1}{DP} = \frac{k_{fm}}{k_p} + \frac{\left(\frac{k_{tc}/2 + k_{td}}{k_p}\right)\left(\frac{2fk_d}{k_{tc} + k_{td}}\right)^{1/2} \int_0^t I \, dt + \frac{k_{fs}}{k_p} \int_0^t \frac{I^{1/2} S v_1}{(v_1 + K_t v_p N_p)^{1/2}} dt}{\int_0^t \frac{I^{1/2}(M_1 + K v_p N_p M_p)}{(v_1 + K_t v_p N_p)^{1/2}} dt} \tag{23}$$

Concentration of catalyst complex I is expressed with a equilibrium constant of redox initiators K_e as follows:

$$I = K_e A^a B^b \tag{24}$$

Decomposition rate of catalyst complex is written as:

$$-dI/dt = k_d I \tag{25}$$

Kinetic parameters in Equations 20–24 were determined from literature and a Simplex method based on the experimental results. The parameters obtained are:

$$a = 1.9\,[-], \qquad b = 0.64\,[-]$$

$$K = 0.134 \exp(11.2 \times 10^3/RT)\,[-]$$

$$k_d = 2.11 \times 10^{13} \exp(-106 \times 10^3/RT)\ s^{-1}$$

$$k_p[2fK_e/(k_{tc} + k_{td})]^{1/2} = 6.84 \times 10^{10} \exp(-43.1 \times 10^3/RT)\ (mol/cc)^{-1/2}\ s^{-1/2}$$

$$k_p^2/(k_{tc}/2 + k_{td}) = 1.61 \times 10^8 \exp(-41.8 \times 10^3/RT)\ (mol/cc)^{-1}\ s^{-1}$$
$$\times\ (k'_{tc} + k'_{td})/k'^2_p \ll 10^{-6}\ (mol/cc)\ s$$

$$k_{fs}/k_p = 5.34 \times 10^{-8} \exp(16.7 \times 10^3/RT)\,[-]$$

$$k_m/k_p = 0.303 \exp(-25.5 \times 10^3/RT)\,[-]$$

The solid lines in Figures 3 and 4 were calculated from Equations 20–23 using the values for the kinetic parameters, showing good agreement with experimental results of monomer conversions and degrees of polymerization, respectively. They reflected the effects of fluid mixing on the kinetics in a continuous operation and the polymer particles size for the precipitation polymerization of acrylonitrile. Concerning the precipitation polymerization initiated by the redox system for acrylonitrile, some rate expressions were recently found in literature [19–21].

PHASE SEPARATION POLYMERIZATION

This representative example is the bulk polymerization of vinyl chloride. No solid polymer particle would be precipitated in the reaction media during the polymerization, but a liquid (solvent-rich or monomer-rich phase)—liquid (polymer-rich phase or swollen polymer phase) separation will occur in the reaction media when the system exceeds the phase separation limit.

Vinyl Chloride

Vinyl chloride was one of the most investigated monomers for the industrial importance [22–29]. The general features of heterogeneous polymerization of vinyl chloride are:

1. The initiator exponent is close to 0.5 in contrast to the value close to 0.9 found for acrylonitrile polymerization.
2. The produced polymer acts as a cocatalyst for the radical polymerization, inducing an auto-accelerating effect.
3. The molecular weight of polymer is dependent on both initiator concentration and conversion over a wide range of both parameters in the bulk polymerization due to the occurrence of chain transfer to the monomer.
4. Polyvinyl chloride prepared by bulk polymerization has a molecular weight that increases with temperature in the range -78 to -30°C, the molecular weight passing through a maximum at -30°C and then decreasing with increasing temperature.
5. The addition of transfer agents markedly reduces the autoacceleration in the bulk polymerization.

The origin of the differences between vinyl chloride and acrylonitrile polymerization systems can be attributed partly to chemical and partly to physical factors. Polyvinyl chloride is readily swollen by its own monomer. Once the particle density is established in the early stages of the reaction, the polymerization system thus consists of two different phases each having a constant composition, at least up to 70% conversion. The bulk polymerization of vinyl chloride would be regarded as a two-phase reaction, proceeding in both the high monomer concentration phase and the high polymer concentration phase. The two phases may exchange radicals, monomer and initiator to hold their equilibria between them. The characteristic features of occluded polymerization observed with acrylonitrile would only be observed for vinyl chloride when the polymerization is carried out below -30°C. In contrast, polyacrylonitrile is totally insoluble in its own monomer so that propagation radicals can undergo virtually no reaction before precipitating and the monomer concentration within the polymer particles is low; polymerization inside the particles can thus be essentially neglected.

Abdel-Alim and Hamielec [23] carried out the bulk polymerization of vinyl chloride initiated by AIBN at temperature levels of 30°C, 50°C and 70°C. They proposed a model similar to that of Talamini et al. (26) with some modifications regarding the change in volume during polymerization as well as the consumption of initiator, which accurately predicts conversion to high levels and molecular weight distribution. Talamini's model assumes a two-phase polymerization, in a monomer-rich and polymer-rich phase. The polymer is treated as a single component, with the concentration of monomer and polymer remaining constant during the polymerization. As reaction proceeds, the mass of polymer-rich phase grows while the monomer-rich phase diminishes. The initiator is assumed to have the same concentration in both phases. Experimental evidence indicates that the onset of two phases begins after less than 1% conversion and lasts until between 70% and 80% conversion, depending on the temperature. In the Hamielec model, the two phases are assumed to be in equilibrium, each of constant composition (x_m and x_p% of polymer, respectively) as shown in Figure 6, where the monomer-rich phase contains only monomer ($x_m = 0$). Since the polymerization in the polymer-rich phase would be diffusion controlled, an autoaccelerating factor γ is introduced to describe the effect, where γ is a constant greater than unity. When conversion is less than x_f (conversion in the polymer-rich phase at equilibrium), the following rate equation can be derived

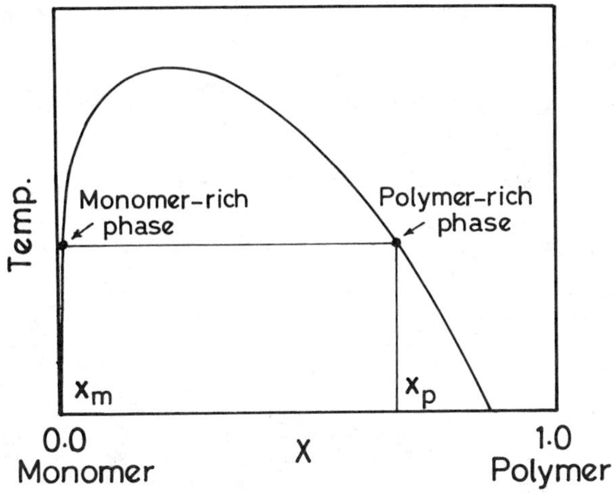

Figure 6. Equilibrium binary diagram between pure monomer and pure polymer [23].

by taking into account the variation of the volume with conversion and the consumption of the initiator:

$$\frac{dx}{dt} = \frac{1 + Q_1 x}{\sqrt{1 - Q_2 x}} \cdot k I_0^{1/2} \exp\left(-\frac{k_d}{2} t\right) \tag{26}$$

where $Q_1 = \{\gamma(1 - x_p) - 1\}/x_f$
$k = k_p(f k_d/k_t)^{1/2}$
$Q_2 = (\rho_p - \rho_m)/\rho_p$

Equation 26 describes the system up to conversion of x_f; it is easily solved analytically with the initial conditions $x = x_m = 0$ at $t = 0$. It is given by

$$t = -\frac{2}{k_d} \ln(1 - H) \tag{27}$$

where

$$H = \frac{k_d}{2kI_0^{1/2}}\left[\frac{2}{Q_1}(\sqrt{1 - Q_2 x} - 1) + \frac{\sqrt{Q_1 + Q_2}}{Q_1\sqrt{Q_2}} \ln\left\{\frac{\dfrac{\sqrt{Q_1(1 - Q_2 x)} - \sqrt{Q_1 + Q_2}}{\sqrt{Q_1} - \sqrt{Q_1 + Q_2}}}{\dfrac{\sqrt{Q_1(1 - Q_2 x)} + \sqrt{Q_1 + Q_2}}{\sqrt{Q_1} + \sqrt{Q_1 + Q_2}}}\right\}\right]$$

When $x > x_p$, k_t, f, and k_p will continue to fall with conversion. Hence, the combined rate parameter k is assumed to change with $(1 - x)$ for x values greater than x_p, so k is expressed as follows:

$$k = \gamma k_m(1 - x)/(1 - x_p)$$

where k_m is k value in the monomer phase, in which no autoacceleration exists. The rate of reaction can then be written as

$$\frac{dx}{dt} = \frac{\gamma k_m}{1 - x_p} I_0^{1/2} \frac{(1 - x)^2}{\sqrt{1 - Q_2 x}} \exp\left(-\frac{k_d}{2} t\right) \tag{28}$$

Again, Equation 28 is easily solved analytically to give the following equation.

$$t = -\frac{2}{k_d} \ln(1 - H_2) + t_p \tag{29}$$

where t_p is the time to reach x_p, and

$$H_2 = \frac{(1 - x_p)k_d}{2\gamma k_m I_0^{1/2}} \left[\frac{\sqrt{1 - Q_2 x}}{1 - x} - \frac{\sqrt{1 - Q_2 x_p}}{1 - x_p} + \frac{Q_2}{2\sqrt{1 - Q_2}} \ln \frac{\left(\dfrac{\sqrt{1 - x} - \sqrt{1 - Q_2}}{\sqrt{1 - x_p} - \sqrt{1 - Q_2}}\right)}{\left(\dfrac{\sqrt{1 - x} + \sqrt{1 - Q_2}}{\sqrt{1 - x_p} + \sqrt{1 - Q_2}}\right)} \right]$$

From homogeneous kinetics, it can be shown that, for termination by disproportionation and transfer to monomer,

$$W_r = \tau^2 r \exp(-\tau r) \tag{30}$$

where τ is given by

$$\tau = T_{fM} + \frac{(fk_d k_t)^{1/2}}{k_p} \frac{I^{1/2}}{M} = T_{fM} + \frac{fk_d I^{1/2}}{kM} \tag{31}$$

The MWD (molecular weight distribution) of the total polymer mixture is obtained from

$$W_r = m_m W_{rm} + m_p W_{rp} \tag{32}$$

C_M is assumed to be the same in both phases. τ_m, τ_p, m_m and m_p are written as

$$\tau_m = T_{fM} + \frac{fk_d I_0^{1/2}}{k_m \sqrt{1 - Q_2 x}} \exp\left(-\frac{k_d}{2} t\right) \tag{33}$$

$$\tau_p = T_{fM} + \frac{fk_d \rho_m I_0^{1/2}}{\gamma k_m \rho_p (1 - x_p)\sqrt{1 - Q_2 x}} \exp\left(-\frac{k_d}{2} t\right) \tag{34}$$

$$m_m = \frac{(Q_1 x_p + 1) \ln(1 + Q_1 x) - Q_1 x}{Q_1^2 x x_p} \tag{35}$$

$$m_p = \frac{\gamma(1 - x_p)[Q_1 x - \ln(1 + Q_1 x)]}{Q_1^2 x x_p} \tag{36}$$

For $x > x_f$, $k \propto (1 - x)$ is assumed, and with small error we can write

$$\frac{fk_d}{kM} \simeq \text{constant} \tag{37}$$

Table 2
Parameters Used in a Model [23]

Temp. [°C]	x_p [−]	Q_1 [−]	$k^m M_0^{1/2}$ [s^{-1}]	$(k_p^2/k_t)M_0$ [s^{-2}]	T_{fm} [−]
30	0.80	4.5	6.39×10^{-4}	5.25×10^{-4}	0.63×10^{-3}
50	0.77	5.5	3.47×10^{-3}	6.69×10^{-4}	1.10×10^{-3}
70	0.72	5.1	1.73×10^{-2}	1.00×10^{-3}	5.71×10^{-3}

or

$$\frac{fk_d}{kM}\text{ (for } x > x_p) = \frac{fk_d}{\gamma k_m M}\text{ (at } x = x_p) \tag{38}$$

From Equation 38 we can see that τ of the polymer produced after x_p is practically the same as that produced in the polymer-rich phase. So, it can be shown that after x_p

$$m_m = (m_m)_{x=x_p} \cdot \frac{x_p}{x} \tag{39}$$

$$m_p = \frac{\gamma(1 - x_p)[Q_1 x_p - \ln(1 + Q_1 x_p)] + Q_1^2 x_p (x - x_p)}{Q_1^2 x x_p} \tag{40}$$

The values of the kinetic parameters in the previously mentioned equations are listed in Table 2, which was determined from literature, and the values chosen to give the best fitting with the data.

The calculated results of conversion and MWD using the model are compared with the experimental data in Figures 7 and 8, respectively.

Excellent agreements in the figures would show a useful aspect of this model in quantitative treatments of monomer conversion and MWD in spite of some questionable assumptions in the model.

Heterogeneous Polymerization of Styrene Within Suspended Isooctane Droplets in Water

Polymerization systems in which polymer particles precipitate in organic solvent media due to the immiscibility of polymer can be found as well as those in which a polymer-rich phase is formed. The polymerizations of acrylonitrile in benzene and styrene in methanol or ethanol would belong to the former systems. Concerning styrene polymerization in ethanol media using an appropriate aqueous polymer stabilizer, we recently classify such polymerization into other specified category, i.e., dispersion polymerization, which will be reviewed later as a useful method to prepare monodispersed microspheres [30].

A typical polymerization in the latter systems is a styrene polymerization in isooctane medium, the kinetics of which are discussed in the following section [31–34]. Since the polymer-rich phase is so sticky that the phase separation polymerization only in organic media results in an unstable condition of adherence of sticky polymer phase to the wall of reactor, forming a sticky polymer wall along the reactor inside, it is better to have the organic phase suspended in water, and to carry out the phase separation polymerization within the organic droplets suspended in water.

Hatate et al. [31] investigated the detailed kinetics of the styrene polymerization within isooctane droplets in water at 70°C to establish a useful quantitative treatment on the polymerization rate and the degree of polymerization.

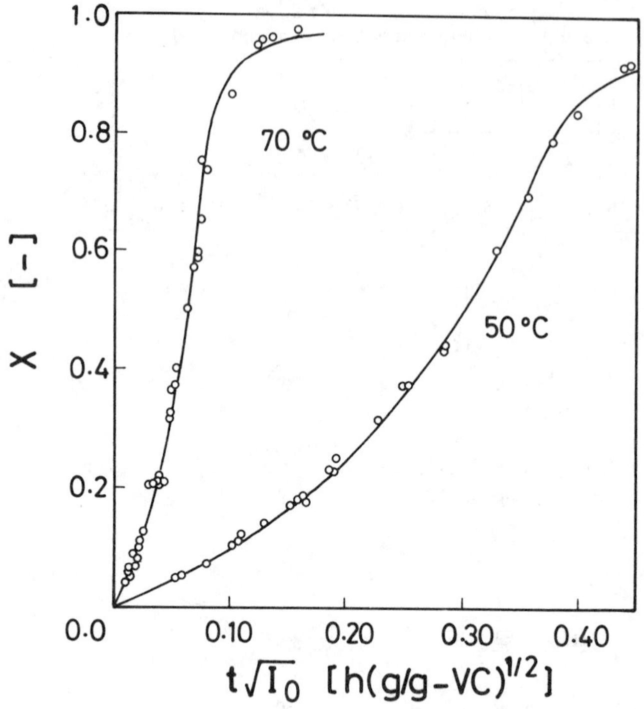

Figure 7. Conversion curves at 50°C and 70°C [23].

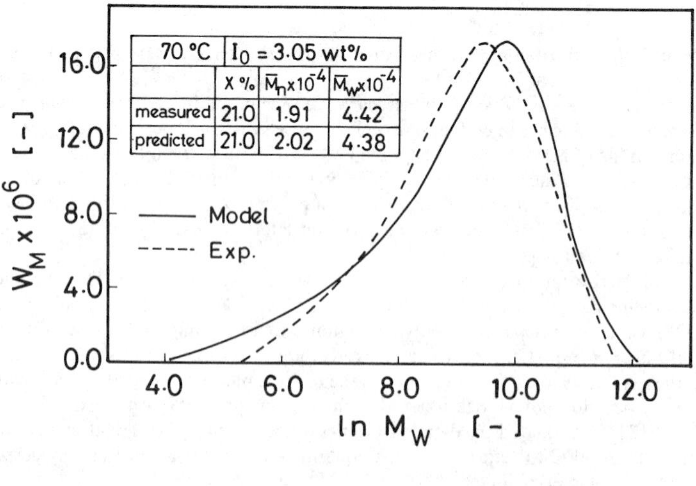

Figure 8. Experimental and theoretical MWD at 70°C [23].

Polymerization Mechanism

In the polymerization, no solid particle exists. (Of course, solid phase may be found at room temperature after completing the polymerization in the case of which we might call it a slurry polymerization.) So, the following homogeneous polymerization mechanisms are assumed for each phase.

	Kinetic rate constant
Initiation	
$I \longrightarrow 2R$	k_d
$R + M \longrightarrow P_1\cdot$	k_i
Propagation	
$P_r\cdot + M \longrightarrow P_{r+1}\cdot$	k_p
Chain transfer	
$P_r\cdot + M \longrightarrow P_r + P_1$	k_{fM}
$P_r\cdot + S \longrightarrow P_r + S^*$	k_{fS}
Reinitiation by solvent radical	
$S^* + M \longrightarrow P_1\cdot$	k_{iS}
Termination	
$P_r\cdot + P_S\cdot \longrightarrow P_{r+S}$	k_{tc}
$P_r\cdot + P_S\cdot \longrightarrow P_r + P_S$	k_{td}
Termination by solvent radical	
$P_r\cdot + S^* \longrightarrow P_r$	k_{tS}

Assuming $k_{ts} = 0$, monomer consumption rate and production rate of dead polymer having r monomer-units are shown by Equations 41 and 42, respectively, when no autoaccelerating effect is predominant.

$$R_p = -\frac{dM}{dt} = \frac{k_p}{k_t^{1/2}} R_i^{1/2} M \tag{41}$$

$$\frac{dP}{dt} = \zeta^r(1-\zeta)R_p\left[T_{fM} + T_{fS}\frac{S}{M} + \frac{R_i}{R_p}\{k_{td} + 0.5k_c(r-1)(1-\zeta)\}/k_t\right] \tag{42}$$

where $R_i = 2k_d fI$

$$\zeta = 1 - P_1\cdot \Big/ \sum_{r=1}^{\infty} P_r\cdot$$

Instantaneous number and weight average degrees of polymerization are written as

$$\bar{P}_{N,inst} = \sum_{r=1}^{\infty} r\left(\frac{dP_r}{dt}\right) \Big/ \sum_{r=0}^{\infty}\left(\frac{dP_r}{dt}\right)$$

$$= \left\{T_{fM} + T_{fS}\frac{S}{M} + \frac{R_i}{2R_p}(2k_{td} + k_{tc})/k_t\right\}^{-1} \tag{43}$$

$$\bar{P}_{w,inst} = \sum_{r=1}^{\infty} r\left(\frac{dP_r}{dt}\right) \Big/ \sum_{r=1}^{\infty}\left(\frac{dP_r}{dt}\right) = 2\bar{P}_{N,inst}\frac{\left(1 + \dfrac{R_i}{R_p}\bar{P}_{N,inst}\dfrac{k_{tc}}{k_t}\right)}{\left(1 + \dfrac{R_i}{2R_p}\bar{P}_{N,inst}\dfrac{k_{tc}}{k_t}\right)} \tag{44}$$

Kinetic Equations from Experimental Results

The effects of operating conditions on the polymerization kinetics were discussed earlier. The effects of PVA concentration on the reaction rate and polymer properties of the polymerization are demonstrated in Figures 9 and 10, respectively. No effect of PVA on the polymerization kinetics is evident from these figures. Furthermore, no effect of rotational speed of impeller and volume fraction of dispersion phase on the polymerization kinetics was experimentally proved in the ranges of 650 to 1,400 rpm in rotational speed and 0.04 to 0.4 in volume fraction of dispersion phase. To investigate the effect of initiator concentration at a comparatively high initial monomer concentration $M_0 = 5.1$ mol/l, plots of conversion and average molecular weight vs. reaction time are shown in Figures 11 and 12, respectively, covering the range of $I_0 = 0.003$ to 0.21 mol/l. In these cases homogeneous polymerization is predominant at low monomer conversions. The same performance as a common homogeneous polymerization is recognized at least at the initial stage of

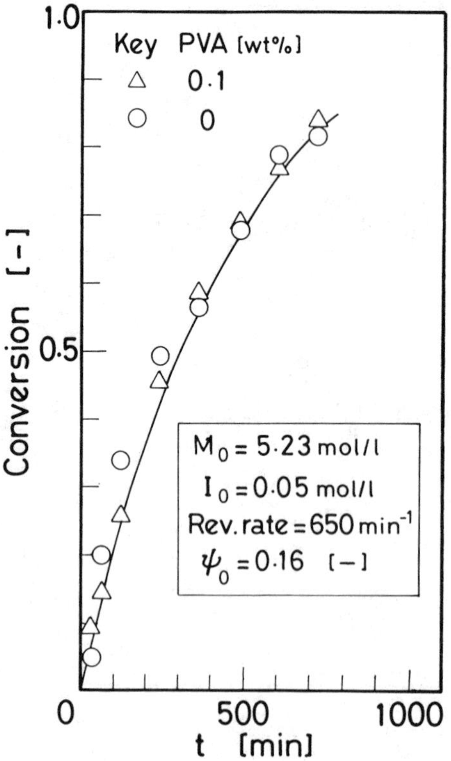

Figure 9. Effect of PVA on polymerization rate [31].

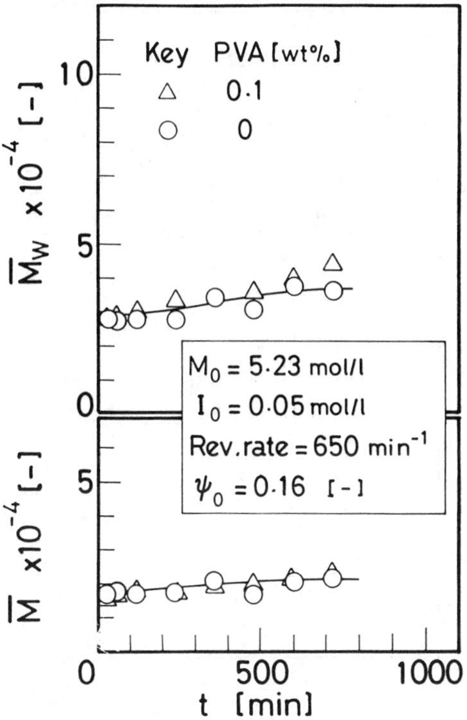

Figure 10. Effect of PVA on average molecular weight [31].

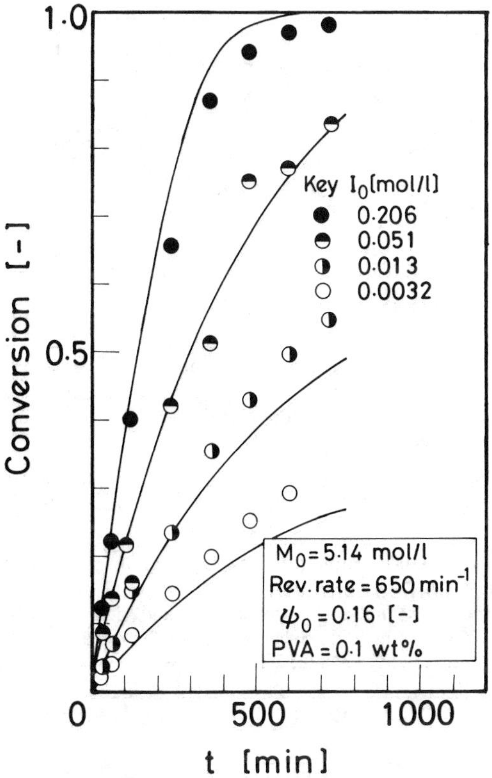

Figure 11. Effect of initiator concentration on polymerization rate (M_0 = 5.14 mol/l) [31].

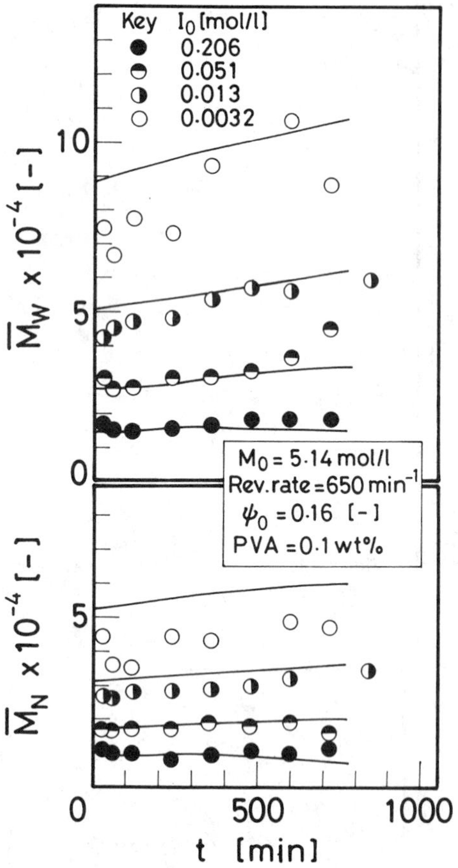

Figure 12. Effect of initiator concentration on average molecular weight ($M_0 = 5.14$ mol/l) [31].

the polymerization. The relation between initial polymerization rate R_{p0} and initial initiator concentration I_0 is shown in Figure 13. The common relation of $R_{p0} \propto I_0^{1/2}$ in the radical polymerization is obvious in the figure. Since the recombination termination is predominant in styrene polymerization, Equation 43 is expressed:

$$\frac{1}{\bar{P}_N} = T_{fM} + T_{fS}\frac{S}{M} + \frac{R_i}{2R_p} = T_{fM} + T_{fS}\frac{S}{M} + k_d f \frac{1}{R_p} \tag{45}$$

Plotting of $1/\bar{P}_{N0}$ vs. I_0/R_{p0} was carried out in Figure 14, and a linear relationship between $1/\bar{P}_{N0}$ and I_0/R_{p0} has been confirmed. Values of $(T_{fM} + T_{fS}S/M)$ and $k_d f$ are, respectively, obtained from the intersection at the ordinate axis and the slope of the linear line.

To investigate the effect of initiator concentration at a comparatively low initial monomer concentration $M_0 = 2$ mol/l, plots of conversion and average molecular weight vs. reaction time are respectively shown in Figures 15 and 16. The initial rate of monomer conversion in the polymerization exhibits almost the same tendency as the homogeneous polymerization. However, a linear

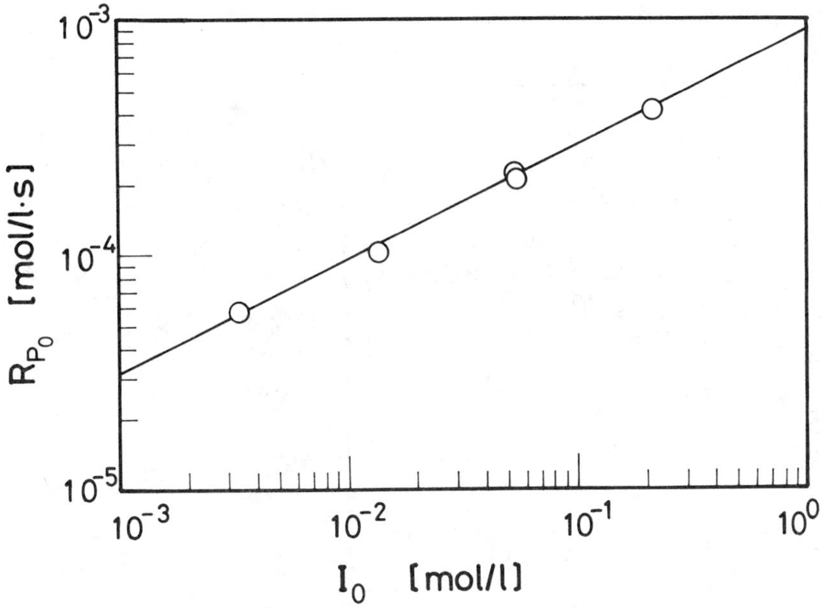

Figure 13. Relation between R_{p0} and I_0 [31].

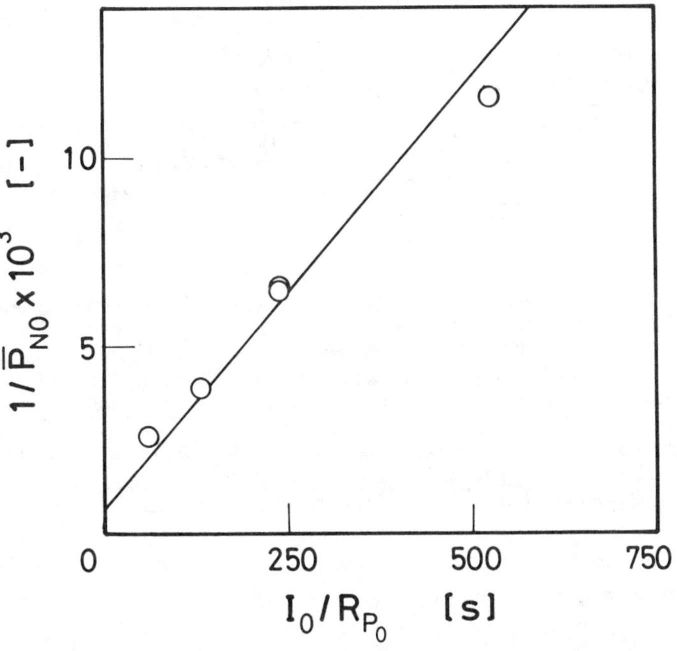

Figure 14. Relation between $1/\bar{P}_{N0}$ and I_0/R_{p0} [31].

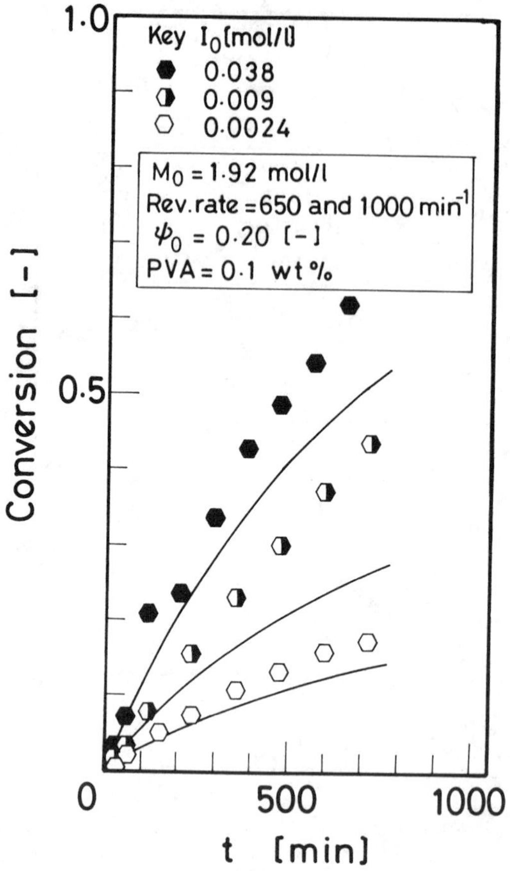

Figure 15. Effect of initiator concentration on polymerization rate (M_0 = 1.92 mol/l) [31].

relation with different slope is found between $1/\bar{P}_{N0}$ and I_0/R_{p0}. If a constant value of f is assumed, Equation 45 is inconsistent with the experimental results. At various initial monomer concentrations except for $M_0 = 5.1$ mol/l, the relations between $1/\bar{P}_{N0}$ and I_0/R_{p0} are represented in Figure 17. It is obvious from the figure that the slopes of the linear lines are different from each other, being steeper with increasing initial monomer concentration. Calculated f-values from the slope of each line in Figures 14 and 17 are listed with each corresponding M_0 in Table 3. It seems reasonable from the table to assume that isooctane, a poor solvent for polymer has a lowering effect in initiator efficiency. Hence, plotting of f vs. solvent weight fraction (SWF) was carried out in Figure 18. The following empirical correlation was obtained for the initiator efficiency.

$$f = 0.838(1 - 1.129\text{SWF}) \qquad \text{for SWF} \leq 0.72 \tag{46}$$

$$f = 0.560(1 - \text{SWF}) \qquad \text{for SWF} > 0.72 \tag{47}$$

From the intersections at the ordinate of the linear lines in Figures 14 and 17, T_{fS} was determined using T_{fM}-value from literature [35] to be 1.35×10^{-3} [–]. Here, $T_{fM} = 0.843 \times 10^{-4}$ [–].

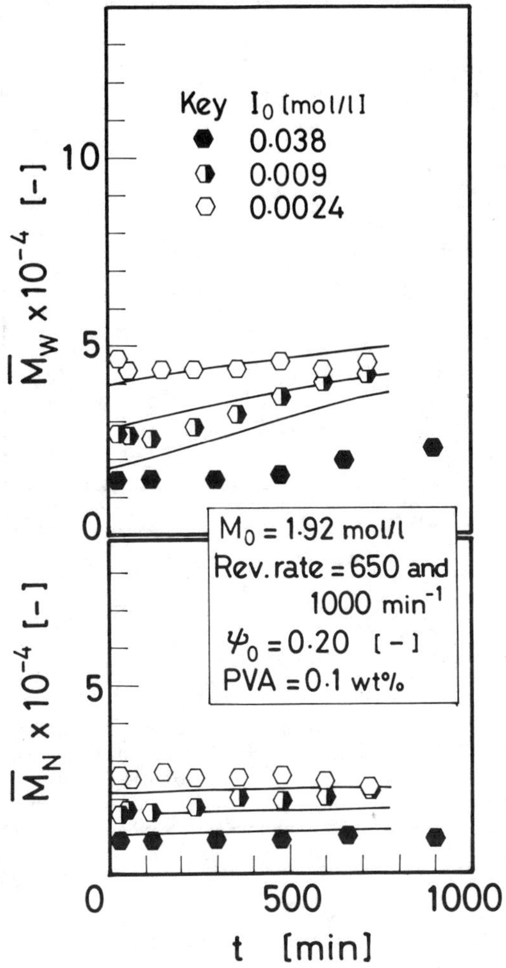

Figure 16. Effect of initiator concentration on average molecular weight (M_0 = 1.92 mol/l) [31].

Table 3
f Values from Figures 14 and 17

f [¯]	M_0 [mol/l]	SWF [¯]
0.838	8.30	0
0.545	5.3	0.32
0.370	3.8	0.47
0.160	1.9	0.72

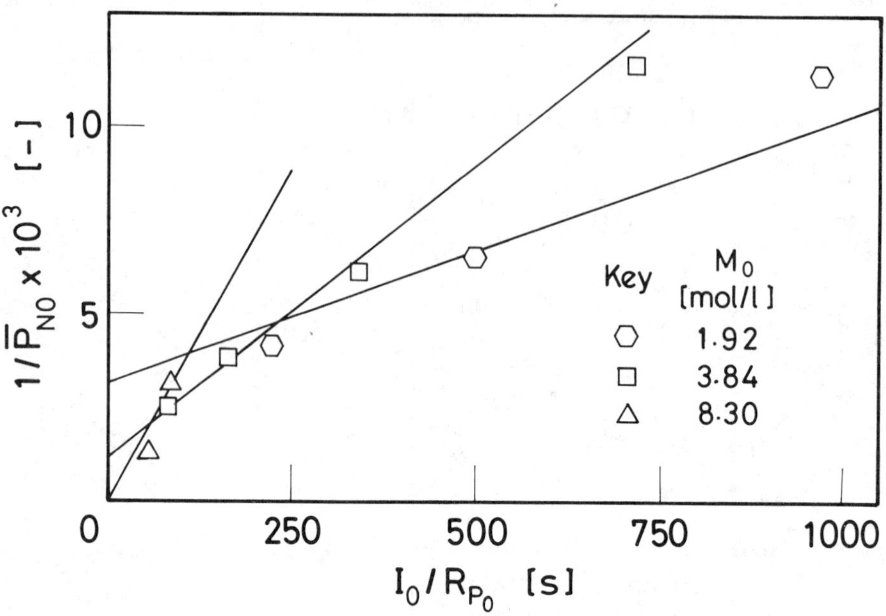

Figure 17. Relations between $1/\bar{P}_{N0}$ and I_0/R_{p0} [31].

Effect of monomer concentration on the rate of polymerization and the average molecular weight is shown in Figures 19 and 20, respectively. With decreasing the initial monomer concentration, monomer conversion rate decreases in the low conversion region. However, the differences of x vs. t relation among data covering a wide range of M are small in the high conversion region. Therefore, S-shaped relations between x and t are observed in the conditions of low initial monomer concentration. Such an x vs. t relation is characteristic in common slurry polymerization.

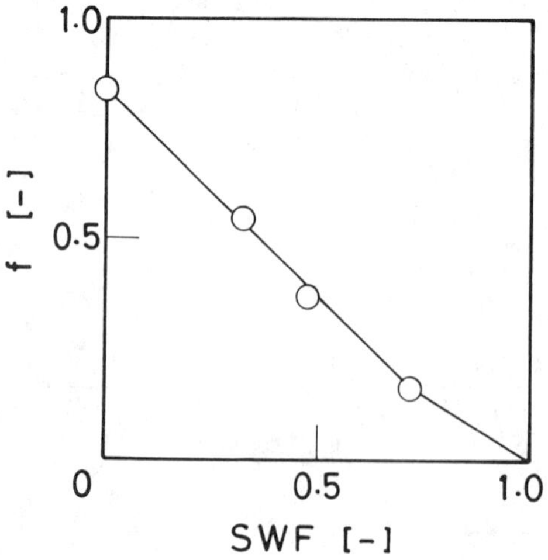

Figure 18. Relation between f and SWF [31].

With decreasing the initial monomer concentration, the average molecular weight of produced polymer also decreases. At low initial monomer concentrations, the following are the characteristics found in this polymerization system:

1. Obtained polymers are confirmed to have much higher average molecular weight than those in the homogeneous solution polymerization.
2. Average molecular weight increases with reaction time or is almost independent of reaction time, which is contrary to the homogeneous solution polymerization.

Two-phase separation model. In this model, the system is assumed to separate into two homogeneous phases, that is, a solvent-rich phase not containing any polymer and a polymer-rich phase. Concentration equilibriums between both phases of monomer, solvent and initiator would be reached. Gel effect would be predominant only in the polymer phase.

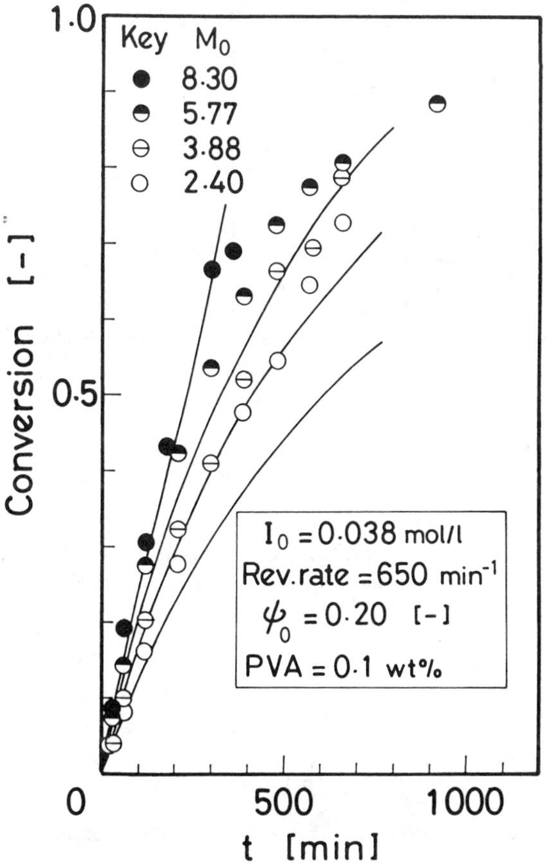

Figure 19. Effect of monomer concentration on polymerization rate [31].

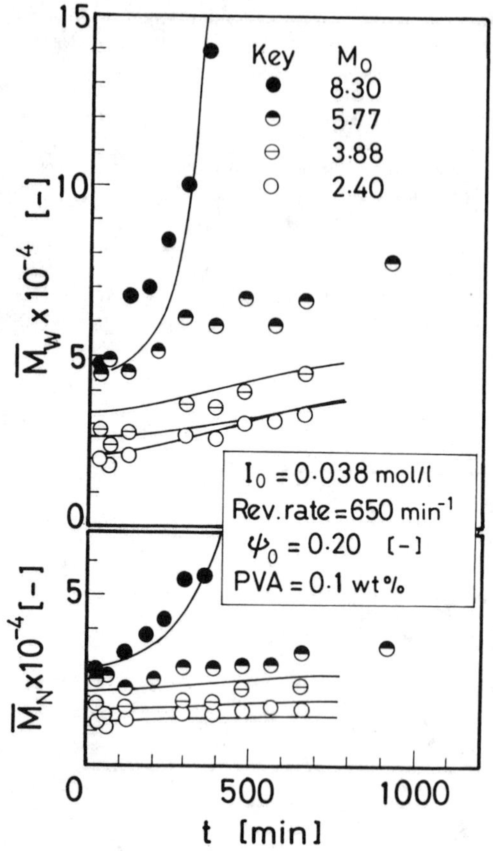

Figure 20. Effect of monomer concentration on average molecular weight [31].

Assigning 1 and 2 to the poor solvent-rich phase and the polymer-rich phase, respectively, the following equilibrium ratios of monomer, solvent and initiator are defined:

$$Q_M = M_2/M_1 \tag{48}$$

$$Q_S = S_2/S_1 \tag{49}$$

$$Q_I = I_2/I_1 \tag{50}$$

Q_M, Q_S and Q_I can be written as functions of only monomer concentration in the solvent-rich phase ($=M_1$).

The volume fraction of the solvent-rich phase ($=\chi_v$) is a solution of the following equation:

$$\frac{a(1-x)}{\chi_v(1-Q_M)+Q_M} + \frac{b}{\chi_v(1-Q_S)+Q_S} = 1 \tag{51}$$

where a and b are, respectively, initial volume fractions of monomer and solvent ($a + b = 1$). Q_M and Q_S are determined from M_1, which satisfies the following equation:

$$M_1 = \frac{M_0(1 - x)}{\chi_v(1 - Q_M) + Q_M} \tag{52}$$

Polymerization rates in the solvent-rich phase, in the polymer-rich phase and in the overall phase (respectively, R_{p1}, R_{p2} and R_p) are written as follows:

$$R_{p1} = \frac{k_p}{k_t^{1/2}}(2k_df)^{1/2}M_1I_1^{1/2} \tag{53}$$

$$R_{p2} = \frac{\gamma}{\varepsilon^{1/2}}\frac{k_p}{k_t^{1/2}}(2k_df\varepsilon)^{1/2}M_2I_2^{1/2} = \gamma\frac{k_p}{k_t^{1/2}}(2k_df)M_2I_2^{1/2} \tag{54}$$

$$\begin{aligned} R_p &= \chi_vR_{p1} + (1 - \chi_v)R_{p2} \\ &= \frac{k_p(2k_df)^{1/2}M_0(1 - x)I_0^{1/2}\exp(-k_dt/2)}{k_t^{1/2}\{\chi_v(1 - Q_M) + Q_M\}\{\chi_v(1 - Q_I) + Q_I\}^{1/2}}[\chi_v + \gamma(1 - \chi_v)Q_MQ_I^{1/2}] \end{aligned} \tag{55}$$

where

$$S_1 = \frac{S_0}{\chi_v(1 - Q_S) + Q_S} \tag{56}$$

$$I_1 = \frac{I_0\exp(-k_dt)}{\chi_v(1 - Q_I) + Q_I} \tag{57}$$

$$Z = T_{fs}\frac{S_0}{M_0(1 - x)}\frac{\chi_v(1 - Q_M) + Q_M}{\chi_v(1 - Q_S) + Q_S} \tag{58}$$

γ and ε are, respectively, correction factors for the overall polymerization rate and the initiator efficiency in the gel effect region. They are described approximately as functions of polymer weight fraction [36, 37].

Overall production rate of P_r is written by the following equation:

$$\begin{aligned} \frac{dP_r}{dt} &= \chi_v\frac{dP_{r1}}{dt} + (1 - \chi_v)\frac{dP_{r2}}{dt} \\ &= \chi_v\zeta_1^{r-1}(1 - \zeta_1)\left[R_{p1}(Z + T_{fM}) + \frac{(r - 1)(1 - \zeta_1)}{2}R_{i1}\right] \\ &\quad + (1 - \chi_v)\zeta_2^{r-1}(1 - \zeta_2)\left[R_{p2}\left(Z\frac{Q_S}{Q_M} + T_{fM}\right) + \frac{(r - 1)(1 - \zeta_2)}{2}R_{i2}\right] \end{aligned} \tag{59}$$

where

$$R_{i1} = 2k_dfI_1, \qquad R_{i2} = 2k_df\varepsilon I_2$$

$$\zeta_1 = 1 - \left(Z + T_{fM} + \frac{R_{i1}}{R_{p1}}\right)$$

$$\zeta_2 = 1 - \left(Z\frac{Q_S}{Q_M} + T_{fM} + \frac{R_{i2}}{R_{p2}}\right)$$

Table 4
Kinetic Parameters Used

$\delta = 35.7$	$(mol\cdot s/1)^{1/2}$
$T_{fA} = 0.843 \times 10^{-4}$	$[-]$
$T_{fS} = 1.35 \times 10^{-3}$	$[-]$
$k_d = 4.25 \times 10^{-5}$	s^{-1}
$f = 0.838(1 - 1.129SWF)$	for $SWF \leq 0.72$
$f = 0.560(1 - SWF)$	for $SWF > 0.72$

Hence, instantaneous number average degree of polymerization is written by the following equation:

$$\bar{P}_{N,inst} = \frac{R_p}{\sum_{r=1}^{\infty} [dP_r/dt]}$$
$$= R_p/[\chi_v\{R_{p1}(Z + T_{fM}) + R_{i1}/2\} + (1 - \chi_v)\{R_{p2}(ZQ_S/Q_M + T_{fM}) + R_{i2}/2\}] \quad (60)$$

Determination of Kinetic Parameters

Homogeneous polymerization. Kinetic parameters in the absence of gel effect are listed in Table 4. Correction factors γ and ε, respectively, for overall polymerization rate and initiator efficiency under

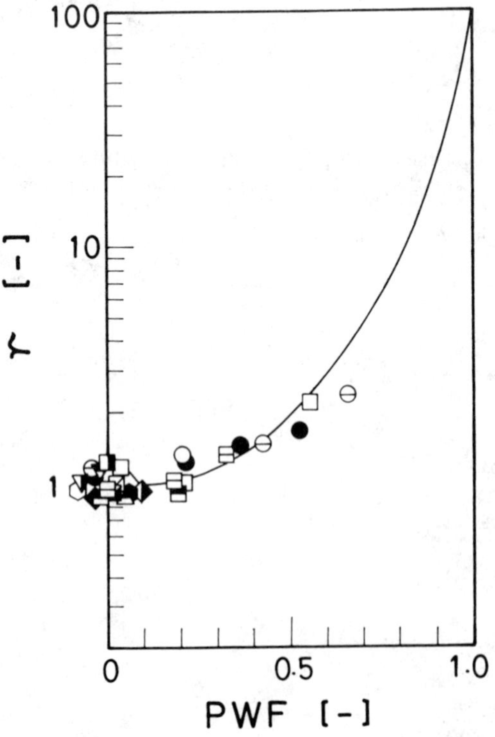

Figure 21. γ versus PWF (homogeneous polymerization) [31].

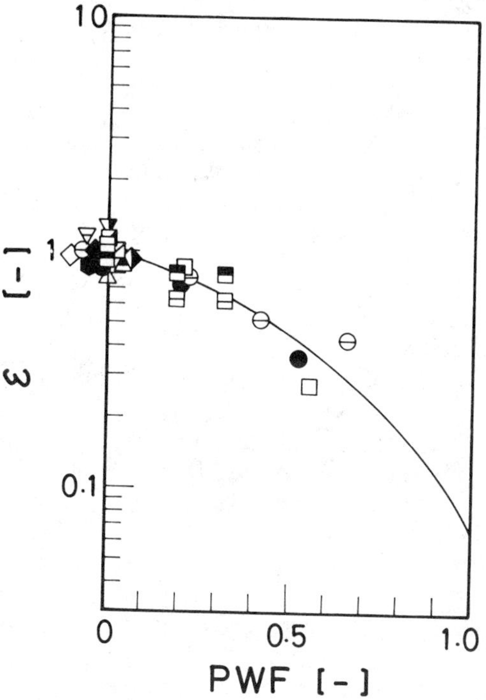

Figure 22. ε versus PWF (homogeneous polymerization) [31].

gel effect were determined from the established method [36, 37] and are shown in Figures 21 and 22 as functions of polymer weight fraction (PWF).

Determination of Kinetic Parameters for Two Separated Phases

Kinetic parameters in the solvent-rich phase are the same as those of the homogeneous polymerization in the absence of gel effect.

Q_M, Q_S and Q_I. To estimate Q_M and Q_S, toluene was used instead of styrene. Equilibrium experiments of toluene-isooctane-polystyrene system were carried out at 70°C. After a small amount of AIBN was charged in the system, Q_I was obtained from AIBN concentrations in both phases. Observed equilibrium compositions are shown on a triangular diagram of Figure 23. Almost no effect of molecular weight of used polymer samples ($\bar{M}_W = 3.19 \times 10^4$ and 17.4×10^4) was detected as shown in Figure 23. The lower area FPG represents the region of immiscibility and the border line curve FPG represents the solubility limits of the system. The bold line PH in the immiscible region is the conjugate line. As expected, almost no polymer content is recognized in the solvent-rich phase. The relation between each Q-value and M_1 is shown in Figure 24.

γ and ε. Since the gel effect is predominant only in the polymer-rich phase, the polymerization rate in the polymer-rich phase, the polymerization rate in the polymer-rich phase is necessary to be regarded as being equal to the overall polymerization rate to obtain γ and ε from the following calculations.

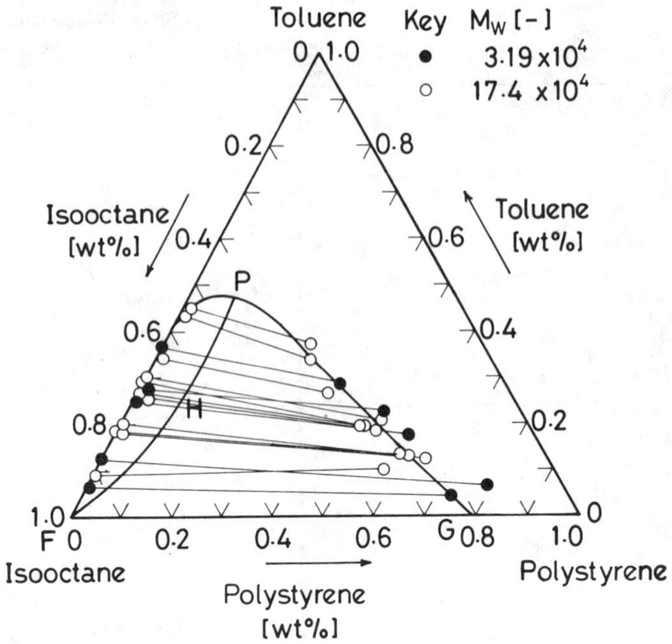

Figure 23. Observed equilibrium composition [31].

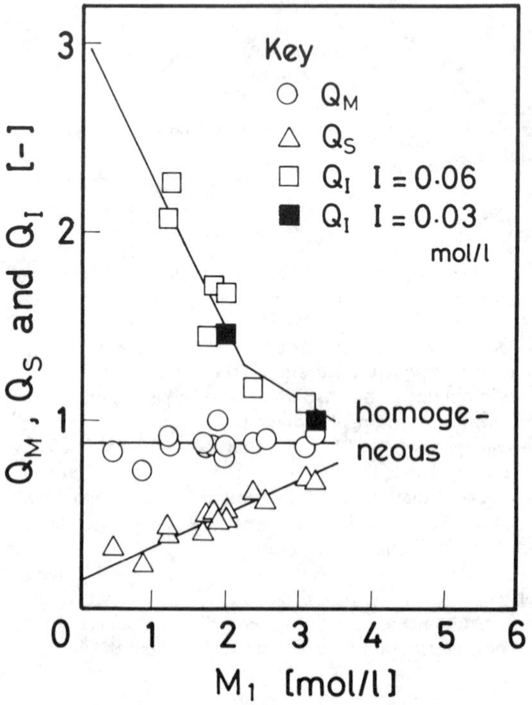

Figure 24. Relation between each Q-value and M_1 [31].

Under the conditions of small contribution of the solvent-rich phase to the overall reaction, γ can be determined from the following equation to be correlated with PWF:

$$\gamma = \frac{R_{p,ob} - \chi_v R_{p1,cal}}{(1-\chi_v)\dfrac{k_p}{k_t^{1/2}}(2k_d f)^{1/2} M_2 I_2^{1/2}} \tag{61}$$

In the condition where $\chi_v R_{p1,cal}/R_{p,ob}$ is almost zero, the obtained polymer is considered to be the polymer from the polymer-rich phase. Instantaneous number average degree of polymerization in this region is obtained from the following equation:

$$\bar{P}_{N,inst} = \frac{\bar{P}_N}{1 - \dfrac{(d\bar{P}_N/dt)M_0(1-x)}{\bar{P}_N \cdot R_p}} \tag{62}$$

ε can be determined using the following equation derived from Equation 60:

$$\varepsilon = \frac{R_p}{fk_d I_2}\left[\frac{1}{\bar{P}_{N,inst}} - \left(Z\frac{Q_S}{Q_M} + T_{fM}\right)\right] \tag{63}$$

γ and ε obtained using these methods are, respectively, shown as functions of PWF in Figures 25 and 26. It is evident in the range of the experimental conditions that γ and ε can be described as a function of only PWF. The same solid lines as in Figures 25 and 26 are, respectively, drawn in Figures 21 and 22 to show the same gel effect in both cases.

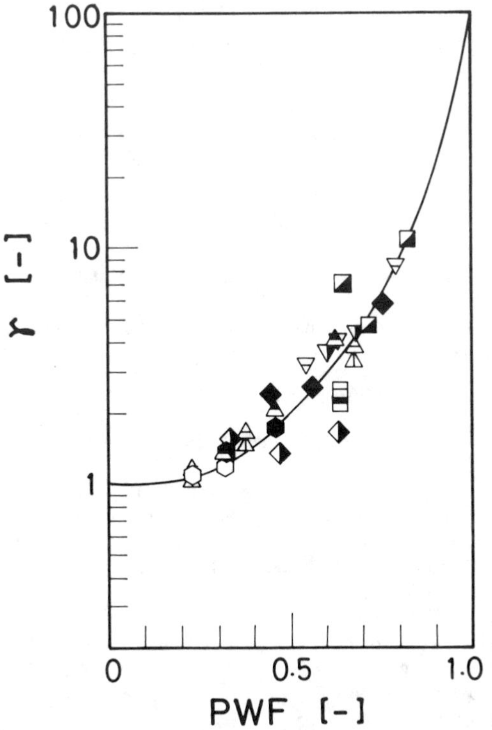

Figure 25. γ versus PWF (heterogeneous polymerization) [31].

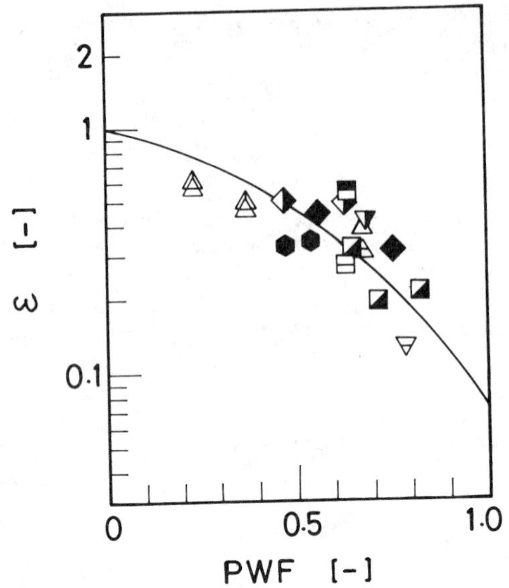

Figure 26. ε versus PWF (heterogeneous polymerization) [31].

Calculation of Conversion and Average Molecular Weight

Number and weight average degrees of polymerization are calculated from:

$$\bar{P}_N = \int_0^t R_p \, dt \Big/ \int_0^t \sum_{r=1}^{\infty} \frac{dP_r}{dt} \, dt \tag{64}$$

$$\bar{P}_W = \int_0^t \sum_{r=1}^{\infty} r^2 \frac{dP_r}{dt} \, dt \Big/ \int_0^t R_p \, dt \tag{65}$$

Using Equations 55, 59, 64, and 65 with the empirical kinetic parameters in Table 4 and Figures 25 and 26, time dependencies of conversion and molecular weight were calculated for each experimental condition. Calculated results are shown as solid lines in Figures 9–12, Figures 15 and 16, and Figures 19 and 20.

Applicability of the two-phase separation model to this polymerization process has been proved by close agreement of both the conversion and the average molecular weight of produced polymer between observed and calculated values.

Styrene-Isooctane-2,2'Azobis(Dimethyl-Valeronitrile) (ADVN) System [34]

This polymerization process is a useful method to prepare the microcapsules with various functions [33, 38]. More rapid polymerization rates than that for the cited polymerization system (St – isooctane – AIBN) are desired to accomplish the practical application of this process. Here, we consider to use 2,2'-azobis (dimethyl-valeronitrile) (ADVN) in place of AIBN. The decomposition rate of ADVN is 4.5 times that of AIBN.

To describe this polymerization system with ADVN, almost the same kinetic parameters as those in the polymerization system initiated by AIBN would be used. However, decomposition rate constant k_d, initiator efficiency f and initiator equilibrium ratio Q_I, being the ratio of initiator concentration in the polymer phase to that in the solvent phase, are considered to be different from those

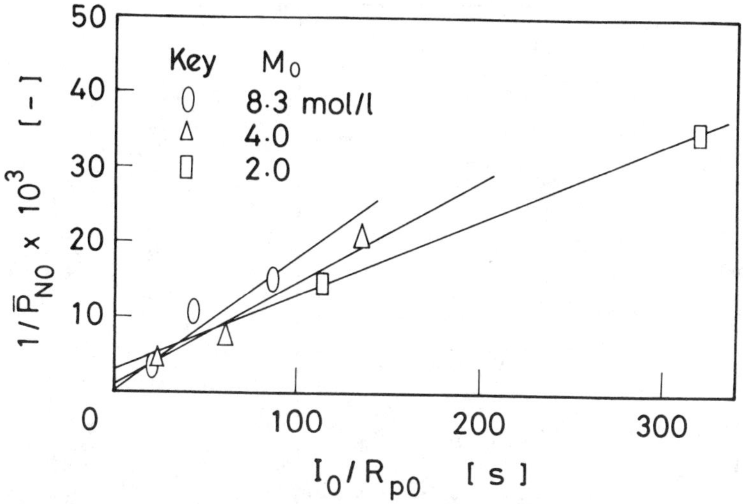

Figure 27. Determination of f according to Equation 45 [34].

determined from AIBN-system because they are the kinetic parameters dependent on the nature of the initiator.

In Figure 27, $1/\bar{P}_{N0}$ were plotted against I_0/R_{p0} according to Equation 45. f-values observed at three levels of M_0 were plotted against the solvent weight fraction (SWF) in Figure 28. f decreases with SWF in the similar manner as shown in Figure 18 using AIBN, being here represented as $f = 0.947 - 0.567$ SWF.

In Figure 29, Q_I-values obtained from equilibrium experiments in an isooctane-toluene (in place of styrene)-polystyrene system were plotted against M_1 (toluene concentrations in the isooctane phase in place of the styrene concentration in that phase). Q_I is described as $Q_I = 1.50 - 0.209M_1$.

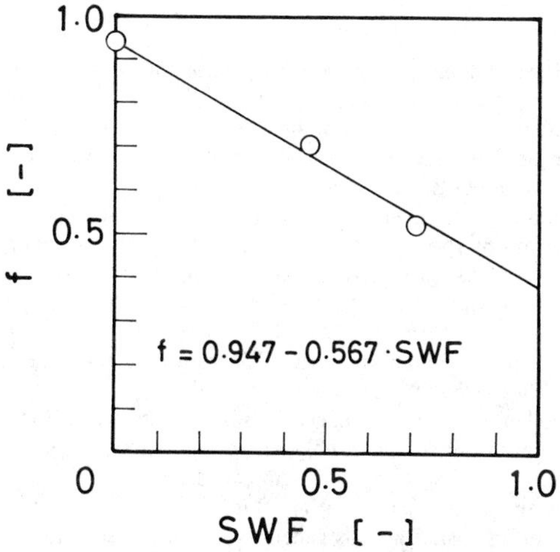

Figure 28. Relation between initiator efficiency and solvent weight fraction [34].

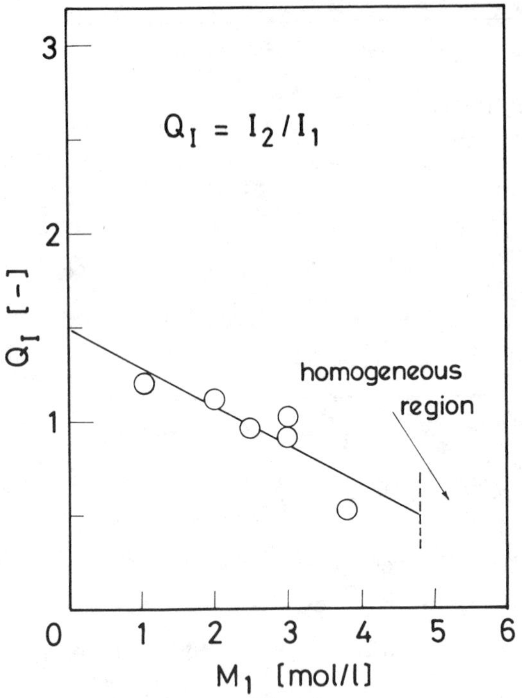

Figure 29. Relation between initiator equilibrium ratio and monomer concentration in solvent phase [34].

The comparisons between the observed and calculated results for monomer conversion and average molecular weights of produced polymer at $M_0 = 4$ mol/l were shown in Figures 30 and 31, respectively. It is obvious that kinetic description of this polymerization system is accomplished using the two-phase separation model.

EMULSION POLYMERIZATION

One of the kinetic characteristics of emulsion polymerization is a proportionality of both the polymerization rate and polymer molecular weight to the number of particles [39]. High polymerization rate and high molecular weight of polymer are generally obtained from the emulsion polymerization due to the free radicals being segregated and the number of loci available for segregation being within a few orders of magnitude of the number of free radicals in the system.

An overall feature of emulsion polymerization is qualitatively explained as follows [39–47]. When the emulsifier (surfactant) is present in concentrations above the critical micelle concentration (cmc), it forms micelles. Hydrophilic groups such as carboxyl groups of emulsifier molecule chains form the outside of the spherical micelles, being contact with water, and lipophilic (hydrophobic) groups of the emulsifier molecule chains associate each other to form the inside of the micelles. If a monomer immisible with water is added to the aqueous solution containing the emulsifier micelles and mixed, a small part of monomer would invade the micelles through aqueous phase from dispersed monomer droplets. The emulsifier micelles would be swollen with the monomer. (This is sometimes called the monomer solubility phenomenon.) At the beginning of emulsion polymerization just after feeding a water-soluble initiator, the emulsifier micelles swollen with the monomer, dispersed monomer droplets, initiator molecules, initiator radicals and a minute amount of soluble monomer coexist in water. According to the initiation-in-micelles mechanism, radicals generated in the aqueous phase

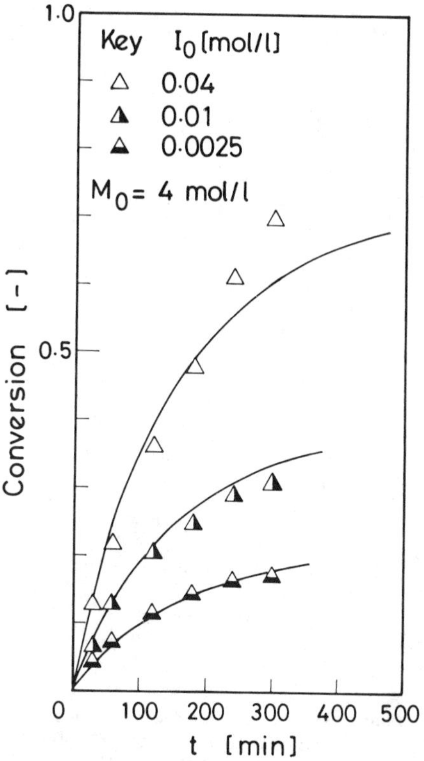

Figure 30. Comparison between observed and calculated results of conversion [34].

enter monomer-swollen micelles and initiate polymerization to form monomer-swollen polymer particles. Such polymer particle formations would continue until the disappearance of the micelles. The polymerization in the dispersed monomer droplets can be neglected because the radicals in the aqueous phase diffuse only into the emulsifier micelles due to their extremely large total surface area relative to that of the monomer droplets. Monomer depletion by the polymerization in the polymer particles would be supplied from the monomer droplets, which act as reservers, feeding monomer to the micelles and polymer particles by diffusion through the aqueous phase. Only one of every 100–1000 micelles captures a radical and becomes a polymer particle; the others give up their monomer and emulsifier to neighboring micelles that have captured a radical. After the disappearance of the micelles, the number of polymer particles would be unchanged until the complete monomer conversion. As the polymerization proceeds, the monomer droplets providing monomer for polymer particles are also depleted to disappear. Unreacted monomer in the polymer particles, then, polymerizes to the complete conversion.

According to the initiation-in-the-aqueous-phase mechanism, radicals generated in the aqueous phase react with monomer molecules in the aqueous phase to add monomer units until the oligomeric radicals exceed their solubility and precipitate. The precipitated oligomeric radicals forms spherical particles that adsorb emulsifier and adsorb monomer to become primary particles. These primary particles persist or flocculate with already existing particles or other primary particles precipitating from the aqueous phase. This mechanism is generally applied to those monomers that have significant solubilities in water. Since the precipitation polymerization based on this mechanism was already mentioned before, no further discussion will be considered concerning the initiation-in-the-aqueous-phase mechanism.

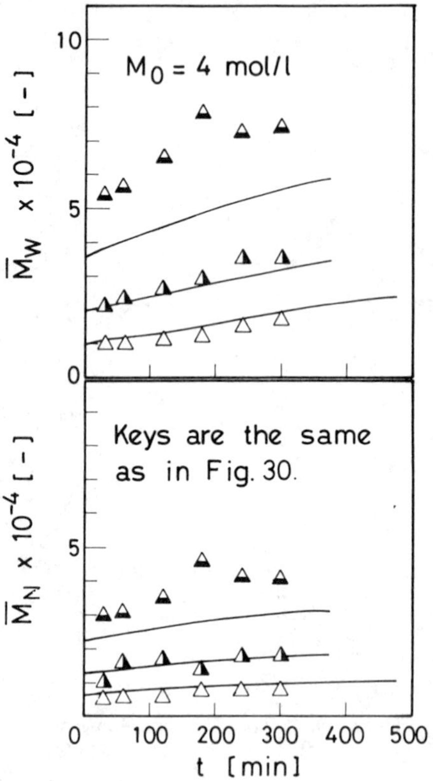

Figure 31. Comparison between observed and calculated results of average molecular weights [34].

Styrene Emulsion Polymerization

Styrene emulsion polymerization is the most popular example kinetically studied so far, showing a typical emulsion polymerization feature previously mentioned [40–47].

Omi et al. [48–50] carried out styrene emulsion polymerization over the entire range of monomer conversion, with changing monomer to water phase ratio, type of emulsifier, emulsifier concentration, and initiator concentration. Figures 32 and 33 show the experimental results of the time dependence of monomer conversion, and the relations between polymerization rate, average degree of polymerization and monomer conversion, respectively, under a representative experimental condition, i.e., water = 640 ml, styrene = 160 ml, sodium oleate(emulsifier) = 1.5 g, potassium persulfate (initiator) = 0.55 g, reaction temperature = 60°C and agitation speed = 700 rpm. As shown in these figures, the following three reaction regions were considered; (a) the first region is defined as the polymerization stage from the beginning of the polymerization until the disappearance of the micelles to reach a constant polymerization rate, which is classified as Region I (the induction reaction region); (b) the second is the stage from the disappearance of the micellles to keep the polymerization rate constant until the disappearance of the monomer droplets, which is classified as Region II (the zero-order reaction region); and (c) the third is the stage from the disappearance of the monomer droplets until the complete conversion, which is classified as Region III (the first-order reaction region) [51, 52].

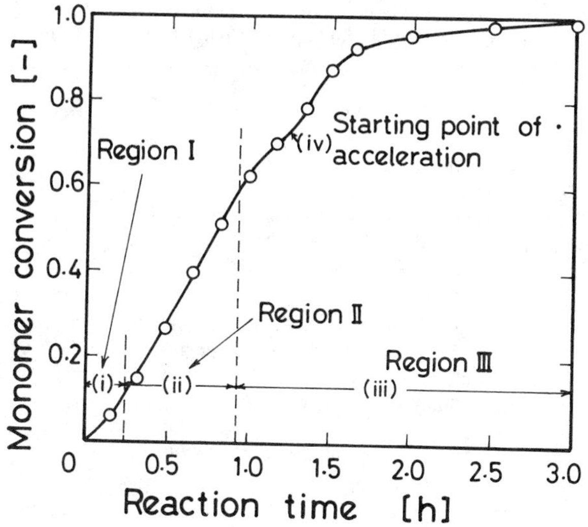

Figure 32. Time dependence of monomer conversion [48].

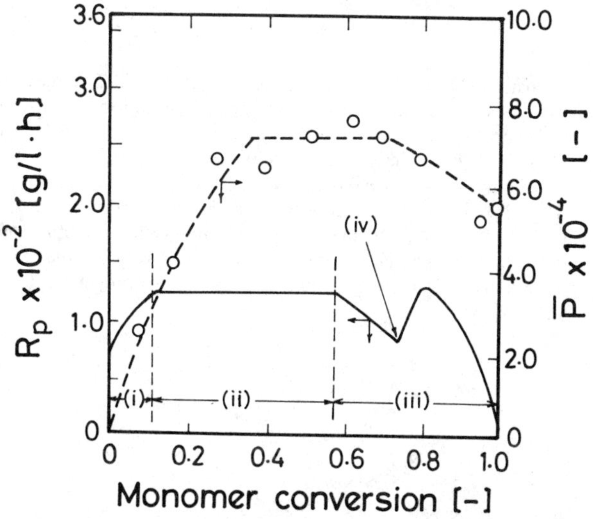

Figure 33. Changes of monomer consumption rate and average degree of polymerization with monomer conversion [48].

Region I. Since polymer particles are continuously produced in this region, the polymerization rate increases with time. The total number of polymer particles produced in this region is given by the following equation [53]:

$$N_I = 0.4(R_i N_A/\mu)^{0.4}(a_S S_0)^{0.6} \tag{66}$$

where R_i = initiation rate [kg-mol/m^{3}h]
N_A = Avogadro number [1/kg-mol]
μ = rate of increase in volume of a polymer particle [m^3/h]
a_S = surface area of polymer particles covered by unit mole of emulsifier [m^2/kg-mol]
S_0 = initial concentration of emulsifier [kg-mol/m^3]

Hence, N_I is estimated to be proportional to $R_i^{0.4}S_0^{0.6}$. This relation is experimentally confirmed for styrene. In this particle nucleation stage, however, N_I depends upon the type of emulsifier, the type and concentration of electrolyte, the temperature, the type and intensity of agitation, as well as other parameters that are often not well understood.

Region II. The monomer consumption rate for homopolymerization is generally expressed as follows,

$$R_p = k_p[M][P\cdot] \tag{67}$$

where [M] and [P·] are the concentrations of monomer and polymer radicals, respectively.
Considering that the polymerization occurs only in the polymer particles, the Equation 67 can be written as

$$R_p = k_p M \frac{\bar{n} N_I}{N_A} \tag{68}$$

where M = monomer concentration in the polymer particles
$\bar{n}$ = average number of radicals existent in a polymer particle

Since M would be constant (M = 5.0 mol/l for styrene) until the disappearence of the monomer droplets, $\bar{n}$ should be estimated to evaluate the monomer consumption rate. $\bar{n}$-value can be easily determined by considering the balance of radicals as mentioned later. The rate of formation of radicals is expressed as $R_i = 2fk_dI$. The invasion rate of a radical from the aqueous phase into the polymer particles containing n radicals is $k_{in}N_n[P]$, where N_n is the number of polymer particles containing n radicals, and [p·] is the radical concentration in the aqueous phase. The disappearance rate of polymer particles containing n radicals by termination reaction is $k_t n(n-1)N_n/v_pN_A$, where v_p is the volume of a polymer particle. The escape rate of a radical from polymer particles containing n radicals is $k_f nN_n/v_p$. From the assumption of quasi-steady state for polymer particles, the following balance equations are derived:

$$\frac{dN_0}{dt} = k_f N_1/v_p + 2k_t N_2/v_p N_A - k_{in}N_0[P\cdot] = 0 \tag{69}$$

$$\frac{dN_n}{dt} = k_{in}N_{n-1}[P\cdot] + k_f(n+1)N_{n+1}/v_p + k_t(n+2)(n+1)N_{n+2}/v_pN_A$$
$$- (k_{in}N_n[P\cdot] + k_f nN_n/v_p + k_t n(n-1)N_n/v_pN_A) = 0 \qquad (n = 1, 2, \ldots, n) \tag{70}$$

or

$$k_{in}N_n[P\cdot] = (k_f/v_p + nk_t/v_pN_A)(n+1)N_{n+1} + (k_t/v_pN_A)(n+1)(n+2)N_{n+2} \tag{71}$$

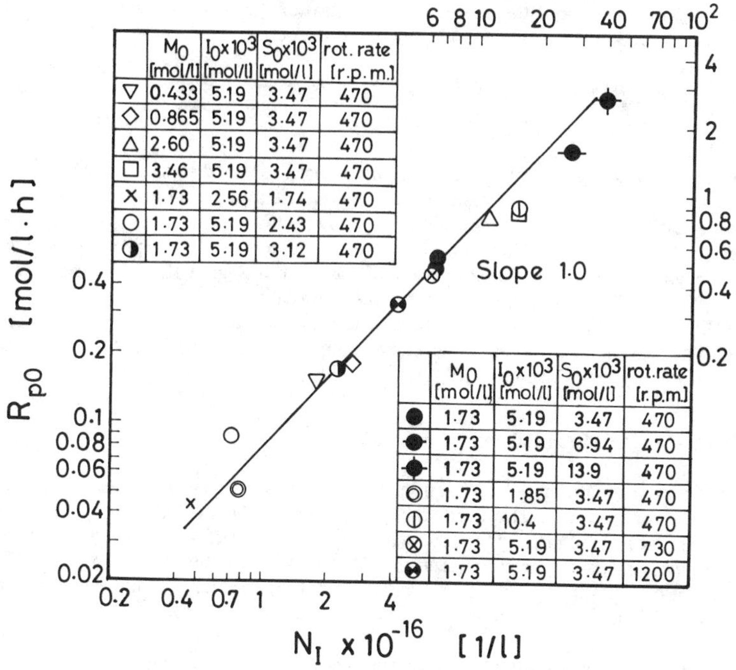

Figure 34. Relation between rate of polymerization and number of polymer particles [50].

Since the termination rate in polymer particles is very fast for styrene, only polymer particles containing zero or one radical would be found in the system. This means $N_2 = N_3 \cdots = 0$, and thus

$$N = N_0 + N_1 \tag{72}$$

Equation 71 is expressed by

$$k_{in}N_0[P\cdot] - k_f\bar{n}N/v - k_{in}N_1[P\cdot] = 0 \tag{73}$$

Since $\bar{n} = N_1/N$ and $k_fN_A/k_t = 0$ for styrene, it is derived that

$$2k_{in}\bar{n}[P\cdot] = k_n[P\cdot] \tag{74}$$

Thus, $\bar{n} = \frac{1}{2}$ is obtained for styrene. Consequently, a constant monomer consumption rate is evident regardless of the change of apparent monomer concentration. R_p is predicted from the rate equation to be directly proportional N_I. This is shown in Figure 34.

The number average degree of polymerization is expressed by

$$\bar{P}_N = R_p/0.5R_i = k_pM\frac{N_I}{R_iN_A} \tag{75}$$

Region III. In this region, the monomer concentration M is not constant, so the first-order reaction will be predominant. The following equation is derived:

$$R_p = k_p M\left(\frac{1 - x}{1 - x_{cr}}\right)\frac{\bar{n}N_I}{N_A} \tag{76}$$

where x_{cr} is the monomer conversion at which monomer droplets disappear. Even in the emulsion polymerization, an abrupt acceleration in the reaction rate may be observed in the later stage of the polymerization. This phenomenon is shown using an arrow in Figures 32 and 33. This auto-accelerating effect is caused by the increase in average number of polymeric radicals in a polymer particle $\bar{n}$ beyond the constant value of one half observed in Region II. This increase in $\bar{n}$ can be connected with the decrease in the termination rate constant k_t.

Other different kinetic discription for the styrene emulsion polymerization was also reported, in which fresh nucleation occurs even at high conversion, causing a continuous shifting toward broadening of particle size distribution [46].

Styrene Soap-Free Emulsion Polymerization

In conventional emulsion polymerization, the concentrations of emulsifier are always above critical micelle concentration. However, stable polystyrene lattices could be prepared without any emulsifier. This is a useful method for producing monodisperse lattices in a single stage up to 1 μm dia with surfaces amenable to characterization [54–60]. Although no essential difference in growth mechanism of particles in both surfactant and surfactant-free systems would be considered, there are two differences in these reactions:

1. The particle number densities involved are significantly different, e.g., for two reactions, identical in all respects save the presence of surfactant in one, it was shown that 100-fold more particles were present at the end of the reaction in the presence of surfactant that was complete in 60 min, (cf. 1,000 min for surfactant-free reaction).
2. The molecular weights formed in surfactant-free systems are a factor of 10 lower.

Goodall et al. [56] assumed that, initially, oligomeric free radicals are formed in the same manner as those for conventional emulsion polymerization, i.e., free radicals are initiated, as for example by persulfate,

$$S_2O_8^{2-} \longrightarrow 2SO_4^{-}\cdot$$

and these react with monomer in the aqueous phase.

$$SO_4^{-}\cdot + M \longrightarrow SO_4^{-}M\cdot$$

$$SO_4^{-}M\cdot + M \longrightarrow SO_4^{-}MM\cdot$$

$$SO_4^{-}MM\cdot + M \longrightarrow SO_4^{-}MMM\cdot$$

As these reactions proceed, the number of monomer units incorporated into the oligomeric ion radical increases until the hydropholic chain length becomes sufficiently long to confer surface-active properties. Their proposed mechanism of particle formation and growth of styrene based on the previously mentioned assumption is shown in Figure 35, where they envisaged several possibilities for particle initiation.

In the first stage of the reaction, the solubility of the monomer increases greatly (beyond 10^{18} molecules/ml) due to the addition of the polar sulfate group, but then decreases as the chain length grows. If chain propagation continued without association, then the oligomeric free radical would eventually become insoluble. Polymerization could still continue, with the polymer chain increasing

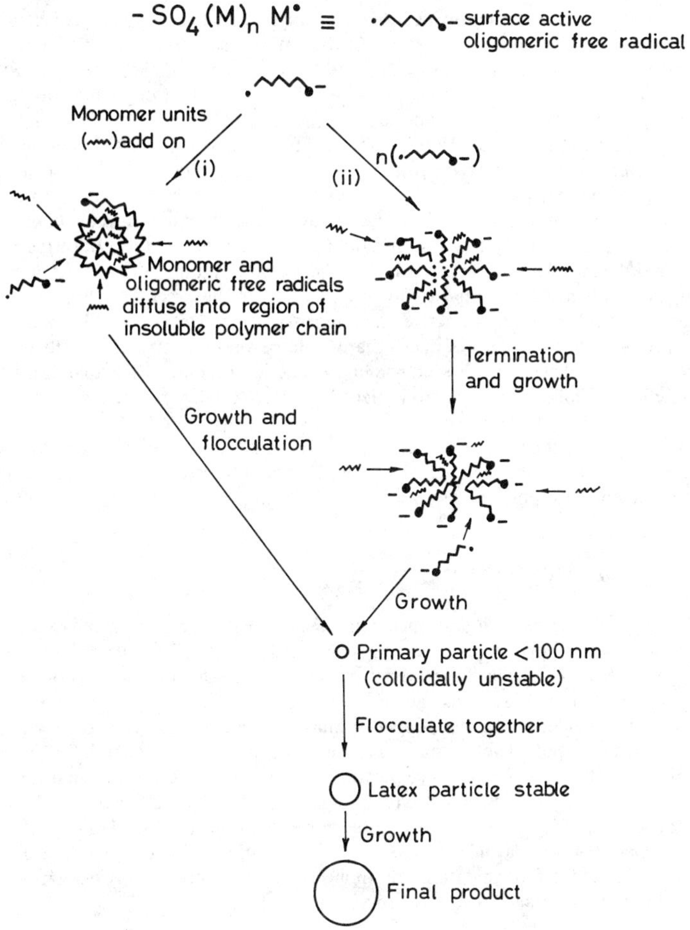

Figure 35. Possible mechanism of particle formation and growth of styrene in the absence of surfactant [56].

in length by addition of monomer. Shorter-chain oligomers and monomer would be preferentially incorporated into this structure and a "particle" would be formed. These small particles would aggregate into groups since they are colloidally unstable and the process would be repeated until a colloidally stable particle was formed. The stable particle would then continue to grow as long as free radicals and monomer are available.

(i) The growing oligomeric radicals eventually reached a concentration in solution at which they precipitated out, subsequent particle growth occurring in these precipitated nuclei.

(ii) The free-radical species could attain a chain length at which they become surface-active. This probably occurs at a shorter chain length than that required for precipitation out of solution.

It has been suggested that micellization could then occur. With radical generation rates of the order of 10^{14}/ml-sec then only 6 sec would be required for oligomers of 500 MW average (4–5 monomer units) to reach a probable micellar concentration of 10^{-6} M.

Once the micelle has become a growing monomer/polymer particle, it no longer has the properties of a conventional micelle, which exists only in a dynamic sense. Monomer and further oligomeric free radicals would be preferentially solubilized in these particles, at the expense of chain growth in solution, since the rates of diffusion of monomer and short-chain oligomers are several orders of magnitude greater than the rate of initiation or propagation.

It is thought that the presence of large amounts of low molecular weight material ($\sim$1,000) in early reaction samples is related both to the mode of particle nucleation and to the presence of anomalous regions within the particles. The presence of large amounts of low molecular weight material cannot be accounted for by the polymerization and termination rates in very small particles; thus, it must have been formed during the particle nucleation stage. Both the precipitation mechanism and the micellar mechanism proposed here would result in the formation of low molecular weight material through mutual termination, either by the precipitation of oligomers or by the formation of micelles by surface-active oligomers. Also, the mechanism of homogenous nucleation would produce large numbers of nuclei that would be very unstable colloidally due to the low surface-charge density; hence, they would coagulate together rapidly until stable. It is unlikely that this process could be followed by electron microscopy due to the very small size of these original nuclei ($\leq$ 10 nm).

Some quantitative kinetic approaches to the soap-free emulsion polymerization have been carried out from the previously mentioned mechanism, which would be essentially the same as that imaged for convertional emulsion polymerization [55, 56, 58–60].

DISPERSION POLYMERIZATION

Dispersion polymerization in organic media has been shown to be a new route to the preparation of small, monodisperse polymer colloids. As mentioned in detail by Barrett [30, 61] this polymerization differs from emulsion polymerization in several key features. In this polymerization, a polymeric steric stabilizer is used instead of the charged surfactant in emulsion polymerization. At the beginning of the polymerization, only one phase is present in contrast to the multiple phases of emulsion polymerization. That is, monomer, initiator, and polymeric stabilizer all dissolve in the organic medium before reaction. Once polymerization occurs, the polymer that is being formed precipitates to produce particles, which are stabilized by dissolved polymeric stabilizer. A graft copolymer or a block copolymer would be used for polymeric stabilizer because of their strong absorptive property on the particle surface and affinity with the solvent. An excellent review by Barrett [30] discusses the fundamentals and applications of dispersion polymerization. Of course, there are many recent approaches to this process [62–69].

NOTATION

A	$Na_2S_2O_5$ or its concentration, [mol/cc-water]
a	volume fraction of monomer, [−]
a_S	surface area of polymer particles covered by unit mole of emulsifier, [m^2/kg-mol]
B	$NaNO_2$ or its concentration, [mol/cc-water]
b	volume fraction of solvent, [−]
f	initiator efficiency, [−]
I	initiator or its concentration, [mol/l]
K_e	equilibrium constant, [$(mol/cc)^{1-a-b}$]
k	kinetic parameter defined by Equation 26, [$(mol/l)^{-1/2}\ s^{-1}$]
k_d	decomposition rate constant of initiator, [s^{-1}]
k_f	escape rate constant of monomer radical from a polymer particle, [cc-polymer phase/particle s]
k_{fm}, k'_{fm}	chain transfer rate constant of polymer radical to monomer, [$(mol/l)^{-1}\ s^{-1}$] or [$(mol/cc)^{-1}\ s^{-1}$]
k_{fS}	chain transfer rate constant of polymer radical to solvent, [$(mol/l)^{-1}\ s^{-1}$] or [$(mol/cc)^{-1}\ s^{-1}$]

k_i initiation rate constant, $[(mol/l)^{-1} s^{-1}]$ or $[(mol/cc)^{-1} s^{-1}]$

k_{im}, k'_{im} reinitiation rate constant by monomer radical, $[(mol/cc)^{-1} s^{-1}]$

k_{in} invasion rate constant from liquid to precipitation phase, [cc-liquid phase/particle s]

k_{iS} reinitiation rate constant by solvent radical, $[(mol/l)^{-1} s^{-1}]$

k_m k value (in Equation 26) in the monomer phase, $[(mol/l)^{-1/2} s^{-1}]$

k_p, k'_p propagation rate constant, $[(mol/l)^{-1} s^{-1}]$ or $[(mol/cc)^{-1} s^{-1}]$

k_t termination rate constant, $[(mol/l)^{-1} s^{-1}]$

k'_t termination rate constant with initiator radical, $[(mol/l)^{-1} s^{-1}]$

k''_t dissipation rate constant of initiator radicals by coupling reaction, $[(mol/l)^{-1} s^{-1}]$

k_{tc}, k'_{tc} termination rate constant for coupling reaction, $[(mol/l)^{-1} s^{-1}]$ or $[(mol/cc)^{-1} s^{-1}]$

k_{td}, k'_{td} termination rate constant for disproportionation, $[(mol/l)^{-1} s^{-1}]$ or $[(mol/cc)^{-1} s^{-1}]$

k_{tS} termination rate constant by solvent radical, $[(mol/l)^{-1} s^{-1}]$

M, M* monomer or its concentration, [mol/l] or [mol/cc-water]

M_1 monomer in liquid phase or its concentration, [mol/l] or [mol/cc-water]

$\bar{M}_N$ number average molecular weight, [−]

M_p monomer in polymer phase or its concentration, [mol/cc-water]

M_{pa} monomer observed in polymer or its concentration, [mol/g]

$\bar{M}_W$ weight average molecular weight, [−]

m_m mass fraction of polymer produced in monomer-rich phase, [−]

m_p mass fraction of polymer produced in polymer-rich phase, [−]

N_A Avogadro number, [1/kg-mol]

N_I total number of polymer particles produced in Region I, $[1/m^3]$

N_n number of polymer particles containing n radicals, $[1/m^3]$

N_p number of polymer particles, [particles/cc-water]

$\bar{n}$ average number of radicals existent in a polymer particle, [−]

$\bar{P}_N$ number average degree of polymerization, [−]

P_n dead polymer of degree of polymerization n or its concentration, [mol/l] or [mol/cc]

$P_n\cdot, P_n^*$ polymer radical of degree of polymerization n or its concentration, [mol/l] or [mol/cc]

$\bar{P}_W$ weight average degree of polymerization, [−]

PVA polyvinyl alcohol or its concentration, [wt%]

PWF polymer weight fraction, [−]

Q_1, Q_2 kinetic parameters in Equation 26, [−]

Q_I, Q_M, Q_S equilibrium ratios defined by Equations 50, 48 and 49, respectively, [−]

R gas constant (=8.314), [J/mol K]

R initiator radical or its concentration, [mol/l]

R_i initiation rate, $[(mol/l)s^{-1}]$ or $[(kg\text{-}mol/m^3)h^{-1}]$

R_p monomer consumption rate, $[(mol/l)s^{-1}]$

r degree of polymerization, [−]

S* solvent radical or its concentration, [mol/l]

S_0 initial concentration of emulsifier, $[kg\text{-}mol/m^3]$

SWF solvent weight fraction, [−]

T_{fM} chain transfer constant to monomer, $(=k_{fm}/k_p)$, [−]

T_{fS} chain transfer constant to solvent, $(=k_{fS}/k_p)$, [−]

t time, [s], [min] or [h]

v_p volume of a polymer particle, [cc/particle]

v_l volume fraction of liquid phase to water, [cc-liquid phase/cc-water]

x conversion, [−]

x_m polymer composition in monomer-rich phase, [−]

x_p polymer composition in polymer-rich phase, [−]

W_r weight fraction of polymer chain length r, [−]

$\beta_1 - \beta_4$ kinetic parameters used in Equation 11
γ correction factor for overall reaction rate under gel effect, [−]
δ kinetic constant ($=k_t/k_p$), $[(mol/l)^{-1/2} s^{1/2}]$
ε correction factor for initiator efficiency under gel effect, [−]
ζ probability factor for calculation of degree of polymerization, [−]
μ rate of increase in volume of a polymer particle, $[m^3/h]$
ρ_m density of monomer, $[g/cm^3]$
ρ_p density of polymer, $[g/cm^3]$
τ probability factor defined by Equation 31, [−]
τ_h half-life, [−]
χ_v volume fraction of solvent-rich phase in organic phase, [−]
ψ volume fraction of organic phase, [−]

Subscript

0 initial state
1 solvent phase, solvent-rich phase or monomer phase
2 polymer-rich phase
inst instantaneous
p polymer phase

REFERENCES

1. Almog, Y., and Levy, M., "Effect of Initiator on the Molecular Weight Distribution in Dispersion Polymerization of Styrene," *J. Polym. Sci. Polym. Chem. Ed.*, 18, 1 (1980).
2. Almog, Y., and Levy, M., "Dispersion Polymerization of Styrene: Effect of Surfactant," *J. Polym. Sci. Polym. Chem. Ed.*, 19, 115 (1981).
3. Mayoral, J. F., and Levy, M., "Dispersion Photopolymerization of Styrene," *J. Polym. Sci. Polym. Chem. Ed.*, 20, 2755 (1982).
4. Almog, Y., and Levy, M., "Studies of Particle Size Distribution and Adsorption of Stabilizers in Dispersion Polymerization," *J. Polym. Sci. Polym. Chem. Ed.*, 20, 417 (1982).
5. Bamford, C. H., and Jenkins, A. D., "Studies in Polymerization VI. Acrylonitrile: The Behavior of Free Radicals in Heterogeneous Systems," *Proc. Roy. Soc. London, Ser. A*, 216, 515 (1953).
6. Ariff, M., Jainuddin, M., Gopalan, V., and Rao, K. V., "Aqueous Polymerization of Acrylonitrile by Ascorbic Acid—Peroxodi-sulfate Redox System," *J. Polym. Sci. Polym. Chem. Ed.*, 23, 2063 (1985).
7. Patnaik, L. N., Satapathy, R. K., Patnaik, S. N., Misra, B. K., and Rout, M. K., "The Kinetics of Retardation by Phenol of the Polymerization of Acrylonitrile," *Eur. Polym. J.*, 16, 117 (1979).
8. Yamazaki, S., Hattori, S., and Hamashima, M., "The Mechanism of Heterogeneous Polymerization of Vinyl Monomer in Aqueous Mediums," *Kobunshi Kagaku*, 27, 611 (1970).
9. Yamazaki, S., Fukuda, M., and Hamashima, M., "The Mechanism of Heterogeneous Polymerization in Aqueous Medium," *Kobunshi Kagaku*, 25, 203 (1968).
10. Lewis, O. G., and King, Jr., R. M., "Free Radical Polymerization Kinetics of Immobilized Chains," *Adv. Chem. Ser.*, 91, 25 (1969).
11. Sugimori, T., Osajima, Y., and Jabara, Y., "Consideration of Polymer Particles in the Precipitation Polymerization of Acrylonitrile," *Kagaku Kogaku Ronbunshu*, 5, 96 (1979).
12. Bamford, C. H., and Jenkins, A. D., "Kinetics of Bulk Polymerization of Acrylonitrile," *J. Polym. Sci.*, 20, 405 (1956).
13. Bamford, C. H., and Jenkins, A. D., "Studies in Polymerization IX. The Occlusion of Free Radicals by Polymers: Physical Factors Determining the Concentration and Behavior of Trapped radicals," *Proc. Roy. Soc. London, Ser. A*, 228, 220 (1955).
14. Bamford, C. H., Jenkins, A. D., Symons, M. C. R., and Townsend, M. G., "Trapped Radicals in Heterogeneous Vinyl Polymerization," *J. Polym. Sci.*, 34, 181 (1959).

15. Allen, P. E. M., and Patrick, C. R., "Diffusion-Controlled Reactions in Free Radical Polymerization," *Makromol. Chem.*, 47, 154 (1961).
16. Sugimori, T., and Nishikawa, S., "Rate of Precipitation Polymerization of Acrylonitrile in Aqueous Solution," *Kagaku Kogaku Ronbunshu*, 3, 323 (1977).
17. Sugimori, T., Akiyama, H., and Tabara, Y., "Effect of the Fluid Mixing on the Continuous Precipitation Polymerization of Acrylonitrile," *Kagaku Kogaku Ronbunshu*, 3, 331 (1977).
18. Mickley, H. S., Michaels, A. S., and Moore, A. L., "Kinetics of Precipitation Polymerization of Vinyl Chloride," *J. Polym. Sci.*, 60, 121 (1962).
19. Samal, R., Nayak, M. C., Panda, G., Suryanarayana, G. V., and Das, D. P., "Polymerization of Acrylonitrile. Kinetics of the Reaction Initiated by the Ce(IV)/Thioacetamide Redox System," *J. Polym. Sci. Polym. Chem. Ed.*, 20, 53 (1982).
20. Misra, G. S., Bassi, P. S., and Abrol, S. L., "Polymerization of Acrylonitrile Initiated by Ceric Ion-Citric Acid Redox System," *J. Polym. Sci. Polym. Chem. Ed.*, 22, 1883 (1984).
21. Senapati, M., Samal, N. C., Mishra, R., Tripathy, B., Rout, S., and Rout, M. K., "Polymerization of Acrylonitrile Initiated by a Manganese(III) Acetate Glycerol Redox System," *J. Polym. Sci. Polym. Chem. Ed.*, 21, 407 (1983).
22. Farber, E., and Koral, M., "Suspension Polymerization Kinetics of Vinyl Chloride," *Society of Plastics Engineers Technical Papers*, 13, 398 (1967).
23. Abdel-Alim, A. H., and Hamielec, A. E., "Bulk Polymerization of Vinyl Chloride," *J. Applied Polym. Sci.*, 16, 783 (1972).
24. Barter, J. A., and Kellar, D. E., "Suspension of Vinyl Chloride Initiated by In Situ Generated Diisobutyryl Peroxide," *J. Polym. Sci. Polym. Chem. Ed.*, 15, 2545 (1977).
25. Ravey, M., Waterman, J. A., Shorr, L. M., and Kramer, M., "Mechanism of Vinyl Chloride Polymerization," *J. Polym. Sci. Polym. Chem. Ed.*, 12, 2821 (1974).
26. Crosato-Arnaldi, A., Gasparini, P., and Talamini, G., "The Bulk and Suspension Polymerization of Vinyl Chloride," *Makromolekulare Chem.*, 117, 140 (1968).
27. Bengough, W. I., and Norrish, R. G. W., "The Mechanism and Kinetics of the Heterogeneous Polymerization of Vinyl Monomers. I. The Benzoyl Peroxide Catalyzed Polymerization of Vinyl Chloride," *Proc. Roy. Soc.*, A200, 301 (1950).
28. Ueda, T., Takeuchi, K., and Kato, M., "Polymer Particle Formation in Suspension Polymerization of Vinyl Chloride and Vinyl Acetate," *J. Polym. Sci. Polym. Chem. Ed.*, 10, 2841 (1972).
29. Cotman, Jr., J. D., Gonzatez, M., and Claver, G. C., "Studies on Poly (Vinyl Chloride). III. The Role of the Precipitated Polymer in the Kinetics of Polymerization of Vinyl Chloride," *J. Polym. Sci.*, 5, 1137 (1967).
30. Barrett, K. E. J., *Dispersion Polymerization in Organic Media*, John Wiley & Sons, New York (1975).
31. Hatate, Y., Kurokawa, Y., Hamada, H., Ikari, A., and Nakashio, F., "Kinetics of Styrene Slurry Polymerization in Suspended Isooctane Droplets," *J. Chem. Eng. Japan*, 18, 293 (1985).
32. Hatate, Y., Hamada, H., Ikari, A., and Nakashio, F., "Styrene Slurry Polymerization within Suspended Droplets in a Continuous Stirred Tank Reactor," *J. Chem. Eng. Japan*, 19, 602 (1986).
33. Hatate, Y., Hamada, H., Ikari, A., and Nakashio, F., "Change of Size Distribution of Polymer Droplets during the Slurry Polymerization of Styrene within Isooctane Droplets Suspended in Water," *J. Chem. Eng. Japan*, 20, 96 (1987).
34. Hatate, Y., Hamada, H., Ikari, A., and Nakashio, F., "Styrene Slurry Polymerization within Suspended Droplets in Water Using 2,2′-Azobis(2,4-Dimethyl-Valeronitrile) as an Initiator," *J. Chem. Eng. Japan*, 20, 644 (1987).
35. Brandrup, J., and Immergut, E. H., *Polymer Handbook*, Jòhn Wiley & Sons, New York (1975).
36. Harada, M., Tanaka, K., Eguchi, W., and Nagata, S., "Rate of Solution Polymerization of Styrene," *Kagaku Kogaku*, 29, 301 (1965).
37. Hatate, Y., Hano, T., Miyata, T., Nakashio, F., and Sakai, W., "The Rate of Copolymerization of Styrene and Acrylonitrile in Solution," *Kagaku Kogaku*, 35, 903 (1971).
38. Hatate, Y., Hamada, H., Nagata, H., and Imafuku, T., "Preparation of Microcapsules Using a Slurry Polymerization in Suspended Droplets," *Kagaku Kogaku*, 51, 519 (1987).
39. Vanderhoff, J. W., "Mechanism of Emulsion Polymerization," *J. Polym. Sci. Polym. Symposium*, 72, 161 (1985).

40. Ballard, M. J., Napper, D. H., and Gilbert, R. G., "Kinetics of Emulsion Polymerization of Methyl Methacrylate," *J. Polym. Sci. Polym. Chem. Ed.*, 22, 3225 (1984).
41. Bataille, P., Van, B. T., and Pham, Q. B., "Emulsion Polymerization of Styrene. II. Effect of Ag(I) and Fe(II) on the Polymerization of Styrene Initiated by Potassium Persulfate," *J. Polym. Sci. Polym. Chem. Ed.*, 20, 811 (1982).
42. Sudol, E. D., El-Aasser, M. S., and Vanderhoff, J. W., "Kinetics of Successive Seeding of Monodisperse Polystyrene Latexes. I. Initiation via Potassium Persulfate," *J. Polym. Sci. A. Polym. Chem.*, 24, 3499 (1986).
43. Turner, S. R., Weiss, R. A., and Lundberg, R. D., "The Emulsion Copolymerization of Styrene and Sodium Styrene Sulfonate," *J. Polym. Sci. Polym. Chem. Ed.*, 23, 535 (1985).
44. Wood, D. F., Whang, B. C. Y., Napper, D. H., and Gilbert, R. G., "Styrene Emulsion Polymerization: Kinetics and Particle Size Distributions in Highly Swollen Latex Systems," *J. Polym. Sci. Polym. Chem. Ed.*, 21, 985 (1983).
45. Purma, I., and Chang, M., "Emulsion Polymerization of Styrene: Nucleation Studies with Nonionic Emulsifier," *J. Polym. Sci. Polym. Chem. Ed.*, 20, 489 (1982).
46. Bataille, P., Van, B. T., and Phan, Q. B., "Emulsion Polymerization of Styrene. I. Review of Experimental Data and Digital Simulation," *J. Polym. Sci. Polym. Chem. Ed.*, 20, 795 (1982).
47. Kao, C. I., Gundlach, D. P., and Nelson, R. T., "Kinetics of Emulsion Polymerization of Styrene—Simulation Model with Varying Free Radical Capture Efficiency," *J. Polym. Sci. Polym. Chem. Ed.*, 22, 3499 (1984).
48. Omi, S., Sato, H., and Kubota, H., "The Kinetic Study of the Emulsion Polymerization of Styrene in the Isothermal Batch Operation," *J. Chem. Eng. Japan*, 2, 55 (1969).
49. Kubota, H., and Omi, S., "Kinetic Consideration of Polymerization with Deposition of Polymer Particles," *J. Chem. Eng. Japan*, 5, 39 (1972).
50. Omi S., Kuwabata, I., and Kubota, H., "Emulsion Polymerization of Styrene in the Vicinity of Critical Micelle Soap Concentration," *J. Chem. Eng. Japan*, 6, 343 (1973).
51. Smith, W. V., "The Kinetics of Styrene Emulsion Polymerization," *J. Amer. Chem. Soc.*, 70, 3695 (1948).
52. Harkins, W. D., "A General Theory of the Mechanism of Emulsion Polymerization," *J. Amer. Chem. Soc.*, 69, 1428 (1947).
53. Smith, W. V., Ewart, R. H., "Kinetics of Emulsion Polymerization," *J. Chem. Phys.*, 16, 592 (1948).
54. Arai, M., Arai, K., and Saito, S., "Polymer Particle Formation in Soapless Emulsion Polymerization," *J. Polym. Sci. Polym. Chem. Ed.*, 17, 3655 (1979).
55. Arai, M., Arai, K., and Saito, S., "On the Rate of Soapless Emulsion Polymerization of Methyl Methacrylate," *J. Polym. Sci. Polym. Chem. Ed.*, 18, 2811 (1980).
56. Goodall, A. R., Wilkinson, M. C., and Hearh, J., "Mechanism of Emulsion Polymerization of Styrene in Soap-Free Styrene," *J. Polym. Sci. Polym. Chem. Ed.*, 15, 2193 (1977).
57. Arai, M., Arai, K., and Saito, S., "Soapless Emulsion Polymerization of Methyl Methacrylate in Water in the Presence of Calcium Sulfite," *J. Polym. Sci. Polym. Chem. Ed.*, 20, 1021 (1982).
58. Hearn, J., "Kinetics of the Surfactant-Free Emulsion Polymerization of Styrene—The Post Nucleation Stage," *J. Polym. Sci. Polym. Chem. Ed.*, 23, 1869 (1985).
59. Show-An Chen and Herng-Show Chang, "Kinetics and Mechanism of Emulsifier-Free Emulsion Polymerization: Styrene/Surface Active Ionic Comonomer Styrene," *J. Polym. Sci. Polym. Chem. Ed.*, 23, 2615 (1985).
60. Chiu Wen-Yen, and Shih Chih-Cho, "A Study on the Soap-Free Emulsion Polymerization of Styrene," *J. Appl. Polym. Sci.*, 31, 2117 (1986).
61. Barrett, K. E., "Dispersion Polymerization in Organic Media," *Br. Polym. J.*, 5, 259 (1973).
62. Akashi, M., Kirikihira, I., and Miyauchi, N., "Synthesis and Polymerization of a Styryl Terminated Oligovinylpyrrolidone Macromonomer," *Angew. Makromol. Chem.*, 132, 81 (1985).
63. Ober, C. K., and Hair, M. L., "The Effect of Temperature and Initiator Levels on the Dispersion Polymerization of Polystyrene," *J. Polym. Sci. A. Polym. Chem.*, 25, 1395 (1987).
64. Ober, C. K., and Lok, K. P., "Formation of Large Monodisperse Copolymer Particles by Dispersion Polymerization," *Amer. Chem. Soc.*, 20, 268 (1987).

65. Zurkova, E., Bouchal, K., Zdenkova, D., Pelzbauer, Z., Svec, F., and Kalal, J., "Preparation of Monodisperse Reactive Styrene-Glycidyl Methacrylate Latexed by the Emulsifier-Free Dispersion Copolymerization Technique," *J. Polym. Sci. Chem. Ed.*, 21, 2949 (1983).
66. Shahar, M., Meshulam, H., and Margel, S., "Synthesis and Characteristics of Microspheres of Polystyrene Derivatives," *J. Polym. Sci. Polym. Chem. Ed.*, 24, 203 (1986).
67. Tseng, C. M., Lu, Y. Y., El-Aasser, M. S., and Vanderhoff, J. W., "Uniform Polymer Particles by Dispersion Polymerization in Alcohol," *J. Polym. Sci. A. Polym. Chem.*, 24, 2995 (1986).
68. Ober, C. K., Lok, K. P., and Hair, M. L., "Monodispersed, Micron-Sized Polystyrene Particles by Dispersion Polymerization," *J. Polym. Sci. Polym. Lett. Ed.*, 23, 103 (1985).
69. Shahar, M., Meshulam, H., and Margel, S., "Synthesis and Characteristics of Microspheres of Polystyrene Derivatives," *J. Polym. Sci. Polym. Chem. Ed.*, 24, 203 (1986).

CHAPTER 15

MONOMER-ISOMERIZATION POLYMERIZATION

Kiyoshi Endo and **Takayuki Otsu**

Department of Applied Chemistry
Osaka City University
Osaka, Japan

CONTENTS

INTRODUCTION

The polymer formation of vinyl monomers usually proceeds via an opening of the double bond without any rearrangements of monomer structure, i.e., the polymers produced have no anomalous units in the chain as comparison with the monomer structure. Along with such polymerization, we often encounter the polymerization accompanying isomerization reaction leading to the formation of a different structure unit in the resulting polymers. The isomerizations take place in a different stage during the course of polymerization. Among them, monomer-isomerization polymerization is that the isomerization occurs prior to polymerization.

The increasing importance and interest in monomer-isomerization polymerization arise mainly from highly selective polymerization of a single monomer from mixed isomers and from the technological-economical points of view. The significant merit of the monomer-isomerization polymerization in polymer synthesis is that compounds that have been known to be unpolymerized can be used as new monomers.

Research for monomer-isomerization polymerization was opened up in 1964 and sufficient information is available for this interesting area of polymer science.

DEFINITION AND CONCEPT OF MONOMER-ISOMERIZATION POLYMERIZATION

Monomer-isomerization polymerization is defined as the polymerization that a charged monomer isomerizes to the polymerizable isomeric monomer prior to polymerization and then polymerizes to give a polymer consisting of the isomerized monomer unit exclusively.

The concept of monomer-isomerization polymerization has been established by the polymerization of 2-butene with Ziegler-Natta catalyst. The first account which mentions the polymerization with monomer-isomerization appeared in a U.S. Patent by J. L. Jezl [1]. Soon after, three independent workers [2, 3, 4] obtained a high molecular weight poly-1-butene from the polymerization of 2-butene in the presence of Ziegler-Natta catalyst. Experimentally the isomerization of 2-butene to 1-butene was observed during the polymerization, and the structure of polymer obtained was identified to be poly-1-butene by spectroscopic analysis.

All evidences gathered in the study of the polymerization of 2-butene with Ziegler-Natta catalysts led to the conclusion that the starting 2-butene isomerized first to highly polymerization 1-butene prior to the propagation, and then homopolymerized to give poly-1-butene, as is depicted in Equation 1. Otsu [5, 6] called this polymerization monomer-isomerization polymerization, and developed as a new polymer synthetic route from various internal olefins which were not utilized as a raw material of polymer.

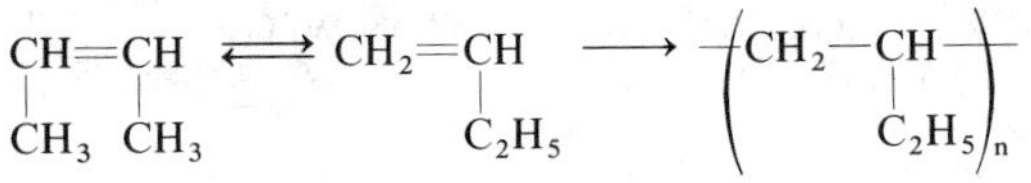

$$
\begin{array}{ccc}
CH{=}CH & \rightleftharpoons & CH_2{=}CH \\
| \quad | & & | \\
CH_3 \ CH_3 & & C_2H_5
\end{array}
\longrightarrow
\left(\!\!\begin{array}{c}
CH_2{-}CH \\
| \\
C_2H_5
\end{array}\!\!\right)_{\!n}
\tag{1}
$$

On the other hand, Kennedy [7, 8, 9, 10] found isomerization polymerization in the cationic polymerization of 3-methyl-1-butene with $AlCl_3$ catalyst at low temperature to give a polymer consisting of the isomerized unit, as is shown in Equation 2:

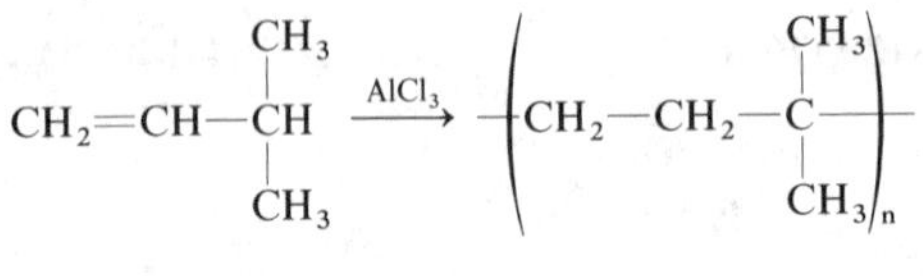

$$
\begin{array}{c}
CH_3 \\
| \\
CH_2{=}CH{-}CH \\
| \\
CH_3
\end{array}
\xrightarrow{AlCl_3}
\left(\!\!\begin{array}{c}
CH_3 \\
| \\
CH_2{-}CH_2{-}C \\
| \\
CH_3
\end{array}\!\!\right)_{\!n}
\tag{2}
$$

The conceptional difference between monomer-isomerization polymerization and isomerization polymerization is that the isomerization to polymerizable isomer occurs prior to the propagation in the former. Whereas in the latter, the propagating cation itself isomerizes to the more stable cation in propagation step (Equation 3). Consequently, isomerization of the unreacted monomer was not observed.

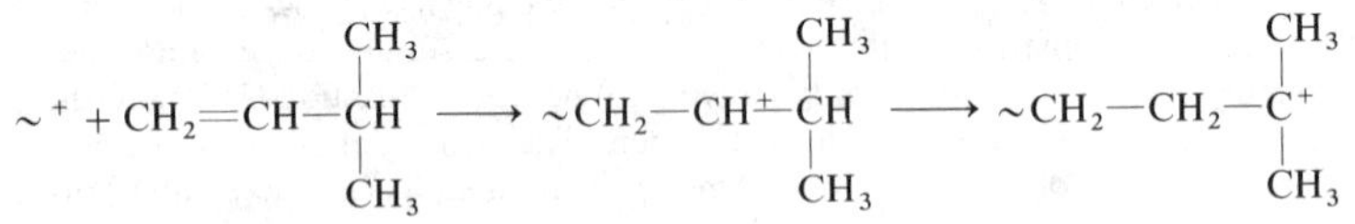

$$
\sim^+ + \begin{array}{c}
CH_3 \\
| \\
CH_2{=}CH{-}CH \\
| \\
CH_3
\end{array}
\longrightarrow
\begin{array}{c}
CH_3 \\
| \\
\sim CH_2{-}CH^{\pm}CH \\
| \\
CH_3
\end{array}
\longrightarrow
\begin{array}{c}
CH_3 \\
| \\
\sim CH_2{-}CH_2{-}C^+ \\
| \\
CH_3
\end{array}
\tag{3}
$$

Therefore, monomer-isomerization polymerization consists of two distinct and independent reactions, i.e. one is the isomerization of the charged monomer to the highly polymerizable monomers and another is the polymerization of the isomerized monomer, and both reactions proceed simultaneously and independently in the same system.

The general scheme for the polymerization of monomer accompanying monomer-isomerization is expressed as follows:

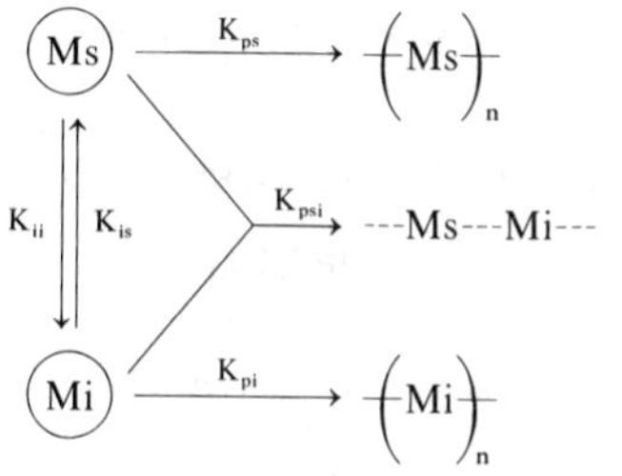

(4)

where Ms is a starting monomer and Mi is the isomerized one.

When Mi is only a highly polymerizable monomer and Ms does not interfere or participate into the polymerization of Mi, a high molecular weight homopolymer of Mi is obtained from the polymerization of Ms in the presence of appropriate catalysts. This case corresponds to a selective polymerization of a single isomer from isomer mixture. We called this polymerization monomer-isomerization polymerization.

If both Ms and Mi are able to polymerize, the copolymer consisting of both units may be formed with a suitable catalyst. The relative amount of Ms and Mi units in the resulting polymer obviously depends on the rates of both isomerization and polymerization. This case is monomer-isomerization copolymerization.

If Ms is only a polymerizable isomeric monomer, the homopolymer of Ms is formed by polymerization even when the isomerization to Mi takes place. This case corresponds to conventional polymerization, but the complete polymerization does not proceed due to the isomerization of a starting monomer [11, 12].

From the above consideration, monomer-isomerization polymerizations have been applicable to all polymerization mechanisms, although most intensive and detailed work has been done for the polymerization of the internal olefins with Ziegler-Natta catalyst. We will describe the monomer-isomerization polymerization for each polymerization mechanism in the following sections.

MONOMER-ISOMERIZATION POLYMERIZATION WITH ZIEGLER-NATTA CATALYST

Internal olefins such as 2-butenes have been known to be not polymerize with Ziegler-Natta catalysts due to steric hindrance of the alkyl substituents [13]. This effect was first pointed out by Alfrey [14] in propagation reaction of radical polymerization between the incoming monomer and the polymer chain end, as depicted in Figure 1.

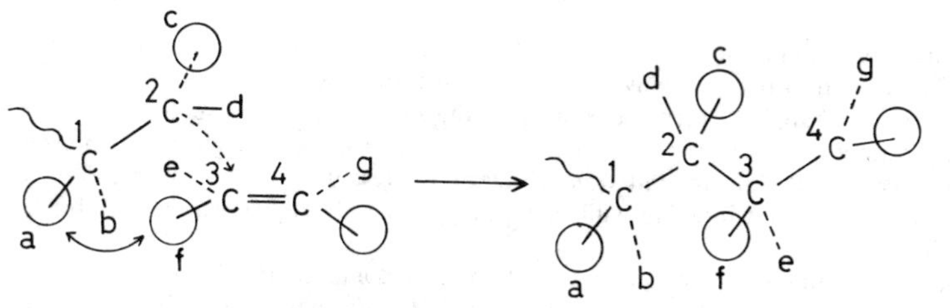

Figure 1. The propagation reaction of polymerization of 1,2-disubstituted ethylenic monomer. Steric repulsion occurs between the substituents, a and b in the propagating chain and e and f in the reacting monomer.

Similar steric effect may be applied to ionic and coordination polymerization of internal olefins despite of the presence of counter ion. Therefore, the high polymerization of these internal olefins is one of the most important problem in synthetic polymer chemistry

Monomer-isomerization polymerization is one of the ways for preparing high polymers from these internal olefins with Ziegler-Natta catalysts along with copolymerization with 1-olefins such as ethylene [15, 16, 17, 18, 19], and metathesis polymerization in the cases of cyclic olefins [20, 21].

Butene Isomers

Butenes isomerize with transition metals complexes including Ziegler-Natta catalysts to give an equilibrium mixture of cis- or trans-2-butene and 1-butene [22]. Among them, only 1-butene is polymerizable isomer toward Ziegler-Natta catalyst [23]. When cis- or trans-2-butene is polymerized in the presence of Ziegler-Natta catalyst such as $TiCl_3$-$(C_2H_5)_3Al$, the polymer was formed. The structure of the polymer obtained was confirmed by the product analysis to be poly-1-butene [1, 2, 3, 24]. This polymer contained the ether insoluble fraction of more than 60%, which consist of isotactic poly-1-butene structure [25].

From the analysis of unreacted butene isomers determined by gas chromatography, a significant change in isomer distribution has been found [23], i.e. the positional and geometric isomerizations of 2-butenes leading to an equilibrium isomer mixture occurred during polymerization. However, no skeletal isomerization to isobutene took place [25]. The rate of polymerization was also found to be proportional to that of isomerization.

Therefore, it was concluded that 2-butenes underwent monomer-isomerization polymerization with Ziegler-Natta catalyst according to Equation 5.

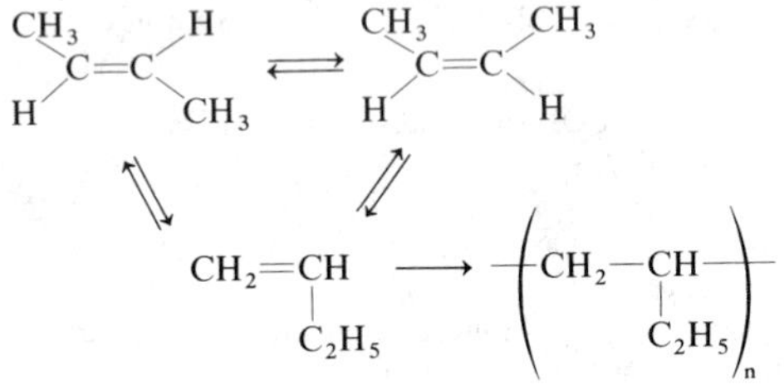

$$
\begin{array}{ccc}
\underset{H}{\overset{CH_3}{}}C=C\underset{CH_3}{\overset{H}{}} & \rightleftharpoons & \underset{H}{\overset{CH_3}{}}C=C\underset{H}{\overset{CH_3}{}} \\
& & \\
& CH_2=CH\underset{C_2H_5}{} \longrightarrow \left(CH_2-CH\underset{C_2H_5}{}\right)_n &
\end{array}
\tag{5}
$$

Although the equilibrium concentration of 1-butene is quite low (about 5%), the reactivity toward Ziegler-Natta catalyst is very highly [23]. Hence, providing the rate of isomerization to produce 1-butene is enough rapid, 1-butene consumed by the polymerization is replenished via a dynamic equilibrium among the isomers so that ultimately a high molecular weight poly-1-butene is formed [25]. A large amount of cis- and trans-2-butene is present in the polymerization system, but nevertheless they do not interfere with or participate in the polymerization of 1-butene and act like a diluent.

Ziegler-Natta catalysts consist of the transition metal compounds of group IV to VIII and metal alkyl of the group I to III in the periodic table [26, 27]. Thus many kinds of combination are available as catalyst systems. Among them, the most effective catalysts for the monomer-isomerization polymerization investigated are composed by $TiCl_3$ and $(C_2H_5)_3Al$, as shown in Table 1. These catalysts showed a maximum rate of the polymerization at Al/Ti molar ratio of about 3.0 and at 80°C for polymerization temperature. Concerning the crystalline form of $TiCl_3$, HA- and Solvay types showed high reactivities for monomer-isomerization polymerization of 2-butenes [28].

Table 1
Monomer-Isomerization Polymerization of *cis*-2-Butene with Transition Metal Compound and $(C_2H_5)_3Al$ Catalyst in *n*-Heptane at 80°C for 24 hr[(a)] [24]

Transition Metal Compound	Yield (%)	Composition of Butenes after Polymerization (%)[(b)]		
		1B[(c)]	t2B[(c)]	c2B[(c)]
$TiCl_3$	34.4	3.2	60.0	36.8
TiH_2	0.0	0.0	2.9	97.1
$(C_5H_5)_2TiCl_2$	0.0	1.0	4.3	94.7
VCl_3	0.0	0.3	4.2	95.5
VCl_4	0.7	4.8	24.0	71.2
$VOCl_3$	1.3	5.6	39.7	54.7
$V(acac)_3$[(d)]	0.2	7.1	25.9	67.0
$ZrCl_4$	0.0	1.4	7.7	90.9

(a) *Polymerization conditions: [c2B] = 4.0 mol/L; [Metal] = 50 mmol/L; Al/Ti = 3.0 molar ratio.*
(b) *Determined by gas chromatography.*
(c) *The abbreviations are as follows: 1B; 1-butene, c2B; cis-2-butene, t2B; trans-2-butene.*
(d) *Acac stands for acetylacetonate.*

The kinetic study for the isomerization of butenes has been performed by $TiCl_3$ and $TiCl_4$ catalyst systems. $TiCl_3$ itself did not catalyze the isomerization of butenes at 40°C [4, 25, 29], but demonstrated the potential for the isomerization of butenes at temperatures higher than 40°C [30]. Furthermore, the isomerization of butenes did not occur with $(C_2H_5)_3Al$ alone below 80°C [25, 29]. However, the isomerization of butenes is accelerated by $TiCl_3$ in combination with $(C_2H_5)_3Al$, and the polymerization proceeds simultaneously [25].

For the isomerization of olefins with transition metal complexes, two different mechanisms have been postulated: one involves σ-alkylmetal complexes [29, 31, 32, 33, 34] and the other π-allyl ones [35, 36], as is depicted in Figure 2.

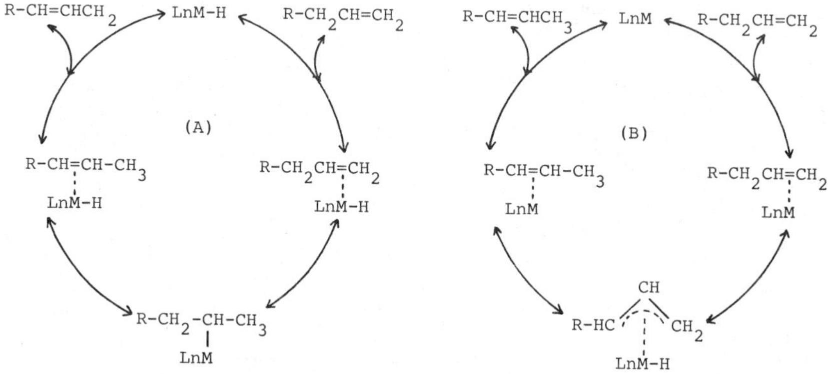

Figure 2. Reaction scheme for isomerization of olefin: (A) σ-alkylmetal complex mechanism; (B) π-allyl complex mechanism; M: metal, Ln: ligand.

Table 2
Activation Energy for Isomerization of Butenes with $TiCl_3$-$(C_2H_5)_3Al$ Catalyst in *n*-Heptane

Charged Butene	Isomerized Product	Ea (kcal/mol)	Ref.
trans-2-butene	1-butene	14.0	29
	cis-2-butene	16.0	29
cis-2-butene	1-butene	10.6	37
	trans-2-butene	12.3	37

In the monomer-isomerization polymerization of *cis*- or *trans*-2-butene with $TiCl_3$-$(C_2H_5)_3Al$ catalyst at 80°C, both positional and geometric isomerizations are found to occur concurrently. Simultaneous positional and geometric isomerizations are explained by assuming σ-alkylmetal complexes mechanism involving Ti-H bond [25, 29, 33, 34].

The activation energy for the isomerization of butene isomers was determined in order to confirm the isomerization mechanism, and the results are shown in Table 2. The energy for positional isomerization is always about 2 kcal/mol lower than that for the geometric one [28, 37].

The positional and geometric isomerizations via σ-alkylmetal complexes can be expressed by Figure 3. According to this mechanism, geometric isomerization requires the additional energy for the rotation of the C-C bond as compared with positional isomerization. The difference in activation

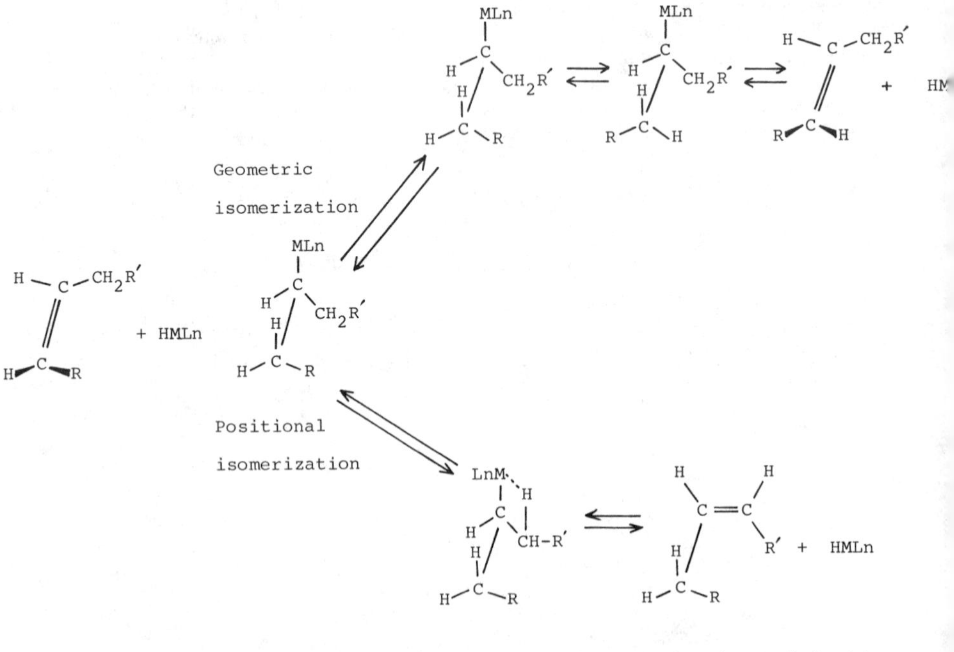

Figure 3. Reaction scheme for geometric and positional isomerization via a σ-alkylmetal complex; M: metal, Ln: ligand, R and R′: alkyl group.

Table 3
Monomer-Isomerization Polymerization of *cis*-2-Butene with $TiCl_3$-R_nAlCl_{n-3} Catalyst in *n*-Heptane at 80°C[(a)] [24]

R_nAlCl_{n-3}	Time (hr)	Yield (%)	Composition of Butenes After Polymerization (%)[(b)]		
			1B[(c)]	t2B[(c)]	c2B[(c)]
$(i\text{-}C_4H_9)_3Al$	7.0	17.6	2.3	65.1	35.6
$(C_2H_5)_3Al$	7.0	12.7	2.3	53.6	44.1
$(C_2H_5)_2AlH$	7.0	12.5	3.1	64.8	32.1
$(C_2H_5)_2AlCl$	24.0	0.5	1.1	2.7	96.2
$C_2H_5AlCl_2$	24.0	0.1	0.6	0.0	99.4

(a) *Polymerization conditions: [c2B] = 4.0 mol/L; [$TiCl_3$] = 50 mmol/L; Al/Ti = 3.0 molar ratio.*
(b) *Determined by gas chromatography.*
(c) *For abbreviations see footnote in Table 1.*

energies observed between positional and geometric isomerization is a reasonable value for the rotation of the C-C bond, indicating that the isomerization with $TiCl_3$-$(C_2H_5)_3Al$ catalyst proceeds via a σ-alkylmetal complex mechanism.

If the isomerization proceeds via a π-allyl complex, only the positional isomerization from 2-butenes to 1-butene takes place, and geometric isomerization of 2-butene must also proceed via 1-butene [35, 36]. Hence, at the initial stage of the reaction the concentration of 1-butene must be higher than that of 2-butene produced by isomerization. Such observations do not recognize with $TiCl_3$-$(C_2H_5)_3Al$ catalyst, indicating that the π-allyl mechanism is excluded in this case.

Consequently, the catalyst site for isomerization involves a Ti-H bond. The rate of the monomer-isomerization polymerization of 2-butenes with $TiCl_3$ in combination of various kinds of trialkyl-aluminum (Table 3) was found to decrease with the following order: $(i\text{-}C_4H_9)_3Al \cong (C_2H_5)_3Al > (CH_3)_3Al > (C_2H_5)_2AlCl$. The effect of Al/Ti molar ratios were observed to give a maximum value at around 3.0. This suggests that the active sites for the isomerization involve the reduced titanium complex.

From the analysis of gaseous materials produced by the reaction of $TiCl_3$ and $(C_2H_5)_3Al$, the amount of ethylene was always higher than that of ethane. Hence the active site of Ti-H is supplied by an intramolecular β-hydrogen elimination of σ-alkyltitanium complex derived from the reaction between $TiCl_3$ and R_3Al as the following process:

$$(C_2H_5)_3Al + TiX_n \longrightarrow C_2H_5TiX_{n-1} + (C_2H_5)_2AlX \tag{6}$$

$$C_2H_5TiX_{n-1} \longrightarrow HTiX_{n-1} + C_2H_4 \tag{7}$$

$TiCl_3$-$(C_2H_5)_2AlCl$ catalyst, which is effective catalyst for polymerization of 1-butene, did not induce monomer-isomerization polymerization of 2-butenes. Only ethylene was produced by the reaction of catalyst components, indicating that reduction of $TiCl_3$ hardly took place in this catalyst system [37]. These evidences suggest that the active site for isomerization involves Ti(II) hydride complexes and that for polymerization is composed of Ti(III) alkyl complexes [34, 37].

Isomerization using $TiCl_4$ as a catalyst component has been investigated also. Neither polymerization nor isomerization of 2-butenes was induced by $TiCl_4$ itself [38]. The addition of $(C_2H_5)_3Al$ to $TiCl_4$, however, initiated both isomerization and monomer-isomerization polymerization of 2-butene. This catalyst system showed different isomerization and polymerization behaviors from $TiCl_3$ systems.

The reactivities for isomerization and polymerization are apparently dependent on Al/Ti molar ratios. When the value of Al/Ti molar ratio was lower than unity, this catalyst did not afford any polymers in the polymerization of 2-butenes but showed a weak activity for polymerization of 1-butene. At above Al/Ti molar ratio of 3, this system induced monomer-isomerization polymerization of 2-butene.

In the isomerization of 1-butene with $TiCl_4$-$(C_2H_5)_3Al$ catalyst, only *cis*-2-butene produced selectivity, and a maximum value was given at Al/Ti molar ratio of 0.5. At the above value, however, such selectivity begins to diminish and as a consequence *cis*-and *trans*-2-butene are produced simultaneously. At lower Al/Ti molar ratio of 0.5, the catalyst system still involves soluble Ti(IV) complex [38]. The amounts of Ti(IV) complex gradually decreased with increasing of Al/Ti molar ratio, and Ti(IV) complex was reduced completely to Ti(III) species at above Al/Ti molar ratio of 3.0 [39]. Hence it was proposed that soluble Ti(IV) complex participates in the isomerization at Al/Ti < 1. For this isomerization, the following mechanism, which was proposed by Bestian and Clausee [40] in the isomerization with $AlCH_3Cl_2/CH_3TiCl_3$ catalyst, was postulated.

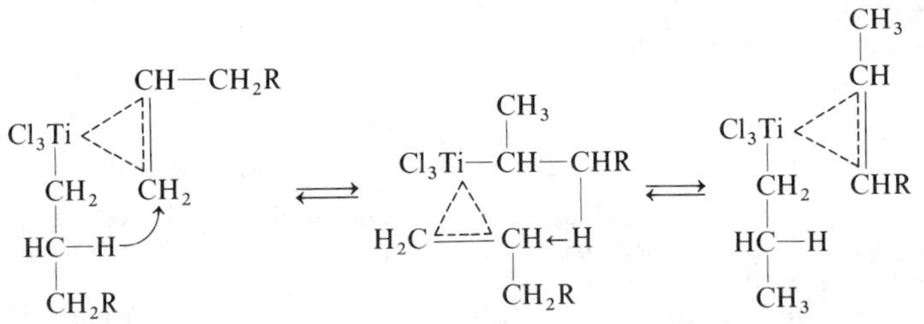

(8)

At Al/Ti molar ratio above 1.0 the reduced Ti(III) complex participates in the isomerization. When the polymerization of 1-butene in the presence of 2-butene was carried out with $TiCl_3$-$(C_2H_5)_3Al$ catalyst (Al/Ti > 1.0), the concentration of 1-butene above the equilibrium value was observed at the initial stage of the reaction. After a few hours, however, the isomerization from 2-butene to 1-butene decreased remarkably due to the change of nature of active sites and to the contamination of the catalyst surface [41].

Since the isomerization of 2-olefin to 1-olefin must be induced prior to the polymerization in monomer-isomerization polymerization, the rate of polymerization will depend on the rate of the isomerization. Thus it is of interest to check the additive effect of isomerization catalysts.

The rate of monomer-isomerization polymerization of 2-butene was found to be influenced by the addition of isomerization catalysts such as transition metal compounds, as is shown in Table 4. When certain transition metal compounds that exhibit pronounced isomerization activity for 2-butene are added to the above Ziegler-Natta catalyst, the overall rate of monomer-isomerization polymerization of 2-butene is greatly increased [42]. As the isomerization catalysts react competitively with alkylaluminum, the ratios of transition metal compounds to $TiCl_3$ give an optimum value.

The addition of an isomerization catalyst such as $NiCl_2$ to VCl_3-$(C_2H_5)_3Al$ catalyst, which is an effective catalyst for the polymerization of 1-butene, induces monomer-isomerization polymerization of 2-butene by producing the active site for isomerization. Various combinations of transition metal compounds for monomer-isomerization polymerization have been disclosed.

The addition of Lewis bases such as triethylamine and pyridine to Ziegler-Natta catalyst also increases the yield of ethyl insoluble isotactic poly-1-butene in the monomer-isomerization polymerization of 2-butene [43].

The monomer-isomerization polymerization of 2-butenes with Ziegler-Natta catalysts are summarized as follows. This reaction occurs at two distinctly different catalyst sites in two independent steps: First, 2-butene isomerizes to 1-butene prior to the polymerization, and the concentration is limited by thermodynamic factor. However, the rate of isomerization is dependent on the reaction conditions and on the nature of the transition metal catalyst component. In the second step 1-butene

Table 4

Effect of Transition Metal Compound (MeX) on Monomer-Isomerization Polymerization of 2-Butene with $TiCl_3$-$(C_2H_5)_3Al$ Catalyst in *n*-Heptane at 80°C for 24 hr[a] [28, 42]

Monomer	MeX	Me/Ti molar ratio	Time (hr)	Yield (%)	Et_2O insoluble wt-%	Et_2O insoluble $[\eta]$[b]	Composition of Butenes After Polymerization (%)[c] 1B	t2B	c2B
t2B	—	—	28.0	17.5	66.5	1.2	2.9	32.3	64.8
t2B	$NiCl_2$	0.65	17.0	32.4	52.5	2.1	3.8	27.3	68.9
t2B	$FeCl_3$	0.35	28.0	17.6	10.3	2.0	2.6	22.7	74.7
t2B	$Fe(acac)_3$[e]	0.81	25.0	0.0	—	—	6.1	28.2	65.7
t2B	$Cr(acac)_3$[e]	0.57	8.0	23.9	74.0	1.6	3.3	26.3	70.4
c2B	—	—	24.0	34.4	46.8	1.0[d]	3.2	60.0	36.8
c2B	$NiCl_2$	3.0	24.0	47.7	64.3	1.2[d]	4.5	52.0	43.5
c2B	$Fe(acac)_3$[e]	0.1	24.0	35.8	62.1	1.0[d]	5.1	69.7	25.2

[a] *Polymerization conditions:* $[TiCl_3] = 50$ *mmol/L; Al/Ti = 3.0 molar ratio;* $[c2B] = 4.0$ *mol/L;* $[t2B] = 6.0$ *mol/L.*

[b] *In teteraline at 135°C.*

[c] *Determined by gas chromatography.*

[d] *In n-heptane at 60°C.*

[e] *Acac stands for acetylacetonate.*

polymerizes and is momentarily removed from the dynamic prevailing at the catalyst site. The polymerization step is visualized as a conventional addition polymerization via a coordination polymerization.

Other Linear Internal Olefins

Table 5 shows the equilibrium concentration of various linear and branched olefins calculated from free energy formation of their respective isomers. The value of the 1-olefins is low in their isomers and diminishes gradually in proportion to the length of the substituted alkyl group.

If the isomerization of 2-olefins to 1-olefins is controlled by thermodynamic stabilities, the possibility of monomer-isomerization polymerization will decrease with an increasing alkyl chain length. However, if isomerization to 1-olefins is sufficiently rapid to replenish the consumed 1-olefins, it will be expected to induce the monomer-isomerization polymerization in higher internal olefins.

2-pentene [25], 2-hexene [25], 2-heptene [44, 45], and 2-octene [44, 46] were found to undergo monomer-isomerization polymerization with $TiCl_3$-$(C_2H_5)_3Al$ catalyst to give high polymers consisting of the corresponding 1-olefin unit, as shown in Table 6. The rate of the polymerization decreased as following: 2-pentene > 2-hexene > 2-heptene > 2-octene. This order is in a good agreement with the calculated equilibrium values of 1-olefins, suggesting that the isomerization of 2-olefins to 1-olefins and the equilibrium concentration of 1-olefins play an important role in this polymerization.

In this polymerization, the enhancement of the isomerization rate will accelerate the polymerization of these olefins as well as 2-butene. The addition of an isomerization catalyst such as

Table 5
Equilibrium Concentration of Olefin Isomers at 80°C

Olefin	Isomers	Concentration in Equilibrium (%)
Butene	1-butene	5.1
	cis-2-butene	22.5
	trans-2-butene	72.4
Pentene	1-pentene	3.1
	cis-2-pentene	33.0
	trans-2-pentene	63.9
Hexene	1-hexene	1.8
	2-hexene	49.1
	3-hexene	49.1
Methylbutene	3-methyl-1-butene	0.5
	2-methyl-2-butene	85.8
	2-methyl-1-butene	13.7
Methylpentene	4-methyl-1-pentene	0.5
	4-methyl-2-pentene	3.7
	2-methyl-2-pentene	82.6
	2-methyl-1-pentene	13.2
Phenylpropene	3-phenyl-1-propene	0.04
	cis-3-phenyl-2-propene	15.18
	trans-3-phenyl-2-propene	84.78

Table 6
Polymerizations of Linear Olefins with $TiCl_3$-$(C_2H_5)_3Al$ Catalyst in *n*-Heptane[a]

Monomer	$[TiCl_3]$ (mmol/L)	Al/Ti molar ratio	Temp. (°C)	Time (hr)	Yield (%)	Composition of 1-olefin After Polymn (%)[b]	Ref.
1-pentene	50	2.0	80	0.02	79.6	—	25
2-pentene	50	2.0	80	28.0	5.1	2.7	25
1-hexene	50	2.0	80	0.5	79.6	97.8	25
2-hexene	50	2.0	80	28.0	1.9	3.0	25
1-heptene	70	3.0	30	1.0	35.7	96.6	45
2-heptene	70	3.0	80	36.0	10.6	2.0	45
3-heptene	70	3.0	80	103.0	4.6[d]	2.0	45
1-octene	70	3.0	29	0.7	95.1	—	46
2-octene	70	3.0	80	36.0	5.6	—	46
3-octene[c]	120	3.0	80	96.0	7.0	—	46
4-octene[c]	120	3.0	80	96.0	2.2	—	46

[a] *Polymerization conditions: [Monomer] = 4.0 mol/L.*
[b] *Determined by gas chromatography.*
[c] *[Monomer] = 3.0 mol/L.*
[d] *In the presence of Ni(acac)$_2$, Ni/Ti = 0.5 molar ratio.*

Ni(acac)$_2$ to $TiCl_3$-$(C_2H_5)_3Al$ catalyst was found to accelerate the rate of monomer-isomerization polymerization of these olefins, but its rate was decreased by the further addition of Ni(acac)$_2$ because the active site for polymerization is destroyed by the polar group in the isomerization catalyst.

3-heptene [45], 3-octene [46], and 4-octene [46], which are further internal olefins than 2-olefins, also underwent monomer-isomerization polymerization to give a polymer consisting of the corresponding 1-olefins unit with $TiCl_3$-$(C_2H_5)_3Al$ catalyst, although the rate of polymerization of these olefins is slower than those of respective 2-olefins (see Table 6). In all internal olefins examined, the rate of monomer-isomerization polymerization on the place of double bond is as follows: 1-olefin > 2-olefin > 3-olefin > 4-olefin. The change of isomer distribution during the polymerization and the rate of polymerization indicate that the isomerization of starting internal olefins to 1-olefins proceeds via a stepwise double bond migration.

It was proved that all internal linear olefins employed undergo monomer-isomerization polymerization to produced polymers consisting of the corresponding 1-olefins unit, and the composition of the unreacted olefins was close to that of the predicted equilibrium values calculated from free energy of their formation.

Branched Internal Olefins

The equilibrium concentration of 1-olefins in branched olefin isomers becomes lower than in linear ones. Thus monomer-isomerization polymerization of branched internal olefins is less favorabe than that of linear ones.

These branched internal olefins, however, will be able to undergo monomer-isomerization polymerization, if the isomerization of these olefins to their corresponding 1-olefins is rapid enough to replenish the 1-olefins consumed by the polymerization. Some branched olefins were found to undergo monomer-isomerization polymerization to give a high molecular weight polymer consisting of the respective 1-olefins unit.

Chauvin [43] reported that 4-methyl-2-pentene polymerized with $TiCl_3$-$CrCl_3$-$(C_2H_5)_3Al$ catalyst at 57°C. The structure of the polymers obtained is identified to be poly-4-methyl-1-pentene and it contains about 60% ether insoluble fraction. 4-Methyl-2-pentene also undergoes monomer-isomerization polymerization with $TiCl_3$-$(C_2H_5)_3Al$ catalyst at 80°C to give a high molecular weight polymer consisting of 4-methyl-1-pentene unit exclusively [47, 48, 49, 50]. The rate of polymerization depends on Al/Ti molar ratios and its optimum was obtained at Al/Ti molar ratio of about 3.0 However, 2-methyl-2-pentene and 2-methyl-1-pentene [50] did not produce any polymers consisting of 4-methyl-1-pentene under the similar conditions, as shown in Table 7. The polymerization reactivity of 2-methyl-2-pentene did not depend on Al/Ti molar ratios and only a trace of polymer was obtained. The structure of the resulting polymer was confirmed to be polyethylene derived from catalyst system. 2-Methyl-1-pentene also gave a polymer with a low yield and it was extracted by benzene. The structure of each fraction was identified to be polyethylene for insoluble fraction and oligomer of 2-methyl-1-pentene for soluble one.

Isomerization was observed in the polymerization of all methylpentenes and the isomer distribution was seen to slowly approach that of an equilibrium mixture as a function of the time, indicating that the isomerization proceeds via a stepwise double bond migration.

The addition of isomerization catalyst such as $Ni(acac)_2$ to $TiCl_3$-$(C_2H_5)_3Al$ catalyst accelerated the monomer-isomerization polymerization of 4-methyl-2-pentene. In the polymerization of 2-methyl-2-pentene and 2-methyl-1-pentene, however, no polymer was obtained even in the presence of $Ni(acac)_2$, suggesting that the isomerization of these olefins to 4-methyl-1-pentene did not occur rapidly.

On the contrary, with a ternary catalyst system such as $TiCl_3$-$(C_2H_5)_2AlCl$-$(PPh_3)_2PdCl_2$ or $TiCl_3$-$(C_2H_5)_2AlCl$-$Ni(SCN)_2$, the polymer with 4-methyl-1-pentene was obtained in a low yield [50]. The observed isomer distribution of methylpentenes recovered after polymerization and the rate of polymerization of four methylpentenes led to the conclusion that the isomerization of 2-methyl-1-pentene to 4-methyl-1-pentene with the above ternary catalyst system proceeded via a direct one-step isomerization mechanism.

Therefore, the monomer-isomerization polymerization of methylpentenes with Ziegler-Natta catalyst can be written:

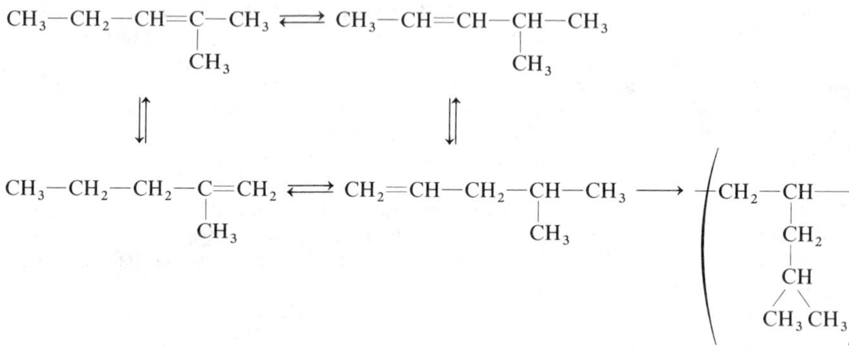

$$CH_3-CH_2-CH\!=\!\underset{\underset{CH_3}{|}}{C}-CH_3 \rightleftharpoons CH_3-CH\!=\!CH-\underset{\underset{CH_3}{|}}{CH}-CH_3$$

$$\Updownarrow \qquad\qquad\qquad\qquad \Updownarrow \tag{9}$$

$$CH_3-CH_2-CH_2-\underset{\underset{CH_3}{|}}{C}\!=\!CH_2 \rightleftharpoons CH_2\!=\!CH-CH_2-\underset{\underset{CH_3}{|}}{CH}-CH_3 \longrightarrow \left(\!CH_2-\underset{\underset{\underset{CH_3\,CH_3}{\diagup\diagdown}}{\underset{|}{CH}}}{\underset{|}{CH}}\!\right)_n$$

Although Chauvin [51] reported that 2-methyl-1-pentene polymerized with $TiCl_3$-$(C_2H_5)_3Al$-Ph_3P-$PdCl_2$ catalyst system to give poly-4-methyl-1-pentene, the reported IR spectrum of the resulting polymer was somewhat different from that of poly-4-methyl-1-pentene, probably due to contamination of 2-methyl-1-pentene unit.

The equilibrium concentration of 3-methyl-1-butene in methybutene isomers (0.5%) was the same as that of 4-methyl-1-pentene in methylpentene isomers. However, 2-methyl-2-butene did not produce a polymer consisting of 3-methyl-1-butene (see Table 8) [52]. This seems to originate in low polymerizability of 3-methyl-1-butene toward the Ziegler-Natta catalyst [53]. This suggests that the polymerizability of 1-olefin also plays an important role in monomer-isomerization polymerization of internal olefins with Ziegler-Natta catalyst.

Table 7
Polymerizations of Methylpentenes with Ziegler-Natta Catalyst[a] [49, 50]

Monomer[b]	Cat.[c]	Temp. (°C)	Time (hr)	Yield (%)	Polymer structure	Composition of Olefins After Polymerization (%)[d]			
						4M1P	4M2P	2M2P	2M1P
4M1P	A	30	1	94.8	Poly(4M1P)	100.0	0.0	0.0	0.0
4M2P	A	80	60	27.5	Poly(4M1P)	0.1	84.8	14.1	0.6
4M2P	B	80	60	35.6	Poly(4M1P)	0.8	68.2	26.8	2.8
2M2P	A	80	100	0.7	PE[e]	0.0	0.2	99.1	0.8
2M2P	C	40	96	0.3	Poly(4M1P)	0.3	3.0	85.6	11.1
2M1P	A	80	100	5.3	Poly(2M1P) + PE	trace	1.5	48.6	49.3
2M1P	C	40	60	4.0	Poly(4M1P)	0.7	12.6	70.9	15.5
2M1P	D	40	60	6.3	Poly(2M1P) + PE	0.0	0.1	3.7	96.2
1M1P	E	40	60	2.6	Poly(4M1P)	0.2	8.1	81.2	10.4

[a] *Polymerization conditions: [Monomer] = 2.7 3.0 mol/L, [$TiCl_3$] = 117 120 mmol/L; Al/Ti = 3.0 molar ratio.*
[b] *Abbreviations are as follows: 4M1P, 4-methyl-1-pentene; 4M2P, 4-methyl-2-pentene; 2M2P, 2-methyl-2-pentene; 2M1P, 2-methyl-1-pentene.*
[c] *Catalyst systems are as follows: A, $TiCl_3$-$(C_2H_5)_3Al$; B, $TiCl_3$-$(C_2H_5)_3Al$-$NiCl_2$; C, $TiCl_3$-$(C_2H_5)_2AlCl$-$(PPh_3)_2PdCl_2$; D, $TiCl_3$-$(C_2H_5)_3Al$-$(PPh_3)_2PdCl_2$; E, $TiCl_3$-$(C_2H_5)_2AlCl$-$Ni(SCN)_2$.*
[d] *Determined by gas chromatography.*
[e] *PE stands for polyethylene derived from catalysts.*

Table 8
Polymerization of Branched Olefins with Ziegler-Natta Catalyst[(a)]

Monomer[(b)]	Al/Ti Molar Ratio	Temp. (°C)	Time (hr)	Yield (%)	Composition of Olefins After Polymerization (%)[(c)]			Ref.
					1-Olefin	2-Olefin	Others	
3M1B	2.0	80	9.0	17.8	93.9	4.0	2.1	52
2M2B	2.0	80	28.0	0.0	0.1	96.0	3.9	52
2M1B	3.0	80	48.0	0.0	—	—	—	52
AB	3.0	40	7.0	40.3	100.0	0.0	0.0	54
PB	2.0	80	30.0	0.7	0.1	99.9	—	54
PB	2.0	80	30.0	1.3[(c)]	0.2	98.8	—	54
ACHA	3.0	40	1.0	15.8	100.0	0.0	0.0	55
PCHA	3.0	80	40.0	12.6	1.2	94.6	4.2	55
4Ph1B	3.0	80	0.25	100	—	—	—	56
4Ph2B	3.0	80	20.0	8.6	1.6	84.0	13.5	56
4Ph2B	3.0	80	100.0	35.1	2.2	65.7	32.0	56
1Ph1B	3.0	80	60.0	1.0	0.1	1.1	98.8	57
5Ph1P	3.0	30	0.3	14.3	100.0	0.0	0.0	59
5Ph2P	3.0	80	36.0	16.1	1.3	77.9	20.8	59
1Ph1P	3.0	80	42.0	trace	0.0	3.0	97.0	59

(a) *Polymerization conditions:* $[TiCl_3] = 120$ *mmol/L;* $[Monomer] = 3.0$ *mol/L.*
(b) *Abbreviations are as follows: 3M1B, 3-methyl-1-butene; 2M2B, 2-methyl-2-butene; 2M1B, 2-methyl-1-butene; AB, allylbenzene; PB, propenylbenzene; ACHA, allycyclohexane; PCHA, propenylcyclohexane; 4Ph1B, 4-phenyl-1-butene; 4Ph2B, 4-phenyl-2-butene; 1Ph1B, 1-phenyl-1-butene; 5Ph1P, 5-phenyl-1-pentene; 5Ph2P, 5-phenyl-2-pentene; 1Ph1P, 1-phenyl-1-pentene.*
(c) *In the presence of* $Fe(C_5H_5)_2$, $Fe/Ti = 0.5$ *molar ratio.*

The results for the polymerizations of some other branched olefins are shown in Table 8. Propenylbenzene polymerized with $TiCl_3$-$(C_2H_5)_3Al$ (Al/Ti = 2.0) catalyst at 80°C. During the polymerization of propenylbenzene, the polymerizable allylbenzene was produced through the monomer-isomerization and the polymer obtained from propenylbenzene was identified to be polyallybenzene, indicating that propenylbenzene underwent monomer-isomerization polymerization to produce a polymer consisting of allylbenzene [54]. The polymer yields, however, was quite low owing to the very low equilibrium concentration of allylbenzene in their isomers (0.04%).

When the benzene ring replaces with cyclohexane, the conjugation between benzene ring and double bond disappear so that the equilibrium concentration of 1-olefin will be higher than that of propenylbenzene isomers. Propenylcyclohexane underwent significant monomer-isomerization polymerization to produce a polymer consisting of allylcyclohexane unit only [55]. Accordingly, the rate of monomer-isomerization polymerization of propenylcyclohexane indicates that the equilibrium concentration of 1-olefin is a very significant factor in monomer-isomerization polymerization.

4-phenyl-2-butene [48, 49, 56] easily underwent monomer-isomerization polymerization to produce high molecular weight homopolymers of 4-phenyl-1-butene. Furthermore, 1-phenyl-1-butene [57], which is a further internal olefin as compared with 4-phenyl-2-butene, also induced monomer-isomerization polymerization with $TiCl_3$-$(C_2H_5)_3Al$ catalyst at 80°C to produce a polymer consisting of 4-phenyl-1-butene. The polymerization rate of phenylbutene isomers decreased in the following order: 4-phenyl-1-butene > 4-phenyl-2-butene > 1-phenyl-1-butene.

It is clear that the isomerization to 4-phenyl-1-butene proceeds via a stepwise double bond migration from both the change of isomer distribution during the polymerization and the order of polymerization rate of the respective phenylbutenes.

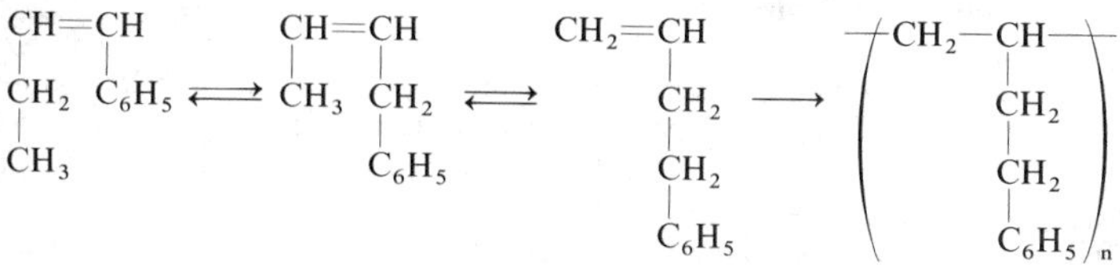

$$
\begin{array}{ccccc}
\underset{\substack{| \\ \text{CH}_2 \ \text{C}_6\text{H}_5 \\ | \\ \text{CH}_3}}{\text{CH}=\text{CH}} & \rightleftarrows &
\underset{\substack{| \\ \text{CH}_3 \ \text{CH}_2 \\ | \\ \text{C}_6\text{H}_5}}{\text{CH}=\text{CH}} & \rightleftarrows &
\underset{\substack{| \\ \text{CH}_2 \\ | \\ \text{CH}_2 \\ | \\ \text{C}_6\text{H}_5}}{\text{CH}_2=\text{CH}} \longrightarrow &
\left(\underset{\substack{| \\ \text{CH}_2 \\ | \\ \text{CH}_2 \\ | \\ \text{C}_6\text{H}_5}}{-\text{CH}_2-\text{CH}-}\right)_n
\end{array} \tag{10}
$$

5-phenyl-2-pentene was prepared by the reaction of butadiene and toluene in the presence of lithium metal in HMPA [58], and polymerized via a monomer-isomerization polymerization mechanism with Ziegler-Natta catalyst to produce a homopolymer of 5-phenyl-1-pentene [59].

Non-Conjugated Diolefins

Conjugated cyclo-diolefins are more thermodynamically stable than non-conjugated ones, and conjugated diolefins are known to polymerize easily with the Ziegler-Natta catalyst, so that non-conjugated diolefins will be expected to induce a new type of monomer-isomerization polymerization.

Marvel [60, 61] reported that the polymerization of 1,5-cyclooctadiene proceeded via a trans-annular mechanism. Whereas in the polymerization of 1,4-cyclohexadiene with the Ziegler-Natta catalyst, such transannular polymerization did not occur, but it produced a poly-1,3-cyclohexadiene with monomer-isomerization. Otsu [62] confirmed that this polymerization proceeds via a monomer-isomerization polymerization mechanism from the observed isomer distribution after polymerization and the analysis of IR and ^{1}H-NMR spectra of the resulting polymer. It was proved that 1,4-cyclohexadiene underwent monomer-isomerization polymerization to produce poly-1,3,-cyclohexadiene according to the following equation:

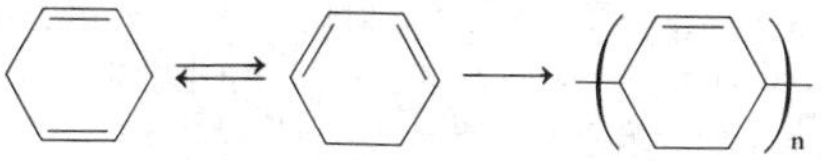

$$
\bigcirc\!\!\!\!\!\!\! \rightleftarrows \bigcirc\!\!\!\!\!\! \longrightarrow \left(\bigcirc\right)_n \tag{11}
$$

Ohara [63] reported the polymerization of 3-vinylcyclopentene. This monomer polymerized with a cationic catalyst to produce a low molecular weight polymer of cyclic structures. When the polymerization was carried out with a Ziegler-Natta catalyst, after passing through the induction periods, the polymerization proceeded, and a polymer with a molecular weight of 2,000 produced. From the change of isomer distribution during the polymerization and spectroscopic analysis of resulting polymers, it was demonstrated that 3-vinylcyclopentene isomerized first to its conjugated diene, i.e., 3-ethylidene cyclopentene, and then this olefin polymerized (Equation 12). Similar monomer-isomerization polymerization were also found in the polymerization of 3-vinylcyclohexene with Ziegler-Natta catalyst (Equation 13).

$$
\begin{array}{ccc}
\text{[}\bigcirc\text{-CH}=\text{CH}_2] & \rightleftarrows & \text{[}\bigcirc\text{=CH}-\text{CH}_3] \longrightarrow \left(\bigcirc\text{-CH-}\atop\ \ \ \ \ \text{CH}_3\right)_n
\end{array} \tag{12}
$$

$$
\begin{array}{ccc}
\text{[}\bigcirc\text{-CH}=\text{CH}_2] & \rightleftarrows & \text{[}\bigcirc\text{=CH}-\text{CH}_3] \longrightarrow \left(\bigcirc\text{-CH-}\atop\ \ \ \ \ \text{CH}_3\right)_n
\end{array} \tag{13}
$$

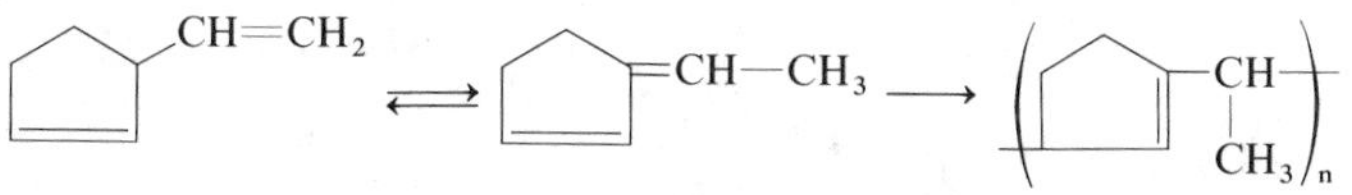

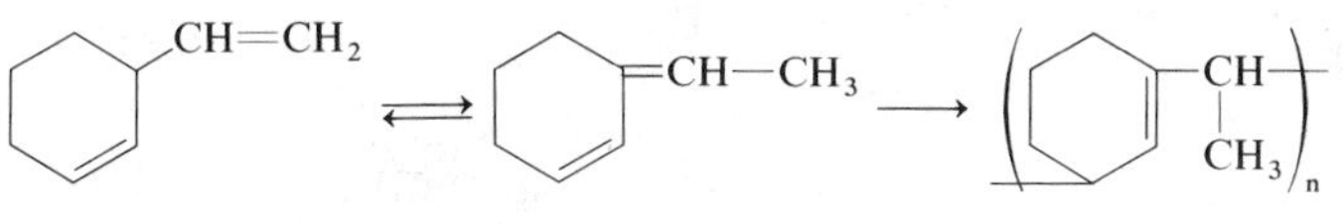

However, the conjugated dienes employed have substituents at 1,4-position so that the high molecular weight polymers are not obtained.

Monomer-Isomerization Copolymerization

In the monomer-isomerization polymerization of internal olefins with a Ziegler-Natta catalyst, a large amount of internal olefins neither participates nor interferes in the polymerization of a small amount of the isomerized 1-olefins. This is most likely due to a selective polymerization of 1-olefin from isomer mixture with a Ziegler-Natta catalyst.

Natta and co-workers [64, 65], however, reported that ethylene copolymerized with 2-butene and cyclopentene without any monomer-isomerization in the presence of VCl_4-(hexyl)$_3$Al or V(acac)$_3$-$(C_2H_5)_3Al$ catalyst to produce an alternating copolymer (Equations 13 and 14, respectively) in addition to a homopolymer of ethylene at sufficiently low ethylene concentration in comonomer feed at temperature as low as $-30°C$.

$$CH_2{=}CH_2 + \underset{CH_3}{\underset{|}{CH}}{=}\underset{CH_3}{\underset{|}{CH}} \longrightarrow \left(CH_2{-}CH_2{-}\underset{CH_3}{\underset{|}{CH}}{-}\underset{CH_3}{\underset{|}{CH}} \right)_n \qquad (14)$$

$$CH_2{=}CH_2 + \underbrace{\underset{CH_2}{\underset{|}{CH}}{=}\underset{CH_2}{\underset{|}{CH}}}_{CH_2} \longrightarrow \left(CH_2{-}CH_2{-}\underbrace{\underset{CH_2}{\underset{|}{CH}}{-}\underset{CH_2}{\underset{|}{CH}}}_{CH_2} \right)_n \qquad (15)$$

On the contrary, a patent by Chauvin et al. [43] stated that ethylene copolymerized with 2-butene, accompanying a monomer-isomerization to 1-butene by using a $Ti(OBu)_4$-$(C_2H_5)_2AlCl$-$NiCl_2$ catalyst at 50°C. The resulting copolymer consisted of ethylene and 1-butene units and the properties of the products changed from crystalline to elastomeric as a function of decreasing ethylene content in the chain.

The polymerization of 2-butene by VCl_4-$(C_2H_5)_3Al$ in combination with nickel dimethylglyoxime [Ni(DMG)$_2$] at 0°C produced a copolymer consisting of both 2-butene and 1-butene units. Although $TiCl_3$-$(C_2H_5)_3Al$-Ni(DMG)$_2$ catalyst is an effective catalyst for monomer-isomerization polymerization of internal olefins at 80°C, this catalyst induced neither isomerization nor polymerization at 0°C. This discrepancy arises from the difference in reactivity of the catalysts with respect to isomerization and polymerization, which are related to the reaction conditions such as temperature.

When a mixture of two kinds of 2-olefins that underwent monomer-isomerization polymerization was allowed to copolymerize in the presence of a catalyst having high activities for both the isomerization and the polymerization, the copolymer consisting of the corresponding 1-olefin units was obtained according to the monomer-isomerization polymerization mechanism. We called this copolymerization monomer-isomerization copolymerization [66].

2-butene underwent monomer-isomerization copolymerization with other internal olefins in the presence of $TiCl_3$-$(C_2H_5)_3Al$ catalyst to yield copolymers consisting of the respective 1-olefin units according to the following equation:

$$\begin{array}{ccccc} \underset{CH_3}{\underset{|}{CH}}{=}\underset{CH_3}{\underset{|}{CH}} & & \underset{CH_3}{\underset{|}{CH}}{=}\underset{R}{\underset{|}{CH}} & & \\ \Updownarrow & & \Updownarrow & & \\ CH_2{=}\underset{C_2H_5}{\underset{|}{CH}} & + & CH_2{=}\underset{CH_2R}{\underset{|}{CH}} & \longrightarrow & \text{---}CH_2{-}\underset{C_2H_5}{\underset{|}{CH}}\text{---}CH_2{-}\underset{CH_2R}{\underset{|}{CH}}\text{---} \end{array} \qquad (16)$$

Table 9
Monomer-Isomerization Copolymerization of *trans*-2-Butene (M_1) and 2-Pentene (M_2) with VCl_3-$(C_2H_5)_3Al$-$Ni(DMG)_2$ Catalyst in *n*-Heptane at 80°C[a] [67]

$[M_1]$ in Comonomer (mol%)	Time (hr)	Copolymer Yield (%)	Copolymer $[M'_1]$ (mol%)	Composition of Olefins after Copolymn. (%)[b] Butenes[d] 1B	t2B	c2B	Pentenes[d] 1P	t2P	c2P
0.0	8	13.5	0.0	—	—	—	3.3	71.8	24.9
20.0	5	10.5	22.4	6.4	66.9	26.7	4.5	71.1	24.4
30.0	5	11.2	28.4	5.4	66.9	27.7	3.8	72.2	24.0
40.0	5	11.0	35.5	5.1	67.2	27.7	3.6	69.7	26.7
50.0	21	23.4	38.2	4.3	67.0	28.7	3.5	70.0	26.5
60.0	5	12.2	43.6	5.6	64.8	29.6	3.5	69.1	27.4
80.0	5	13.9	61.5	5.0	66.7	28.3	3.6	70.1	26.3
100.0	8	17.6	100.0	5.1	67.3	27.6	—	—	—

[a] *Polymerization conditions:* $[VCl_3] = 50$ *mmol/L;* $Al/V = 3.0$ *molar ratio;* $([M_1] + [M_2]) = 4.0$ *mol/L.*
[b] M'_1 *stands for 1-butene unit.*
[c] *Determined by gas chromatography.*
[d] *B and P stand for butene and pentene, respectively.*

where R is the alkyl group such as propyl. The results of copolymerization of 2-butene and 2-pentene, as an example, are shown in Table 9 [66, 67]. The rate of copolymerization between 1-olefins was always faster than that between 2-olefins. The IR spectra of copolymers from copolymerization between 2-olefins were identical to those obtained by direct copolymerization between the respective 1-olefins. Both 2-olefins underwent geometric and positional isomerization during the copolymerization, and the observed isomer distribution of the unreacted olefins gradually approached those of an equilibrium mixture as a function of the time [66, 67].

These behaviors are similar to those observed in the monomer-isomerization polymerization of 2-olefin. Hence it is concluded that both 2-olefins first isomerize to the corresponding 1-olefins prior to the copolymerization and then copolymerize between the 1-olefins.

It is interesting to compare this copolymerization between 2-butene and 2-pentene with that of 1-butene and 1-pentene. Both compositions of copolymer and comonomer feed were determined by IR and gas chromatography, respectively. The copolymer composition curves thus obtained for these system are shown in Figure 4. The copolymer composition curves for the *trans*-2-butene with 2-pentene and 1-butene with 1-pentene systems were for all practical purposes superimposable by plotting the true 2-olefins concentration in comonomer feed. However, a slightly different copolymer composition curve was obtained by using 1-olefins concentration calculated from the observed isomer distribution.

If the isomerization of both 2-olefins to the respective 1-olefins is very fast and the concentration of 1-olefins is very close to the equilibrium ones, the copolymer composition remains constant and independent of the 2-olefins composition in the comonomer feed. The results obtained in this system do not coincide with the predicted compotion. Hence the difference in the rate of isomerization of 2-olefins to the respective 1-olefins is rather significant.

2-butene was also found to undergo monomer-isomerization polymerization with 4-methyl-2-pentene with $TiCl_3$-$(C_2H_5)_3Al$ catalyst to give a copolymer consisting of 1-butene and 4-methyl-1-pentene [68]. The resulting copolymers changed from a white solid to a white powder with an increase in 4-methyl-1-pentene unit and in a greater solubility than that of homopolymer of 4-methyl-1-pentene. The copolymer composition curves for copolymerization of butenes and methylpentenes

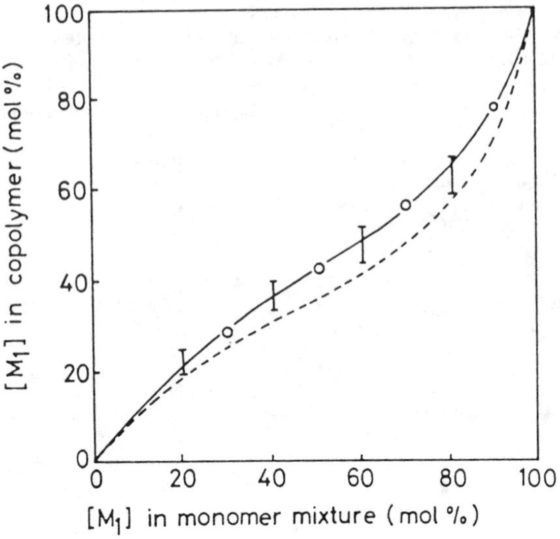

Figure 4. Copolymer composition curves for the copolymerizations of butenes (M_1) and pentenes (M_2) at 80°C (○) 1-butene and 1-pentene system, and (I) trans-2-butene and 2-pentene system in which the compositions of the butenes in the charge were plotted as (——) 2-olefin and (---) 1-olefin, respectively. (Reprinted with permission from Ref. [67].)

are shown in Figure 5. The observed contents of 4-methyl-1-pentene unit in the copolymers obtained from the monomer-isomerization copolymerization are always much lower than those from copolymerization between 1-olefins at the same comonomer feed composition.

In this monomer-isomerization copolymerization system, the equilibrium concentration of polymerizable 1-olefins is quite different (0.5% for methylpentene, 5.1% for butene). Thus, the difference in copolymer composition curves mainly arises from the rate of isomerization between 2-olefins and 1-olefins. Accordingly, it is concluded that the rate of isomerization of 2-olefins to 1-olefins was significant in the monomer-isomerization copolymerization.

In a similar manner, two kinds of internal olefins such as 2-butene/2-hexene [67], 2-butene/2-heptene [45, 69], 2-butene/3-heptene [69], 2-butene/4-phenyl-2-butene [69], and 4-methyl-2-pentene/4-phenyl-2-butene [69] were also found to undergo monomer-isomerization copolymerizations.

The polymerizability of 1-olefin toward Ziegler-Natta catalysts has been known to decrease remarkably when the carbon atom on its 3-position was replaced by an alkyl group, as a result of the increased steric effect of the substituents adjacent to the reacting double bond [52]. Thus, 3-position branched 1-olefins polymerize slowly, and a small amount is incorporated in the copolymers when such olefins copolymerized with much more reactive 1-olefins.

The copolymerization of the less reactive 1-olefin with 2-olefin corresponds to the copolymerization at high concentration of the less reactive 1-olefin, if we take into account the concentration of the polymerizable monomer in the system. Thus, these copolymerization systems produce copolymers containing predominantly less reactive 1-olefin units with a moderate rate. This copolymerization produces a new type of monomer-isomerization copolymerization.

The copolymerization of 3-methyl-1-butene, 2-methyl-2-butene, and 2-methyl-1-butene with 2-butene in the presence of a Ziegler-Natta catalyst has been studied. The copolymerization of 3-methyl-1-butene with 2-butene produced copolymers whose IR spectra were identical to those obtained from a 3-methyl-1-butene with 1-butene system. The isomerization of 2-butene to 1-butene

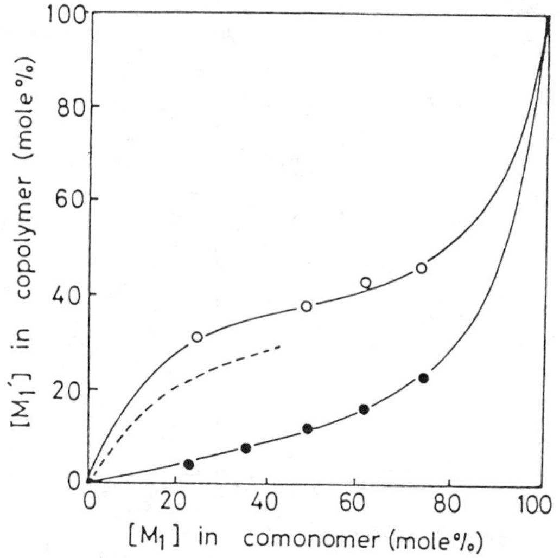

Figure 5. Copolymer composition curves for the copolymerization of methylpentenes (M_1) and butenes (M_2): (●) 4-methyl-1-pentene and 1-butene, and (○) 4-methyl-2-pentene and 2-butene, (---) feed calculated as 1-olefins in the copolymerization of 4-methyl-2-pentene and 2-butene. (Reprinted with permission from Ref. [68].)

and of 3-methyl-1-butene to the unpolymerizable internal olefins was observed during the copolymerization. Thus, monomer-isomerization copolymerization of 3-methyl-1-butene with 2-butene is expressed by:

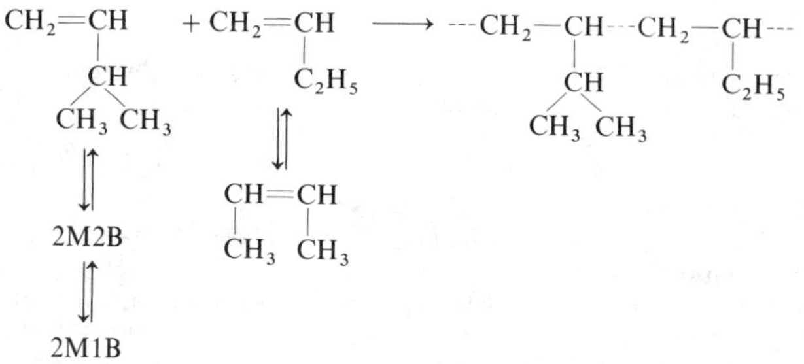

(17)

where 2M2B and 2M1B represent 2-methyl-2-butene and 2-methyl-1-butene, respectively.

Contrary to the monomer-isomerization copolymerization between 2-olefins, in this case only 2-butene is isomerized to 1-butene to copolymerize with 3-methyl-1-butene prior to the copolymerization. The copolymer composition curves for copolymerization of methylbutenes and butenes are shown in Figure 6. The observed curves for both copolymerization systems are different, i.e., the 3-methyl-1-butene content in the copolymer obtained from the copolymerization of the 3-methyl-1-butene and 2-butene system is always higher than that of respective 1-olefins. It is interesting that the apparent copolymerization reactivity of 3-methyl-1-butene widely varies when 1-butene or 2-butene is used as a starting comonomer.

However, 2-methyl-2-butene and 2-methyl-1-butene did not induce monomer-isomerization copolymerization with 2-butene, and only the homopolymer consisting of 1-butene was obtained under the similar conditions.

The copolymerization of 3-methyl-1-butene with 2-pentene [70] proceeded with the above monomer-isomerization copolymerization mechanism, and copolymers consisted of nearly complete 3-methyl-1-butene units were obtained easily. Other 1-olefins belong to this category such as 2,4,4-trimethyl-1-hexene, vinylcyclohexane, styrene, and 4-vinyl-1-cyclohexene were also found to undergo monomer-isomerization copolymerization with 2-butene by the Ziegler-Natta catalyst [71, 72].

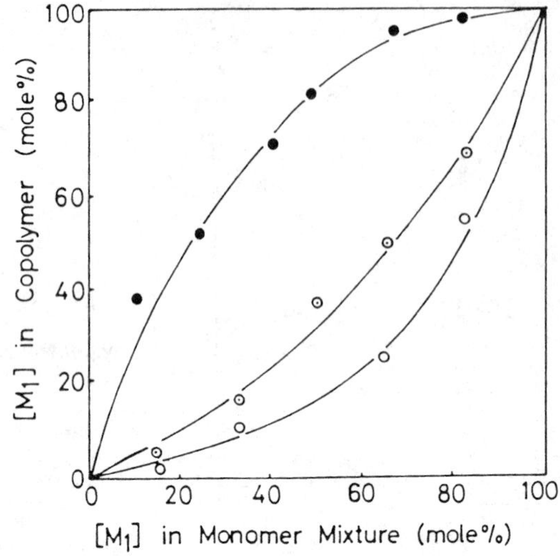

Figure 6. Copolymer composition curves for the copolymerization of methylbutenes (M_1) and butenes (M_2) at 80°C obtained from (●) 3-methyl-1-butene and 1-butene, (◎) 3-methyl-1-butene and 2-butene with $TiCl_3$-$(C_2H_5)_3Al$ catalyst, (○) 3-methyl-1-butene and 2-butene with $TiCl_3$-$(C_2H_5)_3Al$-$NiCl_2$ catalyst. (Reprinted with permission from Ref. [52].)

The rate of polymerization of 3-position branched 1-olefins is quite low, but their polymers have a high melting point. Thus, this copolymerization method has the advantage of producing high melting polymers with rapid rates.

Provided that the catalyst system has a low polymerization reactivity but a high reactivity for the isomerization, the polymerization of 2-olefins produces the polymer consisting of both the charged 2-olefins and the isomerized 1-olefins units. The copolymer composition, of course, depends on the polymerization reactivity for both the olefins.

When the polymerization of propenylbenzene is carried out in the presence of $TiCl_3$-$(C_2H_5)_2AlCl$ catalyst at 80°C, neither isomerization nor polymerization was observed [80]. The addition of $NiCl_2$, however, induced both isomerization and polymerization, and a powder-like polymer was obtained. The analysis of the products led to the conclusion that the resulting polymers consisted of allylbenzene and propenylbenzene units. For the polymerization of propenylbenzene with Ziegler-Natta catalyst, the following scheme can be written:

$$
\begin{array}{c}
\underset{CH_3\ \ C_6H_5}{CH=CH} \longrightarrow \left(\!\!\begin{array}{c}CH-CH\\ \ \ | \ \ \ \ \ |\\ CH_3\ \ C_6H_5\end{array}\!\!\right)_{\!m} \\
\updownarrow \qquad\qquad\qquad ---CH_2-CH---CH-CH--- \\
\qquad\qquad\qquad\qquad\qquad \ \ \ |\qquad\ \ |\qquad| \\
\qquad\qquad\qquad\qquad\qquad CH_2\ \ CH_3\ \ C_6H_5 \\
\qquad\qquad\qquad\qquad\qquad \ \ | \\
\qquad\qquad\qquad\qquad\qquad C_6H_5 \\
\underset{\underset{C_6H_5}{CH_2}}{CH_2=CH} \longrightarrow \left(\!\!\begin{array}{c}CH_2-CH\\ \ \ \ \ \ \ |\\ CH_2\\ |\\ C_6H_5\end{array}\!\!\right)_{\!n}
\end{array}
$$

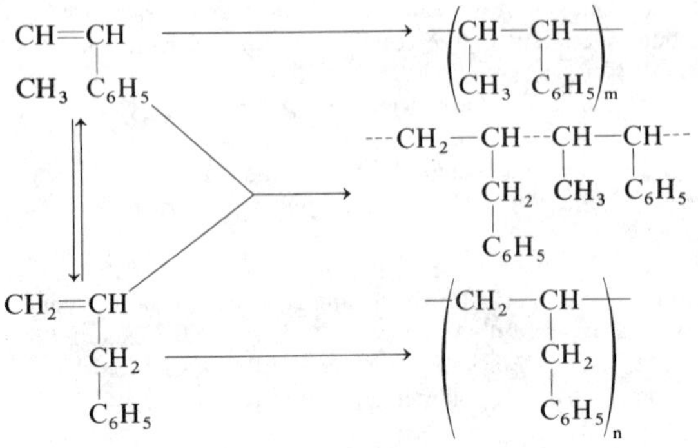

Similarly, the polymerization of 2-butene with VCl_4-$(C_2H_5)_3Al$-$Ni(DMG)_2$ catalyst at low temperature (0°C) led to the formation of a polymer consisting of 1-butene with a minor amount of 2-butene [73].

Therefore, it is concluded that the structure of the polymers produced by this type of polymerization is apparently dependent on the catalyst systems in addition to the polymerizability of the olefins.

MONOMER-ISOMERIZATION POLYMERIZATION WITH CATIONIC CATALYST

In the field of the cationic polymerizations, the case of allylbenzene and propenylbenzene is of interest from historical and scientific points of views [74–76]. The relationship between the reported monomer and polymer structures can be written as follows:

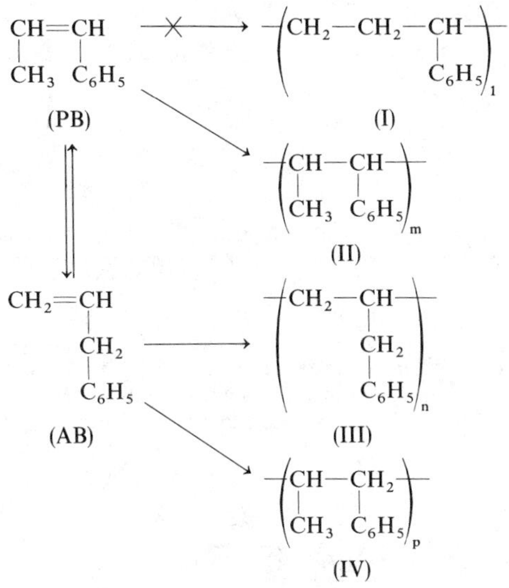

In 1935, H. Staudinger and E. Dreher [74] reported that the polymerization of propenylbenzene and its methoxy derivatives in the presence of cationic catalyst, such as $SnCl_4$ and BF_3, proceeded with isomerization as a part of propagation to give a polymer consisting of a anomalous 1,3-structure unit (PB → I). However, this contention was proven incorrect when it was established that the polymerization of propenylbenzene with cationic catalyst proceeded via a conventional vinylene polymerization mechanism (PB → II) [75].

On the other hand, allylbenzene under similar conditions produced a series of ill defined products. Along with the normal polymerization of allylbenzene, several side reactions can be visualized due to the structure of monomer and carbonium-ion nature of the intermediate (e.g., polyalkylations, copolymerization of rearrangement and unrearrangement unit, etc.).

The isomerization to propenylbenzene was also observed during the polymerization of allylbenzene, and the newly-formed propenylbenzene polymerized with a conventional addition polymerization. This reaction is reasonable from the consideration of both the exothermicity of the isomerization and reluctance to polymerization of allyl compounds. This reaction denotes monomer-isomerization polymerization with cationic catalyst. Similar results were also reported in the polymerization of allylbenzene with Ziegler-Natta catalyst having cationic characters [76].

The polymerization of α-pinene with cationic catalyst has been reported to produce a solid polymer in addition to a large amount of dimer. It is suggested that a part of α-pinene isomerizes first to limonene prior to the polymerization and then the limonene polymerizes [77].

It is well known that a Claisen rearrangement of allyl phenyl ether is induced by thermal treatment at elevated temperatures to yield allylphenol. Such reaction progresses easily in the presence of Lewis acids even at room temperature. Thus, the polymerization of allyl phenyl ether was carried out in the presence of BF_3OEt_2 in bulk to use this reaction for the polymer synthesis. The rate of polymerization of allyl phenyl ether is slower than that of allylphenol. The IR spectra of polymers obtained from both allylphenyl ether and allyl phenol were identical, and allylphenol was detected in the unreacted monomer after the polymerization [78].

Hence, it is clear that allyl phenyl ether isomerized first to allylphenol and then polymerized, i.e., allyl phenyl ether underwent monomer-isomerization polymerization with cationic catalyst (Equation 19). The molecular weight of polymer obtained from monomer-isomerization polymerization of allyl phenyl ether is higher than that from the polymerization of allylphenol suggesting that the propagating cation reacts with phenolic hydroxy group.

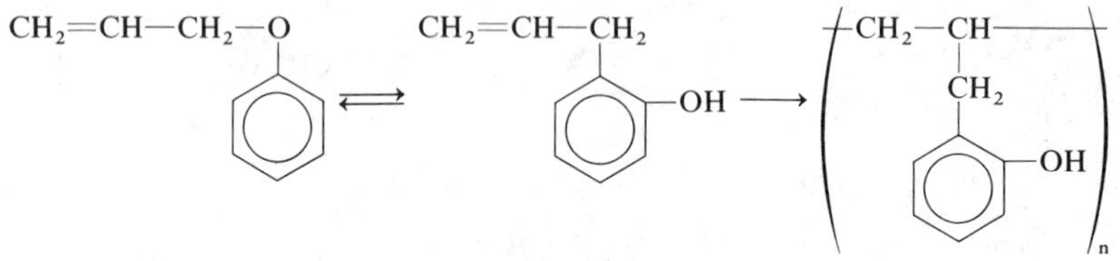

(19)

Higashismura and his co-workers [79, 80] reported that 2-ethyl-1,3-butadiene, methylenecyclohexene, and methylenecyclopentene underwent monomer-isomerization oligomerization in the presence of super acid catalysts such as CF_3SO_3H and $AcClO_4$. When metal halides were used as the polymerization catalysts, the conventional cationic polymerization proceeded without monomer-isomerization.

They confirmed that monomer-isomerization of 2-ethyl-1,3-butadiene (2EBD) to 3-methyl-1,3-pentadiene (3MPD) occurred first and then the isomerized monomer oligomerizes in the presence of super acid catalyst. The monomer-isomerization oligomerization of 2-ethyl-1,3-butadiene is shown in the following:

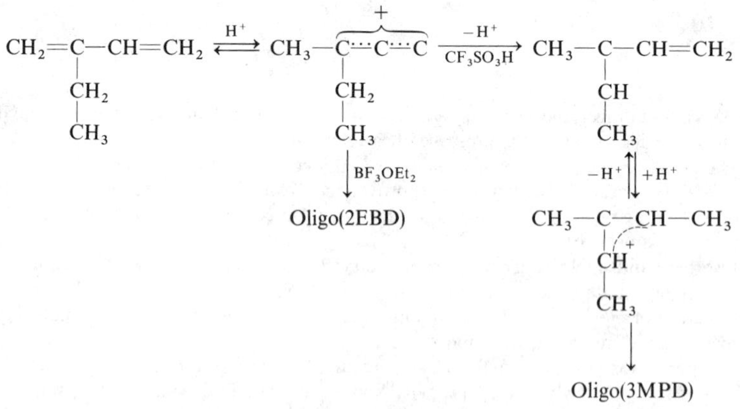

Similarly, methylenecyclohexene and methylenecyclopentene isomerizes first to 1-methyl-1-cyclohexadiene and 1-methyl-1-cyclopentadiene, respectively and then oligomerize. The difference in catalyst function might be attributed to the interaction between propagation cation and its counter anion.

MONOMER-ISOMERIZATION POLYMERIZATION WITH ANIONIC CATALYST

Acrylamide derivatives polymerize by a hydrogen transfer mechanism to give a polymer of amide structure in the main chain, e.g., poly-β-alanine was produced by the polymerization of acrylamide with strong base catalyst such as t-BuONa and $NaNH_2$ in the presence of a radical inhibitor at 80–200°C [81].

$$CH_2{=}CH{-}CONH_2 \longrightarrow {+}CH_2{-}CH_2{-}CONH{+}_n \tag{20}$$

It is reasonable that the non-conjugated acrylamides isomerize to β-substituted conjugated ones by base catalyst based on the thermodynamic stabilities. Thus, the non-conjugated amide compounds such as 3-buteneamide will pave the way to undergo monomer-isomerization polymerization.

Nakayama [82] and Magazzini [83] reported that 3-buteneamide polymerized with n-BuLi or t-BuONa catalyst in pyridine or toluene solvent. The structure of the polymers obtained was confirmed to be identical to that from hydrogen transfer polymerization of crotonamide by the IR and ^{1}H-NMR spectra analysis of the product. The isomerization of 3-buteneamide to crotonamide was also observed during the polymerization.

Therefore, it was concluded that 3-buteneamide isomerized first to high reactive crotonamide and then this crotonamide provoked the hydrogen transfer polymerization to produce a low-molecular-weight and amorphous poly-β-ethyl-alanine. This polymerization denotes monomer-isomerization polymerization with anionic catalyst.

$$CH_2{=}CH{-}CH_2{-}CONH_2 \rightleftarrows \underset{\substack{|\\ CH_3}}{CH}{=}CH{-}CONH_2 \longrightarrow \left(\underset{\substack{|\\ CH_3}}{CH}{-}CH_2{-}CONH\right)_n \tag{21}$$

Similarly, 4-penteneamide [83] was also found to undergo monomer-isomerization polymerization to give a low-molecular weight-polymer ($P_n = 5$) consisting of β-ethyl acrylamide unit.

$$\begin{gathered} CH_2{=}CH{-}CH_2{-}CH_2{-}CONH_2 \rightleftarrows \underset{\substack{|\\ CH_3}}{CH}{=}CH{-}CH_2{-}CONH_2 \rightleftarrows \\ \underset{\substack{|\\ C_2H_5}}{CH}{=}CH{-}CONH_2 \longrightarrow \left(\underset{\substack{|\\ C_2H_5}}{CH}{-}CH_2{-}CONH\right)_n \end{gathered} \tag{22}$$

Monomer-isomerization polymerization of *cis*-crotonamide was also reported, i.e., *cis*-crotonamide isomerizes first to *trans*-crotonamide and then this *trans* isomer homopolymerizes [84]. The polymerization of 1,4-dihydronapthalene also polymerized in the presence of organosodium compounds with monomer-isomerization to 1,2-dihydronapthalene prior of the polymerization [85].

MONOMER-ISOMERIZATION POLYMERIZATION IN RADICAL POLYMERIZATION

In radical polymerization, 1,2-disubstituted ethylenic monomers hardly polymerize with a radical initiator. Recently, the dialkyl fumarates were found to homopolymerize in the presence of a radical initiator under usual conditions to give high molecular weight homopolymers without any rearrangement of monomer. No maleates produced any polymers with a radical initiator under the similar conditions [86, 87, 88, 89, 90].

It is generally accepted that fumarate esters are more reactive than maleate esters in their addition reaction toward the radical [91], and maleates isomerize easily to their fumarate isomers by the addition of catalytic amount of certain amines [92]. These facts suggest that the poly-dialkyl fumarates will be formed by the polymerization of the dialkyl maleates if maleates are allowed to polymerize with a radical polymerization initiator in the presence of isomerization catalyst.

Table 10
Radical Polymerization of Dialkyl Fumarates and Dialkyl Maleates[a]

Monomer (mol/L)	Initiator (mmol/L)	Solvent	[Morphorine] (mol/L)	Temp. (°C)	Time (hr)	Yield (%)	Ref.
DMF (5.3)	ACN (30)	Xylene	0.0	90	12	21.9	93
DMF (5.3)	ACN (30)	Xylene	0.043	90	12	9.3	93
DMM (5.3)	ACN (30)	Xylene	0.0	90	12	0.0	93
DMM (5.3)	ACN (30)	Xylene	0.07	90	8	8.2	93
DEF (6.13)	AIBN (20)	None	0.0	60	16	13.2	94
DEF (6.13)	AIBN (20)	None	0.23	60	16	10.0	94
DEM (6.13)	AIBN (20)	None	0.0	60	16	0.0	94
DEM (6.13)	AIBN (20)	None	0.23	60	16	9.8	94
DEM (6.13)	AIBN (20)	None	0.23[b]	60	16	0.0	94
DtBF (2.2)	AIBN (22)	Benzene	0.0	60	10	42.0	95
DtBF (2.2)	AIBN (22)	Benzene	0.35	60	10	30.0	95
DtBM (2.2)	AIBN (22)	Benzene	0.0	60	10	0.00	95
DtBM (2.2)	AIBN (22)	Benzene	0.22	60	10	27.0	95
DtBM (2.2)	AIBN (22)	Benzene	0.35	60	10	23.0	95

[a] *Abbreviations are as follows: DMF, dimethyl fumarate; DMM, dimethyl maleate; DEF, diethyl fumarate; DEM, diethyl maleate; DtBF, di-tert-butyl fumarate; DtBM, di-tert-butyl maleate; AIBN, 1,1'-azobisisobutyl-nitrile; ACN, 1,1'-azobiscyclohexanecarbonitrile.*
[b] *In the presence of pyridine, [pyridine] = 0.24 mol/L.*

The results for the radical polymerization of various dialkyl fumarates and dialkyl maleates in the presence or absence of morpholine are summarized in Table 10 [90]. The radical polymerization of these maleates proceeded only when the polymerization was carried out in the presence of morpholine. The resulting polymers changed from white or pale yellow powders to viscous materials, depending on the kinds of ester group, i.e., the more the alkyl in ester group bulked, the more the polymers powdered. The IR, ^{1}H-NMR, and ^{13}C-NMR spectra of the polymers obtained from dialkyl maleates are identical to those obtained from the respective dialkyl fumarates isomers [89, 90, 91].

The isomerization of the dialkyl maleates to the dialkyl fumarates was observed during the polymerization only in the presence of morpholine. The isomerization is dependent on the kinds of amines, i.e., primary and secondary amines were affective for this isomerization. Among them morpholine was the most effective isomerization catalyst. On the contrary, the isomerization of dialkyl fumarates to their dialkyl maleate did not progress even in the presence of amines catalyst. When the benzoyl peroxide was used as a radical initiator, the dialkyl maleates did not polymerize due to a fast redox decomposition with the amine.

Therefore, it is clear that the maleates isomerize first to the corresponding fumarates and then newly-formed fumarates undergo radical homopolymerization when the polymerization of maleates was carried out with radical initiators such as AIBN in the presence of isomerization catalyst according to the following scheme:

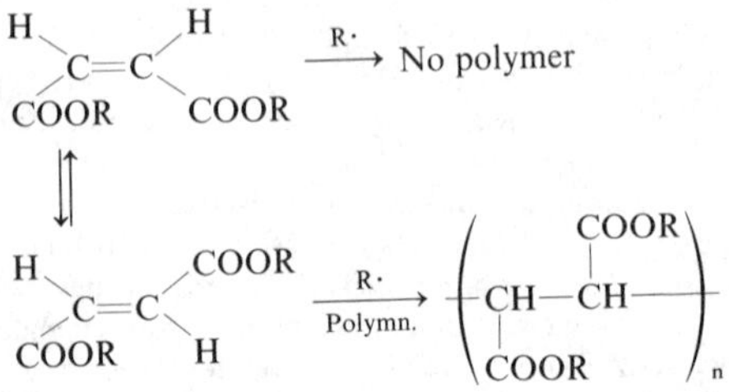

(23)

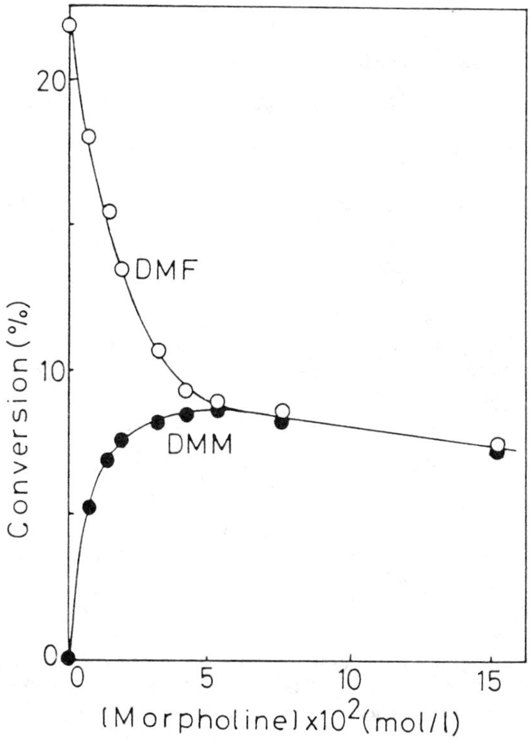

Figure 7. Effect of morpholine on radical polymerizations of dimethyl fumarate (DMF) and dimethyl maleate (DMM) in benzene at 90°C for 8 hr: [DMF] = [DMM] = 5.3 mol/L, [ACN] = 3.0 $\times 10^{-2}$ mol/L. (Reprinted with permission from Ref. [93].)

Otsu called this polymerization monomer-isomerization radical polymerization. This mechanism was confirmed by the copolymerization with styrene in the presence of morpholine and the effect of morpholine on the polymerization of dialkyl maleates and dialkyl fumarates [93].

The effect of morpholine on the polymerization of dimethyl fumarate and on the monomer-isomerization radical polymerization of dimethyl maleate are shown in Figure 7. In radical polymerization of dimethyl fumarate, the polymer yield decreased with the increasing of the concentration of morpholine, indicating that morpholine acts as a retarder in this polymerization. These facts can be explained by the following reasons: the polymer radical of dimethyl fumarate abstracts the hydrogen atom from morpholine yielding nitrogen-centered radical, and this radical does not participate in the reinitiation of the less reactive dimethyl fumarate monomer.

On the other hand, in the polymerization of dimethyl maleate morpholine functions as both isomerization catalyst to dimethyl fumarate and retarder of radical polymerization. Thus, the polymer yield as a function of morpholine is maximized by the balance of the catalyst ability of isomerization and the effectiveness of the retarder. The isomerization of the maleates to the fumarates is catalyzed by a small amount of morpholine, and its rate is faster than that of chain transfer reaction between morpholine and dimethyl fumarate. Hence, the curves for relation between polymer yield and morpholine concentration approached a merged curve.

The effect of dimethyl maleate on radical polymerization of dimethyl fumarate is shown in Figure 8. In the absence of morpholine, the polymer yield decreased linearly with an increase of the feed dimethyl maleate concentration, suggesting that the dimethyl maleate acts as an inert monomer, like a solvent. In the presence of morpholine, however, the polymer yields are almost constant, independent of the feed dimethyl maleate concentration, and also lower than that observed from the bulk polymerization of dimethyl fumarate. This evidence supports the view that morpholine acts

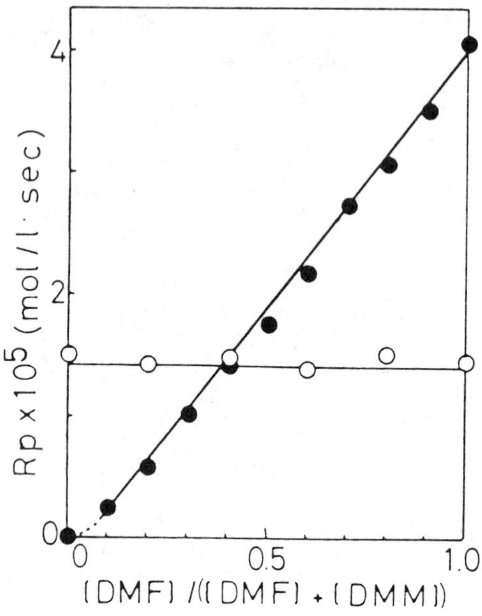

Figure 8. Effect of dimethyl maleate (DMM) on radical polymerization of dimethyl fumarate (DMF) in benzene at 90°C: [DMF] + [DMM] = 5.3 mol/L, [ACN] = 2.1×10^{-2} mol/L, (○) in the presence of morpholine (6.5×10^{-2} mol/L), (●) absence of morpholine. (Reprinted with permission from Ref. [93].)

as both an effective isomerization catalyst and a retarder of the radical polymerization of dimethyl fumarate.

The results of copolymerization of styrene (M_1) with dimethyl maleate (M_2) in the absence or presence of morpholine are shown in Figure 9. When morpholine was added to styrene-dimethyl maleate system, the copolymer compositions were similar to those of styrene-dimethyl fumarate system, in contrast with the curve obtained from the polymerization of styrene-dimethyl fumarate system in the absence of morpholine.

Therefore, it is clear that the copolymerizations are explained satisfactorily by monomer-isomerization polymerization mechanism. Similar results were also reported in the monomer-isomerization radical polymerization of diethyl maleate [94] and di-t-buthyl maleate [95].

REFERENCES

1. Jezl, J. L., (Sun Oil Co.), U.S. Patent 2,956,989, Oct. 18, 1960.
2. Shimizu, A., Otsu, T., and Imoto, M., *J. Polym. Sci., Polym. Lett.*, 3, 449 (1965).
3. Symcox, R. O., *J. Polym. Sci.*, 2B, 947 (1964).
4. Iwamoto, A., and Yuguchi, S., *Bull. Chem. Soc. Jpn.*, 40, 159 (1967).
5. Kennedy, J. P., and Otsu, T., *Adv. Polym. Sci.*, 7, 369 (1970).
6. Otsu, T., Shimizu, A., Itakura, K., and Imoto, M., *Makromol. Chem.*, 123, 284 (1968).
7. Kennedy, J. P., and Thomas, R. M., *Makromol. Chem.*, 53, 28 (1962).
8. Kennedy, J. P., and Thomas, R. M., *J. Polym. Sci.*, A2, 2093 (1964).
9. Kennedy, J. P., and Thomas, R. M., *Polymer*, 6, 287 (1965).
10. Kennedy, J. P., *Encycl. Polym. Sci. Technol.*, Wiley, New York, 1967 7, p 754.

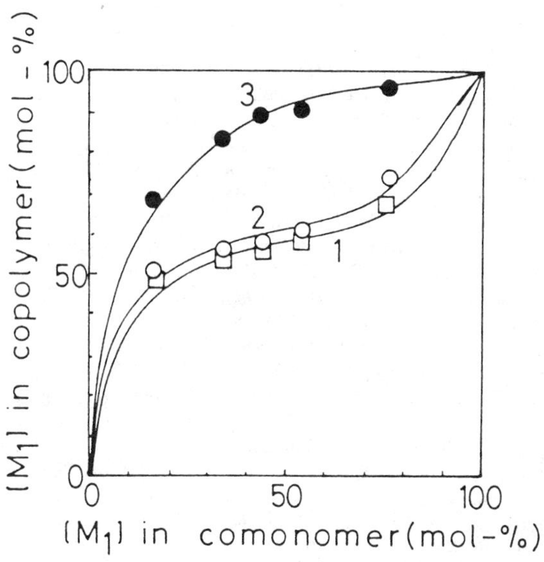

Figure 9. Copolymer composition curves for the copolymerization of styrene (M_1) with dimethyl maleate and dimethyl fumarate (M_2). (1) styrene-DMF, (2) styrene-DMM in the presence of morpholine, (3) styrene-DMM in the absence of morpholine. (Reprinted with permission from Ref. [93].)

11. Marvel, C. S., and Rogers, J. R., *J. Polym. Sci.*, 49, 335 (1961).
12. Pino, P., Lorenz, G. P., and Lardicci, L., *Chim & Ind.* (Milan), 42, 712 (1960).
13. Natta, G., Dall'Asta, G., Mazzanti, G., Pasquon, I., Valassori, A., and Zambelli, A., *J. Am. Chem. Soc.*, 83, 3343 (1961).
14. Alfrey T., Jr., Boher, J. Jr., and Mark, H., *Copolymerizations*, Int. Pub. Inc., New York, 1951, p. 51.
15. Natta, G., Dall'Asta, G., Mazzanti, G., and Motroni, G., *Makromol. Chem.*, 69, 163 (1963).
16. Porri, L., Natta G., and Gallazzi, M. C., *Chim. and Ind.* (milan), 46, 428 (1964).
17. Natta, G., Dall'Asta, G., and Motroni, A., *J. Polym. Sci.*, B, 2, 349 (1964).
18. Natta, G., Dall'Asta, G., and Porri, L., *Makromol. Chem.*, 81, 253, (1965).
19. Dall'Asta, G., and Motroni, G., *Europ. Polym. J.*, 7, 707 (1971).
20. Natta, G., Dall'Asta, G., Mazzanti, G., Pasquon, I., Valassori, A., and Zambelli, A., *Makromol. Chem.*, 54, 95 (1962).
21. Dall'Asta, G., Mazzanti, G., and Natta, G., *Makromol. Chem.*, 61, 178 (1963).
22. Crammer, R., and Lindsey R. V., Jr., *J. Am. Chem. Soc.*, 88, 1535 (1966).
23. Shinizu, A., Otsu, T., and Imoto, M., *Bull. Chem. Soc. Jpn.*, 38, 1535 (1965).
24. Endo, K., Ueda, R., and Otsu, T., Polym. Prepts. Jpn., 28, 662 (1979).
25. Otsu, T., Shimizu, A., and Imoto, M., *J. Polym. Sci.*, A-1, 4, 1579 (1966).
26. Boor J., Jr., *Ziegler-Natta Catalysts and Polymerizations*, Academic Press, New York, 1979.
27. Henrici-Olive, G., and Olive, S., *Coordination and Catalysis*, Verlag Chemie, Weinheim, 1977.
28. Endo, K., Ueda, R., and Otsu, T., Polym. Prepts. Jpn., 27, 768 (1978).
29. Shimizu, A., Itakura, K., Otsu, T., and Imoto, M., *J. Polym. Sci.*, A-1, 7, 3119 (1969).
30. Chauvin, Y., Phung, N. H., G-Loudet, N., and Lefebre, G., *Bull. Soc. Chim. Fr.*, 1966, 3223.
31. Manuel, T. A., *J. Org. Chem.*, 27 (1962).
32. Karapinka, G. L., and Orchin, M., *J. Org. Chem.*, 26, 4187 (1961).

33. Schindler, A., *Makromol. Chem.*, 90, 284 (1966).
34. Schindler, A., *Makromol. Chem.*, 118, 1 (1968).
35. Chauvin, Y., and Lefebre, G., *Compt. Rend.*, 259, 2105 (1964).
36. Phung, N. H., Chauvin, Y., and Lefebre, G., *Bull. Chim. Soc. Fr.*, 1967, 3618.
37. Endo, K., and Otsu, T., Polym. Prepts. Jpn., 29, 735 (1980).
38. Laputte, R., and Guyot, A., *Makromol. Chem.*, 129, 215 (1969).
39. Peyroche, J., Girard, Y., Laputte, R., and Guyot, A., *Makromol. Chem.*, 129, 215 (1969).
40. Bestian, H., and Clauss, K., *Angew. Chem.* 75, 1068 (1963).
41. Laputte, R., and Guyot, A., *Makromol. Chem.*, 132, 179 (1970).
42. Otsu, T., Shimizu, A., and Imoto, M., *J. Polym. Sci.*, A-1, 7, 3111 (1969).
43. Chauvin, Y., and Lefebre, G., Brit. P. 1027758 (April 27, 1966); C.A., 65, 2375 (1966).
44. Otsu, T., Nagahama, H., and Endo, K., *J. Polym. Sci.*, B, 10, 601 (1972).
45. Otsu, T., Nagahama, H., and Endo, K., *J. Macromol. Sci.-Chem.*, A9, 1245 (1975).
46. Endo, K., Nagahama, H., and Otsu, T., *J. Polym. Sci., Polym. Chem. Ed.*, 17, 3647 (1979).
47. Otsu, T., and Endo, K., *J. Macromol. Sci.-Chem.*, A9, 899 (1975).
48. Otsu, T., and Endo, K., *Ionic Polymerization—Unsolved Problems* (O. Vogl and J. Fyrukawa, ed.), Marcel Dekker Inc., New York, 1976, p 259.
49. Otsu, T., Endo, K., Nagahama, H., and Shimizu, A., *Bull. Chem. Soc. Jpn.*, 48, 2470 (1975),
50. Endo, K., and Otsu, T., *J. Polym. Sci., Polym. Chem. Ed.*, 14, 1889 (1976).
51. Phung, N. H., Chauvin, Y., and Lefebre, G., *Bull. Chim. Soc. Fr.*, 1970, 1935.
52. Endo, K., and Otsu, T., *J. Polym. Sci., Polym. Chem. Ed.*, 17, 1453 (1979).
53. Ketley, A. D., *J. Polym. Sci.*, B, 1, 121 (1963).
54. Endo, K., and Otsu, T., *J. Polym. Sci., Polym. Chem. Ed.*, 24 1615 (1986).
55. Endo, K., and Otsu, T., Unpublished results.
56. Endo, K., and Otsu, T., *J. Polym. Sci., Polym. Chem. Ed.*, 14 2083 (1976).
57. Endo, K., and Otsu, T., *Memoirs for Faculty of Eng. Osaka City University*, 26, 109 (1985).
58. Yamaguchi, T., Narita, T., and Tsuruta, T., *Polym. J.*, 3, 573 (1973).
59. Endo, K., Tsujikawa, H., and Otsu, T., *J. Polym. Sci., Polym. Chem. Ed.*, 24, 1633 (1986).
60. Marvel, C. S., and Hartzell, G. E., *J. Am. Chem. Soc.*, 81, 448 (1959).
61. Reichel, B., Marvel, C. S., and Greenley, R. Z., *J. Polym. Sci.*, A1, 2935 (1963).
62. Yousufzai, A. H. K., Endo, K., and Otsu, T., *J. Polym. Sci., Polym. Chem. Ed.*, 13, 1605 (1975).
63. Ohara, O., *Chem. High Polymer Jpn.*, 28, 587 (1971).
64. Natta, G., Dall'Asta, G., Mazzanti, G., and Ciampelli, F., *Kolloid-Z.*, 182, 50 (1962).
65. Natta, G., Allegra, G., Bassi, I. W., Corradini, P., and Ganis, P., *Makromol. Chem.*, 58, 2424 (1962).
66. Otsu, T., Shimizu, A., Itakura, K., and Imoto, M., *Makromol. Chem.*, 123, 289 (1969).
67. Otsu, T., Shimizu, A., Itakura, K., and Endo, K., *J. Polym. Sci., Polym. Chem. Ed.*, 13, 1589 (1975).
68. Otsu, T., Yousufzai, A. H. K., and Endo, K., *J. Polym. Sci., Polym. Chem. Ed.*, 17, 1431 (1979).
69. Endo, K., and Otsu, T., *J. Polym. Sci., Polym. Chem. Ed.*, 17, 1441 (1979).
70. Endo, K., and Otsu, T., *J. Polym. Sci., Polym. Chem. Ed.*, 24, 1505 (1986).
71. Otsu, T., and Endo, K., Japan Kokai 58-8708, 1983.
72. Endo, K., Fujii, K., and Otsu, T., Polym. Prepts. Jpn., 32, 1159 (1983).
73. Otsu, T., Aoki, S., and Nishimura, M., *Makromol. Chem.*, 128, 272 (1969).
74. Staudinger, H., and Dreher, E., *Ann.*, 73, 517 (1935).
75. Kennedy, J. P., and Langer, A., *Adv. Polym. Sci.*, 3, 508 (1964).
76. Shimizu, A., Otsu, T., and Imoto, M., *Bull. Chem. Soc. Jpn.*, 41, 953 (1968).
77. Roberts, W. J., and Day, A. R., *J. Am. Chem. Soc.*, 72, 1226 (1950).
78. Endo, K., and Otsu, T., *Polym. Prepts. Jpn.*, 25, 60 (1976).
79. Higashimura, T., and Hasegawa, H., *J. Polym. Sci., Polym. Chem. Ed.*, 17, 2439 (1979).
80. Aine, T., Hasegawa, H., and Higashimura, T., Polymer Prepts. Jpn., 28, 666 (1979).
81. Kennedy, J. P., and Otsu, T., *J. Macromol. Sci.-Rev. Macromol. Chem.*, C6, 237 (1972).
82. Nakayama, N., Higashimura, H., and Okamura, S., *J. Macromol. Sci.-Chem.*, A2, 52 (1968).
83. Magazzini, M., Vandi, A., and Campadelli, F., *Europ. Polym. J.*, 6, 1331 (1971).
84. Kobuke, Y., Hanzi, K., Fueno, T., and Furukawa, J., *J. Polym. Sci.*, A-1, 9, 43 (1971).
85. Scott et al., N. P., *Ind. & Eng. Chem.*, 32, 312 (1940).
86. Otsu, T., Ito, O., Toyoda, N., and Mori, S., *Makromol. Chem. Rapid Commun.*, 2, 725 (1981).

87. Toyoda, N., and Otsu, T., *J. Macromol. Sci.-Chem.*, A19, 1011 (1983).
88. Otsu, T., Yasuyara, T., Shiraishi, K., and Mori, S., *Polym. Bull.*, 12, 449 (1984).
89. Otsu, T., Minai, H., Toyoda, N., and Yasuhara, T., *Makromol. Chem., Suppl.*, 12, 133 (1985).
90. Otsu, T., Ito, O., Toyoda, N., and Mori, S., *Makromol. Chem., Rapid. Commun.*, 2, 729 (1981).
91. Lewis, M., and Mayo, F. R., *J. Am. Chem. Soc.* 70, 1553 (1968).
92. Inoue, S., Ohashi, S., and Uno, Y., *Polym. J.*, 3, 611 (1972).
93. Otsu, T., Ito, O., Toyoda, N., and Mori, S., *J. Macromol. Sci.-Chem., A*19, 27 (1983).
94. Toyoda, N., Yoshida, M., and Otsu, T., *Polym. J.*, 15, 255 (1983).
95. Otsu, T., and Shiraishi, K., *Macromolecules*, 18, 1795 (1985).

CHAPTER 16

PHOTOREACTOR DESIGN

Alberto E. Cassano and **Orlando M. Alfano**

Instituto de Desarrollo Tecnológico para la Industria Química
Universidad Nacional del Litoral (U.N.L.)
and
Consejo Nacional de Investigaciones Científicas y Técnicas (CONICET)
Argentina

CONTENTS

INTRODUCTION

Kinetic studies of light-sensitized reactions have continued at a sustained rate over many decades. Such systems provide a controllable environment to investigate mechanisms and products of many reactions. Commercial applications, particularly chlorinations, have stimulated interest in designing efficient reactors. Empiricism, experience, and art have been the tools for projecting laboratory apparatuses and procedures to large-scale operations.

Interest in photochemical processes has been motivated mainly because of their selectivity. This unique feature is due to the possibility of raising the energy of a molecule (or atom) to a specific level, by absorption of radiation in a well-defined range of frequencies. This can often be done without disturbing translational and rotational levels—an impossibility by thermal excitation. An illustration is the chlorination of the methyl group of toluene without noticeable reaction in the ring.

When combined with a low operating temperature, characteristic of most light-initiated reactions, the high selectivity is coupled with additional advantages. In fact, this selectivity of photoreactions offers very attractive possibilities. First, the photoprocess may make it feasible to attain a product that would be thermodynamically impossible to be obtained by thermal means. Thus, heating to obtain the required energy for an exothermic reaction may reduce the equilibrium conversion for the desired product to an insignificant level. Another possibility is that a reaction may occur photochemically in the liquid phase, while to obtain the required energy by thermal means would require gaseous conditions (or operation at much higher pressures). This introduces the disadvantages of lower production rate per unit volume, higher temperatures, and more expensive materials of construction. The possibility of reaching a given energy level with the proper wavelength of radiation has other advantages. If the energy is increased thermally, all the intermediate levels are transversed, and at some of these stages other reactions may occur. In other words, kinetic considerations, as well as thermodynamic ones, may indicate the convenience of the photochemical path over the thermal route.

Despite these advantages, photoreactors have been employed industrially only when the reactions are impossible or grossly uneconomical by thermal or conventional catalytic paths. Until recently the few existing commercial photoprocesses have been developed after extensive laboratory and pilot plant activities. Dimensional analysis, of value for conventional reactors, are of little assistance when applied to most photoprocesses. Frequently, the different dimensionless parameters are strongly coupled, generally through some type of concentration or geometric dimensions dependence. This concept will be treated in detail further ahead.

Other reasons are based on size limitations and general construction difficulties. The performance of a photoreactor is always coupled with the behavior of the radiation source—the lamp. The type of light and the configuration of the lamp-reactor system affect the reactor design so strongly that an independent consideration is not possible. With chain reactions, the potential for explosions, instability, wall deposits with associated reduction in yields, and severe inhibition are factors that have mitigated the photo route. The requirement for the use of glass or silica equipment imposes size limitations and breakage costs. Lifetime limits and control problems of the light source are unique operating problems. Finally, the price paid for selectivity in terms of energy can be high since the energy absorbed by the reaction is always a small part of the power consumption of the lamp.

As a conclusion we may say that selectivity with high yields and low operating temperatures seem to be the most attractive features of photoreactors. On the other hand, the requirement for using quartz or glass in some of their parts, poses the main construction and operating difficulties.

When dealing with the design of equipment for carrying out a photochemical reaction, several aspects should be considered. Some of them are common to the design of conventional thermal reactors, such as the kinetic characteristics of the reactions involved, the phases of the system, the necessity of temperature control, the requirements about the material of construction, etc. Besides, a certain number of important photochemical reactions share the common characteristic of presenting products and reactants with highly corrosive properties; a typical example is the chlorination of hydrocarbons where the presence of chlorine, hydrochloric acid and chlorinated solvents creates difficulties in the selection of materials for equipment and seals. In the case of multiphase, heterogeneous systems, the mixing pattern of the reactor is extremely important. Another important aspect in the design is the requirement of temperature control in strongly exothermic or endothermic reactions.

Other aspects arise specifically from the selection of the appropriate radiation source for the reaction under study, i.e., the spectral distribution of the emitted light and the geometrical configuration of the reactor-lamp arrangement. We may add that in some special cases the design can be improved by adding a reflecting device; its use complicates the analysis of the radiation field.

Last, but not least, we should consider the special characteristics of the absorption of radiation associated with *the optical thickness of the reacting media* (concentrations of reactants, products and inerts, their absorptivities, and the length of the optical path), a unique and distinct property of radiation induced processes. This particular combination of variables is responsible for the main difficulties encountered in the application of dimensionless analysis to photoreactor design and, at the same time, constitutes the most important difference between the behavior of photoreactors and other types of reaction processes.

TYPES OF REACTORS

Among a wide range of possible reactor-lamp-reflector configurations, those most widely studied in the literature are the annular reactor, the cylindrical reactor with elliptical reflector and the cylindrical reactor with parabolic reflector; they are briefly described below. Other types of configurations can be used in commercial applications; nevertheless, they arise from different combinations of the three mentioned above.

Annular Reactor

Annular photoreactors are an excellent example of what is one of the most practical types of photochemical reactors to be used for commercial purposes. The use of energy can be the maximum expected and, moreover, they represent the common case of a reaction vessel with a tubular lamp placed at its axis by means of an immersion well.

Figure 1 shows the main features of the system. The reacting stream is contained in the annular space that surrounds the lamp. If the reactor vessel is separated from the lamp, the annular space between them can be used to cool the lamp and/or control the operating temperature of the reactor. However, it must be noted that the requirement of light transmission introduces some limitations in the heat transfer possibilities because at least the inner reactor wall must be made of quartz or glass. Since light transparency is not required in the outer reactor wall, it provides much more

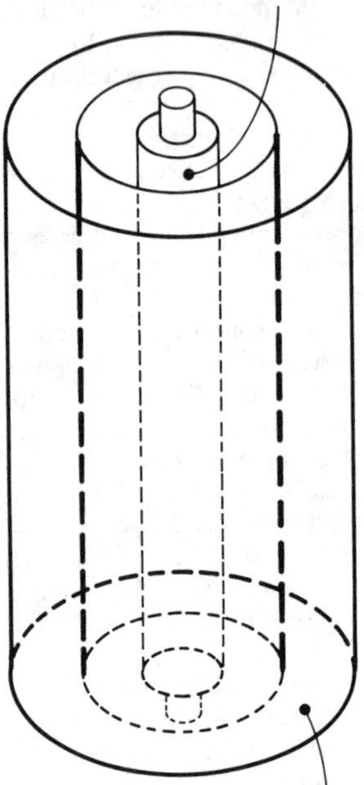

Figure 1. Annular reactor. (Thicker lines indicates the need for using transparent material of construction.)

freedom for design purposes, such as cooling, reflection of nonabsorbed light, and so on. Hence, if one desires to improve the absorption efficiency of the reactor, a reflector surface covering the outer reactor wall can be used.

In dealing with laboratory research, the annular photoreactor cannot be recommended for continuous-flow operations due to its unavoidably large cross-sectional area, which requires the handling of large volumetric flow rates. On the contrary, this characteristic makes it very appropriate for commercial-scale operations.

Cylindrical Reactor with Elliptical Reflector

This system consists of a reactor made with a cylindrical tube placed at one of the focii of a cylindrical reflector of elliptical cross section. A tubular radiation source is placed at the other focus. This particular arrangement is often called an elliptical photoreactor (Figure 2).

The possibility of using cylindrical tubular reactors with a small cross-sectional area together with the generally accepted (but only partially true) concept of the existence of a uniform irradiation from outside, has resulted in a rather extensive application of this reactor for laboratory and bench-scale research work.

On the other hand, since the incidence efficiency of this type of reactor—defined as the capacity of concentrating the energy within the reactor boundaries—is not very high, this is not an advisable device for commercial-scale operation unless other than energetic considerations compel its use.

Cylindrical Reactor with Parabolic Reflector

Another possibility of isolating the reaction system from the radiation source (which could also simplify the solution of the well-known problem of wall deposits, generally more severe at the radiation entrance wall) consists in the use of a cylindrical reactor irradiated from the bottom by

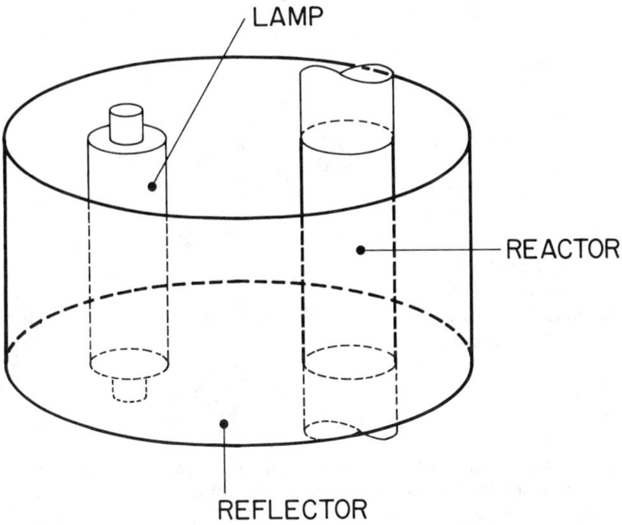

Figure 2. Cylindrical reactor with elliptical reflector. (Thicker lines indicates the need for using transparent material of construction.)

a tubular source located at the focal axis of a cylindrical reflector of parabolic cross-section (Figure 3). Since the cylindrical reactor may be a perfectly stirred tank reactor, this device is especially appropriate to carry out liquid or gas-liquid reactions where a vigorous stirring is required. This type of reactor is indicated for both laboratory and commercial scale work and can be used in batch, semibatch, or continuous operations. Problems of corrosion and sealing can be more easily handled in this system.

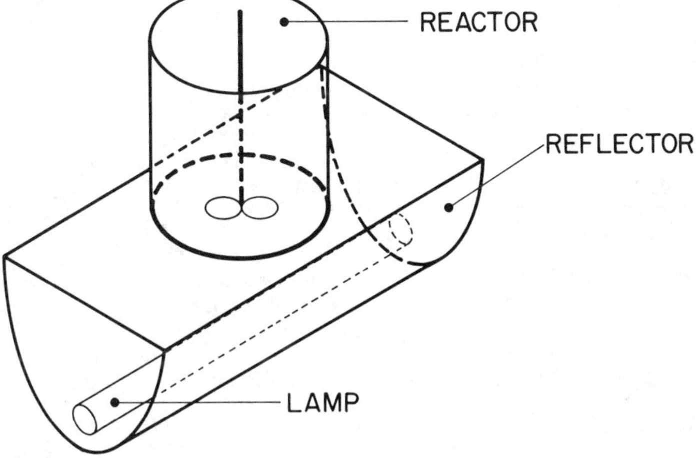

Figure 3. Cylindrical reactor irradiated from the bottom. (Thicker lines indicates the need for using transparent material of construction.)

PHOTOREACTOR DESIGN

In its most general way the problem can be stated as follows:

A. Required information.
  A.1. Several possible radiation sources with:
    A.1.1. A given energy consumption and output power.
    A.1.2. The spectral distribution of their output power.
    A.1.3. Their geometrical dimensions.
    A.1.4. Their operating conditions.
  A.2. Several possible reactors with:
    A.2.1. Their proposed shape.
    A.2.2. In some designs, the transmission characteristics of the wall through which radiation enters the reactor.
    A.2.3. The spectral distribution of this transmission.
    A.2.4. Some general and global information about ranges of operating conditions; for instance: pressure, temperature, required production, etc.,
  A.3. A reaction with:
    A.3.1. A kinetic sequence with the following characteristics:
      a. An initiation step which is activated by absorption of radiation.
      b. One or more "dark" reactions. From the industrial point of view some of the most important ones are special types of dark reactions which are recognized with the name of chain reactions. Starting from an atomic species or a free radical formed in the initiation step, they involve the following constituents:
        b.1 One or more propagation steps.
        b.2 One or more termination steps.
    A.3.2. The radiation absorption characteristics of reactants, inerts, and products.
    A.3.3. The primary quantum yield of the initiation step, i.e., how many atomic or free radical species are effectively produced for each absorbed photon by the desired reactant, in the first reaction of the kinetic sequence.
  A.4. Sometimes, different alternatives regarding a reflecting surface, with the following characteristics:
    A.4.1. Its shape.
    A.4.2. Its size (at least approximately).
    A.4.3. Its reflectivity.
    A.4.4. The spectral distribution of its reflectivity.
B. Answers to be provided by the design.
  B.1. Which is the best source-reactor-reflector arrangement?
  B.2. Which is the optimal size of the reactor?
  B.3. Which is the optimal feed composition?
  B.4. Which is the optimal value of the spectral distribution and overall radiation power output to convert reactants into the desired product?
  B.5. How much conversion can be achieved?
  B.6. How much selectivity can be obtained?

Here, we have pointed out those aspects that are different from conventional reactors. Certainly, other properties are needed such as transport and thermodynamic constants just as in any thermal reactor. In the same way, the final answer will have to include cooling or heating systems, stirring conditions, materials of construction and control requirements. Here, attention will be focused on those points which have no common counterpart with thermal or catalytic systems.

DESIGN EQUATIONS

In addition to momentum, mass, and thermal energy equations, an expression for the conservation of light energy (radiation equation) is necessary to establish the conversion in a photoreactor. The radiation equation is a unique feature of photoreactors, and the mass balance expressions are more complicated than for conventional reactors because of the radiation-dependent kinetics. The momentum expression is the same as for conventional reactors and need not be repeated.

Mass Conservation Equations

The rate of reaction term in the mass balance is a function of composition, temperature, pressure, and volumetric rate of energy absorption. Therefore, a series of differential equations is required covering the overlapping spectra for the emission of the lamp, the absorption of the reactants and reactor walls and reflection of reflecting systems. This overlapping establishes the limits λ_1 and λ_2 between which the reaction can occur. In some cases the absorption characteristics of products and inerts must be included.

A second problem arises because, for all but the most simple photoreactions, the kinetics cannot always be represented by an overall stoichiometric relationship. In order to describe the absorption of radiation, a detailed mechanism, or at least a simplified sequence of steps, is needed to describe the rate. This means that, in general, a mass balance including diffusion terms may be needed for each independent chemical species. Even with a set of differential mass balances to account for the spectral distribution of the source-absorbent system and the various species, the description is not complete if wall reactions are significant.

For constant transport properties, monochromatic light, and incompressible flow, the mass balance may be written:

$$\frac{\partial C_i}{\partial t} = -v_z \underset{\sim}{\nabla} C_i + (D_i + D_i^{(t)}) \underset{\sim}{\nabla}^2 C_i + \Omega_i^* \tag{1}$$

where the molecular and turbulent contributions to the diffusivity are assumed to be additive and Ω_i^* is the local rate of production of species i.

Thermal Energy Equation

Radiation will be used to describe that part of the energy absorbed that causes reaction. The term thermal energy will denote all other forms. The increase in internal energy due to radiation and the accompanying temperature rise are, in most cases, the least significant effects of the light. Hence, the temperature in the reactor can be described by a thermal energy balance. This procedure permits the radiation balance, necessary even for isothermal operation, to be treated separately.

The thermal energy balance may be written for any reactor geometry in vector form as follows:

$$\frac{\partial(\rho U)}{\partial t} = -\sum_i \underset{\sim}{\nabla} \cdot (\text{energy flux}) - (\Delta H)\Omega^* \tag{2}$$

where ΔH is the heat of reaction and U the internal energy. The summation would include all forms of energy transfer.

Due to the energetic features of photochemical reactions (very low and sometimes null "equivalent" activation energy for the global reaction), it is very frequent to find that the reaction behavior can be accurately described with the mass balance and the energy balance reduced exclusively to radiation. In any event, even for the simplest case, the mass and radiation balances are normally coupled through the concentrations of the radiation-absorbing species.

However, in some instances, the description of reactor behavior for design purposes, will necessarily need the use of the complete energy balance, especially if the system is highly exothermic. In this case, in order to maintain the temperature of the reactor within tolerable limits, the energy produced by the reaction should be removed. If this thermal effect is not taken into account, particularly in complex reactions of the chain type, secondary and other side reactions (many of them thermally activated) will produce the loss of selectivity which is precisely one of the most attractive features of photochemical processes. From the operating temperature point of view, the material of construction will also impose restrictions that will have to be taken care of through a heat balance regardless of the fact that the overall "apparent" activation energy of a photochemical reaction may be very low.

Rate of Reaction

When expressing the rate of a photochemical reaction it is necessary to make the distinction between dark and radiation activated steps. To treat the dark reactions one uses the same methodology as for conventional reactors; the main hindrance appears when evaluating the rate of the initiation step. The existence of this very particular step constitutes the main kinetic difference between thermal and radiation activated reactions.

It is known that the rate of a radiation activated step is proportional to the absorbed, useful energy through a property that has been defined as the local volumetric rate of energy absorption (LVREA). The LVREA (e^a) expresses the amount of photons (in units of energy) that are absorbed per unit time and unit reaction volume. The usefulness of the energy absorbed is accounted for by the proper choice of the frequency ranges of radiation that are incorporated in the evaluation of e^a. This property depends on the radiation field existing in the reaction space, hence, we need to know the radiation field within the photoreactor. The radiant energy distribution is not uniform in space due to several causes, among them the attenuation produced by the species absorption is always present. Additional phenomena, usually also important, are the physical properties and geometrical characteristics of the lamp-reactor system. Consequently, the initiation reaction will be spatially dependent, even in the case of absence of concentration gradients. This lack of homogeneity in the radiation field is intrinsically irreducible in practical photochemical reactors.

The evaluation of the LVREA (Figure 4) is performed stating first a balance of radiant energy at steady state for a homogeneous control volume [1]. For simplicity a non-emitting medium is

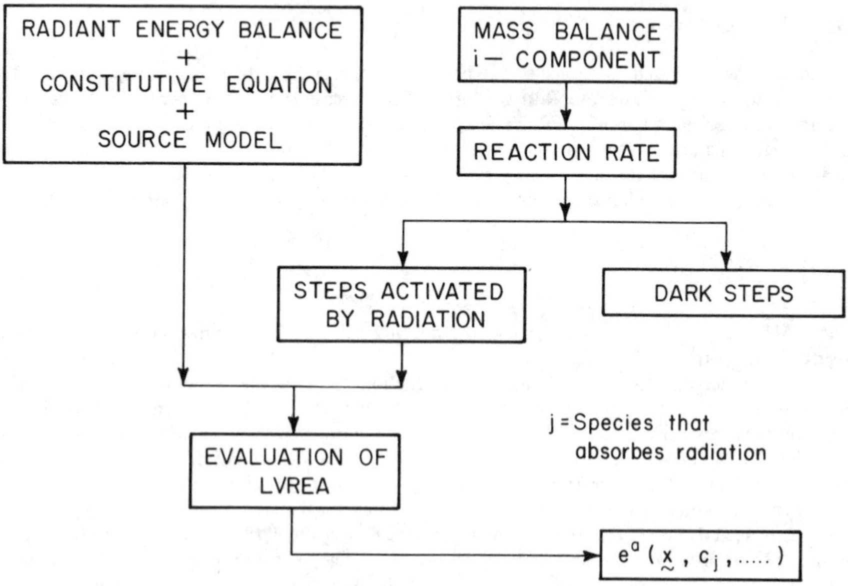

Figure 4. Evaluation of local volumetric rate of energy absorption. (Adapted from Ref. [1].)

generally assumed. Afterwards, it is necessary to incorporate a radiation source model and a constitutive equation (for a homogeneous medium, Lambert's equation for example) in the absorption term. The LVREA is generally a function of the spatial variables, of the concentration of the absorbing species and other physico-chemical parameters. If species (i), which is being considered in the mass balance, is a radiation absorbing species ($i \equiv j$), a coupling between the LVREA and the corresponding mass conservation equation will take place. At the same time, the concentration of the reacting species (j) under consideration, forms part of an integral expression accounting for the radiation attenuation by absorption. Thus, the general problem of modelling a homogeneous photoreactor presents a mathematical problem of integro-differential nature.

However, it is possible to distinguish two cases:

1. Photosensitized reactions. The absorbing species acts as an energy transfer agent, reacts and after a cycle is restored. Its original concentration does not change. If the other reacting species do not absorb light, the radiation field is independent of the extent of the reaction. We can say that "there is no coupling between the attenuation of radiation (caused by absorption) and the extent of the reaction."
2. Non-photosensitized reactions. The absorbing species reacts and its concentration changes with the extent of the reaction. Then the attenuation effects in the radiation field are related to the distribution of concentration in space. Two different situations may occur:
   a. A very well stirred reactor, where the attenuation process is, at most, a function of time.
   b. A reactor with space dependent concentrations, where the problem of the coupling "attenuation of radiation-extent of the reaction" arises.

This coupling is very complicated as shown in Figure 5. The LVREA is not only a point function of position ($e^a = e^a[\underset{\sim}{x}_I, C_{j,I}, \text{etc.}]$), but also a *functional* of all the optical properties of the space through which every ray of radiation reaching point I has traveled. The consequence of this is that there exists a very close association between the extent of the reaction in the whole reactor (which controls the reactant and product absorbing properties) and the radiation absorption rate at each point. Thus, to know the reaction rate at each point I we must know the value of $|\underset{\sim}{q}_\nu|$ at the point; but the value of $|\underset{\sim}{q}_\nu|$ at each point depends on the concentration of the absorbing species along the trajectory of every ray reaching point I from the whole space of reaction. Simultaneously, in order to know the concentration of the absorbing species at each point in the space of reaction we must have the reaction extent at every point (or what is the same, the reaction rate at every point).

It is clear that in any event, be it the case of a radiation field independent of the extent of the reaction (simplest case) or that of a strong coupling between changes in concentration and absorption of radiation, the field of radiant energy must be known. This is also the case, even if one would like to use approximate methods for the design of the reactor. Thus, a key point in the design of a photochemical reactor is the correct formulation of a radiation balance. Once the fundamentals of this aspect are established we will come back to the rate of reaction.

THE RADIATION FIELD*

The problem of incorporating a rigorous treatment of the radiation field has been described in early publications by Cassano and co-workers [2–6]. The most compact way of describing the problem can be found in the work by De Bernardez et al. [6] and it is the one that will be used here.

Foundation of the Analysis

Among the properties of the radiation field defined for a given bundle of rays, one has a distinct physical meaning. This is the specific intensity, which must not be confused with the radiation flux density or its vector (Table 1). The latter is a vector quantity related to the flow rate of energy and

* This section has been partially reprinted from Ref. [6], p. 847–875, by courtesy of Marcel Dekker, Inc.

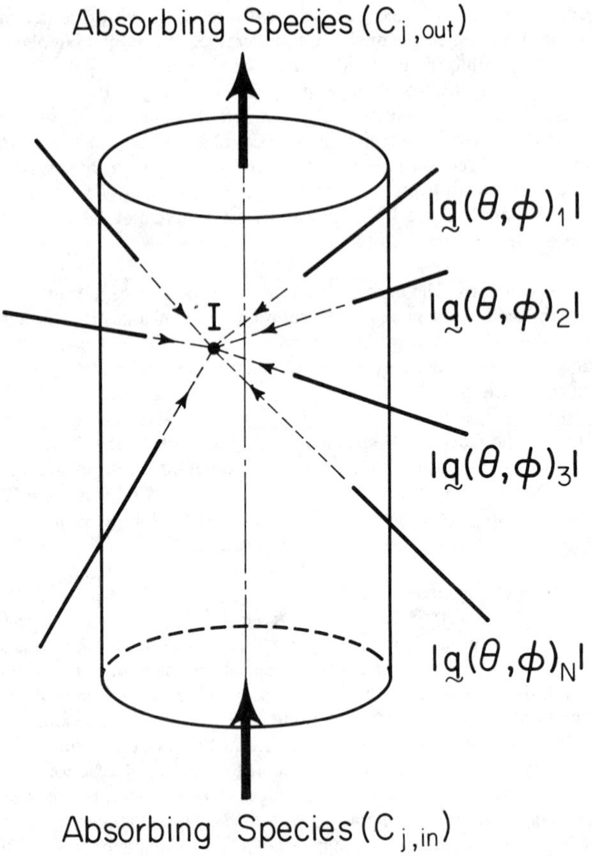

Figure 5. Schematic representation of the coupling "attenuation of radiation-extent of reaction" for the evaluation of e^a at point I. (Adapted from Ref. [5].)

Table 1
Definitions of Radiation Properties*

Property	Symbol	Dimensions
Intensity	I	Unit derived from the way in which the dimensions of the emitting system (lamp) are modelled
Energy flow rate	E	Energy per unit time
Energy flux density vector	$\underset{\sim}{q}$	Energy per unit time and unit area
Energy flux density	$q = \underset{\sim}{q} \cdot \underset{\sim}{n}$	Energy per unit time and unit area
Energy density	e	Energy per unit volume
Volumetric rate of energy absorption	e^a	Energy per unit time and unit volume

* *Adapted from Ref. 5*

the normal area. On the other hand, the specific intensity does not follow the rules of vectorial algebra and is a point function. In a diactinic medium, and for each pencil of radiation, it must be constant throughout the propagation path of the rays and hence independent of distance. Under these conditions, the specific intensity changes only in absorbing and/or nonhomogeneous media (due to absorption, scattering, reflections, and refractions) according to the physical characteristics of the substance in which the rays travel. This is not true for the radiation flux density which, in general, may change for those and other reasons, i.e., it may change not only due to the physical properties of the medium of propagation but also because of the geometry of the system, and hence with distance. Only when the cross-sectional area of the bundle is constant (e.g., for collimated beams of radiation) the numerical values of the specific intensity and the flux density are the same.

The only particular requirement to achieve complete consistency in the theory is to accept that the intensity will change its definition according to the dimensions with which the lamp emission of energy is modelled. With this restriction in mind, all other properties such as energy flow rate, energy flux density vector, energy flux density, and energy density follow from first principles.

The radiation field will be treated in the following sequence: definitions, the Lambert's equation, the radiation balance and finally the evaluation of the LVREA. But first, our approach will require a certain degree of clarification. Our goal is to obtain the value of the LVREA in terms of the properties of the reacting medium and those corresponding to the source of energy (lamp). Hence, the radiation source is part of the analysis. (Here, we will restrict our scope to tubular sources of energy because they are the most widely used in practical applications.) When the energy provided by the lamp is incorporated into the model of the reaction and the reactor, different proposals can be used [7, 8]. Conceptual approaches may be classified into two well-defined groups: (a) those that assume a given radiation distribution in the vicinity of the reactor (*incidence models*); and (b) those that start from a proposal of a model for the source (*emission models*). There is no way of using incidence models without experimentally adjustable parameters. Since we are looking for an a priori design of photoreactors, attention will only be paid to the emission models.

Definitions

The concepts introduced here are based on well-accepted definitions in the areas of radiation engineering and radiation gas dynamics. However, we shall point out some differences between the conventional thermal applications of radiation (e.g., furnaces) and those that involve the use of visible, ultraviolet, and even shorter wavelength radiations.

Specific Intensity

Radiation engineering generally studies the energy exchange between surfaces (Figure 6). To characterize the amount of energy departing from a surface, the concept of specific intensity of radiation is used. The specific intensity of radiation is defined as the amount of energy in the frequency range between ν and $\nu + d\nu$, leaving a surface per unit area normal to the pencil of rays, per unit solid angle, and unit time. From now on we will simplify our notation and call energy in the frequency interval between ν and $\nu + d\nu$ energy of frequency ν. To illustrate the rise of the specific intensity concept, let $d\psi_\nu$ be the radiant energy of frequency ν per unit time and unit area, leaving a given surface dA_e in the direction θ_e and contained within a solid angle $d\omega_e$, then

$$I_\nu = \frac{d\psi_\nu}{d\omega_e \, f(\theta, \phi)} \tag{3}$$

where $f(\theta,\phi)$ takes into account the directional characteristics of the emission (isotropic, diffuse, etc.). We must extend this concept to photoreactor engineering, where the energy exchange may involve not only surfaces but volumes as well.

When the radiation source is a fluorescent lamp, only the external surface of the lamp participates in the emission process. Hence the energy exchange phenomenon involves two surfaces, one for

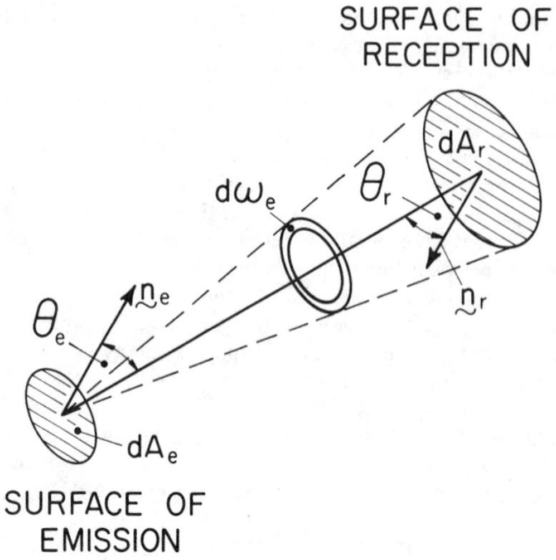

Figure 6. Geometric representation of the emission and reception of radiation energy. (Adapted from Ref. [6].)

emission and the other for reception (Figure 6). On the other hand, if the radiation source is a nonfluorescent arc lamp, the emission is voluminal (i.e., the entire volume of the lamp participates in the emission process). In this case (Figure 7) the energy exchange phenomenon involves an emitting volume (dV_e) and a receiving surface (dA_r). This model is called the extense source with voluminal emission model (ESVE model) whereas the one described by Figure 6 has been named the extense source with superficial emission model (ESSE model).

In spite of the fact that radiation sources have finite spatial dimensions, many authors have used a third model, which considers the lamp as a line (Figure 8). This model is known as the line source

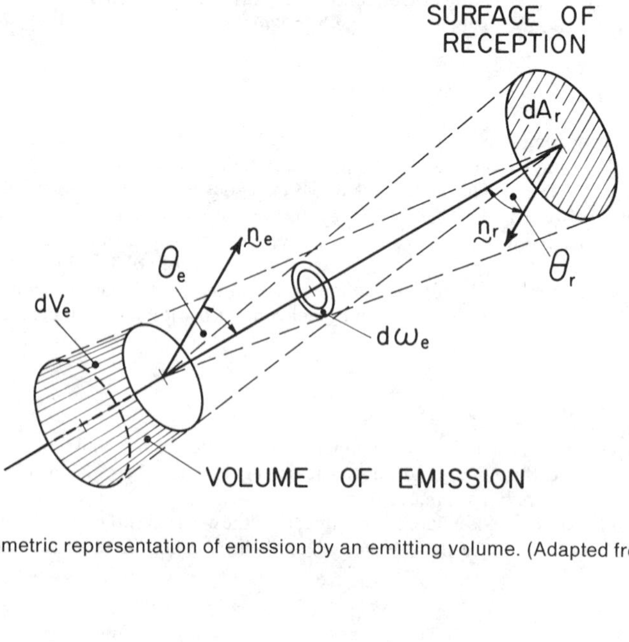

Figure 7. Geometric representation of emission by an emitting volume. (Adapted from Ref. [6].)

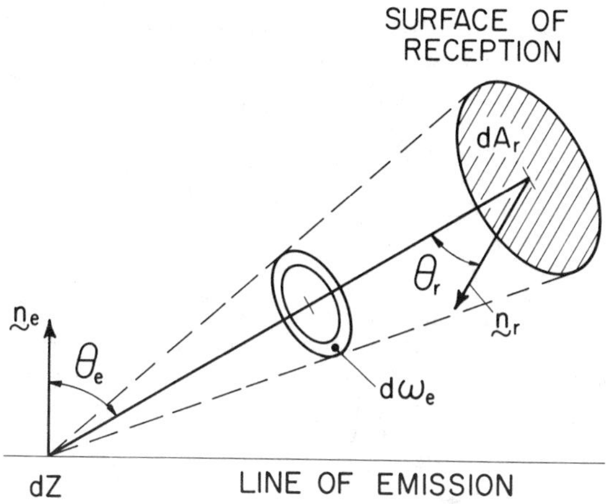

Figure 8. Geometric representation of emission by a line formed by "point" emitters (Adapted from Ref. [6].)

with spherical emission model (LSSE). As we shall see later, the LSSE model can be rigorously used in some special—but very important—reactor designs.

When formulating the equations we make the following assumptions:

1. The emitters of the radiation source are uniformly distributed inside its extension (be it a volume, a surface, or a line).
2. Any elementary extension of the source emits per unit time, at any frequency, an amount of energy proportional to its extension.
3. The emission characteristics are constant along the z-direction. (This assumption does not imply a constant radiation field in the z-direction.)

Maintaining the expression (3) for the definition of I_ν, we may introduce the differences in the energy exchange process in the expression for $d\psi_\nu$. Let us use a generic expression for an "energy flux" ($d\Psi_\nu$) that includes the possibility of emission by either lines, surfaces, or volumes. The generic extent of the lamp will be indicated by $d\Gamma_e$, which may have dimensions of length, area, or volume depending on the case. Then:

$$d\Psi_\nu = \frac{dE_\nu}{d\Gamma_e} \tag{4}$$

where $d\Psi_\nu$ is the amount of energy of frequency ν per unit time that leaves an infinitesimal extent of the lamp, characterized by $d\Gamma_e$. This distinction in the definition of the specific intensity of radiation allows us to achieve complete consistency in a unified theory. Considering Equation 4, the equation for I_ν becomes

$$I_\nu = \frac{dE_\nu}{d\omega_e f(\theta, \phi) d\Gamma_e} \tag{5}$$

In the following analysis we consider three special cases:

1. When the emission is independent of the direction, it is called *isotropic* emission; then $f(\theta, \phi) = 1$.
2. When the emission is *diffuse*, it follows what is known as the "cosine law"; then $f(\theta, \phi) = \cos \theta_e$.
3. When the directional characteristics of the emission are different from cases 1 and 2, the model needs the specification of the function $f(\theta, \phi)$.

From now on we shall consider the first two cases, isotropic and diffuse emission. To simplify the treatment of the equations, we can reduce the two emission cases into a unique expression:

$$I'_\nu = \frac{dE_\nu}{d\omega_e \, d\Gamma_e} \tag{6}$$

For isotropic emission $I'_\nu = I_\nu$. In the case of diffuse emission,

$$I'_\nu = I_\nu \cos \theta_e \tag{7}$$

However, since the product $I_\nu \cos \theta_e$ is independent of direction, in both cases I'_ν is always isotropic. The distinction between the two types of emission will be introduced in the following derivations only when necessary. Table 2 summarizes the final expressions of I_ν for each emission model.

Finally, for polychromatic sources, the radiation intensity is obtained integrating the specific intensity over the whole frequency range, as follows:

$$I = \int_{\nu=0}^{\nu=\infty} I_\nu \, d\nu \tag{8}$$

Specific Energy Flux Density Vector

The amount of energy of frequency ν passing through a surface of extent dA_r, per unit time may be expressed as:

$$dE_\nu = dA_r \underset{\sim}{n} \cdot d\underset{\sim}{q}_\nu \tag{9}$$

where $d\underset{\sim}{q}_\nu$ is the specific energy flux density vector (Figures 6–8). We do not need to make a distinction between the definition of $d\underset{\sim}{q}_\nu$ for each model because it is a property related to the receiving surface. From Equation 9 it follows that

$$dE_\nu = dA_r \cos \theta_r |d\underset{\sim}{q}_\nu| \tag{10}$$

where $|d\underset{\sim}{q}_\nu|$ is the modulus of the specific energy flux density vector.

The relationship between the specific intensity and the modulus of the specific energy flux density vector can be derived relating Equations 6 and 10:

$$I'_\nu = \frac{\rho^2 |d\underset{\sim}{q}_\nu|}{d\Gamma_e} \tag{11}$$

where we used the geometrical relationship

$$d\omega_e = \frac{dA_r \cos \theta_r}{\rho^2} \tag{12}$$

In spite of the fact that $|d\underset{\sim}{q}_\nu|$ and I_ν have different physical meanings, they are often confused in the photoreactor engineering literature. In a diactinic medium while I'_ν remains constant, Equation 11 shows that the modulus of the specific energy flux density vector changes with distance. Table 2 summarizes the expressions of Equation 11 for each emission model.

Lambert's Equation

The second concept that must be applied in the analysis of a photoreactor (strictly speaking only rigorously valid for homogeneous media) is related to the absorption of radiation.

Table 2
Final Equations for the Emission Models*

Model	$d\Gamma_e$	Γ_e	$I'_\nu = \frac{dE_\nu}{d\omega_e\, d\Gamma_e}$	$\lvert d\underset{\sim}{q}_\nu \rvert$	Isotropic Emission e_ν^a	Isotropic Emission κ_ν	Diffuse Emission e_ν^a	Diffuse Emission κ_ν
LSSE	dz	L_L	$\frac{\rho^2\, dE_\nu}{dA_r \cos\theta_r\, dz}$	$\frac{I'_\nu\, dz}{\rho^2}$	$\kappa_\nu \mu_\nu \int_0^{L_L} \frac{dz}{\rho^2} \times \exp\left(-\int_{\rho_0^*}^{\rho^*} \mu_\nu\, d\rho'\right)$	$\frac{E_{L,\nu}}{4\pi L_L}$	$\kappa_\nu \mu_\nu \int_0^{L_L} \frac{\sin\theta\, dz}{\rho^2} \times \exp\left(-\int_{\rho_0^*}^{\rho^*} \mu_\nu\, d\rho'\right)$	$\frac{E_{L,\nu}}{\pi L_L}$
ESSE	$dA_e = \rho^2\, d\omega_r$	$2\pi r_L L_L$	$\frac{\rho^2\, dE_\nu}{dA_r \cos\theta_r\, dA_e}$	$\frac{I'_\nu\, dA_e}{\rho^2} = I'_\nu\, d\omega_r$	$\kappa_\nu \mu_\nu \int_\phi \int_\theta \sin\theta \times \exp\left(-\int_{\rho_0^*}^{\rho^*} \mu_\nu\, d\rho'\right) d\theta\, d\phi$	$\frac{E_{L,\nu}}{8\pi^2 r_L L_L}$	$\kappa_\nu \mu_\nu \int_\phi \int_\theta \sin^2\theta \cos\phi \times \exp\left(-\int_{\rho_0^*}^{\rho^*} \mu_\nu\, d\rho'\right) d\theta\, d\phi$	$\frac{E_{L,\nu}}{2\pi^2 r_L L_L}$
ESVE	$dV_e = \rho^2\, d\omega_r\, d\rho$	$\pi r_L^2 L_L$	$\frac{\rho^2\, dE_\nu}{dA_r \cos\theta_r\, dV_e}$	$\frac{I'_\nu\, dV_e}{\rho^2} = I'_\nu\, d\omega_r\, d\rho$	$\kappa_\nu \mu_\nu \int_\phi \int_\theta \int_\rho \sin\theta \times \exp\left(-\int_{\rho_0^*}^{\rho^*} \mu_\nu\, d\rho'\right) d\rho\, d\theta\, d\phi$	$\frac{E_{L,\nu}}{4\pi^2 r_L^2 L_L}$	$\kappa_\nu \mu_\nu \int_\phi \int_\theta \int_\rho \sin^2\theta \cos\phi \times \exp\left(-\int_{\rho_0^*}^{\rho^*} \mu_\nu\, d\rho'\right) d\rho\, d\theta\, d\phi$	$\frac{E_{L,\nu}}{\pi^2 r_L^2 L_L}$

* *Adapted from Ref. 6*

In general this problem has been solved using a "law" (Lambert's "law"). As it is usually misused, the term "law" has been applied here to what is properly one form of a constitutive equation used to define an attenuation coefficient μ_ν. It is important to investigate the physical and mathematical nature of this "law" of absorption. This will be done here because it must not be confused with a radiation balance, since its use as such is only valid for special cases. The "law" was postulated by Lambert, and it can be derived from the molecular theory. It states that, for an absorbing medium, the contribution of absorption to the gradient of the specific intensity is

$$\left.\frac{dI_\nu}{d\rho}\right|^{a} = -\mu_\nu I_\nu \tag{13}$$

Equation 13 is valid for any form of emission with the proper use of the required definition for I_ν. The radiation conservation equation reduces to Equation 13 at steady-state conditions and for non-emitting and homogenous media. This is so because Lambert's "law" was used in its derivation to formulate the absorption process in the balance of photons. Using index notation, the left side of Equation 13 can be written as:

$$\frac{dI_\nu}{d\rho} = \frac{\partial I_\nu}{\partial x_i}\frac{dx_i}{d\rho} = \frac{\partial I_\nu}{\partial x_i}\cos\alpha_i \tag{14}$$

where $\cos\alpha_i$ are direction cosines of the ray with respect to a Cartesian orthogonal coordinate system x_i (i.e. x, y, z: Figure 9). It is clear that the left-hand side is the directional derivative of I_ν, i.e. the component of the gradient of the scalar function I_ν along the direction of propagation of the ray. The right side of Equation 14 shows the three components of this gradient. In a more general way, if $\underset{\sim}{l}$ is a unit vector in the direction of each ray, with components $\cos\alpha_i$, Equation 13 can be written

$$\underset{\sim}{l}\cdot\underset{\sim}{\nabla} I_\nu = -\mu_\nu I_\nu \tag{15}$$

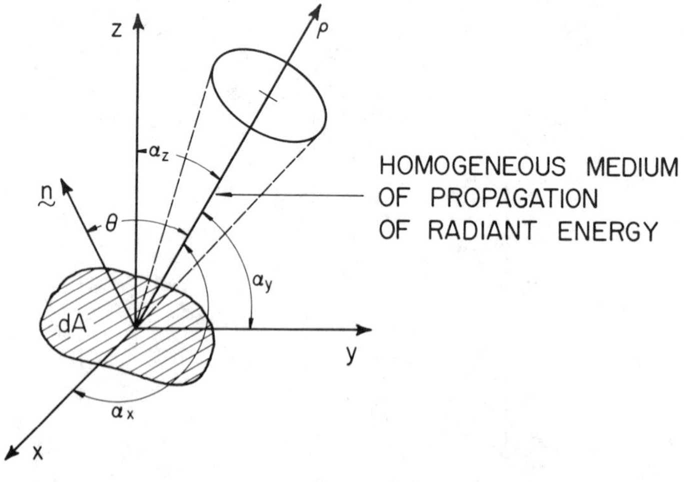

Figure 9. Absorption in homogeneous media. (Adapted from Ref. [5].)

This is the only possible generalization of the absorption constitutive equation which allows it to be used in several coordinate systems. This means that the so-called Lambert's "law" gives the variation of the specific intensity due to absorption along its direction of propagation. In other words, the "law" of absorption is a constitutive equation for homogenous absorbing media, which relates the gradient of the specific intensity to the molecular properties of the space through which the ray travels (e.g. the absorption coefficient and molecular density or, equivalently, the attenuation coefficient μ_v). Note that since $f(\theta, \phi)$ is independent of distance ρ, Equation 15 is also valid for I'_v.

Radiation Balance

We shall state the steady-state radiation balance for a nonemitting, non-dispersing homogeneous control volume (Figure 10). The difference between the energy flux density of frequency v impinging on dA_r at position ρ with direction (θ, ϕ) and the energy flux density of frequency v leaving the fixed control volume with the same direction, at position $\rho + d\rho$, is due to the absorption of radiation:

$$dE_v|_\rho - dE_v|_{\rho + d\rho} = d_\rho E_v^a \tag{16}$$

where in the right side the subscript ρ indicates differentiation with respect to ρ.

Introducing Equations 10 and 12 into Equation 16, we have

$$d_\rho E_v^a = -d\omega_e\, d_\rho[\rho^2 |d\underset{\sim}{q}_v|] \tag{17}$$

Combining Equations 17 and 11 yields

$$d_\rho E_v^a = -d\omega_e\, d_\rho[I'_v\, d\Gamma_e] \tag{18}$$

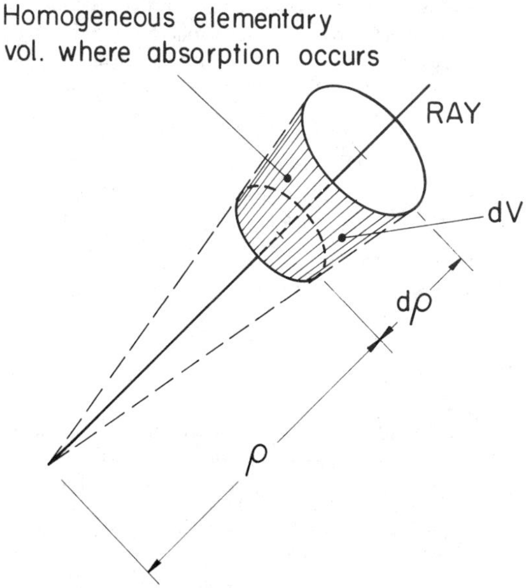

Figure 10. Radiation balance in an homogeneous elementary absorbing volume. (Adapted from Ref. [6].)

Substituting the constitutive Equation 13 into Equation 18 it gives us

$$d_\rho E_v^a = d\omega_e\, I'_v \mu_v d_\rho\, d\Gamma_e \tag{19}$$

Finally, considering Equation 11, 17, and 19, the steady-state radiation balance becomes

$$\frac{1}{\rho^2}\frac{d}{d\rho}(\rho^2 |d\underset{\sim}{q}_v|) = -\mu_v |d\underset{\sim}{q}_v| \tag{20}$$

Volumetric Rate of Energy Absorption

As mentioned earlier, the rate of the activation step is proportional to the LVREA. This property is defined as follows:

$$de_v^a = \frac{dE_v^a}{dV_r} \tag{21}$$

Combining Equation 17 with Equation 21 and considering that $dV_r = \rho^2\, d\omega_e\, d\rho$, we obtain

$$de_v^a = -\frac{1}{\rho^2}\frac{d}{d\rho}(\rho^2 |d\underset{\sim}{q}_v|) \tag{22}$$

Finally, introducing the radiation balance (Equation 20) into Equation 22, we have

$$de_v^a = \mu_v |d\underset{\sim}{q}_v| \tag{23}$$

To evaluate de_v^a we need to know $|d\underset{\sim}{q}_v|$. To do so, we will introduce the source of energy (the lamp) into the radiation balance. Figure 11 shows a typical situation. A ray comes out of the lamp in every direction. (Four of them, R_1, R_2, R_3, and R_4 are shown in the figure.) The ray enters the reactor (where absorption occurs) after travelling through a transparent space. Energy reaches the reactor wall (at points W_1, W_2, W_3, and W_4 for example) with a value of the modulus of the radiation energy density vector that can be designated by $|d\underset{\sim}{q}_v|_0$. For a generic point $W(\rho_0, \theta, \phi)$ this is the value of $|\underset{\sim}{q}_v|$ before absorption by the reactor wall and the reacting medium occurs. Since we are interested in the value of $|\underset{\sim}{q}_v|$ at a point inside the reactor like $I(\rho^*, \theta, \phi)$ for example, we need to relate the energy produced by the lamp $E_{L,v}$ with the value of $|d\underset{\sim}{q}_v|_0$, and to know the way to calculate $|d\underset{\sim}{q}_v|$ at point I from its value at point W (i.e. $|d\underset{\sim}{q}_v|_0$). From the radiation balance and integrating inside the reacting space (where the absorption of the radiation process occurs), we obtain (Figure 11)

$$\rho^2 |d\underset{\sim}{q}_v| = \rho_0^2 |d\underset{\sim}{q}_v|_0 \exp\left[-\int_{\rho_0^*(\theta,\phi)}^{\rho^*(\theta,\phi)} \mu_v\, d\rho'\right] \tag{24}$$

In Equation 24, $|d\underset{\sim}{q}_v|_0$ is precisely the modulus of the specific energy flux density vector for a point $W(\rho^*, \theta, \phi)$ at the surface of entrance of radiation to the reactor volume. To evaluate it, assuming no absorption between the source (points such as S_1, S_2, S_3 and S_4 for example) and the reactor wall (points such as W_1, W_2, W_3 and W_4), because this space is transparent to radiation in the wavelength of interest, we use the equations valid for diactinic media, that is,

$$\rho^2 |d\underset{\sim}{q}_v| = I'_{v,0}\, d\Gamma_e \tag{25}$$

Because I'_v remains constant in a diactinic medium, Equation 25 may be written

$$\rho_0^2 |d\underset{\sim}{q}_v|_0 = I'_{v,0}\, d\Gamma_e \tag{26}$$

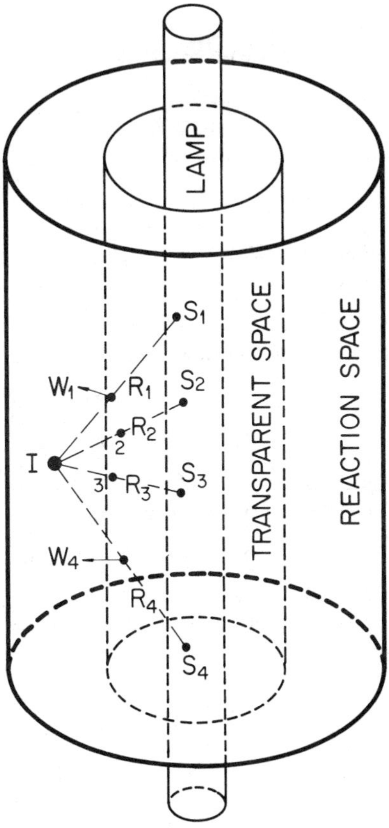

Figure 11. Attenuation process.

Combining Equations 23, 24, and 26, we obtain

$$de_\nu^a = \mu_\nu \frac{I'_{\nu,0}}{\rho^2} \exp\left[-\int_{\rho_0^*(\theta,\phi)}^{\rho^*} \mu_\nu \, d\rho' \right] d\Gamma_e \tag{27}$$

Finally the local volumetric rate of energy absorption at frequency ν is obtained by integrating Equation 27:

$$e_\nu^a = \mu_\nu \int_{\Gamma_e} \frac{I'_{\nu,0}}{\rho^2} \exp\left[-\int_{\rho_0^*(\theta,\phi)}^{\rho^*} \mu_\nu \, d\rho' \right] d\Gamma_e \tag{28}$$

In Equation 28 $I_{\nu,0}$ must be related to the power output of the radiation source. From Equation 6 we have

$$dE_\nu = I'_{\nu,0} \, d\omega_e \, d\Gamma_e \tag{29}$$

for a diactinic medium. Integrating Equation 29 for the whole range of solid angles and for the whole extension of the emission source, we obtain the lamp power output at frequency ν

$$E_{L,\nu} = \int_{\omega_e} \int_{\Gamma_e} I'_{\nu,0} \, d\omega_e \, d\Gamma_e \tag{30}$$

where we have made the following assumptions:

1. In the case of voluminal emission, each elementary volume is transparent to the emission of its surroundings.
2. In the case of three-dimensional emission sources, they are supposed to be bounded by mathematical surfaces of zero thickness. Thus, any bundle of radiation coming out of the lamp does not change its intensity or direction when it crosses this boundary.

To perform the integration in Equation 30, we may distinguish the two emission cases:

1. Isotropic emission

Here $I'_{\nu,0} = I_{\nu,0}$ which is constant (independent of distance). Then Equation 30 becomes

$$E_{L,\nu} = I'_{\nu,0} 4\pi \Gamma_e^* \tag{31}$$

where the expression of Γ^* for each emission model is condensed in Table 2. Finally, we have

$$e_\nu^a = \frac{\mu_\nu E_{L,\nu}}{4\pi \Gamma_e^*} \int_{\Gamma_e} \frac{1}{\rho^2} \exp\left[-\int_{\rho_0^*}^{\rho^*} \mu_\nu \, d\rho' \right] d\Gamma_e \tag{32}$$

2. Diffuse emission

In Equation 30 we must replace $I'_{\nu,0}$ by $I_{\nu,0} \cos \theta_e$ and then perform the integration:

$$E_{L,\nu} = I_{\nu,0} \int_{\omega_e} \cos \theta_e \, d\omega_e \int_{\Gamma_e} d\Gamma_e \tag{33}$$

where $I_{\nu,0}$ is constant (independent of distance). Here, since the intensity of radiation follows the cosine law, the emission solid angle is 2π. Then:

$$E_{L,\nu} = I_{\phi,0} \pi \Gamma_e^* \tag{34}$$

Finally, we have

$$I'_{\nu,0} = I_{\nu,0} \cos \theta_e = \frac{E_{L,\nu}}{\pi \Gamma_e^*} \cos \theta_e \tag{35}$$

and

$$e_\nu^a = \frac{\mu_\nu E_{L,\nu}}{\pi \Gamma_e^*} \int_{\Gamma_e} \frac{\cos \theta_e}{\rho^2} \exp\left[-\int_{\rho_0^*}^{\rho^*} \mu_\nu \, d\rho' \right] d\Gamma_e \tag{36}$$

The final expressions of e^a valid for diffuse emission for each model can be found in Table 2, where $\cos \theta_e$ has been replaced by the appropriate expression for each model.

Equations 32 and 36 are valid for monochromatic light. If we deal with polychromatic radiation, these expressions must be integrated over the entire frequency spectrum, that is,

$$e^a = \int_{\nu=0}^{\nu=\infty} e_\nu^a \, d\nu \tag{37}$$

Table 2 illustrates that for each emission model, the LVREA is a function of the spatial variables, of the physical properties and geometrical characteristics of the lamp-reactor system, and of some physicochemical properties of the reacting mixture. The LVREA dependence on the geometrical characteristics of the lamp-reactor system will be studied in detail further ahead, and it comes from the limits of integration of the LVREA expression for each emission model. The physical properties of the lamp are represented by the parameter κ_ν in the LVREA equations; both are described in Table 2 for each model. Finally, the attenuation coefficient μ_ν involves the dependence on the physicochemical properties of the reacting system.

The Linear Source with Emission in Parallel Planes Model (LSPP model)

This model was first proposed by Harris and Dranoff [9], but here we are very closely following Cassano et al.'s [5] derivation.

As shown in Figure 12 this case is very ideal. The bundle of rays has the shape of a wedge of height dz and an angle of divergence dϕ measured on a plane normal to the z-axis. The specific intensity must be written as:

$$I'_\nu \, d\nu = \frac{dE_\nu}{d\phi \, dz} \tag{38}$$

We know that

$$|d\underset{\sim}{q}_\nu| = \frac{dE_\nu}{dA_r \cos\theta_r} \tag{39}$$

Hence

$$|d\underset{\sim}{q}_\nu| = \frac{I'_\nu \, d\nu}{r} \tag{40}$$

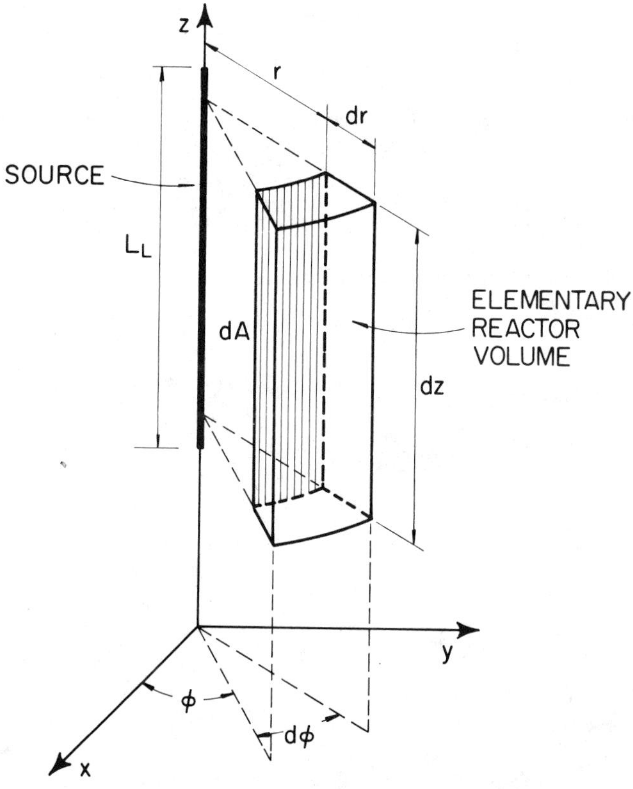

Figure 12. Geometric representation of the LSPP model. (Adapted from Ref. [2].)

and

$$dE = \int_{\nu=0}^{\nu=\infty} dE_\nu = \left(\int_{\nu=0}^{\nu=\infty} I'_\nu \, d\nu \right) d\phi \, dz = I' \, d\phi \, dz \tag{41}$$

It is clear that this model (very attractive because of its simplicity) has very little physical meaning since it requires that every point of the source emits radiation in planes perpendicular to the lamp axis (contradicting the spherical emission of a point source), with zero probability of emission in directions other than those contained in such planes.

Performing a radiation balance in an absorbing medium, at steady-state conditions and for a homogeneous non-emitting control volume, we have

$$d(|\underset{\sim}{dq}_\nu| r) = \left. \frac{dI'_\nu}{dr} \right|^{a} dr \, d\nu \tag{42}$$

We now substitute Lambert's equation in Equation 42 to obtain

$$\frac{1}{r} \frac{d(|\underset{\sim}{q}_\nu| r)}{dr} = \mu_\nu |\underset{\sim}{dq}_\nu| \tag{43}$$

Integrating along the radiation path:

$$|\underset{\sim}{dq}_\nu| = |\underset{\sim}{dq}_\nu|_0 \frac{r_0}{r} \exp\left(-\int_{r_0^*}^{r^*} \mu_\nu \, dr' \right) \tag{44}$$

The flux density must be related to the energy flow rate in order to be able to introduce the radiation characteristics of the U.V. source in the model. It is straightforward to show that

$$|\underset{\sim}{dq}_\nu| = \frac{dE_{\nu,0}}{2\pi L_L} \frac{1}{r} \exp\left(-\int_{r_0^*}^{r^*} \mu_\nu \, dr' \right) \tag{45}$$

From the radiation balance one can also obtain the LVREA. In general, if one identifies the absorbed energy flow rate as dE^a one has:

$$de_\nu^a = \frac{dE_\nu^a}{dV_r} \tag{46}$$

and

$$e^a = \int_{\nu=0}^{\nu=\infty} de_\nu^a \tag{47}$$

Let us now develop the value of e^a for the LSPP model. By definition:

$$dE_\nu|_r - dE_\nu|_{r+dr} = dE_\nu^a \tag{48}$$

Combining Equations 38, 39, and 42 we have

$$dE_\nu^a = -d(|\underset{\sim}{dq}_\nu| r) \, d\phi \, dz = -dI'_\nu|^a \, d\nu \, d\phi \, dz \tag{49}$$

But

$$dE_\nu^a = \mu_\nu I_\nu \, d\nu \, dr \, d\phi \, dz = \mu_\nu \frac{I'_\nu \, d\nu}{r} dV_r \tag{50}$$

since here $dV_r = r\,dr\,d\phi\,dz$. Finally, using Equations 40 and 46 it gives

$$de_\nu^a = \mu_\nu |d\underset{\sim}{q}_\nu| \tag{51}$$

and from Equations 45, 47, and 51 we obtain

$$e^a = \int_{\nu=0}^{\nu=\infty} \mu_\nu \frac{dE_{\nu,0}}{2\pi L_L} \frac{1}{r} \exp\left(-\int_{r_0^*}^{r^*} \mu_\nu\, dr'\right) \tag{52}$$

Even though this model is an ultrasimplified representation of reality, it contains many if not all of the more important characteristics of the problem that we list as:

1. In every initiation step of a photochemical reaction, e^a must be present.
2. Even in the simplest case, e^a is a function of position.
3. Even in the most idealized case (Beer's equation), μ_ν is a linear function of concentration and strongly depends upon the wavelength.
4. The energy flow rate ($dE_{\nu,0}$) also has a complicated dependence on the wavelength (spectral distribution of the radiation source output power).

$dE_{\nu,0}$ is converted into $E_{L,\nu}$ by the procedures described before.

The LVREA as a Kinetic Process

To consider the absorption of energy as a kinetic process, the corresponding state property of the system that allows its quantitative treatment is the previously defined LVREA. As it will be shown later, under the conditions of this analysis, the LVREA can be written with the same formalism as that used for the reaction rate equations for conventional chemical reaction steps.

From Equation 23 at each point inside the reactor we have

$$e_\nu^a = \int_{\Gamma_e} \mu_\nu |d\underset{\sim}{q}_\nu| \tag{53}$$

But

$$|d\underset{\sim}{q}_\nu| = \frac{\partial}{\partial \nu} |\underset{\sim}{q}|\, d\nu \tag{54}$$

Since μ_ν is an intensive property

$$e_\nu^a = \mu_\nu \int_{\Gamma_e} \frac{\partial}{\partial \nu} |\underset{\sim}{q}|\, d\nu \tag{55}$$

From radiation gas dynamics [10, 11] it is well known that the energy density e_ν^d is related to $|d\underset{\sim}{q}_\nu|$ by:

$$e_\nu^d = \frac{1}{c} \int_{\Gamma_e} \frac{\partial}{\partial \nu} |\underset{\sim}{q}| \tag{56}$$

where c is the speed of the light. Consequently:

$$e_\nu^a = c\mu_\nu (e_\nu^d\, d\nu) \tag{57}$$

Clearly, for all frequencies, we have

$$e^a = \int_{\nu=0}^{\nu=\infty} c\mu_\nu(e_\nu^d\, d\nu) \tag{58}$$

$e_\nu\, d\nu$ being the density of energy of frequency ν, which may be considered as moles of photons of frequency ν (Einsteins) per unit volume, in analogy with mass.

An inspection of Equation 57, taking into account the units of each factor, makes it possible to establish an analogy between the LVREA and a reaction rate equation which is first order with respect to one reactant (in this case the photons). Also, in those cases in which μ_ν is not a function of time, $c\mu_\nu$ plays the role of a pseudo-first order reaction rate constant.

The analogy can be further extended after looking at the way in which μ_ν is considered.

The Attenuation Coefficient

The specific intensity (I_ν) does not change with distance only when the propagating medium is transparent. When absorption occurs, I_ν changes as it is established by Lambert's equation for homogeneous media.

It must be clearly emphasized that Lambert's equation is a constitutive equation for a *one-dimensional phenomenon* that is *the absorption of radiation along the direction of propagation*. If other phenomena are present, for example refraction or scattering, it no longer applies.

Consequently, in the evaluation of this coefficient it is necessary to make a distinction between homogeneous and heterogeneous media. The latter are encountered when one attempts to model systems in which gas bubbles are dispersed in a liquid, or solid particles are incorporated into a gas or liquid phase as in photocatalytic applications. The distinction arises from the fact that the presence of heterogeneities introduces unavoidable light dispersion in the radiation field.

When different phenomena other than pure absorption are present, the propagation of a bundle of rays becomes a three-dimensional process. If this is the case, the use of a "Lambertian" form for the attenuation coefficient must be regarded only as a crude, first approximation.

Homogeneous Media

When the medium is homogeneous, the attenuation of radiation changes continuously. As mentioned before, this variation in the specific intensity due to absorption inside an elementary volume of homogeneous media may be expressed by a constitutive equation that involves an attenuation coefficient μ_ν. It is a function of the frequency of radiation ν and the state variables such as temperature, composition and, in some cases, pressure. The exact form of the attenuation coefficient function can be determined from the microscopic theory by studying the absorption of a photon by atoms or molecules exposed to a radiation field. The reader is referred to the specific literature [10, 11].

Macroscopically, the attenuation coefficient (also known as the Naperian absorption coefficient) is considered to be a linear function of the concentration of the absorbing species:

$$\mu_\nu = \alpha_\nu C \tag{59}$$

where α_ν is the absorption coefficient or absorptivity. When more than one species participate in the absorption process, Equation 59 may be written as

$$\mu_\nu = \sum_i \mu_{i,\nu} = \sum_i \alpha_{i,\nu} C_i \tag{60}$$

Both Equations 59 and 60 are strictly valid only for dilute solutions. The range of validity of these equations can be experimentally tested by studying the variation of μ_ν with concentration by means of a spectrophotometer. This type of experiment also allows us to obtain values of the absorption coefficient necessary to model the attenuation process. On the other hand, for many chemical compounds, values of the absorption coefficient and the range of validity of Equations 59 and 60 can generally be found in standard handbooks of physics and chemistry. The absorption characteristics of many other species and mixtures of different compounds may be found in specialized publications in the field of spectroscopy.

Heterogeneous Media

Since homogeneous systems have been the main objective of the research performed so far in photochemical reactor analysis, the information available in the literature about modeling the attenuation in heterogeneous media is particularly scarce. A critical review about this subject can be found in Alfano et al. [8]. The problem can be approached in two different ways: (a) by modeling the process taking into account the scattering of radiation produced by the heterogeneities, or (b) by using the existing formulation on homogeneous media with an *effective* attenuation coefficient. About the first strategy, it can be ascertained that the use of a rigorous radiation source model having no adjustable parameters, together with the complexity provided by the heterogeneities of the medium, have not yet been attempted.

At present, several correlations have been proposed to evaluate the effective attenuation coefficient in gas-liquid dispersions. Among them, we can particularly mention two:

1. The first one, proposed by Otake et al. [12], is a simple empirical expression that accounts for the absorption effects produced by the liquid phase and the reflection, refraction and transmission effects provoked by the gaseous phase. Considering that the latter are proportional to the specific surface area (A_v), $\mu_{eff,v}$ may be represented by the following correlation:

$$\mu_{eff,v} = \mu_v(1 - \varepsilon_G) + kA_v \qquad (61)$$

   where μ_v is the attenuation coefficient of the liquid phase, ε_G the holdup of the dispersed phase, and k is an empirical coefficient depending on the optical properties of the system. Otake et al. plotted the experimental information obtained by them and other authors, finding that the values can be well correlated by using $k = 0.125$ for $\mu_{eff,v}$, μ_v, and A_v in the same units (cm^{-1}).

2. The other correlation was proposed by Yokota et al. [13], in which the effective attenuation coefficient becomes a function of the attenuation coefficient in the liquid phase, the bubble diameter and the gas holdup. The expression is

$$\mu_{eff,v} = \mu_v(1 + h\varepsilon_G) \qquad (62)$$

   and

$$h = \left[\frac{3.6}{d_b}\right]^{0.66} \qquad (63)$$

   where d_b is the bubble diameter in mm for μ_v and $\mu_{eff,v}$ expressed in m^{-1}.

   Both correlations may be used in the case of μ_v smaller than 40 m^{-1}. When μ_v is greater than 40 m^{-1}, the dispersing effect of radiation due to the presence of bubbles may be normally neglected.

Neither similar nor reliable correlation has been found for solid-fluid processes yet. (Either for gas-solid or liquid-solid or gas-liquid-solid systems.)

The Rate of the Initiation Step in a Photochemical Reactor

We have already obtained the value of e_v^a as a function of the energy supplied by the lamp $E_{L,v}$ and the properties of the reacting medium μ_v. This value has been obtained at a point $I(\rho^*, \theta, \phi)$ inside the reactor.

The value of μ_ν for homogeneous media allows us to establish an additional analogy with conventional kinetics. Substituting Equation 60 in Equation 57, we have

$$e_\nu^a = \sum_i (c\alpha_{i,\nu}) C_i (e_\nu^d \, d\nu) \tag{64}$$

Looking for a parallelism with chemical reactions, Equation 64 is a combination of a second-order kinetic constant corresponding to a special reacting system in which a "reactant" (photons of frequence ν) "reacts" simultaneously with other reactants of concentration C_i, $c\alpha_{i,\nu}$ being a second-order reaction rate constant ($\alpha_{i,\nu}$ is a function of P, T, ν and has a different value for each component i which takes part in the "reaction"). The differential character of the "molar" concentration of energy of frequency ν, ($e_\nu \, d\nu$), derives from the consideration of ν as a continuous variable, which is implicit in the definition of I_ν and every related distribution function.

At this point we are in a position of going back to Figure 11 and discuss in some additional detail the link "attenuation of radiation-extent of the reaction" for a reactor with space dependent concentrations. To evaluate $|\underset{\sim}{q}_\nu|$ at point I, every direction (θ, ϕ) must be considered. For each direction (θ, ϕ), in the most general case, the ray travels from the emission source without changing its specific intensity until it reaches the reactor wall, represented by point $W(\rho^*, \theta, \phi)$. In the trajectory between $W(\rho^*, \theta, \phi)$ and $I(\rho^*, \theta, \phi)$ the specific intensity changes due to absorption. This change is represented in the expression of $|\underset{\sim}{q}_\nu|$ for each model by the exponential function

$$\exp\left[-\int_{\rho_0^*(\theta,\phi)}^{\rho^*(\theta,\phi)} \mu_\nu \, d\rho'\right] \tag{65}$$

Due to the concentration dependence of the attenuation coefficient, the modulus of the radiation flux density vector, and hence the LVREA, becomes a functional of the concentration field inside the reactor. This functional characteristic of the LVREA makes the problem of modeling a photochemical reactor more complex than expected. The complexity is due to the coupling between the radiation field evaluation and the resolution of the mass balance equations. The progress of the reaction at each point I depends on the local value of the LVREA, but the LVREA value is a function of the extent of the reaction reached at all points in space through which every ray arriving at point I has previously traveled.

We can now go ahead and formulate the rate for the light activated step (Figure 4).

It has been well established that in a single photon absorption process, the rate of a photochemically initiated step is proportional to the energy absorbed (the LVREA). The proportionality constant is the primary reaction quantum yield:

$$\text{Rate of initiation step} = \int_{\nu=0}^{\nu=\infty} \Phi_{\text{prim},\nu} e^a \tag{66}$$

The definition of this yield will depend on the nature of the process concerned. The primary process may be defined including both the initial act of absorption and those processes following immediately which are determined by the properties of the initially excited electronic state. In almost all cases the primary process leads to a dissociation of the absorbing molecule. In general the primary quantum yield may be defined as

$$\Phi_{\text{prim},\nu} = \left[\frac{\text{number of molecules following the expected path in the primary process}}{\text{number of quanta of radiation absorbed}}\right] \tag{67}$$

Clearly, in the general case, $\Phi_{\text{prim},\nu}$ is a function of frequency.

After absorption of radiation, other processes different from dissociation and reaction can occur; for example: fluorescence, phosphorescence, recombination of the dissociated molecule, deactivation by physical quenching, etc. Each one of them will define different primary quantum yields.

According to the second law of photochemistry [14], the absorption of light by a molecule is a one-quantum process, so that the sum of all primary-process quantum yields must be unity. The validity of the second law depends on the short lifetime of the excited state and the low values of the LVREA, 10^{13}–10^{16} quanta absorbed/$cm^3 \cdot s$, that are common in conventional photochemical systems. In these cases, there is a very low concentration of electronically excited molecules and the probability of absorption of a second photon is low. Under conditions of very high light intensity, ca. 10^{18} quanta absorbed/$cm^3 \cdot s$, eg., in flash-photolysis experiments and in some laser photochemistry, the lifetime of the excited state is long compared to the photon concentration; certain biphotonic processes can take place under these conditions that do not violate the second law.

$\Phi_{prim,\nu}$ cannot be measured easily; to determine its value we must gain information about the relative rates of the other possibilities more likely involved in the primary process (recombination, physical quenching, etc.). Sometimes, these rates may be obtained by inspection of the absorption spectrum. Then, we may be able to estimate the value of $\Phi_{prim,\nu}$. To illustrate this we can consider the photochemical dissociation of chlorine molecules: referring to the potential curves for chlorine [15], they inequivocally show that upper states are unstable and the molecule dissociates very rapidly. Then this process will predominate over all others and we can surely say that, almost independently of the frequency considered, $\Phi_{prim,\nu} \cong 1$.

In some practical applications a different definition of the yield is used. It is called the *overall* quantum yield. This is a highly "process-dependent" value and does not have the quality of a kinetic property (as it is the case of Φ_{prim}). Its definition is

$$\Phi_{ov} = \left[\frac{\text{number of molecules of a given reactant or product finally decomposed or formed}}{\text{number of quanta absorbed}}\right] \tag{68}$$

This property will generally give an indication of the nature of the reaction mechanism. If Φ_{ov} is large, a chain mechanism is indicated; if it is small, either deactivation or recombination is suggested, although other possibilities must not be overlooked. It can be clearly seen that while Φ_{prim} can never be larger than unity, Φ_{ov} can attain very large values. (Depending on the chain length, it can be as large as 10^6.)

Combining Equations 32, 59, and 66, for the simplest case when:

- Emission is isotropic.
- The reactor wall does not absorb or disperse radiation.
- The reacting medium is homogeneous.
- Only one compound (the reactant i) absorbs radiation.
- Absorption of radiation is a single photon process.

the rate of the photochemically initiated step is

$$J^* = \int_{\nu=0}^{\nu=\infty} \frac{\Phi_{prim,\nu}\alpha_\nu E_{L,\nu} C_i}{4\pi\Gamma_e^*} \int_{\Gamma_e} \frac{1}{\rho^2}\left[\exp\left(-\int_{\rho_0^*}^{\rho^*} \alpha_\nu C_i \, d\rho\right)\right] d\Gamma_e \tag{69}$$

Equation 69 shows the main features that distinguish a photochemical reaction from a thermal one:

1. The concentration of the absorbing species comes into play twice:
   a. In a linear way (kinetic effect)
   b. In a negative exponential (attenuating effect).
2. A dimension generally related with a characteristic length of the reactor (ρ) is an important part of the attenuating integral. Hence, the characteristic length affects not only conventional dimensionless numbers such as Re and Pe, but also the one that could be used to characterize the absorption of radiation.

Since J* goes into the mass balance equations, there exits a very strong coupling between the reaction J* that changes C_i, and the attenuation that changes J* but also depends on C_i. Similarly the distance $(\rho^* - \rho_0^*)$ which is proportional to the reactor dimensions, affects the *local value* of the reaction rate in a very inseparable manner from the effects of these dimensions on the reactor hydrodynamical performance.

APPLICATIONS

Annular Reactor

Reaction

Let us choose the following example which represents a decomposition photosensitized by a reactant A. The concentration of A remains unchanged.

$$A + h\nu \xrightarrow{\Phi_{1,\nu}} A^*$$

$$A^* + B \longrightarrow A + C + D$$

$$B + h\nu \xrightarrow{\Phi_{2,\nu}} C + D$$

The values of $\Phi_{2,\nu}$ are known as a function of ν. However, for this first example we will assume monochromatic radiation.

Equation of Change

Concentration of B will be represented by the subindex i. The system can be studied under the following assumptions: (i) steady state; (ii) negligible thermal effects; (iii) unidirectional, incompressible, laminar flow regime; (iv) Newtonian fluid; (v) azimuthal symmetry; (vi) negligible axial diffusion when compared to the convective flux along that direction; (vii) constant diffusion coefficients; (viii) monochromatic radiation; and (ix) nonpermeable reactor walls. The material balance may be written (Figure 13).

$$v_z(r)\frac{\partial C_i}{\partial z} = D_i \frac{1}{r}\frac{\partial}{\partial r}\left(r\frac{\partial C_i}{\partial r}\right) + \Omega_i^* \tag{70}$$

with the following initial and boundary conditions:

$$z = 0, \quad \forall r, \quad C_i = C_i^{\circ} \tag{71a}$$

$$\forall z, \quad r = r_{R_{in}}, \quad \frac{\partial C_i}{\partial r} = 0 \tag{71b}$$

$$\forall z, \quad r = r_{R_{ou}}, \quad \frac{\partial C_i}{\partial r} = 0 \tag{71c}$$

For this case

$$\Omega_i^* = -\Phi_2 e^a \tag{72}$$

$$v_z(r) = 2\langle v\rangle \frac{1 - (r/r_{R_{in}})^2 + [(1 - K^2)/\ln(1/K)]\ln(r/r_{R_{in}})}{1 + K^2 - [(1 - K^2)/\ln(1/K)]} \tag{73}$$

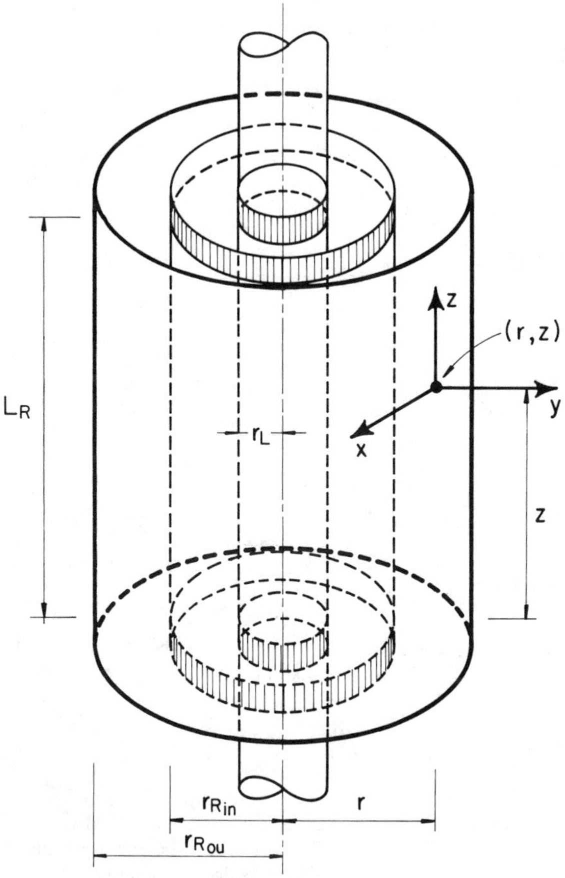

Figure 13. Annular reactor. (Adpated from Ref. [5].)

In dimensionless form:

$$U(\gamma)\frac{\partial \Psi_i}{\partial \zeta} = \frac{1}{\mathrm{Pe_i Ge}}\frac{1}{\gamma}\frac{\partial}{\partial \gamma}\left(\gamma\frac{\partial \Psi_i}{\partial \gamma}\right) + \Omega_i \tag{74}$$

$$\Psi_i(0, \gamma) = 1 \tag{75}$$

$$\frac{\partial \Psi_i}{\partial \gamma}(\zeta, 1) = 0 \tag{76a}$$

$$\frac{\partial \Psi_i}{\partial \gamma}(\zeta, 1/K) = 0 \tag{76b}$$

The following definitions have been used:

$$\Psi_i = \frac{C_i}{C_i^o} \tag{77}$$

$$U(r) = \frac{v_z(r)}{\langle v \rangle} \tag{78}$$

$$\zeta = \frac{z}{L_R} \tag{79}$$

$$\gamma = \frac{r}{r_{R_{in}}} \tag{80}$$

$$Pe_i = \frac{\langle v \rangle r_{R_{in}}}{D_i} \tag{81}$$

$$Ge = \frac{r_{R_{in}}}{L_R} \tag{82}$$

$$\Omega_i = \frac{\Omega_i^* L_R}{\langle v \rangle C_i^0} \tag{83}$$

To solve this differential equation, we must calculate e^a for the annular reactor. Once e^a is known, computations are very similar to those required for any integro-(partial) differential equation.

Evaluation of the LVREA

Expressions for the LVREA for different emission models were presented earlier. There we mentioned that the integration limits will depend on the geometrical configuration of the lamp-reactor system and, perhaps, the reflector. They consititute the major complexity in the evaluation of the radiation field. For the three types of reactors described earlier, they will be derived by applying the ESVE and the LSSE models. The ESSE model requires the same equations for the lamp limiting values as the ESVE model, with the exception of the ρ-coordinate, which is not integrated because the emission is produced by the surface of the lamp only. The final equations for the LVREA and $|\underset{\sim}{q}_\nu|$ also differ in the value of the characteristic constant of the radiation source κ_ν (see Table 2).

To simplify the treatment, we will derive the values of $|\underset{\sim}{q}|$ for monochromatic radiation and isotropic emission. The extension to polychromatic radiation and diffuse emission is straightforward. In addition to the assumptions already described for the emission model and the lamp, we must add the following ones about the reactor [3]:

1. The inner wall of the reactor is bounded by a cylindrical mathematical surface without thickness (i.e., no reflection or refraction occurs).
2. The opaque zones at the top and bottom parts of the reactor do not reflect or emit radiation.

The modulus of the radiation flux density vector at any point in the reacting space, $I(r, \beta, z)$, is the energy flux arriving from all directions in space and from the whole extension of the lamp. It can be obtained after integration of:

$$|\underset{\sim}{q}| = \kappa \int_{\Gamma_e} \frac{1}{\rho^2} \exp\left[-\int_{\rho_0^*}^{\rho^*} \mu \, d\rho' \right] d\Gamma_e \tag{84}$$

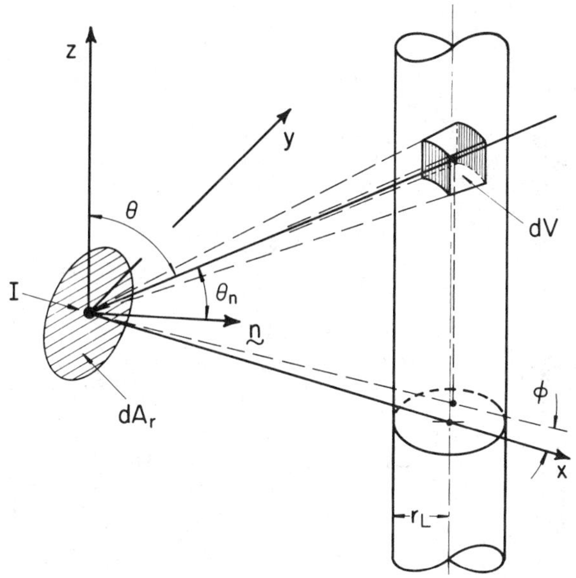

Figure 14. Evaluation of direct radiation from the lamp to the reactor. (Adapted from Ref. [3].)

a) ESVE Model
In this case Equation 84 is written as follows (see Table 2):

$$|\underset{\sim}{q}| = \kappa \int_\theta \int_\phi \int_\rho d\theta \, d\phi \, d\rho \sin\theta \exp\left[-\int_{\rho_0^*(\theta,\phi)}^{\rho^*(\theta,\phi)} \mu \, d\rho' \right] \tag{85}$$

To obtain the integration limits, one starts from the point of reception I(r, β, z) and investigates all the arriving rays with directions (θ, φ). One must find those that intersect the boundaries of the surface of the cylinder representing the lamp (Figure 14).

The limits for variable ρ are the intersections of this coordinate with the front and rear parts of the lamp in any θ, φ direction:

$$\rho_{1,2}(\theta, \phi) = \frac{r \cos\phi \mp [r^2 \cos^2\phi - r^2 + r_L^2]^{1/2}}{\sin\theta} \tag{86}$$

The limits for variable θ are obtained considering that the limiting rays coming from the lamp and reaching the generic point (r, β, z) must satisfy two restrictive conditions: (a) A ray limits the θ angle when its equation has a common solution with the equation of the circumference that defines the non-emitting zones at the upper and lower parts of the lamp; and (b) The ray with be a limit when the common solution above corresponds to the intersection of the ray with that portion of the circumference which, limited by two generatrix lines corresponding to the φ limiting angles, is closer to the generic point I (r, β, z). The second condition is needed because for any plane at constant φ, there are two θ angles that satisfy the first restriction for both

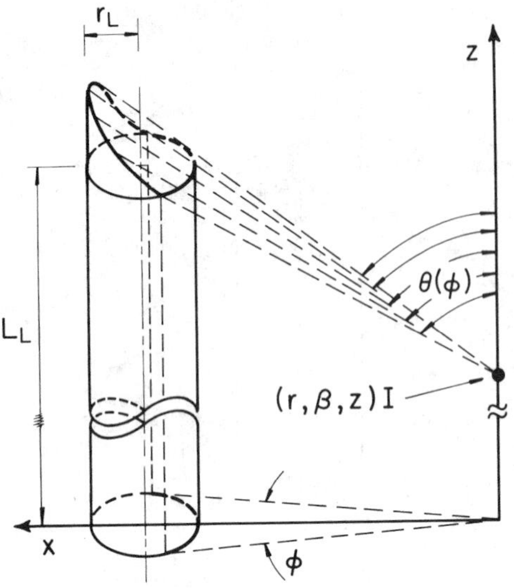

Figure 15. Limits of θ and ϕ for direct irradiation of a point I inside the annular photoreactor. (Adapted from Ref. [3].)

the upper and lower boundaries (Figure 15). In this way, we obtain the following expressions:

$$\theta_1(\phi) = \tan^{-1}\left[\frac{r\cos\phi - [r^2(\cos^2\phi - 1) + r_L^2]^{1/2}}{(L_L - z)}\right] \tag{87a}$$

$$\theta_2(\phi) = \tan^{-1}\left[\frac{r\cos\phi - [r^2(\cos^2\phi - 1) + r_L^2]^{1/2}}{(-z)}\right] \tag{87b}$$

The limiting rays in the ϕ direction can be obtained by imposing the restriction that both intersections of the ρ coordinate with the lamp boundary must coincide, that is,

$$\rho_1 = \rho_2 \tag{88}$$

With Equation 86 and since ϕ can take values only in the closed interval $[-\pi/2, \pi/2]$,

$$-\phi_1 = \phi_2 = \cos^{-1}\left[\frac{(r^2 - r_L^2)^{1/2}}{r}\right] \tag{89}$$

With these limits, Equation (85) can be integrated to obtain:

$$|\underset{\sim}{q}| = 2\kappa \int_{\phi_1}^{\phi_2} d\phi[r_L^2 - r^2\sin\phi]^{1/2} \int_{\theta_1(\phi)}^{\theta_2(\phi)} d\theta \exp\left[-\int_{\rho_0^*(\theta,\phi)}^{\rho^*(\theta,\phi)} \mu\, d\rho'\right] \tag{90}$$

b) LSSE Model.
In this case Equation 84 becomes (see Table 2):

$$|\underset{\sim}{q}| = \kappa \int_0^{L_L} \frac{dz}{\rho^2} \exp\left[-\int_{\rho_0^*(\theta)}^{\rho^*(\theta)} \mu\, d\rho'\right] \tag{91}$$

Let us call

$$\rho(\theta)\cos\theta = r \tag{92}$$

$$\rho(\theta)\sin\theta = z \tag{93}$$

Then, we have

$$\frac{dz}{\rho^2} = \frac{d\theta}{r} \tag{94}$$

and finally

$$|\underset{\sim}{q}| = \frac{\kappa}{r}\int_{\theta_1}^{\theta_2} d\theta \exp\left[-\int_{\rho_0^*(\theta)}^{\rho^*(\theta)} \mu \, d\rho'\right] \tag{95}$$

where θ_1 and θ_2 can be obtained from Equations 87a and 87b, making $r_L = 0$ and $\phi = 0$.

A more rigorous approach should require the computation of the reactor and the lamp wedges. The three-dimensional characteristic of the emission process causes the reactor to be partially irradiated in the incoming and outgoing regions. This fact increases the effective reaction volume. This effect is more noticeable when the inner reactor wall is close to the lamp. The expressions for the θ-limiting angles should be modified in the partially irradiated regions; the reader is referred to Romero et al. [16] for a detailed analysis of the reactor wedge computation. On the other hand, calculations should also be corrected to account for the effective lamp length. If no corrections were introduced we would be computing as emission volumes portions of the cylinder that correspond to regions in the space where there is no emission at all. This effect is also significant when the inner reactor wall is very close to the lamp; for a more detailed analysis, the reader may refer to De Bernardez and Cassano [17].

Photoreactor with a Reflector of Elliptical Cross Section

Reaction

We will illustrate this reacting system with the monohalogenation of saturated hydrocarbons. Let us call X_2 the halogen and RH the hydrocarbon

$$X_2 + h\nu \xrightarrow{\Phi_\nu} 2X\cdot \quad \text{Initiation}$$

Propagation:

$$X\cdot + RH \underset{k_{-2}}{\xrightarrow{k_2}} RX + H\cdot$$

$$H\cdot + X_2 \underset{k_{-3}}{\xrightarrow{k_3}} X\cdot + HX$$

Termination:

$$X\cdot + X\cdot + M \xrightarrow{k_4} X_2 + M$$

$$X\cdot + R\cdot \xrightarrow{k_5} RX$$

$$R\cdot + R\cdot \xrightarrow{k_6} R_2$$

Here, M is a third body needed by thermal reasons to stabilize X_2. It can be either a reactant in excess or an inert. Wall reactions in practical reactors can be safely neglected [18]. It can be easily shown that at atmospheric pressures or greater pressures and for ratios of $V_R/A_R > 0.1$, they do not have significant contributions to the overall rates. Ratios of reactor volume to reactor "wetted" area larger than 0.1 are easily achieved in practice.

The overall reaction is

$$RH + X_2 \xrightarrow{h^{\nu}} RX + XH$$

For simplicity we can designate the intervening species with a subindex as follows:

Species	X_2	X·	RH	RX	R·	XH	R_2	M·
Number	1	2	3	4	5	6	7	8

Equation of Change

De Bernardez and Cassano [19] developed design criteria under which angular asymmetries can be neglected. The key parameter was the ratio r_R/r_L. The established conditions (small ellipse eccentricity, large value of c and $r_R/r_L \ll 1$) can only be achieved in bench scale equipment. For large scale reactors it is only a first approximation. The assumption of angular symmetry is, however, very convenient and it will be used here.

Under these conditions the mass balances can be simplified because they may be written in two dimensions only. The following assumptions were employed: (i) steady state; (ii) stream-line, incompressible flow; (iii) negligible thermal effects; (iv) Newtonian fluid with constant physical properties ($D_{i,m}$, ρ, μ, α, etc.); (v) angular symmetry; and (vi) negligible axial diffusion. Using these assumptions the mass conservation equations may be written

$$v_z(r)\frac{\partial C_i}{\partial z} = \frac{D_{im}}{r}\frac{\partial}{\partial r}\left(r\frac{\partial C_i}{\partial r}\right) + \Omega_i^* \tag{96}$$

with

$$z = 0, \qquad \forall r, \quad C_i = C_i^{\circ} \tag{97}$$

$$\forall z, \quad r = 0, \qquad \frac{\partial C_i}{\partial r} = 0 \tag{98a}$$

$$\forall z, \quad r = r_R, \qquad \frac{\partial C_i}{\partial r} = 0 \tag{98b}$$

If heterogeneous reactions at the wall were present, the boundary conditions for the species at $r = r_R$ would be changed to

$$\forall z, \quad r = r_R, \qquad D_{jm}\frac{\partial C_j}{\partial r} = \sum_h \nu_{jh}\Omega_h^* \tag{99}$$

where the summation must include all the heterogeneous steps where species j participates; Ω_h^* is the rate of the h heterogeneous termination step and ν_{jh} is the stoichiometric coefficient of species j in the h heterogeneous step.

In Equation 96 for the eight homogeneous steps included in the reaction mechanism we have

$$\Omega_i^* = \sum_{r=1}^{r=8} \nu_{ir}\Omega_r^* \tag{100}$$

Hence, the rates of formation of species i are

$$\Omega_1^* = -\Phi e^a - k_{p3}C_1C_5 + k_{t4}C_8C_2^2 + k_{p-3}C_2C_4 \tag{101}$$

$$\Omega_2^* = 2\Phi e^a - k_{p2}C_2C_3 + k_{p-2}C_5C_6 + k_{p3}C_1C_5 - k_{p-3}C_2C_4 - 2k_{t4}C_2^2C_8 - k_{t5}C_2C_5 \tag{102}$$

$$\Omega_3^* = -k_{p2}C_2C_3 + k_{p-2}C_5C_6 \tag{103}$$

$$\Omega_4^* = k_{p3}C_1C_5 - k_{p-3}C_2C_4 + k_{t5}C_2C_5 \tag{104}$$

$$\Omega_5^* = k_{p2}C_2C_3 - k_{p-2}C_5C_6 - k_{p3}C_1C_5 - k_{t5}C_2C_5 - 2k_{t6}C_5^2 + k_{p-3}C_2C_4 \tag{105}$$

$$\Omega_6^* = k_{p2}C_2C_3 - k_{p-2}C_5C_6 \tag{106}$$

$$\Omega_7^* = k_{t6}C_5^2 \tag{107}$$

De Bernardez and Cassano [20] and Clariá et al. [18] showed that in these systems the local or microscopic steady-state approximation for intermediate unstable species can be applied without error. In general it is required that the time needed to reach an "almost steady-state" value for the free radical concentrations be a small fraction of the mean residence time spent by the reactants inside the reactor. This condition depends upon many variables, the most important ones being: L_R, $\langle v\rangle$, e^a, and the relative values of k_2, k_{-2}, k_3, k_{-3}, k_4, k_5 and k_6. For most practical situations, if the mean residence time is longer than 10^{-1} s the hypothesis can be safely used. Very large values of e^a favor its application. Very fast overall reaction rates, on the contrary, may require some precautions in its use (because for a given conversion the system would require rather short mean residence times).

Hence, Equations 102 and 105 can be set equal to zero:

$$\Omega_i^* = 0 \qquad \text{for } i = 2 \text{ and } 5 \tag{108}$$

These two algebraic equations are still coupled with the mass balance equations through the reaction rate term. In addition, Equations 101 and 102 clearly show the coupling of the mass balance equations with the radiation balance through the rate of the activation step.

We also know that for this case

$$v_z(r) = 2\langle v\rangle\left[1 - \left(\frac{r}{R}\right)^2\right] \tag{109}$$

In dimensionless form we have

$$U(\gamma)\frac{\partial \Psi_i}{\partial \zeta} = \frac{1}{Pe_iGe}\frac{1}{\gamma}\frac{\partial}{\partial \gamma}\left(\gamma\frac{\partial \Psi_i}{\partial \gamma}\right) + \Omega_i \tag{110}$$

$$\Psi_1(\gamma, 0) = \Psi_1^\circ = 1 \tag{111a}$$

$$\Psi_3(\gamma, 0) = \Psi_3^\circ \tag{111b}$$

$$\Psi_j(\gamma, 0) = \Psi_j^\circ = 0 \qquad (j = 2, 4\text{–}7) \tag{111c}$$

$$\frac{\partial \Psi_i(0, \zeta)}{\partial \gamma} = 0 \qquad (i = 1\text{–}7) \tag{112a}$$

$$\frac{\partial \Psi_i(1, \zeta)}{\partial \gamma} = 0 \qquad (i = 1\text{–}7) \tag{112b}$$

where in this particular case

$$\Omega_i = \frac{\Omega_i^* L_R}{\langle v \rangle C_1^\circ}$$

and

$$\Omega_1 = -J - K_3\Psi_1\Psi_5 + K_4\Psi_2^2\Psi_8 \quad (113)$$

$$\Omega_2 = 2J - K_2\Psi_2\Psi_3 + K_{-2}\Psi_5\Psi_6 + K_3\Psi_1\Psi_5 - 2K_4\Psi_2^2\Psi_8 - K_5\Psi_2\Psi_5 \quad (114)$$

$$\Omega_3 = -K_2\Psi_2\Psi_3 + K_{-2}\Psi_5\Psi_6 \quad (115)$$

$$\Omega_4 = K_3\Psi_1\Psi_5 + K_5\Psi_2\Psi_5 \quad (116)$$

$$\Omega_5 = K_2\Psi_2\Psi_3 - K_{-2}\Psi_5\Psi_6 - K_3\Psi_1\Psi_5 - K_5\Psi_2\Psi_5 - 2K_6\Psi_5^2 \quad (117)$$

$$\Omega_6 = K_2\Psi_2\Psi_3 - K_{-2}\Psi_5\Psi_6 \quad (118)$$

$$\Omega_7 = K_6\Psi_5^2 \quad (119)$$

with

$$J = \frac{J^* L_R}{\langle v \rangle C_1^\circ} \quad (120)$$

$$K_r = \frac{k_r L_R C_1^\circ}{\langle v \rangle}, \qquad r = 2, -2, 3, 5 \text{ and } 6 \quad (121)$$

$$K_r = \frac{k_r L_R C_1^{\circ 2}}{\langle v \rangle}, \qquad r = 4 \quad (122)$$

Once more, to solve this system of equations we need to calculate e^a for a reactor inside the elliptical reflector. We must also be able to calculate the LVREA for polychromatic radiation. With these particular additions, other computations are similar to those required for any system of integro-(partial) differential equations.

However, the radiation field is now much more complicated than in the case of the annular reactor. Radiation arrives at a point inside the reactor by two different mechanisms:

1. Direct radiation from the lamp to the reactor.
2. Indirect radiation after reflection on the cylindrical reflector. It should also be noted that, strictly speaking, indirect radiation may be the result of one or more than one reflections.

Consequently, the mathematical modelling of the radiation field inside the elliptical reflector is associated with some analytical complexities. Being a radiation problem, these geometrical complications should not be a surprise.

Evaluation of the LVREA

Cassano and coworkers [5] showed that when curved reflecting surfaces are present, extense emission models must be used. Let us have a look at this case, assuming that a non-flourescent, arc lamp is used. The ESVE model will then be applied. Isotropic emission is also assumed.

The reacting system is homogeneous (gas phase), and the halogen is the only absorbing species in the wavelength range of the lamp emission. Hence:

$$e_\nu^a = \mu_\nu |\underset{\sim}{q}_\nu| = \alpha_\nu C_1 |\underset{\sim}{q}_\nu| \tag{123}$$

where α_ν is the absorption coefficient of the halogen. Then:

$$e^a = \int_{\nu=0}^{\nu=\infty} d\nu\, e_\nu^a = \int_{\nu=0}^{\nu=\infty} d\nu\, \alpha_\nu C_1 |\underset{\sim}{q}_\nu| \tag{124}$$

Since the total energy flux density vector results from the contributions of direct and indirect radiation (the latter with one or more reflections), in Equation 124 we have

$$|\underset{\sim}{q}_\nu| = |\underset{\sim}{q}_\nu|_D + |\underset{\sim}{q}_\nu|_{In,1} + \cdots + |\underset{\sim}{q}_\nu|_{In,n} \tag{125}$$

According to De Bernardez and Cassano [19] when the distance between the focal points of the ellipse (c) is sufficiently large, the system can be represented with good approximation considering $|\underset{\sim}{q}|_{IN,1}$ exclusively. (Rigorously speaking; this is an extremely good simplification with, at the same time, the eccentricity (e) is lower than 0.5 and the ratio r_R/r_L is smaller than 0.5.) If this is not the case, direct radiation must also be considered. Inclusion of second reflections are needed only in very special cases. We will show here only the results for direct radiation and indirect radiation with only one reflection. Let us also indicate that the use of two-dimensional mass balances (hypothesis of azimuthal symmetry) can be properly justified when the first reflection is the only significant contribution. Otherwise, the radiation field may have strong angular asymmetries.

Figures 16 and 17 are used to illustrate the geometrical aspects of the lamp-reactor-reflector arrangement. The problem consists in finding the mathematical relationship between the incident

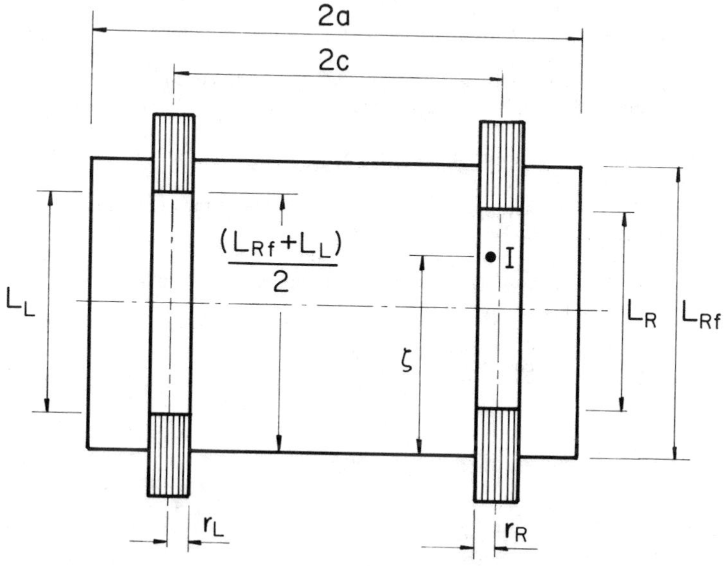

Figure 16. Geometrical characteristics of the "elliptical reactor."

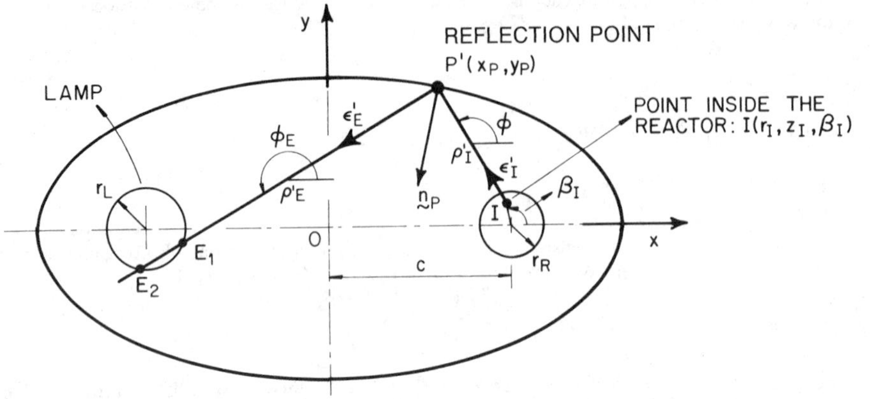

Figure 17. Projection of a ray trajectory on a plane normal to the two focal axis of the elliptical reflector.

radiant energy flux and the reactor, lamp and reflector dimensions, the optical properties of the reflector and the reactor wall, and the physical properties of the radiation coming out of the source. The point of reception (I) on the reactor volume is referred to a cylindrical coordinate system located at the centerline of the cylindrical reactor with origin at the reflector bottom (r_I, β_I, ζ_I).

Five additional assumptions may be added to those given earlier [21]:

1. The reflector is a perfect elliptical cylinder.
2. The lamp is located in such a way that its centerline passes through one of the focuses of the elliptical reflector (F_1).
3. Specular reflection occurs with an average reflection coefficient that is independent of wavelength and direction. (These restrictions could be easily relaxed and are used here for simplicity.)
4. The reflected radiation comes only from the elliptical reflector (i.e., the top and bottom parts of the cylinder do not reflect radiation).
5. Transmittance of the reactor wall is represented by an average coefficient which is only a function of frequency.

Direct Radiation: For this case, the limits of integration may be obtained in a similar way as for the annular reactor. The results are

$$\rho_{1,2}(\theta, \phi) = \frac{\Delta \cos \phi \mp [\Delta^2 \cos^2 \phi - (\Delta^2 - r_L^2)]^{1/2}}{\sin \theta} \tag{126}$$

where

$$\Delta = [(2c + r_I \cos \beta_I)^2 + r_I^2 \sin^2 \beta_I]^{1/2} \tag{127}$$

$$\theta_1(\phi) = \tan^{-1}\left[\frac{\Delta \cos \phi - (r_L^2 - \Delta^2 \sin^2 \phi)^{1/2}}{\frac{1}{2}(L_{Rf} + L_L) - \zeta_I}\right] \tag{128}$$

$$\theta_2(\phi) = \tan^{-1}\left[\frac{\Delta \cos\phi - (r_L^2 - \Delta^2 \sin^2\phi)^{1/2}}{\frac{1}{2}(L_{Rf} - L_L) - \zeta_I}\right] \tag{129}$$

$$\phi_1 = \sin^{-1}\left(\frac{r_L}{\Delta}\right) \tag{130}$$

$$\phi_2 = 2\pi - \phi_1 \tag{131}$$

For direct radiation the final expression is

$$|\underset{\sim}{dq_\nu}| = 2\kappa \Upsilon_{R,\nu} \int_{\phi_1}^{\phi_2} d\phi (r_L^2 - \Delta^2 \sin^2\phi)^{1/2} \int_{\theta_1(\phi)}^{\theta_2(\phi)} d\theta \exp\left[-\int_{\rho_0^*(\theta,\phi)}^{\rho^*(\theta,\phi)} \mu \, d\rho'\right] \tag{132}$$

Indirect Radiation with Only One Reflection: The methodology of analysis for reflected radiation is to follow a ray starting from the point of reception in order to identify the point of reflection, and from this (applying the laws of optical physics) to search in the direction of emission. To understand the analysis it is necessary to locate several key points (Figure 17): first, the point of incidence of the reflected ray (point of reception I); second, the point of reflection (P); and finally, the two points of intersection of the direction of emission with the lamp cylinder (E_1 and E_2). Any ray coming from the lamp will be indicated by an incidence position vector at the point of reflection (ρ_E) and a reflection position vector at the point of reception (ρ_I). The former has its origin at P and the latter at I. The intersections of ρ_E with the cylinder of the lamp tube define two vectors, $\rho_{E,1}$ and $\rho_{E,2}$. The details of the geometrical derivations can be found in the original work of Cerdá et al. [21]. We will show here a summary of the final results.

For monochromatic radiation, the modulus of the radiation energy density vector is

$$|\underset{\sim}{dq_\nu}| = \Gamma_{Rf,\nu} \Upsilon_{R,\nu} \frac{E_\nu}{4\pi V_L} \exp\left[-\int_{\rho_0^*(\theta,\phi)}^{\rho_1^*(\theta,\phi)} \alpha_\nu C_1 \, d\rho'\right] \sin\theta \, d\theta \, d\phi \, d\rho \tag{133}$$

Equation 133 can be integrated analytically for the ρ coordinate. The limits are

$$\rho_{E_{1,2}} = \frac{D \cos\xi \mp (r_L^2 - D^2 \sin^2\xi)^{1/2}}{\sin\theta} \tag{134}$$

where

$$D = [(x_P + h + c)^2 + (y_P + k)^2]^{1/2} \tag{135}$$

$$\sin\xi = -\frac{1}{D}[(x_P + h + c)\sin\phi_E - (y_P + k)\cos\phi_E] \tag{136}$$

$$\cos\xi = -\frac{1}{D}[(x_P + h + c)\cos\phi_E + (y_P + k)\cos\phi_E] \tag{137}$$

$$x_P = \rho_I \sin\theta \cos\phi \tag{138}$$

$$y_P = \rho_I \sin\theta \sin\phi \tag{139}$$

$$z_P = \rho_I \cos\theta \tag{140}$$

$$\rho_I = \frac{-(hb^2\cos\phi + ka^2\sin\phi) + ab[\sigma^2 - (h\sin\phi - k\cos\phi)^2]^{1/2}}{\sigma^2 \sin\theta} \tag{141}$$

and

$$\sigma^2 = b^2 \cos^2 \phi + a^2 \sin^2 \phi \tag{142}$$

$$h = c + r_I \cos \beta_I \tag{143}$$

$$k = r_I \sin \beta_I \tag{144}$$

$$\phi_E = \tan^{-1}\left[\frac{(m^2 - 1)\sin\phi + 2m\cos\phi}{2m\sin\phi - (m^2 - 1)\cos\phi}\right] \tag{145}$$

$$m = \frac{a^2(y_P + k)}{b^2(x_P + h)} \tag{146}$$

Integration along θ and ϕ must be done numerically. The limits are

$$\theta_1 = \tan^{-1}\left[\frac{\rho_I' + D\cos\xi - (r_L^2 - D^2\sin^2\xi)^{1/2}}{\frac{1}{2}(L_{Rf} + L_L) - \zeta_I}\right] \tag{147}$$

$$\theta_2 = \tan^{-1}\left[\frac{\rho_I' + D\cos\xi - (r_L^2 - D^2\sin^2\xi)^{1/2}}{\frac{1}{2}(L_{Rf} - L_L) - \zeta_I}\right] \tag{148}$$

where

$$\rho_I'(\phi) = \frac{-(hb^2\cos\phi + ka^2\sin\phi) + ab[\sigma^2 - (h\sin\phi - k\cos\phi)^2]^{1/2}}{\sigma^2} \tag{149}$$

and

$$D^2 \sin^2 \xi = r_L^2 \tag{150}$$

Solving this implicit equation numerically, since D and ξ are only functions of ϕ, the limiting values of ϕ can be determined.

The equivalent to Equation 90 has now the following expression:

$$|\underline{q}| = 2\kappa\Gamma_{Rf,\nu}\Upsilon_{R,\nu}\int_\phi d\phi(r_L^2 - D^2\sin^2\xi)^{1/2}\int_{\theta_1(\phi)}^{\theta_2(\phi)} d\theta \exp\left[-\int_{\rho_0^*(\theta,\phi)}^{\rho^*(\theta,\phi)} \mu\, d\rho'\right] \tag{151}$$

Analysis for Polychromatic Radiation

A reasonably good approximation (which has shown to be valid for photochlorinations) is to assume that the primary quantum yield is independent of wavelength within the range of continuous absorption of radiation by the molecule. On the other hand, the lamp output power and the absorption by halogens are wavelength dependent. Generally speaking the wavelength dependence of Γ_{Rf} and Υ_R must also be included.

From Equation 151, the dimensionless form of the rate of photoinitiation is

$$J = \frac{J^*L_R}{\langle v\rangle C_1^\circ} = \frac{2\Phi L_R}{4\pi V_L\langle v\rangle}\Psi_1\int_{\nu=0}^{\nu=\infty} d\nu\,\Gamma_{Rf,\nu}E_\nu\alpha_\nu\Upsilon_{R,\nu}$$
$$\times\int_\phi d\phi[r_L^2 - D^2\sin^2\xi]^{1/2}\int_{\theta_1(\phi)}^{\theta_2(\phi)} d\theta \exp\left[-\int_{\rho_0(\theta,\phi)}^{\rho_1^*(\theta,\phi)} \alpha_\nu C_1\, d\rho'\right] \tag{152}$$

Let us concentrate on the frequency integral. It can be written as

$$I = \int_{\nu=0}^{\nu=\infty} d\nu\ \Gamma_{Rf,\nu} \Upsilon_{R,\nu} E_\nu \alpha_\nu \exp\left[- \int_{\rho_0^*(\theta,\phi)}^{\rho_I^*(\theta,\phi)} \alpha_\nu C_1\ d\rho' \right] \tag{153}$$

We can investigate the effect of wavelength on those properties that may be affected by the use of polychromatic light.

Lamp emission is generally (but not always) discrete. Lines of emission are significant between $\lambda_1^L = 200$ nm and $\lambda_2^L = 1{,}400$ nm. The transmission coefficient $\Upsilon_{R,\nu}$ for quartz, has a value which may be considered constant between $\lambda_1^W = 220$ nm and $\lambda_2^W = 2{,}000$ nm (below and above these two limits, values are no longer independent of wavelength). The average reflection coefficient for specularly finished, aluminum reflectors has an almost constant value from $\lambda_1^R = 160$ nm to $\lambda_2^R >$ 2,000 nm. Absorption of radiation by halogens goes from $\lambda_1^H = 200$ nm and $\lambda_2^H = 600$ nm. These limits indicate that one can restrict the range of analysis from $\lambda_1 = 200$ nm to $\lambda_2 = 600$ nm. (In the actual case of chlorine, for example, between 250 and 500 nm.) We may write

$$I = \int_{\lambda_1}^{\lambda_2} d\lambda\ \Gamma_{Rf,\lambda} \Upsilon_{R,\lambda} E_\lambda \alpha_\lambda \exp\left[- \int_{\rho_0^*(\theta,\phi)}^{\rho_I^*(\theta,\phi)} \alpha_\lambda C_1\ d\rho' \right] \tag{154}$$

For the most general case λ_1 is defined by the lower practical bound of the primary quantum yield, lamp emission, reactant (or product) absorption, reactor wall transmission and reflector reflectivity, whichever the larger. Similarly, λ_2 is defined by the upper practical bound of the same properties, whichever the shorter.

Let us write

$$E_\lambda = E_\sigma \delta(\lambda - \lambda_\sigma) \tag{155}$$

with δ being the Dirac function. We can now substitute the polychromatic lamp by a finite number of monochromatic ones, each of them emitting the output power corresponding to each line of emission E_σ. Then:

$$I = \sum_{\sigma=1}^{\sigma=n} \int_{\lambda_1}^{\lambda_2} d\lambda\ E_\sigma \delta(\lambda - \lambda_\sigma) \Upsilon_{R,\sigma} \alpha_\sigma \Gamma_{Rf,\sigma} \exp\left[- \int_{\rho_0^*(\theta,\phi)}^{\rho_I^*(\theta,\phi)} \alpha_\sigma C_1\ d\rho' \right] \tag{156}$$

$$I = \sum_{\sigma=1}^{\sigma=n} E_\sigma \alpha_\sigma \Upsilon_{R,\sigma} \Gamma_{Rf,\sigma} \exp\left[- \int_{\rho_0^*(\theta,\phi)}^{\rho_I^*(\theta,\phi)} \alpha_\sigma C_1\ d\rho' \right] \tag{157}$$

The summation must be performed over all of the spectral lines of the lamp emission spectrum for which $\alpha_\sigma \neq 0$, $\Upsilon_{R,\sigma} \neq 0$ and $\Gamma_{Rf,\sigma} \neq 0$. Here, E_σ is the lamp output power at $\lambda = \lambda_\sigma$; α_σ is the absorption coefficient of the halogen at $\lambda = \lambda_\sigma$; $\Upsilon_{R,\sigma}$ is the wall transmission at $\lambda = \lambda_\sigma$; $\Gamma_{Rf,\sigma}$ is the reflection coefficient at $\lambda = \lambda_\sigma$ and n the number of emission lines produced by the lamp between λ_1 and λ_2.

With the following definitions:

$$\varepsilon = \frac{D \sin \xi}{r_L} \tag{158}$$

$$K_{1\sigma} = \frac{\Phi E_\sigma \alpha_\sigma \Gamma_{Rf,\sigma} L_R}{4\pi^2 \langle v \rangle r_L L_L} \tag{159}$$

$$\Lambda_\sigma = \alpha_\sigma C_1^\circ r_R \tag{160}$$

$$\Delta = \rho^*/r_R \tag{161}$$

Equation 152 is finally written in dimensionless form as

$$J = 2\langle \Upsilon_R \rangle \Psi_1 \int_\phi d\phi (1 - \varepsilon^2)^{1/2} \int_{\theta_1(\phi)}^{\theta_2(\phi)} d\theta \sum_{\sigma=1}^{\sigma=n} K_{1\sigma} \exp\left[-\Lambda_\sigma \int_{\Delta_0(\theta,\phi)}^{\Delta_I(\theta,\phi)} \Psi_1 \, d\Delta' \right] \tag{162}$$

With this equation and the limits of integration previously discussed, the rate of initiation (which includes the LVREA) can be incorporated into the mass balances derived earlier.

The whole system requires numerical integration.

Cylindrical Photoreactor Irradiated from the Bottom with a Parabolic Reflector

Reaction

Let us consider the case of the monosubstitution reaction with chlorine of a liquid saturated hydrocarbon.

The overall reaction

$$R_1 - R_2H + Cl_2 \longrightarrow R_1 - R_2Cl + HCl$$

is well represented by the following sequence:

$$Cl_2 \xrightarrow{\Phi_v} 2\,Cl\cdot$$

$$R_1 - R_2H + Cl\cdot \underset{k_{-2}}{\overset{k_2}{\longrightarrow}} R_1 - R_2\cdot + HCl$$

$$R_1 - R_2\cdot + Cl_2 \underset{k_{-3}}{\overset{k_3}{\longrightarrow}} R_1 - R_2Cl + Cl\cdot$$

$$Cl\cdot + Cl\cdot \xrightarrow{k_4} Cl_2$$

$$Cl\cdot + R_1 - R_2\cdot \xrightarrow{k_5} R_1 - R_2Cl$$

$$2(R_1 - R_2\cdot) \xrightarrow{k_6} \text{products}$$

Here, the reaction between the two chlorine atoms is stabilized by the presence of a liquid phase. Also, in liquid phase systems there exists enough ground to exclude the consideration of significant wall reactions.

Again, to simplify notation, we will designate:

Species	HCl	Cl_2	$R_1 - R_2H$	$R_1 - R_2Cl$	$R\cdot$	$Cl\cdot$
Number	1	2	3	4	5	6

Equation of Change

The reaction will be carried out in a cylindrical vessel, irradiated from the bottom. The reactor will have a continuous feed of pure or diluted (with an inert gas) chlorine gas which bubbles in a well stirred batch of the liquid reactant. Unreacted gas can be continuously eliminated from the reaction chamber. Figure 18 illustrates the semi-batch photoreactor.

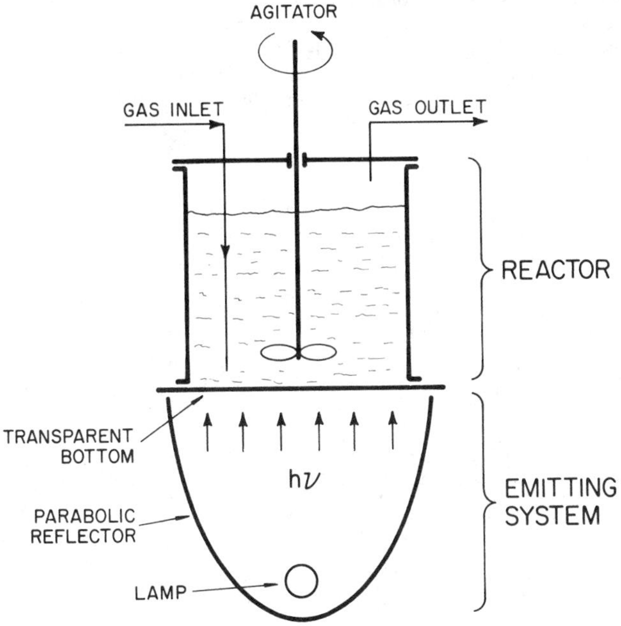

Figure 18. Semi-batch photoreactor irradiated from the bottom. (Adapted from Ref. [27].)

For this particular system, the following phenomena are present [22, 23]:

1. Mass transfer from the gas phase (pure reactant or mixed with an inert) to the liquid phase.
2. Reaction in the liquid phase.

However, we know that photochemical reactions have an initiation step that is always spatially dependent because the radiation field is intrinsically non uniform. Under these circumstances, if an enhancement factor different from one is present, since the reaction rate is spatially dependent, the mass transfer coefficient (modified by the chemical reaction) will also be a function of position. If this is the case, modeling of the mass transfer rate for the photoreactor will be a very difficult task.

Even if we find conditions that permit to overcome the above problem, different mixing conditions can be present in the liquid phase. Two types of species participate in the reaction and their hydrodynamical state of mixing may be different. Under good stirring conditions, stable species may be considered in a state of perfect mixing. On the other hand short lived, intermediate species could have a very short mean lifetime as compared with the characteristic mixing time. Thus, intermediate species could "be born," "live," and "die" in the same place with no chances of interaction with the surrounding fluid. If this is the case, the reactor would not be operating as a perfectly mixed system for these species. If the meanlife time of intermediates species is sufficiently long or the mixing conditions are extremely good, both types of species could be in a state of perfect mixing. Consequently, two models of mixing for the liquid phase can be proposed:

Model I: Perfect mixing for both intermediate and stable species.
Model II: Perfect mixing only for stable species.

Very likely, real situations may show a combination of both cases.

Finally, as it is the case in conventional reactors, mass transfer limitations may exist in the gas phase if the feed composition contains other components besides chlorine.

We will show here the design procedure assuming that the case of model II prevails. Tables describing the problem (Tables 3, 4, and 5) show final results for both models.

Equations have been made dimensionless with the following definitions:

$$\Psi_i = \frac{C_i}{C^{\circ}_{ref}} \tag{163}$$

$$\tau = \frac{t}{t_T} \tag{164}$$

$$\Omega = \frac{\Omega^* t_T}{C^{\circ}_{ref}} \tag{165}$$

$$N_2 = \frac{n_2 t_T A_v}{C^{\circ}_{ref}} \tag{166}$$

$$K_L = k_L A_v t_T \tag{167}$$

$$K_i = \frac{k_i t_T}{C^{\circ}_{ref}} \tag{168}$$

$$J_v = \frac{\alpha_v \Phi_v E_{L,v} t_T}{L_L r_L} \tag{169}$$

$$\Theta_v = \frac{|\underset{\sim}{q}_v| L_L r_L}{E_{L,v}} \tag{170}$$

Table 3
Definitions used in the Analysis of the Gas-Liquid Photoreactor

Denomination	Representation	Definition
Dimensional stable species concentration array	$\underset{\sim}{C}(t)$	$(\langle C_1\rangle, \langle C_2\rangle, \langle C_3\rangle, \langle C_4\rangle)^T$
Dimensionless $\underset{\sim}{C}(t)$	$\underset{\sim}{\Psi}(\tau)$	$(\Psi_1, \Psi_2, \Psi_3, \Psi_4)^T$
Dimensional intermediate species concentration array	$\hat{\underset{\sim}{C}}(t)$ or $\hat{\underset{\sim}{C}}(\underset{\sim}{x}, t)$	$(\hat{C}_6, \hat{C}_5)^T$
Dimensionless $\hat{\underset{\sim}{C}}(t)$ or $\hat{\underset{\sim}{C}}(\underset{\sim}{x}, t)$	$\hat{\underset{\sim}{\Psi}}(\tau)$ or $\hat{\underset{\sim}{\Psi}}(\underset{\sim}{x}, \tau)$	$(\hat{\Psi}_6, \hat{\Psi}_5)^T$
Dimensional stable species reaction rate	$\underset{\sim}{\Omega}^*(\underset{\sim}{x}, t)$	$(\Omega_1^*, \Omega_2^*, \Omega_3^*, \Omega_4^*)^T$
Dimensionless $\underset{\sim}{\Omega}^*(\underset{\sim}{x}, t)$	$\underset{\sim}{\Omega}(\underset{\sim}{x}, \tau)$	$(\Omega_1, \Omega_2, \Omega_3, \Omega_4)^T$
Dimensional intermediate species reaction rate	$\hat{\underset{\sim}{\Omega}}^*(\underset{\sim}{x}, t)$	$(\hat{\Omega}_6^*, \hat{\Omega}_5^*)^T$
Dimensionless $\hat{\underset{\sim}{\Omega}}^*(\underset{\sim}{x}, t)$	$\hat{\underset{\sim}{\Omega}}(\underset{\sim}{x}, \tau)$	$(\hat{\Omega}_6, \hat{\Omega}_5)^T$
Dimensional mass absorption rate	$\underset{\sim}{n}(t)$	$(0, k_L A_v(\langle C_2\rangle^{int} - \langle C_2\rangle), 0, 0)^T$
Dimensionless $\underset{\sim}{n}(t)$	$\underset{\sim}{N}(\tau)$	$(0, K_L(\Psi_2^{int} - \Psi_2), 0, 0)^T$

Table 4
Mass Balances

Species	Mixing State	Equation	Int. Cond.
Stable	Perfect mixing	$\frac{d\underset{\sim}{\Psi}(\tau)}{d\tau} = \underset{\sim}{N}(\tau) - \langle \underset{\sim}{\Omega}(\underset{\sim}{x}, \tau) \rangle$	$\underset{\sim}{\Psi}(0) = \underset{\sim}{\Psi}_0$
Intermediate	Perfect mixing	$\frac{d\hat{\underset{\sim}{\Psi}}(\tau)}{d\tau} = -\langle \hat{\underset{\sim}{\Omega}}(\underset{\sim}{x}, \tau) \rangle$	$\hat{\underset{\sim}{\Psi}}(0) = \underset{\sim}{0}$
Stable	Perfect mixing	$\frac{d\underset{\sim}{\Psi}(\tau)}{d\tau} = \underset{\sim}{N}(\tau) - \langle \underset{\sim}{\Omega}(\underset{\sim}{x}, \tau) \rangle$	$\underset{\sim}{\Psi}(0) = \underset{\sim}{\Psi}_0$
Intermediate	No mixing	$\frac{d\hat{\underset{\sim}{\Psi}}(\underset{\sim}{x}, \tau)}{d\tau} = -\hat{\underset{\sim}{\Omega}}(\underset{\sim}{x}, \tau)$	$\hat{\underset{\sim}{\Psi}}(\underset{\sim}{x}, 0) = \underset{\sim}{0}$

Tables 3 and 4 indicate the array definitions and the dimensionless mass balance equations in the bulk for the models generated considering both states of mixing. A system of integro-differential equations with specified initial values was obtained. Due to the complexity of the problem, some approximation had to be used in order to find the solution of the system. In addition to that, the expressions for the absorption rate $\underset{\sim}{N}(\tau)$ and the reaction rate $\underset{\sim}{\Omega}(\underset{\sim}{x}, \tau)$, must be found to complete the mathematical description of the process.

The vector $\underset{\sim}{N}(\tau)$ represents the absorption rates into the liquid bulk of reactants. If one considers that in the liquid phase only gaseous chlorine is absorbed, the dimensionless expression for each

Table 5
Summary of the Reaction Rates

Denomination of the Array	Representation	Definition
Intermediate species concentrations	$\hat{\underset{\sim}{R}}(\tau)$ or $\hat{\underset{\sim}{R}}(\underset{\sim}{x}, \tau)$	$\begin{bmatrix} \hat{\Psi}_6 & 0 \\ 0 & \hat{\Psi}_5 \end{bmatrix}$
Propagation reactions (without the L.C.A.)	$\underset{\sim}{A}(\tau)$	$\begin{bmatrix} K_2\Psi_3 + K_{-3}\Psi_4 & -K_{-2}\Psi_1 + K_3\Psi_2 \\ -K_2\Psi_3 + K_{-3}\Psi_4 & K_{-2}\Psi_1 + K_3\Psi_2 \end{bmatrix}$
Termination constants	$\underset{\sim}{T}$	$\begin{bmatrix} 2K_4 & K_5 \\ K_5 & 2K_6 \end{bmatrix}$
Initiation reactions	$\underset{\sim}{g}(\underset{\sim}{x}, \tau)$	$\left[\sum_v J_v \Psi_2 \Theta(\underset{\sim}{x}, \tau), 0 \ldots 0\right]^T$
Termination reactions	$\underset{\sim}{t}(\tau)$ or $\underset{\sim}{t}(\underset{\sim}{x}, \tau)$	$\begin{bmatrix} -2K_4\hat{\Psi}_6 & -K_5\hat{\Psi}_5\hat{\Psi}_6 \\ -K_5\hat{\Psi}_5\hat{\Psi}_6 & -2K_6\hat{\Psi}_5 \end{bmatrix}$
Propagation reactions (with the L.C.A.)	$\underset{\sim}{B}(\tau)$	$\begin{bmatrix} -K_2\Psi_3 & K_{-2}\Psi_1 \\ -K_{-3}\Psi_4 & K_3\Psi_2 \\ K_2\Psi_3 & -K_{-2}\Psi_1 \\ K_{-3}\Psi_4 & -K_3\Psi_2 \end{bmatrix}$

component of $N(\tau)$ is given by:

$$N_i(\tau) = 0 \quad (i \neq 2) \tag{171}$$

$$N_2(\tau) = K_L[\Psi_2^{int}(\tau) - \Psi_2(\tau)] \tag{172}$$

where

$$K_L = \frac{t_T}{(1/k_L A_v)} = \left[\frac{\text{Total time of reaction}}{\text{Absorption time}}\right] \tag{173}$$

$$\Psi_2^{int} = \frac{C_2^{int}}{C_{ref}^\circ} = \left[\begin{array}{c}\text{Dimensionless concentration}\\ \text{of chlorine in the gas-liquid interface}\end{array}\right] \tag{174}$$

In order to get some insight about the effect of the reaction rate on the gas absorption rate, an order of magnitude analysis can be performed. One can define two different times:

$$t_{Diff} = \frac{D_i}{(k_L^\circ)^2} \tag{175}$$

$$t_{reac} = \frac{C_2^{int}}{\Omega_2(C_2^{int}, e^a_{x=x\,max})} \tag{176}$$

where the reaction Ω_2 is estimated with C_2 evaluated at the interface conditions and at a point where the value of e^a is maximum.

Under normal conditions [22], it can be shown that the reaction in the liquid phase, in spite of being calculated where C_2 and e^a are maximum, is not fast enough to produce significant changes during the lifetime of the liquid surface elements, i.e.

$$t_{Diff} \ll t_{reac} \tag{177}$$

This condition was defined as a "low reaction regime" [24–26]; if this is the case, the chemical absorption coefficient is equal to the physical absorption coefficient. Hence, the enhancement factor is

$$I = \frac{k_L}{k_L^\circ} \cong 1 \tag{178}$$

In order to evaluate Ψ_2^{int}, a well-mixed gas phase is assumed. Therefore, the outlet mole fraction of chlorine can be calculated using the mass balance for the gas phase under steady-state conditions. The expression for Ψ_2^{int} is given by:

$$\Psi_2^{int}(\tau) = \frac{1}{2}\left[\frac{a}{K_L} + b + \Psi_2(\tau)\right] - \left\{\left[\frac{a}{K_L} + b + \Psi_2(\tau)\right]^2 - 4b\left[y_{2,in}\frac{a}{K_L} + \Psi_2(\tau)\right]\right\}^{1/2} \tag{179}$$

where

$$a = \frac{F_{in}t_T}{V_L C_{ref}^\circ} = \left[\frac{\text{Total moles of gas at the inlet}}{\text{Initial moles of liquid reactant}}\right] \tag{180}$$

$$b = \frac{P}{HC^{\circ}_{ref}} = \left[\frac{\text{Maximum concentration of chlorine in the liquid}}{\text{Initial concentration of liquid reactant}}\right] \quad (181)$$

Finally, from Equation 173 and Equations 178 to 181 one can evaluate $\underset{\sim}{N}(\tau)$ using Equation 172. Note that Equation 179 considers that the gas feed may not be a pure component.

If we restrict our analysis to the conditions of model II we can only apply the steady-state approximation for point concentration expressions. By carrying out the micro-steady-state approximation locally for the free radicals (or MSSA), we obtain

$$\underset{(\text{Propagation rates})}{\underset{\sim}{A}(\tau) \cdot \hat{\underset{\sim}{\Psi}}(\underset{\sim}{x}, \tau)} + \underset{(\text{Termination rates})}{\hat{\underset{\sim}{R}}(\underset{\sim}{x}, \tau) \cdot \underset{\sim}{T} \cdot \hat{\underset{\sim}{\Psi}}(\underset{\sim}{x}, \tau)} - \underset{(\text{Initiation rates})}{2\underset{\sim}{g}(\underset{\sim}{x}, \tau)} = 0 \quad (182)$$

where each term is here a function of position and time. In order to simplify the problem, the long chain approximation (L.C.A.) can be applied:

$$\underset{\sim}{A}(\tau) \cdot \hat{\underset{\sim}{\Psi}}(\underset{\sim}{x}, \tau) = 0 \quad (183)$$

From Equation 183, the value of $\hat{\Psi}_5(\underset{\sim}{x}, \tau)$ can be obtained. Introducing this value into Equation 182 an expression for $\hat{\Psi}_1(\underset{\sim}{x}, \tau)$ can be obtained:

$$\hat{\Psi}_5(\underset{\sim}{x}, \tau) = \frac{\hat{\Psi}_1(\underset{\sim}{x}, \tau)}{\beta} \quad (184)$$

$$\hat{\Psi}_1(\underset{\sim}{x}, \tau) = \left[\frac{1}{K_4 + \frac{K_5}{\beta} + \frac{K_6}{\beta^2}}\right]^{1/2} \left[\sum_v J_v \Psi_2 \Theta_v(\underset{\sim}{x}, \tau)\right]^{1/2} \quad (185)$$

where J_v and Θ_v are values obtained in the evaluation of e^a as it will be described in the next section and

$$\beta = \beta(\tau) = \frac{K_3\Psi_2 + K_{-2}\Psi_1}{K_2\Psi_3 + K_{-3}\Psi_4} \quad (186)$$

It must be noted that here $\hat{\Psi}_1$ and $\hat{\Psi}_5$ are functions of position and time. (Model I renders similar values but the only part of the result which is a function of position is $J_v\Theta_v$.) Consequently, when the intermediate species cannot be assumed to be in a state of complete mixing it is necessary not only to obtain an average value of e^a for the whole reactor but also the volumetric averages of $\hat{\Psi}_1$ and $\hat{\Psi}_5$ in the reacting space. These volumetric-averaged values go into the stable species mass balances. The final results are

$$\langle\hat{\Psi}_5\rangle(\tau) = \frac{\langle\hat{\Psi}_1\rangle(\tau)}{\beta} \quad (187)$$

$$\langle\hat{\Psi}_1\rangle(\tau) = \left[\frac{1}{K_4 + \frac{K_5}{\beta} + \frac{K_6}{\beta^2}}\right]^{1/2} \left\langle\left[\sum_v J_v \Psi_2 \Theta_v(\underset{\sim}{x}, \tau)\right]^{1/2}\right\rangle \quad (188)$$

Hence, for the stable species we obtain

$$\langle\underset{\sim}{\Omega}(\underset{\sim}{x}, \tau)\rangle = \underset{\sim}{B}(\tau) \cdot \langle\hat{\underset{\sim}{\Psi}}(\underset{\sim}{x}, \tau)\rangle + \langle\underset{\sim}{g}(\underset{\sim}{x}, \tau)\rangle - \langle\underset{\sim}{t}(\underset{\sim}{x}, \tau)\rangle \quad (189)$$

In Equation 189, $\langle\hat{\underset{\sim}{\Psi}}(\underset{\sim}{x}, \tau)\rangle$ is given by Equations 187 and 188.

Incidentally, it can be mentioned that for the case in which all species are in a state of complete mixing Equations 188 and 189 take on the following form:

$$\langle\hat{\Psi}_1\rangle(\tau) = \left[\frac{1}{K_4 + \dfrac{K_5}{\beta} + \dfrac{K_6}{\beta^2}}\right]^{1/2} \left[\left\langle \sum_v J_v \Psi_2 \Theta_v(\underset{\sim}{x}, \tau)\right\rangle\right]^{1/2} \tag{190}$$

$$\langle\underset{\sim}{\Omega}(\underset{\sim}{x}, \tau)\rangle = \underset{\sim}{B}(\tau) \cdot \underset{\sim}{\hat{\Psi}}(\tau) + \langle \underset{\sim}{g}(\underset{\sim}{x}, \tau)\rangle - \underset{\sim}{t}(\tau) \tag{191}$$

Clearly two main differences can be observed: (i) in Equation 191 the rate of initiation is the only term that must be averaged to obtain $\langle\Omega\rangle$; and (ii) in Equation 188 the LVREA appears as the volumetric-averaged value of the square root of $(\sum J\Psi_2\Theta)$ whereas in Equation 190 we obtain the square root of the volumetric-averaged value of $(\sum J\Psi_2\Theta)$.

To complete the set of equations needed to design the reactor one must know the value of the rate of initiation. This means to be able to obtain a computable expression for the dimensionless rate of initiation which is the local value of

$$\sum_v J_v \Psi_2(\tau)\Theta_v(\underset{\sim}{x}, \tau) \tag{192}$$

This will be done in the next section.

Evaluation of the LVREA

Results will be shown using the ESVE model (see Figures 19–21). Here again we may have direct and reflected radiation. For the analysis we will require two coordinate systems. The first one $(x_F - y_F - z_F)$ is defined with the origin at point F located at the center of the bottom of the empty cylindrical reactor, with y_F, consequently, being its centerline (Figure 19). An auxiliary coordinate system parallel to the former is also needed. Its center is located at the point of incidence designated by I in Figure 19 and it can be moved all over the space under analysis.

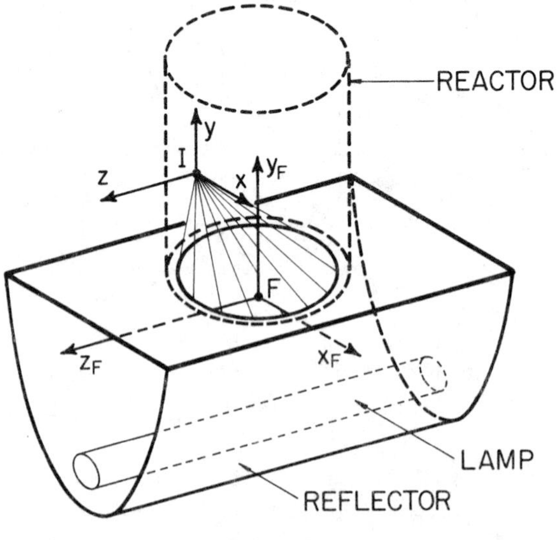

Figure 19. Reactor-reflector-lamp system. (Adapted from Ref. [27].)

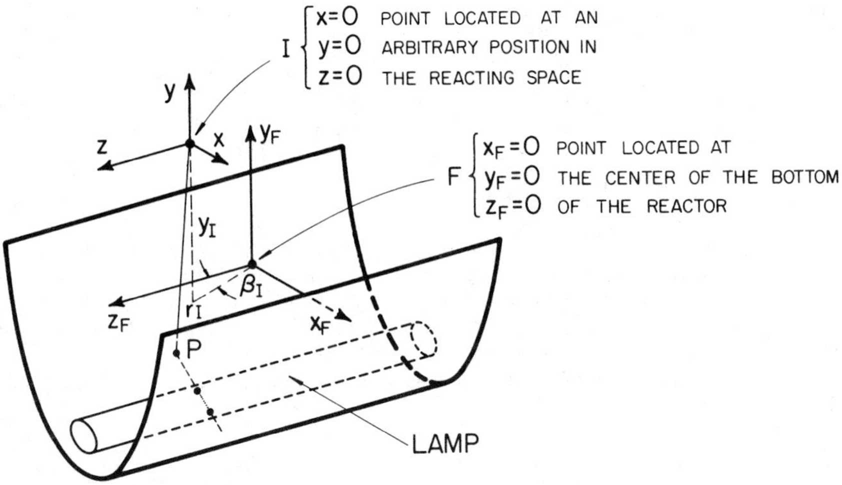

Figure 20. Coordinate systems used in the parabolic reflector analysis. (Adapted from Ref. [27].)

Direct Radiation: For this case, the limits of integration may be obtained in a similar way as for the annular and elliptical reactors. The results are

$$\rho_{1,2}(\theta, \phi) = -\frac{\Delta_1 \sin\phi + \Delta_2 \cos\phi}{\sin\theta} \mp \frac{[r_L^2 - (\Delta_2 \sin\phi - \Delta_1 \cos\phi)^2]^{1/2}}{\sin\theta} \tag{193}$$

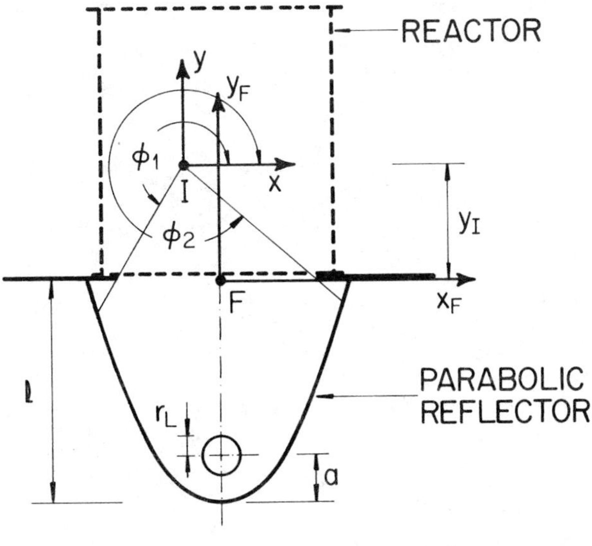

Figure 21. Geometry of the reactor-reflector system.

where

$$\Delta_1 = y_I + 1 - a \tag{194}$$

$$\Delta_2 = r_I \sin \beta_I \tag{195}$$

$$\theta_1(\phi) = \tan^{-1}\left[\frac{\rho'_1}{L_L/2 - z_I}\right] \tag{196}$$

$$\theta_2(\phi) = \tan^{-1}\left[-\frac{\rho'_1}{L_L/2 + z_I}\right] \tag{197}$$

$$\rho'_1 = -\Delta_1 \sin \phi - \Delta_2 \cos \phi - [r_L^2 - (\Delta_2 \sin \phi - \Delta_1 \cos \phi)^2]^{1/2} \tag{198}$$

The limits for ϕ are obtained from the solution of the implicit equation:

$$r_L^2 - (\Delta_2 \sin \phi - \Delta_1 \cos \phi)^2 = 0 \tag{199}$$

and the final expression for $|\underset{\sim}{q}|$ is

$$|\underset{\sim}{q}_\nu| = 2\kappa \int_{\phi_1}^{\phi_2} d\phi[r_L^2 - (\Delta_2 \sin \phi - \Delta_1 \cos \phi)^2]^{1/2} \int_{\theta_1(\phi)}^{\theta_2(\phi)} d\theta \exp\left[-\int_{\rho_0^*(\theta,\phi)}^{\rho^*(\theta,\phi)} \mu \, d\rho'\right] \tag{200}$$

From Equation 200 we can define

$$\Theta^D = \frac{2\Upsilon_{R,\nu}}{4\pi^2 r_L} \int_{\phi_1}^{\phi_2} d\phi[r_L^2 - (\Delta_2 \sin \phi - \Delta_1 \cos \phi)^2]^{1/2} \int_{\theta_1(\phi)}^{\theta_2(\phi)} d\theta \exp\left(-\int_{\rho_0^*(\theta,\phi)}^{\rho^*(\theta,\phi)} d\rho'\right) \tag{201}$$

Indirect Radiation: The methodology of analysis for this type of radiation is similar to that employed with the elliptical photoreactor. The results are

$$\rho_{1,2} = \frac{D \cos \xi \mp (r_L^2 - D^2 \sin^2 \xi)^{1/2}}{\sin \theta} \tag{202}$$

But the meaning of the variables in this case is

$$D = (x_L^2 + y_L^2)^{1/2} \tag{203}$$

$$\sin \xi = -\frac{1}{D}[x_L \sin \phi_E - y_L \cos \phi_E] \tag{204}$$

$$\cos \xi = -\frac{1}{D}[x_L \cos \phi_E + y_L \sin \phi_E] \tag{205}$$

where

$$x_L = \Delta_2 + x_P \tag{206}$$

$$y_L = \Delta_1 + y_P \tag{207}$$

$$\phi_E = \tan^{-1}\left[\frac{(1 - G^2) \sin \phi - 2G \cos \phi}{(G^2 - 1) \cos \phi - 2G \sin \phi}\right] \tag{208}$$

$$G = \frac{-2a}{x_P + \Delta_2} \tag{209}$$

The limits for the θ-variable are represented by the following expressions:

$$\theta_1(\phi) = \tan^{-1}\left[\frac{\rho_I' + D\cos\xi - (r_L^2 - D^2\sin^2\xi)^{1/2}}{L_L/2 - z_I}\right] \tag{210}$$

$$\theta_2(\phi) = \tan^{-1}\left[-\frac{\rho_I' + D\cos\xi - (r_L^2 - D^2\sin^2\xi)^{1/2}}{L_L/2 + z_I}\right] \tag{211}$$

and

$$\rho_I' = \frac{2a\tan\phi - \Delta_2 - 2[a^2(1 + \tan^2\phi) + a(\Delta_1 - \Delta_2\tan\phi)]^{1/2}}{\cos\phi} \tag{212}$$

To obtain the limits for the ϕ-variable, we must solve (as in the case of the elliptical photoreactor) the following implicit equation:

$$r_L^2 = D^2\sin^2\xi \tag{213}$$

with a final value of Θ_v equal to

$$\Theta^{In} = \frac{2\Upsilon_{R,v}\Gamma_{Rf,v}}{4\pi^2 r_L}\int_{\phi_1}^{\phi_2} d\phi[r_L^2 - D^2\sin^2\xi]^{1/2}\int_{\theta_1(\phi)}^{\theta_2(\phi)} d\theta \exp\left(-\int_{\rho_0^*(\theta,\phi)}^{\rho^*(\theta,\phi)} \mu\, d\rho'\right) \tag{214}$$

Finally, it should be mentioned that in certain cases it may be necessary to put a protecting cover over the emission system which can also be used to support the cylindrical reactor (see Figures 19 and 21). If this is the case, there will be totally and partially irradiated zones within the reaction space. Consequently, for each incidence point I, we have to determine which portion of the parabolic reflector or source is capable of illuminating the point. From the mathematical point of view, the integration interval for each point I must be adjusted. To do this, the limiting angles determined by the circular hole of the lamp-reflector cover system must be calculated, and afterwards compared with the limiting angles defined for the integration of the source volume (Equations 210 to 213). For more detailed information the reader is referred to Alfano et al. [27–29].

Finally, the value of Θ_v to be used in Equation 177 is

$$\Theta_v = \Theta_v^D(\underline{x}, \tau) + \Theta_v^{In}(\underline{x}, \tau) \tag{215}$$

It must be noted that in Equation 201 or Equation 214 μ_v must be evaluated for a system where two phases are present. (Equations 61 or 62.) Another observation is that Equation 215 includes only the first reflection.

RESULTS

Cassano and co-workers [2–4, 15–22, 27–29] have solved and experimentally verified all the design equations described in the previous section. The reader interested in the details can resort to the original papers. No attempt will be made to present those results here. However, since several general conclusions (some of them useful for design purposes) have been reached, they will be summarized here.

1. The use of the name absorbed light intensity and the symbol I_a for the absorbed energy by reactants is misleading. The LVREA is not an intensity. We have proposed the symbol e^a.

Similarly the use of the name light intensity and the symbol I for the modulus of the radiation energy density vector is an error. We have proposed the symbol $|\underset{\sim}{q}|$.

2. Lambert's equation can be used to account for the absorption of radiation only in homogeneous media and it is rigorously valid for dilute solutions and very simple mixtures.
3. Line source models can be used if no curved reflectors are present. However, only good results can be expected from the Line Source with Spherical Emission model (LSSE model). The best results are produced by the ESVE model (for non-fluorescent lamps) and the ESSE model with diffuse emission (for fluorescent lamps).
4. When polychromatic radiation is used (and it should always be done unless some special reason advises against it) the wavelength dependence of several components of the reacting system must be considered. They are:
   a. The absorptivities of reactants, products, and inerts.
   b. Reflection coefficients. (When reflectors are used.)
   c. Wall transmittances.
   d. Output power of the radiation source.
   e. Quantum yields.
5. Unless it is absolutely necessary, reflectors should be avoided. Their efficiency cannot be larger than 65%, which is the maximum expected value for the average reflection coefficient in the U.V. range.
6. Only under very restricted conditions does the radiation field produced by a tubular lamp located at one of the focal axes of the elliptical reflector, have angular symmetry on the second focal axis.
7. All radiation source properties (dimensions, output power, wavelength dependence of the output power, etc.) are part of the design equations.
8. With the only exception of photosensitized reactions, the link between the attenuation of radiation and the extent of the reaction cannot be avoided. This situation very often complicates the design of a photoreactor.
9. Temperature effects on the rate of a photochemical reaction are negligible. However, they must be considered to avoid overheating of the system with undesirable consequences in side reactions and safety.
10. The characteristic length in the principal direction of propagation of radiation not only affects the corresponding Pe number (and in some cases the Re number) but also the optical density of the system. This is a very distinct property of photoreactors. This special performance can be easily illustrated for the case in which the radiation characteristic length is the radius. Assuming no thermal or diffusional limitations, in a thermal or catalytic reactor, the conversion in a flow reactor for a given reaction and reaction temperature will be a function of the mean residence time. If we increase the radius, and the flow rate is consequently increased in the corresponding way, conversion will be the same. Under the same conditions, in a photochemical reactor conversion will normally be decreased because such a characteristic length affects also a negative exponential integral that expresses the attenuation of radiation. The increase in the radius—at a constant radiation output power—will decrease the average value of the radiation density inside the reactor and consequently the average value of the rate of initiation. This effect can seldom be overcome by increasing the radiation output power of the source.
11. Unless one is dealing with a photosensitized reaction, the concentration of the radiation absorbing, reactant species affects the reactor behaviour at least in two different ways. They are:
    a. The local value of the rate of the initiation step depends upon the said concentration in a linear form.
    b. When the modulus of the radiation density vector is incorporated into the expression of the rate of the initiation step, the said concentration is also part of a negative exponential integral.

    This means that

$$J^* = f_1\{C_a, p_1\} f_2\{p_2, [\exp - (C_a, p_3)]\} \tag{216}$$

where f_1 and f_2 are known functions, p_1, p_2 and p_3 different reaction and reactor parameters, and C_a is the concentration of the radiation absorbing species. Sometimes C_a also enters into the kinetic expressions of other reaction steps besides the initiation one. Consequently the effect of C_a on the reactor behaviour is very different from that in the case of thermal or catalytic reactors. Equation 216 shows that the linear dependence and the decreasing exponential define a function that goes through a maximum value. Beyond it, increasing C_a will lead to a decrease in reactor conversion.

12. In a practical photoreactor, beside kinetic considerations, there always exists an optimal value for the combination of the radiation characteristic length (for example, the reactor radius) and the concentration of the radiation absorbing species. The optimal value, from the radiation viewpoint, is always a function of the product of both.
13. In practical reactors, particularly in those cases in which well-stirred conditions cannot be assumed, actinometric reactions should be used with great care and always together with a good radiation model.
14. The choice of the proper radiation output power wavelength distribution for a given reaction is a key point in photoreactor design. In fact, for every reaction the corresponding lamp should be especially "designed" whenever possible. The target should be to match the wavelength distribution of the lamp output power with the reacting, radiation absorbing species absorptivity.
15. In practical reactors, at atmospheric pressures or higher pressures, heterogeneous reactions at the wall can be neglected.
16. In practical reactions the *micro* steady state approximation can be generally used. For very fast reactions, it should be applied with great care.
17. In gas-liquid photochemical reactors an additional phenomenon may be present: the existence of a spatially dependent mass transfer coefficient. This is the case when the enhancement factor is different from one. This is due to the intrinsic spatial non-uniformity of the rate of the initiation step.
18. In many cases of gas-liquid reactors, the hypothesis of a state of perfect mixing for stable reacting species can be assumed. However, this is not always the case for *intermediate species*. This is an important consideration for photoreactor design because an a prior design will generally require the use of the mechanistic kinetic sequence.
19. Incidence radiation models cannot be used if experimentally adjustable parameters are to be avoided in practical reactor design [7, 8]. In fact if they are used, these parameters should be measured in the already scaled-up reactor, which will turn the method purposeless.
20. In gas-liquid reactors, when the gas is the reacting and the radiation absorbing species, its concentration in the feed may be adjusted in combination with the value adopted for the radiation flux density vector to increase selectivity in a series reaction sequence. This can be done when the rate of production of at least one of the stable products falls into the kinetic subregime (the reaction is not controlled by diffusion). When this is the case, photochemical control of its rate may allow the achievement of very high selectivities.
21. To design a photochemical reactor, an iterative procedure will be generally needed in order to obtain the best combination of reactor parameters-radiation emission system characteristics (with or without reflectors). The main reason lies in the unavoidable interactions between the properties of the energy supplier (lamp) and energy receptor and user (reactor and reacting species).

DIMENSIONLESS ANALYSIS OF PHOTOCHEMICAL REACTORS

In some cases, the dimensionless analysis of chemical reactors has proved to be a useful tool for designing purposes, particularly in those aspects related to scale-up procedures. As already pointed out [16, 30, 31], it seems that this approach cannot be extended to photoreactors with the same efficiency. The problem can be investigated for a representative case. Let us look at the halogenation of hydrocarbons previously illustrated. For the sake of completeness we will include the possibility of chain reaction heterogeneous terminations, which could occur at the reactor wall.

These reactions could be represented by:

$$X\cdot + W \xrightarrow{k_7} \text{Prod.}$$

$$R\cdot + W \xrightarrow{k_8} \text{Prod.}$$

The system will be analyzed under the following assumptions: (i) steady state; (ii) streamline, incompressible flow; (iii) null "apparent" activation energy; (iv) Newtonian fluid with constant physical properties (diffusivities, viscosities, thermal properties, etc.); (v) angular symmetry and; (vi) negligible axial conduction and diffusion as compared with convective flow. Assumption (iii), which is justified for photochemical reactions, makes much more acceptable the separation of the radiation balance from the thermal energy conservation equation. In fact, the photon balance will only be used to take into account the activation step of the reaction. Moreover, the photochemically useful radiation (at wavelengths between 200 and 600 nm) has always little effect on the reactor temperature.

In dimensionless form (choosing appropriate characteristic scales), the conservation equations, together with the corresponding initial and boundary conditions are:

Mass Balances

$$U(\gamma)\frac{\partial \Psi_i}{\partial \zeta} = \frac{1}{Pe_i Ge}\frac{1}{\gamma}\frac{\partial}{\partial \gamma}\left(\gamma \frac{\partial \Psi_i}{\partial \gamma}\right) + \Omega_i \tag{217}$$

$$\zeta = 0, \quad \forall\gamma \begin{cases} \Psi_1 = \Psi_1^\circ = 1 & (218a) \\ \Psi_3 = \Psi_3^\circ & (218b) \\ \Psi_i = \Psi_i^\circ = 0 \quad (i = 2, 4\text{–}7) & (218c) \end{cases}$$

$$\forall\zeta, \quad \gamma = 0 \left\{ \frac{\partial \Psi_i}{\partial \gamma} = 0 \right. \tag{219}$$

$$\forall\zeta, \quad \gamma = 1 \begin{cases} \dfrac{\partial \Psi_j}{\partial \gamma} = 0 & (220a) \\ \dfrac{\partial \Psi_l}{\partial \gamma} = -Pe_l \Omega_{w,l} & (220b) \end{cases}$$

in which j stands for stable species (j = 1, 3, 4, 6, and 7); l denotes atomic or free radical species and $\Omega_{w,l}$ the rate of heterogeneous termination for species l (l = 2 and 5). We will see further ahead that Boundary Condition 220b can be simplified for this system without losing accuracy in the final results.

The geometric number Ge ($Ge = r_R/L_R$), is an important number in photoreactor analysis. Not only does it affect the Peclet number but it has a strong influence on the optical thickness of the reactor, as well.

In Equations 217 and 220b we defined

$$\Omega_i = \frac{\Omega_i^* L_R}{\langle v \rangle C_1^\circ} \tag{221}$$

and

$$\Omega_{w,l} = \frac{\Omega_{w,l}^*}{\langle v \rangle C_1^\circ} \tag{222}$$

which have the following dimensionless expressions:

$$\Omega_1 = -J - K_3\Psi_1\Psi_5 + K_4\Psi_2^2\Psi_8 \tag{223a}$$

$$\Omega_2 = 2J - K_2\Psi_2\Psi_3 + K_{-2}\Psi_5\Psi_6 + K_3\Psi_1\Psi_5 - 2K_4\Psi_2^2\Psi_8 - K_5\Psi_2\Psi_5 \tag{223b}$$

$$\Omega_3 = -K_2\Psi_2\Psi_3 + K_{-2}\Psi_5\Psi_6 \tag{223c}$$

$$\Omega_4 = K_3\Psi_1\Psi_5 + K_5\Psi_2\Psi_5 \tag{223d}$$

$$\Omega_5 = K_2\Psi_2\Psi_3 - K_{-2}\Psi_5\Psi_6 - K_3\Psi_1\Psi_5 - K_5\Psi_2\Psi_5 - 2K_6\Psi_5^2 \tag{223e}$$

$$\Omega_6 = K_2\Psi_2\Psi_3 - K_{-2}\Psi_5\Psi_6 \tag{223f}$$

$$\Omega_7 = K_6\Psi_5^2 \tag{223g}$$

$$\Omega_{w,2} = K_7\Psi_2 \tag{223h}$$

$$\Omega_{w,5} = K_8\Psi_5 \tag{223i}$$

In all these equations, the following additional definitions were used:

$$J = \frac{J^* L_R}{\langle v \rangle C_1^\circ} \tag{224}$$

$$K_r = \frac{k_r L_R C_1^\circ}{\langle v \rangle}, \qquad r = 2, -2, 3, 5 \text{ and } 6 \tag{225}$$

$$K_r = \frac{k_r L_R C_1^{\circ 2}}{\langle v \rangle}, \qquad r = 4 \tag{226}$$

$$K_j = \frac{k_j}{\langle v \rangle}, \qquad j = 7 \text{ and } 8 \tag{227}$$

We still have to deal with the existence of polychromatic radiation and the explicit form for J^*.

Thermal Energy Balance

$$U(\gamma)\frac{\partial\Theta}{\partial\zeta} = \frac{1}{\text{RePrGe}}\frac{1}{\gamma}\frac{\partial}{\partial\gamma}\left(\gamma\frac{\partial\Theta}{\partial\gamma}\right) + H \tag{228}$$

$$\zeta = 0, \qquad \forall\gamma, \quad \Theta = 0 \tag{229}$$

$$\forall\zeta, \quad \gamma = 0, \qquad \frac{\partial\Theta}{\partial\gamma} = 0 \tag{230a}$$

$$\forall\zeta, \quad \gamma = 1, \qquad \frac{\partial\Theta}{\partial\gamma} = -\text{Nu}(\Theta - 1) \tag{230b}$$

where the following additional definitions have been used:

$$\Theta = \frac{T - T_{in}}{T_w - T_{in}} \tag{231}$$

$$\mathrm{Pr} = \frac{C_p\mu}{k} \tag{232}$$

$$H = \frac{L_R(-\Delta H)\Omega_i^*}{\rho C_p\langle v\rangle(T_w - T_{in})} = \Omega_i H_E \tag{233}$$

$$H_E = \frac{(-\Delta H)C_1^\circ}{\rho C_p(T_w - T_{in})} \tag{234}$$

$$\mathrm{Nu} = \frac{hr_R}{k} \tag{235}$$

The Rate of the Initiation Step

The value is given in terms of the primary quantum yield Φ_v and the LVREA:

$$J^* = \int_{v=0}^{v=\infty} \Phi_v \alpha_v C_1 |\underset{\sim}{q}_v| \, dv \tag{236}$$

If the cylindrical reactor is irradiated by means of a cylindrical reflector of elliptical cross-section area and we accept Cerdá et al.'s [4] conclusions that in many cases the reactor performance can be well represented considering only the first reflection contribution, the value of $|\underset{\sim}{q}_v|$ is

$$|d\underset{\sim}{q}_v| = \Gamma_{Rf,v}\Upsilon_{R,v}\frac{2E_v}{4\pi V_L}\int_\phi d\phi \int_{\theta(\phi)} [r_L^2 - D^2\sin^2\xi]^{1/2} \times \exp\left[-\int_{\rho_0^*(\theta,\phi)}^{\rho_1^*(\theta,\phi)} \alpha_v C_1 \, d\rho'\right] d\theta \tag{237}$$

which is valid for monochromatic radiation.

The limits for the integrals have been presented before and will not be repeated here. However, in the equations governing the emission of radiation, the following dimensionless numbers are significant:

$$e = \frac{c}{a} \tag{238}$$

$$s_1 = \frac{c}{r_L} \tag{239}$$

$$s_2 = \frac{L_L}{r_L} \tag{240}$$

$$s_3 = \frac{L_{Rf}}{r_L} \tag{241}$$

$$s_4 = \frac{r_R}{r_L} \tag{242}$$

$$s_5 = \frac{L_R}{r_L} \tag{243}$$

As it was previously said, e, s_1, and s_4 play an important role in establishing the angular symmetry of the radiation field about the reactor centerline. Certainly, they are not necessary if only direct radiation were used (annular photoreactor, for example). s_2 goes in every formulation of the rate of initiation when the lamp volume (or the lamp surface) appears. s_1, s_2, s_3, s_4, and s_5 participate in the reactor design when lamp and reactor wedges must be taken into account due to the spherical characteristics of the emission of radiation (see References 3, 4, 16, 17, 19, and 21). In the simplest case only s_2, s_4, and s_5 are needed. (Annular reactor with a LSSE model.) It should be noticed that $s_4/s_5 = Ge$.

Making Equation 236 dimensionless we obtain

$$J = \frac{J^* L_R}{\langle v \rangle C_1^\circ} = \Psi_1 \int_{\phi_1}^{\phi_2} d\phi \int_{\theta_1}^{\theta_2} d\theta [1 - \varepsilon^2]^{1/2} \int_{v=0}^{v=\infty} \kappa_{J,v} \exp\left[-\Lambda_v \int_{\Delta_O(\theta,\phi)}^{\Delta_I(\theta,\phi)} \Psi_1 \, d\Delta' \right] \quad (244)$$

with:

$$\Psi_1 = \frac{C_1}{C_1^\circ} \quad (245)$$

$$\varepsilon = \frac{D \sin \xi}{r_L} \quad (246)$$

$$\kappa_{J,v} = \kappa_{J,1,v} \kappa_{J,2} = (\Phi_v \alpha_v E_v \Gamma_{Rf,v} \Upsilon_{R,v}) \left(\frac{L_R}{2\pi r_L L_L \langle v \rangle} \right) \quad (247)$$

$$\Lambda_v = \alpha_v C_1^\circ r_R \quad (248)$$

$$\Delta = \frac{\rho^*}{r_R} \quad (249)$$

$\kappa_{J,v}$ and Λ_v contain all the wavelength dependent information. Equation 247 shows how lamp dimensions (r_L, L_L) and emission characteristics (E_v) enter into the design equations. Equation 244 clearly shows how Ψ_1 enters in two different forms into the rate of initiation of a photoreaction (recall Equation 216). Here, J explicitly shows a linear dependence and a decreasing exponential dependence with Ψ_1. Equation 248 shows how the reactor principal characteristic length (in this case r_R) enters into the optical density of the system. Similarly r_R affects the attenuation path (Equation 249).

Looking at Equations 217 to 249 the complicated interrelationships between several important dimensionless numbers can be analyzed. Table 6 summarizes the results:

1. The appearance of r_R in Λ_v. In conventional reactors, r_R only affects Pe, Re, Nu and Ge. Let us recall that Λ_v participates in an exponential integral (the attenuating decreasing exponential) that influences a function that has a non-monotonous behavior.
2. The appearance of C_1° in Λ_v. In conventional reactors, C_1° only affects H_E and K_r. C_1° also takes part of the attenuating exponential integral.
3. α_v appears in $\kappa_{J,s}$ and Λ_v. Once more, α_v is part of the attenuating function.

These intricate relationships make almost impossible a straightforward application of dimensionless analysis procedures for reactor design purposes, particularly for scale-up considerations.

Consequently, whenever one wishes to extrapolate predictions based upon hydrodynamic or kinetic similarities, they cannot be separated from unavoidable and simultaneous, significant changes in the performance of the radiation field. In other words, changes in C_1° or r_R (and α_v when other system characteristics are affected) cannot be made maintaining, simultaneously, the constancy of the hydrodynamic, kinetic, and radiation similarities.

APPROXIMATE METHODS OF DESIGN

It has been pointed out before that the rigorous formulation of photoreactor design leads to a complex integro-differential problem. Physically its origin must be sought in the existing coupling between the attenuation of radiation (a decreasing exponential integral) and the changes in concentration produced by the progress of the reaction (at least one differential equation). It has also

Table 6

Variable Relationships in Dimensionless Numbers (1: numerator; −1: denominator; 0: the variable does not appear)

	$\langle v\rangle$	r_R	C_1	L_R	D_i	h	k	α_v	Φ_v	E_v	Γ_v	Υ_v	r_L	L_L	ρ	μ	C_p	$T_w - T_{in}$	ΔH	k_r	k_j
Pe	1	1	0	0	−1	0	0	0	0	0	0	0	0	0	0	0	0	0	0	0	0
Re	1	1	0	0	0	0	0	0	0	0	0	0	0	0	1	−1	0	0	0	0	0
Nu	0	1	0	0	0	1	−1	0	0	0	0	0	0	0	0	0	0	0	0	0	0
Pr	0	0	0	0	0	0	−1	0	0	0	0	0	0	0	0	1	1	0	0	0	0
Ge	0	1	0	−1	0	0	0	0	0	0	0	0	0	0	0	0	0	0	0	0	0
H_E	0	0	1	0	0	0	0	0	0	0	0	0	0	0	−1	0	−1	−1	1	0	0
K_r	−1	0	1	1	0	0	0	0	0	0	0	0	0	0	0	0	0	0	0	1	0
K_j	−1	0	0	0	0	0	0	0	0	0	0	0	0	0	0	0	0	0	0	0	1
$\kappa_{J,s}$	−1	0	0	1	0	0	0	1	1	1	1	1	−1	−1	0	0	0	0	0	0	0
Λ_v	0	1	1	0	0	0	0	1	0	0	0	0	0	0	0	0	0	0	0	0	0

been shown that the complexity increases when thermal effects must be included and/or when more than one species mass balance is required. If transport limitations exist and N chemical species are present, assuming that the fluid dynamics is known, the non-isothermal case will require the simultaneous solution of N + 1 partial, integro-differential equations (Figure 22). It seems convenient to look for a reduction of the design complexities in a systematic approach.

First Simplification

One can assume that in the attenuating integral an average, constant concentration can be used. (For instance, the arithmetic mean between the initial and the final radiation absorbing reactant

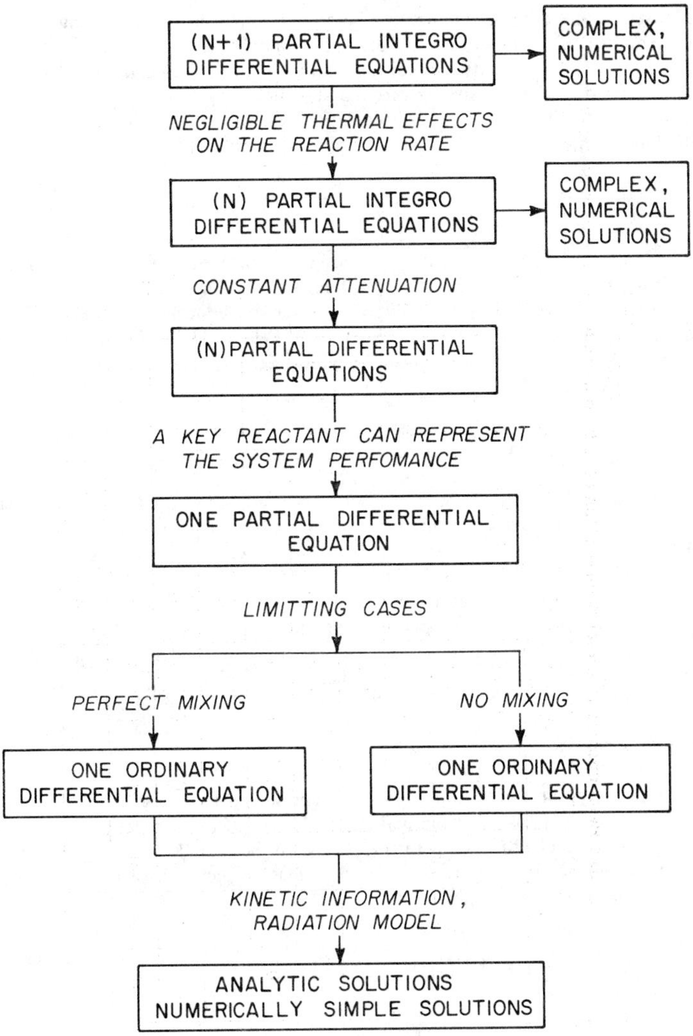

Figure 22. Simplifications used in the approximate methods of design.

concentration). The method that is strictly valid for photosensitized reactions, will be a good approximation for medium and low radiation absorption systems. (Special care must be taken if reaction products also absorb radiation.)

Given the fact that now the exponential integral is independent of the reactant (and/or product) concentration, the integro-differential nature of the problem disappears. It must be noted, however, that the concentration dependence that exists in the linear part of the rate of initiation has not been eliminated. The approximation is also valid for low conversion reactors even if the process imposes recirculation to finally reach a high value for the reaction extent.

Second Simplification

In many cases the reactor performance can be properly described by following one (key) species concentration. When this is possible, only one mass balance will be required. This hypothesis is by no means a loss of accuracy if two conditions can be fulfilled: (i) all other species concentrations can be tightly related to the key species through stoichiometric relationships and (ii) the "kinetic constants" attached to the key species concentration are available or can be calculated from the true specific kinetic rate constants.

Third Simplification

In the differential equations governing the design, a third simplification is possible by considering two limiting cases for the mixing state. Under perfect mixing or no mixing conditions all differential equations (being of the integral type or not) can be reduced to ordinary differential equations. This methodology was first suggested by Hill and Felder [32, 33] for simple kinetics schemes and radiation models. This simplification can be performed even before the first and/or the second simplifications are applied.

Other Simplifications

Although they will not be used here, two other routes can be explored further. They are: (i) flow simplifications in tubular reactors, assuming piston flow behavior and (ii) limiting cases as far as optical thickness is concerned. In this second possibility, two cases have been proposed: infinite optical thickness ("black body reactors") and very low optical density ("diactinic reactors"). These simplications have already been used [3, 4, 20, 34, 35]. Mathematical descriptions resulting from these approximations do not lead to a major reduction in the design complexity.

After application of all three simplifications one can arrive at a final problem description which in certain cases is even amenable of an analytical solution.

Continuous Photoreactors

Let us consider a system that could have been represented by Equations 70 to 95 or alternatively 96 to 162. Let us suppose that thermal effects do not affect the reaction kinetics (which is a good assumption) and that other temperature effects will be considered separately (which is also possible, even though not in a rigorous manner). Let us neglect wall reactions (which, again, is perfectly acceptable). For a reactant i, we have

$$v_z(r)\frac{\partial C_i(\underset{\sim}{x}, z)}{\partial z} = D_{im}\underset{\sim}{\nabla}^2_{(\underset{\sim}{x})}C_i(\underset{\sim}{x}, z) + \Omega_i^*(\underset{\sim}{x}, z) \tag{250}$$

$$C_i(\underset{\sim}{x}, 0) = C_i^{\circ} \tag{251}$$

$$\underset{\sim}{\nabla}_{(\underset{\sim}{x}_n)}C_i\big|_w = 0 \tag{252}$$

where $\underset{\sim}{x}$ is a position vector representing any point inside the reactor cross section and $\underset{\sim}{\nabla}_{(\underset{\sim}{x}_n)} C_i|_w$ is the directional derivative normal to the reactor wall.

Perfect radial mixing (PM)

Integrating Equation 250 over the reactor area, after application of Green's theorem and boundary condition (Equation 252) we get

$$\langle v_z \rangle \frac{dC_i(z)}{dz} = \frac{1}{A_R} \int_{A_R} \Omega_i^*(\underset{\sim}{x}, z)\, dA = \langle \Omega_i^*(\underset{\sim}{x}, z) \rangle_{A_R} \tag{253}$$

$$C_i(z = 0) = C_i^{\circ} \tag{254}$$

In dimensionless form:

$$\frac{d\Psi_i(\zeta)}{d\zeta} = Da \langle \Omega_i(\underset{\sim}{x}, \zeta) \rangle_{A_R} \tag{255}$$

$$\Psi_i\,(\zeta = 0) = 1 \tag{256}$$

where

$$Da = \frac{L(\Omega_i^*)_{ref}}{\langle v_z \rangle C_i^{\circ}} \tag{257}$$

$$\Omega_i = \frac{\Omega_i^*}{(\Omega_i^*)_{ref}} \tag{258}$$

A general expression for the reaction rate can be written in the following way:

$$\Omega_i^*(\underset{\sim}{x}, z) = -f(\underset{\sim}{k}) \left[\left(\int_v \Phi_v\, e_v^a\, dv \right)^n \right] F(C_i) \tag{259}$$

Three factors contribute to Equation 259: a function of the reaction rate constants represented by $f(\underset{\sim}{k})$, a function of all concentrations in terms of a key species i, represented by $F(C_i)$ and finally the effect produced by the radiation field that is represented by the factor between brackets. In the latter, the radiation influence has been raised to a generic power n. Many reaction kinetics can be represented in this way, being chain reactions (chlorinations, polymerizations, etc.) or simpler reactions (isomerizations, nitrosations, photosensitized reactions, etc.). The reference reaction has been defined as

$$(\Omega_i^*)_{ref} = f(\underset{\sim}{k})(\Phi_{ref} e_{ref}^a)^n F(C_i^{\circ}) \tag{260}$$

where Φ_{ref} and e_{ref}^a are calculated at well-defined concentrations and positions.
If we additionally define

$$J_{Mod} = \frac{1}{\Phi_{ref} e_{ref}^a} \int_v \Phi_v e_v^a\, dv \tag{261}$$

we can use a function J_{Mod} that will vary its form according to the emission model that is used to calculate the rate of initiation.

With these definitions we can write

$$\Omega_i(\underset{\sim}{x}, z) = -[J_{Mod}(\underset{\sim}{x}, \zeta)]^n F(\Psi_i) \tag{262}$$

Combining Equation 262 with Equation 259 we obtain

$$\frac{d\Psi_i(\zeta)}{d\zeta} = -Da\langle[J_{Mod}(\underset{\sim}{x}, \zeta)]^n\rangle_{A_R} F(\Psi_i) \tag{263}$$

$$\Psi_i(0) = 1 \tag{264}$$

which, after integration, yields

$$\int_0^{X_i^{PM}(\zeta)} \frac{dX}{F(1 - X)} = Da \int_0^{\zeta} \langle[J_{Mod}(\underset{\sim}{x}, \bar{\zeta})]^n\rangle_{A_R}\, d\bar{\zeta} \tag{265}$$

In Equation 265 we have used

$$X_i^{PM}(\zeta) = 1 - \Psi_i(\zeta) \tag{266}$$

Clearly $X_i^{PM}(\zeta)$ will render the conversion of the i component in the perfectly radially mixed continuous reactor.

Sometimes the reaction kinetics is better represented by an expression of the form

$$\Omega_A^*(\underset{\sim}{x}, z) = -f(\underset{\sim}{k})\left[\left(\int_v \Phi_v e_v^a\, dv\right)^n\right] C_A^m C_B^l \tag{267}$$

For an overall reaction of the form:

$$A + gB \longrightarrow \text{Products}$$

we will have

$$f^\circ = \frac{gC_A^\circ}{C_B^\circ} \tag{268}$$

and

$$F(1 - X_A) = (1 - X_A)^m (1 - f^\circ X_A)^l \tag{269}$$

Substituting Equations 268 and 269 into Equation 265, we obtain

$$\int_0^{X_A^{PM}(\zeta)} \frac{dX}{(1 - X)^n (1 - f^\circ X)^l} = Da \int_0^{\zeta} \langle[J_{Mod}(\underset{\sim}{x}, \bar{\zeta})]^n\rangle_{A_R}\, d\bar{\zeta} \tag{270}$$

Table 7 gives final expressions for different particular cases of Equation 270. The L.H.S. can be solved analytically for certain cases. The R.H.S. can only be analytically solved for very simple radiation models. One of them, which is not very apt for rigorous modeling is he LSPP model, but it will be used here for an approximate design.

Table 7
Continuous Photoreactors

l	m	PM	$\int_0^{X_i(\zeta)} \frac{dX}{(1-X)^m(1-f^\circ X)^l} = Da \int_0^\zeta \langle [J_{Mod}(\underline{x},\bar{\zeta})]^n \rangle_{A_R} d\bar{\zeta}$
		NM	$\int_0^{X_i(\underline{x},\zeta)} \frac{dX}{(1-X)^m(1-f^\circ X)^l} = \frac{Da}{U(\underline{x})} \int_0^\zeta [J_{Mod}(\underline{x},\bar{\zeta})]^n d\bar{\zeta}$
			$X_i(\zeta) = \langle U(\underline{x}) X_i(\underline{x},\zeta) \rangle_{A_R}$
l = 0	m = 1	PM	$X_i(\zeta) = 1 - \exp\left\{-Da \int_0^\zeta \langle [J_{Mod}(\underline{x},\bar{\zeta})]^n \rangle_{A_R} d\bar{\zeta}\right\}$
		NM	$X_i(\zeta) = 1 - \left\langle U(\underline{x}) \exp\left\{-\frac{Da}{U(\underline{x})} \int_0^\zeta [J_{Mod}(\underline{x},\bar{\zeta})]^n d\bar{\zeta}\right\}\right\rangle_{A_R}$
	m ≠ 1	PM	$X_i(\zeta) = 1 - \left\{1 - (1-m) Da \int_0^\zeta \langle [J_{Mod}(\underline{x},\bar{\zeta})]^n \rangle_{A_R} d\bar{\zeta}\right\}^{1/1-m}$
		NM	$X_i(\zeta) = 1 - \left\langle U(\underline{x}) \left\{1 - (1-m) \frac{Da}{U(\underline{x})} \int_0^\zeta [J_{Mod}(\underline{x},\bar{\zeta})]^n d\bar{\zeta}\right\}^{1/1-m}\right\rangle_{A_R}$
l = 1	m = 1	PM	$X_i(\zeta) = \frac{\exp\left\{(1-f^\circ) Da \int_0^\zeta \langle [J_{Mod}(\underline{x},\bar{\zeta})]^n \rangle_{A_R} d\bar{\zeta}\right\} - 1}{\exp\left\{(1-f^\circ) Da \int_0^\zeta \langle [J_{Mod}(\underline{x},\bar{\zeta})]^n \rangle_{A_R} d\bar{\zeta}\right\} - f^\circ}$
		NM	$X_i(\zeta) = \left\langle U(\underline{x}) \frac{\exp\left\{(1-f^\circ) \frac{Da}{U(\underline{x})} \int_0^\zeta [J_{Mod}(\underline{x},\bar{\zeta})]^n d\bar{\zeta}\right\} - 1}{\exp\left\{(1-f^\circ) \frac{Da}{U(\underline{x})} \int_0^\zeta [J_{Mod}(\underline{x},\bar{\zeta})]^n d\bar{\zeta}\right\} - f^\circ}\right\rangle_{A_R}$

No radial mixing (NM)

Here $D_{im} = 0$ and we obtain

$$v_z(\underline{x}) \frac{\partial C_i(\underline{x}, z)}{\partial z} = \Omega_i^*(\underline{x}, z)$$

$$C_i(\underline{x}, 0) = C_i^\circ \tag{271}$$

which in dimensionless form results

$$\frac{\partial \Psi_i(\underline{x}, \zeta)}{\partial \zeta} = -Da \frac{[J_{Mod}(\underline{x}, \zeta)]^n}{U(\underline{x})} F(\Psi_i) \tag{272}$$

$$\Psi_i(\underline{x}, 0) = 1 \tag{273}$$

If we define a local value of conversion as

$$X_i^{NM}(\underset{\sim}{x}, \zeta) = 1 - \Psi_i(\underset{\sim}{x}, \zeta) \tag{274}$$

after integration we get

$$\int_0^{X_i^{NM}(\underset{\sim}{x},\zeta)} \frac{dX}{F(1 - X)} = Da \int_0^{\zeta} \frac{[J_{Mod}(\underset{\sim}{x}, \bar{\zeta})]^n}{U(\underset{\sim}{x})} d\bar{\zeta} \tag{275}$$

The average conversion at any axial position is given by

$$X_i^{NM}(\zeta) = \frac{1}{A_R} \int_{A_R} X_i^{NM}(\underset{\sim}{x}, \zeta) U(\underset{\sim}{x})\, dA \tag{276}$$

where $X_i^{NM}(\zeta)$ is obtained from Equation 275.

When the kinetic expression is of the type given by Equation 267, Equation 275 must be substituted by

$$\int_0^{X_i^{NM}(\underset{\sim}{x},\zeta)} \frac{dX}{(1 - X)^m(1 - f^{\circ}X)^l} = Da \int_0^{\zeta} \frac{[J_{Mod}(\underset{\sim}{x}, \bar{\zeta})]^n}{U(\underset{\sim}{x})} d\bar{\zeta} \tag{277}$$

Table 7 also gives the results for this limiting case.

We will now show, through several examples, a comparison between the results obtained with the approximate models and those derived from the rigorous treatment present in the first section. In some cases, comparisons are made with results from bench-scale experiments. It should be noted that rigorous models can be applied to bench-scale dimensions or larger dimensions. They can be readily used with no changes or loss of accuracy. Some precautions should be taken however, when approximate models are applied. This is so because, as far as the quality of the results is concerned, the behavior of simple radiation models is very sensitive to changes in geometric dimensions, particularly the radiation characteristics dimension.

Example No. 1

The conversion of an annular photoreactor whose characteristics are described below must be investigated. Results are required in order to have an estimation of the radiation energy available in the reactor. Hence a well known photosensitized reaction will be carried out. Average exit conversion for the photodecomposition of oxalic acid, using uranyl ions as photosensitizers, must not exceed 20%, otherwise a concentration dependent attenuation coefficient must be used [17]. The prediction of an approximate value of the required flow rate is desired.

Reaction description:

$$C_2O_4H_2 + UO_2^{++} + h\nu \longrightarrow UO_2^{++} + CO_2 + CO + H_2O$$

$$C_{Ox}^{\circ} = 0.005\ M$$

$$C_{Ur}^{\circ} = 0.001\ M$$

$$\Omega_{Ox}^{*} = \Phi e^{a}$$

$$\Phi_{253.7\ nm} = 0.6\ \text{mole Einstein}^{-1}$$

$$\mu_{253.7\ nm} = 6.93\ cm^{-1}$$

Reactor description:

U.V. source: G.E. G-15T8, 15 w

$L_L = 35.6$ cm

$2r_L = 2.54$ cm

Output power: 3.6 w at $\lambda = 253{,}7$ nm. (Emission outside the 253,7 nm line, which is less than 10% of total emission, is neglected.)

Reactor: Annular type

$L_R = 30$ cm

$r_{R_{in}} = 2.3$ cm

$r_{R_{ou}} = 2.7$ cm

Solution

It is known that under carefully controlled conditions [17, 36], these reactions can be represented with the following kinetic parameters (Table 7):

$l = 0;\quad m = 0;\quad n = 1\quad \text{and}\quad f(\underset{\sim}{k}) = 1$

From Table 7 at $\zeta = 1$, we have

$$X_{Ox}^{PM}(1) = Da \int_0^1 \langle J_{Mod}(\underset{\sim}{x}, \bar{\zeta}) \rangle_{A_R}\, d\bar{\zeta} \tag{278}$$

$$X_{Ox}^{NM}(1) = Da \left\langle \int_0^1 J_{Mod}(\underset{\sim}{x}, \bar{\zeta})\, d\bar{\zeta} \right\rangle_{A_R} \tag{279}$$

It should be noticed that if no changes in the kinetics occur [17], for this particular reaction:

$X_{Qx}^{PM}(1) = X_{Ox}^{NM}(1)$

a) LSPP model:
Equation 261 gives for this case:

$$J_{LSPP}(\gamma) = \frac{\gamma_{ou}^2 - \gamma_{in}^2}{2}\, \varepsilon \frac{1}{\gamma} \exp[-\varepsilon(\gamma - \gamma_{in})] \tag{280}$$

where we have used

$$\varepsilon = \mu(r_{R_{ou}} - r_{R_{in}}) \tag{281}$$

$$\gamma = \frac{r}{r_{R_{ou}} - r_{R_{in}}} \tag{282}$$

$$\Phi_{ref} = \Phi \tag{283}$$

$$e_{ref}^{a} = \frac{E_L}{V_R} = \frac{E_L}{\pi(r_{R_{ou}}^2 - r_{R_{in}}^2)L_R} \tag{284}$$

Substituting Equation 280 into Equation 278, we obtain

$$X_{Ox}(1) = Da[1 - \exp(-\varepsilon)] \tag{285}$$

From which

$$\mathrm{Da} = \frac{0.2}{1 - \exp(-2.772)} = 0.213$$

Since

$$\mathrm{Da} = \frac{L_R/\langle v\rangle}{C^{\circ}_{Ox}/(\Phi E_L/V_R)} = \frac{\Phi E_L}{F_v C^{\circ}_{Ox}} \tag{286}$$

From Equation 286 we obtain

$$F_v = 4.3\ \mathrm{cm^3\,s^{-1}}$$

b) LSSE model:
Equation 261 gives for this model:

$$J_{LSSE}(\gamma, \zeta) = \frac{\gamma_{ou}^2 - \gamma_{in}^2}{2}\, \varepsilon \frac{1}{\gamma} \int_{\theta_1}^{\theta_2} \exp\left[- \frac{\varepsilon(\gamma - \gamma_{in})}{\sin\theta} \right] d\theta \tag{287}$$

where the limiting angles are

$$\theta_1(\gamma, \zeta) = \tan^{-1}\left(\mathrm{Ge}^* \frac{\gamma}{1 - \zeta} \right) \tag{288}$$

$$\theta_2(\gamma, \zeta) = \tan^{-1}\left(\mathrm{Ge}^* \frac{\gamma}{\zeta} \right) \tag{289}$$

$$\mathrm{Ge}^* = \frac{r_{R_{ou}} - r_{R_{in}}}{L_R} \tag{290}$$

After substitution of Equation 287 into Equation 278:

$$X_{Ox}(1) = \mathrm{Da}\, \frac{1}{2}\, \varepsilon \int_0^1 d\zeta \int_{\gamma_{in}}^{\gamma_{ou}} d\gamma \int_{\theta_1}^{\theta_2} d\theta \exp\left[- \frac{\varepsilon(\gamma - \gamma_{in})}{\sin\theta} \right] \tag{291}$$

Equation 291 is easily solved with a small calculator. (For example a TI 59.) From the solution:

$$\mathrm{Da} = \frac{0.2}{(0.5)(2.772)(0.634)} = 0.228$$

and from Equation 286,

$$F_v = 4.0\ \mathrm{cm^3\,s^{-1}}$$

The problem was rigorously solved by De Bernardez and Cassano [17] using the ESVE model. They also performed an experimental verification for the conditions here described. The results are:

c) ESVE model (Equations 70 to 90):

$$F_v = 3.6\ \mathrm{cm^3\,s^{-1}}$$

d) Experimental:

$$F_v = 3.3\ \mathrm{cm^3\,s^{-1}}$$

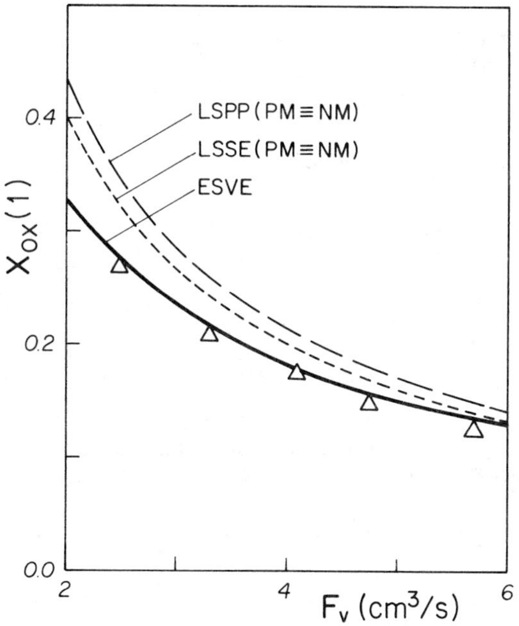

Figure 23. Uranyl oxalate decomposition in an annular photoreactor.

Figure 23 shows results for an extended range of conversions. It should be noted that beyond a conversion value of 20%, both limiting cases (PM and NM) are a poor assumption as it is described in Reference 17. In this particular case, the simplification about the constant attenuation coefficient is the first one to collapse. This is so because the kinetic expression used in the approximation is valid only under well-controlled conditions and the simplified models cannot properly take into account deviations from those prescribed operating conditions.

Example No. 2

In an annular photoreactor whose characteristics are indicated below, an isomerization reaction of the type A → B is carried out in the gas phase at atmospheric pressure. The inside reactor radius is fixed from the lamp dimensions and the required precautions for cooling. We wish to know the outside reactor radius for an average exit conversion of 50%.

Reaction description:

$$A + h\nu \xrightarrow{\Phi e^a} A^*$$

$$A^* \xrightarrow{k_2} B$$

$$A^* + M \xrightarrow{k_3} A + M \qquad (M = \text{inert})$$

$C_A^o = 0.017$ M

$k_2 = 10^{12}\ s^{-1}$

$k_3 = 10^{14}\ cm^3\ mole^{-1}\ s^{-1}$

$\Phi = 0.7$ mole Einstein^{-1}

$\alpha = 10^5\ cm^2\ mole^{-1}$

Reactor description:

U.V. source: $E_L = 3.08 \times 10^{-3}$ Einstein s^{-1}
$L_L = 75$ cm
$2r_L = 1.5$ cm
The output power here considered is monochromatic.

Reactor: Annular type
$L_R = 75$ cm
$r_{R_{in}} = 4$ cm
$\langle v \rangle = 5$ cm s^{-1}

Solution

The LSPP model will be used. Since the residence time is higher than 10 s the microsteady state approximation is valid. Hence, for species A* we have

$$C_{A*} = \frac{\Phi e^a}{k_2 + k_3 C_M} \tag{292}$$

For the stable species A, the rate of reaction results

$$\Omega_A^* = -\frac{k_2}{k_2 + k_3 C_M} \Phi e^a$$

Consequently, resorting to Table 7 we have

$$l = 0; \qquad m = 0; \qquad n = 1; \qquad f(\underset{\sim}{k}) = \frac{k_2}{k_2 + k_3 C_M} \cong 1$$

Assumption is made here that the attenuation coefficient (αC_A) in the exponential integral is constant and equal to αC_A°. With this simplification, for monochromatic radiation, Equation 261 gives for the LSPP model:

$$J_{LSPP}^*(\gamma) = \frac{\gamma_{ou}^2 - \gamma_{in}^2}{2} \varepsilon \Psi_A \frac{1}{\gamma} \exp[-\varepsilon(\gamma - \gamma_{in})] = J_{LSPP}(\gamma)\Psi_A \tag{293}$$

Since species A has a linear participation on the evaluation of e^a and here $n = 1$, in practice, the reaction order for species A, after the assumption of constant attenuation becomes:

$$m + n = 0 + 1 = 1$$

From Table 7, the average exit conversion will be

$$X_A^{PM}(1) = 1 - \exp\left\{-Da \int_0^1 \langle J_{LSPP}(\gamma)\rangle_{A_R} d\bar{\zeta}\right\}$$
$$= 1 - \exp\{-Da[1 - \exp(-\varepsilon)]\} \tag{294}$$

$$X_A^{NM}(1) = 1 - \left\langle U(\gamma) \exp\left\{ -Da \int_0^1 \frac{J_{LSPP}(\gamma)}{U(\gamma)} d\bar{\zeta} \right\} \right\rangle_{A_R}$$

$$= 1 - \left\langle U(\gamma) \exp\left[-Da \frac{J_{LSPP}(\gamma)}{U(\gamma)} \right] \right\rangle_{A_R} \tag{295}$$

In Equation 295 for the laminar flow regime, the value of $U(\gamma)$ is

$$U(\gamma) = \frac{2}{a+b}\left[1 - \left(\frac{\gamma}{\gamma_{ou}}\right)^2 - a \ln\left(\frac{\gamma}{\gamma_{ou}}\right)\right] \tag{296}$$

with

$$a = \frac{1-K^2}{\ln K} \tag{297}$$

$$b = 1 - K^2 \tag{298}$$

$$K = \frac{r_{R_{in}}}{r_{R_{ou}}} \tag{299}$$

After substitution of Equation 296 into Equation 295 and making the required area average explicit, we finally obtain

$$X_A^{NM}(1) = 1 - \frac{4}{(1-K^2)(a+b)\gamma_{ou}^2} \int_{\gamma_{in}}^{\gamma_{ou}} d\gamma\, \gamma \left[1 - \left(\frac{\gamma}{\gamma_{ou}}\right)^2 - a \ln\left(\frac{\gamma}{\gamma_{ou}}\right)\right]$$
$$\times \exp\left\{ -Da\varepsilon \frac{(1-K^2)(a+b)\gamma_{ou}^2}{4} \frac{\exp[-\varepsilon(\gamma - K\gamma_{ou})]}{\gamma\left[1 - \left(\frac{\gamma}{\gamma_{ou}}\right)^2 - a \ln\left(\frac{\gamma}{\gamma_{ou}}\right)\right]} \right\} \tag{300}$$

Again Equation 300 can be solved with a small calculator. However, Equations 294 and 300 require a trial and error solution. Results for an average exit conversion of 50%, are provided in terms of outside radii in the two limiting cases:

$r_{R_{ou}}^{PM} = 5.08$ cm

$r_{R_{ou}}^{NM} = 4.78$ cm

Romero et al. [16] solved the problem in a rigorous form, using the ESVE model, a variable attenuation, with no application of the microsteady state approximation and accounting for lamp wedges. For the values of the parameters employed here, they obtained

$r_{R_{ou}} = 5.00$ cm

Actually one should not extrapolate from these results a very optimistic view of these approximate methods. Figure 24 is a plot of $X_A(1)$ vs. $r_{R_{ou}}$ that shows that not always the coincidence is so good.

Example No. 3

The manufacturing of methyl chloride by photochlorination of methane is studied in a bench scale reactor. To simplify the preliminary analysis, an almost monchromatic U.V. source is adopted. (It will be later substituted by a more efficient polychromatic lamp.) Data from the literature indicate that good selectivity can be obtained if the feed concentration ratio of chlorine to methane is about 0.1. It is required to have a rapid estimation of the mean residence time to reach an exit conversion of about 40%, under the desired operating conditions.

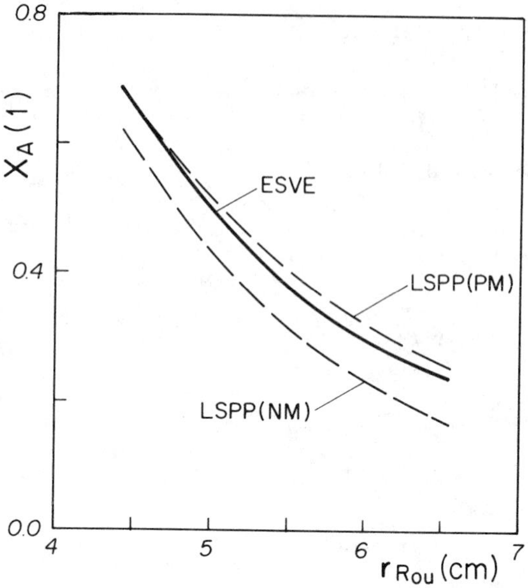

Figure 24. Isomerization reaction in an annular photoreactor.

Reaction description:

$$Cl_2 + h\nu \xrightarrow{\Phi e^a} 2\,Cl\cdot$$

$$CH_4 + Cl\cdot \xrightarrow{k_1} HCl + CH_3\cdot$$

$$CH_3\cdot + Cl_2 \xrightarrow{k_2} CH_3Cl + Cl\cdot$$

$$2\,Cl\cdot + M \xrightarrow{k_{t_1}} Cl_2 + M \qquad (M = \text{inert})$$

$$2\,CH_3\cdot \xrightarrow{k_{t_2}} C_2H_6$$

$$CH_3\cdot + Cl\cdot \xrightarrow{k_{t_3}} CH_3Cl$$

Successive chlorinations of methane after the first one are neglected.

$k_1 = 6.89 \times 10^{10}\ cm^3\ mol^{-1}\ s^{-1}$

$k_2 = 1.63 \times 10^{11}\ cm^3\ mol^{-1}\ s^{-1}$

$k_{t_1} = 4.06 \times 10^{15}\ cm^3\ mol^{-1}\ s^{-1}$

$k_{t_2} = 3.16 \times 10^{13}\ cm^3\ mol^{-1}\ s^{-1}$

$k_{t_3} = 3.98 \times 10^{14}\ cm^3\ mol^{-1}\ s^{-1}$

$\Phi = 1$

Reactor description:

U.V. source: G.E. G-30T8, 30 w

$L_L = 81$ cm

$2r_L = 2.54$ cm

Output power: 8.3 w at $\lambda = 253{,}7$ nm. (Emission outside the 253,7 nm line is neglected.)

Reactor: Annular type

$L_R = 81$ cm

$r_{R_{in}} = 3$ cm

$r_{R_{ou}} = 5$ cm

$C^{\circ}_{Cl_2}/C^{\circ}_{CH_4} = 0.1$

P = 1 atm.

T = 20 C

The molar fraction of chlorine in the inlet stream is 5%; an inert being the make up gas.

Solution

In order to obtain a simple kinetic expression, the microsteady state and the long chain approximations will be applied to the kinetic sequence. The result for the rate of disappearance of chlorine is

$$\Omega^*_{Cl_2} = -\left[\int_v \Phi_v e^a_v \, dv\right]^{1/2} \frac{k_1 C_{CH_4}}{\left[k_{t_1} + \dfrac{k_{t_2}}{\beta^2} + \dfrac{k_{t_3}}{\beta}\right]^{1/2}} \tag{301}$$

with

$$\beta = \frac{k_2}{k_1}\frac{C_{Cl_2}}{C_{CH_4}} \tag{302}$$

Replacing the known numerical values in Equation 301 it can be seen that the controlling termination step is the recombination of atomic chlorine and the methyl radical. This special situation allows an additional simplification. For application of the design methodology its use is not required, but since it will not introduce a large error and this is an approximate method, we incorporate it to the design; the result is

$$\Omega^*_{Cl_2} = -\left(\frac{k_1 k_2}{k_{t_3}}\right)^{1/2}\left(\int_v \Phi_v e^a_v \, dv\right)^{1/2} C^{1/2}_{CH_4} C^{1/2}_{Cl_2} \tag{303}$$

Another simplification is also possible. Since F = 0.1, the excess of methane allows us to consider the methane concentration constant and equal to the initial value. Later on, for comparison purposes, this particular case will be solved with a variable methane concentration.

Considering the previous discussions, the following parameters are obtained:

$$l = 0; \quad m = \tfrac{1}{2}; \quad n = \tfrac{1}{2}; \quad f(\underline{k}) = \left(\frac{k_1 k_2}{k_{t_3}}\right)^{1/2} (C^{\circ}_{CH_4})^{1/2} \tag{304}$$

The expressions for ε and Da are

$$\varepsilon = \alpha C^{\circ}_{Cl_2}(r_{R_{ou}} - r_{R_{in}}) \tag{305}$$

$$Da = \tau_R (F^{\circ})^{1/2} \left(\frac{k_1 k_2}{k_{t_3}}\right)^{1/2} \left[\frac{\Phi E_L}{\pi L_R (r^2_{R_{ou}} - r^2_{R_{in}})}\right] \tag{306}$$

In this case, chlorine absorbs radiation and reacts. It is possible to consider C_{Cl_2} constant for the attenuating integral because we have an inert and an excess of methane; hence, the system is typically an optically thin medium.

Since $(r_{R_{in}})/L_R$ is small and $L_R = L_L$, but specially because $(r_{R_{ou}} - r_{R_{in}})$ is also small, we may assume that the LSPP model can be used. Following the same approach as for Example No. 2, we get

$$J^*_{LSPP}(\gamma) = J_{LSPP}(\gamma)\Psi_{Cl_2} \tag{307}$$

The reaction order with respect to Cl_2 is

$$m + n = \tfrac{1}{2} + \tfrac{1}{2} = 1$$

From Table 7 the chlorine conversion results

$$X^{PM}_{Cl_2}(1) = 1 - \exp\{-Da\langle[J_{LSPP}(\gamma)]^{1/2}\rangle_{AR}\} \tag{308}$$

$$X^{NM}_{Cl_2}(1) = 1 - \exp\left\langle U(\gamma)\exp\left\{-Da\frac{[J_{LSPP}(\gamma)]^{1/2}}{U(\gamma)}\right\}\right\rangle_{AR} \tag{309}$$

In Equation 309 the values of $J_{LSPP}(\gamma)$ and $U(\gamma)$ are given by Equations 280 and 296. After substitution into Equations 308 and 309, the final equations are:

$$X^{PM}_{Cl_2}(1) = 1 - \exp\left\{-Da\left(\frac{2\varepsilon}{\gamma^2_{ou} - \gamma^2_{in}}\right)^{1/2} \int_{\gamma_{in}}^{\gamma_{ou}} d\gamma\, \gamma^{1/2} \exp\left[-\frac{\varepsilon}{2}(\gamma - \gamma_{in})\right]\right\} \tag{310}$$

$$X^{NM}_{Cl_2}(1) = 1 - \frac{2}{\gamma^2_{ou} - \gamma^2_{in}} \int_{\gamma_{in}}^{\gamma_{ou}} d\gamma\, \gamma \frac{2}{a+b}\left[1 - \left(\frac{\gamma}{\gamma_{ou}}\right)^2 - a\ln\left(\frac{\gamma}{\gamma_{in}}\right)\right] \times \exp\left\{-Da\left(\frac{\varepsilon}{\gamma}\right)^{1/2}\left(\frac{\gamma^2_{ou} - \gamma^2_{in}}{2}\right)^{1/2} \frac{\exp\left[-\frac{\varepsilon}{2}(\gamma - \gamma_{in})\right]}{\frac{2}{a+b}\left[1 - \left(\frac{\gamma}{\gamma_{ou}}\right)^2 - a\ln\left(\frac{\gamma}{\gamma_{ou}}\right)\right]}\right\} \tag{311}$$

Equations 310 and 311 can again be solved by trial and error with a small calculator (the TI-59 for example). The results for a chlorine conversion of 40% are:

$$\tau^{PM}_R\ (X = 40\%) = 4.1\ s$$

$$\tau^{NM}_R\ (X = 40\%) = 4.5\ s$$

De Bernardez and Cassano [20] solved the complete system (including the four chloromethanes) using the ESVE model. They neither used the steady state approximation nor the long chain approximation. Lamp and reactor wedges were not neglected, either. The only simplification was to assume negligible thermal effects which for this special situation (low chlorine concentration) is

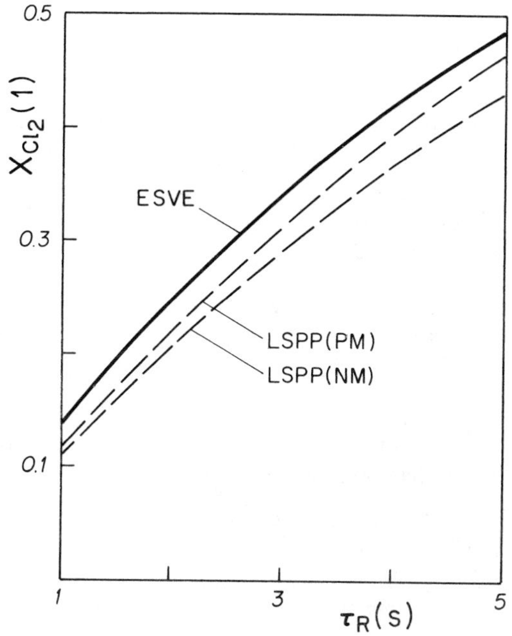

Figure 25. Monochlorination of methane in a continuous annular photoreactor.

perfectly satisfactory. For the conditions of this example the obtained result is

$$\tau_R = 3.7 \text{ s}$$

With the complete sequence, De Bernardez and Cassano found that the methyl chloride selectivity was 95%. Also, they showed that the microsteady state approximation can be used with confidence and that wall reactions can be safely neglected. Hence, the approximate results can be used to compare the simplified design methodology with almost exact results. Figure 25 is a plot of $X_{Cl_2}(1)$ vs. τ_R for both methods.

If one uses a variable methane concentration, Table 7 must be used with

$$l = \tfrac{1}{2}; \qquad m = \tfrac{1}{2}; \qquad n = \tfrac{1}{2}; \qquad f(\underset{\sim}{k}) = \left(\frac{k_1 k_2}{k_{t_3}}\right)^{1/2}$$

The reaction order for chlorine is

$$m + n = \tfrac{1}{2} + \tfrac{1}{2} = 1$$

Solving the resulting equations, the obtained mean residence times are slightly longer but in no case the difference from the previous results is larger than 1%.

Inspecting Figures 23, 24, and 25 one may conclude that the approximate design methods are a useful tool for first estimations. Very likely, they can provide very good results to initialize a process simulation procedure.

Batch Photoreactors

For a generic species i, the mass conservation equation gives

$$\frac{\partial C_i(\underset{\sim}{x}, t)}{\partial t} + \underset{\sim}{\nabla}_{(x)} \cdot \underset{\sim}{N}_i(\underset{\sim}{x}, t) = \Omega_i^*(\underset{\sim}{x}, t) \tag{312}$$

$$C_i(\underset{\sim}{x}, 0) = C_i^\circ \tag{313}$$

$$\underset{\sim}{\nabla}_{(\underset{\sim}{x}_n)} C_i\big|_w = 0 \tag{314}$$

In this case $\underset{\sim}{x}$ is a position vector inside the reactor volume and $\underset{\sim}{\nabla}_{(\underset{\sim}{x}_n)} C_i\big|_w$ is the directional derivative normal to the reactor wall.

Perfect Mixing (PM)

Integrating Equation 312 in the batch reactor volume and applying Green's theorem, after application of boundary condition (314) one finally obtains:

$$\frac{dC_i(t)}{dt} = \frac{1}{V_R} \int_{V_R} \Omega_i^*(\underset{\sim}{x}, t)\, dV = \langle \Omega_i^*(\underset{\sim}{x}, t) \rangle_{V_R} \tag{315}$$

$$C_i\,(t = 0) = C_i^\circ \tag{316}$$

Putting this result in dimensionless form, the result is:

$$\frac{d\Psi_i(\tau)}{d\tau} = -\langle [J_{Mod}(\underset{\sim}{x}, \tau)]^n \rangle_{V_R} F(\Psi_i) \tag{317}$$

$$\Psi_i(0) = 1 \tag{318}$$

where the dimensionless time τ has been defined as

$$\tau = \frac{t}{C_i^\circ/(\Omega_i^*)_{ref}} = \frac{\text{(Reaction time)}}{\text{(Characteristic reaction time)}} \tag{319}$$

Integrating Equation 317 from the initial reaction time, we get

$$\int_1^{\Psi_i(\tau)} \frac{d\Psi}{F(\Psi)} = -\int_0^\tau \langle [J_{Mod}(\underset{\sim}{x}, \bar{\tau})]^n \rangle_{V_R}\, d\bar{\tau} \tag{320}$$

When Equation 320 is written in terms of conversion, the result is:

$$\int_0^{X_i^{PM}(\tau)} \frac{dX}{F(1 - X)} = -\int_0^\tau \langle [J_{Mod}(\underset{\sim}{x}, \bar{\tau})]^n \rangle_{V_R}\, d\bar{\tau} \tag{321}$$

If an equation of the type represented by Equation 267 instead of the one corresponding to Equation 259 is used, the result is:

$$\int_0^{X_i^{PM}(\tau)} \frac{dX}{(1 - X)^m (1 - f^\circ X)^l} = -\int_0^\tau \langle [J_{Mod}(\underset{\sim}{x}, \bar{\tau})]^n \rangle_{V_R}\, d\bar{\tau} \tag{322}$$

Table 8
Batch Photoreactors

l	m	PM	$\int_0^{X_i(\tau)} \frac{dX}{(1-X)^m(1-f^\circ X)^l} = Da \int_0^\tau \langle [J_{Mod}(\underset{\sim}{x}, \bar{\tau})]^n \rangle_{V_R} \, d\bar{\tau}$
		NM	$\int_0^{X_i(\underset{\sim}{x},\tau)} \frac{dX}{(1-X)^m(1-f^\circ X)^l} = \int_0^\tau [J_{Mod}(\underset{\sim}{x}, \bar{\tau})]^n \, d\bar{\tau}$
			$X_i(\tau) = \langle X_i(\underset{\sim}{x}, \tau) \rangle_{V_R}$
l = 0	m = 1	PM	$X_i(\tau) = 1 - \exp\left\{-\int_0^\tau \langle [J_{Mod}(\underset{\sim}{x}, \bar{\tau})]^n \rangle_{V_R} \, d\bar{\tau}\right\}$
		NM	$X_i(\tau) = 1 - \left\langle \exp\left\{-\int_0^\tau [J_{Mod}(\underset{\sim}{x}, \bar{\tau})]^n \, d\bar{\tau}\right\} \right\rangle_{V_R}$
	m ≠ 1	PM	$X_i(\tau) = 1 - \left\{1 - (1-m) \int_0^\tau \langle [J_{Mod}(\underset{\sim}{x}, \bar{\tau})]^n \rangle_{V_R} \, d\bar{\tau}\right\}^{1/1-m}$
		NM	$X_i(\tau) = 1 - \left\langle \left\{1 - (1-m) \int_0^\tau [J_{Mod}(\underset{\sim}{x}, \bar{\tau})]^n \, d\bar{\tau}\right\}^{1/1-m} \right\rangle_{V_R}$
l = 1	m = 1	PM	$X_i(\tau) = \frac{\exp\left\{(1-f^\circ) \int_0^\tau \langle [J_{Mod}(\underset{\sim}{x}, \bar{\tau})]^n \rangle_{V_R} \, d\bar{\tau}\right\} - 1}{\exp\left\{(1-f^\circ) \int_0^\tau \langle [J_{Mod}(\underset{\sim}{x}, \bar{\tau})]^n \rangle_{V_R} \, d\bar{\tau}\right\} - f^\circ}$
		NM	$X_i(\tau) = \left\langle \frac{\exp\left\{(1-f^\circ) \int_0^\tau [J_{Mod}(\underset{\sim}{x}, \bar{\tau})]^n \, d\bar{\tau}\right\} - 1}{\exp\left\{(1-f^\circ) \int_0^\tau [J_{Mod}(\underset{\sim}{x}, \bar{\tau})]^n \, d\bar{\tau}\right\} - f^\circ} \right\rangle_{V_R}$

Different particular cases are illustrated in Table 8. The L.H.S. can be analytically solved for some values of m and l of practical interest. The complexity of the R.H.S. depends on the model used to calculate $J_{Mod}(\underset{\sim}{x}, \tau)$.

No Mixing (NM)

For this limiting case the mass balance is

$$\frac{\partial C_i(\underset{\sim}{x}, t)}{\partial t} = \Omega_i^*(\underset{\sim}{x}, t) \tag{323}$$

$$C_i(\underset{\sim}{x}, 0) = C_i^\circ \tag{324}$$

In dimensionless form:

$$\frac{\partial \Psi_i(\underset{\sim}{x}, \tau)}{\partial \tau} = -[J_{Mod}(\underset{\sim}{x}, \tau)]^n F(\Psi_i) \tag{325}$$

Integrating from $\tau = 0$ to $\tau = \tau$, the result is:

$$\int_{1}^{\Psi_i(\underset{\sim}{x},\tau)} \frac{d\Psi}{F(\Psi)} = -\int_0^{\tau} [J_{Mod}(\underset{\sim}{x}, \bar{\tau})]^n \, d\bar{\tau} \tag{326}$$

In terms of a conversion for species i we obtain

$$\int_{0}^{X_i(\underset{\sim}{x},\tau)} \frac{dX}{F(1-X)} = -\int_0^{\tau} [J_{Mod}(\underset{\sim}{x}, \bar{\tau})]^n \, d\bar{\tau} \tag{327}$$

It is important to note that in Equation 327, $X_i(\underset{\sim}{x}, \tau)$ is a local value of conversion. The average reactor conversion is:

$$X_i^{NM}(\tau) = \frac{1}{V_R} \int_{V_R} X_i(\underset{\sim}{x}, \tau) \, dV \tag{328}$$

Hence, the problem here is to calculate first the local value of X_i and then the volumetric average for the whole reactor must be obtained from Equation 328.

When an Equation like 267 is required, the result is:

$$\int_{0}^{X_i(\underset{\sim}{x},\tau)} \frac{dX}{(1-X)^m(1-f^{\circ}X)^l} = -\int_0^{\tau} \langle [J_{Mod}(\underset{\sim}{x}, \bar{\tau})]^n \rangle_{V_R} \, d\bar{\tau} \tag{329}$$

As in the previous case, after solving Equation 329, the volumetric average of $X_i(\underset{\sim}{x}, \tau)$ must be obtained by application of Equation 328.

Table 7 also presents the equations for some particular cases under no mixing conditions. One example of a batch photoreactor will be illustrated in the next paragraphs.

Example No. 4

In order to compare different possible U.V. sources to be used in a batch photoreactor irradiated from the bottom (Figure 3), in a reacting system of medium to high optical thickness, an experimental evaluation of the radiation field generated by them will be performed. It is required to know if there will be enough time for sampling before a critical value of conversion is reached. This is so because one of the classical actinometers—the uranyl oxalate—can be used (even under well-stirred conditions), for reaction times in which oxalic acid conversion never exceeds 80%. It should also be noticed that the use of a constant attenuation coefficient, also under well-stirred conditions, for conversions of oxalic acid beyond 20% is only an approximation.

In this case, since a curved reflector of parabolic cross section is used, linear models cannot be used [5, 6, 27]. Hence, the ESVE or the ESSE models should be employed depending upon the type of U.V. lamp.

For the reacting system described below it is required to estimate the reaction time for an oxalic acid conversion of 60%.

Reaction description:

The uranyl oxalate reaction: $C_2O_4H_2 + UO_2^{++} + h\nu \longrightarrow UO_2^{++} + CO_2 + CO + H_2O$

$C_{Ox}^{\circ} = 0.005$ M

$C_{Ur}^{\circ} = 0.001$ M

Reactor description:

U.V. source: G.E. UA-3 Uviarc, 360 w

$L_L = 15.2$ cm

$2r_L = 1.9$ cm

Reflector: Parabolic cross section

$L_{Rf} = 15.8$ cm

$a = 2.1$ cm

$l = 8.4$ cm

Reactor: A cylinder with a bottom made of quartz.

Diameter = 14.4 cm

$V_R = 2{,}000 \text{ cm}^3$

The lamp is polychromatic. Details of the value of Φ, E_L, and α as a function of radiation frequency can be found in previously quoted references [19, 22, 23, 27–29, 36]. An average reflection coefficient for the parabolic reflector equal to 0.65 is used as suggested by the aluminum manufacturer and adopted by Cassano and co-workers in previous work.

Since we are dealing with a photosensitized reaction, the attenuation coefficient $\mu = \alpha C_{Ur}$ remains constant, but we will have to take its wavelength dependence into account. (As well as the one corresponding to α and E_L.)

Solution

From Example No. 1 we know that $l = 0$; $m = 0$; $n = 1$; $f(\underset{\sim}{k}) = 1$. From Table 8, we have:

$$X_{Ox}^{PM}(\tau) = 1 - \left\{1 - \int_0^\tau \langle J_{ESVE}(\underset{\sim}{x})\rangle_{V_R}\, d\bar{\tau}\right\} = \tau\langle J_{ESVE}(\underset{\sim}{x})\rangle_{V_R} \tag{330}$$

$$X_{Ox}^{NM}(\tau) = 1 - \left\langle\left\{1 - \int_0^\tau J_{ESVE}(\underset{\sim}{x})\, d\bar{\tau}\right\}\right\rangle_{V_R} = \tau\langle J_{ESVE}(\underset{\sim}{x})\rangle_{V_R} \tag{331}$$

It must be noticed that for this particular kinetics $X^{PM}(\tau) = X^{NM}(\tau)$.

Although this result is valid, it should be remarked that the used kinetic expression

$$\Omega_{Ox}^* = -\Phi e^a$$

with $\mu \neq \mu(C_{Ox})$ is valid when at any point inside the reactor, conversion never exceeds 20%. This condition can be fulfilled only under perfectly stirred conditions. When local conversions exceed this value, a different kinetic behavior should be modeled in some regions of the reactor volume. The NM case has not incorporated enough information to account for such deviations. Only a rigorous formulation like the one used by De Bernardez and Cassano [17] for a segregated flow, continuous photoreactor will show these effects. For more details the reader is referred to the quoted work.

Here we adopt

$$\Phi_{ref} = 1; \qquad e_{ref}^a = \frac{E_L}{V_R}$$

and

$$\tau = \frac{t}{C_{Ox}^\circ/(E_L/V_R)} = \left(\frac{E_L}{V_R C_{Ox}^\circ}\right) t \tag{332}$$

With previous definitions and using Equation 261 we have for the ESVE model:

$$J_{ESVE}(\underset{\sim}{x}) = \frac{V_R}{E_L}\int_\nu \Phi_\nu e_{ESVE,\nu}^a(\underset{\sim}{x})\, d\nu \tag{333}$$

From Equations 193 to 215 we can obtain

$$\int_V \Phi_v e^a_{ESVE,v}\,dv = \frac{1}{4\pi^2 r_L^2 L_L}\left\{\int_{\phi_1^P}^{\phi_2^P} \Delta\rho'(\underset{\sim}{x},\phi)\int_{\theta_1^P(\phi)}^{\theta_2^P(\phi)} I_v^*(y,\theta,\phi)\,d\theta\,d\phi\right.$$
$$+\langle\Gamma_{Rf}\rangle\int_{\phi_1^{In}}^{\phi_2^{In}} \Delta\rho_E'(\underset{\sim}{x},\phi)\int_{\theta_1^{In}(\phi)}^{\theta_2^{In}(\phi)} I_v^*(y,\theta,\phi)\,d\theta\,d\phi \tag{334}$$

where for the polychromatic problem we have made

$$I_v^*(y,\theta,\phi) = \sum_v \Phi_v E_{L,v}\mu_v \exp\left(-\frac{\mu_v}{\sin\theta\sin\phi}\,y\right) \tag{335}$$

Equation 334 must be replaced into Equation 333 and the latter into either Equation 330 or 331. The resulting problem, particularly the volumetric average, can be solved in a small personal computer.

The value of $\langle J_{ESVE}(\underset{\sim}{x})\rangle_{V_R}$ obtained for this case is

$$\langle J_{ESVE}(\underset{\sim}{x})\rangle_{V_R} = 0.0669$$

Finally, from Equations 330 or 331, we have

$$\tau = \frac{X_{Ox}(\tau)}{\langle J_{ESVE}(\underset{\sim}{x})\rangle_{V_R}} = \frac{0.6}{0.0699} = 8.97$$

and from Equation 332

$$t = 678\ s$$

One experiment was conducted by Alfano and Cassano as part of their previous work [22, 23] and an oxalic acid conversion of 60% was obtained for

$$t_{exp} \cong 780\,s$$

Figure 26 is a plot of X_{Ox} vs. t. Approximate values and experimental values are presented. It can be observed that the error increases for higher values of conversion. It is also clearly shown that for conversion values above 80% predictions are no longer valid. Clearly, a drastic change in the kinetics has occurred. Beyond $X_{Ox} = 80\%$ the problem cannot be tackled with a kinetics of the form $\Omega^*_{Ox} = \Phi e^a$, even if a variable attenuation coefficient is used.

PHOTOCHEMICAL REACTIONS IN INDUSTRIAL PRACTICE

Presently, it should be hard to argue against the idea that the great effort that has been put into basic photochemistry has no equivalent counterpart in practical, commercial applications, particularly in the chemical process industry.

Some of the main hindrances were described at the beginning of this chapter, yet, successful applications exist and they will be briefly described in this section. The subject has been discussed in several publications, among which the interested reader can resort to References 37–48. An interesting way of presenting applications has been used by Pape [41] and we will follow his approach.

A photochemical reaction has always a primary step of the type:

$$\begin{pmatrix}\text{Radiation}\\ \text{absorbing}\\ \text{species}\end{pmatrix} + (\text{radiation}) \longrightarrow \begin{pmatrix}\text{Radiation}\\ \text{activated}\\ \text{species}\end{pmatrix}$$
$$A \quad + \quad h\nu_1 \quad \longrightarrow \quad A^*$$

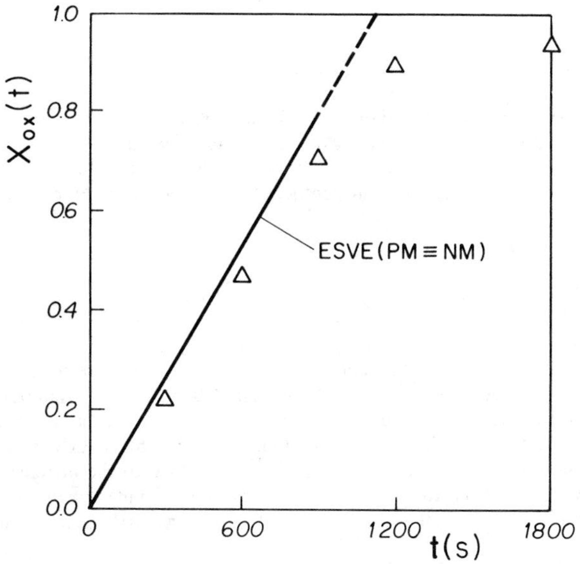

Figure 26. Uranyl oxalate decomposition in a batch photoreactor irradiated from the bottom.

Species A* may undergo different processes and these processes have been clearly separated by Pape to show application possibilities. They are:

Luminiscence

$$A^* \longrightarrow A + h\nu_2$$

This type of reaction is used to develop optical brighterners. When a body does not reflect all visible light it does not show an appearance of complete whiteness. This has been called the "blue defect". By adding blue fluorescent compounds that absorb in the ultraviolet range and are deactivated by fluorescence in the blue range, the yellowish coloration is transformed into a very white aspect. Paper and particularly fiber-made fabrics are the main applications.

Other applications of luminiscence include: luminous colours in advertising, warning signals in traffic, automatic sorting of letters, marking dials, light switches, emergency lightings, etc..

Non-Radiative Deactivation

$$A^* \longrightarrow A + \text{heat}$$

One of the main applications is for sun-screening cosmetics that filter dangerous radiations and allow the passing of the harmless one. Thus, the desired tan is obtained without affecting the skin and avoiding sunburn. The absorbed energy may be transformed into heat or partially re-emitted as fluorescent radiation.

Electron Transfer

$$A^* \longrightarrow A^+ + e^-$$

As a result of the absorption of radiation and further reaction, electrons are normally removed from the valence band into the conduction band. In this way they can be used in a reduction reaction or for carrying electrical current. The main applications are photographic, photoelectrostatic (for instance the Xerox process) and photoelectrophoretical (for color prints) reproductions.

Energy Transfer

$$A^* + B \longrightarrow A + B^*$$

This process is also known with the name of photosensitization. Here the main objective is to extend the spectral sensitivity to radiation of compound B by using an intermediate absorbing species represented by A. Generally, the main target is to move the absorption range into the longer wavelengths. This effect has been used in the development of panchromatic films and high-wattage lamps for street illumination. Thus, some compounds are added to the mercury vapor lamps so that upon energy transfer from the mercury atoms, light more similar to the solar color may be produced. Here the mercury vapor acts as a photosensitizer and thalium iodide has been used as the acceptor of energy.

Photosensitizers are also used in photocatalytic reactions to extend the absorption range into the solar spectrum. In fact, some of these reactions are produced by doped oxides that absorb mainly in the U.V. and short wavelength visible radiation. By using photosensitizers the absorption range has been extended well inside the whole visible region, facilitating a better use of solar energy. This application has been focused to reactions that will produce hydrogen from water aiming at the production of a clean fuel from an almost infinite raw material. Pt and Ru oxides co-supported on colloidal Ti-oxide particles have been used as a photocatalyst. Several dyes have been used as photosensitizers.

Other sensitizers have found application in synthesis reactions.

The energy transfer may also be used in the reverse way, i.e., having a compound that will receive the transferred energy by a radiation activated substance. Thus, energy acceptors are used to stabilize plastics and fibers, quenching polymer excited molecules avoiding in this way fast degradation. This is a problem of great economic importance and deserves further comments.

The absorption of light may be followed by subsequent photochemical reactions. The molecular chains of polymeric plastics and fibers may be broken leading to gradual disintegration. Also, new links (cross-links for example), may be formed leading to undesirable brittleness. Sometimes this light activation forms free radicals that promote chain degradations thus making the disintegration even faster. The solution has been sought resorting to an imitation of plant behavior. It is known that β-carotene protects chlorophyll from oxidation. Much in the same way, energy sinks have been incorporated into the polymer structure. They can absorb the U.V. energy and exercise the ability of wasting the electronic energy, protecting the plastic or fiber from changes in its desirable properties. Ortosubstituted benzophenones have been used with this purpose.

On the other hand, efforts have also been made to accelerate the photodegradation of polymers, but in this case the energy transfer is not the predominant mechanism. In this case all the methods employed are based on producing systems capable of generating a greater concentration of radicals to initiate an oxidation chain. Obviously, the objective here is to accelerate degradation of disposed plastics rather than to preserve the life of the polymer structure, environmental considerations being the main concern.

Isomerization

$$A^* \longrightarrow B$$

Although many photoisomerization reactions are very well known, only a few of them have found commercial application. Important photochemical isomerizations are the synthesis of vitamin D_3 from dehydrocholesterol, the synthesis of dehydrogesterone and the vitamin A acetate.

Not to be forgotten is the plastic stabilization produced by certain compounds that absorb U.V. radiation avoiding polymer degradation. These compounds undergo a reversible photochemical isomerization that transforms the absorbed U.V. energy into heat by regenerating, in a cyclic way, the U.V. absorber concentration in the polymeric substance.

Photochromism is another application of photoisomerizations. Some of the reported uses are: photochromic systems for computer data display, microimage formation for information storage, self-darkening glasses for windshields, windows, and sun glasses, etc., the main features in all cases being the control of the speed, degree, and duration of changes in one or the other direction.

Addition

$$A^* + B \longrightarrow AB$$

No important applications of this type of outcome have been reported so far. Some interesting reactions have been patented, for instance the addition of carbonyl groups to olefins, but no commercial processes have been put into practice. Pape [41] indicates that these addition reactions offer a very attractive system to facilitate the penetration of cell membranes by certain functional groups, opening in this way the route for significant biological breakthroughs.

Hydrogen Abstractions

$$A^* + R - H \longrightarrow AH + R\cdot$$

This is a well known way of producing free radicals ($R\cdot$). The hydrogen abstraction reaction is a suitable way for triggering off polymerizations and other chain reactions frequently found in free-radical chemistry. The main applications will be described in the next paragraph.

Fragmentation

In this case we have a primary process of the type:

$$(A - B) + h\nu \longrightarrow (A - B)^*$$

followed by:

$$(A - B)^* \longrightarrow A\cdot + B\cdot$$

with $A = B$ being a particular case.

This is a more important way of producing free radicals than hydrogen abstraction and perhaps the route that has produced more large-scale industrial applications in the chemical process industry.

Chlorinations

$$R - H + Cl_2 + h\nu \longrightarrow R - Cl + HCl$$

The most important commercial uses of photochlorinations are:

1. Monochloroalkanes from linear C_{11}–C_{14} paraffin cut. They are produced as intermediates to give alkylbenzenes that serve as starting materials for linear alquilbenzenesulfonates, an important group of biodegradable detergents.

2. γ-isomer of the hexachlorocyclohexane by direct chlorination of benzene at low reaction temperatures that favor the γ-isomer production.
3. Chlorination of the methyl group of toluene without noticeable reaction in the ring. Similar reactions lead to benzylidene dichloride and benzotrichloride, all of them valuable intermediates in industrial synthesis.
4. Production of chloromethanes (methyl chloride, methylene chloride, chloroform and carbon tetrachloride) from methane.
5. Production of ethylchloride from ethane.
6. Production of 1-1-1 trichloroethane from 1,1-dichloroethane.

Sulfochlorinations

$$RH + SO_2 + Cl_2 + h\nu \longrightarrow RSO_2Cl + HCl$$

Alkanesulfonyl chlorides obtained in this way may be used to produce water soluble alkanesulfonates used mainly as polymerization emulsifiers or sulfonamides used in the textile industries.

Sulfoxidations

$$RH + SO_2 + O_2 + h\nu \longrightarrow RSO_3H$$

The product has the same applications as the one discussed in above with the exception that now no HCl is obtained as a by-product, which is an economic advantage.

Oximation

$$\begin{matrix} R_1 \\ R_2 \end{matrix}\!\!>\!CH_2 + NOCl + h\nu \longrightarrow \begin{matrix} R_1 \\ R_2 \end{matrix}\!\!>\!C{=}NOH\cdot HCl$$

Application of photooximation cyclohexane opened the shortest route to caprolactame for subsequent production of Nylon 6.

The same reaction is used to produce lauryl-lactam from cyclodecane which is used to produce Nylon 12, a polyamide of important special applications.

During many years it was an accepted concept that photoinduced reactions were economic only when radical chain reactions with overall quantum yields of up to 10^3 moles per einstein or more were involved, or when a very expensive specialty chemical was produced. This prejudice about photochemical reactions, originated mainly in the practical success of chlorinations and vitamin D_3 synthesis, was dramatically overthrown by the photooximation processes. Here, stoichiometrical energy consumption led to the production of a commodity that has shown to compete very well in the international market.

Hydrogen Sulphide Addition to Alkenes

This reaction is produced via fragmentation of H_2S in two free radicals: H· and HS·. The reaction has application in the production of antioxidants and volatile primary mercaptans.

Polymerizations and Cross-Linking

Several applications have resulted from the use of photochemical methods in polymer technology besides the existing interest in preventing undesirable photodegradation or stimulating an easier and faster destruction after plastics and fibers have been disposed.

Photopolymerization and photoinduced cross-linking includes: solventless coatings for metals and wood; solventless, rapid drying ink; printed coatings, photomillings, etc.

Photopolymer systems are mainly used for U.V. curable coatings. By this technology changes in physical properties are brought about such as adhesive characteristics, mechanical strength and solubility. In every application an optimal combination of the monomer (or mixtures of polymers) and the photoinitiator is required.

Photopolymeric printing plates are some of the most important products in the market. They consist in a polymer matrix, a cross-linking substance, a photoinitiator and a metalic or plastic carrrier. The plate is exposed to radiation through a given pattern. A developer washes out the unexposed part of the polymeric matrix and the remaining photopolymeric relief is the required matrix for printing. Different washing techniques have been used in commercial systems.

Not always a radical fragmentation is required, and as a matter of fact some of the modern positive offset printing are based on non-radical fragmentation. Photosensitive polymers formed by o-diazoquinones and lippophilic polymers can change solubility in alkalis after exposure to light. After washing the image thus obtained, the surface of the carrier has hydrophobic and hydrophilic regions. The first ones take up the printing ink, which is of an oily nature.

Copying techniques also make use of photochemistry, starting from the old and well known system of reproduction made by mixtures of a diazonium salt and a phenol, with moist ammonia as a developer.

Photoresists, printed circuits, precision scales, precision mouldings in micromechanics, etc. are among other applications of photopolymerizations.

In the field of synthetic chemistry, visible and ultraviolet light has been used in polymerization by two different mechanisms:

1. Polyinitiated or "photoaddition" polymerization, that involves the production of an excited molecule that initiates a radical process. It can be generated in the polymer, in the monomer (by homolytic cleavage of a weak bond) or in an initiator. Once the radical is formed, the chain reaction follows the known polymerization mechanisms.
2. "Photocondensation" polymerization that involves reactions of an excited polymer or monomer in which it adds more polymers or monomers to produce the structure of the polymeric chain.

Cross-linking is also another example of photopolymerizations and it has been used to change physical properties of existing polymers. Similar processes have been developed in photochemical polymer grafting. It consists in polymerizing a thin layer of a monomer on a high molecular weight polymer. In this way, for example, polyethylene may be grafted to polystyrene producing a resultant film of drastically improved physical properties.

Other Applications

Here we would like to list a series of processes that involve a mixture of many different photochemical routes. They can be better described by the application purpose. Following Legan [45], we can mention:

1. Disinfection of wastewater prior to deepwell disposal to prevent plugging by slimes produced by microorganisms.
2. Purification of raw materials in fermentation processes to avoid the production of undesirable side-products.
3. Pretreatment of feed streams in reverse osmosis to produce algae and bacteria free water, to avoid fouling of membranes.
4. General algae and slime control in process water, to avoid plugging of on line instrument control.
5. Disinfection of secondary effluents from sewage plants by means of U.V. alone or in combination with an oxidant.
6. Disinfection and sterilization of process and drinking water by U.V. alone or in the presence of an oxidant like hydrogen peroxide.

7. Supply of high-purity water for industries such as: electronics, brewing, pharmaceuticals, foods, and soft-drink bottling.
8. Control of biofouling in cooling-water systems by using U.V. radiation and hydrogen peroxide.
9. Removal of pollutants, particularly those very refractary to biodegradation. This will also require the combination of U.V. radiation and an oxidizing agent. Pesticides, polychlorinated biphenols, as well as many other harmful organic chemicals can be subjected to photolysis in the presence of an oxidant.
10. Elimination of chromium from sludges by attack with U.V. radiation and hydrogen peroxide.
11. Removal of chelated heavy metals that otherwise offer difficulties to precipitate. They can be treated by U.V. oxidizing processes that destroy the chelating agent.
12. Color removal of kraft-mill effluents. Also by combining an oxidant and U.V. action.
13. Removal of iron cyanide from wastewaters produced in the electroplating and photographic industries. This can be accomplished by using U.V. light and ozone.
14. An important and modern field of photochemical processes is the storage of energy via photochemical reactions. It is required to have a substance A that can absorb in the solar region of the radiation spectrum. Then, it can be converted into an excited state A* and from it again transformed in a new material B of much higher ground energy than A. Part of the solar energy originally absorbed by A (because not all can be transformed when A → B) is stored as chemical energy in B. Promoting the conversion of B back to A (initiating the reaction by heating or by the presence of a catalyst), an exothermic reaction is produced that liberates the stored energy. Several properties and conditions must be fulfilled by the system of substances formed by A and B. They have been carefully outlined by Laird [44] and will not be repeated here. Several reactions have also been described that can be used for energy storage. The reader interested in the subject can resort to the quoted reference.
15. Closing this area of applications one should mention the increasing significance that photochemical vapor deposition techniques have developed in the past years. The economic impact being more effective in microcircuits and microcomponents technology in the electronic industry.

Water cleavage using solar energy and applications in microelectronics seem to be the most new promising fields for photochemical technology. Both cases present new challenging areas that have not been thoroughly explored yet. More than ever, it is clear that an interdisciplinary effort is indispensable to enhance their possibilities of success.

Acknowledgment

A proposal to use approximate methods in photoreactor design is a novel part of this chapter. Credit must be given to Prof. H.A. Irasoqui of INTEC for his suggestion of including a section with this type of approach.

Miss Y. Pereyra deserves our gratitude for her excellent job in typing the manuscript. Prof. E. Grimaldi has contributed with her usual devotion in helping us with the English edition. The Reference section includes a concise list of all my co-workers who have contributed to the development of the concepts and methods here described. I am pleased to extend my thanks to all of them.

We also thank Universidad Nacional del Litoral (U.N.L.) and Consejo Nacional de Investigaciones Científicas y Técnicas (CONICET), Argentina, which provided the financial support for the edition of this monography.

NOTATION

a	ellipse semimajor axis or characteristic constant of the parabola, m
A	area, m^2
A_v	interfacial area per unit volume, m^{-1}
b	ellipse semiminor axis, m
c	half distance between foci, m or velocity of light, $m\ s^{-1}$
C	concentration, $mole\ m^{-3}$

d_b bubble diameter, m
D diffusion coefficient, $m^2\,s^{-1}$
Da Damköhler number, dimensionless
e ellipse eccentricity, dimensionless
e^a local volumetric rate of energy absorption, einstein $s^{-1}\,m^{-3}$
E energy flow rate, einstein s^{-1}
$f(\theta, \phi)$ function that takes into account the directional characteristics of the emission, dimensionless
F molar flow rate, mole s^{-1}
F_v volumetric flow rate, $m^3\,s^{-1}$
Ge geometric number, dimensionless
h Planck's constant, J s
H Henry's constant, Pa m^3 $mole^{-1}$
I intensity of radiation, dimensions are source-model dependent
I' isotropic intensity of radiation, dimensions are source-model dependent
J rate of initiation step, dimensionless
J^* rate of initiation step, mole $m^{-3}\,s^{-1}$
k_i reaction rate constant for i-step, s^{-1} (first order) or $m^3\,mole^{-1}\,s^{-1}$ (second order).
k_L° physical absorption coefficient, m s^{-1}
k_L chemical absorption coefficient, m s^{-1}
K ratio of the inner radius to outer radius (annular reactor), dimensionless
K_i reaction rate constant for i-step, dimensionless
K_L ratio of reaction time to absorption time, dimensionless
L length, m
$\underset{\sim}{n}$ unit normal vector, or mass absorption rate, mole $m^{-2}\,s^{-1}$
N mass absorption rate, dimensionless
P total pressure, Pa
Pe Peclet number, dimensionless
$\underset{\sim}{q}$ radiation flux density vector, einstein $m^{-2}\,s^{-1}$
q $\underset{\sim}{q} \cdot \underset{\sim}{n}$, radiation flux density, einstein $m^{-2}\,s^{-1}$
r radial coordinate, m
R radius, m
Re Reynolds number, dimensionless
t time, s
T temperature, K
U velocity, dimensionless
v velocity, m s^{-1}
V volume, m^3
x, y, z rectangular Cartesian coordinates, m
X fractional conversion, dimensionless

Greek Letters

α absorption coefficient, $m^2\,mole^{-1}$
β cylindrical coordinate, rad
γ radial coordinate, dimensionless
Γ reflection coefficient, dimensionless or emitting extension, dimensions are source-model dependent
ΔH heat of reaction, J $mole^{-1}$
$\underset{\sim}{\varepsilon}$ unit vector representing the direction of a ray
ε absorption number, dimensionless or volume fraction, dimensionless
ζ axial coordinate, dimensionless
θ angular coordinate, rad
Θ temperature, dimensionless
κ characteristic property of the lamp emission, einstein $m^{-3}\,s^{-1}\,sr^{-1}$
λ wavelength, m
μ attenuation coefficient, m^{-1}
ν frequency, s^{-1}
ρ spherical coordinate, m
τ time, dimensionless
Υ reactor wall transmittance, dimensionless
ϕ spherical coordinate, rad
Φ quantum yield, mole $einstein^{-1}$
ψ radian energy per unit time and unit area, einstein $s^{-1}\,m^{-2}$
Ψ concentration, dimensionless or radiant energy per unit time and unit of source extent, dimensions are source-model dependent
ω solid angle, sr
Ω reaction rate, dimensionless
Ω^* reaction rate, mole $m^{-3}\,s^{-1}$

Subscripts

D direct radiation
Diff diffusion value
e emission value
eff effective property
exp experimental value
E property of an emerging ray from the source
ESVE relative to the Extense Source Model with Voluminal Emission
G relative to the gas phase

h	relative to a heterogeneous termination step
i	i-species
in	relative to the inner wall of the reactor or inlet condition
I	incident point or an incident ray property
In	indirect radiation
L	lamp property or relative to liquid phase
LSPP	relative to the Line Source Model with emission in Parallel Planes
LSSE	relative to the Line Source Model with Spherical Emission
m	relative to a multicomponent mixture
mod	relative to the radiation model
n	relative to the normal
o	at the surface of entrance of radiation
Ox	relative to oxalic acid
ou	relative to the outer wall of the reactor or outlet condition
ov	relative to an overall quantum yield
p	relative to a propagation step
prim	relative to a primary quantum yield
P	relative to the point of reflection
r	reception value
reac	characteristic reaction time
R	reactor property or relative to the mean residence time
ref	reference value
Rf	reflector property
t	relative to a termination step
T	denotes total value
Ur	relative to the uranyl ion
w	wall property
z	relative to the z-axis
1	lower limit of integration
2	upper limit of integration
ν	frequency dependence

Superscripts

a	absorbed value
D	direct radiation
int	interface value
In	indirect radiation
NM	no mixing
PM	perfect mixing
(t)	turbulent diffusivity
$^{\circ}$	initial value
$'$	values projected on the x-y plane
*	relative to attenuation path

Special Symbols

$\langle\ \rangle$	average value
$\wedge$	denotes a free radical

REFERENCES

1. Alfano, O. M., Romero, R. L., and Cassano, A. E., "Modeling of radiation transport and energy absorption in photoreactors," *Adv. Transport Processes, 4* 201 (1985).
2. Irazoqui, H. A., Cerdá, J., and Cassano, A. E., "The radiation field for the point and line source approximations and the three-dimensional source models: applications to photoreactors," *The Chem Eng. Journal, 11* 27 (1976).
3. Irazoqui, H. A., Cerdá, J., and Cassano, A. E., "Radiation profiles in an empty annular photoreactor with a source of finite spatial dimensions," *A.I.Ch.E. J., 19* 460 (1973).
4. Cerdá, J., Marchetti, J. L., and Cassano, A. E., "Radiation efficiencies in elliptical photoreactors," *Lat. Am. J. Heat and Mass Transfer, 1* 33 (1977).
5. Cassano, A. E., Alfano, O. M., and Romero, R. L., Photoreactor Engineering: Analysis and Design, *Concepts and Design of Chemical Reactors* (S. Whitaker and A. E. Cassano, eds.), Gordon and Breach Science Pub., New York, 1986, p. 339.
6. De Bernardez, E. R., Clariá M. A., and Cassano, A. E., Analysis and Design of Photoreactors, *Chemical Reaction and Reactor Engineering* (J. J. Carberry and A. Varma, eds.), Marcel Dekker Inc., New York, 1987, p. 839.
7. Alfano, O. M., Romero, R. L., and Cassano, A. E., "Radiation field modelling in photoreactors—I. Homogeneous media," *Chem. Eng. Sci., 41* 421 (1986).

8. Alfano, O. M., Romero, R. L., and Cassano, A. E., "Radiation field modelling in photoreactors—II. Heterogeneous media," *Chem. Eng. Sci.*, *41* 1137 (1986).
9. Harris, P. R., and Dranoff, J. S., "A study of perfectly mixed photochemical reactors," *A.I.Ch.E. J.*, *11* 497 (1965).
10. Pai, S., *Radiation Gas Dynamics*, Springer-Verlag, Berlin, 1966.
11. Vincenti, W. G., and Kruger, C. H., Jr., *Introduction to Physical Gas Dynamics*, J. Wiley and Sons, New York, 1965.
12. Otake, T., Tone, S., Higuchi K., and Nakao, K., "Light intensity profile in gas-liquid dispersion. Applicability of effective absorption coefficient," *Kagaku Kogaku Ronbunshu*, *7* 57 (1981).
13. Yokota, T., Iwano, T., Deguchi, H., and Tadaki, T., "Light absorption rate in a bubble column photochemical reactor," *Kagaku Kogaku Ronbunshu*, *7* 157 (1981).
14. Calvert, J. C., and Pitts, J. N., Jr., *Photochemistry*, J. Wiley and Sons, New York, 1966.
15. Herzberg, G., Spectra of Diatomic Molecules, *Molecular Spectra and Molecular Structure*, Vol. I, 2nd. Ed., Van Nostrand Reinhold, New York, 1950.
16. Romero, R. L., Alfano, O. M., Marchetti, J. L., and Cassano, A. E., "Modelling and parametric sensitivity of an annular photoreactor with complex kinetics," *Chem. Eng. Sci.*, *38* 1593 (1983).
17. De Bernardez, E. R., and Cassano, A. E., "A priori design of a continuous annular photochemical reactor. Experimental validation for simple reactions," *J. Photochem.*, *30* 285 (1985).
18. Clariá, M. A., Irazoqui, H. A., and Cassano, A. E., "A priori design of a photochemical reactor for the monochlorination of ethane. Modelling and experimental validation," accepted for publication in the *A.I.Ch.E. J.* (1987).
19. De Bernardez, E. R., and Cassano, A. E., "Azimuthal asymmetries in tubular photoreactors," *Lat. Am. J. Heat and Mass Transfer*, *6* 333 (1982).
20. De Bernardez, E. R., and Cassano, A. E., "Methodology for an optimal design of a photoreactor. Application to methane chloroderivatives production," *Ind. Eng. Chem. Process Des. Dev.*, *25* 601 (1986).
21. Cerdá, J., Irazoqui, H. A., and Cassano, A. E., "Radiation fields inside an elliptical photoreflector with a source of finite spatial dimensions," *A.I.Ch.E. J.*, *19* 963 (1973).
22. Alfano, O. M., and Cassano, A. E., "Modelling of a gas-liquid tank photoreactor irradiated from the bottom. I. Theory," accepted for publication in *Ind. Eng. Chem. Res.* (1987).
23. Alfano, O. M., and Cassano, A. E., "Modelling of a gas-liquid tank photoreactor irradiated from the bottom. II. Experiments," accepted for publication in *Ind. Eng. Chem. Res.* (1987).
24. Astarita, G., "Regimes of mass transfer with chemical reaction," *Ind. Eng. Chem.*, *58* 18 (1966).
25. Astarita, G., *Mass Transfer with Chemical Reaction*, Elsevier Pub., New York, 1967.
26. Astarita, G., Savage, D. W., and Bisio, A., *Gas Treating with Chemical Solvents*, J. Wiley and Sons, New York, 1983.
27. Alfano, O. M., Romero, R. L., and Cassano, A. E., "A cylindrical photoreactor irradiated from the bottom. I. Radiation flux density generated by a tubular source with a parabolic reflector," *Chem. Eng. Sci.*, *40* 2119 (1985).
28. Alfano, O. M., Romero, R. L., and Cassano, A. E., "A cylindrical photoreactor irradiated from the bottom. II. Model for the local volumetric rate of energy absorption with polychromatic radiation and their evaluation," *Chem. Eng. Sci.*, *41* 1155 (1986).
29. Alfano, O. M., Romero, R. L., Negro, A. C., and Cassano, A. E., "A cylindrical photoreactor irradiated from the bottom. III. Measurement of absolute values of the local volumetric rate of energy absorption. Experiments with polychromatic radiation," *Chem. Eng. Sci.*, *41* 1163 (1986).
30. Foraboschi, F. P., "La conversione in un reattore fotochimico continuo," *Chem. Ind.* (Milan), *41* 731 (1959).
31. Dolan, W. J., Dimon, C. A., and Dranoff, J. S., "Dimensional analysis in photochemical reactor design," *A.I.Ch.E. J.*, *24* 1134 (1965).
32. Felder, R. M., and Hill, F. B., "Mixing effects in chemical reactors—I. Reactant mixing in batch and flow systems," *Chem. Eng. Sci.*, *24* 385 (1969).
33. Felder, R. M., and Hill, F. B., "Mixing effects in chemical reactors. Chain reactions in batch and flow systems," *Ind. Eng. Chem. Fundam.*, *9* 360 (1970).

34. Harano, Y., and Smith, J. M., "Design of tubular flow reactor for photochemical systems," *A.I.Ch.E. J., 14* 584 (1968).
35. Williams, J. A., and Ragonese, F. P., "Asymptotic solutions and limits of transport equations for tubular flow reactors," *Chem. Eng. Sci., 25* 1751 (1970).
36. Clariá, M. A., Irazoqui, H. A., and Cassano, A. E., "Modelling and experimental validation of the radiation field inside an elliptical reflector," *The Chem. Eng. Journal, 33* 119 (1986).
37. Doede, C. M., and Walker, C. A., "Photochemical engineering," *Chem. Eng., 62* 159 (1959).
38. Marcus, R. J., Kent, J. A., and Schenck, G. O., "Industrial photochemistry," *Ind. Eng. Chem., 54* 20 (1962).
39. Arnold, D. R., and de Mayo, P., "Photochemistry and industry," *Chem. Tech, 1* 615 (1971).
40. Mellor, J. M., Phillips, D., and Salisbury, K., "Photochemistry: new technological applications," *Chem. in Britain, 10* 160 (1974).
41. Pape, M., "Industrial applications of photochemistry," *Pure and App. Chem. 41* 535 (1975).
42. Fisher, M., "Industrial applications of photochemical synthesis," *Angew. Chem. Int. Ed. Engl., 17* 16 (1978).
43. Davidson, R. S., "Practical aspects of photochemistry," *Chem. Ind.*, 180 (1978).
44. Laird, T., "Energy storage via photochemical reactions," *Chem. Ind.*, 186 (1978).
45. Legan, R. W., "Ultraviolet light takes on CPI role," *Chem. Eng., 89* 95 (1982).
46. Yue, P. L., Studies of photoreactions in homogeneous photoreactors, *Photoelectrochemistry, Photocatalysis and Photoreactors* (M. Schiavello, ed.), D. Reidel Pub. Co., Dordrecht, Holland, 1985, p. 561.
47. Yue, P. L., Studies of photoreactions in heterogeneous photoreactors, *Photoelectrochemistry, Photocatalysis and Photoreactors* (M. Schiavello, ed.), D. Reidel Pub. Co., Dordrecht, Holland, 1985, p. 575.
48. Cassano, A. E., Silveston, P. L., and Smith, J. M., "Photochemical reaction engineering," *Ind. Eng. Chem., 59* 18 (1966).

CHAPTER 17

THE SYNTHESIS OF METHANOL

A. A. C. M. Beenackers, G. H. Graaf, and E. J. Stamhuis

Department of Chemical Engineering
University of Groningen
Groningen, The Netherlands

CONTENTS

INTRODUCTION

Methanol from synthesis gas is a bulk chemical since the early twenties. World production nowadays is in the order of twenty million tons per year with plant capacities typically in the order of 1,000 tons per day. All modern commercial processes are of the so-called "low pressure" type (50–100 bar), where the equilibrium reactions in the synthesis reactor

$$CO + 2\,H_2 = CH_3OH \tag{1}$$

$$CO_2 + H_2 = CO + H_2O \tag{2}$$

$$CO_2 + 3\,H_2 = CH_3OH + H_2O \tag{3}$$

are catalyzed by Cu—Zn—Al or Cu—Zn—Cr mixed oxides. Various processes are in use (ICI, Lurgi, Haldor-Topsoe), all of the so-called packed bed reactor type.

It is well known that the packed bed reactor technology has several disadvantages if applied for strongly exothermic processes where by-product formation and/or catalyst deactivation are temperature sensitive. Both are the case in the methanol synthesis. Reason why we decided to investigate the opportunities of a methanol synthesis process based on slurry reactor technology that potentially can be attractive if good temperature control is a major item. However, the commercial feasibility of such a new reactor concept exclusively depends on the performance of the slurry reactor relative to the conventional packed bed reactors. So we also decided to develop a chemical reaction engineering model for the methanol synthesis in conventional packed bed reactors. It asks for detailed knowledge of the chemical equilibrium constants of the reactions (1–3), of the reaction kinetics, and ultimately for a model of mass transfer with complex equilibrium kinetics to describe the local conversion rates inside the catalyst particles. For such a classical process one would expect that at least accurate equilibrium data and probably also reliable kinetic data can be readily obtained from open literature. However, our search showed that the published data both on kinetics and equilibria are either incomplete or conflicting. For that reason we decided to investigate these topics experimentally. The results are given in the second and third part of this chapter, respectively. The incorporation of these results in a dusty gas model for mass transfer with complex methanol synthesis equilibrium reactions will be discussed in the fourth part.

CHEMICAL EQUILIBRIA

Theory

From the three equilibria (1–3) playing a role in methanol synthesis, only two are independent. Arbitrarily we select the equilibria of Reactions 1 and 2, and define the equilibrium constants as:

$$K_{f1} = \left[\frac{f_{CH_3OH}}{f_{CO}f_{H_2}^2}\right]_{Eq} = \left[\frac{\phi_{CH_3OH}}{\phi_{CO}\phi_{H_2}^2}\right]_{Eq}\left[\frac{y_{CH_3OH}}{y_{CO}y_{H_2}^2}\right]_{Eq}\frac{1}{p^2} = K_{\phi,1}K_{p,1} \tag{4}$$

$$K_{f2} = \left[\frac{f_{CO}f_{H_2O}}{f_{CO_2}f_{H_2}}\right]_{Eq} = \left[\frac{\phi_{CO}\phi_{H_2O}}{\phi_{CO_2}\phi_{H_2}}\right]_{Eq}\left[\frac{y_{CO}y_{H_2O}}{y_{CO_2}y_{H_2}}\right]_{Eq} = K_{\phi,2}K_{p,2} \tag{5}$$

Since most gases show ideal behaviour at 1 bar, we may assume:

$$K_f = K_p^\circ \tag{6}$$

Then K_p° is a function of temperature only. However, K_ϕ can be a function of temperature, pressure and composition.

The value of K_p° can be calculated from

$$-\Delta G^\circ(T) = RT \ln K_p^\circ(T) \tag{7}$$

$$\frac{-\Delta G^\circ(T)}{T} = \frac{-\Delta G^\circ(T_{ref})}{T_{ref}} - \int_{T_{ref}}^{T} \frac{\Delta H^\circ(T)}{T^2}\,dT \tag{8}$$

$$\Delta H^\circ(T) = \Delta H^\circ(T_{ref}) + \int_{T_{ref}}^{T} \Delta C_p^\circ(T)\,dT \tag{9}$$

Since the specific heats of the components are known to be polynomial functions of T, the integrations in Equations 8 and 9 can easily be carried out. Using ΔH_f° (25°C) and ΔG_f° (25°C) values [1] in combination with specific heat data [2], we get:

$$\log_{10} K^{\circ}_{p,1} = \frac{5139}{T} - 12.621 \qquad \text{(pressures in bars)} \tag{10}$$

$$\log_{10} K^{\circ}_{p,2} = \frac{-2073}{T} + 2.029 \tag{11}$$

It is possible to calculate K_{ϕ}-values using an equation of state. For a pressure-explicit equation of state, the fugacity coefficient of a component i in a mixture is given by [3]:

$$\ln \phi_i = \frac{1}{RT} \int_V^{\infty} \left[\left(\frac{\partial P}{\partial n_i} \right)_{T,V,n_j} - \frac{RT}{V} \right] dV - \ln Z \tag{12}$$

There are many equations of state available. The choice is not easily made as the system is a complicated one. It is a high-pressure system containing polar and non-polar molecules, some of which are above and some of which are below their critical temperatures. We investigated which of the equations of state listed in Table 1 is superior in describing the equilibria in "low pressure" methanol synthesis.

The parameters a and b in the van der Waals type of equations of state (RK, RKS, and PR, see Table 1) and B in the virial equation can be calculated from the critical pressures, temperatures, and the acentric factors of the components present in the methanol synthesis. Numerical values are published in Reference 7. The original mixing rules are used without interaction coefficients [4].

$$a = \sum_i \sum_j y_i y_j \sqrt{(a_i a_j)} \tag{13}$$

$$b = \sum_i y_i b_i \tag{14}$$

and for the second virial coefficient:

$$B_M = \sum_i \sum_j y_i y_j B_{ij} \tag{15}$$

Data from Literature

Literature data on $K_{p,1}$ do scatter substantially (see Figure 1) while data for the water gas shift reaction are scarce in the temperature range 475–575 K (see Figure 2). Very little information on non-ideal behavior is available for the conditions in the methanol synthesis. Ewell [19] calculated the fugacity coefficients for carbon monoxide, hydrogen, and methanol using Lewis and Randall's rule [20]:

$$\phi_i \text{ (mixture)} = \phi_i \text{ (pure component, same P, T)}$$

The result of this simplification is that the fugacity coefficients become a function of pressure and temperature only and not of composition.

Additional Experiments

From the previous discussion it follows that additional experiments are needed to get at accurate data for the equilibrium constants under conditions relevant for the methanol synthesis. We have carried out these experiments. For the techniques applied see Graaf and co-workers [7].

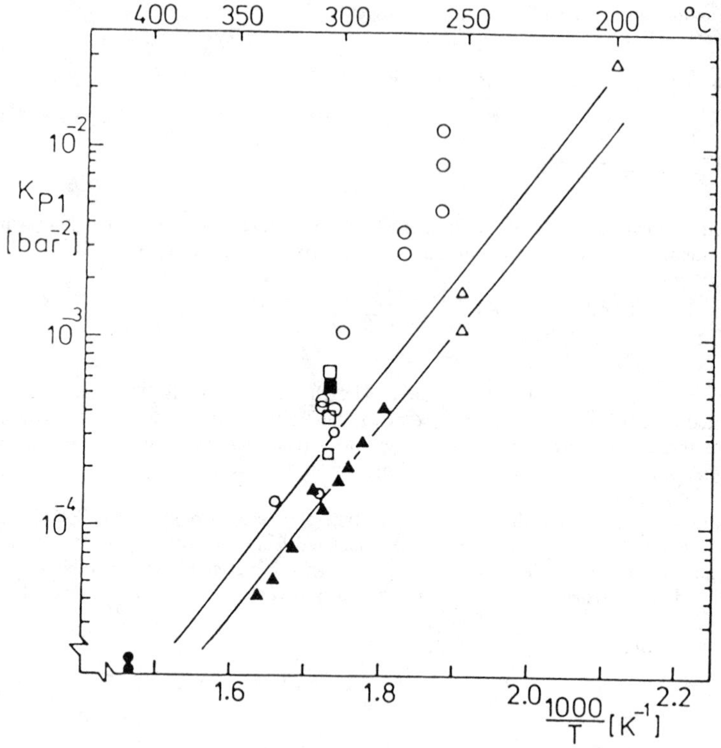

Figure 1. Literature data on K_{p1}: ○, Ref. [8]; ●, Ref. [9]; □, Ref. [10]; ■, Ref. [11]; △, Ref. [12]; ▲, Ref. [13]; upper line, Ref. [14]; lower line, Ref. [15]. (Reprinted with permission from Ref. [7], Pergamon Books Ltd.)

Results

$K_{p,1}$ and $K_{p,2}$ were measured in the range $10 < p < 75$ bar and $470 < T < 540$ K. These equilibrium constants can also be calculated from Equations 10 and 11 using successively one of the equations of state listed in Table 1 to calculate K.

For each equation of state the relative variance, S^2, between calculated and experimental value was calculated from

$$S^2 = \frac{1}{N} \sum_{i=1}^{N} \left[\frac{K_{p,calc} - K_{p,exp}}{K_{p,exp}} \right]^2 \tag{16}$$

The results are shown in Table 2.

From Table 2 it is clear that the best results are obtained when the Soave-Redlich-Kwong equation of state or the Peng-Robinson equation of state is used to desccribe the experimental data. Although the former gives slightly better results than the latter, the difference is not significant.

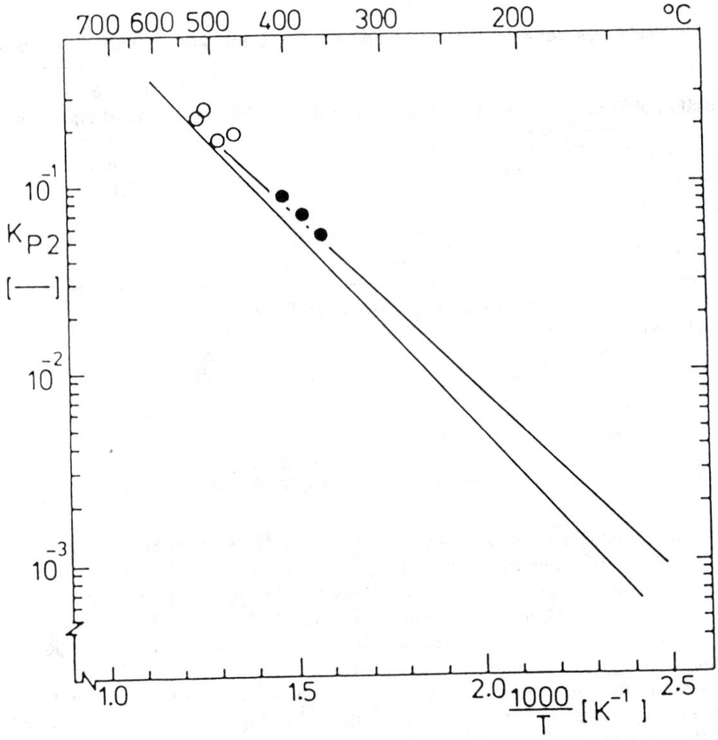

Figure 2. Literature data on K_{p2}: ○, Ref. [16]; ●, Ref. [17]; upper line, Ref. [15]; lower line, Ref. [18]. (Reprinted with permission from Ref. [7], Pergamon Books Ltd.)

Table 1
Equations of State Evaluated in This Study

Equations of State	Ref.	Abbreviation	Formula $z = Pv/RT$
Ideal gas law		IGL	1
Redlich-Kwong equation of state	[4]	RK	$\frac{v}{v-b} - \frac{1}{RT^{3/2}(v+b)}$
Soave-Redlich-Kwong equation of state	[5]	RKS	$\frac{v}{v-b} - \frac{a(T)}{RT(v+b)}$
Peng-Robinson equation of state	[6]	PR	$\frac{v}{v-b} - \frac{a(T)v}{RT(v(v+b)+b(v-b))}$
Virial equation		Vir	$1 + \frac{B}{v} + \cdots$

Reprinted with permission from Ref. 7, Pergamon Books Ltd.

Table 2
Relative Variances between the Calculated and Experimental Equilibrium Constants

Equation of State	$10^3 \times S_1^2$ (Methanol Equilibrium)	$10^3 \times S_2^2$ (Water-Gas Shift Equilibrium)
IGL	5.54	5.49
RK	10.9	7.44
RKS	3.32	4.34
PR	3.33	4.37
Vii*	5.14	4.98

* *The Virial equation of state was truncated after the second virial coefficient*
Reprinted with permission from Ref. 7, Pergamon Books Ltd.

In the Figures 3 and 4 the experimental equilibrium constants corrected to a pressure of 1 bar with the Soave-Redlich-Kwong equation of state, are given, as well as Equations 10 and 11.

It can be seen that there is good agreement between the (semi-)experimental points and the relationships derived from thermochemical data assuming ideal gas behavior. For comparison purposes, some experiments are also corrected to a pressure of 1 bar using Lewis and Randall's rule [20]. As can be clearly seen, this leads to serious errors.

Comparison of our results with the literature data shows that our results for the methanol equilibrium are in fairly good agreement with those of Ewell [19]. This can be seen in Table 3.

Extrapolating our results for the water-gas shift equilibrium to temperatures between 625 and 825 K shows that our results are in agreement with the experimental values of Oki and Mezaki [16], and those of Podolski and Kim [17]. This can be seen in Table 4.

REACTION KINETICS

Data from Literature

The Limiting Role Given to Carbon Dioxide

The kinetic data as published in open literature are conflicting. Particularly the rate of carbon dioxide has been much discussed (see Table 5).

Most kinetic models published until now assume formation of methanol from carbon monoxide only. The role of carbon dioxide in these models, if present, is restricted to competitive adsorption on the active sites of the catalyst. In contrast, some authors, Dybkjaer [32], and Chinchen et al. [28], claim methanol to be formed from carbon dioxide only. According to Dybkjaer, this is because strong adsorption of carbon dioxide prevents the co-adsorption of carbon monoxide. Chinchen and co-workers based their conclusions on experiments with labeled carbon in carbon dioxide. A third group of authors conclude that methanol is formed from both carbon monoxide and carbon dioxide. Liu et al. [35] come to this conclusion based on experiments with labeled oxygen in carbon dioxide. Based on kinetic experiments Denise and Sneeden [25] and Klier et al. [26] reach the same conclusion.

Most of the authors mentioned in Table 5 present kinetic rate expressions. The rate equations published more recently are listed in Table 6. Seyfert and Luft [31] (see Table 6) assume a Langmuir-Hinshelwood mechanism in which carbon monoxide and hydrogen are believed to be

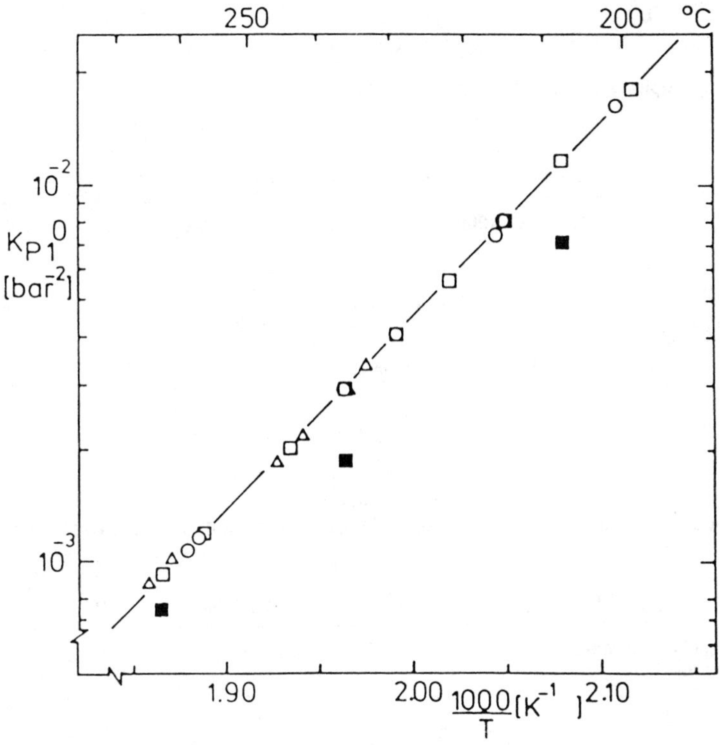

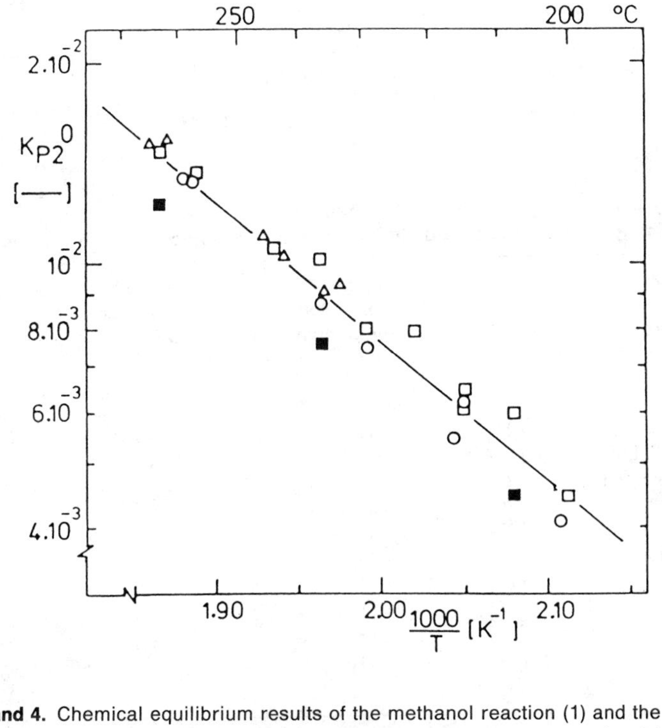

Figures 3 and 4. Chemical equilibrium results of the methanol reaction (1) and the water-gas-shift reaction (2), respectively. Open symbols: experimental points corrected to 1 bar with the Soave-Redlich-Kwong equation of state: ○, $p < 20$ bar; △, $20 < p < 40$ bar; □, $p > 40$ bar; ■ experimental points ($p > 40$ bar) corrected with Lewis and Randall's rule. (Reprinted with permission from Ref. [7], Pergamon Books Ltd.)

Table 3
Comparison of Data on the Methanol Equilibrium

Ref.	$10^2 \times K^{\circ}_{p1}$ (200°C) (bar^{-2})	$10^3 \times K^{\circ}_{p1}$ (250°C) (bar^{-2})	$10^4 \times K^{\circ}_{p1}$ (300°C) (bar^{-2})
Ewell [19]	1.74	1.67	2.38
This work	1.74	1.59	2.21

Reprinted with permission from Ref. 7, Pergamon Books Ltd.

Table 4
Comparison of the Literature Data on the Water-Gas Shift Equilibrium with Our Results

Ref.	T (°C)	$10^1 \times K^{\circ}_{p2}$	$10^1 \times K^{\circ}_{p2}$ (this work)
Oki and Mezaki [16]	467	1.9	1.7
	489	1.8	2.0
	522	2.3	2.6
	511	2.6	2.4
Podolski and Kim [17]	360	0.55	0.57
	381	0.70	0.72
	404	0.89	0.93

Reprinted with permission from Ref. 7, Pergamon Books Ltd.

Table 5
The Role of Carbon Dioxide in Methanol Synthesis According to Literature

Authors	Ref.	Carbon Source for Methanol	Adsorption of Carbon Dioxide?	Catalyst
Natta	[21]	CO	—	Zn—Cr
Bakemeier et al.	[22]	CO	yes	Zn—Cr
Leonov et al.	[23]	CO	no	Cu—Zn—Al
Schermuly & Luft	[24]	CO	yes	Cu—?
Denise & Sneeden	[25]	$CO + CO_2$	—	Cu—Zn—Al
Klier et al.	[26]	$CO + CO_2$	yes	Cu—Zn
Monnier et al.	[27]	CO	yes	Cu—Cr
Chinchen et al.	[28]	CO_2	yes	Cu—Zn—Al
Villa et al.	[29]	CO	yes	Cu—Zn—Al
Liu et al.	[35]	$CO + CO_2$	yes	Cu—Zn
Seyfert & Luft	[31]	CO	yes	Cu—Zn
Dybkjaer	[32]	CO_2	yes	Cu—Zn—Al Al—Zn—Cr

Table 6
Kinetic Rate Expressions for the Methanol Formation on Cu-Containing Catalysts Found in Recent Literature

Authors and Ref.	Kinetic Rate Expression $r'_{CH_3OH} =$	p / bar	T / °C
Seyfert & Luft [31]	$\dfrac{f_{CO}f_{H_2}^2 - f_{CH_3OH}/K_{p1}^\circ}{(A_1 + A_2f_{CO} + A_3f_{H_2} + A_4f_{CH_3OH} + A_5f_{CO}f_{H_2} + A_6f_{CO_2})^2}$	80–140	235–265
Villa et al. [29]	$\dfrac{f_{CO}f_{H_2}^2 - f_{CH_3OH}/K_{p1}^\circ}{(A_1 + A_2f_{CO} + A_3f_{CO_2} + A_4f_{H_2})}$	30–95	215–245
Klier et al [26]	$\dfrac{A_1A_2^3(p_{CO_2}/p_{CO})^3A_3A_5^2(p_{CO}p_{H_2}^2 - p_{CH_3OH}/K_{p1})}{(1 + A_2p_{CO_2}/p_{CO})^3(1 + A_3p_{CO} + A_4p_{CO_2} + A_5p_{H_2})^3} + A_6(p_{CO_2} - p_{CH_3OH}p_{H_2O}/(p_{H_2}^3K_{p3}))$	75	225–250
Dybkjaer [32]	$\dfrac{A_1A_2A_3^{1/2}(f_{CO_2}f_{H_2} - f_{CH_3OH}f_{H_2O}/(f_{H_2}^2K_{p3}^\circ))}{(1 + A_2f_{CO_2})(1 + A_3^{1/2}f_{H_2}^{1/2} + A_4f_{H_2O}/(A_3f_{H_2})^{1/2})}$	—	—

non-dissociatively adsorbed on the same kind of active sites. Methanol is made in a two-step reaction. In the first step formaldehyde is formed in an equilibrium reaction; the second step, in which adsorbed hydrogen and adsorbed formaldehyde react to form methanol, is believed to be rate determining. Villa et al. [29] (see Table 6) also assume a Langmuir-Hinshelwood mechanism in combination with non-dissociative adsorption of carbon monoxide and hydrogen. The rate determining step is believed to be a trimolecular surface reaction between adsorbed carbon monoxide and two adsorbed hydrogen-molecules as proposed originally by Natta [21].

Klier et al. [26] (see Table 6) presented a kinetic rate expression based on two synthesis routes. The first term in their kinetic rate expression describes the methanol formation from carbon monoxide and hydrogen. They furthermore assumed that the active sites can be reduced to inactive sites by a redox equilibrium involving carbon monoxide and carbon dioxide. The second term in their kinetic rate expression describes the methanol formation from carbon dioxide.

The kinetic rate expression as proposed by Dybkjaer [32] (see Table 6) is based on a dual-site Langmuir-Hinshelwood mechanism in which hydrogen is believed to adsorb dissociatively and reacts with adsorbed carbon dioxide. Dybkjaer also reported the results of studies on chemisorption of hydrogen, water, carbon monoxide, carbon dioxide on Cu—Zn—Cr and Cu—Zn—Al catalysts. Hydrogen and water are believed to adsorb competitively on one sort of active site, while carbon monoxide and carbon dioxide are adsorbed on a second sort of active site.

Also Herman et al. [33] noted the probability of a dual-site mechanism, because ZnO is a good hydrogenation catalyst that activates hydrogen by dissociative adsorption, while carbon monoxide is poorly adsorbed on ZnO and because univalent copper is known to absorb carbon monoxide but not hydrogen.

Matulewicz [34] concluded from "initial-rate" experiments that a dual-site mechanism is more likely than a single-site mechanism. He also concluded that no distinction can be made between molecular hydrogen adsorption and dissociative hydrogen adsorption. Liu et al. [30] reported an inhibiting effect of water on the methanol production. The results of Dybkjaer [32] are in agreement with this observation.

Table 7
Kinetic Rate Expressions for the Water-Gas-Shift Reaction on Cu—Zn—Al Catalysis Found in Recent Literature

Authors and Ref.	Kinetic Rate Expression $r'_{H_2O} =$	$\frac{p}{bar}$	$\frac{T}{°C}$
Villa et al. [29]	$\{f_{CO_2}f_{H_2} - f_{H_2O}f_{CO}/K^{\circ}_{p2}\}/A_5$	30–95	215–245
Dybkjaer [32]	$\dfrac{A_5A_2A_3^{1/2}[f_{CO_2}f_{H_2}^{1/2} - f_{CO}f_{H_2O}/(f_{H_2}^{1/2}K^{\circ}_{p2})]}{(1 + A_2f_{CO_2})[1 + A_3^{1/2}f_{H_2}^{1/2} + A_4f_{H_2O}/(A_3f_{H_2})^{1/2}]}$	—	—

From the authors mentioned in Table 6 only Villa and co-workers and Dybkjaer presented kinetic rate expressions for the water-gas-shift reaction. These rate expressions are summarized in Table 7.

The Ignorance of the Water-Gas-Shift Reaction

From the literature survey presented here it follows that still no agreement exists on the kinetics of methanol synthesis. The confusion is caused by the complicating effects of the simultaneously proceeding water-gas-shift reaction. This makes it in no way a simple matter to conclude unambiguously from which carbon source methanol is actually formed. Therefore, concerning methanol formation kinetics, our main objective has been to quantify the relative contribution of carbon monoxide and carbon dioxide in the synthesis of methanol.

Additionally, improved kinetic rate equations could be derived for each of the three parallel reactions relevant to the synthesis of methanol.

Proposed Reaction Schemes and Kinetic Rate Expressions

Without knowing whether methanol is formed from carbon monoxide, carbon dioxide or both, the safest way of writing down a reaction scheme is to include both routes. Because the Cu—Zn—Al catalysts are known to catalyze the water-gas-shift reaction as well, this reaction should be modeled too. So the three reactions (1–3) are the basis for the derivation of the kinetic rate expressions.

Based on the results of Dybkjaer [32], Herman et al. [33], and Matulewicz [34] all reactions are assumed to be based on a dual-site Langmuir-Hinshelwood mechanism. On site 1 carbon monoxide and carbon dioxide adsorb competitively, while on site 2 hydrogen and water adsorb competitively. The adsorption of methanol is assumed to be negligible. Hydrogen is believed to adsorb dissociatively. However, it is quite straightforward to derive alternative kinetic rate expressions that are based on molecular adsorption of hydrogen. It is now possible to write down the elementary reactions necessary for the overall reactions A, B, and C.

Adsorption equilibria:

$$CO + s1 = COs1 \tag{17}$$

$$CO_2 + s1 = CO_2s1 \tag{18}$$

$$H_2 + 2s2 = 2Hs2 \tag{19}$$

$$H_2O + s2 = H_2Os2 \tag{20}$$

Reaction A:

A1: $COs1 + Hs2 = HCOs1 + s2$ (21)

A2: $HCOs1 + Hs2 = H_2COs1 + s2$ (22)

A3: $H_2COs1 + Hs2 = H_3COs1 + s2$ (23)

A4: $H_3COs1 + Hs2 = CH_3OH + s1 + s2$ (24)

Reaction B:

B1: $CO_2s1 + Hs2 = HCO_2s1 + s2$ (25)

B2: $HCO_2s1 + Hs2 = COs1 + H_2Os2$ (26)

Reaction C:

C1: $CO_2s1 + Hs2 = HCO_2s1 + s2$ (27)

C2: $HCO_2s1 + Hs2 = H_2CO_2s1 + s2$ (28)

C3: $H_2CO_2s1 + Hs2 = H_3CO_2s1 + s2$ (29)

C4: $H_3CO_2s1 + Hs2 = H_2COs1 + H_2Os2$ (30)

C5: $H_2COs1 + Hs2 = H_3COs1 + s2$ (31)

C6: $H_3COs1 + Hs2 = CH_3OH + s1 + s2$ (32)

Assuming the total number of sites 1 and 2 being constant per weight of catalyst and neglecting terms originating from intermediate products, we obtain the following equations:

$$c_{s1,tot} = c_{s1} + c_{COs1} + c_{CO_2s1} \tag{33}$$

$$c_{s2,tot} = c_{s2} + c_{Hs2} + c_{H_2Os2} \tag{34}$$

Kinetic rate expressions can be easily obtained by choosing rate-determining steps for each overall reaction (A, B, and C) and assuming that all the other elementary reactions are at equilibrium. Assuming also that adsorption or desorption steps are not rate-controlling, then there are 48 possible combinations of kinetic rate expressions. Such a combination we will call a kinetic model.

Each kinetic model contains 7 kinetic constants, which have to be estimated from experimental results. These experimental results are sets of the following data:

$$r'_{CH_3OH},\ r'_{H_2O},\ T,\ p,\ y_{CO},\ y_{CO_2},\ y_{H_2},\ y_{CH_3OH},\ y_{H_2O}.$$

From the temperature, the total pressure and the mole fractions fugacities of each component are calculated with the Soave-Redlich-Kwong equation of state [5].

For a chosen kinetic model $r'_{CH_3OH} = (r'_{CH_3OH,A} + r'_{CH_3OH,C})$ and $r'_{H_2O} = (r'_{H_2O,B} + r'_{H_2O,C})$ can be calculated using these fugacities in combination with the estimated values of the kinetic constants. The equilibrium constants K°_{p1} and K°_{p2} in the rate expressions are taken from the previous section. Because reaction C is the stoichiometric sum of reactions A and B, K°_{p3} follows from:

$$K^\circ_{p3} = K^\circ_{p1} \cdot K^\circ_{p2} \tag{35}$$

For the parameter estimation a direct search algorithm was developed in which the parameters were adjusted towards optimum values.

Once a set of optimal constants was found for a given model, the variances of this model for both the methanol and the water production rates were calculated.

$$S^2_{A,C} = \frac{\sum_{j=1}^{N} (\hat{r}'_{CH_3OH} - r'_{CH_3OH})^2_j}{(N - m)} \tag{36}$$

$$S^2_{B,C} = \frac{\sum_{j=1}^{N} (\hat{r}'_{H_2O} - r'_{H_2O})^2_j}{(N - m)} \tag{37}$$

The values of these variances are due to experimental inaccuracies and to "lack of fit" of the kinetic model used.

The variances of all models were tested upon their equality with Bartlett's χ^2-test [36]. Models that passed this test were subsequently tested by two other methods: physico-chemical constraints, and residual analysis.

The estimates of the kinetic parameters must have physico-chemical meanings. Therefore, with reference to [37], [38], and [39]:

1. With respect to reaction rate constants, both the actual reaction rates and the activation energies must have positive values.
2. With respect to adsorption equilibrium constants, $K > 0$; $\Delta H^\circ_{ads} < 0$ and $0 < -\Delta S^\circ_{ads} < S^\circ_{gas}$.

The residuals, $(\hat{r}'_{CH_3OH} - r'_{CH_3OH})$ and $(\hat{r}'_{H_2O} - r'_{H_2O})$ should be normally distributed with zero mean. Also, the residuals should have no trending effects as a function of any of the independent variables, f_{CO}, f_{CO_2}, f_{H_2}, f_{CH_3OH}, f_{H_2O}.

Experiments

The kinetic study was carried out with a spinning basket reactor as described by Tajbl et al [40]. A commercial catalyst was used (Haldor Topsoe MK 101). Properties of this catalyst are reported by Dybkjaer [41]. The kinetic experiments were always carried out under steady state conditions. External mass-transfer limitations and heat-transfer limitations were negligible during experimental conditions chosen, as were both calculated and experimentally verified. A broad range of experimental conditions was examined in order to gain a good insight into the kinetics. These conditions are summarized in Table 8. The spinning basket reactor behaved as a perfect mixer [40]. Reaction rates for water and methanol were calculated from mixed-flow material balances over the reactor.

$$r'_j = y_j \Phi_v p/(WRT) \tag{38}$$

Results

Water Formation in the Methanol Synthesis

The amount of water formed in the methanol synthesis as a function of the gas-flow rate shows some peculiar features (see Figure 5). Here, the quantity put at the vertical axis is a dimensionless measure for the extent the shift reaction is away from equilibrium in the well-mixed basket reactor outlet. Its numerical value is plotted as a function of space velocity for one particular feed composition (feed 7) at various pressures. If the water-gas shift reaction is at equilibrium, its numerical value will be one.

Table 8
Experimental Conditions Selected in the Present Study on Synthesis Kinetics (Catalyst: Cu—Zn—Al)

Feed No.	Feed Composition y_{CO}	y_{CO_2}	y_{H_2}	$\frac{p}{bar}$	$\frac{T}{K}$	$\frac{10^3\ \phi_v/W}{m^3\ s^{-1}\ kg^{-1}}$
1	0.065	0.261	0.674	15 30 50	483.5 499.3 516.7	1–6
2	0.053	0.047	0.900	" "	" "	"
3	0.220	0.155	0.625	" "	" "	"
4	0.120	0.021	0.859	" "	" "	"
5	0.179	0.067	0.754	" "	" "	"
6	0	0.115	0.885	" "	483.5	0.3–7
7	0.092	0.105	0.803	" "	499.3	0.1–6

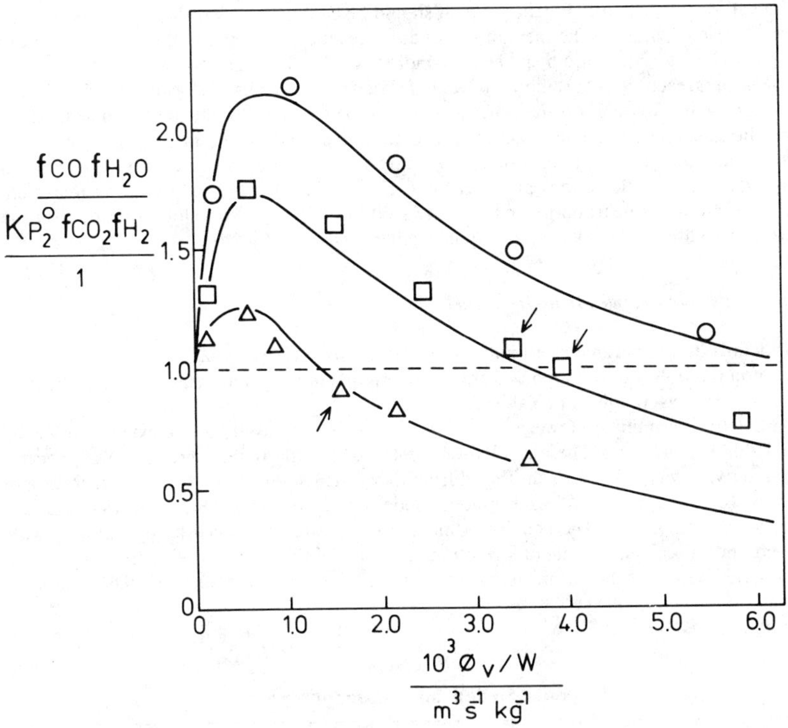

Figure 5. Water formation in methanol synthesis; ○, p = 50 bar; □, p = 30 bar; △, p = 15 bar. Symbols: results of feed 7 (see Table 8). Lines: calculated with model A3B2C3 after correcting for the difference in catalyst used in feed 7 (with respect to methanol).

Table 9
Relative Amounts of Methanol Formed from Carbon Monoxide and from Carbon Dioxide for Experiments with Feed 7 (See Table 8)

$\frac{10^3 f_{CO} f_{H_2O}}{f_{CO_2} f_{H_2}}$	$10^3\ K^{\circ}_{p2}$	y_{CH_3OH}	y_{H_2O}	% CH_3OH from CO	% CH_3OH from CO_2
6.9	7.54	0.0109	0.0061	44	56
8.2	7.54	0.0122	0.0074	39	61
7.5	7.54	0.0110	0.0067	39	61

Under certain conditions more water is formed than is predicted thermodynamically. We see only one possible explanation for this phenomenon: In addition to the water-gas-shift reaction still a second water yielding reaction must proceed. Since no by-products in detectable amounts were formed in these experiments, the surplus of water must result from the direct synthesis of methanol from carbon dioxide, which indeed yields water. Still another interesting feature can be detected from Figure 5. In some experiments (marked with an arrow) the water content is about the same as predicted from the chemical equilibrium of the water-gas-shift reaction. In this situation no driving force is left for this reaction. Furthermore, it should be emphasized that the water-gas-shift is not a fast reaction compared to the methanol formation reaction. Otherwise, the water content would have been close to equilibrium under all conditions. For these reasons, the contribution of the water-gas-shift reaction to the amount of water formed will be negligible for the experiments marked with an arrow in Figure 5. All the water formed will be the result of the methanol formation from carbon dioxide. Since hydrogenation of carbon monoxide yields only methanol, we can now calculate the amounts of methanol formed from carbon monoxide and carbon dioxide respectively. The results of these calculations are listed in Table 9. They prove unambiguously that methanol is produced from both carbon monoxide and carbon dioxide. It also follows that none of the two independent synthesis routes is relatively negligible.

Parameter Estimation and Model Discrimination

For details on the parameter estimation procedure, see Reference 42.

Based on the χ^2-test only 3 models from the 48 original models were retained at a 95% confidence level. These models are given in Table 10.

In order to discriminate between these 3 rival models, the results of the experiments with feed 6 (see Table 8) were used. These results were not used for the parameter estimation, because the catalyst activity was different from that during experiments with feeds 1–5. For each experiment of feed 6 (18 experiments) and each kinetic model of Table 10 the relative methanol and water activities were calculated. The activity of methanol or water is defined as the ratio between the observed and the calculated rate of formation using one of the kinetic models in combination with the estimated values of the parameters. The results of these calculations are listed in Table 11.

Table 10
Kinetic Models that Passed the χ^2-Test

Kinetic Model	$\Delta(r'_{CH_3OH})$	$\Delta(r'_{H_2O})$
A3B1C2	7.9%	28.7%
A3B1C3	6.4%	26.8%
A3B2C3	6.4%	24.2%

Table 11
Relative Catalyst Activities with Respect to Methanol and Water

Kinetic Model	Activity for Methanol	Activity for Water
A3B1C2	1.45 +/− 0.27	1.75 +/− 0.30
A3B1C3	1.34 +/− 0.05	1.38 +/− 0.07
A3B2C3	1.36 +/− 0.04	1.35 +/− 0.05

For the correct kinetic model equal catalyst activities might be expected for both methanol and water. Based on the results listed in Table 11 in combination with those listed in Table 10 we conclude that the best kinetic model is A3B2C3.

In Figure 6 rates of methanol and water production as predicted by model A3B2C3 are compared with the experimental results of feed 6. As can be seen there is a good agreement between the model calculations and the experimental data.

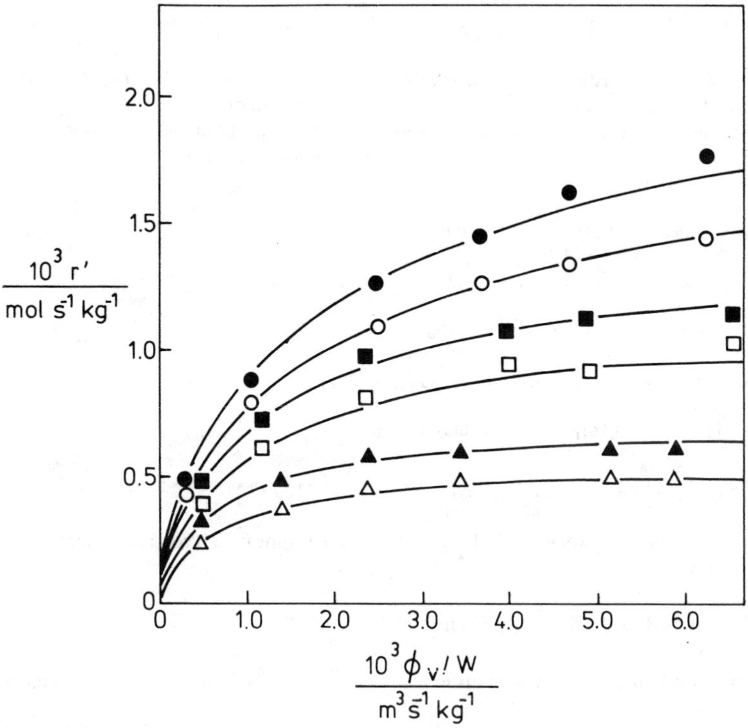

Figure 6. Reaction rates for methanol and water: ○, ●, p = 50 bar; □, ■, p = 30 bar; △, ▲, p = 15 bar. Open symbols: reaction rates for methanol, results of feed 6 (see Table 8). Closed symbols: reaction rates for water, results of feed 6 (see Table 8). Lines: calculated with model A3B2C3 after correcting for the difference in catalyst activity of the catalyst used in feed 6 (with respect to methanol).

The same agreement can be seen in Figure 5: the solid lines were calculated with model A3B2C3 in combination with a correction for catalyst activity (with respect to methanol).

From a thorough residual analysis on model A3B2C3, which is not given here, it was found that trending effects of the residuals as a function of any of the independent variables were normally distributed with zero mean.

It turned out that the kinetic model could be simplified, because the number of free sites 2 is negligible, which means:

$$1 \ll K_{H_2}^{1/2} f_{H_2}^{1/2} + K_{H_2O} f_{H_2O} \tag{39}$$

Model A3B2C3 can now be expressed kinetically as:

$$r'_{CH_3OH,A3} = \frac{k'_{ps,A3} K_{CO}(f_{CO} f_{H_2}^{3/2} - f_{CH_3OH}/f_{H_2}^{1/2} K_{p1}^{\circ})}{(1 + K_{CO} f_{CO} + K_{CO_2} f_{CO_2})(f_{H_2}^{1/2} + f_{H_2O} K_{H_2O}/K_{H_2}^{1/2})} \tag{40}$$

$$r'_{H_2O,B2} = \frac{k'_{ps,B2} K_{CO_2}(f_{CO_2} f_{H_2} - f_{H_2O} f_{CO}/K_{p2}^{\circ})}{(1 + K_{CO} f_{CO} + K_{CO_2} f_{CO_2})(f_{H_2}^{1/2} + f_{H_2O} K_{H_2O}/K_{H_2}^{1/2})} \tag{41}$$

$$r'_{CH_3OH,C3} = r'_{H_2O,C3} = \frac{k'_{ps,C3} K_{CO_2}(f_{CO_2} f_{H_2}^{3/2} - f_{CH_3OH} f_{H_2O}/f_{H_2}^{3/2} K_{p3}^{\circ})}{(1 + K_{CO} f_{CO} + K_{CO_2} f_{CO_2})(f_{H_2}^{1/2} + f_{H_2O} K_{H_2O}/K_{H_2}^{1/2})} \tag{42}$$

The reaction rate constants are marked with the subscript ps (pseudo), because they now contain the adsorption equilibrium constant of hydrogen. The parameter estimation was carried out again for this simplified form of model A3B2C3. It should be noted that the model predictions as presented in Figures 5 and 6 did not change noticeably after the simplification mentioned above. The following results were obtained:

$$k'_{ps,A3} = (2.69 +/- 0.14)10^7 \exp((-109900 +/- 200)/RT) \tag{43}$$

$$k'_{ps,B2} = (7.31 +/- 4.90)10^8 \exp((-123400 +/- 1600)/RT) \tag{44}$$

$$k'_{ps,C3} = (4.36 +/- 0.25)10^2 \exp((-65200 +/- 200)/RT) \tag{45}$$

$$K_{CO} = (7.99 +/- 1.28)10^{-7} \exp((58100 +/- 600)/RT) \tag{46}$$

$$K_{CO_2} = (1.02 +/- 0.16)10^{-7} \exp((67400 +/- 600)/RT) \tag{47}$$

$$K_{H_2O}/K_{H_2}^{1/2} = (4.13 +/- 1.51)10^{-11} \exp((104500 +/- 1100)/RT) \tag{48}$$

The Arrhenius' diagrams are given in Figures 7 and 8. The (linearized) confidence intervals in these equations were calculated from:

$$SSR(0.99) = SSR_{min} + SSR_{min} m/(N - m) F(m, N - m, 0.99) \tag{49}$$

In this equation F(m, N − m, 0.99) is Fisher's F-value with (m, N − m) degrees of freedom at a 99% significance level [43].

From Equations 43–48 it can be seen that the physico chemical constraints with respect to the numerical values of k, E_A, K, and ΔH_{ads}° all are satisfied.

The entropies of adsorption can be calculated from:

$$K = \exp(\Delta S_{ads}^{\circ}/R) \exp(-\Delta H_{ads}^{\circ}/RT) \tag{50}$$

The result is listed in Table 12, together with the S_{gas}° values.

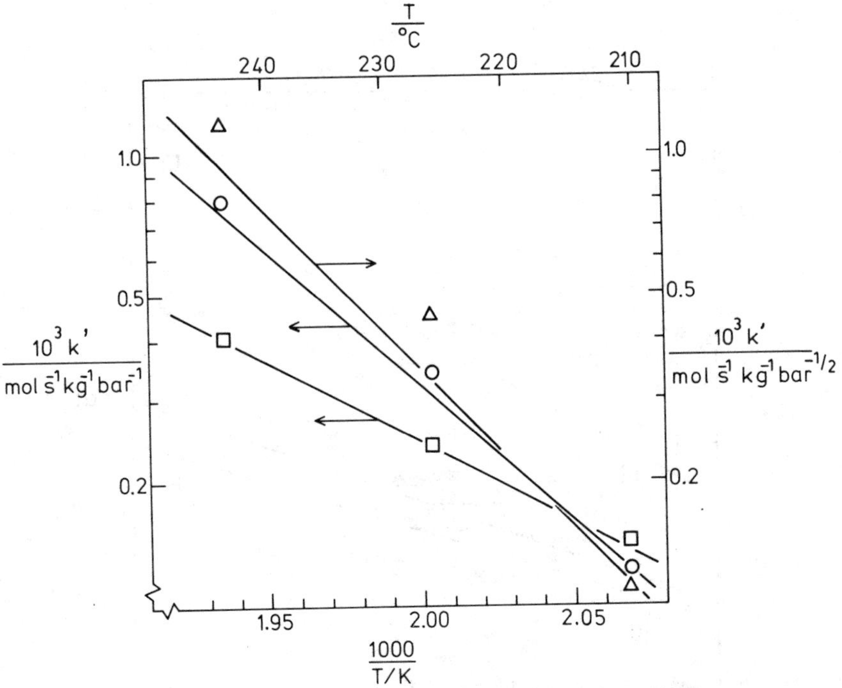

Figure 7. Reaction rate constants versus temperature: ○, $k'_{ps,A3}$; △, $k'_{ps,B2}$; □, $k'_{ps,3}$. Symbols: regression per temperature. Lines: regression with all temperatures.

Clearly, the adsorption entropies have reasonable values. For hydrogen and water, only the ratio of adsorption constants was determined; this gives no information about the adsorption entropies, however. We therefore may conclude, that the kinetic model A3B2C3 obeys to all physico-chemical constraints.

From the results of feed 6 the adsorption of hydrogen, which was assumed to be dissociative, can be studied in more detail. Because feed 6 did not contain carbon monoxide, it may be assumed that methanol is formed almost exclusively from CO_2 ($r'_{CH_3OH} \simeq r'_{CH_3OH,C3}$).This was confirmed by model calculations, which are not given here. After rearrangement of Equation 42 the following equation is obtained:

$$\frac{k'_{ps,C3}K_{CO_2}(f_{CO_2}f_{H_2}^{3/2} - f_{CH_3OH}f_{H_2O}/f_{H_2}^{3/2}K^{\circ}_{p3})}{r'_{CH_3OH}(1 + K_{CO}f_{CO} + K_{CO_2}f_{CO_2})f_{H_2}^{1/2}} = 1 + \frac{K_{H_2O}f_{H_2O}}{K_{H_2}^{1/2}f_{H_2}^{1/2}} \tag{51}$$

Thus, by plotting the left side of Equation 51 against $f_{H_2O}/f_{H_2}^{1/2}$ a straight line should be obtained. As can be seen from Figure 9 the results are in complete agreement with our expectations, thus supporting the assumption that hydrogen is adsorbed dissociatively.

Comparison with Literature

Parameter estimation was also carried out with the models taken from the literature as given in Tables 6 and 7 using the experimental data of feeds 1–5. Because Seyfert and Luft [31], and Klier et al. [26] do not give kinetic rate expressions for the water-gas shift reaction, these literature models

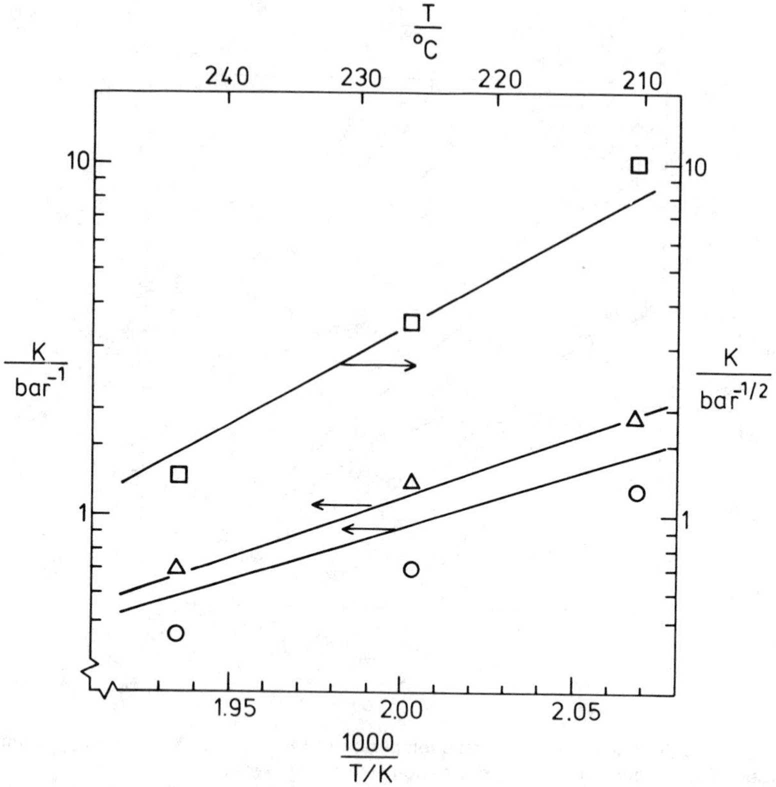

Figure 8. Adsorption constants versus temperature: ○, K_{CO}; △, K_{CO_2}; □, $K_{H_2O}/K_{H_2}^{1/2}$. Symbols: regression per temperature. Lines: regression with all temperatures.

were completed with the kinetic rate expression for the latter reaction as reported by Villa et al. [29]. The optimal parameters were determined for each of these models. Using these optimal parameters the deviations for the methanol and water production rates were calculated. These values are summarized in Table 13. Comparing the results with the results of model A3B2C3 show that the latter describes the kinetics in methanol synthesis much better. This was confirmed by the χ^2-test: using this criterion the four models from the literature were rejected, thus favoring model A3B2C3.

Table 12
Adsorption Entropies of CO and CO_2

Compound	$-\Delta S_{ads}$ / $J\ mol^{-1}\ K^{-1}$	S^{o}_{gas} (500 K) * / $J\ mol^{-1}\ K^{-1}$
CO	116.7	213.2
CO_2	133.9	243.9

* *taken from Ref. 44.*

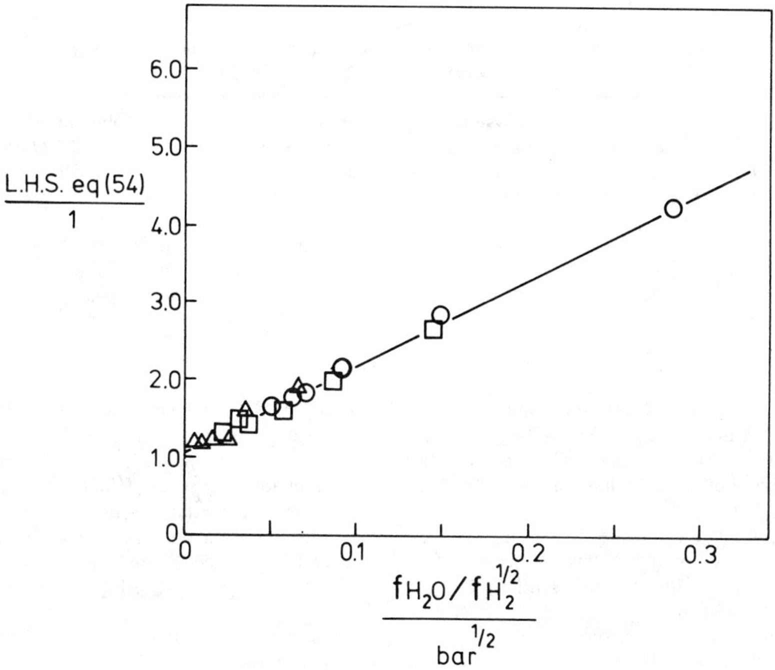

Figure 9. Adsorption of hydrogen and water: ○, p = 50 bar; □, p = 30 bar; △, p = 15 bar. Symbols: results of feed 6 (see Table 8). Line: best fit based on sum of squares of residuals.

MASS TRANSPORT AND CHEMICAL REACTION INSIDE THE CATALYST PELLET

Intra-particle Diffusion Limitation

Under practical reaction conditions diffusion limitation usually plays a role and various authors recently paid attention to it (see Table 14). Seyfert and Luft [31] experimentally observed diffusion limitations and used a modified Thiele modulus to describe the effects quantitatively. In this Thiele modulus they built in an adaption parameter instead of a diffusion coefficient. From their results

Table 13
Accuracies of the Kinetic Models Taken from Recent Literature Compared with the Model Proposed in This Study

Kinetic Model from (Author and Ref.)	$\Delta(r'_{CH_3OH})$	$\Delta(r'_{H_2O})$
Seyfert & Luft [31]	10.8%	100%
Villa et al. [29]	12.3%	100%
Klier et al. [26]	10.0%	57%
Dybkjaer [32]	14.7	167%
this study	6.4%	24%

Table 14
The Role of Intra-Particle Diffusion Limitations in Methanol Synthesis as Reported in the Open Literature

Authors	Diffusion Limitations Observed?	Diffusion Limitations Described?	Diffusion Model or Criterion Used
Berty et al. [45]	yes	no	Weisz-modulus
Seyfert & Luft [31]	yes	yes	(adapted) Thiele modulus
Dybkjaer [32]	—	yes	pore diffusion model
Skrzypek et al. [46]	—	yes	dusty gas model

we calculated an effective diffusion coefficient of about $10^{-9}\ m^2\ s^{-1}$, which is a very low value even for high pressure gas diffusion. The reverse problem was encountered by Berty et al. [45], who used the Weisz-Prater criterion [47] in combination with reasonable diffusion coefficients. Although they observed diffusion limitations, the Weisz-Prater criterion predicted absence of diffusion limitations.

Dybkjaer [32] reported effectiveness factors for the low-pressure methanol synthesis ranging from 80% to 40%. These effectiveness factors were obtained from a multicomponent diffusion-reaction model based on pore diffusion. Recently, Skrzypek et al. [46] applied the dusty-gas model for the description of the methanol synthesis in a single isothermal catalyst pellet, using simplified kinetic rate-expressions.

From this literature survey it follows that simple methods of determining effectiveness factors are not reliable for a complex system such as the methanol synthesis.

On the other hand, the perspectives of complex diffusion models, as used byDybkjaer [32] and Skrzypek et al. [46] are encouraging. With the number of molecules changing during reaction we have a preference for the dusty gas model. Combination of such a sophisticated diffusion model with the complex kinetic rate equations governing the methanol synthesis has not yet been undertaken, as far as the authors know. It is the aim of the final part of this contribution.

The Dusty-Gas Model

As pointed out by Skrzypek et al. [49] the dusty gas flux relations for each component can be presented as:

$$\frac{N_i}{D_i^{EFF}} + \sum_{s \neq i} \frac{(y_s N_i - y_i N_s)}{D_{is}^{EFF}} = -\frac{p}{RT}\frac{dy_i}{dl} - \frac{y_i}{RT}\left(1 + \frac{B_0 p}{\mu D_i^{EFF}}\right)\frac{dp}{dl} \tag{52}$$

Here, the effective diffusion coefficients are defined as [48]:

$$D_i^{EFF} = \alpha \frac{\varepsilon}{\tau} \frac{2}{3} \sqrt{\frac{8RT}{\pi M_i}} \tag{53}$$

$$D_{is}^{EFF} = \frac{\varepsilon}{\tau} D_{is} \tag{54}$$

Using d'Arcy's law [48]:

$$B_0 = a^2/8 \tag{55}$$

the model contains only two catalyst carrier dependent parameters: a and ε/τ. The flux relations described by Equation 52 can be transformed into a set of first order differential equations, yielding expressions for dy_i/dl. See Reference 49.

The material balances and the stoichiometric relations have to be added to the flux relations in order to describe the multicomponent reaction-diffusion problem.

Since three kinetically independent reactions occur simultaneously in the methanol synthesis, the same number of kinetic rate expressions is needed. Similar to Skrzypek et al. [46] this yields the following set of equations for a spherical catalyst particle:

$$d\Omega_k/dl = l^2 r_k \qquad (k = 1, 2, 3) \tag{56}$$

$$dy_i/dl = \left(\sum_{k=1}^{3} \Omega_k \sum_{j=1}^{Nc} \upsilon_{jk} F_{ij}\right) \Big/ l^2 \qquad (i = 1, 2, \ldots, Nc - 1) \tag{57}$$

with

$$F_{ii} = \frac{RT}{p}\left[\frac{1}{D_i^{EFF}} + \sum_{j \neq i}^{Nc} \frac{y_i}{D_{ij}^{EFF}} - \frac{y_i}{D_i^{EFF}}\left(1 + \frac{B_0 p}{\mu D_i^{EFF}}\right)\right]\frac{1}{w} \tag{58}$$

$$F_{ij} = -\frac{RT}{p}\left[\frac{y_i}{D_{ij}^{EFF}} + \frac{y_i}{D_i^{EFF}}\left(1 + \frac{B_0 p}{\mu D_i^{EFF}}\right)\right]\frac{1}{w} \tag{59}$$

$$w = 1 + \frac{B_0 p}{\mu} \sum_{i=1}^{Nc} \frac{y_i}{D_i^{EFF}} \tag{60}$$

and for the pressure gradient:

$$\frac{dp}{dl} = -\frac{1}{l^2}\frac{RT}{w} \sum_{i=1}^{Nc} \frac{1}{D_i^{EFF}} \sum_{k=1}^{3} \upsilon_{ik}\Omega_k \tag{61}$$

The kinetic rate expressions used are given by Equations 40–42. The multicomponent reaction-diffusion problem is now described by 8 coupled nonlinear first-order differential equations, which must be solved numerically, subject to the boundary conditions:

$$\Omega_k = 0 \qquad (k = 1, 2, 3) \qquad \text{at } l = 0 \tag{62}$$

$$y_i = y_i^S \qquad (i = 1, 2, 3, 4) \qquad \text{at } l = r \tag{63}$$

$$p = p^S \qquad \text{at } l = r \tag{64}$$

The effectiveness factor for each reaction can be calculated subsequently from:

$$\eta_k = \frac{3\Omega_k^S}{r^3 r_k^S} \tag{65}$$

Experiments

The experiments under conditions of diffusion limitation were carried out in the same spinning basket reactor as used for the kinetic investigations. For reference purposes, kinetic measurements were carried out parallel in a small packed bed with crushed particles ($d_p = 0.15$–0.2 mm).

For an overview of the experimental programme, see Table 15.

Table 15
Experimental Conditions for Experiments under Internal Diffusion Limitation

Feed No.	Feed Composition y_{CO}	y_{CO_2}	y_{H_2}	10^3 d_p m	p bar	T K	10^3 ϕ_v/W $m^3 s^{-1} kg^{-1}$
1	0.065	0.261	0.674	4.2*	15–50	483–548	1–6
2	0.053	0.047	0.900	"	"	"	"
3	0.220	0.155	0.625	"	"	"	"
4	0.120	0.021	0.859	"	"	"	"
5	0.179	0.067	0.754	"	"	"	"
6	0.131	0.023	0.846	"	20	"	4–18
7	0.131	0.023	0.846	"	10–15	"	5–15
8	0.131	0.023	0.846	0.15–0.2**	20	"	2–27

* *cylindrical with: height = diameter.*
** *assumed to be spherical.*

Results

Demonstration of the Presence of Intra-Particle Diffusion Limitations

The methanol formation kinetics can be simplified for feed conditions with a high CO/CO_2-ratio. Then, the rate of formation of methanol is almost first order with respect to hydrogen:

$$r'_{CH_3OH} = k'_{ps}\left(f_{H_2} - \frac{f_{CH_3OH}}{f_{CO}f_{H_2 3}K^{\circ}_{p1}}\right) \tag{66}$$

In order to check where intra-particle diffusion limitations enter the picture, the results of experiments with commercial size catalyst particles (feed 6, Table 15) are compared with the results of experiments with small particles (feed 8, Table 15). The Arrhenius' diagrams for k'_{ps} are presented in Figure 10.

For small size catalyst particles (● in Figure 10) the energy of activation found is E = 67 kJ/mol. For full size particles (○ in Figure 10) the apparent energy of activation reduces to 34 kJ/mol above 500 K, while at lower temperatures the energy of activation corresponds to the value obtained with the small particles.

This reduction of the observed energy of activation by almost a factor of two is a strong indication for the presence of intra-particle diffusion limitations. This indication is further supported by the results of partially deactivated (aged) catalysts (△ and □ in Figure 10). As expected, the temperature at which diffusion limitation becomes noticeable increases with decreasing catalyst activity.

Parameterization of the Dusty-Gas Model

Binary diffusion coefficients were calculated according to Fuller et al. [50]. From Petrini and Schneider [51], who studied the water-gas-shift reaction on a similar catalyst, the mean pore diameter was taken as 20 nm. In the reaction-diffusion model the reaction rates have to be based on volume of catalyst. Since the kinetic rate expressions are based on weight of catalyst, the apparent density of the catalyst is needed. It was estimated to be 1,950 kg m^{-3}. Furthermore, the catalyst particles were assumed to be spherical with a radius of 2.1 10^{-3} m. The value of ε/τ was determined from experimental data. For this purpose the experiments of feeds 4 and 5 at 547.8 K (see Table

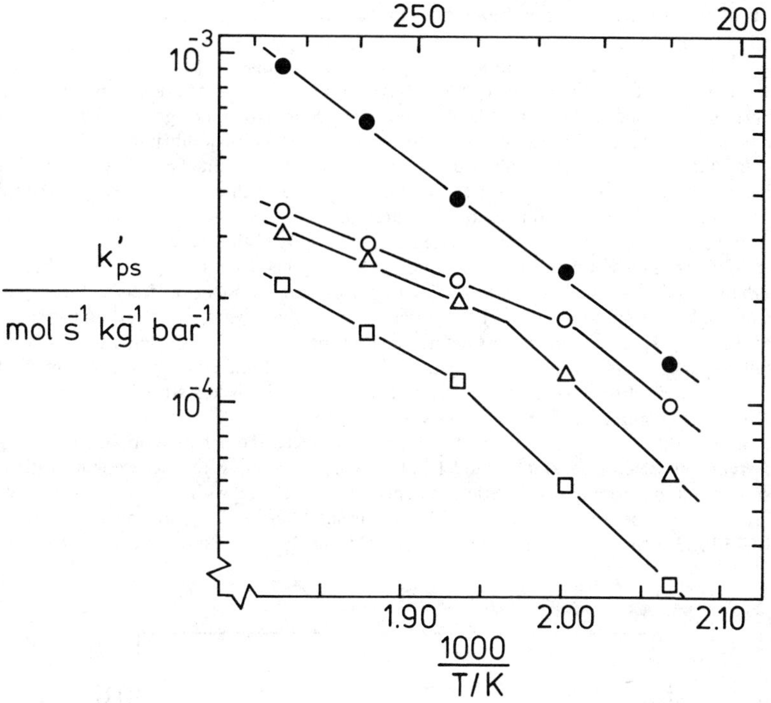

Figure 10. Arrhenius diagrams of the pseudo first-order reaction rate constant with respect to H_2 (Equation 66); ●, results of feed 8 (see Table 15); ○, ibid, feed 6; △, ibid, feed 7; □, ibid, feed 5.

15) were used, because the reaction rates of methanol are nearly first order in hydrogen for these feed conditions. This allows a safe extrapolation of the kinetics with temperature. For each experiment the reaction rate of methanol was calculated with the use of the dusty-gas model in combination with the kinetic rate expressions (40–42). By varying ε/τ in these calculations, an optimal value of ε/τ was obtained if the experimental and calculated reaction rates of methanol were identical. For the solution of the differential equations a standard computer library routine was used [52].

Initial estimates of the remaining boundary values were taken as follows:

$$\Omega_k = \frac{1}{6} R^3 r_k^S \qquad \text{at } l = r \tag{67}$$

$$y_i = y_{i,Eq} \qquad \text{at } l = 0 \tag{68}$$

$$P = 0.99 p^S \qquad \text{at } l = 0 \tag{69}$$

In this way an average value for ε/τ of 0.087 was obtained. This value has been used in the subsequent calculations.

Aspects of Intraparticle Diffusion Limitations in the Low-Pressure Methanol Synthesis

Figure 11 shows typical concentration profiles in the catalyst particle calculated with the dusty-gas model. It shows that in the center of the catalyst particle the composition is nearly at chemical equilibrium. The concentration profile of carbon dioxide is redrawn in greater detail in Figure 12 together with the fraction of water relative to the water-gas shift equilibrium.

The peculiar concentration profile of carbon dioxide can be explained as follows: at $l > l^*$ carbon dioxide is consumed both via the water-gas shift reaction and the methanol from carbon dioxide reaction. Because of this second reaction the water-gas shift is pushed over its chemical equilibrium at $l < l^*$. Therefore carbon dioxide is formed by the water-gas shift reaction at $l < l^*$.

The influence of the temperature and the pressure on the effectiveness factors of both the formation of methanol and of water is given in the Figures 13 and 14. As can be seen in these figures the effectiveness factors fall monotonously with rising temperature, which is according to expectations.

The effectiveness factors are almost independent of the pressure. This is less obvious because the pressure dependency is affected by two effects: the decrease of diffusivity with pressure results in a decrease of the effectiveness factor, but the influence of kinetics is less straightforward in a system with kinetics so complex as in the synthesis of methanol.

A final remarkable result, supporting the dusty-gas model approach, was obtained after repeating the exercise on selecting a kinetic model but now also including the experiments with internal diffusion limitation from which kinetic constants were calculated with the dusty-gas model. Based on a total of 146 experiments, with and without internal diffusion limitation, again the same kinetic model A3B2C3 turned out to give the best results of the 48 kinetic models taken into account.

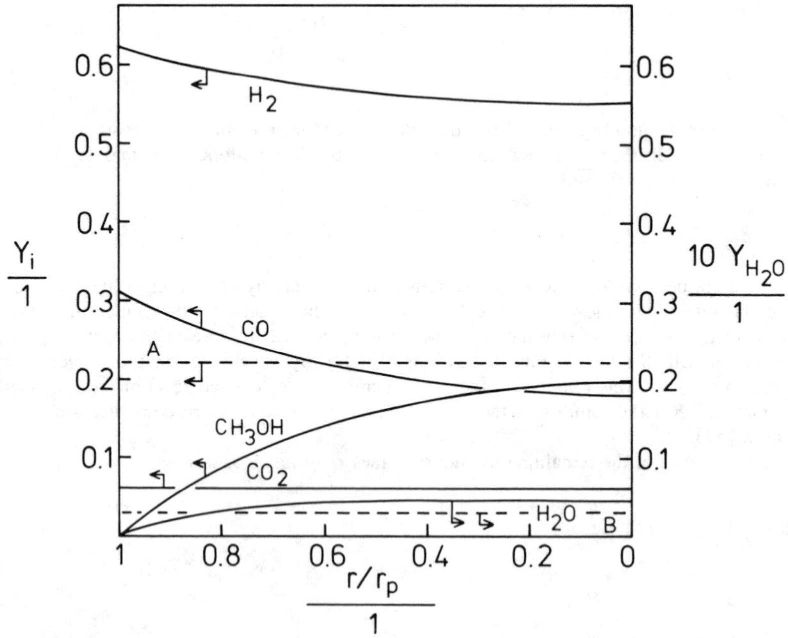

Figure 11. Calculated concentration profiles in the catalyst pellet. Conditions outside the catalyst particle: p = 100 bar; T = 548 K; $y_{CO} = 0.31$; $y_{CO_2} = 0.063$; $y_{H_2} = 0.63$; $y_{CH_3OH} = 0$. Note: The profile of H_2O is 10 × enlarged. A = $y_{CH_3OH,Eq}$; B = $y_{H_2O,Eq}$ (10 × enlarged).

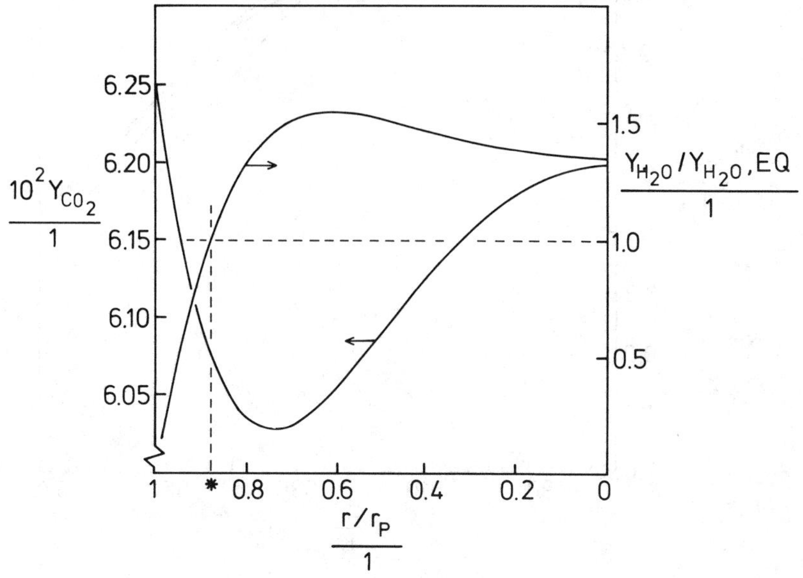

Figure 12. Water formation and consumption in the catalyst pellet. Conditions outside the particle as in Figure 11.

Obviously, this exercise resulted in slightly adapted optimal numerical values of the model parameters mentioned in Equations 43–48. With the adapted rate constants the methanol and water production rates could be predicted with accuracies of 9.7 and 21%, respectively, over the whole range of temperatures (483–565 K), pressures (15–50 bar), and effectiveness factors between 0.3 and 1. These results are satisfactory considering the uncertainties caused by Relation 55 and by the inaccuracy in guessing the mean pore diameter.

CONCLUSION

- The chemical equilibria of the methanol reaction and the water-gas shift reaction can be described very well by relationships derived from thermochemical data assuming ideal gas behavior and correcting for non-ideal gas behavior by using the Soave-Redlich-Kwong equation of state [5]. Significantly less satisfactory are corrections based on the original Redlich-Kwong equation of state, the Peng-Robinson equation of state, the virial equation of state truncated after the second virial coefficient, Lewis and Randall's rule, or not correcting at all for non-ideality, thus assuming ideal gas behavior.
- Experimental evidence shows that methanol can be formed simultaneously from both carbon monoxide and carbon dioxide in the low-pressure methanol synthesis.
- The experimental results on the kinetics of the synthesis of methanol can be explained by a dual-site Langmuir-Hinshelwood mechanism based on dissociative hydrogen adsorption and three independent reactions: methanol formation from carbon monoxide, methanol formation from carbon dioxide and the water-gas shift reaction.
- Depending on which elementary reaction step is rate controlling in each of these three parallel reactions, 48 different kinetic models are possible. Based on statistics and consistency tests one single optimal final model could be selected.

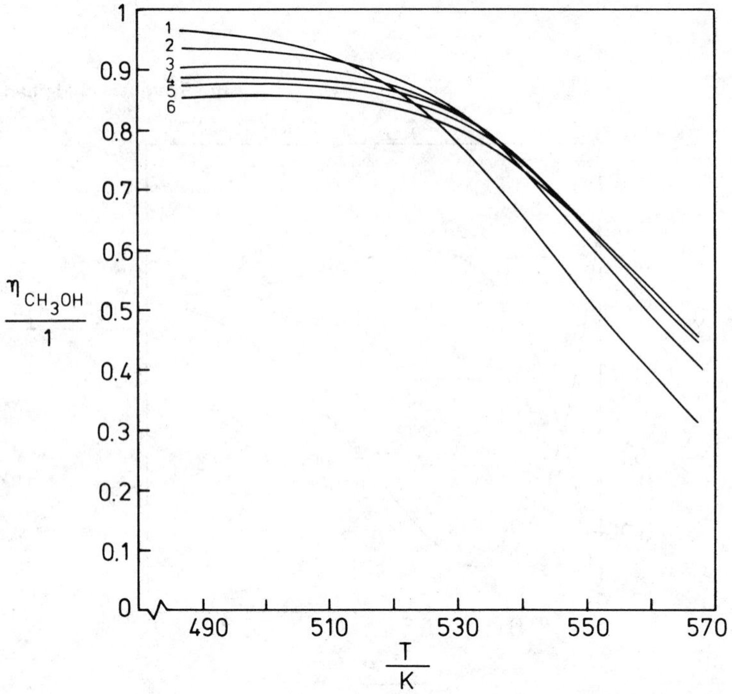

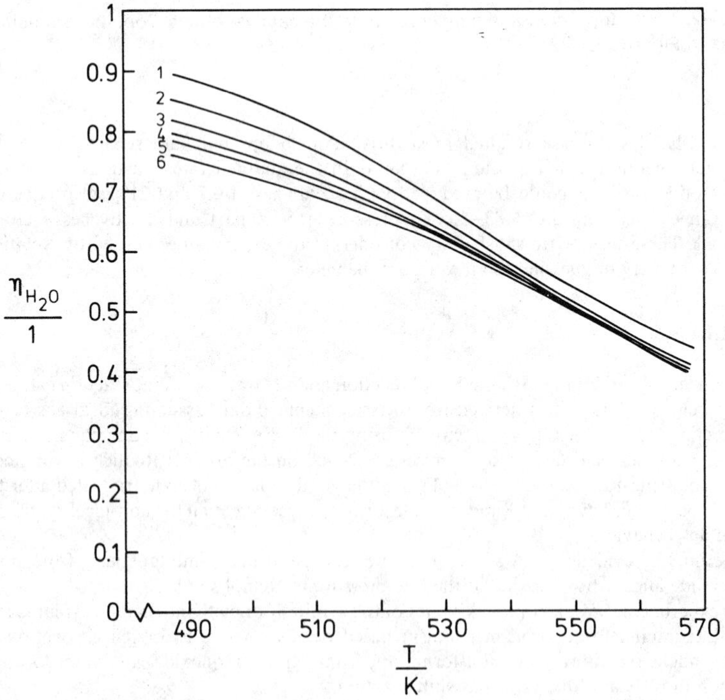

Figures 13 and 14. Methanol and water formation, respectively. Calculated effectiveness factors versus p and T. Composition outside the catalyst particle: $y_{CO} = 0.15$; $y_{CO_2} = 0.05$; $y_{H_2} = 0.80$; $y_{CH_3OH} = 0$; $y_{H_2O} = 0$; 1, p = 20 bar; 2, p = 40 bar; 3, p = 60 bar; 4, p = 80 bar; 5, p = 100 bar; 6, p = 120 bar.

- The kinetic parameters could be determined as functions of temperature between 485–520 K. The values of these parameters are not conflicting with the physico-chemical constraints.
- The experiments further support the assumption of dissociative hydrogen adsorption.
- At least for the commercial catalyst applied in this study, the kinetic model proposed here explains the experimental results with a significantly improved accuracy relative to the kinetic models proposed by Seyfert and Luft [31], Villa et al. [29], Klier et al. [26], and Dybkjaer [32].
- Above 520 K, intraparticle diffusion becomes significant. The effect of this transport limitation on the conversion rate can be described by the dusty-gas model. The model predictions obtained in this way are in excellent agreement with the experimental results.

Acknowledgments

We thank Haldor Topsoe for delivering catalyst Mk 101 and N. V. Nederlandse Gasunie for gas mixtures for calibration purposes.

NOTATION

Abbreviations

IGL	ideal gas law
PR	Peng-Robinson equation of state
RK	Redlich-Kwong equation of state
RKS	Soave-Redlich-Kwong equation of state
Vir	virial equation
SSR	sum of squares of residuals

Symbols

a	constant in PR, RK and RKS
a	mean pore diameter, m
a_1–a_6	constants in K_p° equation
A	pre-exponential factor
A_{1-6}	kinetic constants in literature
b	constant in PR, RK and RKS, $m^3\,mol^{-1}$
b_1–b_2	constants in K_p° equation
B	second virial coefficient, $m^3\,mol^{-1}$
B_0	permeability, m^2
c	concentration, $mol\,kg^{-1}$
d_p	catalyst particle diameter, m
D_i	Knudsen diffusion coefficient, $m^2\,s^{-1}$
D_{is}	binary diffusion coefficient, $m^2\,s^{-1}$
E	energy of activation, $J\,mol^{-1}$
f	partial fugacity, bar
F_{ii}, F_{ij}	auxiliary variables, $m\,s\,mol^{-1}$
k'	reaction rate constant
K_f	equilibrium constant based on partial fugacities
K_i	adsorption equilibrium constant, bar^{-1}, e.g. for CO: $(c_{COs1}/f_{CO}c_{s1})_{Eq}$
K_p	equilibrium constant based on partial pressures
K	ratio of fugacity coefficients
$K_{A1} \cdots K_{A4}$, K_{B1}, K_{B2}, $K_{C1} \cdots K_{C6}$	elementary reaction equilibrium constants, e.g.: $K_{A1} = c_{HCOs1}c_{s2}/(c_{COs1}c_{Hs2})_{Eq}$
l	coordinate along radius of catalyst pellet, m
m	number of parameters
M	molecular weight, $kg\,mol^{-1}$
n	quantity, mol
N	number of experiments
Nc	number of components
N_i	molar flux of components i, $mol\,s^{-1}\,m^{-2}$
p	total pressure, bar

p_i	partial pressure, bar
r'	reaction rate per unit weight of catalyst, mol kg^{-1} s^{-1}
r_k	reaction rate per unit volume of catalyst, mol s^{-1} m^{-3}
r_p	radius of the particle, m
R	gas constant (8.314), J mol^{-1} K^{-1}
s	number of neighboring sites
S	entropy, J mol^{-1} K^{-1}
S^2	variance
T	temperature, K
v	molar volume, m^3 mol^{-1}
V	volume, m^3
w	auxiliary variable
W	weight of catalyst, kg
y	mole fraction
Z	compressibility factor

Greek Letters

α	mean pore diameter of the catalyst, m
ΔC_p	specific heat change, J mol^{-1} K^{-1}
ΔG	Gibbs energy change, J mol^{-1}
ε	porosity of the catalyst = void fraction of the catalyst
μ	dynamic viscosity, N m^{-2} s
υ	stoichiometric coefficient
τ	tortuosity of the catalyst
ϕ	fugacity coefficient
Ω	auxiliary variable
Δ	relative error
ΔH	enthalpy change, J mol^{-1}
ΔS	entropy change, J mol^{-1} K^{-1}
ϕ_v	gas flow rate at standard temperature and pressure (298.2 K, 1.013 bar), m^3 s^{-1}
η	effectivity of the catalyst

Subscripts

ads	of adsorption
A1 ··· A4	indicates rate determining step of the methanol from CO reaction
B1 ··· B2	indicates rate determining step of water-gas shift reaction
c	at the critical point
calc	calculated
C1 ··· C6	indicates rate determining step of the methanol from CO_2 reaction
CO, CO_2, CH_3OH	indicates component CO, CO_2, CH_3OH, respectively
Eq	at equilibrium
exp	experimental
f	of formation
gas	of gaseous component
H_2, H_2O	indicates component H_2, H_2O, respectively
i, j, s	indicates component
k	indicates reaction 1, 2 or 3
max	maximum value
min	minimum value
M	mixture
ps	pseudo
ref	reference
sr	surface reaction
s1	of site 1
s2	of site 2
tot	total
0	feed conditions
1, 2, 3	indicator reaction (1), (2), or (3)

Superscripts

EFF	effective
S	at the surface of the catalyst
^	indicates calculated value
°	standard pressure (1 bar)

REFERENCES

1. Rossini, F. D., Wagman, D. D., Evans, W. H., Levine, S., and Jaffe, I., *Selected Values of Thermodynamic Properties*, Part I, Tables, National Bureau of Standards, circ. 500, Washington, DC, 1961.
2. Reid, R. C., Prausnitz, J. M., and Sherwood, T. K., *The Properties of Gases and Liquids*, 3rd ed., McGraw-Hill, New York, 1977, Appendix B.
3. Prausnitz, J. M., *Molecular Thermodynamics of Fluid-Phase Equilibria*, Prentice Hall, Englewood Cliffs, NJ, 1969, p. 74, 89, 162.
4. Redlich, O., and Kwong, J. N. S., "On the Thermodynamics of Solutions. V. An Equation of State. Fugacities of Gaseous Solutions," *Chem. Rev.*, *44*, 233 (1949).
5. Soave, G., "Equilibrium Constants from a Modified Redlich-Kwong Equation of State," *Chem. Eng. Sci.*, *27*, 1197 (1972).
6. Peng, D., and Robinson, D. B., "A New Two-Constant Equation of State," *Ind. Eng. Chem., Fundam.*, *15*, 59 (1976).
7. Graaf, G. H., Sijtsema, P. J. J. M., Stamhuis, E. J., and Joosten, G. E. H., "Chemical Equilibria in Methanol Synthesis," *Chem. Eng. Sci.*, *41*, 2883 (1986).
8. von Wettberg, E. F., and Dodge, B. F., "The Methanol Equilibrium," *Ind. Eng. Chem.*, *22*, 1040 (1930).
9. Brown, R. L., and Galloway, A. E., "Methanol from Hydrogen and Carbon Monoxide," *Ind. Eng. Chem.*, *20*, 960 (1928).
10. Smith, D. F., and Hirst, L. L., "Reactions that Occur on a Methanol Catalyst," *Ind. Eng. Chem.*, *22*, 1037 (1930).
11. Smith, D. F., and Branting, B. F., "The Equilibrium between Methanol, Carbon Monoxide, and Hydrogen," *J. Amer, Chem. Soc.*, *51*, 129 (1929).
12. Lacy, B. S., Dunning, R. G., and Storch, H. H., "Equilibrium in the Synthesis and Composition of Methanol," *J. Amer. Chem. Soc.*, *52*, 926 (1930).
13. Newitt, D. M., Byrne, B. J., and Strong, H. W., "Equilibrium in the System Methyl Alcohol-Hydrogen-Carbonic Oxide," *Proc. Roy. Soc.*, *A123*, 236 (1928).
14. Cherednichenko, V. M., Dissertation, Karpova Physico-Chemical Institute, Moscow (1953).
15. Zeise, H., *Thermodynamik auf den Grundlagen der Quantentheorie, Quantenstatistik und Spektroskopie, Bd. III*, S. Hirzel, Leibzig, 1954, p. 132.
16. Oki, S., and Mezaki, R., "Identification of Rate-Controlling Steps for the Water-Gas-Shift Reaction over an Iron-Oxide Catalyst," *J. Phys. Chem.*, *77*, 447 (1973).
17. Podolski, W., and Kim, I., "Modeling the Water-Gas-Shift Reaction," *Ind. Eng. Chem., Process Des. Develop.*, *13*, 415 (1974).
18. Hahn, O., "Beitrage zur Thermodynamik des Wassergases. Das Gleichgewicht $CO_2 + H_2 = CO + H_2O$," *Z. Phys. Chem.*, *44*, 513 (1903).
19. Ewell, R. M., "Calculation of Chemical Equilibrium at High Pressures," *Ind. Eng. Chem.*, *32*, 149 (1940).
20. Lewis, G. N., and Randall, M., *Thermodynamics and Free Energy of Chemical Substances*, McGraw-Hill, New York, 1923.
21. Natta, G., *Synthesis of Methanol, Catalysis: Hydrogenation and Dehydrogenation.* (P. H. Emmett, ed.), Rheinhold Publishing Corp., New York, *3* 1955, p. 349–411.
22. Bakemeier, H., Laurer, P. R., and Schroder, W., "Development and Application of a Mathematical Model of the Methanol Synthesis," *Chem. Eng. Progr., Symp. Ser. 66*, *98*, 1 (1970).
23. Leonov, V. E., Karavaev, M. M., Tsybina, E. N., and Petrishcheva, G. S., "Kinetics of Methanol Synthesis on a Low-Temperature Catalyst," *Kinet. Katal.*, *14*, 970 (1973).
24. Schermuly, O., and Luft, G., "Untersuchung der Niederdruck-Methanolsynthese im Treibstrahlreaktor," *Chem.-Ing.-Tech. MS* 536/77, *Chem.-Ing.-Tech.*, *49*, 907 (1977).
25. Denise, B., and Sneeden, R. P. A., "Hydrocondensation of Carbon Dioxide, IV," *J. Mol. Catal.*, *17*, 359 (1982).
26. Klier, K., Chatikavanij, V., Herman, R. G., and Simmons, G. W., "Catalytic Synthesis of Methanol from CO/H_2," *J. Catal.*, *74*, 343 (1982).
27. Monnier, J. R., Apai, G., and Hanrakan, H. J., "Effect of CO_2 on the Conversion of H_2/CO to Methanol over Copper-Chromia Catalysts," *J. Catal.*, *88*, 523 (1984).

28. Chinchen, G. C., Denny, P. J., Parker, D. G., Short, G. D., Spencer, M. S., Waugh, K. C., and Whan, D. A. "The Activity of Copper-Zinc Oxide-Aluminium Oxide Methanol Synthesis Catalyst," *Prep. Pap. Chem. Soc., Div. Fuel Chem.*, 29, 178 (1984).
29. Villa, P., Forzatti, P., Buzzi-Ferraris, G., Garone, G., and Pasquon, I., "Synthesis of Alcohols from Carbon Oxides and Hydrogen," *Ind. Eng. Chem., Process Des. Develop., 24*, 12 (1984).
30. Liu, G., Willcox, D., Garland, M., and Kung, H. H., "The Rate of Methanol Production on a Copper-Zinc Oxide Catalyst. The Dependence on the Feed Composition," *J. Catal.*, 90, 139 (1984).
31. Seyfert, W., and Luft, G., "Untersuchung zur Methanolsynthese im Mitteldruckbereich," *Chem.-Ing.-Tech. MS* 1358/85, *Chem.-Ing.-Tech., 57*, 482 (1985).
32. Dybkjaer, I., "Design of Ammonia and Methanol Synthesis Reactors," Paper presented at the NATO conference: Chemical Reactor Design and Technology, Canada, 1985.
33. Herman, R. G., Klier, K., Simmons, G. W., Finn, B. P., Bulko, J. B., and Kobylinski, T. P., "Catalytic Synthesis of Methanol from CO/H_2," *J. Catal., 56*, 407 (1979).
34. Matulewicz, E. R. A., *Kinetics and Spectroscopic Investigations of Propene Metathesis and Methanol Synthesis*, Dissertation, The University of Amsterdam, The Netherlands, 1984.
35. Liu, G., Willcox, D., Garland, M., and Kung, H. H., "The Role of CO_2 in Methanol Synthesis on Cu-Zn Oxide: An Isotope Labeling Study," *J. Catal., 96*, 251 (1985).
36. Bartlett, M. S., "Properties of Sufficiency and Statistical Tests," *Proc. Roy. Soc., Ser. A, 160*, 268 (1937).
37. Boudart, M., "Two-Step Catalytic Reactions," *A.I.Ch.E.J., 18*, 465 (1972)
38. Vannice, M. A., Hyun, S. H., Kalpakci, B., and Liauh, W. C., "Entropies of Adsorption in Heterogeneous Catalytic Reactions," *J. Catal., 56*, 358 (1979).
39. Kapteyn, F., *The Metathesis of Alkenes over Rhenium Oxide-Alumina*, Dissertation, The University of Amsterdam, The Netherlands, 1980, p. 77.
40. Tajbl, D. G., Simons, J. B., and Carberry, J. J., "Heterogeneous Catalysis in a Continuous Stirred Tank Reactor," *Ind. Eng. Chem., Fundam., 5*, 171 (1966).
41. Dybkjaer, I., "Topsoe Methanol Technology," *Chem. Econ. Eng. Rev., 13*, 17 (1981).
42. Graaf, G. H., Stamhuis, E. J., and Beenackers, A.A.C.M., "Kinetics of the Methanol Synthesis," accepted for publication by Chem. Eng. Sci.
43. Fisher, R. A., *Statistical Methods for Research Workers*, Hafner, New York, 13th ed., 1958.
44. Stull, D. R., Westrum, E. F., and Simke, G. C., *The Chemical Thermodynamics of Organic Compounds*, Wiley, New York, 1969, p. 219, 220.
45. Berty, J. M., Lee, S., Parekh, V., Gandhi, R., and Sivagnanam, K., "Diffusional Kinetics of Low Pressure Methanol Synthesis," Proceedings Pachec '83/ The third pacific Chem. Eng. Congress, 1983, p. 191.
46. Skrzypek, J., Grzesik, M., and Szopa, R., "Analysis of the Low-Temperature Methanol Synthesis in a Single Commercial Isothermal Cu-Zn-Al Catalyst Pellet Using the Dusty-Gas Diffusion Model," *Chem. Eng. Sci., 40*, 671 (1985).
47. Weisz, P. B., and Prater, C. D., "Interpretation of Measurements in Experimental Catalysis," *Advan. Catal., 6*, 143 (1954).
48. Jackson, R., *Transport in Porous Catalysts*, Elsevier Scientific Publishing Company, Amsterdam, 1977, p. 10, 11, and 15.
49. Skrzypek, J., Grzesik, M., and Szopa, R., "Theoretical Analysis of Two Parallel and Consecutive Reactions in Isothermal Symmetrical Catalyst Pellets Using the Dusty-Gas Model," *Chem. Eng. Sci., 39*, 515 (1984).
50. Fuller, E. N., Schettler, P. D., and Giddings, J. C., "A New Method for Prediction of Binary Gas-Phase Diffusion Coefficients," *Ind. Eng. Chem., 58*, 19–27 (1966).
51. Petrini, G., and Schneider, P., "Catalyst Effectiveness in Low-temperature Water-Gas Shift Reaction," *Chem. Eng. Sci., 39*, 637 (1984).
52. Naglib: 1823/0: Mk10: November 15th, 1982, Nag Fortran Library routine document, D02GAF.

CHAPTER 18

BIOLOGICAL ASPECTS OF ANAEROBIC DIGESTION

Shiro Nagai and **Naomichi Nishio**

Department of Fermentation Technology
Faculty of Engineering, Hiroshima University,
Saijo, Higashi - Hiroshima, Japan

CONTENTS

INTRODUCTION

Anaerobic digestion is the versatile biotechnology capable of converting almost all sorts of polymeric materials to C_1 compounds, i.e., methane and carbon dioxide. This has been achieved as the results of consecutive biochemical breakdown of polymers to C_1 compounds where the variety of microorganisms such as fermentative microbes, acetogens, methanogens, etc. are harmoniously growing and producing reduced end-products. Anaerobes existing in the respective phase play an important role in an orchestra—methane fermentation—to establish a stable environment.

This chapter first deals with biochemistry and microbiology on the anaerobic breakdown of polymeric materials to methane and the role of the related microorganisms.

BIOLOGICAL ASPECTS OF ANAEROBIC DIGESTION

Anaerobic digestion leads to the overall gasification of organic deposits into methane and carbon dioxide. This process has gradually proved its superiority to the conventional aerobic process as an effective means of pollution reduction. Although the digestion processes have been practiced for decades, interest has increased recently for economical recovery of fuel gas from industrial and agricultural surpluses due to changing socio-economical situation.

Anaerobic digestion is recognized to be the consequence of a series of metabolic interactions among various groups of microbial population such as hydrolytic and/or acidogenic bacteria, acetogens, and methanogens, in which methanogens may play a vital role as a metabolic regulator of the whole process [1]. Also the methanogens are extremely sensitive to environmental changes with their inherent nature of a slow growth rate, and are often outnumbered by the hydrolytic and acidogenic bacteria, thus making the whole process unstable.

These facts indicate that comprehension of the fundamental aspects of related microorganisms is essential to establish and control a stable fermentation, and to exploit all the potentialities concerned. This chapter reviews the present understanding of bacterial populations involved in anaerobic digestion into CH_4 and CO_2(biogas) including microbiology, biochemistry, and growth kinetics.

Microbiology and Biochemistry

The combined and coordinated metabolic activities brought from anaerobic microbial populations are capable of completely degrading any organic compounds to methane and carbon dioxide. The intermediate substrates necessary for certain microorganisms are supplied from the end-products produced by predecessor microbes, therefore microbial consortia must stably exist together in the anaerobic biodegradation system. Despite continuous studies on the major non-methanogenic bacteria present in anaerobic digesters, detailed information on the generic nature and specific growth characteristics of the hydrolytic and fermentative microbes have not been fully analyzed due to the difficulties of their systematic analyses.

Present understanding of bacterial populations involved in anaerobic digestion is mostly based on analysis of bacteria isolated from sewage sludge digesters or from the rumina of some animals [2, 3]. Sometimes in past years, e.g., 1956, methane fermentations were discussed on the basis of degradation stages of organic compounds, i.e., the acid-forming and methane-forming stages [4], in which the acid-forming stage involved the acidogenic bacteria that hydrolyze polymers and convert the products to organic acids, alcohols, CO_2 and H_2; whereas the methanogenic bacteria in the methane-forming stage catabolize these compounds to the final products, CH_4 and CO_2. However, methanogenic bacteria are not able to catabolize alcohols other than methanol or organic acids other than acetate and formate [5, 6], which is why at least three groups of bacteria are coordinately existing to decompose organic material into CH_4 and CO_2 (Figure 1). In the figure, the first group hydrolyzes polymeric materials to monomers such as glucose and amino acids, and then these are converted to higher volatile fatty acids together with H_2 and acetic acid. In the second stage, hydrogen-producing acetogenic bacteria converts the previous products, e.g., propionic acid to H_2, CO_2, and acetate, and then, finally, the third group, the methanogenic bacteria capable of using H_2, CO_2, and acetate convert them to CH_4 and CO_2.

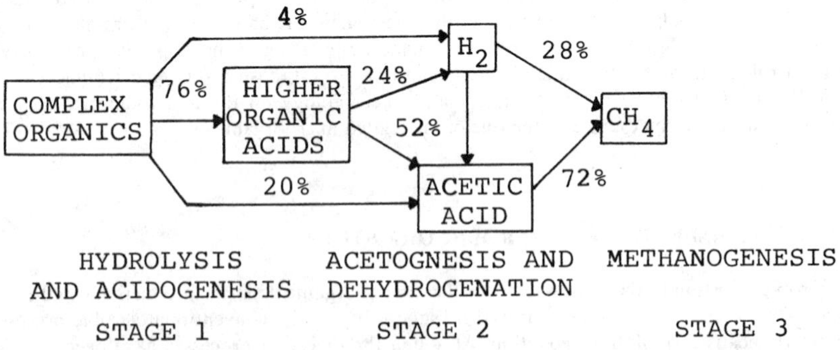

Figure 1. The three stages of the methane fermentation. Percentages represent the flow of electrons from organic compounds to methane. (Reprinted with permission from Ref. [7].)

Hydrolysis and Acidogenesis

Polymeric materials such as lipids, proteins, carbohydrates, and lignin under anaerobic conditions are primarily hydrolyzed by extracellular enzymes, hydrolases, excreted from microbes existing in stage 1 (Figure 1). Hydrolytic enzymes, such as amylase, cellulase, protease, lipase, etc. can hydrolyze respective polymers into small molecules, mostly to each unit, then these are consumed by microbes. In anaerobic digestion where a wastewater contains the high concentration of organic polymers, the hydrolyzing activities relevant to each polymer are paramountly significant because their activities may become a rate-limiting step for the production of simpler substrates for the succeeding bacteria in the next degradation step (see upper part in Figure 2) [8].

Lipid decompositions. Lipid hydrolysis under anaerobic culture conditions has not been extensively documented so far. The extracellular enzymes responsible for the conversion of the glycerol esters of lipids to long chain fatty acids are lipases, which attack the 1 and 3 positions on the glyceride, but some can attack all three positions to give free fatty acids and glycerol [9]:

$$C_3H_5(RCOO)_3 + 3\,H_2O \xrightarrow[\text{lipase}]{} 3\,RCOOH + C_3H_5(OH)_3$$

A population density of 10^4–10^5 lipolytic bacteria per ml of the digester fluid has been recorded [10], and an enrichment technique for lipolytic bacteria has succeeded to isolate lipolytic microorganisms [11]. The clostridia and the micrococci appear to be responsible for most of the extracellular lipase producers in anaerobic digesters.

The further oxidation of the long chain fatty acids proceeds by β-oxidation to produce acetyl-CoA (Figure 3A). On the other hand, glycerol produced could be converted to acetyl-CoA from pyruvate via E.M.P. pathway (Figure 3B) [12].

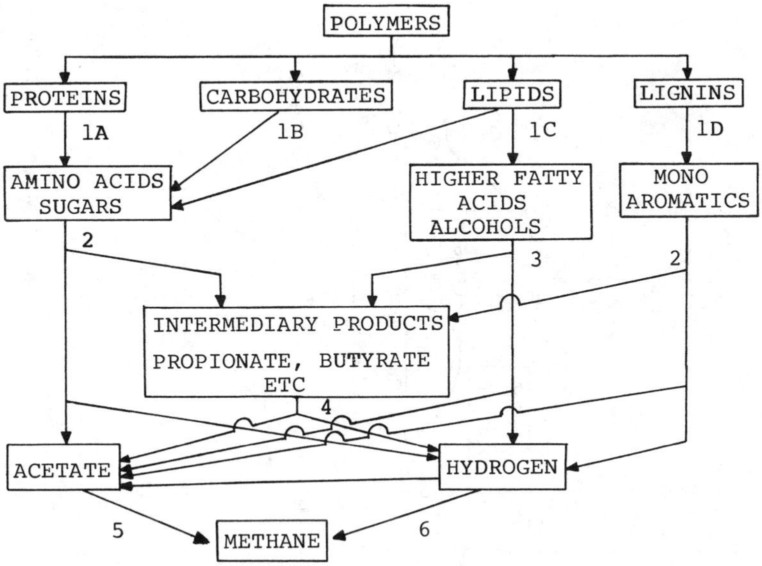

Figure 2. The breakdown of organic polymers: (1) hydrolysis; (2) fermentation; (3) anaerobic (β) oxidation; (4) anaerobic oxidation; (5) decarboxylation of acetate, $CH_3COO^- + H_2O \rightarrow CH_4 + HCO_3^-$; (6) hydrogen oxidation, $CO_2 + 4H_2 \rightarrow CH_4 + 2H_2O$. (Reprinted with permission from Ref. [8].)

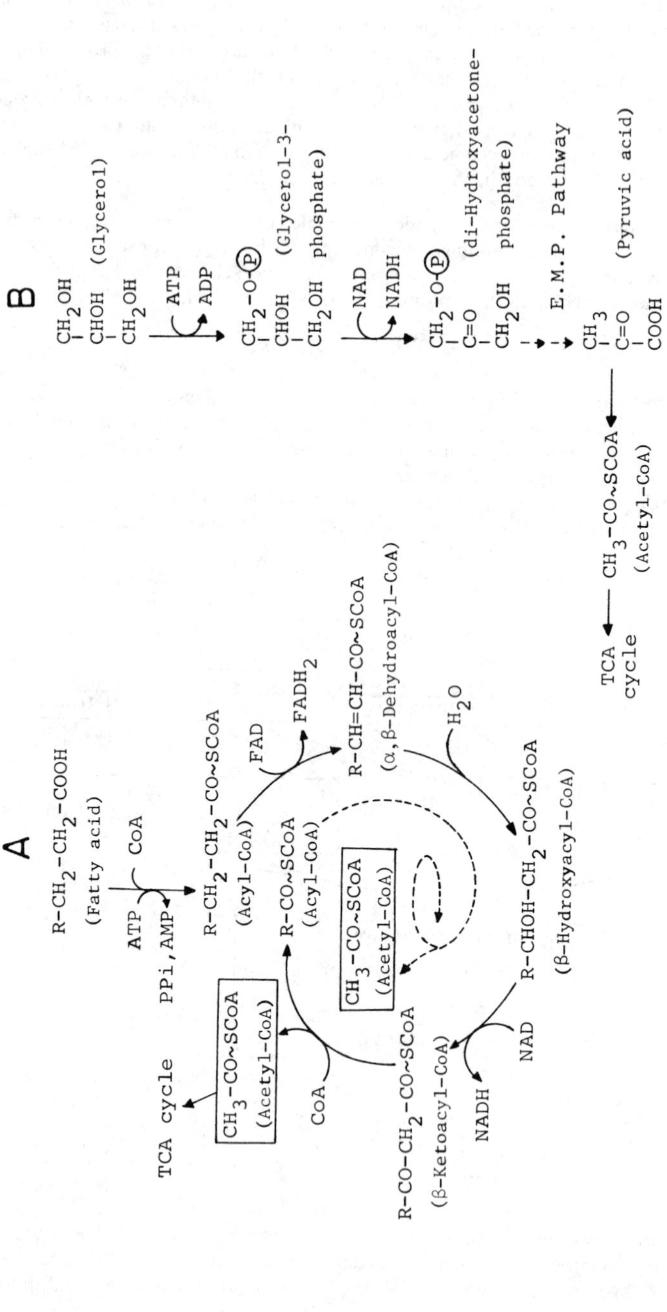

Figure 3. Metabolisms of fatty acid (β-oxidation) and glycerol.

Table 1
Growth of Proteolytic Isolates on Different Sources of Nitrogen [13]

Nitrogen Source	Concn (g/l)	*Bacteroides ruminicola* M384	*Butyrivibrio fibrisolvens* SH1	*Clostridium* spp. M361	*Fusobacterium* spp. JW7	*Selenomonas ruminantium* JW2	*Streptococcus bovis* C277
NH_4Cl	0.54	+++	++++	++	++	++++	++++
Casamino acids	1.0	++++	++++	++++	+++	++++	++++
Casitone	1.0	++++	+++	++++	++++	++++	++++
Casein	1.0	++++	++++	+	+++	+	+++
Casein + NH_4Cl	1.0 + 0.54	++++	++++	++++	+++	++++	++++
Lactoglobulin	1.0	+++	+++	+	+++	+	+
Albumin	1.0	++	++	+	−	+	+
γ-Globulins	1.0	++	++	+	−	+	+
Proteolytic activity (mg casein/mg/day)		0.79	4.3	0.20	12.8	0.13	0.21
Maximum cell density (g/l)		0.51	0.15	0.22	0.17	0.26	0.30

−, <0.02 × maximum cell density; +, 0.02–0.20; ++, 0.2–0.5; +++, 0.5–0.8; ++++, 0.8–1.0

Table 2
Microbial Degradation of Amino Acids [18]

1. Single amino acids (examples)

$$3\ \text{Alanine} + 3\ H_2O \longrightarrow 2\ \text{Propionate}^- + \text{Acetate}^- + HCO_3^- + 3\ NH_4^+ + H^+$$
$$4\ \text{Glycine} + 4\ H_2O \longrightarrow 3\ \text{Acetate}^- + 2\ HCO_3^- + 4\ NH_4^+ + H^+$$

2. A pair of amino acids (examples)

Oxidative deamination

$$\text{(A) Alanine} + 3\ H_2O \longrightarrow \text{Acetate}^- + NH_4^+ + HCO_3^- + 2\ H_2 + H^+$$
$$\text{(B) Valine} + 3\ H_2O \longrightarrow \text{Isobutyrate}^- + NH_4^+ + HCO_3^- + 2\ H_2 + H^+$$
$$\text{(C) Leucine} + 3\ H_2O \longrightarrow \text{Isovalerate}^- + NH_4^+ + HCO_3^- + 2\ H_2 + H^+$$

Reductive deamination

$$\text{(D) Glycine} + H_2 \longrightarrow \text{Acetate}^- + NH_4^+$$

Sum

$$\text{A+D} \quad \text{Alanine} + 2\ \text{Glycine} + 3\ H_2O \longrightarrow 3\ \text{Acetate}^- + 3\ NH_4^+ + HCO_3^- + H^+$$
$$\text{B+D} \quad \text{Valine} + 2\ \text{Glycine} + 3\ H_2O \longrightarrow \text{Isobutyrate}^- + 2\ \text{Acetate}^- + 3\ NH_4^+ + HCO_3^- + H^+$$
$$\text{C+D} \quad \text{Leucine} + 2\ \text{Glycine} + 3\ H_2O \longrightarrow \text{Isovalerate}^- + 2\ \text{Acetate}^- + 3\ NH_4^+ + HCO_3^- + H^+$$

Protein decompositions. The degradation of protein has not been fully studied compared with carbohydrate metabolisms. Proteins are generally hydrolyzed to amino acids by extracellular enzymes, proteases.

Proteolytic bacteria isolated from rumen source were in Table 1 [13]. In addition, *Succinivibrio, Lachnospira, Bacillus* have been isolated as proteolytic bacteria [14–16]. Proteolytic isolates are also able to hydrolyze carbohydrate [17], indicating the versatility of hydrolyzing bacteria.

The amino acids produced are then degraded to fatty acids such as acetate and propionate, and ammonia. The general processes of amino acid degradation are summarized in Table 2 [18]. Two pathways are known:

1. Single amino acid is directly degraded to volatile fatty acids (Table 2, 1).
2. A pair of amino acids is degraded by coupled oxidation-reductions (see Table 2, 2). This coupled deamination is designated as the Stickland reaction where one member of the pair is oxidized (dehydrogenated) while the other is reduced (hydrogenated) (Figure 4) [18].

Amino acid degradations by anaerobic bacteria are listed in Table 3. In many cases, the products are lower fatty acids such as acetic, propionic, and butyric acids. As an example, a hypothetical pathway for the fermentation of glutamate by *Selenomonas acidaminophila* is shown in Figure 5 [24].

Carbohydrate decompositions

Microorganisms and enzymes. Anaerobic bacteria actively hydroylze and solubilize homopolysaccharides such as starch, cellulose, and pectin with amylases, cellulases, and pectinases.

Cellulose is the most abundant biopolymer on the earth and exists as a highly ordered crystalline structure composed of glucose moieties linked by β1-4 bonds. Most microbial cellulases comprise three species [26, 27]: (a) endo-β-1,4-glucanases that act randomly on non-crystalline cellulose and are assayed with carboxymethyl-cellulose; (b) exo-β-1,4-glucanases that are cellobiohydrolases that act on the non-reducing end of the cellulose chain and are assayed using a variety of crystalline celluloses as substrates; (c) cellobiase or β-glucosidase, which cleaves cellobiose into glucose (Table 4). The three enzymes synergistically act to cellulose [28] so as to effectively hydrolyze crystalline cellulose to produce glucose.

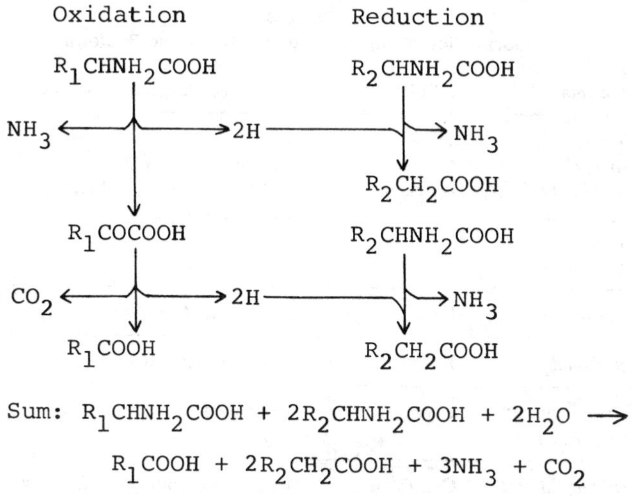

Figure 4. Scheme for the Stickland reaction. (Reprinted with permission from Ref. [18].)

Starch is a glycosidic polymer linked by a α1-4 and α1-6 bonds and is composed of branched amylopectin (ca 80%) and unbranched amylose (ca 20%). Microbial hydrolysis of raw starch to glucose requires amylases which consist of 5 species: (a) α-amylases that endocleave α1-4 bonds; (b) β-amylases that exocleave α1-4 bonds liberating maltose; (c) amyloglucosidases that exocleave α1-4 and α1-6 bonds; (d) debranching enzymes that act on α1-6 bonds; (e) maltases that act on maltose liberating glucose. α-Amylases have been isolated in some anaerobic bacteria (Table 4) and characterized in mesophilic starch-fermenting anaerobes [29–33].

Pectin is a galactopyranosiduronic acid polymer linked by α1-4 bonds. Pectins present in ligno-cellulosic materials are covalently linked to hemicellulosic materials by glucosidic bonds. Pectinases contain several different activities, including pectinesterases that form methanol and depolymerases (i.e., pectin transeliminases and pectin hydrolases) that solubilize pectin into various saccharide including hexoses and pentoses [34].

Xylans, polymer of β-D-xylose, which are major components of hemicellulose, are widely distributed in ligno-cellulosic materials such as crops and woods, and are degraded enzymatically with β-endo-xylanase and β-xylosidase to produce xylose. Pectinase and xylanase producing bacteria are summarized in Table 4.

Fermentation pathways of hexoses and pentoses. Hexoses and pentoses are generally converted to C_2 and C_3 intermediates and the reduced electron carriers (e.g., NADH) via common pathways [46]. Most anaerobic bacteria have the Emden-Meyerhof-Parnas pathway (EMP) for hexose metabolism (i.e. glycolysis) (Figure 6) where hexoses are converted into 2 mol of pyruvate and 2 mol of NADH. The intermediates formed in EMP pathway can also be combined into other cycles, e.g., the oxidative pentose-pathway, the hexose-monophosphate pathway (HMP), or the Warburg-Dicken-Horecker scheme (i.e., xylolysis) (Figure 6). The Entner-Doudoroff (ED) pathway is popular for the oxidative catabolism of glucose (Figure 6) [47].

The C_3 intermediate (pyruvate) and reduced pyridine nucleotides (NADH) generated by these common pathways for hexolysis and pentolysis are transformed into fermentation endo-products by other enzymatic activities that vary tremendously depending on microbial species.

The typical pathways for glucose conversion to acids and ethanol are comparatively shown in Figures 7–9 [1]. In homolactic and homoacetic fermentations it is interesting to note that glucose is completely converted to lactic and acetic acids, respectively without producing CO_2 (Figure 7).

Table 3
Degradation of Amino Acids by Anaerobic Bacteria

Microorganism	Substrate	Organic Product	Ref.
Clostridium histlyticum *sporopheroides* *sticklandii* *subterminale* *difficile* *scatologenes*	Threonine Leucine Isoleucine Valine	Acetic, Propionic, *n*-Butyric, iso-Butyric, *n*-Valeric, 2-Methylbutyric, 3-Methylbutyric, iso-Caproic acids	19
Clostridium sporogenes	Leucine	iso-Butyric, Acetic acids	20
Clostridium sticklandii	Proline	δ-Aminovaleric acid	21
Clostridium sticklandii *sporogenes*	Glycine	Acetic acid	21
Clostridium sticklandii	Ornithine	Acetic acid, Alanine, δ-Aminovaleric acid	22
Clostridium bifermentans *sticklandii* *difficile* *tetani*	Phenylalanine	Phenylacetic, Phenylpropionic, Phenyllactic acids	23
	Tyrosine	Hydroxyphenylacetic, Hydroxyphenyllactic, Hydroxyphenylpropionic acids, Phenol, *p*-Cresol	
	Tryptophan	Indole, Indoleacetic acid, Indolepropionic acid	
Clostridium tetanomorphum *Peptococcus aerogenes*	Glutamate	Acetic, Butyric acids	21
Selenomonas acidaminophila	Glutamate	Acetic, Propionic, Succinic acids	24
Clostridium subterminale *sticklandii*	Lysine	Acetic, Butyric acids	25
Campylobacter spp. *Bacteroides melaninogenicus*	Aspartate	Acetic, Succinic acids	21
Selenomonas acidaminophila	Aspartate	Acetic, Propionic, Succinic acids	24

Although many facultative anaerobes ferment glucose to lactic acid, only one species, *Clostridium thermoaceticum* [48], has been reported to have the homoacetic fermentation pathway. As shown in Figure 8, the succinate fermentation pathway of *Bacteroides succinogenes* was proposed [49] in which succinate, acetate, and formate are equimolarly formed.

Propionate production from glucose by *Propionibacterium* spp. [50–52] is popular (Figure 8) and a similar pathway also operates for lactate fermentation by *Propionibacterium* spp.

Three different pathways for glucose conversion to ethanol are known in anaerobic bacteria [46, 53] and they are distinguished by the mechanism of key carbon cleavage enzymes (see Figure 9). The ketoclastic pathway can produce ethanol from acetyl phosphate by lactic acid bacteria

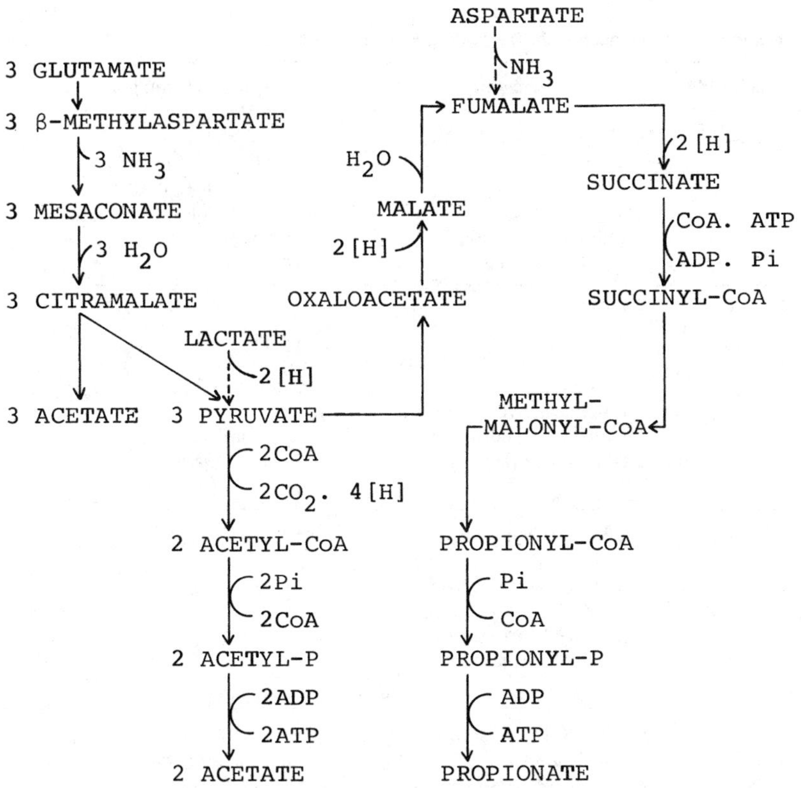

Figure 5. Hypothetical pathway for the fermentation of glutamate by *Selenomonas acidaminophila* strain DKglul6. (Reprinted with permission from Ref. [24].)

(e.g., *Lactobacillus brevis*). The phosphoroclastic pathway can produce lactic and acetic acids with ethanol and this pathway distributes widely in anaerobes (e.g., *Clostridium*, *Thermoanaerobium*, *Sarcina*, *Ruminococcus*). The decarboxyclastic pathway is common in yeasts for alcohol fermentation but not in bacteria, except for *Sarcina ventriculi*, an obligate anaerobic species [54].

Representative fermentation results of selected acidogenic bacteria are summarized in Table 5. Lactic acid and ethanol produced are further converted to acetic acid, H_2 and CO_2 i.e., substrates for methanogens.

Lignin decompositions. Lignin is composed of highly branched polymeric molecules consisting of phenylpropane based monomeric units linked together by different types of bonds, including alkyl-aryl, alkyl-alkyl, and aryl-aryl ether bonds.

Little research study has been done with regard to the anaerobic metabolism of native lignin. Lignin monomers such as ferulic, syringic, and vanillic acids (structure see Figure 10) have been shown to be sequentially metabolized to CH_4 under strictly anaerobic conditions [74–76]. However, the question still remains as to whether larger lignin fragments can be anaerobically attacked and the extent to which native lignin can be anaerobically metabolized. Benner et al. [77] showed that labeled methane and carbon dioxide (13–23%) was produced from [^{14}C]lignin in thermophilic

Table 4
Some Important Polysaccharide-Degrading Enzymes and Related Anaerobic Microorganisms

Polysaccharide	Enzyme	Microorganism	Ref.
Cellulose	Endo-β-1,4-glucanase (C_x cellulase, carboxy methyl cellulase)	*Ruminococcus albus*	35
		Clostridium thermocellum	36
		Bacteroides succinogenes	26
	Exo-β-1,4-glucanase (C_1 cellulase, avicelase, cellobiohydrolase)	*Acetivibrio celluolyticus*	37
		Bacteroids celluosolvens	38
		Clostridium stercorarium	39
Starch	α-1,4-Glucan 4-glucanhydrolase (α-Amylase)	*Clostridium butyricum*	40
		Bacteroides spp.	40
	α-1,4-Glucan maltohydrolase (β-Amylase)	*Lactobacillus* spp.	40
		Bacillus subtilis	41
	α-1,4-Glucanglycohydrolase (Amyloglucosidase)	*B. cereus*	41
		B. licheniformis	41
	α-Glucosidase (Maltase)	*Clostridium thermosulfurogenes*	42
		C. thermohydrosulfuricum	43
Pectin	Pectin pectylhydrolase (Pectinesterase)	*Clostridium multifermentans*	44
	α-1,4-D-Galactrosiduronate lyase (Pectin transeliminase)		
	α-1,4-D-Galactrosiduronate glycanohydrolase (pectin hydrolase)		
Hemicellulose (Xylan)	β-1,4-D-Xylan xylanohydrolase (β-xylanase)	*Clostridium thermocellum*	45
		C. thermohydrosulfuricum	45
	β-Xylosidase	*C. thermosaccharolyticum*	45
		Thermoanaerobacter ethanolicum	45
		Thermobacteroides acetoethylicus	45
		Bacteroides rumicola	40

(55°C) anaerobic enrichment cultures. Colberg et al. [78] first demonstrated that soluble fragment of lignin obtained by thermochemical treatment of [^{14}C]lignin-labeled lignocellulose served as substrate for anaerobic enrichment cultures, and could be degraded to lower molecular weight compounds and to methane and carbon dioxide. They demonstrated, then, by using [^{14}C]lignin-derived substrate with molecular weight of 600 as a sole carbon source that 2-bromoethanesulfonic acid seemed to effectively block CH_4 formation in the anaerobic food chain resulting in the buildup of volatile fatty acids and monoaromatic intermediates, and they proposed anaerobic metabolism of the lignin-derived substrate (Figure 10) [79].

Healy et al. [75] proposed a methanogenic degradation of ferulic acid, which included various acids as possible intermediate (Figure 11).

Native lignin degrading anaerobic microorganisms are still obscure. A lignin related compound, dehydrovanillin was degraded by *Fusobacterium varium* and *Enterococcus faecium* [80]. Phenylpropionate stimulated the growth of *Ruminococcus albus* [81] and phenolic monomers, syringic, *p*-hydroxybenzoic, and hydrocinnamic acids, stimulated the growth of *Ruminococcus albus, R. flavefaciens, Butyrivibrio fibrisolvens* and *Lachnospira multiparus* [82].

Although most of the biopolymers are easily degradable, the cellulosic materials of highly lignified plants (straw, wood, etc.) are extremely undegradable for hydrolysis [83].

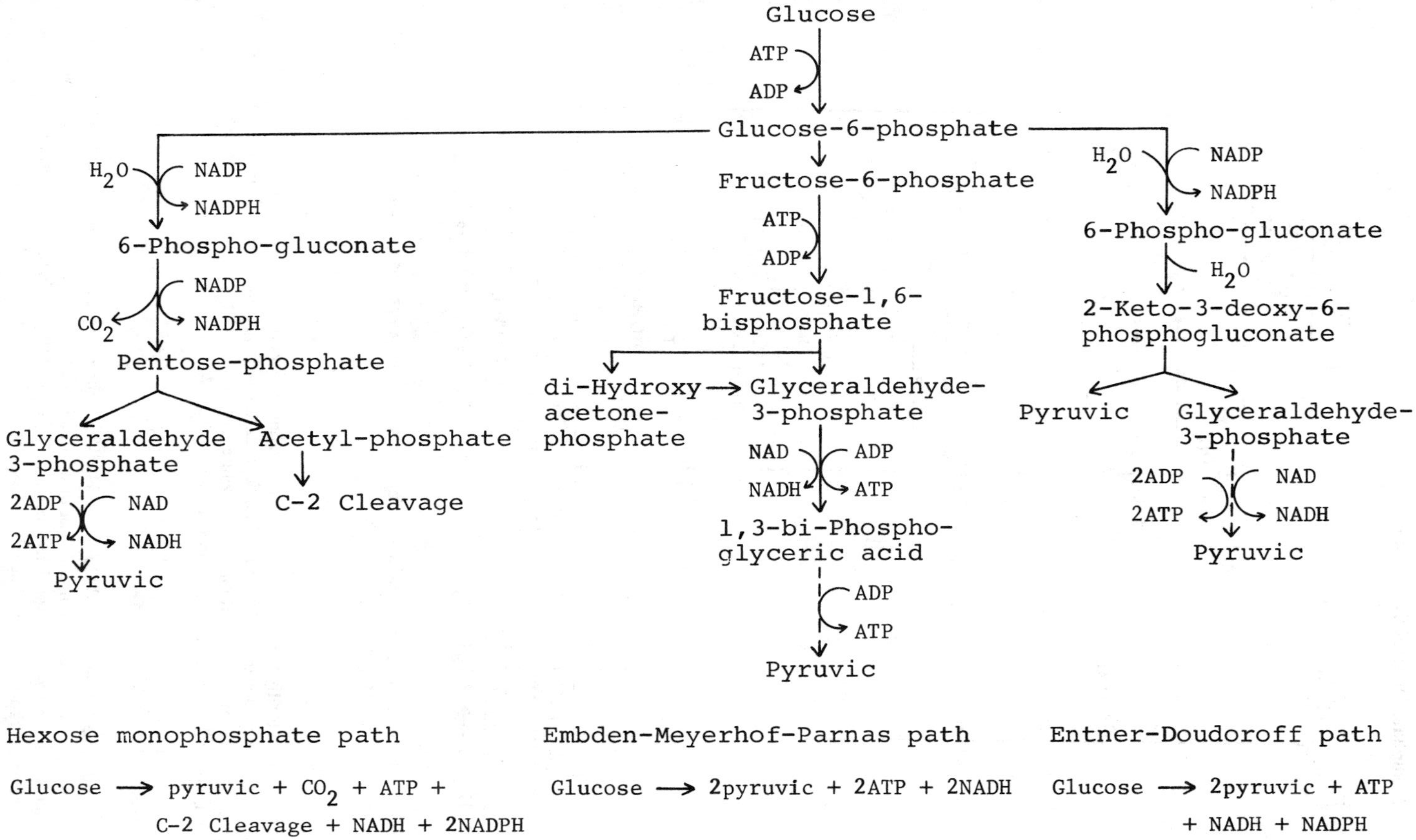

Figure 6. Pathways of glucose breakdown to pyruvic acid.

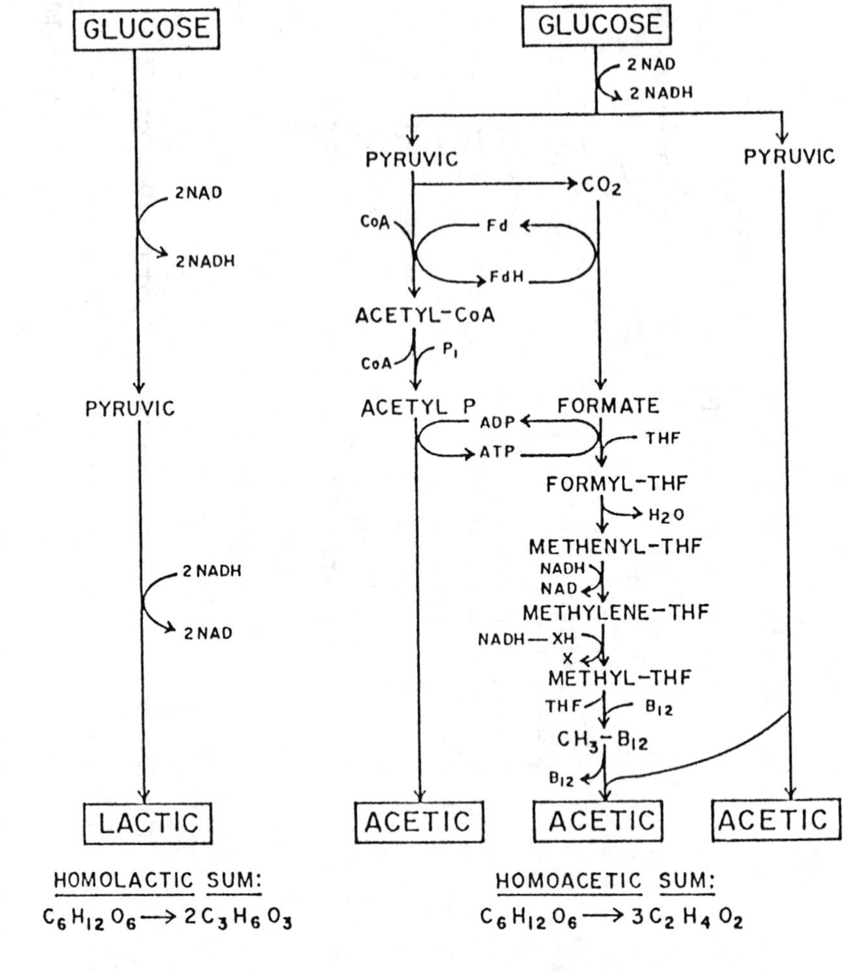

Figure 7. Homolactic and homoacetic fermentation pathways for glucose. (Reprinted with permission from Ref. [1].)

In conclusion for hydrolysis and acidogenesis (stage 1, Figure 1), sugars, amino acids, fatty acids, and monoaromatics produced by microbial degradation of biopolymers are taken up by the successive bacteria and are fermented mainly to acetate, propionate, butyrate, lactate, formate, succinate, ethanol, glycerol, carbon dioxide, and hydrogen.

Acetogenesis and Dehydrogenation

Although a part of acetic acid (20%) and H_2 (4%) is directly produced from sugars, amino acids and so on in acidogenic fermentation, both products are mainly derived from the higher volatile fatty acids via acetogenesis and dehydrogenation (see stage 2 in Figure 1). Microorganisms and biochemical breakdown in the stage 2 are described here.

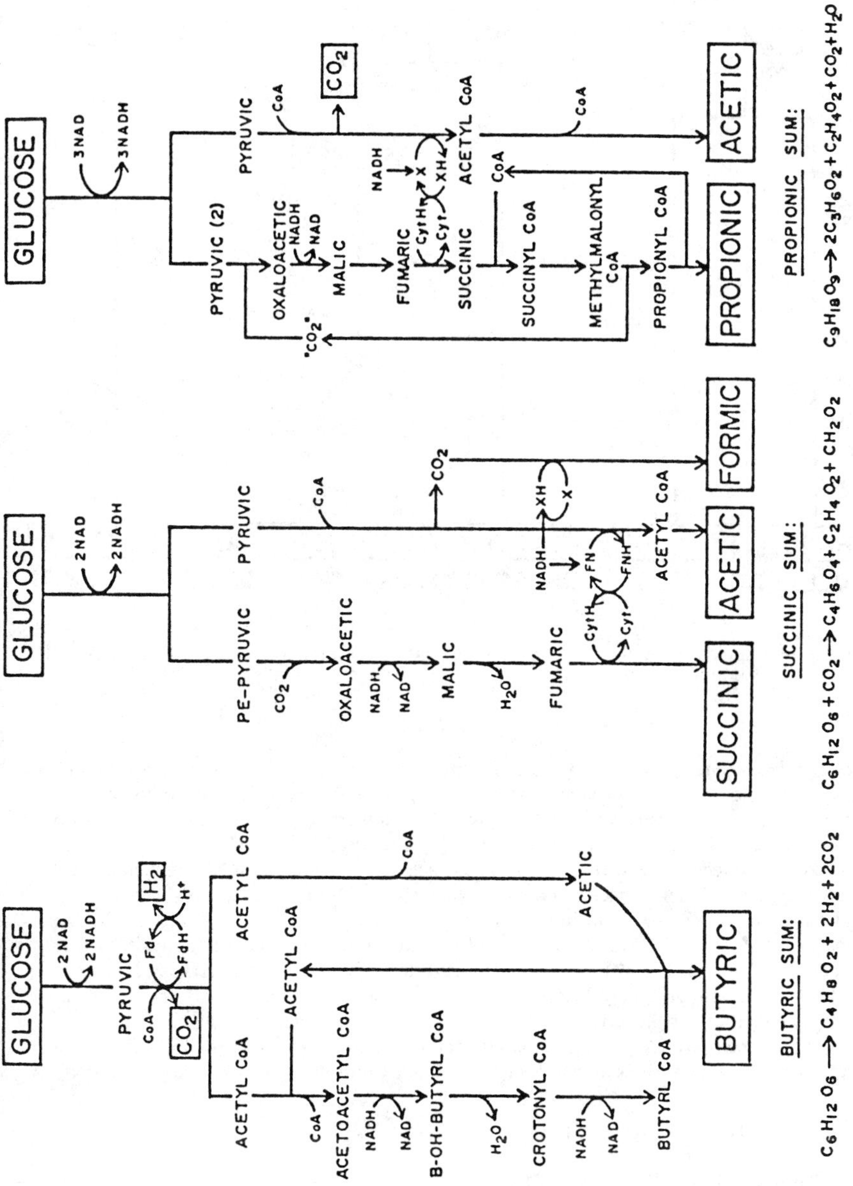

Figure 8. Heteroacidic fermentation pathways for glucose. (Reprinted with permission from Ref. [1].)

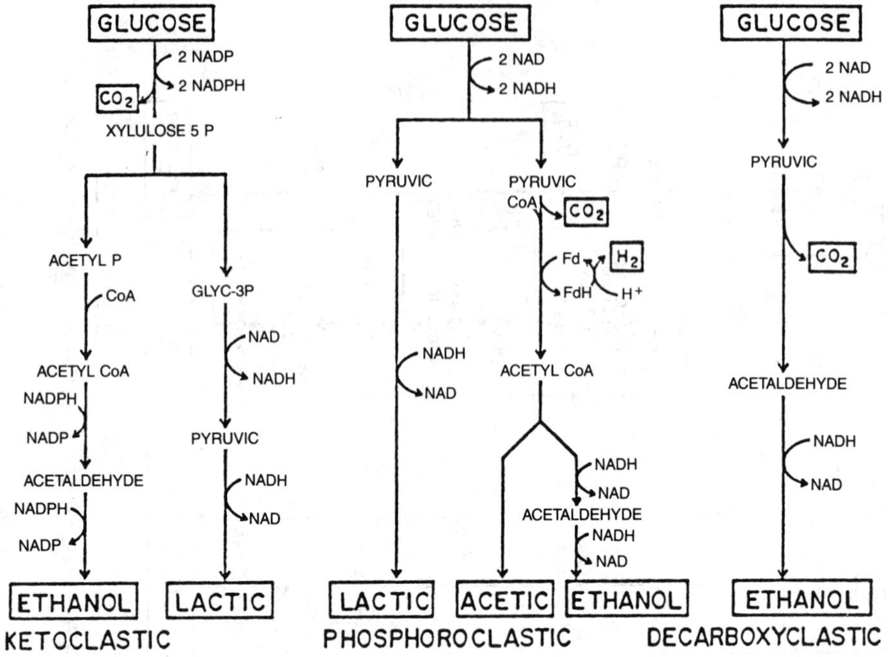

Figure 9. Ethanolic fermentation pathways for glucose. (Reprinted with permission from Ref. [1].)

Fatty acids decompositions. The obligate H_2-producing acetogenic bacteria are capable of producing acetic acid and H_2 from higher fatty acids. *Syntrophobacter wolinii*, a propionate decomposer [84] and *Syntrophomonas wolfei*, a butyrate decomposer [85] have been only isolated so far due to technical difficulties of pure isolation since the produced H_2 severely inhibits their growth. Hence, co-culture techniques with H_2 consumers such as methanogens, sulfate reducing bacteria, etc. may help the study on biochemical breakdown of fatty acids and consequently, microbiological and physiological studies have not been fully developed so far.

Tables 6 and 7 show the overall reactions of breakdown for long chain fatty acids. Generally, H_2 producing acetogens (see Table 7, I) are energetically unfavorable due to $\Delta G^{o\prime} > 0$, hence, with a combination of H_2-consuming bacteria (see Table 7, III), co-culture systems are able to make a favorable condition for the fatty acid decomposition to acetate and methane or H_2S.

Besides the decomposition of long chain fatty acids, ethanol [86] and lactate [87] are converted to acetic acid and H_2 by an acetogen (S organism) and *Clostridium formicoaceticum*, respectively.

$$C_2H_5OH + H_2O = CH_3COO^- + H^+ + 2\,H_2$$

$$CH_3CHOHCOO^- + 2\,H_2O = CH_3COO^- + HCO_3^- + H^+ + 2\,H_2$$

Figure 12 shows the effect of H_2 partial pressure on the free energy of conversion of ethanol, propionate, acetate, and H_2/CO_2 during methane fermentation [7]. An extremely low partial pressure of H_2, e.g. 10^{-5} atm seems to be significant factor for the propionate degradation to methane. This can be done in the co-culture with H_2-consuming bacteria previously mentioned (Table 7, III).

Table 5
Carbohydrate Fermentation by Acidogenic Bacteria

Microorganism	Opt. Temp. (°C)	Substrate	Production (g/l) or (mol/mol Glucose)* or (mol/mol Fructose)**										Ref.
			Formic Acid	Acetic Acid	Propionic Acid	Butyric Acid	Lactic Acid	Succinic Acid	Methanol	Ethanol	Butanol	Acetone	
Acetovibrio cellulolyticus ATCC 33288	37	Cellulose (5 g/l)		0.78						0.92			55
Clostridium butyricum LMD 77-11	30	Glucose (10 g/l)		1.06		2.36							56
Clostridium cellulolyticum ATCC 35319		Cellulose (7.6 g/l)		0.90			0.86			0.17			57
Clostridium cellulovorans ATCC 35296	37	Cellobiose (3.42 g/l)	0.47	0.31		1.55	0.29						58
Clostridium sporogenes 3121	37	Glucose (5 g/l)	0.14	0.90	0.13	1.50							59
Clostridium thermocellum strain TC11	60	Cellulose (10 g/l)	0.31	1.68			1.32			2.12			60
Clostridium thermocellum ATCC 31549	60	Hemicellulose		1.43			1.36			0.46			45

(Continued)

Table 5 (Continued)

Microorganism	Opt. Temp. (°C)	Substrate	Production (g/l) or (mol/mol Glucose)* or (mol/mol Fructose)**										Ref.
			Formic Acid	Acetic Acid	Propionic Acid	Butyric Acid	Lactic Acid	Succinic Acid	Methanol	Ethanol	Butanol	Acetone	
Clostridium thermocellum type culture	60	Cellulose (15 g/l)		1.13						0.89			61
Clostridium thermocellum LQ 8	60	Cellulose (7.1 g/l)		0.25		0.59	0.42			0.96			62
		Cellobiose (7.1 g/l)		1.22		0.73	0.35			1.46			
Clostridium thermohydro-sulfuricum DSM 2247	65–70	Hemicellulose		1.75			0.30			0.87			45
Clostridium thermohydro-sulfuricum DSM 2355	65	Soluble starch (25 g/l)		0.42			2.97			2.39			63
Clostridium thermosaccha-rolyticum ATCC 7956	55–60	Hemicellulose		1.56			0.23						45
Clostridium thermosulfurogenes ATCC 33743	60	Soluble starch (25 g/l)		1.38			2.97			1.70			63

Eubacterium limosum strain 11A	37	Betaine (50 mmol/*l*)		0.54		0.79							64
Eubacterium limosum strain RF	37	Pectin (2 g/*l*)		0.10		0.02							65
Lachnospira multiparus ATCC 19207	37	Pectin (2 g/*l*)	0.16	0.72	0.01		0.18		0.18	0.06			65
Thermoanaerobacter ethanolicus	65–70	Hemicellulose		1.08			0.22			1.49			45
Thermoanaerobium brockii ATCC 33075	65	Hemicellulose		0.92			0.26			1.21			45
Thermobacteroides acetoethylicus ATCC 33265	65	Hemicellulose		0.94			0.19			1.21			45
Clostridium acetobutylicum ATCC 39236	35	Hydrolyzed starch (60 g/*l*)		2.7		1.0				1.0	13.0	5.0	66
Clostridium acetobutyricum DSM 1731	33–37	Glucose (18–60 g/*l*)		0.54		0.81				0.78	12.6	4.9	67
Bacteroides succinogenes C-1-A	37	Glucose		0.63				1.89		0.05			68

(*Continued*)

Table 5 (Continued)

Microorganism	Opt. Temp. (°C)	Substrate	Production (g/l) or (mol/mol Glucose)* or (mol/mol Fructose)**										Ref.
			Formic Acid	Acetic Acid	Propionic Acid	Butyric Acid	Lactic Acid	Succinic Acid	Methanol	Ethanol	Butanol	Acetone	
Bacteroides succinogenes C-1-B	37	Glucose		0.51				1.52					68
Rumicococcus flavefaciens	37	Cellobiose		0.79				1.02		0.09			68
Clostridium thermohydrosulfuricum 39E	65	Cellulose (MN 300)		0.37						0.51			69
Clostridium thermohydrosulfuricum 39E	65	Cellulose (Solka Floc)		0.38						0.60			69
Clostridium chartatabidum	39	Cellobiose		0.48*		0.48*				0.2*			70
Clostridium chartatabium	39	Cellulose		0.47*		0.86*				0.08*			70
Clostridium formicoaceticum		Fructose		3**									71
Lactobacillus casei	37	Glucose	0.1*	0.05*			1.6*						72
Thermoanaerobium brockii	65	Glucose		0.18*			1.52*			0.65*			73

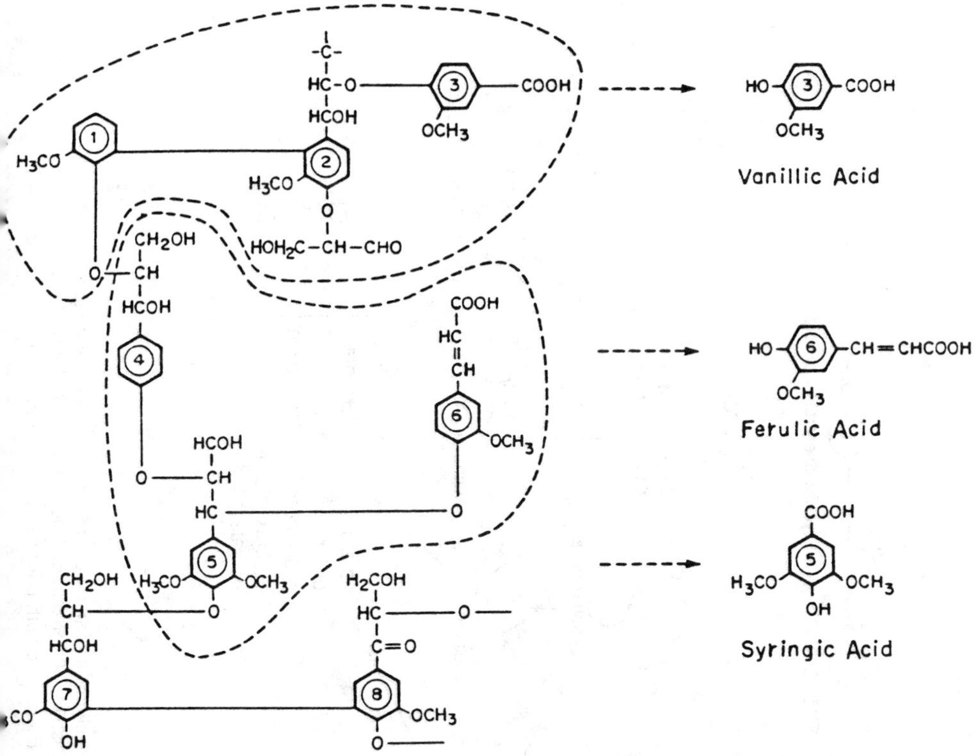

Figure 10. Model depicting the lignin-derived substrate (MW. 600) represented by the trilignols and its anaerobic metabolism with the release of the lignin monomers. (Reprinted with permission from Ref. [79].)

Acetogenesis from H_2/CO_2. Historically, *Clostridium aceticum* was isolated in 1936 [88] as an acetic acid producer from H_2 and CO_2. Afterwards, *Acetobacterium woodii* [89] was isolated as H_2/CO_2 using acetogen.

$$4\,H_2 + 2\,CO_2 = CH_3COOH + 2\,H_2O$$

Physiological aspects and substrate availabilities of so far isolated acetogens are summarized in Tables 8 and 9. All the acetogens are strictly anaerobes and capable of using a variety of substrates other than H_2/CO_2. In Table 8, most acetogens grow at 30°C and some of them, *C. thermoaceticum, C. thermoautotrophicum, A. kivui,* at 60°C. Fructose seems to be a favorable substrate capable of converting one mole fructose to 3 moles of acetic acid, which corresponds to acidogenesis (stage 1, Figure 1).

Besides, *Eubacterium limosum* and *Butyribacterium methylotrophicum* can also produce acetate together with butyrate from glucose, methanol and H_2/CO_2 [98].

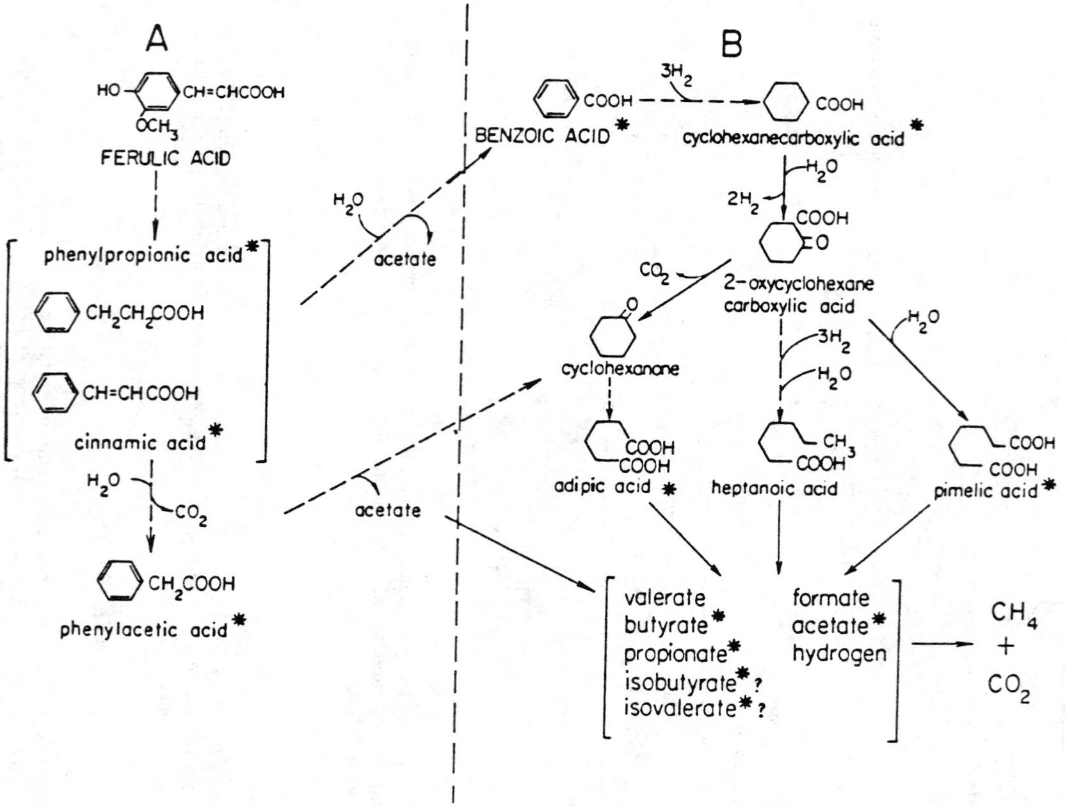

Figure 11. Suggested model for decomposition of ferulic acid to methane: (A) Initial steps in ferulic acid decomposition; (B) Decomposition of benzoic acid to methane. Asterisk denotes intermediates observed in enrichments. (Reprinted with permission from Ref. [75].)

Table 6
Proposed Reactions Involved in Catabolism of Fatty Acids by *Syntrophomonas wolfei*

Fatty Acids	Reaction
Even-numbered	
$CH_3CH_2CH_2COO^-$	$+ 2\,H_2O \rightleftharpoons 2\,CH_3COO^- + 2\,H_2 + H^+$
$CH_3CH_2CH_2CH_2CH_2COO^-$	$+ 4\,H_2O \rightleftharpoons 3\,CH_3COO^- + 4\,H_2 + 2\,H^+$
$CH_3CH_2CH_2CH_2CH_2CH_2CH_2COO^-$	$+ 6\,H_2O \rightleftharpoons 4\,CH_3COO^- + 6\,H_2 + 3\,H^+$
Odd-numbered	
$CH_3CH_2CH_2CH_2COO^-$	$+ 2\,H_2O \rightleftharpoons CH_3CH_2COO^- + CH_3COO^- + 2\,H_2 + H^+$
$CH_3CH_2CH_2CH_2CH_2CH_2COO^-$	$+ 4\,H_2O \rightleftharpoons CH_3CH_2COO^- + 2CH_3COO^- + 4\,H_2 + H^+$
Branched-chained	
$CH_3CH(CH_3)CH_2CH_2CH_2COO^-$	$+ 2\,H_2O \rightleftharpoons CH_3CH(CH_3)CH_2COO^- + CH_3COO^- + 2\,H_2 + H^+$

[Reprinted with permission from Ref. 85]

Table 7
Equations and Free-Energy Changes for Reactions Involving Anaerobic Oxidation of Butyrate and Propionate to Acetate and HCO_3^-, with Protons, HCO_3^-, or SO_4^{2-} Serving as Electron Acceptor, by Butyrate- or Propionate-Catabolizing Bacteria in Pure Culture or in Co-Culture with H_2-Utilizing Methanogens or *Desulfovibrio* spp.

Equation	$\Delta G^{\circ\prime}$ (kJ/Reaction)
I. Proton-reducing (H_2-producing) acetogenic bacteria	
A. $CH_3CH_2CH_2COO^- + 2\,H_2O \rightleftharpoons 2\,CH_3COO^- + 2\,H_2 + H^+$	+48.1
B. $CH_3CH_2COO^- + 3\,H_2O \rightleftharpoons CH_3COO^- + HCO_3^- + H^+ + 3\,H_2$	+76.1
II. H_2-using methanogens and desulfovibrios	
C. $4\,H_2 + HCO_3^- + H^+ \rightleftharpoons CH_4 + 3\,H_2O$	−135.6
D. $4\,H_2 + SO_4^= + H^+ \rightleftharpoons HS^- + 4\,H_2O$	−151.9
III. Co-cultures of I and II	
A + C $2\,CH_3CH_2CH_2COO^- + HCO_3^- + H_2O \rightleftharpoons 4\,CH_3COO^- + H^+ + CH_4$	−39.4
A + D $2\,CH_3CH_2CH_2COO^- + SO_4^= \rightleftharpoons 4\,CH_3COO^- + H^+ + HS^-$	−55.7
B + C $4\,CH_3CH_2COO^- + 12\,H_2 \rightleftharpoons 4\,CH_3COO^- + HCO_3^- + H^+ + 3\,CH_4$	−102.4
B + D $4\,CH_3CH_2COO^- + 3\,SO_4^= \rightleftharpoons 4\,CH_3COO^- + 4\,HCO_3^- + H^+ + 3\,HS^-$	−151.3

[Reprinted with permission from Ref. 84]

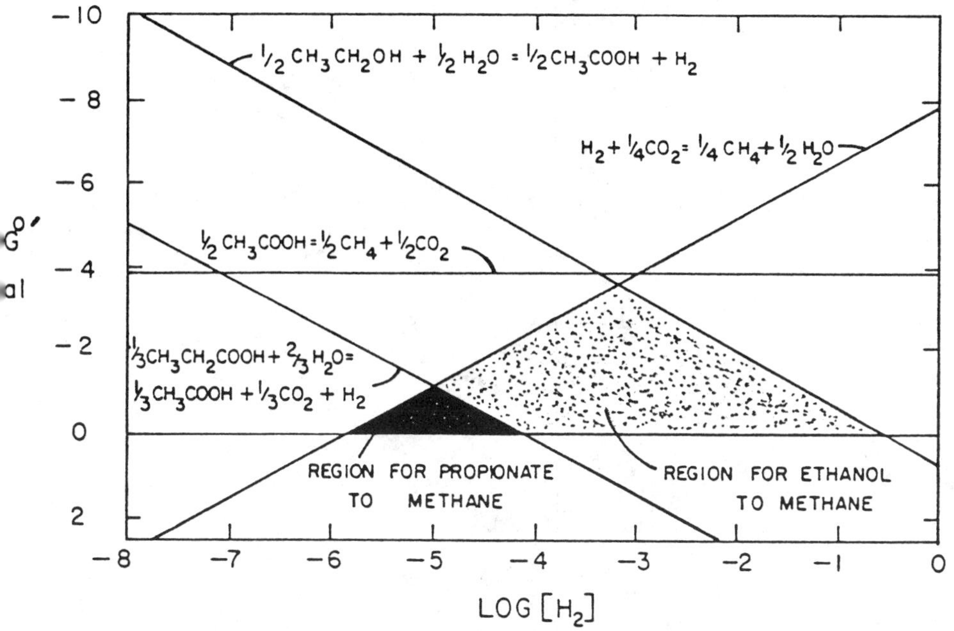

Figure 12. Effect of hydrogen partial pressure on the free energy of conversion of ethanol, propionate, acetate, and hydrogen during methane fermentation. (Reprinted with permission from Ref. [7].)

Methanogenesis

Methanogens are physiologically united as methane producer in anaerobic digestion (see Figure 1, stage 3). Although acetate and H_2/CO_2 are main substrates available in natural environments, formate, methanol, methylamines, and CO are also converted to methane (see Table 10) [99].

All the methanogens have a common feature in which a methyl-group acts as a terminal electron acceptor to form methane, which is an energetically favorable reaction ($\Delta G^{o\prime} = -112$ kJ) [100, 101]. In other words, this reaction serves as an "electron sink" for anaerobic oxidative reactions of all the substrates cited in Table 10.

Isolated methanogens. Methanogens, obligate anaerobes, require a negative redox potential less than −300 mV for their growth. Therefore, the isolation and cultivation of methanogens have not succeeded for a long time due to the technical difficulties of handling the methanogens under the completely O_2-free condition. Owing to the remarkable developments for the isolation technique of methanogens by Hungate [102, 103], pure methanogens have been produced as listed in Table 11.

Table 11 lists 40 methanogens that can be divided in two groups, i.e. H_2/CO_2 (31 strains) and acetate consumers (8 strains). A part of H_2/CO_2 consumers can use formate (18 strains), however, acetate was consumed by limited strains, *Methanosarcina* spp. and *Methanothrix* spp. being incapable of using formate but mostly capable of using methanol, methylamines, and H_2/CO_2. In the natural environments, since a large quantity of acetate was produced (see Figure 1), *Methanosarcina* spp. and *Methanothrix* spp. play an important role in completing the whole anaerobic digestion and for H_2 accumulation, which inhibit acetogens and methanogens, the H_2-consuming

Table 8
Characteristics of Acetogenic Bacteria

Acetogen	Size (μm)	Spore Formation	Fragellium	G + C Content (Mol%)	Growth Temp. (°C)	Opt. Temp. (°C)	Growth pH	Opt. pH	Ref.
Clostridium									
aceticum	0.8–1.0 × 5	+	+	33	20–55	30	7–9.5	8.3	90
thermoaceticum	0.4 × 2.8	+	+	54	45–65	55–60	6–8.5	7	91
thermoautotrophicum	0.8–1.0 × 3–6	+	+	54–55	36–70	56–60	4.5–7.6	5.7	92
Acetobacterium									
woodii	1 × 2	−	+	39	<40	30		6.7–7.5	89
wieringae	1 × 1–2	−	+	43	20–45	30	5.7–8.3	7.2–7.8	93
carbinolicum	0.8–1.3 × 1.8–3.5	−	+	38.5	15–40	27	6.0–8.0	7.0–7.2	94
kivui	0.7 × 2–7.5	−	−	38	50–72	66	5.3–7.3	6.4	95
Sporomusa									
sphaeroides	0.5–0.8 × 2–4	+	+	46.7–47.4	15–45	35–39	5.7–8.7	6.4–7.6	96
ovata	0.7–1.0 × 1–5	+	+	41.3–42.2	15–45	34–39	5.0–8.1	5.3–7.2	96
acidovorans	0.7–1.0 × 2–8	+	+	42	20–40	35	5.4–7.5	6.5–7.0	97

Table 9
Use of Various Substrates by Acetogenic Bacteria

Substrate	*Clostridium aceticum*	*C. thermoaceticum*	*C. thermoautotrophicum*	*Acetobacterium woodii*	*A. wieringae*	*A. carbinolicum*	*A. kivui*	*Sporomusa sphaeroides*	*S. ovata*	*S. acidovorans*
Fructose	+	+	+	+	+	+	+	−	+	+
Glucose	−	+	+	+	−	+	+	−	−	−
Galactose	−	−	+	−	−	nd	−	nd	−	−
Mannose	−	−	−	−	nd	nd	+	−	−	nd
Xylose	−	+	+	−	−	nd	nd	−	−	−
Ribose	+	−	−	−	−	nd	−	−	−	+
Mannitol	−	−	nd	−	−	nd	−	−	−	−
Glutamate	+	−	−	−	−	nd	nd	nd	nd	+
Fumarate	+	−	nd	−	−	nd	−	−	−	+
Malate	+	−	−	−	−	−	−	nd	−	+
Serine	+	nd	nd	−	−	nd	−	+	−	+
Lactate	−	−	−	+	+	+	nd	+	+	−
Pyruvate	+	+	−	+	−	+	+	+	+	+
Ethylene glycol	+	nd	−	+	+	+	nd	+	−	nd
Ethanol	+	nd	−	−	−	+	−	+	+	+
Glycerol	−	−	−	+	+	+	−	+	−	nd
Glycerate	nd	nd	+	+	−	nd	−	+	−	−
CO_2/H_2	+	+	+	+	+	+	+	+	+	+
CO	nd	+	+	nd	nd	nd	nd	nd	nd	nd
Formate	+	nd	+	+	+	+	+	+	+	+
Methanol/CO_2	−	nd	+	+	−	+	−	+	+	+
Methylamine/CO_2	nd	nd	+	nd	nd	nd	nd	nd	nd	nd
Ref.	90	91	92	89	93	94	95	96	96	97

+: growth, −: no growth, nd; not determined.

Table 10
Reactions Yielding Energy ($\Delta G^{o\prime}$) in Methanogens

Reaction	$\Delta G^{o\prime}$ (kJ/mol Substrate)
1. $CO_2 + 4\,H_2 \longrightarrow CH_4 + 2\,H_2O$	−130.7
$HCO_3^- + 4\,H_2 + H^+ \longrightarrow CH_4 + 3\,H_2O$	−135.5
2. $CH_3COO^- + H^+ \longrightarrow CH_4 + CO_2$	−37.0
$CH_3COO^- + H_2O \longrightarrow CH_4 + HCO_3^-$	−32.3
3. $HCOO^- + H^+ \longrightarrow 0.25\,CH_4 + 0.75\,CO_2 + 0.5\,H_2O$	−36.1
4. $CO + 0.5\,H_2O \longrightarrow 0.25\,CH_4 + 0.75\,CO_2$	−52.7
5. $CH_3OH \longrightarrow 0.75\,CH_4 + 0.25\,CO_2 + 0.5\,H_2O$	−79.9
6. $CH_3NH_3^+ + 0.5\,H_2O \longrightarrow 0.75\,CH_4 + 0.25\,CO_2 + NH_4^+$	−57.4
7. $(CH_3)_2NH_2^+ + H_2O \longrightarrow 1.5\,CH_4 + 0.5\,CO_2 + NH_4^+$	−112.2
8. $(CH_3)_2NCH_2CH_3 \cdot H^+ + H_2O \longrightarrow 1.5\,CH_4 + 0.5\,CO_2 + {}^+H_3NCH_2CH_3$	−105
9. $(CH_3)_3NH^+ + 1.5\,H_2O \longrightarrow 2.25\,CH_4 + 0.75\,CO_2 + NH_4^+$	−170.8

[Calculated from data of Ref. 99].

Substrates and Optimal Growth Conditions of Pure Methanogenic Bacteria

Methanogenic bacteria	Substrate					Opt. Temp. (°C)	Opt. pH	Ref.
	H_2/CO_2	Formate	Methanol	Methylamines	Acetate			
Methanobacterium								
formicicum	+	+				56	8.0	104
bryantii	+					38–45	7.2–7.6	105
thermoautotrophicum	+					65–70	7.2–7.6	106
thermoaggregans	+					65	7.0–7.5	107
thermoalcaliphilum	+					58–62	7.5–8.5	108
wolfei	+					55–65	7.0–7.5	109
uliginosum	+					40	6.0–8.5	110
Methanobrevibacter								
ruminantium	+	+				37–43	6.0–8.0	111
arboriphilus	+	+				30–40	7.5–8.0	112
smithii	+	+				37		113
Methanothermus								
fervidus	+					83	6.5	114
Methanoplanus								
limicola	+	+				40	7.0	115
Methanococcus								
deltae	+					36–40	7.0	116
vannielii	+	+				36–40	8.0	117
voltae	+	+				35–45	6.0–7.0	118
thermolithotrophicus	+	+				65	6.5–7.5	119
maripaludis	+	+				38	6.8–7.2	120
jannaschii	+					85	5.0	121
halophilus			+	+	+	26–36	6.5–7.4	122

(*Continued*)

Table 11 (Continued)

Methanogenic bacteria	Substrate					Opt. Temp. (°C)	Opt. pH	Ref.
	H_2/CO_2	Formate	Methanol	Methylamines	Acetate			
Methanomicrobium								
mobile	+	+				40	6.1–6.9	123
paynteri	+					40	7.0	124
Methanogenium								
cariaci	+	+				20–25	6.8–7.3	125
marisnigri	+	+				20–25	6.2–6.6	125
tatii	+	+				40–45	7.0	126
frittonii	+	+				57	7.0–7.5	127
thermophilicum	+	+				55	7.0	128
olentangyi	+						7.0	116
Methanolobus								
tindarius			+	+		25		129
Methanospirillum								
hungatei	+	+				35	7.0	130

Methanosarcina							
mazei	+		+	+	+	35	7.0	131
barkeri	+		+	+	+	37–40	7.0	132
acetivorans			+	+	+	35–40	6.5–7.0	133
vacuolata	+		+	+	+	40	7.5	134
Methanothrix								
soehngenii					+	37	7.4–7.8	135
spp.	+				+	60		136
concilii					+	35–40	7.1–7.5	137
Methanococcoides								
methylutens			+	+		30–35	7.0–7.5	138
Methanocorpusculum								
parvum	+	+				37	7.0	139
Methanosphaera								
stadtmaniae			+			36–40	6.5–6.9	140
Methanoplanus								
endosymbiosus	+	+				32	7.0	141

methanogens also play an important role in maintaining a low atmospheric condition of H_2. Besides, some methanogens can also use CO to produce methane.

The most methanogens (Table 11) grow at mesophilic temperature (25–40°C) where a part of them (11 strains) grow at thermophilic temperature (45–85°C) which were isolated from hot springs, volcanic regions, the sea bottoms, etc. For optimum pHs for methanogens are almost neutral pHs between 6 and 8 except for *M. thermoalcaliphilum* (7.5 to 8.5) and *M. jannaschii* (5.0).

These methanogens are considerably different from usual heterotrophic bacteria and eucaryotic microorganisms with respect to several biochemical aspects as follows.

1. A typical cell wall component, i.e. muramic acid of usual bacteria is not of the methanogens, instead of, L-talosaminuronic acid is the unit for pseudomurein [142].
2. Lipid compositions markedly differ from usual bacteria, consisting of glycerol ethers with saturated C_{20} and C_{40} isoprenoid hydrocarbons [143].
3. Specific coenzymes, CoM, F_{420}, F_{430}, methanopterin and methanofuran have been found.
4. Ribosomal RNA sequences of the methanogens are quite unique from the classical bacteria (eubacteria) [144].

Hence, the methanogens so far isolated are classified in the *Archaebacteria* together with extreme halophiles, *Halobacteriaceae* and thermoacidophiles, *Sulfolobus* and *Thermoplasma* [145].

Methanation from H_2/CO_2. H_2/CO_2-consuming methanogens reduce CO_2 as electron acceptor via the formyl, methenyl, and methyl levels with the association of unusual coenzymes and finally produce methane [146] (see Figure 13). In the figure, the C_1-cycle for the reduction of CO_2 involves 6 steps based on very pioneering works by Wolfe group [146].

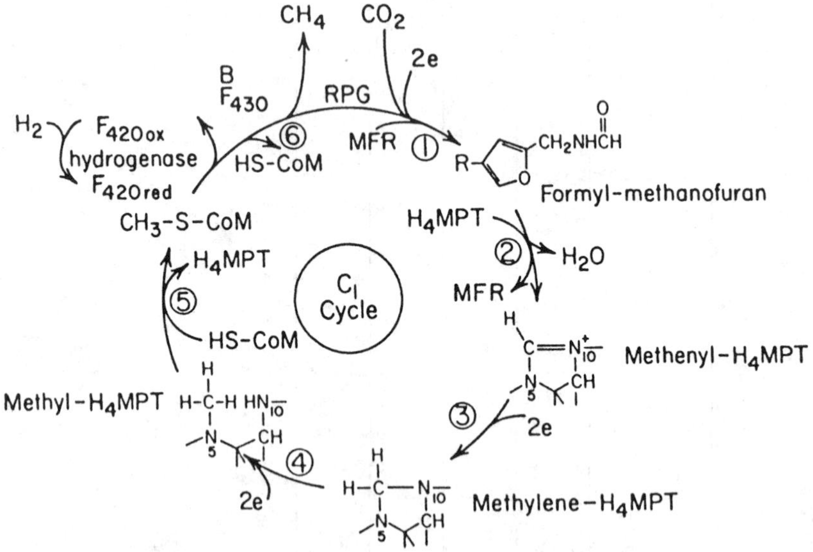

Figure 13. The C_1 cycle for the reduction of CO_2 to CH_4: MFR, methanofuran; H_4MPT, tetrahydromethanopterin; CH_3-S-CoM, 2-(methylthio)ethanesulfonic acid; HS-CoM, 2-mercaptoethanesulfonic acid; F_{420}, deazaflavin; F_{430}, nickel tetrapyrrole; B, essential coenzyme of unknown structure; RPG effect, coupling of the methylreductase to CO_2 activation. (Reprinted with permission from Ref. [146].)

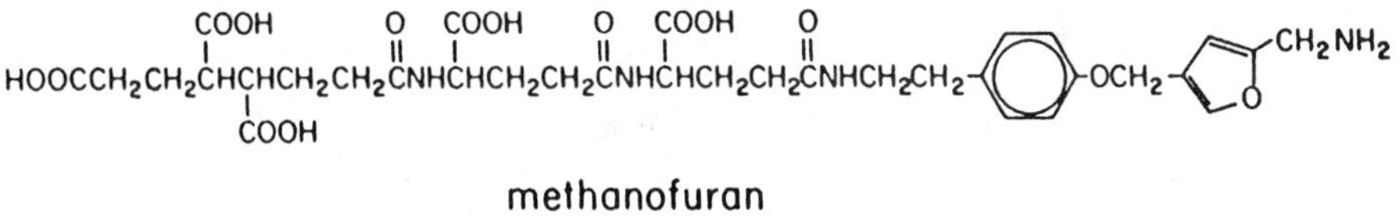

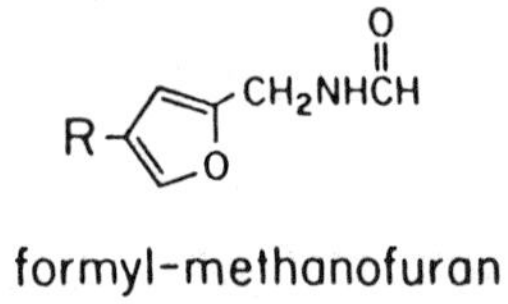

Figure 14. Structure of methanofuran (MFR) and of formylmethanofuran (F-MFR). (Reprinted with permission from Ref. [146].)

1. Methanofuran (MFR) (Figure 14) [146–149]. This unique fixation of CO_2 to formyl-methanofuran (Figure 13, reaction 1) with MFR is triggered when the methylreductase system (Figure 13, reaction 6) was actively reducing methyl-group to CH_4.

$$CO_2 + MFR \xrightarrow{2e} \text{Formyl-MFR (F-MFR)}$$

2. Methanopterins (Figure 15). A fluorescent compound (F_{342}) isolated from the methanogen [150] was determined as methenyl-tetrahydromethanopterin (Methenyl-H_4MPT) [151] and further tetrahydromethanopterin (H_4MPT) was also identified [152]. These methanopterins act as the cofactors on the reactions 2, 3, and 4 in Figure 13.

$$\text{F-MFR} + H_4MPT \longrightarrow \text{MFR} + \text{Methenyl-}H_4MPT$$

$$\text{Methenyl-}H_4MPT \xrightarrow{2e} \text{Methylene-}H_4MPT \xrightarrow{2e} \text{Methyl-}H_4MPT$$

(a)

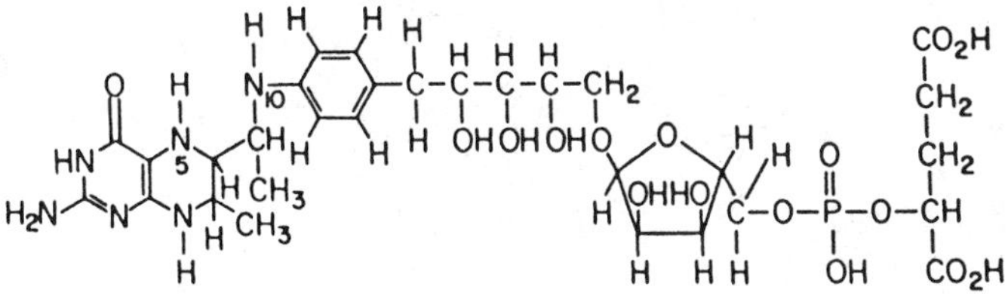

(b)

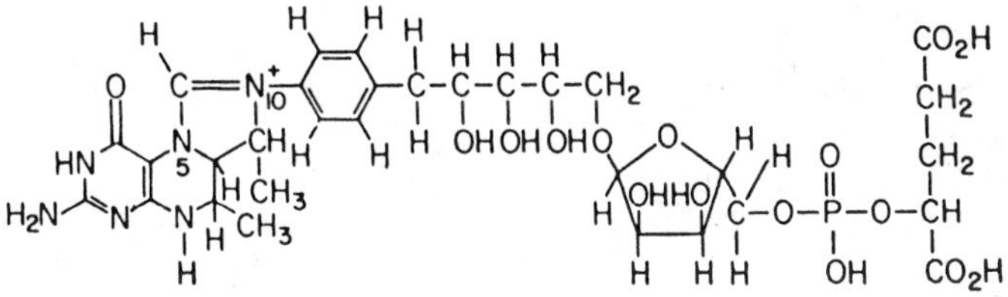

Figure 15. Structure of tetrahydromethanopterin (H_4MPT) (a) and of methenyl-tetrahydromethanopterin (methenyl-H_4MPT) (b). (Reprinted with permission from Ref. [146].)

(a) $HS-CH_2-CH_2-SO_3^-$

(b) $CH_3-S-CH_2-CH_2-SO_3^-$

Figure 16. Structure of coenzyme M(HS-CoM, 2-mercaptoethanesulfonic acid) and of methyl coenzyme M(CH_3-S-CoM, 2-(methylthio)ethanesulfonic acid. (Reprinted with permission from Ref. [146].)

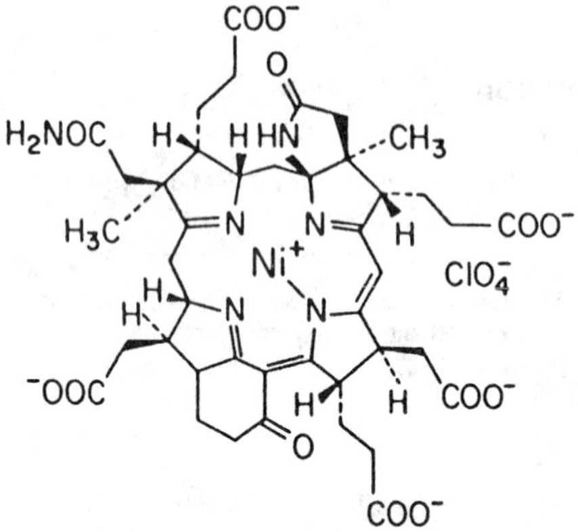

Figure 17. The nickel tetrapyrrole, F_{430} of Methanobacterium after acid-methanolysis of the natural compound. (Reprinted with permission from Ref. [146].)

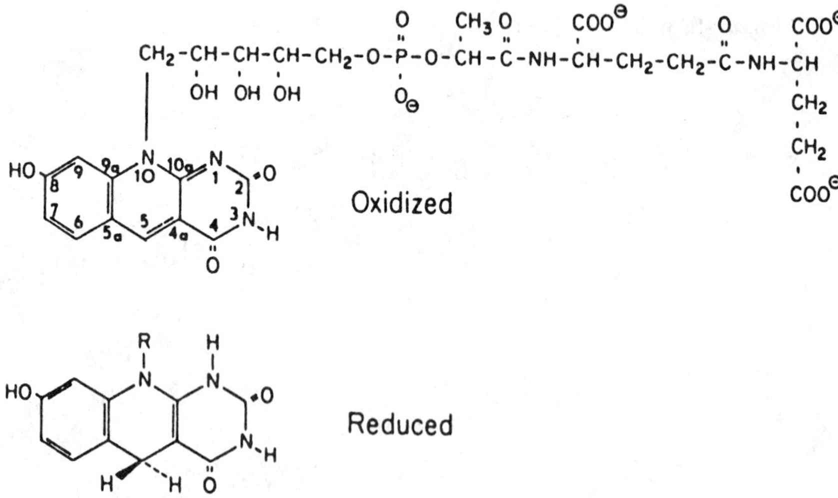

Figure 18. F_{420} (the 8-hydroxy-, 7-demethyl-, 5-deazaflavin) from Methanobacterium. (Reprinted with permission from Ref. [146].)

3. Coenzyme M (HS-CoM, 2-mercaptoethanesulfonic acid) (Figure 16). This unique coenzyme [153] carries a methyl-group (Figure 13, reaction 5) to produce 2-(methylthio)ethanesulfonic acid (CH_3-S-CoM) which is the substrate for the methyl-reductase [153].

$$\text{Methyl-}H_4\text{MPT} + \text{HS-CoM} \longrightarrow H_4\text{MPT} + CH_3\text{-S-CoM}$$

4. Nickel tetrapyrrole (F_{430}) [146], (Figure 17). F_{430} (absorption maximum, 430 nm) functions on the final step (Figure 13, reaction 6) to produce methane from CH_3-S-CoM.
5. 5-Deazaflavin (F_{420}) [146], (Figure 18). F_{420} serves as an electron carrier at the reaction 6 in Figure 13 [100, 101, 145] and probably at the reaction 1 with no evidence.
6. Methyl reductase system (Figure 13, reaction 6). The reduction mechanism of CH_3-S-CoM to CH_4 has not fully been analyzed. Four protein factors (A-1, -2, -3 and C) have been identified in this reaction [154] and a component B, a coenzyme, has not been fully analyzed, either (see Figure 19).

To sum up the C_1-cycle for the reduction of CO_2 to CH_4 (Figure 13), the overall reaction becomes,

$$4\,H_2 + CO_2 = CH_4 + 2\,H_2O$$

(Cofactors)
Component B
F_{430}
F_{420}
FAD
ATP
Mg^{2+}

$$CH_3\text{-S-CoM} + H_2 \longrightarrow CH_4 + \text{HS-CoM}$$

(Protein Components)
A-1
A-2
A-3
C

Figure 19. The methylreductase system. Cofactors: component B, an essential coenzyme of unknown structure; F_{430}, nickel tetrapyrrole; F_{420}, deazaflavin. Protein components: A-1, a hydrogenase-containing crude fraction; A-2, a homogeneous protein of unknown enzymic function; A-3, an oxygen-sensitive protein fraction; C, a homogeneous protein that contains 2 mol F_{430} per mol protein. (Reprinted with permission from Ref. [146].)

Methanation from acetate. In spite of acetate being mainly accumulated and converted to methane in natural environments, biochemistry for methanation from acetate are still obscure. The overall aceticlastic reaction can be expressed as follows:

$$\overset{*}{C}H_3\overset{\circ}{C}OOH \longrightarrow \overset{*}{C}H_4 + \overset{\circ}{C}O_2$$

However, since a small part of CO_2 was also formed from methyl-bound, it is suspected that the reduced potential produced from the methyl-bound may reduce CO_2 to CH_4 [155–158]. When used mixed substrates, e.g., acetate with methanol [159, 160] or trimethylamine [161], acetate was mainly oxidized to CO_2 yielding the reducing power so as to reduce methanol and trimethylamine

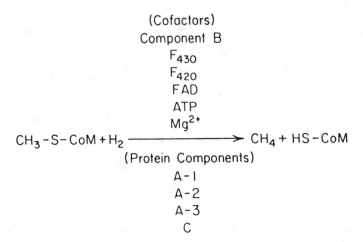

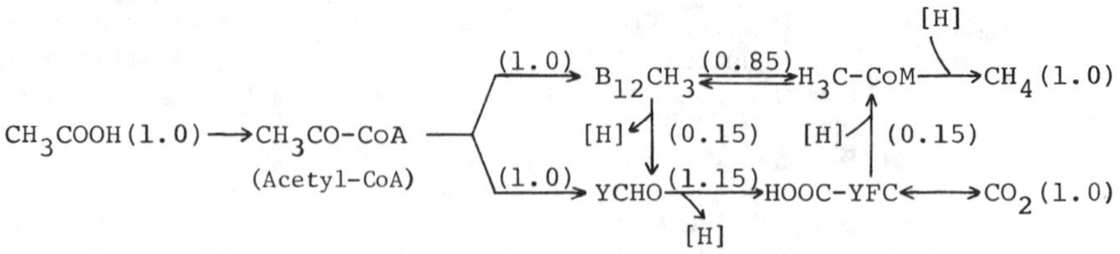

Figure 20. Scheme for carbon and electron flow proposed for methanogenesis during growth of a *Methanosarcina barkeri* strain adapted to grow on acetate as sole carbon and electron donor. B_{12}, a corrinoid; Y, unknown formyl carrier; CoA, coenzyme A; CoM, coenzyme M; YFC, methanopterin; numbers refer to moles of metabolite. This model suggests that carbon monoxide dehydrogenase is a key cleavage enzyme in oxidoreduction of acetate. (Reprinted with permission from Ref. [170].)

for CH_4 formation. However, when methanol or trimethylamine had been completely consumed during the culture, CH_4 was produced from acetate itself.

Coenzyme M was found in *Methanosarcina* spp. [162–164] and *Methanothrix* spp. [137, 157] and the methylreductase system was found in *Methanosarcina* spp. [162–165]. Another very specific enzyme, carbon monoxide dehydrogenase [164, 166, 167] which can undergo cleavage in oxidoreduction of acetate, i.e., aceticlastic reaction, was found in *Methanosarcina barkeri* with a high content [166]. In addition, acetate kinase (converting acetate to acetyl-phosphate) and phosphotransacetylase (converting acetyl-phosphate to acetyl-CoA) were detected in *Methanosarcina barkeri* [168], and acetate thiokinase (converting acetate to acetyl-CoA) was detected in *Methanothrix soehngenii* [167] with a high content of vitamin B_{12} [169].

Based on these facts, Zeikus [170] proposed a scheme for carbon and electron flows from acetate to CH_4 and CO_2 (Figure 20). In this scheme, after the aceticlastic reaction of acetyl-CoA by carbon monoxide dehydrogenase, the major parts of methyl-bound (B_{12}-CH_3) convert to CH_4 via CH_3-S-CoM with methylreductase (Figure 19), whereas a part of B_{12}-CH_3 (15% of the total) is oxidized to form the reducing potential to reduce CH_3-S-CoM to CH_4, although another scheme for methanation from acetate has been proposed [158].

Carbon monoxide dehydrogenase acts also in methane production from carbon monoxide at a initial step ($CO + H_2O \rightarrow H_2 + CO_2$) [170].

Methanation from methanol. Methanol accumulation in natural environments originated from pectin and lignin so that its accumulation seems to be minor compared with acetate accumulation. However, *Methanosarcina* spp. (see Table 11) can use methanol more quickly than acetate. A proposed reaction sequence from methanol to methane (Figure 21) [171] indicates that the methyl-bound of methanol is split by the cobalamin (vitamin B_{12})-containing protein and then transferred to the coenzyme M to produce CH_3-S-CoM. However, the final step for the reduction of CH_3-S-CoM is still obscure suggesting that a certain intermediate with highly reduced potential formed from methanol oxidation [172] (discussed in Figure 20) seems to be associated for the reduction of CH_3-S-CoM$\cdot F_{430}$ (see Figure 21) to methane.

Cell Synthesis of Methanogens

Assimilation pathways from H_2/CO_2, acetate and methanol for the cell synthesis have not been fully analyzed especially for the initial stage of acetyl-CoA synthesis. A conceptual model of carbon assimilation during growth is shown in Figure 22 [170]. When starting from acetate, the acetate is converted to acetyl-phosphate by acetate kinase and then to acetyl-CoA by phosphotransacetylase [168] or convert directly to acetyl-CoA by acetate thiokinase [167]. Second, in the case of methanol, methyl-B_{12} (see Figure 21) seems to be responsible for the reversible production of acetyl-CoA by

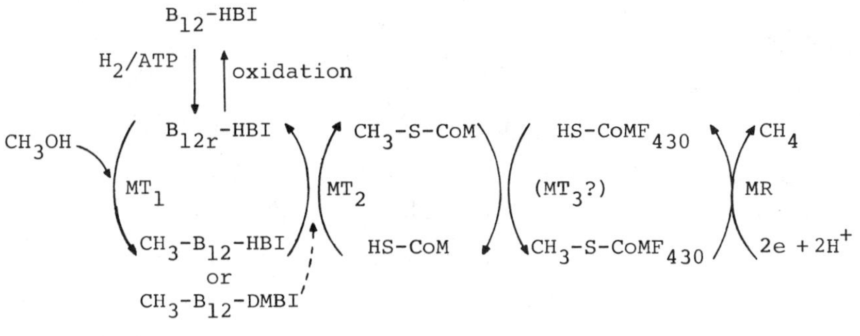

Figure 21. Proposed reaction sequence of the conversion of methanol to methane by *Methanosarcina barkeri*.

MT_1 = Methanol: B_{12r}-HBI methyltransferase;

MT_2 = CH_3-B_{12}-HBI: HS-CoM methyltransferase;

MT_3 = CH_3-S-CoM: HS-$CoMF_{430}$ methyltransferase; and

MR = CH_3-S-$CoMF_{430}$ methylreductase.

(Reprinted with permission from Ref. [171].)

carbon monoxide dehydrogenase (see Figure 20). Finally, when started from H_2/CO_2, although it is still obscure how acetyl-CoA is synthesized from CO_2, an assimilation pathway is proposed (see Figure 23) [173] in which one of two CO_2 is activated to CH_3-pterin and the other to bound carbon monoxide, then these are combined and finally converted to acetyl-CoA.

Further, pyruvate is produced by CO_2 condensation with acetyl-CoA, followed by oxaloacetate formation. Other interesting features for the synthesis of oxoglutarate (C_5) are that, *M. barkeri* [174] produces it via citrate and iso-citrate, whereas, *M. thermoautotrophicum* [175] does it via malate, fumarate, and succinate, indicating that the unification of the both pathways can create the so-called TCA cycle (see Figure 22).

KINETICS ON GROWTH AND SUBSTRATE—UPTAKE

Any sorts of microorganism exponentially growing on a given nutritional medium can be defined as follows.

$$dX/dt = \mu X \tag{1}$$

where X = cell mass concentration, g/*l*
μ = specific growth rate, 1/h
t = time, h

In most cases, specific growth rate can expressed as a function of a growth limiting substrate, so-called Monod equation.

$$\mu \equiv \frac{1}{X}\frac{dX}{dt} = \frac{\mu_m S}{K_s + S} \tag{2}$$

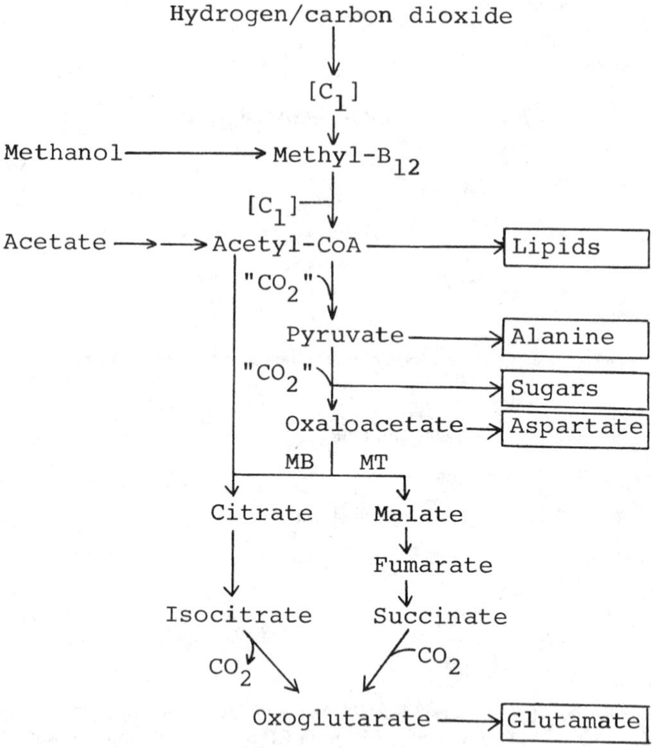

Figure 22. A proposed model for cell carbon synthesis in *Methanosarcina barkeri* (MB) and *Methanobacterium thermoautotrophicum* (MT). (Reprinted with permission from Ref. [170].)

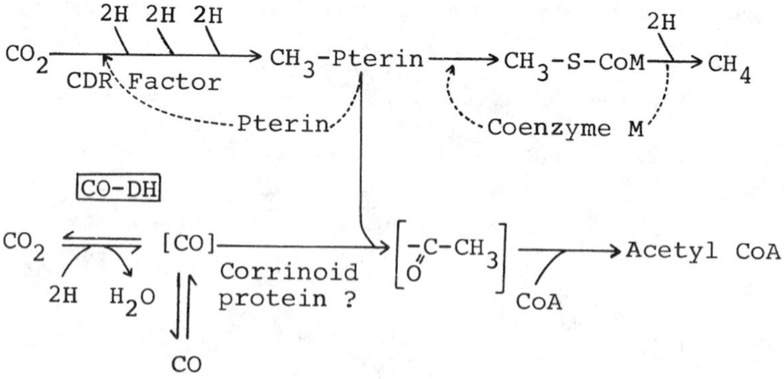

Figure 23. Proposed pathway of synthesis of activated acetic acid from two CO_2 in *Methano-bacterium thermoautotrophicum*. CDR Factor, carbon dioxide reducing factor; CoM, coenzyme M; CO-DH, carbon monoxide dehydrogenase; [CO], bound carbon monoxide. (Reprinted with permission from Ref. [173].)

where μ_m = maximum μ, l/h
K_s = saturation constant, mol/l
S = substrate concentration, mol/l

Growth yield from the substrate consumed is defined as

$$Y_{X/S} = dX/dS \tag{3}$$

where, $Y_{X/S}$ = growth yield from substrate, g/mol

Then combining Equation 3 with Equation 2, one obtains that

$$v \equiv \frac{1}{X}\frac{dS}{dt} = \frac{1}{Y_{X/S}}\frac{\mu_m S}{K_s + S} = \frac{v_m S}{K_s + S} \tag{4}$$

where v = specific substrate utilization rate, mol/g/h
v_m = maximum $v = \mu_m/Y_{X/S}$, mol/g/h

Growth yield, $Y_{X/S}$ does not always take a constant value, but also becomes "variable" as a function of environmental factors.

Kinetic Parameters in Hydrolysis and Acidogenesis

The anaerobic degradation of urban refuse, cellulose as a major component, is important to energy fuel recovery and pollution reduction. However, kinetic studies on hydrolysis and acidogenesis from carbohydrate polymers have been poorly reported. Some available data are summarized in Table 12, which indicates that from hydrolysis of cellulose and starch, further H_2, acetate, ethanol and lactate are mainly produced as the common end products. And specific growth rates observed from starch and pectin media are considerably higher than those of a cellulose medium, suggesting that cellulose hydrolysis which cellulases is more difficult than starch hydrolysis.

Another example (see Table 13) [176] is the acidogenic fermentation of orange peel, which mainly consists of soluble sugars (sucrose, glucose, fructose) and pectin. In semi-continuous cultures with mixed microorganisms, a considerably high μ_m 0.2 l/h was attained with $Y_{X/S}$ values between 0.11 and 0.16 g/g, and methane production was completely ceased by a relatively short retention time (5–10 h), suggesting that the initially existing methanogens had been almost completely eliminated from the fermentor (176]. The end-products were typical acidogenic products, mainly acetate with formic, propionic and butyric acids. Based on the results obtained in rapid acidogenic fermentation, a two-phase anaerobic digestions, i.e., acidogenesis and methanogenesis, may be realized. However, the problem in acidogenic fermentation is how to avoid the severe inhibitory effect of the produced volatile fatty acids on the microbial activities in this fermentation.

For example, when the influent concentration of glucose was increased from 10 to 380 mmol/l in a model experiment of acidogenic fermentation, the bacterial growth was drastically decreased from 0.52 to 0.05 l/h in terms of specific growth rate [177]. This inhibition is due to the produced volatile acids [178, 179] and further studies point out that the undissociated fatty acids, rather than the dissociated ones [180–182] cease bacterial growth.

Besides the inhibitory effect of volatile fatty acid on bacterial growth, a high concentration of substrate, e.g. glucose, inhibits the growth. This can be expressed by the Haldane equation [183–185].

$$\mu = \frac{\mu_m S}{K_s + S + S^2/Ki} \tag{5}$$

where, Ki = substrate-inhibition constant, mol/l

Table 12
Kinetic Data in Hydrolysis and Acidogenesis

Microorganism	Temp. (°C)	pH	Carbon Source	Product								Degradation (mg/l/h)	μ (l/h)	$Y_{X/S}$ (g/mol hexose)	Ref.
				H_2	CO_2	Acetate	Methanol	Ethanol	Lactate	Formate	Butyrate				
Clostridium thermocellum	65	7.4	Cellulose powder	1.1	1.5	0.6		1.0	0.3	0.2		470			60
	65	6.8		2.4	1.8	1.2		0.6	0.2	nd		48			
						(mmol/mol glucose fermented)									
Lachnospira multiparus	35		Pectin	1.6	17.2	12.0 (mmol/*l*)	5.5	1.3	2.1	3.4			0.37		65
Acetivibrio cellulolyticus	35	6.8	Cellulose powder	16.6	2.1	0.5		0.8							55
						(mmol/mol glucose fermented)									
Clostridium cellulovorans	37	7.0	Cellulose powder	1.5	1.6	0.5			0.3	1.0	1.8	19			58
						(mmol/mol cellobiose fermented)									
Clostridium thermosulfurogenes	60	4.3	Starch	24.4	43.9	15.9 (mmol/*l*)		28.0	6.6				0.46		63
Clostridium thermohydrosulfuricum	65	6.1	Starch	4.3	64.0	10.0 (mmol/*l*)		5.4	13.0				0.17		63
Clostridium cellulolyticum	37	7.0	Cellulose MN 300			15.0 (mmol/*l*)		4.0	100.0				0.03	36.2	57

Table 13
Steady State Data in Anaerobic Acidogenic Fermentation of Mandarin Orange Peel [176]

				Volatile Materials (g/l)						Gas Evolved	
μ (l/h)	X (g/l)	Peel Residue (g/l)	$Y_{X/S}$ (g/g)	Formic Acid	Acetic Acid	Propionic Acid	Butyric Acid	Methanol	Ethanol	Total Gas (m/l)	H_2/CO_2
0.01	3.6	2.4	0.15	0.0	5.5	1.5	1.9	0.3	0.7	129	1.2
0.03	3.5	3.5	0.15	0.1	5.8	1.4	1.8	0.3	0.9	83	1.5
0.04	3.8	3.6	0.16	2.1	5.8	0.8	1.8	0.5	0.8	59	1.8
0.06	3.2	4.9	0.14	2.1	6.2	0.8	1.2	0.2	0.7	72	14.1
0.08	3.0	5.0	0.14	2.5	6.8	0.3	0.8	0.2	0.6	34	21.6
0.10	2.9	5.0	0.13	2.7	6.6	0.2	0.7	0.2	0.8	27	27.8
0.12	2.7	5.8	0.13	3.1	6.2	0.2	0.4	0.2	0.8	27	40.9
0.16	2.2	7.5	0.11	3.2	3.8	0.1	0.0	0.1	0.7	18	nd
0.20	2.0	9.3	0.11	3.2	2.8	0.0	0.0	0.2	0.7	10	nd

Peel concentration in fresh medium: 27 g/l; pH, 8. nd; not determined.

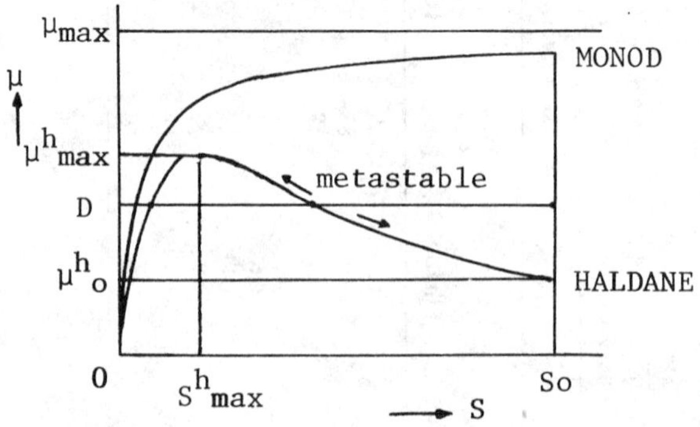

Figure 24. Haldane kinetics for inhibitory substrate. For pure Haldane kinetics, the multiple steady-state region lies between μ^h_{max} and μ^h_0; the lower boundary depends on So.

Figure 24 indicates how a high concentration of substrate inhibits bacterial growth according to Equation 5. As an example, *Propionibacterium shermanii* growing on a glucose medium producing acetic and propionic acids is shown in Figure 25 [180]. Other data analyzed by Equation 5 described mixed acidogenic microorganisms growing on a glucose medium with the results being $\mu_m = 1.16$ 1/h, $K_s = 8.3$ mmol/*l* and $K_i = 27$ mmol/*l* [177].

For the product inhibition on the growth, a general expression of a noncompetitive inhibition model is considered [180, 186–188].

$$\mu = \frac{\mu_m S}{(K_s + S)[1 + (P/K_p)^n]} \tag{6}$$

where n = exponent of inhibition,
P = product concentration, mol/*l*
K_p = product-inhibition constant, mol/*l*

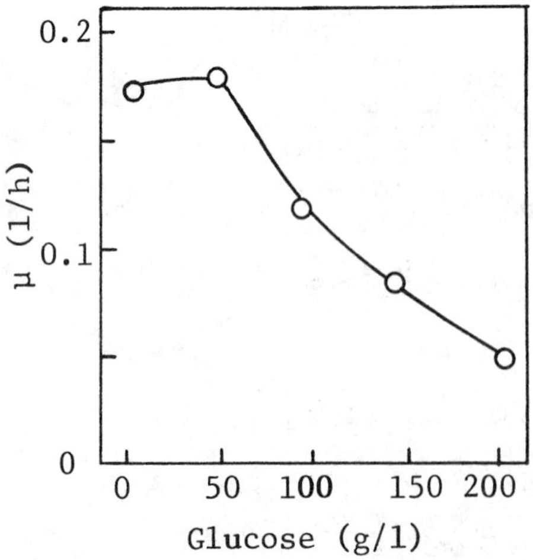

Figure 25. Effects of glucose concentration on growth rate of *Propionibacterium shermanii*. pH, 6.8 and temperature 30°C. (Reprinted with permission from Ref. [180].)

When n = 1, it becomes [186]

$$\mu = \frac{\mu_m S}{(K_s + S)(1 + P/K_p)} \tag{7}$$

In a case of $S \gg K_s$ in Equation 6, it becomes [180]

$$\mu = \frac{\mu_m}{1 + (P/K_p)^n} \tag{8}$$

When *Propionibacterium shermanii* grows on a glucose medium, the produced acetic and propionic acids inhibit the growth indicating that for acetic acid, $\mu_m = 0.169$ 1/h, $K_p = 692$ mmol acetic acid/*l* and n = 2, and for propionic acid, $\mu_m = 0.169$ 1/h, $K_p = 2$ mmol undissociated propionic acid/*l* and n = 1. This indicates propionic acid was much more inhibitory than acetic acid [180].

Kinetic Parameters of H_2-Producing Acetogens

As mentioned, fatty acid-decomposing bacteria are important for providing acetic acid and H_2 for methanogens. Kinetic parameters available from the published reports are few because of technical difficulties for the pure cultivation. Table 14 shows the data available concerned. Specific growth rates observed in Table 14 are considerably low compared with usual heterotrophic bacteria (e.g., 0.1–1.0 1/h).

Kinetic Parameters of Methanogens

Recent progress for the microbiological technologies enabled to isolate the pure culture of methanogen. Table 15 summarizes the available data for methanogens. Although several thermophilic methanogens have high growth rate, i.e., *M. thermoautotrophicum* (65°C, $\mu = 0.69$), *M. fervidus* (83°C, $\mu = 0.25$), *M. jannaschii* (85°C, $\mu = 1.60$), *M. thermolithotrophicus* (65°C, $\mu = 0.75$), the specific growth rates of methanogens are relatively low ranging from 10^{-3} to 10^{-2} 1/h compared with usual heterotrophic bacteria (e.g. 0.1–1.0 1/h). However, specific consumption rates of substrate, e.g. 10^{-3} to 10^{-2} mol/g cell/h for acetate and 10^{-2} mol/g cell/h for methanol are not so much different compared with aerobically grown cells on the same substrates, suggesting that the most part of substrate consumed by methanogens are metabolized catabolically to produce methane and CO_2, not anabolism to cell synthesis.

In aceticlastic methanogens, i.e., *Methanosarcina* spp. and *Methanothrix* spp., *Methanothrix* spp. will predominate in low concentration of acetate as it has a high affinity (and thus a small K_s) for acetate (0.3–0.7) compared with that in *Methanosarcina* spp. (4.5–5). At high acetate concentration, however, the comparison of the kinetic parameters (μ and v) of *Methanosarcina* spp. and *Methanothrix* spp. shows that probably the former may become dominant.

Acknowledgment

The authors thank Mr. Tsuyoshi Morinaga, Manager of Research Center, Daicel Chemical Industries Ltd., for his devotion in the preparation of Tables 8 and 9.

REFERENCES

1. Zeikus, J. G., "Chemical and Fuel Production by Anaerobic Bacteria," *Ann. Rev. Microbiol.*, 34, 423 (1980).
2. Hobson, P. N., Bousfield, S., and Summers, R., "Anaerobic Digestion of Organic Matter," *CRC Critical Reviews in Environmental Control*, 1974, p. 131.

Table 14
Growth Kinetics of Obligate H_2-Producing Acetogens in Co-Culture or Enrichment Culture

Microorganism	Co-Culture with	Substrate	μ (l/h)	K_s (μmol/l)	v (mol/g/h)	$Y_{X/S}$ (g/mol)	Ref.
Syntrophobacter wolinii	*Desulfovibrio* spp.	Propionate	0.0079				84
Syntrophobacter wolinii	*Methanospirillum hungatei*	Propionate	0.0042				
Syntrophomonas wolfei	*Methanospirillum hungatei*	Butyrate	0.0083				85
Mesophilic enrichment cultures		Butyrate	0.015	57			189
		Propionate	0.017	432			
Mesophilic sludge digestor		Propionate	0.0054	149			190
		Propionate	0.05	4460			
Thermophilic butyrate-utilizing bacterium	*Methanobacterium thermoautotrophicum* + Thermophilic acetate-utilizing methanogen (TAM organism)	Butyrate	0.032	76	0.006	1.5	191

Table 15
Growth Kinetics of Pure Methanogenic Cultures

Microorganism	Substrate	μ (l/h)	K_s (mmol/l)	v (mol/g/h)	$Y_{X/S}$ (g/mol)	Ref.
Methanobacterium formicicum JF-1	H_2/CO_2	0.082				104
	Formate	0.055		0.05	1.17	
Methanobacterium formicicum MF	Formate	0.08	3.5	0.057	1.4	192
Methanobrevibacter arboriphilus	H_2/CO_2	0.012	0.005	0.12	0.61	193
Methanobacterium thermoautotrophicum	H_2/CO_2	0.69	$K_{H_2} = 20\%$ $K_{CO_2} = 11\%$	0.43 (from $v = \mu/Y_{X/S}$)	1.6	194
Thermophiric acetate-utilizing methanogen (TAM)	Acetate	0.032	0.8	0.019 (from $v = \mu/Y_{X/S}$)	1.7	191
Methanothrix spp.	Acetate	0.022	0.3			136
Methanothrix soehngenii	Acetate	0.008	0.7	0.0016	1.1–1.4	135
Methanosarcina spp. strain 227	Acetate	0.01–0.02	5	0.0091	2.1	195
	Methanol	0.06		0.016 (from $v = \mu/Y_{X/S}$)	3.8	
Methanosarcina spp. strain TM-1	Acetate	0.058	4.5	0.032	1.8	196
	Methanol	0.069–0.099		0.02–0.029 (from $v = \mu/Y_{X/S}$)	3.4	
Methanothermus fervidus	H_2/CO_2	0.25				114
Methanococcus jannaschii	H_2/CO_2	1.60				121
Methanococcus thermolithotrophicus	H_2/CO_2	0.75				119

3. Hungate, R. E., *The Rumen and Its Microbes*, Acad. Press, New York, 1966, p. 67.
4. Barker, H. A., *Bacterial Fermentations*, John Wiley & Sons Inc., New York, 1956, p. 1.
5. Bryant, M. P., Wolin, E. A., Wolin, M. J., and Wolfe, R. S., "*Methanobacillus omelianskii*, A Symbiotic Association of Two Species of Bacteria," *Arch. Microbiol.*, 59, 20 (1967).
6. Bryant, M. P., Campbell, L. L., Reddy, C. A., and Crabill, M. R., "Growth of *Desulfovibrio* in Lactate or Ethanol Media Low in Sulfate in Association with H_2-Utilizing Methanogenic Bacteria," *Appl. Environ. Microbiol.*, 33, 1162 (1977).
7. McCarty, P. L., "One Hundred Years of Anaerobic Treatment," *Anaerobic Digestion* 1981 (D. E. Hughes et al., eds.), Elsevier Biomedical Press B.V., Amsterdam, 1982, p. 3.
8. Stronach, S. M., Rudd, T., and Lester, J. N., *Anaerobic Digestion Process in Industrial Wastewater Treatment*, Springer-Verlag, Berlin, Heidelberg, 1986, p. 2.
9. Scott, R., *Rennets and Cheese, Topics in Enzyme and Fermentation Biotechnology* 3 (A. Wiseman, ed.), Ellis Horwood, Chichester, 1979, p. 101.
10. Hobson, P. N., Production of Biogas from Agricultural Waste, *Advances in Agricultural Microbiology* (N. S. Subba Rao, ed.), Butterworth Scientific, London, 1982, p. 523.
11. Toerien, D. F., "Enrichment Culture Studies on Aerobic and Facultative Anaerobic Bacteria Found in Anaerobic Digesters," *Water Res.*, 1, 147 (1967).
12. Kotzé, J. P., Thiel, P. G., and Hattingh, W. H. J., "Anaerobic Digestion II. The Characterization and Control of Anaerobic Digestion," *Water Res.*, 3, 459 (1969).
13. Wallace, R. J., and Brammall, M. L., "The Role of Different Species of Bacteria in the Hydrolysis of Protein in the Rumen," *J. Gen. Microbiol.*, 131, 821 (1985).
14. Blackburn, T. H., and Hobson, P. N., "Further Studies on the Isolation of Proteolytic Bacteria from the Sheep Rumen," *J. Gen. Microbiol.*, 29, 69 (1962).
15. Fulghum, R. S., and Moore, W. E. C., "Isolation, Enumeration and Characteristics of Proteolytic Ruminal Bacteria," *J. Bacteriol.*, 85, 808 (1963).
16. Hungate, R. E., *The Rumen and Its Microbes*, Academic Press, New York, 1966.
17. Siebert, M. L., and Toerien, D. F., "The Proteolytic Bacteria Present in the Anaerobic Digestion of Raw Sewage Sludge," *Water Res.*, 3, 241 (1969).
18. Nagase, M., and Matsuo, T., "Interactions between Amino Acid-Degrading Bacteria and Methanogenic Bacteria in Anaerobic Digestion," *Biotech. Bioeng.*, 24, 2227 (1982).
19. Elsden, S. R., and Hilton, M. G., "Volatile Acid Production from Threonine, Valine, Leucine, and Isoleucine by *Clostridia*," *Arch. Microbiol.*, 117, 165 (1978).
20. Poston, J. M., "Leucine 2,3-Aminomutase, an Enzyme of Leucine Catabolism," *J. Biol. Chem.*, 251, 1859 (1976).
21. Barker, H. A., "Amino Acid Degradation by Anaerobic Bacteria," *Ann. Rev. Biochem.*, 50, 23 (1981).
22. Dyer, J. K., and Costilow, R. N., "Fermentation of Ornithine by *Clostridium sticklandii*," *J. Bacteriol.*, 96, 1617 (1968).
23. Elsden, S. R., Hilton, M. G., and Waller, J. M., "The End Products of the Metabolism of Aromatic Amino Acids by *Clostridia*," *Arch. Microbiol.*, 107, 283 (1976).
24. Nanninga, H. J., Drent, W. J., and Gottschal, J. C., "Fermentation of Glutamate by *Selenomonas acidaminophila* sp. nov.," *Arch. Microbiol.*, 147, 152 (1987).
25. Stadtman, T. C., "Lysine Metabolism by *Clostridia*," *Adv. Enzymol.*, 38, 413 (1973).
26. Halliwell, G., "Microbial β-Glucanases," *Prog. Ind. Microbiol.*, 15, 1 (1979).
27. Reese, E. T., "Summary Statement on the Enzyme System," *Biotechnol. Bioeng. Symp.*, 5, 77 (1975).
28. Wood, T. M., "Properties and Mode of Action of Cellulases," *Biotechnol. Bioeng. Symp.*, 5, 111 (1975).
29. Ensley, B., McHugh, J. L., and Barton, L. L., "Effect of Carbon Sources on Formation of α-Amylase and Glucoamylase by *Clostridium acetobutyricum*," *J. Gen. Appl. Microbiol.*, 21, 51 (1975).
30. French, D., and Knapp, D. W., "The Maltase of *Clostridium acetobutylicum* Its Specificity Range and Mode of Action," *J. Biol. Chem.*, 187, 463 (1950).
31. Hobson, P. N., and MacPherson, M., "Amylases of *Clostridium butyricum* and *Streptococcus* Isolated from the Rumen of the Sheep," *Biochem. J.*, 52, 671 (1952).

32. McWethy, S. J., and Hartman, P. A., "Purification and Some Properties of an Extracellular Alpha-Amylase from *Bacteroides amylophilus*," *J. Bacteriol.*, 129, 1537 (1977).
33. Nakamura, L. K., and Crowell, C. D., "*Lactobacillus amylophilus*, a New Starch-Hydrolyzing Species from Swine Waste-Corn Fermentation," *Dev. Ind. Microbiol.*, 20, 531 (1979).
34. Rexova-Benkova, L., and MarKovic, O., "Pectic Enzymes," *Adv. Carbohydr. Chem. Biochem.*, 33, 323 (1976).
35. Wood, T. M., Wilson, C. A., and Stewart, C. S., "Preparation of the Cellulase from the Cellulolytic Anaerobic Rumen Bacterium *Rumicococcus albus* and Its Release from the Bacterial Cell Wall," *Biochem. J.*, 205, 129 (1982).
36. Lee, B. H., and Blackburn, T. H., "Cellulase Production by a Thermophilic *Clostridium* Species," *Appl. Microbiol.*, 30, 346 (1975).
37. Mackenzie, C. R., Bilous D., and Patel, G. B., "Studies on Cellulose Hydrolysis by *Acetivibrio cellulolyticus*," *Appl. Environ. Microbiol.*, 50, 243 (1985).
38. Giuliano, C., and Khan, A. W., "Conversion of Cellulose to Sugars by Resting Cells of a Mesophilic Anaerobe, *Bacteroides cellulosolvens*," *Biotechnol. Bioeng.*, 27, 980 (1985).
39. Madden, R. H., "Isolation and Characterization of *Clostridium stercorarium* Sp. Nov., Cellulolytic Thermophile," *Int. J. Syst. Bacteriol.*, 33, 837 (1983).
40. Hobson, P. N., and Shaw, B. G., "The Bacterial Population of Piggery Waste Digesters," *Water Res.*, 8, 507 (1974).
41. van Assche, P. F., "Microbiological Aspects of Anaerobic Digestion," *Antonie van Leeuwenhoek*, 48, 520 (1982).
42. Schink, B., and Zeikus, J. G., "*Clostridium thermosulfurogens* Sp. Nov., a New Thermophile that Produces Elemental Sulphur from Thiosulphate," *J. Gen. Microbiol.*, 129, 1149 (1983).
43. Zeikus, J. G., Ben-Bassat, A., and Hegge, P. W., "Microbiology of Methanogenesis in Thermal, Volcanic Environments," *J. Bacteriol.*, 143, 432 (1980).
44. Lee, M., Miller, L., and Macmillan, J. D., "Similarities in the Action Patterns of Exopolygalacturonate Lyase and Pectinase from *Clostridium multifermentans*," *J. Bacteriol.*, 103, 595 (1970).
45. Wiegel, J., Mothershed, C. P., and Puls, J., "Differences in Xylan Degradation by Various Noncellulolytic Thermophilic Anaerobes and *Clostridium thermocellum*," *Appl. Environ. Microbiol.*, 49, 656 (1985).
46. Doelle, W. H., *Bacteriol Metabolism* (2nd ed.) Academic Press, New York, 1975, p. 738.
47. Schlegel, H. G., *General Microbiology*, Cambridge University Press, Cambridge, 1986.
48. Welty, F. K., and Wood, H. G., "Purification of the "Corrinoid" Enzyme Involved in the Synthesis of Acetate by *Clostridium thermoaceticum*," *J. Biol. Chem.*, 253, 5832 (1978).
49. Miller, T. L., "The Pathway of Formation of Acetate and Succinate from Pyruvate by *Bacteroides succinogenes*," *Arch. Microbiol.*, 117, 145 (1978).
50. Johns, A. T., "The Mechanism of Propionic Acid Formation by Propionibacteria," *J. Gen. Microbiol.*, 5, 337 (1951).
51. Leaver, F. W., Wood, H. G., and Stjernholm, R., "The Fermentation of Three Carbon Substrates by *Clostridium propionicum* and *Propionibacterium*," *J. Bacteriol.*, 70, 521 (1955).
52. Wood, H. G., and Stjernholm, R., "Transcarboxylase, II. Purification and Properties of Methylmalonyl-Oxaloacetic Transcarboxylase," *Proc. Natl. Acad. Sci. U.S.A.* 47, 289 (1961).
53. DeMoss, R. D., "Routes of Ethanol Formation in Bacteria," *J. Cell Comp. Physiol.*, 41, 207 (1955).
54. Canale-Porola, E., "Biology of the Sugar-fermenting Sarcinae," *Bacteriol. Rev.*, 34, 82 (1970).
55. Laube, V. M., and Martin, S. M., "Conversion of Cellulose to Methane and Carbon Dioxide by Triculture of *Acetivibrio cellulolyticus*, *Desulfovibrio* Sp., and *Methanosarcina barkeri*," *Appl. Environ. Microbiol.*, 42, 413 (1981).
56. van Andel, J. G., Zoutberg, G. R., Crabbendam, P. M., and Breure, A. M., "Glucose Fermentation by *Clostridium butyricum* Grown Under a Self Generated Gas Atmosphere in Chemostat Culture," *Appl. Microbiol. Biotechnol.*, 23, 21 (1985).
57. Giallo, J., Gaudin, C., and Belaich, J.-P., "Metabolism and Solubilization of Cellulose by *Clostridium cellulolyticum* HlO," *Appl. Environ. Microbiol.*, 49, 1216 (1985).

58. Sleat, R., Mah, R. A., and Robinson, R., "Isolation and Characterization of an Anaerobic, Cellulolytic Bacterium, *Clostridium cellulovorans* Sp. Nov.," *Appl. Environ. Microbiol.*, 48, 88 (1984).
59. Montiville, T. J., Parris, N., and Conway, L. K., "Influence of pH on Organic Acid Production by *Clostridium sporogenes* in Test Tube and Fermentor Cultures," *Appl. Environ. Microbiol.*, 49, 733 (1985).
60. Ruyet, P. L., Dubourguier, H. C., and Albagnac, G., "Homoacetogenic Fermentation of Cellulose by a Coculture of *Clostridium thermocellum* and *Acetogenium kivui*," *Appl. Environ. Microbiol.*, 48, 893 (1984).
61. Bender, J., Vatcharapijarn, Y., and Jeffries, T. W., "Characteristics and Adaptability of Some New Isolates of *Clostridium thermocellum*," *Appl. Environ. Microbiol.*, 49, 475 (1985).
62. Weimer, P. J., and Zeikus, J. G., "Fermentation of Cellulose and Cellobiose by *Clostridium thermocellum* in Presence of *Methanobacterium thermoautotrophicum*," *Appl. Environ. Microbiol.*, 33, 289 (1977).
63. Hyun, H. H., and Zeikus, J. G., "Simultaneous and Enhanced Production of Thermostable Amylases and Ethanol from Starch by Cocultures of *Clostridium thermosulfurogenes* and *Clostridium thermohydrosulfuricum*," *Appl. Environ. Microbiol.*, 49, 1174 (1985).
64. Müller, E., Fahlbusch, K., Walther, R., and Gottschalk, G., "Formation of N,N-dimethylglycine, Acetic Acid, and Butyric Acid from Betaine by *Eubacterium limosum*," *Appl. Environ. Microbiol.*, 42, 439, (1981).
65. Rode, L. M., Genthner, B. R. S., and Bryant, M. P., "Syntrophic Association by Cocultures of the Methanol- and CO_2-H_2-Utilizing Species *Eubacterium limosum* and Pectin-Fermenting *Lachnospira multiparus* During Growth in a Pectin Medium," *Appl. Environ. Microbiol.*, 42, 20 (1981).
66. Datta, R., and Zeikus, J. G., "Modulation of Acetone-Butanol-Ethanol Fermentation by Carbon Monoxide and Organic Acids," *Appl. Environ. Microbiol.*, 49, 522 (1985).
67. Bahl, H., Andersch, W., and Gottschalk, G., "Continuous Production of Acetone and Butanol by *Clostridium acetobutylicum* in a Two-Stage Phosphate-Limited Chemostat," *Eur. J. Appl. Microbiol. Biotechnol.*, 15, 201 (1982).
68. Varel, V. H., Fryda, S. J., and Robinson, I. M., "Cellulolytic Bacteria from Pig Large Intestine," *Appl. Environ. Microbiol.*, 47, 219 (1984).
69. Ng, T. K., Ben-Bassat, A., and Zeikus, J. G., "Ethanol Production by Thermophilic Bacteria: Fermentation of Cellulosic Substrates by Cocultures by *Clostridium thermocellum* and *Clostridium thermohydrosulfuricum*," *Appl. Environ. Microbiol.*, 41, 1337 (1981).
70. Kelly, W. J., Asmundson, R. V., and Hopcroft, D. H., "Isolation and Characterization of a Strictly Anaerobic, Cellulolytic Spore Former: *Clostridium chartatabidum* Sp. Nov.," *Arch. Microbiol.*, 147, 169 (1987).
71. Andreesen, J. R., Gottschalk, G., and Schlegel, H. G., "*Clostridium formicoaceticum* Nov. Spec. Isolation, Description, and Distinction from *C. aceticum* and *C. thermoaceticum*," *Arch. Microbiol.*, 72, 154 (1970).
72. Devries, W., van Wyck-Kapteyn, W. M. C., van der Beek, E. G., and Stouthamer, A. H., "Molar Growth Yields and Fermentation Balances of *Lactobacillus casei* L3 in Batch Cultures and in Continuous Cultures," *J. Gen. Microbiol.*, 63, 333 (1970).
73. Lamed, R., and Zeikus, J. G., "Glucose Fermentation Pathway of *Thermoanaerobium brockii*," *J. Bacteriol.*, 141, 1251 (1980).
74. Healy, J. B., Jr., and Young, L. Y., "Anaerobic Biodegradation of Eleven Aromatic Compounds to Methane," *Appl. Environ. Microbiol.*, 38, 84 (1979).
75. Healy, J. B., Jr., Young, L. Y., and Reinhard, M., "Methanogenic Decomposition of Ferulic Acid, a Model Lignin Derivative," *Appl. Environ. Microbiol.*, 39, 436 (1980).
76. Kaiser, J. P., and Hanselmann, K., "Fermentative Metabolism of Substituted Monoaromatic Compounds by a Bacterial Community from Anaerobic Sediments," *Arch. Microbiol.*, 133, 185 (1983).
77. Benner, R., and Hodson, R., "Thermophilic Anaerobic Biodegradation of [^{14}C]Lignin, [^{14}C]Cellulose, and [^{14}C]Ligno-Cellulose Preparations," *Appl. Environ. Microbiol.*, 50, 971 (1985).

78. Colberg, P. J., and Young, L. Y., "Biodegradation of Lignin-Derived Molecules under Anaerobic Conditions," *Can. J. Microbiol.*, 28, 886 (1982).
79. Colberg, P. J., and Young, L. Y., "Aromatic and Volatile Acid Intermediates Observed During Anaerobic Metabolism of Lignin-Derived Oligomers," *Appl. Environ. Microbiol.*, 49, 350 (1985).
80. Chen, W., Ohmiya, K., and Shimizu, S., "Protoplast Formation and Regeneration of Dehydrovanillin-Degrading Strains of *Fusobacterium varium* and *Enterococcus faecium*," *Appl. Environ. Microbiol.*, 52, 612 (1986).
81. Hungate, R. E., and Stack, R. T., "Phenylpropionic Acid: Growth Factor for *Ruminococcus albus*," *Appl. Environ. Microbiol.*, 44, 79 (1982).
82. Borneman, W. S., Akin, D. E., and van Eseltine, W. P., "Effects of Phenolic Monomers on Rumen Bacteria," *Appl. Environ. Microbiol.*, 52, 1331 (1986).
83. Khan, A. W., "Anaerobic Degradation of Cellulose by Mixed Culture," *Can. J. Microbiol.*, 23, 1700 (1977).
84. Boone, D. R., and Bryant, M. P., "Propionate-Degrading Bacterium, *Syntrophobacter wolinii* Sp. Nov. Gen. Nov., from Methanogenic Ecosystems," *Appl. Environ. Microbiol.*, 40, 626 (1980).
85. McInerney, M. J., Bryant, M. P., Hespell, R. B., and Costerton, J. W., "*Syntrophomonas wolfei* Gen. Nov. Sp. Nov., an Anaerobic, Syntrophic, Fatty Acid-Oxidizing Bacterium," *Appl. Environ. Microbiol.*, 41, 1029 (1981).
86. Reddy, C. A., Bryant, M. P., and Wolin, M. J., "Characteristics of S Organism Isolated from *Methanobacillus omelianskii*," *J. Bacteriol.*, 109, 539 (1972).
87. Yang, S., Tang, I., and Okos, M. R., "Kinetics of Homoacetic Fermentation of Lactate by *Clostridium formicoaceticum*," *Appl. Environ. Microbiol.*, 53, 823 (1987).
88. Wieringa, K. T., "Over het Verdwijnen van Waterstofen Koolzuur onder Anaerobe Voorwaarden," *Antonie van Leeuwenhoek, J. Microbiol. Serol.*, 3, 263 (1936).
89. Balch. W. E., Schoberth, S., Tanner, R. S., and Wolfe, R. S., "*Acetobacterium*, a New Genus of Hydrogen-Oxidizing, Carbon Oxidize-Reducing, Anaerobic Bacteria," *Int. J. Syst. Bacteriol.*, 27, 355 (1977).
90. Braun, M., Mayer, F., and Gottschalk, G., "*Clostridium aceticum* (Wieringa), a Microorganism Producing Acetic Acid from Molecular Hydrogen and Carbon Dioxide," *Arch. Microbiol.*, 128, 288 (1981).
91. Kerby, R., and Zeikus, J. G., "Growth of *Clostridium thermoaceticum* on H_2/CO_2 or CO as Energy Source," *Curr. Microbiol.*, 8, 27 (1983).
92. Wiegel, J., Braun, M., and Gottschalk, G., "*Clostridium thermoautotrophicum* Species Novum, a Thermophile Producing Acetate from Molecular Hydrogen and Carbon Dioxide," *Curr. Microbiol.*, 5, 255 (1981).
93. Braun, M., and Gottschalk, G., "*Acetobacterium wieringae* Sp. Nov., a New Species Producing Acetic Acid from Molecular Hydrogen and Carbon Dioxide," *Zbl. Bakt. Hyg., I. Abt. Orig. C3*, 368 (1982).
94. Eichler, B., and Schink, B., "Oxidation of Primary Aliphatic Alcohols by *Acetobacterium carbinolicum* Sp. Nov., a Homoacetogenic Anaerobe," *Arch. Microbiol.*, 140, 147 (1984).
95. Leigh, J. A., Mayer, F., and Wolfe, R. S., "*Acetogenium kivui*, a New Thermophilic Hydrogen-Oxidizing Acetogenic Bacterium," *Arch. Microbiol.*, 129, 275 (1981).
96. Möller, B., Ossmer, R., Howard, B. H., Gottschalk, G., and Hippe, H., "*Sporomusa*, a New Genus of Gram Negative Anaerobic Bacteria Including *Sporomusa sphaeroides* Spec. Nov. and *Sporomusa ovata* Spec. Nov.," *Arch. Microbiol.*, 139, 388 (1984).
97. Ollivier, B., Cordruwisch, R., Lambardo, A., and Garcia, J. -L., "Isolation and Characterization of *Sporomusa acidovorans* Sp. Nov., a Methylotrophic Homoacetogenic Bacterium," *Arch. Microbiol.*, 142, 307 (1985).
98. Lynd, L. H., and Zeikus, J. G., "Metabolism of H_2—CO_2, Methanol, and Glucose by *Butyribacterium methylotrophicum*," *J. Bacteriol.*, 153, 1415 (1983).
99. Thauer, R. K., Jungermann, K., and Decker, K., "Energy Conservation in Chemotrophic Anaerobic Bacteria," *Bact. Rev.*, 41, 100 (1977).
100. Whitman, W. B., "The Archaebacteria," *The Bacteria Vol. 8* (C. R. Woose and R. S. Wolfe, eds.), Academic Press, New York, 1985, p. 3.

101. Daniels, L., Sparling, R., and Sprott, G. D., "The Bioenergetics of Methanogenesis," *Biochim. Biophys. Acta.*, 768, 113 (1984).
102. Hungate, R. E., "The Anaerobic Mesophilic Cellulolytic Bacteria," *Bacteriol. Rev.*, 14, 1 (1950).
103. Hungate, R. E., "A Roll Tube Method for Cultivation of Strict Anaerobes," *Methods in Microbiology, Vol. 3B* (I. R. Norris and D. W. Ribbons, eds.), Academic Press, New York, 1969, p. 117.
104. Schauer, N. L., and Ferry, J. G., "Metabolism of Formate in *Methanobacterium formicicum*," *J. Bacteriol.*, 142, 800 (1980).
105. Godsy, E. M., "Isolation of *Methanobacterium bryantii* from a Deep Aquifer by Using a Novel Broth-Antibiotic Disk Method," *Appl. Environ. Microbiol.*, 39, 1074 (1980).
106. Zeikus, J. G., and Wolfe, R. S., "*Methanobacterium thermoautotrophicum* Sp. Nov., an Anaerobic, Autotrophic, Extreme Thermophile," *J. Bacteriol.*, 109, 707 (1972).
107. Blotevogel, K. H., and Fischer, U., "Isolation and Characterization of a New Thermophilic and Autotrophic Methane Producing Bacterium: *Methanobacterium thermoaggregans* Spec. Nov.," *Arch. Microbiol.*, 142, 218 (1985).
108. Blotevogel, K. H., Fischer, U., Mocha, M., and Jannsen, S., "*Methanobacterium thermoalcaliphilum* Spec. Nov., a New Moderately Alkaliphilic and Thermophilic Autotrophic Methanogen," *Arch. Microbiol.*, 142, 211 (1985).
109. Winter, J., Lerp, C., Zabel, H. P., Wildenauer, F. X., König, H., and Schindler, F., "*Methanobacterium wolfei* Sp. Nov., a New Tungsten-Requiring Thermophilic, Autotrophic Methanogen," *System. Appl. Microbiol.*, 5, 457 (1984).
110. König, H., "Isolation and Characterization of *Methanobacterium uliginosum* Sp. Nov. from a Marshy Soil," *Can. J. Microbiol.*, 30, 1477 (1984).
111. Smith, P. H., and Hungate, R. E., "Isolation and Characterization of *Methanobacterium ruminantium* N. Sp.," *J. Bacteriol.*, 75, 713 (1958).
112. Morii, H., Nishihara, M., and Koga, Y., "Isolation and Characterization and Physiology of a New Formate-Assimilable Methanogenic Strain (A2) of *Methanobrevibacter arboriphilus*," *Agric. Biol. Chem.*, 47, 2781 (1983).
113. Smith, P. H., "Microbiology of Sludge Methanogenesis," *Dev. Ind. Microbiol.*, 7, 156 (1966).
114. Stetter, K. O., Thomm, M., Winter, J., Wildgruber, G., Huber, H., Zillig, W., Janecovic, D., König, H., Palm, P., and Wunderl, S., "*Methanothermus fervidus*, Sp. Nov., a Novel Extremely Thermophilic Methanogen Isolated from an Icelandic Hot Spring," *Zentralhl. Bakteriol. Parasitekd. Infektionskr. Hyg. Abt. 1 Orig. Reihe A, C2*, 166 (1981).
115. Wildgruber, G., Thomm, M., König, H., Ober, K., Ricchiuto, T., and Stetter, K. O., "*Methanoplanus limicola*, a Plate-Shaped Methanogen Representing a Novel Family, the Methanoplanaceae," *Arch. Microbiol.*, 132, 31 (1982).
116. Corder, R. E., Hook, L. A., Larkin, J. M., and Frea, J. I., "Isolation and Characterization of Two New Methane Producing Cocci: *Methanogenium olentangyi*, Sp. Nov., and *Methanococcus deltae*, Sp. Nov.," *Arch. Microbiol.*, 134, 28 (1983).
117. Stadtman, T. C., and Barker, H. A., "Studies on the Methane Fermentation. X. A New Formate-Decomposing Bacterium, *Methanococcus vanielii*," *J. Bacteriol.*, 62, 269 (1951).
118. Whitman, W. B., Ankwanda, E., and Wolfe, R. S., "Nutrition and Carbon Metabolism of *Methanococcus voltae*," *J. Bacteriol.*, 149, 852 (1982).
119. Huber, H., Thomm, M., König, H., Thies, G., and Stetter, K. O., "*Methanococcus thermolithotrophicus*, a Novel Thermophilic Lithotrophic Methanogen," *Arch. Microbiol.*, 132, 47 (1982).
120. Jones, W. J., Paynter, M. J. B., and Gupta, R., "Characterization of *Methanococcus maripaludis* Sp. Nov., a New Methanogen Isolated from Salt Marsh Sediment," *Arch. Microbiol.*, 135, 91 (1983).
121. Jones, W. J., Leigh, J. A., Mayer, F., Woese, C. R., and Wolfe, R. S., "*Methanococcus jannaschi* Sp. Nov., an Extremely Thermophilic Methanogen from a Submarine Hydrothermal Vent," *Arch. Microbiol.*, 136, 254 (1983).
122. Zhilina, T. N., "A New Obligate Halophilic Methane-Producing Bacteria," *Mikrobiologiya 52*, 375 (1983).
123. Paynter, M. J. B., and Hungate, R. E., "Characterization of *Methanobacterium mobilis*, Sp. N., Isolated from the Bovine Rumen," *J. Bacteriol.*, 95, 1943 (1968).

124. Rivard, C. J., Henson, J. M., Thomas, M. V., and Smith, P. H., "Isolation and Characterization of *Methanomicrobium paynteri* Sp. Nov., a Mesophilic Methanogen Isolated from Marine Sediments," *Appl. Environ. Microbiol.*, 46, 484 (1983).
125. Romesser, J. A., Wolfe, R. S., Mayer, F., Spiess, E., and Walther-Mauruschat, "*Methanogenium*, a New Genus of Marine Methanogenic Bacteria, and Characterization of *Methanogenium cariaci* Sp. Nov. and *Methanogenium marisnigri* Sp. Nov.," *Arch. Microbiol.*, 121, 147 (1979).
126. Zabel, H. P., König, H., and Winter, J., "Isolation and Characterization of a New Coccoid Methanogen, *Methanogenium tatii* Spec. Nov. from a Solfataric Field on Mount Tatio," *Arch. Microbiol.*, 137, 308 (1984).
127. Harris, J. E., Pinn, P. A., and Davis, R. P., "Isolation and Characterization of a Novel Thermophilic, Freshwater Methanogen," *Appl. Environ. Microbiol.*, 48, 1123 (1984).
128. Rivard, C. J., and Smith, P. H., "Isolation and Characterization of a Thermophilic Marine Methanogenic Bacterium, *Methanogenium thermophilicum* Sp. Nov.," *Int. J. Syst. Bacteriol.*, 32, 430 (1982).
129. König, H., and Stetter, K. O., "Isolation and Characterization of *Methanolobus tindarius*, Sp. Nov., a Coccoid Methanogen Growing only on Methanol and Methyamines," *System. Appl. Microbiol.*, 3, 478 (1982).
130. Patel, G. B., Roth, L. A., van den Berg, L., and Clark, D. S., "Characterization of a Strain of *Methanospirillum hungatii*," *Can. J. Microbiol.*, 22, 1404 (1976).
131. Mah, R. A., "Isolation and Characterization of *Methanococcus mazei*," *Curr. Microbiol.*, 3, 321 (1980).
132. Bryant, M. P., *Bergey's Manual for Determinative Bacteriology, 8th Ed.*, The Willians and Wilkins, Baltimore, 1974, p. 472.
133. Sowers, K. R., Baron, S. F., and Ferry, J. G., "*Methanosarcina acetivorans* Sp. Nov., an Acetophilic Methane-Producing Bacterium Isolated from Marine Sediments," *Appl. Environ. Microbiol.*, 47, 971 (1984).
134. Zhilina, T. N., Zararzin, G. A., "Comparative Cytology of Methanosarcinae and Description of *Methanosarcina vacuolata* N. Sp.," *Mikrobiologiya*, 48, 279 (1979).
135. Huser, B. A., Wuhrmann, K., and Zehnder, A. J. B., "*Methanothrix soehngenii* Gen. Nov. Sp. Nov., a New Acetotrophic Non-Hydrogen-Oxidizing Methane Bacterium," *Arch. Microbiol.*, 132, 1 (1982).
136. Zinder, S. H., Cardwell, S. C., Anguish, T., Lee, M., and Koch, M., "Methanogenesis in a Thermophilic (58°C) Anaerobic Digestor: *Methanothrix* Sp. as an Important Aceticlastic Methanogen," *Appl. Environ. Microbiol.*, 47, 796 (1984).
137. Patel, G. B., "Characterization and Nutritional Properties of *Methanothrix concilii* Sp. Nov., a Mesophilic, Aceticlastic Methanogen," *Can. J. Microbiol.*, 30, 1383 (1984).
138. Sowers, K. R., and Ferry, J. G., "Isolation and Characterization of a Methylotrophic Marine Methanogen, *Methanococcoides methylutens* Gen. Nov., Sp. Nov., "*Appl. Environ. Microbiol.*, 45, 684 (1983).
139. Zellner, G., Alten, C., Stackebrandt, E., Conway de Macario, E., and Winter, J., "Isolation and Characterization of *Methanocorpusculum parvum*, Gen. Nov., Spec. Nov., a New Tungsten Requiring, Coccoid Methanogen," *Arch. Microbiol.*, 147, 13 (1987).
140. Miller, T. L., and Wolin, M. J., "*Methanospaera stadtmaniae* Gen. Nov., Sp. Nov.: A Species that Forms Methane by Reducing Methanol with Hydrogen," *Arch. Microbiol.*, 141, 116 (1985).
141. van Bruggen, J. J. A., Zwart, K. B., Hermans, J. G. F., van Hove, E. M., Stumm, C. K., and Vogels, G. O., "Isolation and Characterization of *Methanoplanus endosymbiosus* Sp. Nov., an Endosymbiont of the Marine Sapropelic Ciliate *Metopus contortus* Quennerstedt," *Arch. Microbiol.*, 144, 367 (1986).
142. Kandler, O., "Cell Wall Structures and Their Phylogenetic Implications," *Zbl. Bakt. Hyg., I. Abt. Orig. C3*, 149 (1982).
143. Langworthy, T. A., Tornabene, T. G., and Holzer, G., "Lipids of Archaebacteria," *Zbl. Bakt. Hyg., I. Abt. Orig. C3*, 228 (1982).
144. Woese, C. R., "Archaebacteria and Cellular Origins: An Overview," *Zbl. Bakt. Hyg., I. Abt. Orig. C3*, 1 (1982).

145. Balch, W. E., Fox, G. E., Magrum, L. J., Woese, C. R., and Wolfe, R. S., "Methanogens: Reevaluation of a Unique Biological Group," *Microbiol. Rev.*, 43, 260 (1979).
146. Wolfe, R. S., "Unusual Coenzymes of Methanogenesis," *Trends in Biochemical Sciences*, 10, 396 (1985).
147. Romesser, J. A., and Wolfe, R. S., "CDR Factor, a New Coenzymes Required for Carbon Dioxide Reduction to Methane by Extracts of *Methanobacterium thermoautotrophicum*," *Zbl. Bakt. Hyg., I. Abt. Orig. C3*, 271 (1982).
148. Leigh, J. A., Rinehart, K. L., Jr., and Wolfe, R. S., "Structure of Methanofuran, the Carbon Dioxide Reduction Factor of *Methanobacterium thermoautotrophicum*," *J. Am. Chem. Soc.*, 106, 3636 (1984).
149. Leigh, J. A., Rinehart, K. L., Jr., and Wolfe, R. S., "Methanofuran (Carbon Dioxide Reduction Factor), a Formyl Carrier in Methane Production from Carbon Dioxide in *Methanobacterium*," *Biochemistry*, 24, 995 (1985).
150. Gunsalus, R. P., and Wolfe, R. S., "Chromophoric Factors F_{342} and F_{430} of *Methanobacterium thermoautotrophicum*," *FEMS Microbiol. Lett.*, 3, 191 (1978).
151. van Beelen, P., van Neck, J. W., de Cock, R. M., Vogels, G. D., Guijt, W., and Haasnoot, C. A. G., "5,10-Methenyl-5,6,7,8-Tetrahydromethanopterin, a One-Carbon Carrier in the Process of Methanogenesis," *Biochemistry*, 23, 4448 (1984).
152. Escalante-Semerena, J. C., Leigh, J. A., Rinehart, K. L., Jr., and Wolfe, R. S., "Formaldehyde Activation Factor, Tetrahydromethanopterin, a Coenzyme of Methanogenesis," *Proc. Natl. Acad. Sci. U.S.A.*, 81, 1976 (1984).
153. Taylor, C. D., and Wolfe, R. S., "Structure and Methylation of Coenzyme M," *J. Biol. Chem.*, 249, 4879 (1974).
154. Nagle, D. P., Jr., and Wolfe, R. S., "Component A of the Methyl·Coenzyme M Methylreductase System of *Methanobacterium*: Resolution into Four Components," *Proc. Natl. Acad. Sci. U.S.A.*, 80, 2151 (1983).
155. Smith, M. R., Zinder, S. H., and Mah, R. A., "Microbial Methanogenesis from Acetate," *Process Biochem., May* 34 (1980).
156. Krzycki, J. A., Wolkin, R. H., and Zeikus, J. G., "Comparison of Unitrophic and Mixotrophic Substrate Metabolism by an Acetate-Adapted Strain of *Methanosarcina barkeri*," *J. Bacteriol.*, 149, 247 (1982).
157. Zehnder, A. J. B., Huser, B. A., Brock, T. D., and Wuhrmann, K., "Characterization of an Acetate-Decarboxylating, Non-hydrogen-Oxidizing Methane Bacterium," *Arch. Microbiol.*, 124, 1 (1980).
158. Vogels, G. D., and Visser, C. M., "Interconnection of Methanogenic and Acetogenic Pathways," *FEMS Microbiol. Lett.*, 20, 291 (1984).
159. Smith, M. R., and Mah, R. A., "Growth and Methanogenesis by *Methanosarcina* Strain 227 on Acetate and Methanol," *Appl. Environ. Microbiol.*, 36, 870 (1978).
160. Weimer, P. J., and Zeikus, J. G., "Acetate Metabolism in *Methanosarcina barkeri*," *Arch. Microbiol.*, 119, 175 (1978).
161. Blaut, M., and Gottschalk, G., "Effect of Trimethylamine on Acetate Utilization by *Methanosarcina barkeri*," *Arch. Microbiol.*, 133, 230 (1982).
162. Baresi, L., and Wolfe, R. S., "Levels of Coenzyme F_{420}, Coenzyme M, Hydrogenase, and Methylcoenzyme M Methylreductase in Acetate-Grown *Methanosarcina*," *Appl. Environ. Microbiol.*, 41, 388 (1981).
163. Lovely, D. R., White, R. H., and Ferry, J. G., "Identification of Methylcoenzyme M as an Intermediate in Methanogenesis from *Methanosarcina* Spp.," *J. Bacteriol.*, 160, 521 (1984).
164. Krzycki, J. A., Lehman, L. J., and Zeikus, J. G., "Acetate Catabolism by *Methanosarcina barkeri*: Evidence for Involvement of Carbon Monoxide Dehydrogenase, Methyl Coenzyme M and Methylreductase," *J. Bacteriol.*, 163, 1000 (1985).
165. Nelson, M. J. K., and Ferry, J. G., "Carbon Monoxide-Dependent Methyl Coenzyme M Methyl Reductase in Acetotrophic *Methanosarcina* Spp.," *J. Bacteriol.*, 160, 526 (1984).
166. Krzycki, J. A., and Zeikus, J. G., "Characterization and Purification of Carbon Monoxide Dehydrogenase from *Methanosarcina backeri*," *J. Bacteriol.*, 158, 231 (1984).

167. Kohler, H. -P. E., and Zehnder, A. J. B., "Carbon Monoxide Dehydrogenase and Acetate Thiokinase in *Methanothrix soehngenii*," *FEMS Microbiol. Lett.*, 21, 287 (1984).
168. Kenealy, W. R., and Zeikus, J. G., "One-Carbon Metabolism in Methanogens: Evidence for Synthesis of a Two-Carbon Cellular Intermediate and Unification of Catabolism and Anabolism in *Methanosarcina barkeri*," *J. Bacteriol.*, 151, 932 (1982).
169. Kenealy, W. R., and Zeikus, J. G., "Influence of Corrinoid Antogonists on Methanogen Metabolism," *J. Bacteriol.*, 146, 133 (1981).
170. Zeikus, J. G., "Metabolism of One-Carbon Compounds by Chemotrophic Anaerobes," *Adv. Microbiol. Physiol.*, 24, 215 (1983).
171. van der Meijden, P., Heythuysen, H. J., Pouwels, A., Houwen, F. P., van der Drift, C., and Vogels, G. D., "Methyltransferases Involved in Methanol Conversion by *Methanosarcina barkeri*," *Arch. Microbiol.*, 134, 238 (1983).
172. Blaut, M., Müller, V., Fiebig, K., and Gottschalk, G., "Sodium Ions and an Energized Membrane Required by *Methanosarcina barkeri* for the Oxidation of Methanol to the Level of Formaldehyde," *J. Bacteriol.*, 164, 95 (1985).
173. Stupperich, E., and Fuchs, G., "Autotrophic Synthesis of Activated Acetic Acid from Two CO_2 in *Methanobacterium thermoautotrophicum* II. Evidence for Different Origins of Acetate Carbon Atoms," *Arch. Microbiol.*, 139, 14 (1984).
174. Weimer, P. J., and Zeikus, J. G., "Acetate Assimilation Pathway of *Methanosarcina barkeri*," *J. Bacteriol.*, 137, 332 (1979).
175. Zeikus, J. G., Fuchs, G., Keneally, W., and Thauer, R. K., "Oxidoreductase Involved in Cell Carbon Synthesis of *Methanobacterium thermoautotrophicum*," *J. Bacteriol.*, 132, 604 (1977).
176. Nishio, N., Kitaura, S., and Nagai, S., "Volatile Fatty Acids Production from Mandarin Orange Peel in an Acidogenic Fermentation," *J. Ferment. Technol.*, 60, 423 (1982).
177. Zoetemeyer, R. J., Matthijsen, A. J. C. M., Cohen, A., and Boelhouwer, C., "Product Inhibition in the Acid Forming Stage of the Anaerobic Digestion Process," *Water Res.*, 16, 633 (1982).
178. Hueting, S., and Tempest, D. W., "Effects of Formate, Acetate and Propionate on the Behavior of *Klebsiella aerogenes* NCTC 418, Growing in Continuous Culture on Glucose: Inhibition and Uncoupling of Oxydative Phosphorylation," *Arch. Microbiol.*, 123, 189 (1979).
179. Bahl, H., Andersch, W., Braun, K., and Gottschalk, G., "Effect of pH and Butyrate Concentration on the Production of Acetone and Butanol by *Clostridium acetobutylicum* Grown in Continuous Culture," *Eur. J. Appl. Microbiol. Biotechnol.*, 14, 17 (1982).
180. Nanba, A., Nukada, R., and Nagai, S., "Inhibition by Acetic and Propionic Acids of the Growth of *Propionibacterium shermanii*," *J. Ferment. Technol.*, 61, 551 (1983).
181. Wang, G., and Wang, D. I. C., "Elucidation of Growth Inhibition and Acetic Acid Production by *Clostridium thermoaceticum*," *Appl. Environ. Microbiol.*, 47, 294 (1984).
182. Monot, F., Engasser, J., and Petitdemange, H., "Influence of pH and Undissociated Butyric Acid on the Production of Acetone and Butanol in Batch Cultures of *Clostridium acetobutylicum*," *Appl. Microbiol. Biotechnol.*, 19, 422 (1984).
183. Yano, T., and Koga, S., "Dynamic Behavior of the Chemostat Subject to Substrate Inhibition," Biotechnol. Bioeng., 11, 139 (1969).
184. Edwards, V. H., "The Influence of High Substrate Concentrations on Microbial Kinetics," *Biotechnol. Bioeng.*, 12, 679 (1970).
185. Andrews, J. F., "A Mathematical Model for the Continuous Culture of Microorganisms Utilizing Inhibitory Substrates," *Biotechnol. Bioeng.*, 10, 707 (1968).
186. Ierusalimsky, N. D., *Microbial Phisiology and Continuous Culture* (E. O. Powell, C. G. T. Evans, R. R. Strange, and D. W. Tempest, eds.), Her Majesty's Stationary Office, London, 1967, p. 23.
187. Yano, T., and Koga, S., "Dynamic Behavior of the Chemostat Subject to Product Inhibition," *J. Gen. Appl. Microbiol.*, 19, 97 (1973).
188. Takamatsu, T., Shioya, S., and Okuda, K., "A Comparison of Unstructured Growth Models of Microorganism," *J. Ferment. Technol.*, 59, 131 (1981).
189. Lawrence, A. W., and McCarty, P. L., "Kinetics of Methane Fermentation in Anaerobic Treatment," *J. Water Pollut. Control Fed.*, 41, R1 (1969).

190. Heyes, R. H., and Hall, R. J., "Kinetics of Two Subgroups of Propionate-Using Organisms in Anaerobic Digestion," *Appl. Environ. Microbiol.*, 46, 710 (1983).
191. Ahring, B. K., and Westermann, P., "Kinetics of Butyrate, Acetate, and Hydrogen Metabolism in a Thermophilic, Anaerobic, Butyrate-Degrading Coculture," *Appl. Environ. Microbiol.*, 53, 434 (1987).
192. Chua, H. B., and Robinson, J. P., "Formate-Limited Growth of *Methanobacterium formicium* in Steady-State Cultures," *Arch. Microbiol.*, 135, 158 (1983).
193. Zehnder, A. J. B., and Wuhrmann, K., "Physiology of a *Methanobacterium* Strain AZ," *Arch. Microbiol.*, 111, 199 (1977).
194. Schönheit, P., Moll, J., and Thauer, R. H., "Growth Parameters (K_s, μ_{max}, Y_s) of *Methanobacterium thermoautotrophicum*," *Arch. Microbiol.*, 127, 59 (1980).
195. Smith, M. R., and Mah, R. A., "Acetate as Sole Carbon and Energy Source for Growth of *Methanosarcina* Strain 227," *Appl. Environ. Microbiol.*, 39, 993 (1980).
196. Zinder, S. H., and Mah, R. A., "Isolation and Characterization of a Thermophilic Strain of *Methanosarcina* Unable to Use H_2—CO_2 for methanogenesis," *Appl. Environ. Microbiol.*, 38, 996 (1979).

CHAPTER 19

CONVENTIONAL ANAEROBIC DIGESTION

Yorikazu Sonoda and **Kenji Kida**

Department of Applied Chemistry
Faculty of Engineering, Kumamoto University
Kurokami, Kumamoto, Japan

Shiro Nagai

Department of Fermentation Technology
Faculty of Engineering, Hiroshima University
Saijo, Higashi—Hiroshima, Japan 724

CONTENTS

INTRODUCTION

Anaerobic digestion has long been used for treating the excess sludge discharged from sewage treatment works, e.g., since 1900 in London, U.K. Since then, anaerobic digestions have been developed to treat other wastewaters, such as those from alcohol distillationer, antibiotics production, and baker's yeast productions.

Flowsheets of anaerobic digestion combined with activated sludge treatment (aerobic) for the pre- and post-treatments are shown in Figure 1.

This chapter discusses the fundamental aspects of conventional anaerobic digestion processes.

CONSTRUCTION OF ANAEROBIC DIGESTION SYSTEMS

Fundamental construction of anaerobic digestion systems (Figure 2) consists of pre-treatment of wastewater, anaerobic digestion tank(s), and maintenance facilities, fuel gas separator, and post-treatment of the discharged sludge.

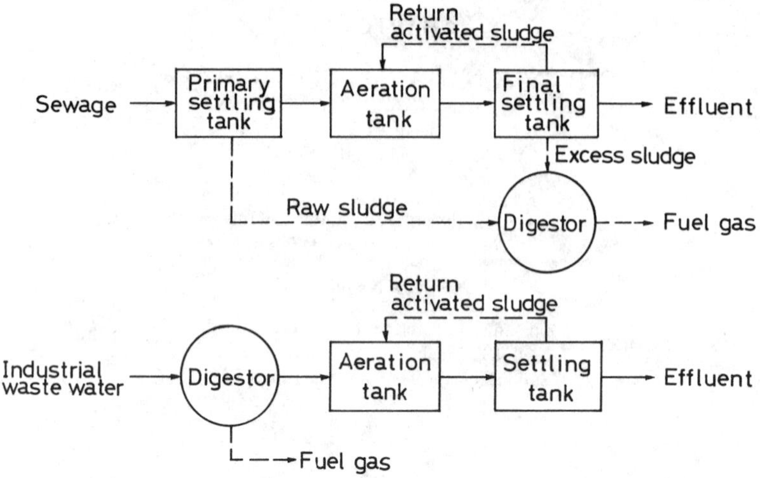

Figure 1. Roles of conventional anaerobic digestion for sewage treatments and industrial wastewater treatments.

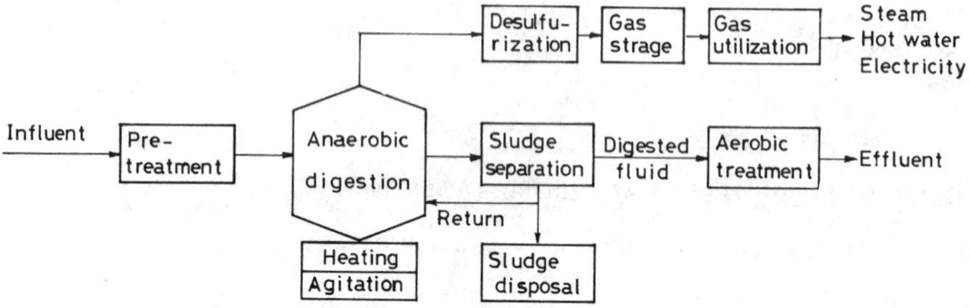

Figure 2. Fundamental construction of anaerobic digestion system.

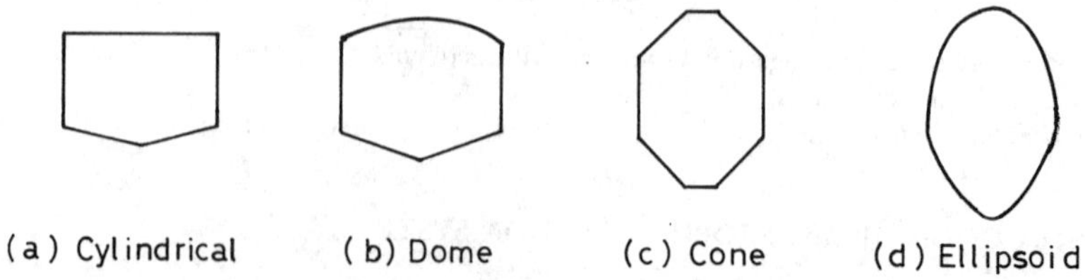

Figure 3. Types of anaerobic digestor.

In the pre-treatment process, after separating the grits and scums in the influent, temperature, pH, COD concentration, and organic load are adjusted, if necessary; nutrient supplement and the removal of inhibitory substances contained must be carried out.

The digestion tank has facilities for temperature control, agitation and control of sludge concentration.

In the post-treatment after anaerobic digestion, it is necessary to have a separation facility to effectively separate solid, liquid, and gas for further use.

The units in the whole digestion system are described in the following sections.

Digestor

Many varieties of digestion tanks are available (Figure 3):

a. Cylindrical type. This popular design has a large dead space that inhibits agitation.
b. Dome type. This type allows large-scale construction because of its resistance to high pressure.
c. Cone type. This is characterized with a small dead space for agitation, i.e., efficient mixing and ease of discharging the sludge produced.
d. Ellipsoid type. This type has been popular in domestic sewage treatment in West Germany since 1960. It is a good design and the digestor bottom has a sharp grade over the rest angle of sludge, which allows discharging of the settled sludge. Ellipsoid digestors can be constructed with pre-stressed concrete, so their great structural strength permits very large-scale construction, e.g., a 12,000 m^3 in Düsseldorf, W. Germany (Figure 4).

Agitation in Digestor

Mixing inside the digestor enhances gas production, so several means for mixing have been devised (Figure 5).

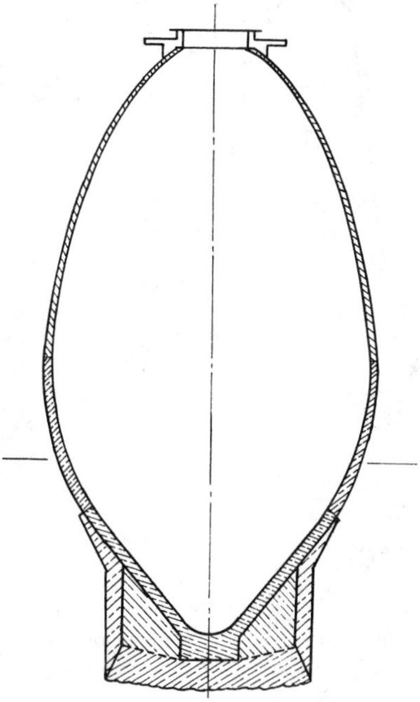

Figure 4. Sectional view of ellipsoid type digestor [1]. (Düsseldorf South Sewage Treatment Works, West Germany)

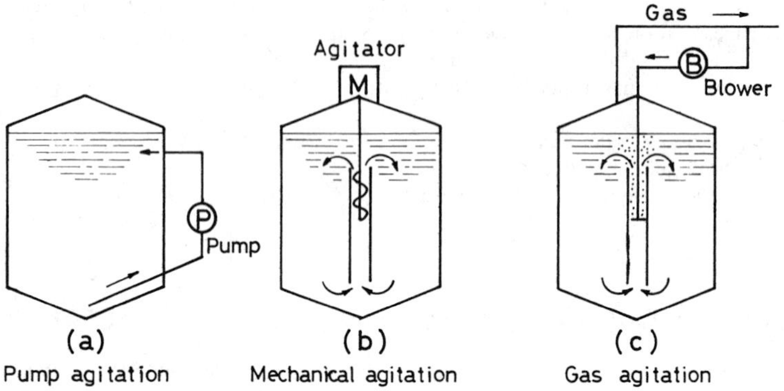

Figure 5. Agitation system in digestor.

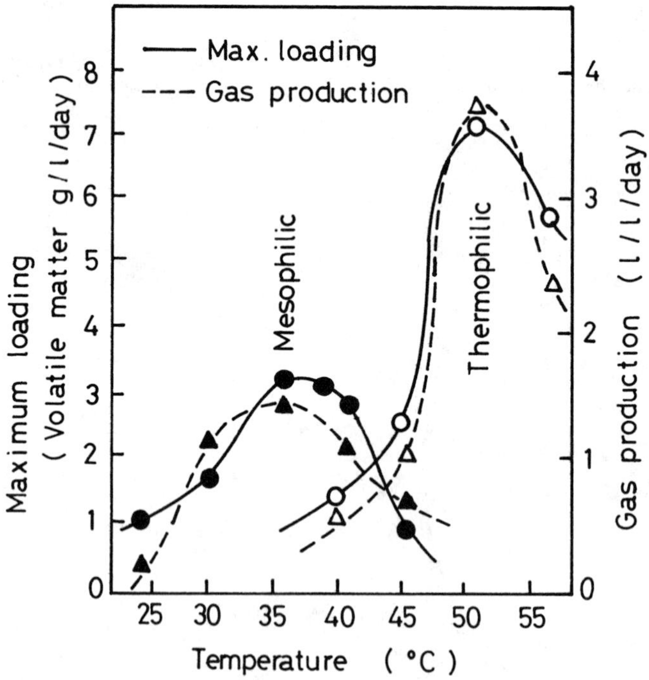

Figure 6. Gas production and organic load in mesophilic and thermophilic anaerobic digestions [2].

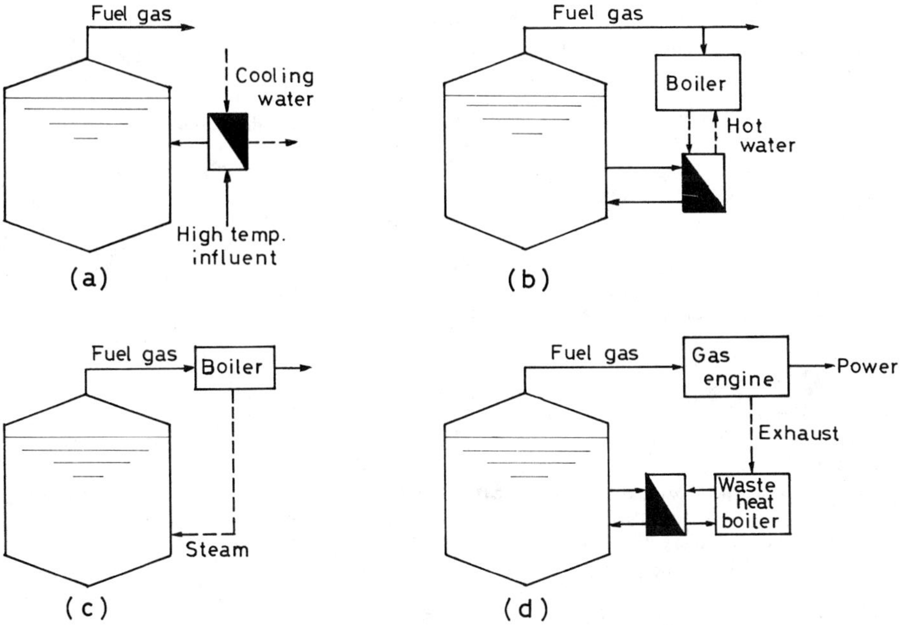

Figure 7. Heating system in digestor: ◣ heat exchanger.

In contrast to mechanical agitation, which occurs submerged in the medium, gas agitation is simpler, easier to maintain, and allows control of the liquid flow pattern by adjusting the gas flow-rate. Hence, the gas agitation methods are more practically distributed, especially, when the fermentation medium contains a relatively high H_2S. The desulfurized gas circulation enhances the removal of sulfide, and thus, stabilizes the whole methane fermentation.

Heating in Digestor

Temperature control to maintain an optimum condition for methane fermentation is essential. Mesophilic (36–38°C) and thermophilic (53–55°C) digestions are practical, and the treatment efficiency of the latter can be 2 to 3 times that of the former (Figure 6).

When high-temperature wastewater is discharged (Figure 7, a), e.g., in an ethanol distillery (70–80°C), it can be used to replace the radiation heat loss from the digestor.

In the case of low-temperature wastewater, e.g., domestic sewage, the produced biogas must be used for heating (Figure 7, b, c and d).

Use of Fuel Gas

Fuel gas produced consists of CH_4 (50–70%) and CO_2 (30–50%) with a byproduct of H_2S (0.01 to 2% of the gas). Even a small fraction of H_2S causes corrosion and air pollution after combustion as fuel gas, hence, the desulfurization is essential.

Table 1
Gas Composition from Anaerobic digestion of Sewage Sludge after Desulfurization [3]

Content	Inlet	After desulfurization
CH_4 (%)	63.2	63.3
CO_2 (%)	35.4	35.4
Air (%)	1.3	1.3
H_2S (ppm)	255	90
Calorie (kcal/m^3)	5,600	5,600

Dry desulfurization process by Fe_2O_3 Shibaura Sewage Treatment Works, Tokyo, Japan

As a dry desulfurization process, a pellet desulfurizer, Fe_2O_3 is used, while as a liquid type, Na_2CO_3 and monoethanolamine are used. An example of desulfurization of biogas is shown in Table 1.

Figure 8 is a typical example of how fuel gas is used for electric generation to supply the electricity for the process treatment, and the exhaust wasteheat is used for digestor heating.

In an ethanol distillery, the gas is used to fuel the boiler(s).

OPERATIONS IN INDUSTRIAL FACILITIES

Sewage Sludge

Anaerobic digestions have been widely used in many countries. A typical example (Figure 9) indicates that the sludge discharged from the primary settling tank settles in the sludge thickener, and the thickened sludge is transferred to the digestor (1,400 m^3/day, solid matter 56 t/day), where it is anaerobically digested (retention time: 10 days, temp: 34.5°C). Then, the biogas produced (15,000 m^3/day, CH_4: 63%) is used for the gas engine(s) (6 units) and for the boiler(s) (3 units).

The electric power obtained from 3-unit gas engines is used for the facility's equipment, and that from the rest of the 3-unit gas engines is connected directly to an air compressor and the produced compressed air is used to aerate a tank.

The effluent discharged from the digestor (8,500 $m^3 \times 2$) settles in the thickener (2,000 $m^3 \times 2$) units and the thickened sludge is conditioned with iron chloride, aluminium chloride and slaked lime. It is then automatically dehydrated up to the water content of 55%. The dehydrated cake (110 m^3/day) is used as a fertilizer for a sugar beet farm.

Table 2 shows the results obtained from 15 municipal sewage treatment works in London, U.K. (1972) where the biogas production was 90 to 150 ℓ/m^3 sewage and total biogas produced was about $8{,}800 \times 10^4$ m^3/year (6,000 kcal/m^3).

Wastewater from Alcohol Distillery

Anaerobic digestions for alcohol distillery wastewater have been carried out since 1956 in Japan's governmental alcohol distilleries so as to practically use the biogas. However, since distillery wastewater from cane sugar molasses is a biologically undegradable dark-brownish color, many distilleries have changed the anaerobic treatment to the combustion process in which the condensed distillery wastewater is directly burned. It is suspected that in 1970, when anaerobic digestion was most widely used, about 20 million m^3/year of the biogas were produced in all of Japan's distilleries. Table 3 shows the results obtained from 5 governmental alcohol distilleries where the recovered biogas could supply 30 to 50% of the total fuel energy required in the factory.

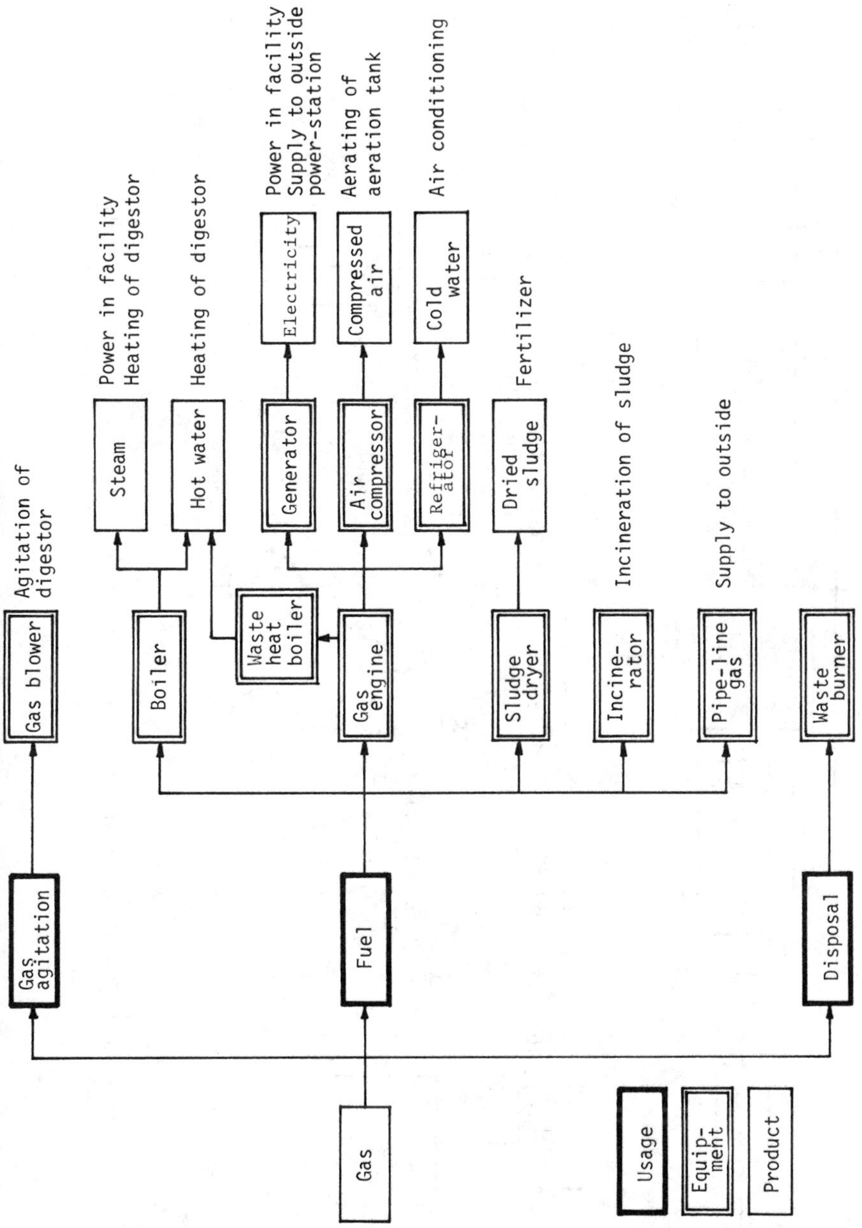

Figure 8. Utilization scheme of produced fuel gas.

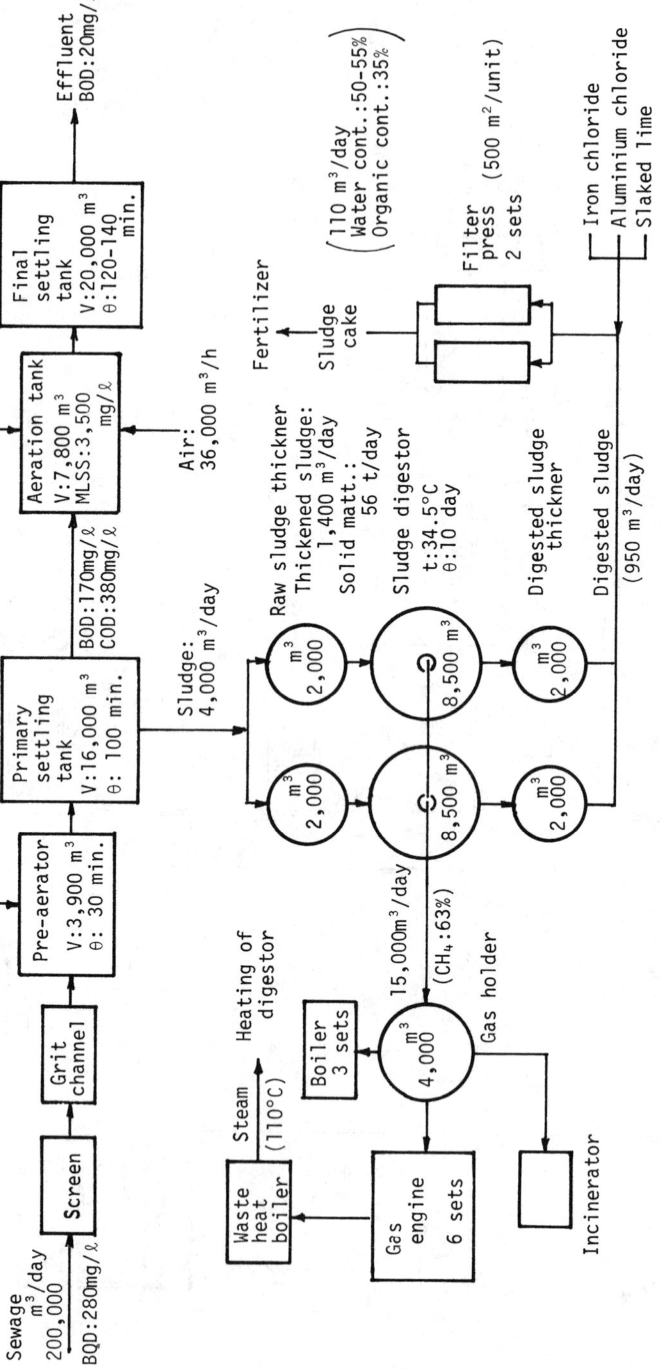

Figure 9. Flow-sheet of sewage treatment works (Düsseldorf North Sewage Treatment Works) [3].

Table 2
Actual Results of Anaerobic Digestion in Municipal Sewage Works, London, U.K. (1972/73) [5]

Works	Area Served (km^2)	Population Served (million)	Sewage received: Total (10^4 m^3/year)	Sewage received: Average (10^4 m^3/day)	Influent: BOD (ppm)	Influent: SS (ppm)	Effluent: BOD (ppm)	Sludge Produced (m^3/day)	Sludge Gas Produced (m^3/day)
Beckton	282	2.39	32,600	89.2	304	353	66	7,750	77,000
Crossness	205	1.53	18,900	51.7	479	571	19	4,950	52,600
Mogden	427	1.35	14,400	39.1	275	331	7.9	3,570	57,700
Deephams	249	0.69	6,110	16.7	357	431	5.7	1,740	21,800
Riverside	127	0.34	6,983	8.1	400	547	70	720	10,600
Beddington	140	0.34	2,741	7.5	342	561	5	650	10,700
Hogsmill Vally }	70 }	0.2 }	1,671	4.6	362	412	9.5	478 }	5,484
Surbiton			237	0.65	246	264	12.6		
Wandle Valley	23	0.09	1,000	2.7	286	296	7.6	300	—
Kew	23	0.08	1,142	3.1	175	218	3.1	115	2,807
Worcester Park	36	0.08	556	1.5	408	524	12.5	150 }	2,500
Sutton	9	0.04	313	0.85	417	427	7.4		
Redbridge E	8	0.04	316	0.8	353	341	12.9	—	—
Redbridge S	6.5	0.03	217	0.6	330	339	8.9	36	—
Bury Farm	23	0.02	150	0.4	338	466	5.0	30	—
Total	1,628	7.2	83,335					20,489	240,471

Table 3
Actual Results of Anaerobic Digestion in Alcohol Distilleries [4]

Name of plant	Waste Treated per Year		Gas Production			Power Consumed		BOD		
	Waste volume (k1)	Volatile matter (ton)	Total gas production (m^3/year)	CH_4(%)	Gas/volatile matter (m^3/ton)	Agitator, Pump, Lighting (kwh/year)	kwh/1,000m^3 of gas	Influent (ppm)	Digested effluent (ppm)	Removal ratio (%)
Chiba	55,850	3,749	1,986,788	50.5	530	216,062	109	36,350	5,300	85
Ishioka	37,450	987	682,815	56.0	692	72,978	107	15,128	1,139	92
Iwata	36,716	979	720,738	54.3	736	75,181	104	23,194	1,986	91
Higo-Oozu	30,945	941	635,351	52.5	695	120,702	190	28,709	2,882	90
Izumi	72,440	2,632	1,559,711	50.1	593	209,647	134	22,998	5,451	76
Sum or Average	233,401	9,261	5,585,403	51.8	603	694,572	124	25,718	3,352	87

(Governmental alcohol distilleries, Japan. 1970 fiscal year)

Wastewater from Baker's Yeast Factory

Cane sugar molasses has been widely used in baker's yeast factories, and the separated wastewater (28,400 VS mg/ℓ, 175 m^3/day, see Table 4) from the yeast separator is the main pollutant. The wastewater is anaerobically and aerobically treated (Figure 10). It is first anaerobically digested at 55°C and a retention time of 7 days in a digestor (1,822 m^3), then the digested effluent enters a floatator, where the produced gas separates the solid sludge. About 80% of the sludge from the digested effluent is separated and returned to the digestor.

As a result, the sludge concentration in the digestor can be held at 9,000 to 11,000 mg/ℓ in a dry state, which contributes to digestion efficiency. As shown in Table 4, BOD removal in the digestor is about 85.2%, followed by 95.3% in the aeration tank. The result is that the total BOD removal is about 97.2%.

Wastewater from Paper-Mill Factory

In a chemical digestion process of wood-chip in a paper-mill, a large amount of evaporate condensate is discharged. An example of anaerobic digestion of the evaporate condensate with the

Table 4
Operation Results of Anaerobic Digestion and Activated Sludge Process of Wastewater from a Baker's Yeast Factory, Oriental Yeast Co. Ltd., Japan [6]

Anaerobic digestion process	Influent		Wastewater flow-rate (m^3/day)	175
			Volatile matter content (mg/ℓ)	28,400
			Total amount of volatile matter (kg/day)	4,978
			BOD (mg/ℓ)	13,400
			Volatile matter loading (kg/SSkg·day)	0.266
	Digested effluent		pH	7.0 ~ 7.4
			BOD (mg/ℓ)	1,800 ~ 2,300
			Digested sludge content (mg/ℓ)	9,000 ~ 11,000
			Volatile acid content (mg/ℓ)	1,400 ~ 2,700
	Gas produced		CH_4 content (%)	51
			Total production (m^3/day)	1,900
			Gas/Volatile matter (ℓ/kg)	390
Activated sludge process	Influent	Digested effluent	Flow-rate (m^3/day)	360
			BOD (mg/ℓ)	2,000
		Other waste	Flow-rate (m^3/day)	370
			BOD (mg/ℓ)	1,700
	Aeration tank		BOD loading (kg/m^3·day)	1.45
			BOD loading (kg/SSkg·day)	0.226
			MLSS (mg/ℓ)	6,500
			SVI (mℓ/g)	135
	Effluent		BOD (mg/ℓ)	48
			pH	7.0 ~ 7.9

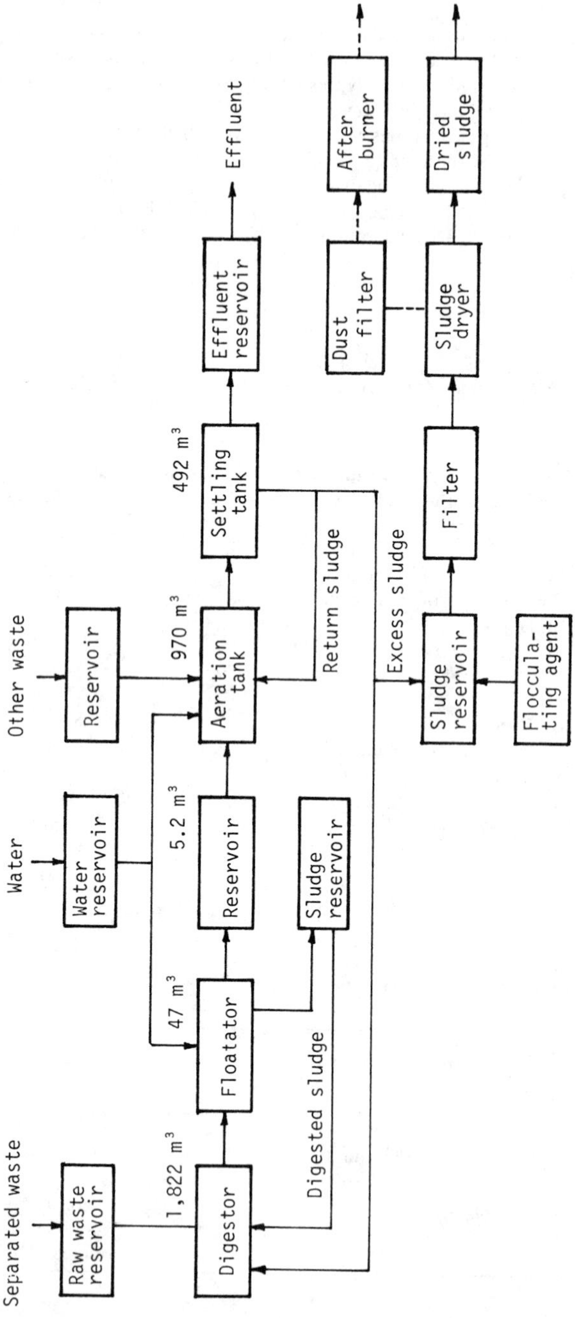

Figure 10. Flow-sheet of wastewater treatment of a baker's yeast factory [6].

Table 5
Chemical Composition of Evaporate Condensate and RNA Extraction Wastewater of a Sulfite Pulp Industry, Sanyo-Kokusaku Pulp Co. Ltd., Gohtsu Mill, Japan. [7]

Item	SSL Evaporation Condensate	RNA Extraction Waste
pH	2.2 ~ 2.5	1.9 ~ 2.2
CODcr (mg/ℓ)	8,000 ~ 12,000	14,000 ~ 16,000
COD_{Mn} (mg/ℓ)	2,000 ~ 2,400	7,000 ~ 8,500
BOD_5 (mg/ℓ)	5,500 ~ 6,500	6,000 ~ 7,000
Total S (mg/ℓ)	300 ~ 400	250 ~ 300
Total N (mg/ℓ)	N.D.	600 ~ 750
Total P (mg/ℓ)	N.D.	180 ~ 250
Components (mg/ℓ)	Acetic acid 8,000 ~ 12,000 Furfural 500 ~ 1,300 Methanol 500 ~ 600 Free SO_2 70 ~ 120 Loosely combined SO_2 350 ~ 500	Soluble organic compounds from *Candida* yeast cell

SSL: Sulfite Spent Liquor
RNA: Ribonucleic Acid

wastewater from a RNA extraction process is shown in Table 5 and Figure 11. As shown in Table 5, sulfite-spent liquor mainly contains acetate, methanol, and furfural. Because this factory is producing RNA from *Candida* sp. using sulfite-spent liquor, the wastewater from RNA production process is treated together with sulfite-spent liquor (see Table 5).

As shown in a flowsheet of anaerobic digestion (Figure 11) and a material balance of the whole system (Figure 12), the wastewater and its flow are adjusted in the mixing tank and in the digestor (2,950 m^3, 2 units).

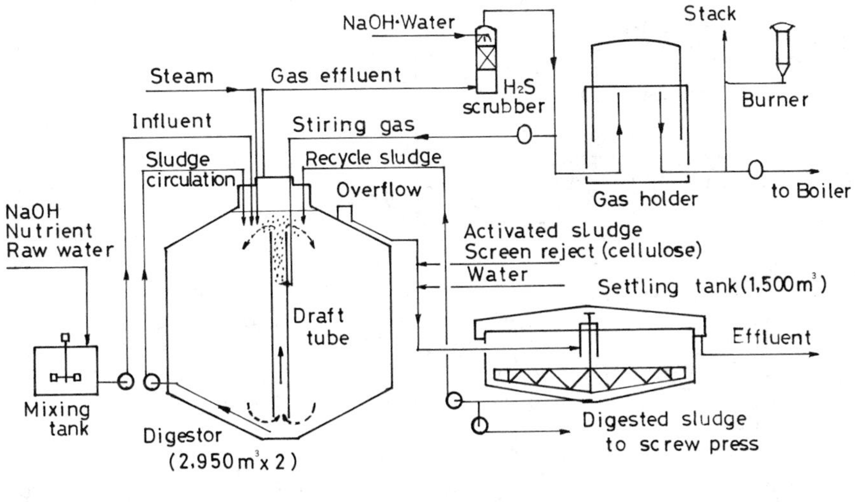

Figure 11. Flow-sheet of the anaerobic digestion in a paper-mill factory (see Table 5) [7]. Flow-rate: 2,200 m^3/day; Retention: 1.8 days; COD_{cr} load: 30 t/day.

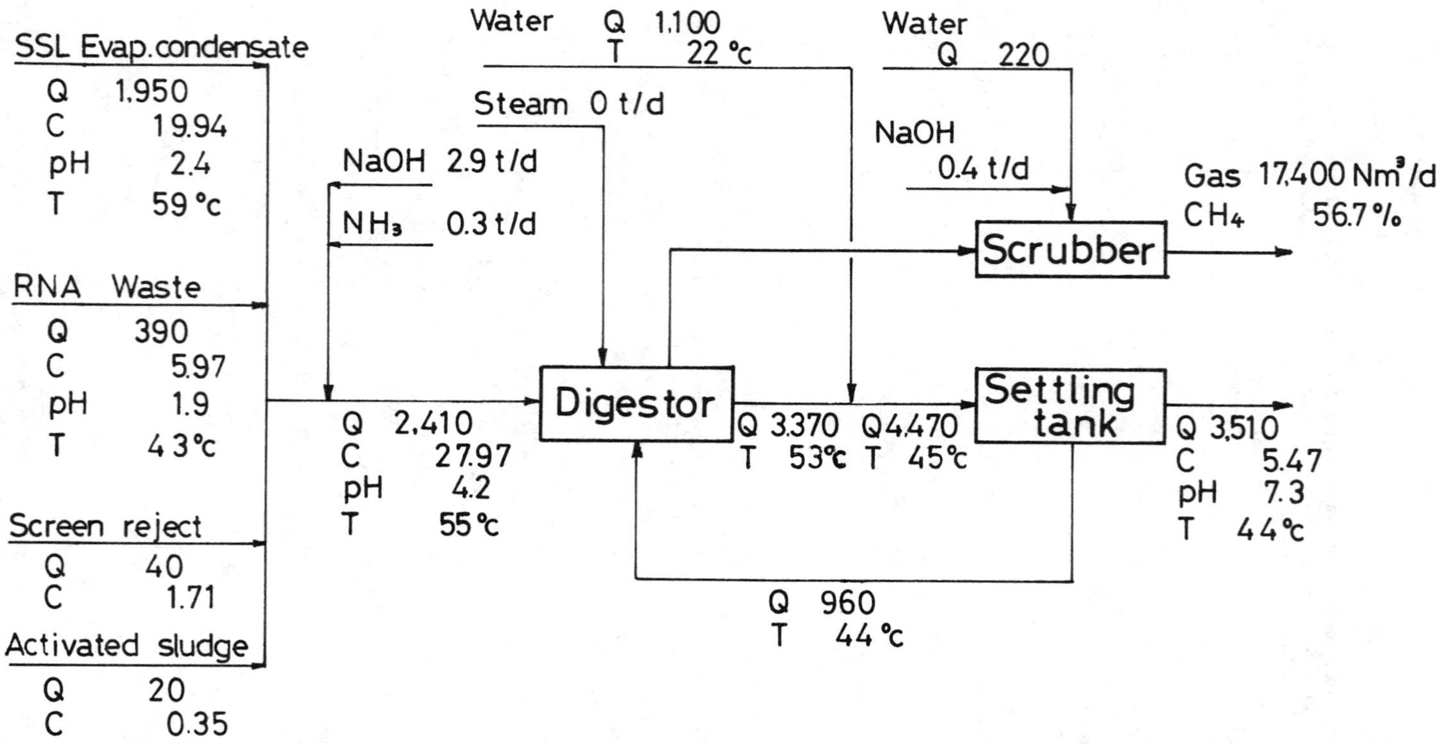

Figure 12. Material balance of anaerobic digestion of a paper-mill factory (see Table 5 and Figure 11) (1982) [7]. Q: Flow-rate t/d; C: COD_{cr}, t/d.

After being anaerobically fermented at 52 to 55°C for about 2 days, the effluent is transferred to the settling tank (1,500 m^3). The produced gas contains 50 to 65% CH_4 at a production rate of 15,000 to 17,000 Nm^3/day. H_2S (0.5 to 1.5%) in the gas effluent is removed by an H_2S-scrubber and the fuel gas is used for a boiler fuel to produce steam for generating electricity. In addition, the COD and BOD removals were 81 and 91% respectively at COD load, 5 kg/m^3/day.

HEAT REQUIREMENTS FOR ANAEROBIC DIGESTION

Methane formation in anaerobic digestion is the ultimate end as a result of sequential reduction reactions starting from organic matters. Hence, in order to maintain an optimum temperature for anaerobic digestion, in many cases, heating for the digestor (cooling for aerobic cultivation) is essentially required. The heating quantity required is assessed by summing up the heating of wastewater (Q_1) and the heat loss during fermentation (Q_2).

$$Q_1 = S \cdot W(T_i - T_w) \tag{1}$$

where Q_1 = heating quantity of wastewater (inlet) (kcal/day)
S = specific heat of wastewater (= 1) (kcal/kg·°C)
W = wastewater load (kg/day)
T_i = temperature of digestor inside (°C)
T_w = temperature of wastewater (inlet) (°C)

And for Q_2,

$$Q_2 = K \cdot A(T_i - T_0) \times 24 \tag{2}$$

where Q_2 = heat loss from digestor (kcal/day)
K = thermal conductivity of digestor's wall (kcal/m^3·h·°C)
A = surface area of digestor (m^2)
T_0 = temperature of digestor outside (air)(°C)

For example, to assess the heating quantities required for heating wastewater (inlet) Q_1 and to compensate the heat loss from digestor surface, Q_2, a model plant is considered (Figure 13) for a case study.

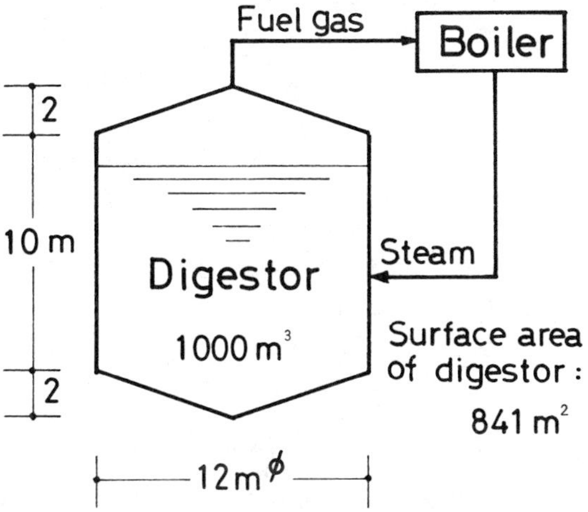

Figure 13. A model plant of anaerobic digestion to assess the heating requirements [3].

Table 6
Assessments of the Heat Required for Wastewater (Inlet) and for Digestor Based on the Heat Generated with the Biogas Obtained [3]

Process	Volatile Matter Loading (kg/m³·day)	Volatile Matter Content (%)	Waste Water Flow Rate (m³/day)	Quantity of Heat Demanded (10^3 kcal/day): Influent Heating	Digester Heating	Total	Heat Demand Corrected (A)*	Quantity of Heat in Gas Produced (B) (10^3 kcal/day)	Balance of Heat Supply and Demand (B) − (A) (10^3 kcal/day)	Heat Demand per Heat Produced (A)/(B) (%)
		1	200	3,400		3,657	5,486		△ 486	110
		1.5	133	2,261		2,518	3,777		1,233	76
		2	100	1,700		1,957	2,936		2,064	59
Mesophilic Digestion (37°C)	2	3	67	1,139	257	1,396	2,094	5,000 (1,000 m³/day)	2,906	42
		4	50	850		1,107	1,661		3,339	33
		5	40	680		937	1,406		3,594	28
		7	29	493		750	1,125		3,875	23
		10	20	340		597	896		4,104	18
		1	500	16,500		17,000	25,500		△13,000	204
		1.5	333	10,989		11,489	17,234		△ 4,734	138
		2	250	8,250		8,750	13,125		△ 625	105
Thermophilic Digestion (53°C)	5	3	167	5,511	500	6,011	9,017	12,500 (2,500 m³/day)	3,483	72
		4	125	4,125		4,625	6,938		5,562	56
		5	100	3,300		3,800	5,700		6,800	46
		7	71	2,343		2,843	4,265		8,235	34
		10	50	1,650		2,150	3,225		9,275	26

* *Based on corrected by boiler efficiency (80%) and the heat loss of pipe line (20%) (see Figure 13).*

The heat balances are shown in Table 6 in the cases of mesophilic (2 kg/m^3/day, 37°C) and thermophilic (5 kg/m^2/day, 53°C) digestions as a function of volatile matter concentration.

For assessing Q_1 and Q_2, assume T_0 and $T_w = 20°C$, $K = 0.75$ kcal/m$^2 \cdot$h$\cdot$°C.

The heat demand assessed was corrected by the heat losses of boiler efficiency (80%) and the pipe line concerned (20%), and the biogas produced was assumed to be 500ℓ (=5,000 kcal/m^3) from 1 kg volatile matter. The relationship between the heat demand ($Q_1 + Q_2$) per the heat produced from the gas (see (A)/(B) in Table 6) and the volatile matter content of wastewater is depicted in Figure 14, which contrasts the case of $T_0 = T_w = 10°C$. Figure 14 indicates that in the case of more than 1% volatile matter concentration in a mesophilic condition, a part of the fuel gas produced can be used, except for the heat demand for digestion maintenance at $T_0 = T_w = 20°C$; whereas in a thermophilic condition, more than 2% volatile matter concentration is required to use the biogas, suggesting that the extra gas is more available in a high COD wastewater and when $T_w > T_i$, as in alcohol distillery wastewater, all the produced gas can be available, but not for digestion maintenance heat.

STIMULATION AND INHIBITION OF ANAEROBIC DIGESTION

In principle, microbial density (=sludge) in the digestor can significantly enhance the treatment efficiency. The example shown in Figure 15 indicates that the sludge (anaerobic microorganism) concentration exponentially stimulates the anaerobic digestion although this result is not applicable for all the cases. Sometimes, nutrients of nitrogen, phosphate, etc. must be supplied empirically, leaving some problems to be solved.

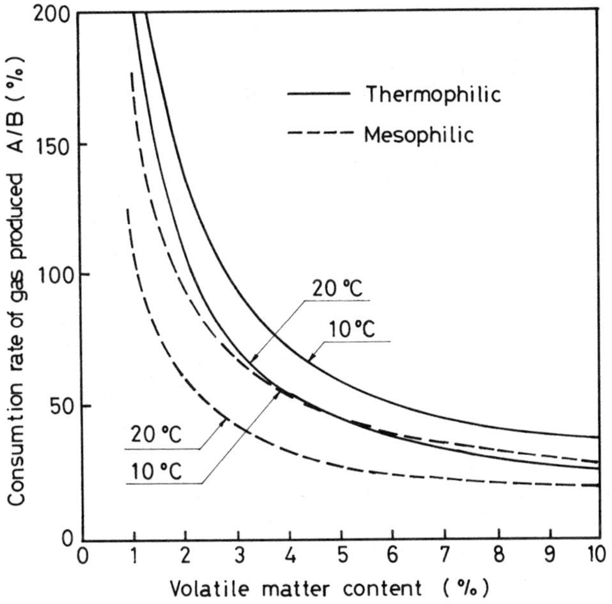

Figure 14. Relationships between heat demand per heat produced, A/B and volatile matter content of wastewater (see Table 6) [3]. 100: digestor self-maintenance with biogas produced; $T_0 = T_w = 10$ or 20°C.

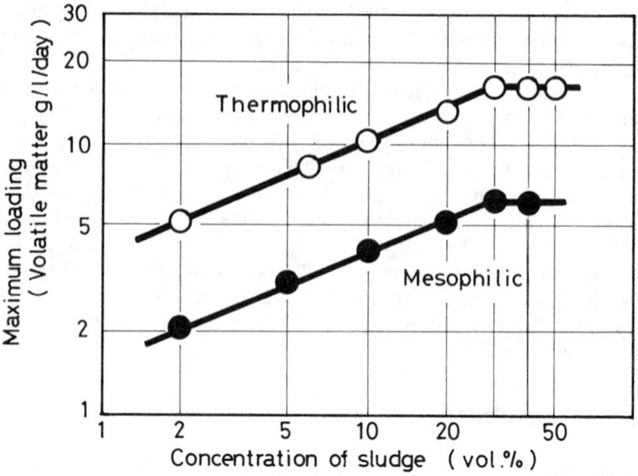

Figure 15. Relationships between digested sludge concentration and organic loading of alcohol distillery wastewater vol.%: sludge volume centrifuged at 1,500G, 10 min. [8].

Table 7
Permissible Concentration of Heavy Metal Compounds in Anaerobic Digestion [9]

Compound	Permissible Conc. (ppm)
$CuSO_4 \cdot 5H_2O$	700 (178 as Cu)
Cu_2O	300 (266 as Cu)
CuO	500 (399 as Cu)
$CuCl$	500 (321 as Cu)
$CuCl_2 \cdot 2H_2O$	700 (261 as Cu)
$Cu(OH)_2$	700 (456 as Cu)
CuS	700 (465 as Cu)
$Cu(CN)_2$	70 (38 as Cu)
$K_2Cr_2O_7$	500 (88 as Cr)
$Cr(OH)_3$	1,000 (505 as Cr)
Cr_2O_3	>5,000 (>3,422 as Cr)
$CrCl_3 \cdot 6H_2O$	1,000 (195 as Cr)
$K_2Cr_2(SO_4)_4 \cdot 24H_2O$	3,000 (156 as Cr)
$Cr(NO_3)_3 \cdot 9H_2O$	100 (13 as Cr)
$NiSO_4 \cdot 7H_2O$	300 (63 as Ni)
$NiCl_2 \cdot 6H_2O$	500 (123 as Ni)
$Ni(NO_3)_2 \cdot 6H_2O$	200 (40 as Ni)
$Ni(CH_3COO)_2 \cdot 4H_2O$	300 (71 as Ni)
NiS	700 (453 as Ni)
$HgCl_2$	2,000 (1,478 as Hg)
$HgNO_3$	1,000> (764> as Hg)

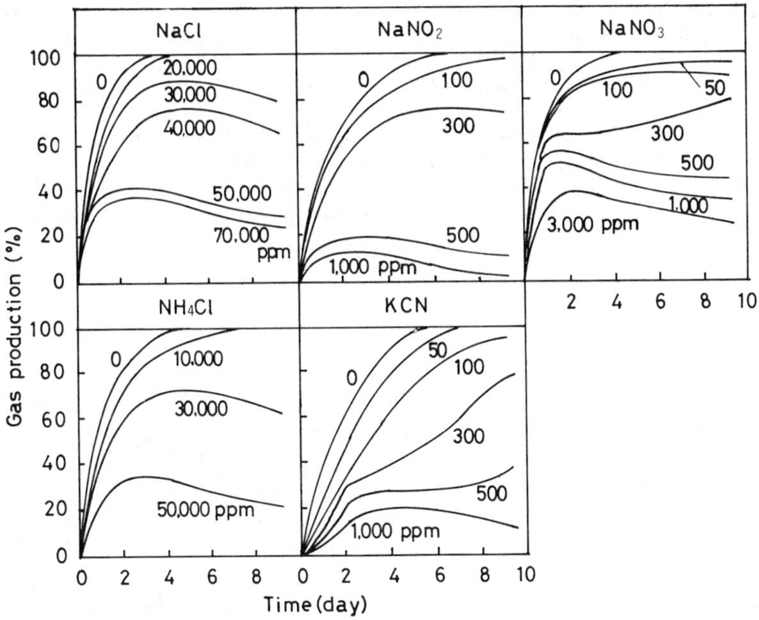

Figure 16. Effect of inorganic salts on gas production in thermophilic digestion [9].

On the other hand, the contaminated substances in wastewaters occasionally inhibit the methane fermentation. Sulfate and organic sulfur compounds are very inhibitory since the excess sulfide produced by sulfate-reducing bacteria remarkably inhibit the methanogen's growth. In this case, the dilution of wastewater, the addition of iron salts, and gasification of biogas to remove H_2S have been done, although they are temporary means.

Heavy metal contamination in anaerobic digestion is not severe because the evolved H_2S acts as a precipitator of metal ions, although it depends upon both concentrations concerned. For example, permissible concentrations of heavy metal compounds in anaerobic digestion are investigated using synthetic media (Table 7) indicating that the combination of cations (metal) and anions, mutually affect the anaerobic digestion.

In addition, an example of the effects of inorganic salts on the gas production is shown in Figure 16, which indicates that a low concentration of NO_2, NO_3, and CN^- is relatively responsible for the inhibition of methane fermentation.

REFERENCES

1. Düsseldorf South Sewage Treatment Works, from "Guide Pamphlet," W. Germany (1974)
2. Ono, H., Tanaka, M., Fukuoka, S., and Seiko, Y., "Studies on the Methane Fermentation of Alcohol Distillers Slop (Part 10) (in Japanese), "*Report of Ferm. Res. Inst.*, 15, 121 (1958).
3. Sonoda, Y., *Anaerobic Digestion, Biological Treatment of Industrial Wastewaters* (Y. Takahara, ed.), Chikyu-sha, Tokyo, 1980, p. 167.
4. Sonoda, Y., "Organic Waste Treatment and Fuel Gas Production by Methane Fermentation (in Japanese)," *Fermentation and Industry*, 34, 248 (1976).
5. Public Information Branch of the Director-General's Dept., Greater London Council, from Guide Pamphlet "London's Main Drainage," London, 1974, p. 7.

6. Ishikawa, T., Sato, K., Ookura, T., and Turuoka, A., "Methane Fermentation combined with Activated Sludge Treatment of Baker's Yeast Wastewater (in Japanese)," *Techanical Report of Yeast Industries*, 45, 23 (1976).
7. Nihei, H., "Methane Fermentation of Sulfite Pulp Mill Wastewater (in Japanese)," *Kami-Pa Technical Rep.*, 37, 523 (1983).
8. Sonoda, Y., Ono, H., and Nomura, S., "Effects of Digested Sludge in Mesophilic Methane Fermentation (in Japanese)," *Hakkokogaku Kaishi*, 43, 396 (1965).
9. Sonoda, Y., and Seiko, Y., "Effects of Heavy Metal Compounds, Inorganic Salts, Hydrocarbon Compounds and Antibiotics on Methane Fermentation (in Japanese)," *Hakkokogaku Kaishi*, 55, 22 (1977).

CHAPTER 20

RECENT DEVELOPMENTS IN ANAEROBIC DIGESTION

Kenji Kida and **Yorikazu Sonoda**

Department of Applied Chemistry
Faculty of Engineering, Kumamoto University
Kurokami, Kumamoto, Japan

Shiro Nagai

Department of Fermentation Technology
Faculty of Engineering, Hiroshima University
Saijo, Higashi–Hiroshima, Japan

CONTENTS

INTRODUCTION

To improve the drawback of conventional anaerobic digestion, i.e., rather slow digestion rate due to a low microbial concentration and unstability against environmental shocks, etc., R & D efforts have been carried out how to retain useful microorganisms at a high density to achieve rapid and effective anaerobic digestions. To do this, technological developments for microbial floc formation and microbial adhesion onto the carrier materials to retain the cells in the reactor have progressed considerably. For the former, the following processes are being developed, i.e., anaerobic activated processes [1] and upflow anaerobic sludge blanket (UASB) [2]; while, for the latter, upflow anaerobic filter process (UAFP) [3]. In addition, anaerobic attached film expanded-bed reactor (AAFEB) [4] and anaerobic fluidized-bed reactor (AFBR) [5] have been put to practical use. In all the newly developing processes, sometimes, acidogenesis occurs more than the methanogenesis, which leads to accumulation of the inhibitory end-product, volatile fatty acids. To solve the problems, two-phase anaerobic digestion processes are also developing [6]. In addition to the liquid-type anaerobic digestion previously mentioned, a solid-state anaerobic digestion using solid biomasses is also under development [7].

UPFLOW ANAEROBIC SLUDGE BLANKET (UASB)

Lettinga et al. [8] were first to successfully construct a UASB process capable of forming a self-granulation (floculation) of the anaerobic microbes concerned. As shown in Figure 1, the waste influent that entered from the bottom of reactor passes through the sludge bed and the sludge blanket where the organic materials are anaerobically decomposed. Then, the produced gas is separated by a gas-solid separator and the clarified liquid is discharged over the weir; whereas the granular sludges are naturally settled to the bottom. The granule size is 0.5–2.5 mm, and the granule concentration is 50–100 kg VSS/m^3 at the bottom, and 5–40 kg VSS/m^3 at the upper part of the reactor [9]. Bench and pilot plant scale experiments indicate it is possible to operate at a COD loading of 40 kg/m^3/day at a hydraulic retention time (HRT) of 4–24 h [10].

Engineering firms such Esmil, CSM, Grontmij, Paques, Sulzer, and Joseph Oat in Europe EC and the USA recently constructed 20 plants of UASB. As shown in Table 1, in the full-scale operations of UASB plants, COD concentration in inlet wastewater ranges from 2,000 to 20,000 mg/l at HRT of 2–47 h depending on inlet COD concentration, in which COD loads are 6–14 kg/m^3/day, resulting in a COD reduction of more than 85%. In addition, the UASB plant operating in a brewery seems to have the largest capacity in the world (inlet flow rate = 23,000 m^3/day and HRT = 0.21 day), capable of producing a biofuel of 600×10^6 Btu/month.

Significant parameters for the operation of UASB are floc diameter, microbial density (concentration), and structure of gas-solid separator to effectively retain the microbial granule in the reactor. To achieve a successful UASB operation (a) select a proper wastewater capable of self-forming a granule; (b) operate without mechanical agitation; (c) start up at a relatively low COD load; (d) wastewater contains Ca^{2+} and Ba^{2+} [11]; and (e) avoid a bulking formation caused by filamentous microbial growth. Granule formation in a UASB system is influenced by the growth of rod-type *Methanothrix* spp. in making a spherical granule. Brummeler et al. [12] investigated how to form a spherical granule using *Methanosarcina* sp., however, this has not yet succeeded because *Methanothrix soehngenii* has become a dominant species, excluding *Methanosarcina* sp. when acetic acid concentration is at a low level. Endo [13] reported that *Methanothrix* sp. becomes a dominant species in a high load operation in a mesophilic UASB system; however, in a thermo-

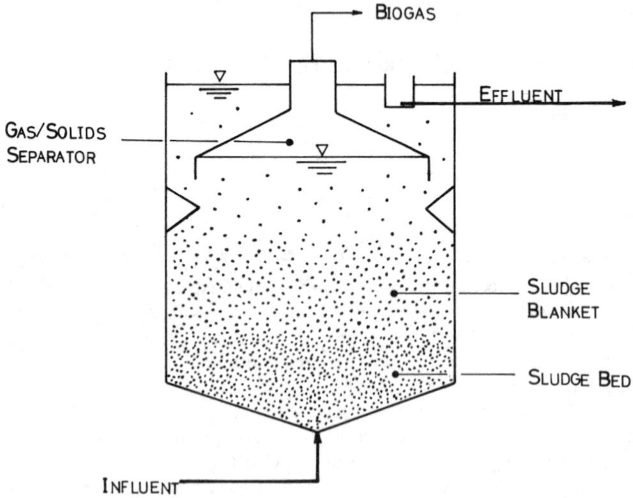

Figure 1. Schematic of the upflow anaerobic sludge-blanket process (UASB). (Reprinted with permission from Ref. 9.)

Table 1
Full-Scale Upflow Anaerobic Sludge Blanket (UASB) Installations

	Waste Characteristics			Design		
Location	**Type**	**COD (mg/l)**	**Flow (m^3/day)**	**HRT (hours)**	**COD Load. kg/m^3/day**	**COD Removal (%)**
USA						
LaCrosse, Wis.	Brewery	2,500	23,000	4.9	14.1	86
Caribou, Me.*	Starch	22,000	910	47	11	85
Plover, Wis.*	Potato	4,300	3,000	17.5	6.0	80
Europe (partial list)						
Netherlands	Sugar	17,000	3,000	24	13.3	94
Netherlands	Sugar beet	3,000	6,960	4.9	14.5	85
Netherlands	Starch	7,700	1,750	2.4	8	85
Switenland	Potato	2,260	2,210	6.5	8.3	80
Germany	Sugar beet	7,500	2,400	15	12	86
Netherlands	Alcohol	5,330	2,090	8	16	90

* *Start-up 9/82*
[Reprinted with permission from Ref. 9].

philic condition, an unstable UASB system has succeeded when the COD load became more than 12 kg/m^3/day. However, Wiegent and Lettinga [14] reported that in a thermophilic UASB system using wastewater containing sugar, the granule formation consisting of acidogens and methanogens succeeded at a high COD load, but failed with a wastewater mainly composed of volatile fatty acid.

For a gas-liquid separator, van der Meer [15] pointed out that in the settling compartment gas, liquid and sludge must be completely separated and the horizontal flow rate of clarified effluent should be adjusted slightly lower than that of the sludge granule sedimentation rate. To correlate this, Homoda and van der Berg [16] proposed using a settler outside of the reactor rather than in the upper part of the reactor. As a result, a stable UASB system could be operated at a relatively high COD load, 30 kg/m^3/day.

As mentioned, UASB systems are now widely used to treat the wastewater mainly from food industries (Table 1). An application of this system in a domestic sewage (a low COD concentration) indicated that the UASB system can operate at a rather long HRT, 22 h with a relatively low COD reduction, 60 to 80% [17].

UPFLOW ANAEROBIC FILTER PROCESS (UAFP)

UAFP systems were initially developed by Young and McCarty [18] using rocks and plastics for microbial fixation. These UAFP systems have been applied for domestic sewage and industrial wastewater containing a relatively low organic materials.

As shown in Figure 2, a reactor contains "media," i.e., microbial supporter. The granulated microorganisms not only exist in the spaces of the media, but also attach to the surface of the media; hence, a high-density microbial population can be retained in the reactor creating a hybridization of microbial floc and adhesion.

To avoid short-circuiting the flow through the packed column, a distributor is set at the bottom to make a homogeneous up-flow of wastewater. At the top, the treated wastewater and the produced biogas are separated by a free board. At the beginning stage of development, rocks (25 to 38 mm

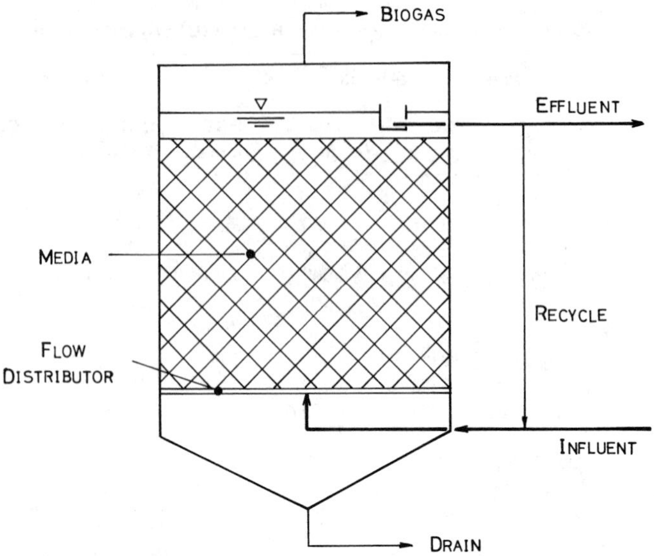

Figure 2. Schematic of the upflow anaerobic filter process (UAFP). (Reprinted with permission from Ref. 9.)

in diameter, 42% of void fraction in the reactor) were packed in the reactor, and at a COD loading of 3.4 kg/m^3/day, relatively low COD removals of 37 and 63% were respectively observed at inlet COD of 1,500 and 3,000 mg/l [18]. Afterward, the void fraction of medium to the total reactor volume was increased to 80 to 90%, as a result, it operated at a COD load of 10 to 20 kg COD/m^3/day with 20 g VSS/l of sludge concentration and removed more than 70% of the input COD [19]. From the data of full-scale UAFP (Table 2), alcohol distillery wastewater (COD = 95,000 mg/l) can be treated at a HRT of 7.8 days (COD load = 8.9 kg/m^3/day) with 75% COD removal. Besides, this UAFP was applied to a domestic sewage treatment using Raschig rings (2.5 cm ϕ) as microbial supporter (medium), resulting in BOD and SS removal of 50 to 60% and 70 to 80%, respectively, at HRT, 5–33 h (19 m^3 wastewater/day) [9].

The most significant parameter for UAFP is the selection of "medium," in which the microbial adhesion is greatly influenced by the SS content and the chemical composition of wastewater. For that, Young and Dahab [20] investigated the effects of "medium" characteristics, such as size and shape, on COD removal using the modular corrugated blocks (porosity > 95%), pall rings, and perforated spheres. As a result, at a COD load of 2 kg/m^3/day, modular corrugated blocks exhibited superior behavior by removing COD at 88% [20]. And when the COD removal is compared between cross- and tubular-flows, in most cases, COD removal is greater in cross-flow type, in the range of 20–30%, than in tubular-flow experiments. In further investigation of cross-flow systems, it was suggested that the redistributed flow in the media matrix might be a more significant parameter than the surface area of media [21].

Except for plastic media, baked clay and a melted slug (void fraction of reactor: 56%) were also useful media in the laboratory model experiments for the methanogenesis from formic, acetic, and methanol [22]. Pumice was used as microbial supporter for methanogenesis from methanol-rich wastewater of evaporate condensate from a pulp mill (COD load: 12 kg/m^3/day, COD removal: 96%) [23].

Table 2
Full-Scale Upflow Anaerobic Filter(UAFP) Installations

	Waste Characteristics		Design				
Location	Type	COD (mg/l)	Design Flow (m^3/day)	HRT (days)	Media	COD Load. kg/m^3/day	COD Removal (%)
Spokane, Washington*	Stachgluten	8,800	490	0.9	Graded rock 2.5–7.6 cm	3.8	64
Vernon, Texas	Guar Gum	9,140	823	1	9 cm Pall Rings	16	60
San Juan, Puerto Ricol**	Rum Distillery	95,000	1,325	7–8	Synthetic ("Vinyl Core")	8.9	75
Bishop, Texas	Chemical	12,000	3,785	1.5	9 cm Pall Rings	9.6	80
Pampa, Texas	Chemical	14,400	3,785	1.5	9 cm Pall Rings	10.4	90

* *No longer in operation.*
** *Downflow anaerobic filter.*
[Reprinted with permission from Ref. 9].

As a quantitative approach for UAFP in a rock-filled reactor, COD removal, E can be expressed as an empirical equation [20, 24].

$$E = 100\,(1 - \alpha/\mathrm{HRT}) \tag{1}$$

where E = COD removal (%)
α = coefficient depending on media type and size

ANAEROBIC FLUIDIZED-BED REACTOR (AFBR)

Originally, fluidized bed reactors were developed as a combustion fireplace in chemical engineering processes. Later, they were applied in biological systems for activated sludge [25] and biological denitrification treatments [26]. During the development of aerobic activated sludge processes, AFBR systems were switched to use in anaerobic sludge processes because they require a considerable energy power for aeration. A diagram of an anaerobic fluidized-bed process is shown in Figure 3. Here the media on which the microbes are adhering are fluidizing in the reactor to convert the organic materials to CH_4 and CO_2. In this system, anaerobic microbes are growing on the surface of the medium, expanding the apparent medium volume, called "expanded bed reactor." Callander and Barford [27] defined that if the expanded volume is about 10–20%, it is called a "expanded bed reactor," however, if the expanded volume is about 30–100%, it is called "fluidized bed reactor." Here, both reactors are called "fluidized bed reactors" (FBR).

When using an artificial sewage in an anaerobic FBR, more than 80% COD removal was attained at 20°C [28] and this system, at COD load 2.4 g/l/day, can tolerate shock loading for the step

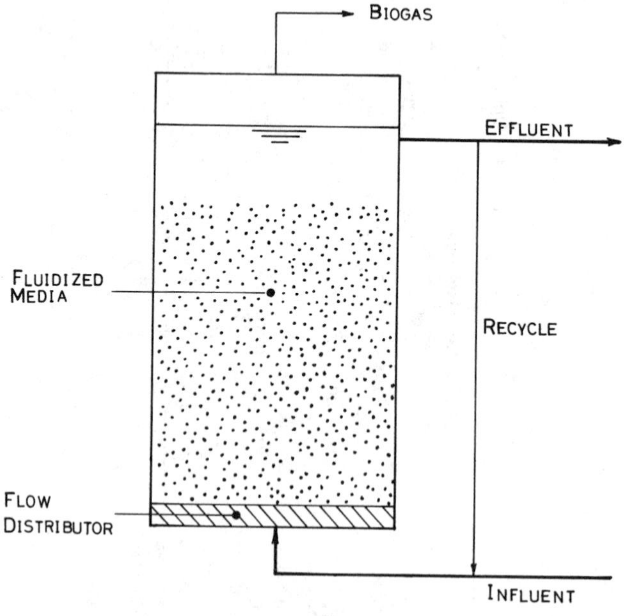

Figure 3. Schematic of the anaerobic fluidized-bed reactor (FBR). (Reprinted with permission from Ref. 9.)

Table 3
Summary—Industrial Waste Treatment with Anaerobic Fluidized Bed Reactor

Waste	COD g/l Inf	COD g/l Eff	% COD Rem.	COD Load (kg/m³/day)	HRT (days)
Whey (35°C)	54	8–14	72–84	13–38	1.4–4.9
Whey (24°C)	53	15–19	65–71	15–37	1.5–3.5
Whey (S)	52	3	94	10	5.0
Food	8	1–2	75–86	3–24	0.3–2.1
Chemical	11	0.8–3	79–93	4–27	0.6–2.8
Soft Drink	5	0.5–2	68–90	4–19	0.3–1.3
Barkery	9	1.8	80	4–12	1–2
Zimpro Sup't.	8*	0.4–3*	66–95*	3–17	0.3–2

* *Based on BOD ultimate, 35 days*

changes of temperature from 13 to 35°C and from 35 to 13°C. In the case of a COD shock loading from 1.3 to 24 g/l/day, it is observed that a steady state is established after 6 days [4].

As shown in Table 3, the anaerobic FBRs can be used not only low COD wastewater but also high COD wastewater. The table shows (see whey, 35°C) that in case of a high COD load, e.g., 13 to 38 kg/m³/day, a high COD removal (72–84%) was achieved in a relatively low HRTs, 1.4 to 4.9 days. In a two FBRs in series (see whey in Table 3), the highest COD removal (94%) was achieved. As a whole HRTs were remarkably reduced in FBR systems [29].

For two-series FBRs, Kida and Nakata [30] achieved a high BOD removal (98%) when they treated distillery wastewater from sweet potato spirits with two-FBRs in series in which crystobalite was packed as a fluidized medium.

As shock loading experiments, first, a sudden change of BOD from 2,500–3,000 mg/l to 8,700 was tested, almost no problems were observed, and even after a drastic change to 45,700, steady operation was attained after 700-min operation [31]. Second, in thermophilic anaerobic digestion [32], when COD concentration was step changed, the COD removal was affected by the COD load, not the COD concentration, and at a steady state COD removal was 80%, even at a high COD load of 30 kg/m³/day.

In conclusion, the anaerobic FBRs seem to be capable of treating at lower temperatures with low and high COD wastewaters, without a significant effects from shock loading.

The anaerobic FBRs have been progressively developed as shown by the full-scale operation data in Table 4. This anaerobic FBR is commercially available from Dorr-Oliver, Austgen Biojet, and Gist-Brocades Companies.

Significant engineering improvements can minimize the mechanical power for fluidization for anaerobic FBRs. To achieve this, the following criteria are required: (a) reduce the expanded volume; (b) select a medium with a low density and a high specific area; and (c) avoid fragility. Usually, media such as sand, quartzite, almina, anthracite, granular activated carbon, and crystobalite are available in a particle size, about 0.5 mm.

Fluidization characteristics of media have been analyzed in a biological denitrification [33], and bed voidage ε could be expressed as a function of superficial liquid velocity in the bed, υ_z (m/s) as follows.

$$\ln \varepsilon = \frac{1}{n} \ln \upsilon_z - \frac{1}{n} \ln v_i \quad (2)$$

where v_i, n = constants
ε = [(total expanded bed volume) – (total volume of medium particles with attached growth)]/(total expanded bed volume)

Table 4
Full-Scale Anaerobic Fluidized Bed Reactors(Industrial)

	Waste Characteristics			Design			
Location	Type	COD (mg/l)	Flow (m^3/day)	HRT (hours)	COD Load. (kg/m^3/day)	Media	COD Removal (%)
Birmingham, Ala.	Soft-drink bottling waste	6,900	380	6	9.6	0.6 mm E.S. sand	77
Midwest	Soy-processing waste	9,000	—	<24	13	0.4 mm E.S. sand	—

[Reprinted with permission from Ref. 9].

And for the attached cells on the medium, the following empirical equation was proposed [34].

$$x = \rho_{bd}(1 - \varepsilon)\left[1 - \left(\frac{dm}{dp}\right)^3\right] \quad (3)$$

where x = bacterial concentration (mg/l)
ρ_{bd} = biofilm density in dry basis (g/ml)
dp = diameter of medium particle (μm)
dm = diameter of medium particle with attached growth (μm)

In anaerobic fluidized bed reactor, a biofilm thickness on the medium is generally about 20 μm, and this thickness increases with the increase of COD load, e.g. up to maximum 120 μm [28].

ANAEROBIC FIXED-FILM REACTOR (AFFR)

Anaerobic FFRs have a fixed supporter with a channel or tubular type on which anaerobes can adhere (see Figure 4). Wastewater flows downstream along a fixed-film support and anaerobic digestion occurs from organic materials to CH_4 and CO_2. When changed to an upstream type, it becomes similar to a UAFP; however, this system tends to clog the flow at the bottom area with a high density of microbial cells, caused by the laminar flow at the bottom of reactor. Hence, to avoid the excess formation of biofilm, a downstream type (see Figure 4) may be better for practical use. Generally, the interval between fixed-film supports is 20–100 mm with 600–1,400 mm in length and 50–250 m^2 specific area per m^3 reactor.

Support materials used are glass, PVC, needle punched polyester (NPP), potter's clay, etc. [27]. An example that used potter's clay for anaerobic digestion of chemical waste and bean blanching waste indicates that, even at a quite low temperature, 10°C, 80% COD removal was achieved at a COD load of 5 kg/m³/day [35]. And in a intermittent COD feeding treatment, e.g., 7-h supply/day,

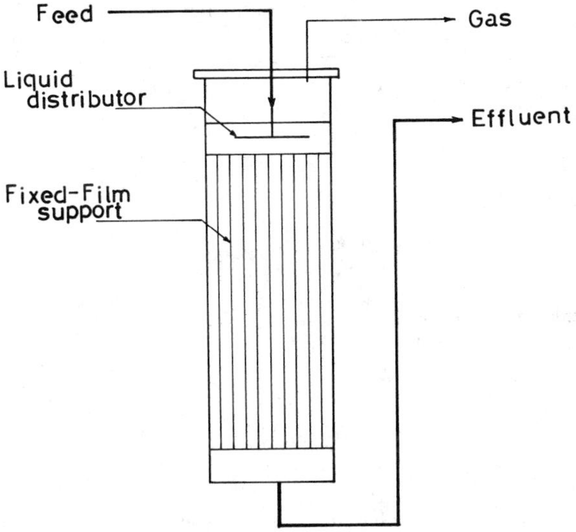

Figure 4. Schematic of the anaerobic fixed-film reactor (FFR). (Reprinted with permission from Ref. 36.)

it was possible to increase the COD load to 26 kg/m^3/day with higher gas production than that of continuous operation [36]. In a second example that used a needle punched polyester (void space 88%) as a supporter, when a COD load (=30 kg/m^3/day) suddenly increased 6 times from the previous operation, it was observed that an unsteady state developed into a new steady state after a 2-day operation using a well-buffered wastewater [37]. Although it was reported that a maximum COD load of 20 kg/m^3/day might be possible to digest at 35°C in a laboratory scale, there have been few reported in full-scale operation.

TWO-PHASE ANAEROBIC DIGESTION

Novel bioreactors for anaerobic digestion such as UASB, UAFP, and AFBR have inherent problems when operating at a high COD loads because the overall growth rate of acidogenic bacteria proceeds faster, e.g., 10-fold than that of methanogenic bacteria [38]. When this happens, the inhibitory products, such as volatile fatty acids and H_2, accumulate in the reactor, consequently, the whole digestion is slowed down. To overcome the problem, two-phase anaerobic digestion consisting of acidogenic and methanogenic fermentations has been proposed [39]. A full-scale process, e.g., Anodek process (Konincks Co., Belgium) claims that a 70–97% COD removal, and a biogas production of 3–13 Nm^3/m^3/day with methane content of 65 to 80% were obtained when operated at a COD load of 20–60 kg/m^3/day for acidogenic fermentation (1st phase) and at a COD load of 6–30 kg/m^3/day in methanogenic one (2nd phase) [40]. As other examples, Cohen et al. [41] constructed a two-phase system consisting of a complete stirred reactor for the first phase and a UASB for the second phase. Using glucose (1%) in a model experiment they obtain 1 l methane from 1 g TOC (theoretical value) with a growth yield of 0.11 g/g glucose. Pipyn et al. [6] reported that, by a similar two-phase fermentation of Cohen, they treated alcohol distillery waste (COD = 10,000 mg/l) at HRTs of 16–72 h in first phase, and 14 h in the second phase, with 84% COD removal and 92% BOD removal. They also investigated the effects of shock operation of COD load, temperature, and pH on the anaerobic digestion.

Messing [42] proposed a two-phase system consisting of UAFP for the first phase and a horizontal AFP for the second phase. In both phases, ceramics as a medium (pore size: ~5 times of bacterial cell size) was used. They treated sewage wastewater (COD 800 to 2,600 mg/l) at HRT of 2–5.5 h with a high concentration of methane (~90%) and a low concentration of CO_2 (~5%). Kishimoto et al. [43] studied the kinetics of two-phase system in mesophilic methane fermentation. In acidogenic fermentation, Monod's equation relationship was obtained between total sugar concentration and removal rate.

$$V_1 = \frac{455S_1}{1.5 + S_1} \tag{4}$$

where V_1 = removal rate of total sugar (g/l/day)
S_1 = total sugar concentration (g/l)

In the methanogenic phase, there exists first-order relationship between volatile fatty acid concentration and the removal rate of volatile fatty acids. However, the removal

$$V_2 = 0.82S_2 \tag{5}$$

where V_2 = removal rate of volatile fatty acid (g/l/day)
S_2 = volatile fatty acid concentration (g/l)

rate of volatile fatty acid was greatly inhibited when the presence of volatile fatty acids was greater than 3,000 mg/l. In addition, it was ascertained that the overall growth rate of acidogenic bacteria is much faster than that of methanogenic bacteria.

In acidogenic fermentation, the produced propionic and butyric acids severely inhibit the bacterial growth and are thermodynamically undergradable to acetic acid and H_2 at the standard condition. In acidogenic fermentation, culture pH affects the sorts of volatile fatty acid produced, i.e., acetic acid is mainly accumulated at pHs between 4 and 7, propionic acid at neutral pH, butyric acid between 6 and 7, and lactic acid and ethanol at nearly 4, although this tendency is considerably dependent upon microbial ecosystem, type of wastewater, fermentation conditions, etc. [38, 41, 44, 45]. In addition, since the contained suspended solids in wastewater greatly depend upon the performance of UASB and UAFP, the acidogenic fermentation (first stage) is useful in combination with UASB and UAFP (second phase) so as to reduce the suspended solids which enter in the second phase.

OTHERS

Upflow tower digesters (UFTD) [46] were developed as a modification of UASBs. Upflow blanket filter reactors [47], which are hybrids of UASBs and UAFPs were also developed. In an upflow tower digester (see Figure 5), chemical flocculants are supplied for floc formation in contrast with natural microbial granulation in UASB. Sludge concentration in this digester can be achieved at 20–70 g/l. In treating cane juice stillage (COD: 26,000 mg/l) with a high concentration of SO_4^{2-} (1,470 mg/l), a maximum COD load of 5.3 kg/m^3/day was achieved with addition of iron [48].

An example of an upflow blanket filter process is shown in Figure 6 where the upper part of reactor (1/3 in total volume, UAFP) contains plastic ring to maintain a high bacterial population, while the lower part is a sludge blanket space (UASB). Guiot and Berg [47] tested a sugar wastewater (COD: 2,500 mg/l, COD:N:P = 100:5:0.8) in this reactor at 25°C, where COD removal of 96% was obtained at a high COD load of 25 kg/m^3/day and a high SS reduction.

Anaerobic rotating biological contactors are similar to rotating biological contactors [49], which were originally developed for aerobic treatments. Tait and Fridman [50] used polymethylmethacrylate for a disk steeping (70% depth) in sugar wastewater. As a result, a TOC removal of 96% was achieved at a TOC load of 21.7 g/m^2 disk/day (=4.2 kg/m^3/day), indicating a pseudo-first-order relationship between residual TOC and HRT.

$$\ln C = \ln Ci - (0.3744 - 7.96 \times 10^{-5}\, Ci)T \tag{6}$$

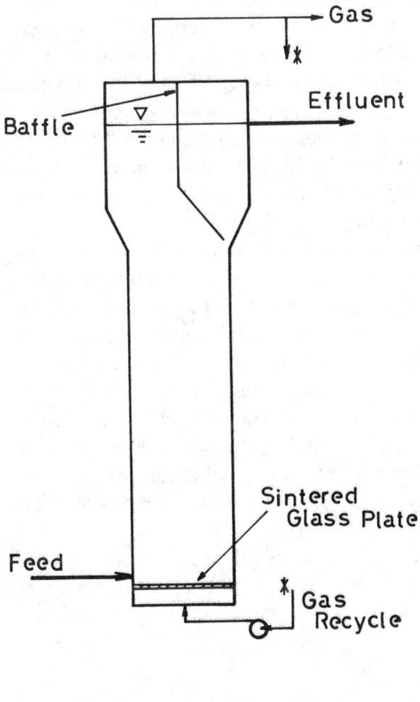

Figure 5. Schematic of the upflow tower digestor. (Adapted from Ref. 48.)

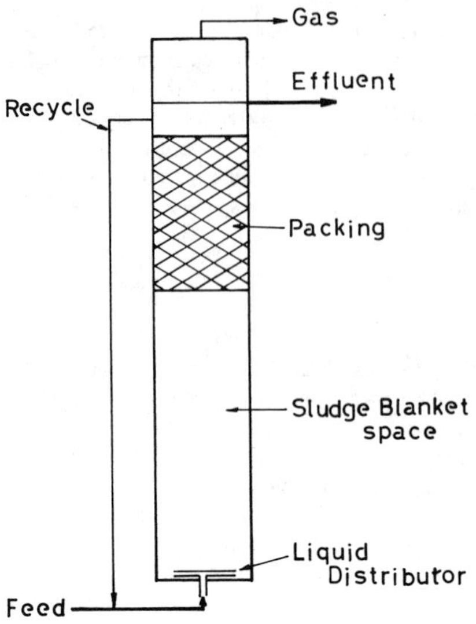

Figure 6. Sketch of the upflow blanket filter reactor. (Adapted from Ref. 47.)

where C = residual TOC (mg/l)
Ci = initial TOC (mg/l)
T = HRT (h)

DENSE AND SOLID-STATE ANAEROBIC DIGESTIONS

Slurry type and solid state wastes are discharged from food processing factories, slaughterhouses and agro-industries. As an example of slurry type waste, pig manure was treated in two-phase anaerobic digestion by Colleran et al. [51]. The solubilization of pig manure first conducted resulted in 50–80% of total COD being solubilized at HRT of 12 to 15 days at mesophilic temperature, and 88% COD removal was achieved in UAFP at a COD load of 20 kg/m^3/day (30°C, HRT = 3 days). Garbage mixed with sewage sludge (VS 13–15%) was also treated in a two-phase system in conjunction with alkali pretreatment (pH 9.8). The pretreated substrate increased the production of volatile fatty acids up to 3 times compared to that without pretreatment. A pilot-scale test of this two-phase anaerobic digestion [52] was carried out with the feed substrate (VS 8–16%) and resulted in a gas production rate of 3.2 m^3 CH_4/m^3/day at a loading rate of 9.4 kg VS/m^3/day.

Dry anaerobic digestion is generally in order when solids concentration is greater than 25%. Compared to the usual liquid wastes, the low water content of dry anaerobic digestion allows lower post-treatment costs and smaller reactor volume. Also heating costs are reduced for maintaining an optimum fermentation condition because of the relatively slow heat radiation from the reactor wall, and the power consumption cost is eliminated because agitation is not required. Wujcik and Jewell [53] investigated a dry anaerobic digestion of straw mixed with dairy cow manure (TS = 25%), which showed that the rate of conversion and the efficiency of conversion were similarly close to those of a 10% solid mixture. They also tested corn stover and wheat straw for anaerobic digestion and found that increased fermentation temperature could enhance the biogas production up to 7 v/v/day (average: 3 v/v/day) and 60% of total volatile solids had been decomposed to biogas after 60-day fermentation [7].

Ghosh et al. [54] proposed a solid-bed anaerobic digestion rather than a dense-fermentation (see Figure 7). In this solid-bed two-phase digestion process, the main products from acidogenic fermentation were volatile fatty acids and ethanol, and methane concentration of biogas from methane

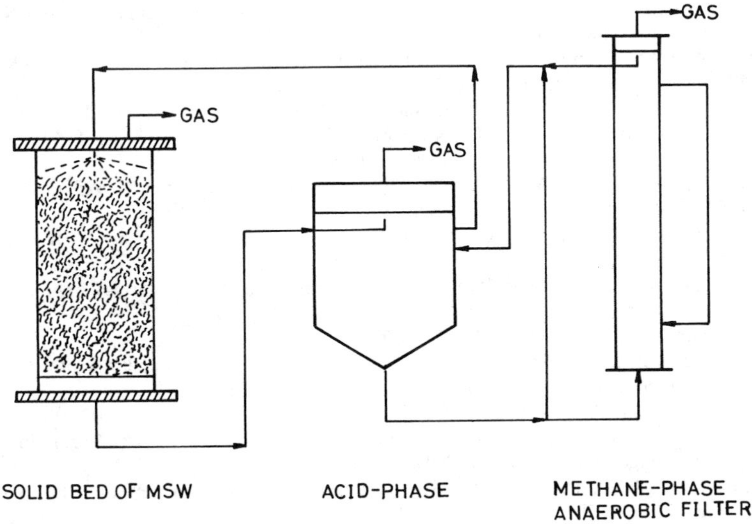

Figure 7. Solid-bed two-phase digestion of synthetic refuse. MSW: municipal solid waste. (Reprinted with permission from Ref. 54.)

phase anaerobic filter was about 88%. A methane yield from municipal solid waste (simulated) was found to be 0.063 m^3/kg VS.

Baere et al. [55] developed a dry anaerobic composting process consisting of "dry fermentation" and "composting" (commercially named "Dranco Process"), where available substrates (TS = 30 to 35%) were first selected from household refuse and then anaerobically digested for 12 to 18 days. Results from a pilot plant test (digestion tank = 56.5 m^3) indicated that gas evolution in a mesophilic condition was 2–3 m^3/m^3/day, but in a thermophilic condition, this increased to 6–8 m^3/m^3/day with a methane yield of 0.1 m^3/kg VS. The obtained compost after the post-digestion, followed by drying, was a useful fertilizer (named Humotex) that was better than a compost aerobically produced.

It would be expected that anaerobic digestion is not only applicable for dilute wastewaters, but also for dense ones involving solid waste. These wastewater treatment processes are not only less-energy consuming, but also provide useful technologies to recover biogas from renewable biomass wastes.

REFERENCES

1. Dague, R. R., Mckinney, R. E., and Pfeffer, J. T., "Anaerobic Activated Sludge," *J. WPCF*, 38, 220 (1966).
2. Lettinga, G., Roersma, R., and Grin, P., "Anaerobic Treatment of Raw Domestic Sewage an Ambient Temperatures Using a Granular Bed UASB Reactor," *Biotechnol. Bioeng.*, 25, 1701 (1983).
3. Bories, A., Raynal, I., and Jover, J. P., "Fixed Film Reactor with Plastic Media for Methane Fermentation," *Energy from Biomass*, Applied Science Pub. (1983).
4. Jewell, W. J., Switzenbaum, M. S., and Morris, J. W., "Municipal Wastewater Treatment With the Anaerobic Attached Microbial Film Expanded Bed Reactor," *J. WPCF*, 53, 482 (1981).
5. Sutton, P. M., and Li, A., "Anitron and Oxitron System: High-Rate Anaerobic and Aerobic Biological Treatment System for Industry," Proceedings of Industrial Waste Conference. 36th (1981), p. 665.

6. Pipyn, P., Verstraete, W., and Ombregt, J. P., "A Pilot Scale Anaerobic Upflow Reactor Treating Distillery Wastewaters," *Biotechnol. Letts.*, 1, 495 (1979).
7. Jewell, W. J., "New Approaches in Anaerobic Digestor Design," 1981 International Gas Research Conference, Los Angeles, Calif., 796 (1982).
8. Lettinga, G., van Velsen, A. F. M., Hobma, S. W., de Zeeum, W., and Klapwijk, A., "Use of the Upflow Sludge Blanket (UASB) Reactor Concept for Biological Wastewater Treatment Especially for Anaerobic Treatment," *Biotechnol. Bioeng.*, 22, 699 (1980).
9. Bowker, R. P. G., "New Wastewater Treatment for Industrial Applications," *Environmental Progress*, 2, 235 (1983).
10. Switzenbaum, M. S., "Anaerobic fixed film wastewater treatment," *Enzyme Microb. Technol.*, 5, 242 (1983)
11. Lettinga, G., de Zeeuw, W., and Ouborg, E., "Anaerobic Treatment of Wastes Containing Methanol and Higher Alcohols," *Water Research*, 15, 171 (1981).
12. ten Brummeler, E., Hulshoff Poi, L. W., Dolfing, J., Lettinga, G., and Zehnder, A. J. B., "Methanogenesis in an Upflow Anaerobic Sludge Blanket Reactor at pH 6 on an Acetate-Propionate Mixture," *Applied and Environmental Microbiology*, 49, 1472 (1985).
13. Endo, G., "Recent Progress in Methane Fermentation," *Hakkokogaku*, 64, 202 (1986).
14. Wiegant, W. M., and Lettinga, G., "Thermophilic Anaerobic Digestion of Sugars in Upflow Anaerobic Sludge Blanket Reactors," *Biotechnol. Bioeng.*, 27, 1603 (1985).
15. van der Meer, R. R., and de Vletter, R., "Anaerobic treatment of wastewater: the gas-liquid-sludge separator," *J. WPCF*, 54, 1482 (1982).
16. Hamoda, M. F., and van den Berg, L., "Effect of Settling on Performance of the Upflow Anaerobic Sludge Bed Reactors," *Water Res.*, 18, 1561 (1984).
17. Lettinga, G., and Vinken, J. N., "Feasibility of the Upflow Anaerobic Sludge Blanket (UASB) Process for the treatment of Low-Strength Waters," Proceedings of the 35th Industrial Waste Conference, Purdue University (May 13–15, 1980).
18. Young, J. C., and MaCarty, P. L., "The anaerobic filter for waste treatment," *J. WPCF*, 41, 161 (1969).
19. Braun, R., and Huss, S., "Anaerobic Filter Treatment of Molasses Distillery Slops," *Water Research*, 16, 1167 (1982).
20. Young, J. C., and Dahab, M. F., "Effect of Media Design on the Performance of Fixed-Bed Anaerobic Reactors," *Wat. Sci. Tech.* 15, 369 (1987).
21. Song, K., and Young, J. C., "Media design factors for fixed-bed filters," *J. WPCF*, 58, 115 (1986).
22. Nishio, N., Kayawake, E., and Nagai, S., "Rapid Methane Production from Formate or Acetate in Fixed Bed Bioreactors," *J. Ferment. Technol.*, 63, 205 (1985).
23. Minami, K., Horiyama, T., Tasaki, M., and Tanimoto, Y., "Methane Production Using a Bio-Reactor Packed with Pumice Stone on an Evaporator Condensate of a Kraft Pulp Mill," *J. Ferment. Tech.*, 64, 523 (1986).
24. Young, J. C., and McCarty, P. L., "The anaerobic filter for waste treatment," Technical Report No. 87, Department of Civil Engineering, Stanford University, Stanford, California.
25. Jewell, W. J., and Cummings, R. J., "An Optimized Biological Waste Treatment Process for Oxygen Utilization," Paper presented at the 47th Annual Conference, Water Poll. Control Fed., Denver, Colo., (Oct. 1974).
26. Jeris, J. S., and Owens, R. W., "Pilot-scale, high-rate biological denitrification," *J. WPCF*, 47, 2043 (1975).
27. Callander, I. J., and Barford, J. P., "Recent Advances in Anaerobic Digestion Technology," *Process Biochemistry, August*, 24 (1983).
28. Switzenbaum, M. S., and Jewell, W. J., "Anaerobic attached-film expanded-bed reactor treatment," *J. WPCF*, 52, 1953 (1980).
29. Jeris, J. S., "Industrial Wastewater Treatment Using Anaerobic Fluidized Bed Reactors," *Wat. Sci. Tech.*, 15, 169 (1983).
30. Kida, K., and Nakata, T., "Treatment of distillery wastewater by a series of two anaerobic fluidization method (in Japanese)." *Bioscience and Industry*, 45, 107 (1987).
31. Barnes, D., Bliss, P. J., Grauer, B., Kuo, E. M., Robins, K., and Maclean, G., "Influence of Organic Shock Loads on the Performance of an Anaerobic Fluidized Bed System," Proc. of Industrial Waste Conf. 1983, 38th, 715 (1984).

32. Schraa, G., and Jewell, W. J., "High rate conversions of soluble organics with a thermophilic anaerobic attached film expanded bed," *J. WPCF*, 56, 226 (1984).
33. Ngian, K., and Martin, W. R. B., "Bed Expansion Characteristics of Liquid Fluidized Particles with Attached Microbial Growth," *Biotechnol. Bioeng.*, 22, 1843 (1980).
34. Shieh, W. K., Sutton, P. M., and Kos, P., "Predicting reactor biomass concentration in a fluidized-bed system," *J. WPCF*, 53, 1574 (1981).
35. Kennedy, K. J., and van den Berg, L., "Stability and Performance of Anaerobic Fixed Film Reactors during Hydraulic Overloading at 10–35°C," *Water Res.*, 16, 1391 (1981).
36. van den Berg, L., and Kennedy, K. J., "Comparison of Intermittent and Continuous Loading of Stationary Fixed-Film Reactors for Methane Production from Waste," *J. Chem. Tech. Biotechnol.*, 32, 427 (1982).
37. Kennedy, K. J., Muzar, M., and Copp, G. H., "Stability and Performance of Mesophilic Anaerobic Fixed-Film Reactors during Organic Overloading," *Biotechnol. Bioeng.*, 27, 86 (1985).
38. Noike, T., "Purification Mechanism of Anaerobic Digestion and Approach to Two-phase Digestion Process," *J. Environmental Pollution Control*, 17, 751, (1981).
39. Ghosh, S., Conrad, J. R., and Klass, D. L., "Anaerobic acidogenesis of wastewater sludge," *J. WPCF*, 47, 30 (1975).
40. Teraoka, H., "BIOTIM–A," *Zousui Gijitsu (in Japanese)* 11, 61 (1985).
41. Cohen, A., Zoetemeyer, R. J., van Deursen, A., and van Andel, J. G., "Anaerobic Digestion of Glucose with Separated Acid Production and Methane Formation," *Water Res.*, 13, 571 (1979).
42. Messing, R. A., "Immobilized Microbes and a high-rate, continuous waste processor for the production of high Btu gas and the reduction of pollutants," *Biotechnol. Bioeng.*, 24, 1115 (1982).
43. Kishimoto, M., Shima, N., Miyazawa, T., Kida, K., and Nakata, T., "Methane Production from Distillery Waste Water by Two-phase Methane Fermentation," *The Hitachi Zosen Technical Review*, 45, 1 (1984).
44. Roy, D., and Jones, L. M., "Acidogenesis in the two-phase anaerobic process," *J. Environ. Sci. Health*, A20(1), 1 (1985).
45. Belgian patents 866.935, 890.724, "Method and Device for Producing Methane Gas from and the Treatment of Aqueous Substrate Containing Organic Compounds by an Anaerobic Fermentation Process".
46. Callander, I. J., "The Development of the Tower Fermentor for Anaerobic Digestion," 1982, Ph.D. Thesis, The University of Sydney, Sydney, Australia.
47. Guiot, S. R., and van den Berg, L., "Performance and Biomass Retention of an Upflow Anaerobic Reactor Combining a Sludge Blanket and a Filter," *Biotechnol. Letts.*, 6, 161 (1984).
48. Callander, I. J., and Barford, J. P., "Anaerobic Digestion of High Sulphate Cane Juice Stillage in a Tower Fermenter," *Biotechnol. Letts.*, 5, 755 (1983).
49. Anthonie, R. L., Kluge, D. L., and Mielke, J. H., "Evaluation of a rotating disk waste water plant," *J. WPCF*, 46, 498 (1974).
50. Tait, S. J., and Friedman, A. A., "Anaerobic rotating biological contactor for carbonaceous wastewaters," *J. WPCF*, 52, 2257 (1980).
51. Colleran, E., Barry, M., Wilkie, A., and Newell, P. J., "Anaerobic Digestion of Agricultural Wastes Using the Upflow Anaerobic Filter Design" *Process Biochemistry, March/April.* 12 (1982).
52. Ishida, M., Odawara, Y., Geyo, T., and Okum, A. H., Biogasification of municipal waste, p. 797," Proceedings of Recycling Berlin '79., In K. J. Thome-Kozmiensky (ed.) Freitag Verlag, Berlin, 1979.
53. Wujcik, W. J., and Jewell, W. J., "Dry Anaerobic Fermentation," In Biotechnology and Bioengineering Symposium No. 10, 43 (1980).
54. Ghosh, S., Henry, M. P., and Sajjad, A., "Novel two-phase anaerobic gasification with solid-bed acid digestion in tandem with fixed-film methane fermentation," Proceedings of 1983 International gas research conference, London, June, 330 (1983).
55. de Baere, L., van Meenen, P., and Verstraete, W., "Anaerobic Fermentation of Refuse," Proceedings of 3rd International Symposium on Materials and Energy from Refuse, Antwerten, 1986, 6.1–6.14.

CHAPTER 21

SOLVENT EXTRACTION WITH CHELATING AGENTS

Makoto Harada

Institute of Atomic Energy
Kyoto University, Japan

and

Yoshikazu Miyake

Kyoto Institute of Technology, Japan

CONTENTS

INTRODUCTION

Solvent extraction of metals is a selective separation procedure for isolating and concentrating metals from aqueous solutions with the aid of an immiscible organic solvent. Metals in ionic form have a strong affinity for the aqueous phase, whereas they are energetically less favorable to the organic solvent. For extracting metal ions to the organic phase, metal ions must be neutralized by forming organic-soluble neutral metal complexes. The reaction of this complex formation must be reversible because of the necessity of back extraction to another aqueous phase for succeeding processes of metal purification.

The solvent extraction can be classified as shown in Table 1, according to the nature of the chemical reaction, which provides the metal complex in neutral form. The solvent extraction with chelating extractants has become increasingly important in connection with hydrometallurgical extraction processes. In the early and mid 1970s, several chelating extractants were produced. The first is the LIX series of hydroxyoxime extractants, which were provided from General Mills Chemical Company Inc. (now Henkel Corporation). The LIX oximes are widely applied to copper and nickel separation processes. The Kelex extractants of oxine type were originally proposed by Ashland Chemical Company for alternative copper extractant. In the 1970s, chelating extractants of β-diketone and quinolyl sulfonamide types have been produced. These chelating extractants and their application to the separation of primary metals and the secondary resources of metals such as scrup and sludges have been reviewed in [1–9].

The investigators who are interested in solvent extraction of metals are mainly analytical chemists and in part solution chemists, or the persons who are engaged in the application of it to nuclear fuel cycle processes. In the mid of 1970, the research on chelating extraction processes had become very active in many fields due to their hydrometallurgical applications.

The metal complex formation is usually very fast in the extractions with the aid of ion-pair and solvation interactions, whereas, in the extraction with chelating agents, the rate is relatively slow. The rate strongly depends upon the metal species and also upon the solubility and pK_a of the extractants, the pK_a being usually high. Therefore, kinetics of metal extraction is of primary concern together with extraction equilibrium for selecting optimal extractor type and for the design and operation of the extractor. The selective separation with the aid of the difference in extraction rates is also important for developing the advanced separation methods.

Metal extraction with chelating agents can occur by completing several processes; first dissolution of the chelating agent in the aqueous phase, followed by the complex formation in the aqueous phase, and thereafter partition of the produced metal complex in neutral form into the organic phase. Interface itself is of considerable importance as providing the reaction location of the complex formation. The phrase, interface, denotes the phase boundary between aqueous and organic phases where steep concentration changes of substances are observed, and distinguishes from the diffusion boundary layer and from thin reaction layer in the aqueous phase adjacent to the interface. The

Table 1
Classification of Solvent Extraction Systems

Extraction Type	Interaction Type	Extractants
Compound formation	Mainly coordination bond	*Chelating extractant: acidic chelating agents* Non-chelating extractant: carboxylic-, sulfonic phosphoric-, phosphonic-, phosphinic acids
Ion-pair formation	Mainly electrostatic bond	High molecular amine salts, polyphenyl-metalloids polyalkyl-ammonium or sulfonium types
Solvation adduct formation	Solvation-electrostatic bond	Carbon-, sulfur-, or phosphorous-bonded oxygen-bearing extractants such as TBP, TOPO etc., alkyl sulfides

mass transfer accompanied with complex formation reaction is essentially the same as the gas absorption processes, but a variety of reaction processes are concerned with the extraction. At this point, the metal extraction process differs from the simple gas absorption process.

In recent years, many reports have appeared on the kinetics of metal extraction with chelating agents. This chapter does not aim at reviewing the subject of solvent extraction in full. The reader should consult the other books [1, 10–14]. Rational understanding of the extraction kinetics is important for developing new solvent extraction systems that need the molecular designs of the extractants and the design of separation field, and also provides an important basis for the extractor design. Therefore, we focus on the principles governing the kinetics of metal extraction with chelating agents, as they are presently understood. The first section provides the minimum requirement of the equilibrium relationship concerned with the solvent extraction with chelating agents. The second section is concerned with the interfacial properties of chelating extractants, which are required for understanding the kinetics. Thirdly, we highlight reaction kinetics in homogeneous phase, which provides an important basis of the heterogeneous kinetics of metal extraction. The kinetics of the metal extraction is reviewed in the fourth section. The effects of the substituent hydrocarbon group of the extractant and of the diluent for the extractant on the metal extraction rate are then discussed. The fifth section discusses the catalytic role in the chelating extraction systems. The last section briefly highlights the rational methods of designing the extraction system.

EXTRACTION EQUILIBRIUM

Chelating Extractants

Chelating agents must contain at least two donor groups. These donor atoms are usually oxygen, nitrogen, sulfur or phosphorus elements. Chelating agents used as extractants have a dissociative proton, such as carboxyl group —COOH, hydroxyl group —OH, oxime group =NOH, imino group =NH, and thiol group —SH, etc., being a monobasic acid. The other donor group, which contains non-dissociative protons such as carbonyl group =CO, nitroso group —NO, amino group $=NH_2$, trivalent nitrogen atom =N, and thiocarbonyl group =CS, is arranged to form the chelating ring with metal ion. These chelating extractants are used for the analysis of metal ions and for the recovery of metals in leaching solution of ores and others. There are several chelating agents with the combinations of donor groups. We shall confine our attention to the important chelating agents in commercial use. The typical chelating extractants are shown in Table 2.

Chelating extractants generally have following characteristics: The solubility of commercial extractants with a long alkyl chain is low in the aqueous phase to prevent the loss of these into the aqueous phase. The acidity of chelating extractants is weak, the pK_a in the aqueous phase being large as shown in Table 2. The commercial chelating extractants have a high selectivity for metal ion, e.g., the β-hydroxyoxime used for hydrometallurgy of copper extracts only slightly the iron that is involved in the leaching solution. The selectivity of metal ion can be controlled by changing pH in aqueous phase. The rate of metal extraction with chelating agents, however, is slower than in the extractions with basic and neutral extractants such as trioctyl amine (TOA) and tributyl phosphate (TBP)

There are many excellent books and reviews [10–14] that contain the extensive data concerning the equilibrium of metal extraction by chelating agents. Here we confine ourselves to discussing the equilibrium concerned with metal extraction and the commercially useful chelating agents from the standpoint of the Linear Free Energy Relationship (LFER) and the other correlations.

Distribution of Chelating Extractants

The distribution coefficent of a chelating agent is defined by

$$D_{HR} = \bar{C}_{HR}/C_{HR} \tag{1}$$

where C_{HR} and $\bar{C}_{HR}$ represent the total concentration of HR species in the aqueous and the organic phases, respectively. The overbar represents the species present in organic phase. The chemical

Table 2
Typical Chelating Agents

Structure	R_1	R_2	X	Commercial Name	pK_a
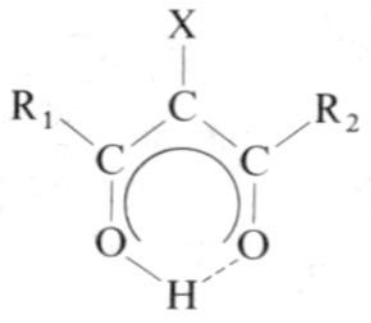	$-CH_3$	$-CH_3$	$-H$	Acetylacetone	8.9
	$-CH_3$	$-C_6H_5$	$-H$	Benzoylacetone	8.6
	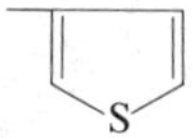	$-CF_3$	$-H$	Thenoyltrifuluoroacetone	6.2
	$-R'_1$	branched alkyl chain	$-H$ or $-CN$	LIX54 (Henkel)	
	$-C_{12}H_{25}$	$-CF_3$ or $-C_2F_5$	$-H$	LIX51 (Henkel)	
	$-C_6H_2R'_1R'_2R'_3$	$-H$	$-H$	Hostarex DK16 (Hoechst)	
β-diketone	R'_1, R'_2, R'_3 alkyl, alkoxy	$-Cl$ or $-F$			
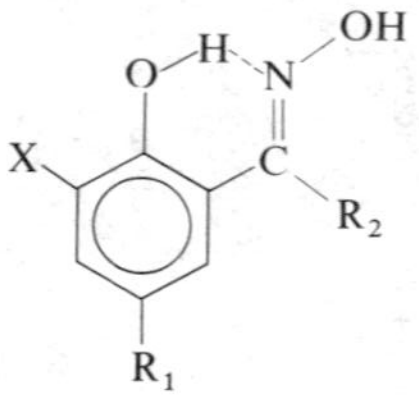	$-H$	$-H$	$-H$	Salicylaldoxime	10.7 (75% dioxane)
	$-C_9H_{19}$	$-C_6H_5$	$-H$	LIX65N (Henkel)	8.5
	$-C_9H_{19}$	$-CH_3$	$-H$	SME529 (Henkel)	10.5
	$-C_9H_{19}$	$-H$	$-H$	P1 (Acorga)	
	$-C_9H_{19}$	$-C_6H_5$	$-Cl$	LIX70 (Henkel)	
	$-CH_2C_6H_5$	$-H$	$-H$	P17 (Acorga)	
(β-hydroxyoxime)					
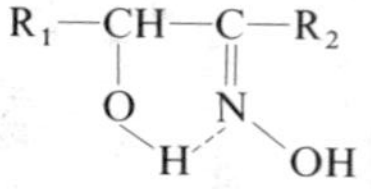	$-C_6H_5$	$-C_6H_5$		α-benzoinoxime	
	$-CH(C_2H_5)C_4H_9$ ($R_1 = R_2$)			LIX63 (Henkel)	
(α-hydroxyoxime)					

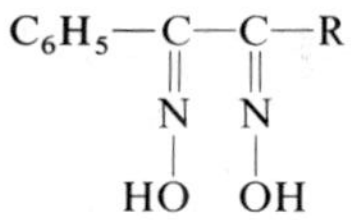 (α-dioxime)		RD573 (Shell)	
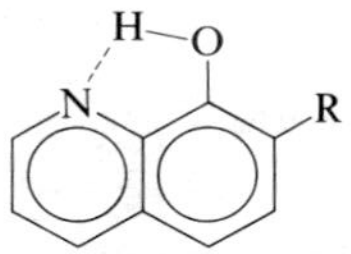 (oxine)	R: —H R: —$CH(CHCH_2)C_9H_{19}$ Kelex 100 + p-nonylphenol	8-hydroxyquinoline Kelex 100 (Sherex) Kelex 120	9.7
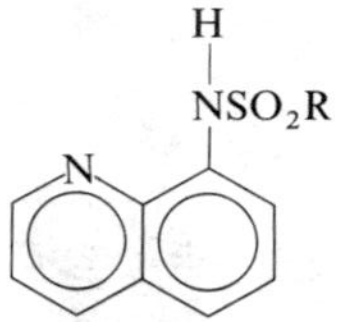 (sulfoneamidoquinoline)	R: -alkylaryl	LIX34 (Henkel)	
$C_6H_5NH{-}NH{-}C(=S)N{=}NC_6H_5$		Dithizone	12.5

species of the agent in the organic phase, which has low dielectric constant and is insoluble in the aqueous phase, are the tautomers, HR and HR*, and the aggregates, $(HR)_m$ and $(HR^*)_n$, of the agent. $\bar{C}_{HR}$ in Equation (1) is expressed as

$$\bar{C}_{HR} = [\overline{HR}] + [\overline{HR^*}] + \sum_m m[\overline{(HR)_m}] + \sum_n n[\overline{(HR^*)_n}] \tag{2}$$

The chemical species in the aqueous phase consist of the tautomer and the conjugate base, R^-, which is formed by release of proton from the extractant, when the protonation reaction of the agents is ignored:

$$C_{HR} = [HR] + [HR^*] + [R^-] \tag{3}$$

Here, the aggregation of the agent is neglected in the aqueous phase, because water has high dielectric constant. The distribution of chelating agents depends on many factors, the tautomerization constants in both phases, the aggregation constant in the organic phase, the acid dissociation constant in the aqueous phase, and also the partition constant of the extractants in monomeric form between both phases.

Isomerization of Chelating Agents

The tautomer of the β-diketone is well known to be the enol and keto isomers such as

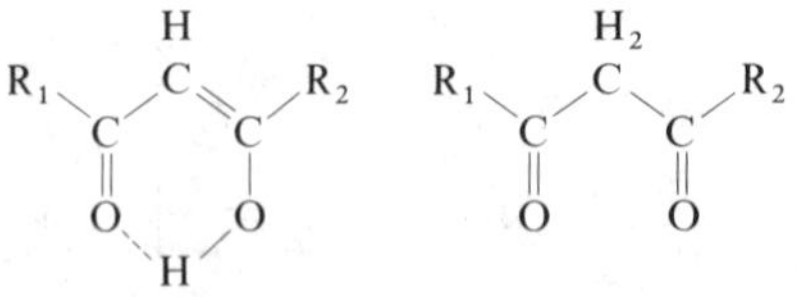

(4)

[enol] [keto]

$$\bar{K}_T = [\overline{HR}]/[\overline{HR^*}], \qquad K_T = [HR]/[HR^*]$$

The tautomerization constants $\bar{K}_T$ and K_T of typical β-diketones in the several organic and aqueous phases are shown in Table 3. The enolic isomer is more stable than the keto form in the organic phase of low dielectric constant, due to intramolecular hydrogen bonding in the enolic form. The

Table 3
Equilibrium Constant of Tautomerization for β-diketones at 298 K

β-diketone[a]	Solvent	K_T = [enol]/[keto]	Ref.
AA	gas (T = 306 K)	11.7	[15]
	n-hexane	19	[15]
	CCl_4	24	[15]
	benzene	8.1	[15]
	ethanol	4.6	[15]
	methanol	2.8	[15]
	water (I = 0.1 mol dm^{-3})[b]	0.16	[16]
BA	CCl_4	49	[17]
	H_2O (I = 0.2 mol dm^{-3})	0.43	[18]
TTA	H_2O (I = 1.0 mol dm^{-3})	4.4×10^{-3}	[19]

[a] *Abbreviations, AA: acetylacetone, BA: benzoylacetone, TTA: thenoyltrifluoroacetone*
[b] *I: ionic strength*

fraction of enol isomer, $\bar{f}_{enol} = \bar{K}_T/(1 + \bar{K}_T)$, in the organic phase that is used as the diluent of the extractant, is more than 0.9. Therefore, we assume that the presence of keto form in the organic phase is neglected. The keto form of β-diketone in the aqueous phase must be considered for evaluating the distribution constant of β-diketone between both phases.

The oxime used as the chelating agents has a dissociative proton. Typical hydroxyoximes in commercial use are listed in Table 2. If the alkyl group with the dissociative proton is expressed by R_1, the syn-anti isomerism of a hydroxyoxime can be shown as

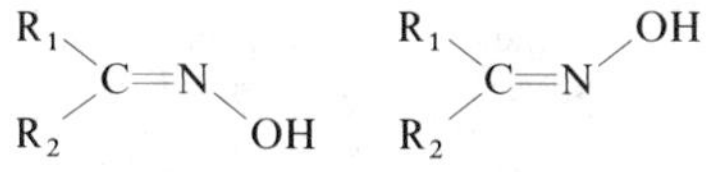

(5)

[anti-isomer] [syn-isomer]

Since the donor atom of the hydroxyoxime is nitrogen in oxime group, anti-isomer alone can react with metal ion. The anti-isomer of hydroxyoxime is very stable and the fraction of anti-isomer is almost unchanged for several or several ten days at room temperature [20]. Therefore, syn-isomer is not necessary to be accounted for the equilibrium reaction concerned with metal extraction, if long time change of equilibrium is disregarded.

Aggregation of Chelating Agent in the Organic Phase

Since the chelating agents used for the extractants in general have an intramolecular hydrogen bonding as shown in Table 2, the intermolecular interaction between the agents is much weaker in the organic phase than that of the other extractants such as amine and organophosphorus acids. Therefore, the aggregation is weak in the organic phase. When the dimerization of the agents is accounted, the total concentration of a chelating agent can be expressed by Equation 6 instead of Equation 2,

$$\bar{C}_{HR} = [\overline{HR}] + 2[(\overline{HR})_2] = [\overline{HR}](1 + 2K_d[\overline{HR}]) \quad (6)$$

$$\text{where} \quad K_d = [(\overline{HR})_2]/[\overline{HR}]^2 \quad (7)$$

The dimerization constants of several hydroxyoximes are summarized in Table 4. The K_d value of β-hydroxyoxime in aromatic solvent is smaller than that in aliphatic solvent due to stronger solute-solvent interaction in the aromatic diluent.

Acid Dissociation Constant of Chelating Agents

Since the chelating agent used for an extractant is monobasic acid, the proton dissociation in the aqueous phase is expressed by

$$HR \rightleftarrows R^- + H^+, \qquad K_a = [R^-][H^+]/[HR] \quad (8)$$

The pK_a values are also shown in Table 2, the acidity of chelating agents being very weak. The effect of substituent groups on the pK_a value can be correlated by Linear Free Energy Relationship such as Hammett's and Taft's rules. Taft equation is expressed as

$$pK_a = pK_a^o - \rho^* \textstyle\sum \sigma^* \quad (9)$$

where pK_a^o is the dissociation constant of the parent compound, ρ^* a constant for a given class of reaction, and σ^* a constant specific to a given substituent. The σ^* values for several substituents are summerized in organic chemistry books [28, 29].

Table 4
Dimerization Constant of Hydroxyoxime at 298 K.

Reagents[a] R₁	R₂	Solvent	Method	K_d [dm^3 mol^{-1}]	Ref.
C_9H_{19}	C_6H_5	toluene	distribution	3	[21]
C_9H_{19} (anti)	C_6H_5	toluene		4.5	[23]
C_9H_{19} (syn)	C_6H_5	toluene		8.3	[23]
C_9H_{19}	C_6H_5	benzene	distribution	2	[21]
C_9H_{19}	C_6H_5	Dispersol[b]	distribution	11	[22]
C_9H_{19}	C_6H_5	n-heptane	distribution	120	[21]
C_9H_{19} (syn)	C_6H_5	isooctane		32	[23]
C_9H_{19}	CH_3	benzene	V.P.O.	6 (313 K)	[24]
C_9H_{19}	CH_3	Dispersol[b]	distribution	4.4	[25]
C_8H_{17}	H	toluene	IR	11.5	[26]
C_8H_{17}	H	hexane	IR	117	[26]
C_8H_{17}	H	toluene		8.9	[23]
C_8H_{17}	H	isooctane		70	[23]
C_8H_{17}	H	toluene		5.0	[23]
C_8H_{17}	H	isooctane		62	[23]

[a]
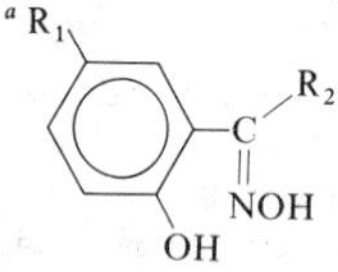

[b] *Dispersol is a sort of kerosene and the commercial name of Shell Chemical Co Ltd.*

When acetylacetone is taken as a parent compound ($pK_a^\circ = 8.99$), the effect of the substituents at both sides of β-diketone on the pK_a can be correlated by Equation 9 as shown in Figure 1. The ρ^* value of this system is calculated as 0.89. Few Linear Free Energy relationships for the pK_a values of the chelating extractants in commercial use are reported, because the solubility of the extractant is so low in the aqueous phase that the analysis of agents is very difficult.

Recently, Yuan et al. [30] reported the pK_a values of several hydroxyoximes in methanol solution. The results are shown in Table 5. The change of pK_a by the addition of substituents to hydroxyaryloxime has a qualitative trends that the addition of long alkyl and alkoxy groups slightly increases the pK_a value of phenolic proton, whereas the addition of the nucleophilic substituents such as nitro group to ortho-position greatly decreases pK_a values. The pK_a values for these hydroxyoximes increase with the increase in the electron density of the phenolic hydroxyl oxygen atom, q_O, which is calculated by the Hückel Molecular Orbital method.

Partition Constant of Chelating Agents

Partition constant of the extractant in monomeric form between both phases is defined as

$$P_{HR} = [\overline{HR}]/[HR] \tag{10}$$

This property is important both for evaluating the extraction capability of chelating agent and for understanding the extraction rate and mechanism. The partition constant of the extractant in commercial use is in general very large, because the agent is designed to prevent its loss into aqueous phase. Therefore, the experimental determination of this property is very difficult, and few data are reported systematically.

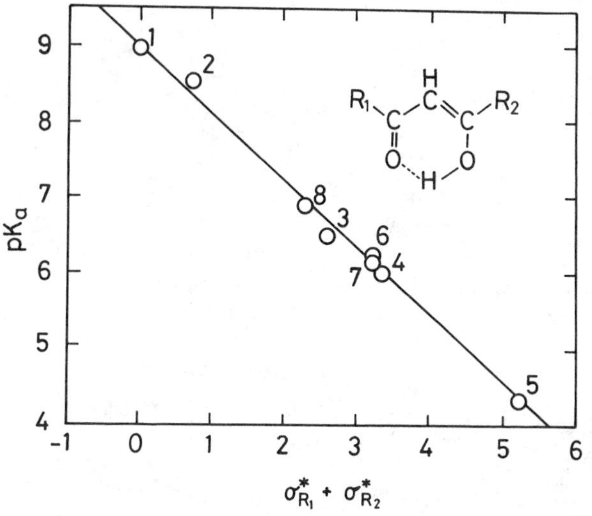

Figure 1. Taft Relation for pKa values of several β-diketone derivatives.
R_1—CO—CH_2—CO—R_2 (R_1, R_2)
1: (CH_3, CH_3), 2: (C_6H_5, CH_3), 3: (CF_3, CH_3), 4: (C_6H_5, CF_3)
5: (CF_3, CF_3), 6: (CF_3, 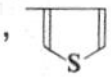), 7: (CF_3, 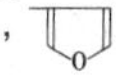), 8: (CF_3, $C(CH_3)_3$)
(data from Ref. 10.)

Table 5
pK_a in methanol and K_{ex}(Cu(II)) Values of Several hydroxyoximes[a] [30]

No.	R_1	R_2	pK_a	q_0[b]	q_N[c]	log K_{ex}
1	H	C_6H_5	10.78	1.9347	1.3293	−0.96
2	5-s-C_8H_{17}	C_6H_5	11.12	1.9369	1.3294	−0.78
3	5-s-$C_8H_{17}O$	C_6H_5	11.48	1.9376	1.3294	−1.08
4	4-s-$C_8H_{17}O$	C_6H_5	10.99	1.9347	1.3452	0.29
5	3-NO_2, 5-t-C_8H_{17}	C_6H_5	7.7	1.9311	1.3298	2.41
6	3-Cl, 5-s-C_8H_{17}	C_6H_5	10.45	1.9377	1.3294	1.97
7	H	4′-$C_{12}H_{25}C_6H_4$	11.29	1.9347	1.3409	−0.31
8	5-s-C_8H_{17}	2′-ClC_6H_4	11.08	1.9369	1.3337	−0.73
9	5-s-C_8H_{17}	4′-$CH_3OC_6H_4$	11.08	1.9369	1.3444	−0.92
10	5-s-$C_8H_{17}O$	CH_3	10.83	1.9371	1.3781	−0.61
11	4-s-$C_8H_{17}O$	CH_3	10.56	1.9342	1.3934	0.51
12	4-s-$C_8H_{17}O$	C_3H_7	10.94	1.9342	1.3934	0.48
13	4-s-$C_8H_{17}O$	C_5H_{11}	10.46	1.9342	1.3934	0.32
14	4-s-$C_8H_{17}O$	C_7H_{15}	10.68	1.9342	1.3934	1.28
15	4-i-$C_8H_{17}O$	CH_3	10.02	1.9342	1.3934	0.14

[a] 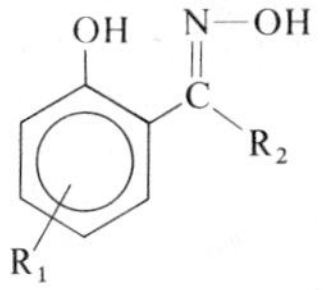

[b] *electron density on phenolic oxygen*
[c] *electron density on nitrogen atom*

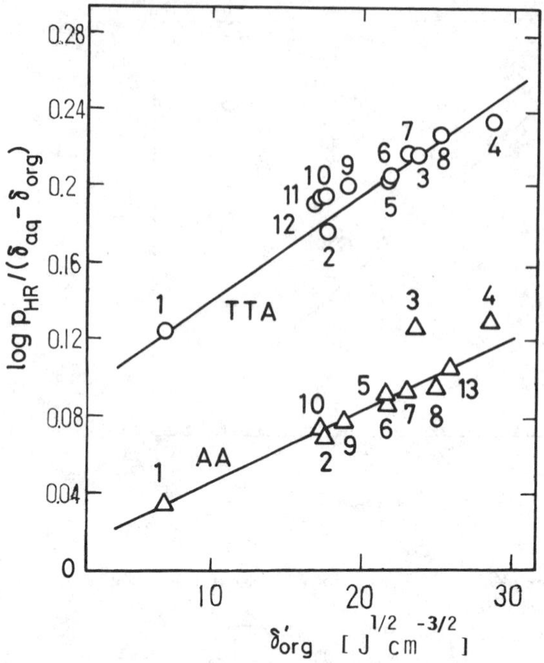

Figure 2. Correlation of partition constant for β-diketones with solubility parameters, δ's in $J^{1/2}\ cm^{-3/2}$ 1, n-hexane; 2, carbon tetrachloride; 3, chloroform; 4, methylene chloride; 5, ethyl bromide; 6, benzene; 7, chlorobenzene; 8, o-dichlorobenzene; 9, toluene; 10, m-xylene; 11, p-xylene; 12, mesitylene; 13, nitrobenzene. (Reprinted with permission from Ref. 32.)

There are two important factors concerning the partition constant. The one is the solvent effect and the other is the substituent effect. The solvent effect can be explained by use of the Hildebrand regular solution theory [31]. When the concentration of extractant is sufficiently low in both phases, the partition constant defined by Equation 10 can be expressed [32] as

$$\log P_{HR} = (V_{HR}/2.3RT)[(\delta_{aq} + \delta_{org} - 2\delta_{HR})(\delta_{aq} - \delta_{org}) + RT(1/V_{org} - 1/V_{aq})] \quad (11)$$

where, the δ and V are the solubility parameter and the molar volume, and the subscripts, aq, org, and HR represent the aqueous phase, organic phase and chelating agent, respectively. Equation 11 is arranged as

$$\log P_{HR}/(\delta_{aq} - \delta_{org}) = (V_{HR}/2.3RT)(\delta_{aq} + \delta_{org}' - 2\delta_{HR}) \quad (12)$$

$$\delta_{org}' = \delta_{org} + RT(1/V_{org} - 1/V_{aq})/(\delta_{aq} - \delta_{org}). \quad (13)$$

Figure 2 shows an example of the relationship, Equation 12, for some β-diketones. The solubility parameter and the molar volume of the chelating agents are obtained from the slope and the intercept of the linear relationship, these values being listed in Table 6.

There are some problems in predicting the partition constant of a chelating agent by using the regular solution theory because the solubility parameters are difficult to measure for complicated molecules such as a chelating complex. Also, the regular solution theory cannot be rigorously applied to the aqueous phase. Therefore, it is important how to apply the new and modern solution chemistry, which is based on the statistical thermodynamics, to this fields.

There are a few data about the solvent effect on the partition constant of hydroxyoxime as shown in Table 7. The partition constant of β-hydroxyoxime in the aromatic solvent is greater than that in the aliphatic diluent due to π-electron interaction between β-hydroxyoxime and diluent.

Table 6
Solubility Parameters and Molar Volumes of β-Diketones and Oxines

Reagent	δ_{HR} [(J cm^{-3})$^{1/2}$]	V_{HR} [cm^3 mol^{-1}]	Ref.
AA[a]	21.7	102	[32]
TTA[b]	20.6	160	[32]
oxine	22.1	124	[33]
2-methyloxine	21.93	139	[33]
4-methyloxine	21.83	139	[33]

[a] *Acetylacetone*
[b] *Thenoyltrifluoroacetone*

Few data were reported for the effect of substituents of chelating extractant on the partition constant. The P_{HR} values increases with the increase in the molar volume of extractant. Figure 3 shows the effect of carbon number, n_c, of alkyl chain group in 2-hydroxy-5-alkyl acetophenone oxime and 3-alkyl-2,4-pentane dione (derivative of acetylacetone) on the P_{HR} between the benzene and aqueous phases. The other data of non-chelating extractants are also shown in Figure 3. There exists a linear relationship between log P_{HR} and n_c, but the slope for chelating agents is smaller than those for non-chelating agents. The transferring free energy per one methylen group from the organic phase to the aqueous phase, $\Delta_{tr}G^0$, can be calculated from the slope of this relationship and the values are listed in Table 8. The values of the non-chelating agents are almost constant, regardless of the diluent. This suggests that the transferring free energy change per one methylene group is independent of the hydrophilic group of non-chelating agents. However, the values of chelating agents are much lower than those for the other reagents.

Further systematic data are required to elucidate the substituent effect on the partition constant.

Table 7
P_{HR} of Hydroxyoximes at 298 K

Reagent[a] R$_1$	R$_2$	Solvent	I[b] [mol dm^{-3}]	log P_{HR}	Ref.
CH_3	H	toluene	0.15	1.67	[34]
*C_8H_{17}	H	toluene	0.15	4.55	[34]
C_9H_{19}	H	n-heptane	—	4.02	[36]
H	CH_3	benzene	0.20	1.60	[24]
CH_3	CH_3	toluene	0.15	2.15	[34]
C_2H_5	CH_3	benzene	0.20	2.11	[24]
n-C_8H_{17}	CH_3	toluene	0.15	4.86	[34]
C_9H_{19}	CH_3	benzene	0.20	4.57	[35]
C_9H_{19}	CH_3	n-heptane	0.20	3.58	[35]
C_9H_{19}	CH_3	Dispersol	0.20	3.87	[25]
CH_3	C_6H_5	toluene	0.15	3.11	[34]
*C_8H_{17}	C_6H_5	toluene	0.15	4.90	[34]
C_9H_{19}	C_6H_5	toluene	0.0	4.85	[21]
C_9H_{19}	C_6H_5	n-heptane	0.0	3.96	[21]
C_9H_{19}	C_6H_5	Dispersol	0.06	3.96	[22]
LIX63		Dispersol	0.06	4.03	[27]

* $C_8H_{17} = (CH_3)_3CCH_2C(CH_3)_2$
[a] *Oxime structure is the same as in Table 4*
[b] *Ionic strength*

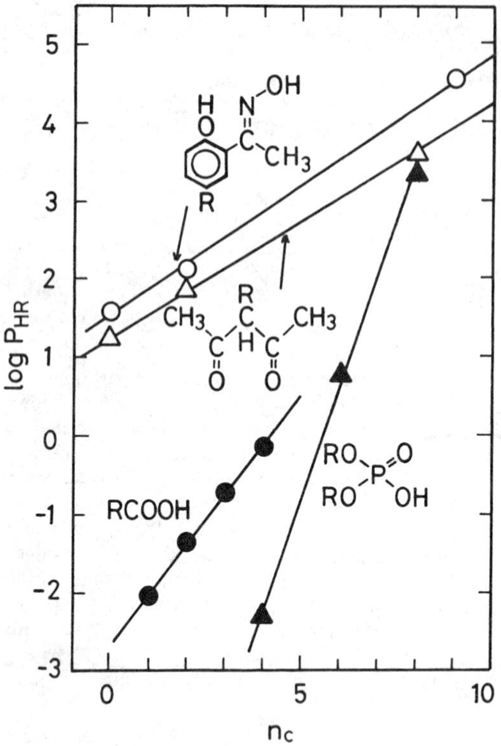

Figure 3. Effect of carbon number on the partition constants of chelating agents and non-chelating ligands. n_c: carbon no. in R. (Data from Refs. 24, 37, 38, and 39.)

Metal Extraction Equilibrium

Metal ions can react with acidic chelating extractant to form neutral complexes that are preferentially dissolved in the organic phase. For the sake of simplicity, consider the extraction of the divalent metal ion with a bidentate chelating agent. The overall reaction can be expressed as

$$M(H_2O)_n^{2+} + 2\overline{HR} \rightleftarrows \overline{MR_2} + 2H^+ + nH_2O;\ K_{ex} = [\overline{MR_2}][H^+]^2/([M(H_2O)_n^{2+}][\overline{HR}]^2) \quad (14a)$$

Table 8
Transferring Free Energy Per One Methylen Group from Aqueous Phase to Organic Phase

Reagent	Solvent	$\Delta_{tr}G^0$ [kJ mol^{-1}][a]	Ref.
β-diketone	C_6H_6	−1.74	[37]
β-hydroxyoxime	C_6H_6	−1.88	[24]
RCOOH	C_6H_6	−3.66	[38]
$(RO)_2POOH$	C_6H_{14}	−3.95	[39]
	$CHCl_3$	−3.47	[39]
$R(CH_3)_3NX$	C_6H_{14}	−3.83	[40]
	$CHCl_3$	−3.77	[40]

[a] $-\Delta_{tr}G^0 = RT\ \partial \ln P_{HR}/\partial(n_c m)$, *m = 2 for* $(RO)_2POOH$, *m = 1 for the others*

If the hydrophilic ligand except water molecule, which is monodentate ligand coordinated to the metal ion (denoted as L), is involved in the aqueous phase, the overall reaction can be rewritten,

$$ML_m(H_2O)^{2+}_{n-m} + 2\overline{HR} \rightleftarrows \overline{MR_2} + 2H^+ + mL + (n-m)H_2O;$$
$$K_{ex,m} = [\overline{MR_2}][H^+]^2[L]^m/([ML_m(H_2O)^{2+}_{n-m}][\overline{HR}]^2) \quad (14b)$$

The relation between K_{ex} and $K_{ex,m}$ can be expressed

$$K_{ex}/K_{ex,m} = [ML_m(H_2O)^{2+}_{n-m}]/([M(H_2O)^{2+}_n][L]^m) = \beta_{L,m} \quad (15)$$

where, $\beta_{L,m}$ represents the stability constant of the complex composed of m-molecules of hydrophilic ligand of L and metal ion, and the values are summarized in the book [41].

When the metal species $ML_m(H_2O)^{2+}_{n-m}$ is neglected, the overall distribution of metal ion between the organic and aqueous phases can be expressed as

$$D_M = [\overline{MR_2}]/[M(H_2O)^{2+}_n] = K_{ex}[\overline{HR}]^2/[H^+]^2 \quad (16)$$

$$K_{ex} = \beta_1\beta_2(P^2_{HR}/P_{MR_2})^{-1}K^2_a \quad (17)$$

where, β_1 and β_2 are defined as the stability constant of Equations 18 and 19, respectively, and P_{MR_2} is the partition constant of neutral metal complex between the organic and aqueous phases, Equation 20.

$$M(H_2O)^{2+}_n + R^- \rightleftarrows M(H_2O)_{n-2}R^+ + 2H_2O; \beta_1 = [M(H_2O)_{n-2}R^+]/([M(H_2O)^{2+}_n][R^-] \quad (18)$$

$$M(H_2O)_{n-2}R^+ + R^- \rightleftarrows MR_2 + (n-2)H_2O; \beta_2 = [MR_2]/([M(H_2O)_{n-2}R^+][R^-] \quad (19)$$

$$MR_2 \rightleftarrows \overline{MR_2}; P_{MR_2} = [\overline{MR_2}]/[MR_2] \quad (20)$$

If the metal-ligand complexes, $ML_m(H_2O)_{n-m}$ $(m = 0, 1, 2 \cdots n)$, exist in the aqueous phase, the overall distribution of metal ion between the organic and aqueous phases can be expressed as

$$D_M = [\overline{MR_2}]/(\sum m[ML_m(H_2O)^{2+}_{n-m}]) = [\overline{MR_2}]/\{[M(H_2O)^{2+}_n](1 + \sum_m \beta_{L,m}[L]^m)\}$$
$$= K_{ex}[\overline{HR}]^2/\{(1 + \sum_m \beta_{L,m}[L]^m)[H^+]^2\} \quad (21)$$

The distribution constant of metal ion depends on the value of K_{ex} and also on the concentration ratio of chelating extractant in the organic phase to proton in the aqueous phase. When the hydrophilic ligand exists in the aqueous phase, the value of D_M depends on the stability constant and the concentration of the uncombined ligand, L.

The extraction ability of chelating agents for a metal ion can be expressed by the $pH_{1/2}$, which is the pH in aqueous phase when the concentrations of the metal species in both aqueous and organic phases agree with each other. The $pH_{1/2}$ values for several chelating agents and metal ions are summarized in the several reviews or handbooks [1, 10–14]. This $pH_{1/2}$ value represents the degree of selectivity of metal ions. The metal ions with the distinct difference in these values are easily separated from each other by controlling the pH in the aqueous phase.

Kraus et al. [42] have correlated the observed $pH_{1/2}$ values for Cu(II) extraction by the homologous α- and β-hydroxyoximes [34, 43], with the Taft's parameters and the steric factors for the substituents. Figure 4a shows the plot of the $pH_{1/2}$ value of copper extraction with α-hydroxyoximes against the sum of Taft's parameters of substituents, without considering the steric factor. As shown in Figure 4b, the values of the distribution constant of copper for β-hydroxyoxime derivatives can be correlated with the Hammett's parameter σ_o and σ_p of the substituents at ortho- and para-positions, by considering the steric factor of the substituent of R_2, E_s [29]. These results suggest that extraction ability of the hydroxyoxime for copper strongly depends on the proton dissociation constant of the hydroxyoximes, pK_a. Recently, the similar result was reported by Yuan

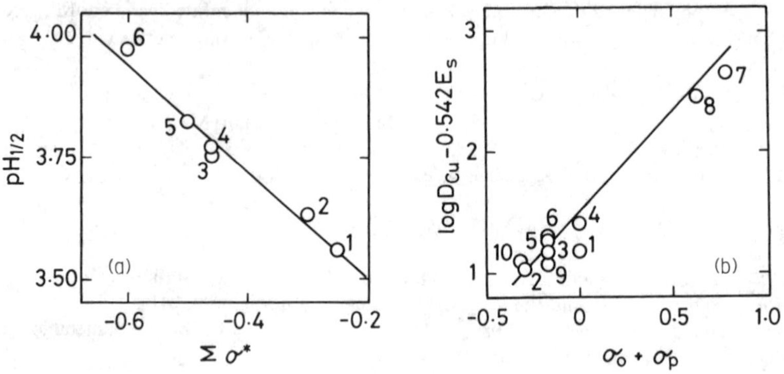

Figure 4a. Correlation of $pH_{1/2}$ of Cu(II) with the Taft parameter of substituents of α-hydroxyoxime R—CH(OH)—C(=NOH)—R: 1, 3-methyl-1-butyl; 2, 1-pentyl; 3, 3-pentyl; 4, 2-pentyl; 5, 2-ethyl-1-hexyl; 6, t-butyl. (Reprinted with permission from Ref. 42.)
b. Correlation of distribution of Cu(III) D_{Cu} with Hammett's parameters of substituents of β-hydroxyoxime. (R_1, R_2, X) in Table 1: 1, (H, CH_3, H); 2, (CH_3, CH_3, H); 3, (CH_3, C_2H_5, H); 4, (H, C_7H_{15}, H); 5, (CH_3, C_6H_{13}, H); 6, (CH_3, C_7H_{15}, H); 7, (CH_3, C_7H_{15}, NO_2); 8, (CH_3, Cl, C_7H_{15}); 9, (C_8H_{17}, CH_3, H); 10, (CH_3, CH_3, C_7H_{15}). (Reprinted with permission from Ref. 42.)

et al. [30]. Their data are listed in Table 5. The K_{ex} value increases with the decrease in the pK_a of β-hydroxyoximes. They reported a correlation of the K_{ex} values with the charge densities of phenolic hydroxyl oxygen q_O and oxime nitrogen atom q_N, which were calculated by the Hückel Molecular Orbital method.

Figure 5a shows that relationship between the pK_a and the stability constants of some metal-salicylaldoxime complexes, β_1, which were obtained by Burger et al. [44]. The stability constants decrease with the decrease in pK_a, approaching a constant value. The chelate complex formation can be expressed

$$M(H_2O)_n^{2+} + HR \rightleftarrows M(H_2O)_{n-2}R^+ + H^+ + 2H_2O;$$
$$K_1 = [M(H_2O)_{n-2}R^+][H^+]/[M(H_2O)_n^{2+}][HR] \quad (22)$$

$$M(H_2O)_{n-2}R^+ + HR \rightleftarrows MR_2 + H^+ + (n-2)H_2O;$$
$$K_2 = [MR_2][H^+]/[M(H_2O)_{n-2}R^+][HR] \quad (23)$$

The equilibrium constants K_i (i = 1 or 2) are expressed in terms of the stability constants β_i and the proton dissociation constant K_a:

$$K_i = \beta_i K_a, \qquad (\log K_i = \log \beta_i - pK_a) \quad (24)$$

In this system, the β_1 value is proportional to the K_a^{-1} at high pK_a region, whereas at lower pK_a region, the K_1 value is proportional to K_a. The value for copper(II) was not reported, because the 1:1 complex of copper-salicylaldoxime complex is very unstable. The stability constants β_1 of some metal-β-diketone complexes are proportional to K_a^{-1} as shown in Figure 5b [45]. However, the equilibrium constant of 1:1 complex of copper and 3-alkyl 2,4-pentane dione, K_1, is proportional to K_a of the β-diketone [37]. Stability of chelate-metal complex depends on the ligand-metal coordinative σ- and metal-ligand donor π-bonds. A change of electron density on the donor atom in a ligand probably has an opposite effect on these two types of bonds [44]. The increase in the electron density enhances the basicity of the donor atom, favoring the formation of the coordinative σ-bond and giving it greater stability. Then, the stability constant increases with the increase in the

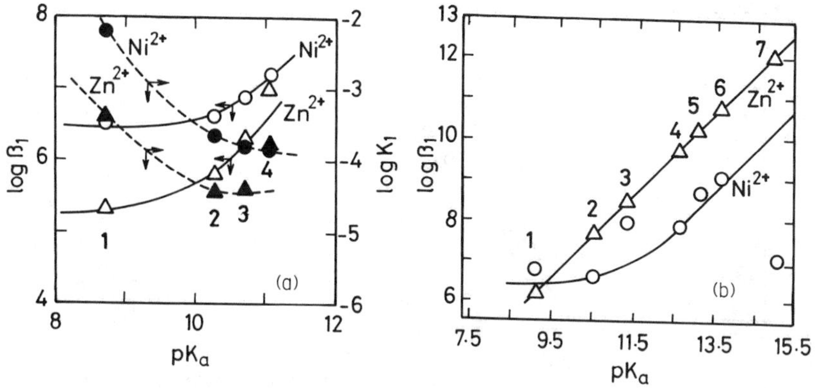

Figure 5a. Relation of stability constants of some metal ion with pK_a values of salicylaldoxime derivatives. β_1: value in $mol^{-1}\,dm^3$ 1, 5-nitrosalicylaldoxime; 2, 5-chlorosalicylaldoxime; 3, salicylaldoxime; 4; 5-metylsalicylaldoxime. (Data from Ref. 44.)
b. Relation of stability constants of some metal ion with pK_a values of β-diketone derivatives. β_1: value in $mol^{-1}\,dm^3$ 1, 2-thenoyltrifluoroacetone; 2, N-Indolecarboxyl (phenylpropioloyl) methane; 3, 4-phenylbenzoyl(phenylpropioloyl)methane; 5, acetylacetone; 6, benzoylacetone; 7, dibenzoylmethane. (Reprinted with permission from Ref. 45.)

pK_a value of ligand. Whereas, the increase in the electron density on the donor atom reduces the π-acceptor capability of the ligand and prevents the formation of the donor π-bond, resulting in the decrease in its stability. In this case, the stability constant increases as the pK_a value of the ligand decreases. The relationship between the stability constant and the pK_a of the chelating agent strongly depends on the species of metal ion and the chelating agent.

The solvent effect on K_{ex} is affected by the partition constants P_{HR} and P_{MR_2} only. If the regular solution theory can be applied to P_{MR_2}, log P_{MR_2} is expressed by a similar equation to Equation 11:

$$\log P_{MR_2}/(\delta_{aq} - \delta_{org}) = (V_{MR_2}/2.3RT)(\delta_{aq} - \delta_{org'} - 2\delta_{MR_2}) \tag{25}$$

The combination of Equation 11 with Equation 25 yields

$$\log P_{MR_2} = (V_{MR_2}/V_{HR})\log P_{HR} + 2V_{MR_2}(\delta_{aq} - \delta_{org})(\delta_{HR} - \delta_{MR_2})/(2.3RT)$$

If the solubility parameters of HR and MR_2 almost agree with each other and the molar volume of MR_2 is twice that of HR, the relation of log P_{MR_2} and log P_{HR} gives a straight line with slope 2. In this case, K_{ex} value is independent of the diluent. An example is shown in Figure 6. However, this relationship is not always satisfied for chelating extraction system, the extraction constant depending on the species of diluents. The selection of diluents is very important for designing the optimum solvent extraction system, but the general guideline for selecting the diluent species is not yet established.

INTERFACIAL PROPERTIES OF CHELATING EXTRACTANTS

Needs of Interfacial Properties

The extractants used in hydrometallurgical liquid-liquid extraction must interact with the species existing in the aqueous phase, while maintaining a high solubility in the organic phase in order to prevent the loss of the extractant into the aqueous phase. Therefore, the extractants display an am-

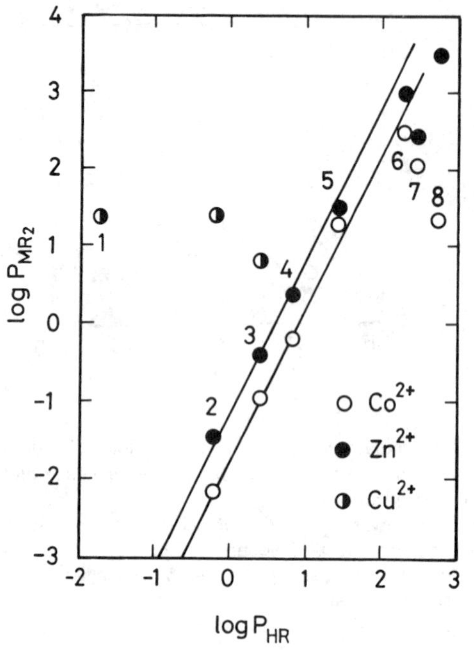

Figure 6. Correlation of partition constants of chelating agents with the chelate complexes. Diluent is carbon tetrachloride and the aqueous phase is 1 mol dm^{-3} $NaClO_4$. 1, hexafluoroacetylacetone; 2, trifluoroacetylacetone; 3, acetylacetone; 4, 2-fluoroyltrfluoroacetone; 5, 2-thenoyltrifluoroacetone; 6, pivaloyltrifluroacetone; 7, benzoyltrifluoroacetone; 8, benzoylacetone. (Data from Refs. 10, 46.)

phiphilic nature. The extractant molecule consists of a hydrophobic tail mainly of a hydrocarbon group and a polar head group, which provides a metal-ligand bond. The polar head group of the chelating agents is mainly non-ionic in nature, e.g., hydroxyoxime, β-diketone or oxine, and the hydrophobic tail is hydrocarbon chain, benzene or naphthalen ring groups.

Due to the amphiphilic nature, adsorption of the chelating agent occurs at the interface between the aqueous and organic bulk phases, followed by the accumulation of the agents in the interfacial zone. If the chelating agent has a high solubility in the aqueous phase, the chemical reaction concerned with metal extraction could occur mainly in the aqueous phase [24, 47]. However, the chelating agents of commercial use have very low solubility in the aqueous phase, and the chemical reaction to form the metal chelating agent complexes can occur at the interface due to the accumulation of the agents [48, 49], still lacking a complete agreement about the significance of the interface role [50, 51]. The nature of the interface provides significant information about the mechanism of metal extraction and also about the molecular design of chelating agents used in the metal extraction.

Adsorption process of chelating agent is of primary importance from a kinetic viewpoint in a variety of the interfacial phenomena. This process has been extensively studied in the colloid and interface science fields; however, in the solvent extraction with chelating agents, there exist few systematic works due to experimental difficulties involved in the system. This section provides information on the interfacial adsorption for the solvent extraction system with chelating agents.

Basic Concept of Interfacial Adsorption

The interfacial tension at a constant temperature changes significantly with the addition of surface-active reagents into the liquid-liquid system. Gibbs [52] derived an important equation, which relates the change of the interfacial tension with the reagent concentration in the bulk phase.

Consider a liquid column containing j-number of species, where two bulk phases, α and β, are separated from each other by an interfacial region as shown in Figure 7. The hatched region in

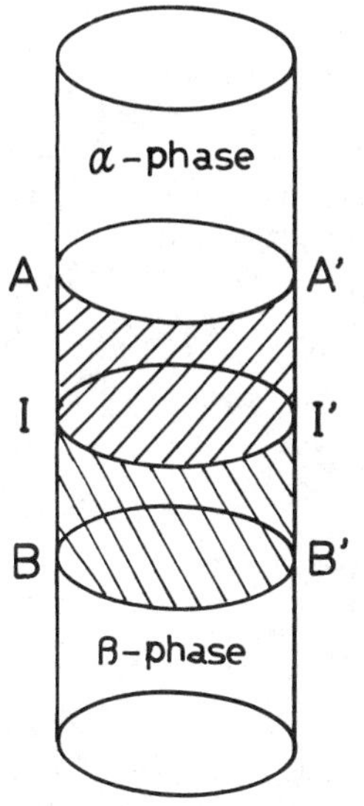

Figure 7. Conceptual figure of interfacial zone.

the figure, AA'BB', represents the interfacial zone where the species concentrations differ from the ones in the bulk phases. The nature of the interface is characterized by a hypothetical membrane, I − I', in which an uniform tension is imposed. This tension is called the interfacial tension σ. The hypothetical membrane is a mathematical plane without thickness. The side surface of the cylinder contracts, the resultant volume change of the total system being represented by dV. Simultaneously, the area A of the membrane changes by dA. Since the work done during the above change is given by

$$dw = -p\,dV + \sigma\,dA,$$

the Helmholtz free energy F of the two phases is expressed at a thermodynamic equilibrium:

$$dF = -S\,dT - p\,dV + \sigma\,dA \tag{26}$$

Here, the pressure p and the temperature T are uniform throughout the system because these are of intensive properties. S represents the entropy of the total system.

The concentration of a species present in the system changes continuously through the interfacial zone from α to β-phases. The volume above the mathematical plane II' is designated as V^α, the volume below the plane being V^β. We consider the idealized system where the chemical compositions in the α and β phases are imaging to remain unchanged up to the mathematical dividing plane so that their concentrations are kept constant at those in the bulk phases, C_i^α and C_i^β, the subscript i representing the species i. The moles of the species i involved in the imaginary α and β phases are equal to $n_i^\alpha = V^\alpha C_i^\alpha$ and $n_i^\beta = V^\beta C_i^\beta$, respectively. When n_i is the total moles of the species i present in the system, the surface excess quantity is defined as

$$A\Gamma_i = n_i - n_i^\alpha - n_i^\beta, \tag{27}$$

where Γ_i is the excess surface concentration, representing a measure of the degree of adsorption at the interface.

Similarly, we define the surface excess of free energy density ψ;

$$A\psi = F - F^\alpha - F^\beta \tag{28}$$

Here, F and F^{ν} represent the total and the ν-phase free energies.

In the open system, the free energy change is written

$$dF = -S\,dT - p\,dV + \sigma\,dA + \sum_i \mu_i\,dn_i \tag{29}$$

The chemical potential of the i-species, μ_i, is kept constant throughout the system at equilibrium. The free energy is a homogeneous function with respect to the volume, the interfacial area and the moles of components. Euler's theorem provides

$$F = V(\partial F/\partial V)_{T,A,ni} + A(\partial F/\partial A)_{T,v,ni} + \sum_i n_i(\partial F/\partial n_i)_{T,V,A,nj\neq i} = -pV + \sigma A + \sum_i n_i\mu_i \tag{30}$$

Here, we used the thermodynamic relationship:

$$p = -(\partial F/\partial V)_{T,A,ni};\ \sigma = (\partial F/\partial A)_{T,V,ni}$$

The free energy of the ν-phase for the idealized system is expressed by

$$F^{\nu} = -pV^{\nu} + \sum_i \mu_i n_i^{\nu}, \qquad \nu = \alpha \quad \text{or} \quad \beta, \qquad V = V^{\alpha} + V^{\beta} \tag{31}$$

Subtracting Equation 31 from Equation 30 yields

$$\sigma = \psi - \sum_i \mu_i \Gamma_i \tag{32}$$

The change of free energy of the ν-phase is written similarly to Equation (29):

$$dF^{\nu} = -S^{\nu}\,dT - p\,dV^{\nu} + \sum_i \mu_i\,dn_i^{\nu} \tag{33}$$

Equations 29 and 33 provide

$$d\psi \equiv d\{(F - F^{\alpha} - F^{\beta})/A\} = -\tau\,dT + \sum_i \mu_i\,d\Gamma_i \tag{34}$$

where τ represents the surface-excess density of the entropy. Differentiating Equation 32 and combining this with Equation 34, one obtains

$$d\sigma = -\tau\,dT - \sum_i \Gamma_i\,d\mu_i \tag{35}$$

Equation 35 corresponds to the Gibbs-Duhem equation for the bulk phase, and is simplified at constant temperature:

$$d\sigma = -\sum_i \Gamma_i\,d\mu_i \tag{36}$$

This equation is called the Gibbs isotherm for adsorption. The Γ_i value is evaluated from the change of the interfacial tension due to variation of the chemical potential.

Gibbs [52] decided the position of the divided plane so that $\Gamma_1 = 0$. More meaningful surface-excess concentration was treated by Defay [53]. The Gibbs-Duhem equations for two bulk phases are written at isothermal condition:

$$dp = \sum_i C_i^{\nu}\,d\mu_i, \qquad \nu = \alpha \quad \text{and} \quad \beta; \qquad C_i^{\nu} = n_i^{\nu}/V^{\nu}$$

Eliminating the dp-term from the above equations yields

$$d\mu_1 = -\sum_{i\geq 2} (C_i^{\alpha} - C_i^{\beta})\,d\mu_i/(C_1^{\alpha} - C_1^{\beta}) \tag{37}$$

Introduction of Equation 37 into Equation 36 leads to

$$-d\sigma = \sum_{i \geq 2} \Gamma_i^{(1)} \, d\mu_i \tag{38a}$$

$$\Gamma_i^{(1)} = \Gamma_i - \Gamma_1(C_i^\alpha - C_i^\beta)/(C_1^\alpha - C_1^\beta) \tag{38b}$$

When the relative excess concentrations are defined by Equation 38b, their values are independent of the fixation of the dividing plane and are definite for any fixation of the plane.

In a hydrometallurgical process, the mutual solubilities of water (i = 1) and the organic diluent (i = 2) are low enough to be neglected. We consider a ternary component system consisting of water, organic diluent, and a solute (i = 3), which involves the ligand polar group. In this case, the Gibbs-Duhem equations at a fixed pressure are given by

$$\begin{aligned} &C_1^\alpha \, d\mu_1 + C_3^\alpha \, d\mu_3 = 0, \qquad C_2^\alpha = 0 \\ &C_2^\beta \, d\mu_2 + C_3^\beta \, d\mu_3 = 0, \qquad C_1^\beta = 0 \end{aligned} \tag{39}$$

The Gibbs equation of Equation 36 is simplified by using Equation 39:

$$(\partial\sigma/\partial\mu_3) = -(\Gamma_3 - \Gamma_2 C_3^\beta/C_2^\beta - \Gamma_1 C_3^\alpha/C_1^\alpha) \equiv -\Gamma_3^{(1,2)} \tag{40}$$

This equation can be used for the adsorption of a solute at liquid-liquid interface. $\Gamma_3^{(1,2)}$ is the surface excess concentration of the solute relative to the water and the organic diluent.

The moles of the i-species in the real interfacial zone is denoted as Δn_i (in Domain AA′ – BB′ in Figure 7). The volumes of the domains (AA′II′) and BB′II′) are taken as ΔV^α and ΔV^β, respectively. The Γ_i values in Equation 40 are expressed with the help of Δn_i and ΔV^ν's:

$$A\Gamma_3 = \Delta n_3 - (C_3^\alpha \, \Delta V^\alpha + C_3^\beta \, \Delta V^\beta)$$

$$A\Gamma_2 = \Delta n_2 - C_2^\beta \, \Delta V^\beta$$

$$A\Gamma_1 = \Delta n_1 - C_1^\alpha \, \Delta V^\alpha$$

Equation 40 can be rewritten with use of the above absolute values Δn_i in the interfacial zone [54].

$$A\Gamma_3^{(1,2)} = (\Delta n_3 - \Delta n_2 C_3^\beta/C_2^\beta - \Delta n_1 C_3^\alpha/C_1^\alpha) \tag{41}$$

The absolute surface concentration is given by the sum of excess concentration and the solute concentrations, which are evaluated from the solute concentrations in the bulk phases by assuming that the solute exists in the interfacial zone in proportion to $\Delta n_2/C_2^\beta$ and $\Delta n_1/C_1^\alpha$.

$$\Delta n_3/A = \Gamma_3^{(1,2)} + \{\Delta n_2 C_3^\beta/(AC_2^\beta) + \Delta n_1 C_3^\alpha/(AC_1^\alpha)\} \tag{42}$$

The chemical potential μ_3 is usually expressed by

$$\mu_3 = \mu_3^0 + RT \ln(C_3\mu_3), \tag{43}$$

where μ_3^0 is the standard chemical potential on a basis of infinite dilution, and μ_3 is the corresponding activity coefficient. When the solute is in a state of infinite dilution, the Gibbs isotherm can be written as

$$-\partial\sigma/\partial \ln C_3^\nu = RT\Gamma_3^{(1,2)}, \qquad \nu = \alpha, \beta \tag{44}$$

The reagent with amphiphilic nature has a strong tendency to be accumulated at the interfacial zone, resulting in the lowering of the interfacial tension. The adsorbed surface-active reagent yields a monomolecular layer at the interface, as is shown by many investigators [55, 56]. This layer is called the monolayer. The molecules existing in the monolayer exhibit the two dimensional thermal motion parallel to the interface. The force exerted by the molecules per unit length is denoted by the interfacial pressure Π, which is related to

$$\Pi = \sigma_0 - \sigma \tag{45}$$

σ_0 is the interfacial tension for the binary phases in the absence of solute molecule.

The interfacial pressure is related with the mean interfacial area A_3 occupied by unit amount of surface-active reagent molecule in the monolayer, in a similar way to the pressure-vs.-molar-volume relationship in three dimensions. Several equations of states for the monolayer have been reported [54, 55]. The detailed features of the adsorbed state can be deduced from the equation of states in two dimensions.

At low concentration of the solute, an empirical equation is reported [55, 56]:

$$\Pi = bC_3^\alpha \tag{46}$$

Equation 46 can be written with the help of Equation 44:

$$\Pi = RT\Gamma_3^{(1,2)} = bC_3^\alpha, \qquad b = RT\Gamma_3^{(1,2)}/C_3^\alpha \tag{47}$$

If we take

$$\Gamma_3^{(1,2)} = 1/A_3 \tag{48}$$

the equation of states of ideal gas type is obtained:

$$\Pi A_3 = RT \tag{49}$$

Equation 47 displays that a distribution of solute between the interface and the bulk phase can be defined,

$$P_3^{(\alpha,s)} \equiv \Gamma_3^{(1,2)}/C_3^\alpha = b/RT \tag{50}$$

if the solute is in extreme dilution. The distribution coefficient $P_3^{(\alpha,s)}$ becomes a measure of interfacial activity at the condition that the interaction between the adsorbed molecules is negligibly small.

The Π value is approximately fitted to an empirical equation of the Szyszkowski type [57], which was originally proposed for air/water system.

$$\Pi = RT\Gamma_3^{(\infty)} \ln[1 + C_3^\alpha K_3^{(\alpha,s)}] = RT\Gamma_3^{(\infty)} \ln[1 + C_3^\beta K_3^{(\beta,s)}] \tag{51}$$

This equation can be derived from the Gibbs isotherm with the Langmuir adsorption isotherm for immobile site adsorption,

$$\begin{aligned}\Gamma_3^{(1,2)} &= \Gamma_3^{(\infty)} K_3^{(\alpha,s)} C_3^\alpha/(1 + K_3^{(\alpha,s)} C_3^\alpha) \\ &= \Gamma_3^{(\infty)} K_3^{(\beta,s)} C_3^\beta/(1 + K_3^{(\beta,s)} C_3^\beta)\end{aligned} \tag{52}$$

where $\Gamma_3^{(\infty)}$ is the surface-excess concentration at the state of solute saturation. $K_3^{(\nu,s)}$ represents the apparent adsorption equilibrium constant. The adsorbed molecule is mobile in nature at the liquid-liquid interface, however, the difference between the immobile and mobile interface does not make a drastic change for the equation of states [55]. The area at the saturation is related to the equation:

$$A_3^{(\infty)} = 1/\Gamma_3^{(\infty)}$$

This limiting area provides significant information on the adsorbed state of the molecule in the monolayer.

Interfacial concentration of the extractant reagent can be evaluated by measuring the lowering of the interfacial tension due to the addition of the reagent to the system, with the help of the Gibbs isotherm. The Gibbs isotherm can be reduced to a simple form, Equation 44, only when a single solute is added to the liquid-liquid system which is composed of water and the organic diluent, the mutual solubility of these being negligibly small. Due to this limitation, caution must be paid for obtaining the quantitative information on the adsorbed states in the solvent extraction systems.

Direct determination of the interfacial pressure [58] can be performed by using Langmuir trough in the case of an insoluble monolayer. In solvent extraction, the solute usually dissolves in the aqueous and organic phases, and the insoluble monolayer cannot be formed. This prevents the application of the above technique to the solvent extraction system. The usual techniques for measuring interfacial tension [54, 56] are the drop-weight method, the pendant drop method, and DuNouy ring method. Special care must be taken for applying the last method.

Another important phenomenon concerning the interface is the electrostatic potential that is imposed between the interface and the bulk phase. This potential is important for the systems containing the charged species.

The penetration of a polar group of the chelating reagent adsorbed at a water-organic interface into the aqueous phase is observed because the polar group shows the preferential affinity with water molecule. This penetration causes the conformation change of the water molecule, resulting in the change of water molecule dipole. The adsorbed chelating reagent itself causes the systematic dipole at the interface. These dipoles at the interface cause the electrical potential difference across the interface region. Another origin of the interfacial potential is the specific adsorption of charged molecule at the interface. This potential is electrostatic in nature concerning with the charged ionic species. Generally, these two types of potential are called Volta potential, Ψ. The change of the Volta potential, $\Delta\Psi$, which is caused by the adsorption layer at the previously clean interface, is characteristic of the electrostatic environment near the interfacial zone. $\Delta\Psi$ is expressed [55] by

$$\Delta\Psi = 4\pi\Gamma_3^{(1,2)}\mu_D + \psi_0 \tag{53}$$

The first term on the right side of Equation 53 represents the potential due to the change of overall dipole at the interfacial zone, which involves the changes of water molecule dipole, and of the adsorbed solute molecule dipole caused by the adsorption of the solute at the interface. The overall dipole moment depends on the orientation of the adsorbed molecules at the interface. The second term is a term due to the electrostatic potential formed by the adsorption of charged molecules, which is relative to the adjacent bulk aqueous phase. In surface layers carrying no net electrical charge, ψ_0 is zero.

Gouy and Chapman established their theory of the diffused double layer that accounts for the ψ_0 [55, 59]. The basic assumptions are shown as follows.

1. The interface is uniformly charged. The charge density is denoted by σ_e per unit area.
2. The ions in the aqueous phase behave as point charges, which are distributed from the charged plane of the surface to the aqueous phase by thermal motion. Thus, a diffused electrical double layer is built up.

The Poisson-Boltzmann equation is given as follows for one dimensional case;

$$d^2\psi/dx^2 = -(1/\varepsilon)\sum_i \rho_i \tag{54}$$

$$\rho_i = z_i e C_i(x) = z_i e C_i \exp(-z_i e\psi/k_B T) \tag{55}$$

The ε is the dielectric constant of the aqueous medium. The ρ_i is the charge density of ith-ions. $C_i(x)$ is the ith-ion concentration in molecule/cm^3 unit at the position x and is related to the corresponding concentration in the bulk aqueous phase C_i with the help of the Boltzmann relationship.

For the sake of simplicity, we consider $z-(-z)$ valent electrolyte, i.e., $Z_+ = z$, $Z_- = -z$, and $C_+ = C_-$. The above equation can be solved with the boundary conditions.

$$\psi = \psi_0 \text{ at } x = 0 \quad \text{and} \quad \psi = 0 \text{ at } x \to \infty \tag{56}$$

The ψ_0 is determined from the electro-neutrality condition:

$$\sigma_e = -\sum_i \int_0^\infty \rho_i \, dx = -\varepsilon(d\psi/dx)_{x=0} \tag{57}$$

The resultant ψ_0 value at the interface is given by

$$\begin{aligned}\psi_0 &= (2k_BT/ze)\sinh^{-1}[\sigma_e(8C_+\varepsilon RT)^{-0.5}] \\ &= (2k_BT/ze)\sinh^{-1}[\sigma_e(8C_E\varepsilon RT)^{-0.5}]\end{aligned} \tag{58}$$

C_E is the concentration of the $z-(-z)$ valent electrolyte in mole/cm^3-unit.

The concentration of the ion i with valence Z_i at the interface is given from Equation 55:

$$(C_i)_s = C_i \exp(-Z_i e\psi_0/k_BT) \tag{59}$$

Equation 58 is obtained from the Gouy's assumption as mentioned previously. The other models, e.g., Stern's specific adsorption of the counter ion have been proposed [54, 59, 60].

Another origin of the potential difference between the aqueous and organic bulk phases is the difference in the affinities of the anion and the cation in both phases [55]. For example, if the anion is preferentially distributed from the aqueous phase to the organic phase, the organic phase is negatively charged, resulting in the potential difference between both bulk phases. This potential, being called the distribution potential, is built up so that the electrochemical potentials in both phases agree with each other.

So far as a nonpolar diluent, usually used in the metal extraction, is considered, the charged ion solubility in these diluent is very low and the distribution potential is possibly neglected even though the weak charge separation due to the difference in the distributions of anion and cation makes strong effect on the formation of the electrostatic potential difference.

Extensive works on the surface potential at an air-water interface have been performed, but few data are available in the liquid-liquid system due to experimental difficulty associated with this system. No systematic work on the interfacial potential has been published for hydrometallurgical systems, though this potential would play a significant role in the reaction processes concerning the interface.

The ζ-potential, which is the potential at the surface of shear between the charged surface and the electrolyte solution, can be measured more easily by the particle or droplet electrophoresis than the interface potential. The ζ-potential does not directly give the actual interface potential at liquid-liquid interface, but provides information on the interfacial potential [61, 62, 63], though caution must be paid for estimating the electrostatic structure at the interface.

Adsorption of Chelating Extractants

When a pure chelating extractant, e.g., hydroxyoxime, is dissolved in an organic diluent, the surface tension on the air-organic interface is independent of the oxime concentration from 0 to 0.1 mol dm^{-3} [64, 65]. However, the interfacial tension lowering at the aqueous-organic interface is observed with the increase in the oxime concentration. The solute molecules are preferentially adsorbed and oriented at this interface probably due to the interaction with water molecules by hydrogen bonding [64, 66].

Typical examples of the interfacial tension lowering, in other words, the interfacial pressures Π, are shown in Figure 8 against the concentration of the chelating agents HR in the organic diluents, $\bar{C}_{HR}$. The relations of Π with $\bar{C}_{HR}$ are affected by many factors. To fully discuss the contribution

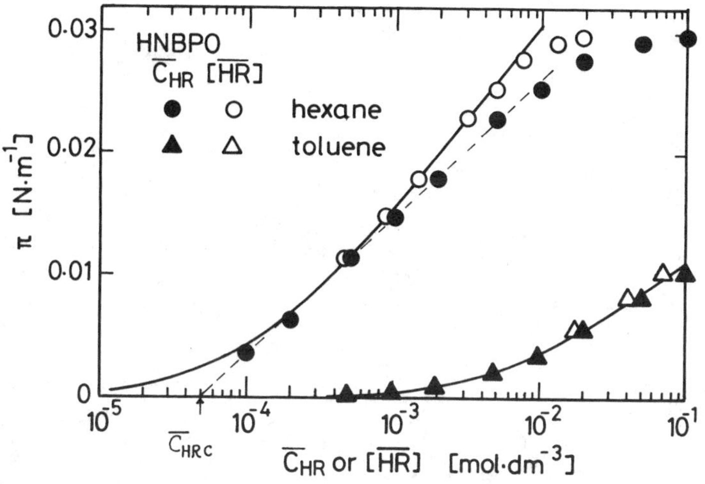

Figure 8. Typical examples of interfacial pressure against the concentration of chelating agent. HNBPO, in hexane and toluene at 28°C. The solid curves are calculated from Equation (51). (Data from Ref. 65)

of these factors to the interfacial adsorption requires many systematic studies on the solvent extraction system. However, the available data at present, which are mainly concerned with hydroxyoximes, provide some general trend of the chelating agent adsorption.

From a kinetic viewpoint, the characteristics of the adsorption, the interfacial activity, and the interfacial concentration of the chelating agents are important. From Figure 8, there appears to be a quasi-threshold concentration, above which the chelating agent molecules tend to be accumulated at the interface. The threshold concentration is defined as the $\bar{C}_{HRC}$ at which the apparently straight line of Π against $\log C_{HR}$ crosses the $\Pi = 0$ line. The pC_{HR} defined by $-\log \bar{C}_{HRC}$ is a measure of the interfacial activity [67]. The straight line apparently gives the surface-excess concentration of the chelating agents at saturation, $\Gamma_{HR}^{(\infty)}$. The pC_{HR} and $A_{HR}^{(\infty)}$ $(=1/\Gamma_{HR}^{(\infty)})$ values for several hydroxyoximes are shown in Table 9.

Hydroxyoxime tends to form dimer in a less polar diluent, due to hydrogen bonding between the oximes themselves, as is shown earlier. Since the chemical potential of the oxime-species agrees with that of the oxime monomer, the Gibbs isotherm is expressed in a diluent-oxime solution:

$$d\Pi/d\ln[\overline{HR}] = RT\Gamma_{HR}^{(1,2)} \qquad (60)$$

Here, $[\overline{HR}]$ represents the concentration of the oxime monomer. The plots of Π against $\log[\overline{HR}]$ are also shown in Figure 8. The Π value is in linear relation to the $[\overline{HR}]$ in the lower concentration, satisfying Equation 47. The distribution constant of HR between the interface and the organic diluent phase, $\bar{P}_{HR}^{s}$, can be evaluated from Equation 50, as shown in Table 10.

$\bar{P}_{HR}^{s}$ would be mainly determined by the difference of the interaction between the polar group-diluent molecule pair and the polar group-water molecule pair. If the polar group of the hydroxyoxime is common, the $\bar{P}_{HR}^{s}$ values for the oximes with hydrocarbon chain groups or the aromatic hydrocarbon agree with each other within a factor two as is clear from Table 10 for a common diluent. This result shows that the polar head group mainly interacts with water molecules, while the rest of the reagent interacts with the diluent molecules in the interfacial zone. The $\bar{P}_{HR}^{s}$ value for the hydroxy aryl oxime with two long hydrocarbon chains such as C_7 and C_8 is also affected by the hydrocarbon group as is shown in Table 10. The nonylphenol composing of hydroxyl polar head group is less surface-active than the hydroxyoxime.

Table 9
Adsorption of Chelating Agents

Chelating Agent	Structure	Aq. Phase	Org. Phase	Temp. [°C]	Method	$A_{ax}^{(\infty)} \times 10^{16}$ [cm^2]	pC_{HR} [d]	$A_s \times 10^{16}$ [cm^2]	$\bar{K}_{HR}^{s}$ [dm^3/mol] [b]	Ref.
anti-HNBPO	1) $R_1 = C_9H_{19}$, $R_2 = C_6H_5$	pH: 2, I[c]: 0.5M Na_2SO_4—H_2SO_4	hexane	28	drop-wt.	81	4.30	61.2[a]	9.0×10^{3}[a]	[65]
HNBPO	1) $R_1 = C_9H_{19}$, $R_2 = C_6H_5$	1M Na_2SO_4	n-heptane			83.4				[66]
HNBPO	1) $R_1 = C_9H_{19}$, $R_2 = C_6H_5$	distill. water	n-heptane	25	pendant-drop	95.2				[21]
anti-HNBPO	1) $R_1 = C_9H_{19}$, $R_2 = C_6H_5$	pH: 2, I: 0.5M Na_2SO_4—H_2SO_4	toluene	28	drop-wt.	152	2.60	93.0	1.8×10^2	[65]
HNBPO	1) $R_1 = C_9H_{19}$, $R_2 = C_6H_5$	1M Na_2SO_4	toluene			114				[66]
HNBPO	1) $R_1 = C_9H_{19}$, $R_2 = C_6H_5$	water	toluene	26		151	2.74			[68]
HNBPO	1) $R_1 = C_9H_{19}$, $R_2 = C_6H_5$	1M Na_2SO_4	toluene/ n-heptane = 1/1			102				[66]
HNAPO	1) $R_1 = C_9H_{19}$, $R_2 = CH_3$	0.5M Na_2SO_4 pH: 2	n-heptane	25	drop-wt.	78.1				[64]
HNAPO	1) $R_1 = C_9H_{19}$, $R_2 = CH_3$	0.5M Na_2SO_4 pH: 2	toluene	25	drop-wt.	105				[64]
HNAPO	1) $R_1 = C_9H_{19}$, $R_2 = CH_3$	0.2M $NaClO_4$	benzene	25	pendant-drop			92.0	2.1×10^3	[24]
HNAPO	1) $R_1 = C_9H_{19}$, $R_2 = CH_3$	0.2M $NaClO_4$	kerosene	25	pendant-drop			50.3	7.7×10^2	[25]
HOAPO	1) $R_1 = C_8H_{17}$, $R_2 = CH_3$	0.2M Na_2SO_4 pH: 2	n-heptane	25	drop-wt.	82.6	3.60	59.1	1.7×10^3	[64]
HOAPO	1) $R_1 = C_8H_{17}$, $R_2 = CH_3$	0.2M Na_2SO_4 pH: 2	toluene	25	drop-wt.	139	2.20			[24]
HBAPO	1) $R_1 = C_4H_9$, $R_2 = CH_3$	0.2M Na_2SO_4 pH: 2	n-heptane	25	drop-wt.	68.5				[64]
HEAPO	1) $R_1 = C_2H_5$, $R_2 = CH_3$	0.2M $NaClO_4$	benzene	25	pendant-drop		3.0	55.3	2.4×10^2	[24]

HMPOO	1) $R_1 = CH_3$, $R_2 = C_7H_{15}$	0.2M Na_2SO_4 pH: 2	n-heptane	25	drop-wt.	91.7				[64]
HMPOO	1) $R_1 = CH_3$, $R_2 = C_7H_{15}$	0.2M Na_2SO_4 pH: 2	toluene	25	drop-wt.	147				[64]
HOPOO	1) $R_1 = t\text{-}C_8H_{17}$, $R_2 = C_7H_{15}$	0.2M Na_2SO_4 pH: 2	n-heptane	25	drop-wt.	58.5				[64]
HOPOO	1) $R_1 = t\text{-}C_8H_{17}$, $R_2 = C_7H_{15}$	0.2M Na_2SO_4 pH: 2	toluene	25	drop-wt.	105				[64]
DEHDO	2)	I: 0.5M, pH: 2 0.167M Na_2SO_4	hexane	28	drop-wt.	101	3.7			[65]
DEHDO	2)	I: 0.5M, pH: 2	toluene	28	drop-wt.	176	2.0			[65]
DEHDO	2)	0.5M KNO_3 pH: 2.5	hexane	25	DuNouy	108	3.7			[67]
nonyl phenol	3)	I: 0.5M, pH: 2 0.167M Na_2SO_4	hexane	28	drop-wt.	73	2.7	52.5	3.3×10^2	[65]
nonyl phenol	3)	I: 0.5M, pH: 2 0.167M Na_2SO_4	toluene	28	drop-wt.	106	4.7			[65]

HNBPO: 2-hydroxy 5-nonyl benzophenone oxime, HNAPO: 2-hydroxy 5-nonyl acetophenone oxime, HOAPO: 2-hydroxy 5-t-octyl acetophenone oxime, HBAPO: 2-hydroxy 5-t-butyl acetophenone oxime, HEAPO: 2-hydroxy 5-ethyl acetophenone oxime, HMPOO: 1-(2-hydroxy 5-methyphenyl) octane-1-one oxime, HOPOO: 1-(2-hydroxy 5-t-octylphenyl) octane-1-one oxime, DEHDO: 5,8-diethy 7-hydroxy 6-dodecanone oxime

[a] *Assuming equilibrium constant of dimer formation,* $\bar{K}_d = 110\ dm^3/mol$

[b] *Constants in Szyszkowski's adsorption equation*

[c] *I: ionic strength*

[d] $pC_{HR} = -\log \bar{C}_{HRc}$

1) 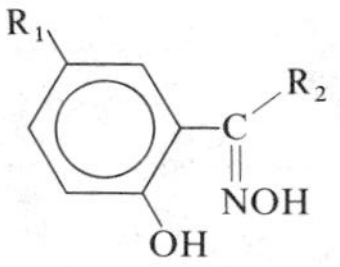

2) 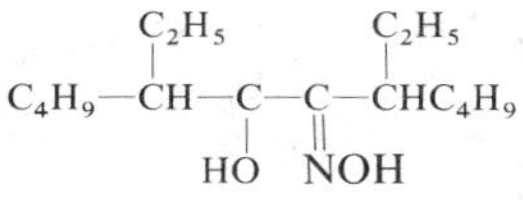

3) 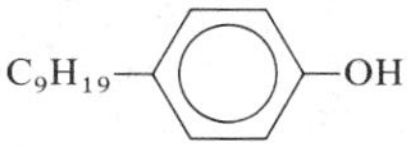

4) 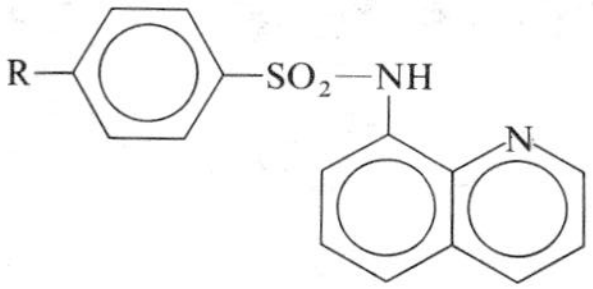

5) 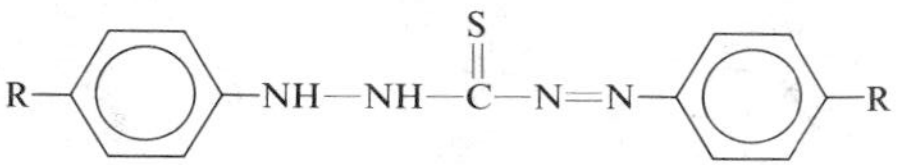

(Continued)

Table 9 (*Continued*)

Chelating Agent	Structure	Aq. Phase	Org. Phase	Temp. [°C]	Method	$A_{ax}^{(\infty)} \times 10^{16}$ [cm²] pC_{HR} [d]	$A_s \times 10^{16}$ [cm²]	$\bar{K}_{HR}^{s}$ [dm³/mol] [b]	Ref.
N-8-quinolyl p-n-hexyl benzene	4) R = n-C_6H_{13}	pH: 6.0	toluene	30	drop-wt. pendant-drop		48	1.58×10^0	[69]
N-8-quinolyl p-n-dodecyl benzene	4) R = n-$C_{12}H_{25}$	pH: 6.0	toluene	30	drop-wt. pendant-drop		49	4.10×10^0	[69]
N-8-quinolyl p-dodecyl benzene	4) R = $C_{12}H_{25}$		toluene	30	drop-wt. pendant-drop		53	2.0×10^1	[69]
N-8-quinolyl p-n-octadecyl benzene	4) R = n-$C_{18}H_{37}$	pH: 6.0	toluene	30	drop-wt. pendant-drop		61	2.25×10^2	[69]
dithizone	5) R = H	pH: 11.96	$CHCl_3$	25	drop-wt.	2.2			[70]
di-butyl dithizone	5) R = C_4H_9	pH: 11.95	CCl_4	25	drop-wt.	3.7			[70]
di-butyl dithizone	5) R = C_4H_9	pH: 11.75	$CHCl_3$	25	drop-wt.	2.8			[70]

Table 10
Distribution of Chelating Agents Between Interface and Organic Bulk Phase

Chelating Agent	Organic Phase	temp. [°C]	$\bar{P}^s_{HR}$ [cm]	$\bar{P}^s_{HR} = \bar{K}^s_{HR}\Gamma^{(\infty)}_{HR}$ [cm][a]	Ref.
anti-HNBPO	hexane	28	1.4×10^{-3}	2.5×10^{-3}	[65]
anti-HNBPO	*n*-heptane	25	1.0×10^{-3}		[71]
HNAPO	*n*-heptane	25	5.1×10^{-4}		[72]
HOAPO	*n*-heptane	25		4.7×10^{-4}	[64]
DEHDO	*n*-heptane	28	5.7×10^{-4}		[65]
nonyl phenol	hexane	25	6.5×10^{-5}	1.0×10^{-4}	[65]
anti-HNBPO	toluene	28	2.3×10^{-5}	3.0×10^{-5}	[65]
HNAPO	toluene	25	1.1×10^{-5}		[73]
HOAPO	toluene	25	1.4×10^{-5}		[73]
HNBAO	toluene	25	0.7×10^{-5}		[73]
HMPOO	toluene	30	1.2×10^{-5}		[34]
HOPOO	toluene	25	0.42×10^{-5}		[73]
DEHDO	toluene	28	2.3×10^{-5}		[65]
DEHDO	benzene	25		2.2×10^{-5}	[35]

HNBAO: 2-hydroxy 5-nonyl benzaldehydeoxime
[a] *Values obtained from Szyszkowski's equation*
Other abbreviations are the same as in Table 9.

The $\bar{P}^s_{HR}$ values for hydroxyoxime is strongly affected by the organic diluent. Generally, the $\bar{P}^s_{HR}$ value for aliphatic hydrocarbon is larger than that for aromatic diluent. The aromatic ring group with delocalized π-electron strongly interacts with the hydroxyoxime compared with aliphatic hydrocarbon, thus preventing the dimer formation of the hydroxyoxime in aromatic diluents. The greater the extent of the interaction, the lower is the tendency of the hydroxyoxime to adsorb at the interface. The $\bar{P}^s_{HR}$ for 2-hydroxy-5-nonyl benzophenoneoxime (HNBPO, active component of LIX65N), which has two benzene ring, is greater than that for the reagent with one benzene ring. This is probably caused by the weak interaction of the benzene ring with water.

The $\bar{P}^s_{HR}$ values are obtained from the values in low concentration of the oximes. As mentioned previously, the Π-$[\overline{HR}]$ relationship can be fitted by the Szyszkowski equation (Equation 51), which provides the same equation as Equation 50 in low range of $[\overline{HR}]$:

$$\bar{P}^s_{HR} = b/RT = \bar{K}^s_{HR}\Gamma^{(\infty)}_{HR} \tag{61}$$

Here, $\bar{K}^s_{HR}$ denotes the adsorption constant of HR from organic phase($K^{(\alpha,s)}_{HR}$, α = org. phase). The $\bar{P}^s_{HR}$ values obtained from Equation 61 are also shown in Table 10. These values almost agree with those obtained from the linear relationship of Π-[HR] in low concentrations.

The $\bar{P}^s_{HR}$ obtained from the Szyszkowski equation is an apparent value, because the $\bar{P}^s_{HR}$ is determined from the Π-$[\overline{HR}]$ curves in greater $[\overline{HR}]$ concentration region than in the range of linear Π-$[\overline{HR}]$ relationship. Since both $\bar{P}^s_{HR}$ values roughly agree with each other, the interaction between the adsorbed molecules may be weak at a moderately high range of the surface-excess concentration.

A comparison of the $A^{(\infty)}_{HR}$ with the value derived from the molecular model provides useful information concerning the adsorption state or the orientation of the interfacial molecules at saturate adsorption equilibrium. For neutral monolayer, Langmuir proposed the modified equation of states by accounting for the excluded area due to adsorbed molecules [74]:

$$\Pi(A_{HR} - A^{(\infty)}_{HR}) = k_B T \tag{62}$$

The value of $A^{(\infty)}_{HR}$ obtained from the interfacial pressure for homologous series of mono-basic fatty acids is found to be 24 Å^2 per molecule [75]. The effective cross-sectional area of the hydrocarbon chain is known to be 12 Å^2 [76]. The excluded area per pair molecules is four times the cross-sectional area and the above $A_{HR}^{(\infty)}$ value is well interpreted by twice the cross-sectional area. The hard disk model for the $A_{HR}^{(\infty)}$ value can interpret the experimental result only qualitatively, but gives important information on the adsorbed state.

The $A_{HR}^{(\infty)}$ values obtained from the Szyszkowski equation, $A_s^{(\infty)}$, and those from the $d\Pi/d \ln \bar{C}_{HR}$ values at high concentrations, $A_a^{(\infty)}$ are shown in Table 9 for several hydroxyoximes together with nonylphenol. The $A_s^{(\infty)}$ is lower than the $A_a^{(\infty)}$, which is an apparent value because no account is paid for the variation of the activity coefficient and also for the gradual asymptote to the straight line of the Π-$\ln \bar{C}_{HR}$ relationship. We consider, firstly, the $A_s^{(\infty)}$ values for hydroxyoximes in the aliphatic hydrocarbon. As shown in Table 9, the $A_s^{(\infty)}$ values for the *β*-hydroxyoximes with only one benzene ring are similar values with each other, 50–60 Å^2/molecule.

This result indicates that the long chain hydrocarbon tail part of the *β*-hydroxyoxime has little effect on the $A_s^{(\infty)}$ value, while *o*-hydroxy aryl oxime group greatly contributing to the $A_s^{(\infty)}$. Corey-Pauling-Koltun (CPK) molecular model of space filling type provides some information on the cross-sectional area of this group. The *o*-hydroxy aryl oxime group has a plane-like structure, whose area is about 45 Å^2. The hard disk model of this group provides 90 Å^2 for the $A^{(\infty)}$ value, which is much greater than the observed $A_s^{(\infty)}$. The cross-sectional shape observed from the plane perpendicular to the *o*-hydroxy aryl oxime plane is like a rectangular one, its area being about 35 Å^2. From this result, a qualitative estimation can be made for the adsorbed molecular state that the *o*-hydroxy aryl oxime group is oriented perpendicular to the interface so that the hydroxyl and oxime groups are favored to interact with the water molecules.

The conformation of the hydroxyl and oxime at the interface prevents the formation of hydroxyoxime dimer at the interface. Even if the dimer formation is assumed at the interface [26], the dimer is formed with the help of the water molecule, being much different from the dimer in the organic bulk phase.

The area of the benzene ring plane is about 28 Å^2, yielding $A^{(\infty)} = 56$ Å^2 on the basis of the hard disk model. This value is close to the observed value 53 Å^2 for nonylphenol, but caution must be paid for the observed value, which is obtained by neglecting the dimerization of nonylphenol in *n*-hexane due to lack of the dimerization constant.

The CPK molecular models are shown in Figure 9 for two hydroxyoximes. HNBPO has two benzene rings, the planes of which locate vertically with each other. Due to this configuration the $A_s^{(\infty)}$ for anti-HNBPO is greater than those for 2-hydroxy 5-alkylacetophenone oximes.

The $A_s^{(\infty)}$ of DEHDO (active component of LIX63) in hexane and toluene diluents is an extraordinarily large value, reflecting the branched hydrocarbon tail in this reagents, which is bulky as shown in Figure 9.

The interfacial activity of *β*-diketone has not been well investigated. The interfacial tension lowering with the addition of benzoylacetone is weak [49], and the *β*-diketone without a long chain hydrocarbon tail does not show strong adsorption at the interface.

The interfacial lowering for the *n*-alkyl-substituted dithizone was measured at high pH (11.96 – 11.75) [70]. The adsorbed species is probably in a dissociated form because pKa's of these are relatively small. The parameters of adsorption are also shown in Table 9.

Recently, the adsorptions of N-8-quinolyl-sulfonamides are measured by Yoshizuka et al. [69]. The results are also shown in Table 9. The $A_s^{(\infty)}$ values for the amides with several hydrocarbon tail groups are about 50–60 Å^2 irrespective of the tail groups.

Next we consider the effect of the diluent on the $A_{HR}^{(\infty)}$ value for aromatic diluent. The $A_{HR}^{(\infty)}$ is much larger than that for aliphatic diluent, this being caused by the interaction between the benzene rings in the hydroxyoxime and in the diluent. Flett [66] also reported the effect of diluent species including naphthenes on the $A_{HR}^{(\infty)}$ value.

The final problem of the adsorption of chelating extractant concerns the aqueous phase environment. Chelating extractant has an acidic property. If the chelating extractant remains in a neutral form, the ionic strength in the aqueous phase has little effect on the interfacial tension and the effect plays a minor role in the extraction. In ionic form, the adsorption of chelating reagents is probably affected by the counter ion existing in the aqueous phase.

The interfacial tension is found to be strongly affected by the pH value in the aqueous bulk phase. Al-Diwan et al. [65] showed some experimental results for commercial hydroxyoxime that the interfacial tension goes through a maximum with the increase in pH value, followed by the

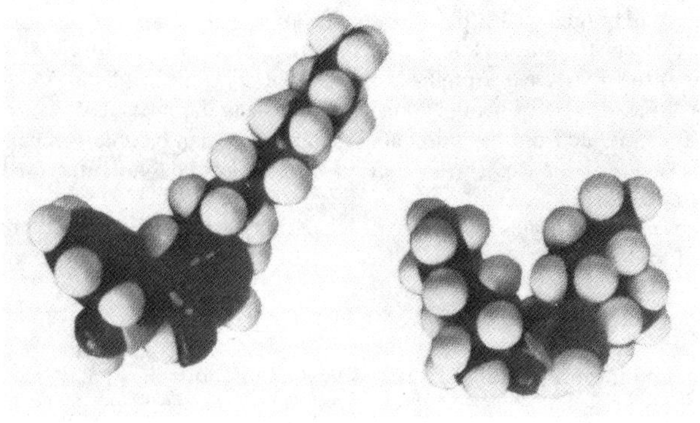

Figure 9. Corey-Pauling-Koltun (CPK) model of β-hydroxyoxime A: (HNBPO) and α-hydroxyoxime B: (DEHDO).

decrease as the pH increases further. The increase in the interfacial tension at lower pH values was interpreted in terms of the protonation of the oxime molecule to give a charged species of higher interfacial activity than neutral oxime:

$$HR + H^+ \rightleftharpoons H_2R^+ \tag{63}$$

The protonation has been investigated by titration of the oximes with perchloric acid in a glacial acetic acid medium. The most ready to be protonated is LIX63 and the second is SME529; the other oximes P50, P17, LIX65N show slight protonation. Other experimental results for LIX65N have been reported for the effect of the pH on the interfacial tension [63, 71]. From these results, the interfacial tension is almost constant until pH reached 9, followed by the decrease as the pH increases. The results by Al-Diwan et al. [65] on the commercial reagents are most probably associated with the impurity in the experimental system.

Al-Diwan's data reporting the interfacial tension lowering at high pH values agrees with the other investigator's results, though the pH values of the onset of the interfacial tension lowering disagree with each other. This lowering is caused by the proton dissociation of the oximes at high pH values:

$$HR \rightleftharpoons R^- + H^+ \tag{64}$$

When a long chain acid adsorbs at the benzene-water interface, a change occurs at about 3 pH units to the alkaline side of the point at which such reagents are half-ionized in the bulk aqueous environment [77]. As the head group of the polar part has an aqueous environment, the pK_a value of the head group is now assumed not to change [55]. This assumption leads to an interpretation of the shift of the pH units as the change of the pH value at the interface from the measured pH in the bulk aqueous phase. This change is caused by the interfacial electrical potential, ψ_0.

The hydrogen ion concentration adjacent to the interface $[H^+]_s$ is given by taking into account the Boltzmann factor:

$$[H^+]_s = [H^+]\exp(-ze\psi_0/k_BT) \tag{65}$$

The z and e represent the electrical valence of the hydrogen ion (in this case $z = 1$) and the elementary electrical charge. The pH value at the interface, pH_s, is related to the bulk phase pH value;

$$pH_s = pH + e\psi_0/2.30k_BT \tag{66}$$

Only when $\psi_0 = 0$, pH_s agrees with pH. If ψ_0 is negative, $pH_s < pH$ because the negative charge at the interface collects the positive ion. The potential may arise from either ionization of the adsorbed groups at the interface or from fixed charge. The ψ_0 value is difficult to know in the liquid-liquid system. A typical value of being 200 mV accounts for the measured change of the pH-shift of 3–4 pH unit as estimated from Equation 66. Similar results can be obtained from the ζ-potential. A relationship between pH_s and pH was reported with use of the ζ-potential for lauric acid in the liquid-liquid systems [78].

Surface-active weak-electrolytes such as acidic chelating agents are adsorbed both as ion R^- and as the uncharged molecule. If the excess salt is present, the Gibbs isotherm is given by the form:

$$-d\sigma/RT = \Gamma_{HR}\, d\ln[HR] + \Gamma_{R^-}\, d\ln[R^-] + \Gamma_{H^+}\, d\ln[H^+] \tag{67}$$

The dissociation equilibrium of HR is expressed in the bulk aqueous phase,

$$K_a = [R^-][H^+]/[HR] \tag{68}$$

from which, if $[H^+]$ is held constant,

$$d\ln[HR] = d\ln[R^-]$$

Hence, Equation 67 is rewritten as a simpler form:

$$-d\sigma/RT = (\Gamma_{HR} + \Gamma_{R^-})\, d\ln[HR] \tag{69}$$

Since partition equilibrium is attained for HR,

$$P_{HR} = [\overline{HR}]/[HR] \tag{70}$$

The change of the interfacial tension is expressed in terms of $[\overline{HR}]$.

$$d\Pi/d\ln[\overline{HR}] = RT(\Gamma_{HR} + \Gamma_{R^-}) \tag{71}$$

At an extremely low concentration of HR, an empirical equation is obtained as is shown in Equation 47.

$$\Pi = b\,[\overline{HR}], \qquad b = RT(\Gamma_{HR}/[\overline{HR}] + \Gamma_{R^-}/[\overline{HR}]) \tag{72}$$

This equation makes the dissociation process at the interface clear form. The dissociation equilibrium for the oxime at the interface and the distribution coefficient between the interface and bulk aqueous phase are respectively defined as

$$K_a^s = \Gamma_{R^-}[H^+]_s/\Gamma_{HR} \quad \text{and} \quad \bar{P}_{HR}^s = \Gamma_{HR}/[\overline{HR}] \tag{73}$$

The distribution coefficient of R^- can be related to the dissociation of HR in the bulk aqueous phase:

$$P_{R^-}^s = \Gamma_{R^-}/[R^-] = (K_a^s/K_a)\{[H^+]/[H^+]_s\}P_{HR}^s,\ P_{HR}^s = \Gamma_{HR}/[HR] \tag{74}$$

The surface activity of R^-, i.e., the $P_{R^-}^s$, differs from P_{HR}^s by the factor, $(K_a^s/K_a)[H^+]/[H^+]_s$. If we assume $K_a^s/K_a = 1$, the surface activity of R^- differs from that of the neutral species HR by a factor $[H^+]/[H^+]_s$.

Equation 72 can be rewritten as

$$b = RT\bar{P}_{HR}^s\{1 + K_a^s([H^+]/[H^+]_s)[H^+]^{-1}\} \tag{75}$$

Watarai et al. [71] measured the Π-$\bar{C}_{HR}$ relationship at constant pH for purified LIX65N in water-*n*-heptane system. Equation 72 was satisfied at low concentration of LIX65N. The b-values

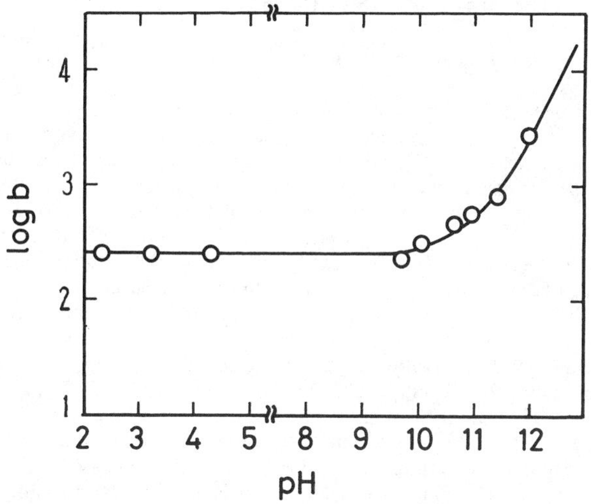

Figure 10. Adsorption of oxime anion at interface at high pH in aqueous phase. (oxime: HNBPO, diluent: n-heptane, 25°C). b: value in Ncm^2/mol (Reproduced with permission from Ref. 71).

obtained are plotted against pH in Figure 10. The log b value is independent of the pH at low pH region, followed by the linear increase in log b with the pH at high pH region. The data can be explained by Equation 75 with the values of the parameters

$$\bar{P}^{s}_{HR} = 1.0 \times 10^{-3}\ \text{cm and } K^{s}_{a}[H^+]/[H^+]_s = 1 \times 10^{-11}\ \text{dm}^3\ \text{mol}^{-1}$$

The second term was originally reported as 1×10^{-9} dm^3 mol^{-1}, which is incorrect. The pK_a is reported to be 8.7, and if we assume $K^s_a = K_a$, the $[H^+]_s/[H^+]$ is estimated to be 200, suggesting the presence of negatively charged interface. Since $\Gamma_{R^-}/[R^-] = (1/200)\Gamma_{HR}/[HR]$, the adsorption of R^- from the aqueous phase is reduced to 1/200 times compared with that of HR, due to the presence of the interfacial potential.

Adsorption of Metal Complexes

The interfacial activity of metal complexes relative to that of the chelating ligand is a factor determining the rate of metal release from the metal complex at the interfacial zone. The neutral metal-hydroxyoxime complexes are less interface-active than the hydroxyoximes, which are free from metal ions, due to the molecular form of the complexes [24, 63, 69]. From a kinetic viewpoint, the interfacial activity of the charged complex, e.g., the complex cation consisting of the divalent metal ion with a ligand species, is more important than that of the metal complex in neutral form. However, the purified metal complex cation cannot be obtained and no work has been reported on the interfacial activity.

The interfacial lowering of the mixture of the uncombined ligand and the metal complex is mainly determined by the uncombined ligand concentration, and this result also indicates that the uncombined ligand preferentially adsorbs at the interface [63]. Some investigators reported that the metal hydroxyoxime complex adsorbs strongly at the interface [79, 80]. However, special caution must be taken for determining interfacial activity of the metal complex in neutral form, because uncombined chelating agent slightly involved in the metal complex leads to misjudgment of the interfacial activity of the complex.

REACTION KINETICS IN HOMOGENEOUS PHASE

Reaction Scheme of Metal-Ligand Complex Formation

Let the divalent metal case be considered for the sake of simplicity. The reaction processes to yield divalent-metal complexes in an aqueous phase are described as shown in Figure 11a for the chelating agents of β-diketone type, which are composed of the enol and keto tautomers. In these chelating agents, there exists the tautomerization reaction through the deprotonation reaction. The ionic metal-ligand complex is formed by the reactions of metal ion with three different species of the chelating agent. The metal complex in neutral form is produced from the metal-ligand cation by reacting with the chelating ligand. The reaction processes concerned with the hydroxyoximes and oxines are described as shown in Figure 11b. In this case, the chelating agents do not involve enol-keto tautomers, the tautomerization reaction being omitted from Figure 11a.

The rates of the reaction processes in Figure 11 are required for evaluating the metal extraction rate. In hydrometallurgical process, the chelating reagents dissolve in aqueous phase only very slightly, due to preventing the loss of the reagents into the aqueous phase. From this characteristic, the concentration of the chelating ligand in the aqueous phase is in general very low. The reaction processes are usually fast, but the overall rate of the reaction to yield the metal complex is rather slow due to low level of the reactant concentrations in the aqueous phase.

The fast reaction can be characterized with the help of chemical relaxation methods, e.g., temperature jump, pressure jump, electrical field jump, concentration jump methods, and the acoustic method that we greatly owe to Eigen's school [81].

General Features of Reaction Kinetics

The reaction in a solution occurs according to the scheme:

$$A + B \underset{k'_D}{\overset{k_D}{\rightleftharpoons}} A \cdots B \underset{}{\overset{k_R}{\rightleftharpoons}} AB \qquad (76)$$

step: D step: R

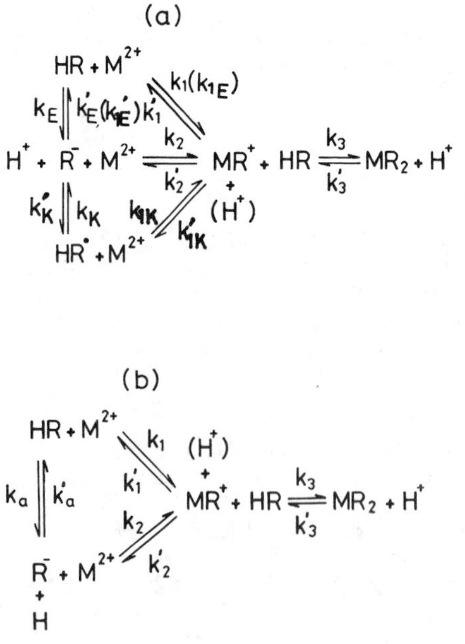

Figure 11a. Reaction scheme of producing metal chelate complexes for β-diketone system in homogeneous phase.
b. Reaction scheme of producing metal chelate complexes for β-hydroxyoxime type.

The reactants A and B encounter with each other by diffusion in the solution, yielding the intermediate aggregate of short life, A ··· B. Thereafter, the aggregate is converted to the product AB. The first step "D" is controlled by the diffusion of the reactants, and the second step "R" is a process to yield complex product. The overall reaction rate is determined by the slower reaction process of the steps D and R.

The formation rate of the intermediate aggregate, A ··· B, is determined by the diffusion step. We consider a simple case in which no electrical potential field is imposed.

$$A + B \underset{k'_D}{\overset{k_D}{\rightleftarrows}} A \cdots B \xrightarrow{k_R} AB \tag{77}$$

Let $C_B(x)$ be the concentration of the center of B-molecule at a distance x from the center of an A molecule. The diffusion flux of B at x is balanced with the reaction flow $\tilde{r}$ per an A-molecule at steady state:

$$4\pi x^2 D' dC_B(x)/dx = \tilde{r} \tag{78}$$

Here, D′ is the relative diffusion coefficient, which is given by the sum of the self-diffusion coefficients of A and B, i.e., $(D_A + D_B)$. Equation 78 is solved as

$$C_B(x) = C_B(\infty) - \tilde{r}/(4\pi D' x) \tag{79}$$

The flow $\tilde{r}$ can be expressed in terms of $C_B(d)$:

$$\tilde{r} \equiv \tilde{k}_R C_B(d) = (k_R/N_A)C_B(d) \tag{80}$$

Here, k_R is the reaction rate constant in usual unit, $cm^3\ mol^{-1}\ s^{-1}$, and N_A is the Avogadro number. The d-value is minimum separation distance (center to center) between A and B molecules. From Equations 79 and 80, $C_B(d)$ is expressed by

$$C_B(d) = C_B(\infty)/[1 + \tilde{k}_R/(4\pi D' d)] \tag{81}$$

The reaction flow $\tilde{r}$ is usually expressed in terms of $C_B(\infty) = C_B$, because $C_B(d)$ is not measurable.

$$\tilde{r} \equiv \tilde{k} C_B(\infty) = (k/N_A)C_B$$

Here, k is the overall reaction rate constant of the reaction of Equation 77. Combination of this equation with Equation 81 gives

$$k = N_A \tilde{r}/C_B = \tilde{k}_R N_A/[1 + \tilde{k}_R/(4\pi D' d)] \tag{82}$$

If $\tilde{k}_R \gg 4\pi D' d$, Equation 82 becomes

$$k = k_D \equiv 4\pi D' d N_A \tag{83}$$

This equation corresponds to the diffusion-controlled rate constant of the intermediate formation [82]. For ordinary molecules, d is of the order of a few Å, and D′ is of the order $10^{-5}\ cm^2\ s^{-1}$. Then the approximation $k = k_D$ will be satisfied if k_R is much greater than $10^{10}\ dm^3\ mol^{-1}\ s^{-1}$.

When both A and B are ionic forms with the electric valence, Z_A and Z_B, respectively, an electrostatic potential is imposed around the A ion, the potential being shielded by the presence of the B and A ions. Debye modified the rate constant of Equation 83 by taking into account the electrostatic potential without the shielding effect [83]:

$$k_D = 4\pi\, d\, (D_A + D_B) N_A \xi_e/(\exp(\xi_e) - 1) \tag{84}$$

Here, the ξ_e value is the Coulomb potential between A and B at x = d divided by the thermal energy:

$$\xi_e = Z_A Z_B e^2/(4\pi\varepsilon\, dk_B T) \tag{85}$$

When $\xi_e \ll 1$, Equation 84 reduces to Equation 83.

The dissociation of the product AB is controlled by the diffusional separation of A and B, when the product is rapidly converted to the intermediate aggregate due to fast rearrangement of electronic structure. In this case, the rate constant of the diffusional separation is expressed by

$$k_{D'} = 3\xi_e(D_A + D_B)/[d^2(1 - \exp(-\xi_e))] \tag{86}$$

Next, we consider another case that the step D of the reaction processes in Equation 76 is fast enough for the product formation to be controlled by the chemical reaction step R. In this case, an equilibrium state is attained between the reactants (A and B) and the diffusional-encounter intermediate A · · · B. The equilibrium constant $K'_{A,B}$ is determined from Equations 84 and 86:

$$K'_{A,B} = C_{A\cdot\cdot B}/C_A C_B = k_D/k'_D = (4\pi\, d^3 N_A/3)\exp(-\xi_e) \tag{87}$$

Fuoss [84] developed a theory of the ionic association, showing that Equation 87 gives a thermodynamic equilibrium constant if C_A and C_B are replaced by the corresponding activities. We must account for the activity coefficients of A, B and A · · · B.

$$K_{A,B} = \gamma_{AB} C_{AB}/\gamma_A \gamma_B C_A C_B = (4\pi\, d^3 N_A/3)\exp(-\xi_e) \tag{88}$$

$$\gamma_A \gamma_B = \gamma_\pm^2 = \exp(-|\xi_e|\kappa\, d/(1 + \kappa\, d)),\ \kappa^2 = e^2 \sum_i C_i Z_i^2 N_A/(\varepsilon k_B T) \tag{89}$$

where, the $\gamma_\pm$ is the mean activity coefficient for the ions A and B which is expressed by Debye-Hückel expression for a dilute electrolyte solution. The κ is the reciprocal of Debye's screening length. The γ_{AB} is taken as unity, because the concentration of encounter intermediate is usually very low. Substitution of the $\gamma_\pm$ value into Equation 88 results in Equation 90:

$$K_{A,B} = C_{A\cdot\cdot B}/C_A C_B = (4\pi\, d^3 N_A/3)\exp(\xi_e/(1 + \kappa\, d)),\ \text{for } \xi_e < 0 \tag{90}$$

In this case, the rate of reaction to form the product is expressed by

$$r = k_R K_{A,B} C_A C_B \tag{91}$$

Diffusion-Controlled Reaction

A typical example of the diffusion-controlled reaction is the recombination process between a proton and a hydroxide ions:

$$H^+ + OH^- \underset{}{\overset{k_D}{\rightleftharpoons}} [H^+ \cdots OH^-] \rightleftharpoons H_2O \tag{92}$$

The charge transfer of the hydrogen bond in the intermediate is very fast, and then the reaction to produce H_2O is controlled by the diffusion process of the step D. The rate constant obtained by the relaxation method [85] are

$$k_D = 1.4 \times 10^{11} \cdot dm^3\, mol^{-1}\, s^{-1} \tag{93}$$

The d value calculated from Equations 84 and 93 with the D'(=1.45 × 10^{-4} $cm^2\, s^{-1}$ from ion conduction) is 8 Å. Discussions on this d-value appeared in several reports. The diffusion coefficients of proton is extraordinarily large due to Grotthuss mechanism, and the value (Equation 93) would provide an upper limit of the diffusion-controlled reaction.

Reaction of Metal Complex Formation

The process of the metal complex formation in aqueous solution is a reaction of substituting the solvent molecule coordinated to the metal ion with the ligand. This process has been extensively studied [86]. The reaction between metal M and the ligand L is simply described by the same scheme as Equation 76;

$$M + L \underset{}{\overset{\text{step D}}{\rightleftharpoons}} M \cdots L \underset{}{\overset{\text{step R}}{\rightleftharpoons}} ML \qquad (94)$$

where M is the metal ion that carries coordinated water molecules around it. The ligand anion L approaches the metal ion, followed by the formation of the intermediate complex. This intermediate is an aggregate, whose constituents M and L interact through the Coulombic potential, taking a form that the outer-sphere-coordinated water around M is substituted by the ligand L, leaving the inner sphere of coordinated water around M unchanged. This aggregate is called outer-sphere complex. The outer-sphere water molecule is weakly bonded with the inner sphere water molecule, and then the formation process of the outer-sphere complex is considered to be diffusional process of encounter and separation. The relaxation time concerned with the step D is $10^{-9}\ s^{-1}$ in order of magnitude.

The step R is a process in which the inner-sphere water is substituted by the ligand L, and is, in many cases, the rate-determining step for the reaction of Equation 94. This step is greatly affected by the nature of the metal species.

Eigen et al. [81, 87] measured the reaction rate constants, k_R, for many sets of metals and ligand species, by using chemical relaxation techniques, and found that the rate constants are almost independent of the ligand species for a given metal ion. These results strongly suggest that the inner-water substitution by a ligand is determined by the release of the inner-sphere water molecule from the metal ion:

$$M(H_2O)_n + L \overset{K_{M,L}}{\rightleftharpoons} M(H_2O)_n \cdots L \overset{k_M^{-H_2O}}{\rightleftharpoons} LM(H_2O)_{n-1} + H_2O \qquad (95)$$

In this case, the rate of ML formation can be expressed by

$$r = k_M^{-H_2O} K_{M,L} C_M C_L \qquad (96)$$

where $K_{M,L}$ represents the formation constant of the outer-sphere complex given by Equation 90. Since the formation constant of ML is strongly affected by the ligand species, the rate constant of the reaction in the reverse direction is strongly dependent on the ligand species.

Langford et al. [88] classified the metal ions into three groups by taking into account the magnitude of the $k_M^{-H_2O}$ value, as shown in Figure 12. The $k_M^{-H_2O}$ of the metal ions belonging to the class I is comparable to the rate constant of the diffusion controlled reactions, whereas the metals in the class II obeying the S_N1 mechanism. The $k_M^{-H_2O}$ for the class III is less than $10^4\ s^{-1}$. Besides these, there exists a class of metal ions, e.g., Cr(III), Pt(II), Rh(III), and Ir(III) in which the substitution of inner water by ligands is markedly slow.

The rate constants, $k_M^{-H_2O}$, for metals with rare gas electronic structure (d^0, d^{10} metal ion) can be roughly correlated with the ion radius as shown in Figure 13 for uni-, di-, and tri-valent ions [81]. This result shows that the interaction energy between M and inner sphere is mainly determined by the Coulombic potential field due to the central metal ion.

The $k_M^{-H_2O}$ values for transient series of metals are affected by the electronic structure together with the Coulombic interaction, changing regularly with the number of d-electron as shown in Figure 14 for divalent metals [81]. The decreases in $k_M^{-H_2O}$ from d^0 to d^3 and d^5 to d^8 correspond to the difference in the energy of stabilization due to coordination field, which also affects the hydration energy and ionic radius. The strong increase in the $k_M^{-H_2O}$'s at d^4 [Cr(II)] and d^9 [Cu(II)] [81] is due to labilization of ligand substitution by Jahn-Teller effect.

The $k_M^{-H_2O}$ values for metal ions are shown in Figure 15. The rate constant of the inner-sphere complex formation from the outer-sphere one is mainly determined by the metal species, as

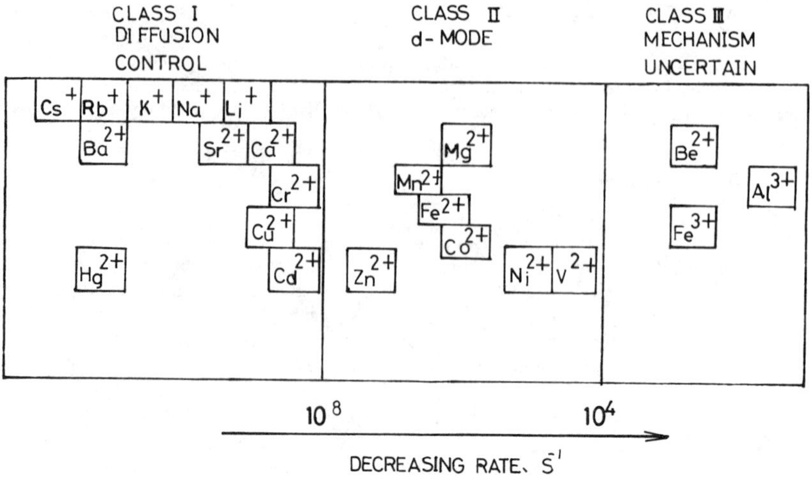

Figure 12. Classification of metal ions by considering the magnitude of $k_M^{-H_2O}$ values. (Reprinted with permission from Ref. 88.)

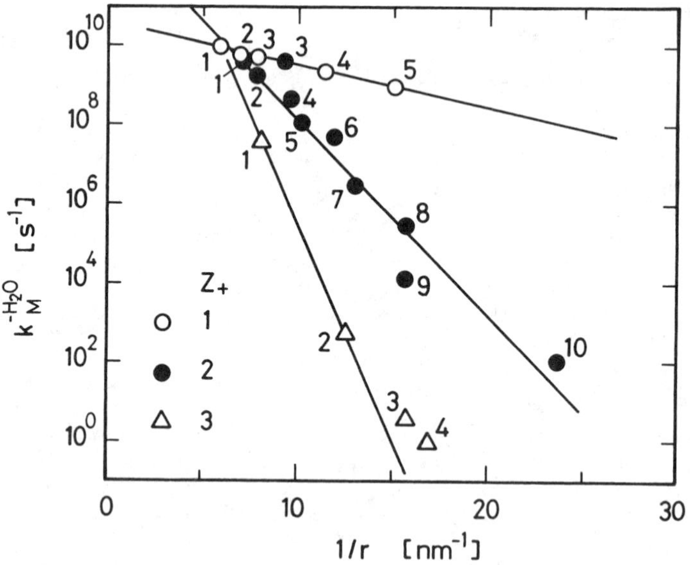

Figure 13. $k_M^{-H_2O}$ values against ionic radii r for uni-, di- and tri-valent metal ions. Univalent (1, Cs^+; 2, Rb^+; 3, K^+; 4, Na^+; 5, Li^+), Divalent (1, Ba^{2+}; 2, Sr^{2+}; 3, Hg^{2+}; 4, Cd^{2+}; 5, Ca^{2+}; 6, Zn^{2+}; 7, Mg^{2+}; 8, $GaOH^{2+}$; 9, Be^{2+}), Trivalent (1, La^{3+}; 2, In^{3+}; 3, Ga^{3+}; 4, Al^{3+}). (Reprinted with permission from Ref. 81.)

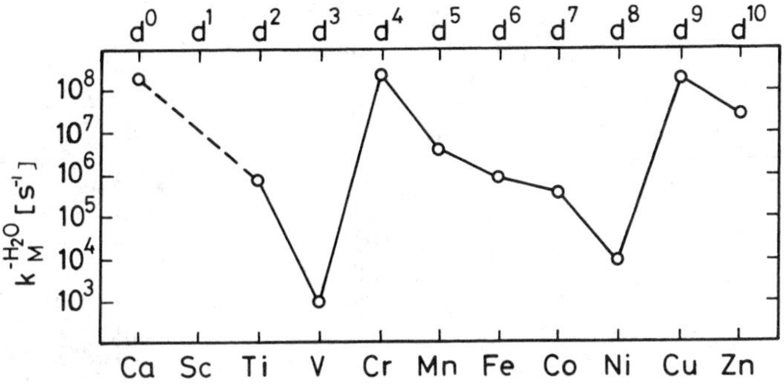

Figure 14. Relation of $k_M^{-H_2O}$ for transient series of metal with the number of d-electron. (Reprinted with permission from Ref. 81.)

mentioned previously. However, there exist some data that the rate constant is also affected by the ligand species [89, 90, 91]. Table 11 shows the effects of the ligand species for Ni(II) and Co(II) [89]. The intra-hydrogen bonding in the ligand species has also an effect on the rate of metal chelate formation [92, 93].

Addition of a monodentate and mono-valent ligand, L, such as hydroxide, acetate, and chloride ions to the aqueous solution with metal ion strongly increases the rate of metal extraction. These catalytic role will be shown later.

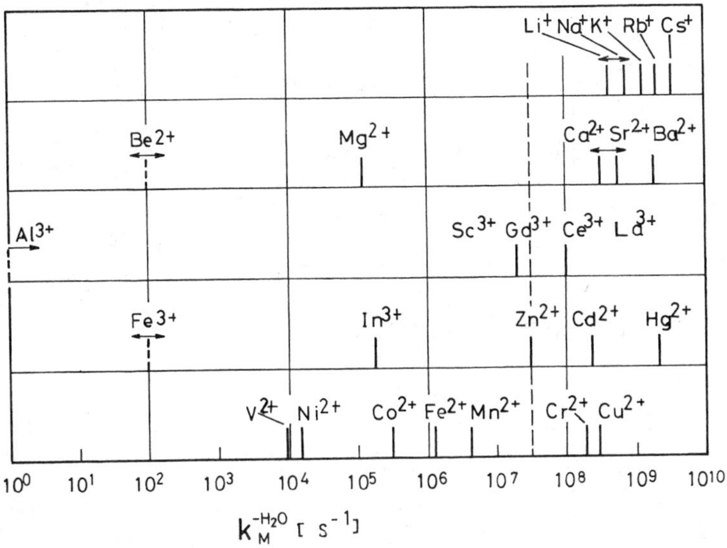

Figure 15. $k_M^{-H_2O}$ for metal ions. (Reproduced with permission from Ref. 81.)

Table 11
Rate Constant of Complex Formation. [$dm^3\ mol^{-1}\ s^{-1}$]
$M(H_2O)_6^{2+} \cdots L \rightarrow M(H_2O)_{6-n}L^{2+} + nH_2O$ (298 K)

Ligand	$Co(H_2O)_6^{2+}$	$Ni(H_2O)_6^{2+}$
H_2O	1.1×10^6	2.7×10^4
SCN^-	—	0.6×10^4
SO_4^{2-}	0.20×10^6	1.5×10^4
$HP_2O_7^{3-}$	0.48×10^6	1.2×10^4
$HP_3O_{10}^{4-}$	0.72×10^6	1.2×10^4
$C_2O_4^{2-}$	—	0.6×10^4
$HC_2O_4^-$	—	0.9×10^4
imidazole	0.44×10^6	1.6×10^4
glycine	0.26×10^6	0.7×10^4
diglycine	0.26×10^6	1.2×10^4
triglycine	—	0.5×10^4

(Reprinted with Permission from Ref. 89)

Reactions of Metal Chelate Complex Formation

Tautomerization of β-diketone

β-diketone comprises the enol and keto forms, between which a tautomerization reaction occurs as shown in Figure 11a:

$$\begin{array}{ccccc} k_K{:}O[10^{-2}\ s^{-1}] & & k'_E{:}O[10^{10}\ dm^3\ mol^{-1}\ s^{-1}] & & \\ HR^* \rightleftharpoons H^+ & + & R^- \rightleftharpoons HR & & (97) \\ \text{(keto)} & & \text{(enolate ion)} \quad \text{(enol)} & & \\ k'_K{:}O[10^6 \sim 10^7\ dm^3\ mol^{-1}\ s^{-1}] & & k_E{:}O[10^2\ s^{-1}] & & \end{array}$$

The enolization of β-diketones does not in general proceed by the direct transfer of a proton from carbon to oxygen [19].

The rate constants for several β-diketones are shown in Table 12. The recombination reaction of the enolate ion with a proton to yield the enol form is much faster than that of yielding the

Table 12
Rate Constants of Tautomerization for β-Diketones at 298 K

β-Diketone	k'_k ($dm^3\ mol^{-1}\ s^{-1}$)	k_k (s^{-1})	k'_E ($dm^3\ mol^{-1}\ s^{-1}$)	k_E (s^{-1})	I^a	Ref.
AA	1.2×10^7	1.4×10^{-2}	3.0×10^{10}	1.7×10^2		[93]
		1.32×10^{-2}			0.2	[94, 95]
		1.67×10^{-2}				[96]
		3.6×10^{-2}		1.6×10^2	0.1	[37]
BA	7.9×10^6	1.8×10^{-2}	1.5×10^{10}	8.1×10	0.1	[18]
TTA		8.4×10^{-3b}		1.9^b	1.0	[19]
AApH		1.9×10^{-3}		1.4×10	0.1	[37]
AAE		8.9×10^{-4}		1.1×10	0.1	[37]

[a] *ionic strength, in mol/dm³*, [b] *Rate constants for the reaction,* $HR \underset{k_K}{\overset{k_E}{\rightleftharpoons}} HR$.
AA: acetylacetone, BA: benzoylacetone, TTA: thenoyltrifluoroacetone, $CH_3COCHRCOCH_3$, *AApH: R = phenyl-, AAE:* CH_3CH_2-

keto form. The enolate ion takes resonance structures of oxygen-negative and carbon-negative types. The recombination to yield HR, k'_E, takes the magnitude of the diffusion-controlled reaction, whereas that to yield HR*, k'_K, is much smaller than k'_E, this result suggesting that the oxygen-negative form is energetically more stable than the carbon-negative form.

Reaction of Metal Complex Formation in β-Diketone System

The reaction processes to form metal complexes of β-diketone are divided into three paths. The first is the reaction of metal ion M with the enolate ion (Path I). Let k_2 be the rate constant of this reaction in a forward direction. The second and the third are the direct reactions of M with the undissociated enol and keto forms (Path II and Path III), the rate constants being expressed by k_{1E} and k_{1K}, respectively. The data of these rate constants are listed in Table 13 for several divalent metal ions.

The reaction Path I is a reaction process obeying Eigen's mechanism, which involves the loss of water from the metal ion. The k_2 value for Cu(II) is large enough to be considered as diffusion-controlling rate constant, due to Jahn-Teller effect. The reaction between Ni(II) and enolate ion is a typical reaction that proceeds according to S_N1 mechanism. Equation 96 gives the magnitude of the k_2 value.

The direct reactions of metal ion with the undissociated β-diketone (Paths II & III) play a significant role in the metal extraction, when the pH is much lower than the pK_a value of the β-diketone. The rate constants, k_{1E} and k_{1K}, are extraordinarily low compared with that for the reaction involving the loss of water molecules from the metal ion as the rate-determining step. In general, the k_{1K} is less than the k_{1E}.

The slow rate of the reaction of the enol tautomer with metal ion has been interpreted in terms of three factors [99, 98]:

1. Sterically controlled six-membered chelate ring closure contributes to the slow rate of the above reaction.
2. Relatively strong intramolecular hydrogen bonding in the enol tautomer, which converts the protonated ligand to a poor entering ligand for metal ion.
3. The energetics of the proton release from half-bonded intermediate with metal ion, which slows down the rate of chelate ring closure.

The first mechanism postulated that the closing of six- (and seven-) membered rings is in general sterically hindered, in contrast to the five-membered chelate ring closure [101–103], in which the coordinated water release from a metal ion controls the rate. Then, the six-membered metal-chelate complex formation is controlled by the step of the chelate ring closure. This postulation predicts that the enolate ion should also react with metal ions at abnormally slow rate, while the k_2 is still of large value as estimated from the water release mechanism [19]. This result suggests that the slow rate chelate ring closure is not due to the steric factor, but by the other factors.

The intramolecular hydrogen bonding in a ligand is a mechanism to slow down the entering of metal ion into the ligand, for example, the reaction of hydroxide ion with the enol form of acetylacetone proceeds as follows [93].

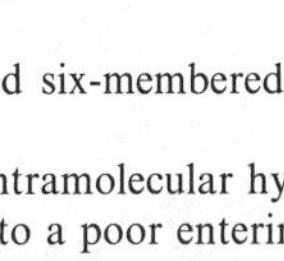

$$+ \quad OH^- \underset{}{\overset{k = 1.6 \times 10^7\ dm^3\,mol^{-1}\,s^{-1},}{\rightleftharpoons}} R^- + H_2O \qquad (98)$$

The rate constant, $1.6 \times 10^7\ dm^3\,mol^{-1}\,s^{-1}$, is still higher than the k_{1E} values, but is about three orders of magnitude lower than the normal diffusion-controlled mechanism.

The release of a proton from the enol tautomer would be one important factor of slowing down the direct reaction between enol tautomer and metal ion. Pearson et al. [99] argued that the k_{1E} value for acetylacetone and Cu(II) system remains unchanged when the solvent is changed from

Table 13

Rate Constants of the 1:1 Metal-Ligand Complex Formation in Aqueous Phase in $dm^3\ mol^{-1}\ s^{-1}$ at 298 K

Reagent Metal	Ligand	AA [Ref.]	BA [Ref.]	TTA [Ref.]	AApH [Ref.]	AAE [Ref.]
Cu^{2+}	R^-	9×10^8 [97]	1.1×10^9 [18]	$>3 \times 10^6$ [19]		
	HE	2×10^4 [99]	2×10^3 [18]		1.5×10^3 [37]	6×10^2 [37]
		3.6×10^3 [37]				
	HK	1.5×10 [99]	12 [18]		1.1×10^{-2} [37]	1.2×10^{-3} [37]
Ni^{2+}	R^-			1.0×10^4 [19]		
	HE	2.7 [99]		2.3 [19]		
		19.3 [100]				
	HK					
Co^{2+}	R^-			$\geqslant 3 \times 10^4$ [19]		
	HE					
	HK					
$Fe(OH)^{2+}$	R^-					
	HE	4.4×10^3 [98]		(1.3×10^3) [19]		
	HK	5.4 [98]				
Fe^{3+}	R^-	8×10^8 [98]		(2.4×10^4) [19]		
	HE	5.2 [98]		1.4 [19]		
	HK	0.29 [98]				

Abbreviations are the same as in Table 12., HE = enol, R^- = enolate ion, HK = keto

water to methanol, suggesting the proton release mechanism is unreasonable. However, the magnitude of the rate constant change expected for this solvent exchange is difficult to access [19].

The previous three factors are of primary importance, but it is not easy to distinguish between them. It is of interest that the k_{1E} value is insensitive to ligand species with six-membered ring closure for a given metal ion.

The rate constant of the reaction of metal ion with keto tautomer is much slower than that with enol tautomer. It has been proposed that the first step in the reaction between Cu(II) and the keto tautomer of acetylacetone involves the formation of a symmetrical precursor complex in which the metal ion is bonded to both keto groups [99]. The cupric ion acts as an electron sink and the rate determining step involves the slower, metal ion-catalyzed proton release from the three-carbon acid. The keto form of thenoyltrifluoroacetone (TTA) is relatively unreactive compared with acetylacetone keto form. This unreactivity may be due to its unsymmetrical hydrated structure [19, 98]. The reaction process involving the keto tautomer is less important than that involving the enol tautomer, and can be neglected in the interpretation of the kinetics in metal extraction process. Thus, the reaction scheme shown in Figure 11a is simplified as Figure 11b.

We can postulate two extreme cases in metal complex formation. The first case (abbreviated as Case I) postulates that the concentration of the 1:1 metal-ligand complex is much larger than that of 1:2 metal-ligand complex. This case is frequently realized in β-diketone systems. The rate of MR^+ formation is simply described by Equation 99, when the pK_a value of the chelating agents is much higher than the pH in the extraction operation. This condition results in low concentration of the dissociated form of the ligand, making a stationary state approximation available for the dissociated ligand [104].

$$r_{MR} = k_I([HR] - [MR^+][H^+]/K_1[M^{2+}]) \tag{99}$$

$$k_I = k_1[M^{2+}] + k_2[M^{2+}]/([H^+]/K_a + k_2[M^{2+}]/k_a) \tag{100}$$

The first and second terms of the right side of Equation 100 represent the mobilities of HR flow through the path of MR^+ direct formation and the path of the reaction between the dissociated ligand and metal ion, respectively. The second case (abbreviated as Case II) postulates the preferential formation of MR_2, the yield of MR^+ being much less than that of MR_2. In addition to this, we postulate $pK_a \gg pH$. In this case, the stationary state approximations for the species R^- and MR^+ are available. These postulations yield the MR_2 formation rate [104]:

$$r_{MR_2} = k_{II}([HR] - [MR_2][H^+]^2/K_1K_2[HR][M]) \tag{101}$$

$$1/k_{II} = 1/k_I + 1/(k_3K_1[HR][M^{2+}]/[H^+]) \tag{102}$$

The first term of the right side of Equation 102 is the resistance in the 1:1 complex formation step and the second term is the resistance in the 1:2 complex formation step from MR^+. These resistances in series contribute to the overall reaction resistance. If the 1:2 complex formation is rapid, Equation 102 reduces to Equation 100, while, when the reaction is slow, the 1:2 complex formation from MR^+ controls the overall reaction rate.

Reactions of Metal Complex Formation in Hydroxyoxime System

Hydroxyoximes of commercial importance, e.g., 2-hydroxy 5-nonyl benzophenone oxime (oxime component of LIX65N) comprises of anti- and syn-isomers. Anti-isomer alone is active component of metal extraction due to its steric conformation. Since the conversion rate from anti-isomer to syn-isomer is very slow [20], the metal extraction rate can be evaluated with the help of the concentration of anti-isomer. Hydroxyoximes with long hydrocarbon chain tails dissolve in the aqueous phase only slightly, and the metal-ligand complex produced in the aqueous phase often precipitates in the phase. Due to these characteristics, the rate of metal complex formation is difficult to measure in the aqueous phase. Instead, the reaction rate in a neutral protic solvent, such as ethanol or ethanol-water mixtures, can be measured. β-hydroxyoxime has a similar electric structure to the enol form of β-diketone as shown in Figure 16.

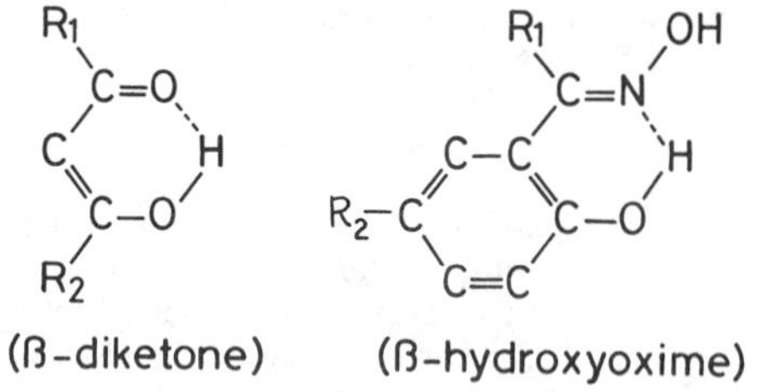

Figure 16. Similarity of β-diketones and β-hydroxyoximes.

The production rate of Cu(II)-hydroxyoxime complex in neutral form, CuR_2, can be measured by using the stopped flow spectrophotometer. The reaction scheme to give the neutral complex is described as

$$M^{2+} + HR \underset{k_1'}{\overset{k_1}{\rightleftarrows}} MR^+ + H^+ : K_1 \tag{103}$$

$$MR^+ + HR \underset{k_3'}{\overset{k_3}{\rightleftarrows}} MR_2 + H^+ : K_2 \tag{104}$$

when the anion species R^- is neglected.

Nicol et al. [105] determined the reaction rate constants for salicylaldoxime-Cu(II) in 80% ethanol aqueous solution at 284 K. The resultant constants are given by

$$k_1 = 3.7 \times 10^4 \ dm^3 \, mol^{-1} \, s^{-1}, \qquad k_3' = 2.55 \times 10^4 \ dm^3 \, mol^{-1} \, s^{-1}$$
$$k_1'/k_3 = 1.28, \qquad K \equiv K_1 K_2 = 1.13 \tag{105}$$

The overall equilibrium constant, K, decreased from 0.92 in 75% dioxane to 0.07 in 46% dioxane, and for LIX65N the K value being 1.4 at 298 K in 90% ethanol aqueous solution. The overall rate of the MR_2 formation is determined by the direct reaction step of the MR^+ formation, when $[HR]/[H^+] \gg (k_1'/k_3)$ in Nicol case $[HR]/[H^+] \gg 1.28$. Pratt et al. [106] also reported for LIX65N system that the MR^+ formation step controls the MR_2 formation at their experimental condition, $7 > [HR]/[H^+] > 0.03$, and the resultant k_1 value takes a similar value to the salicylaldoxime system. The data for the k_1 values reported for Cu(II) are shown in Table 14.

The rate constants of the oxime-Cu(II) complex, k_1, take the values similar to those of β-diketone-Cu(II) systems, which are much less than the value estimated from the mechanism of water release from the Cu(II) ion as the rate-determining step. The causes of extraordinarily low value can be interpreted in terms of three factors as mentioned previously.

Nicol et al. [105] also reported the k_1 values (see Table 14) for the hydroxyoximes that are different from each other in the substituent group: The faster rate for X=NO_2 is interpreted in terms of a displacement of the hydrogen bond normally present between the phenolic proton and the oxime group towards the nitro group, thus facilitating conformation to a metal ion.

This effect on the conformation of the phenolic proton could also explain the reduced rate of reaction for the oxime, X=Br, in which the bulky bromine atom hinders proton away from the coordination site. The relatively slight effect of the substituent groups, R_1 and R_2, on the k_1 is because these groups are located far from the coordination site of metal ions. From these results, it is deduced that the three factors cooperatively slow down the rate constant, k_1.

Finally, let the reaction process of Equation 104 be considered. The formation of 1:2 metal-ligand complexes in neutral form is, in general, much faster than the preceding reaction process. The condition at which the 1:2 complex formation controls the overall reaction rate is given with the help of Equation 102.

$$[HR]/[H^+] \ll k_1'/k_3 \tag{106}$$

If the magnitude of k_1'/k_3 is assumed to be unity as mentioned in Equation 105, the condition results in that $[HR] \ll [H^+]$. At low pH, this condition would be frequently realized. It is reported

Table 14
k_1 Values for Hydroxyoximes—Cu(II) System

Oxime			Solvent	Temp. [K]	k_1 [$dm^3\ mol^{-1}\ s^{-1}$]	Ref.
salicylaldoxime			80% ethanol	284	3.7×10^4	[105]
β-hydroxyoxime[a]						
$R_2 = H$	$R_1 = H$	$X = H$	80% ethanol	277	7.4×10^3	[105]
H	t-C_4H_9	H	in water at pH = 5	277	5.3×10^3	[105]
CH_3	H	H	in water at pH = 5	277	14.5×10^3	[105]
CH_3	Cl	H	in water at pH = 5	277	12.2×10^3	[105]
C_7H_{15}	CH_3	H	in water at pH = 5	277	9.5×10^3	[105]
C_7H_{15}	Cl	H	in water at pH = 5	277	8.6×10^3	[105]
C_7H_{15}	Br	H	in water at pH = 5	277	8.0×10^3	[105]
C_7H_{15}	CH_3	Br	in water at pH = 5	277	2.7×10^3	[105]
C_7H_{15}	CH_3	NO_2	in water at pH = 5	277	34.8×10^3	[105]
ph	C_9H_{19}	H	ethanol	298	29.0×10^3	[106]
CH_3	H	H	80% ethanol	298	2.5×10^3	[24]

[a]
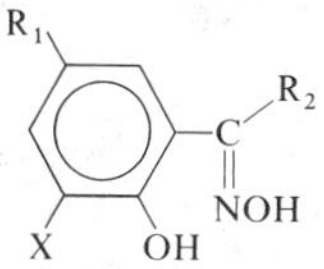

that the rate constant for the 1:2 complex formation is never larger than that for the 1:1 complex, this result being unique for Cu(II) [107].

The 1:1 metal complex formation for hydroxyoximes occurs in general through two paths, one being the reaction, Equation 103 and the other the reaction process with the help of the dissociated ligand species, R^-. The presence of the 1:1 Cu(II)-ligand complex is hardly detected, suggesting that $K_1 \ll K_2$. From this feature for the hydroxyoxime systems, a stationary state approximation can be applicable for the 1:1 complex. In this case, the overall rate of MR_2 formation r_{MR_2} can be described by Equations 101 and 102.

The protonation of oximes, $HR + H^+ \rightarrow H_2R^+$, is probably important in the evaluation of metal extraction rate, and in some cases this reaction should be accounted for in metal complex formation. In this treatment, this reaction is disregarded for the sake of simplicity.

KINETICS OF METAL EXTRACTION BY CHELATING AGENTS

Experimental Techniques

The metal extraction is performed by diffusional flow of metal across the interface between two liquid phases, accompanied with the chemical reaction of metal complex formation. The diffusional processes of several species participating in the chemical reaction in both phases are of great significance, together with both the location where the chemical reaction proceed and its rate. To understand the kinetics of the metal extraction, one must precisely evaluate the effect of diffusion on the metal transfer. Several techniques have been developed for the evaluation, some of the more important are classified into two groups, the violent mixing and the known interfacial area types. A critical review appeared in Reference [108].

Violent Mixing Type

This type is employed when the reaction processes in the bulk phase control the extraction rate due to fast diffusion caused by a violent mixing. The typical apparatus of this type, e.g.,

AKUFVE apparatus [109], has a defect that the interfacial area of the liquid droplets is difficult to measure and also the hydrodynamic conditions cannot be well controlled. The fast reaction limits the reaction location to a thin boundary phase adjacent to the interface, and requires a precise interfacial area. If the reaction occurs at the interface, the interfacial area must be known for understanding the kinetics of interfacial reaction. Due to these reasons, this experimental technique is worthwhile only when the reaction is so slow that the reaction proceeds in the bulk liquid phase.

Early works on kinetics of metal extraction assert that the rate of extraction increases as the stirring speed increases and approaches a plateau value. However, the plateau value does not always suggest the presence of the chemical reaction-controlled process, because the liquid droplets are not divided to more fine droplets due to coalescence of droplets, even if the stirring speed increases. Also, the diffusional flow to droplets approaches a saturated value, because of the saturation of droplet subdivision. Therefore, special caution must be taken when using this technique.

Known Interfacial Area Type

This type is classified into several methods:

1. Lewis cell [110]—This constant-area stirred cell overcomes the many disadvantages of violent mixing type, though the hydrodynamic conditions must be determined by preliminary experiments. In some cases, the interface is established by a filter membrane, which separates two liquid phases.
2. Rotating diffusion cell [111]—In this method, the liquid-liquid interface is established by surface tension on the pore of a Milipore filter of disk type, which is rotated. This apparatus provides a known interfacial area and better control of the hydrodynamic condition because the mass transfer near a rotating disk is well defined [112].
3. Laminar jet method [113]—The hydrodynamic condition is well defined in the gas-liquid system, and this method is frequently used in the gas-liquid system. However, for liquid-liquid system, there exist some problems with the hydrodynamic condition. In liquid-liquid system a free jet motion cannot be obtained due to the presence of the liquid phase around the liquid jet. Further, there is the difficult problem of forming a stable laminar jet. Due to these defects, this method is not used now, except for examining the very fast reaction behavior.
4. Freely rising or falling single drop method [114]—Though this method provides a known interfacial area, the evaluation of the end effects present at drop formation and coalesence is difficult. The hydrodynamic condition inside the drop also prevents clear insight into the mass transport effect.
5. Diffusion cell—This is frequently used in measuring the diffusion constant in liquid phase. Recently a powerful technique was developed [115] that provides multicomponent concentration profiles with the help of position-scanning spectrophotometer. This can be used for examining the kinetics of extraction accompanied with relatively slow reaction superimposed on the diffusion process.

The selection of the experimental technique depends upon the nature of the extraction system. If the reaction process is not fast enough to be considered as a diffusion-control, techniques (1) or (2) are suited for the kinetic research on metal extraction.

Kinetics of Metal Extraction

Brief Review on Kinetic Data

Large amounts of kinetic data have been published and are summarized in Tables 15–18. Some data assert that the rate determining reactions proceed in a bulk phase or in a thin boundary layer adjacent to the interface, whereas in other data the kinetically important reactions are estimated to occur at the interface itself.

Table 15
Kinetic Studies on Dithizone and Derivatives

Chelating Agent	Metal	Aq. Phase	Org. Phase	Method	Reaction Location	Rate-Determining Step & Rate Expression	Ref.
dithizone	Zn(II)	Cl^-	CCl_4, $CHCl_3$	mixing cell	aq. bulk phase	reaction of metal with dithizonate ion $j \propto [Zn^{2+}][\overline{HR}]/[H^+]$ (approximately)	[116]
dithizone, di-2-methyl- & di-α-naphtyl-dithizones	Zn(II) Co(II) Ni(II)	ClO_4^-	$CHCl_3$	mixing cell	aq. bulk phase	reaction of metal with dithizonate ion $j \propto [M^{2+}][\overline{HR}]/[H^+]$ (approximately) $j \propto [Zn^{2+}][\overline{HR}]^2/[H^+]^2$ for di-α-naphtyl dithizone-Zn(II) system	[117]
dithizone-derivatives	Zn(II) Co(II)	ClO_4^-	$CHCl_3$	mixing cell	aq. bulk phase	reaction of metal with dithizonate ion $j \propto [M^{2+}][\overline{HR}]/[H^+]$	[118]
dithizone	Zn(II)	ClO_4^-	$CHCl_3$	mixing cell	aq. bulk phase	discussion on loss of coordinate water from metal ion	[119]
dithizone	Ni(II)		CCl_4, $CHCl_3$	const. area stirred cell	interface	interfacial reaction to yield 1:1 metal-ligand complex formation with diffusional resistance	[120]
di(p-alkylphenyl) thiocarbazones	Zn(II)	ClO_4^-	$CHCl_3$	mixing cell	interface & aq. bulk phase	aq. bulk phase reaction to yield 1:1 complex for dithizone, interfacial reaction to yield 1:1 complex for alkyls, ethy & butyl-groups. $j \propto [M^{2+}][\overline{HR}][H^+]$	[121]

Table 16
Kinetic Studies on β-Diketones

Chelating Agent	Metal	Aq. Phase	Org. Phase	Method	Reaction Location	Rate Determining Step & Rate Expression	Ref.
TTA	Be(II)	ClO_4^-, Cl^- NO_3^-	CCl_4	mixing cell	aq. bulk phase	1:1 metal complex formation from enolate ion $j \propto [Be^{2+}][\overline{HR}]/[H^+]$, Anion species cause no effect on the rate.	[47]
			MIBK			Ion pair extracted was replaced by TTA in org. phase for MIBK. $j \propto \sum_a k_a[Be^{2+}][\overline{HR}]/[H^+]^a$, a = 1, 2, 3	
TTA	Ga(III)	ClO_4^-	$CHCl_3$	mixing cell	aq. bulk phase	reaction of $Ga(OH)^{2+}$ with enolate ion for forward extraction and reaction to form $Ga(OH)^{2+}$ and R^- for back extraction $j \propto k[Ga(OH)^{2+}][\overline{HR}]/[H^+]\text{-}k'[\overline{GaR_3}][\overline{HR}]^{-2}[H^+]$	[122]
TTA	Fe(III)	ClO_4^-	CCl_4, $CHCl_3$	mixing cell	aq. bulk phase	reaction of Fe(III) with undissociated and dissociated TTA for ClO_4^--(CCl_4, $CHCl_3$) $j \propto [Fe^{3+}][\overline{HR}][1 + K[H^+]^{-1}]$	[123] [124]
		ClO_4^-, Cl^-	MIBK	mixing cell	aq. bulk phase	additional reaction of Fe(III)-ClO_4^- ion pair with TTA in MIBK phase $j \propto [Fe^{3+}][\overline{HR}][1 + K[H^+]^{-1}][1 + K'[ClO_4^-]^3]$ $FeCl^{2+}$ formation enhances iron extraction.	

TTA	Co(II) Ni(II) Cu(II)	SO_4^{2-}, NO_3^-	benzene	mixing cell	aq. bulk phase	$j \propto [M^{2+}][\overline{HR}][1 + K[H^+]^{-1}]$	[125]
acetylacetone, & other β-diketones	Fe(III)	ClO_4^-	CCl_4	mixing cell	aq. bulk phase	reaction of Fe^{3+} with dissociated β-diketones or reaction of $FeOH^{2+}$ with undissociated ketones, the latter being acceptable. $j \propto [Fe^{3+}][\overline{HR}]/[H^+]$ when acidity is not high.	[126]
acetylacetone	Cr(III)	ClO_4^-	4-methyl 2-pentanone 4-methyl 2-pentanol	mixing cell	aq. bulk phase	complex formation between $Cr(OH)^{2+}$ extracted as ion pair with two ClO_4^- ions and organic AA $j \propto [Cr^{3+}][\overline{HR}][H^+]^{-1}[ClO_4^-]^2$	[127]
Benzoylacetone	Cu(II)	NO_3	benzene	const. area stirring cell	aq. stagnant film	1:1 metal complex formation, analyzed using solution of diffusion equation with reaction	[128]
benzoylacetone	Cu(II)	ClO_4	benzene	const. area stirring cell	aq. stagnant film & interface	1:1 metal complex formation in aq. stagnant film and at interface	[49]
3-alkyl pentane 2,4-diones	Cu(II)	ClO_4	benzene	const. area stirring cell	aq. stagnant film & interface	1:1 metal complex formation in aq. stagnant film and at interface. Interfacial reaction plays dominant role for less aq.-soluble agents	[37]

Table 17
Kinetic Studies on Hydroxyoximes

Chelating Agent	Metal	Aq. Phase	Org. Phase	Method	Reaction Location	Rate Determining Step & Rate Expression	Ref.
LIX65N, LIX65N-LIX63	Cu(II)	SO_4^{-2}	toluene	mixing cell	interface	1:2 metal complex formation at interface $j \propto [Cu^{2+}][\overline{HR}]/[H^+]$ for LIX65N(HR) $j \propto [Cu^{2+}][\overline{HR}][\overline{HB}]^{0.5}/[H^+]$ for LIX65N-63(HB)	[48]
LIX64N	Cu(II)	SO_4^{2-}	Escaid-100	single drop		Chemical step at least partially controlling the extraction rate: $j \propto fn([Cu^{2+}]/[H^+])$ for forward extraction $j \propto fn([\overline{CuR_2}][\overline{H^+}])$ for back extraction Catalytic effect of LIX63 was discussed.	[129] [130] [131]
LIX64N	Cu(II)	NO_3^-	xylene	single drop	interface	Reaction not limited by mass transfer $j \propto [Cu^{2+}][\overline{HB}]^{0.5}[HR]^{0.5}$, LIX63:HB, LIX65N:HR	[132]
anti-LIX65N	Cu(II)	SO_4^{2-}	n-heptane	single-drop		Nonylphenol slows down copper extraction rate	[133]
LIX65N	Cu(II)	SO_4^{2-}		single drop		Both mass transfer and chemical reaction are important.	[134]
LIX65N	Cu(II)	SO_4^{2-}	dispersol	const. area stirring cell with & without membrane	aq. stagnant film	Reaction to yield 1:1 complex in aq. stagnant film, when $[Cu^{2+}]/[H^+] > 1$, for forward, extraction, back extraction rate, $j \propto [\overline{CuR_2}][H^+]/[\overline{HR}]$, when $[H^+]/[\overline{HR}] > 10^4$	[135] [136]
LIX64N & salicylaldoxime	Cu(II)	ClO_4^- acetate-buffer	$CHCl_3$ kerosene	const. area mixing cell	aq. stagnant film	Reaction to yield 1:1 complex in aq. stagnant film	[137]

LIX65N	Cu(II)	SO_4^{2-}	toluene	liquid jet	interface	1:1 complex formation from adsorbed HR $j \propto [Cu^{2+}][\overline{HR}]/([H^+] + K[\overline{HR}])$, if diffusion effect is eliminated from the observed data.	[68]
LIX65N	Cu(II)	SO_4^{2-}	kerosene	const. area		Forward extraction rate: $j \propto [Cu^{2+}]^{0.85}([\overline{HR}]/[H^+])^{1.4}$ (a) $j \propto [Cu^{2+}]([\overline{HR}]/[H^+])^{0.5}$ (b) Rate shifts from Eq. (b) to Eq. (a) by washing LIX65N in kerosene with H_2SO_4 aq. solution. Back extraction rate $j \propto [\overline{CuR_2}]^{0.85}[H^+]^a$, $a = 0.7$, $[H^+] > 0.3M$, $a = 0.16$, $[H^+] < 0.3M$	[138] [139]
LIX64N	Cu(II)	SO_4^{2-}	kerosene	const. area stirring cell		Co-existing iron ion slows down copper extraction rate, when iron conc. > 0.1M	[140]
LIX65N	Cu(II)	NO_3^-	$CHCl_3$ & several diluents	mixing cell	aq. bulk phase	1:2 metal complex formation in aq. bulk phase $j \propto [\overline{HR}]^2[Cu^{2+}]/[H^+]$ for several diluents	[141] [142]
anti-HNBPO	Cu(II)	SO_4^{2-}	$CHCl_3$	const. area stirring cell	interface	1:2 complex formation at interface $j \propto [Cu^{2+}][\overline{HR}]^a/[H^+]$, $a = 1.2$–1.3 for HNBPO	[63]
DEHDO						$j \propto [Cu^{2+}][\overline{HR}]^a/[H^+]$, $a = 1.45$ for DEHDO Co-existing ions, Fe(III), Ga(III), slow down copper extraction rate.	
2-hydroxy 5-tert octyl phenyl-heptyl ketoxime	Cu(II)	SO_4^{2-}	toluene n-heptane	mixer cell	interface	Reaction between dimer HR and Cu^{2+} Diluent effect is explained by this, dimer formation being much more favoured to n-heptane than toluene $j \propto k[\overline{HR}]^2[Cu^{2+}]/[H^+]\text{-}k'[H^+][\overline{CuR_2}]$	[143]
HMPOO	Cu(II)	ClO_4^-	toluene	single drop	interface	1:2 complex formation at interface $j \propto [Cu^{2+}][\overline{HR}]^a/[H^+]$, $a = 1$–2	[34]

(Continued)

Table 17 (Continued)

Chelating Agent	Metal	Aq. Phase	Org. Phase	Method	Reaction Location	Rate Determining Step & Rate Expression	Ref.
anti-HNBPO LIX65N	Cu(II)	SO_4^{2-}	toluene n-heptane	single drop const. area stirred cell	interface	1:2 complex formation at interface $j \propto [Cu^{2+}][HR]/[H^+]$ if diffusion effect is eliminated from observed data.	[144] [145]
HOAPO	Cu(II)	NO_3^-	toluene n-heptane	const. area stirred cell	interface	1:2 complex formation at interface $j \propto [Cu^{2+}][\overline{HR}]/[H^+]$ if diffusion effect is eliminated from observed data.	[146]
HOAPO	Cu(II)	Cl^-	toluene	mixing cell	interface	1:1 complex formation from Cu^{2+} and R^- $j \propto [Cu^{2+}][\overline{HR}]/[H^+]$	[147]
Acorga P50	Cu(II)	SO_4^{2-}	n-heptane	rotating diffusion cell	interface	Attachment of the first oxime to Cu^{2+}	[51]
HNAPO	Cu(II)	ClO_4^-	dispersol	const. area	interface	1:2 complex formation $j \propto [Cu^{2+}][\overline{HR}]^a/[H^+]$, a = 1–2 for forward extraction $j \propto [\overline{CuR_2}][H^+]f([\overline{HR}])$, f decreases as $[\overline{HR}]$ increases, for backward extraction	[25] [148]
HNAPO	Cu(II)	ClO_4^-	benzene	const. area	interface & aq. stagnant film	1:2 complex formation at interface for HNAPO $j \propto [Cu^{2+}][\overline{HR}]/[H^+]$	[24]
HAPO						1:1 complex formation in aq. stagnant film for HAPO	
HNAPO	Cu(II)	ClO_4^-	n-heptane toluene, benzene, & their mixture	const. area stirred cell	interface	1:2 complex formation at interface. Diluent effect is interpreted in terms of P_{HR}. $j \propto [Cu^{2+}][\overline{HR}][H^+]^{-1}P_{HR}^{-1}$	[35]

HNBPO	Cu(II)	SO_4^{2-}, Cl^-	$CHCl_3$	const. area stirred cell & mixing cell	interface	Reorientation of adsorbed metal-oxime cation at interface. Cl^- enhances the extraction rate. Discussion on catalitic role of LIX 63.	[149]
HOAPO	Fe(III)	Cl^-	toluene	mixing cell	interface	$j \propto k[Fe^{3+}][\overline{HR}](1 + K[H^+]^{-1})$ Reaction processes: $Fe(OH)^{2+} + HR \rightarrow FeR^{2+}$, $Fe^{3+} + R^- \rightarrow FeR^{2+}$, $Fe^{3+} + HR \rightarrow FeR^{2+} + H^+$	[147]
LIX65N	Ni(II)	ClO_4^-	several diluents	mixing cell	aq. bulk phase	1:1 complex formation in aq. bulk phase $j \propto [Ni^{2+}][\overline{HR}][H^+]^{-1}P_{HR}^{-1}$	[142]
HNAPO	Ni(II)	NO_3^- NH_4^+	MSB210	const. area stirred cell	interface	1:2 complex formation at interface $j \propto [Ni^{2+}][\overline{HR}]/[H^+]$ when $[Ni^{2+}][\overline{HR}]/[H^+] < 3 \times 10^4$ mol/dm^3	[150]
LIX65N	Pd(II)	Cl^-	$CHCl_3$	mixing cell	aq. bulk phase	Reaction between $PdCl_3^-$ and HR $j \propto [Pd]_t[\overline{HR}](1 + K[H^+])^{-1}$	[151]
HNAPO	Pd(II)	Cl	MSB210	mixing cell	interface	Reaction between $PdRCl_2^{2-}$ and HR at interface $j \propto [Pd]_t[\overline{HR}][H^+]^{-1}[Cl^-]^{-1}$ $(1 + K[H^+])^{-1}$	[152]
HNAPO	Pd(II)	Cl^-	n-heptane	const. area stirred cell	aq. bulk phase	Reaction between $PdCl_3^-$ and HR $j \propto [Pd]_t[\overline{HR}]\,(1 + K[H^+])^{-1}$	[153]

Table 18
Kinetic Studies on Oxine and Related Extractants

Chelating Agent	Metal	Aq. Phase	Org. Phase	Method	Reaction Location	Rate-Determining Step & Rate Expression	Ref.
KELEX 100	Cu(II)	SO_4^{2-}	toluene	mixing cell	interface	1:2 complex formation $j \propto [Cu^{2+}][\overline{HR}]/[H^+]$ (approximately)	[154]
KELEX 100	Cu(II)	SO_4^{2-}	$CHCl_3$	const. area stirred cell	interface	1:2 complex formation (deduced)	[63]
KELEX 100	Ga(III)	NaOH	kerosene	mixing cell		$j \propto [Ga^{3+}][Na^+][OH^-]^{0.3}[\overline{HR}]^{0.1}$ at low NaOH conc. $j \propto [Ga^{3+}][Na^+][OH^-]^{-1}[\overline{HR}]$ at high NaOH conc.	[155]
alkylbenzene substituted	Cu(II)	NO_3^-	toluene	hollow-fiber extractor	interface	Reaction between CuR^+ and HR (both species adsorbed at interface) for forward extraction	[156] [157]
N-8-quinolyl-sulfonamides		Cl^-				Reaction between CuR_2 and HCl at interface for back extraction	[158]

Table 15 summarizes the mechanisms of the metal extractions for dithizone and its derivatives. The earlier studies were performed by means of a mixing cell of droplet dispersion in which the interfacial area is unknown. The data taken by using this method postulate, a priori, that the rate-determining reaction occurs in the aqueous bulk phase. Freiser group [116–119] performed systematic studies on the extraction of Ni(II), Zn(II) and other metals, showing that the extraction rates are, in many cases, proportional to the concentrations of metals and ligands, and are inversely proportional to that of hydrogen ion:

$$(A/V)j = k[R^-][M^{2+}] = k'[\overline{HR}][M^{2+}]/[H^+] \qquad (107)$$

Their data were interpreted in terms of 1:1 metal ligand formation as a rate-determining step. The resultant rate constant k as defined in Equation 107 agreed in some cases with the data obtained from the relaxation method in homogeneous phase, however, the rate constants being strongly dependent on the species of dithizone derivatives. On the contrary, Nitsch et al. [120] showed by using the Lewis cell technique that the Zn(II)-ligand complex formation in neutral form was controlled by the reaction of Zn(II) with dissociated dithizone ion adsorbed on the interface. Freiser et al. [121] changed their opinion of 1:1 metal complex formation in the aqueous bulk phase as the rate determining step for long-chain alkyl-group-substituted dithizones, to the one in which the interfacial reaction plays a dominated role in metal extraction.

The kinetic mechanism of extraction by β-diketones reported are summarized in Table 16. Most extensively studied were the metal extractions with thenoyltrifluoroacetone (TTA). Earlier data were taken by using a mixing cell that postulates the presence of the rate-determining reaction in an aqueous bulk phase. Sekine group [47, 122–124, 126, 127] examined extensively the TTA system. Some of their data satisfy Equation 107, the resultant rate constants k_e agreeing with the magnitude of the rate constants obtained by using the relaxation method for homogeneous phase reaction. There are many data showing a strong effect of metal counter anion species on the extraction rate as was observed in dithizone systems. The Lewis cell was used in recent works. Kondo et al. [128] reported for Cu(II)-benzoylacetone system that the rate of Cu(II) extraction was determined by 1:1 metal-ligand complex formation from enolate anion in the aqueous boundary phase adjacent to the interface, but the resultant rate constant of reaction exceeding that of diffusion-controlled reaction. Harada et al. [49] interpreted their data of the same system in terms of the 1:1 metal complex formation as rate-determining both in the aqueous phase and at the interface itself.

Since copper extraction with hydroxyoximes is ot commercial importance, a target is spotted on the Cu(II) metal ion, the other metal ions being studied recently. In the early stage of the kinetic studies, commercial extractants such as LIX65N and LIX64N were used for their practical importance. The physical picture of the extraction rate is difficult to grasp, because the commercial extractants contain several impurities. Nonylphenol involved in LIX65N slows down the copper extraction rate [133]. Also, the extraction rate was proportional to $([\overline{HR}]/[H^+])^{0.5}$, if crude LIX65N is used, whereas if the LIX65N in diluent was washed several times with sulfuric acid aqueous solution, the rate becomes proportional to $([\overline{HR}]/[H^+])^a$ $(a > 1)$ [138]. Addition of syn-2-hydroxy-5-nonyl benzophenone oxime to its anti-isomer solution greatly slows down the rate of Cu(II) extraction from sulfuric acid aqueous solution, whereas from chloride solution, no effect of syn-isomer was observed [159]. This was interpreted in terms of the formation of mixed anti-syn-neutral complex at the interface. Due to these complicated factors, the results of kinetic studies by use of the commercial extractants are of controversy as shown in Table 17. Many recent studies aim at elucidating the kinetic features of the metal extractions using purified oximes.

The extraction rates for hydroxyoximes are frequently characterized by

$$j = k_f'[\overline{HR}][M^{2+}]/[H^+] \qquad (108)$$

though a variety of dependencies of the rate on the previous three kinds of species have been reported. Equation 108 agrees in form with the last form of Equation 107. Kinetic data on Cu(II)-LIX65N obtained by Freiser group by means of a mixing cell satisfy Equation 109 instead of Equations 107 and 108 and they asserted that the 1:2 metal-ligand complex formation in the aqueous phase controlled the Cu(II) extraction.

$$j = k_f[\overline{HR}]^2[Cu^{2+}]/[H^+] \tag{109}$$

Freiser's assertion is based on the experimental results that the rate of extraction was strongly affected by the diluent species, i.e., the more soluble LIX65N is in the aqueous phase, the faster the extraction rate is. On the contrary, Flett et al. [48] focused on the distribution of LIX65N to the aqueous phase being extremely low, making the kinetically important reaction interfacial in nature. They obtained the rate equation of Equation 108 and described it in terms of the reaction scheme: firstly, 1:1 metal-ligand complex is formed by the reaction between Cu(II) and the ligand adsorbed at the interface, thereafter being converted into neutral complex, followed by the desorption of the neutral complex into the organic bulk phase. The rate-determining step is assumed to be the neutral complex formation, this assumption yielding Equation 110 with the help of Equation 52:

$$j = k_f K_{1f}[\Gamma_{HR}^{(\infty)}\bar{K}_{HR}^{s}[\overline{HR}]/(1 + \bar{K}_{HR}^{s}[\overline{HR}])][M^{2+}][\overline{HR}]/[H^+] \tag{110}$$

Here, K_{1f} is the apparent formation constant of MR^+ at the interface, k_f is the rate constant of the 1:2 complex formation from the 1:1 complex that is attained to be equilibrated with the species involved in the reaction. If the interface is saturated with HR, the interfacial excess concentration of HR becomes a constant value $\Gamma_{HR}^{(\infty)}$, thus yielding Equation 109. When $[\overline{HR}]$ is so low that the interfacial concentration is given by the equation $\Gamma_{HR}^{(\infty)}\bar{K}_{HR}^{s}[\overline{HR}]$, Equation 110 can be simplified to

$$j = k_f K_{1f}\Gamma_{HR}^{(\infty)}K_{HR}^{s}[\overline{HR}]^2[M^{2+}]/[H^+] \tag{111}$$

The feature approaching from Equation 111 to Equation 110 with the increase in $[\overline{HR}]$ has been ascertained by Preston et al. [34] and Miyake et al. [25].

Few works have been carried out for the extraction of the other metals with hydroxyoximes such as Ni(II), Fe(III) and Pd(II). The effect of a ligand present in the aqueous phase should be elucidated. The extraction of Cu(II) is reported to be faster from a chloride medium than from sulfate medium [160]. The Pd(II) extraction rate is also affected by the chloride ion concentration in the aqueous phase [151].

The kinetic studies of metal extraction with 8-quinolinol and the related extractants have been reported as shown in Table 18. The kinetic data were interpreted in terms of the interfacial reaction. Kelex 100 developed by Ashland Chemical Company was also examined for kinetic behavior. Recently, Yoshizuka et al. [156–158] examined the rate of Cu(II) extraction with N-8-quinolyl-alkyl-sulfonamides, reporting the significance of the interfacial reaction.

Several studies as shown in Tables 15–18 have been performed, but many of them are only qualitative; in a few of them even units of the kinetic data were lacking. The quantitative data are required for elucidating the dynamic behaviors of metal extractions. Earlier works discussed the kinetic nature of the rate determining reaction without elucidating a simple diffusional contribution to the observed extraction rate. The complicated nature of extraction with chelating agents also prevents clear insight into the kinetics. Since the kinetic models involve many parameters, many models could fit the kinetic data by adjusting the parameter values. It is, therefore, necessary for elucidating the kinetics to discuss how the model parameters are rational. The essential problems to be solved are summarized as follows:

1. Location where rate-determining reaction can occur.
2. Effects of diluents and a variety of extractants on the extraction rate.

The first problem is concerned with the location where rate-determining reaction mainly occurs. The reported locations are in the bulk phase, in the aqueous stagnant film or at the interface. This problem is important for designing the extractor type and its operation, and also for selecting the most powerful separation system. Therefore, the critical conditions to determine dominate reaction location are required for them.

The concept of the interfacial reaction is still of controversy. The distinction between an interfacial reaction and the reaction in a thin boundary layer in the aqueous phase may not be clearly defined and is only a semantic one. From this point of view, Hughes et al. [50] formulated the extraction rate expression by using the Astarita's integral method [161]. In a rapid reaction case, the reaction location is limited to a thin aqueous layer adjacent to the interface, the magnitude of the thickness being expressed by using the absorption theory for reacting gas species in the liquid phase:

$$X_r = (D/k[M])^{0.5} \tag{112}$$

Here, D is the diffusion coefficient and k the overall rate coefficient of the reaction concerned with the reactant M. The enhancement factor of the extraction rate becomes (X_L/X_r), X_L being the stagnant phase film thickness. When the X_r is small, the reaction in the aqueous phase looks like an interfacial reaction. Some experimental works [128, 135] assumed the reaction in the aqueous stagnant film for less soluble chelating agents in the aqueous phase. To explain the copper extraction rates by this, the rate constant of the rate-determining step must be an extraordinarily large value, resulting in a small value of the X_r, e.g., 10 Å, which is a similar order of magnitude to the real interfacial zone thickness. Therefore, this assumed model is only artificial without sound physical meanings. The interfacial reaction is real and originates from the peculiar property of the interface. Albery et al. [51], and Freeman et al. [68] proposed formal description of the interfacial rate. In our treatment, we call the reaction in the real interfacial zone the interfacial reaction.

Another problem is concerned with the rate-determining step of the reaction in the metal extraction. Usually, the reaction process of the complex formation of neutral form is estimated to be much faster than that of the precursor 1:1 complex formation. If we accept the interfacial reaction model, a rather slow reaction of 1:2 complex formation, as expected from the model (Equation 110), should be explained.

A modification of interfacial properties by the adsorption of strongly surface-active agents markedly influences the rate of extraction. Harada et al. [49] reported for Cu(II) extraction with benzoylacetone that the addition of anionic surface-active reagent to the extraction system causes the increase in the Cu(II) extraction rate, whereas the surface-active agents of nonion and cation types cause marked decrease in the rate. These experimental results support the concept of the interfacial reaction.

The second problem to be solved is concerned with the effect of diluents on the extraction rate. Diluent affects strongly the extraction rates. The hydroxyoximes aggregate in a non-polar diluent, which is important for analyzing the mechanism of extraction rate process as is mentioned earlier. Besides this aggregation effect, the nature of diluent affects the rate of extraction [35, 142]. Also important is the effect of the alkyl-chain tail of the chelating agents on the extraction rate. This problem is closely related to the first problem and is solved for molecular design of the extractants.

Now required is the comprehensive treatment of the metal extraction kinetics, which will be presented in succeeding sections.

Rate Equations in Interfacial Zone

The structural properties of water adjacent to the oil-water interface are different from those of bulk water. The thickness of the interfacial zone is about 20 Å, which was decided from Raman spectra for microemulsion system [162]. At the water-air surface, the interfacial zone thickness is similar to that of the oil-water interface system, 20 Å [163]. Also, the water structure adjacent to the interface is similar to that in electrolyte solutions [164].

As mentioned previously, the chelating agent in commercial use such as hydroxyoximes has an amphiphilic nature, and is adsorbed at the water-oil interface by interacting with water molecules through hydrogen bonding. From a kinetic viewpoint, the interfacial zone, where the polar part of the chelating agent exists, acts as a phase similar to aqueous phase. This interfacial zone provides a location of the metal complex formation by collecting the reactant due to adsorption. Therefore, the interfacial reaction plays a key role in the metal extraction.

Let us first consider the case in which the chelating agent is strongly surface-active. Formulation of the interfacial reaction rate was provided by Harada and Miyake [104]. Consider the following type reactions;

$$J + W \underset{k'}{\overset{k}{\rightleftarrows}} I + Q\text{: aqueous bulk phase, K} \tag{113}$$

$$J^* + W \underset{k'^*}{\overset{k^*}{\rightleftarrows}} I^* + Q\text{: interfacial zone, } K^* \tag{114}$$

Here, the asterisk represents the adsorbed species. The equilibrium constants, K and K^*, are defined by

$$K = [I][Q]/[J][W], \qquad K^* = [Q]_s\theta_I/[W]_s\theta_J \tag{115}$$

The subscript, s, represents the aqueous phase adjacent to the interface. θ_J is the fraction covered by the species J and is described by the Langmuir adsorption as shown earlier:

$$\theta_J = K_J^s[J]_s \bigg/ \left(1 + \sum_J K_J^s[J]_s\right) = \bar{K}_J^s[\bar{J}]_s \bigg/ \left(1 + \sum_J \bar{K}_J^s[\bar{J}]_s\right) \tag{116}$$

The K_J^s and $\bar{K}_J^s$ are the equilibrium constants of J adsorbed from the aqueous and organic phases, respectively. The reaction rates of Equations 113 and 114 are expressed by

$$r = k[J][W] - k'[I][Q] \tag{117}$$

$$r^* = (1/2)k^*\theta_J[W]_s - (1/2)k'^*\theta_I[Q]_s \tag{118}$$

The r* has a unit, mol $cm^{-2} s^{-1}$. The coefficient 1/2 in Equation 118 is introduced because the species reacting with adsorbed molecule exists only in 2π solid angle, in comparison with 4π in the bulk solution. The adsorption and desorption of I and J species are assumed to be very fast, this yielding that the θ_I and θ_J can be expressed by Equation 116. Thus, Equation 118 is rewritten with the use of the driving force expressed in terms of the concentrations of the species in the aqueous phase adjacent to the interface.

$$r^* = (1/2)\left[k^*K_J^s \bigg/ \left(1 + \sum_J K_J^s[J]\right)\right]\{[J]_s[W]_s - [I]_s[Q]_s/K\} \tag{119}$$

Since the reaction of the polar part of the reactant occurs in the atmosphere similar to the aqueous phase, we assume as a first approximation:

$$k^*/\Gamma^{(\infty)} = k \tag{120}$$

This equation relates the k* with the rate constant in the bulk aqueous phase, k, Equations 117–120 can be used for any reactions that occur in an atmosphere similar to the homogeneous aqueous phase.

Now, consider the metal-chelating ligand complex formation. The reaction scheme at the interface can be expressed as shown in Figure 17 by referring to the reaction processes in the bulk phase, Figure 11. In Figure 17a, the 1:1 complex is formed at the interface, followed by the reaction with X_{HR} to yield neutral form complex. The MR^+ in the interfacial zone takes an orientation that the polar part dips into the water atmosphere, the rest being oriented toward the organic phase.

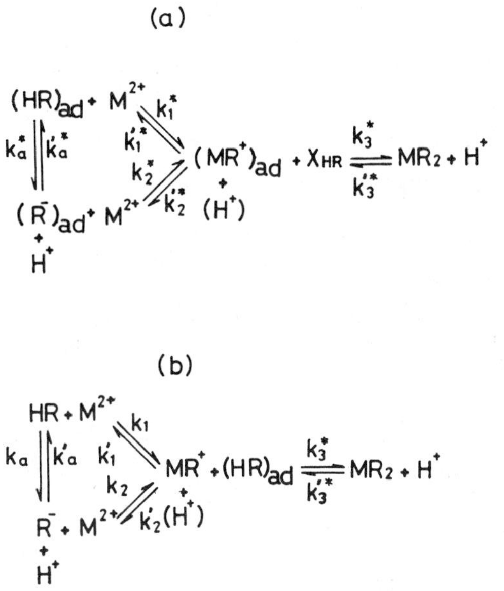

Figure 17. Reaction scheme of metal complex formation at interface.

Since the rotational motion of MR^+ is strongly restricted due to amphiphilic nature of the chelating agent, it is natural to consider that the MR^+ complex in the interfacial zone reacts with chelating agent that is dissolved in the aqueous phase. In this case,

$$X_{HR} = HR \tag{121}$$

In Figure 17b, the MR^+ formed in the aqueous phase is converted to MR_2 by reacting with the HR adsorbed at the interface. Applying Equation 117 or 118 to these reaction scheme, the reaction rates to form metal complexes at the interfacial zone are expressed in Case I (cf. Equation 99)

$$r^*_{MR^+} = k_{sI}([HR] - [H^+][MR^+]/K_1[M^{2+}]) \tag{122}$$

and also for Case II (cf. Equation 101),

$$r^*_{MR_2} = k_{sII}([HR] - [H^+]^2[MR_2]/K_1K_2[M^{2+}][HR]) \tag{123}$$

where,

$$k_{sI} = (k_1[M^{2+}]_s + k_a[M^{2+}]_s/([M^{2+}]_s + (K^s_{HR}/K^s_{R^-})\{k_a/(K_a k_2)\}[H^+]_s]) \times (1/2)K^s_{HR}\Gamma^{(\infty)}\Big/\Big(1 + \sum_J K^s_J[J]\Big) \tag{124}$$

$$1/k_{sII} = 1/k_{sI} + \{(K^s_{HR}/K^s_{MR^+})/(k_3K_1)\}[H^+][X_{HR}]^{-1}[M^{2+}]^{-1} \times \left\{\Gamma^{(\infty)}_{HR}K^s_{HR}\Big/\Big(1 + \sum_J K^s_J[J]\Big)\right\}^{-1} \tag{125}$$

$$[X_{HR}] = [HR]$$

Equation 122 or 124 can be applied to the case that $K_2[HR]/[H^+] \ll 1$ and Equation 123 or 125 is for $K_2[HR]/[H^+] \gg 1$ case. These equations are applicable for surface-active chelating agents.

In the case of a surface-inactive chelating agent, the agent is not accumulated by the adsorption at the interface, but the concentration of the ligand in the interfacial zone is still high in comparison with that in the aqueous phase, being equal to that in the organic phase. In this case, the rate expressions corresponding to Equations 122–125 are

$$r^{*}_{MR^{+}} = (1/2)\delta k_{I}P_{HR}\{[HR] - [H^{+}][MR^{+}]/K_{1}[M^{2+}])\} \quad (126)$$

$$r^{*}_{MR_2} = \delta k_{II}P_{HR}\{[HR] - [H^{+}]^{2}[MR_2]/K_1K_2[M^{2+}][HR])\} \quad (127)$$

where δ is the characteristic thickness of the interfacial zone. The overall rate of complex formation can be expressed by adding Equations 122 and 126, or Equations 123 and 127 by referring to Equation 42.

The $K^{s}_{MR^{+}}$ and $K^{s}_{R^{-}}$ are affected by the electrostatic potential at the interface. Since the information about this potential is lacking, we neglected the effect for the sake of simplicity. In this case, the following equation is approximately satisfied:

$$K^{s}_{HR} = K^{s}_{MR^{+}} = K^{s}_{R^{-}}$$

Then, the interfacial reaction rates can be simplified:

$$\begin{aligned} r^{*}_{MR^{+}} &= k^{*}_{s1}\{[HR] - (1/K_1)[H^{+}][MR^{+}]/[M^{2+}]\} \\ k^{*}_{sI} &= \frac{1}{2}k_{I}\{\delta P_{HR} + \Gamma^{\infty}_{HR}K^{s}_{HR}/(1 + K^{s}_{HR}[HR] + K^{s}_{HR}[MR^{+}]_{s})\} \end{aligned} \quad (128)$$

$$\begin{aligned} r^{*}_{MR_2} &= k^{*}_{sII}\{[HR] - (1/K_1K_2)[H^{+}]^{2}[MR_2]/[M^{2+}][HR]\} \\ k^{*}_{sII} &= k_{II}\{\delta P_{HR} + \Gamma^{\infty}_{HR}K^{s}_{HR}/(1 + K^{s}_{HR}[HR])\} \end{aligned} \quad (129)$$

Some investigators assumed that the X_{HR} species is the HR in the organic phase [48]. In this case, the $[X_{HR}]$ is replaced by [HR] in Equation 125. Yoshizuke et al. [156] assumed that the X_{HR} is the HR adsorbed at the interface. This case needs another expression of the interfacial rate instead of Equations 122–129.

Formulations of Metal Extraction Rates

The metal extraction rate can be obtained by solving the diffusion equations accompanied with the complex formation reaction processes. When the interfacial reaction is neglected, the problem of solving the diffusion equations is the same as in the case of gas absorption with chemical reaction. The diffusion equation for the complex formation in the stagnant film of the aqueous phase was solved applying the Astalita's method [161] in the gas absorption problems [165, 166, 167], and was also solved using a linearization approximation for the governing equation [128, 135]. However, the interfacial reaction not involved in the gas absorption problem is important. The interfacial reaction can be accounted for by the boundary condition at the interface position for the diffusion equation with the chemical reaction in the aqueous phase. The diffusion equation should be linearized with respect to the reaction term. Harada and Miyake [104] solved the diffusion equation with the chemical reactions, which are combined with the interfacial reactions Equations 128 and 129 as the boundary conditions. Also, they accounted for the chemical reactions in the bulk aqueous phase, the volume of which is V/A per unit interfacial area. The diffusion equations with the boundary conditions and the solutions at a steady state are summarized in Table 19.

The metal flow is balanced with the ligand flow at steady state. The metal flow can be described in terms of the equivalent circuit for the HR flow as shown in Figure 18. The R's represent the resistances. The R_s and R_f values are the resistances due to the reactions in the interfacial zone

Diffusion Equations and Their Solutions [104]

	General Forms	Case I	Case II
Diffusion Eqs.	$Dd^2u/dx^2 = \tilde{r}$ $Dd^2v/dx^2 = -\tilde{r}$	$u = [HR]$ $v = [MR^+]$	$u = [HR]$ $v = 2[MR_2]$
Reaction rate	$\tilde{r} = \tilde{k}(u - v/\tilde{K})$	$\tilde{k} = k_1$ $\tilde{K} = K_1[M^{2+}]/[H^+]$	$\tilde{k} = 2k_{II}$ $\tilde{K} = 2K_1K_2[M^{2+}][HR][H^+]^{-2}$
B.C. at $x = L$	$u = u_b$ $Ddu/dx + Ddv/dx = 0$ $-Ddu/dx = (V/A)\tilde{r}$	$u_b = [HR]_b$	$u_b = [HR]_b$
B.C. at $x = 0$	$Ddv/dx + r^* = k_0(m_i - m_b)$ $r^* = k_s(u_s - v_s/\tilde{K})$ $m_s/v_s = \tilde{K}'$	$m = [\overline{MR_2}]$ $k_s = k^*_{sI}$ $\tilde{K}' = P_{MR_2}K_2[HR]_s/[H^+]_s$	$m = 2[\overline{MR_2}]$ $k_s = 2k^*_{sII}$ $\tilde{K}' = P_{MR_2}$
Flux of metal	$j = \dfrac{1}{nR_0}\dfrac{R_a^{-1} + R_s^{-1}}{R_a^{-1} + R_s^{-1} + R_0^{-1}}(u_s - m_b/(\tilde{K}'\tilde{K}u_s))$ $= \dfrac{R_a^{-1} + R_s^{-1}}{R_a^{-1} + R_s^{-1} + R_0^{-1}}k_0K_1K_3P_{MR_2}$ $\times\left(\dfrac{[HR]_s^2[M^{2+}]_s}{[H^+]_s^2} - \dfrac{[\overline{MR_2}]_b}{K_1K_2P_{MR_2}}\right)$ $R_a^{-1} = R_f^{-1} + R_B^{-1}$ $R_B = \vec{R}_f + \overleftarrow{R}_f + R_b$ $j = \dfrac{1}{R_0'}([\overline{HR}]_b - [\overline{HR}]_s)$ $R_0' = 2/k_0$ k_0 = mass transfer coeff. in org. phase k_w = mass transfer coeff. in aq. phase D = diffusion coefficient in aqueous phase	$n = 1$ $R_0^{-1} = k_0P_{MR_2}K_1K_2\dfrac{[M^{2+}]_s[HR]_s}{[H^+]_s^2}$ $R_s^{-1} = k^*_{sI}$ $R_f = \left(1 + \dfrac{[H^+]_s}{K_1[M^{2+}]_s}\right)\coth\zeta_b/(\zeta_bk_w)$ $\vec{R}_f = \sinh(2\zeta_b)/(2k_w\zeta_b)$ $\overleftarrow{R}_f = \vec{R}_f[H^+]_s[M^{2+}]_s^{-1}K_1^{-1}$ $R_b = (A/V)\dfrac{\coth\zeta_b \sinh 2\zeta_b}{2k_I}$ $\zeta_b = (1/k_w)\sqrt{k_ID(1 + \tilde{K}^{-1})}$	$n = 2$ $R_0^{-1} = 2k_0P_{MR_2}K_1K_2\dfrac{[M^{2+}]_s[HR]_s}{[H^+]_s^2}$ $R_s^{-1} = 2k^*_{sII}$ $R_f = \left(1 + \dfrac{[H^+]_s^2}{2K_1K_2[M^{2+}]_s[HR]_s}\right)\coth\zeta_b/(\zeta_bk_w)$ $\vec{R}_f = \sinh(2\zeta_b)/(2k_w\zeta_b)$ $\overleftarrow{R}_f = \vec{R}_f[H^+]_s^2(2K_1K_2[M^{2+}]_s[HR]_s)^{-1}$ $R_b = (A/V)\dfrac{\coth\zeta_b \sinh 2\zeta_b}{2\cdot 2k_{II}}$ $\zeta_b = (1/k_w)\sqrt{2k_{II}D(1 + \tilde{K}^{-1})}$

The concentrations adjacent to interface, $[\overline{HR}]_s$, $[H^+]_s$ and, $[M^{2+}]_s$ can be estimated from the approximate relations: $j = kw([M^{2+}]_b - [M^{2+}]_s) = (kw,_{H^+}/2)([H^+]_s - [H^+]_b)$ and $[\overline{HR}]_s = P_{HR}[HR]_s$. Subscript, b: bulk phase

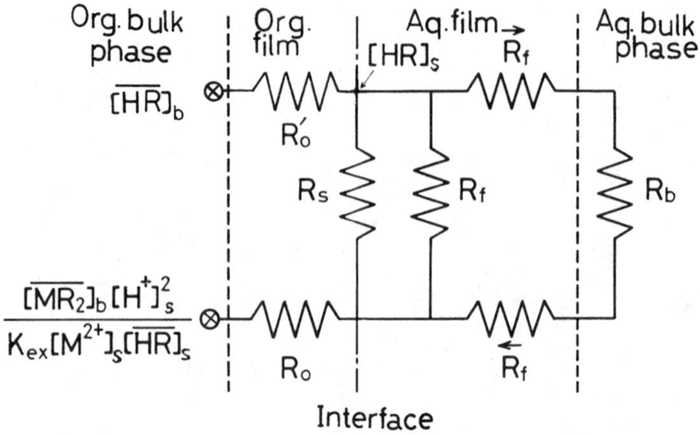

Figure 18. Equivalent circuit of metal and ligand-group flow.

and in the aqueous stagnant film, respectively. The $(\vec{R}_f + \overleftarrow{R}_f)$ value is the resistance for the ligand-group through the aqueous stagnant film, and the R_b corresponds to the resistance of the reaction in the aqueous bulk phase. The Ro′ and Ro are the resistances for the diffusions of the HR species and of the metal complex MR_2 in the organic phase, respectively. The metal extraction rates are shown in Table 20 in terms of these resistances.

The ratio R_B/R_f is an index of the role of reaction in the aqueous stagnant film compared with that in the aqueous bulk phase:

$$R_B/R_f = [\sinh(2\zeta_b)/(2\xi_b)][(\zeta_b/\coth\zeta_b) + (V_f/V)] \tag{130}$$

Here, V_f is the total volume of the aqueous stagnant film, being the interfacial area multiplied by the film thickness x_L. As shown in Figure 19, the ratio is mainly dependent on the parameter ζ_b,

Table 20
Rate-Determining Steps and Extraction Rate Expression

Rate-Determining Step	Extraction Rate
Diffusion of complex in organic stagnant film	$j = k_0K_{ex}[\overline{HR}]^2_s[M^{2+}]_s[H^+]_s^{-2}$
Interfacial reaction	$j = R_s^{-1}[\overline{HR}]_s/P_{HR}$
Reaction in aqueous stagnant film	$j = R_f^{-1}[\overline{HR}]_s/(P_{HR}\xi)$ $j = [kD(1 + \tilde{K}^{-1})^{-1}]^{1/2}[\overline{HR}]_s/(P_{HR}\xi)$ $k = k_I$ (Case 1), $2k_{II}$ (Case 2) when $\zeta_b > 3$
Aqueous bulk phase reaction with diffusional resistances of HR and MR_2 in aqueous stagnant film	$j = R_B^{-1}[\overline{HR}]_s/(P_{HR}\xi)$ $R_B = (1 + \tilde{K}^{-1})/k_w + (A/V)/k$ $k = k_I$ (Case 1), k_{II} (Case 2)

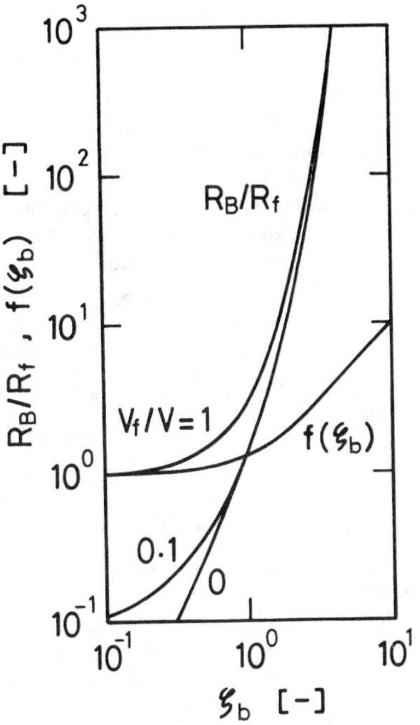

Figure 19. R_B/R_f and $f(\zeta_b)$ against ζ_b value. (Reprinted with permission from Ref. 104.)

which represents the degree of reactant depletion by the reaction in the film per reactant fed to the aqueous bulk phase by diffusion through the film.

The R_B/R_f becomes larger than unity as ζ_b increases, and the reaction is completed in the aqueous film. This ratio, which also depends on the volume ratio V_f/V, approaches V_f/V when $\zeta_b \to 0$. In this case, the reaction proceeds in the total volume of the aqueous phase due to slowness of the reaction.

The ratio, R_f/R_s, is an index of the role of the interfacial reaction compared to that in the aqueous film, and is given by

$$R_f/R_s = [P_{HR}\delta + \Gamma_{HR}^{(\infty)}K_{HR}^s/(1 + K_{HR}^s[HR] + K_{MR^+}^s[MR^+])(\xi/2x_L)f(\zeta_b) \quad (131)$$

$$f(\zeta_b) = \zeta_b \coth(\zeta_b), \qquad \xi = 1 \text{ for case I} \quad \text{and} \quad \xi = 2 \text{ for case II}$$

The $f(\zeta_b)$ value is also shown in Figure 19. For surface-inactive chelating agents, Equation 131 is reduced to

$$R_f/R_s = (\xi/2)P_{HR}(\delta/x_L)f(\zeta_b) \quad (132)$$

In usual case, the δ and x_L values are 10^{-7} cm and 10^{-2} cm in orders of magnitude, respectively. Then, the condition satisfying $R_f/R_s \gg 1$ is given by

$$P_{HR}f(\zeta_b) \gg 10^5 \quad (133)$$

For surface-active chelating agents, equation 131 can be simplified if the adsorption of MR^+ is neglected.

$$R_f/R_s = (\xi/2x_L)[\Gamma_{HR}^{(\infty)}P_{HR}K_{HR}^s/(1 + K_{HR}^s[HR])]f(\zeta_b) \quad (134)$$

A condition for $R_f \gg R_s$ is expressed by

$$P_{HR}f(\zeta_b) \gg x_L(1 + \overline{K}^s_{HR}[\overline{HR}])/(\Gamma^{(\infty)}_{HR}\overline{K}^s_{HR}) \sim 10^3 \tag{135}$$

The rates of metal extraction are reduced to simple forms according to the rate-determining paths, which are shown in Table 20. These simplified forms are also divided into a variety of forms as shown in Table 21, depending on the main chemical reactions, and on the locations where main chemical reaction occurs [168]. The exponents (a, b, c) for the concentrations of chelating agents, metal ions, and hydrogen ions take a variety of sets. Therefore, the extraction mechanism cannot be determined only from the information on a set (a, b, c) that is experimentally determined.

Mechanism of Metal Extraction and Important Factors

The kinetic researches on metal extraction with chelating agents have been extensively performed. There are, however, few studies that provide quantitative informations on the kinetics of metal extraction.

Hydroxyoxime-Extractants

Due to commercial importance the Cu(II) extraction rates have been most extensively studied for hydroxyoximes of the types, 2-hydroxy-5-alkyl(R) acetophenone oximes and 2-hydroxy-5- alkyl(R) benzophenone oximes. The rate of Cu(II) extraction with *o*-hydroxy acetophenone oximes (HAPO, R=H), which is more soluble in the aqueous phase ($P_{HR} = 40$ in benzene diluent), can be correlated by Equation 136 at low pH, when the mass transfer resistance in the organic phase can be neglected [168].

$$j = 0.82 \times 10^{-2}[\overline{HR}]_s^{3/2}[Cu^{2+}]_s[H^+]_s^{-1} \text{ mol cm}^{-2}\text{ s}^{-1} \tag{136}$$

This oxime is surface-inactive and the $P_{HR}f(\zeta_b)$ values are in the range of 10^3 order of magnitude, these characteristics suggesting that the main reaction location is in the aqueous stagnant film. This extraction system corresponds to the Case XI in Table 21, i.e., the rate control of the 1:1 metal-ligand complex formation in the aqueous stagnant film. From the coefficient of Equation 136, the rate constant k_1 can be evaluated to be 1.0×10^6 $cm^3\ mol^{-1}\ s^{-1}$, which is close to the value determined from the reaction in homogeneous phase (see Table 14).

The chelating agent, 2-hydroxy 5-nonylacetophenone oxime (HNAPO), has a long chain hydrocarbon group and is less soluble in the aqueous phase than HAPO, the P_{HR} being 4.1×10^3 (in heptane) and 3.2×10^4 (in benzene). This oxime is strongly surface-active. Since the rate constant of Cu(II)-ligand complex formation is large, the main reaction proceeds at the interface. The rate of Cu(II) extraction is empirically expressed by

$$j = k_f[\overline{HR}]_s[Cu^{2+}]_s[H^+]_s^{-1} \text{ mol cm}^{-2}\text{ s}^{-1} \tag{137}$$

$k_f = 6.2 \times 10^{-6}$ $cm\ s^{-1}$ in *n*-heptane diluent

which corresponds to the Case XXVII in Table 21. The same set (a, b, c) can be found in the Case XXI, which is rejected because $[\overline{HR}]_s \gg \overline{K}^{s\,-1}_{HR}$ and $pH \ll pK_a$ in the experiment. The coefficients k_f in Equation 137, which are observed for different diluents, are inversely proportional to the P_{HR} as is mentioned later. This experimental results assert the justice of the presumption of Equation 121. The k_3K_1 value obtained from these coefficients is 10^8 $cm^3\ mol^{-1}\ s^{-1}$, which is close to the value determined from the homogeneous phase reaction for Cu(II)-salicylaldoxime in ethanol solution, i.e., Equation 105.

Figure 20 shows the effects of chain length of alkyl groups and of the diluent species on Cu(II)-extraction rate in terms of the P_{HR} [35]. The rate is controlled by the 1:1 metal ligand complex formation in the aqueous phase in lower range of P_{HR}, whereas at high P_{HR} the rate is controlled

Table 21

Overall Rate Constant, k_f, and Exponents (a, b, c) When the Extraction Rate Is Expressed in the Form, $j = k_f[\overline{HR}]_s^a[M^{+2}]_s^b/[H^+]_s^c$ [168]

Rate-Determining Reaction: Rate Eq.	Reaction in Aq. Bulk Phase	Reaction in Aq. Stagnant Film			Interfacial Reaction[a]		
			$\tilde{K}^{-1} \gg 1$		Surface-Inactive Agents	Surface-Active Agents	
		$\tilde{K}^{-1} \ll 1$	Case I	Case II		$[\overline{HR}]_I \gg \overline{K_{HR}^{S}}^{-1}$	$[\overline{HR}]_I \ll \overline{K_{HR}^{S}}^{-1}$
$k_a[HR]$	No. I (1, 0, 0) $(V/A)k_a/P_{HR}$	No. II (1, 0, 0) $(Dk_a/\xi)^{0.5}/P_{HR}$	No. III (1, 0.5, 0.5) $(Dk_aK_1)^{0.5}/P_{HR}$	No. IV (1.5, 0.5, 1) $(Dk_aK_1K_2)^{0.5}/P_{HR}^{1.5}$	No. V (1, 0, 0) $\xi k_a\delta/2$	No. VI (0, 0, 0) $\xi k_a\Gamma_{HR}^{\infty}/2$	No. VII (1, 0, 0) $\xi k_a\overline{K_{HR}^{S}}\Gamma_{HR}^{\infty}/2$
$k_1[M^{2+}][HR]$	No. IIX (1, 1, 0) $(V/A)k_1/P_{HR}$	No. IX (1, 0.5, 0) $(Dk_1/\xi)^{0.5}/P_{HR}$	No. X (1, 1, 0.5) $(Dk_1K_1)^{0.5}/P_{HR}$	No. XI (1.5, 1, 1) $(Dk_1K_1K_2)^{0.5}/P_{HR}^{1.5}$	No. XII (1, 1, 0) $\xi k_1\delta/2$	No. XIII (0, 1, 0) $\xi k_1\Gamma_{HR}^{\infty}/2$	No. XIV (1, 1, 0) $\xi k_1\overline{K_{HR}^{S}}\Gamma_{HR}^{\infty}/2$
$\frac{k_2K_a[M^{2+}][HR]}{[H^+]}$	No. XV (1, 1, 1) $(V/A)k_2K_a/P_{HR}$	No. XVI (1, 0.5, 0.5) $(Dk_2K_a/\xi)^{0.5}/P_{HR}$	No. XVII (1, 1, 1) $(Dk_2K_aK_1)^{0.5}/P_{HR}$	No. XIIX (1.5, 1, 1.5) $(Dk_2K_aK_1K_2)^{0.5}/P_{HR}^{1.5}$	No. XIX (1, 1, 1) $\xi k_2K_a\delta/2$	No. XX (0, 1, 1) $\xi k_2K_a\Gamma_{HR}^{\infty}/2$	No. XXI (1, 1, 1) $\xi k_2K_a\overline{K_{HR}^{S}}\Gamma_{HR}^{\infty}/2$
$\frac{k_3K_1[HR]^2[M^{2+}]}{[H^+]}$	No. XXII (2, 1, 1) $(V/A)k_3K_1/P_{HR}^2$	No. XXIII (1.5, 0.5, 0.5) $(Dk_3K_1/\xi)^{0.5}/P_{HR}^{1.5}$	No. XXIV (1.5, 1, 1) $(Dk_3K_1^2)^{0.5}/P_{HR}^{1.5}$	No. XXV (2, 1, 1.5) $(Dk_3K_1^2K_2)^{0.5}/P_{HR}^2$	No. XXVI (2, 1, 1) $\xi k_3K_1\delta/(2P_{HR})$	No. XXVII (1, 1, 1) $\xi k_3K_1\Gamma_{HR}^{\infty}/(2P_{HR})$	No. XXVIII (2, 1, 1) $\xi k_3K_1\overline{K_{HR}^{S}}\Gamma_{HR}^{\infty}/(2P_{HR})$

[a] *$\xi = 1$ (Case I), $\xi = 2$ (Case II)*

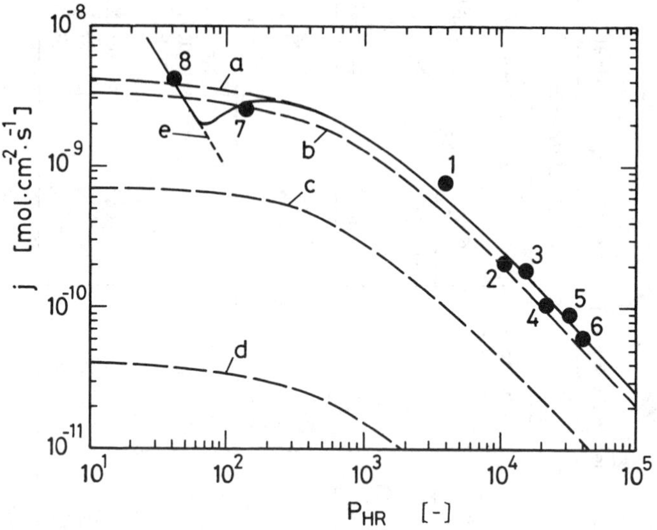

Figure 20. Effects of chain length of alkyl group and diluent species on the rate of extraction of copper with β-hydroxyoximes at 25°C. $[\overline{HR}]_s = 2.12 \times 10^{-5}$, $[Cu^{2+}]_s = 2.0 \times 10^{-5}$ $[H^+]_s = 4.0 \times 10^{-6}$ mol/dm^3, $\Gamma_{HR}^{(\infty)} = 2 \times 10^{-10}$ mol/cm^2

	alkyl-group	diluent
1	nonyl (HNAPO)	n-heptane (Abbrev. as H)
2	nonyl (HNAPO)	H/T = 2/1 (mole ratio)
3	nonyl (HNAPO)	H/T = 1/1 (mole ratio)
4	nonyl (HNAPO)	H/T = 1/2 (mole ratio)
5	nonyl (HNAPO)	toluene (Abbrev. as T)
6	nonyl (HNAPO)	benzene
7	ethyl (HEAPO)	benzene
8	hydrogen (HAPO)	benzene

Broken curves: a, b, c, d = interfacial reactions, calculated with $K_1k_3 = 1.2 \times 10^8$ cm^3 mol^{-1} s^{-1}, $\bar{K}_{HR}^s = \infty$ (a), 2.4×10^5 (b), 10^4 (c), 0 (d), cm^3/mol

Broken curve: e = reaction in aqueous stagnant film

Solid curve: estimated values for the sum of interfacial reaction and reaction in aqueous stagnant film

by the 1:2 metal-ligand complex formation at the interface. The effect of diluent species is attributed to the change of the P_{HR} value. The shift of the rate determining step from 1:1 complex formation to 1:2 complex formation is caused by the decrease in the driving force of HR to promote the 1:2 complex formation reaction due to high P_{HR}.

The effect of the HR adsorption on the extraction rate appears in the two terms, $\Gamma_{HR}^{(\infty)}$ and $\bar{K}_{HR}^s$. The $\Gamma_{HR}^{(\infty)}$ is of similar magnitude for the species containing β-hydroxyoxime functional group, the substitutional groups playing a minor role as seen earlier. The adsorption equilibrium constant

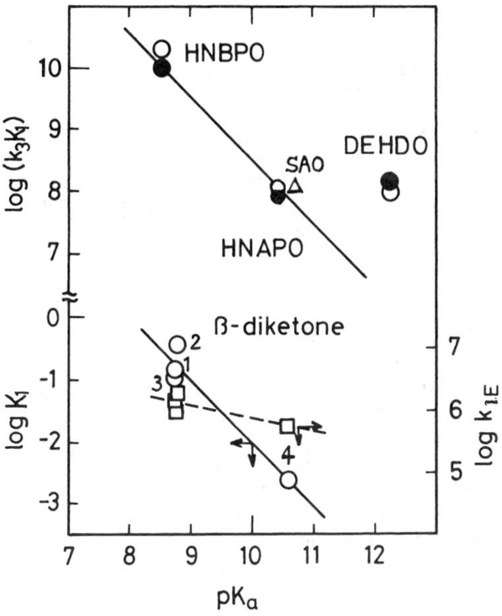

Figure 21. Relation between the k_3K_1 value for several hydroxyoximes and the pK_a and comparison of oxime system with β-diketones system. SAO: salicylaldoxime (pK_a is the value in 75% dioxane) β-diketones: $CH_3COCHRCOR'$, 1: R—H, R'=CH_3, 2: R=H, R'=C_6H_5, 3: R=C_6H_5, R'=CH_3, 4: R=CH_3, R'=C_2H_5, open keys=benzene or toluene, closed keys=n-heptane, k_3K_1 of SAO is given in Equation 105. k_3K_1, k_{1E}: values in $cm^3\ mol^{-1}\ s^{-1}$

$\overline{K}^s_{HR}$ is dependent on the alkyl chain group when the carbon number in the chain group is small and also by the diluent species, but this affects the extraction rate only when $\overline{K}^s_{HR}[\overline{HR}]_s < 1$. Therefore, the HR-adsorption plays a secondary role, in the metal extraction for a given class of β-hydroxyoximes.

The rate of Cu(II)-extraction with 2-hydroxy 5-nonylbenzophenone oxime is also described by the same empirical equation as Equation 137 [144], if the diffusion resistances are eliminated from the overall resistance. This result shows that the interfacial reaction to produce 1:2 complex controls the extraction rate. The k_3K_1 value in this oxime is much greater than that of HNAPO. The k_3K_1 values for several hydroxyoximes are plotted against the pK_a values of the oximes in Figure 21.

There exist few works on the quantitative analysis of the rate of Cu(II) extraction in the reverse direction. Miyake et al. [148] reported that the rate data can be interpreted by the theory described earlier.

The P_{HR} values, which play a significant role in the rate of metal extraction rate are shown in Figure 3 for 2-hydroxy-5-alkyl aceto- or benzo-phenone oximes in aromatic and aliphatic diluents. Though the P_{HR} is difficult to determine precisely for a high P_{HR} region, this figure provides a rough estimate of the P_{HR} value for the oximes with different carbon number in alkyl chain.

The reaction rates concerned with Ni(II) are much less than those for Cu(II), the k_1 and k_2 being 10^3 and 10^7 $cm^3\ mol^{-1}\ s^{-1}$ in orders of magnitude according to Table 13. For Ni(II) extraction with long chain ortho-hydroxyoximes, the 1:1 complex formation can be detected in the aqueous phase [44], suggesting that the rate-determining step is considered to be a 1:1 complex formation. Akiba and Freiser [142] reported for Ni(II) extraction with LIX65N that the rate of Ni(II) extraction was controlled by the 1:1 complex formation in the aqueous bulk phase. This result corresponds to Case XXII in Table 21, and the rate constant obtained in this experiment was $4.6 \times 10^8\ dm^3\ mol^{-1}\ s^{-1}$, which is close to the value observed in homogeneous reaction experiment. Though this experiment was performed with a cell with drop dispersion, the result seems to be reasonable due to slowness of the complex formation reaction. However, caution must be paid for the interfacial reaction, when violent stirring technique is used. If the reaction is slow enough to be considered as $\zeta_b > 1$, the R_B/R_s ratio is simply expressed by

$$R_B/R_s = (A/V)P_{HR}\Gamma_{HR}^{(\infty)}\overline{K_{HR}^s}/(1 + \overline{K_{HR}^s}[\overline{HR}]) \tag{138}$$

where A/V is the interfacial area per unit volume of the aqueous phase. The A/V is a relatively small value for a Lewis cell, yielding $R_B/R_s \ll 1$, whereas, in a violent stirring cell, this value becomes so large that $R_B/R_s \gg 1$ at high P_{HR} value. Inoue et al. [150] obtained the kinetic data for the extraction of Ni(II) in ammonium solution with 2-hydroxy 5-nonylacetophenone oxime at relatively high pH. Their data can be rearranged as follows.

$$j = 1.7 \times 10^{-8}[HR]_s[Ni^{2+}]_s^{1/2}[H^+]_s^{-1/2} \text{ mol cm}^{-2}\text{ s}^{-1} \tag{139}$$

This result corresponds to Case XVI in Table 21, and the rate constant k_2 is chosen as 2×10^9 cm^3 mol^{-1} s^{-1}, which is considered a reasonable magnitude if one considers the presence of the ligand species, NH_3. The interfacial reaction probably takes part in the overall extraction rate.

Recently, palladium extraction was studied by several investigators, because of its commercial importance as well as the kinetic interest in the transition metal complex formation of the Pt-group. Hydroxyoxime well extracts Pd(II), but the extraction process is markedly slow. Pd(II) forms a square planar complex. The strong tendency of forming a chloro-complex in chloride solutions is in marked contrast to copper and nickel ions. At high Cl^- concentration, chloro-complex $PdCl_4^{2-}$ is a predominant species. The $PdCl_3^-$ present in small amounts is much more labile than $PdCl_4^{2-}$, reacting preferentially with oximes. The $PdCl_3^-$ concentration is related with

$$[PdCl_3^-] = C_{Pd}/(1 + \beta_4[Cl^-]/\beta_3) \tag{140}$$

where C_{Pd} represents the total concentration of Pd. β_3 and β_4 are the cumulative stability constants for tri- and tetra-palladium chloride, respectively. Here, we postulate the reaction schemes:

$$PdCl_3^- + HR \overset{k_1}{\rightleftarrows} PdRCl_2^- + H^+ + Cl^-;\ K_1 \tag{141}$$

$$PdRCl_2^- + HR \overset{k_3}{\rightleftarrows} PdR_2 + H^+ + 2Cl^-;\ K_2 \tag{142}$$

The rate of PdR_2 formation in the aqueous phase is formulated in the same form as Equations 101 and 102:

$$\begin{aligned} r_{PdR_2} &= k_{II}\{[HR] - [PdR_2][H^+]^2[Cl^-]^3/(K_1K_2[HR][PdCl_3^-])\} \\ C_{Pd}/\{(1 + \beta_4[Cl^-]/\beta_3)k_{II}\} &= (1/k_1 + [H^+][Cl^-]/k_3K_1[HR]) \end{aligned} \tag{143}$$

The rate of Pd complex formation at the interface can be expressed with use of the R_s value in Table 20:

$$\begin{aligned} r_{PdR_2}^* = {} & k_{II}\Gamma^{(\infty)}K_{HR}^s/(1 + K_{HR}^s[HR]) \\ & \times ([HR] - [PdR_2][H^+]^2[Cl^-]^3/K_1K_2[HR][PdCl_3^-]) \end{aligned} \tag{144}$$

The kinetic data obtained with the help of violent stirring cell were reported for 2-hydroxy 5-nonylbenzophenone oxime in chloroform by Ma et al. [151] and for 2-hydroxy 5-nonylacetophenone oxime by Inoue et al. [152]. The data correlation reported by Ma et al. [151] is incorrect and should be rewritten as

$$\begin{aligned} r_{Pd} &= Aj_{PdR_2}/V \propto [\overline{HR}]C_{Pd}/\{(1 + \beta_4[Cl^-]/\beta_3)(P_{HR} + k_1P_{HR}^2/k_3K_1[Cl^-][H^+]/[\overline{HR}])\} \\ k_1P_{HR}/k_3K_1 &= 1.1 \times 10^{-2} \text{ dm}^3 \text{ mol}^{-1} \end{aligned} \tag{145}$$

Also, Inoue's data can be correlated by Equation 144 with $\bar{K}^{s}_{HR}[\overline{HR}] \gg 1$

$$r_{Pd} \propto \Gamma^{(\infty)}_{HR} C_{Pd} \bigg/ \left\{ (1 + \beta_4[Cl^-]/\beta_3)\left(1 + \frac{k_1}{k_3}\frac{P_{HR}}{K_1}[Cl^-][H^+]/[\overline{HR}]\right)\right\} \quad (146)$$

These results suggest that both 1:1 and 1:2 Pd-oxime complex formations control the overall extraction rate. The form of Equation 145 corresponds to the cases whether the reaction occurs in the bulk aqueous phase or at the interface that is not saturated by HR. The effect of the area to aqueous phase volume ratio on the extraction rate provides an information whether the reaction location is in the aqueous bulk phase or at the interface. Miyake et al. [153] studied the extraction rate of Pd from the chloride medium with 2-hydroxy 5-nonylacetophenone oxime in n-heptane by means of a Lewis cell with the constant interfacial area. The extraction rate is proportional to the concentrations of $PdCl_3^-$ and oxime when the $[Cl^-][H^+]/[\overline{HR}]$ value is lower than 1 mol dm^{-3}. Under this condition, the following equation can be obtained from Equation 145.

$$j = k_1[\overline{HR}]C_{Pd}/[(1 + \beta_4[Cl^-]/\beta_3)P_{HR}] \quad (147)$$

This equation satisfies the observed data, suggesting that the rate-determining step is the 1:1 complex formation in the aqueous bulk phase and the rate constant of Equation 141 can be evaluated as 1.1 dm^3 mol^{-1} s^{-1}, which is close to that observed in the 80 wt% methanol-water mixture, 1.7 dm^3 mol^{-1} s^{-1}.

β-Diketones and Dithizones

The Cu(II) extraction with benzoylacetone is a typical system in which quantitative kinetic data set have extensively been reported [18]. The kinetic data of reaction processes in the aqueous bulk phase are usable for evaluating the rate of metal extraction as shown earlier. When Cu(II) is extracted by benzoylacetone in benzene solution, $P_{HR} = 3.6 \times 10^3$ and the ζ_b value is in several tens order of magnitude. In this case, the R_f takes a value of similar order of magnitude to the R_s value. The kinetic data of Cu(II) extraction by benzoylacetone in benzene solution are also available [49]. Benzoylacetone is surface inactive. Then, as shown in Figure 22, the metal extraction rates observed experimentally can be explained by the rate expression for Case I in Table 19, if the interfacial zone thickness δ value, the only parameter left to be known, is taken to be 14 Å, which is of reasonable order of magnitude. The contribution of each resistance to the overall one can also be evaluated from the equations for Case I in Table 19 with the rate constants obtained in the reaction in aqueous bulk phase (see Figure 22). Miyake et al. [37] reported for β-diketones with several substituents at C_3-position of acetyl acetone that the theoretical rate of extraction model in Table 21 can estimate the rates of Cu(II) extraction. In this case, the larger the P_{HR}, the more important is the role of interfacial reaction.

The kinetic data for TTA and dithizones by means of a mixing cell with drop dispersion have been interpreted in terms of the 1:1 metal ligand complex formation in aqueous bulk phase as the rate determining step [47, 116]. The P_{HR} values for TTA are relatively low and the distribution of TTA in the aqueous phase is high. Then, the reactions in the aqueous bulk phase probably control the metal extraction rate if the ζ_b is less than unity. Whereas for dithizone derivatives, the P_{HR} is much larger than that for TTA. The kinetic mechanism by Freiser group [116–118] should be checked for their validity. The reaction rate constant of the 1:1 metal-dithizone complex formation, which was obtained by assuming the aqueous bulk phase reaction, agree in order of magnitude with those determined by means of the relaxation method for homogeneous phase reaction, whereas the rate constants for 2,2′-dimethyl dithizone and di-α-naphtyl dithizone were much larger than those for dithizone. This discrepancy is probably caused by the difference in the P_{HR} values, the P_{HR}'s for the above derivatives being two and more orders of magnitude larger than that of dithizone.

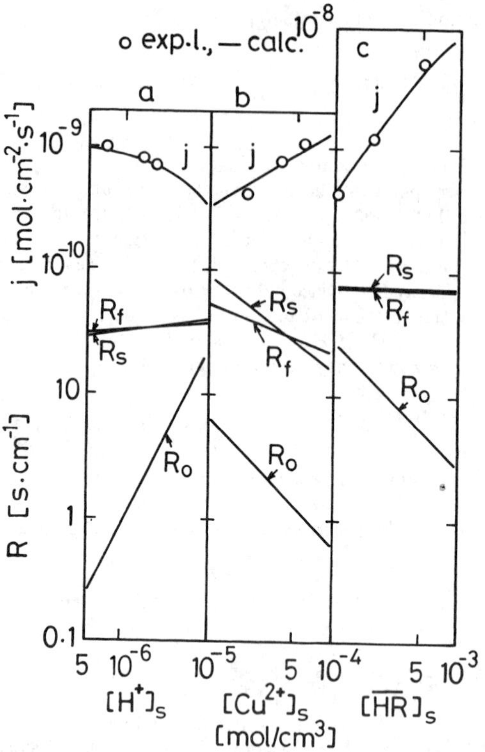

Figure 22. Rate of copper(II) extraction with benzoylacetone in benzene at 298 K, and the resistances in equivalent circuit of metal flow. The R_B value is much larger than those of other resistances. a) $[Cu^{2+}]_s = 3.75 \times 10^{-5}$, $[\overline{HR}]_s = 4.7 \times 10^{-5}$, b) $[H^+]_s = 1.35 \times 10^{-6}$, $[\overline{HR}]_s = 4.7 \times 10^{-5}$ c) $[H^+]_s = 6.0 \times 10^{-6}$, $[Cu^{2+}]_s = 1.9 \times 10^{-5}$ in mol/dm^3. (Reprinted with permission from Ref. 104.)

The ratio R_B/R_s is given for less surface-active extractants:

$$R_B/R_s = (1/2)(A/V)\delta P_{HR} = (3/d_P)(1/\phi - 1)\delta P_{HR}, \text{ for } \zeta_b < 1$$

Here, ϕ is the hold-up volume fraction of the aqueous phase and d_P repesents the drop diameter of the dispersed phase. If $\phi = 0.5$ and $\delta = 10^{-7}$ cm, the R_B/R_s ratio is 3×10^{-7} P_{HR}/d_P. Since the P_{HR} for dithizone in $CHCl_3$ is 8×10^5 [117], main reaction location is in the aqueous bulk phase when d_P is larger than 1 mm in order of magnitude. In their experiments, d_P is probably smaller than 1 mm, and the interfacial reaction cannot be neglected. The P_{HR} magnitude of the dithizone derivatives previously mentioned are reported to be 10^7–10^8, thus yielding $R_B/R_s \gg 1$. The k′ value in Equation 107 divided by K_a, in fact, agrees with each other for two kinds of dithizone derivatives, whereas the reaction rate constants obtained by assuming the 1:1 metal-complex formation in the aqueous bulk phase as rate-determining step do not agree with each other. Recently, Watarai and Freiser [121] revised their opinion, reporting that the interfacial reaction plays a key role in the Ni(II) and Zn(II) extractions with di(p-alkyl phenyl)thiocarbazones of relatively long alkyl chain length.

Quinoline and Related Extractants

Quantitative data were reported by Yoshizuka et al. [156, 157] for the Cu(II)-extraction with N-8-quinonlyl sulfonamides in toluene. The extraction mechanism proposed by them involves the interfacial reaction:

$$\overline{HR} \rightleftarrows (HR)_{ad}: \bar{K}^{s}_{HR} \tag{148}$$

$$Cu^{2+} + (HR)_{ad} \rightleftarrows (CuR^{+})_{ad} + H^{+}: K_1^* \tag{149}$$

$$(CuR^{+})_{ad} + (HR)_{ad} \overset{k_3^*}{\rightleftarrows} CuR_2 + H^{+}: K_2^* \tag{150}$$

The rate determining step is assumed as the reaction step Equation 150, in which two adsorbed species, CuR^+ and HR, react with each other. In this case, the extraction rate is described with the help of Langmuir adsorption.

$$j = k_3^* K_1^* (\Gamma_{HR}^{(\infty)} \bar{K}^{s}_{HR})^2 / (1 + \bar{K}^{s}_{HR}[\overline{HR}]_s + K_1^* \bar{K}^{s}_{HR}[Cu^{2+}]_s[\overline{HR}]_s/[H^+]_s)^2 \times ([Cu^{2+}]_s[\overline{HR}]_s^2/[H^+]_s - [CuR_2][H^+]_s/K_{ex}) \tag{151}$$

Equation 151 fits the observed data well, but the interfacial reaction between two adsorbed species is probably hard to achieve. Their data can also be interpreted by Equation 121, where the 1:2 complex formation reaction between the adsorbed CuR^+ and the HR dissolved in the aqueous phase is assumed as rate-determining step. The resultant k_3K_1 value is 9.0×10^{10} cm^3 mol^{-1} s^{-1}.

CATALYSIS

Classification of Catalyst

The metal extraction with chelating agents is much slower than those with the other types of extractants. It is, therefore, of practical importance how to enhance the extraction rate. To solve this problem, we must know what process controls the extraction rate. If the rate of extraction is controlled by a diffusional process, addition of a compound acting as catalyst or accelerator to the extraction system causes no effect on the rate. When a chemical reaction process at least partially determines the rate, the location for the reaction to proceed must be elucidated, because different catalytic roles will be expected according to the main location of the reaction.

The phrase "catalysis" denotes the kinetic synergism, which differs from the simple synergism affecting the equilibrium relationship of the extraction. The catalysts can be classified into two categories as shown in Table 22, according to their hydrophobic and hydrophilic nature and the catalytic roles.

The hydrophobic reagents belonging to the first category are divided into two groups. The first is a chelating agent such as aliphatic α-hydroxyoximes in copper extraction with β-hydroxyoximes.

Table 22
Classification of Accelerators for Metal Extraction with Chelating Agents

Nature of Accelerator	Mode of Catalytic Action	Example
I. Hydrophobic		
(a) chelating agent	Formation of intermediate metal chelate complex	LIX63
(b) non-chelating agent	Phase transfer catalysis	RCOOH
	Reversed micellar catalysis	Aerosol OT
	Modification of interface	SDS
II. Hydrophilic		
(a) chelating agent	Formation of chelate with metal ion in aqueous phase (masking agent)	EDTA
(b) non-chelating agent	Coordinate to metal ion in aqueous phase	Cl^-

The chelating agent acting as a catalyst increases the extraction rate without substantial effect on the extraction equilibrium. This suggests that metal-catalyst ligand complex is thermodynamically unstable. The second group involves non-chelating agents such as carboxylic acid with a long alkyl chain, which makes metals more favorable to organic solvent by the specific interaction with metal ions through coordination or electrostatic bonding. This type of catalysis is known as a phase transfer catalysis. The second group also involves the hydrophobic surface-active reagent, such as sodium di-2-ethylhexyl-sulfosuccinate (Aerosol-OT), which tends to aggregate to form the reverse micelles in the organic phase. These increase both overall distribution of metals in the organic phase and the rate of extraction.

The addition of hydrophilic surface-active reagents, such as sodium dodecyl sulfate, (SDS) to the extraction system enhances the extraction rate, because the electrostatic surface potential due to adsorption of these reagents strongly increases the metal ion concentration just outside of the interfacial zone.

The hydrophilic reagents in second category are divided into two groups, non-chelating and chelating agents. The non-chelating agent involves a ligand such as the conjugate base of mineral acid, which is important in hydrometallurgy. This ligand is coordinated to metal ion. Since the rate of ligand-exchange reaction depends on the ligand species coordinated to metal ions, this reagent enhances the reaction rate concerning metal complex formation in the aqueous phase, resulting in the enhancement of the extraction rate. The hydrophilic chelating agents such as ethylenediamine tetraacetic acid (EDTA) are used as the masking reagent in analytical chemistry, which forms a stable chelate complex of specific metal ion in aqueous phase. The reader should refer to typical books [46, 169] on the masking effect, bacause here we do not discuss it.

Catalytic Roles of Hydrophobic Agents

Hydrophobic Chelating Agents

It is well known that aliphatic α-hydroxyoxime, LIX63, functions as an efficient catalyst for copper extraction with aromatic β-hydroxyoxime such as LIX65N and SME529. The LIX64N, a mixture of LIX63 and LIX65N, became an important extractant in copper hydrometallurgy. van der Zeeuw et al. [170] inferred that the extraction accelerator has a structure to form the five-membered chelate-ring with metal ion. To confirm this, they synthesized the aliphatic β-hydroxyoximes that provide the six-membered chelate-ring with copper ion. As is expected, this compound exerts no accelerating action at all. They also pointed out that the accelerator must have a characteristic structure: The C—C bond between the active groups, which are located in the middle of the chain, is singly bonded and can freely rotate around the axis of the bond. This structure results in the formation of a metal complex that provides a thermodynamically unfavorable influence on the stability constant. Therefore, this type of accelerator acts as the catalyst because the copper-accelerators complex concentration becomes low level.

They [170] synthesized several compounds possessing the structure previously mentioned, and evaluated the degree of the catalytic effect of these compounds on the extraction rate of copper with SME529 in a practical mixer-settler extractor. The results are shown in Table 23. The open-chain vicinal dioximes are extremely powerful accelerators. Theoretically, there exists four isomers of the dioxime, anti, syn, and two amphi isomers; the anti-isomer being the most active as an accelerator. This result means that the formation of a five-membered chelate-ring is of primary importance. The similar conclusion was also reported by Preston [171], as shown in Table 24. He observed that the visible-UV absorption spectrum of α-dioxime-Cu(II) complex in the toluene solution shifts to that of the ortho-hydroxyoxime-Cu(II) complex with the addition of the ortho-hydroxyoxime to the toluene solution, which contains α-hydroxyoxime-Cu(II) complex. This means that the α-dioxime acts as catalyst for extraction of copper with ortho-hydroxyoxime, the five-membered chelate-ring complex being thermodynamically unstable than the six-membered chelate-ring complex.

Several models have been proposed for the mechanism of catalysis of α-hydroxyoxime and are summarized in Table 25. Most of these models assume that the final copper complex, CuR_2, is formed through the intermediate mixed complex, CuBR, [171, 174]. Whereas, Atwood et al. [132,

Table 23
Relative Effects of Catalyst on the Extraction Rate of Copper by SME 529. The Value Is the Relative Molar Amounts of Catalyst Needed to Achieve Same Performance for LIX63. [170]

	LIX 63		1 (standard)
I	$C_8H_{17}-C(C_6H_{13})(OH)-CH{=}NOH$		1
II	$R-C_6H_5-C({=}NOH)-CH_2(OH)$		0.5
III	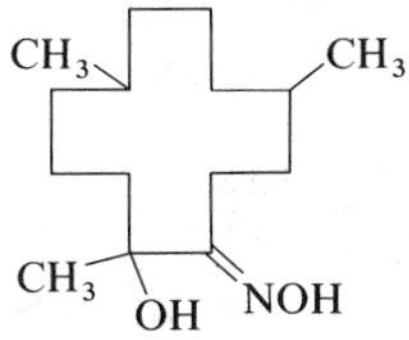		1
IV	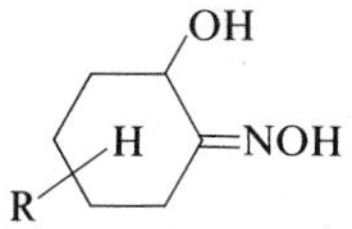	R = tert-nonyl	>1
V	$R-C_6H_5-C({=}NOH)-C({=}NOH)-R'$	$R' = H$ $R = C_{10} \sim C_{14}$ alkyl	0.05
VI	$R-C_6H_5-C({=}NOH)-C({=}NOH)-R'$	$R' = CH_3$ $R = C_{15} \sim C_{18}$ alkyl	0.05
VII	$R-C_6H_5-C({=}NOH)-C({=}NOH)-R'$	$R' = C_7H_{15}$ $R = C_{10} \sim C_{14}$ alkyl	0.1
IIX	$R-C_6H_5-C({=}NOH)-C({=}NOH)-R'$	$R' = C_7H_{15}$ $R = C_7H_{15}$	0.2
IX	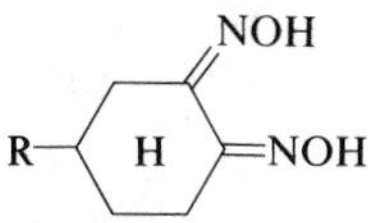	R = tert-nonyl	0.4

173] proposed the other mechanism that the α-hydroxyoxime acts as a proton acceptor. This mechanism suggests that the activity of α-hydroxyoxime increases with the increase in pK_a. The pK_a values for some aliphatic oximes shown in Table 24 lie in the order, anti I > III > syn I = VI > II > V > IV. There exists no correlation between the base strength of the aliphatic oximes and their influence on the rate of Cu(II) extraction with ortho-hydroxyoxime. Thus, their mechanism might be rejected [171].

Table 24
Effect of Aliphatic Oximes on the Rate of Extraction of Copper(II) with an Ortho-Hydroxyoxime[b] at 298K.

	Aliphatic Oxime[a]		Extraction Rate[c] at pH 0.9	1.4	1.8	Interfacial Pressure[d]
I	R—CH—C—R HO NOH	a(anti) c(anti) c(syn)	0.89 0.51	1.63 0.89	2.21 1.32 0.68	3.2 5.3
II	R—CH—C—R HO $NOCH_3$	a		0.91		0.4
III	R—CH_2C—R NOH	a b c		0.53 0.76 0.79	0.63	3.6
IV	R—C—C—R O NOH	a b c		0.91 0.86 1.01	 0.93	0.7
V	R—C—C—R HON NOH	a(anti) b(anti) c(syn)	2.15 4.77 0.45	4.47		0.7
VI	R—CH—C—R CH_3O NOH	a		0.53		3.2

[a] *Alkyl-group, a = nBuCHEt, b = nPrCHMe, c = MeCHMe*
[b] *1-(2-hydroxy-5-methylphenyl)octan-1-one oxime at 0.04M*
[c] *Rates are initial rates relative to that of o-hydroxyoxime. Aliphatic oxime conc. is 0.008M*
[d] *Measured between 0.008M oximes in toluene and 0.02M ClO_4^- aqueous phase at pH = 1.4 and 298K. (in dyn/cm)*
(Reprinted with permission from Ref. 171.)

The reaction mechanism of copper extraction with the mixed chelating agents α-hydroxyoxime and ortho-hydroxyoxime are summarized as follows [35]. As described earlier, the 1:1 complexes of Cu(II) with α-hydroxyoxime and ortho-hydroxyoxime, CuB^+ and CuR^+, are formed at the interface or in the aqueous phase adjacent to the interface. These complexes exist at the interface by the adsorption, and in aqueous phase due to the hydrophilic properties of 1:1 complex. Taking account of the reaction between the adsorbed species and the species existing in the aqueous phase, there exist four reaction paths to form the intermediate mixed chelate-complex, CuBR.

$$(CuR^+)_{ad} + HB \overset{k_3^{RB}}{\rightleftarrows} \overline{CuRB} + H^+ \tag{152}$$

$$CuR^+ + (HB)_{ad} \overset{k_3^{RB}}{\rightleftarrows} \overline{CuRB} + H^+ \tag{153}$$

$$(CuB^+)_{ad} + HR \overset{k_3^{BR}}{\rightleftarrows} \overline{CuBR} + H^+ \tag{154}$$

$$CuB^+ + (HR)_{ad} \overset{k_3^{BR}}{\rightleftarrows} \overline{CuBR} + H^+ \tag{155}$$

Table 25
Several proposed Mechanisms on the Catalysis of LIX63 in the Copper Extraction with β-hydroxyoxime

Researcher	Extractor	Chelating Agent (Solvent)	Catalytic Role of LIX63	Ref.
Flett et al. (1973)	AKUFVE	LIX65N + LIX63 (toluene)	$CuR^+ + (HB)_{ad} \rightarrow (CuBR)_{ad} + H^+$	[48]
Ashbrook (1975)	—	—	$(CuB^+)_{ad} + (HR)_{ad} \rightarrow (CuBR)_{ad} + H^+$	[172]
Atwood et al. (1975)	single drop	LIX65N + LIX63 (xylene)	$(HR)_{ad} + (HB)_{ad} \rightarrow (R^-)_{ad} + (H_2B^+)_{ad}$ $(Cu^{2+})_{ad} + (R^-)_{ad} \rightarrow (CuR^+)_{ad}$	[132, 173]
Fleming et al. (1976)	Lewis cell	LIX65N + LIX63 (chloroform)	Intermediate, CuBR, $CuB^+ + (HR)_{ad} \rightarrow (CuBR)_{ad} + H^+$	[173]
Preston (1980)	Single drop	HNBPO + aliphatic oxime(toluene)	Intermediate, CuBR No-correlation between pKa of aliphatic oxime and catalytic ability.	[171]
Kojima et al. (1981)	Lewis Cell	LIX65N + LIX63 (Dispersol)	$MB^+ + 2\,HR \rightarrow MR_2 + HB + H^+$ $MB_2 + 2\,HR \rightarrow MR_2 + 2\,HB$ in aqueous phase	[175]
Harada et al. (1986)	Diff. Cell	HNAPO + DEHDO (toluene, n-heptane)	Reaction mechanism Equations 152–155	[35]

The extraction rates for each reaction can be written with the aid of the rate expression mentioned earlier. When the interface is saturated with the oximes, the rates are

$$j_1 = (k_3^{RB}K_1^R\Gamma_{HR}^{(\infty)}/2P_{HB})f \tag{156}$$

$$j_2 = (k_3^{RB}K_1^R\Gamma_{HB}^{(\infty)}/2P_{HR})(\bar{K}_{HB}^s/\bar{K}_{HR}^s)f \tag{157}$$

$$j_3 = (k_3^{BR}K_1^B\Gamma_{HB}^{(\infty)}/2P_{HR})(\bar{K}_{HB}^s/\bar{K}_{HR}^s)f \tag{158}$$

$$j_4 = (k_3^{BR}K_1^B\Gamma_{HR}^{(\infty)}/2P_{HB})f \tag{159}$$

$$f = [\overline{HB}]_s[Cu^{2+}]_s/[[H^+]_s\{1 + (\bar{K}_{HB}^s/\bar{K}_{HR}^s)([\overline{HB}]_s/[\overline{HR}]_s)\}] \tag{160}$$

Here, k_3^{RB} and k_3^{BR} represent the rate constants for the reactions between CuR^+ and HB and between CuB^+ and HR, respectively. K_1^R and K_1^B represent the stability constants of 1:1 complex CuR^+ and CuB^+, respectively. $\Gamma_J^{(\infty)}$, $\bar{K}_J^s$ and P_J (J = HR or HB) represent the saturated interface concentration, the Langmuir adsorption constant and the partition constant of ortho-hydroxyoxime (HR) or α-hydroxyoxime (HB, catalyst), respectively.

The kinetic data concerning the catalytic effect have been expressed in the form:

$$j \propto [\overline{HR}]^a[\overline{HB}]^c[H^+]^d[Cu^{2+}]^e \tag{161}$$

This type of expression neglects the rate of the extraction without catalysis, providing no quantitative information on the catalysis. We must evaluate the catalytic effect by the comparison of the rate with catalysis and that without catalysis. The extraction rate in the absence of the α-hydroxyoxime, can be expressed by

$$j_0 = (k_3^{RR}K_1^R\Gamma_{HR}^{(\infty)}/P_{HR})[\overline{HR}]_s[Cu^{2+}]_s/[H^+]_s \tag{162}$$

Therefore, the ratio of extraction rates, $(j_0 + j_1 + j_2 + j_3 + j_4)/j_0 = j_c/j_0$, can be expressed as

$$j_c/j_0 = 1 + G([\overline{HB}]_s/[\overline{HR}]_s)\{1 + (\bar{K}_{HB}^s/\bar{K}_{HR}^s)([\overline{HB}]_s/[\overline{HR}]_s)\}^{-1} \tag{163}$$

where

$$G = (k_3^{RB}K_1^R + k_3^{BR}K_1^B)/(2k_3^{RR}K_1^R) \times \{\Gamma_{HB}^{(\infty)}\bar{K}_{HB}^s/(\Gamma_{HR}^{(\infty)}\bar{K}_{HR}^s) + P_{HR}/P_{HB}\} \tag{164}$$

The G value is a measure describing the catalytic effect, and hereafter will be called the enhancement factor.

Notice that the ratio of extraction rate, j_c/j_0, is decided by the concentration ratio alone, $[\overline{HB}]_s/[\overline{HR}]_s$, for a given extraction system. Figure 23 shows this relationship for the copper extraction with HNAPO (active species of SME529) in benzene solution in the presence of the catalyst 5,8-diethyl-7-hydroxy 6-dodecanone oxime (abbreviated as DEHDO, active species of LIX63). The solid line is the result calculated from Equation 163 with G = 10. G = 6 was obtained for the heptane solution. The data reported by Hummelstadt et al. [149] and Whewell et al. [131], which were obtained in the copper extraction with HNBPO (active species of LIX65N) in the presence of the catalyst DEHDO in toluene and Escaid 100 diluents, respectively, can also be correlated with Equation 163, the G values being 4 and 15, respectively. The other data for copper extraction system have been reported. However, most of these data are not available for confirming this correlation, because the extraction rate in the absence of catalyst was not reported and the concentration range of chelating agent was very narrow, together with the unknown contribution of the diffusional resistance to the extraction rate.

If k_3^{RB} and k_3^{BR} agree with each other, the enhancement factor can be rewritten as

$$G = (k_3^{RB}/k_3^{RR})[(1 + K_1^B/K_1^R)/2]\{\Gamma_{HB}^{(\infty)}\bar{K}_{HB}^s/(\Gamma_{HR}^{(\infty)}\bar{K}_{HR}^s) + P_{HR}/P_{HB}\} \tag{165}$$

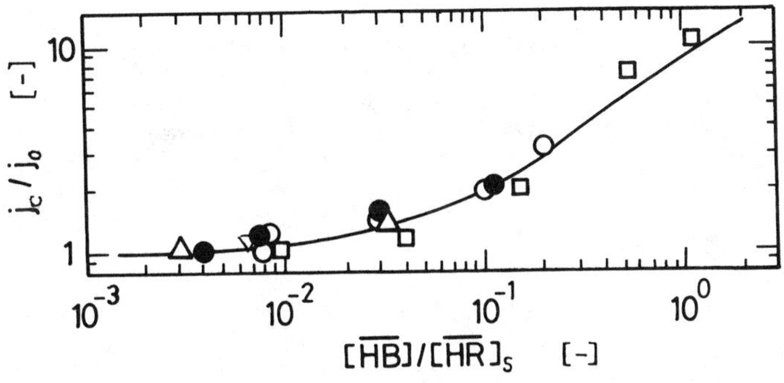

Figure 23. Catalytic role of DEHDO in copper(II) extraction with HNAPO in benzene at 298 K [35]

Key	$\bar{C}_{HR}$[mM]	$[Cu^{2+}]$[mM]	$[H^+]$[mM]
○	50.8	20	3.0
▽	50.8	80	6.0
●	50.8	20	5.0
□	10.2	20	4.0
△	21.1	20	4.5

where, the values of $(k_3^{BR}/k_3^{RR})(1 + K_1^B/K_1^R)/2$ can be evaluated using the physico-chemical properties of the chelating agents, HNAPO-DEHDO. The values of 6 and 38 were obtained for the n-heptane and benzene diluents, respectively. These values take the same order of magnitude, the difference between them probably arising from the uncertainty of physico-chemical properties of chelating agents due to difficulties in measuring these.

Preston et al. [171] pointed out that the enhancement of extraction rate arises from the increase in the rate constant, because the five-membered chelate-ring is more thermodynamically unstable than the six-membered ring chelate, i.e., the ratio K_1^B/K_1^R is less than unity. The rates of Cu(II) extraction with DEHDO alone in benzene and heptane diluents provide the parameter value, $k_3^{BB}K_1^B$, being 1.0×10^8 $cm^3\,mol^{-1}\,s^{-1}$. In Figure 20 the relation of $\log(k_3K_1)$ against pKa is shown for some hydroxyoximes. There exists a linear relation with slope -1.0 between ortho-hydroxyoxime, HNAPO and HNBPO, but the values for DEHDO is larger than that estimated from the linear relationship. The relations between K_1 and pK_a and between k_1 and pK_a for β-diketones are also shown in Figure 21. In this case, K_1 is proportional to K_a^{-1}, but the rate constant slightly decreases with the increase in pK_a. It is deduced from these results that the change of (k_3K_1) with pK_a for ortho-hydroxyoxime is attributed to the change in K_1 and that the extra-large value of the k_3K_1 for DEHDO arises from the large value of the rate constant k_3^{BB} due to fast five-membered chelate-ring closure.

The enhancement factor depends on the ratios of physico-chemical properties, k_3^{RB}/k_3^{RR}, K_1^B/K_1^R, $\Gamma_{HB}^{(\infty)}/\Gamma_{HR}^{(\infty)}$, $\bar{K}_{HB}^s/\bar{K}_{HR}^s$ and P_{HR}/P_{HB}. As shown in Table 23, the catalytic activity of the dioximes decreases in order V > VI > VII > IIX. This decreasing trend can be qualitatively interpreted by the increase in the P_{HB} values of these dioximes.

Hydrophobic Non-chelating Agent

Several compounds were found to act as accelerators for the metal extraction with chelating agent as summarized in Table 26. These compounds have a few common characteristics: There exists at least one long alkyl chain group to increase the solubility into the organic diluent. Some compounds such as dinonylnaphthalene sulfonic acid (DNNSA) and Aerosol-OT in low dielectric

Table 26
Several Accelerators and Inhibitors in the Chelating System

Chelating Agent[a]	Accelerator[b]	Metal	Mode of Action[c]	Remarks Equilibria	Rate	Ref.
HNBPO	D2EHPA	Cu^{2+}	2	none (low con.) decrease (high con.)	increase increase	[179]
	nonyl-phenol	Cu^{2+}	3	—	decrease	[133]
HNAPO	SDS	Cu^{2+}	3	none	increase	[181]
	polyethylene glycol alkyl ether	Cu^{2+}	3	none	decrease	[181]
LIX65N	sulfo-succinate	Cu^{2+}	2	increase	—	[180]
LIX64N	D2EHPA	Cu^{2+}	2	decrease	increase	[182]
	versatic acid	Cu^{2+}	2	none (1%) decrease (5%)	increase increase	[182] [182]
	oleic acid	Cu^{2+}	2	none	none	[182]
LIX63	DNNSA	Cu^{2+}	1	increase	none	[178]
	DNNSA	Ni^{2+}	1	increase	increase	[67]
	carboxylic acid	Ni^{2+}	2	increase	increase	[183]
Kelex 120	D2EHPA	Cu^{2+}	2	decrease	decrease	[182]
LIX70	D2EHPA (1%)	Cu^{2+}	2	none	increase	[182]
BA	SDS	Cu^{2+}	3	none	increase	[42]
	Tween	Cu^{2+}	3	none	decrease	[42]
TTA	TOPO	Fe^{3+}	2	none	increase	[184]
	TBP	Fe^{3+}	2	none	increase	[185]
	TOMACI	Fe^{3+}	2	none	increase	[186]
	pyridine	Ni^{2+} Co^{2+}	coordinate		increase increase	[125]
Dithizone	SDS	Cu^{2+}	3	none	increase	[187]
	polyethelene glycol alkyl ether	Cu^{2+}	3	none	decrease	[187]

[a] *See Table 2*
[b] *D2EHPA: di-2-ethylhexyl phosphoric acid, SDS: sodium dodecyl sulfate, DNNSA: dinonylnapthalene sulfonic acid, TOPO: trioctyl phosphine oxide TBP: tributylphosphate, TOMACl: trioctylmethyl ammonium chloride*
[c] *See text*

diluent tend to form spontaneously the large aggregate, which is well known as a reversed micelle. These compounds also have a polar head group that interacts with the metal ion through the coordination bond or electro-static bonding with metal ion. The polar group frequently contains a dissociating proton, and the acidity of this compound is higher than that of chelating agents. Therefore, these exist in an anionic species at the interface or in the aqueous phase, even at lower pH. Due to this amphiphilic nature of a molecule, these compounds tend to adsorb at the organic-aqueous interface, which provides the main reaction field for the metal-chelate complex formation, especially in the extraction by commercial chelating agents as described earlier.

Taking account of these characteristics, the modes of the action as accelerator are classified as

1. Reversed micellar catalysis—Reversed micelles formed in the organic phase solubilize water molecules into the core of micelle accompanying with the metal ion.

2. Phase transfer catalysis—Ionic pair between metal ion and the agent preferentially dissolves into the organic phase.
3. Modification of interface—Agent adsorbed at the interface changes the physico-chemical interfacial properties such as interfacial potential.

Since these modes of catalysis reveal themselves simultaneously in many cases, it is difficult to distinguish from each other.

Reversed micellar catalysis. Several reactions catalyzed by the reversed micelles are summarized in the literature [176, 177]. The principal role of reversed micelle is to concentrate the metal ion and chelating agents into the core of reversed micelle that provides a hydrophilic environment different more or less from the bulk aqueous phase. This catalytic role has not been interpreted quantitatively.

For the solvent extraction system, the reversed micelle carrying chelating agent is formed in the organic phase due to the surface-active properties of chelating agent. Recently, Osseo-Asare et al. [67, 178] reported the synergism of DNNSA and LIX63, which form a mixed reversed micelle by the hydrogen bonding between these agents. The distribution ratio of both Co(II) and Ni(II) increases with the coexistance of DNNSA and LIX63 due to the formation of mixed reversed micelle. The extraction rate of Ni(II) is also enhanced by the presence of mixed reversed micelle at lower DNNSA concentration region.

Phase transfer catalysis. The term "phase transfer catalysis" was used by Starks who studied the role of tetraalkylammonium salt used for the reaction between the hydrophilic reactant in the aqueous phase and the hydrophobic reagent in the organic phase. Since the metal ion usually exists as a cation in the solvent extraction system, the anionic species with a suitable hydrophobic group acts as a phase transfer catalysis. Several anionic species acting as a phase transfer catalyst in the solvent extraction of metal ion have been found, but most studies are only qualitative.

Komasawa et al. [179] studied quantitatively the enhancement mechanism of copper extraction with HNBPO in the presence of di-2-ethylhexyl phosphoric acid (D2EHPA). The proposed extraction scheme is similar to that of the copper extraction enhanced by the presence of DEHDO, which is described previously. Then, the rate ratio of Cu(II) extraction with D2EHPA to without D2EHPA, j_c/j_O, is expressed as

$$j_c/j_O = 1 + G'[\overline{HB}]_s/[\overline{HR}]_s = 1 + (G'/K_d^{1/2})\bar{C}_{HB}^{1/2}/[\overline{HR}]_s \tag{166}$$

where, $[\overline{HB}]$ represents the concentration of monomeric D2EHPA in the organic phase, and can be expressed by $(\bar{C}_{HB}/K_d)^{1/2}$ because D2EHPA exists as dimer in the organic diluent. $\bar{C}_{HB}$ is the analytical concentration of D2EHPA. The values of $(G'/K_d^{1/2})$ are obtained as 1.7 for n-heptane and 100 for xylene diluent, respectively. The difference between both diluents is probably caused by the larger P_{HR} and also smaller P_{HB} and K_d in aromatic diluent than those in aliphatic diluent.

Modification of interface by adsorption of surface active agent. The chelate complex formation proceeds at the organic-aqueous interface and in some cases in the aqueous phase. As discussed in the previous section, the metal complex formation with a commercial chelating agents mainly occurs at the interface. Now, consider the rate of copper extraction by β-hydroxyoxime, in which the interfacial reaction controls the rate. In this case, the extraction rate is expressed by

$$j_O = (k_3K_1/P_{HR})\Gamma_{HR}^{(\infty)}\bar{K}_{HR}^s(1 + \bar{K}_{HR}^s[\overline{HR}])^{-1}[\overline{HR}]^2[Cu^{2+}]_s/[H^+]_s \tag{167}$$

Note that the term, $\{1 + \bar{K}_{HR}^s[\overline{HR}]\}$, in the denominator is introduced to account for the interfacial activity of β-hydroxyoxime in terms of Langmuir adsorption. When an anionic surface-active agent A is added to this system, the interfacial concentration of β-hydroxyoxime, Γ_{HR}, can be expressed as

$$\Gamma_{HR} = \Gamma_{HR}^{(\infty)}\bar{K}_{HR}^s[\overline{HR}]/(1 + \bar{K}_{HR}^s[\overline{HR}] + \bar{K}_A^s[\bar{A}]) \tag{168}$$

where we assumed that the Langmuir adsorption can be applied to this multi-component system. The adsorption of anionic agent at the interface brings about the negative interfacial potential. As a result, the cationic species in the aqueous phase are attracted to the interface by the Coulombic interaction. If the cation is assumed to have a point charge, the concentration of cationic species with the valence of Z_+ at the position adjacent to interface can be expressed,

$$[C^{Z+}]_{es} = [C^{Z+}]_s \exp(-Z_+ e\psi_0/k_B T) \quad (169)$$

Introduction of Equations 168 and 169 into Equation 167 provides the extraction rate of copper in the presence of the anionic surface-active species:

$$j_c = (k_3K_1/P_{HR})\Gamma_{HR}^{(\infty)}\bar{K}_{HR}^{s}(1 + \bar{K}_{HR}^{s}[\overline{HR}] + \bar{K}_{A}^{s}[\bar{A}])^{-1} \exp(-e\psi_0/k_BT) \times [\overline{HR}]_s^2[Cu^{2+}]_s/[H^+]_s \quad (170)$$

Here, the subscript, s, represents the concentration in the absence of surface potential. If the parameters k_3K_1, P_{HR}, $\Gamma_{HR}^{(\infty)}$ and $\bar{K}_{HR}^{s}$ are not affected by the presence of anionic surface-active species, the ratio of extraction rate is expressed as

$$j_c/j_0 = (1 + \bar{K}_{HR}^{s}[HR])/(1 + \bar{K}_{HR}^{s}[\overline{HR}] + \bar{K}_{A}^{s}[\bar{A}]) \exp(-e\psi_0/k_BT) \quad (171)$$

The effect of a surface-active agent, A, can be qualitatively explained by this equation. The adsorption of anionic species at interface strongly enhances the extraction rate when the interfacial reaction dominates the extraction rate. Whereas, the adsorption of cationic species slows down the extraction.

It is of practical importance that the adsorption of non-reactive surface-active species decreases the extraction rate. The degree of the retardation depends on the adsorption ability denoted by $\bar{K}_{A}^{s}$ and the concentration of A. As shown in Table 24, the addition of non-chelating agent (Ic, III, IV, Vc, and VI) retards the extraction of copper. The degree of retardation of the strongly surface-active agents, IIIa and VIa, becomes greater than that of weakly surface-active agents such as II and IV aliphatic oximes. The syn-isomers, Ic and Vc, which do not act as a chelating agent also retard the extraction rate, due to their adsorption. van der Zeeuw et al. [170] also found the retardation effect of syn-isomer of hydroxyoxime, which is contained in the commercial products LIX65N and SME529. This retarding effect was interpreted in terms of the formation of mixed anti-syn-neutral complex at the interface [159] in addition to the retarding effect by the adsorption of syn-isomer.

Catalytic Role of Hydrophilic Agents

Several extraction systems in which the extraction rate is enhanced by the presence of ligands coordinating to metal ion in the aqueous phase have been reported and are summarized in Table 27. The catalysis of a hydrophilic ligand A is interpreted in terms of the ligand exchange reaction. The mechanism of loss of water molecule from the central metal ion is extended to the ligand exchange reaction:

$$MA + L \underset{}{\overset{K_{MA,L}}{\rightleftharpoons}} MA \cdots L \underset{k_{MAL}^{-L}}{\overset{k_{MA}^{-H_2O}}{\rightleftharpoons}} MAL \quad (172)$$

Here, MA represents the metal-ligand A complex, and MAL the metal mixed ligand complex. Insofar as the loss of water molecule from the metal ion is rate-determining step, the overall reaction rate constant of Equation 172 is expressed in the same equation as Equation 96:

$$k_{MAL} = K_{MA,L}k_{MA}^{-H_2O} \quad (173)$$

The $K_{MA,L}$ denotes the formation constant of the outer-sphere complex MA ... L. The $k_{MA}^{-H_2O}$ is the rate constant of the exchange of water molecule with the incoming ligand L, and the k_{MAL}^{-L}

Table 27
Accelerator of Hydrophilic Ligand

Chelating Agent	Metal	Ligand (i)	Solvent	Extractor	Remarks	Ref.
LIX64N	Cu^{2+}	Cl^{-} SO_4^{2-} (1 M)(0.5 M)	kerosene	single drop	$j(Cl^{-})/j(SO_4^{2-}) = 4.5$	[160]
LIX65N					$j(Cl^{-})/j(SO_4^{2-}) = 5.5$	
LIX70					$j(Cl^{-})/j(SO_4^{2-}) = 4.5$	
P17					$j(Cl^{-})/j(SO_4^{2-}) = 5$	
SME529					$j(Cl^{-})/j(SO_4^{2-}) = 8.1$	
Kelex 100					$j(Cl^{-})/j(SO_4^{2-}) = 4.1$	
TTA	Fe^{3+}	SCN^{-}	benzene	drop disp.	Fe-SCN complex formation replacement of SCN^{-} with TTA in organic phase (phase transfer)	[188, 189]
TTA	Ni^{2+}	pyridine	benzene	drop disp.	$k_i/k_0 = 8.8$	[125]
	Co^{2+}	pyridine	benzene	drop disp.	$k_i/k_0 = 85$	
TTA	Fe^{3+}	Cl^{-}	benzene	drop disp.	$k_i/k_0 = 40$	[190]
	Fe^{3+}	OH^{-}	benzene	drop disp.	$k_i/k_0 = 880$	
TTA	Fe^{3+}	Cl^{-}	CCl_4	drop disp.	$k_i/k_0 = 28$	[123]
Dithizone	Ni^{2+}	CH_3COO^{-}	$CHCl_3$	drop disp.	$k_i/k_0 = 1.0$	[119]
		SCN^{-}	$CHCl_3$	drop disp.	$k_i/k_0 = 2.5$	
		CH_3CSO^{-}	$CHCl_3$	drop disp.	$k_i/k_0 = 14.0$	
Dithizone	Zn^{2+}	CH_3COO^{-}	$CHCl_3$	drop disp.	$k_i/k_0 = 25.0$	[119]
		SCN^{-}	$CHCl_3$	drop disp.	$k_i/k_0 = 10.0$	
		CH_3CSO^{-}	$CHCl_3$	drop disp.	$k_i/k_0 = 7.0$	

k_i/k_0 represents rate constant ratio with ligand i to without the ligand.

is the rate constant of the reaction in reverse direction. The formation constant of MAL is described by

$$K_{MAL} = K_{MA,L}k_{MA}^{-H_2O}/k_{MAL}^{-L} \tag{174}$$

Now, we assume that the rate of dissociation of the ligand L from the complex MAL is inversely proportional to both the Brønsted basicity and the electron donating properties of leaving ligand L and is proportional to the electron donating properties of the remaining ligand A. This assumption yields a relation:

$$\log(k_{MAL}^{-L}/k_{M}^{-H_2O}) = \tilde{\mu}E(A) - \tilde{\alpha}E(L) - \tilde{\beta}H(L) \tag{175}$$

The $k_{MAL}^{-L}/k_{M}^{-H_2O}$ is the rate constant ratio of the removal of the ligand L to that of the ligand H_2O. E and H represent the measures of the electron donating property and of the basicity of the argumented ligand. The coefficients $\tilde{\alpha}$, $\tilde{\beta}$ and $\tilde{\gamma}$ are dependent on the metal ion M. The E and H are defined zero for H_2O as a standard. Then,

$$\log(k_{ML}^{-L}/k_{M}^{-H_2O}) = -\tilde{\alpha}E(L) - \tilde{\beta}H(L), \text{ for } A = H_2O \tag{176}$$

$$\log(k_{MA}^{-H_2O}/k_{M}^{-H_2O}) = \tilde{\mu}E(A), \text{ for } L = H_2O \tag{177}$$

The complex formation of ML corresponds to Equation 172 with $A = H_2O$ and the formation constant is given from Equations 173 and 175.

$$\log K_{ML} = \log K_{M,L} + \tilde{\alpha}E(L) + \tilde{\beta}H(L) \tag{178}$$

Table 28
Electrode Potentials and Doner Constants

A	E(A)	H(A)
NO_3^-	0.29	(0.40)
SO_4^{2-}	0.59	3.74
$ClCH_2COO^-$	0.79	4.54
CH_3COO^-	0.95	6.46
C_5H_5N	1.20	7.04
Cl^-	1.24	(−3.00)
$C_6H_5O^-$	1.46	11.74
Br^-	1.51	(−6.00)
N_3^-	1.58	6.46
OH^-	1.65	17.48
NO_2^-	1.73	5.09
$C_6H_5NH_2$	1.78	6.28
SCN^-	1.83	(1.00)
NH_3	1.84	11.22
$(CH_3O)_2POS^-$	2.04	(4.00)
$C_2H_5SO_2S^-$	2.06	(−5.00)
I^-	2.06	(−9.00)
$(C_2H_5O)_2POS^-$	2.07	(4.00)
$CH_3C_6H_4SO_2S^-$	2.11	(−6.00)
$SC(NH_2)_2$	2.18	0.80
$S_2O_3^{2-}$	2.52	3.60
SO_3^{2-}	2.57	9.00
CN^-	2.79	10.88
S^{2-}	3.08	14.66

(Reprinted with Permission from Ref. 192.)

The H scale is selected as the normal pK_a values of the conjugated acid in the aqueous solution, being defined [192] by

$$H = pK_a + 1.74 \tag{179}$$

The E scale is related with the oxidation potential of the donar E^0, being defined [192] by

$$E = E^0 + 2.6 \tag{180}$$

These values are shown in Table 28. Tanaka et al. [191, 193] evaluated the $\tilde{\alpha}$ and $\tilde{\beta}$ values from Equation 178 with the $K_{M,L}$ of Fuoss's equation. The resultant $\tilde{\alpha}$ and $\tilde{\beta}$ values are summarized in Table 29. The $\tilde{\mu}$ value is also determined for several metals [193];

$$\tilde{\mu} = -5.8\tilde{\sigma} + 5.7 \tag{181}$$

where, $\tilde{\sigma}$ is defined by $\tilde{\sigma} = \tilde{\alpha}/(\tilde{\alpha} + \tilde{\beta})$.

The catalysis of the hydrophilic ligand A is estimated from Equation 177. If we take into account the statistical factor arising from the number of water molecules available for exchange, Equation 177 is modified [191] as

$$\log(k_{MA}^{-H_2O}/\text{No. of } H_2O) - \log(k_M^{-H_2O}/\text{No. of } H_2O) = \tilde{\mu}E(A) \tag{182}$$

Table 29
$\tilde{\alpha}$, $\tilde{\beta}$ and $\tilde{\sigma}$ Values for Metal Ions

Metal Ions	$\tilde{\alpha}$	$\tilde{\beta}$	$\tilde{\sigma}$
Ag^+	3.60	−0.09	1.03
Pd^{2+}	5.33	−0.12	1.02
Hg^{2+}	5.83	−0.07	1.01
Tl^-	1.24	0.03	0.98
CH_3Hg^+	4.21	0.11	0.97
Cu^+	3.92	0.18	0.96
Cd^{2+}	1.66	0.07	0.96
Ni^{2+}	1.41	0.09	0.94
In^{3+}	1.57	0.15	0.93
Co^{2+}	1.39	0.12	0.92
Zn^{2+}	1.25	0.13	0.91
Cu^{2+}	1.64	0.21	0.89
Bi^{3+}	0.89	0.13	0.87
Pb^{2+}	1.21	0.22	0.85
Fe^{2+}	1.13	0.21	0.84
Mn^{2+}	1.04	0.23	0.82
Fe^{3+}	1.62	0.47	0.78
Sn^{2+}	1.35	0.50	0.73
VO^{2+}	1.37	0.57	0.71
Cr^{3+}	1.29	0.68	0.65
UO_2^{2+}	0.95	0.58	0.62
Ce^{3+}	0.79	0.48	0.62
Ga^{3+}	1.01	0.73	0.58
Zr^{4+}	1.45	1.10	0.57
Hf^{4+}	1.19	0.93	0.56
U^{4+}	0.67	1.01	0.40
Alkali and alkaline earth metal ions	0	0	—

(Reprinted with Permission from Ref. 193.)

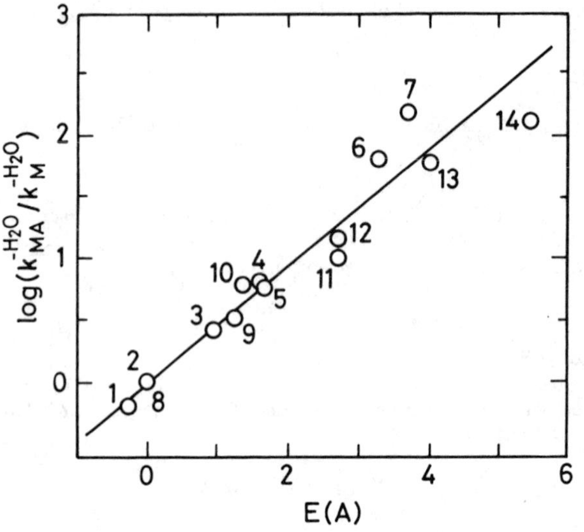

Figure 24. Relation between $\log(k_{MA}^{-H_2O}/k_M^{-H_2O})$ and E(A). 1, $Ni(H_2O)_5F^+$; 2, $Ni(H_2O)_6^{2+}$; 3, $Ni(H_2O)_5CH_3COO^+$; 4, $Ni(H_2O)_5OH^+$; 5, $Ni(H_2O)_5N_3$; 6, $Ni(H_2O)_3nta^-$; 7, $Ni(H_2O)_3edda$; 8, $Ni(H_2O)_6^{2+}$; 9, $Ni(H_2O)_5Cl^+$; 10, $Ni(H_2O)_5NH_3^+$; 11, $Ni(H_2O)_4en^{2+}$; 12, $Ni(H_2O)_4(NH_3)_2^{2+}$; 13, $Ni(H_2O)_3(NH_3)_3^{2+}$; 14, Ni $(H_2O)_2(en)_2^{2+}$. (Reprinted with permission from Ref. 195.)

An example of catalysis of the ligand A for Ni(II) complex formation [194, 195] is shown in Figure 24, which indicates that the bond-ligand effect of NiA on the water-exchange rate is reasonably well described by Equation 182. The ligand species Cl^-, OH^- and NH_3 greatly enhances the rate of loss of water molecule from the central metal ion. When the formation rate of complex MAL is determined by the release of water molecule from outer-sphere complex, the ratio of reaction rate with hydrophilic ligand, A, to that without A can be expressed by

$$r_{MAL}/r_{ML} = \{(K_{MA,L}/K_{M,L})10^{\bar{\gamma}E(A)} - 1\}\{\beta_A[A]/(1 + \beta_A[A])\} + 1 \tag{183}$$

If the chelating agent L is neutral, the $K_{MA,L}/K_{M,L}$ term of the right side of Equation 183 vanishes due to the Fuoss's equation. Therefore, the degree of enhancement in the presence of hydrophilic ligand can be mainly determined by both E(A) and $\bar{\gamma}$ values. When the central metal is the same, the degree of enhancement increases with the increase in E(A). As shown in Table 27, the extraction rate of copper with hydroxyoxime in the chloride media is greater than that in the sulphate media. This behavior may be due to greater $E(Cl^-)$ value than $E(SO_4^{2-})$ as shown in Table 28.

This theory is based on the loss of water from central metal ion as the rate determining step, and provides important information on the catalysis of hydrophilic ligand.

CONCLUSION

This chapter summarized the principles of designing the separation system with chelating agents by focusing on the kinetics of metal extraction. The schematic diagram of rational procedures of designing the metal separation system is shown in Table 30.

The first problem is how to select the optimal chelating ligand species for a given metal. This is concerned with the solution chemistry, and we postulated that the ligand species is given a priori for a metal to be separated.

TABLE 30
Procedures of Designing Metal Extraction System Based on Fundamental Principles

Procedures	Important Factors	Fundamental Basis
Metal ions to be selected in aqueous phase (a priori given) Selection of extractant ligand (a priori given)		
Modification of extractant by introducing hydrophobic groups Selection of diluent for extractant	pK_a of the extractant Stability constants, β_1 and β_2 or K_1 and K_2 Dimerization constant of extractant, K_d	Linear Free Energy Relationship (LFER-correlation)
	Partition constants of extractant and neutral metal complex, P_{HR} and P_{MR_2}	Regular solution theory Needs of developing the estimation method of transferring free energy and modern theory of solution
Estimation of equilibrium constant metal of extraction	Overall extraction constant, $K_{ex} = K_1K_2(P_{MR_2}/P_{HR}^2)$	LFER-correlation and molecular orbital theory
Estimation of interfacial properties (adsorption)	Saturated surface concentration of extractants, $\Gamma_{HR}^{(\infty)}$ Adsorption equilibrium constant of extractant, $\bar{K}_{HR}^{s}$	Information only qualitative
Estimation of extraction rate: Location of main reaction and estimation of each resistance of mass transfer	Rate constants of complex formation in homogeneous phase, partition constant of extractant, P_{HR} and interfacial properties	Mechanism of complex formation in homogeneous phase Critical conditions determining reaction location, and kinetic theory of metal extraction
To check the selected hydrophobic groups of modifying extraction ligand and the diluent Decision of introducing catalytic role		
To select what catalytic roles should be introduced to the system	Hydrophobic catalysis or hydrophilic catalysis? P_{HR} and interfacial properties, and formation constant of metal-catalyst ligand complex	Qualitative rules of catalysis of hydrophobic reagents Ligand exchange reaction rate for hydrophilic ligand species
Selection of extractor type and design of its operation		

The second problem is concerned with the modification of the extractant, which involves the given chelating ligand, i.e., introduction of hydrophobic groups to the ligand in order to prevent the loss of the extractant and to provide full power of the extraction ability for the extractant. Once the modification of the extractant is decided, the basic properties of the extractant, e.g., the pK_a, are determined. Linear free energy relationship is available for estimating the pK_a value for rather simple systems. The stability constants of the metal-chelate complexes are determined at this stage, though the estimation of these is difficult at present.

The third problem is to select the diluent species for the extractant. The dimerization constant of the extractant, K_d, and the partition constants of the extractant and the metal-complex in neutral form, P_{HR} and P_{MR_2}, are determined at this stage. The chelating extractant displays some behaviors different from the extractants of strongly acidic phosphorous compounds and ion-exchange extractants, such as high-molecular-weight amines, i.e., the change of the transfer free energy with the hydrocarbon chain length is different from those of the extractants, such as phosphoric acids and amines. This prevents the development of an estimation method for P_{HR} and P_{MR_2}. The method is to be developed in future. The overall extraction constant K_{ex} is also determined at this stage. The linear free energy correlation and molecular orbital methods are being developed for estimating the K_{ex} values. We highlighted the equilibrium relationships of the metal extraction.

The main problems in this chapter are concerned with the metal extraction kinetics. We first judge where and at what rate the metal complex formation reaction proceeds. The fundamental factors to determine the main reaction locale are the partition constant P_{HR}, the interfacial properties of adsorption (the saturated surface concentration of HR and the adsorption constant), and also the complex forming reaction rate in the homogeneous phase.

The interfacial properties of the chelating agent and the reaction kinetics in homogeneous phase were given. The modification of the extractant ligand by introducing the hydrophobic group into the ligand has a strong effect on the rate of extraction through the factors of the P_{HR} and the interfacial properties of the extractant. If the physico-chemical properties are known, one can estimate the critical condition that gives information on the main reaction field of the complex formation. Also, we can estimate what rate processes control the extraction rate. If the estimated value is inadequate in order of magnitude, one must return to the steps of modification of the extractant and the selection of the diluent, and/or consider the introduction of a catalytic role into the extraction system. The main catalyses and the classification were summarized.

Finally, we arrive at the selection of extractor type and the design of the extractor operation.

The selection and design of the extraction system including molecular design of the extractant and the separation field design could be performed with the help of semi-theoretical or theoretical methods. At present, these methods are not satisfactory, and we need preliminary experimental results, especially for the equilibrium relationships. The development of rational design method of deciding the separation field is now an important problem imposed on the chemical engineer.

NOTATION

A	area
A_i	area occupied by unit amount of species i
$A_i^{(\infty)}$	area occupied by unit amount of species i at saturation
$A_a^{(\infty)}$	apparent area occupied by unit amount of HR at saturation
$A_s^{(\infty)}$	area occupied by unit amount of HR at saturation, evaluated from Szyszkowski's equation
b	coefficient of the relation between interfacial pressure and solute concentration
C_E	concentration of electrolyte
C_i	concentration of species i in total
D, D_i	diffusion coefficient
D′	relative diffusion coefficient
D_{HR}	distribution coefficient of HR
D_M	distribution of metal M
d	minimum separation distance between molecules (center-to-center)
d_p	diameter of droplet
E(L)	electron-donating function
e	elementary charge
F	Helmholtz free energy
$f(\zeta_b)$	defined in Table 19
$\bar{f}_{enol}$	fraction of enol form in β-diketone
G, G′	enhancement factor of catalysis

$\Delta_{tr}G^0$ transferring free energy change
$H(L)$ basicity function
j flux of metal (extraction rate)
j_c flux of metal in the presence of catalyst
j_0 flux of metal in the absence of catalyst
K_a dissociation constant of HR
K_a^s dissociation constant of HR at interface
$K_{A,B}$ formation constant of A · · · B aggregate
K_d equilibrium constant of HR-dimerization
K_{ex} overall equilibrium constant of extraction of metal
K_i^s equilibrium constant of adsorption of species i
$K_i^{(\alpha,s)}$ equilibrium constant of adsorption of species i between α-phase and interface
K_{MAL} formation constant of metal-mixed ligands (A, L) complex
K_T equilibrium constant of tautomerization
K_1 formation constant of 1:1 metal complex from HR
K_1^B formation constant of 1:1 metal complex MB^+
K_1^* formation constant of 1:1 metal complex at interface
K_2 formation constant of 1:2 metal complex from MR^+ and HR
K_2^* formation constant of metal-mixed complex from MR^+ and HR at interface
k reaction rate constant or rate coefficient
k^* reaction rate constant at interface
k_a, k'_a rate constants of HR dissociation and reverse reaction
$k_a^*, k_a^{*\prime}$ rate constants of HR dissociation and reverse reaction at interface
k_B Boltzmann constant
k_D, k'_D rate constants of diffusion-controlled reaction and reverse reaction
k_E, k'_E rate constants of enol-enolate ion transformation
k_f apparent constant of extraction
k_k, k'_k rate constant of keto-enolate ion transformation
$k_M^{-H_2O}$ rate constant of loss of water molecule from central metal ion
k_{MAL}^{-L} rate constant of loss of ligand L from complex MAL
k_0 mass transfer coefficient in organic phase
k_R rate constant of reaction occurring after diffusion-controlled reaction
k_{sI} rate constant of interfacial reaction defined by Equations 122
k_{sII} rate constant of interfacial reaction defined by Equation 123
k_{sI}^* rate constant of interfacial reaction defined by Equation 128
k_{sII}^* rate constant of interfacial reaction defined by Equation 129
k_w mass transfer coefficient in aqueous phase
$k_{w,H}$ mass transfer coefficient of proton in aqueous phase
k_1, k'_1 rate constants of reaction between metal ion and HR and reverse reaction
k_{1E} rate constant of reaction between metal ion and enol-HR
k_{1K} rate constant of reaction between metal ion and keto-HR
k_2, k'_2 rate constants of reaction between metal ion and R^- and reverse reaction
k_3, k'_3 rate constants of reaction between MR^+ and HR and reverse reaction
k_3^{RB} rate constant of reaction between MR^+ and HB
k_I rate constant defined by Equations 99/100
k_{II} rate constant defined by Equations 101/102
n_i moles of species i
Δn_i quantity of species i in interfacial zone
n_c carbon number in alkyl-group
P_{HR} partition constant of HR between organic and aqueous phases
P_i^s partition constant of species i between aqueous phase and interface
$\bar{P}_i^s$ partition constant of species i between organic phase and interface
P_{MR_2} partition constant of MR_2 between aqueous and organic phases
p pressure
$p_i^{(\alpha,s)}$ partition constant of species i between interface and α-phase
pC_{HR} a measure of adsorption for HR
R gas constant
R_j resistance of J-rate process

r_i	reaction rate of i-species
r_i^*	reaction rate of i-species at interface
S	entropy
T	temperature
V	volume
V_i	molar volume of i-species
V_{aq}	molar volume of aqueous phase molecule
V_{org}	molar volume of organic phase molecule
w	work
x	distance
x_L	thickness of stagnant film
x_r	reaction zone thickness
Z	valence

Greek Symbols

$\tilde{\alpha}$	a coefficient defined in Equation 175
$\tilde{\beta}$	a coefficient defined by Equation 175
β_1	stability constant of MR^+
β_2	stability constant of MR_2
β_i	stability constant of ML_i
β_A	stability constant of MA
γ	entropy density
γ_i	activity coefficient of species i
$\tilde{\gamma}$	a coefficient defined by Equation 175
Γ_i	excess surface-concentration of species i
$\Gamma_i^{(1,2)}$	excess surface-concentration of species i relative to species 1 and 2
$\Gamma_i^{(\infty)}$	excess surface-concentration of species i at saturation
ε	dielectric constant
ζ_b	reaction parameter defined in Table 19
κ	Debye's reciprocal screening length
μ_D	dipole moment
μ_i	chemical potential of i-species
μ_i^0	standard chemical potential of i-species
ξ	a parameter in Table 20
ξ_e	electrostatic to thermal energy ratio
Π	interfacial pressure
ρ^*	Taft parameter
ρ_i	charge density of species i
σ	interfacial tension
$\tilde{\sigma}$	$\tilde{\alpha}/(\tilde{\alpha} + \tilde{\beta})$
σ^*	Taft or Hammett parameter
σ_e	electrical charge density per unit area
ϕ	hold-up volume ratio
Ψ	Volta potential
ψ_0	electrostatic potential at interface
ψ	electrostatic potential near interface
[ ]	concentration
over bar	organic phase

REFERENCES

1. Lo, T. C., Baird, M. H. I., and Hanson, C., *Handbook of Solvent Extraction*, John Wiley & Sons, New York, 1983.
2. Fleming, C. A., "Origin of Selectivity of Oxines and Oximes for Copper(II) over Iron(III)," *Trans. Instn. Min. Metall.* (sect. C: Mineral Process, Extr. Metall.) 85, C211, (1976).
3. Flett, D. S., "Selectivity of LIX64N and LIX65N for Copper(II) over Iron(III)," *Trans. Instn. Min. Metall.* (sect. C: Mineral Process, Extr. Metall.) 88, C256, (1979).
4. Hughes, M. A., "The Recovery of Metals from Secondary Sources: Solvent Extraction Routes," *Chem. Ind.*, 20, (Dec.) 1042, (1975).
5. Flett, D. S., and Pearson, D., "Recovery of the Metal Values from Effluents," *Chem. Ind.* 2 (Aug.), 639, (1975).
6. Reinhardt, H., "Solvent Extraction for Recovery of Metal Waste," *Chem. Ind.* 1, 20, (1975).
7. Flett, D. S., "Solvent Extraction in Scrap and Waste Processing," *J. Chem. Tech. Biotech.*, 29, 210, (1979).
8. Cleare, M. J., Charlesworth, P., and Bryson, D. J., "Solvent Extraction in Platinum Group Metal Processing," *J. Chem. Tech. Biotech.*, 29, 210, (1979).
9. Maclunis, M. B., and Kim, T. K., "The Impact of Solvent Extraction and Ion Exchange on the Hydrometallurgy of Tungsten and Molybdenum," *J. Chem. Tech. Biotech.*, 29, 225, (1979).
10. Sekine, T., and Hasegawa, Y., *Solvent Extraction Chemistry*, Marcel Dekker Inc. 1976.

11. Marcus, Y., and Kertes, A. S., *Ion Exchange and Solvent Extraction of Metal Complexes*, Wiley-Interscience, 1969.
12. Золотов, Ю. А., Зкстракция Внутрикомплексных Соелинеий, Издательство, Москва, 1968
13. Мазуренко, Е. А., Справочник по Зкстракции, Издательство, Киев, 1972
14. Freiser, H., "Extraction," *Anal. Chem.*, 38, 131R (1966).
15. Reichardt, C., *Solvent Effects in Organic Chemistry*, Verlag Chemie Weisnheim, New York 1979, p. 61.
16. Schwarzenbach, G., and Felder, E., "Determination of Keto-Enol Equilibrium in Water" *Helv. Chim. Acta.*, 27, 1044, (1944).
17. Allen, G., and Dwek, R. A., "An N.M.R. Study of Keto-Enol Tautomerism in β-diketones" *J. Chem. Soc(B)*, 161 (1966).
18. Harada, M., Mori, M., Adachi, M., and Eguchi, W., "Rates of Reactions in Cu(II)-Benzoylacetone System in Aqueous Phase," *J. Chem. Eng. Japan*, 16, 187, (1983).
19. Jaffe, M. R., Fay, D. P., Cefola, M., and Sutin, N., "Kinetics and Mechanism of the Formation of the Monothenoyltrifluoroacetone Complex of Nickel(II), Cobalt(II), Copper(II) and Iron(III)," *J. Amer. Chem. Soc.*, 93, 2878, (1971).
20. Paatero, E., and Hummelstedt, L., "The Behaviour of Syn-2-Hydroxy-5-Nonylbenzophenone Oxime in the Extraction of Copper with LIX65N and LIX64N," Proceedings of ISEC '80, 80–72, 1980.
21. Komasawa, I., Otake, T., and Yamada, A., "Equilibrium Studies of Copper from Sulphate Media with Hydroxyoxime Extractant," *J. Chem. Eng. Japan*, 13, 130, (1980).
22. Kojima, T., Tomita, T., and Miyauchi, T., "Extraction Equilibrium of Copper by LIX65N," *Kagaku Kogaku Ronbunsyu* 5, 476, (1979).
23. van der Zeeuw, A. J., and Kok, R., "Kinetics and Mechanism of Copper Extraction with 5-Alkyl-2-Hydroxyphenyl Alkyl Ketoximes," Proceedings of ISEC '77, p. 210. 1977.
24. Miyake, Y., Imanishi, Y., Katayama, Y., Hamatani, T., and Teramoto, M., "Effect of Alkyl Chain length of o-Hydroxyoxime on the Extraction of Copper," *J. Chem. Eng. Japan*, 19, 117, (1986).
25. Miyake, Y., Takenoshita, Y., and Teramoto, M., "Extraction of Copper with SME529," *J. Chem. Eng. Japan*, 16, 203, (1983).
26. Dalton, R. F., Hauxwell, F., and Tumilty, J. A., "Diluent Effects on the Hydrometallurgical Extraction of Metals by o-Hydroxyaryl Oximes," *Chem. and Ind.*, 181 (1976).
27. Kojima, T., and Miyauchi, T., "Extraction Equilibrium of Copper by LIX63", *Kagaku Kogaku Ronbunsyu*, 7, 200 (1981).
28. Perrin, D. D., Dempsey, B., and Serjeant, E. P., *pK_a Prediction for Organic Acids and Bases*, Chapman and Hall Ltd., 1981.
29. Lowry, T. H., and Richardson, K. S., *Mechanism and Theory in Organic Chemistry*, Harper & Row, Publishers, 1976, p. 67.
30. Yuan, C., Li, S., and Hu, S., "Structural Effects of Organic Ligand in Metal Extraction" Proceedings of ISEC '86, Münhen, 1986. p. II–487.
31. Hildebrand, J. H., and Scott, R. L., *The Solubility of Nonelectrolyte* (*3rd Ed.*) Dover Publications, Inc. 1964.
32. Wakahayashi, T., Oki, S., Omori, T., and Suzuki, N., "Some Applications of the Regular Solution Theory to Solvent Extraction I," *J. Inorg. Nucl. Chem.*, 26, 2255 (1964).
33. Wakahayashi, T., "Some Applications of the Regular Solution Theory to Solvent Extraction IV. Oxine-inert Solvent System," *Bull. Chem. Soc. Japan.*, 40, 2836 (1967).
34. Preston, J. S., and Luklinska, Z. B., "Solvent Extraction of Copper(II) with Orthohydroxyoxime-I" *J. Inorg. Nucl. Chem.* 42, 431, (1980).
35. Harada, M., Miyake, Y., and Kayahara, Y., "Metal Extraction Rates in Solvent Extraction with Chelating Agents," Proceedings of ISEC '86, 1986, II–309.
36. Foakes, H. J., Preston, J. S., and Whewell, R. J., "Aqueous Phase Solubilities and Partition Data for Commercial Copper Extractants," *Anal. Chim. Acta*, 97, 349. (1978).

37. Miyake, Y., Ohtsuki, K., and Teramoto, M., "Extraction Rate of Cu(II) by 3-Alkyl 2,4-pentane-dione," Proceedings of Symp. Sol. Ext. Japan, '86, 1986, p. 113.
38. Harada, M., Imamura, T., Fujiyoshi, K., and Eguchi, W., "Interfacial Resistance in Liquid-Liquid Mass Transfer," *J. Chem. Eng. Japan* 8, 233, (1975).
39. Kolarik, Z., "Interactions of Acidic Organophosphorous Extractants in the Organic Phase." *Solvent Extraction Reviews vol.* 1, Marcel Dekker, Inc. 1971 p. 1.
40. Czapkiewincz, J., and Czapkiewicz-Tutaj, B., "Partition Isotherms of Long Chain—Alkyl trimethylammonium Bromides in the Chloroform-Water or Aqueous NaBr System," *J., Colloid. Inter. Sci.*, 94 399 (1983).
41. Ringbom, A., *Complexation in Analytical Chemistry*, John Wiley & Sons Inc., New York 1963.
42. Kraus, M., and Rod, V., "Structural Effects on Equilibria and Rates of Metal Extraction," *Hydrometallurgy*, 13, 305, (1985).
43. Preston, J. S., "Alpha-substituted Oxime Extractants. I. Extraction of Copper(II), Nickel(II), Cobalt(II) and Iron(III) by Aliphatic α-Hydroxyoximes," *Inorg. Nucl. Chem.* 37, 1235 (1975).
44. Burger, K., and Egyed, I., "Some Theoretical and Practical Problems in the Use of Organic Reagents in Chemical Analysis. V.," *J. Inorg. Nucl. Chem.* 27, 2361, (1965).
45. Al-Niaimi, M. S., and Hamid, H. A., "Stabilities of Nickel(II), Copper(II), Zinc(II) and Dioxouranium(II) Complexes of Some β-Diketones," *J. Inorg. Nucl. Chem.* 39, 849, (1977).
46. Sekine, T., Murai, R., Takahashi K., and Iwahori, S., "The Formation and Extraction Equilibria of Several Manganese(II) β-Diketones and Their Trioctyl-Phosphine Oxide Adducts," *Bull. Chem. Soc. Japan*, 50, 3415 (1977).
47. Sekine, T., Koike, Y., and Komatsu, Y., "Kinetics Studies of the Solvent Extraction of Metal Complex I: The Extraction of the Beryllium(II)-TTA Chelated from Aqueous Perchlorate Media into Carbon Tetrachloride and Methyl Isobutyl Ketonë," *Bull. Chem. Soc. Japan* 44, 2903, (1971).
48. Flett, D. S., Okuhara, D. N., and Spink, D. R., "Solvent Extraction of Copper by Hydroxyoximes," *J. Inorg. Nucl. Chem.*, 35, 2471, (1973).
49. Harada, M., Mori, M., Adachi, M., and Eguchi, W., "Kinetics of Copper Extraction by Benzoylacetone," *J. Chem. Eng. Japan*, 16, 193 (1983).
50. Hughes, M. A., and Rod, V., "A General Model to Account for the Liquid/Liquid Kinetics of Extraction of Metals by Organic Acid," *Faraday Discuss. Chem. Soc.*, 77, 75, (1984).
51. Albery, W. J., Choudhery, R. A., and Fisk, P. R., "Kinetics and Mechanism of Interfacial Reactions in the Solvent Extraction of Copper," *Faraday Disc. Chem. Soc.*, 77, 53 (1984).
52. Gibbs, J. W., *The Collected Works of J. W. Gibbs, Vol. 1* Longmans, Green, New York, 1931.
53. Defay, R., Prigogine, I., and Bellmans, A., *Surface Tension and Adsorption*, D. H. Everett Trans. Longmans Green, London, 1966.
54. Chattoraj, D. K., and Birdi, K. S., *Adsorption and the Gibbs Surface Excess*, Plenum Pres., New York (1984).
55. Davies, J. T., and Riedeal, E. K., *Interfacial Phenomena*, Acad. Press New York, (1963).
56. Adamson, A. W., *Physical Chemistry of Surface* (*3rd Ed.*), Wiley-Interscience Pub., New York, (1976).
57. Szyszkowski, B. V., "Experimental Studies of Capillary Properties of Aqueous Solutions of Fatty Acids," *Z. Phys. Chem.*, 64, 385 (1908).
58. Askew, F. A., and Danielli, J. F., "Measurement of the Pressure due to Monolayers at Oil-Water Interfaces," *Trans. Faraday Soc.*, 36, 785, (1940).
59. Watanabe, A., "Electrochemistry of Oil-Water Interface," *Surface and Colloid Science*, 13, 7 (1984).
60. Bockris, J. O. M., Devanathan, M. A. V., Muller, K., "On the Structure of Charged Interfaces," *Proc. Roy. Soc.*, (*London*) A274, 55, (1863).
61. Paartero, E. Y. O., "Study of the Electrophoretic Mobility of Oil Droplets Containing Some α- and β-hydroxyoxime Extractants," *Hydrometallurgy*, 17, 39, (1986).
62. Lin, K. L., and Osseo-Asare, K., "Electrophoretic Mobility of Oil Drops in the Presence of Solvent Extraction Reagents" *Solv. Extr. & Ion Exchange*, 2, 365, (1984).
63. Fleming, C. A., "The Kinetics and Mechanism of Solvent Extraction of Copper by LIX64N and KELEX100," *Nat, Inst, for Metallurgy Report* No. 1793 (1976).

64. Dobson, S., and Van der Zeeuw, A. J., "Hydrocarbon Solvent Diluents in Hydroxyoxime Solvent Extraction Processes," *Chem. Ind.* (*London*) 6, 175, (1976).
65. Al-Diwan, T. A. B., Hughes, M. A., and Whewell, R. J., "Behaviour of Interfacial Tension in Solvent Extraction Involving Hydroxyoxime Extractants for Copper," *J. Inorg. Nucl. Chem.*, 39, 1419, (1977).
66. Flett, D. S., "Chemical Kinetics and Mechanism in Solvent Extraction of Copper Chelate," *Accounts. Chem. Res.*, 10, 99, (1977).
67. Osseo-Assare, K., "Interfacial Phenomena in Hydrometallurgical Liquid-Liquid Extraction Systems," *Hydrometallurgical Process Fundamentals*, (R. G. Bautista ed) NATO Conference Series VI," vol. 10, Plenum Press, New York, (1982).
68. Freeman, R. W., and Tavlarides, L. L., "Studies of Interfacial Kinetics for Liquid-Liquid Systems II," *Chem. Eng. Sci.* 37, 1547 (1982).
69. Yoshizuka, K., Kondo, K., and Nakashio, F., "Effect of Hydrophobicity on Distribution and Interfacial Adsorption Equilibria of 8-Quinolylsulfonamides," *J. Chem. Eng. Japan*, 19, 258, (1986).
70. Watarai, H., and Frieser, H., "Effect of Stirring on the Distribution Equilibria of n-Alkyl-Substituted Dithizones," *J. Amer. Chem. Soc.* 105, 191 (1983).
71. Watarai, H., and Sasabashi, K., "Interfacial Adsorption of 2-hydroxy-5-nonylbenzopheno-neoxime in Static and Vigorously Stirred Distribution System," *Solv. Extr. & Ion Exchange*, 31, 881, (1985).
72. Watarai, H., Takahashi M., and Shibata, K., "Interfacial Phenomena in the Extraction Kinetics of Ni(II) with 5-Hydroxy-5-Nonylacetophenoneoxime," *Bull. Chem. Soc. Japan.* 59, 3469, (1986).
73. van der Zeeuw, "On the Kinetics and Mechanism of Extraction of Copper with β-Hydroxyoximes in the Absence of Mass Transfer Limitations," *Hydrometallurgy*, 17, 295 (1987).
74. Langmuir, I., "The Constitution and Fundamental Properties of Solid and Liquids," *J. Amer. Chem. Soc.*, 38, 2221, (1916).
75. Chatterjee, A., and Chattoraj, D. K., "Adsorption of Short-chain Fatty Acids and Their Ions at Oil/water Interface," *J. Coll. Inter. Sci.* 26, 1 (1968).
76. Jasper, J. J., and Vandelt, R. D., "The Shapes and Closed-Packed Areas of Oriented Long-chain Dipoles at the Water-Octane Interface," *J. Phys. Chem.* 69, 481, (1965).
77. Peters, R. A., "Interfacial Tension and Hydrogen Ion Concentration," *Proc. Roy. Soc.*, A133, 140 (1931).
78. Cante, C. J., McDermott, J. E., and Saleeb, F. Z., "Surface pH from Electrokinetic Potentials and Titration of Lauratè Salts," *J. Coll. Inter. Sci.* 50, 1 (1975).
79. Takahashi, K., and Takeuchi, H., "Behaviour of Interfacial Tension during Copper Extraction by LIX65N," *J. Chem. Eng. Japan*, 19, 161 (1986).
80. Inoue, K., Tsunomachi, H., and Maruuchi, T., "Interfacial Adsorption Equilibrium of a Hydro-xyoxime and Its Metal Complex," *J. Chem. Eng. Japan*, 19, 131 (1986).
81. Eigen, M., "Ionen-und Ladungsubertragungsreactionen in Lösungen," *Ber. Bunsenges. Physik. Chem.*, 67, 753, (1963).
82. Noyes, R. M., *Progress in Reaction Kinetics* 1 (G. Porter, ed), Pergamon Press. London (1961).
83. Debye, P., "Reaction Rates in Ionic Solutions," *Trans. Electochem. Soc.* 82, 265, (1942).
84. Fuoss, R. M., "Ionic Association III. The Equilibrium Ion Pairs and Free Ions," *J. Am.* Chem. Soc., 80, 5059, (1958).
85. Eigen, M., de Maeyer, L., and Spatz, H. Ch., "Uber das Kinetische Verhalten von Protonen und Deuteronen in Eiskristallen" *Ber. Bunsenges. Physik. Chem.*, 68, 19, (1964); "Die Geschwindigkeit der Neutralisationreaction," *Naturwiss*, 42, 413, (1955).
86. Basolo, F., and Pearson, R., *Mechanism of Inoganic Reactions—A Study of Metal Complexes in Solutions* (*2nd Ed.*), John-Wiley & Sons. (1967).
87. Eigen, M., and de Maeyer, L., *Techniques of Organic Chemistry vol. 8. Pt.II* (S. L. Friess, E. S. Lewis and A. Weisshergen, ed) Interscience, Pub. New York (1963).
88. Langford, C., and Stengle, T. R., "Ligand Substitution Dynamics," *Ann. Rev. Phys. Chem.* 19, 193, (1968).
89. Hammes, G. G., and Moarell, M. L., "A Study of Nickel(II) and Cobalt(II) Phosphate Complexes," *J. Amer. Chem. Soc.*, 86, 1497, (1964).

90. Hammes, G. G., and Steinfeld, J. I., "Relaxation Spectra of Some Nickel(II) and Cobalt(II) Complexes," *J. Amer. Chem. Soc.*, 84, 4639 (1962).
91. Suttin, N., Nancollas, G. H., "The Kinetics of Formation of the Nickel Monooxalate Complex in Solution," *Inorg. Chem.*, 3, 360 (1964).
92. Onodera, T., and Fujimoto, M., "Kinetics of Chelate Formation between Lanthanum(II) and 4-(2-Pyridylazo)-Resorcinol," *Bull. Chem. Soc. Japan* 44, 2003, (1971).
93. Eigen, M., Kruse, W., Maass, G., and de Maeyer, L., "Rate Constants of Protolytic Reactions in Aqueous Solution," *Progr. Reaction Kinetics*, 2, 285 (1964).
94. Bell, R. P., Gelles, E., and Moller, E., "Kinetics of the Base-Catalyzed Halogenation of Some Ketons and Esters," *Proc. Roy. Soc.* A198, 438, (1948).
95. Bell, R. P., and Crooks, J. E., "Kinetic Hydrogen Isotope Effects in the Ionization of Some Ketonic Substances," *Proc. Roy. Soc.* A286, 285(1965).
96. Pearson, R. G., and Dillon, R. L., "Rates of Ionization of Pseudo Acids IV. Relation between Rates and Equilibria," *J. Amer. Chem. Soc.* 75, 2439, (1953).
97. Munakata, M., "Kinetics Studies on the Stability Enhancement of Mixed Ligand Copper(II) Complexes with 2,2',Bipyridyl and Acetylactone," *Bull. Chem. Soc., Japan* 51, 3500, (1978).
98. Fay, D. P., Nichols, A. R., and Sutin, N., "The Kinetics and Mechanism of the Reactions of iron(III) with β-Diketone, The Formation of Monoacetylacetonato Iron(III) and the Effect of Copper(II) on the Formation of Monothenoyltrifluoroacetonato Iron(III)," *Inorg. Chem.*, 10, 2096 (1971).
99. Pearson, R. G., and Anderson, O. P., "Rates and Mechanism of Formation of Mono (Acetylacetonato) Copper(II) Ion in Water and Methanol," *Inorg. Chem.*, 9, 39, (1970).
100. Hynes, M. R., and O'Regan, B. D., "Kinetics and Mechanism of the Reactions of Nickel(II) and Pentane-2,4-Dione," *J. Chem. Soc. Dalton*, 162 (1978).
101. Kustin, K., Pasternack, R. F., and Weistrock, M. E., "Steric Effect in Fast Metal Complexes Substitution Reactions I," *J. Amer. Chem. Soc.* 88, 4610, (1966).
102. Pasternack, R. F., and Kustin, K., "The Reactions of L-Carnosine with Metal Ions. Copper(II)," *J. Amer. Chem. Soc.*, 90, 2295, (1968).
103. Kustin, K., and Pasternack, R. F., "The Reaction of L-Carnosine with Cobalt(II)," *J. Amer. Chem. Soc.*, 90, 2805, (1968)
104. Harada, M., and Miyake, Y., "Formulation for Metal Extraction Rates in Solvent Extraction with Chelating Agents," *J. Chem. Eng. Japan* 19, 196 (1986).
105. Nicol, M. J., Preston, J. S., Rasden, J. A., and Mooiman, M., "The Kinetics of the Reaction between Copper(II) and Ortho- Hydroxyoximes," *Hydrometallurgy* 14, 83, (1985).
106. Pratt, J. M., and Telly, R. L., "The Reaction of Cu(II) with LIX65N in Homogeneous Solution," *Hydrometallurgy* 5, 29, (1979).
107. Brubaker, J. W., Pearlmutter, A. F., Jr., Stuehr, J. E., and Vu, T. V., "Copper(II) Chelation Kinetics III. Steric Effects," *Inorg. Chem.* 13, 559, (1974).
108. Hanna, G. J., and Noble, R. D., "Measurement of Liquid-Liquid Interface Kinetics," *Chem. Rev.*, 85, 583 (1985).
109. Reinhardt, H., and Rydberg, J. H. A., "The AKUFVE Solvent Extraction System" *Handbook of Solvent Extraction*, John Wiley & Sons, New York (1983).
110. Lewis, J. B., "The Mechanism of Mass Transfer of Solutes across Liquid-Liquid Interface Part I. The Determination of Individual Transfer Coefficients for Binary Systems," *Chem. Eng. Sci.* 3, 248 (1954).
111. Albery, W. J., Burke, J. F., Leffler E. B., and Hadgraft, J., "Interfacial Transfer Studied with a Rotating Diffusion Cell," *J. Chem. Soc. Faraday Transaction I.*, 72, 1618, (1976).
112. Levich, V. G., *Physico-chemical Hydrodynamic*, Prentice-Hall, Englewood, Cliffs N.J. 1962.
113. Kimura, S., and Miyauchi, T., "Mass Transfer in a Liquid-Liquid Laminar Jet," Chem. Eng. Sci., 21, 1057 (1966)
114. Heertjes, P. M., and De Nie, Litt., "Mass Transfer to Drops," *Recent Advances in Liquid-Liquid Extraction*, (C. Hanson, ed.) Pergamon Pres. Oxford 1971.
115. Eguchi, W., Harada, M., Adachi, M., and Tanigaki, M., "Position-scanning Spectrophotometer as a means of Observing Multl-Component Diffusion Phenomena," *J. Chem. Eng. Japan* 17, 466 (1984).

116. Honaker, C. B., and Freiser, H., "Kinetics of Extraction of Zinc Dithizonate," *Anal. Chem.* 66, 127, (1962).
117. McClellan, B. E., and Freiser, H., "Kinetics and Mechanism of Extraction of Zinc, Nickel, Cobalt and Cadmium with Dipheny-thiocarbazone, Di-o-Tolylthiocarbazone and Di-α-Naphthyl-thiocarbazone," *Anal. Chem.* 36, 2262 (1964).
118. Oh, J. S., and Freiser, H., "Kinetics and Mechanism of Extraction of Zinc and Nickel with Substituted Diphenylthiocarbazones," *Anal. Chem.* 39, 295 (1967).
119. Subbaraman, P. R., Cordes, S. M., and Freiser, H., "Effect of Auxiliary Complexing Agents on the Rate of Extraction of Zinc(II) and Nickel(II) with Diphenylthiocarbazone," *Anal. Chem.* 41, 1878 (1969).
120. Nitsch, W., and Kruis, B., "The Influence of Flow and Concentration on the Mass Transfer Mechanism in Chelateing Liquid/Liquid Extractions," *J. Inorg. Nucl. Chem.*, 40, 857 (1978).
121. Watarai, H., and Frieser, H., "Role of the Interface in the Extraction Kinetics of Zinc and Nickel Ions with Alkyl-Substituted Dithizone," *J. Amer. Chem. Soc.*, 105, 189 (1983).
122. Sekine, T., Komatsu, Y., and Yumikura, J., "Kinetics Studies of the Solvent Extraction of Metal Complexes III—The Rate of Hydroxyoxime and Back Extraction of Gallium(II) Thenoyltrifluoroacetonate Chelate in Aqueous Perchlorate Solution-Chloroform Systems," *J. Inorg. Nucl. Chem.*, 35, 3891 (1973).
123. Sekine, T., Yumikura, J., and Komatsu, Y., "Kinetics Studies of the Solvent Extraction of metal Complex II Rate of the Extraction of Iron(III) with Thenoyltrifluoroacetone into Carbon Tetrachloride," *Bull. Chem. Soc. Japan* 46, 2356 (1973).
124. Sekine, T., and Komatsu, Y., "Kinetics Studies of the Solvent Extraction of Metal Complexes IV—The Increase in the Rate of Iron(III) Extraction with Thenoyltrifluoroacetone with Methyl Isobutyl Ketone as a Solvent," *J. Inorg. Nucl. Chem.*, 37, 185 (1975).
125. Akaiwa, H., Kawamoto, H., and Ishii, T., "Kinetics Studies of Synergestic Extraction of Nickel(II) and Cobalt(II) with Thenoyltrifluoroacetone," *J. Inog. Nucl. Chem.*, 36, 2077 (1974).
126. Komatsu, Y., Honda, H., and Sekine, T., "Kinetics Studies of the Solvent Extraction of Metal Complexes V—Rate of Solvent Extraction of Iron(III) with Several β-Diketones," *J. Inorg. Nucl. Chem.*, 38, 1861, (1976).
127. Sekine, T., and Inagaki, H., "Kinetics Studies of Solvent Extraction Complexes VII—Extraction of Chromium(III) with Acetylacetone into 4-Metyl-2-pentanol," *J. Inorg. Nucl. Chem.*, 42, 115 (1980).
128. Kondo, K., Takahasi, S., Tsuneyuki, T., and Nakashio, F., "Solvent Extraction of Copper by Benzoylacetone in a Stirred Transfer Cell," *J. Chem. Eng. Japan*, 11, 193 (1978).
129. Whewell, R. J., Hughes, M. A., and Hanson, C., "The Kinetics of the Solvent Extraction of Copper(II) with LIX Reagents I-Single Drop Experiments," *J. Inorg. Nucl. Chem.*, 38, 2067, (1976).
130. Hughes, M. A., Preston, J. S., and Whewell, R. J., "The Kinetics of the Solvent Extraction of Copper(II) with LIX64N Reagents II-Active Energy," *J. Inorg. Nucl. Chem.* 38, 2067 (1976).
131. Whewell, R. J., Hughes, M. A., and Hanson, C., "The Kinetics of the Solvent Extraction of Copper(II) with LIX Reagents III—The Effect of LIX63 in LIX 64N," *J. Inorg. Nucl. Chem.*, 3, 2071 (1976).
132. Atwood, R. L., Thatcher, D. N., and Miller, J. P., "Kinetics of Copper Extraction from Nitrate Solutions by LIX64N," *Mett. Trans. B.* 6B, 465 (1975).
133. Hanson, C., Hughes, M. A., Preston, J. S., and Whewell, R. J., "The Kinetics of the Solvent Extraction of Copper(II) with LIX Reagents IV-Effects of Nonylphenol," *J. Inorg. Nucl. Chem.*, 38, 2306 (1976).
134. Perez de Ortiz, E. S., Cox, M., and Flett, D. S., "The Effect of Hydrodynamic Conditions on the Kinetics of Copper Extraction by LIX65N," *CIM Special Volume* 21, 198, ISEC77.
135. Kojima, T., and Miyauchi, T., "Extraction Kinetics of Copper-LIX65N System 1. Forward Extraction Rate," *Ind. Eng. Chem. Fundam.*, 20, 14 (1981).
136. Kojima, T., and Miyauchi, T., "Extraction Kinetics of Copper-LIX65N System 2. Stripping Rate of Copper," *Ind. Eng. Chem. Fundam.*, 20, 20 (1981).
137. Rod, V., Stmadova, L., Hancil, V., and Sir, Z., "Kinetics of Metal Extraction by Chelate Formation, Part II Extraction of Cu(II) by Hydroxyoximes," *Chem. Eng. J.* 21, 187 (1981).

138. Takahashi, K., and Takeuchi, H., "Rate of Copper Extraction by LIX65N," *Kagaku Kogaku Ronbunshu* 10, 409 (1984).
139. Takahashi, K., and Takeuchi, H., "Stripping Rates of Copper for LIX65N-Copper System," *Kagaku Kougaku Ronbunshu* 9, 567 (1983).
140. Kojima, T., Kaneko, N., and Furusaki, D., "Effect of Ferric Ion on Copper Extraction by LIX64N," *Kagaku Kougaku Ronbunshu* 9, 567 (1983).
141. Carter, S. P., and Freiser, H., "Kinetics and Mechanism of the Extraction of Copper with 2-Hydroxy-5-Nonylbenzophenone Oxime," *Anal. Chem.* 52, 511 (1980).
142. Akiba, K., and Freiser, H., "The Roll of the Solvent in Equilibrium and Kinetic Aspects of Metal Chelate Extractions," *Anal. Chem. Acta*, 136, 329 (1982).
143. Van der Zeeuw, A. J., and Kok, R., "Kinetics and Mechanism of Copper Extraction with 5-Alkyl-2-Hydroxyphenyl Alkyl Ketoximes," *CIM special* vol. 21, 210, ISEC77
144. Komasawa, I., Otake, T., and Kuraoka, T., "Extraction Kinetics of Copper with Hydroxyoxime Extractant," *J. Chem. Eng. Japan* 13, 204 (1980).
145. Komasawa, I., Otake, T., and Yamada, A., "Diffusion Resistance in Extraction Rate of Copper with Hydroxyoxime Extractant," *J. Chem. Eng. Japan* 13, 209 (1980).
146. Cox, M., and Hirons, C. G., "Kinetics and Mechanism of Extraction of Copper by Hydroxyoximes under Quiescent and Turbulent Mixing," Proceedings of ISEC '80, 80–118 (1980).
147. Danesi, P. R., Chiarizia, R., and Vandegrift, G. F., "Kinetics and Mechanism of the Complex Formation Reactions between Cu(II) and Fe(III) Aqueous Species and a α-Hydroxy Oxime in Toulene," *J. Phys. Chem.*, 84, 3455 (1980).
148. Miyake, Y., Mitsumoto, A., and Teramoto, M., "Stripping Rate of Copper in Copper-SME529 System," *Solv. Extr. Ion Exchange* 2, 1069 (1984).
149. Hummelstedt, L., Paatero, E., Nyberg, T., and Rosenback, L., "Investigation of the Catalytic Mechanism in the Extraction of Copper with Mixtures of the Pure Active Hydroxyoxime Isomers of LIX64N." Proceedings of ISEC '80, 80–73 (1980).
150. Inoue, K., Tomita, S., and Maruuchi, T., "Extraction Kinetics of Nickel with a Hydroxyoxime Extractant," *J. Chem. Eng. Japan* 18, 445 (1985).
151. Ma, E., and Freiser, H., "Mechanistic Studies on the Extraction of Palladium(II) with 2-Hydroxy-5-Nonylbenzophenone Oxime (LIX65N)" *Solv. Extr. Ion Exchange* 1, 485 (1983).
152. Inoue, K., and Maruuchi, T., "Solvent Extraction of Palladium with SME529 Equilibrium and Kinetics" *Hydrometallugy* 16, 93 (1986).
153. Miyake, Y., Okada, A., Wakishige, K., and Teramoto, M., "Extraction Rate of Palladium with 2-Hydroxy-5-Nonylacetophenone Oxime". *Proc. Solv. Extr. Metals* '87, 1987, p. 19.
154. Flett, P. S., Hartlage, J. A., Spink, D. R., and Okuhara, D. N., "The Extraction of Copper by Alkylated 8-Hydroxy Quinoline," *J. Inorg. Nucl. Chem.* 37, 1967 (1975).
155. Sato, T., and Ohishi, H., "Solvent Extraction of Gallium(II) from Sodium Hydroxide Solution by Alkylated Hydroxy-Quinoline," *Hydrometallurgy* 16, 315 (1986).
156. Yoshizuka, K., Kondo, K., and Nakashio, F., "Kinetics of Copper Extraction with N-8-Quinolyl-p-Dodecylbenzene-sulfonamide," *J. Chem. Eng. Japan* 18, 163 (1985).
157. Yoshizuka, K., Kondo, K., and Nakashio, F., "Effect of Hydrophobicity of Extractant on Extraction Kinetics of Copper with N-8-Quinonylsulfonamide" *J. Chem. Eng. Japan* 19, 396 (1986).
158. Yoshizuka, K., Kondo, K., and Nakashio, F., "Kinetics of Stripping of N-8-Quinolyl-p-Dodecylbenzenesulfonamide-Copper Chelate Complex with Hydrochloric Acid," *J. Chem. Eng. Japan* 18, 342, (1985).
159. Paatero, E. Y. O., "The Interaction between Syn- and Anti-Isomers of 2-Hydroxy-5-Nonylbenzophenone Oxime in the Extraction of Copper(II) with LIX65N and LIX64N," *Hydrometallurgy* 11, 135 (1983).
160. Ellender, P. S., and Lawson, G. J., "Kinetic Investigations of the Extraction of Copper from Chloride and Sulphate Media with Commercial Selective Extractants," *J. Appl. Chem. Biotechnol.*, 28, 435 (1978).
161. Astarita, G., *Mass Transfer with Chemical Reaction*, Elsevier Amsterdam, 1967.
162. Mallamace, F., Mogliardo, P., Vasi C., and Wanderlingh, F., "Structure of Water in Microemulsions Investigated by Raman Scattering," *Phys. Chem. Liq.* 11, 47 (1981).

163. Croxton, C. A., *Statistical Mechanics of Liquid Surface* Wiley Rep. Pub. Chicheater (1980).
164. Drost-Hanson, W., "Water at Biological Interfaces-Structural and Functional Aspects," *Phys. Chem. Liq.* 7, 243 (1978).
165. Hanson, C., Hughes, M. A., and Whewell, R. J., "The Rate of Mass Transfer to Single Drops. The Copper Hydroxyoxime System," *J. Appl. Chem. Biotechnol.*, 28, 426 (1978).
166. Rod, V., "Kinetics of Metal Extraction by Chelate Formation Part I, Mass Transfer with a Fast Reversible Chemical Reaction and Product Extraction," *Chem. Eng. J.* 20, 131 (1980).
167. Danesi, P. R., and Chiarizina, R., "The Kinetics of Metal Solvent Extraction," CRC Critical Reviews in Analytical Chemistry (1980).
168. Miyake, Y., "Metal Extraction Rates with Chelating Agents," *Bull. Atomic Energy Inst. Kyoto Univ.* 71, 14 (1987).
169. Freiser, H., and Fernands, Q., *Ionic Equilibria in Analytical Chemistry*, John Wiley & Sons Inc. 1963
170. van der Zeeuw, A. Z., and Kok, R., "Ideas and Practice in the Design of Solvent Extraction Reagents," International Solvent Extraction Conference 77, *CIM Special volume* 21, 17 (1977).
171. Preston, J. S., "Solvent Extraction of Copper(II) with ortho-Hydroxyoxime II Effect of Aliphatic Oximes on Extraction Kinetics," *J. Inorg. Nucl. Chem.*, 42, 441 (1980).
172. Ashbrook, A. W., "Chelating Reagents in Solvent Extraction Process: The Present Position," *Coordination Chemistry Reviews*, 16, 285 (1975).
173. Miller, J. D., and Atwood, R. L., "Discussion of the Kinetics of Copper Solvent Extraction with Hydroxy Oximes," *J. Inorg. Nucl. Chem.*, 37, 2539 (1975).
174. Fleming, C. A., Nicol, M. J., Hancock, R. D., and Finkelstein, N. P., "The Kinetics of the Extraction of Copper by LIX65N and the Catalytic Role of LIX63 in this Reaction," *J. Appl. Chem. Biotech.*, 28, 443 (1978).
175. Kojima, T., and Miyauchi, T., "Catalytic Effect of LIX 63 on Copper Extraction in the LIX63/LIX65N System," *Ind. Eng. Chem. Fundam.*, 21, 220 (1982).
176. Fendler, J. H., and Fendler, E. J., *Catalysis in Micellar and Macromolecular Systems*, Academic press Inc. 1975.
177. Fendler, J. H., *Membrane Mimetic Chemistry*, John Wiley & Sons (1982).
178. Osseo-Asare, K., and Renninger, D. R., "Synergic Extraction of Nickel and Cobalt by LIX63-Dinonylnaphthalene Sulfonic Acid Mixtures," *Hydrometallurgy* 13, 45 (1984).
179. Komasawa, I., and Otake, T., "Extraction of Copper with 2-Hydroxy-5-nonylbenzophenone Oxime and the Catalytic Role of Bis(2-ethylhexyl)phosphoric Acid," *Ind. Eng. Chem. Fundam.* 22, 122, (1983).
180. Morin, E. A., and Peterson, H. D., "Process for Recovering Copper from Aqueous Solutions," *United States Patent No. 3*, 878, 286 (1975).
181. Miyake, Y., Takenoshita, Y., and Teramoto, M., "Extraction Rates of Copper with SME529 Mechanism and Effects of Surfactants," Proceedings of ISEC '83, p. 301, Americal Institute of Chemical Engineers, 1986.
182. Hazen, W. C., Coltrinari, El., "Ion Exchange Process for the Recovery of Metals," *United States Patent No. 3*, 872, 209 (1975).
183. Flett, D. S., and West, D. W., "Extraction of Metal ions by LIX63/Carboxylic acid Mixtures" Proceedings of ISEC '71 p. 214 Society of Chemical Industry, London (1971).
184. Fischman, A. J., Finston, H. L., and Goldberg, D. E., "Further Studies of the Rate Affected Synergic Solvent Extraction of Fe(III)-TTA-I, The Effect of Tri-n-octylphosphine Oxide on the Solvent Extraction of Iron(III) with 2-Thenoyltrifluoroacetone," *J. Inorg. Nucl. Chem.*, 35, 2497 (1973).
185. Raphael, D. M., Finston, H. L., and Fischman, A. J., "Further Studies of the Rate Affected Synergic Solvent Extraction of Fe(III)-TTA-II, The Effect of Tributyl Phosphate on the Extraction of Iron(III) with 2-Thenoyltrifluoroacetone," *J. Inorg. Nucl. Chem.*, 35, 2507, (1973).
186. Akaiwa, H., Kawamoto, H., and Matsumura, T., "Effect of Trioctylmethylammonium Chloride on the Extraction Rate of Iron(III)-TTA Complex. *Nihon Kagakukaishi*, 612 (1979).
187. Miyake, Y., Nishimura, Y., Okabe, H., and Teramoto, M., "Effect of Surfactants on the Extraction Rate of Copper," Proceedings of Sol. Extr. of Metals '81, 1981 p. 57.

188. Finston, H. L., and Inoue, Y., "The Effect of SCN^- on the Extraction of Fe(III)-TTA," *J. Inorg. Nucl. Chem.*, 29, 199 (1967).
189. Finston, H. L., and Inoue, Y., "A Rate Promoted Synergistic Effect on the Solvent Extraction System Fe(III)-TTA-SCN," *J. Inorg. Nucl. Chem.*, 29, 2431, (1967).
190. Dind, A., and Newman, L., "The Formation of the Aqueous Iron(III)-Thenoyltrifluoracetone Complex in Relation to the Uncatalyzed and Chloride Catalyzed Extraction of Iron(III) by Thenoyltrifluoroacetone into Benzene," *J. Inorg. Nucl. Chem.*, 32, 3321 (1970).
191. Tanaka, M., "A Mechanistic Consideration on the Formation Constant of Metal Complexes with Special Reference to Ligand Complexes of Nickel Involving Amines and Aminocarboxylates," *J. Inorg. Nucl. Chem.*, 35, 965 (1973).
192. Edwards, J. O., "Correlation of Relative Rates and Equilibria with a Double Basicity Scale," *J. Amer. Chem. Soc.*, 76, 1540 (1954).
193. Yamada, S., and Tanaka, M., "Softness of Some Metal Ions," *J. Inorg. Nucl. Chem.*, 37, 587 (1975).
194. Funahashi, S., and Tanaka, M., "Kinetics of the Reaction of Some Monoacidopentaaquonickel(II) Complexes with 4-(2-Pridylazo)resorcinol," *Inorg. Chem.*, 8, 2159 (1969).
195. Funahashi, S., and Tanaka, M., "Kinetics and Mechanism of the Ligand Substitution Reactions of the Ethylenediamine-N,N′-Diacetate and Nitrilotriacetate Complexes of Nickel(II) with 4-(2-Pyridylazo)resorcinol," *Inorg. Chem.*, 9, 2092 (1970).

CHAPTER 22

SEPARATION BY GAS-LIQUID CHROMATOGRAPHY

Kyung Ho Row and **Won Kook Lee**

Department of Chemical Engineering
Korea Advanced Institute of Science & Technology
Dongdaemoon, Seoul, Korea

CONTENTS

INTRODUCTION

Gas-liquid chromatography is a separation method based on differences in the partition coefficients of substances distributed between a stationary liquid phase (SLP) and a mobile phase. Since the introduction of the chromatography, over the past 30 years much effort has been made to increase the throughput capabilities.

By use of conventional gas-liquid chromatography, partition coefficients were obtained in terms of column temperature. The feed materials were chosen by close-boiling points as dichloromethane, diethylether, and dimethoxymethane.

In a preparative chromatographic column (I.D. 1 cm), the three close-boiling components were separated with dinonylphtalate-coated Chromosorb A as a SLP and helium as an eluant.

A scaled-up chromatographic system was used to separate the two close-boiling components, diethylether and dichloromethane. The system was composed of 12 segmented columns and 60 solenoids valves controlled by a programmable controller.

From the experimental results, the efficient separation method was that the less-absorbed component was obtained purely in the partition section, the remaining components were separated in a desorption section by an increase in column length, and the whole process was to be finished within a designated time. This new process was developed and used for separating the binary feed materials continuously by the gas-liquid chromatography. Uniqueness of the system was that several columns were added in series in the desorption section to separate the non-eluted components effectively, compared to other continuous chromatographic systems.

The theoretical concentration profiles assumed by uniform film thickness and linear partition equilibrium were in good agreement with the experimental data for the combined continuous and preparative chromatographic system.

The earliest reported experiments that can be regarded as chromatography are those of Tswett [1], who separated the components of plant pigments by passing their solutions through the columns of solid adsorbents. James et al. [2] introduced gas-liquid chromatography in 1952, and it came into being as one of the most powerful analytical tools.

Advantages of chromatography are fast speed of analysis, simplicity of the apparatus, sensitivity of detection [3]. But it is known that chromatography is inherently difficult to scale up on an industrial size for the following reasons [4]:

1. The separating power depends upon thin phases.
2. Conventional chromatography uses the batch method for handling the feed mixture as a pulse, and requires substantial dilution of the components with the mobile phase.
3. It represents a problem of stabilizing the system against mixing or natural convection on scale-up.

Although many works are related to separation by adsorption characteristics [5, 6], which are known as gas-solid chromatography, those by partition (known as gas-liquid chromatography) are comparatively rare [7]. The separation in the partition systems is mainly affected by different solubilities in the SLP. The main advantages of the partition systems over the adsorption are as follows [8]:

1. Easier desorption of the partitioned products.
2. Wider fields of application (for heat-sensitive or high boiling-point liquid mixtures).
3. More-versatile separation system (more availability of stationary liquid phases than adsorbents).

From the start, it was recognized this technology could be used for quantitative separation on an industrial scale. Until now, many attempts have been made to scale up lab-sized chromatography units to treat more substances, and much effort has been put in to make the system a continuous operation.

Continuous chromatographic system may be classified as follows:

1. Moving-bed system
2. Moving-port system
3. Simulated moving-bed system

The simulated moving-bed system is a more complicated apparatus and cannot do multicomponent separations. Thus, modified systems such as moving feed-injection [9, 10], moving product-withdrawal, moving port chromatography [11], and semicontinuous counter-current simulated moving-bed [12] have been developed to increase the throughput from the apparatus.

This chapter investigates the applicability of the uniform film thickness model to the system and usefulness of the scaled-up chromatographic system by simulations as well as the experimental verifications.

PREPARATIVE GAS-LIQUID CHROMATOGRAPHY

Basic Equations

The distribution of SLP on the solid support is seemed to be very complex in the particle because of irregularity of pore size and shape [13] (see Figure 1). Schematic processes of interparticle mass transfer, pore diffusion, and diffusion in SLP and the coordinate of each step are shown in the

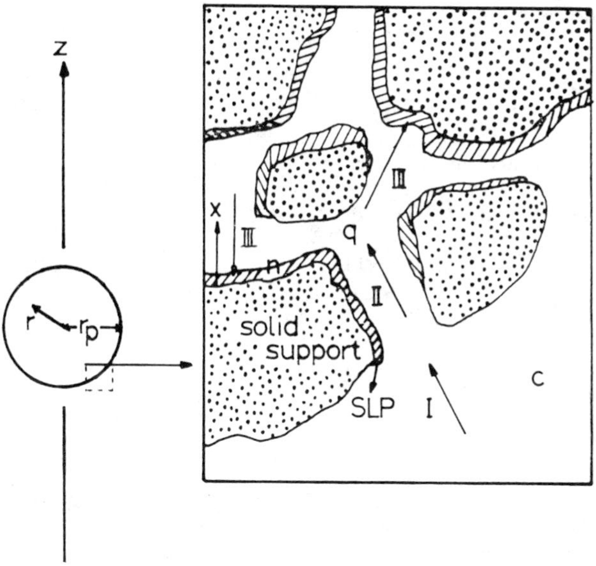

Figure 1. Scheme of pore structure and mass transport processes in gas-liquid chromatography. (I = interparticle mass transfer, II = pore diffusion, III = diffusion in SLP). (Adapted from Ref. 17.)

figure. The assumptions for establishing the governing equations of the processes are:

1. SLP is distributed uniformly on the surface of the inert solid particle.
2. The partition isotherm is linear.
3. Sorption effects for two or more solutes are considered to have no interaction on each other.
4. The pressure drops along the column as well as any effects due to injection of the sample are ignored.
5. Adsorption effects between SLP and the surface in the particle are negligible.
6. The solid particle is assumed to be a sphere.

As the concept of uniform film thickness simplifies the phenomena of SLP-coated porous particle, transient material balances of a solute with three steps are [14, 15]:

$$\frac{\partial c}{\partial t} + u\frac{\partial c}{\partial z} = \frac{E}{\epsilon}\frac{\partial^2 c}{\partial z^2} - \frac{3}{r_p}\frac{1-\epsilon}{\epsilon} D_e \left.\frac{\partial q}{\partial r}\right|_{r=r_p} \tag{1}$$

for the mobile phase,

$$\epsilon_p \frac{\partial q}{\partial t} = D_e \frac{1}{r^2}\frac{\partial}{\partial r}\left(r^2 \frac{\partial q}{\partial r}\right) - A_p k_g\left(q - \frac{n|x=\delta}{K}\right) \tag{2}$$

for the intraparticle phase, and

$$\frac{\partial n}{\partial t} = D_1 \frac{\partial^2 n}{\partial x^2} \tag{3}$$

for the SLP.

The initial and boundary conditions are:

$$c = q = n = 0 \qquad \text{(for } t = 0, z > 0) \tag{4}$$

$$c = c_0(t) \qquad \text{(for } t > 0, z = 0) \tag{5}$$

$$c = \text{finite} \qquad \text{(for } t > 0, z \to \infty) \tag{6}$$

$$\frac{\partial q}{\partial r} = 0 \qquad \text{(for } t > 0, r = 0) \tag{7}$$

$$\frac{\partial n}{\partial x} = 0 \qquad \text{(for } t > 0, x = 0) \tag{8}$$

$$D_e \frac{\partial q}{\partial r} = k_f(c - q) \qquad \text{(for } t > 0, r = r_p) \tag{9}$$

$$D_1 \frac{\partial n}{\partial x} = k_g\left(q - \frac{n}{K}\right) \qquad \text{(for } t > 0, x = \delta) \tag{10}$$

It is assumed that the partition effect is dominant to that of adsorption with a linear equilibrium isotherm. The solution of Equation 1 to Equation 10 in the Laplace domain is [16, 17]

$$C(s) = C_0(s) \exp\left(\frac{L}{2}\left[\frac{u_0}{E} - \left\{\left(\frac{u_0}{E}\right)^2 + 4\lambda\right\}^{1/2}\right]\right) \tag{11}$$

at the bed exit, z = L, where

$$\lambda = \frac{\epsilon}{E}\left(s + \frac{3(1-\epsilon)}{r_p \epsilon} k_f \left\{1 - \frac{\sinh(\lambda_2 r_p)}{r_p} \lambda_1\right\}\right) \tag{12}$$

$$\lambda_1 = \frac{r_p k_f}{D_e \lambda_2 \cosh(\lambda_2 r_p) + \left(k_f - \frac{D_e}{r_p}\right) \sinh(\lambda_2 r_p)} \tag{13}$$

$$\lambda_2 = \left(\frac{1}{D_e}\left[\{\epsilon_p s + A_p k_g\} - \frac{A_p k_g^2 \cosh \lambda_3}{D_e K \sqrt{\frac{s}{D_1}} \lambda_3 + D_e k_g \cosh \lambda_3}\right]\right)^{1/2} \tag{14}$$

$$\lambda_3 = \delta \sqrt{\frac{s}{D_1}} \tag{15}$$

The solution of Equations 1–10 in the Laplace domain with the dimensionless groups is

$$\bar{\psi}(s) = \frac{1}{s} \exp\left\{\frac{1}{2}(P_e - \sqrt{P_e^2 + 4\lambda_4})\right\} \tag{16}$$

at the bed exit, z = L, where

$$\lambda_4 = \{s + S_t(1 - \lambda_5 \sinh \lambda_6)\}P_e \tag{17}$$

$$\lambda_5 = B_i/\{\lambda_6 \cosh \lambda_6 - \sinh \lambda_6 + B_i \sinh \lambda_6\} \tag{18}$$

$$\lambda_6 = \left\{P_i(s + S_t M) - \frac{B_i M \sqrt{S_t} M \sqrt{P_i} \cosh(\sqrt{P_i s})}{B_i M \cosh \sqrt{P_1 s} + K\sqrt{P_1 s} \sinh \sqrt{P_1 s}}\right\}^{1/2} \tag{19}$$

The solutions in the frequency domain are obtained by substituting $s = j\omega$ in the s-domain, and the frequency response is computed as the magnitude and phase of the impulse response in the Fourier transformed system,

$$C(s)_{s=j\omega} = R + jI \tag{20}$$

then

$$m(\omega) = |G(j\omega)| = \sqrt{R^2 + I^2} \tag{21}$$

$$\phi(\omega) = \text{angle } G(j\omega) = \arctan(I/R) \tag{22}$$

If the objective function, ψ_{obj}, is defined as

$$\psi_{obj} = \int_0^\infty \{f_0(t) - f_p(t)\}^2 \, dt \tag{23}$$

and using the Parseval theorem, it becomes

$$\psi_{obj} = \frac{1}{\pi} \int_0^\infty |F_0(j\omega) - F_p(j\omega)| \, d\omega \tag{24}$$

$$= \frac{1}{\pi} \int_0^\infty [\{R_0(\omega) - R_p(\omega)\}^2 + \{I_0(\omega) - I_p(\omega)\}^2] \, d\omega \tag{25}$$

Thus, minimization of ψ_{obj} minimizes simultaneously both the integral of squared scalar distance between data and model in the time domain, and the integral of the squared vector distance between data and model in the frequency domain.

Determination of Fixed Parameters

The column was packed with Chromosorb A obtained from Alltech Associates (U.S.A.). The particles have good capacity to hold SLP, and are not easily broken down with handling, so it is mainly used for large-scale chromatographic separation [18]. Table 1 shows characteristics of the solid support [19].

The Chromosorb A of three particle sizes (r_p = 0.0001, 0.000136, and 0.000314 m) selected from 60/80, 45/60, and 20/30 mesh commercially obtained were used. Average particle sizes were determined by screen analysis. Interparticle porosity was assumed to be 0.41 for all three particle sizes (20).

The intraparticle porosity of uncoated porous particle was estimated as;

$$\epsilon'_p = 1 - \frac{\rho_{app}}{\rho_{true}} \tag{26}$$

Table 1
Characteristics of Chromosorb A

Properties	Chromosorb A
Color	pink
Type	flux-calcined
Density (kg/m^3)	
loose weight	400
packed weight	480
Surface area (m^2/kg)	2,700
(m^2/m^3)	1,300,000
Maximum liquid loading	25%
pH	7.1
Handling characteristics	good

Apparent density, measured by a mercury porosimeter at atmospheric pressure, was 0.5, 0.5, and 0.78 g/cm^3 for 60/80, 45/60, and 20/30 mesh, respectively. True density of Chromosorb A was fixed as 2.3 g/cm^3.

Figure 2 shows schematic representation of porous particle. From the figure,

$$V = V' - \delta A \tag{27}$$

divided by V_{tot}, then

$$\text{so} \quad \frac{V}{V_{tot}} = \frac{V'}{V_{tot}} - \frac{\delta A}{V_{tot}} \tag{28}$$

$$\text{that is} \quad \epsilon_p = \epsilon'_p - \delta A_p \tag{29}$$

$$\text{where} \quad A_p = A/V_{tot} \tag{30}$$

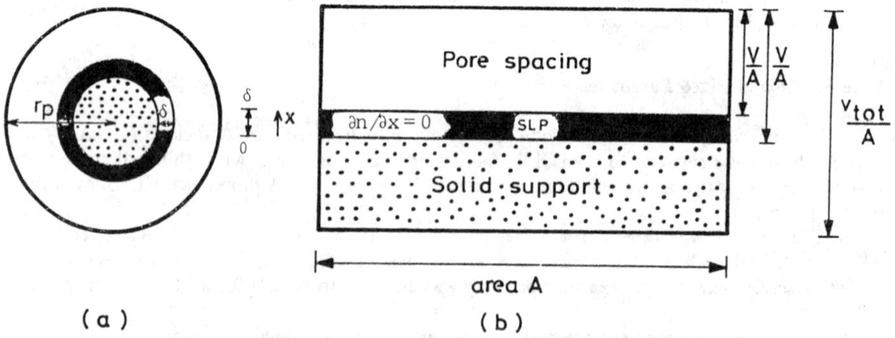

Figure 2. Schematic representation of porous particle. (a) = particle, (b) = SLP on surface of particle. (Reprinted with permission of Ref. 16.)

Table 2
Intraparticle Porosity with Particle Size and % Liquid Loading

% Liquid Loading	60/80 Mesh	45/60 Mesh	20/30 Mesh
0	0.78	0.78	0.66
15	0.69	0.69	0.57
20	0.66	0.66	0.54
25	0.62	0.62	0.50

Assuming that SLP was spread with uniform film thickness, δ can be calculated as follows [21]:

$$\delta = \frac{W_L}{\rho_L A_s W_s} \tag{31}$$

Therefore, the intraparticle porosity of SLP-coated porous particle with uniform thickness, ϵ_p, could be obtained. Table 2 shows the intraparticle porosity for the three particle sizes and % liquid loading. The calculated film thickness were 0.067, 0.095, and 0.127 m for 15%, 20%, and 25% liquid loading, respectively.

The partition coefficient may be related to the corrected retention volume and the column packing, and its relation is derived as [22];

$$K = \frac{V_N}{V_L} = \frac{\text{net retention volume}}{\text{volume of SLP}} \tag{32}$$

where $V_N = (\text{retention volume} - \text{air retention volume}) \times J$

Figure 3 indicates that retention volumes were independent from the solute concentration in inlet flow. For different temperatures, the partition coefficients were obtained by measuring the volume of SLP.

Littlewood [23] showed that a plot of log K vs. 1/T for a component was linear and that the slope of this plot was a function of the heat of solution. Therefore, the effect of the column temperature on the partition coefficient can be correlated by the following exponential term:

$$K = K_0 \exp(-\Delta H_s/R_G T) \tag{33}$$

where $-\Delta H_s$(J/mol) = heat of solution
R_G(J/mol k) = gas constant

Figure 4 shows the effect of the column temperature on the partition coefficient, and the linear regressions give the following correlation [24];

$$K_{DCM} = 2.98 \times 10^{-3} \exp(3545/T) \tag{34}$$

$$K_{DEE} = 1.67 \times 10^{-3} \exp(3460/T) \tag{35}$$

$$K_{DMM} = 2.31 \times 10^{-3} \exp(3470/T) \tag{36}$$

Diffusion coefficients and rate coefficients were estimated by the equations listed in Table 3.

Parameter Estimations in the Frequency Domain

Each of the response curves was fit to the transient material balance with the two adjustable parameters, E and D_e. Fourier analysis was used to estimate the parameters. Because of high flow

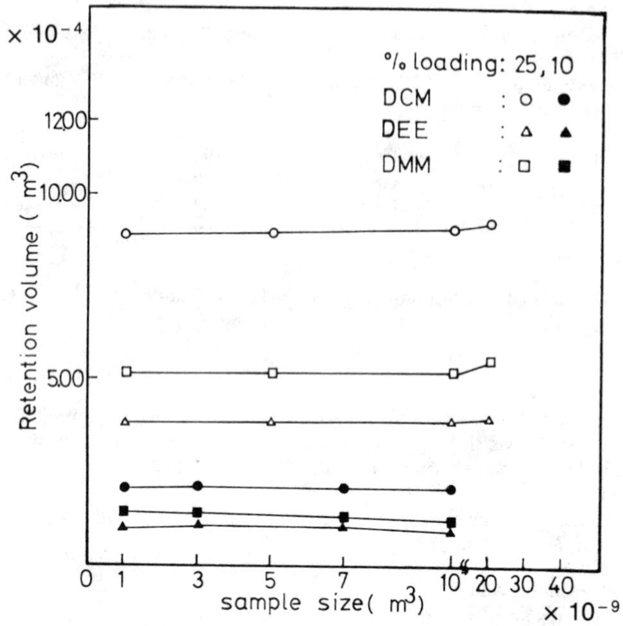

Figure 3. Effect of sample size on retention volume. (45/60 mesh, L = 4.00 m, 55°C).

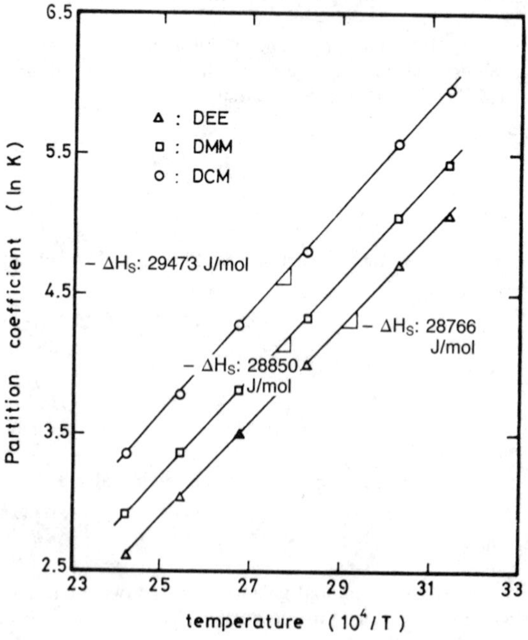

Figure 4. Effect of column temperature on partition coefficient. (Reprinted with permission of Ref. 16.)

Table 3
Fixed Parameters Used in this Work

Parameter [Ref.]	Relation
D_M [25] (m^2/sec)	$D_M = \dfrac{0.0150\, T^{1.81}}{P(T_{CN_2}T_{Ci})^{0.1405}(V_{CN_2}^{0.4} + V_{Ci}^{0.4})^2} \times \sqrt{\dfrac{1}{M_{N_2}} + \dfrac{1}{M_i}}$
D_1 [26] (m^2/sec)	$D_1 = 7.4 \times 10^{-8} \dfrac{(\phi M_B)^{1/2}\, T}{\eta_B V_A^{0.6}}$
k_f [27] (m/sec)	$k_f = \dfrac{D_M}{r_p}(1 + 0.725\, Re^{1/2}\, Sc^{1/3})$
k_g [28] (m/sec)	$k_g = \dfrac{12.5\, D_M}{r_p}\left(\dfrac{1-\epsilon_p}{\epsilon_p}\right)$

rate in this system, the effect of superficial velocity of eluant may be large. It is possible to estimate external tortuosity, η_{ext}, from impulse-injection tests at different superficial velocities of eluant and particle sizes using the following relation [29]:

$$E = \eta_{ext} D_M + r_p u_0 \tag{37}$$

The results showed that the η_{ext} strongly depended on the superficial velocity of eluant as in Table 4. This result was obviously inconsistent to the fact that η_{ext} should be constant in a specified system.

Table 4
Results of η_{ext} from Frequency Domain Analysis of DCM

L (cm)	$r_p \times 10^{-4}$ (m)	$u_0 \times 10^{-2}$ (m/sec)	η_{ext}
0.75	1.36	7.73	1.26
		4.08	0.70
		2.43	0.45
0.50	3.13	6.28	1.05
		4.54	1.04
		2.65	0.85
0.50	1.36	5.77	1.08
		4.11	0.88
		2.13	0.45
0.50	1.00	5.07	0.85
		4.99	0.82
		2.82	0.32
0.25	1.36	3.71	0.68
		2.58	0.40
		1.51	0.23

Reprinted with permission of Ref. [16].

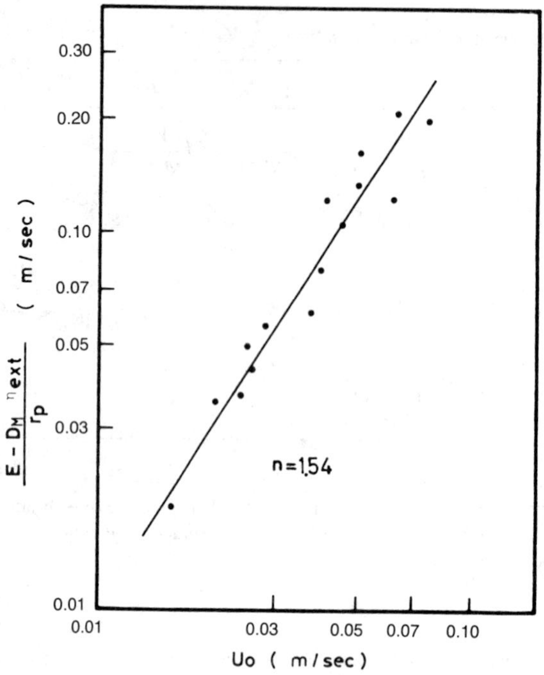

Figure 5. Effect of superficial velocity of eluant on $\log\left(\frac{E - D_M\eta_{ext}}{r_p}\right)$. (Reprinted with permission of Ref. 16.)

Also, considering the finding of Hsiang and Haynes [30, 31] that the effect of the velocity was not linear to the axial dispersion coefficient at high Reynolds numbers, the following form of the coefficient was adopted for modification of Equation 37:

$$E = 0.71D_M + r_p u_0^n \tag{38}$$

Figure 5 shows that $\log(E - 0.71D_M/r_p)$ vs. $\log u_0$ plot with $\eta_{ext} = 0.71$, the average value of the external tortuosities in Table 4. From the slope of the plot, n was found to be 1.54. The fact of n greater than unity seems to be attributed to the increased average velocity from the drop pressure caused by fine particles.

The intraparticle diffusion coefficient for DCM was obtained as about 2.00×10^{-7} m^2/sec, for DEE 1.00×10^{-7} m^2/sec, and for DMM 1.19×10^{-7} m^2/sec.

The liquid film with the assumption of uniform thickness at 25% liquid loading was determined to be 0.127 μm from Equation 31. But effective liquid film thickness calculated on the basis of the relationship between HETP and superficial velocity of eluant from the van Deemter equation for a sorbent was 16 μm.

The greater effective film thickness found from the van Deemter equation seemed to be a result of the interpretation that a major portion of the SLP filled smaller pores and the other left the wider pores unwetted [32]. But usually the pore diameter of diatomaceous earth ranged from 1 to 10 μm [21], and this means that the film thickness from the van Deemter equation is greater than the pore size. When the surface area of porous particle per unit volume, A_p, is 1,300,000 m^2/m^3, as in this case, Equation 29 was not satisfied with this larger thickness because ϵ_p would be negative value. For packed column, the ratio of fraction occupied by SLP to that by mobile phase normally lies between 0.2 and 0.028. In this work, the values of 0.09187 for 45/60 and 60/80 mesh, and 0.19832 for 20/30 mesh in the condition of uniform film thickness, explain the distribution of SLP in uniform film thickness is better than that from the van Deemter equation.

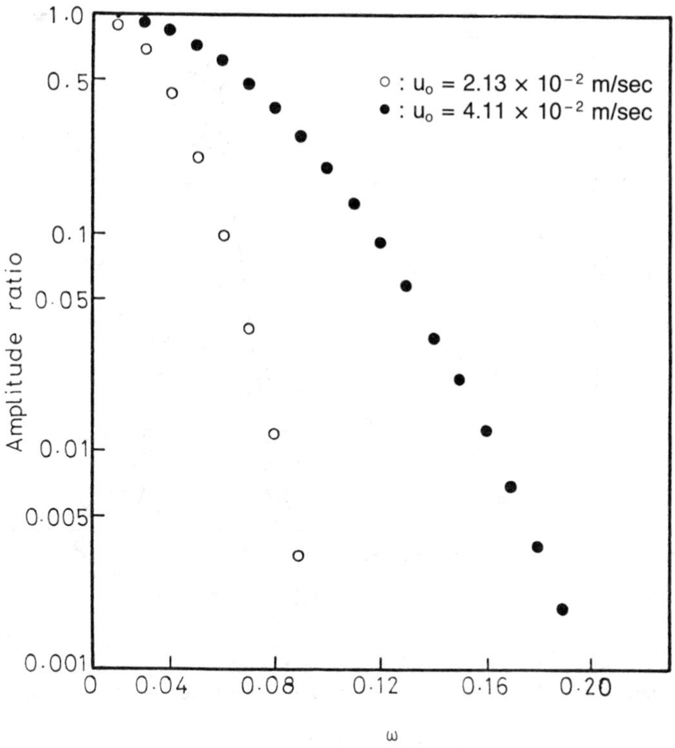

Figure 6. Amplitude ratio for DCM. (45/60 mesh, L = 0.50 m). (Reprinted with permission of Ref. 15.)

Rotavapor was used to coat SLP on the Chromosorb A in this experiment. Even though this coating method was used, it might be thought that the SLP were not coated uniformly on the surface of the porous support. It seems that distribution of the SLP is very complicated. Therefore, the relevant model for describing the distribution of SLP is necessary to investigate the characteristics of gas-liquid chromatographic column.

By the nature of interaction of SLP with the solid support, physical properties of the SLP, the technique used to prepare the sorbent, and subsequent treatment, the SLP may be distributed over the surface of the solid support in the form of continuous film or dropwise. But relatively higher liquid loading (20% in the work) gave good assurance that the form of dropwise did not likely exist (usually, dropwise exists at less than 10% liquid loading). The only way to ensure the uniformity of SLP-thickness is to compare the calculated values from the model equations with the experimental data in the time domain.

In a chromatographic column, the mean residence time of carrier gas decreased with the increase in the flow rate [15]. In such a case, the maximum frequency, ω_{max}, was also increased because of the large amplitude ratio (Figure 6).

Sensitivity analyses of the response curves with respect to $S_t(k_f)$ and $S_tM(k_g)$ gave useful indications of how these parameters influenced to the shape of the curves. The effect of the intraparticle film resistance on the response curve is illustrated in Figure 7, from which it is found that the effect was not greatly influenced when the dimensionless group, S_t, was greater than about 1,500. Curve II was obtained by using the interparticle mass transfer coefficient calculated from the equation in Table 3.

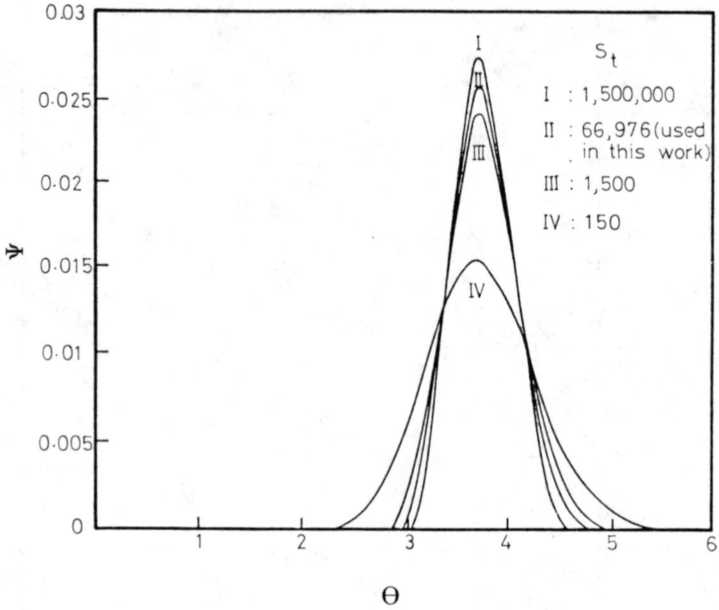

Figure 7. Dependence of the response curve upon the interparticle mass transfer coefficient, k_f. (45/60 mesh, $u_0 = 2.13 \times 10^{-2}$ m/sec, L = 0.50 m, DMM). (Reprinted with permission of Ref. 15.)

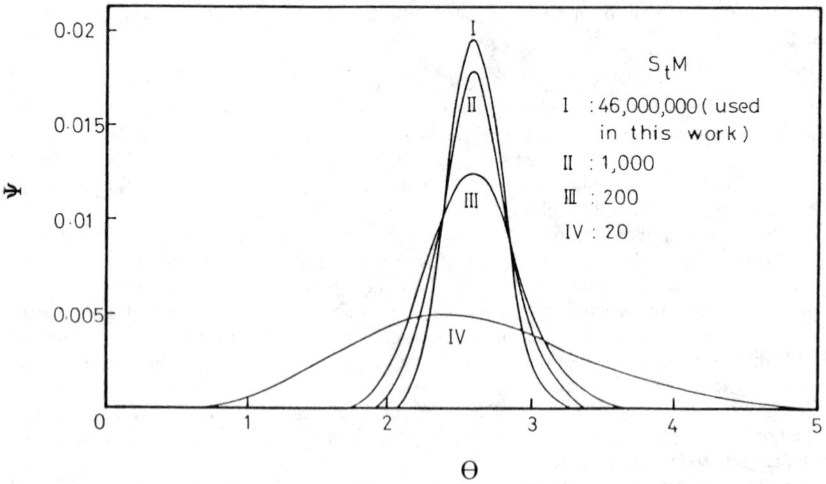

Figure 8. Dependence of the response curve upon the intraparticle mass transfer coefficient, k_g. (45/60 mesh, $u_0 = 2.13 \times 10^{-2}$ m/sec, L = 0.50 m, DEE). (Reprinted with permission of Ref. 15.)

Figure 8 shows the effect of the intraparticle film resistance on the response curve. Decrease in the dimensionless group, S_tM, gáve progressively broader peak in response curve. The theoretical Curve I was obtained by using the intraparticle mass transfer coefficient for this work. The shape of the theoretical curve was not changed even though the dimensionless group S_tM approached infinity. It was known that the interparticle and intraparticle film resistance to the second moment of the frequency was linearly additive [14]. So it could be concluded that the liquid film resistance was small and the diffusion in the SLP was not a rate-determining step.

Effect of Operating Conditions on Resolution

The resolution between the chromatographic curves of component 1 and 2 is given by [18]:

$$\text{Res} = \frac{2(b_2 - b_1)}{a_2 + a_1} \tag{39}$$

where a and b are peak width in unit of volume and retention volume, respectively.

Superficial velocity of eluant and column length are mainly influenced by the resolution between the given two components [33]. Two resolutions between DEE and DMM, and between DEE and DCM were respectively considered.

Figure 9 shows the comparisons between experimental and calculated resolutions with changes in column length. For 0.25 m and 0.5 m of column lengths, differences between experimental and

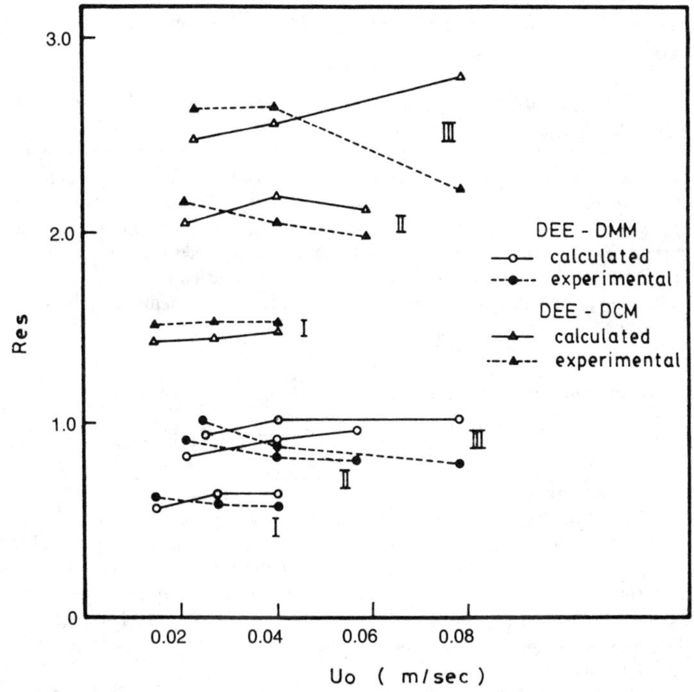

Figure 9. Comparison between experimental and calculated resolution. (45/60 mesh, (I) L = 0.25 m, (II) L = 0.50 m, (III) L = 0.75 m). (Reprinted with permission of Ref. 16.)

calculated values were relatively small, while for 0.75-m column length, the deviations of the calculated from experimental values were large at 7.73×10^{-2} m/sec. That is, the resolution was worse at longer column and higher superficial velocity of eluant. As basic model equations in this work ignored the pressure drop, the superficial velocity of eluant was treated as constant along the column. However, for larger pressure drop in an actual column, superficial velocity of eluant would not be constant. If the pressure-velocity product is said to be a constant at uniform flow rate and column temperature, as an ideal gas, the velocity at the end of the column differs from that at the inlet of the column. The deviation in Figure 9 can be explained that the calculation of resolutions were done as the constant velocity, while experimental value were measured at the inlet velocity into the column.

For instance, in 0.75 m column packed with 45/60 mesh size and 7.73×10^{-2} m/sec, pressure drop along the column was measured as 16,000 N/m^2, so that the outlet velocity increased to 8.95×10^{-2} m/sec with the assumption of constant pressure-velocity product. Therefore, in a large pressure drop caused by a longer column, finer particle size, and higher flow rate, average superficial velocity of eluant at inlet and outlet must be used. The average velocity is usually calculated by $u_{ave} = Ju_0$, and correction factor J is defined by

$$J = \frac{3\{(P_i/Po)^2 - 1\}}{2\{(P_i/Po)^3 - 1\}} \tag{40}$$

Generally, as a longer column is used, a considerable time is required to separate completely, and when achieved, the outlet streams might be so dilute as to be undetectable.

COMBINED CONTINUOUS AND PREPARATIVE CHROMATOGRAPHIC SEPARATION

Much interest has been aroused over the years in the use of chromatography as a method of handling large preparative-scale separations (34).

The most direct scale-up was to increase the size of the column in diameter and length. The research and development works have concentrated on column design and packing techniques [35, 36]. But, as the dimension of the column is increased, the efficiency is decreased sharply [37]. Another approach is to achieve a continuous separation of a feed mixture into each component by a counter-current flow of mobile phase and stationary phase. Based on the counter-current flow, simulated moving beds (UOP process) have been developed and used on a commercial size [38].

After the introduction of the UOP process, considerable developments have been made toward the separation using the continuous chromatography.

Operational Principles of the System (39)

This chapter introduces a new separation method in which the feed mixtures (binary) are separated continuously with the combined operation of the continuous and preparative chromatography in two sections, partition and desorption sections.

As a feed mixture is injected into the column, the less-absorbed component is eluted initially by the solubility difference of the feed mixture to the SLP. After a while, as the more-absorbed component also begins to be eluted, the components whose composition are same as the feed mixture come out from the column. As observed in Figure 10, the less-absorbed component for the time being exists in a pure product (the portion of inclined lines in the figure). The normalized concentration used in the system means the ratio of the concentration of a component in the mobile phase to that at the inlet of the column, c/c_0.

If the column in the system is divided into two sections, the less-absorbed component can be obtained purely before the elution of the more-absorbed component in one of the sections (partition section). During that time, in the other section (desorption section) the less-absorbed component that remained in the column with the more-absorbed component can be separated by adjusting the

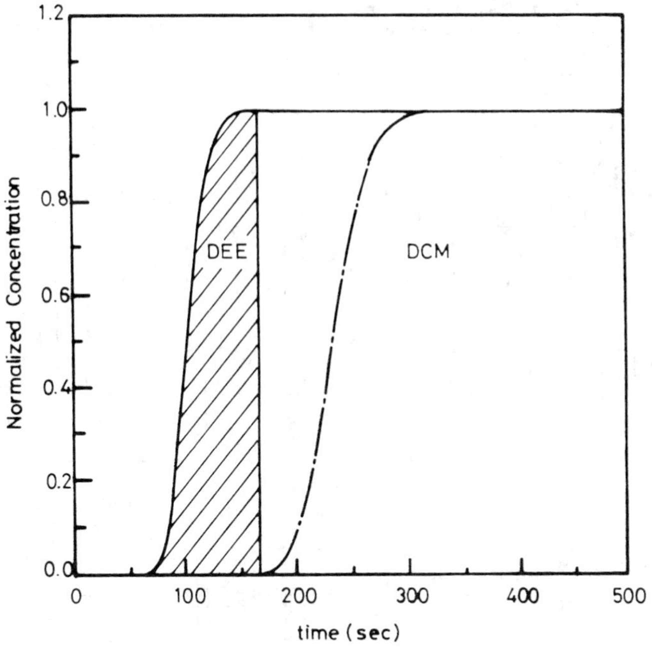

Figure 10. Theoretical concentration profile in case of step input. (20/30 mesh, 35°C, $u_0 = 9.53 \times 10^{-2}$ m/sec, L = 1.00 m, 20% liquid loading).

additional column length and desorbent velocity. If these two steps can be completed simultaneously within a certain time (switching time), the feed mixture can be separated continuously. The switching time is varied by the characteristic combination of the stationary liquid and the feed mixtures. In the desorption section the remained components should be separated within the switching time by change of the operating conditions.

Figure 11 shows the arrangement of segmented columns and solenoid valves in the equipment for the operating principle. During the operation, two streams—carrier gas with feed and desorbent—enter the system, and the two streams are withdrawn through the partition section and the desorption section.

The system is binary separation process, but by the careful selection of SLP and the operating conditions it can be extended to various feed mixtures.

Experimental Equipments and Results

A general view of the main system is shown in Figure 12 and schematic diagram of the overall experimental apparatus is shown in Figure 13 [40]. Nitrogen was used as the carrier gas and the desorbent. The flow rates were controlled by the microneedle valves (A_4, A_5). The carrier gas and the desorbent were put into the main chromatographic system (I) through preheaters (F) and heating wires (H) with desired temperatures.

The feed reservoir (C) was made of stainless-steel, 6-cm I.D., 50-cm height, and filled with 1/8-in. and 1/2-in. ceramic Raschig rings to enlarge the interfacial area between the carrier gas and the liquid feed mixtures.

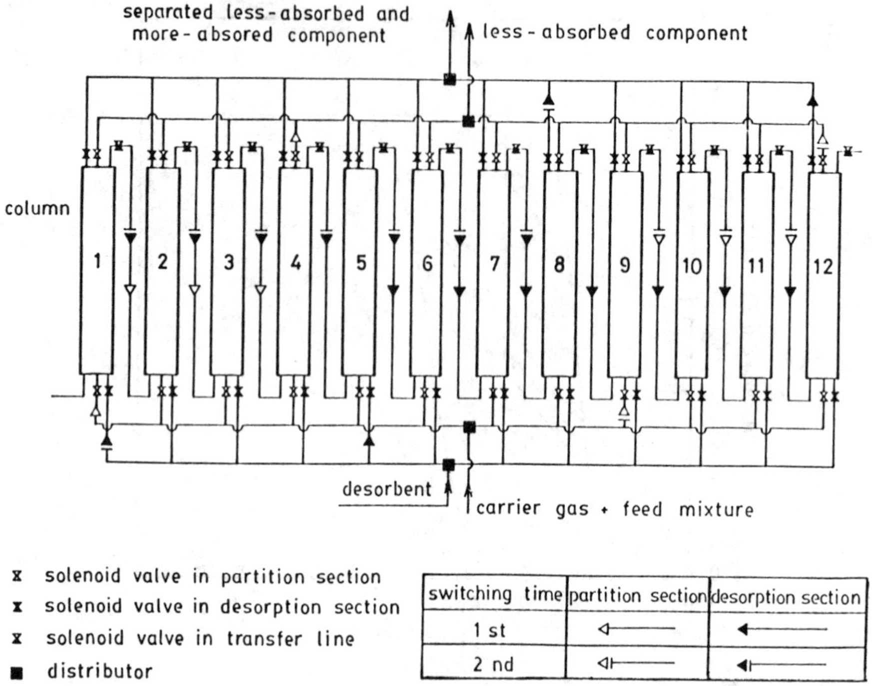

Figure 11. Schematic diagram of combined continuous and preparative chromatographic beds. (Reprinted with permission of Ref. 39.)

Twelve columns were arranged in a circular form. The column was made of stainless-steel, 1-cm I.D., 30-cm height, and the packed height was 25 cm. In both ends of the column, glass wool was used for solid particles retained in place. Each column had 4 openings, 2 for entering streams and 2 for withdrawing streams, and it was covered with ceramic insulation to keep the column temperature constant.

All the lines were made of 1/8-in. copper tube to reduce the dead volume in the system and tygon tube was used in the connection part to prevent possibility of the gas leakage.

Five solenoid valves (CKD, AB31-01-4) were used for each column (see Figure 14). A supporter was made to fix the 12 columns, 60 solenoid valves, and 4 distributors, and was enclosed with covers to maintain desired temperature in the system. The 4 distributors (see Figure 15), 2 for the entering streams and 2 withdrawing streams, were set up. Each distributor formed a cylindrical type whose upperside had one central bore, and the side of the distributors had twelve screwed openings. The entering stream passed through the central bore and put into one of the openings in the distributor, and it entered to the inlet of the column through the solenoid valve connected to the opening. Conversely, through the solenoid valve from the outlet of the column, the withdrawing stream was collected through one of the openings and the central bore in the distributor, and this was sent for analysis.

An electric heater (P) in circular form was set in the inner side of the main system (I) to change the column temperature easily. Two outlet streams and inlet feed mixtures were analyzed by a conventional gas chromatograph (Gow Mac 550P thermal conductivity detector, L_1 and L_2) with a syringe (Hamilton Co.) and 10-port multi-functional sampling valves (Valco Instruments Co., **M**),

Figure 12. Photograph of the chromatographic unit.

in which desired amount of samples were taken and transferred to the chromatograph. The sampling valve was used to measure the outlet concentrations of the components in the carrier gas and the desorbent alternately. Figure 16 shows the flow path used in this experiment. A single carrier inlet, column, and detector were employed as shown in the figure. This technique replaced a 4-port selector valve and 6-port sampling valve. The signal was analyzed by HP 3390 A integrator.

A programmable controller (J) was used to control the solenoid valves used for the main chromatographic system (I), and it consisted of 6 parts. These were the input, which could receive the program of the flow paths. Transistor Transistor Logic (TTL) RAM, a counter for presettable time of 5 to 600 sec, a logic gate for turning to a next step after a switching time, a relay to control the solenoid valves, and the display.

Total elution volumes of the mixture, DEE and DCM, are plotted with the feed concentration and the column temperature in Figure 17. The volume is the quantity of the gas that can elute the components completely in the length of the column. It is shown that the slope of each component is distinguishable. Although the slope of elution profile of DEE was low and that of DCM was

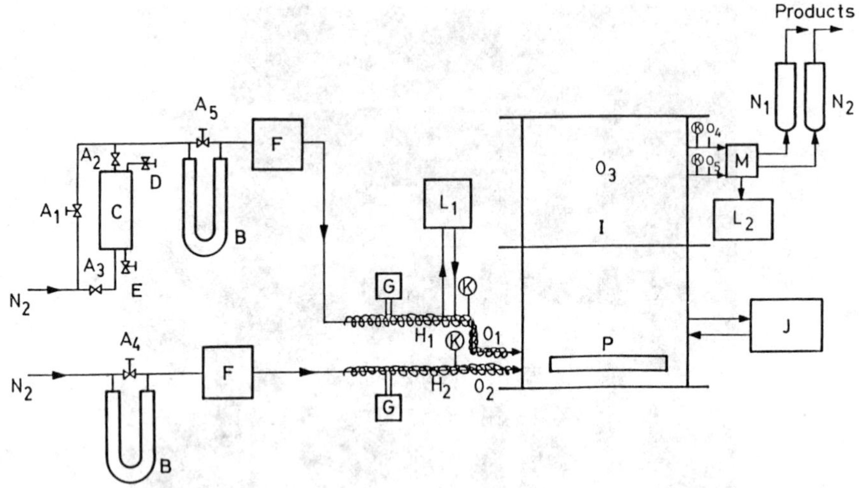

Figure 13. Schematic diagram of experimental apparatus. A_1, A_4, A_5—microneedle valves; A_2, A_3—solenoid valves; B—manometers for adjustment of flow rates; C—feed reservoir; D—inlet of feed; E—outlet of feed; F—preheaters for carrier gas and desorbent; G—temperature controllers; H_1, H_2—heating wires; I—main chromatographic system; J—programmable controller; K—pressure gauge; L_1, L_2—gas chromatographs; M—multi-functional sampling valves; N_1, N_2—bubble flow meters for carrier gas and desorbent; 0_1–0_3—thermocouples; P—electric heaters. (Reprinted with permission of Ref. 39.)

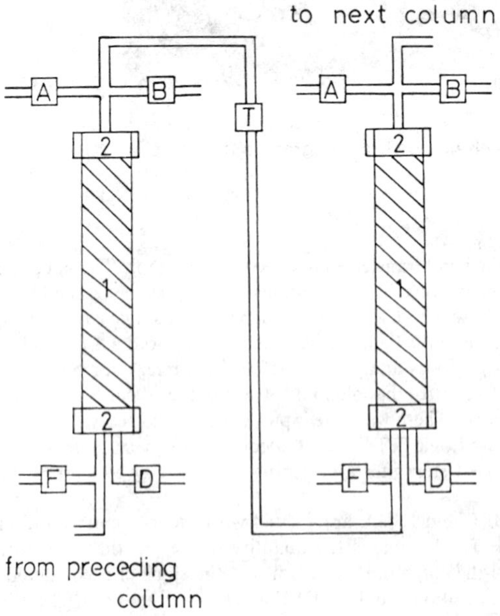

Figure 14. Schematic arrangement of solenoid valves per column. (A, B = valves for outlet streams, D = for desorbent, F = for feed stream, T = for transfer line, l = packed column, 2 = glass wool).

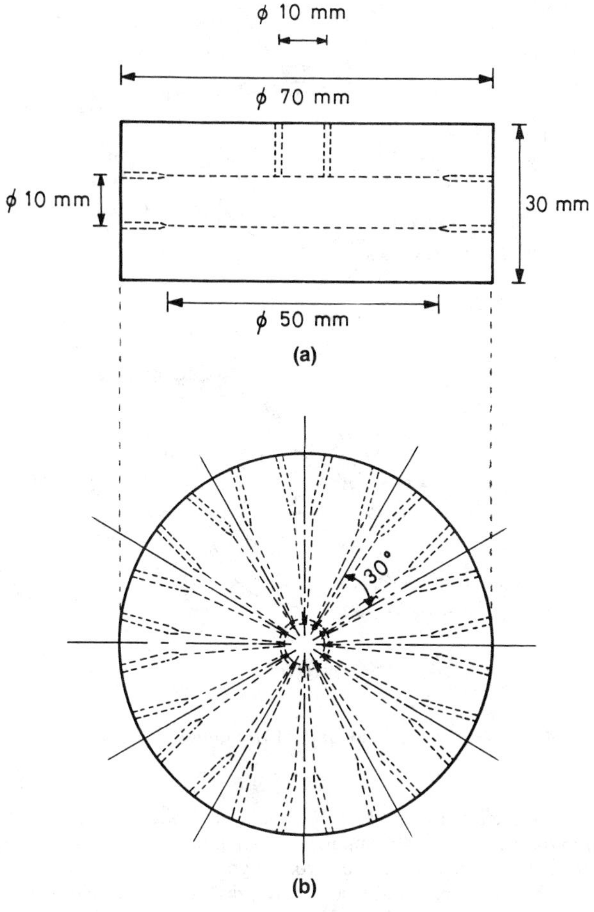

Figure 15. Construction and dimensions distributor. (a) side-view, (b) top-view.

high, the bandwidth of the components was observed to be wider with increasing the feed concentration and decreasing the columnn temperature, which resulted from the limited capacity of vaporization when the more feed mixtures were injected.

In order to examine the applicability of this system over a wide range of operating conditions, the outlet concentrations of DEE and DCM were measured, and the concentration profiles of the components in each experimental runs were obtained. Experimental conditions of some runs in the partition section are listed in Table 5, in which the peak width in unit of second is defined by the time elapsed from start to reach the feed concentration.

The stationary liquid should be chosen to have as high a selectivity with feed materials as possible. Once the system was determined, the switching time could be experimentally obtained as the elapsed time from the start to just before the elution of the more-absorbed component, DCM. Experimental runs in the desorption section were performed (see Table 6), after the same average carrier velocity was applied in the partition section. As seen in Table 6, the column temperature and the column length had mainly affected the switching time. Experimental conditions of some

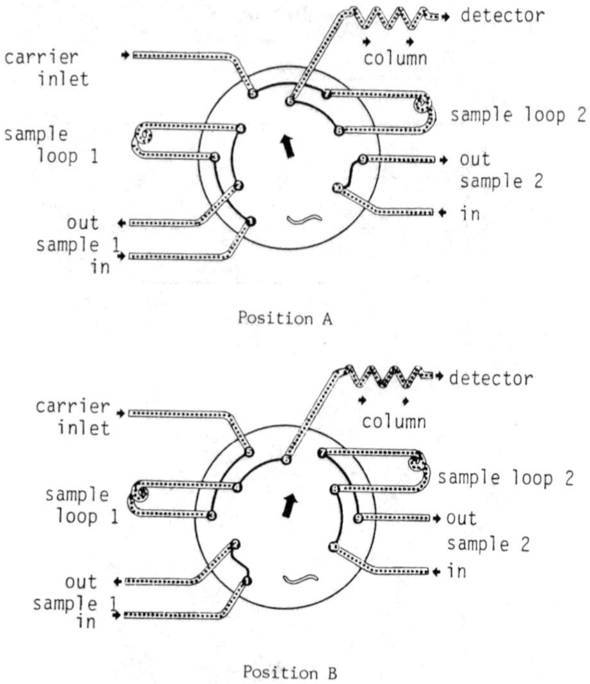

Figure 16. Flow path of two outlet streams.

runs in the desorption section are listed in the table to understand the effects of the unseparated DEE and DCM in the section, and the impurity shown in the table is defined by the ratio of overlapped section to the total areas of the two chromatograms.

Figure 18 shows that this separation method can prevent the possibility of the more-absorbed component eluted in the partition section, and increase the resolution of the two components in the desorption section by using the additional column length [41].

Mathematical Models [17]

The usual method of operating fixed beds for preparative scale is to use a large pulse of feed input to the column followed by a longer period of flow of carrier gas. In case of pulse input, $C_0(s)$ has the following form:

$$C_0(s) = \frac{1 - e^{-st_0}}{s} \tag{41}$$

where t_0 = time of feed-injection, then Equation 11 becomes

$$C(s) = \frac{1 - e^{-st_0}}{s} \exp\left(\frac{L}{2}\left\{\frac{u_0}{E} - \left[\left(\frac{u_0}{E}\right)^2 + 4\lambda\right]^{1/2}\right\}\right) \tag{42}$$

Equation 42 can be used to describe the less-absorbed component in the partition section.

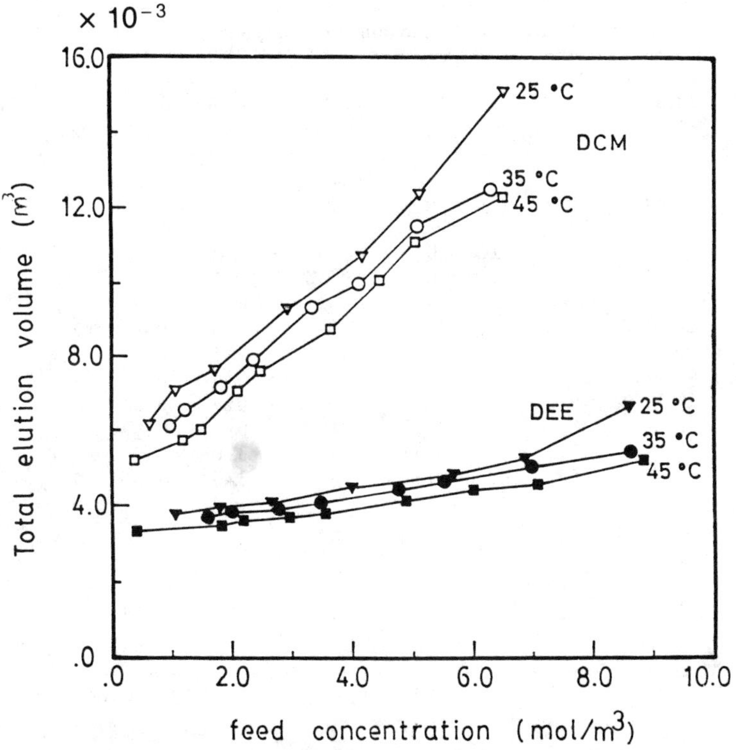

Figure 17. Effect of feed concentration on total elution volume with column temperature. (20/30 mesh, $u_{ave} = 9.53 \times 10^{-2}$ m/sec, L = 1.00 m, t_0 = 300 sec). (Reprinted with permission of Ref. 39.)

Table 5
Experimental Conditions in Partition Section

Run #	Mesh Size	Column Temp. (°C)	L (m)	u_{ave} ($\times 10^{-2}$ m/sec)	c_θ (mol/m^3) DEE	DCM	Peak Width of DEE (sec)
1	20/30	45	1.00	9.53	0.99	0.89	113.8
2	45/60	45	1.00	8.76	0.98	0.91	98.9
3	60/80	45	1.00	7.70	0.99	0.88	87.2
4	60/80	45	1.50	8.47	1.35	1.28	97.0
5	60/80	45	1.50	7.35	1.35	1.29	110.6
6	60/80	45	1.50	5.23	1.34	1.31	112.2
7	20/30	45	1.50	9.09	0.90	0.88	100.0
8	20/30	35	1.50	9.09	3.40	0.90	63.0
9	20/30	35	1.50	9.09	0.90	0.91	169.6
10	20/30	35	1.50	9.09	0.88	0.89	265.2

Reprinted with permission of Ref. [39].

Table 6
Experimental Conditions in Desorption Section

Run #	Mesh Size	Col. Temp. (°C)	L (m)	L′ (m)	u_{ave} ($\times 10^{-2}$, m/sec)	c_0 (mol/m³) DEE	DCM	SW (sec)	Impurity (%)
11	45/60	35	1.00	0.	12.41	0.92	0.70	240	28.7
12	45/60	35	1.50	0.	10.22	0.94	0.75	360	18.3
13	60/80	45	1.00	0.	13.03	0.94	0.78	180	13.1
14	45/60	45	1.00	0.	12.62	0.98	0.82	180	18.6
15	20/30	35	1.00	0.25	19.40	0.61	0.57	240	12.0
16	20/30	35	1.00	0.75	19.83	0.45	0.46	240	3.9
17	20/30	35	1.00	1.00	18.53	0.85	0.78	240	1.6
18	20/30	35	1.00	1.00	21.87	0.84	0.82	240	1.9
19	20/30	45	1.50	0.50	14.46	0.64	0.73	270	12.6
20	20/30	35	1.50	0.50	16.65	0.68	0.77	240	8.6
21	20/30	35	1.50	0.50	14.97	3.40	0.20	360	8.6
22	20/30	35	1.50	0.50	17.92	3.40	0.20	360	15.2

Reprinted with permission of Ref. [39].

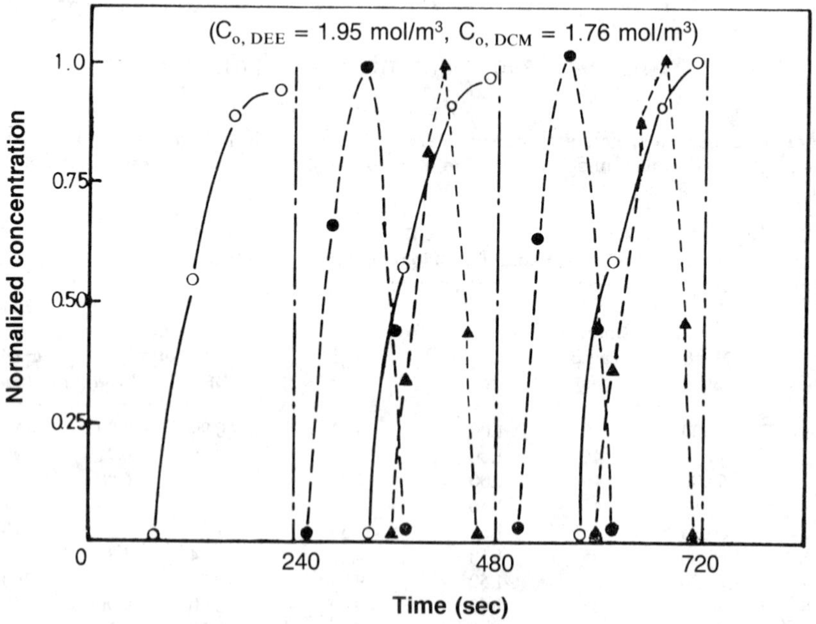

Figure 18. Concentration profile in partition section and desorption section. (45/60 mesh, 25°C. $u_{ave} = 2.53 \times 10^{-2}$ m/sec, L = 1.00 m, L′ = 1.00 m, 20% liquid loading, SW = 240 sec).

It is assumed that in the desorption section the components are partitioned initially with the inlet concentration of the feed, c_0. In the desorption section of the main column, governing equations are the same as in the partition section. However, some of initial and boundary conditions are different from those of the partition section. The initial condition, Equation 4, and the boundary condition, Equation 5 in the partition section are changed as follows:

$$c = q = c_0 \qquad (\text{for } t = 0, z > 0) \tag{43}$$

$$n = Kc_0 \qquad (\text{for } t = 0, z > 0) \tag{44}$$

$$c = 0 \qquad (\text{for } t > 0, z = 0) \tag{45}$$

Under the condition, the solution in the Laplace domain is

$$C(s) = \gamma\left(\exp\left\{\frac{L}{2}\left(\frac{u_0}{E} - \left[\left(\frac{u_0}{E}\right) + 4\gamma_1\right]^{1/2}\right)\right\} - 1\right) \tag{46}$$

where

$$\gamma = \left(-\frac{\epsilon_p c_0}{E} + \frac{3(1-\epsilon_p)}{r_p E} k_f \left\{\frac{\gamma_2 \sinh(\sqrt{\gamma_4} r_p)}{r_p} + \frac{\gamma_5}{\gamma_4}\right\}\right) \Big/ \gamma_1 \tag{47}$$

$$\gamma_1 = \frac{\epsilon s}{E} + \frac{3(1-\epsilon_p)}{r_p E} k_f \left\{1 - \frac{\gamma_3 \sinh(\sqrt{\gamma_4} r_p)}{r_p}\right\} \tag{48}$$

$$\gamma_2 = -\gamma_5 k_f/\gamma_4 (D_e\{\sqrt{\gamma_4} r_p \cosh(\sqrt{\gamma_4} r_p) - \sinh(\sqrt{\gamma_4} r_p)\}/r_p^2 + k_f \sinh(\sqrt{\gamma_4} r_p)/r_p) \tag{49}$$

$$\gamma_3 = \frac{-\gamma_4}{\gamma_5 \gamma_2} \tag{50}$$

$$\gamma_4 = \frac{1}{D_e}(\epsilon_p s + A_p k_g) - \frac{A_p k_g^2 \cosh\left(\sqrt{\frac{s}{D_1}}\,\delta\right)}{D_e K\left\{\sqrt{D_1 s} \sinh\left(\sqrt{\frac{s}{D_1}}\,\delta\right) + k_g \cosh\left(\sqrt{\frac{s}{D_1}}\,\delta\right) \Big/ K\right\}} \tag{51}$$

$$\gamma_5 = \frac{A_p k_g}{D_e K}\left\{\frac{Kc_0}{s} - \frac{\frac{k_g c_0}{s} \cosh\left(\sqrt{\frac{s}{D_1}}\,\delta\right)}{\sqrt{D_1 s} \sinh\left(\sqrt{\frac{s}{D_1}}\,\delta\right) + k_g \cosh\left(\sqrt{\frac{s}{D_1}}\,\delta\right) \Big/ K}\right\} + \frac{c_0}{D_e} \tag{52}$$

Equation 46 is used as the input function for the inlet of the additional column. That is

$$C_0(s) = \gamma\left(\exp\left\{\frac{L}{2}\left(\frac{u_0}{E} - \left[\left(\frac{u_0}{E}\right)^2 + 4\gamma_1\right)^{1/2}\right]\right\} - 1\right) \tag{53}$$

As the governing equations, initial conditions, and other boundary conditions are the same as those in the partition section, the solution in s-domain is, therefore

$$C(s) = \gamma\left(\exp\left\{\frac{L}{2}\left(\frac{u_0}{E} - \left[\left(\frac{u_0}{E}\right)^2 + 4\gamma_1\right]^{1/2}\right)\right\} - 1\right) \times \exp\left(\frac{L'}{2}\left\{\frac{u_0}{E} - \left[\left(\frac{u_0}{E}\right)^2 + 4\lambda\right]^{1/2}\right\}\right) \tag{54}$$

where L' = additional column length

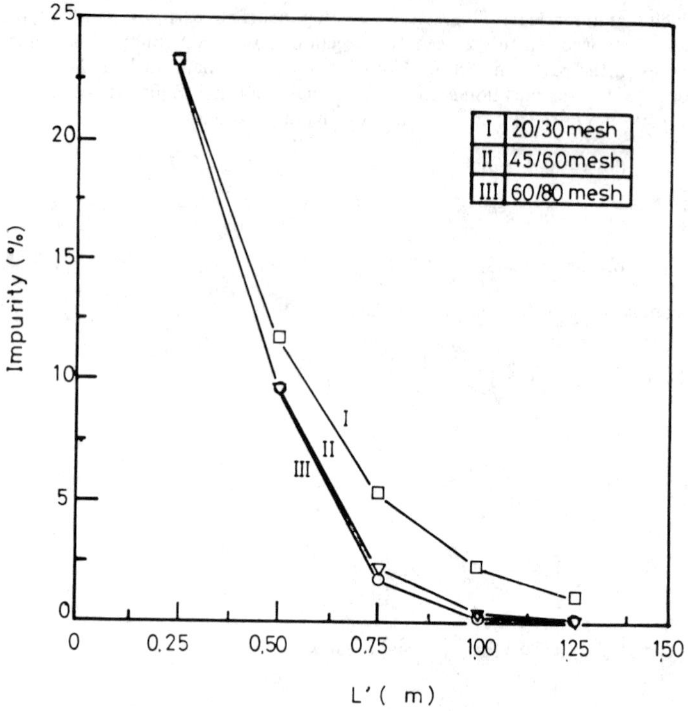

Figure 19. Effect of additional column length on impurity with particle size in desorption section. (35°C, $u_0 = 10.35 \times 10^{-2}$ m/sec, L = 1.00 m, 20% liquid loading). (Data from Ref. 17.)

The resulting Laplace transformed equations (Equations 42, 46, 54) should be converted into the real time domain, but an analytical method is highly unlikely. For an approximation technique, the equations are inverted numerically with the curve fitting procedure suggested by Dang and Gibilaro [42]. In the numerical inversion, the infinite upper integration limit is taken as the corresponding value of the frequency to the amplitude ratio of the Laplace transformed equations of 0.001, and it takes several minutes using HP 3000 to transform the equations into the real time domain.

Figures 19 and 20 show that the separation of two components in the desorption section was decisively affected by an increase in the additional column length more than particle size and % liquid loading. The effects of the latter have their own optimum values on the impurity. In the desorption section, the remained components should be separated within a switching time to perform the operation of the system continuously. Therefore, too small of a particle size and too large of a loading of SLP should be avoided.

An increase in the % liquid loading decreased the impurity, but it increased the total elution time (Figure 21). Because the higher temperature decreases the total elution time, the impurity increases due to the fast elution of the components. It is also observed that with higher loading of SLP, cross points by sets of the two lines (solid line and chain line in the figure) were shifted to higher temperature.

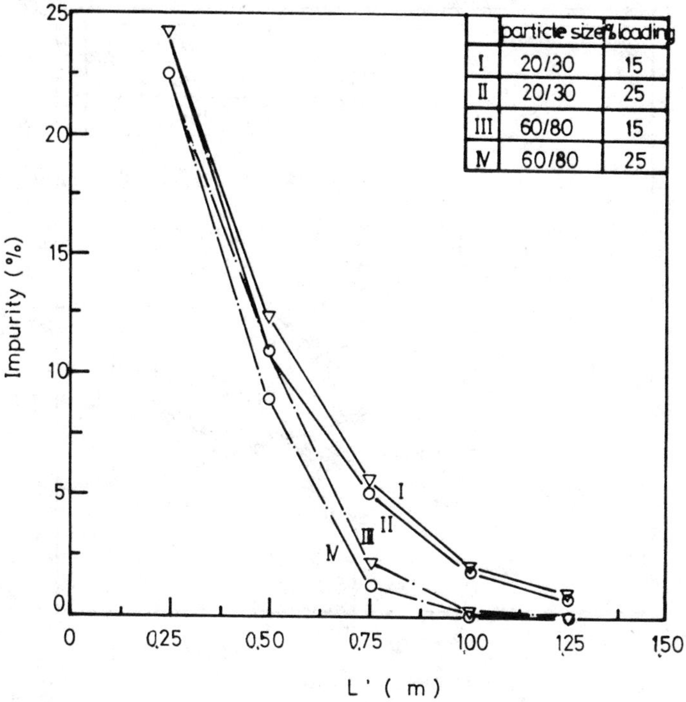

Figure 20. Effect of column length on impurity with particle size and liquid loading in desorption section. (35°C, $u_0 = 10.35 \times 10^{-2}$ m/sec, L = 1.00 m). (Data from Ref. 17.)

Another significant factor to be discussed is desorbent velocity. Based on the previous results of column temperature and % liquid loading in Figure 21, the effects of desorbent velocity on impurity and total elution time with the column length are shown in Figure 22 at 35°C and 20% liquid loading with switching time of 240 sec. When the allowable impurity is assumed to be a value of 10%, optimum operating condition exists below the time of 400 sec.

Continuous operation, however, can be achieved by connecting the additional column length to the end of the desorption section. The resolution between the two components was improved gradually by increasing the additional column length from 50 to 100 cm (43). The difference in the trailing edge of the concentration profile of DEE and in the leading edge of DCM is caused by somewhat higher concentration of the feed. It was assumed that in the model equations, the partition isotherm was linear and no interaction between the two components existed, but the mixture to be separated shows the some degree of deviation from the assumptions. With adjustment of the desorbent velocity alone, separation in the desorption section with the additional column length can be completed in accordance with the switching time of 240 sec (Figure 23).

When the feed concentration is increased, the phenomena in the column become more complex, and the information about the nonlinear isotherm is needed for better prediction. Moreover, the assumption that the velocity of carrier gas and desorbent remained constant throughout a column is not thought to be reasonable, because higher pressure drop by smaller particle size and longer column length caused the variation of the gas velocity, and the solute concentration changes along the length of the column by absorption are necessarily accompanied by change in the velocity.

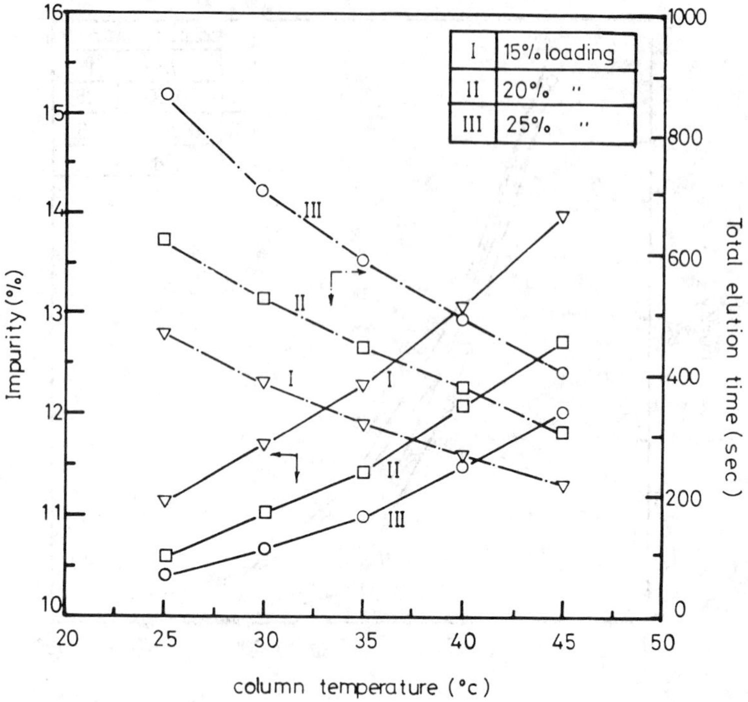

Figure 21. Effect of column temperature on impurity and total elution time with liquid loading in desorption section. (20/30 mesh, $u_0 = 10.00 \times {}^{-2}$ m/sec. L = 1.00 m, L′ = 0.50 m). (Data from Ref. 17.)

Although it was assumed in Equation 43 that the components, DEE and DCM, were partitioned in the desorption section with the feed concentration, c_0, the more-absorbed component, DCM, was not exactly the case, because during the previous SW, the component was not withdrawn from the partition section [17].

In spite of the some deviations, the theoretical concentration profiles are in relatively good agreement with the experimental data. Hence, the uniform film thickness model with the governing equations can be used as a suitable estimation of optimum operating conditions for the combined continuous and preparative chromatographic system.

NOTATION

a	peak width cut by the two tangents in unit of volume, m^3
A	surface area of porous particle, m^2
A_p	surface area of porous particle per unit volume, m^2/m^3
A_s	surface area of porous particle per unit mass, m^2/kg
b	retention volume from injection to peak maximum, m^3
B_i	Biot number $(= k_f r_p/D_e)$
B_iM	modified Biot number $(= \delta k_g/D_1)$

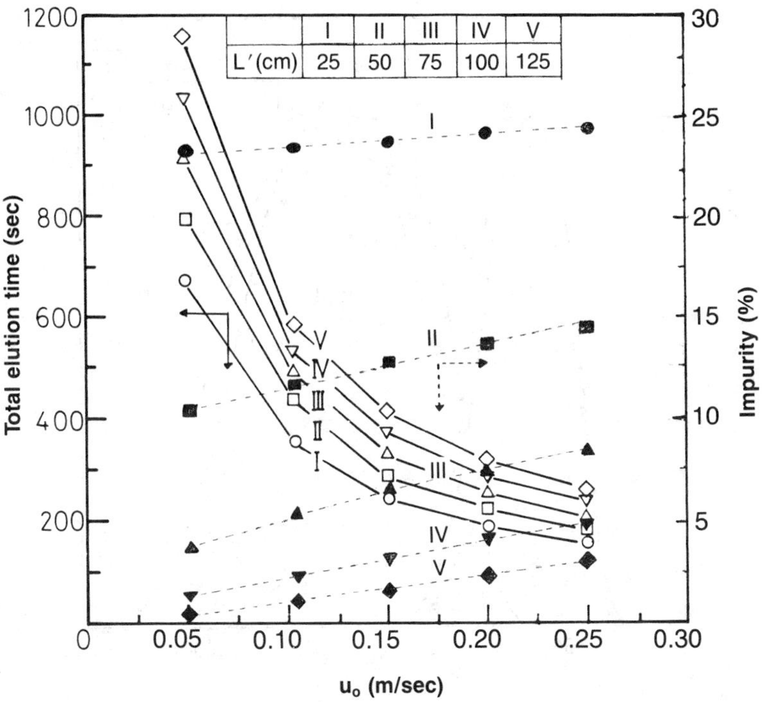

Figure 22. Effect of desorbent velocity on impurity with additional column length in desorption section. (20/30 mesh, 35°C, L = 1.00 m, 20% liquid loading). (Data from Ref. 17.)

- c concentration of solute in the mobile phase, mol/m^3
- c_0 inlet concentration of solute, mol/m^3
- $C(s)$ Laplace transform of $c(t)$
- D_e diffusion coefficient in the pore spacing, m^2/sec
- D_1 diffusion coefficient in the SLP, m^2/sec
- D_M molecular diffusivity, m^2/sec
- E axial dispersion coefficient, m^2/sec
- $f_0(t)$, $f_p(t)$ observed value and predicted value, respectively
- $F_0(t)$, $F_p(t)$ Fourier transform of $f_0(t)$ and $f_p(t)$, respectively
- $G(j\omega)$ Fourier transformed transfer function
- $-\Delta H_s$ heat of solution, J/mol
- I imaginary part
- j $\sqrt{-1}$
- J correction factor defined by Equation 40
- k_f interparticle mass transfer coefficient, m/sec
- k_g intraparticle mass transfer coefficient with respect to SLP-film, m/sec
- K, K_i partition coefficient, of component i, respectively
- K_0 constant used in Equation 33
- L column length in the partition section or desorption section, m
- L' additional column length in the desorption section, m
- $m(\omega)$ magnitude ratio
- M, M_B molecular weight, of SLP, respectively, kg/mol

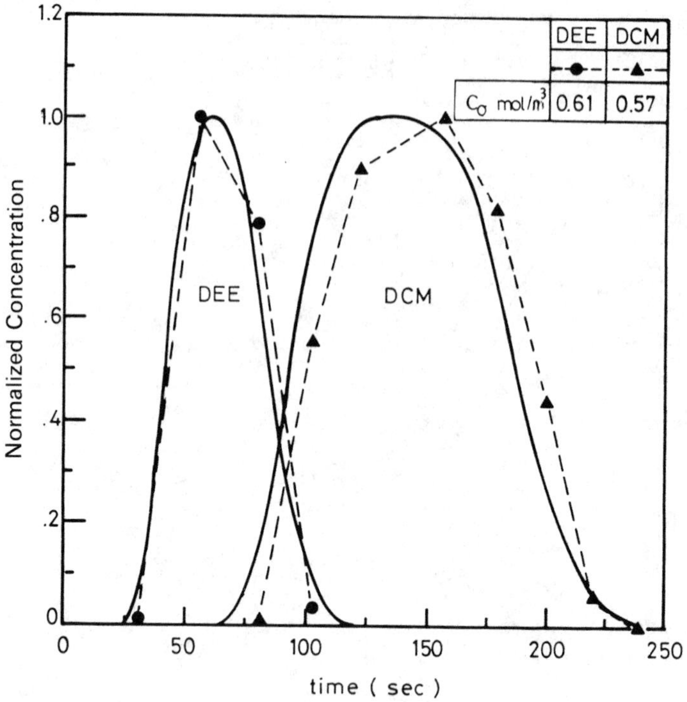

Figure 23. Comparison of experimental data with calculated values. (20/30 mesh, 35°C. u_{ave} = 20.57×10^{-2} m/sec, L = 1.00 m, L′ = 1.00 m, SW = 240 sec). (Data from Ref. 43.)

n concentration of solute in the SLP, mol/m^3

P_e Peclet number ($= uL\epsilon/E$)

Pi, Po pressure of inlet and outlet, respectively, N/m^2

P_i dimensionless group ($= r_p^2 u \epsilon_p / D_e L$)

P_1 dimensionless group ($= \delta^2 u / D_1 L$)

q concentration of solute in the pore spacing, mol/m^3

r radial distance, m

r_p radius of porous particle, m

R real part

Re Reynolds number ($= 2 r_p u_0 \rho_G / \nu$)

R_G gas constant (8.314 J/mol K)

Res resolution defined by Equation 39

s variable of Laplace transform

S_c Schmidt number ($= \nu / D_M \rho_G$)

S_t Stanton number ($= 3(1 - \epsilon) k_f L / \epsilon r_p u$)

S_tM modified Stanton number ($= A_p k_g L / \epsilon_p u$)

t time, sec

t_0 time of feed-injection, sec

T column temperature, K

T_c critical temperature, K

u interstitial velocity of carrier gas or desorbent, m/sec

u_{ave} average velocity corrected by J ($= u_{out} \times J$), m/sec

u_0 superficial velocity of carrier gas or desorbent, m/sec

u_{out} outlet velocity of carrier gas or desorbent, m/sec
V volume of intraparticle without SLP, m^3
V′ volume of intraparticle with the presence of SLP, m^3
V_A molar volume of solute at boiling temperature, m^3/mol
V_C critical volume, m^3/mol
V_{tot} total volume of a porous particle
V_L volume of SLP, m^3
W_L total weight of SLP in the column, kg
W_s total weight of solid particle in the column, kg
x distance perpendicular to surface of porous particle, m
z axial distance, m

Greek Letters

$\gamma, \gamma_1, \gamma_2, \gamma_3, \gamma_4, \gamma_5$ values defined by Equations 47–52
δ film thickness of SLP, m
ϵ void fraction of chromatographic column
ϵ_p porosity with the presence of SLP
ϵ'_p intraparticle porosity with the uncoated porous particle
η_B viscosity of SLP, kg m/sec
η_{ext} external tortuosity
$\lambda, \lambda_1, \lambda_2, \lambda_3$ values defined by Equations 11–15
$\lambda_4, \lambda_5, \lambda_6$ values defined by Equations 17–19
ν viscosity of carrier gas or desorbent, kg m/sec
ρ_G density of carrier gas or desorbent, kg/m^3
ρ_L density of SLP, kg/m^3
ρ_{app} apparent density of porous particle, kg/m^3
ρ_{true} true density of porous particle, kg/m^3
ψ dimensionless group ($=c/c_0$)
ψ_{obj} objective function defined by Equation 24
ϕ association factor of SLP
$\phi(\omega)$ angle $G(j\omega)$
ω frequency
ω_{max} ω value at which the amplitude ratio of $F(j\omega)$ is 0.001

Abbreviations

DCM dichloromethane
DEE diethylether
DMM dimethoxymethane
SLP stationary liquid phase
SW switching time

REFERENCES

1. Tswett, M., Ber dent., botan, Ges., *Physikalisch-chemische Studien uber das Chlorophyll. Die Adsorptionen,*" 24, 316, 384 (1906).
2. James, A. T., and Martin, A. J. P., "Gas-Liquid Partition Chromatography. Technique for Analysis of Volatile Materials," *Analyst*, 77, 915 (1952).
3. Purnell, H., *Gas Chromatography*, 2nd Ed., John Wiley, New York (1967), p. 3.
4. King, C. J., *Separation Process*, 2nd Ed., McGraw-Hill (1980), p. 191.
5. Ghim, Y. S., and Chang, H. N., "Adsorption Characteristics of Glucose and Fructose in Ion-Exchange Resin Columns," *Ind. Eng. Chem. Fundamen.*, 21, 369 (1982).
6. Schneider, P., and Smith, J. M., "Adsorption of Rate Constants from Chromatography," *AIChE J.*, 14, 762 (1968).
7. Huang, S. D., Wilson, J. W., Wilson, D. J., and Overhosler, K. A., "Non-Ideal Line Shapes in Gas-Liquid Chromatography," *J. Chromatogr.*, 82, 119 (1974).

8. Husband, W. H., Barker, P. E., and Kini, K. D., "The Separation of Liquid Mixtures by Vapor Phase Adsorption in a Moving-Bed Column," *Trans. Instn. Chem., Engineers.*, 42, T387 (1964).
9. Ha, H. Y., Row, K. H., and Lee, W. K., "A Theoretical Plate Model for the Moving Feed-Injection Chromatography: I. Simulation Results," *Sep. Sci. and Technol.*, 22, 141 (1987).
10. Ha, H. Y., Row, K. H., and Lee, W. K., "A Theoretical Plate Model for the Moving Feed-Chromatography: II. Experimental Results," *Sep. Sci. and Technol.*, 22, 1281 (1987).
11. Wankat, P. C., "Moving Port Chromatography," *Ind. Eng. Chem. Fundamen.*, 23, 256 (1984).
12. Barker, P. E., and Chuah, C. H., "A Sequential Chromatographic Process for the Separation of Glucose/Fructose Mixtures," *Chemical Engineer*, 389 (Aug./Sept., 1981).
13. Berezikin, V. G., "Adsorption in Gas-Liquid Chromatography," *J. Chromatogr.*, 159, 359 (1978).
14. Alkarasani, M. A., and McCoy, B. J., "Gas-Liquid Partition Chromatographic Separation in Columns Packed with Porous Particles—A Model for Uniform Thickness Liquid Film," *Chem. Eng. J.*, 23, 81 (1982).
15. Row, K. H., and Lee, W. K., "Partition of Close-Boiling Components in a Chromatographic Column," *Korean J. Chem. Eng.*, 3, 7 (1986).
16. Row, K. H., and Lee, W. K., "Separation of Close-Boiling Components by Gas-Liquid Chromatography," *J. Chem. Eng. Japan*, 19, 173 (1986).
17. Row, K. H., and Lee, W. K., "Separation of Close-Boiling Components by Continuous Chromatography: I. Computational Results," submitted to *Ind. Eng. Chem. Research* (1986).
18. McNair, H. M., and Bonelli, E. J., "Basic Gas Chromatography," Varian Instrument Div. (1969), p. 49.
19. Chromosorb Diatomite Supports for Gas-Liquid Chromatography, Johns-Manville (1984).
20. Nogare, S. D., and Juvet, R. S., *Gas-Liquid Chromatography: Theory and Practice*, John Wiley & Sons, Inc., New York, (1962), p. 135.
21. Giddings, J. C., "Liquid Distribution on Gas Chromatographic Support: Relation to Plate Height," *Anal. Chem.*, 34, 458 (1962).
22. Conder, J. R., Locke, D. C., and Purnell, J. H., "Concurrent Solution and Adsorption Phenomena in Chromatography: I. General Consideration," *J. Phys. Chem.*, 73, 700 (1969).
23. Littlewood, A., *Gas Chromatography*, Academic Press, New York, (1970), p. 112.
24. Moon, I., Row, K. H., and Lee, W. K., "Characteristics of Gas-Liquid Chromatography," *Korean J. of Chem. Eng.*, 2, 155 (1985).
25. Chen, N. H., and Othmer, D. F., "New Generalized for Gas Diffusion Coefficient," *J. Chem. Eng. Data*, 7, 37 (1962).
26. Wilke, C. R., and Chang, P., "Correlation of Diffusion Coefficients in Dilute Solutions," *AIChE J.*, 1, 264 (1955).
27. Foo, S. C., and Rice, R. G., "On the Prediction of Ultimate Separation in Parametric Pump," *AIChE J.*, 21, 1149 (1975).
28. Ergun, S., Mass Transfer Rate in Packed Column: Its Analogy to Pressure Loss, *Chem. Eng. Pro.*, 48, 227 (1952).
29. Wen, C. Y., and Fan, L. T., *Models for Flow Systems and Chemical Reactors*, Marcel Dekker, New York (1975), p. 169.
30. Hsiang, T. C. S., and Haynes, H. W., Jr., "Axial Dispersion in Small Particle Beds of Large Spherical Particles," *Chem. Eng. Sci.*, 32, 678 (1977).
31. Hsu, L. K. W., and Haynes, H. W., Jr., "Effective Diffusivity by the Gas Chromatography Technique: Analysis and Application to Measurements of Diffusion of Various Hydrocarbons in Zeolite NaY," *AIChE J.*, 27, 81 (1981).
32. Keulemans, A. J. P., *Gas Chromatography*, Reinhold, Chapman Hill, New York (1959), p. 157.
33. Giddings, J. C., *Dynamics of Chromatography: Part I. Principles and Theory*, Marcel Dekker, New York (1965), p. 278.
34. Bonmati, R. G., Chapelet-Letourneux, G., and Margulis, J. R., "Gas Chromatography Analysis to Production," *Chem. Eng.*, 86, 70 (1980).
35. Albrecht, J., and Verzele, M., "Preparative Scale Gas Chromatography: X. Improved Packing Method for Large Diameter Columns," *J. Chromatogr. Sci.*, 8, 856 (1970).
36. Albrecht, J., and Verzele, M., "Preparative Scale Gas Chromatography: XI. Factors Affecting Performance of Large Diameter Columns," *J. Chromatogr., Sci.*, 9, 745 (1971).

37. Giddings, J. C., "Principles of Column Performance in Large Scale Gas Chromatography," *J. Gas Chromatogr.*, 1, 12 (1963).
38. Bourghton, D. B., "Molex; Case History of a Process," *Chem. Eng. Pro.*, 64, 60 (1968).
39. Row, K. H., and Lee, W. K., "Separation of Close-Boiling Components Using A New Chromatographic Method," *Sep. Sci. and Technol.*, 22, 1761, (1987).
40. Row, K. H., Ph.D. Thesis, KAIST, Seoul (1986).
41. Row, K. H., and Lee, W. K., "Effect of Flow Path on Separation of Binary Components by Gas-Liquid Chromatography," *Korean J. of Chem. Eng.*, 4, 23 (1987).
42. Dang, N. D. P., and Gibilaro, L. G., "Numerical Inversion of Laplace Transforms by a Simple Curve Fitting Technique," *Chem. Eng. J.*, 8, 157 (1974).
43. Row, K. H., and Lee, W. K., "Separation of Close-Boiling Components by Continuous Chromatography: II. Comparison of Experimental Data to Calculated Values," submitted to *Ind. Eng. Chem. Research* (1986).

SECTION III

ADVANCED METHODS OF SYSTEMS ANALYSIS

CONTENTS

CHAPTER 23

EXERGY METHOD OF THERMAL AND CHEMICAL PLANT ANALYSIS

T. J. Kotas

Department of Mechanical Engineering
Queen Mary College
University of London
London, United Kingdom

CONTENT

INTRODUCTION

The exergy method is a method of thermodynamic analysis in which the basis of evaluation of thermodynamic losses follows from both the First and the Second Laws rather than just from the First Law of Thermodynamics. Because of this it belongs to the category of thermodynamic analyses known under the name of Second Law analyses. Another name that has been applied to it is "availability analysis."

Since, as is well known, the Second Law governs the limits of convertibility between various forms of energy, its use is indispensable for the assessment of grades of energy as well as the degradation of energy that occurs in all real processes.

This Chapter introduces the basic concepts and techniques of the exergy method and reviews some of the more important contributions that have been made to this subject.

The birth of the Second Law Analysis corresponds to the first attempts at assessing various energy forms according to their convertibility to useful work. These attempts were directly connected with the beginnings of the formulation of the Second Law of Thermodynamics and thus initially were mainly of theoretical interest. The practical applications of the concept of "usable energy" to closed systems was demonstrated by Gouy in 1889 [1] who also showed that the loss of "usable energy" in a given process is equal to the product of the temperature of the environment and the sum of the entropy changes of all the bodies participating in the process. In 1898, Stodola [2], apparently quite independently, developed the same concepts for the more important, as far as engineering processes are concerned, steady flow processes. The development of these concepts in the following years was slow until the 1930s when interest in their practical applications was stimulated by industrial growth and new technological developments. Two papers published by Bošnjaković in 1939 [3, 4] mark a new era in the development of the Second Law Analysis. These papers made some important contributions toward the formulation of new criteria of performance and techniques of evaluation of the thermodynamic perfection of processes. This work was interrupted by World War II but was renewed again in the early 1950s with new vigor. Some of the developments during that decade are of particular relevance ot the application of exergy in chemical engineering. The first known application of the Second Law Analysis to chemical processes was published in 1951 by Rant [5] in which he used the entropy method to analyze the process of the production of soda (Na_2CO_3). A few years later, Denbigh [6] extended the techniques of the availability analysis to the analysis of ammonia oxidation process and calculated a form of Second Law efficiency for it. Another important development was the formulation by Szargut [7] of the theory of reference substances for evaluating standard chemical energy of substances. This decade also saw the introduction by Rant [8] of the word "exergy." This term has now gained almost general international acceptance, replacing a confusing variety of terms such as availability, usable energy, work capability, and others.

The 1950s mark a sharp increase in the number of papers published on various aspects of the Second Law analysis, which for that decade alone was more than three times greater than for the whole of the preceding period. This trend continues unabated with the total number of papers published to data approaching 1,500. Among the factors for the more recent surge in the number of publications, particularly in North America, is without doubt the increase in the cost of fuels.

BASIC CONCEPTS

The Concept of Exergy

Exergy may be defined as the maximum work potential of a system or of a particular form of energy in relation to the state of the environment. Or putting it in another way, exergy is a measure, expressed in terms of work, of the capacity of a given form of energy to cause change. As follows from the first definition, the environment plays a most important in the exergy method. The conceptual environment is an idealization of the real environment, its main characteristic being a perfect state of equilibrium, i.e., absence of any gradients or differences involving pressure, temperature, chemical potential, kinetic energy, and potential energy. The conceptual environment is usually assumed to be so large that its parameters (pressure, temperature, composition) are unaffected by its interaction with any manmade system. Because of its size the environment constitutes a natural reference medium with respect to which the exergy of different systems is evaluated. When evaluating the exergy of a stream of matter the environment is treated as a reservoir of zero grade thermal energy and common environmental substances that can be drawn upon freely. The common environmental substances are in equilibrium with each other and are said to be in the *dead state.*

The exergy method can be applied to both closed systems and open systems. Since most of the important industrial systems are of the open type, operating most of the time under steady-state conditions, we shall confine this discussion to the *control region* method of analysis.* Accordingly, the energy transfers across the control surface for which we have to determine the corresponding exergy transfers using the above definition, are:

1. Energy transfer, through work interaction.
2. Energy transfer through heat interaction.
3. Energy transfer associated with streams of matter entering or leaving the control region.

Since, as follows from this definition, work is used as a measure of the exergy associated with a given form of energy transfer, the first form of energy transfer listed is easiest to deal with. In the case of systems operating under steady conditions, the quantity of interest is the exergy flow rate $\dot{E}^W$ associated with a given work transfer rate, or shaft power, $\dot{W}_x$. The relationship between these two quantities is clearly

$$\dot{E}^W = \dot{W}_x \tag{1}$$

Because of the identity between $\dot{E}^W$ and $\dot{W}_x$, it is usual to use the latter symbol for both of them.

The exergy associated with a given heat transfer rate, $\dot{Q}$, is called *thermal exergy* flow, and is denoted by the symbol $\dot{E}^Q$. According to the definition the relationship between these two quantities is given by

$$\dot{E}^Q = \dot{Q}(1 - T_0/T) \tag{2}$$

where, T is the temperature at the control surface at which the heat transfer occurs, and T_0 is the temperature of the environment.

To determine the exergy flow rate, $\dot{E}$, associated with a stream of matter crossing the control surface we must use ideal devices such as reversible expanders and compressors, semipermeable membranes, etc. in order to reduce reversibly the stream from its original state (at the control surface) to a state of equilibrium with the environment. A diagrammatic representation of this type of arrangement is shown in Figure 1. The power output obtainable from this device is equal to the exergy flow rate of the stream. The calculation of $\dot{E}$ involves much more complex considerations than in the case of $\dot{E}^W$ and $\dot{E}^Q$. Some aspects of these considerations will be discussed at some length below.

Exergy Balance

The exergy balance is one of the basic tools of the exergy method. Figure 2 shows the exergy flows $\dot{W}_x$, $\dot{E}^Q$, $\dot{E}_{IN}$ and $\dot{E}_{OUT}$ crossing the control surface.* If the processes taking place within the control region are reversible, the total exergy inflow will be equal to the total exergy outflow, i.e., there will be no loss of exergy. However, if the process under consideration is a real one then it must be, to some degree, irreversible. Under these conditions a proportion of the inflow energy will be lost and hence the exergy outflow will be smaller than the inflow by this amount. Thus, with reference to

---

* The concepts and techniques relating to closed system analysis are dealt with in Reference 15. Some expressions, definitions and the exergy balance applicable to closed system analysis will be found at the end of this chapter.

* In the sign convention adopted, the work done by the system and the heating done on the system are taken as positive quantities.

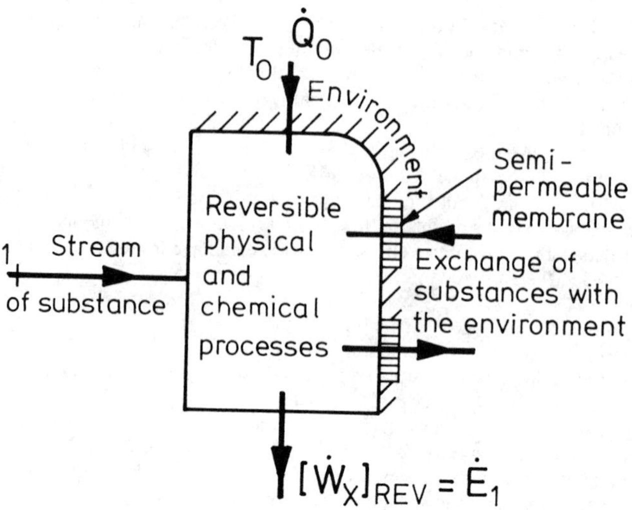

Figure 1. Determination of the exergy flow rate of a steady stream of matter.

Figure 2 we can write

$$(\dot{E}_{IN} + \dot{E}^Q) - (\dot{W}_x + \dot{E}_{OUT}) = \dot{I} \tag{3}$$

where $\dot{I}$ is the rate of loss of exergy or the irreversibility rate of the process. Since we have defined independently the exergy of the various forms of energy that are transferred across the control surface, the exergy balance may be looked upon as a definition of the irreversibility rate of the process. The exergy balance can also be obtained by combining the steady flow energy equation with the expression for the entropy production rate [9].

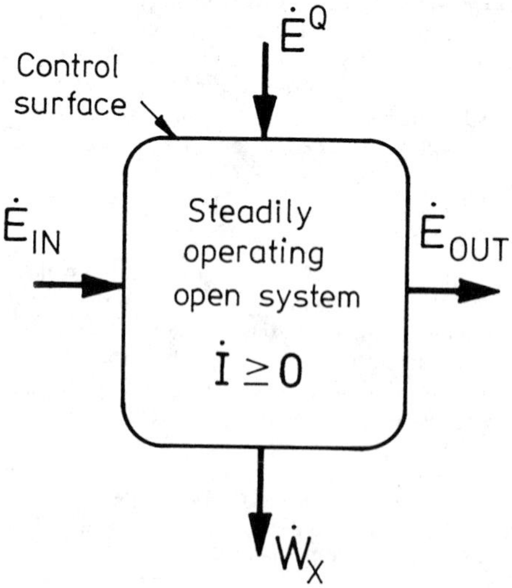

Figure 2. Exergy balance for an open system.

Irreversibility Rate

The principal area of application of the exergy balance is in the calculation of the irreversibility rate of a process. The irreversibility rate is a generally applicable measure of thermodynamic imperfection of the process. Depending on how the control surface is drawn, it can be calculated for a single component, a group of components or the whole plant. Since $\dot{I}$ obeys the additive law we can write, with reference to Figure 3.

$$\dot{I}_T = \sum_N \dot{I}_i \qquad (4)$$

where $\dot{I}_T$ is the irreversibility rate of a system consisting of N components and $\dot{I}_i$ that of the i-th component. Irreversibility rate provides a means of identifying the plant components that cause the great contribution to plant inefficiency. The cause of irreversibility is, partly, the fact that if a process is to proceed at a finite rate it must occur in virtue of finite driving (generalized) forces. The driving forces of particular interest in chemical engineering processes are temperature differences, pressure differences, and differences in chemical potential. For a given size of equipment, the bigger are the driving potentials, the bigger is the irreversibility rate, and the greater is the process rate. The process rate can also be increased by increasing the size of the equipment and, hence in general its cost, without the need to increase irreversibility. This trade-off between the cost of irreversibility rate and the cost of equipment forms the basis of the technique of thermoeconomic optimization of plant components described later. As follows from this discussion and from the exergy balance (Equation 3). In any productive process (i.e., one in which there is an output expressible in terms of exergy) the irreversibility rate is that part of the exergy input that must be consumed in the process to make it proceed at the required rate. Thus, as will be noted, it is exergy and not energy that is consumed in a process.

It is possible to assess that proportion of the total irreversibility of a plant or a component that is intrinsic to the process, i.e., that part that cannot be reduced owing to limits imposed by physical, technological, economic, and other constraints. Thus, one can represent the irreversibility rate in two parts, the intrinsic part and the avoidable part, i.e.

$$\dot{I} = \dot{I}_{intrinsic} + \dot{I}_{avoidable} \qquad (5)$$

The importance of identifying the intrinsic and the unavoidable parts of irreversibility has been first put forward by Denbigh [6] in his work on chemical processes. This concept has been subsequently generalized and developed by Linnhoff and his co-workers [10 to 14] who have also been largely responsible for the popularization of these concepts.

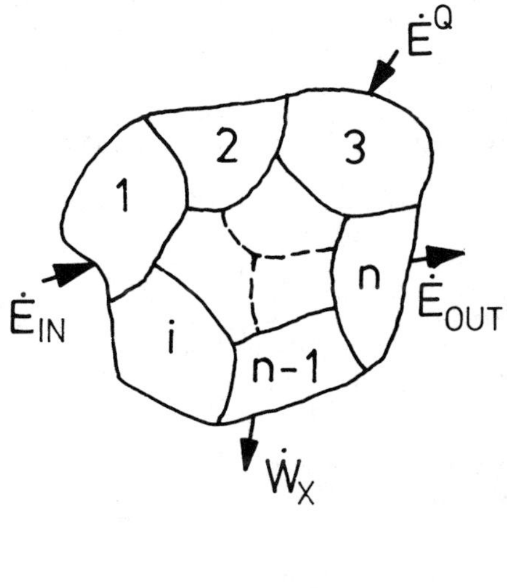

Figure 3. A multi-component open system.

As an alternative to calculating the irreversibility rate of a process from the exergy balance, we can use the Gouy-Stodola relation [15]

$$\dot{I} = T_0 \dot{\Pi} \tag{6}$$

where T_0 = environmental temperature
$\dot{\Pi}$ = entropy production rate in the control region

The choice of one or the other relation for calculating $\dot{I}$ depends on the type of data available and the kind of under process being considered. The Gouy-Stodola relation will be found generally simpler to apply to physical processes. In chemical reactions and in processes involving exchange of substances with the environment the exergy balance may be found more convenient particularly if tables of standard chemical exergy of substances are available.

Exergy of a Stream of Matter

Determining the exergy of a steady stream of matter is based on the following definition: *The exergy of a steady stream of matter is equal to the maximum amount of work obtainable when the stream is brought from its initial state to the state of thermal, mechanical, and chemical equilibrium with the environment by means of processes during which the stream may interact thermally and chemically only with the environment.* Clearly, for maximum work these interactions and all the processes must occur reversibly.

The exergy of a stream of matter may be divided into four basic components. This can be written, per mole of the substance, as follows

$$\tilde{\epsilon} = \tilde{\epsilon}_{kin} + \tilde{\epsilon}_{pot} + \tilde{\epsilon}_{ph} + \tilde{\epsilon}_0 \tag{7}$$

where $\tilde{\epsilon}_{kin}$ = molar kinetic exergy
$\tilde{\epsilon}_{pot}$ = molar potential exergy
$\tilde{\epsilon}_{ph}$ = molar physical exergy
$\tilde{\epsilon}_0$ = molar chemical exergy

The first two components of exergy, $\tilde{\epsilon}_{kin}$ and $\tilde{\epsilon}_{pot}$, are associated with forms of energy that are stored in an ordered manner and are fully convertible into other forms of energy [15]. Thus, in the case of an ordered stream of matter, the kinetic exergy of the stream is equal to its kinetic energy when the velocity of the stream is reckoned with respect to the surface of the Earth. Similarly potential exergy of the stream is equal to its potential energy reckoned with respect to the sea level.

The forms of energy associated with the physical and the chemical components of exergy are stored in a manner that involves an element of disorder. Thus, the determination of these two components of exergy involves very much more complex considerations than that of the previous two, since in this case we have to invoke the Second Law and also we must consider the environment as a reference medium.

The general principles underlying the evaluation of the exergy of a substance in steady flow and its decomposition into the physical component, $\tilde{\epsilon}_{ph}$, and the chemical component $\tilde{\epsilon}_0$ will be discussed with reference to Figure 4. In the ideal device illustrated the stream is brought from its initial state to the state of unrestricted equilibrium with the environment using fully (i.e. internally and externally) reversible processes so that the work obtainable is the maximum. The whole process occurs in three modules. The work output derived from Module X is equal to the physical component of exergy. $\tilde{\epsilon}_{ph}$, while the combined output from Modules Y and Z is equal to the chemical component $\tilde{\epsilon}_0$.

Module X. In this module all the processes are physical in character. The change of state of the stream is from the initial state, state 1, to the environmental state, the state defined by the environmental pressure, P_0, and temperature, T_0. As can be easily shown [15, 16] the work obtainable for

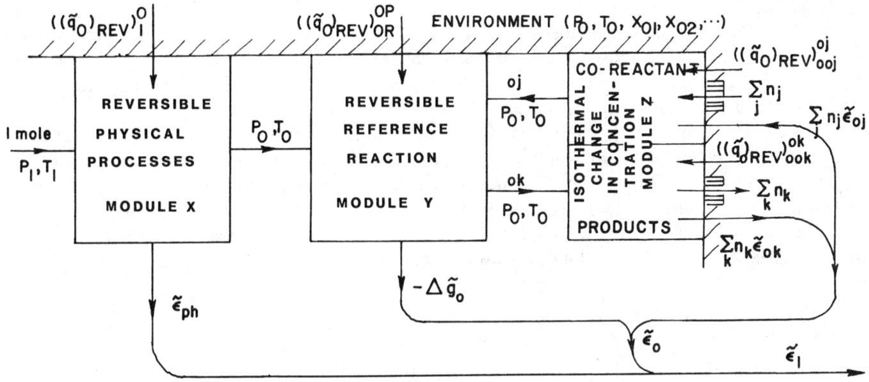

Figure 4. An ideal model for determining the physical and the chemical components of molar exergy of a steady stream of a pure simple substance (with $\epsilon_{kin} = 0$ and $\epsilon_{pot} = 0$).

any combination of fully reversible processes between these two states is given by

$$[(W_x)_{REV}]_1^0 = (\tilde{h}_1 - \tilde{h}_0) - T_0(\tilde{s}_1 - \tilde{s}_0) \tag{8}$$

Module Y. Within this module the substance undergoes a reversible chemical reaction with some environmental substances called here co-reactants, to form products that are also environmental substances. The purpose of this reaction is to modify the original substance in the stream so that it can be brought subsequently into a state of chemical equilibrium with the substances of which the conceptual environment is made up. If, for example, the substance under consideration is methane the reaction is

$$CH_4 + \underbrace{2O_2}_{\text{co-reactant}} \longrightarrow \underbrace{CO_2 + 2H_2O}_{\text{products}} \tag{9}$$

i.e. in this reaction oxygen is the co-reactant while carbon dioxide and water substance are the products. All three substances are common environmental substances that co-exist in the environment in a state of equilibrium. They are delivered to this module and removed from it at the environmental pressure P_0, and temperature T_0. The function of this module can be fulfilled by such idealized devices as the van't Hoff equilibrium box or a reversible fuel cell with, in either case, the necessary compressors and expanders. The reversible work delivered by the module can be shown to be equal to the difference between the chemical potential of the reactants and the products, which is equal in turn to the Gibbs function of the reaction. Thus, per mole of the substance under consideration we have

$$[(W_x)_{REV}]_{OR}^{OP} = \mu_0 - \left(\sum_k n_k\mu_{0k} - \sum_j n_j\mu_{0j}\right) = -\Delta\tilde{g}_0 \tag{10}$$

where $\Delta\tilde{g}_0$ = molar Gibbs function of the reaction
n_k, n_j = numbers of moles
μ_{0k}, μ_{0j} = chemical potentials of the co-reactants and products, respectively necessary for the stoichiometric reaction with 1 mole of the substance under consideration with chemical potential μ_0

Module Z. The purpose of this module is to bring about reversibly an isothermal change of concentration of the environmental substances that are either delivered from the environment to Module Y or vice versa. Module Z consists of several cells equal to the number of environmental substances involved in the reaction. For the purpose of illustration only two cells, one for a co-reactant and one for a product are shown in Figure 4.

Each cell is equipped with semipermeable membranes to enable the required substance to be separated from the environmental mixture. The calculation of the reversible work associated with the changes of concentration of the substances passing through the cells involves, in general, complex calculations, particularly in the case of non-gaseous environmental substances. Reversible isothermal work is given by the change in the chemical potential of the substance, hence we can express the total work required by the cells handling the co-reactants as

$$[(W_x)_{REV}]^{0j}_{00j} = -\sum_j n_j \tilde{\epsilon}_{0j} = \sum_j n_j(\mu_{0j} - \mu_{00j}) \qquad (11)$$

Similarly, the work delivered by the cells handling the products is

$$[(W_x)_{REV}]^{0k}_{00k} = \sum_k n_k \tilde{\epsilon}_{0k} = \sum_k n_k(\mu_{0k} - \mu_{00k}) \qquad (12)$$

The symbols $\tilde{\epsilon}_{0j}$ and $\tilde{\epsilon}_{0k}$ denote the molar chemical exergy of the co-reactants and the products respectively.

The net work delivered by Modules Y and Z combined is equal, according to the definition, to the chemical exergy of the substances. This can be written as

$$\tilde{\epsilon}_0 = -\Delta\tilde{g}_0 - \sum_j n_j(\mu_{0j} - \mu_{00j}) + \sum_k n_k(\mu_{0k} - \mu_{00k}) \qquad (13)$$

$$\tilde{\epsilon}_0 = -\Delta\tilde{g}_0 - \sum_j n_j \epsilon_{0j} + \sum_k n_k \epsilon_{0k} \qquad (14)$$

In the case when the stream under consideration is a mixture the molar chemical exergy is given by [15]

$$\tilde{\epsilon}_{0m} = \sum_i x_i \tilde{\epsilon}_{0i} + \tilde{R}T_0 \sum_i x_i \ln \gamma_i x_i \qquad (15)$$

where $\tilde{R}$ = universal gas constant
x_i = mole function of the i-th constituent
$\tilde{\epsilon}_{0i}$ = molar chemical energy
γ_i = activity coefficient

Standard Chemical Exergy

As seen from Expression 13 the calculation of ϵ_0 requires information regarding the chemical potential in the environment of the common environmental substances that pass through the cells of Module Z. To simplify these calculations it was found convenient to select a number of *reference substances*, one for each chemical element, from among the various possible common environmental substances of low chemical potential containing the element in question. These substances were then allocated standard concentrations that correspond to the average values in their sphere of incidence, i.e., on the Earth's surface, the atmosphere or in the oceans. Using these values, and appropriate activity coefficients, the standard values of the chemical exergy of the reference substances and of the chemical element are then calculated. The *standard environmental state* for which the values of chemical exergy have been computed is the same as the standard state that is used for quoting thermochemical data, i.e., $T^0 = 298.15$ K and $P^0 = 1.0132$ bar.*

---

* Whereas the actual environmental values of P are marked with the subscript 0 the corresponding standard values are marked with a superscript 0.

Table 1
Some Selected Standard Values of Enthalpy of Devaluation and Chemical Exergy of Chemical Elements and Substances [15, 78].

Chemical Element or Substance		Enthalpy of Devaluation		Chemical Exergy	
Chemical Symbol	**Standard Reference State**	**Reference Substance**	**Standard Enthalpy of Devaluation kJ/kmol**	**Reference Substance**	**Standard Chemical Exergy kJ/kmol**
Al	s	Al_2SiO_5, s sillimanite	927 800	Al_2SiO_5, s	887 890
C	g, graphite	CO_2, g	393 780	CO_2, g	410 820
Ca	s, II	$CaCO_3$, s calcite	813 910	Ca^{2+}, i	717 400
Al_2SiO_5	s, sillimanite	—	0	—	15 400
CH_4	g, methane	—	802 870	—	836 930
Fe_3O_4	s, magnetite	—	116 170	—	126 960

Key: s—solid, g—gaseous, i—ions in aqueous solution

This work was first done by Szargut and his co-workers [17] who originally selected reference substances from the atmosphere and the Earth's crust. Subsequently [18] this system of reference substances was modified by dropping most of the reference substances from the Earth's crust and replacing these by ionic reference substances from the oceans. The resulting values of standard chemical exergy of the elements were only marginally different from those calculated from reference substances in the solid state. This confirmed the assumption implicit in this work that the Earth's crust and the oceans as well as the atmosphere are in a state of equilibrium.

Table 1 gives by way of an example the standard chemical exergies of a few chemical elements and the corresponding reference substances. Using these exergy values and the appropriate value of the Gibbs function of formation the standard molar chemical exergy $\tilde{\epsilon}^0$, of any chemical compound can be calculated, from the following expression [15, 16]:

$$\tilde{\epsilon}^0 = \Delta\tilde{g}_f^0 + \sum_i n_i\tilde{\epsilon}_i \qquad (16)$$

where $\Delta\tilde{g}_f^0$ = standard Gibbs functions of formation
$\tilde{\epsilon}_j$ = standard molar chemical exergy of the i-th element making up the compound
n_i = corresponding number of moles per mole of the compound

In addition to the table of standard chemical exergy of chemical elements these values have also been computed and tabulated for a variety of organic and inorganic chemical compounds [15, 17]. The use of such tables greatly facilitate calculating exergy balances for chemical processes.

Chemical Exergy of Industrial Fuels

Solid and liquid industrial fuels are solutions of numerous chemical compounds of, usually, unknown nature. This makes the calculation of their chemical exergy from Expression 13 or 16 very difficult. To overcome this problem, Szargut and Styrylska [19] determine the correlations that exists between chemical exergy and the net calorific value, (NCV), for pure organic substances. They assumed in their work that the ratio

$$\varphi = \frac{\epsilon_0}{(NCV)} \qquad (17)$$

for solid and liquid industrial fuels is the same as for pure chemical substances having the same atomic ratios of their constituent elements. After computing values of φ for numerous pure dry organic substances, correlations expressing the dependence of φ on the atomic ratios H/C, O/C, N/C, and in some cases S/C, were worked out. A correction is made for the moisture content of solid industrial fuels [15].

When the processes occurring within the control region are purely physical, the chemical exergy of the streams entering and leaving the control region is the same and therefore will cancel out in the exergy balance. Under these conditions only the physical components of exergy need to be considered. However, outside this special area the use of some form of chemical exergy is essential. In particular this applies when the processes under consideration include chemical reactions, and the processes occurring within the control region include exchange of substances with the environment.

"Relative" Chemical Exergy

The form of chemical exergy based on a system of reference substances selected from among common environmental substances as previously described is of general utility and can be used in both the cases just given. However, in the case of a chemical process *without* the exchange of substances with the environment the use of chemical exergy based on environmental substances is not essential. For such cases an alternative form of chemical exergy, which may be called *relative chemical energy* proposed by Sussman [20] may be used. If we consider Equation 16 as the basis of evaluation of chemical exergy, it will be realized that in the case of an open system operating under steady flow conditions the part of the chemical exergy contributed by the second term on the RHS of Equation 16 will be the same for the streams entering and leaving the control region and hence will cancel out in an exergy balance. Thus for any processes for which the states of the streams at the control surfaces are known, a "relative" form of chemical exergy can be used that is equal to the negative value of the Gibbs function of formation of the substance under consideration. As will be realized, the reference substances in this case are the chemical elements in the environmental state (P_0, T_0). However, when the open system under consideration involves exchange of substances with the environment, the substances exchanged must be referred to some suitable reference substances in the environment, and thus under these circumstances the use of the "absolute" form of chemical exergy will be found more convenient. Furthermore, this form of chemical exergy does not possess the physical significance that can usually be attached to the absolute values of chemical exergy.

To overcome the difficulty of finding the entropy data necessary for the exergy analysis of chemical processes Linnhoff et al. [11, 12, 13, 14, 21, 22] developed expressions for entropy and exergy change "across the unit," which make use of enthalpy data calculated as part of the energy analysis of the plant. Thus, for exergy change of a stream he gives the following expression:

$$\dot{E}_2 - \dot{E}_1 = \dot{m}\left[(h_2 - h_1)\left(1 - \frac{T_0}{T_2 - T_1}\ln\frac{T_2}{T_1}\right) - RT_0 \ln\frac{P_2}{P_1}\right] \tag{18}$$

which is specifically applicable to the case when $T_1 \neq T_2$. For a process or a part of a process for which T = const and P = const the expression is

$$\dot{E}_2 - \dot{E}_1 = \dot{m}(h_2 - h_1)\left(1 - \frac{T_0}{T}\right) \tag{19}$$

Although the derivation of Expression 18 involves the assumption that c_p = const, the error involved is usually small, and hence the accuracy of the "short-cut" technique is adequate for most practical applications.

In the case of a process involving a chemical reaction or separation of components from a mixture, appropriate terms that account for exergy changes due to these phenomena must be introduced into the exergy balance.

Reference States for Chemical Exergy

As previously stated, the values of chemical exergy calculated by Szargut and his co-workers are based on a system of reference substances using the average values of the concentrations at which they are found in the natural environment. Such a standard system of reference substances and the resulting standard chemical exergies of substances may be found very convenient in the calculation of exergy balances for a variety of chemical processes. There are, however, circumstances where the use of the standard reference substances would be inappropriate. For example in the case of a sea water desalination plant, zero exergy value is allocated to sea water, which under these circumstances must be looked upon as the reference substance for H_2O. A more thorough discussion of the theory of reference states applicable to exergy analysis will be found in References 23 and 24.

Enthalpy of Devaluation

In the case of processes that include chemical reactions it is convenient to consider chemical energy by including it in the enthalpy of each substance involved in the reactions. For this purpose the enthalpy may, as in the case of exergy, be divided into the physical and the chemical components. In the form of chemical enthalpy proposed by Szargut [17] common environmental substances of low chemical potential are used as reference substances. In this respect it is similar to chemical exergy although the substances selected are limited to those from the atmosphere and the Earth's crust (substances from the oceans are not used). The name given to this form of chemical enthalpy is *enthalpy of devaluation* and the symbol h_d is used for its specific value. In the special case of fuels enthalpy of devaluation is identical to the calorific value. Thus, as follows from the previous description the specific enthalpy of a substance may be written in the following form

$$h = h_{ph}\Big|_{T_0 P_0}^{T,P} + h_d(T_0, P_0) \tag{20}$$

where h_{ph} is the physical component of enthalpy. The standard values of molar enthalpy of devaluation, $\tilde{h}_d$, for the most common chemical elements and chemical compounds are available in tabular form [15]. Using these values the steady flow energy equation for a chemically reacting open system can be written as follows (with the kinetic and potential energy terms neglected):

$$\dot{Q} - \dot{W}_x = \sum_k n_k \tilde{h}_{ph,k} - \sum_j n_j \tilde{h}_{ph,j} + \sum_k n_k \tilde{h}_{d,k} - \sum_j n_j \tilde{h}_{d,j} \tag{21}$$

where the subscripts j and k refer to the incoming and the outgoing streams respectively.

The use of enthalpy of devaluation is based on the same philosophy as that of chemical exergy, namely that in any balance (energy or exergy) all the terms (except irreversibility rate) refer to states on the control surface rather than to the processes taking place inside it. In the "across the unit" approach an energy or exergy balance has a mixture of terms that refer to states at the control surface and to the process, i.e., ethalpy of the reaction and the Gibbs function of the reaction. The similarity of the concept of enthalpy of devaluation with chemical exergy makes the use of the two in chemical process calculations most convenient. Some selected standard values of both enthalpy of devaluation and the corresponding reference substances of the chemical elements listed are given in Table 1.

Study Objectives

In a competitive free market economy the primary objective aimed for in plant design will, more often than not, be the lowest manufacturing cost of the product. Additional requirements may include safety, process flexibility, controllability, protection of the environment, etc. Attaining this primary objective is dependent on the plant designer's success in achieving an optimal synthesis of the production system. The main elements of the process of optimal synthesis are:

1. Synthesis of an optimal system structure i.e. an optimal arrangement of appropriate components in the system.
2. Assessment of economically justified costs of the plant components.

The first element is usually the more difficult of the two. There are no formal techniques of general applicability for determining an optimal system structure. The only systematic techniques of synthesis of thermal systems that have been successfully developed up to now are special techniques for specific areas of application. One of these areas of application is the synthesis of heat exchanger networks which, since it is a well-defined, close-ended problem, can be dealt with in a systematic way [25 to 28]. More open-ended types in the problem of synthesis of distillation systems [29 to 31] and integration of heat and power networks [28, 32], for which specific techniques are available. For most other types of systems, the synthesis of optimal system structure still amounts to a succession of alternating steps of analysis and synthesis. Consequently, in this type of approach the availability of effective techniques of system analysis and evaluation is most important. These techniques have two roles to play in the overall process. One of these roles is to help in the learning process. The study of simple and complex systems with the object of revealing their performance characteristics under different operating conditions leads to an accumulation of knowledge that can be subsequently applied in the design process. The techniques developed as part of the exergy method can be particularly useful in this context because the information of interest is easily quantifiable in terms of the concepts of exergy, irreversibility rate, and performance indicators derived from them. Several studies [15] of this type have been carried out for simple systems such as heat exchangers, expanders, compressors, throttling devices, as well as for complex systems, e.g., air liquefaction plants. The other role of analysis is to assess the performance of the plant configuration arrived at a particular stage of the process of system synthesis and to provide pointers for possible improvements in the next step of this process. Thus, clearly plant analysis, through its two-fold role is an essential element of an evolutionary process of system synthesis.

Another aspect of study objectives that ought to be clarified is the question of how the overall control surface should be drawn for a thermal or chemical plant. Most of these plants interact with the environment by exchanging with it heat and substances. The irreversibilities associated with these interactions should be reflected in the value of the efficiency calculated for the plant. Clearly, plants that reject high grade heat to the environment should surface a reduction in the overall efficiency commensurate with the energy degradation resulting from it. The same applies to chemical plants that reject to the environment substances with high chemical potential. To take these effects into account the control surface of the plant must be extended to include parts of the environment in which degradation of energy and substances occurs. In the latter case the loss of energy can be easily calculated if chemical exergy values evaluated with reference to common environmental substance of low chemical potential are used.

EXERGY AND TOOLS AND TECHNIQUES

Criteria of Performance

The concept of exergy affords means of formulating new criteria of performance that offer some advantages over the traditional ones. Several workers in this area, among them Bošnjaković [33] and Fratzscher [34], have proposed some general criteria of performance based on the concept of exergy. Also Szargut and Petela [17] defined exergy-based efficiencies applicable to particular plants. Rational efficiency [9] is a criterion of performance that can be formulated for any steadily operating thermal plant or plant component for which the output is expressible in terms of exergy. Unless the process under consideration is purely dissipative (i.e., it has no exergy output) the exergy balance for it can be put in the following form.

$$\sum \Delta\dot{E}_{OUT} = \sum \Delta\dot{E}_{IN} - \dot{I} \qquad (22)$$

where $\sum \Delta\dot{E}_{OUT}$ = sum of all energy transfer making up the desired output
$\sum \Delta\dot{E}_{IN}$ = sum of all energy transfers making up the necessary input
$\dot{I}$ = irreversibility rate associated with the process under consideration

Defining the rational efficiency*, ψ, as a ratio of exergy output to exergy input and dividing Equation 22 by $\sum \Delta \dot{E}_{IN}$ we get

$$\psi = \frac{\sum \Delta \dot{E}_{OUT}}{\sum \Delta \dot{E}_{IN}}$$

$$= 1 - \frac{\dot{I}}{\sum \Delta \dot{E}_{IN}} \tag{23}$$

Thus, as shown in Equation 23 the use of the exergy balance yields an alternative expression for ψ. Since from the Second Law

$$\dot{I} \geq 0 \tag{24}$$

and also since

$$\sum \Delta \dot{E}_{OUT} \geq 0 \tag{25}$$

the range of values of ψ lies within the following limits

$$0 \leq \psi \leq 1 \tag{26}$$

By introducing $\dot{I} = \dot{I}_{intrinsic}$ into the second of the two expressions for ψ given by Equation 23 we obtain the maximum practical value of ψ corresponding to the set of physical, technological, and economic constraints, applicable to the plant under consideration.

Note that not all forms of efficiency formulated as a ratio of two exergy values or exergy changes will satisfy the inequality given by Equation 26. In this respect rational efficiency occupies a special position among the different possible forms of exergetic efficiencies [34] and, perhaps, has not been accorded the adjective "rational" undeservedly. When dealing with a multi-component plant the total irreversibility in the form given by Equation 25 can be used. This leads to

$$1 - \psi = \frac{\sum_{N} \dot{I}_i}{\sum \Delta \dot{E}_{IN}} \tag{27}$$

The difference $(1 - \psi)$ is clearly that fraction of the input that is lost through irreversibility and is known as efficiency defect, δ. As can be seen from the RHS of Equation 27 it is made up of contributions from the different components of the plant. If the contribution of the i-th component is expressed as

$$\delta_i = \frac{\dot{I}_i}{\sum \Delta \dot{E}_{IN}} \tag{28}$$

expression Equation 27 can be written as follows

$$1 = \psi + \delta_1 + \delta_2 + \cdots + \delta_N \tag{29}$$

The RHS of Expression 29 shows in dimensionless form how the exergy input to the plant (unity) is split up into the useful output, represented by ψ, and the part that is dissipated in the different plant components given by δ_i's. This information can be represented in graphic form as a pie diagram or, as a Grassmann diagram.

* Rational efficiency is a particular form of exergetic efficiency.

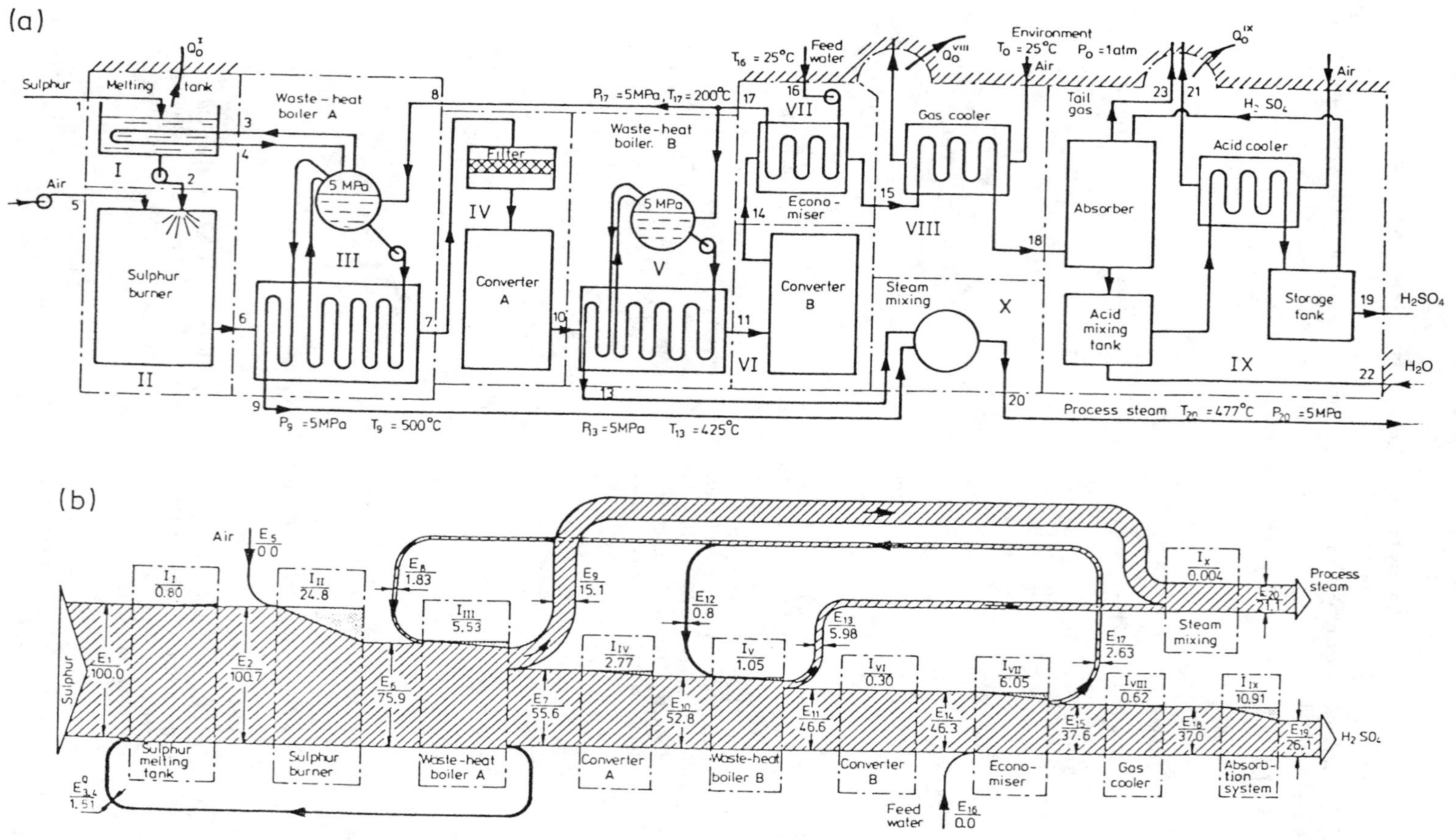

Figure 5. Sulphuric acid plant, (a) plant diagram (b) Grassmann diagram. (Reproduced with permission from Ref. 15.)

Grassmann Diagram

A list of component irreversibilities may provide suitable means of examining the performance of a simple plant. However, in the case of more complex plants consisting of a number of components, there is a distinct advantage in presenting the information in a pictorial way. A very useful diagram for the pictorial representation of exergy flows and losses is known as *Grassmann diagram.* This diagram may be considered as an adaptation of the Sankey diagram, which is used to represent energy transfers within a plant. Figure 5 is an example of this pictorial presentation of exergy analysis. The width of the band is a measure of the magnitude of the exergy flow at the entry or the exit of a particular sub-region. Each sub-region is represented as a rectangular box and the reduction in the width of the band, shown dotted, is a measure of the exergy loss, or irreversibility rate, in a given sub-region. In more complex plants the Grassmann diagram can be particularly valuable since it shows not only energy losses but also the splitting of exergy streams and recirculation of exergy. It also shows graphically how the original input of exergy is dissipated in the successive stages of energy transformation in the plant.

The diagram can be presented either in a dimensional or dimensionless form. In the former case the values of exergy and irreversibility rate can be expressed in units of power, say, kW.

Exergy Based Property Diagrams

Several exergy-based property diagrams has been devised for analyzing processes by the exergy method. A particularly useful one for analyzing power cycles, refrigeration cycles, and cryogenic processes is the exergy-enthalpy diagram. The $\epsilon - h$ diagram shown in Figure 6, is typical in its form of substances such as water, substance, ammonia, and a number of fluorinated refrigerants. By drawing the cycle or the process under analysis on such a chart a number of different quantities such as

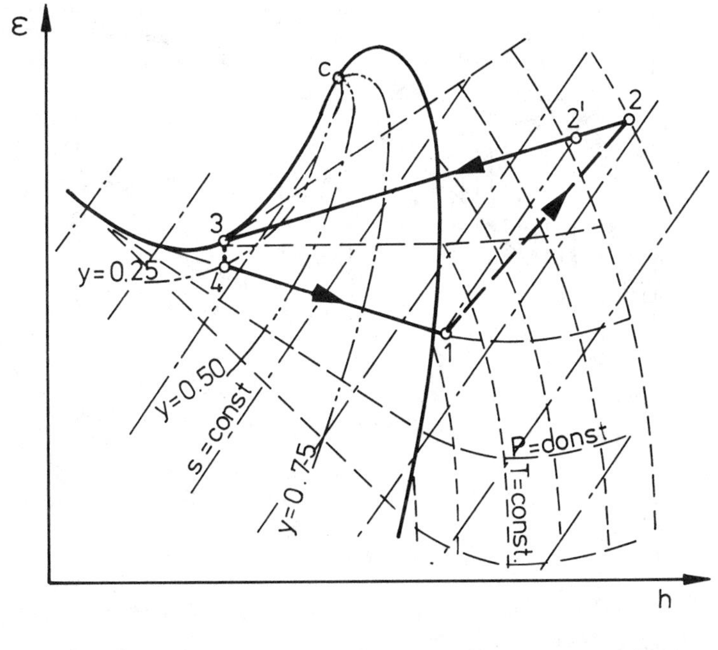

Figure 6. $\epsilon - h$ diagram for a refrigeration cycle. (Reproduced with permission from Ref. 15.)

exergy change, enthalpy change and irreversibility can be read off directly. Since the processes analyzed on such charts are of a physical type, the exergy coordinate plotted is usually physical exergy or exergy with an arbitrary reference level of the following type

$$\epsilon = h - T_0 s + C \tag{30}$$

where C is an arbitrary constant. Some examples of such diagrams and their method of application are given by Glaser [35] Brodyanskii and Ishkin [36] and Auracher [37]. The $\epsilon - h$ diagram can be also found useful for demonstrating the thermodynamic principles of cycles and processes including those involving ideal gases [15].

An exergy-concentration chart for a binary mixture consisting of O_2 and N_2 in the molar ratio of 0.21 to 0.79 has been constructed by Brodyanskii [38]. This type of chart can be used for reading off directly the minimum work of separation for products of different degree of purity. Although this appears to be the only example of an exergy-concentration chart, similar charts could be easily constructed for other binary mixtures given the necessary data.

Heat transfer processes in which the main source of irreversibility is heat transfer over a finite temperature difference can be conveniently analyzed by means of a *dimensionless exergetic temperature – enthalpy* diagram. Dimensionless exergetic temperature, τ, is the name given to the Carnot efficiency based on the temperature of the environment (see Equation 2), i.e.

$$\tau = 1 - T_0/T \tag{31}$$

An example of application of this type of diagram to the regenerative heat exchanger of a Linde air liquefaction plant is shown in Figure 7. The difference between the two cross-hatched area shows the

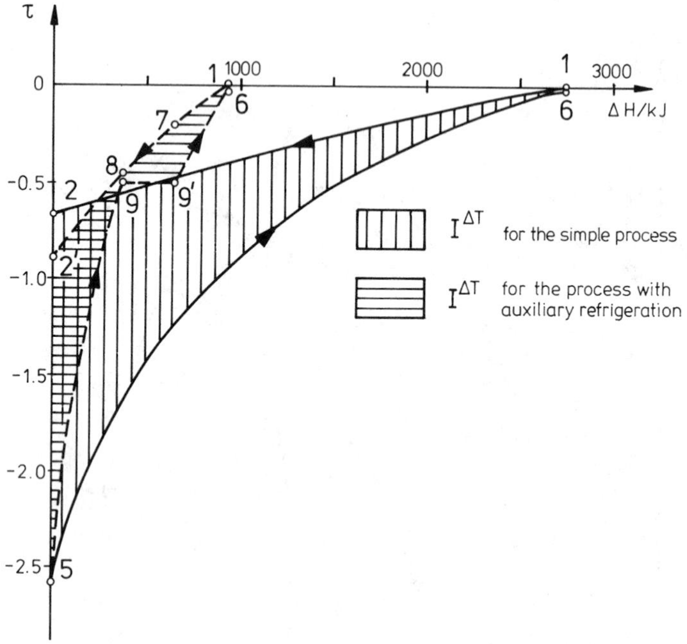

Figure 7. Evaluation of heat exchange process irreversibility from $\tau - \Delta H$ diagram. (Reproduced with permission from Ref. 15.)

effect of the introduction of auxiliary refrigeration on the irreversibility of the heat exchange process [15].

Exergy Based Property Tables

The availability of tables [15, 17] of standard values of chemical energy and enthalpy of devaluation can be of great help in chemical process calculations.

To facilitate the calculation of the physical component of exergy of ideal gases it can be expressed as a sum of two components, the isobaric component, $\tilde{\epsilon}^{\Delta T}$, and the isothermal component, $\tilde{\epsilon}^{\Delta P}$, i.e.

$$\tilde{\epsilon}_{ph} = \tilde{\epsilon}^{\Delta T} + \tilde{\epsilon}^{\Delta P}$$

$$= \tilde{c}_p^{\epsilon}(T - T_0) + \tilde{R}T_0 \ln \frac{P}{P_0} \tag{32}$$

where $$\tilde{c}_p^{\epsilon} = \frac{\tilde{\epsilon}^{\Delta T}}{(T - T_0)} \tag{33}$$

The thermodynamic function $\tilde{c}_p^{\epsilon}$ has been called the *mean molar isobaric exergy capacity*. Two forms of mean molar isobaric heat capacities may be defined one for enthalpy and the other for entropy evaluation. They are respectively

$$\tilde{c}_p^h = \frac{1}{T - T_0} \int_{T_0}^{T} \tilde{c}_p \, dT \tag{34}$$

$$c_p^s = \frac{1}{\ln(T/T_0)} \int_{T_0}^{T} \frac{\tilde{c}_p \, dT}{T} \tag{35}$$

where $\tilde{c}_p$ is the molar isobaric specific heat capacity. Using a polynomial expression for $\tilde{c}_p$ [39] both $\tilde{c}_p^h$ and $\tilde{c}_p^s$ can be evaluated. Hence c_p^{ϵ} can be calculated from

$$\tilde{c}_p^{\epsilon} = \tilde{c}_p^h - T_0\tilde{c}_p^s \frac{\ln(T/T_0)}{T - T_0} \tag{36}$$

Values of $\tilde{c}_p^h$, $\tilde{c}_p^s$ and $\tilde{c}_p^{\epsilon}$ have been tabulated for a number of common gases over a range of temperatures with $T_0 = 298$ K [15].

By using tables of $\tilde{h}_d^0$, $\tilde{\epsilon}^0$, $\tilde{c}_p^h$ and $\tilde{c}_p^{\epsilon}$ energy and exergy balances for physical and chemical processes can be carried out speedily.

Coefficient of Structural Bonds

Irreversibility rate provides means of assessment of the thermodynamic performance of individual plant components as well as that of the whole plant. This makes it possible not only to compare the exergy losses of the different plant components under static conditions but also to investigate their relative changes as a result of a change in a selected plant parameter. These relative changes can be conveniently expressed in the form of the *coefficient of structural bonds* or CSB for short. The CSB is defined by the following relation

$$\sigma_{k,i} = \left[\frac{\partial \dot{I}_T}{\partial x_i}\right] \bigg/ \left[\frac{\partial \dot{I}_k}{\partial x_i}\right] \tag{37}$$

where $\dot{I}_T$ = irreversibility rate of the whole plant
$\dot{I}_k$ = irreversibility rate of the k-th plant component
x_i = plant parameter which is varied

If the exergy output rate of the plant under analysis is fixed and the exergy input is of only one type and of invariable quality (e.g., fuel or electricity) a reduction in the plant irreversibility rate, $\Delta\dot{I}_T$, leads to an equal reduction in the plant exergy input rate, $\Delta\dot{E}_{IN}$, i.e.

$$\Delta\dot{I}_T = \Delta\dot{E}_{IN} \tag{38}$$

Hence, for a finite change in the parameter x_i, Equation 37 may be put in the following form

$$\Delta\dot{E}_{IN} = \sigma_{k,i}\,\Delta\dot{I}_k \tag{39}$$

This expression shows clearly the effect of changes in local irreversibility rates on the exergy input to the plant. As values of $\sigma_{k,i}$ are different for different plant components, Equation 39 may be said to demonstrate the *thermodynamic non-equivalence of exergy and exergy losses.*

It is instructive to examine the significance of the following possible ranges of values of $\sigma_{k,i}$.

1. In the case when

$$\sigma_{k,i} > 1 \tag{40}$$

the reduction in the input to the system (saving in primary exergy) is greater than the reduction in the irreversibility of the element under consideration (k-th element). Clearly in this case, the change in x_i affects favorably not only the k-th element but also, owing to the existence of bonds between them, other elements. When this situation exists, it is particularly advantageous to optimize the k-th element because of its potentially favorable impact on the overall plant efficiency.

2. In the case when

$$\sigma_{k,i} < 1 \tag{41}$$

the reduction in the input to the system is less than the reduction in the irreversibility of the k-th element. Clearly, here a *reduction* in the irreversibility rate in the k-th element is accompanied by *increases* in the irreversibility rates in other elements of the plant. This range of values of $\sigma_{k,i}$ demonstrates an unfavorable structure of the system.

3. As a special case we have

$$\sigma_{k,i} = 0 \tag{42}$$

which means that the improvement in the performance of the k-th element is counterbalanced by an equal reduction in performance of other elements (as measured by $\dot{I}$) so that there is no effect on the overall plant efficiency. This case demonstrates a rigid structure of the system that does not permit the benefits of a local improvement in performance to be passed on to the plant as a whole.

4. It is possible to have

$$\sigma_{k,i} < 0 \tag{43}$$

which would indicate that the parameter x_i affects other elements more strongly than it affects the k-th element and in the opposite sense, i.e., when the irreversibility rate in the k-th element *decreases*, it *increases* in other plant elements by a greater amount. This clearly demonstrates a very unfavorable system structure.

Among these four cases only Case 1 represents a really favorable system structure. The other three cases represent, to different degrees, unfavorable system structures that, subject to economic and other constraints, should be changed through the introduction of suitable plant modifications.

The concept of CSB has been found useful in the following two areas of application:

- Values of CSB's calculated for the plant components in conjunction with suitable variables have been used as means of studying system structure [40 to 44]. Although this area of application is probably the least developed in the whole field of exergy analysis, there is no doubt that CSB is a most powerful thermodynamic indicator, which, together with other information derived from exergy analysis, offers a possible basis for the development of a more systematic approach to the study and improvement of system structures.
- The CSB is used in a technique of thermoeconomic optimization of plant components. This technique will be described below.

The concept of the CSB has been originally put forward by Beyer who also developed some of the associated techniques of analysis and optimization [40 to 44]. Several contributions to the development of this subject have been made by Brodyanskii and his co-workers [38, 45, 46].

THERMOECONOMIC APPLICATIONS OF EXERGY

Thermoeconomics combines concepts of the exergy method with those belonging to economic analysis. The purpose of thermoeconomic optimization is to achieve, within a given system structure, a balance between expenditure on capital costs and exergy costs that result in a minimum cost of the plant product. The complexity of thermal systems makes their thermoeconomic optimization often very difficult. Therefore, the basic objective of the research into the methodology of thermoeconomic optimization is to simplify the optimization procedure while ensuring that the results obtained are within acceptable limits of accuracy. Thermoeconomic optimization is usually carried out after an efficient system structure has been arrived at.

The advantage of using the exergy method of thermoeconomic optimization is that the various elements of the system can be optimized on their own, the effect of the interaction between the given element and the whole system being taken into account by local unit costs of exergy flows or those of exergy losses. The individual optimization of system elements is made possible in these methods because of the universality of exergy as a standard of quality of energy and the availability of the concept of irreversibility rate as a measure of process imperfection.

There are currently in existence basically two different methods that use the exergy concepts. One of these, which is based on concepts introduced by Beyer [42, 43, 44], depends on the use of structural coefficients and related concepts for the evaluation of local unit costs of irreversibilities. This method will be called the *structural method.* In the other method [47, 48] the autonomous thermoeconomic optimization of system elements is made possible through the use of local unit costs of exergy flows entering and leaving the elements under consideration. This method will be called the *autonomous method.*

The Structural Method of Thermoeconomic Optimization

The applicability of this method is restricted to plants with exergy input of one type (e.g. fuel oil or electricity, etc). More than one form of exergy input is admissible only if their relative exergy flow rates remain the same so that a single unit cost can be attached to the input exergy. In order to optimize the cost of one of the components it is assumed that there is one parameter, x_i, which can influence its performance and, in most cases, also indirectly affect the performance of the whole plant. Any variation in the parameter x_i will also, in general, cause changes in the irreversibility rates of other plant elements and also may necessitate changes in their capital costs. Taking the plant output to be fixed the objective function is the annual operating cost, which can be expressed as follows

$$C_T(x_i) = t_{op} c^{\varepsilon}_{IN} \dot{E}_{IN}(x_i) + a^c \sum_{l=1}^{n} C^c_l(x_i) + b^c \tag{44}$$

where t_{op} = period of operation per year
c^{ϵ}_{IN} = unit cost of input exergy to the system
a^c = capital recovery factor, which when multiplied by the total investment gives the annual repayment necessary to pay back the investment after a specified period
C^c_l = capital cost of the l-th element of the system consisting of n elements
b^c = the part of the annual cost which is not affected by the optimization

The optimum condition corresponds to

$$C_T(x_i) \longrightarrow \min$$

and is given by

$$\left[\frac{\partial \dot{I}_k}{\partial x_i}\right]_{OPT} = -\frac{a^c}{t_{op} c^I_{k,i}} \frac{\partial C^c_k}{\partial x_i} \tag{45}$$

where

$$c^I_{k,i} = c^{\epsilon}_{IN} \sigma_{k,i} + \frac{a^c}{t_{op}} \xi_{k,i} \tag{46}$$

$$\xi_{k,i} = \sum_{l'=1}^{n} \frac{\partial C^c_{l'}}{\partial \dot{I}_k} \tag{47}$$

with $l' \neq k$

i.e., subscript l′ marks any of the plant components except the one that is the subject of the optimization procedure. The expression defines the *capital cost coefficient*.

Equation 46 defines the unit cost of irreversibility in the k-th plant element, and may be said to demonstrate the *thermoeconomic non-equivalence of irreversibilities* occurring in the differing plant components. What this means is that although the unit cost of primary exergy supplied to the whole system is fixed at the value determined by external economic factors, the unit cost of compensation for the loss of exergy (irreversibility) will vary from component to component. This thermoeconomic indicator takes into account the thermodynamic non-equivalence of irreversibilities through $\sigma_{k,i}$, while the capital investment (the economic) contribution to this indicator comes from the term containing $\xi_{k,i}$. This coefficient gives a measure of the changes in the capital costs of the elements (other than the k-th element) resulting from the change in the irreversibility rate in the k-th element. For some elements of a plant the contribution to the value of this coefficient may be very small. This may lead to a situation when the second term on the RHS of equation 46 may be neglected leading to a substantial saving in calculations. In an illustrative example of thermoeconomic optimization of a heat exchanger in a back-pressure CHP plant, it was shown [15] that the term involving $\xi_{k,i}$ accounted only for about 12% of the value of $c^I_{k,i}$.

The structural method has not been as yet adapted to the optimization of multi-component plants. Consequently, it will require some more development work before it can compete with existing computer package programs that have been designed for this purpose.

The Autonomous Method of Thermoeconomic Optimization

In this approach the system is decomposed into several suitably selected sub-systems or zones. The technique is based on the assumption that the balance between the capital cost rate and the expenditure rate necessary to compensate for process irreversibility can be applied to each zone in the same way as to the whole plant i.e. the zone is treated as if it was an *autonomous* system. The general cost equation for an autonomous *Zone X* can be expressed in the following form.

$$\sum_{OUT,\,x} (\dot{E}_i c_i^{\epsilon}) = \sum_{IN,\,x} (\dot{E}_i c_i^{\epsilon}) + \dot{Z}_x \tag{48}$$

where $\dot{E}_i$ = is the exergy flux rate of the i-th stream
c_i^{ϵ} = is the corresponding unit cost of exergy, and
$\dot{Z}_x$ = is the capital expenditure rate for Zone X

Since, owing to irreversibility of all real processes, the total exergy output for a zone is always less than the exergy input, and because of the additional cost $\dot{Z}_x$ involved in the process the unit cost of exergy tends to increase in the direction of its flow.

The key to the success of this method lies in the determination of the proper values of unit costs of exergy for the exergy fluxes crossing the zone boundary. Where there is only one exergy input and one exergy output stream, c_{OUT}^{ϵ} can be easily determined provided c_{IN}^{ϵ} and the other parameters in Equation 48 are known. In such a case the unit cost of exergy at a point of a zone boundary can be obtained by following the path of exergy flow from the input point to the plant where the unit cost will be generally known from commercial considerations. Where there is more than one input or output exergy stream involved in the zone under consideration additional information or assumptions are required.

El-Sayed and Evans [48] demonstrated mathematically the basic elements of this technique, namely the decomposition of a system into autonomous zones and the method of determination of the unit costs of exergy fluxes, on a simple system consisting of three elements in series. The autonomous method has been applied to a number of technical problems.

Among these we have the optimization of a vapor compression desalination plant [49], costing of the heating and the power output of a CHP plant [50], and maintenance and operating decisions concerning defective feed heaters in a steam power plant [51].

The autonomous method is quite time consuming and for its successful application requires a high level of expertise, so that in its present state of development it is unlikely to find many followers particularly in its application to cost optimization of multi-component plants.

APPLICATIONS

Cryogenic Processes

The application of the exergy method to low-temperature processes can be particularly fruitful since in this area the overall plant efficiency is particularly sensitive to component efficiencies. As can be shown by means of the exergy method [15] the mean temperature difference in heat exchange must decrease with decreasing operating temperature if a particular value of the rational efficiency of the heat exchanger is to be maintained. It has also been shown that the irreversibility rate associated with the operation of expanders and compressors of a given isentropic efficiency increases with decreasing temperature. One of the earliest examples of application of the Second Law analysis is due to Kapitsa [52] who analyzed the individual processes of an air liquefaction plant and found that the throttling process accounted for an inordinatedly high proportion of total plant irreversibility. This led him to the replacement of the throttling valve with an expander.

Papers by Gardner and Smith [53] and Benedict and Gyftopoulos [54] represent early yet effective examples of analysis of air liquefaction plants. In fact, the latter of the two papers is based on an unpublished lecture given at MIT in 1949. The analysis of the plants consisted of calculation of both intrinsic and actual irreversibilities of the plant components. In both papers simple forms of thermoeconomic optimization of the main heat exchangers were carried out by trading off "lost work" against the capital cost of these components.

In an interesting study Brodyanskii and Ishkin [55] analyzed the distribution of irreversibilities in both the simple Linde plant and in one with auxiliary refrigeration. Particularly effective is the use of the τ-ΔH diagram (see Figure 7), which shows the two-fold effect of auxiliary refrigeration on the reduction in the irreversibility of the heat exchange process. This is due to the reduction both in the mean temperature difference and in the mass flow rate of fresh air necessary for given output of liquified air. The latter factor leads to the reduction in the irreversibility rate of other plant components. Thus, this study is particularly successful in highlighting the structural bonds between the plant components.

Distillation Processes

The publications involving the application of exergy concepts to the analysis of distillation processes fall mainly into the following two categories.

1. Analysis of the whole distillation plant with the object of determining the principal factors contributing to the overall plant irreversibility.
2. Analysis of the processes occurring in a distillation column with the aim of arriving at new, thermodynamically more efficient designs.

In the first category are two publications on air liquefaction plant namely those by Gardner and Smith [53] and Benedict and Gyftopoulos [54] which were just referred to in connection with cryogenic processes. Similar analysis was carried out on an oil distillation plant by Michalek [57].

The work corresponding to this second category has been dealt with at some length in References 15 and 57. The paper by Fitzmorris and Mah [58] is also largely concerned with the thermodynamic performance of distillation columns. In this paper the authors discussed in terms of exergy the losses that occur in a distillation column and proposed four different forms of thermodynamic, second law efficiencies. Using these tools they calculated component irreversibilities and efficiencies for the column and the systems as a whole for the conventional distillation process, vapor compression process and secondary reflux and vaporization (SRV) process. By varying in turn the reflux ratio and the number of stages they demonstrated the effect of these two parameters on the irreversibilities and the efficiencies.

Linnhoff and Smith [59] concerned about the low thermodynamic efficiency of distillation columns apply exergy analysis to the problem. In order to select the most suitable criterion for the assessment of the performance of a distillation column they consider the merits and drawbacks of various alternative forms of exergetic efficiencies. Then they examine the behavior of these efficiencies using a computer package simulating distillation over a range of practical applications. They conclude that an assessment of the variable scope for improvement in the efficiency of the distillation column should be made with reference to an "ideal distillation" process, i.e., one in which (for binary feed) the process is arranged to occur reversibly.

The efficiency of the distillation process is also the subject of a paper by Fonyo and Rev [60]. Their main contribution is a detailed analysis and identificatiion of losses expressed in terms of entropy production inside and outside the column. The authors then give a comprehensive list of energy-saving policies aiming to reduce the different types of irreversibilities. Drawing on their own theoretical studies and practical experience, they recommend the use of interboilers and intercondensers as well as energy integration concepts as the most effective energy conservation methods.

Chemical Processes

The steep rise in the cost of fuels that occurred in the last decade has led to a search for ways of upgrading and modifying fuels in an efficient manner to fit in with the pattern of demand in the national economies of different countries. Many authors have accordingly turned to the Second Law analysis for means of improving the performance of the production plants.

In an effort to pinpoint the causes of plant inefficiency Singh et al. [61] have calculated the irreversibilities of the various constituent processes making up the HYGAS process of producing substitute natural gas from bituminous coal. They found that the largest irreversibilities were associated with three major chemical conversion process steps, namely pre-treatment, gasification, and combustion for steam generation. A similar type of plant was analyzed by the exergy method by Tsatsaronis et al. [62]. However, in this case the plant was a pilot plant for the hydrogasification of coal with the aid of thermal energy delivered by a HTGR nuclear plant. From the results of the analysis the authors produced some recommendation for improving the plant performance.

Kapner and Lannus [63] analyzed a catalytic reforming process for upgrading low-octane petroleum containing significant quantities of aromatic hydrocarbons. The object of this analysis was to compare the theoretical minimum irreversibility of the process with that calculated for the actual process. From this analysis the authors have concluded that there is a substantial potential for improvement in the performance of the plant, and identified areas where plant modification or long-term research were required.

As a result of the general energy conservation drive of the recent years, the efficiency of production of a number of basic chemicals was assessed using the exergy Method. Riekert calculated the irreversibilities associated with various stages of production of ammonia from natural gas and nitric acid from ammonia [64] using values of chemical exergy based on reference substances present in the atmosphere. In a later publication [65] Riekert analyzed by similar techniques the processes of methanol from naphtha and natural gas and the subsequent production of formaldehyde from methanol. In all cases Riekert represented the flows and losses of energy with the aid of Grassmann diagrams.

Cremer analyzed [66] a synthesis-gas plant and an ammonia plant operating in series by calculating the entropy rates from the various streams entering and leaving plant components. From these values he calculated entropy production and hence using the Gouy-Stodola relation (see Equation 6) the irreversibility rate for each plant component. This technique, however, does not give absolute values of exergy of the streams entering or leaving the plant, and consequently, it is not possible to evaluate external irreversibilities such as that due to discharge of waste products into the environment. This technique also does not provide the necessary quantities for the evaluation of the rational efficiency of the process.

The technique of chemical plant analysis described in Reference 15 does not suffer from these drawbacks. It provides a systematic approach to the calculation of quantities necessary for the application energy and exergy balances to the plant and the sub-regions into which it may be divided. Figure 5a shows a simplified diagram of a plant producing sulfuric acid, using the sulfur-burning contact method. The results of the calculations are presented in the form of the Grassmann diagram in Figure 5b. Because of the exothermic nature of the process substantial quantities of process steam are produced. The integration of the two parallel processes of the production of H_2SO_4 and steam makes the overall rational efficiency relatively high. From Figure 5b we have $\psi_{0v} = (\dot{E}_{19} + \dot{E}_{20})/\dot{E}_1 = 0.211 + 0.261 = 0.472$. Since some of the sub-regions, namely the sulfur burner, the economizer and the absorption system, show appreciable irreversibilities, further improvement in the performance of the plant through better integration of the two processes is possible.

The relatively large consumption of fossil fuels in metallurgical plants has provided an incentive for a search for fuel economies. One of the earliest but also one of the most comprehensive analyses was carried out by Szargut et al. [67] on a complete steel production plant. The plant analyzed consisted of a coking plant, CHP plant, sinter plant, blast furnance, open hearth furnace, rolling mill, and several auxiliary installations. A more recent contribution to this subject area is due to Morris et al. [68]. The initial part of this paper is devoted to an outline of the theory on which determination of chemical exergy is based and to the actual calculation of the values of chemical exergy for a number of elements, compounds, and complex substances such as coke, slag, and sinter, which are of interest in the process under consideration. The plant analyzed included all the major components, namely the sinter plant, acid plan, blast furnace, and refinery. For all these components irreversibility rates were calculated. The results of this analysis were discussed and recommendations for improving the plant performance were made.

Several papers give accounts of the type of plant analysis that consists basically of calculation of irreversibilities of plant components. This approach can have in some cases a useful function by alerting the design engineer to the need for improving the thermodynamic efficiency of the components with the largest avoidable irreversibilities. Also, given the necessary degree of understanding of the nature of these irreversibilities and their causes, the information obtained from the analysis can serve as a basis for a step towards a more efficient process. However, in many cases substantial improvements in performance are only possible through a thorough rearangement of the system structure. To do this successfully a systematic approach to process synthesis is needed.

Process Synthesis

Although the analysis of thermal systems by the exergy method may have reached an advanced state of development, exergy concepts and techniques in process synthesis is still in its infancy. The principal types of approaches to process synthesis that have been developed so far were briefly reviewed under "Study Objectives." Also the importance of analysis in the evolutionary type of process synthesis has been emphasized. We shall now review some of the published work covering this subject area.

One of the earliest attempts, due to King et al. [69], is a general technique for a systematic evolutionary process synthesis. The plant selected for this experimental technique was a methane liquefaction plant. Starting with the simplest plant arrangement a procedure of alternaing processes of analysis and local improvements was put into effect. As a rule the component selected for improvement was either one with the highest irreversibility or if this was not feasible, with the second highest irreversibility. The procedure adopted was probably the best available considering the state of the art of exergy at the time of publication. However, as is well understood now, the key to the reduction in the irreversibility of one plant component is often to be found in another component. The procedure selected worked reasonably well in the case of the chosen plant, but, as the authors have pointed out, the final form of the plant had some undesirable features that arose owing to some inherent defects in the technique.

The techniques of process synthesis proposed by Umeda et al. [30] and Naka et al. [31] are designed for specific types of plants, namely distillation plants. The technique described in the first of the two papers is restricted to plants with one heat source and one heat sink. The principal tool used was the τ-ΔH diagram on which the composite cooling and heating curves were assembled. The area between the two curves in these coordinates gives the irreversibility of the process (see Figure 7). To reduce this irreversibility the curves are shifted and pinch-points are located. These are subsequently eliminated by either changing the column pressure or the temperature of a segment of the composite line (without pressure change). The latter change is brought about by increasing the plant complexity through the introduction of interboilers and/or intercondensers. The irreversibility of the plant decreases monotonically with each repeated set of operations. Economic and operability criteria are finally applied. The main advantage of this technique is its simplicity and ease of application.

The technique described in the other paper, Naka et al. [31], is designed to cope with a rather more complex problem of a multicomponent distillation systems with heat integration, involving multiple heat sources and heat sinks with fixed loads (from other processes) as well as process utilities. The synthesis problem is equivalent to the problem of how to minimize the exergy consumption of the process utilities by maximizing energy recovery between condensers and reboilers. Heat integration arising from sensible heat was neglected. To make heat recovery possible operating pressures had to be selected for the different columns. Because of the large number of pressure combinations a tree searching method was employed. The physical meanings of the computing processes were visually represented in the τ-ΔH coordinates. This work represents a successful attempt to use the advantages offered by the exergy concepts to solve a fairly complex problem of process synthesis.

Papers by Grant and Anozie [70] and Parker [71] are representatives of a new kind of approach to process analysis and process synthesis, which appears to be gaining grounds among chemical plant designers. The authors of both papers look upon the exergy method as a very useful tool, particularly when dealing with new processes. They recommend that exergy analysis should be incorporated into process simulation programs together with energy and mass balances. The use of exergy criteria was considered useful in such simulation techniques for studying the effect of changes in operating conditions on the thermodynamic efficiency of the process. Some initial steps to put such a scheme into effect have been taken [70]. Further studies including sensitivity analysis and optimization of operating conditions were to be implemented in the second stage of the investigation. One of the main difficulties that has been stressed in both papers is lack of entropy data. The authors proposed various approximate techniques to deal with this problem.

Chiu [72] discusses at some length different exergy techniques that can be applied to improve the efficiency of cryogenic plants. These included empirical trial and error approach in conjunction with exergy analysis of the plant, analytical optimization process, and what he calls "iterative and comparative exergy analysis," which basically consists of exergy analysis of the process alongside other processes fulfilling similar function. The comparative approach constitutes a form of process synthesis and leads to generation of ideas for improving process efficiency. Chiu reviews several papers that describe the application of these techniques. He also recommends the use of exergy-enthalpy property diagrams and various forms of exergetic efficiencies as effective tools that can aid exergy analysis in cryogenic engineering.

A paper by Trepp [73] provides a good example of how the study of performance of simple components under different operating conditions can help in the design of complex systems. The particular system to which he applies this approach is a refrigeration system for temperatures below 25 K. He uses the results of an earlier study on low-temperature heat exchange, which shows that for optimum performance the temperature difference between streams must be a certain function of the local operating temperature. Another element in the design is Trepp's own study of exergy losses in expansion processes as function of the number of stages of expansion and gas inlet temperature. Using this information Trepp synthesizes an efficient multi-expander, hydrogen refrigerator.

The following three papers reviewed here, in which the authors consider optimization of whole petrochemical industries, represent a new departure in exergy analysis. As is well known, there is a multiplicity of technological paths available for arriving at a given product from basic raw materials. In the production processes of the petrochemical industry the outputs of the different plants may be used as final products or as raw materials for other subsystems. This interaction makes it necessary to study whole industrial sectors since optimization of individual production units will not necessarily result in optimum performance of the whole system. Stephanopoulos et al. [74, 75] apply multiobjective analysis to the petrochemical industry of the USA. In the first of the two papers dealing with this subject the authors use the following two objective functions:

1. Maximization of the ideal reversible exergy change associated with the production process.
2. Minimization of the actual exergy requirement.

In the second paper they bring in an additional objective namely minimization of feedstock consumption. In the overall optimization procedure an optimum structure is determined for each objective. However, since these cannot be satisfied in full at the same time, a whole set of compromised structures is put forward in which all the objectives are considered simultaneously. From these a designer can choose one that is most appropriate, giving, as necessary, preference to selected objectives.

Similar work to those just reviewed was done by Balli [76] for the European petrochemical industry. In his particular approach to multiobjective modeling, Balli optimized one of the objective functions incorporating the others as inequality constraints. This work is essentially a study into the feasibility of optimizing the system using different techniques and different combinations of objectives. One of the studies was to be modeled on the American study by incorporating exergy objectives. However, Balli found it difficult to obtain sufficiently reliable data and consequently had to abandon this approach in favor of using primary energy requirement as the objective.

Stephanopoulos and Townsend [77] address a very general question of the issues and methodologies involved in the synthesis of new reaction pathways. The authors discuss the idea of the existence of structure and patterns in the search space that can be used as a valuable aid in the systematic generation of desirable chemical reaction schemes. Among the group of parameters that can be used for this purpose, the Gibbs function of reaction is mentioned because of its usefulness as a measure of the expected equilibrium conversion for a chemical reaction. Although exergy concepts as such are not used in this paper, Gibbs function, of reaction, which is used, can be regarded [15] (as follows from Equations 13 and 14) as a form of relative chemical exergy for the purpose of analyzing processes that do not involve exchange of substances with the environment.

In a search for a systematic approach to process synthesis several investigators have developed non-exergy, "rules-of-thumb" techniques for application to specific problems. The most successful of these is a group of techniques known under the name of "pinch technology." These techniques have been originated by Linnhoff and Flower at Leeds University and subsequently developed further with the aid of their co-workers at ICI and UMIST. Pinch technology has been developed for use in heat exchanger networks [25 to 28]; distillation systems [29]; and heat and power integration [28, 32].

These are fully developed techniques with their own terminology, rules, and guidelines. The most important concept on which these techniques depend is the point of closest temperature approach of the composite curves or "the pinch." The main form of irreversibility that these techniques aim to minimize is the one associated with energy degradation in heat transfer over a finite temperature difference, which clearly is a Second Law concept. However, by assuming constant temperatures for the hot and cold utilities, the authors reduce the problem of minimization of this form of irreversibility to one of energy recovery, i.e. to a First Law problem. As these techniques are designed to be used in specific areas of application, they tend to be more incisive than any general technique and therefore quite effective. However, there is little doubt that these techniques cannot be applied mechanically, without a "good understanding and some creative flexibility on behalf of the user" [28]. A background of Second Law analysis should help by providing the necessary understanding of the principles underlying the basic rules.

Future Outlook

As will be seen from this review, the exergy method has reached now a stage of development of its techniques of analysis when practically any type of chemical process can be analysed without difficulty. Useful forms of efficiency and other performance indicators based on exergy concepts are available for evaluating the performance of both unit processes as well as whole plants. Charts, tables, and short-cut techniques have been developed to facilitate the calculations.

The more recent published papers on the use of exergy concepts in a structured form of process synthesis give grounds for optimism for the future of the exergy method in this area of application. Some useful techniques of process synthesis for specific areas of application have been developed in parallel with similar non-exergy techniques (e.g., pinch technology).

A further example of a new, interesting development is the use of exergy concepts in multi-objective optimization of process routes in macroeconomic systems. The area of application that is not served well by any of the existing techniques of process synthesis are cryogenic systems and other systems in which irreversibility due to heat transfer over a finite temperature difference is not the dominant form of irreversibility. The way forward in this area may be the heuristic approach to evolutionary process synthesis as exemplified by the experimental technique produced by King et al. [69]. The use of coefficients of structural bonds may prove useful in this context, although much more work is required before we learn how to apply them in a systematic way.

There are some successful examples of thermoeconomic optimization of components in plants of moderate complexity. However, these techniques require further development work before they can be considered suitable for application to large multicomponent systems. In the case of the structural method of thermoeconomic optimization, the graph theoretic approach to the calculation of CSB's should help to make the optimization of large systems more systematic.

The usefulness of charts such as exergy-enthalpy and exergy-concentration charts has been pointed out. Although these charts are available for several fluids, there is a need for further development to include among these more of the important working fluids.

Finally, the question of notation for exergy analysis must be mentioned. At present there is a lack of uniformity in the use of names and symbols in this subject area, particularly in English language publications. This is, without doubt, a significant factor in the resistance to the use of the exergy method as well as to its more widespread teaching. Steps have now been taken to remedy this situation. A working party has been set up by the Exergy Group* to prepare, in consultation with leading workers in this subject area from a number of different countries, a proposal for what it is hoped will be a generally acceptable notation. The glossary presented below is based on this proposal [79].

Glossary

Entropy production associated with a process is equal to the entropy increase of an isolated system consisting of all systems involved in the process.

Conceptual environment is an idealization of the real environment that is characterized by a perfect state of equilibrium, i.e., absence of any gradients or differences involving pressure, temperature, chemical potential, kinetic energy and potential energy. The environment constitutes a natural reference medium with respect to which the maximum work potential (exergy) of different systems is assessed. The unqualified term *environment* used in this document always means *conceptual environment.*

Exergy is a generic term for a group of concepts which define the maximum work potential of a system, a stream of matter or a heat interaction, the state of the (conceptual) environment being used as the datum state. The following terms are derived from it:

1. *Exergy* refers to the exergy of a stream of matter.
2. *Non-flow exergy* is the exergy of a closed system.
3. *Thermal exergy* is the exergy associated with a heat interaction.

Each of these forms of exergy is defined separately:

Exergy: The maximum amount of shaft work obtainable when a *steady stream of matter* is brought from its initial state to the dead state by means of processes involving interaction only with the environment is called *exergy.*

Non-flow exergy: The maximum net usable work obtainable when the *closed system* under consideration is brought from its initial state to the dead state by means of processes involving interaction only with the environment is called *non-flow exergy.*

Thermal exergy: The maximum shaft work obtainable from a given *heat interaction* using the environment as a thermal energy reservoir is called *thermal exergy.*

Components of exergy:

1. *Physical exergy* of a substance is equal to the maximum amount of shaft work obtainable when it is brought from its initial state to the environmental state (P_0, T_0), by means of physical processes involving interaction only with the environment.
2. *Chemical exergy* is the exergy of a substance when in the environmental state.
3. *Kinetic exergy* is equal to kinetic energy when the latter is expressed in terms of velocity relative to the quiescent environment.
4. *Potential exergy* is equal to potential energy when the latter is expressed in terms of altitude relative to the sea level.

Exergy function is a thermodynamic function defined by $(H - T_0S)$.

Non-flow exergy function is a thermodynamic function defined by

$$(U + P_0V - T_0S).$$

* Exergy Group is an association of teachers and workers in exergy analysis with a common interest in the development of this technique.

Irreversibility (in addition to the use of the word as an abstract noun) is a quantitative concept. It is equal to the amount of exergy lost in a process within the physical space defined by the system boundary or the control surface *Irreversibility rate* denotes of loss of exergy in a system.

Reference substance is a selected common environmental substance of low chemical potential with reference to which the chemical exergy of a chemical element is calculated.

Reference states

1. *Environmental state*: When a system is in a state of thermal and mechanical equilibrium with the environment it is said to be in the *environmental state*. The environmental state is defined by the actual pressure and temperature of the environment P_0 and T_0.
2. *Dead state* is the state of the common environmental substances, called reference substances, which make up the conceptual environment. The state of the conceptual environment is defined by the pressure P_0, temperature T_0 and the chemical potential, μ_{00}, of the reference substances in their respective dead states.
3. *Standard States*. Although the two previous states may vary and need to be defined, it is often convenient to use a *standard environment* in terms of which the *standard environmental state*, P^0, T^0, and the *standard dead state* P^0, T^0, μ_1^{00}, μ_2^{00}, . . . are defined.

Exergetic efficiency is a general criterion of performance which can be formulated for any steady state process taking place in a plant, or plant component, which produces a useful output expressible in terms of exergy. Exergetic efficiency is formed as a ratio of the exergy transfer rate associated with the output to the exergy transfer rate associated with the necessary input.

Symbols in the Context of the Equations

The applicability of the expressions given below is, in general, restricted to systems or streams of matter involving simple compressible fluids.

Basic Quantities

For a closed system:

Non-flow exergy

$$\Xi = m\xi \tag{49}$$

Specific non-flow exergy

$$\xi = \xi_{ph} + \xi_0 \tag{50}$$

Specific physical non-flow exergy

$$\xi_{ph} = \alpha - \alpha_0 \tag{51}$$

Specific non-flow exergy function

$$\alpha = u + P_0 v - T_0 s \tag{52}$$

Specific chemical exergy, ξ_0, is evaluated relative to the environment, (dead state), according to the definition.

For a stream of matter:

Exergy flow rate

$$\dot{E} = \dot{m}\epsilon \tag{53}$$

Specific exergy

$$\epsilon = \epsilon_{ph} + \epsilon_0 + \epsilon_{pot} + \epsilon_{kin} \tag{54}$$

Specific physical exergy

$$\epsilon_{ph} = \beta - \beta_0 \tag{55}$$

Specific exergy function

$$\beta = h - T_0 s \tag{56}$$

Specific chemical exergy, (available in tables as standard molar chemical exergy, $\tilde{\epsilon}^0$) is evaluated relative to the environment (dead state) according to the definition. Note that $\epsilon_0 \equiv \xi_0$.

Specific potential exergy

$$\epsilon_{pot} = g_E Z \qquad Z - \text{altitude relative to sea level} \tag{57}$$

Specific kinetic exergy

$$\epsilon_{kin} = C^2/2 \qquad C - \text{velocity relative to the earth's surface} \tag{58}$$

For a heat transfer:

Thermal exergy

$$E^Q = Q\frac{T - T_0}{T} \tag{59}$$

Thermal exergy transfer rate

$$\dot{E}^Q = \dot{Q}\frac{T - T_0}{T} \tag{60}$$

For a work transfer:

Net usable work – due to volume change of a system during process 1 → 2

$$(W_{NET})_{1,2} = W_{1,2} - P_0(V_2 - V_1) \tag{61}$$

$W_{1,2}$ = work done by the system due to volume change

$(V_2 - V_1)$ = change in the volume of the system

Shaft work done during process 1 → 2

$(W_x)_{1,2}$

Gouy-Stodola relation:

Irreversibility

$$I = T_0 \Pi \tag{62}$$

Irreversibility rate

$$\dot{I} = T_0 \dot{\Pi} \tag{63}$$

Exergy balance, non-steady flow process in the time interval t_1 to t_2:

$$(W_x)_{1,2} + (W_{NET})_{1,2}\} \text{ exergy transfer due to work*}$$

$$= \Xi_1 - \Xi_2\} \text{ reduction of exergy of the control region}$$

$$+ \sum_i m_i \epsilon_i - \sum_e m_e \epsilon_e \left.\right\} \text{net import of exergy into the control region with the flow of matter} \quad (64)$$

$$+ \sum_r (E_r^Q)_{1,2} \left.\right\} \text{net transfer of exergy to the control region with heat transfer}$$

$$- I_{1,2}\} \text{ process irreversibility}$$

Special cases:

1. Exergy balance for a closed system
   With $m_i = 0$ and $m_e = 0$
   Equation 64 becomes the exergy balance for a closed system:

$$\Xi_1 - \Xi_2 = (W_x)_{1,2} + (W_{NET})_{1,2} - \sum_r (E_r^Q)_{1,2} - I_{1,2} \quad (65)$$

2. Exergy balance for a steady-state process in an open system (control region) in this case we have

$$\Xi_1 - \Xi_2 = 0 \text{ and } (W_{NET})_{1,2} = 0$$

Hence, when differentiated with respect to time, Equation 64 becomes

$$\dot{E}_{IN} + \dot{E}^Q = \dot{W}_x + \dot{E}_{OUT} + \dot{I} \quad (66)$$

where $\dot{E}_{IN} = \sum_i \dot{m}_i \epsilon_i$

$$\dot{E}_{OUT} = \sum_e \dot{m}_e \epsilon_e$$

$$\dot{E}^Q = \sum_r (\dot{E}_r^Q)$$

NOTATION

g_E	specific force due to gravity
H, h	enthalpy, specific enthalpy
I, i	irreversibility, specific irreversibility
m	mass
T	thermodynamic temperature
P	absolute pressure
Q	heat interaction
S, s	entropy, specific entropy
U, u	internal energy, specific internal energy
V, v	volume, specific volume
W	work done by a system due to change in its volume
W_{NET}	net useful work done by a system due to change in its volume
W_x	shaft work

* In the sign convention used here work done by the system and heat transfer to the system are positive.

Greek Symbols

A, α	non-flow exergy function, specific non-flow exergy function
B, β	exergy function, specific exergy function
E, ϵ	exergy, specific exergy*
E_{ph}, ϵ_{ph}	physical exergy, specific physical exergy
E_0, ϵ_0	chemical exergy, specific chemical exergy
E_{kin}, ϵ_{kin}	kinetic exergy, specific kinetic exergy
E_{pot}, ϵ_{pot}	potential exergy, specific potential exergy
E^Q, ϵ^Q	thermal exergy transfer, specific thermal exergy transfer
Ξ, ξ	non-flow exergy, specific non-flow exergy
Π, π	entropy production, specific entropy production
ψ	exergetic efficiency

Subscripts

0	environmental state, chemical exergy
00	dead state
ph	physical component
kin	kinetic component
pot	potential component
i	inlet
e	exit
r	thermal energy reservoir

Superscripts

·	rate with respect to time
~	molar quantity
0	standard environmental state, standard chemical exergy
00	standard dead state

REFERENCES

1. Gouy, G., "Sur l'energie utilisable" ("On Usable Energy"), *Journal de physique*, 8 (2nd Series), 501–518, (1889).
2. Stodola, A., "Die Kreisprozesse der Gasmachinen," ("Gas Engine Cycles"), *Z.d. VDI*, 32, (38), 1086–91, (1898).
3. Bošnjaković, F., "Kampf den Nichtumkehrbarkeiten" (Fight irreversibilities), *Arch. Wärmewirtsch*, 19 No. 1, 1–2, (1938).
4. Bošnjaković, F., "Güte vom Wärmeanlagen und die Leistungsregein," ("The Degree of Perfection of Thermal Plants and Load Control"), *Tech, Mitt. Essen*, 32, No. 15, 439–445, (1939).
5. Rant, Z., "Energetska ocenitev postopka fabrikacije sode (Na_2CO_3)" ("Energy Evaluation of the Process of Production of Soda"), Techniška visoka šola v Ljubljani, *Acta technica*, 3 (Series machinarium No. 1), 1–72, 1951.
6. Denbigh, K. G., "The Second Law Efficiency of Chemical Processes," *Chemical Engineering Science*, 6, No. 1, 1–9, (1956).
7. Szargut, J., "Ogólne zasady bilansowania energetycznego procesów chemicznych oraz nowa metoda bilansowania," (General Principles of Drawing up Energy Balances for Chemical Processes and a New Method"), *Zeszyty Naukowe Politechniki Ślaskiej*, No. 5, *Energetyka*, (1), 81–152, (1956).

* Where a suitable type is available and in hand written texts, the curly capital epsilon, ε, may be used instead of the usual Greek capital epsilon, E.

8. Rant, Z., "Exergie, ein neues Wort für "technische Arbeitsfähigkeit," (Exergy, A New Word for "Technical Work Capacity"), *Forsch. Gebiete Ingenieurwes.* (1956).
9. Kotas, T. J., "Exergy Criteria of Performance for Thermal Plant," *Int. J. Heat and Fluid Flow*, 2, 147–163, (1980).
10. Linnhoff, B., "*Thermodynamic Analysis in the Design of Process Networks*," Ph.D. Thesis, University of Leeds, (1979).
11. Linnhoff, B., and Turner, J. A., "Simple Concepts in Process Synthesis Give Energy Savings and Elegant Designs," *The Chemical Engineer*, 742–747, (1980).
12. Townsend, D. W., "Second Law Analysis in Practice," *The Chemical Engineer*, 628–633, (1980).
13. Linnhoff, B., et al., "*Exergy Analysis of Chemical Process Network*," I. Chem. E approved User Course, printed notes, UMIST.
14. Linnhoff, B., "New Concepts in Thermodynamics for Better Chemical Process Design," *Proc. Royal Society of London*, 386, 1–33, (1983).
15. Kotas, T. J., *The Exergy Method of Thermal Plant Analysis*, Butterworths, 1985.
16. Kotas, T. J., "Exergy Concepts for Thermal Plant," *Int. J. Heat and Fluid Flows*, 2, No. 3 pp. 105–114, (1980).
17. Szargut, J., and Petela, R., "*Egzergia*," (Wydawnictwa Naukowo-Techniczne, Warsaw, (in Polish), (1965).
18. Szargut, J., and Dziedziniewicz, K., "Energie utilisable des substances chimiques inorganiques," *Entropie*, July–August 1971, No. 40. 1. English Translation "Exergy of Chemical Substances." Queen Mary College, Faculty Report No. E.P. 5018.
19. Szargut, J., and Styrylska, T., "Angenäherte Bestimmung der Exergie von Brennstoffen," *Brennstoff-Wärme-Kraft*, 16, No. 12, 589–596, (1964).
20. Sussman, M. V., "Steady-Flow Availability and the Standard Chemical Availability," *Energy*, 5, pp. 793–802, (1980).
21. Linnhoff, B., and Carpenter, K. Y., "Energy Conservation by Exergy Analysis—The Quick and Simple Way." *Proceedings 2nd World Congress of Chem. Eng.*, Vol. II, paper 6.7.4, p. 248, Montreal Canada, October (1981).
22. Linnhoff, B., "Interpreting Exergy Analysis: A Case Study," *I. Chem. E. Jubilee Symposium*, (1982).
23. Ahrendts, J., "Reference states," *Energy*, 5, 667–677, (1980).
24. Wepfer, W. J., and Gaggioli, R. A., "Reference Datums for Available Energy," *Thermodynamics: Second Law Analysis.* Gaggioli, R. A. (ed.), 77–92. American Chemical Society, Washington, D.C. (1980).
25. Linnhoff, B., and Flower, J. R., "Synthesis of Heat Exchanger Networks," *AICHE Journal*, 24, No. 4, 633–654, (1978).
26. Flower, J. R., and Linnhoff, B., "Thermodynamic Analysis in the Design of Process Networks," Paper presented at *CACE Conference*, 214th event of EFCE, Montreux, 8–11 April (1979).
27. Linnhoff, B., and Turner, J. A., "Efficient use of Energy in the Process Industries," *The Chemical Engineer*, p. 621, October (1980).
28. Collective Work, "*A User Guide on Process, Integration for the Efficient Use of Energy*," *I. Chem.* E, Rugby, UK, (1982).
29. Hindmarsh, E., and Townsend, D. W., "Heat Integration of Distillation Systems into Total Flowsheets—A Complete Approach," paper No. 88b, *AIChE Annual Meeting*, San Francisco, (1984).
30. Umeda, T., et al., "A Thermodynamic Approach to Heat Integration in Distillation Systems," *AIChE Journal*, 25, No. 3, 423–429, (1979).
31. Naka, Y., et al., "A Thermodynamic Approach to Multicomponent Distillation System Synthesis," *AIChE Journal*, 28, No. 5, 812–820, (1982).
32. Townsend, D. W., and Linnhoff, B., "Heat and power Networks in process design," *AIChE Journal*, 29, No. 5, 742–771, (1983).
33. Bosňjaković, F., *Technical Thermodynamic*, Holt, Rinehart and Winston, (1965).
34. Fratzscher, W., "Exergetical efficiency," *B.W.K.* 13, (11), 483, (1961).
35. Glaser, H., "Die Thermodynamische Untersuchung von Kalte prozessen mit Hilfe der Technischen Arbeitsfahigkeit" ("Thermodynamic Investigation of Refrigeration Processes by Means of the Concept of Availability") *Kaltetechnik*, 15, No. 11, 344–353, (1963).

36. Brodyanskii, V. M., and Ishkin, I. P., "The Application of Enthalpy-Exergy Diagrams to Thermodynamic Calculations," (in Russian) *Kholodilnaya tekhnika*, No. 1, 19–24, (1962).
37. Auracher, H., "The Application of Energy to Refrigeration Process Optimization," XVth *Int. Congress of Refrigeration* Proceedings Vol. 11, 241–256, Venice, (1979).
38. Brodyanskii, V. M., "*Exergy Method of Thermodynamic Analysis*" (in Russian), Energiya, Moscow, (1973).
39. Perry, R. H., Chilton, C. H., and Kirkpatrick, C. H., (eds.) *Chemical Engineers Handbook*, 4th Edition, McGraw-Hill Book Co., New York, (1963).
40. Beyer, J., "Strukturuntersuchungen notwendiger Bestandteil der Effektivitatsanalyse von Warmeverbrauchersysteme". ("Structural Investigations—An Essential Part of the Analysis of the Efficiency of Thermal Systems") *Energieanwendung*, 19, No. 12, 358–361, (1970).
41. Beyer, J., "Strukturuntersuchung des Wärmeverbrauchs in Zuckerfabriken". ("Structural Investigations of Heat Consumption in Sugar Plants") *Energieanwendung*, 21, No. 3. 70–82, (1972).
42. Beyer, J., "Zur Aufteilung der Primarenergiekosten in Koppelprozessen auf Grundlage der Strukturanalyse" (Distribution of Primary Energy Costs in Multi-Purpose Processes on the Basis of Structural Analysis,). *Energieanwendung*, 21, No. 6, 179–183, (1972).
43. Beyer, J., "Strukturwärmetechnischer Systeme und ökonomische Optimirung der Systemparameter" (Structure of thermal systems and economic optimization of system parameters). *Energieanwendung*, 23, No. 9, 274–279, (1974).
44. Beyer, J., "Einige Probleme der praktischen Anwendung der exergetischen Methode in Wärmewirtschaftlichen Untersuchungen industrieller Produktionsprozesse" (Some problems on the practical application of the exergy method in thermoeconomic investigation of industrial production processes.) *Energieanwendung*,
Part I—Nov/Dec 1978, 27, (6), 204–208.
Part II—March/April 1979, 28, (2), 66–70.
Part III—May/June 1979, 28, (2), 86–90.
Part IV—July/August 1979, 28, (4), 137–139.
45. Kalinina, E. I., and Brodyanskii, V. M., "Basic Rules of the Method of Thermodynamic Analysis of Complex Processes," *Izvestia Vuzov, Energyetika*, (12), 57–64 (in Russian), (1973).
46. Kalinina, E. I., and Brodyanskii, V. M., "Thermoeconomic Method of Distribution of Expenditure in a Multi-Purpose Technical System" *Izvestia Vuzov, Energyetika*, No. 3, 58–63, (in Russian), 32, (1974).
47. Tribus, M., Evans, R. B., and Crellin, G. L., "Thermoeconomic Demineralization" *Principles of Desalination*, Spiegler, K. W., ed., Academic Press, New York, Chapter 2, 1966.
48. El-Sayed, Y. M., and Evans, R. B., "Thermoeconomics and the Design of Heat Systems," *Trans. of the ASME, Journal of Engineering for Power*, 27–35, (1970).
49. El-Sayed, Y. M., and Aplenc, A. J., "Application of the Thermoeconomic Approach to the Analysis and Optimization of a Vapor-Compression Desalting System." *Trans of the ASME, Journal of Engineering for Power*, 17–26, (1970).
50. Reistad, G. M., and Gaggioli, R. A., "Available-Energy Costing," *Thermodynamics: Second Law Analysis*, Gaggioli, R. A., ed., 143, American Chemical Society, Washington, D.C. 1980.
51. Fehring, T. J., and Gaggioli, R. A., "Economics of Feedwater Heater Replacement, *Trans. of the ASME Journal of Engineering for Power*, 482–489, (1977).
52. Kapitsa, P. L., "Rotary Expander for Obtaining Low Temperatures and its Application for the Liquefaction of Air," *Zh.T.F.* 9, 99–123 (in Russian), (1939).
53. Gardner, J. B., and Smith, K. C., "Power Consumption and Thermodynamics Reversibility in Low Temperature Refrigeration and Separation Processes." *Advances in Cryogenic Engineering* 3. Plenum, New York, (1960).
54. Benedict, M., and Gyftopoulos, E. P., "Economic Selection of the Components of an Air Separation Process," *Thermodynamics: Second Law Analysis*, Gaggioll, R. A., ed. American Chemical Society, Washington, D.C. 195–202, (1980).
55. Brodyanskii, V. M., and Ishkin, I. P., "Thermodynamic Analysis of Gas Liquefaction Process." Inzhenerno-fizicheskii zhurnal, 6, 19–26 (English translation: J. of Engineering Physics), (1963).
56. Michalek, K., "Exergetische Analyse einer Rohöldestillationsanlage" (Exergy analysis of a crude-oil distillation plant). *Energieanvendung*, Oct. 1976, 25, No. 10, 308–312.

57. Sokolov, E. Y., and Brodyanskii, V. M., *Energy Fundamentals for Heat Transformation and Refrigeration Processes, Energoizdat*, Moscow, (in Russian), (1981).
58. Fitzmorris, R. E., and Mah, R. S. H., "Improving Distillation Column Design Using Thermodynamic Availability Analysis," *AICHE* Journal, 26, (2), 265–274, (1980).
59. Linnhoff, B., and Smith, R., "The Thermodynamic Efficiency of Distillation," *Int. Chem. Eng. Symp.* Ser. No. 56, (1979).
60. Fonyo, Z., and Rev, E., "The Thermodynamic Efficiency and Energy Conservation of Industrial distillation systems," *Proceedings 2nd World Congress of Chem. Eng.* Vol. II, paper 6.9.4, p. 298, Montreal, Canada, (1981).
61. Singh, S. P., et al., "Thermodynamic Analysis of Coal Gasification Process," *Energy*, 5, 905–914, (1980).
62. Tsatsarouis, G., et al., "Exergy Analysis of the Nuclear Coal Hydrogasification Process", *Proceedings, Summer Meeting of AIChE*, Detroit, August (1981).
63. Kapner, R. S., and Lannus, A., "Thermodynamic Analysis of Energy Efficiency in Catalytic Reforming," *Energy*, 5, 915–924, (1980).
64. Riekert, L., "The Efficiency of Energy-Utilization in Chemical Processes," *Chemical Engineering Science*, 29, 1613–1620, (1974).
65. Riekert, L., "Flow and Conversion of Energy in Chemical Processing Networks," *Large Chemical Plant*, Proceedings 4th Int. Symp. Froment, G. F., ed., Antwerp, 35–44, Oct. (1979).
66. Cremer, H., "Thermodynamic Balance and Analysis of a Synthesis Gas and Ammonia Plant," *Thermodynamics: Second Law Analysis*, Gaggioli, R. A., ed. (American Chemical Society, Washington D.C.) 111–127, (1980).
67. Szargut, J., et al., "Exergy Balance for a Steel Plant," *Hutnik*, 31, (4), 123–128, (in Polish) (1964).
68. Morris, D. R., et al., "Energy efficiency of a Lead Smelter," *Energy* 8 (5), 337–349, (1983).
69. King, C. J., et al., "Systematic Evolutionary Process Synthesis," *Ind. Eng. Chem. Process Des. Develop.*, 11, (2), 271–283, (1972).
70. Grant, C. D., and Anozie, A. N., "The Use of Exergy Analysis for Process Plant Improvements". *Proceedings 2nd World Congress of Chem. Eng.*, Vol. II, paper 7.4.4., p. 392, Montreal, Canada, October (1981).
71. Parker, A. L., "Availability Energy Analysis Within a Chemical Simultator." *Proceedings 2nd World Congress of Chem. Eng.*, Vol. II, paper 6.9.2, p. 289, Montreal, Canada, October (1981).
72. Chiu, C. H., "Exergy analysis for Cryogenic Process and Equipment Optimization," *Proceedings 2nd World Congress of Chem. Eng.*, Vol. II, paper 6.8.3. p. 269, Montreal, Canada, October (1981).
73. Trepp, C., "Refrigeration System for Temperatures Below 25K with Turboexpanders." *Advances in Cryogenic Engineering*, 7, 251–261, (1964).
74. Stephanopoulos, G., et al., "Thermodynamic bounds and the Selection of Technologies in the Petrochemical industry," *Chemical Engineering Science*, 35, 1049–1065, (1980).
75. Stephanopoulos, G., et al., "Multiobjective analysis in modelling the petrochemical industry"; *Chemical Engineering Science*, 35, 2415–2426, (1980).
76. Balli, V., "*Modelling the European Petrochemical Industry by linear programming with multiple objective functions*," Diploma Thesis, ETH Switzerland, (1982).
77. Stephanopoulos, G., and Townsend, D. W., "Synthesis in process development: Issues and solution methodologies," *Int. Ch. E. Symposium Series No. 92.*
78. Szargut, J., "*Analiza termodynamiczna i ekonomiczna w energetyce przemyslowej*", (*Thermodynamic and economic analysis in power generation industry*). Wydawnictwa Naukowo-Techniczne, Warsaw, (in Polish), (1983).
79. Working Party for Nomenclature, "*Proposed Nomenclature for the Exergy Method of Thermodynamic Analysis*," Exergy Group, Dept. of Mechanical Engineering, Queen Mary College, University of London, Mile End Road, London, E1 4NS, U.K.

CHAPTER 24

TOMOGRAPHIC MEASUREMENT TECHNIQUES FOR PROCESS ENGINEERING STUDIES

Dieter Mewes, Michael Friederich, Wilhelm Haarde, and **Wilfried Ostendorf**

Institut fur Verfahrenstechnik
Universitat Hannover
Hannover, Federal Republic of Germany

CONTENTS

INTRODUCTION

In all the process-engineering studies that are concerned with three-dimensional fields with variable velocities, temperatures, or concentrations, it is desirable to be able insofar as possible to measure these parameters simultaneously at all points in the space. Probes of very small volumetric dimensions and special optical procedures have made it possible to determine experimentally with considerable accuracy the three-dimensional velocity, temperature, and concentration fields in stationary fluids or fluids in steady flow. In general, the probes are moved through the volume of the apparatus and their measured signals can then be related to the respective positions. Optical procedures, such as laser-Doppler anemometry, for instance, can only obtain measurements at one position at a given point in time. Transmission methods have an integrating effect on the measured parameter over the beam path in the volume being observed. In dealing with a flow field, in which arbitrary timewise variations of the local measured values occur, the results from the probes can only give information on the temporal variation of the measured parameter at one point of the flow field. Fluids in turbulent flow or those having flows coupled with unsteady-state energy and mass transport are of particular interest in this respect. It is therefore the objective of every process engineer carrying out experimental work to obtain a representative three-dimensional picture of the parameter of interest for each point in time.

For this purpose, tomographic measurement techniques are available that have been developed over more than 50 years of medical, electron-microscopic and radio-astronomic uses and have been used more recently in materials science investigations, With the help of these techniques it is possible to represent the measured parameter for each point of a given cross-section that can be selected from a given volumetric zone. Building up the total volume from individual layers, each with their measured parameter distributions, then provides the three-dimensional field of the measured parameter.

Depending upon the problem, it may be necessary to consider, for instance, the density, the temperature, the concentration, etc., as the measured parameter. This procedure has been used recently for the three-dimensional spatial determination of time-independent and temporally varying field parameters. The measurement of temporally and spatially varying field parameters in an arbitrary apparatus volume thus represents a significant extension of this measurement technique. Further development of the evaluation procedures in the mathematical area is still required. Because of the large expenditure of numerical effort required, it is understandable that tomographic measurement techniques are only now becoming of importance for process-engineering applications.

This chapter explains the different measurement techniques to obtain tomograms. The mathematical basis for the calculation of tomographic representations are described in so far as they are necessary for a clear interpretation of tomography. In the last section tested measurement techniques will be introduced and their applications explained.

TECHNIQUES FOR DETERMINING EXPERIMENTAL PARAMETERS

Tomographic measurement techniques so far have been applied mainly in medicine, but also to an increasing extent in the testing of materials and in process engineering investigations. Depending on the problem being investigated they require, like all other systems used for parameter detection, a signal and a sensor for measurement purposes. Since the signal should be related to the time and the differential volume of space, radiations of all kinds of wavelength and energy are suitable for this purpose. The wavelength of the best-known forms of electromagnetic radiation are shown in Figure 1. Wavelength and amplitude of the radiation are influenced by the physical properties of the material such as density or refractive factor. These are called field parameters. The variation of the field parameters is caused by the temperature-, concentration-, density- or velocity-fields under investigation. The field parameters are indicated by probes that are positioned outside the volume. Their signals are related to the line integral of the field parameter.

In Figure 2, this relationship is shown schematically for one plane of the volume to be measured. The field parameter f, which is variable in the plane, is projected onto an image plane. Field parameters include the absorption coefficient or the index of refraction of transparent fluids or solid-state bodies. If several projections can be related to different directions, the field parameter can be determined from the measured projections with the use of suitable algorithms. Such a procedure is shown schematically in Figure 3.

The following mathematical correlation exists for the relationship between the field parameter f and its projections in different directions θ:

$$\int_{s_i} f(x, y, z, t)\, ds = \Phi_i(\rho_i, \theta, z, t) \tag{1}$$

Φ_i is the measured physical parameter and s_i is equivalent to the length of the path through the measurement volume.

As shown in Figure 4, the measurement volume is divided into several two-dimensional fields, for which the coordinate z is constant. If the field parameter is observed for one particular point in time only, Equation 1 will become simplified

$$\int_{s_i} f(x, y, z_0, t_0)\, ds = \Phi_i(\rho_i, \theta, z_0, t_0) \tag{2}$$

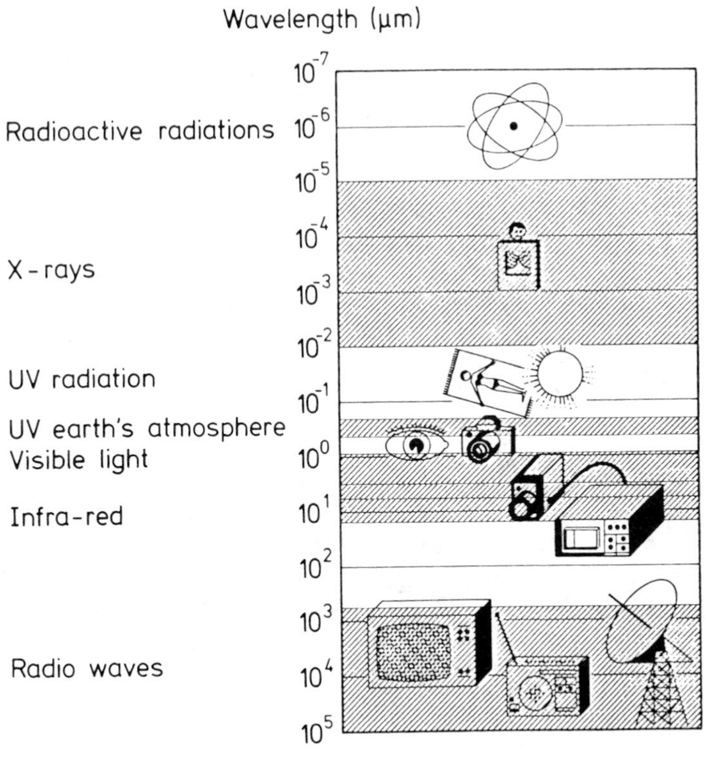

Figure 1. Electromagnetic radiations of various wavelengths and their corresponding uses in practice.

For a height coordinate z_0, a time t_0 and a projection direction at the angle θ, Equation 2 can be simplified as follows:

$$\int_{s_i} f(x, y,)\, ds = \Phi_i(\rho_i, \theta) \tag{3}$$

Depending on the field parameter that is to be determined experimentally, there are different possibilities to measure the individual projected parameters. The methods for taking such measurements will be explained in the following.

Absorption Techniques

Absorption measurement techniques make use of the decrease of the intensity of a radiation or a wave during the irradiation of fluids or solid matter. They belong to the category of absorption techniques. The field parameter indicated in Equation 1 is equivalent to the location-dependent absorption coefficient μ.

The experimental parameter in Equation 1 is equal to the natural logarithm of the ratio between the intensity of the radiation entering the measurement volume and the intensity of the

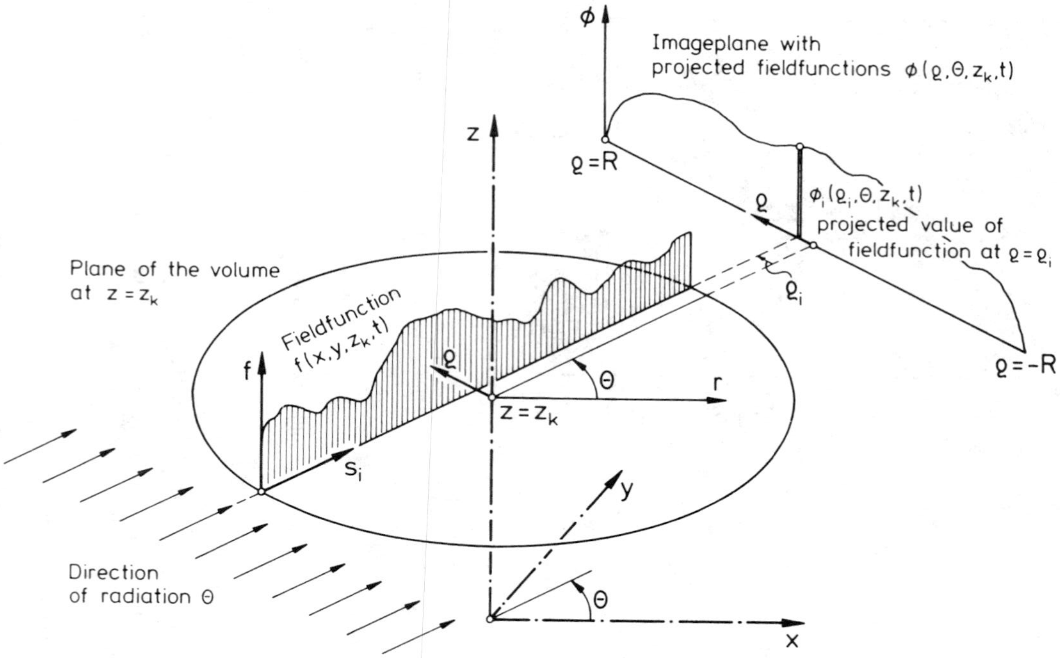

Figure 2. Line integral of a field function along one defined path through the measurement volume.

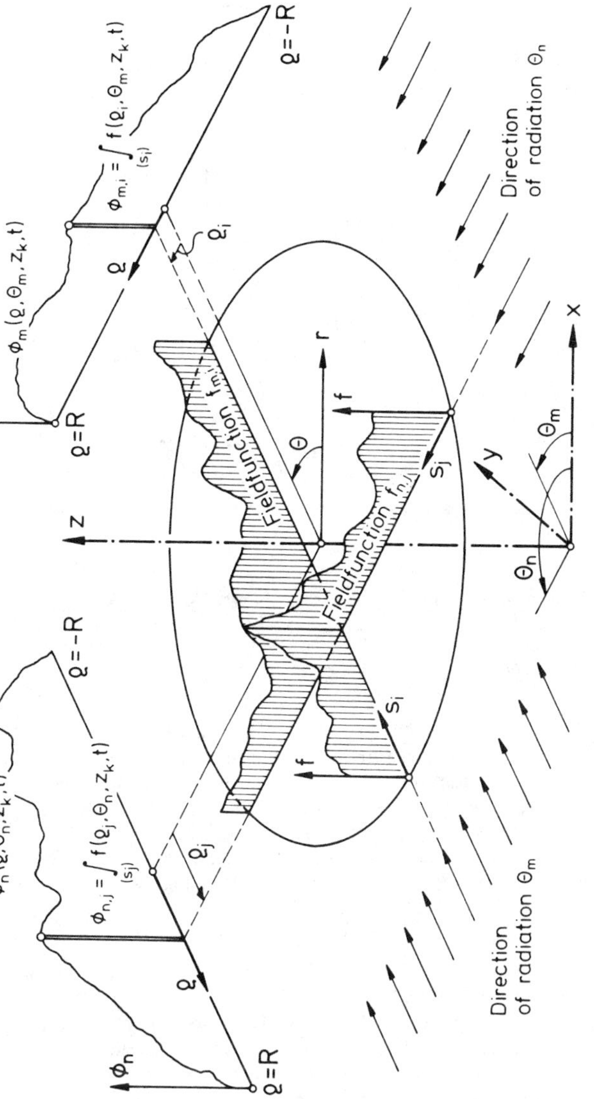

Figure 3. Line integrals along different paths through the measurement volume.

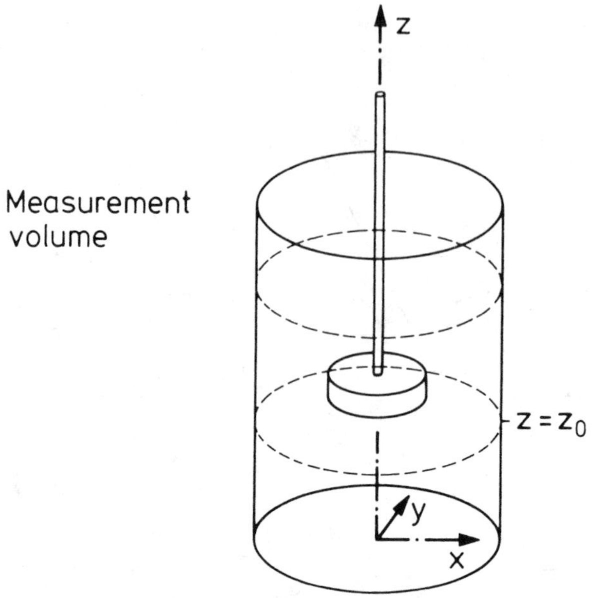

Figure 4. Planes at various heights in the measurement volume.

radiation leaving the measurement volume. Consequently, Equation 1 must be transformed into

$$\ln\left(\frac{I}{I_0}\right) = \int_{s_i} \mu(x, y, z, t)\, ds \tag{4}$$

for absorption techniques.

For tomographic techniques, the measurement volume is irradiated from different directions. The reduced intensity of the radiation becomes visible as projections with the use of sensors that are selected according to the type of radiation. Since the absorption coefficient depends on the wavelength of the applied wave type as well as the material properties of the fluids or the solid matter contained in the measurement volume, monochromatic waves must be applied to obtain a holographic recording of the experimental parameter. This is the only way to relate the reconstructed absorption coefficient to one particular material property.

Electromagnetic Waves

In the range of electromagnetic waves, X-rays or visible light are mainly used to record the experimental parameter. In special applications, infra-red light and γ-radiation are used as well [1]. Visible light is used to measure concentration differences in the measurement volume. Concentration differences can be marked with color change reactions. X-rays are used to measure density differences in solid matter or in opaque fluids.

Figure 5 shows a simple tomographic arrangement schematically. The source of radiation and the detector are coupled and can be rotated through the angle θ with respect to the measurement volume to be scanned. The measurement volume is located on the axis of rotation of the arrangement. As a source of radiation, a laser could be used for visible light, and an X-ray tube for X-ray

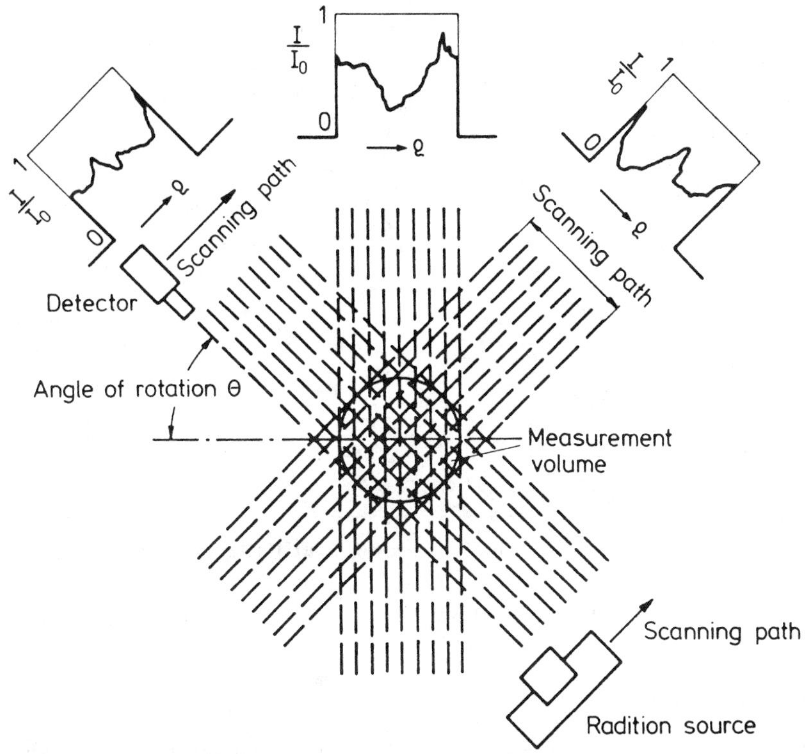

Figure 5. Schematic representation of a simple tomograph with one beam and one detector for linear scanning and rotation.

radiation. As a detector for visible light, either a photographic plate or a photographic diode can be used. An X-ray film is used for the X-ray radiation.

For each angular position, the source of radiation and the detector are shifted step by step across the entire cross-section to be scanned. For logical reasons, the step width will be no larger than the width of the beam. Each experimental result represents the experimental parameter for the applied radiation. The result of the tomographic reconstruction is the three-dimensional profile of the location-dependent absorption coefficient. The experimental parameter recorded by the detector is the integral change of the field parameter along the irradiation path. Therefore, the irradiation path must be known for the reconstruction of the field parameter. It is therefore necessary to minimize scattering or even eliminate it for special requirements.

If X-ray radiation is used to record the experimental parameter, the effect of beam hardening has to be considered during the evaluation of the measured projections [20]. The X-ray radiation produced in X-rays contains a spectrum of quanta of different energies. Since the absorption coefficient also depends on the radiation energy, beam hardening must be considered. Figure 6 shows the natural logarithm of the absorbed radiation intensity as a function of the thickness of a homogeneously absorbing matter. Without beam hardening the logarithm of the relative intensity decrease $\ln((I_0 - I)/I_0)$ is proportional to the thickness of the material. With beam hardening the absorption of the radiation no longer increases linearly with increasing thickness.

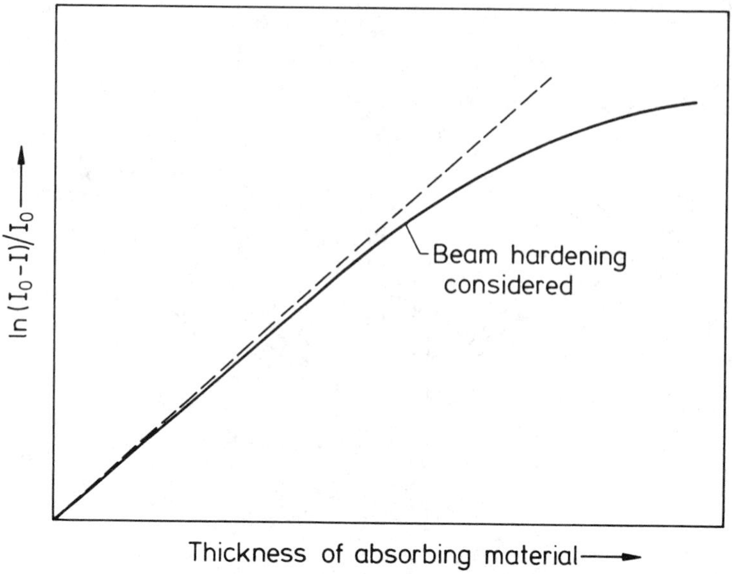

Figure 6. Intensity of the absorbed radiation as a function of the material thickness.

Corpuscular Radiation

The mathematical relationship described in Equation 4 between the decrease of the intensity of electromagnetic radiation and the location-dependent absorption coefficient generally applies for corpuscular radiation as well [2]. In this case, the absorption coefficient indicated in Equation 4 must be replaced with the product of the density ρ of the material by the mass absorption coefficient μ'. The ratio of the intensities of the electromagnetic waves I/I_0 is replaced with the ratio of the number of particles entering into the measurement volume to the number of particles leaving the measurement volume.

With the use of a collimator, an intensely bundled neutron beam is emitted from the neutron source shown in Figure 7. Part of the neutron beam entering into the measurement volume penetrates the measurement volume and is recorded by a neutron detector (scintillation counter). This neutron detector must have a high probability of detection and a good neutron-gamma discrimination property [2]. The measurement volume can be shifted transversely with a transport carriage. With the use of a rotating table, the measurement volume can be irradiated from different directions. The source of radiation, the measurement volume, and the detector must be installed in a chamber protected against scattering.

The advantage of a neutron tomographic arrangement compared to an X-ray tomographic arrangement is a better resolution of place and contrast. Such an arrangement is especially suitable for investigations of measurement volumes with highly inhomogeneous densities.

Sound Waves

In addition to electromagnetic waves, ultra sound waves can also be used to irradiate fluids or solid-state bodies. This is a way to record projections of the density field in the measurement volume. If an even sound wave expands in a medium, part of the sound energy is transformed into other forms of energy. The sound wave is weakened. The sound intensity I_0 of the sound wave be-

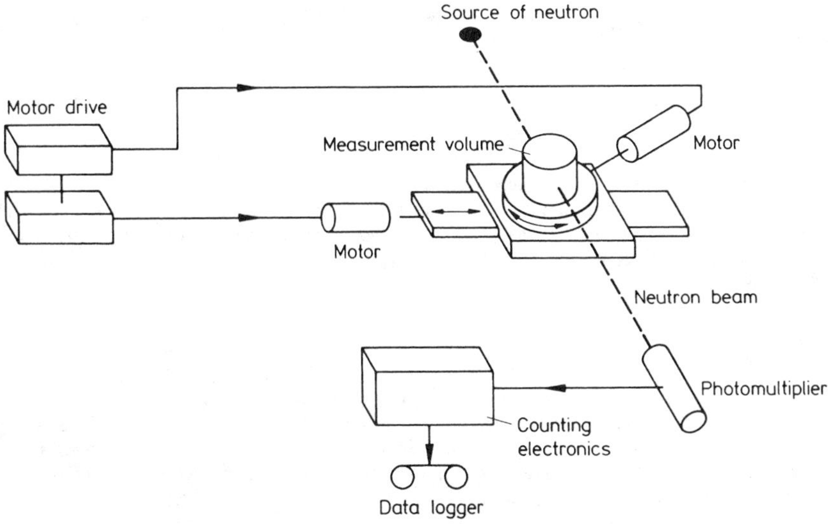

Figure 7. Experimental facility for neutron tomography [2].

fore entering into the measurement volume decreases to the sound intensity I after penetrating the measurement volume. This exit intensity I is

$$I = I_0 \exp\left(-\int_s \mu^*(x, y, z, t)\, ds \right) \tag{5}$$

The parameter μ^* is called sound absorption coefficient. It depends on the density of the sound-transferring medium and on the frequency of the sound wave.

The structure of an ultra sound tomographic arrangement generally corresponds with the schematic representation shown in Figure 5. Oscillator crystals, which can produce sound waves of a certain frequency, are used as sound sources. A sound wave with a frequency of about 2 MHz is emitted by the source during the time $t = 1\ \mu s$. The sound energy is approximately 100 dB. After penetrating the measurement volume, the sound wave is received by a microphone. Either a voltmeter or an oscilloscope can be connected to the microphone. The different readings are proportional to the sound intensity. The absorption of the sound intensity is about 20 to 30 dB. The density differences between the various density regions in the measurement volume must not exceed a certain limit. If this limit is exceeded, the decrease of the sound intensity due to the reflection of the sound wave at the boundary areas between the density zones and the decrease of the transmitted wave are identical.

Interferometric Techniques

In addition to the change of the intensity of a wave, the change of the phase of a wave, with respect to a reference wave, during the irradiation of a measurement volume can be used to record projections of three-dimensional field parameters in a measurement chamber. The respective shifting of the phase of a wave, called phase shift, is equivalent to the integral change of the field parameter along the irradiation path. In accordance with the relationship between the field parameter f and the experimental parameter Φ indicated in Equation 1, the following equation results for interferometric techniques:

$$\Phi_i(\rho_i, \theta, z, t) = \int_{s_i} \Delta f(x, y, z, t)\, ds \tag{6}$$

The function Δf is the change of the field parameter with respect to a reference condition.

The advantage of interferometric techniques compared to absorption techniques is the fact that the recorded experimental parameters are equivalent to the integral change of the field parameter. For the absorption techniques, the recorded experimental parameter is proportional to the integral change of the field parameter. Therefore, the experimental results of interferometric techniques need not be calibrated.

Coherent Light Waves

Coherent monochromatic light waves traveling through different optical distances are interfering in the plane of the hologram. However, the interference pattern disappears, as soon as the difference between the optical distances of the waves becomes larger than the so-called coherence length. Since recent developments of the laser technique, light sources of high energy are now available. The light originating from these laser beams has a long coherence length. The coherence length of an argon-ion laser operated with a beam splitter is about 1 m. These light sources are used for tomographic measurement techniques. For light waves, transparent measurement volumes are irradiated from different directions and the results recorded with the use of holographic interferometry. Figure 8 shows a schematic representation of the irradiation of a stirred vessel as measurement volume with light. Interferograms are obtained as projections of the field of refractive indices existing in the measurement volume.

The measurement principle of holographic interferometry has already been described in numerous publications [4–7]. Therefore, the following only contains the basic knowledge required for tomographic applications.

The holographic interferometer. Contrary to the commonly known operation of classical interferometers (Mach-Zehnder interferometer), the measurement with holographic interferometry is done by two time steps. These two steps are the recording of the hologram and the formation of the interferogram, with which the processes in the experimental setup become measurable and visible.

The general structure of a holographic transillumination interferometer is shown in Figure 9. A He-Ne or argon-ion laser usually serves as light source. With a beam splitter, the light beam is separated into two portions, called object beam and reference beam. The object beam then penetrates a system of lenses to produce a parallel light beam of larger diameter and then passes through the test chamber. The reference beam, which is necessary for holographic storage and reconstruction of the object wave, is enlarged and superimposed on the object wave behind the experimental setup. The storage itself, i.e. the formation of the hologram, occurs by exposure of a photographic plate of high resolution, which is installed in the area of the superposition of the object wave and reference wave. The photographic image on this photographic plate of the microscopic interference pattern resulting from both waves is called a hologram. It contains the complete required information about the object wave. This information consists of the amplitude in the form of different intensities and the length and the phase of the wave through distance and shape of the interference pattern.

Holographic double exposure technique. The principle of holographic double exposure technique is shown in Figure 10. The example used is the determination of a temperature field near a heated wall. In the first holographic image, the object wave is stored at a time when the fluid-dynamic or heat-transferring process to be examined in the measurement volume has not yet started. It is not absolutely necessary that the object wave pass through the test chamber with ideally parallel wave fronts. The wave may already be deformed due to optical inadequacies of the mirrors and cell windows.

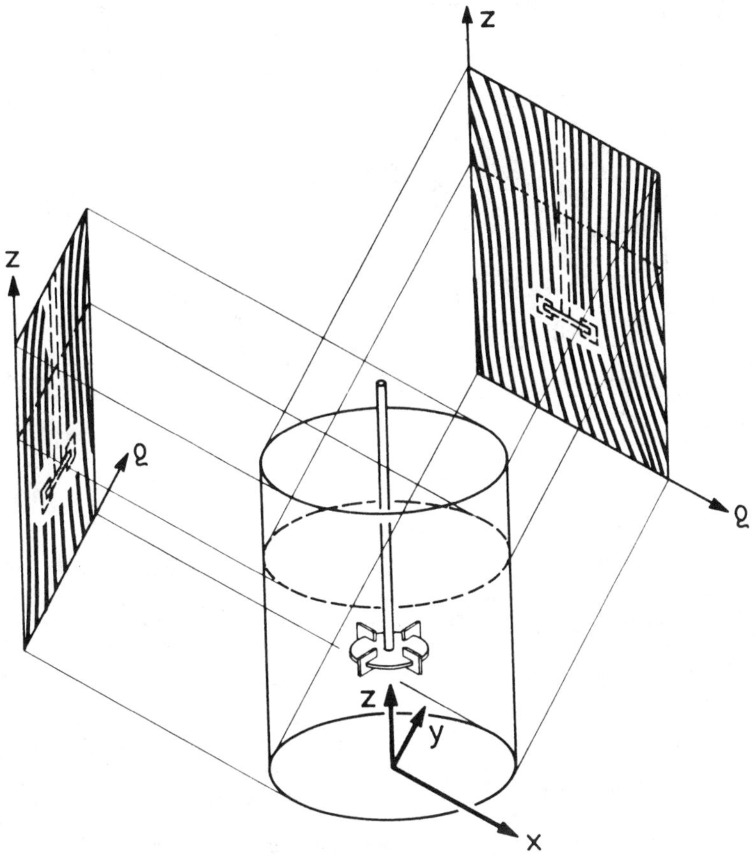

Figure 8. Schematic representation of the different projections by two transmission angles obtained by holographic interferometry.

The heat and mass transport to be examined is then established and the second holographic recording implemented. Compared to the first recording, the object wave penetrating the measurement volume is now also affected by the changes resulting from the transport process. The storage with the use of the reference wave occurs on the same photographic plate. Consequently, this plate contains information about two object waves, i.e., before and after the beginning of the transport process to be measured. The interference occurs during the reconstruction of the hologram, as shown in the lower section of Figure 10. For this purpose, the photographic plate must be developed and illuminated with the reference wave. The reference wave now assumes the function of a reconstruction wave. During this illumination, the hologram acts as a diffraction grid with locally variable grid constants. The reconstructed object waves from the first and second recording, leaving simultaneously behind the hologram, become superimposed. An interference pattern is created. It describes the integral change of the temperature or concentration field resulting from the transport process.

Holographic real-time interferometry. The described holographic interferometry with the double exposure technique permits only the examination of individual instantaneous conditions. Continuous

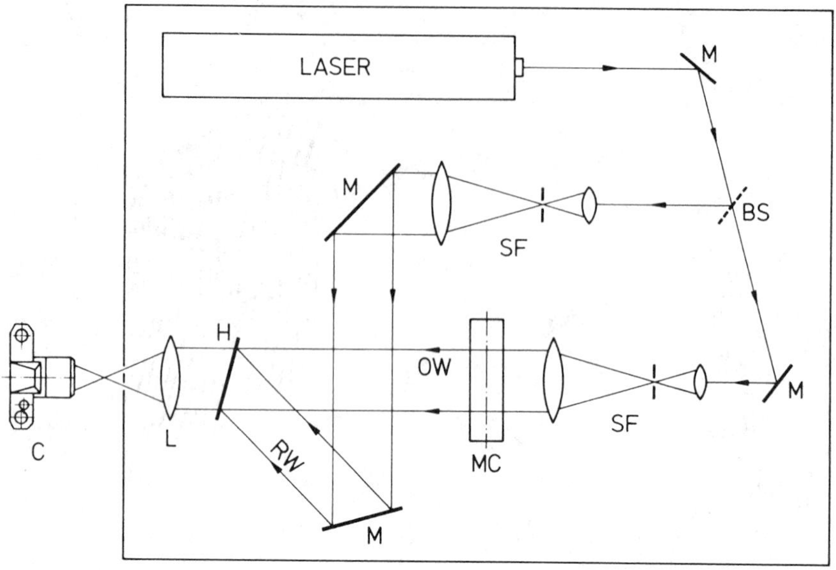

Figure 9. Optical setup for holographic interferometry: M—mirror, BS—beam splitter; SF—spatial filter; MC—measurement chamber; RW—reference wave; OW—objective wave, H—hologram; C—camera, L—lens.

observation and recording of the processes in the experimental setup is not possible, because the interference field does not become visible until the hologram is developed and reconstructed by the reference wave. This disadvantage can be avoided with the so-called real-time method. This requires minor modifications of the recording technique. Figure 11 again shows this principle on the basis of the heated wall. The first exposure of the photographic plate occurs when the process to be examined has not yet started. The photographic plate is then developed. A hologram is obtained, which stores only the information of the object wave in the reference condition. If the photographic plate is removed from the optical arrangement for chemical treatment, it must later be reinstalled at half of the wave length of the light at its exact original position. This can be achieved with a finely adjustable precision plate holder, e.g., with the use of a piezo crystal. Controlling is possible by repositioning. The stored object wave, which is released with the use of the reference wave, is superimposed on the instantaneous, unaffected object wave. The position of the hologram is exact, if no interference pattern becomes visible. The heat transport to be observed is then initiated. The continuously reconstructed object wave, which serves as a reference wave, now interferes behind the hologram with the object wave penetrating the measurement volume at this instant. This object wave is also affected by the temperature field. The resulting instantaneous interference image can now be continuously observed, photographed or recorded with a film camera.

The finite-fringe-field technique. Interferometry offers two possibilities for the representation of the phase shift between the instantaneous object wave and the reconstructed object wave [7]. The fringe-field technique uses interference stripes, which develop due to the superposition of two wave fronts. In the finite-fringe-field technique, a given interference pattern is deflected due to the phase shift. The advantage of the finite-fringe-field technique is the possibility to prescribe the number of interference stripes, i.e. the information density of the interferograms, and the possibility to determine the direction of the temperature change, i.e., whether the fluid has heated up or cooled off. In Figure 12, a gas flame is used to demonstrate the difference between the two techniques. In the

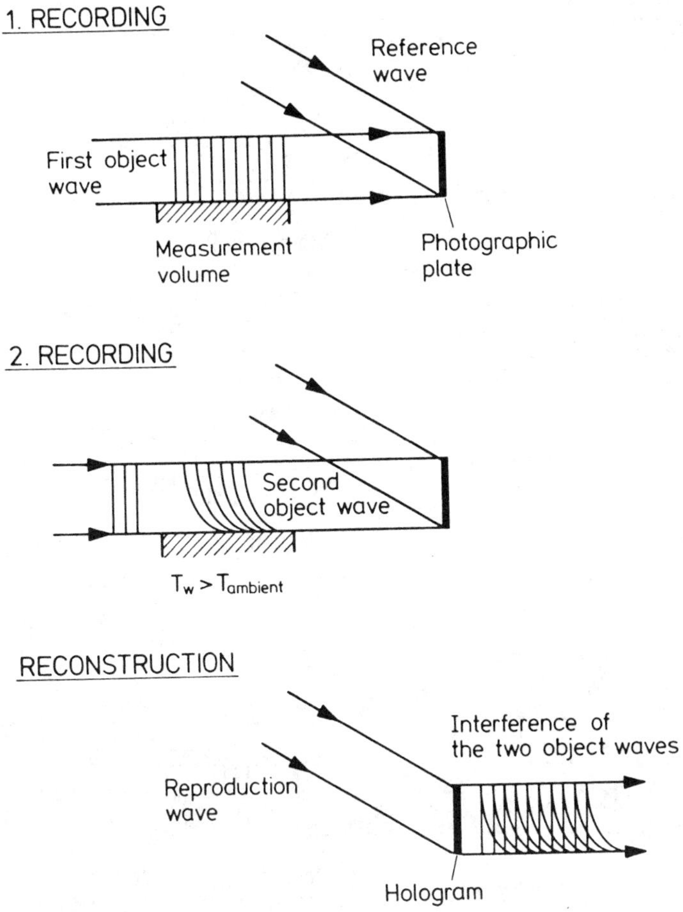

Figure 10. Double exposure technique.

upper left picture, the interference lines result from the temperature field around a gas flame. The interference lines can be interpreted as isotherms. In the other three pictures, the reference wave was tilted by a small angle at the time of the recording of the interferogram in comparison to the recording of the hologram. Therefore, an even striped pattern already develops before the measurement effect is initiated. The position and the number of the given stripes can be changed by varying the tilting angle. The temperature field around the gas flame is reflected by the deflection of the interference stripes. If the temperature of the air had been cooled off, the interference stripes would have been deflected into the opposite direction.

Without the use of the fringe-field technique in investigations of temperature fields, it is not possible to determine only with the use of the interferograms, whether the fluid has heated up or cooled off, because the interferograms for heating and cooling of a fluid are identical.

Holographic interferometry with diffuse light. The irradiation of the volume under investigation with diffuse light belongs to the category of interference techniques that can only be implemented

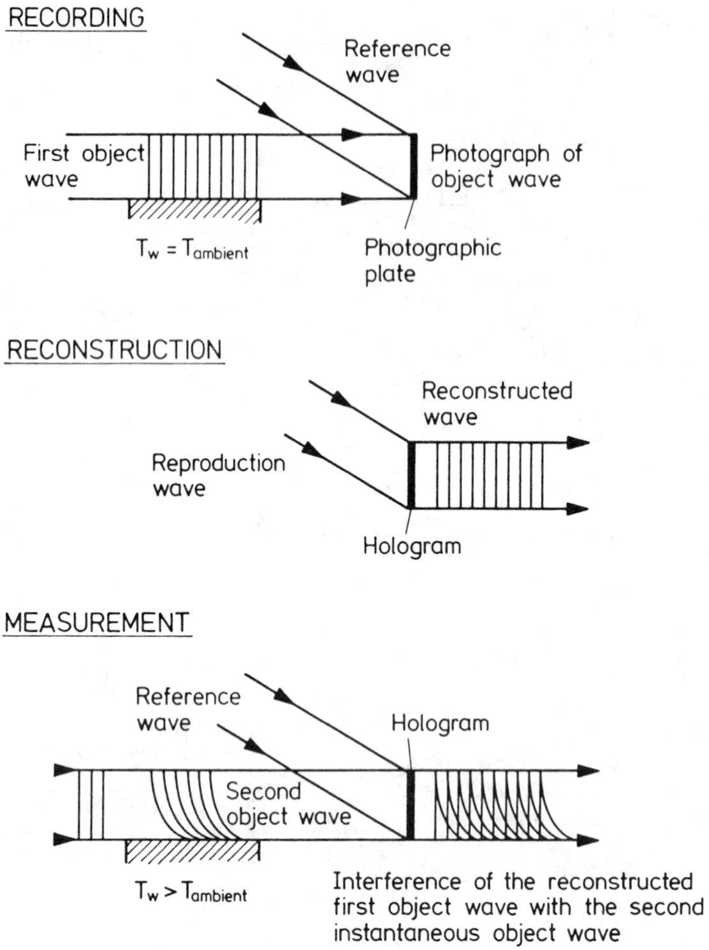

Figure 11. Explanation of holographic real-time interferometry.

with the use of holography. In general, exact measurements are possible only with parallel light, however, in some cases it is of advantage to irradiate the measurement chamber with diffuse light. The only difference between the optical arrangement used here (Figure 13) and the one used for normal holographic transillumination interferometry is the installation of a matte screen in the object beam before the experimental setup [8]. Contrary to the parallel beams, the measurement volume is irradiated at different directions. As a result, different interferograms are obtained that depend on the position of the camera.

Sound Waves

In general, it is possible to obtain interferograms from superposition of sound waves [9, 10]. The shifting of the phase between the sound wave leaving the measurement volume and a reference

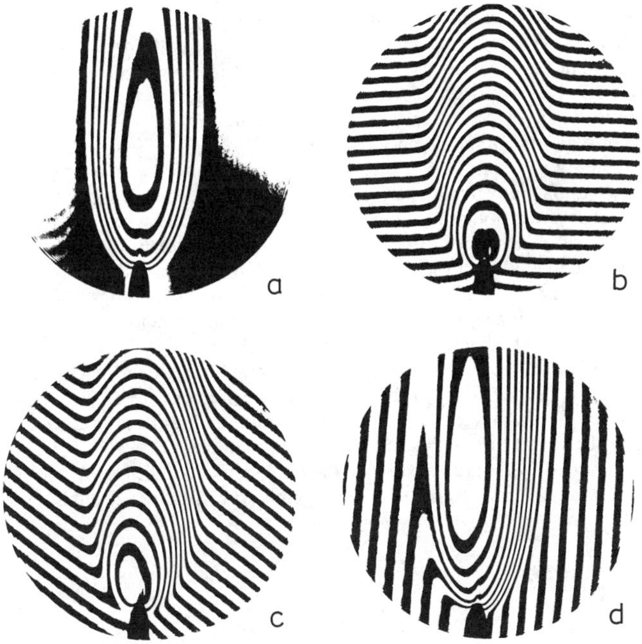

Figure 12. Demonstration of the finite-fringe-field technique by a temperature field of a gas flame.

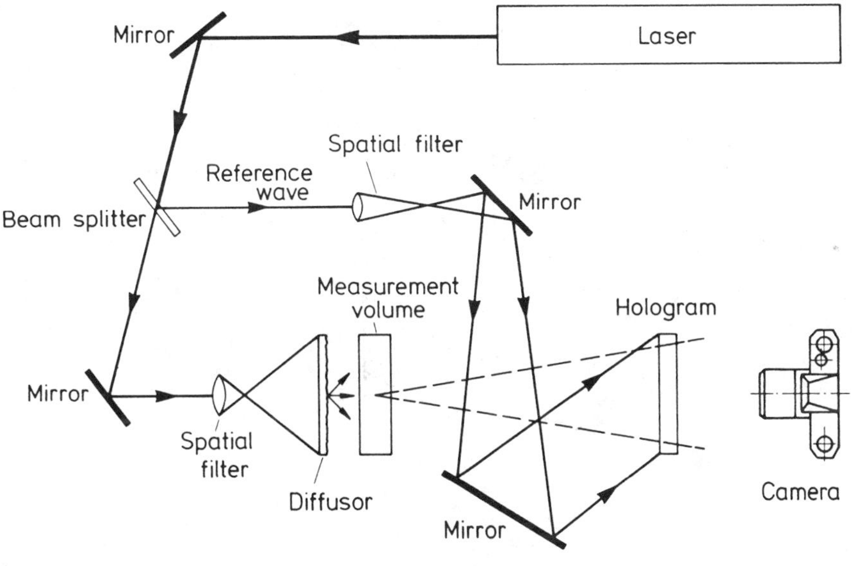

Figure 13. Holographic interferometry using diffusive light [8].

wave is a measure for the integral change of the sound velocity and the density along the path of the sound wave. The enlargement of the developing interference pattern, however, is more complicated here than in optical interferometry. The techniques applied so far for recording the interference images can be divided into two groups. On one hand, the interference pattern can be recorded directly with piezoelectric detectors, and on the other hand, the acoustic interference pattern can be transformed into an optical interference pattern.

In Figure 14 the transformation of an acoustic hologram into an optical hologram is shown schematically. S_1 and S_2 are two frequency generators that create two waves with coupled phases.

Generator S_1 sends out the object wave, generator S_2 the reference wave. Due to the interference of the two sound waves, the surface of the liquid in which the object is located is deformed. If the liquied surface is illuminated with the light source L, a light intensity that is proportional to the deformation of the liquid surface is obtained in every point of the photographic plate. When the photographic plate is developed, the photograph is a real optical hologram. Illumination from a coherent light source would reconstruct a picture of the object.

If a reference condition is stored at first on the photographic plate and then the measured condition after the change of the density in the measurement volume is stored as well, an interference image will be stored on the photographic plate that contains the integral change of the density along the path of the sound through the measurement volume.

Another interferometric technique is based on the measurement of the travel time of sound waves. The difference between the travel time of the measured wave passing through the measurement

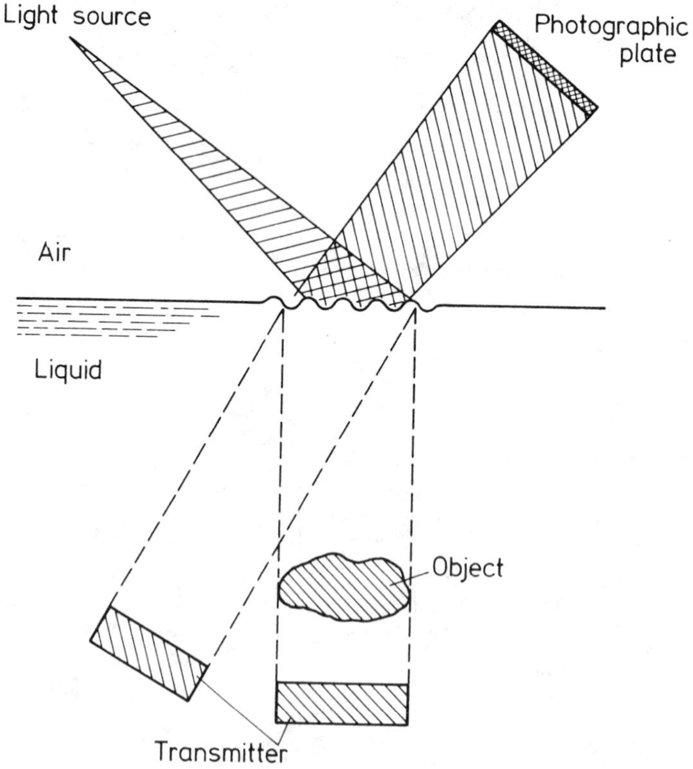

Figure 14. Transformation of an acoustical hologram into an optical hologram [9].

volume and the travel time of the reference wave passing through a medium of constant density is measured. Both sound waves cover the same distance.

From the measured difference in travel time $\Delta\tau$, the sound velocity and also the density in the measurement volume can be calculated with:

$$\Delta\tau = \int_{s_i} \left(\frac{1}{w_R} - \frac{1}{w_M(x, y, z, t)} \right) ds \tag{7}$$

w_R is the sound velocity of the reference wave, w_M the sound velocity of the measured wave.

Nuclear Spin Resonance

For the reconstruction of the composition of a three-dimensional object with the use of nuclear spin tomography, the atomic nuclei of the object to be examined must have a magnetic momentum [11]. This means that the atomic nuclei must have an uneven number of nucleons. Magnetic momenta can be pictured as microscopic rod magnets.

In a chamber without magnetic fields, the magnetic momenta are distributed evenly and they point into all chamber directions. This is shown schematically in Figure 15. If an exterior static

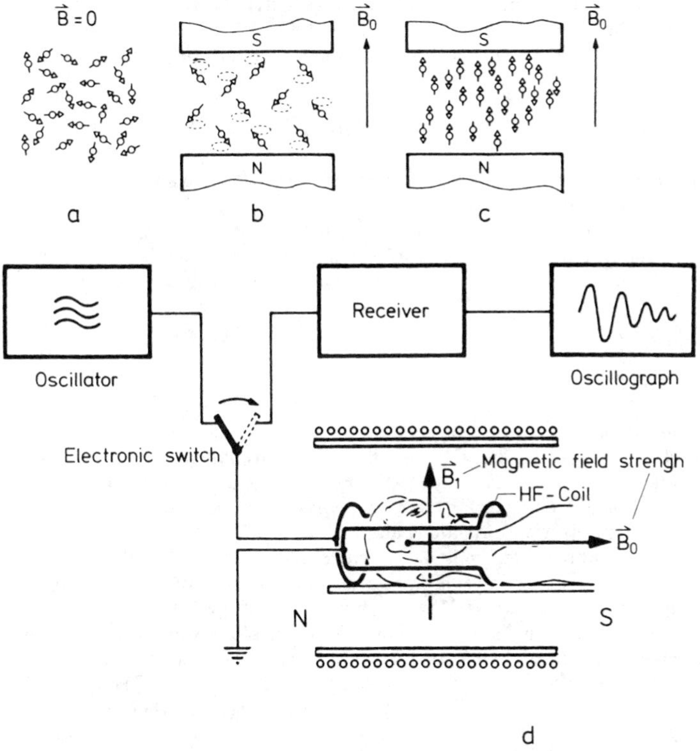

Figure 15. Nuclear spin resonance tomography: a) even distribution of magnetic momenta; b) alignement of magnetic momenta in an anti-parallel manner; c) alignement of magnetic momenta in a parallel manner; d) experimental setup for nuclear spin resonance tomography [11].

magnetic field B_0 is established, the magnetic momenta are aligned either in a parallel or an anti-parallel manner with respect to this magnetic field (Figures 15b and c). The magnetic momenta aligned in a parallel manner with respect to the magnetic field have a lower energy level than the magnetic momenta aligned in an anti-parallel manner. If a high-frequency alternating electromagnetic field is fed in at a right between the two energy levels can be induced. The fed radiation energy, however, must be equivalent to the difference between the two energy levels. When the additional magnetic field is switched off, the system returns to its original condition of equilibrium. A signal that is decreasing in time is received by an antenna installed at a right angle to the exterior magnetic field. The magnetic coupling of the examined atomic nuclei to each other and to the surrounding medium can be reconstructed from the type of the signal.

The image reconstruction requires exact information about the individual area of development of the answer signal. A unique attribution of the signal to one volume element of the object is therefore mandatory.

The local information is obtained with additional fields beyond the static magnetic field B_0 along the three space coordinates. The magnetic field values of these fields are locally variable. A different magnetic field exists in each volume element of the object. The radiation energy to be fed is different for each volume element. Therefore, only one signal in one particular volume element is obtained after an inducement with a certain frequency or radiation energy. This way, an image of the object can be created point by point.

This explanation of image creation is only a general description. The methods most commonly used in practical application for image reconstruction are much faster and much more elegant [11]. Figure 15d shows the general structrure of a nuclear spin tomographic arrangement.

MATHEMATICAL BASIS OF TOMOGRAPHIC TECHNIQUES

The techniques described in the previous section make it possible to determine the measured field parameters in the form of their projections for the examined volume. Mathematical methods that permit the calculation of the unknown field parameter for each space coordinate from several projections in different directions are called tomographic techniques. The experimental values are the results of a line integration of the field parameter along defined beam paths, according to Equation 3 [12].

Principal Solution Techniques

A calculation of the local field parameters is not possible, if only one of their projections is available. If the object is irradiated from several directions, a reconstruction can be implemented. In this case, several linearly independent integral equations are available. Depending on the algorithm used for the solution, the methods for the calculation of the field function can be subdivided into grid methods and integral transformations [13, 14].

For the application of grid methods, each plane of the measurement volume is divided up into a grid, and the integral equation (2) is transformed into a summation equation. The result is a relatively simple system of equations. However, a multitude of angles of view is required for a good approximate solution. The quality of the reconstruction can be improved this way, and objects of increasing size can be recorded. In integral transformations, the mathematical method of the Fourier transformation is applied to reconstruct the required field parameters. These methods are most commonly used in practical application. They permit a fast and accurate calculation [15] and are therefore used mainly for medical diagnosis. These methods have a high quality of reconstruction However, they are not suitable for an analysis in all cases. Many irradiations obtained from a wide range of angles are required for the reconstruction. Some methods precisely belong to one of the two mentioned groups. However, there are other methods that have the characteristics of both groups. A frequently used method of this type is the sample method developed by Sweeney [16]. The following contains a short description of the mathematical basis of the mentioned methods.

Grid Method

The most simple method, from a mathematical point of view, is the grid method. Each plane of the volume is covered with a close-meshed grid. A constant value of the field parameter is assumed in each field element of the grid. The irradiation can be considered as the summation of these values across all field elements that are hit by a beam. The integral equation (3) is written as a summation equation:

$$\Phi_i(\rho_i, \theta) = \sum_{i=1}^{N} f(x, y)\, \Delta s \tag{8}$$

In Equation 8, N means the number of field elements with the linear expansion of Δs in the direction of the observed beam. The beam is located at the distance ρ_i from the center of the axialsymmetric measurement plane and runs in the direction of θ. f(x, y) means the averaged value of the field function for one grid element. The center of the grid element is located at the coordinates x and y. The mathematical solution is a system of equations, in which the number of unknown parameters is equal to the number of existing grid elements. If there is an identical number of linearly independent experimental results, it is possible to formulate a system of equations that can be solved elementally. Since the grid must be as close-meshed as possible, the number of required experimental results quickly becomes very high. The number of required equations changes exponentially with the change of the grid size or the size of the examined range. The requirement for an increased number of equations can be met only with a growing number of irradiation directions and, consequently, increased experimental effort.

The number and direction of the angles at which the irradiation must occur is given only by the required linear independence of the summation equations. It is not necessary to view each local field parameter from all directions.

Since the equations must be solved simultaneously, the required calculation capacity is relatively high. Therefore, this method is suitable only for the reconstruction of field parameters in small measurement volumes, if a very high quality of reconstruction is not required [13]. In this case, the number of equations to be solved and the experimental effort can be kept low.

Integral Transformations

So far, each grid element was related to exactly one field parameter. Actually, however, the graph of the required field function is a continuous one. It can be approximated with the use of methods that assume discrete values for each point instead of finite area elements. This approximate calculation of the required field function can be implemented with the use of integral transformations. The reconstruction is implemented with the use of the Fourier transformation.

Each periodic function of the location can be transformed uniquely and reversibly into a spectral representation. This is achieved with the use of the Fourier series, which represents a periodic signal as the sum of sine oscillations. Figure 16a shows an example: A periodic signal consisting of two sine waves in the local range is transferred into the frequency range. Thus, the periodic functions can be shown in the frequency range by a corresponding line spectrum. The sine function in Figure 16b is represented by one single line. The rectangular function in Figure 16b, however, is described by an infinitely large number of lines in the frequency range. For locally limited, non-recurrent processes, the disintegration of the function into its spectral components in the form of a Fourier series is not possible any more. Parameters such as periodic interval or basic frequency do not exist, if the function is locally limited. Examples are shown in Figure 16b.

A representation with continuous amplitude and phase spectrum is used to describe non-periodic functions in the frequency range. The frequencies of the sine functions, from which the local function can be obtained, approach each other infinitesimally. The representation of the local function in the frequency range is implemented with the use of the Fourier transformation. This transformation can be applied only, if the local function $\Phi(\rho, \theta)$ is monotonic and if the integral $\int_{-\infty}^{\infty} |\Phi(\rho, \theta)|\, d\rho$ converges.

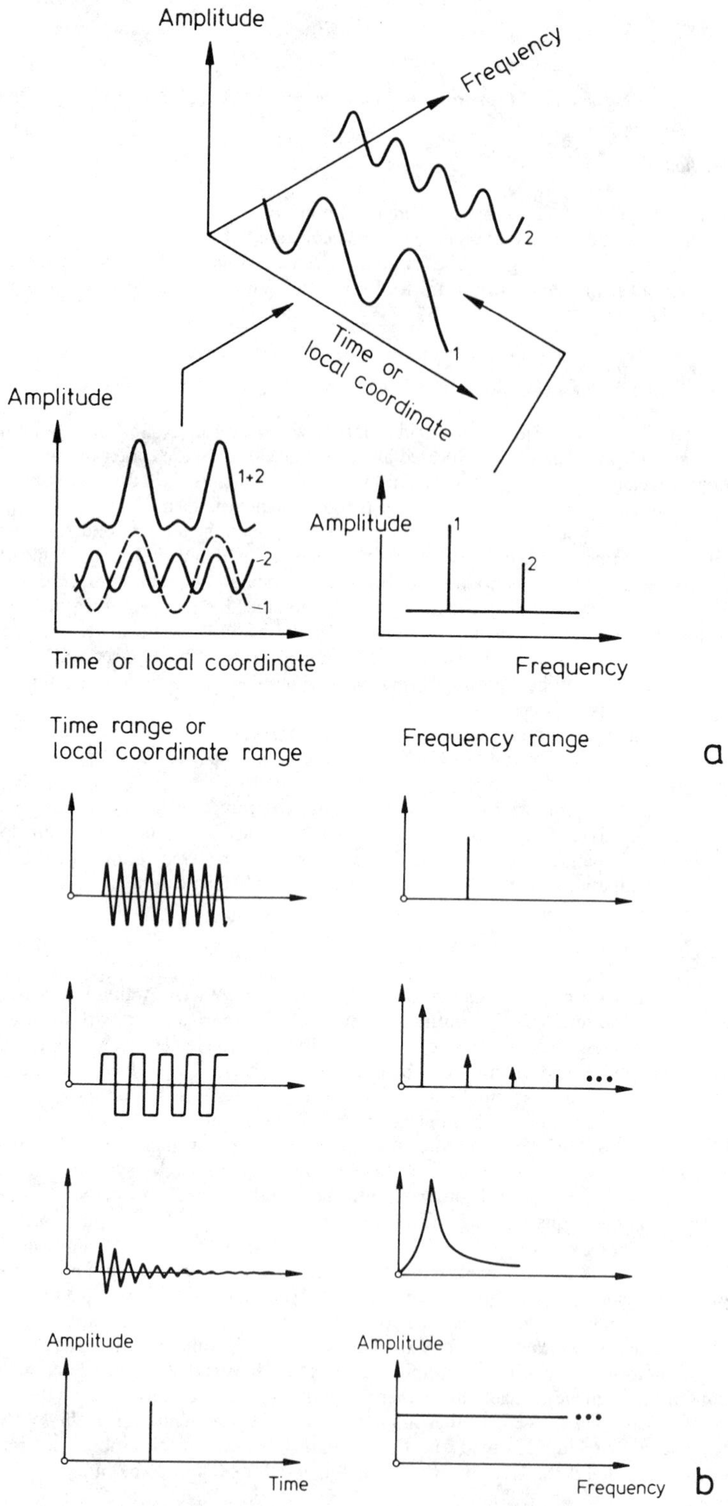

Figure 16. a) Example for the transformation of a periodic signal consisting of two sine waves from the local range into the frequency range. b) Transformation of different types of periodic functions.

The result of the Fourier transformation is called spectrum. The experimental results are plotted in the frequency range as amplitudes above the corresponding frequencies. By means of back projection, the original function can be obtained again. Smith and Keinert [17] have established an exact mathematical justification for the application of the integral transformation in tomography.

Numerous mathematical operations, such as filter operations, can be implemented more easily in the frequency range than in the time range. This technique is used for digital signal processing [18]. The experimental results are projected into the frequency range, processed, and then projected back into the local range. The filtered initial parameters are obtained again. This makes it possible to eliminate any disturbances that may be superimposed on a measurement. The transformation can be either uni- or multi-dimensional. If the experimental result depends on only one coordinate, e.g., the location, the uni-dimensional Fourier transformation describes the process. If the experimental result depends on two coordinates, the transformation must be two-dimensional as well. Picture processing is an example. Brightness and color value in the picture plane generally depend on two coordinates. The dependence of the required field parameter on two coordinates is given in Equation 8.

In order to reconstruct the field parameter for all points of one plane from their projections, the uni-dimensional Fourier transformation of the projection is used. It is identical to the two-dimensional Fourier transformation of the field parameter [12]. With the two-dimensional back projection of the uni-dimensional Fourier-transformed projection, it is now possible to calculate the required field parameter. The principle is shown in Figure 17. It is called the Radon theorem and is described in detail in the following: The problem described in Equation 3 is:

$$\Phi_i(\rho_i, \theta) = \int_{s_i} f(x, y)\, ds \tag{9}$$

Φ_i is the experimental result; Φ_i is determined by the applied measurement technique and it is obtained by means of integration of the required field parameter along the radiation path. For the further observations it is necessary to replace the fixed coordinates x and y of the examined plane with a coordinate system that is related to the path of the beam. The coordinate system is shown in Figure 18. The coordinate transformation is implemented with the equations

$$\rho = x \cos \theta + y \sin \theta \tag{10}$$

and

$$s = -x \sin \theta + y \cos \theta \tag{11}$$

The ρ, s-system is rotated through the angle θ with respect to the x, y-system. The s-coordinate is parallel to the beam. After the coordinate transformation, Equation 9 becomes:

$$\Phi_i(\rho_i, \theta) = \int_{s_i} f(\rho, s)\, ds \tag{12}$$

By definition of the Fourier transformation, the uni-dimensional Fourier transformation of function $\Phi(\rho, \theta)$ is [13]:

$$P(\tau_\rho, \theta) = \int_{-\infty}^{\infty} \Phi(\rho, \theta) \exp(-2\pi i \rho \tau_\rho)\, d\rho \tag{13}$$

If Equation 12 is inserted into Equation 13, the result is:

$$P(\tau_\rho, \theta) = \iint_{-\infty}^{\infty} f(\rho, s) \exp(-2\pi i \rho \tau_\rho)\, d\rho\, ds \tag{14}$$

The two-dimensional Fourier transformation of the field parameter $f(\rho, s)$ is:

$$F(\tau_\rho, \tau_s) = \iint_{-\infty}^{\infty} f(\rho, s) \exp(-2\pi i(\tau_\rho \rho + \tau_s s))\, d\rho\, ds \tag{15}$$

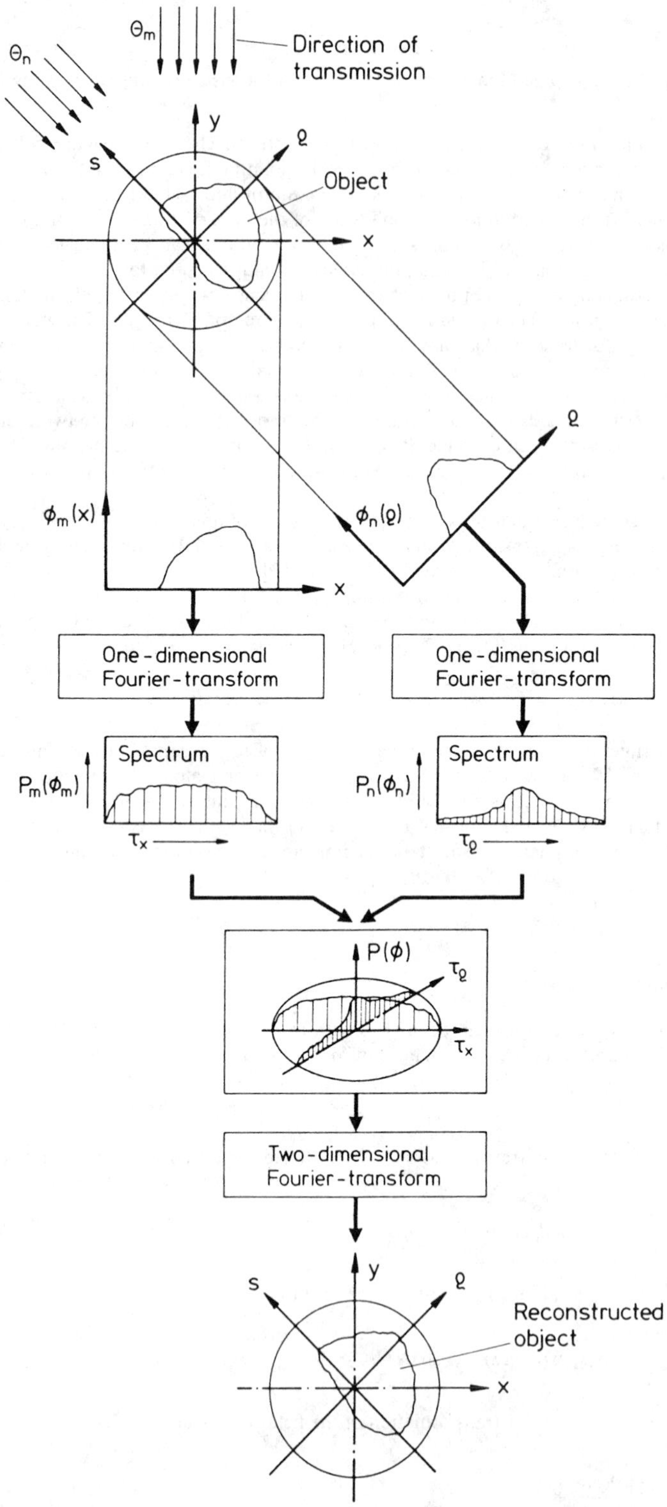

Figure 17. Principles of the tomographic reconstruction with integral transformations.

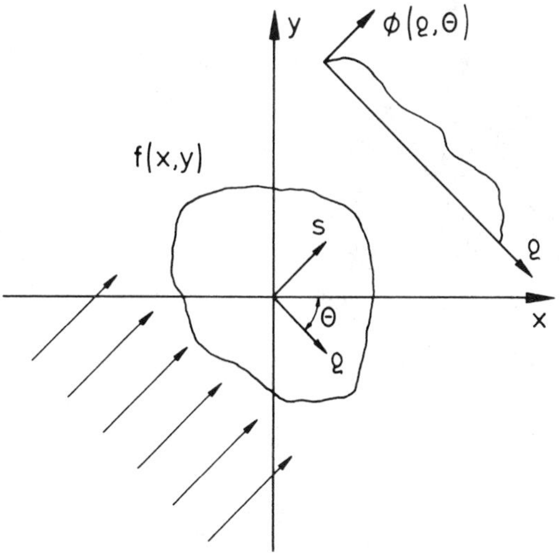

$$\phi(\varrho,\Theta) = \int_S f(\varrho, s)\, ds$$

Figure 18. Transformation of coordinates for the projection of a field function.

A comparison between Equation 15 and Equation 14 shows that both equations become identical for $\tau_s = 0$. Consequently, the condition $\tau_s = 0$ is fulfilled, if the s-axis of the coordinate system is parallel to the path of the beam [18]. Therefore, the uni-dimensional Fourier transformation of the experimental results is identical to the two-dimensional Fourier transformation of the experimental results is identical to the two-dimensional Fourier tansformation of the field parameters. If the projections from all angles between 0° and 180° are known, all values of the field parameter can be calculated in the frequency plane. By means of back projection, the field parameter can be calculated numerically in every place.

With a method suggested by Junginger and Heringen [19], it is possible to eliminate the extensive numerical back projection. The final equation for the calculation of the field parameter is:

$$f(x, y) = \frac{1}{2\pi^2} \int_{-\pi/2}^{\pi/2} d\theta \int_{-\infty}^{\infty} \left[\Phi(\rho_0 + \rho_1 \theta) + \Phi(\rho_0 - \rho_1 \theta) - 2\Phi(\rho_0, \theta) \frac{1}{\rho^2} \right] d\rho \tag{16}$$

With Equation 16 it is possible to calculate the field parameter point by point. However, this equation also shows the disadvantage of this method. For an exact calculation, it is necessary to know the experimental results for all angles between 0° and 180°. However, an indefinitely large number of angles cannot be achieved in experimental setups. The quality of reconstruction deteriorates with the decrease of the number of angles at which the object can be observed. Therefore, the reconstruction of the field parameter with this method is always out of focus.

In the Fourier plane, the lack of the projections from angles that were not included in the tests means that the amplitudes for certain ranges in the frequency plane are missing. This phenomenon is called aliasing. During back projection, the missing amplitudes cause a so-called "spreading" of the reconstruction values. The aliasing effect can be suppressed with the use of a filter function [15, 20]. With the filter function, the amplitudes in the excluded ranges of the frequency plane are set at zero. The result is that the reconstruction of the field parameter becomes more focussed.

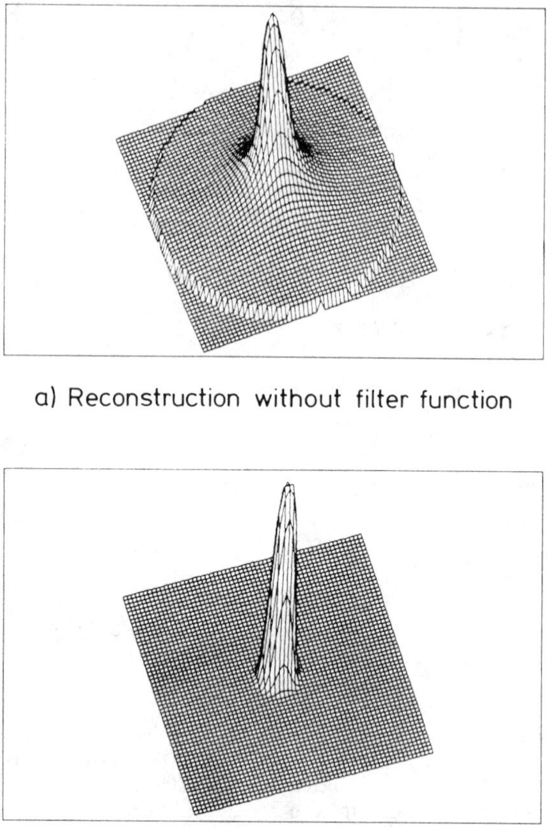

a) Reconstruction without filter function

b) Reconstruction with filter function

Figure 19. Reconstruction of a rod shaped body with integral transformation a) without filter function and b) with filter function [21].

Figure 19 shows a simple example: the reconstruction of a single rod implemented with and without the filter function [21]. It is clearly obvious that the gradient at the edge of the rod is steeper with the filter than it is without the filter.

Methods operating with integral transformations provide very exact reconstruction after short calculation times. However, the high processing speed is usually achieved only with the application of special computers [15]. Another disadvantage is the relatively large required number of projections and the wide range of required observation angles. For the investigation of unsteady-state processes, all projections must be recorded simultaneously. This would require very extensive experimental effort. Integral transformation methods are therefore preferred for the investigation of static objects.

The investigation of periodic events is a special application. By triggering the recordings with the frequency of the events, the recording of the individual projections and the events can be synchronized [15]. This technique is applied in medicine to examine the surroundings of the heart. This method can also be used for the solution of technical problems.

Combined Techniques

In addition to methods that either belong to the category of integral transformations or the category of grid methods, there are methods that have the characteristics of both techniques. These methods combine the high quality of reconstruction of the integral transformations and the low number of required irradiation angles of the grid method. The sample method belongs to this category that combines different calculation methods. This method was described by Sweeney [16] and it was applied for the measurement of three-dimensional temperature fields.

The sample method is derived from the Whittacker-Shannon sampling theorem. The theorem states that a function can be exactly represented by a sum of discrete values. For this purpose, the function must be band-restricted within known limits. A function is called band-restricted, if its Fourier transformation is different from zero in the restricted range only.

Figure 20 shows the importance of band restriction for the uni-dimensional case. The figure shows the schematic representation of a function f(x) and the corresponding Fourier transformation $F(f_x)$. If the values of the Fourier transformation $F(f_x)$ of the function f(x) are different from zero only in the interval $-B_x, B_x$, the function is band-restricted.

It can be shown that functions that differ from zero in a finite interval of the local range are generally not band-restricted [16]. Even for very large frequencies, the Fourier transformation of such a function has an amplitude that differs from zero. The rect-function is a simple example. The function is defined with the equation:

$$\begin{aligned} &\text{rect}(x) = 1 \qquad \text{for } -1 \leq x \leq 1 \\ \text{and} \quad &\text{rect}(x) = 0 \qquad \text{for all other } x \end{aligned} \tag{17}$$

The corresponding Fourier transformation is the sinc-function. It is defined as:

$$\text{sinc}(x) = \frac{\sin(\pi x)}{\pi x} \tag{18}$$

The functions are shown in Figure 21. The function according to Equation 18 has an amplitude that differs from zero even for infinite frequencies. However, the amplitude decreases quickly with rising frequency. Therefore, the deviation from the exact solution becomes very small, if the higher frequencies are not included in the Whittacker-Shannon sampling theorem.

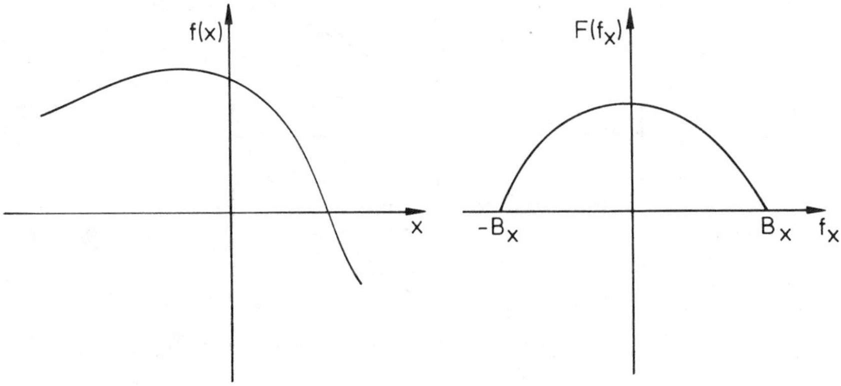

Figure 20. A function f_x and its bandlimited Fourier-transformation $F(f_x)$.

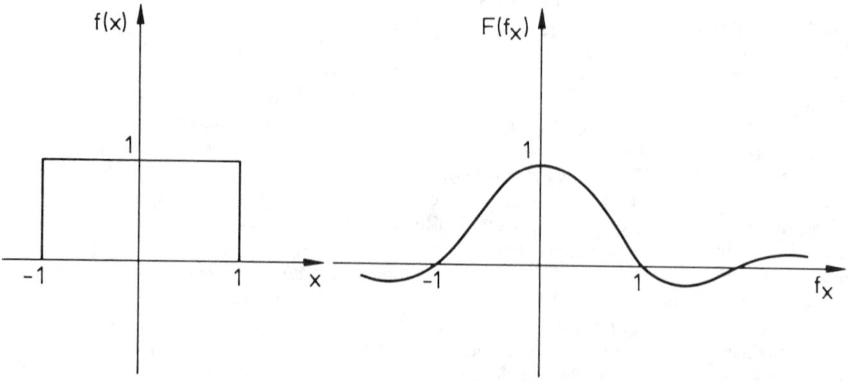

Figure 21. Graphical presentation of the rect-function and its Fourier-transformation the sine-function.

According to the Whittacker-Shannon sampling theorem, a band-restricted function g(x, y) can be calculated as the sum of discrete values of this function along defined beam paths. The summation equation is:

$$g(x, y) = \sum_m \sum_n g(ml_x, nl_y) \operatorname{sinc} \frac{x - ml_x}{l_x} \operatorname{sinc} \frac{y - nl_y}{l_y} \tag{19}$$

with $l_x = 1/2B_x$ as grid distance in x-direction and $l_y = 1/2B_y$ as grid distance in y-direction.

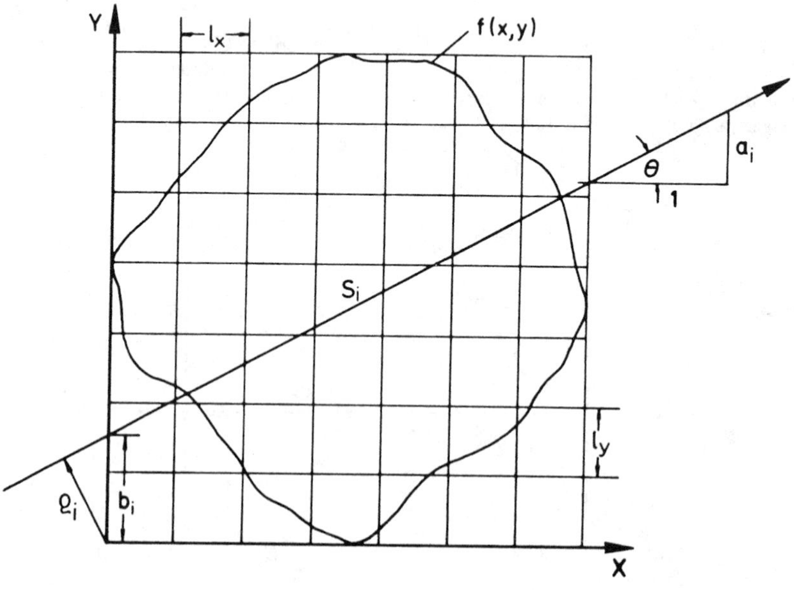

Figure 22. Coordinate system and geometrical parameters used for the sample method.

The parameters B_x and B_y are the limitations of the band restriction. The right side of Equation 19 is understood as the integral given by the experimental result, the left side as the required field function. If the function is not band-restricted, Equation 19 applies in approximation, if B_x and B_y are selected sufficiently large. With growing grid distance or decreasing limitations of the band restriction, the approximate calculation of the integral value g(x, y) becomes more and more difficult.

For further investigations, a coordinate system rotated through the angle θ is introduced again. Figure 22 shows the investigated range of a selected plane with the beam s_i penetrating this range. After inserting Equation 19 into Equation 9 in consideration of the rotation of the coordinate system through the angle θ and after transformation, the following equation results:

$$\sum_m \sum_n w(a_i, b_i) f(ml_x, nl_y) = \Phi(\rho, \theta) \tag{20}$$

Φ describes the experimental results in the projection plane. The coefficients $w(a_i, b_i)$ depend on the geometric parameters. They are defined as follows:

$0 < |a_i| < l_y/l_x$:

$$w(a_i, b_i) = \sqrt{1 + a_i^2}\, l_x \operatorname{sinc}\left(\frac{b_i + a_i l_x m - l_y n}{l_y}\right) \tag{21a}$$

$l_y/l_x < |a_i| < \infty$:

$$w(a_i, b_i) = \frac{l_y}{a_i}\sqrt{1 + a_i^2} \operatorname{sinc}\left(\frac{b_i + a_i l_x m - l_y n}{a_i l_x}\right) \tag{21b}$$

$a_i = \infty$:

$$w(a_i, b_i) = l_y \operatorname{sinc}\left(\frac{b_i + m l_x}{l_x}\right) \tag{21c}$$

Again, this system of equations contains as many unknown parameters for each plane as there are points in the grid. An identical number of linearly independent equations is required. With the sample theorem, larger distances l_x, l_y can be used than with the conventional grid method, without affecting the quality of reconstruction [16]. However, the experimental and computing effort is considerably lower for the same quality of reconstruction. The requirements for the experimental setup are still considerable. According to Sweeney, it is desirable to have more experimental results than unknown parameters, because the experimental results always contain inaccuracies. The error quota can be reduced and the reconstruction improved, if the values are redundant.

Solution of Ill-Conditioned Systems of Equations

If the number of experimental results that are independent of each other and available for the solution of a system of equations is smaller than the number of unknown parameters, the system of equations can be solved in approximation with the use of iterative methods. Zonneveld [20] suggests three possible solutions. The approximation is implemented either for a single element of the field function (simultaneous iterative reconstruction technique; SIRT) or for an entire beam (algebraic reconstruction technique; ART). A third possibility is the suppression of the oscillation of the iteration with attenuators (iterative least square technique; ILST). The ART-method developed by Gordon, Bender and Herman [22] is explained briefly here, because it is the one most frequently used in practical applications. The method can be used for a system of equations, such as the grid method or the sample method. The number of required equations can be reduced this way.

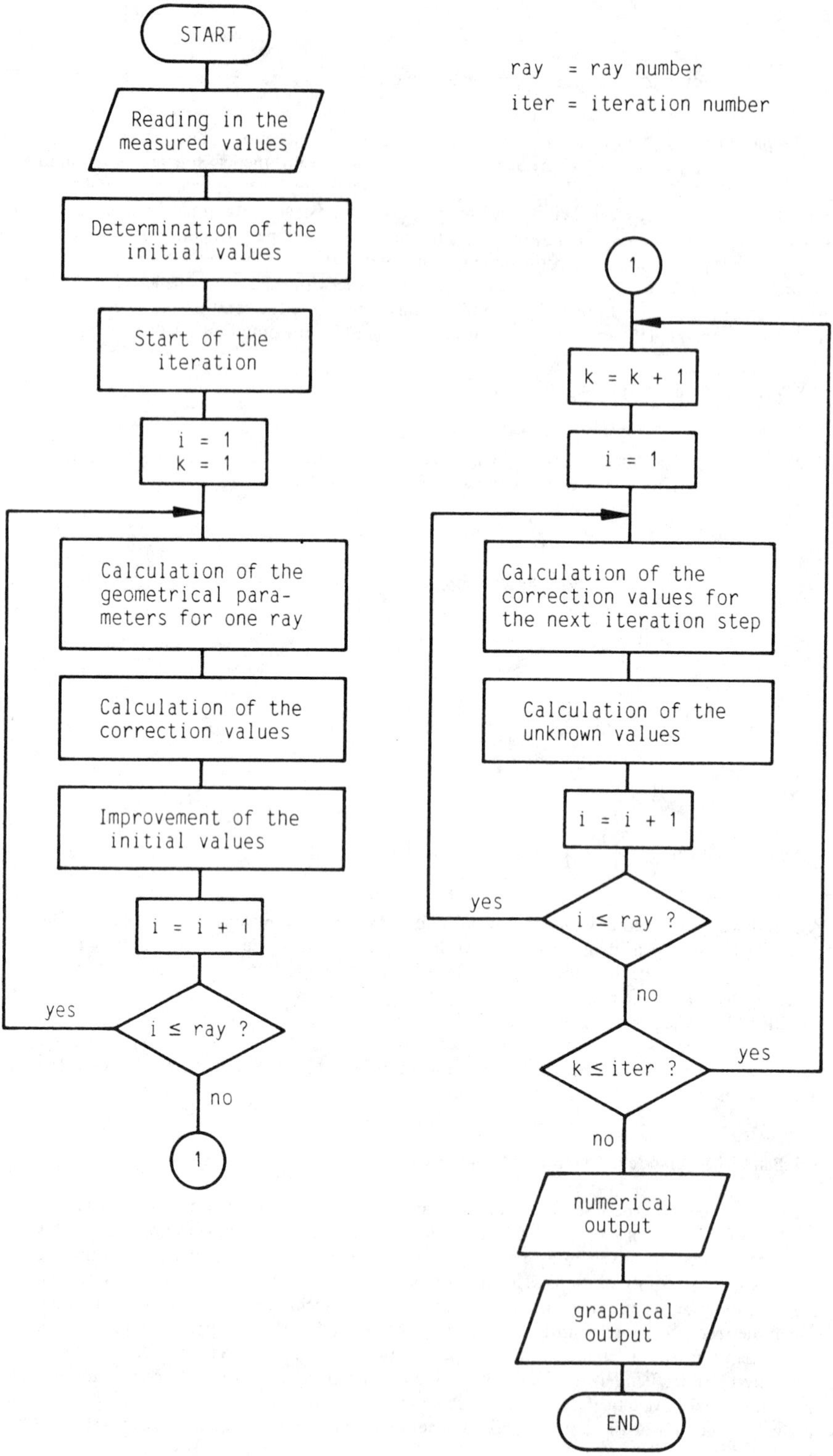

Figure 23. Flow chart for computations using the sample-method.

The calculation is based on Equation 20, which can be considered as a matrix equation and written as follows:

$$w_{ij}f_j = \Phi_i \tag{22}$$

Matrix w_{ij} describes geometric parameters according to Equation 21; f_j are the required values of the function, Φ_i the experimental results. At first, an initial value $f_j^{(1)}$ is applied to each f_j. This initial value is then corrected iteratively. The result of the k-th iteration step $w_{ij}f_j^{(k)} = \Phi_i^{(k)}$ usually deviates from the experimental value Φ_i. The difference $\Delta\Phi_i^{(k)}$ results as

$$\Delta\Phi_i^{(k)} = \Phi_i - w_{ij}f_j^{(k)} \tag{23}$$

With this value, the (k + 1)-th iteration step is corrected. The correction occurs according to

$$f_j^{(k+1)} = f_j^{(k)} + (w_{ij}\,\Delta\Phi^{(k)})/\alpha_i \tag{24}$$

with

$$\alpha_i = \sum_j (w_{ij})^2 \tag{25}$$

The iteration is continued until all $\Delta\Phi_i^{(k)}$ assume a sufficiently small value.

The flow chart for the reconstruction of the field function with the use of this algorithm is shown in Figure 23. At first, the experimental results of all beams are entered. Initial values are applied to the matrix of the required field parameters. In the following, this matrix is called objective matrix. If any pre-information about the investigated object is available, it can be taken into consideration for the setting of the initial values. This reduces the required calculation effort. In the first iteration process the matrix defined in Equation 21 is calculated with the geometric parameters. Then the first correction of the objective matrix is implemented according to Equation 24 with the use of the experimental results. Each element of the objective matrix is corrected along all beams. When the correction for all beams is completed, the correction in the next iteration process again begins with the first beam.

Each correction of an element in the objective matrix affects all other elements in the matrix. For this reason, it is not possible to formulate a convergence criterion that leads to the end of the iteration. If the convergence criterion is fulfilled for the field elements of one beam, the elements are changed again due to the correction of the next beam. The convergence criterion may become ineffective. Another convergence criterion must be found that differs from the usual information about the discrepancy between two parameters.

One possibility is to prescribe the number of iteration steps. For the determination of the required number, the quality of reconstruction is observed in dependence of the number of iteration processes with the use of a test function. Two-dimensional analytic functions are used for text purposes. In these functions, the dimensions of the values of the function and the number of extreme values in the investigated range correspond with the course of the assumed field parameter. The applied functions should have no symmetrical axes in the direction of the beam. The test functions are integrated along defined paths. The obtained integral values represent simulated experimental results, which reconstruct the required analytic functions with the use of the mentioned method. The quality of the obtained reconstructions depends on the number of completed iteration processes. When the desired quality of reconstruction is achieved, the determined number of iteration steps can be used as a measure for the number of iterations required for the calculation of the field function from experimental results. In Figure 23, the number of iteration processes is marked with "iter." This number must be determined for each individual application and for the required quality of reconstruction.

With the described methods, representations of temperature, density, and concentration fields can be obtained for process engineering purposes. Integral transformations can be used for static or at least stationary, moving objects. With suitable synchronization facilities, the integral methods can be used for periodic processes as well. They deliver most exact results for the reconstruction of the required field function. If the field parameter is time dependent or if it cannot be viewed from all sides, a reconstruction of the field function is possible with the use of a grid method or a combined technique.

THE APPLICATION OF TOMOGRAPHIC TECHNIQUES IN PROCESS-ENGINEERING STUDIES

Applied measurement techniques and the mathematical basis of computerized tomography were described in the previous sections. It is therefore possible to select suitable measurement techniques for special applications. The individual experimental results must be processed mathematically, before they can be used for tomographic purposes.

In the field of medicine, computerized tomography has already become an important part of diagnosis. Various techniques are applied here, which use an integral transformation for the evaluation. Ultrasonics and nuclear magnetic resonance are used in addition to X-ray radiation. As already explained, only stationary or quasi-stationary objects can be examined with this technique. The success of computerized tomography in medical applications resulted in its use for non-destructive material testing. However, due to the higher densities and frequently complicated pieces of material, the necessary correction methods require increased effort. The application of computerized tomographies common in medicine proved suitable for the examination of materials of low ordinal numbers, such as plastics, aluminum, etc. [23, 25].

In recent times, computerized tomography has also been used more and more for investigations of unsteady-state processes. An example is the investigation of unsteady-state temperature fields in stirred vessels [24, 26]. The following describes the measurement techniques applied so far in process-engineering studies and their results.

Measurements in Gases

Application of Radiation Sources for Incoherent Light

Computerized tomographic techniques for the measurement of aerosol density. A technique for the measurement of the aerosol density in enclosed spaces was established by Willms [27] with the objective to develop a system for automatic fire detection. It is designed to measure the concentration of aerosol particles in the air. The experimental parameter is the decrease of infrared beams on their path through the measurement volume (Lambert-Beer law).

Figure 24 shows the applied experimental setup. In a frame measuring 26 × 26 cm, there are 16 diodes (S1–S16), which emit infrared radiation, as well as 16 photo-diodes (E1–E16), which receive the radiation. The emitting diodes have an emission angle of 140°. The emitted radiation has a wavelength of 0.93 μm. The emitting diodes are activated in sequence. The individual intensities of the radiation are measured simultaneously at the various photo-diodes. A connected computer controls the switching of the emitting diodes and the sequence of the individual measurements. The measured intensities of the infrared radiation at the photo-diodes are then stored and processed in the computer.

Willms uses an iterative method to reconstruct the aerosol density in the measurement volume, which was derived from the method developed by Gordon [22]. The duration of one measurement cycle is 0.2 second. This makes it possible to measure unsteady-state processes as well. With the use of the connected computer, the experimental results can be processed with the real-time method.

Measurement of the temperature distribution in flames by means of infrared radiation. A new technique for the measurement of the temperature distribution in flames is introduced by Uchiyama, Nakajima, and Yuta [28]. Thermometry is used to measure the temperature. The radiation emitted by an object or a flame is recorded with a pyrometer. The radiation measured by the detector is the sum of the radiation intensities emitted at individual locations in the flame along the path

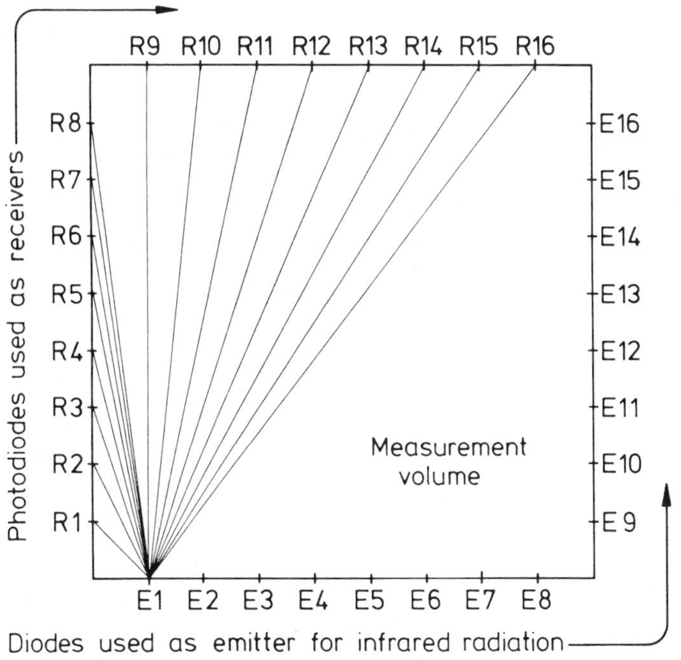

Figure 24. Experimental facility for measurement of aerosol densities [27].

of the assumed measured beams. These beams come in at a right angle, with respect to the detector surface. A simple block diagram of the structure of the experimental setup is shown in Figure 25.

The infrared radiation of a flame penetrates two orifices. With the use of a filter plate, only the radiation of a certain range of wavelengths is recorded by the detector and transformed into a voltage signal. The signal is amplified and filtered. A mixture of methane and air was used in the tests. The diameter of the burner was 10 mm. The flame was laminar. Thirty projections in a range of angles of 180° were recorded for one tomogram. Each projection contained 96 steps with a distance of 1 mm. The reconstruction was implemented with the integral transformation described by Barret and Swindel [29]. In order to double-check the measurement technique, the temperature profiles were measured simultaneously with thermocouples.

Figure 26 shows the temperature profiles reconstructed with the use of the infrared emission computerized tomography and the temperature profiles recorded with the use of thermocouples for two cross sections. The differences between the reconstructed and the measured temperature profiles are caused by the applied experimental setup. The aperture angle of the orifices is $\alpha = 3°$. Therefore, the beam expands to a bundle with a diameter of 7.9 mm in the flame, before it hits the detector. This large aperture angle could be reduced by selecting a much more sensitive detector. Further possible causes for errors in the measurements are the absorption of infrared radiation by polyatomic molecules, such as water and carbon dioxide, as well as the flickering of the flame. In order to reduce the effect of the absorption on the measurements, the use of an additional detector is suggested, which records the radiation of the environment. The flickering of the flame depends on the burner and the environment. It can be made visible with the use of highly sensitive detectors, i.e. much shorter recording times.

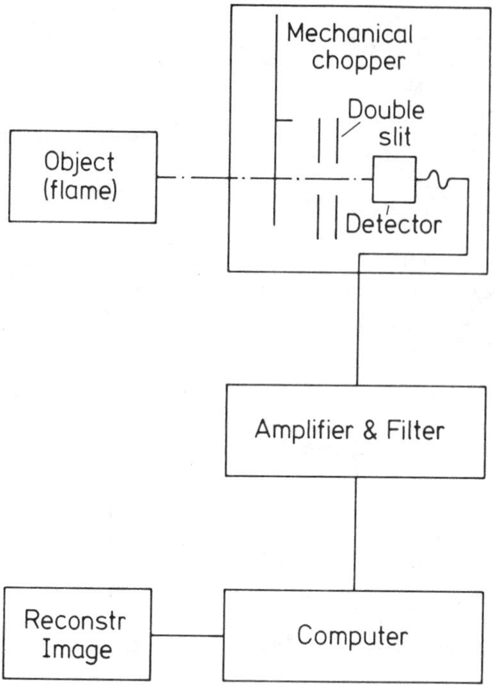

Figure 25. Experimental facility for infrared emission computer tomography (IRECT) [28].

Application of Coherent Light

Application of tomography for the determination of concentration profiles in free jets. Santoro and Emmermann [30, 31] introduced the application of optical tomography for the analysis of fumes. The concentration profiles of different gases in a free jet are examined. The experimental parameter is the absorption of light waves in the measurement volume. The absorption is described by the Lambert-Beer law. In order to determine whether the method is generally suitable and in order to keep the experimental difficulties as low as possible, air/methane or argon/methane mixtures were used instead of fumes. The tests were implemented at ambient temperature and at ambient pressure as well as stationary flow conditions.

The experimental setup is shown in Figure 27. The mixtures are prepared in a mixing chamber filled with glass pellets. They enter into the measurement chamber at a velocity of 35 ms^{-1} through a brass pipe with a diameter of d = 10 mm. A He-Ne laser was used for the transillumination of the measurement chamber. The light beam of the laser is enlarged to a diameter of d = 1.3 mm with a lens. After penetrating the measurement chamber, the light beam is bundled again with the use of a second lens. The intensity of the light is measured with a detector. The developing electric signal is amplified, digitalized, and stored by the computer. The experimental results were registered for three planes spaced at distances of 1.27, 12.7, and 25.4 cm from the jet outlet. 12 angles of view were implemented for each plane. The gas jet was guided step by step through the laser beam for each angle of view with the use of a movable table. When the recording of the experimental results for one angle was completed, the gas jet was turned by an angle of 15°, in order to repeat the measurement. The experimental results obtained this way are projections of the mean values of optical absorption coefficients establishing along the optical axes.

The profiles of linear absorption coefficients along the optical axes were then reconstructed with the integral transformation method introduced earlier. A modified Shepp-Logan filter function [32]

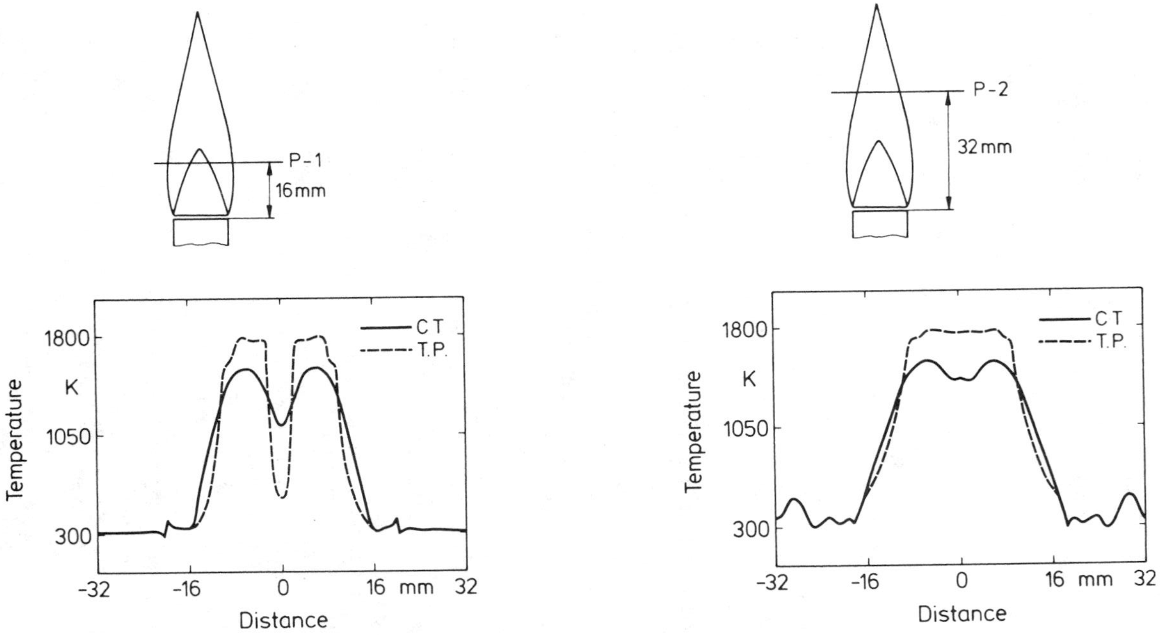

(a) P-1

(b) P-2

Figure 26. Comparison of temperature profiles between IRECT and thermocouple measurements: a) P-1 layer; b) P-2 layer; CT—temperature profile obtained by IRECT; TP—temperature profile obtained by thermocouple probe measurement [28].

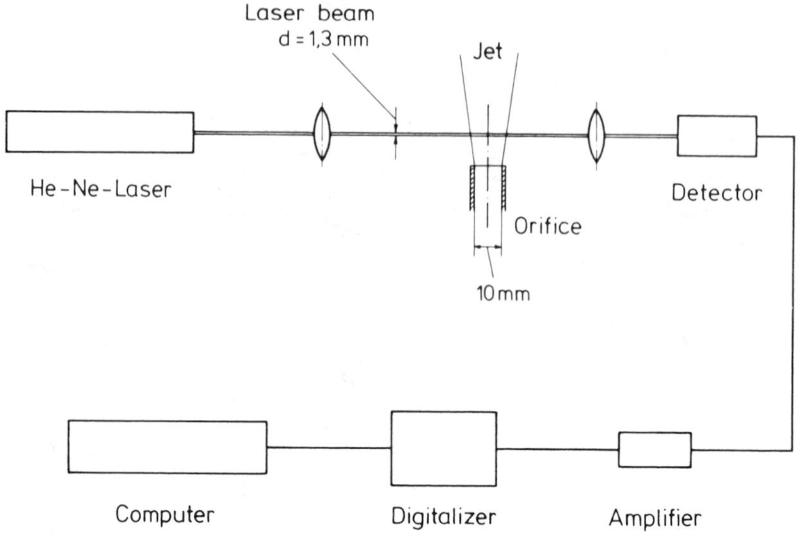

Figure 27. Experimental facility for measurement of concentration profiles in a free jet of gas mixtures [30].

was used as well. The following relationship applies between the local concentration N_i of the component i in the mixture and the local absorption coefficient μ:

$$\mu = \sum_i N_i Q_{\lambda i} \tag{26}$$

$Q_{\lambda i}$ is the absorption coefficient of the component i for the wavelength λ. For the measurement of the concentration in mixtures with several components, measurements with different wavelengths of the laser light would have to be implemented, in order to obtain a uniquely resolvable system of equations for N_i from Equation 26.

The reconstructed absorption coefficients are shown in Figure 28 for a mixture of 10% methane and 90% air in the plane z = 1.27 cm. Even for the satisfactory reconstruction of a simple Gauss test function, at least 10 angles of view are required. Therefore, many angles of view are required for measurements in complicated turbulent gas flows with strongly varying concentration profiles. With the use of the ART method described earlier, the required number of angles of view can be reduced. A comparison with published experimental results for a free jet of methane and air shows that the measurement of concentration profiles with the use of optical tomography provides very exact results.

The development of tomographic techniques for the measurement of concentration profiles in unsteady-state, turbulent gas flows requires additional intensive experimental effort. The measurement volume must be irradiated simultaneously from all angles of view. This requires a high-capacity computer to process the simultaneous measurement signals.

In general, the described experimental setup is also suitable to record experimental results of unsteady-state field parameters. However, the tested object would have to rotate faster in the laser beam. Furthermore, the experimental results would have to be recorded simultaneously across the entire diameter of the measurement volume. This would make it possible to survey all projections of the field parameter within fractions of seconds. However, difficulties would probably arise especially with asymmetric profiles of the field parameters, due to the resulting centrifugal forces, which would cause a distortion of the experimental results.

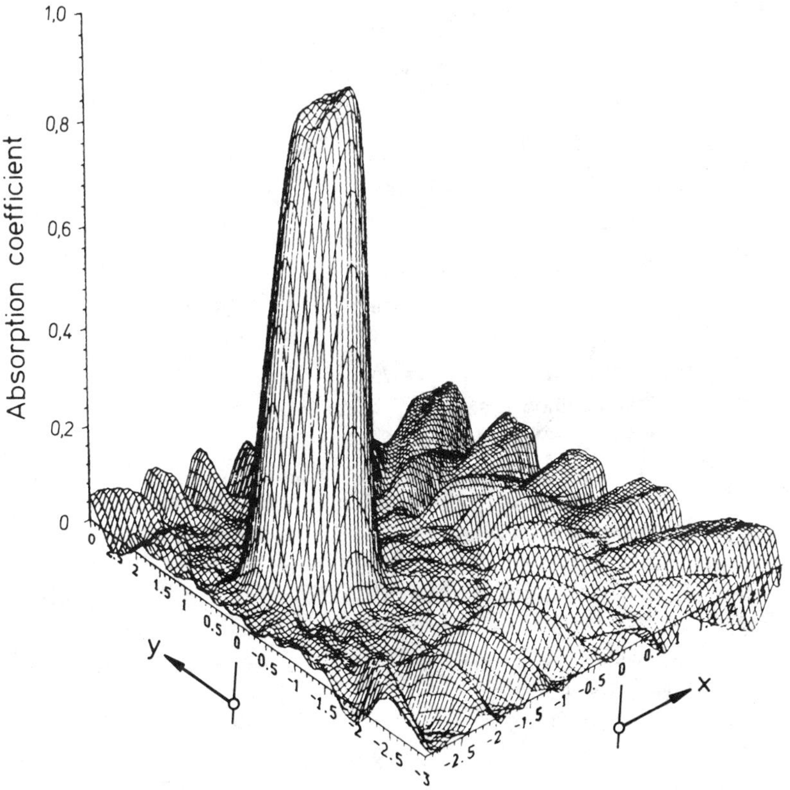

Figure 28. Absorption coefficients for a He–Ne laser beam penetrating one plane of a methane-air jet at 1.27 cm from the orifice [28].

Measurement of air pollution with the use of optical tomography. So far, air pollution has been measured with the use of measuring stations, which take samples of the air at certain time intervals, followed by a chemical analysis of the samples. These examinations are very time-consuming. Also, the operation of such measuring stations is very expensive, which means that the spatial and timely resolution of the measured values is very low. Wolfe and Byer [33] describe a tomographic method, with the use of which it is possible to implement two-dimensional measurements of the air pollution in an area of 6-km diameter simultaneously. The area is subdivided into grid cells, the sides of which are 200 m long. The experimental parameter is the decrease of the intensity of a light wave due to absorption in the air. The relationship is described by the Lambert-Beer law.

The experimental setup shown schematically in Figure 29 is used for the measurements. A laser beam rotates and sweeps across the circular measurement area. Mirrors and detectors are arranged on a concentric circle of larger diameter around the measurement area. The laser beam illuminates the mirrors in sequence. The laser beam is enlarged and reflected by these mirrors. This way, the mirrors act as light sources, which irradiate the measurement area in sequence with a fanned-out bundle of light beams. After the irradiation of the measurement area, the fanned-out bundle of light beams hits the detectors that are arranged within the radiation angle. By rotating the laser beam, the experimental results required for the reconstruction of the concentration field are obtained.

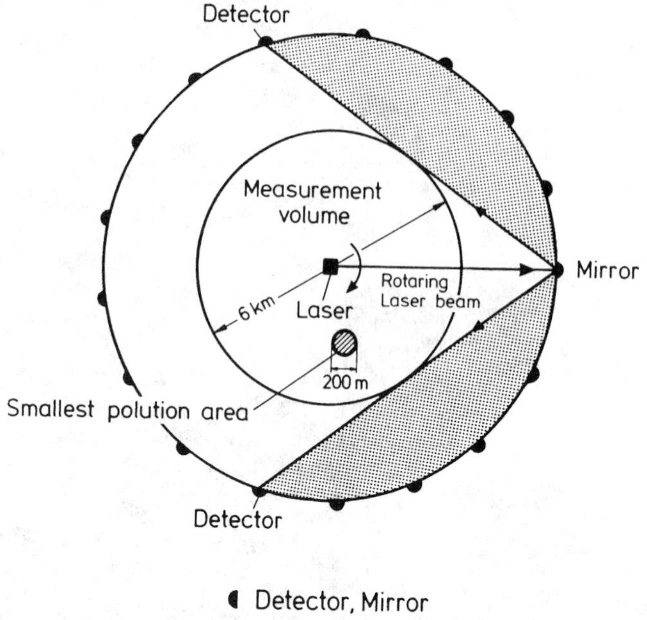

Figure 29. Measurement equipment for the estimation of concentration fields with a tomographic reconstruction technique [33].

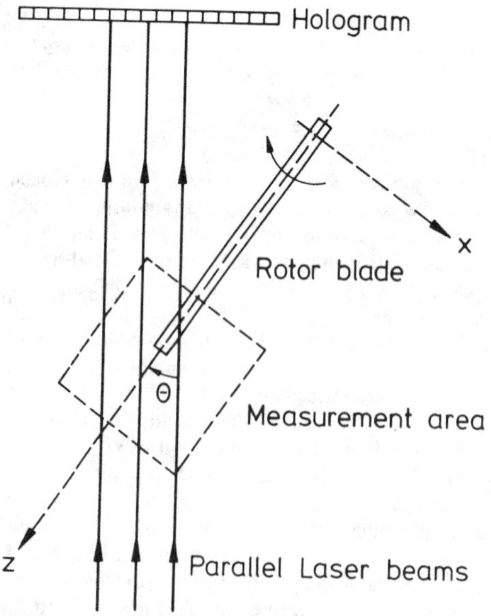

Figure 30. Experimental facility for measurement of density fields at the tip of rotating helicopter blades [34].

Measurements were implemented with the experimental setup shown in Figure 29. The total beam absorption in regions of the measurement volume, the selection of the wavelength of the laser light, the sensitivity of the detectors and their effect on the reconstruction result were examined. The recording of all projections requires approximately 13 seconds. The reconstruction was implemented by iteration on the basis of the integral transformation. With the use of this measurement technique, concentrations in the ranges from ppm to ppb can be identified, which makes the technique interesting for many different applications.

Measurement of the density field at a rotating helicopter rotor blade. The density fields around rotating helicopter rotor blades were measured by Hesselink [34] with the optical tomographic method. The applied measurement method is based on the technique for the measurement of the phase shift of coherent light waves described earlier. A stationary density field establishes in a coordinate system rotating with the rotor blade. The investigation is restricted to the area around the rotor tip.

The relatively simple experimental setup shown schematically in Figure 30 was used for the measurements. The rotor blade rotates in an enlarged bundle of parallel laser beams. The different angles of view result from the movement of the measurement field due to the pulsed laser light. The number of the angles of view is determined by the frequency of the laser pulses. Difficulties are caused by the large dimensions of the experimental setup. The hologram area was located about 9 m away from the rotor blade. Therefore, the experimental result was affected strongly even by minor density changes in the path of the beam.

For the reconstruction of the local index of refraction, a reconstruction technique described by Cha and Vest [35] was used, which is based on the Fourier transformation. A filter function described by Shepp and Logan [38] was used as well. Figure 31 shows the calculated density distribution for an investigated plane. Forty projections at distances of two radians each (total of 80°)

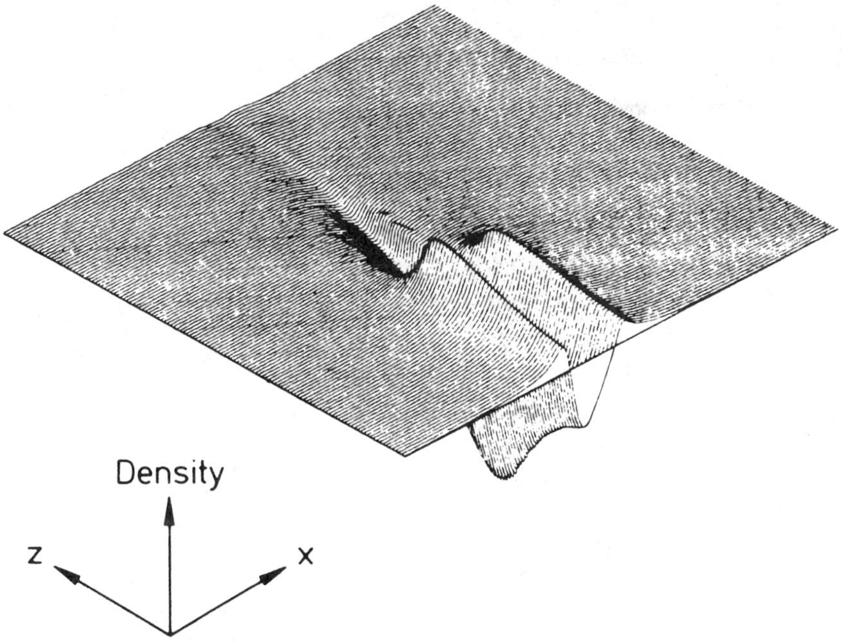

Figure 31. Reconstructed density field at the tip of a rotating helicopter blade [34].

were used for the reconstruction. The zero level of the density is identical to the density of the surrounding air.

Experimental setup for the tomographic measurement of unsteady-state density and concentration profiles. With the measurement techniques introduced so far, it was not possible to record timely variable field parameters. Snyder and Hesselink [36] describe an experimental setup for the measurement of density and concentration profiles in unsteady-state flows. Although only time-independent measurements have been tested with this technique to date, the optical setup will be described briefly in the following.

The phase shift between two coherent laser light beams is measured as described earlier. The finite-fringe-field method is used for this purpose. From the phase shift, the three-dimensional distribution of the index of refraction can be reconstructed and the density profile can be calculated. The calculation of the concentration profiles would also require the measurement of the decrease of the light intensity and the reconstruction of the local absorption coefficient.

Figure 32 shows the experimental setup schematically. A laser beam is subdivided into two partial beams with a beam splitter. One of these partial beams is the reference wave. The second beam is enlarged, filtered, and reflected onto a so-called "holographic optical element" via a mirror S_1. There, the beam is transformed into a bundle of parallel light beams and reflected again. The parallel light waves illuminate the measurement volume across a width of 5 cm. After penetrating the measurement volume, the beam is bundled again by a second "holographic optical element" and reflected onto a mirror S_2. From this mirror, the beam is projected onto a picture plane. The reference wave can now be superimposed on this beam, which results in the development of an interferogram or the possibility to measure the intensity distribution.

In order to implement several angles of view, several "holographic optical elements" were arranged on two semicircles displaced with respect to each other. The two mirrors rotate so that the "holographic optical elements" are illuminated in sequence. At a rotational speed of the mirrors of $n = 15{,}000\ \text{min}^{-1}$, it is possible to record 100 projections per millisecond from different angles of view with this setup. The number of projections depends on the number of "holographic optical elements." Photographs of the resulting interferograms can be taken with a high-speed camera. Figure 33 shows an interferogram recorded with this technique.

With this experimental setup, it would be possible to conduct the concentration measurements implemented by Emmerman, Goulard, Santoro and Semerjians [31] in turbulent, unsteady-state flows.

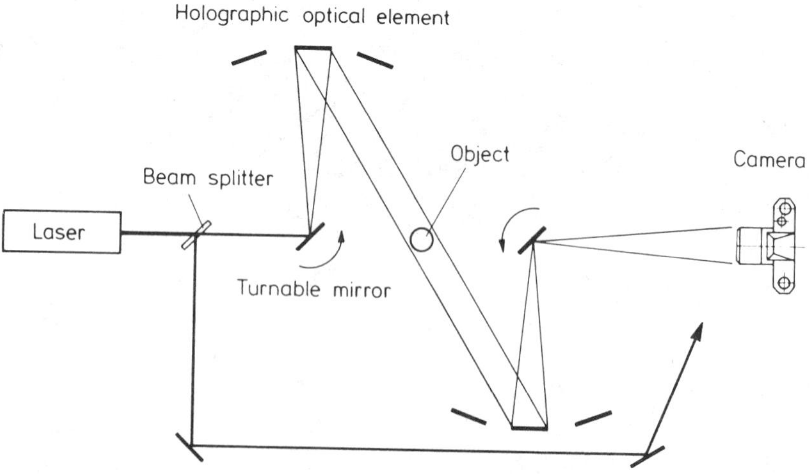

Figure 32. Experimental facility for measurement of instationary field functions [36].

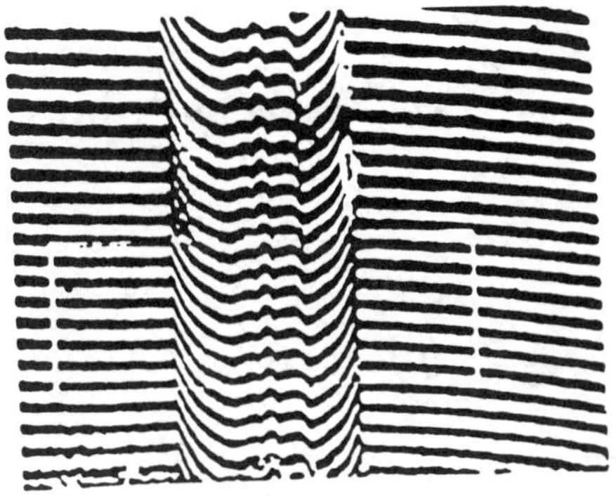

Figure 33. Interferogram of a glass cylinder in the measurement volume [36].

Application of Acoustic Waves

Measurements of temperature and velocity in fumes with the use of sound waves. Green [37] describes a technique for measuring temperatures and velocities in fumes with the use of sound waves. For this purpose, microphones and sound transmitters were installed in two planes in the waste gas duct of a furnace with a cross-sectional area of 5.2 × 3.5 m. Three microphones and three sound transmitters were located at each end of the waste gas duct. The frequency of the sound waves was selected as 2 kHz.

The time of flight of the sound waves on their way through the duct was measured. The relationship between time of flight and local sound velocity is described in Equation 7. The local function of the sound velocity was then reconstructed with the use of the integral transformation. With

$$c = \sqrt{\kappa RT/M} \tag{27}$$

the temperature profile in the examined cross section can be determined for gases. The sound velocity c depends on the gas constant R, the isentropic exponent κ, on the temperature T, and the molar mass M of the gas.

Figure 34 shows a comparison between the experimental results from acoustic tomography and the experimental results obtained with thermocouples. The cross section of the waste gas duct was subdivided into 6 × 6 grid cells. For a comparison, it must be considered that the measurement with the thermocouples lasted one half hour, whereas the acoustic measurement reflects the temperature profile for one point in time. The achieved accuracy of the measurement makes the technique suitable especially for the three-dimensional measurement of high temperatures. With this technique, measurements at a 1,500 MW boiler with waste gas temperatures of up to 1,900 K have already been implemented.

The axial flow velocities in the waste gas duct can be calculated from the measured times of flight of the sound waves. The Doppler effect is used for this purpose, according to which sound waves in flowing media expand faster in flow direction than against flow direction.

Measurements in Liquids

Measurement of Temperature Fields in Stirred Vessels

Mayinger and Lübbe [24] as well as Ostendorf [26] have measured three-dimensional temperature fields with the use of optical tomography. They examined the time- and location-dependent mixing of a liquid component in a stirred vessel. The two liquids used for the mixture had different temperatures but the same concentration. The rotational speed of the stirrer was varied during the tests. With the use of holographic interferometry, the temperature fields were recorded simultaneously from four different directions. The so-called real-time method was used for this purpose.

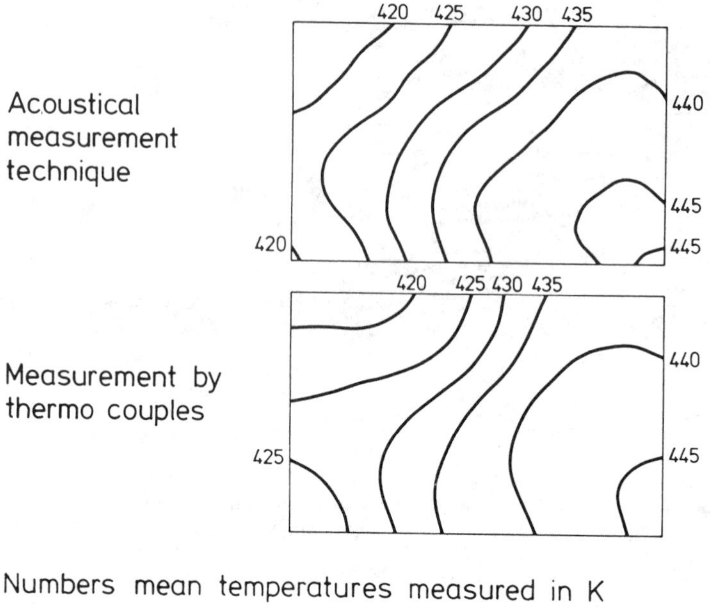

Figure 34. Results of temperature measurement using sound waves [37].

The optical setup is shown in Figure 35. The light beam emitted from the argon-ion laser reaches a beam splitter (BS), where it is divided into an object beam and a reference beam. The ratio between the intensity of the object beam and the intensity of the reference beam can be varied with this beam splitter. At the following beam splitter, the object beam is divided into two portions, each of which is divided into two object waves of identical value via two large beam splitters, after passing through the enlargement optics (BE). Thus, they irradiate the measurement chamber at displacement angles of 45°. The object waves are then bundled with lenses (L), which results in an increase of the intensity of the light in the holographic plane (H). The exposure times for the holograms are reduced, which is of special importance for the recording of unsteady-state processes. Two object waves can be projected onto a holographic plate with mirror (M). The reference beam is also enlarged. It bypasses the measurement chamber and is divided into two reference beams for one holographic plate each with a beam splitter. The holographic plates are installed in clamped frames in fixed mountings with three-point bearings. This makes an exact repositioning of the holograms after the development possible. Pictures of the interferograms developing behind the holographic plates are taken from a motor-driven camera with synchronized shutter release.

The measurement chamber is shown in Figure 36. It is irradiated by the four enlarged parallel object beams. It consists of an octagonal exterior vessel. The walls of this vessel are made of glass, top and bottom of anodized (eloxadized) aluminum. The measurement chamber is located on a plate with adjustment pins. This plate is attached to the hologram table with fixed mountings. The measurement chamber can therefore be inserted in the optical setup without time-consuming adjustments. The cylindrical stirred vessel itself is installed in the center of a tempering vessel. Both areas are sealed off against each other. The diameter of the stirred vessel is 98 mm. The height is H = 105 mm. Since the liquids in the exterior vessel and the stirred vessel have the same index of refraction as the applied glass, the light is not refracted at any boundary area in the measurement chamber. The light traverses the measurement chamber in straight lines. The measured phase shifts can therefore be applied to certain optical paths in the measurement chamber.

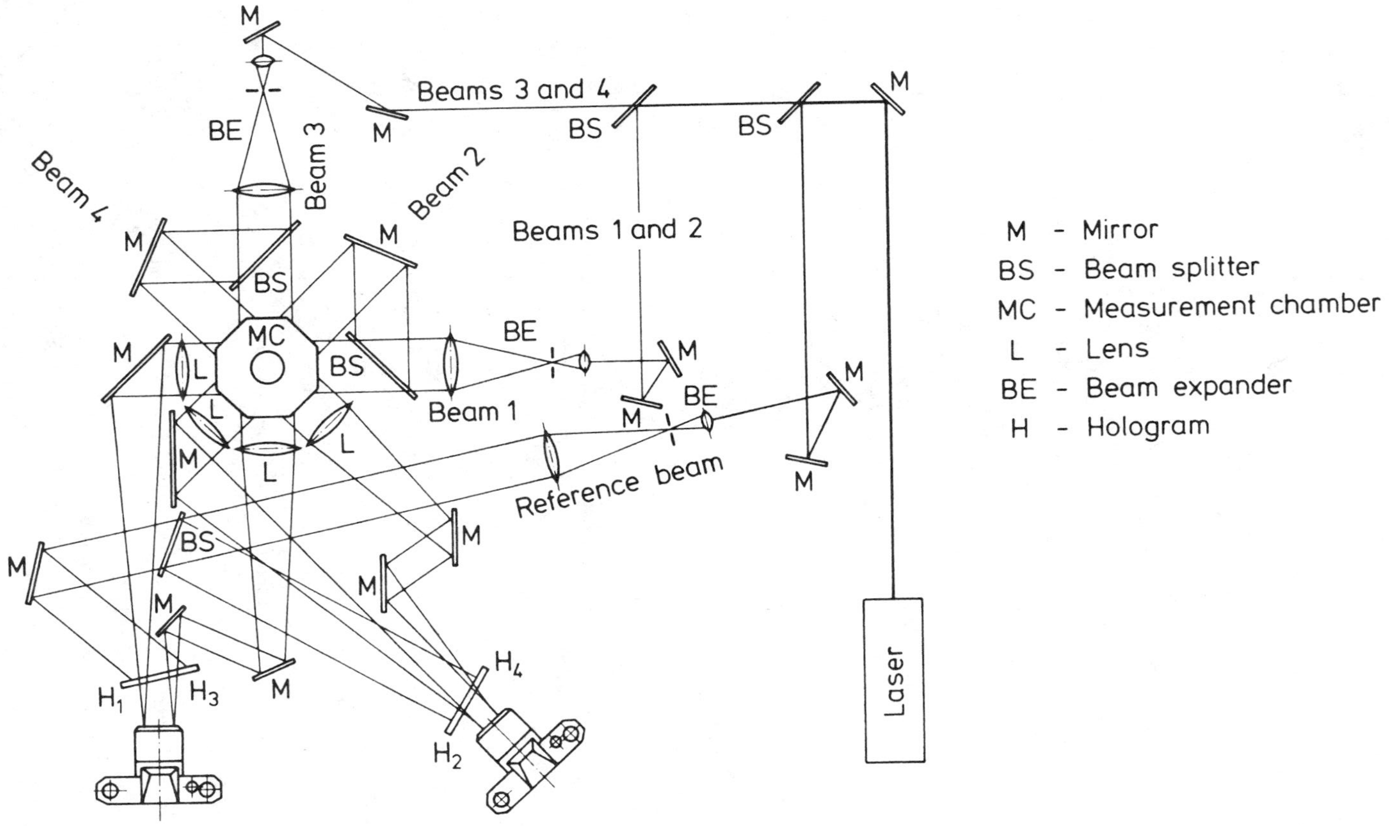

Figure 35. Experimental facility for optical tomography [24, 26].

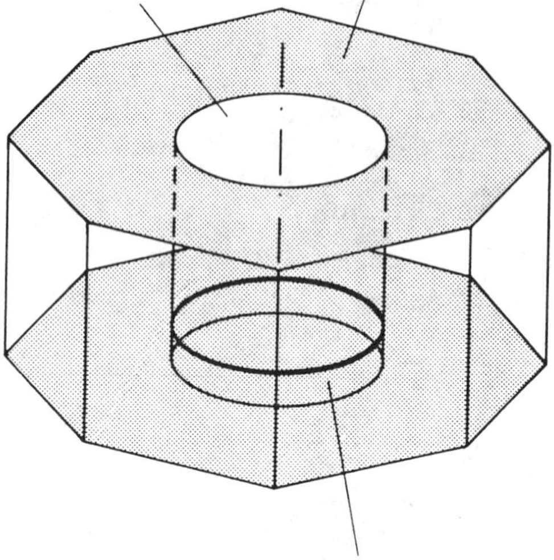

Figure 36. Measurement chamber used for tomographic registration of temperature fields in mixing vessels [24, 26].

Lübbe [13] used the organic solvent dimethylsulfoxide for the tests. It mixes completely with water and reaches the index of refraction of the applied glass type for a mixing ratio of approximately 95% dimethylsulfoxide and 5% water. Ostendorf [26] used mean viscosity mixtures of 34 V% benzine (gasoline) and 66 V% palatinol as well as highly viscous mixtures of 99.5 V% glycerin and water. Turbines with six blades and a simple cylindrical disk were used as stirrers.

The mixture of differently tempered liquid volumes as well as the dissipation was examined in the test series. The results of these tests are described in the following.

Stirring of two mixable liquids of different temperatures. A small volume of the same liquid but of different temperature is injected into the liquid volume contained in the stirred vessel. The mixing process in the stirred vessel and the equalization of the temperatures are observed. Figure 37 shows the interference images for an irradiation angle at certain points in time after the warmer liquid is added.

Before the warmer liquid is added, the interference pattern has even stripes. This pattern is obtained by changing the angle between reference and object wave slightly after the development and the back positioning of the hologram. During the mixing process, a temperature change occurs. It can be calculated from the deflection of the interference stripes for each plane of the vessel and from the distance between the stripes in the zero-field interference image.

The procedure for evaluating interference images consists of the following four steps:

1. Digitalizing the interference images.
2. Skeletonizing the interference stripes.
3. Calculating the relative shifting of the interference stripes for the individual selected sections of height.
4. Calculating the phase shift of the light wave for each place of projection in the selected plane of the vessel.

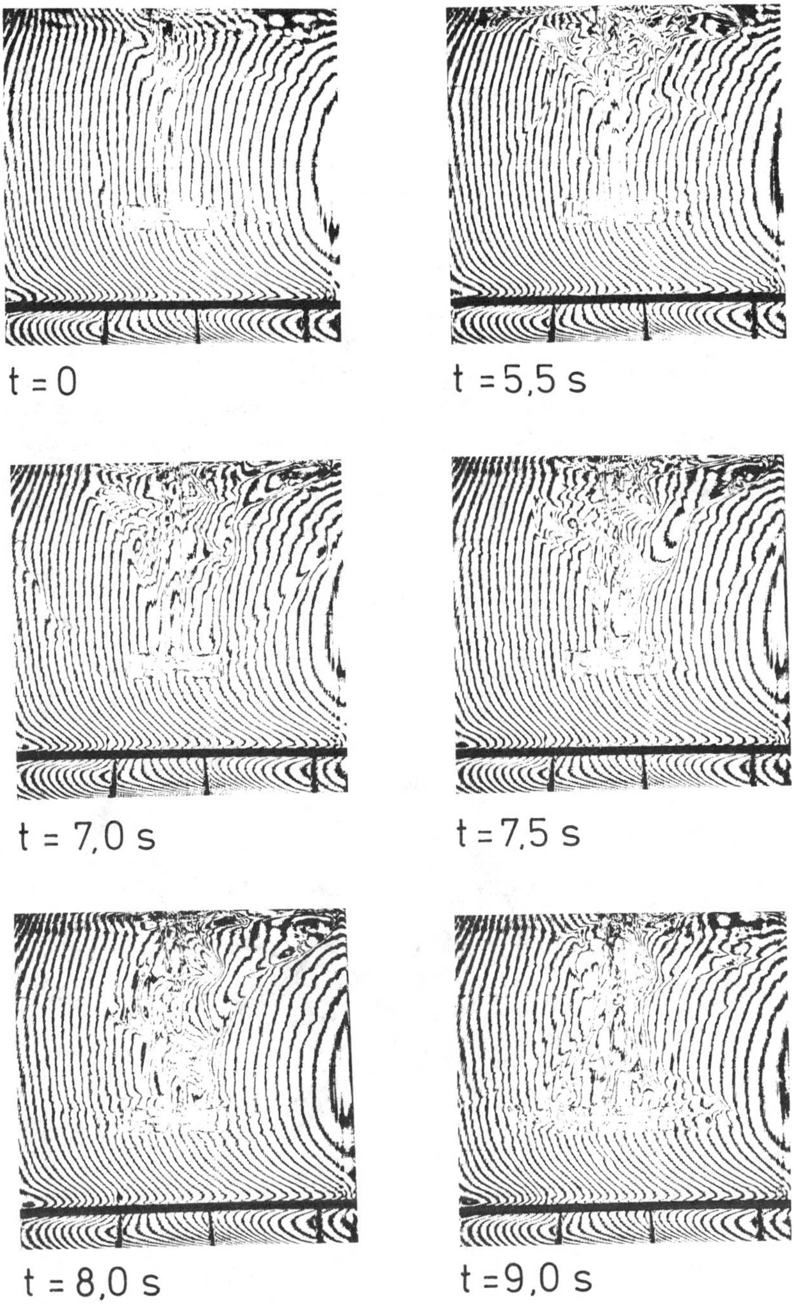

Figure 37. Interferograms at different times of a mixing vessel. At the top of the vessel a small heated fluid volume is supplied [26].

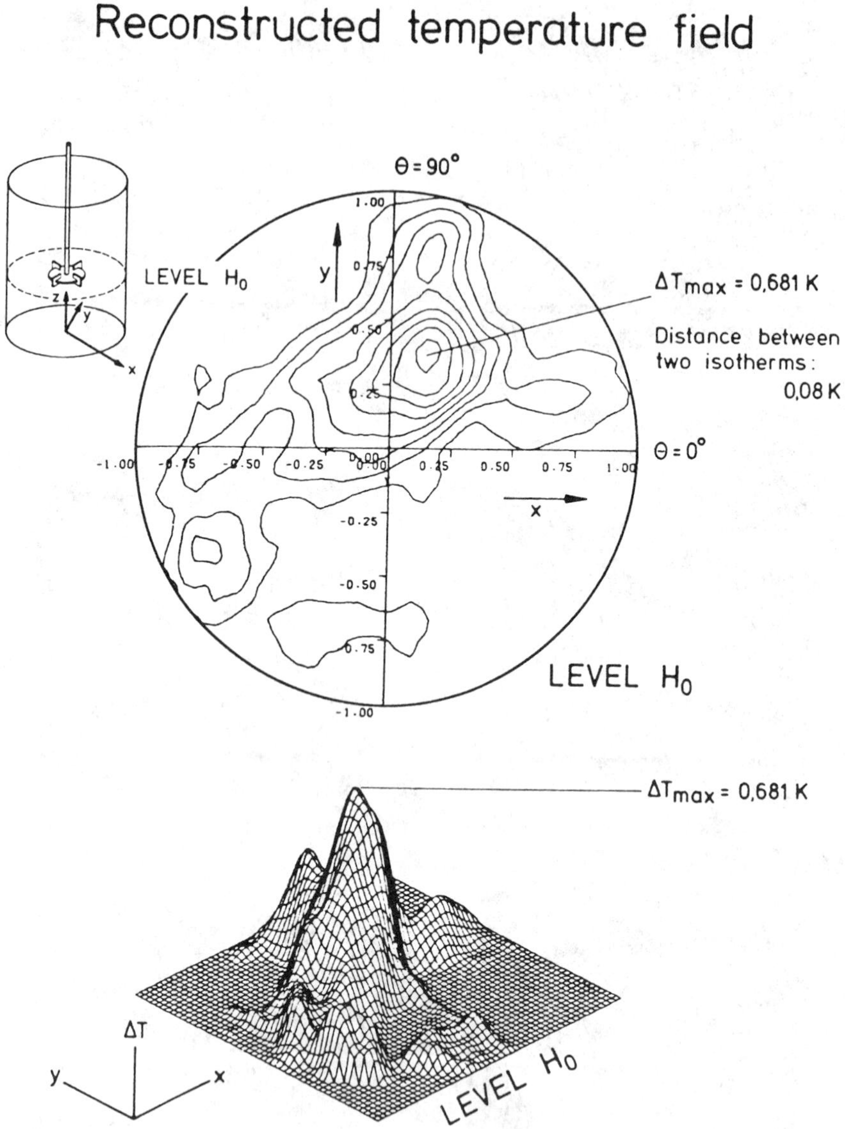

Figure 38. Temperature profiles in one cross section of the mixing vessel computed by tomographical method [26].

The local phase shift is determined for each section of height and for each irradiation direction across the diameter of the stirred vessel. The local phase shifts are the entry data for the tomographic evaluation method. The reconstructed temperature fields are shown in Figure 38. They are drawn either as isotherms for a vessel cross section or as three-dimensional pictures of the local temperature profiles.

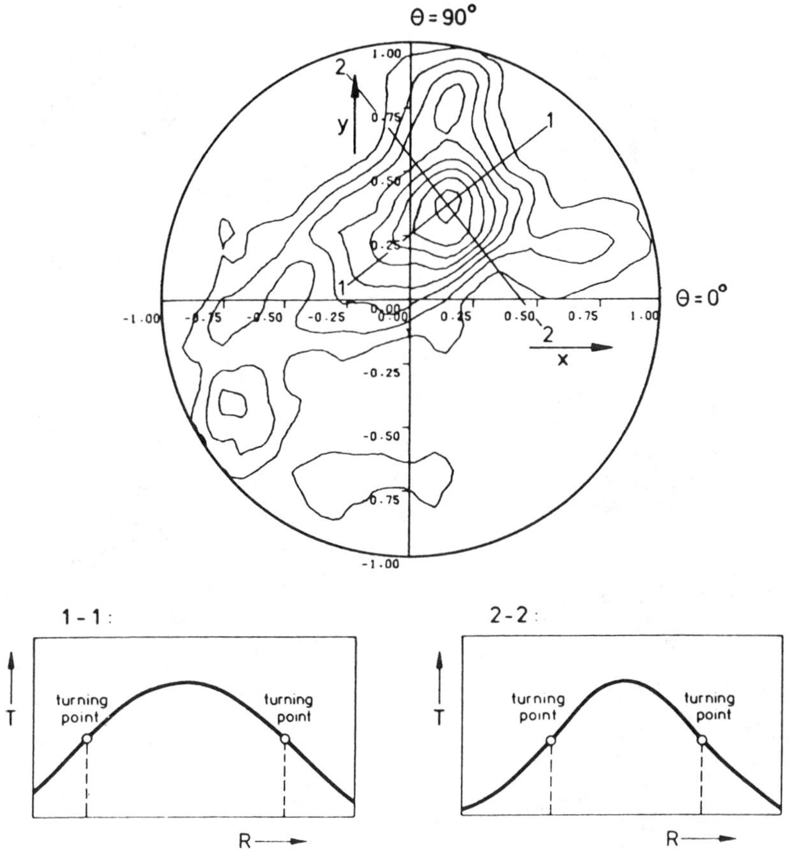

Figure 39. Determination of a limit between a heated liquid volume and its environment [26].

Representation of fluid elements of identical temperatures. In the turbulent region of the flow, the mixing can be interpreted as a separation and distribution of fluid elements in the macroscopic scale with subsequent mass exchange between fluid elements in the microscopic scale. To date, a unique determination of the geometrical expansion of macroscopic fluid elements has not been possible.

With reference to the definition of fluid elements that have an increased concentration of one of the components to be mixed, compared to their environment, liquid volumes can be defined as fluid elements that have an increased temperature compared to their environment. The laws of unsteady-state heat transport can be used to determine the limit between a liquid volume and its environment. This limit is defined by the turning points of the temperature profiles along discrete sections to the ring-shaped isotherms. In Figure 39, the determination of the limit between the heated liquid volume and its environment is shown schematically.

In order to obtain the spatial expansion of the liquid volume, the temperature profiles at several levels are reconstructed in the immediate vicinity of the stirrer. The plane cuts through this liquid volume at 6 superimposed levels, as marked in Figure 40 in order to present a picture of the vertical expansion of the liquid volume. The temperature difference between adjacent isotherms amounts to $\Delta T = 0.02°C$.

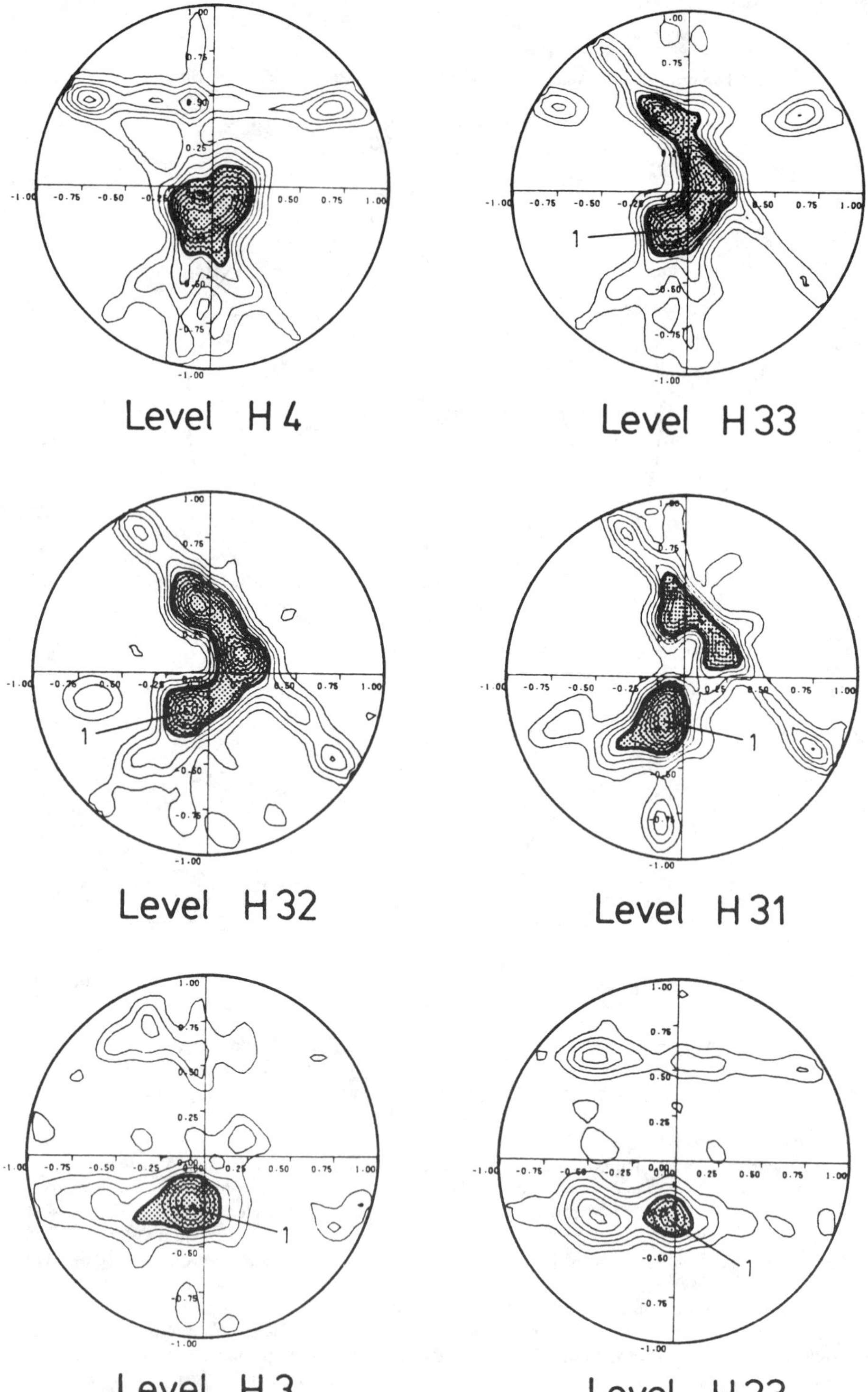

Figure 40. Reconstructed temperature profiles after a duration of 7.5 s after adding the heated liquid volume [26].

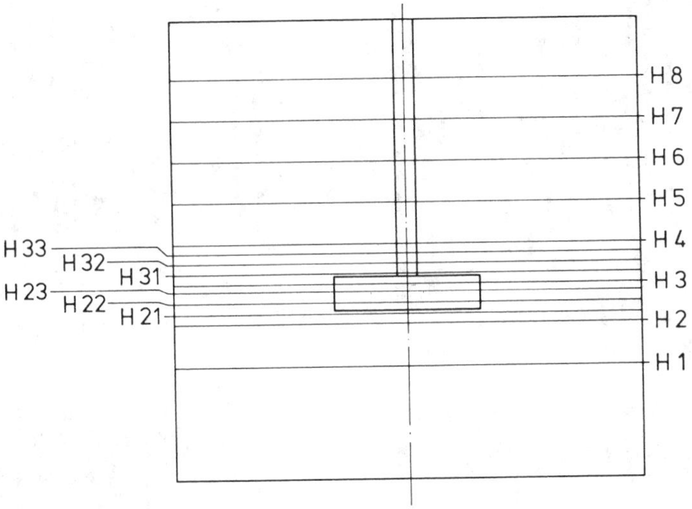

Figure 41. Position of the different levels in the agitated vessel [26].

In the cross section of the stirrer (H31), the volume flow of the liquid is divided up into two smaller streams of liquid of different vertical expansions. The vertical position of the other mentioned temperature profiles in the agitated vessels are presented in Figure 41. In order to give an impression of the spatial shape of the described liquid volume, a picture of the volume is given in Figure 42.

Dissipation phenomenon occurring in laminar mixing. Ostendorf [26] uses a cylindrical model stirrer and a 6-blade disk stirrer to investigate the mixing in the laminar region of a flow. The stirrers are installed in the center between the top and the bottom of the stirred vessel. The ratio between the diameter of the stirrer d and the diameter of the stirred vessel D is $d/D = 0.4$. For the disk stirrer, the ratio is $d/D = 0.3$. The rotational speed of the stirrer was selected in such a way that the Reynolds numbers $Re = 2$, $Re = 4$ and $Re = 8$ result in consideration of the mass values of the glycerin.

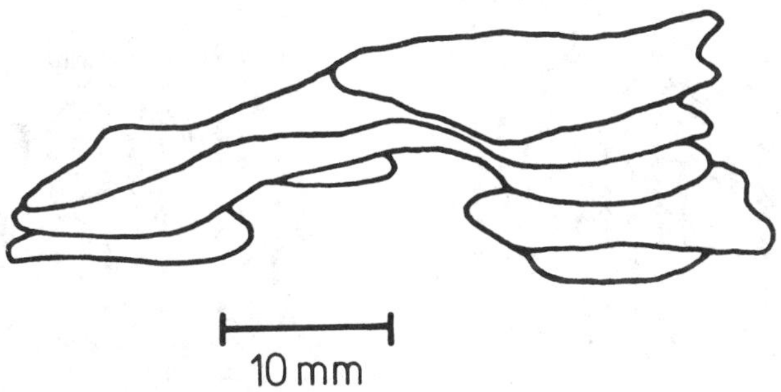

Figure 42. Picture of a fluid element in a volume above the stirrer 7.5 s after adding the liquid volume with different temperature [26].

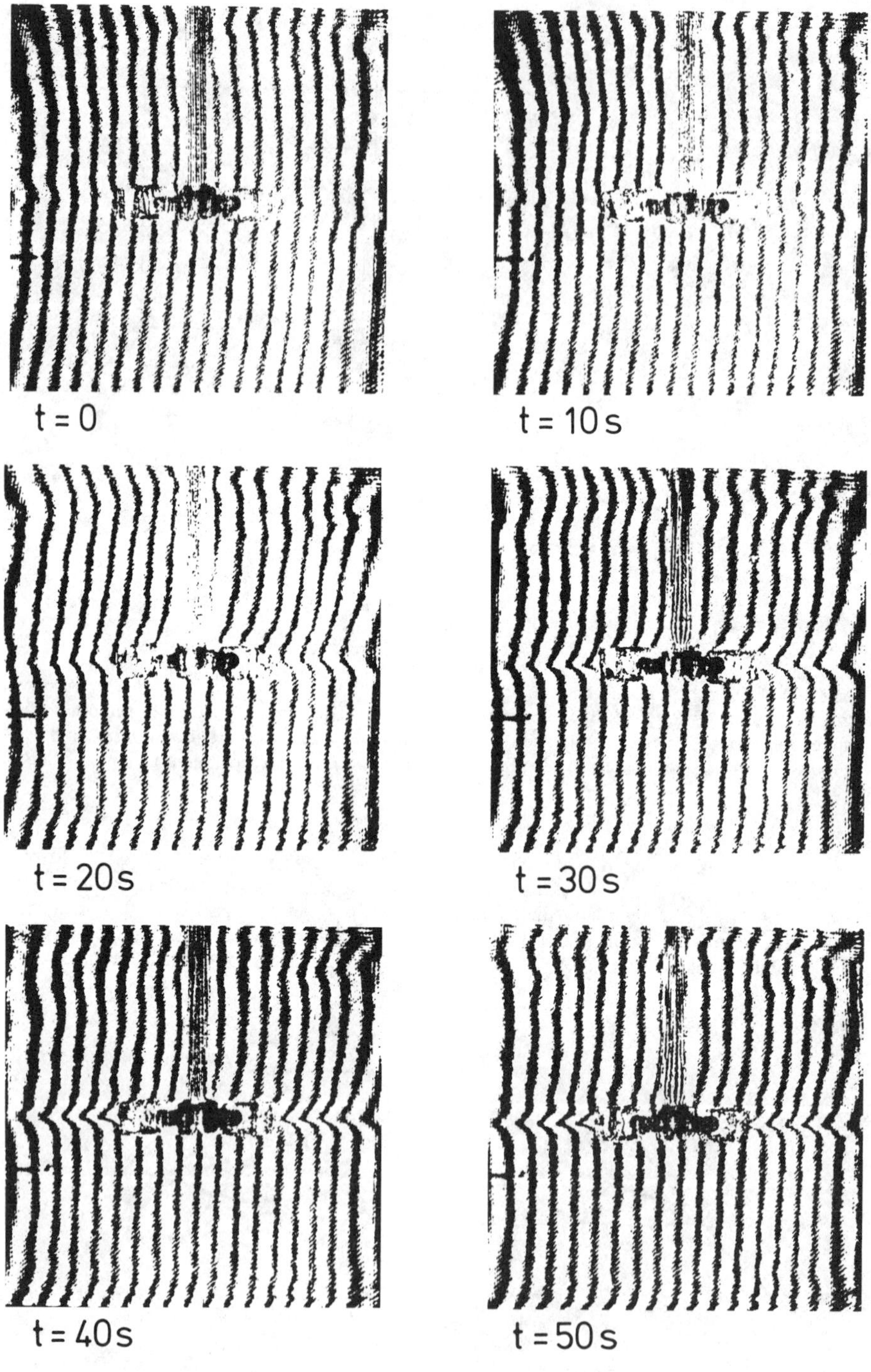

Figure 43. Interference pictures of temperature fields with dissipation effects at different times of viscous mixing [38].

Figure 43 shows the interference images of a test series implemented with a 6-blade disk stirrer. The interference stripes are deformed into wedge shapes in the height of the stirrer. In the rest of the volume of the stirred vessel, their position remains constant throughout the entire stirring process. Temperature profiles were reconstructed after different stirring times from the interference images of Figure 43. They are shown in Figures 44a–c. After the stirring time $t = 12$ s, the liquid volume in Figure 44a has heated up around the stirrer. The change of temperature is $0.02\ K > \Delta T \geq 0.01\ K$. The maximum axial expansion of the temperature profile is located along the axis of the stirrer. In radial direction, it expands most in the height of the stirrer. Nine seconds later, the liquid has heated up further in the immediate vicinity of the stirrer. The heated liquid volume shown in Figure 44b has increased as well. Thirty seconds after the beginning of the stirring process, the temperature profile shown in Figure 44c has established. The region of maximum temperature is located around the stirrer. Above the stirrer, the heating of the liquid in axial direction has progressed further than below the stirrer. In the height of the stirrer, the isotherm $\Delta T = 0.01$ K almost reaches the vessel wall.

Representation of Concentration Fields in a Jet-Mixed Vessel

Haarde [39] developed the experimental setup shown in Figure 45 for the observation of unsteady-state mass exchange processes occurring during jet mixing. In this setup, the concentration profiles of a dye can be observed with the use of optical tomography. The dyes are either injected or they develop during a color change reaction. They cause a decrease of the light in the cylindrical mixing vessel. The experimental results are recorded with diverging light in the form of transillumination projections from four angles of view with divergent light. The axes of the light bundles cross each other in the center of the vessel at an angle of 45° each. Thus, the light bundles cover a range of 180°. The light is guided through the measurement chamber from four directions via mirrors and two beam splitters. With cylindrical lenses, the vessel can be illuminated in sections of 50 mm (overall) height each. For this purpose, the measurement chamber, which is about 200 mm high and has a diameter of 200 mm, must be divided up into four sections that are located above each other. In order to implement this investigation, the measurement chamber must be located on a table with variable height that is positioned opposite of the optical setup. The cylindrical measurement chamber is located in the octagonal measurement chamber. The space between the octagonal exterior chamber and the cylindrical interior chamber is filled with water. This is necessary to suppress total reflection as much as possible. After penetrating the chamber, the beams hit matte screens. Photographs of the four matte screens are taken with synchronized, motor-driven microphotographic cameras. The negatives are fed into a picture processing unit and the film density is digitalized.

The three-dimensional concentration field obtained with the use of tomographic reconstruction is shown in Figure 46 for one plane. The lines connect points of identical film densities and identical concentrations. The dye distribution in the volume can be reconstructed from several of these tomograms. Mass-exchanging regions can be made visible this way. Figure 47 shows the reconstruction of section B-B. Lines of constant concentration have been entered. The maximum local values are shaded in the shown section. If the method is applied in sequential time steps, the movement and the change of the mass-exchanging regions can be observed. Figure 48 shows a sequence of 4 tomograms.

The maximum local values are shaded. The tomograms show the dye profile in the plane 72 mm below the liquid surface at different points in time. The first tomogram developed 3.2 seconds after the beginning of the process. The beam penetrating into the axis of the vessel appears as the maximum decrease of the light. Another 3.2 seconds later, no new dye develops, the entire quantity of dye has been added to the vessel. The colored volume elements rise along the walls of the vessel. The maximum values for the decrease of the light are now in the vicinity of the wall. During the further progress of the mixing, the dye is distributed, the maximum values take up a wide range of the cross section and they are not localized as much any longer. The maximum values of the decrease of the light become smaller and the concentration profiles are more even.

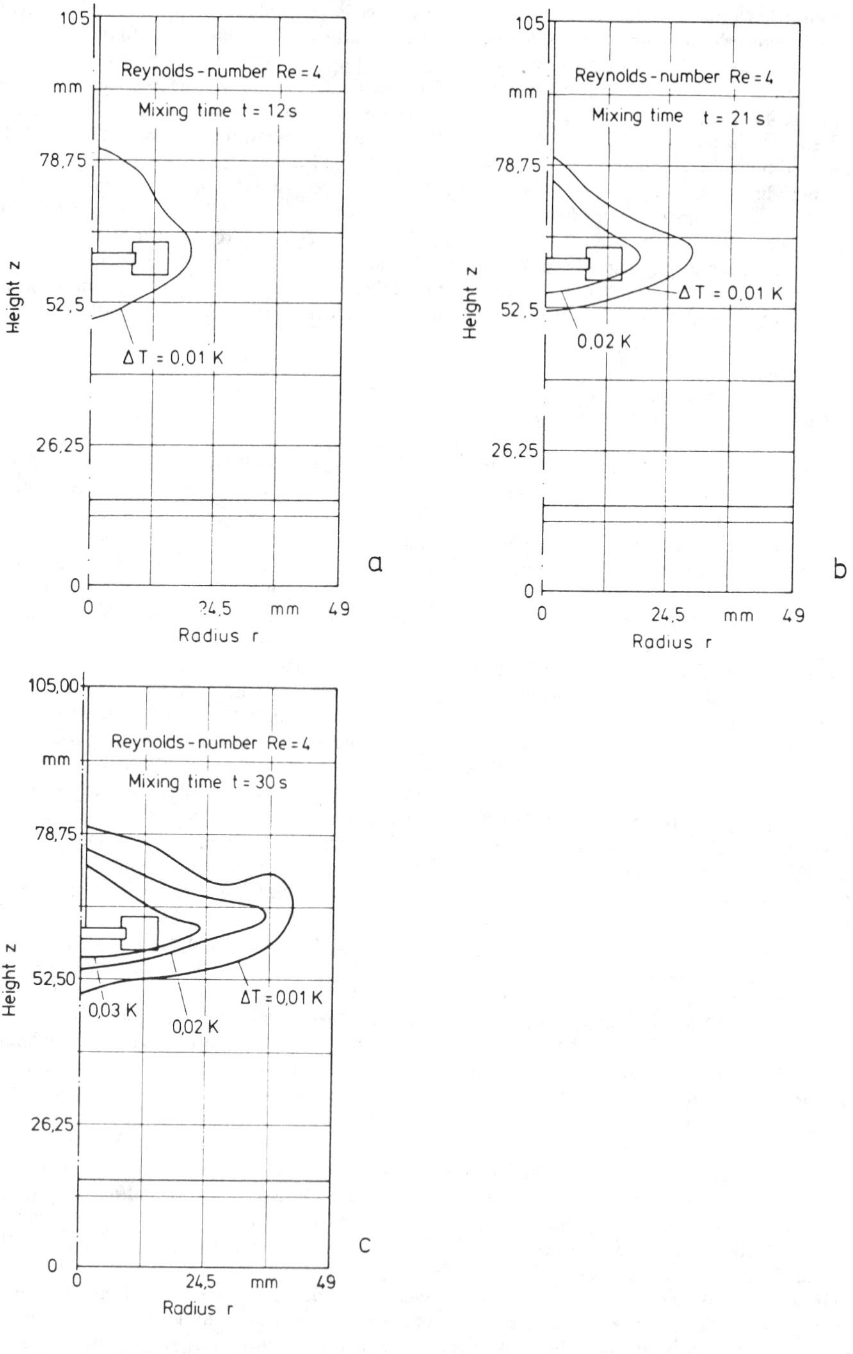

Figure 44. Reconstructed temperature profiles after different stirring times [38].

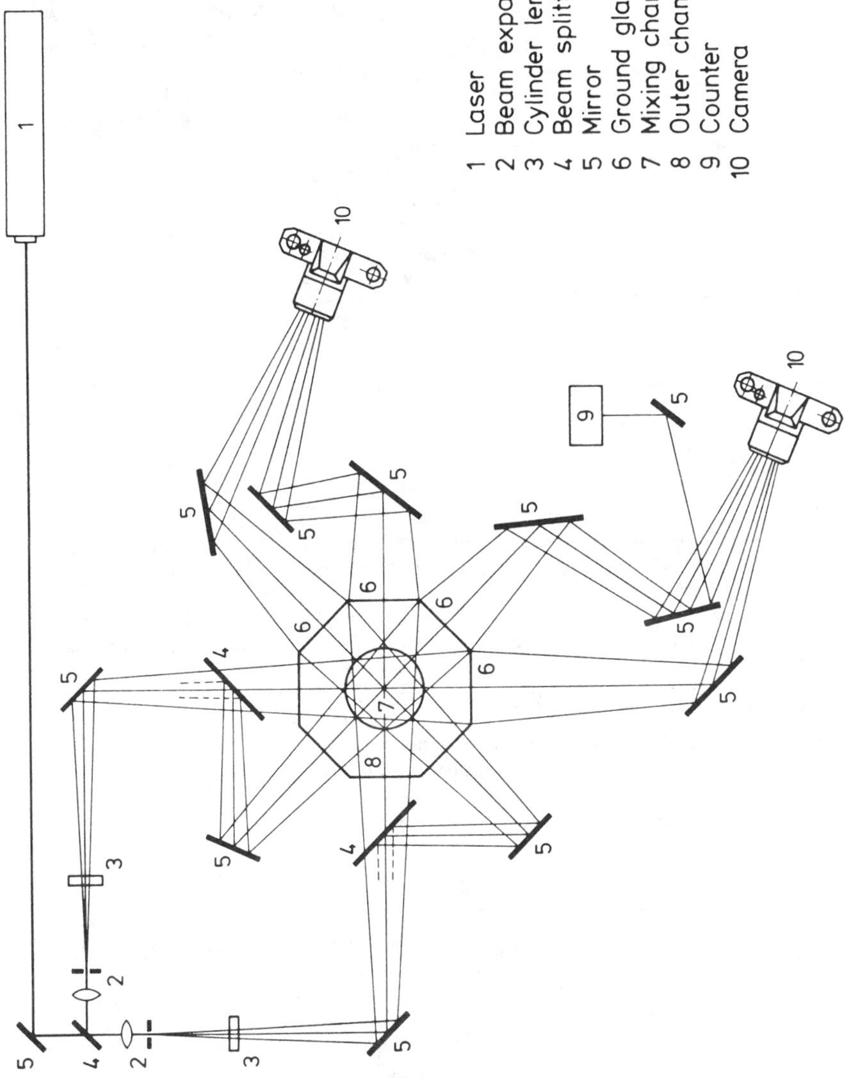

Figure 45. Experimental facility for the measurement of instationary mass transfer processes [39].

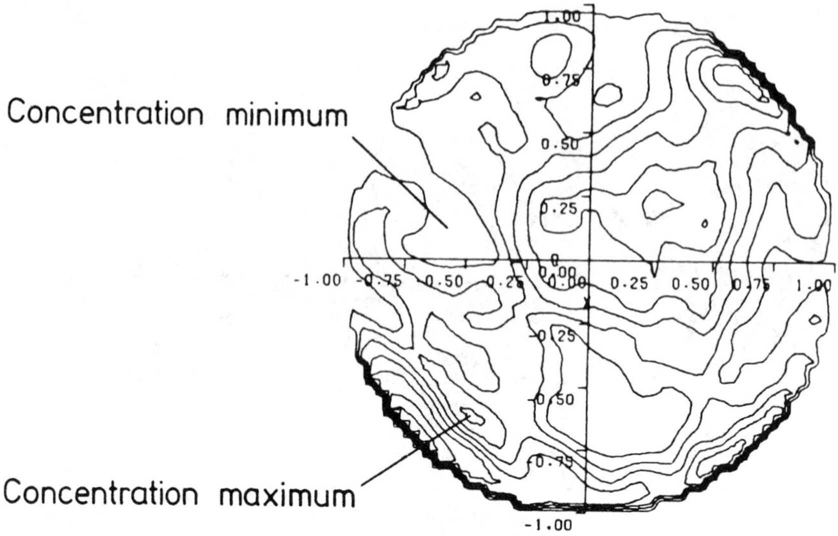

Figure 46. Tomographic reconstruction of the concentration field in a horizontal plane of the vessel [39].

Application of Sound Waves

Reconstruction of three-dimensional velocity and temperature fields with the use of ultrasonics. Johnson, Greenleaf, Tanaka and Flandro [40] describe a technique for the measurement of three-dimensional velocity and temperature fields in liquids with the use of ultrasonics.

They examined the velocity field of a liquid vortex. Figure 49 shows the applied experimental setup schematically. It shows the geometric arrangement of the sensors and detectors. The sensors are arranged at the locations a and b on a circle with the radius r = 15 cm. The area surrounded by the points C_1, C_2, C_3, C_4 is recorded tomographically. The radius OB is 9.55 cm. The radius OA is 4.24 cm. During the investigations, the transmitter is located at a, the detector at b. The detector is moved around the center a along a circular curve on the line F_1, b′, M, F_2. Transmitter and detector are rotated around the object when a picture is taken. The difference in time

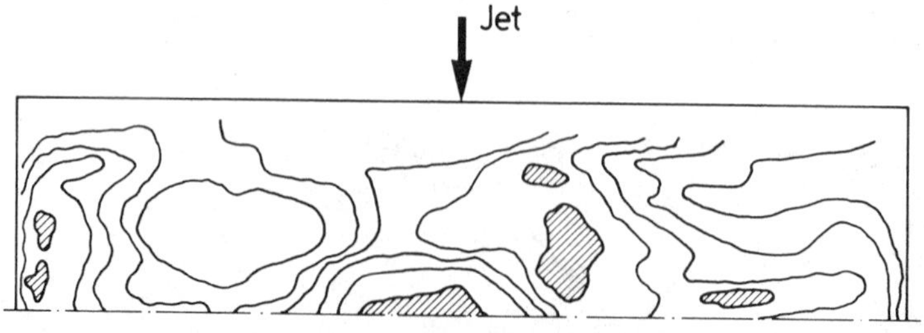

Figure 47. Tomographic reconstruction of the concentration field in a vertical plane of the mixing vessel.

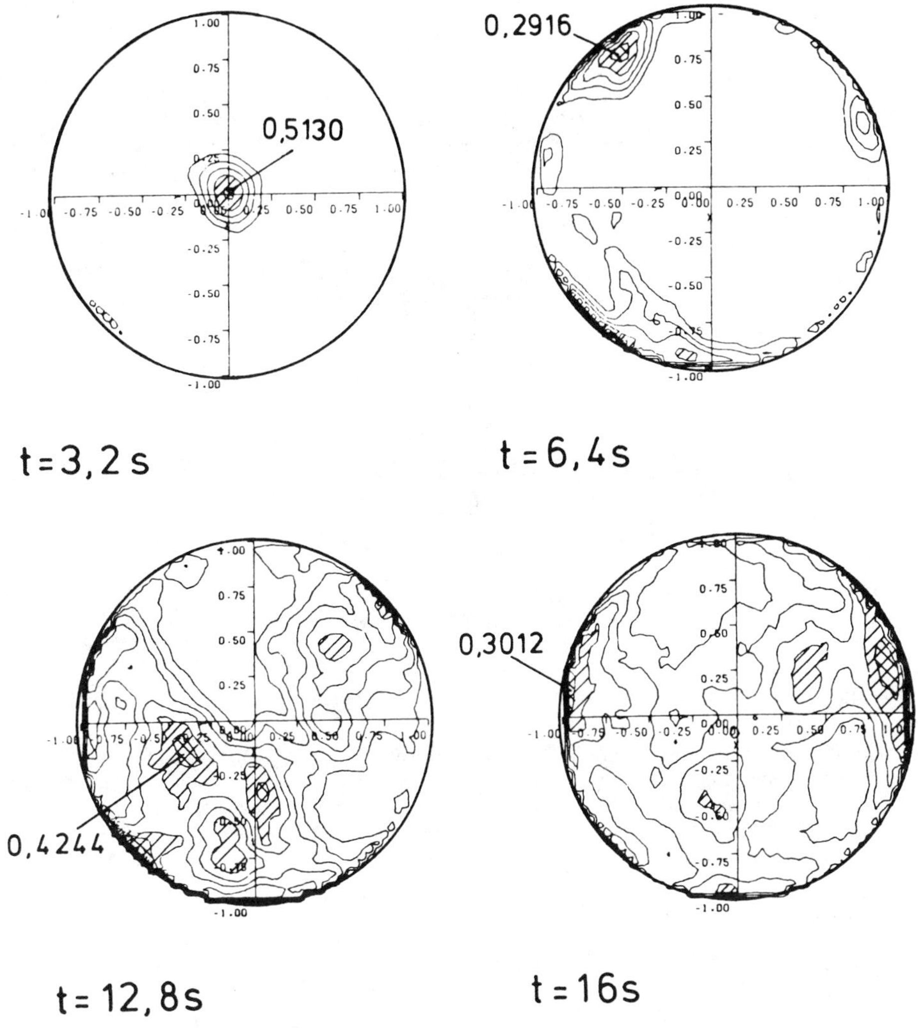

Figure 48. Concentration profiles in one plane at various times [39].

of flight $t_{ab} - t_{ba}$ is determined. Separate measurements for t_{ab} and t_{ba} are obtained with a time of flight detector. The differences in time of flight are measured for 60 angles of view and 150 beams per angle of view. The distances between the beams are identical. Only stationary or quasi-stationary velocity fields can be recorded with these measurements.

The same applies for measurements in temperature fields of fluids or solid-state bodies. In order to determine the temperature fields, the density change with the temperature is measured in an experimental area. Tests were implemented with three balloons arranged in a tempered water bath. The temperatures of the water in the balloons were varied. A fourth balloon was arranged in the center of the water bath. This balloon was filled with diluted sodium chloride. It represents a region of identical temperature but changed density. With this balloon, an inhomogeneous materal is

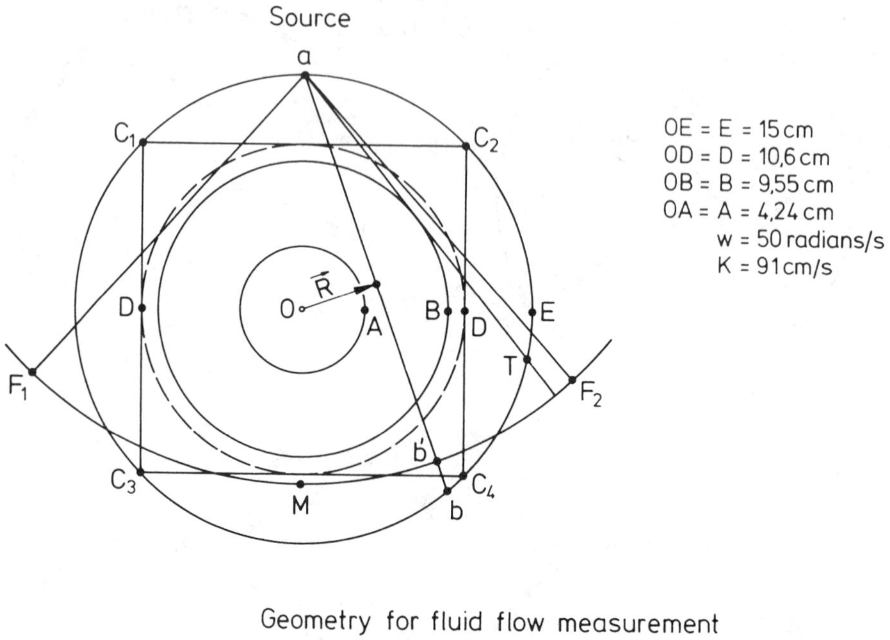

Figure 49. Experimental facility for fluid flow measurements with ultrasound waves [40].

simulated. For the reconstruction of the temperature differences, the difference between the temperature distribution at a certain point in time and the initial temperature distribution was determined. The temperature-independent distribution of refractive indices in the test chamber is suppressed this way and temperature changes of $\Delta T = 0.5$ K can be measured. For all tests, the evaluation of the experimental results was implemented with the algebraic reconstruction technique (ART).

Measurements on Solid Matter

Application of X-Rays

Measurement of timber rings of live trees. A mobile experimental setup for the measurement of timber rings of live trees is introduced by Onoe, Isao, Yamada, Nakamura, Kongure, Kawamura and Yoshimatsu [41]. The scanner consists of two U-shaped plates that are located above each other and attached coaxially. If the openings are located above each other, the setup can be moved in such a way that a vertical object, such as a live tree, can be arranged in the center. The bottom plate with four adjustable legs serves as fixed platform. A source for X-ray radiation and a group of detectors are attached to the top plate. Both plates are connected with each other by means of a rotating mechanism. After each scan, the top plate is rotated by a few degrees. The entire scanning process and the collection of the experimental data is controlled by a microprocessor. An X-ray tube with a variable voltage of 40–120 KV and three sodium-iodid-scintillation counters are used. The tube and the detectors are connected with each other with fixed mountings. This unit rotates around the focal point of the X-ray tube. Three beams traverse the object.

In the upper part of Figure 50, the reconstruction of the timber rings of a Douglas fir is shown. The lower part shows photographs of the examined cross section. A satisfactory coincidence between the reconstructions and the photographs can be observed.

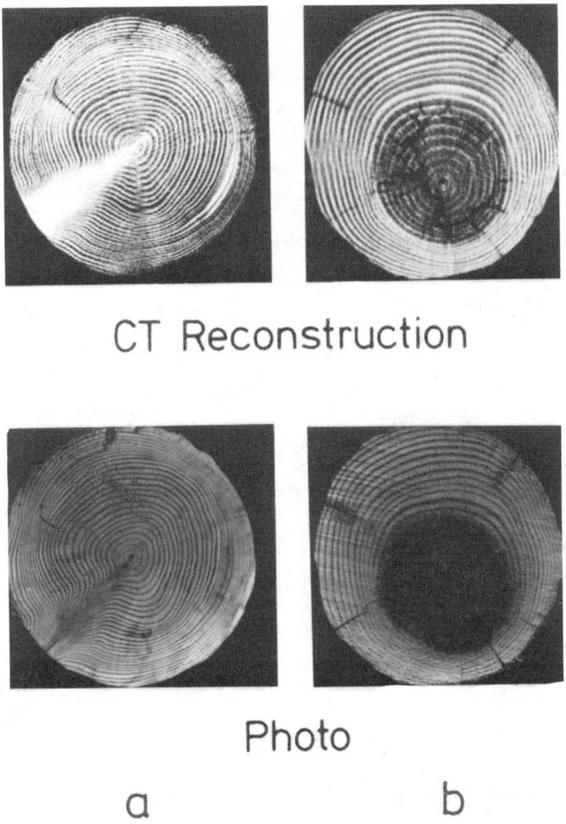

Figure 50. Comparison of computer tomographic reconstruction and photographs of actual cross sections of wooden poles: a) the wrapping pattern of annual rings around a branch, b) severe decay in the heartwood region [41].

Application of x-ray radiation for tomographic examinations in oil production. Wang, Ayral, Castellano and Gryte [42] published investigations about the measurement of the oil distribution in minerals.

They used a tomographic computer with an X-ray energy of 125 KeV. Cylindrical sandstone test pieces with a diameter of 5 cm and a length of 25 cm, as well as artificial cylindrical objects were used for the investigations. These objects consist of a PVC pipe with an interior diameter of 7.5 cm and a length of 27 cm, which are filled with a mixture of sand and epoxy resin. A rectangular chamber measuring 5 × 5 × 27 cm is filled either with glass pellets (45–90 μm in diameter) or sandstone. The two ends of the cylinder are closed with a porous plate. At first, the test pieces are evacuated and oil is filled in, until the entire cavity volume is filled up. Then the test pieces are mounted in the annulus of the tomographic computer. A liquid feed is attached to the top end. A 1M-potassium-iodide/water-solution is used as test liquid and pumped into the test piece. Reconstructions of cylinders that contain only potassium iodide solution or oil are used for calibration. The height of the examined region is about 8 mm. Figure 51 shows tomograms of a cylindrical sandstone test piece. These recordings represent the reconstructed distributions of oil

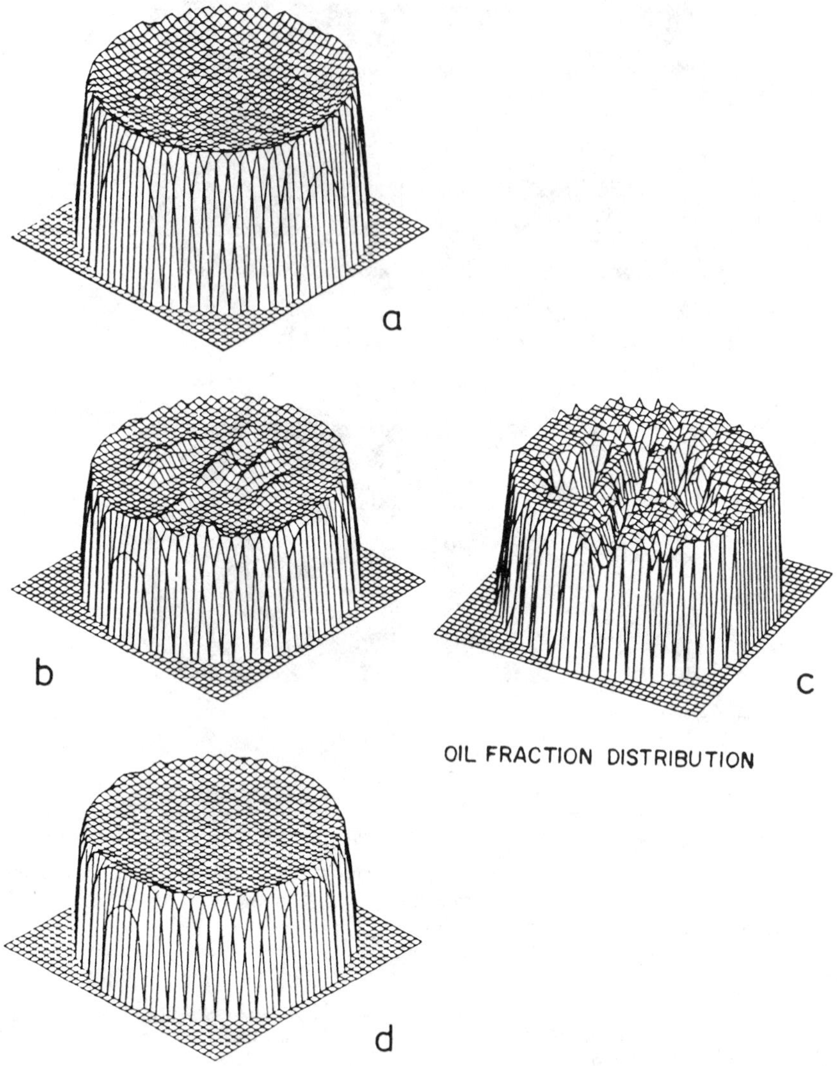

Figure 51. Oil fraction distribution computed from X-ray attenuation coefficient distribution obtained from computer tomographic scanner. a) X-ray attenuation coefficient of a core filled with 1 M-potassium-iodine-water-solution; b) X-ray attenuation coefficient of a core filled with 1 M-potassium-iodine-water-solution/oil mixture; c) X-ray attenuation coefficient of an oil filled core; d) Oil fraction distribution of a core filled 1 M-potassium-iodine-water-solution/oil mixture [42].

and potassium iodide solution in a cross section of a cylindrical sandstone test piece, at a distance of 7.6 cm from the inlet for the potassium iodide solution. The quantity of potassium iodide solution added to this point is 4.5% of the volume of voids. Figure 51 shows the distribution of the oil fraction in the cross section of the test piece. In aqueous potassium iodid solutions, the decrease of the X-ray radiation is higher than in oil. Therefore, high values indicate a high oil content in the test piece and low values indicate a low oil content.

Application of x-ray radiation for tomographic examinations of three-phase distributions in sandstone. Vinegar and Wellington [44] describe the use of X-ray radiation for determining the different phases oil, water, and gas in porous solid-state bodies with the application of tomography. The applied X-ray tube can be operated at a voltage of up to 120 KV at a currency of 25 mA. The voltage can be varied between two predetermined values, in order to obtain reconstructions for two different energy conditions. The change from one predetermined voltage to another one takes place automatically.

For the investigations, the solid-state bodies are placed in a pressurized cylinder. The pressurized cylinder is made of aluminum, in order to keep the decrease of the X-ray radiation as low as possible. The cylinder can be heated from the outside. For the recording of a tomogram, the pressurized cylinder is mounted onto a table that can be rotated and shifted, in the center of a tomographic computer. The entire recording process is controlled electronically. The data are processed and stored by the computer.

The maximum voltage of the X-ray tube is used in the tests. For a recording with low energy, it is important to make sure that the X-ray radiation is not decreased too much by the wall of the pressurized vessel. Materials with stronger absorption can be added to improve the contrast between the phases oil, gas, and water. Table 1 lists different materials for the individual phases that are suitable for the tests. The solubility in water and the position of the absorption spectra are also indicated. One material can be selected for each phase. Depending on the phase to be examined, the material can be added in one or two phases. First investigations of the phase distribution in oleiferous sandstone with forced-in carbon monoxide were implemented.

Table 1
Dopants for Brine, Oil, and Gas Phases

Compound	Solubility ($g/100g\ H_2O$)	K-edge (keV)
Brine phase		
NaBr	90	13.2
Na_2MoO_4	65	20.0
NaI	178	33.2
Na_2WO_4	73	69.5
TlF	78	85.5
Tl-EDTA		85.5
$Pb(NO_3)_2$	54	88.0
Pb-EDTA		88.0
Bi-EDTA		90.5
Oil phase		
Bromated oils		13.2
Iodated oils		33.2
$(C_2H_5)_4Pb$	Tetraethyl lead	88.0
$(CH_3)_4Pb$	Tetramethyl lead	88.0
Gas phase		
Krypton		14.3
Xenon		34.6

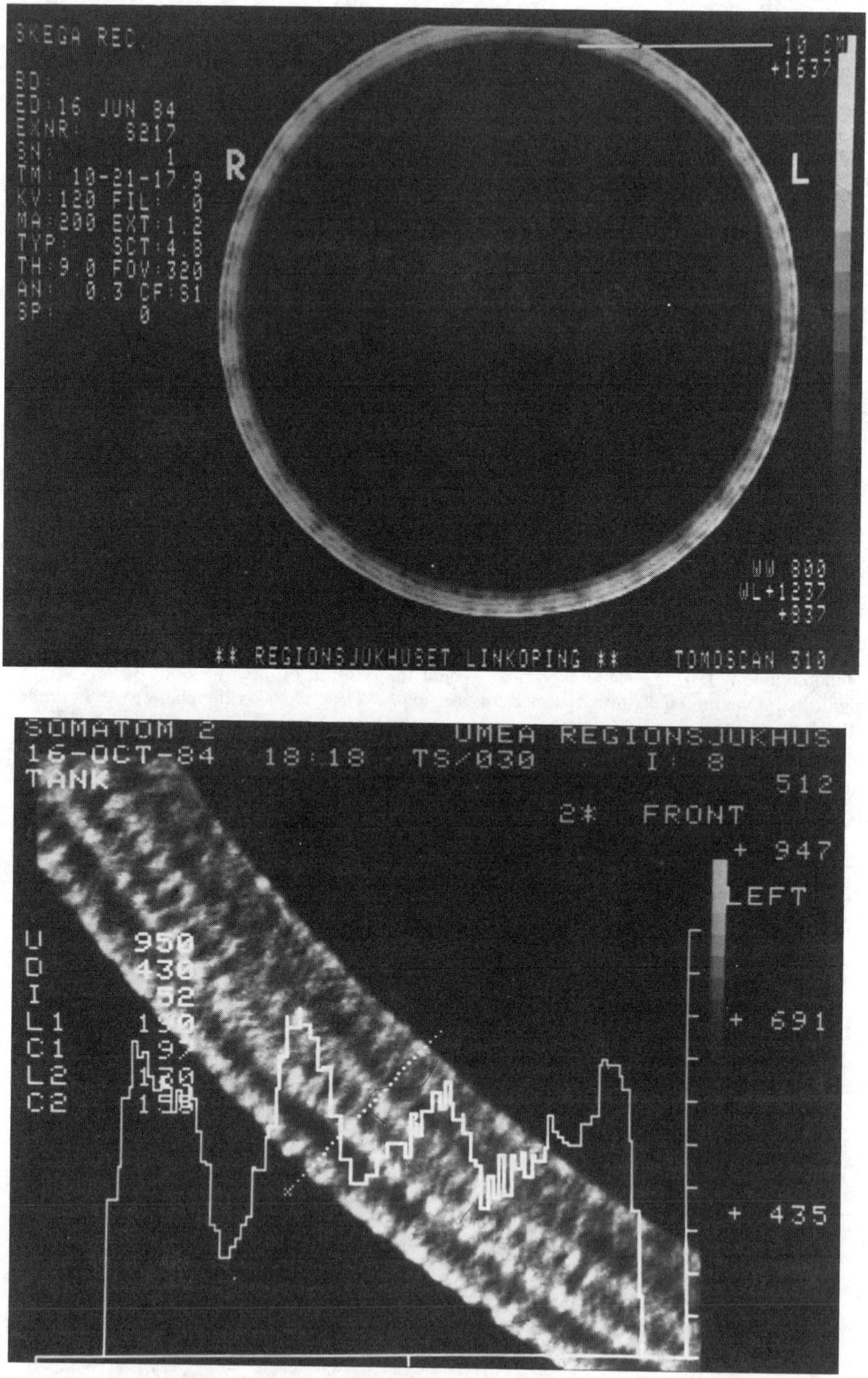

Figure 52. a) Computer tomographic image of a high-pressure tank; b) Magnification of a part of the high-pressure tank showing the structure of the wall of the tank [25].

Application of Gamma Rays

Investigation of elastomers with the use of gamma rays. Many types of plastic and rubber have densities that come close to the density of the human body. Computerized tomography can therefore be easily modified for non-destructive testing of such materials. Persson and Östman [25] used common tomographic computers, such as the ones used for medical purposes. Investigations were implemented with airplane tires, shock absorbers, thick-walled rubber cylinders, and welded automotive parts made of thermoplastic material. The tests were subdivided into two groups. In the first group, several polymeric products were examined. The tests were implemented with the objective to determine, whether computerized tomography is suitable for the detection and localization of defects, which may lead to the destruction or the impairment of the service life of the product. The second group of tests was implemented to determine possibilities for the examination of cross-link density differences in vulcanized rubber with the use of computerized tomography. Tomograms of a plastic container and a rubber cylinder are shown as examples.

Figure 52a shows a fiber-reinforced high-pressure vessel for air with a pressure resistance of up to 40 MPa. The wall thickness is approximately 15 mm. The interior wall of the vessel is covered with a 2 mm butyl rubber coating. The brighter contours represent the glass fiber reinforced epoxy resin. Figure 52b shows an enlargement of a section of the vessel. The vessel consists of four glass fiber reinforced layers. Between the brighter layers—glass fiber—there are darker regions with a lower density. These regions of lower density mainly contain the resin. The degree of age-hardening also has an effect on the density. Resin that is not age-hardened has a lower density than fully age-hardened resin. These factors lead to the observed phenomena.

As a second example, Figure 53 shows the reconstruction of a rubber cylinder with a wall thickness of 100 mm and a diameter of 300 mm. Due to the low heat-conductivity of rubber, there

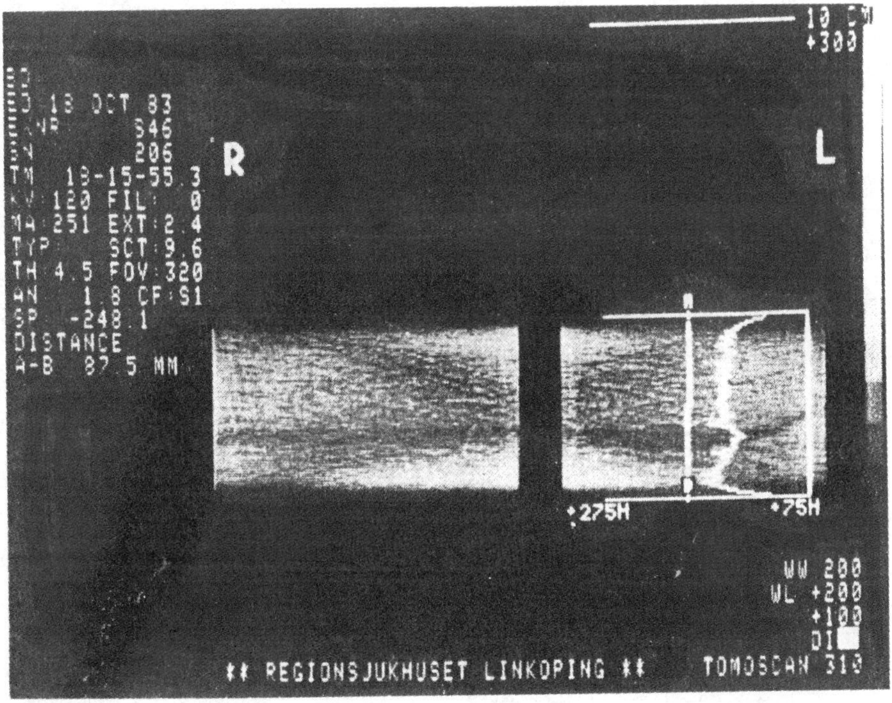

Figure 53. Computer tomographic picture of the density-field of a rubber cylinder [25].

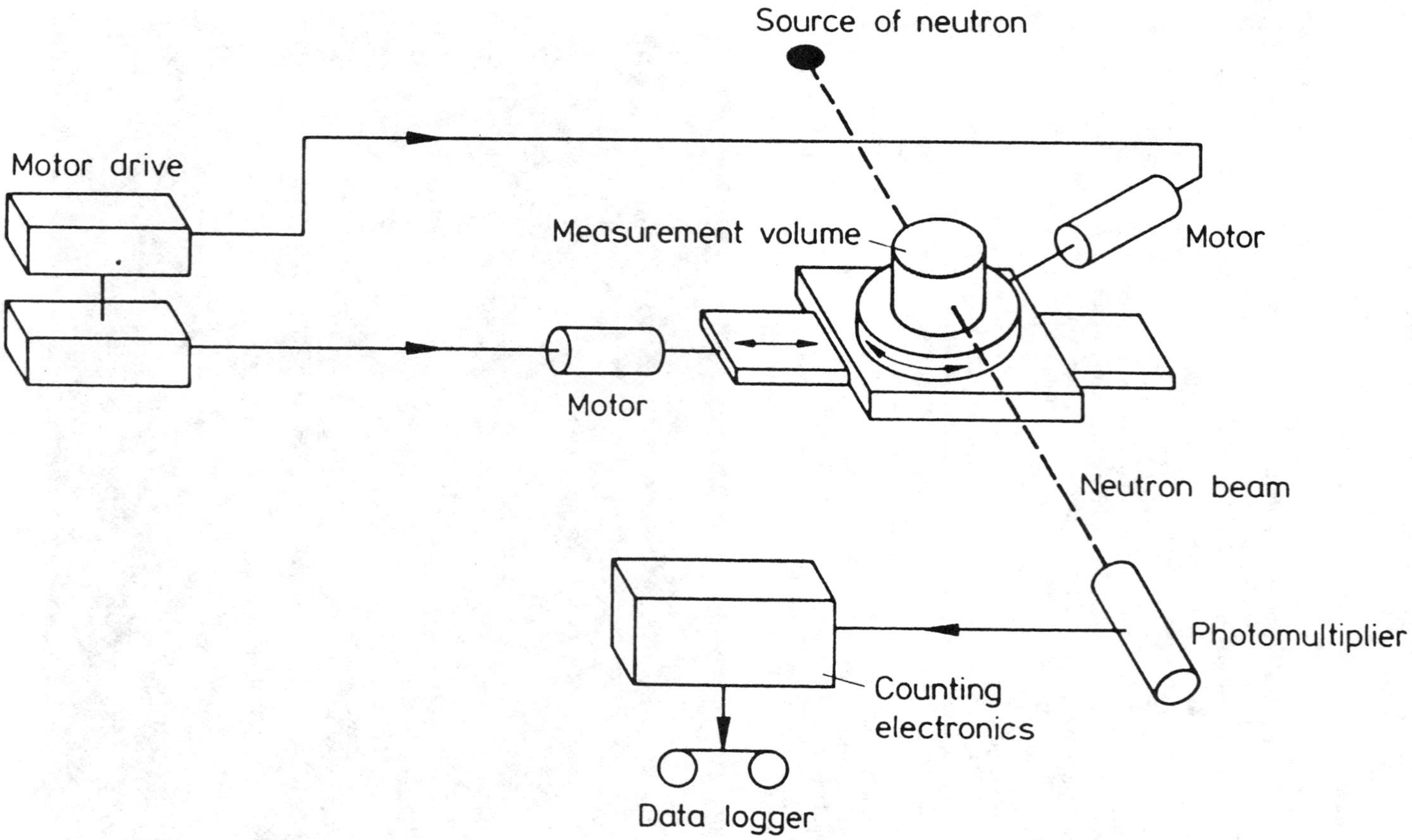

Figure 54. Experimental facility for neutron tomography.

are strong temperature gradients in the material during the production of thick-walled products. Furthermore, an increase of the cross-link density causes a decrease of the heat-conductivity. These two phenomena lead to variations of the cross-link density in thick-walled rubber products. In Figure 53, a dark stripe can be noticed across the entire width of the cylinder. In this area, the density is lower than in the rest of the cylinder. The axial hole shows the location, at which a rubber sample was taken. The cross-link density was measured on this sample with the wet chemical method. A satisfactory coincidence of the cross-link densities in the rubber cylinder determined with the different methods is required.

Application of gamma rays for the investigation of oleiferous minerals. In addition to X-rays and nuclear magnetic resonance, gamma rays can be used to investigate the distribution of liquids in minerals. Nicholas, MacCuaig and Gilboy [45] determined several advantages of gamma rays in comparison to X-rays. For example, beam hardening does not occur with gamma rays. Also, the costs of the radioactive source are lower. The source of gamma radiation is also much smaller than an X-ray tube. However, the radiation is lower by a magnitude of four, compared to an X-ray tube. The recording time lasts at least 100 s. A single ^{241} Am-source with a gamma radiation energy of 59.5 KeV is used for the investigations.

The attenuation coefficients of three synthetic materials soaked with air, saltwater, or oil were determined. The determined attenuation coefficient for oil was 20% higher than for air. The coefficient for saltwater was 30% higher. Ions can be added to increase the difference between the attenuation coefficients. In order to keep the change of the physical properties of the fluids low, the number of added ions should be kept as low as possible. Due to the monoenergetic radiation of a gamma source, a small quantity is already sufficient to cause major changes of the attenuation coefficient.

Application of Corpuscular Beams

Pfister, et al. [2] report about the application of neutron beams for non-destructive material testing with the use of computerized tomography. The application of fast neutrons offers some advantages compared to photons. Contrary to photons, which mainly interact with the atom shell, the linear attenuation coefficient of neutrons is determined by nuclear interactions. Due to the high penetration capacity of neutrons in steel, it is possible to examine large structural components.

The mobile unit shown schematically in Figure 54 consists of a setup that can be rotated and shifted. With this setup, the object to be examined can be moved through the bundled neutron beam in random translations and rotations. With the use of a collimator, the beams from the neutron source are sharply bundled. A neutron detector is located opposite of the neutron source. The detector is connected with an electronic counter. The motors controlling the translation and rotation of the examined object are oprated with a computer. The experimental results are stored on tape. Due to the statistical fluctuations of all nuclear processes, the experimental results vary considerably. They must be evened out. Furthermore, a correction of the experimental results, called spectral correction by the authors, is implemented. This is necessary, because a neutron source emits neutrons as well as gamma rays and both radiations are measured by the detector. Additional filter processes are implemented for image reconstruction.

First examinations of test pieces have been implemented. A cylindrical plastic test piece was equipped with cylindrical iron inserts with diameters from 15 mm to 1 mm. Inserts with a diameter of 2 mm and more can be detected satisfactorily in this test piece. The contrast between plastic and iron is lower with the use of neutron beams than with the use of X-rays. Therefore, even the size of the inserts is shown satisfactorily. An iron test piece with welded air inclusion was examined as well. The obtained reconstruction was of much lower quality.

Application of Electromagnetic Waves

Determining apparent impedance of solid-state bodies. Methods for the determination of electric impedance are used for geological and mineralogical examinations. All methods for determining impedance require an artificial currency source with ground connections. The potential is measured at other electrodes in the surrounding area. In most cases, the currency is also measured. Otherwise it is possible to measure an effective or apparent impedance below the surface. Methods for the determination of apparent impedance are used in medicine as well. These methods are considered as possibilities for diagnosis because of the high conductivity differences in human bodies, which are caused by the different salt contents within and outside of the organs. Price [46] describes an application of this technique in medicine.

Wexler, Fry, and Neumann [47, 48] introduced a measurement technique for determining impedance for process-technological studies. Sixteen electrodes are installed at each side of a square measurement vessel. With the use of a computer program, currency flows are generated between selected pairs of electrodes and the voltage is measured at all electrodes.

For the first tests, the measurement vessel was filled with a small quantity of water. The water formed a thin layer on the bottom of the vessel. It served as a current-conducting medium.

A rectangular steel can was positioned in one corner of the measurement vessel and a plastic vessel in the opposite corner. A 1 kHz signal with a currency of approximately 1 mA was used. The shape of the steel can was reconstructed satisfactorily with this method. Due to its high conductivity, it can be easily reproduced. The shape of the plastic vessel could also be reconstructed. Due to the lower conductivity, the contrast is much worse than that of the steel can.

The authors also produced test pictures to double-check the technique. With the use of these test pictures it could be shown that it is possible to reconstruct the shape of a rectangular object satisfactorily. However, the conductivity of the object is not reflected correctly.

Application of Nuclear Magnetic Resonance

Petrophysical application of nuclear magnetic resonance. Rothwell and Vinegar [49] describe an application of nuclear magnetic resonance for the tomography of drill cores from oil exploration. The applied setup uses an electric magnet, with which a field force of 0.84 T can be produced. Frequency changes of 1.4 Khz/min can be produced in all three directions. Normally, 120 projections are obtained from each direction. The recording time for a typical cross section is about 5 minutes. The image reconstruction is implemented by a minicomputer connected to the setup. After the reconstruction, the data are stored on magnetic tape and transferred to a computer with color graphics screen. During an experiment, different pulse sequences are used to measure the nuclear magnetic resonance. Due to the short relaxation times of fluids in porous minerals, short intervals between the pulse sequences are necessary. They last about 0.5–2.0 ms. These intervals are much shorter than the ones used in medicine. Still dissipating tomograms were obtained of typical drill cores. The authors found out that for many systems the differences of the relaxation times are large enough to make a definite determination possible. The possibility to analyze the distribution of oil and water with the use of nuclear magnetic resonance is based on the different relaxation times of the liquids.

In cases in which the viscosity of the oil and the pore size of the mineral cause similar relaxation times of the two phases, the test piece can be doped with a paramagnetic ion such as Mn^{24}. This results in a reduction of the relaxation time of the water protons. With high concentrations of Mn^{24}, the water cannot be analyzed any longer with the nuclear magnetic resonance technique. Only the oil distribution in the test piece is reflected.

Measurements in Multiphase Systems

Application of Gamma Radiation

Investigating fluidized beds with gamma rays. Mac Cuaig, Seville, Gilboy and Clift [50] introduced a technique for tomographically investigating fluidized beds with gamma rays. The fluidized bed is located in a transparent cylinder with a height of 200 mm and a diameter of 51 mm. Different gas distributor plates can be inserted into the cylinder. A plate with a 2-mm borehole in its center and a sintered metal plate are used. The sintered metal plate also has a 2-mm borehole in its center. Air is fed to this borehole separately. Therefore, the gas flow in the core can be adjusted independent of the remaining gas flow through the plate. Pressurized air is used as gas. Two different materials are used as solids: quartz sand with a diameter of 300–355 μm and spherical "soda glass ballotini" with a dimater of 210–250 μm. The height of the bed is 60 mm in most of the tests.

A monoenergetic ^{241}Am source is used to produce the projections. The gamma rays have an energy of 59.6 KeV, the disintegration rate is $3.7 \cdot 10^9$ 1/s. The object is rotated and traversed by the radiation. Forty steps at a distance of 2 mm are selected for the tests. Thirty angles of view, differing by 6° each, are adjusted.

First results are published in research reports. Figure 55 shows the density profiles of a fixed bed and a fluidized bed.

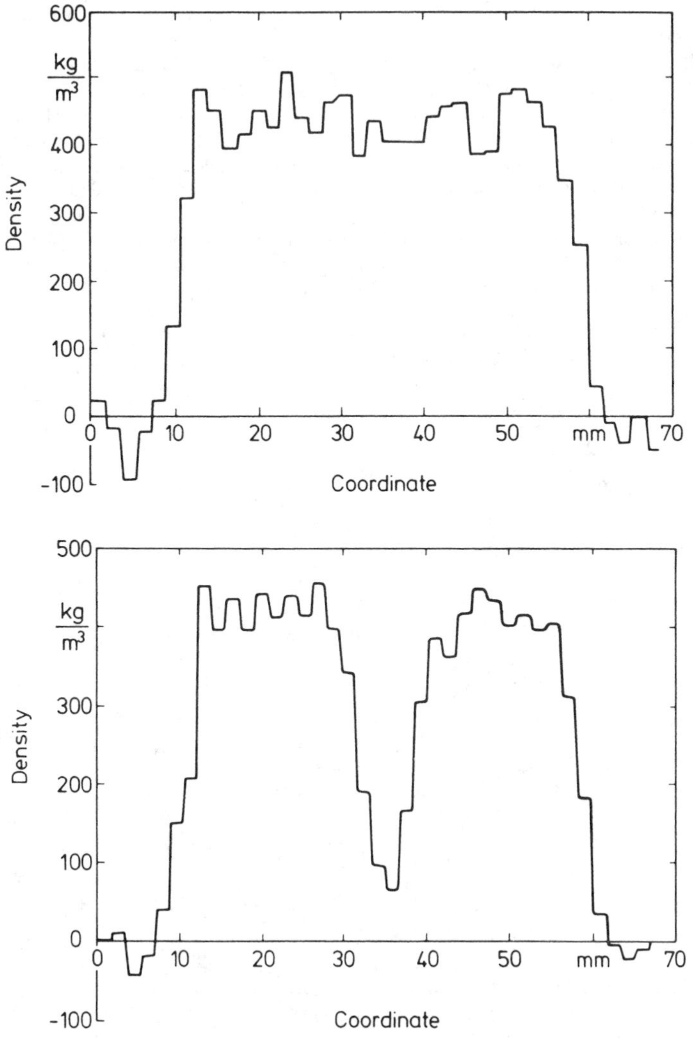

Figure 55. a) Density profile of the settled bed of particles; b) Density profile of the bed with central orifice flow only [50].

Using gamma rays to investigate two-phase flows. In an experimental investigation, a rotating gamma radiation source was used for tomographic purposes by Kulacki, Schlosser, De Vuono and Munshi [51] to measure the void fraction of an air/water flow.

The two-phase flow is produced by blowing air into a vertical pipe of 150 mm diameter and 1.8 m height that is filled with water. The gas content is determined with a tomographic reconstruction of the density distribution. For this purpose, the gamma radiation traverses different planes of the bubble column at various angular positions. ^{137}Cs is used as a radiation source. It is mounted onto a platform located around the pipe. On the side of the point-shaped radiation source, the platform can be rotated, which means that the detector located opposite of the platform can be rotated by an angle of $\pm 25°$. This angle is necessary for an irradiation of the entire pipe. The radiation source and the detector are rotated horizontally at intervals of 2.5°. The recording time for each interval is 100 s.

The authors examined the local gas content in dependence of the mean gas content in the column. The results for a bubble flow are shown in Figure 56. Values for the void fraction determined with the measurements sometimes are lower than 0 or higher than 1, which is unrealistic from a physical point of view. This is partially due to the applied mathematical reconstruction technique by Shepp and Logan [32]. The filter function used in this technique was developed for the low density variations in the human body. However, the density differences in the described investigations were large. Therefore, the development of a new filter function for two-phase flows is considered necessary.

Another setup for the measurement of the void fraction in two-phase flows was described by Fincke, Gheever, Fachrell, Scown, Thornton and Ward [52]. The setup is used for the investigation of two-phase flows in horizontal pipes. It can be rotated around the axis of the pipe. The rotation

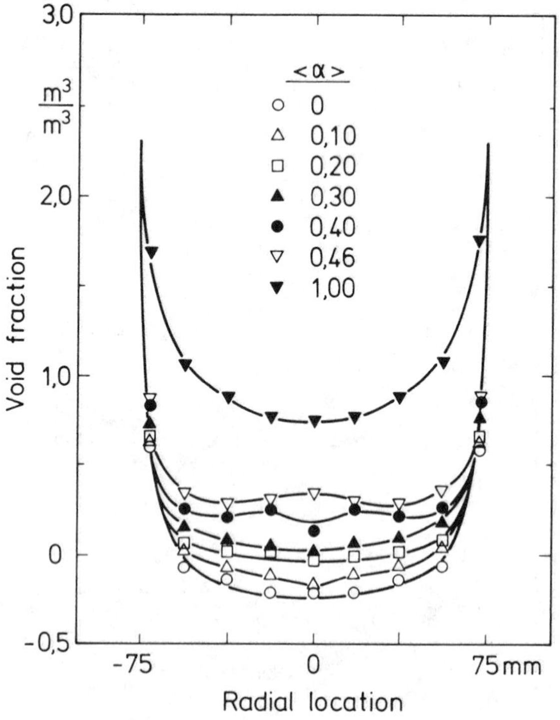

Figure 56. Variation of reconstructed void fraction across pipe diameter [51].

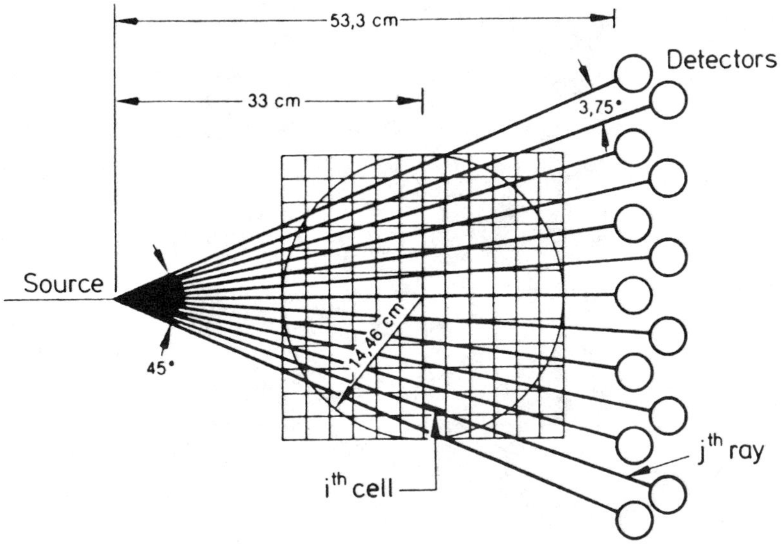

Figure 57. Tomographic densitometer ray geometry and pixel array for iterative reconstruction [52].

occurs step by step with a stepping motor at discrete angles. A radiation source for gamma rays is used to investigate the void fraction. Caesium is used as a radioactive element. The photons have an energy of 662 KeV. The gamma rays are emitted across an angular range of 45°. The opening of the protective screen has a size of 0.64 × 1.78 cm. Thirteen detectors are arranged opposite of the gamma radiation source at angular distances of 3.75° each. The protective screen of the detectors is 7.62 cm thick and has openings measuring 0.64 × 2.54 cm. The longer side is located in direction of the pipe axis. The detectors are cooled with water. Figure 57 shows a drawing of the experimental setup. The interior diameter of the examined pipe is 28.92 cm.

Seventeen different test pieces made of plexiglass, wood, and polyethylene were used to check the quality of reconstruction. Figure 58a shows an object that contains a bubble with eccentric position. The reconstruction of this object from 16 angles of view is shown in Figure 58b. The number of angles of view was varied between 11 and 31. The lowest background noise level was determined for 31 angles of view. For a field of 15 × 15 pixels and 13 detectors, 11 angles of view were considered as necessary, 16 or more as desirable.

Fincke, Vince and Jeffry [53] used a much smaller setup to measure the void fraction in two-phase flows. It consists of an americium source with a photon energy of 60 KeV. The setup shown schematically in Figure 59 is basically identical to the one previously described. The gamma rays are emitted at an angle of 32 degrees. Nine detectors are used. The interior diameter of the examined pipe is 6.66 cm. Figure 60 shows a tomogram of a slug flow with 144 pixels.

Application of Acoustic Waves

Investigating bubble flows with ultrasonic tomography. Wolf [54] developed a measurement technique suitable for the determining the local distribution of the specific phase interface in the cross section of a bubble column.

At a bubble column with a diameter of 150 mm, 108 ultrasonic elements are distributed evenly and in annular manner around the pipe circumference. The elements can be used either as transmitters

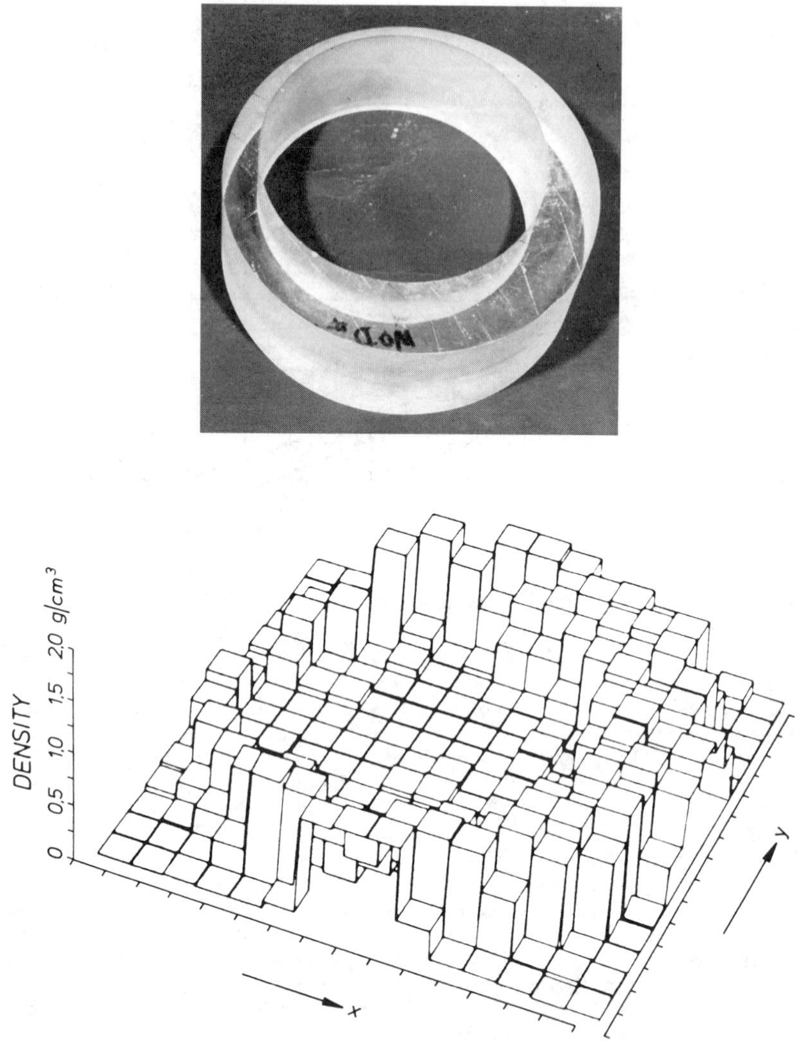

Figure 58. Eccentric bubble plexiglas phantom and reconstruction of the density-field [52].

or detectors. With a lens-shaped element that is cast onto the ultrasonic element, it is possible to emit ultrasonic waves at an angle of up to 120°. For the recording of a projection, the ultrasonic elements are activated in pulses. The arrangement of the individual elements around a bubble column is shown in Figure 61.

In order to produce projections of parallel beams, the activation of the elements is staggered. The scanning process is controlled electronically. Only two elements, one as transmitter and one as detector, are operated at the same time. Projections of parallel beams are obtained this way and a Fourier transformation can be used for the evaluation.

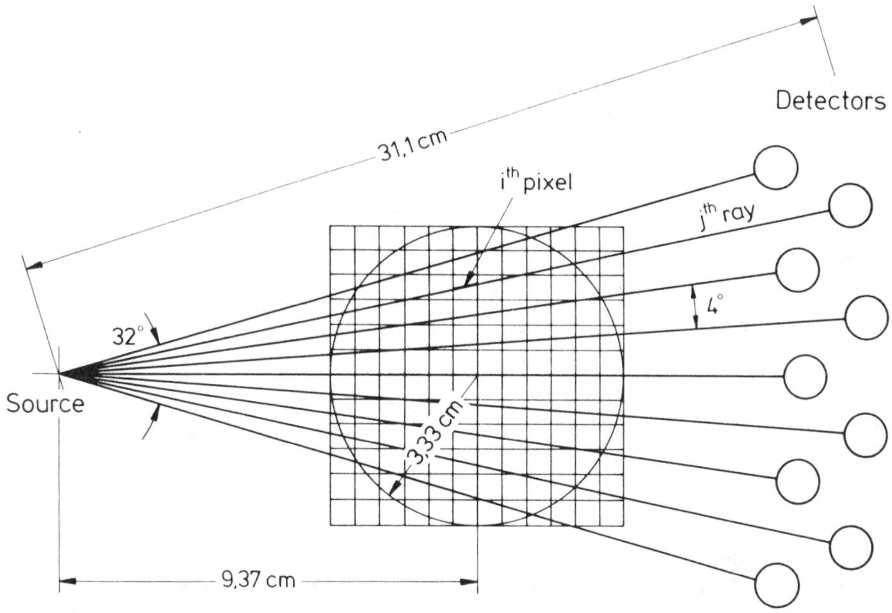

Figure 59. Tomographic densitometer ray geometry and detector array to measure two-phase flow [53].

The recording time depends on the time of flight of the ultrasonic pulses through the bubble column and the switching time of the control mechanism. The duration of one recording for 32 projection angles with 32 scans each is indicated as approximately 0.2 s.

Due to the pulsed operation of the elements, high capacities can be emitted with the piezoceramic elements for short periods of time. In continuous operation, such capacities would act

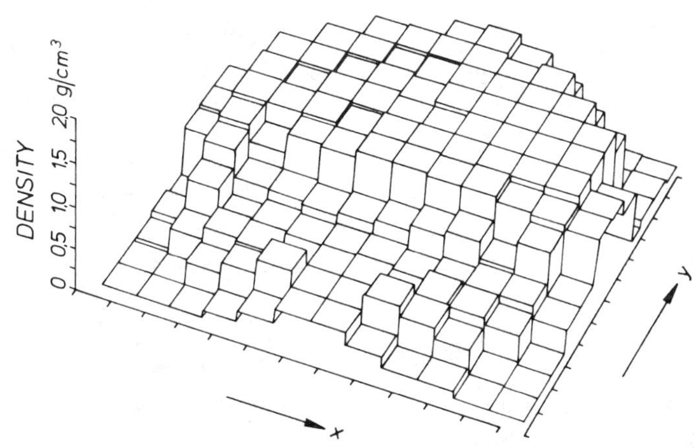

Figure 60. Reconstruction of void fraction profiles in a cross section with slug flow [53].

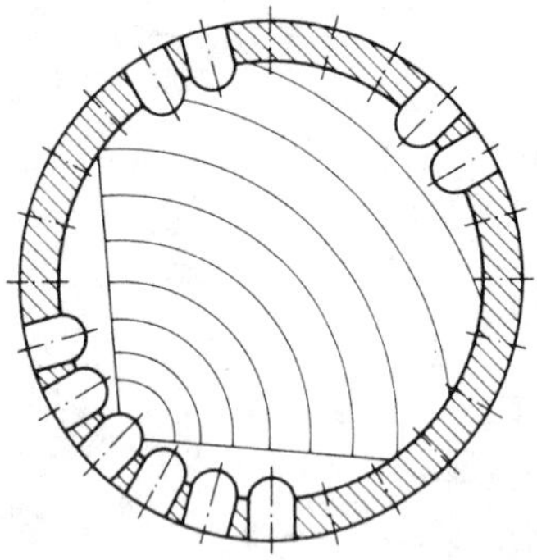

Figure 61. Experimental arrangement to measure the phase distribution in two phase flow with ultrasonic waves [54].

destructive. This is a way of increasing the distance between signal and background noise in the experimental setup considerably. Another advantage of the pulsed operation is the possibility to limit the detection time of the emitted pulses.

NOTATION

- a gradient of the straight line
- b y-axis distance of the straight line at x = 0, m
- B limitation of the band restriction
- c sound velocity, m/s
- f field parameter
- F two dimensional Fourier transformation of the field parameter
- g mathematical function
- I intensity of a radiation, W/m^2
- l grid distance, m
- m running variable
- M molar mass of the gas, kg/Kmol
- n running variable
- N local concentration, kg/m^3
- N number of field elements
- P uni-dimensional Fourier transformation of the physical parameter ϕ
- Q light absorption coefficient, m^2/kg
- R gas constant, J/mol K
- s length, m
- s length coordinate rotated through the angle θ to the x, y-system in Equation 11, m
- t time, s
- T temperature, K
- w velocity m/s
- w coefficient in Equations 20–25
- x length coordinate, m
- y length coordinate, m
- z length coordinate, m

Greek symbols

- α correction factor of ART iteration
- θ angle, °
- κ isentropic exponent
- μ absorption coefficient, 1/m
- μ^* sound absorption coefficient, 1/m
- ρ density, kg/m^3
- ρ radial coordinate, m
- ρ coordinate rotated through the angle θ to the x, y-system in equation 10, m
- τ travel time, s
- Φ physical parameter

Subscripts

- i component, ray i
- j component, ray j
- M measurement wave
- R reference wave
- s direction of rotated coordinate system
- x x-direction
- y y-direction
- o initial state
- ρ direction of rotated coordinate system

Superscripts

k number of iteration steps

REFERENCES

1. Vogg, H., "Strahlendiagnostik-in der Medizin ja, für die Verfahrenstechnik nein? Ein kritischer Vergleich," *Chem.-Ing.-Techn.*, 55, 457 (1983).
2. Pfister, G., Maier, P., Hehn, G., Kegriss, H., and Stier, G., "Neutronentomographie zur zerstörungsfreien Werkstoffprüfung," *Atomenergie, Kernenergie*, 47, 242 (1985).
3. Heyser, R. C., and Croisette, D. H., "Transmission ultrasonography," Proc. Ultrasonics Symp., 1973.
4. Wernike, G., and Osten, W., *Holographische Interferometrie*, Physik Verlag, Weinheim, 1982.
5. Hauf, W., and Grigull, U., "Optical Methods in Heat Transfer," *Advances in Heat Transfer*, 6 (1970).
6. Mayinger, F., and Panknin, W., "Holography in heat and mass transfer," *Proc.* 5th Int. Heat Transfer Conf., Tokio, 1974.
7. Panknin, W., "Einige Techniken und Anwendungen der holographischen Durchlicht Interferometrie," *Chemie Technik*, 3, 219 (1974).
8. Hunter, J. C., and Collins, M. W., "Problems Using Holographic Interferometry to Resolve the Four-Dimensional Character of Turbulence," IV. Congresso Nazionale sulla Transmissione del Calore, 1986.
9. Hildebrand, B. P., and Brasden, B. B., *An Introduction to Acoustical Holography*, Adam Hilger Ltd., London, 1972.
10. Green, P. S., *Acoustical Holography*, Vol. 5, Plenum Press, New York, London, 1974.
11. Ramm, B., Semmler, W., and Laniado, M., *Einführung in die MR-Tomographie*, Ferdinand Enke Verlag Stuttgart, 1986.
12. Rangayyan, R., Dhawan, A. T., and Gordon, R., "Algorithms for limited-view computed tomography: an annotated bibliography and a challenge," *Applied Optics*, 24, 4000 (1985).
13. Lübbe, D., *Ein Meßverfahren für instationäre, dreiaimensionale Verteilungen und seine Anwendung auf Mischvorgänge*, Diss. Universität Hannover, 1982.
14. Hesselink, L., "Flow visulisation and digital image processing," v. Karman Institut of Fluid Dynamics, Lecture Series 1986-09, Bruxelles 1986.
15. Keil, P., "Fortschritte auf dem Gebiet der Röntgen-Computer-Tomographie," *Phys. Bl.*, 39, 1 (1983).
16. Sweeney, D. W., *Interferometric measurement of three-dimensional temperature fields*, Diss. University of Michigan, 1972.
17. Smith, K. T., and Keinert, F., "Mathematical foundations of computed tomography," *Applied Optics*, 24, 3950 (1985).
18. Achilles, D., *Die Fourier-Transformation in der Signalverarbeitung*, Springer-Verlag, Berlin, Heidelberg, New York, 1978.
19. Junginger, H. G., and van Haeringen, W., "Calculation of three-dimensional refractive-index fields using phase integrals," *Opt. Comm.*, 5, 1 (1972).
20. Zonneveld, F. W., *Computer Tomographie*, Philips Medical Systems, Eindhoven.
21. Ridder, H. W., "Computer-Tomographie," *Pascal*, 2, 20 (1987).
22. Gordon, R., Bender, R., and Herman, G. T., "Algebraic reconstruction techniques (ART) for three-dimensional electron microscopy and x-ray photography," *J. of Theor. Biol.*, 29, 471 (1970).
23. Reimers, P., Heidt, H., Stade, J., and Weise, H. P., "Beispiele für die Anwendung der Computertomographie in der zerstörungsfreien Werkstoffprüfung," *Materialprüfung*, 22, 214 (1980).
24. Mayinger, F., and Lübbe, D., "Ein tomographisches Meßverfahren und seine Anwendung auf Mischvorgänge und Stoffaustausch," *Wärme- und Stoffübertragung*, 18, 49 (1984).
25. Persson, S., and Östman, E., "Use of computed tomography in nondestructive testing of polymeric materials," *Applied Optics*, 24, 4095 (1985).

26. Ostendorf, W., *Einsatz der optischen Tomographie zur Messung von Temperaturfeldern in Rührgefäßen*, Diss. Universität Hannover, 1987.
27. Willms, I., *Anwendung computertomographischer Verfahren bei Aerosoldichtemessungen*, Diss. Universität Duisburg, 1983.
28. Ushiyama, H., Nakajima, M., and Yuta, S., "Measurement of flame temperature distribution by IR emission computed tomography," *Applied Optics*, 24, 4111 (1985).
29. Barret, H. H., and Swindel, W., "Analog reconstruction methods for transaxial tomography," Proc. IEEE, 65, 1977.
30. Santoro, R. J., Semerjians, H. G., Emmerman, P. J., and Goulard, R., "Optical tomography for flow field diagnostics," *Int. J. Heat Mass Transfer*, 24, 1139 (1981).
31. Emmerman, P. J., Goulard, R., Santoro, R. J., and Semerjians, H. G., "Multiangular absorption diagnostics of a turbulent argon-methane-jet," *J. Energy*, 4, 70 (1980).
32. Shepp, L. A., Logan, B. F., "The Fourier reconstruction of a head section," *IEEE Trans. Nucl. Sci., NS*-21, 21, (1974).
33. Wolfe, D. C., and Byer, R. L., "Model studies of laser absorption computed tomography for remote air pollution measurement," *Applied Optics*, 21, 1165 (1982).
34. Snyder, R., and Hesselink, L., "Optical tomography for flow visualisation of the density field around a revolving helicopter rotor blade," *Applied Optics*, 23, 3650 (1984).
35. Cha, S., and Vest, C. M., "Tomographic reconstruction of strongly refracting fields and its application to interferometric measurements of boundary layers," *Applied Optics*, 20, 2787 (1981).
36. Snyder, R., and Hesselink, L., "High speed optical tomography for flow visualisation," *Applied Optics*, 24, 4046 (1985).
37. Green, S. F., "Acoustic temperature and velocity measurement in combustion gases," Proc. 8th Int. Heat Transfer Conf., San Franzisco, 1986.
38. Ostendorf, W., Mayinger, F., and Mewes, D., "A tomographical method using holographic interferometry for the registration of three-dimensional unsteady temperature profiles in laminar and turbulent flow," Proc. 8th int. heat transfer conference, MT-10, San Franzisco, 1986.
39. Haarde, W., Ostendorf, W., and Mewes, D., Dosieren und Vermischen geringer Flüssigkeitsmengen in chemischen Reaktoren und Lagertanks, *Dechema Monographien*, 107, VCH Verlagsgesellschaft, Weinheim, 1987.
40. Johnson, S. A ., Greenleaf, J. F., Tanaka, M., and Flandra, G., "Reconstructing three-dimensional fluid velocity vector and temperature fields from acoustic transmission measurements" NBS special publications 484, US Department of Commerce, Washington, 1977.
41. Onoe, M., Tsao, J. W., Yamada, H., Nakamura, H., Kogure, J., Kawamura, H., and Yoshimatsu, M., "Computed tomography for measuring annual rings of a live tree," Proc. of the IEEE, A1, 1983.
42. Wang, S. Y., Ayral, S., Castellana, F. S., and Gryte, C. C., "Reconstruction of oil saturation distribution histories during immiscible liquid-liquid displacement by computer-assisted tomography," *AIChE J.*, 30, 642 (1984).
43. Wang, S. Y., Huang, Y. B., Pereira, V., and Gryte, C. C., "Application of computed tomography to oil recovery from porous media," *Applied Optics*, 24, 4021 (1985).
44. Vinegar, H. J., and Wellington, S., "Tomographic imaging of three-phase flow experiments," *Rev. Sci. Instr.*, 58, 96 (1987).
45. Nicholls, C. I., MacCuaig, N., and Gilboy, W. B., "The application of gamma ray computer tomography to oil recovery studies," Topical meeting on industrial applications of computed tomography and NMR imaging, Hecla Island, Canada 1984.
46. Price, L. R., "Electrical impedance computed tomography (ICT): A new imaging technique," *IEEE Trans. Nuc. Sci. NS*-26 1979.
47. Wexler, A., Fry, B., and Neumann, M. R., "Impedance computed tomography algorithm and system," *Applied Optics*, 24, 3985 (1985).
48. Wexler, A., Fry, B., and Neumann, M. R., "An impedance computed tomography algorithm and system," Topical meeting on industrial applications of computed tomography and NMR imaging, Hecla Island, Canada 1984.

49. Rothwell, W. P., and Vinegar, H. J., "Petrophysical applications of NMR imaging," *Applied Optics*, 24, 3969 (1985).
50. MacCuaig, N., Seville, J. P. W., Gilboy, W. B., and Cliff, R., "Application of gamma ray tomography to gas fluidized beds," *Applied Optics*, 24, 4083 (1985).
51. Kulacki, F. A., Schlosser, P. A., DeVuono, A. C., and Munshi, P., "A preliminary study of the application of reconstruction tomography to void fraction measurements in two-phase flow," *NUREG/CP*-0014 Vol. 2, 1980.
52. Finke, J. R., Cheever, G. C., Fackrell, L. S., Scown, V. S., Thornton, V. B., and Ward, M. B., "The development of reconstructive tomography for the measurement of density distribution in large pipe steady-state multi-phase flows," *NUREG/CP-0015*, 1980.
53. Finke, J. R., Vince, M. A., and Jeffry, C. L., "Measurements of time-average density distribution in horizontal multi-phase flow using reconstructive tomography," *ASME 82-FE*, 23, 1982.
54. Wolf, J., "Untersuchung von Blasenströmungen mittels Ultraschalltomographie," *BMFT-Report, SFB 62, Teilprojekt B12*, 1985.

CHAPTER 25

DYNAMIC BEHAVIOR OF NONISOTHERMAL CONTINUOUS STIRRED TANK REACTORS

J. L. Hudson

Department of Chemical Engineering
University of Virginia
Charlottesville, VA

and

I. G. KeVrekidis

Department of Chemical Engineering
Princeton University
Princeton, N.J.

CONTENTS

INTRODUCTION

In this chapter we discuss the dynamics of nonisothermal continuous stirred chemical reactors. Such stirred reactors, commonly referred to as CSTRs, can produce interesting behavior because of the highly nonlinear dependence of the rate of reaction on the system variables, particularly temperature. Multiple states are discussed elsewhere in this volume. We concentrate on the oscillatory behavior in CSTRs, and show how many of the interesting phenomena predicted by nonlinear dynamics have been observed in mathematical models and/or experiments is nonisothermal stirred reactors.

CSTRs are comparatively easy to set up experimentally or model theoretically, due to their spatial uniformity; only a few variables (usually conversions and temperature) are adequate to describe the state of the system. They come in many forms: liquid or gas phase for homogeneous reactions, differential packed beds or heterogeneous CSTRs for catalytic reactions, multiphase CSTRs, etc. CSTRs have been the workhorse of experimental kinetic studies as well as the cornerstone of reaction engineering modeling. The strong nonlinearity of the Arrhenius temperature dependence of the reaction rate underlies most of the interesting and nontrivial dynamic behavior observed in CSTRs. Thermal as well as kinetic instabilities have long been observed in both experimental and simulation studies of CSTRs, along with the resulting steady state multiplicities and oscillations.

Starting in the fifties (see, for example, the papers of Van Heerden [1], Bilous and Amundson [2], and Aris and Amundson [3]) a number of case studies of nonlinear dynamics in CSTRs were made. In addition, the mathematical theory of dynamical systems made enormous steps, culminating in a virtual explosion of interdisciplinary research activities during the last decade. This theoretical progress revealed the fundamental relationship between nonlinear dynamic phenomena in a variety of scientific disciplines. It has allowed the transcription of phenomenology and methodologies between disciplines, and has acted as motivation and guidance for further research. Because of their comparative simplicity, CSTRs and their models have served as examples of many of the new theories and methods, both analytically and computationally. They have also been used to test the predictive strength of these theories. The power and elegance of such theories and methods lies in the unification of scattered previous observations into a common framework. This is beautifully illustrated through Singularity Theory, dealing with steady state multiplicity phenomena. It is remarkable that CSTR examples can be found in mathematical treatises of the method, and that chemical engineers have catalyzed the development of the theory and participated in its applications.

It has been a long time since multiple steady states or simple oscillations were considered "exotic" dynamics for CSTRs; we are now—especially through the availability of large computing power—capable of probing more complicated phenomena: infinite period and multifrequency oscillations; the onset of deterministic chaos and global bifurcations; dynamics of many coupled systems. The frontiers of what is amenable to systematic analysis have been growing in an explosive fashion. One might consider prohibitive even just the amount of "jargon" associated with the new phenomena. Nevertheless, the study of the complex dynamic behavior of nonisothermal CSTRs has aided the understanding and designing of non-steady state processes. The variety of theoretical, analytical, computational, graphical and data-processing tools developed in the context of dynamical systems will make this task immensely easier. This chapter is a conscious effort to promote this perspective.

We start with a discussion of a single exothermic reaction in a CSTR with external cooling. This system is governed by two ordinary differential equations, one for concentration or conversion, the other for temperature. This system has been the starting point for studies of the dynamics of chemical reactors. Even in this simplest situation both the steady state and oscillatory behavior of the reactor can be quite complicated. This provides a convenient setting for illustrating the basic interactions of steady states with oscillations: the Hopf bifurcation and the infinite period bifurcation. We will describe the methods available for their systematic study and their implications for the observable system behavior.

The next section is on multiple chemical reactions with emphasis on the sequential reactions $A \rightarrow B \rightarrow C$ in a nonisothermal reactor. Such reactors are governed by three or more ordinary differential equations and thus are capable of exhibiting more complex behavior such as complex periodic oscillations and chaos i.e., nonperiodic time dependence. We describe certain universal characteristics of routes to chaos (period doubling, the Feigenbaum ratio) and ways of efficiently representing chaotic data (Poincaré maps). We also discuss certain quantitative characteristics of chaotic trajectories (dimension of the attractor, Lyapounov exponents).

We then discuss forced reactors in which some parameter, such as the coolant temperature, is varied periodically. We discuss phenomena associated with the nonlinear interplay of the external forcing frequency with the system natural frequency. Such phenomena involve quasiperiodicity and frequency locking (entrainment) along with a different set of routes to chaos. Complicated transitions termed *global*—as opposed to local—bifurcations arise. Even for the simplest model, a maze of different behaviors is possible, and a combination of analysis, computation and graphics becomes necessary to chart transitions in parameter space and set the stage for systematic experimental verification.

Finally, we discuss coupled nonisothermal reactors. Coupled reactors can exhibit all the interesting phenomena of a forced oscillator since the latter is a limiting case of coupled oscillators in which one oscillator is unaffected by the other. Other effects are also possible: two different oscillators can become phase locked, or, through coupling, the oscillations in each can be completely stopped. On the other hand, two identical coupled reactors can undergo symmetry breaking so that their concentrations and temperatures are different at a given time. There exists, of course, a wide class of ways to couple CSTRs in arrays or in pairs. We will start with a treatment of two identical or similar CSTRs at the limit of small coupling; this allows us to understand how, as the coupling strengthens, the dynamics of the individual reactors are affected by it. Eventually, for strong enough coupling the identity of each reactor as a separate entity fades and the system dynamics cannot be predicted from the dynamics of the parts. This involves to a large extent global bifurcations related to those encountered in the periodically forced CSTRs. During the last few years a wealth of phenomena has been discovered in this low coupling region: chemical engineers have played a pioneering role in these advances. We believe that the phenomenology associated with such dynamic transitions will eventually become as commonplace as the phenomenology of S-shaped steady state curves.

Much of the discussion in this chapter is mathematical. We do refer to experimental studies where they exist. Although the emphasis is on nonisothermal reactors, reference is made on occasion to isothermal reactors, particularly when referring to experiments. It is sometimes the case that experiments with isothermal reactors illustrate a point made with a nonisothermal analysis.

We have tried to discuss all of the interesting dynamics possible in nonisothermal stirred chemical reactors. Examples are chosen from the literature to illustrate each type of behavior, and some attempt was made to mention the first papers in a particular area. On the other hand we have tried to write a handbook section rather than make a complete review of the literature. Many interesting and worthwhile papers are not included. We do refer, however, to some review articles and textbooks with more complete reference sections.

THE SINGLE EXOTHERMIC REACTION

We start by discussing the single, irreversible chemical reaction which takes place in a continuous stirred reactor. In most, but not all, analyses the reaction is assumed to be first order. The reactor is cooled or heated by means of heat exchange with an external fluid.

It is, of course, somewhat limiting to consider the case of a single irreversible reaction. We relax this restriction in the next section in which multiple reactions are considered. Nevertheless, even the single reaction in a well-stirred fluid can exhibit interesting behavior. Multiple steady states are possible over a range of parameter values. More directly of relevance to this discussion, however, is the fact that periodic oscillations can also occur even though all external constraints such as residence time, inlet concentration, and coolant temperature are held constant.

Stability and oscillations in a nonisothermal continuous stirred reactor (CSTR) have been treated in now classic papers by Van Heerden [1], Bilous and Amundson [2], and Aris and Amundson [3] and have been discussed in several books and review articles [4–16]. Uppal et al. [17, 18] have extended these studies and published a comprehensive treatment of the status of work to 1976.

In the late fifties and early sixties the interest was in demonstrating that for certain parameter values the system exhibited some interesting behavior. In more recent years the emphasis has shifted to systematic ways of patching together behavior occurring for isolated parameter values, and to charting boundaries between different behaviors (bifurcations) in multiparameter space.

The equations governing the nonisothermal CSTR in dimensionless form are:

$$dx/dt = -x + Da\,(1 - x)\exp[\theta/(1 + \theta/\gamma)] \equiv f_1(x, \theta) \tag{1}$$

$$d\theta/dt = -\theta + B\,Da\,(1 - x)\exp[\theta/(1 + \theta/\gamma)] - \beta(\theta - \theta_c) \equiv f_2(x, \theta)$$

where x, θ = dimensionless conversion and temperature, respectively
t = dimensionless time
Da = Damköhler number
B = dimensionless adiabatic temperature rise
β = dimensionless heat transfer coefficient
γ = dimensionless activation energy.

In Equation(s) 1 a first order, irreversible reaction is assumed.

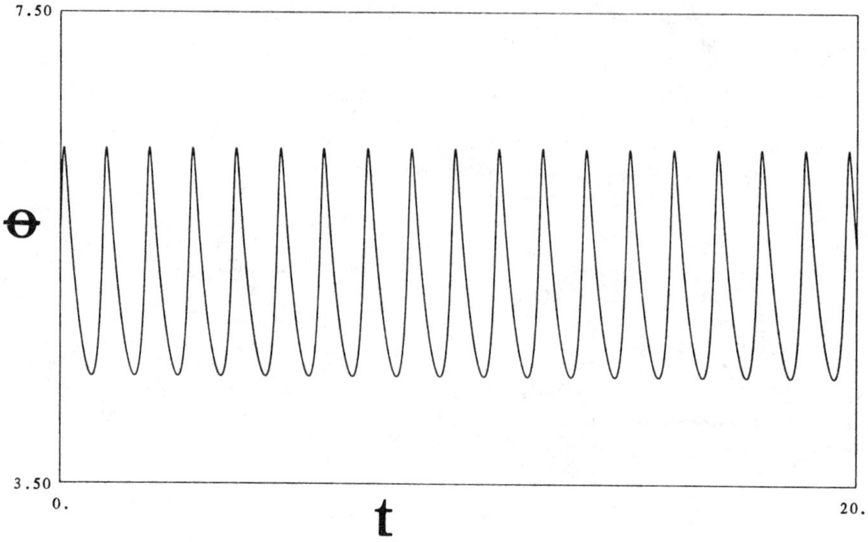

Figure 1. Dimensionless temperature vs. time for the nonisothermal CSTR; Da = 0.085, B = 22.0, $\gamma = \infty$, $\beta = 3.0$, $T_c = 0.0$.

Equation 1 will sometimes be written in the shorthand notation

$$d\mathbf{x}/dt = \mathbf{f}(\mathbf{x})$$

where **x** is the vector (x, θ) and **f** is the vector (f_1, f_2) of the nonlinear right sides.

Equation(s) 1 governs the nonisothermal CSTR for which all parameters such as inlet, flow rate, inlet concentration, and coolant temperature are held constant. After initial transients have died down, the reactor will often reach a steady state. Under some conditions, however, self-sustained oscillations can occur. An example of such sustained oscillations is given in Figure 1 for one set of parameter values. Here the dimensionless reactor temperature is shown as a function of dimensionless time. A plot of conversion versus time (not shown) looks similar. Note that these oscillations have a very simple form. Second order systems, such as Equation(s) 1, can only produce steady states or simple limit cycles. We shall see in later sections that third order systems can yield complicated periodic behavior and even chaos.

Uppal et al. considered the steady state solutions of Equation(s) 1 i.e., the solution of the equations with the left side set identically equal to zero, as well as the stability of the steady states and oscillatory behavior. Although the emphasis of this article is on oscillatory behavior, we consider briefly steady state behavior and stability as way of background.

At steady state Equation(s) 1 can be rearranged, by elimination of θ_s, to yield

$$Da = \{x_s/(1 - x_s)\}\{-(Bx_s + \beta\theta_c)/(1 + \beta + [Bx_s + \beta\theta_c]/\gamma)\} \quad (2)$$

where the subscript s is added to denote steady state. Equation 2 can then be solved for the steady state conversion x_s as a function of the parameters. Consider the behavior as a function of the Damköhler number, with all the other parameters held constant. Although Equation 2 could be solved for x_s as a function of Da, in practice it is easier to choose values for x_s between 0 and 1 and then evaluate the corresponding value for Da. There are two possible results as shown in Figures 2 and 3. For the moment ignore the dots in the figures and consider only the solid and

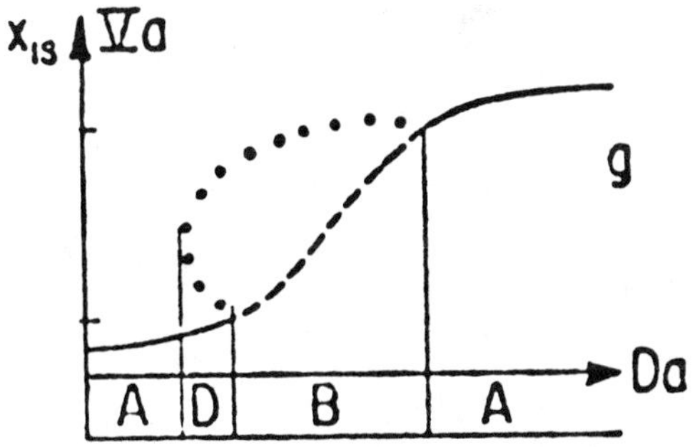

Figure 2. Conversion vs. Da. (Reprinted with permission from Ref. 17.)

broken lines. In Figure 2 there is everywhere a single steady state, i.e., only one value of x_s for each value of Da; in Figure 3, however, obtained for other values of the remaining parameters γ, B, β, and θ_c there is a region in which three steady states can occur. Such diagrams (behavior vs. parameter) are called bifurcation diagrams.

These steady states can be stable or unstable, i.e., if the reactor is disturbed very slightly away from a steady state, the concentration and temperature will either return to the steady state or will continue to move away from it. In the former case the reactor is said to be locally stable since small disturbances are damped out. If disturbances grow, the steady state is said to be unstable.

The local stability of a state can usually be determined by linearization about it. Let

$$x = x_s + \eta_1 \qquad \theta = \theta_s + \eta_2 \tag{3}$$

where η_1 and η_2 are distances from the steady state values of conversion and dimensionless temperature respectively. The right sides of Equation(s) 1 are expanded in Taylor series and truncated, yielding two linear differential equations that can be written in vector form as:

$$d\boldsymbol{\eta}/dt = \mathbf{A}\boldsymbol{\eta} \tag{4}$$

where the vector $\boldsymbol{\eta}$ has components η_1 and η_2. These linear equations can be solved exactly and have solutions whose time dependence is of the form

$$\eta_{1 \text{ or } 2} \propto \exp(\lambda t) \tag{5}$$

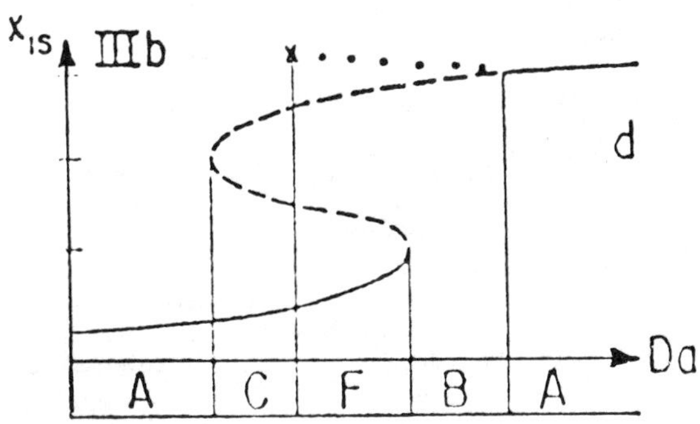

Figure 3. Conversion vs. Da. (Reprinted with permission from Ref. 17.)

The values of λ (there are two in this second order problem) determine the stability. If the real parts of the λ are negative, then the disturbances go to zero and the reactor returns to the stable steady state (and conversely).

The necessary and sufficient conditions for stability are

$$\det \mathbf{A} > 0$$

$$\text{and} \quad \text{tr}\,\mathbf{A} < 0 \tag{6}$$

where det **A** and tr **A** are the determinant and trace of the matrix of coefficient of the linearized equations and are given by

$$\text{tr}(\mathbf{A}) = \{-Bx_s^2 + (1 + \beta + B)x_s - (2 + \beta)\}/(1 - x_s)$$

$$\det(\mathbf{A}) = (Bx_s^2 - Bx_s + 1 + \beta)/(1 - x_s) \tag{7}$$

We have taken $\gamma \to \infty$ in Equation 7 to simplify the form of the expressions.

The behavior of the linearized equations depends on the values of the eigenvalues λ. If both λ's are real and negative, the steady state is termed a stable node. If both λ are real and greater than zero, disturbances grow (as can be seen from equation 5) and the state is termed an unstable node. If one of the eigenvalues is positive and the other negative, trajectories in state space that approach the steady state from one direction will move away from it in another (in directions given by the eigenvectors of A) so that the net effect is that the state is unstable; this is known as a saddle point.

If the eigenvalues are complex then the disturbance creates either a damped oscillatory motion (Re $\lambda < 0$) or a growing oscillatory motion (Re $\lambda > 0$); such states are known as stable and unstable foci respectively.

The linearized equations fail to describe the stability of the steady state for the nonlinear system when some eigenvalue of the matrix A lies on the imaginary axis (i.e., one or both eigenvalues are zero, or both are purely imaginary and conjugate). In this case, second order terms in the Taylor expansion of the equations of change become necessary in order to determine what occurs for the nonlinear system. If the second order terms happened to be zero too, the third order terms would become necessary, and so on. These first and higher order derivatives are evaluated at the steady state; they constitute *local* information.

In an analytical or computational study, in order to predict the sign of the eigenvalues of A as a function of the parameters, one must first evaluate the steady state around which the linearization is performed. This requires solution of the steady state equations, and expression of the (possibly multiple) steady states as a function of the parameters. While for simple systems such solutions may be obtained in closed form, in general the nonlinear coupled algebraic steady state equations must be solved numerically, through an iterative procedure. One technique that can be employed for this purpose is the Newton-Raphson scheme:

$$[\partial \mathbf{f}(\mathbf{x}_n)/\partial \mathbf{x}] \cdot (\mathbf{x}_{n+1} - \mathbf{x}_n) = -\mathbf{f}(\mathbf{x}_n)$$

where $\mathbf{x}_1$ is a guess of the steady state solution $\mathbf{f}(\mathbf{x}_s) = 0$. If $\mathbf{A} = [\partial \mathbf{f}(\mathbf{x}_s)/\partial \mathbf{x}]$ is nonsingular, for a good initial guess $\mathbf{x}_n \to \mathbf{x}_s$ as $n \to \infty$.

It is important to discuss the contrast between this iterative way of computing the steady states of CSTRs as opposed to solving the initial value problem (which is in a sense equivalent to performing an experiment). Only *stable* states (attractors, since they attract trajectories that pass in their neighborhood) are visible to the experiment or to the initial value problem. Moreover, the *rate* of approach of a transient to the stable steady state will be governed—close enough to the steady state—by the eigenvalue with the absolutely smallest negative real part. Thus, the approach can be extremely slow when the steady state is not strongly attracting. With the Newton-Raphson procedure however, both stable and unstable steady states may be found, given a good initial guess. In addition, the Jacobian of the Newton-Raphson upon convergence contains *all* the eigenvalues (and corresponding eigenvectors) that govern the linearized stability. It is finally important to notice that when an eigenvalue is in the process of crossing from the left to the right plane through zero (loss of stability for the steady state), the determinant of A will instantaneously become zero, and A will not be invertible, destroying the convergence of the Newton iteration. This can be used to detect certain bifurcations numerically.

From the previous discussion it becomes apparent that algorithms for the systematic tracking of branches of solutions of simultaneous coupled nonlinear algebraic equations in multiparameter space play an important role in the dynamical study of CSTRs. The problem of providing a good initial guess for these algorithms is solved through the use of continuation or sometimes homotopy methods. A number of bifurcation algorithms for small systems of ODEs have become available during the last decade; such algorithms include AUTO, BIFPACK, PITCON, DERPAR, BIFOR2, PEFLOQ etc. [19–22]. Some of these algorithms are "smart" enough to recognize and then go around turning points, thus connecting the lower and upper parts of S-shaped branches. They can also recognize Hopf bifurcation points and oscillatory solution branches which are born there.

In Figure 2 two such transitions occur as the complex conjugate eigenvalues of A cross the imaginary axis and pass to the right hand plane. When this happens, the steady state becomes locally unstable, which means that trajectories starting in its vicinity spiral away from it. For a linear system the trajectories would grow without bound towards infinity; however, the nonlinearity of the CSTR "saturates" this outward growth and keeps the trajectories bounded for all positive time. (See the phase plot in Figure 4b). The transition from type A to type B is a *supercritical Hopf bifurcation*. It is possible to show analytically that just to the left of the critical value of Da_{cr} the trajectories will become attracted to a *limit cycle*, a simple periodic oscillation. It is also possible to approximate this limit cycle and its period analytically as a series expansion in terms of the distance $Da\text{-}Da_{cr}$. The stability of the limit cycle, the direction of the bifurcation (i.e. whether the limit cycle exists for $Da\text{-}Da_{cr} < 0$ or >0) as well as the coefficients of the above series are again derived from *local* information (derivatives, eigenvalues and eigenvectors) evaluated *at* the Hopf bifurcation point [23, 24]. The sign or the magnitude of the relevant quantities depend on the specific model and parameter values, but the qualitative dynamic behavior in the neighborhood of such a simple supercritical Hopf bifurcation is almost independent of the particular system. Most of the general purpose algorithms we referred to previously are capable of determining that a Hopf bifurcation has occurred, and of switching onto the limit cycle branch; the initial guess for the computation of the limit cycles is obtained through numerical implementation of the analytical procedures.

The computation and quantitative stability analysis of limit cycles constitutes the basis for the study of more complex dynamics. It is easy to see that a limit cycle is the solution of a two-point free boundary value problem in time: a trajectory starting at one point of the limit cycle comes back to itself after precisely one (unknown) period. This problem is traditionally solved through shooting or collocation [19]. It is worth describing certain aspects of the shooting procedure.

Let us consider the set of ODEs

$$d\mathbf{x}/dt = \mathbf{f}(\mathbf{x}) \tag{8}$$

If the (unknown) period of the oscillation is T, and the result of integrating [8] with initial conditions $\mathbf{x}(t = 0) = \mathbf{x}_0$ for time T is $\mathbf{F}(\mathbf{x}_0, t)$, a point on the limit cycle is a solution of the fixed point problem

$$\mathbf{x} - \mathbf{F}(\mathbf{x}, T) = \mathbf{0} \tag{9}$$

The n simultaneous nonlinear Equation(s) 9 have n + 1 unknowns and a one-parameter infinity of solutions, since every point on the limit cycle satisfied (Equation 9). By arbitrarily selecting one solution out of the one-parameter infinity—"anchoring" the limit cycle [19]—the problem becomes well posed, and can be solved through an iterative procedure (say, a Newton-Raphson) for **x** and T. Evaluation of the Jacobian matrix of the nonlinear Equation(s) 9 requires evaluation of the matrix

$$\mathbf{A}(t = T) \equiv \partial\mathbf{F}/\partial\mathbf{x} \tag{10}$$

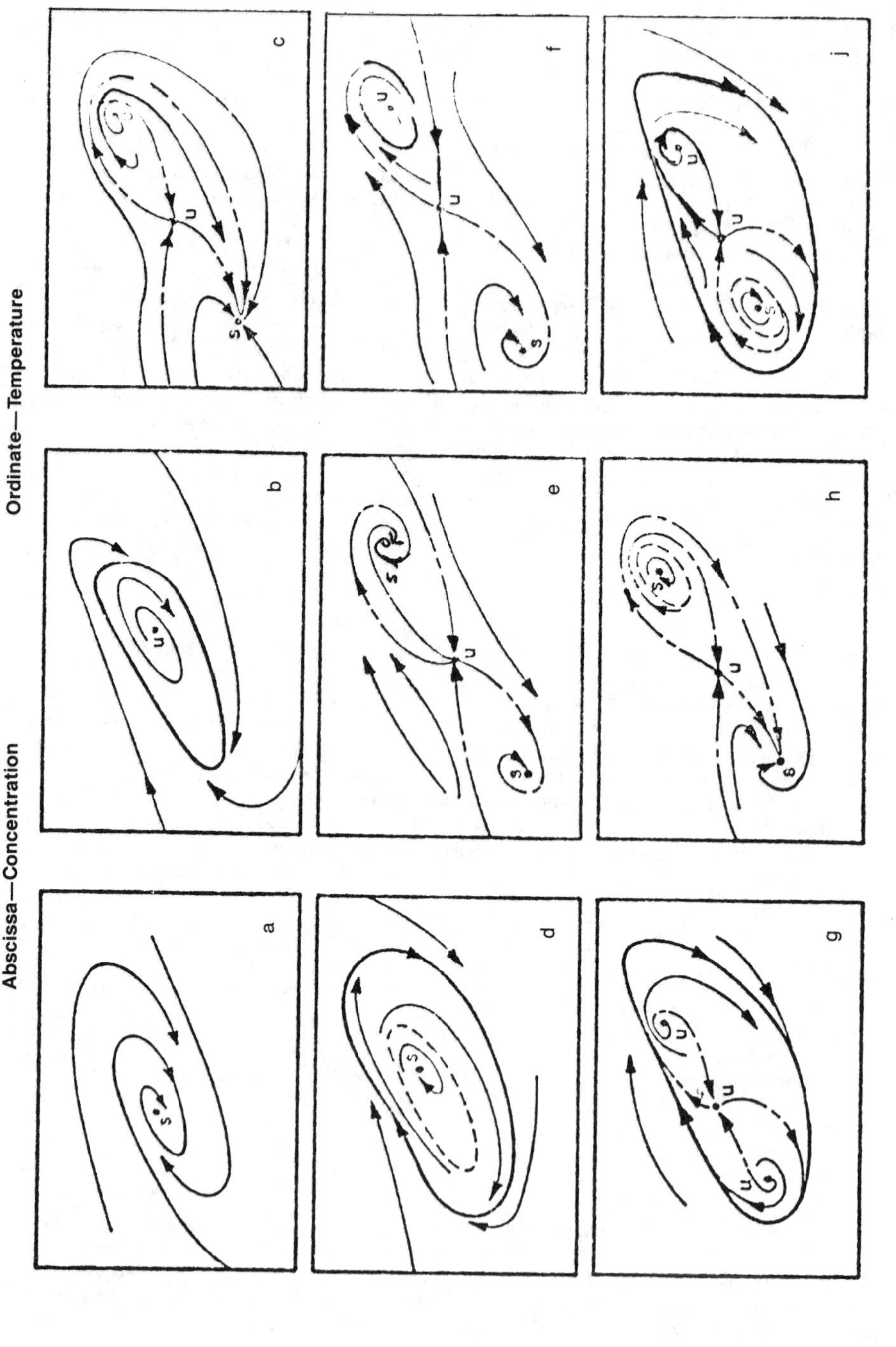

Figure 4. Classes of state plots. (Reprinted with permission from Ref. 17.)

where $\mathbf{A}(t = T)$ is the solution at time T to the matrix initial value problem

$$d\mathbf{A}/dt = [\partial \mathbf{f}(\mathbf{x})/\partial \mathbf{x}] \cdot \mathbf{A}, \qquad \mathbf{A}(t = 0) = \mathbf{I} \tag{11}$$

that is, the result of integrating the variational equations. We emphasize the following points:

1. The Newton-Raphson on the fixed point problem *converges* (for a good initial guess) on the limit cycle *independent* of whether integration of the dynamical equations would converge on it. This means that we can accurately locate and analyze unstable limit cycles, which cannot be easily observed experimentally.
2. The Jacobian of the Newton-Raphson upon convergence contains quantitative stability information for the located solution. The eigenvalues of $\mathbf{A}(t = T)$ (the Floquet or characteristic multipliers) govern the evolution of small perturbations around the limit cycle. For the CSTR $\mathbf{A}$ is a 2×2 matrix and has two multipliers. Their physical meaning is loosely the following: if a transient, starting very close to the limit cycle is monitored and its distance from the limit cycle is recorded after one revolution, this distance should shrink if the trajectory is to become attracted to the limit cycle; the characteristic or Floquet multipliers quantify by how much components of this distance have shrunk. Since two trajectories starting close to one another *on* the limit cycle keep their relative distance after one revolution, *one* of these Floquet multipliers should be exactly 1 (thus providing a numerical check of the accuracy of the computation). For the limit cycle to be stable *all* other multipliers should have absolute value less than unity (so that $|\lambda|^n \to 0$ as $n \to \infty$, i.e. asymptotically after many revolutions).
3. Computation of this Jacobian elements requires variational integrations [11] concurrently with the system integration [8]. These can be performed very efficiently through a shortcut that has recently been published as a modification of DASSL [25].

Characteristics (1) and (2) are shared with the computation through Newton-Raphson of the steady state solutions. Given a good model, the computer allows us not only to reproduce the experimental results for a time-dependent experiment (simple simulation), it also allows us—through computational bifurcation work—to find many important characteristics in the phase place (unstable solutions etc.) that affect the system dynamics but are very difficult to observe experimentally. This knowledge facilitates enormously the systematic search of the parameter space for new transitions.

Uppal et. al. have classified a number of types of phase planes some of which are shown in Figure 4, with the letters corresponding to the ranges of parameter values of Figures 2 and 3. At the bifurcation from type A to type B (a supercritical Hopf bifurcation) there is a transition from a stable to an unstable focus. Surrounding the unstable focus is a limit cycle as can be seen in Figure 4B. The transition from region D to B in Figure 2 is termed a subcritical Hopf bifurcation in which the oscillatory branch starts back in the direction of the stable steady state. Note that in region D there is a stable steady state surrounded by an unstable limit cycle which itself is surrounded by a stable limit cycle.

The unstable limit cycle is a *separatrix*. It separates—in phase space—those initial conditions that will be attracted eventually to the stable steady state from those that will eventually end on the stable limit cycle. As the Damköhler number is further decreased, the unstable limit cycle collides with the stable one and they both disappear (transition from A to D). This is a *turning point* on a branch of limit cycles. This is a typical example of an unstable solution affecting the visible system dynamics, both as a separatrix and by colliding with a stable solution and annihilating it. Once more, only local information evaluated *at* the steady state is enough to determine whether a transition of the type B-A or B-D will be observed.

Figure 3 shows even more complicated behavior. There are now three steady states, the middle one of which is unstable (a saddle point). The upper steady state is also unstable over a region. The transition from A to B is again a supercritical Hopf bifurcation. The transition from F to C is particularly interesting. In region F, trajectories will go either to the lower steady state or to the upper limit cycle depending on whether they are below or above the stable manifold of the saddle, i.e., the almost horizontal lines with arrows pointing in toward the saddle point. The set of initial conditions that gives rise to trajectories asymptotically approaching one or the other stable state constitute the *basin of attraction* of this stable state (*attractor*). The boundary that separates the two basins is a *separatix*. It is very interesting to observe that this separatrix is associated with the *saddle* steady state. In particular, this separatix consists of the *stable manifold* of the saddle, i.e. the set of initial conditions that get attracted to the saddle. This curve can be shown to be *tangent* to the eigenvector of A corresponding to the stable ($\lambda < 0$) eigenvalue of the saddle [26]. The *unstable manifold* of the saddle is the set of initial conditions that would be attracted by the saddle *backwards* in time. It is tangent to the eigenvector of the *unstable* ($\lambda > 0$) eigenvalue of the saddle, and connects the saddle with the various attractors.

As one moves to the left in region F, i.e., lowers the Damköhler number, the limit cycle grows until it merges with the stable and unstable manifolds of the saddle point. The period of the oscillation is infinite at this value of Da; the trajectory leaves and returns to the saddle point and the time required to reach the saddle is infinite since the distance from it decays exponentially. Such a cycle is known as a homoclinic orbit [27, 28]. This is the first-and simplest-example of a *global* bifurcation: an attractor (the limit cycle) interacts with the boundary of its basin of attraction (a branch of the stable manifold of the saddle) and disappears. While the saddle type steady state participates in the bifurcation, it remains a saddle (i.e. it does not change its stability characteristics). Local information (i.e., linearization and higher derivatives evaluated at the saddle) cannot detect the bifurcation. Since a finite (as opposed to infinitesimal) part of the phase plane is involved, this is termed a global bifurcation. We will observe such bifurcations again with different forms in later sections.

Integrating phase-plane and one-parameter bifurcation diagrams in a multi parameter picture was performed by Uppal et. al. in diagrams of the type of Figure 5 at a suggestion of R. Aris. The curves in the two-parameter diagram in the center represent transition boundaries between qualitatively different one-parameter diagrams.

The emphasis in the study (analytical, computational, experimental) of the dynamics of the CSTR has therefore shifted from the demonstration of interesting phase planes and bifurcation diagrams to the *systematic* charting of a multiparameter space. What we try to obtain is a *global*, integrated picture of all possible diagrams and all possible transitions between them in a given model [29–41]. This point will underpin most future research, and for this reason it is worth belaboring.

Searching a multiparameter space for transitions is a horrendous task if performed naively; even the representation of the results becomes prohibitive as the number of parameter grows. The alternative is to attempt to locate a set of parameter values—and the corresponding equilibrium state—such that every possible qualitative phase plane of the system can be found for parameter values arbitrarily close to this singularity. If such a state exists, it is possible to predict by studying local information around this most degenerate set of parameter values, all possible qualitative behavior for the system. This is usually studied through a *normal form*, the simplest dynamical system (a truncated Taylor series) that exhibits the same qualitative behavior with the system we study [26]. Since a large number of possible singularities, the normal forms for them and the possible behavior in their neighborhood have been—and continue being—tabulated and classified, the problem becomes one of recognition: how, given a model dynamical system, is it possible to find the most degenerate point(s) in its parameter space and the corresponding normal form? After the recognition is successfully concluded, analytical procedures are available to quantify the analogy between the dynamics of the normal form and those of the system in question.

It is possible to pose the recognition problem as a set of nonlinear simultaneous algebraic equations to be solved for the parameter values at which a given singularity occurs; unfortunately, precisely because of the nature of the equations, it is almost never a priori known whether they might possess a solution, especially for high-codimension bifurcations.

An "educated" guess may be obtained through two distinct rational procedures; the first is based on a hierarchical search: a single transition—say a turning point—is located in a one-parameter diagram. The turning point is then continued in two-parameter space to a hysteresis point; and the hysteresis point is then continued in a further parameter to say a pitchfork bifurcation [23]. On the other hand the turning point may be continued to a double zero eigenvalue, where one may switch to either a branch of Hopf bifurcation points or to a branch of infinite period bifurcations [26]. It is evident that such multiparameter continuation cannot be realistically performed in an

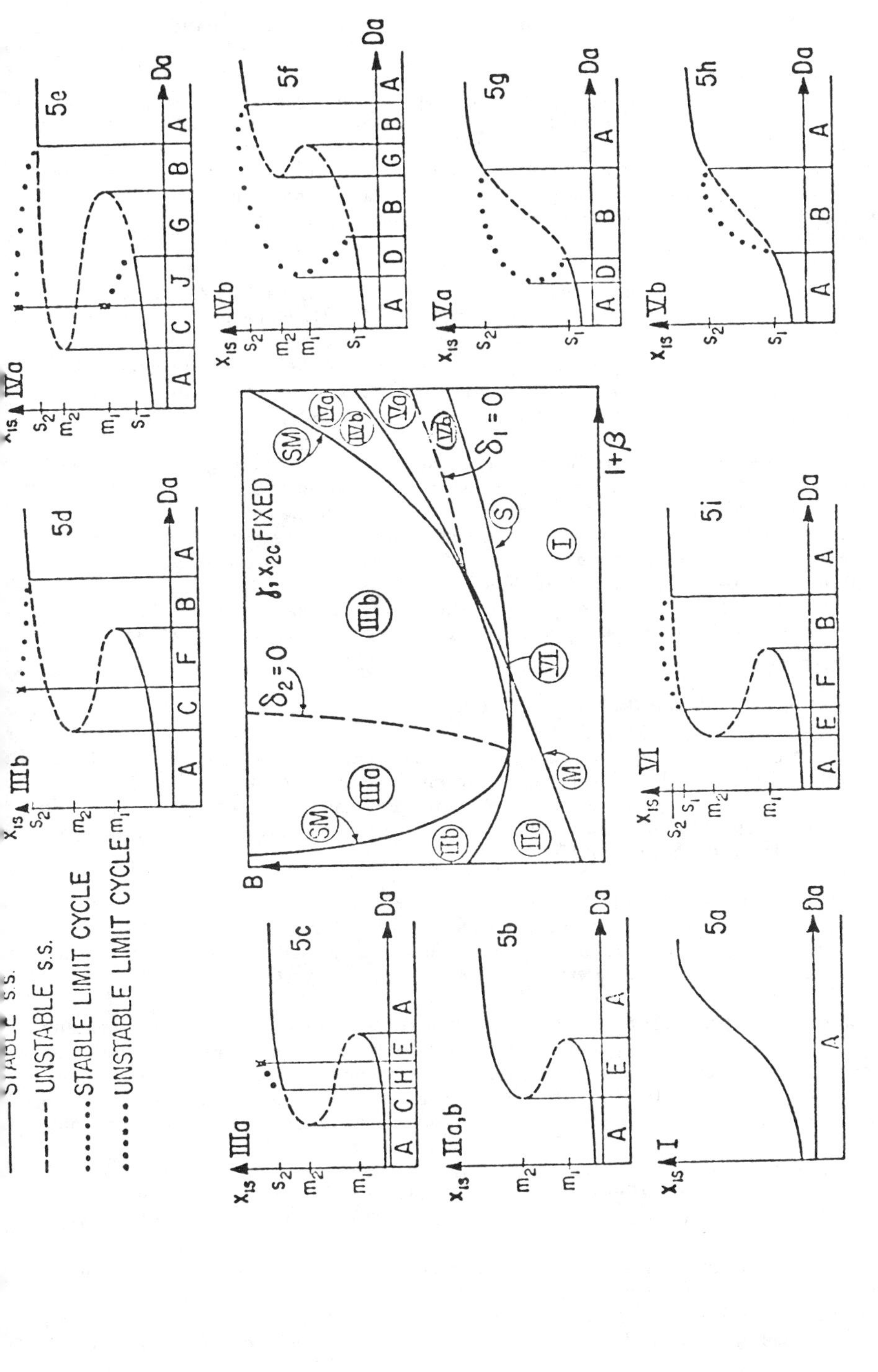

Figure 5. Representative conversion vs Da bifurcation diagram in B, $1 + \beta$ parameter space.

experiment. Systematic experiments normally produce sequences of one-parameter diagrams. One needs to discard scenarios that are inconsistent with the available data and design experiments to discriminate between the remaining possibilities.

Two important elements become apparent from this simplified exposition. The first is that both modeling and experimental researchers should become acquainted with the "tabulated" normal forms and the qualitative behaviors predicted by them. The second is that the search for global behavior can be automated in a rational way: codes like AUTO are intelligent enough to perform a variety of recognition and switching tasks. We expect that very powerful general purpose codes will become available in the near future for the study of global behavior. They will combine symbolic, computational, and graphical capabilities and possibly some degree of intelligence for automating the search.

There have been a few experimental studies on nonisothermal reactions in CSTRs showing the existence of multiple states and sustained oscillations [42–46]. The liquid phase studies employed highly exothermic reactions such as the catalyzed reaction of an alcohol with hydrogen peroxide [42], the reaction of sodium thiosulfate and hydrogen peroxide [44–46], or the hydrolysis of acetyl chloride [43]. These studies show that there is reasonable agreement between experiment and the mathematical studies both as to the appearance of the oscillations and their location in parameter space.

Self-sustained oscillations can also occur in stirred gas phase reactions [47–49]. The oxidation of organic compounds with oxygen in the temperature range of about 500 to 800 K is known as a cool flame. Such reactions are complicated by the fact that in addition to temperature oscillations of around 100 K there is a concommitant switching of chemical mechanism from a predominantly branching to a predominantly nonbranching mode [48]. Such cool flames can be distinguished from normal, hot flames by the former's lower heat of reaction.

Sheintuch and Luss [50] have recently presented a scheme for identification of the bifurcation types that may occur in experimental systems. They demonstrated their method by analyzing cool flame data.

MULTIPLE NONISOTHERMAL REACTIONS

We now turn to a more complicated situation, viz., multiple reactions occurring in a CSTR. The individual reactions can be exothermic or endothermic. The reactor is cooled or heated by means of heat exchange with a heat transfer fluid. As in the preceding section, the inlet concentrations and flow rate as well as the coolant temperature are held constant, so that oscillations, if they occur, are due to the interaction of reaction, flow, and heat exchange and not to any external forcing.

Such nonisothermal reactors are, of course, also governed by the equations of conservation of mass and energy with the appropriate reaction kinetics and heat transfer expressions. There is now one material balance for each independent chemical reaction as well as a single energy balance for the entire reactor so that a system of N independent chemical reactions in a CSTR is governed by $N + 1$ first-order ordinary differential equations.

Most studies of multiple reactions in nonisothermal CSTRs have dealt with two consecutive first-order reactions, either both exothermic or one exothermic and the other endothermic. These are governed by three ordinary differential equations. The emphasis of this section will be on such consecutive nonisothermal reactions. We do draw some analogies, however, to some studies on the dynamics of multiple isothermal reactions which are modelled by three (or more) ordinary differential equations.

Systems of three ordinary differential equations can, of course, exhibit all the types of behavior that we saw above with two equations, i.e., both steady states and self-sustained oscillations can occur. In addition, however, both complicated periodic oscillations and non-periodic behavior, or chaos, are possible.

The steady state behavior of multiple nonisothermal reactions is, in of itself, an interesting topic. Bilous and Amundson [2] pointed out in 1955 that two consecutive exothermic reactions in a CSTR can yield five steady states (at least two of which are unstable). Such questions have been explored in more detail by others; both consecutive and parallel reactions have been considered [51–53].

Our discussion will concentrate on oscillations and chaos in reactors in which multiple reactions occur. Sabo and Dranoff [54], Cohen and Keener [55], and Halbe and Poore [56] have investigated the stability of the steady states and the oscillatory solutions that bifurate from them for the case of consecutive reactions; Hlavacek et. al. [51] and Doedel and Heineman [57] have calculated some limit cycles.

The dimensionless equations governing the consecutive first-order reactions in a CSTR are similar to those for a single reaction, Equation(s) 1. The governing equations for the reactions A → B → C are:

$$\begin{aligned} dx/dt &= -x + \mathrm{Da}\,(1 - x)\exp[\theta/(1 + \theta/\gamma)] \\ dy/dt &= -y + \mathrm{Da}\,(1 - x)\exp[\theta/(1 + \theta/\gamma)] - \mathrm{Da\,Sy}\exp[\kappa\theta/(1 + \theta/\gamma)] \\ d\theta/dt &= -\theta + \mathrm{B\,Da}\,(1 - x)\exp[\theta/(1 + \theta/\gamma)] + \mathrm{B\,Da\,Sy}\exp[\kappa\theta/(1 + \theta/\gamma)] - \beta(\theta - \theta_c) \end{aligned} \tag{12}$$

where x, the dimensionless conversion of A and θ, the dimensionless temperature, are defined as in Equation 1 and y is the dimensionless concentration of B. The dimensionless parameters Da, B, and β are defined as in the preceding section. Additional dimensionless parameters are required; α is the ratio of the heat of reaction for B → C to the heat of reaction for A → B; it is positive when both reactions are exothermic and negative when the second is endothermic. S is defined as the ratio of the rate constant for the second reaction to that of the first, and κ is the ratio of the activation energies. In some of the numerical simulations that we discuss below, it is assumed that $\kappa = 1.0$ and that $\gamma \to \infty$.

Kahlert et al. [60] have carried out simulations with Equation(s) 8 with $\alpha < 0$, i.e., they considered the case of an exothermic reaction followed by an endothermic reaction. They studied the system as a function of the parameter β, the dimensionless heat transfer coefficient holding all other parameters fixed. Some of their results are reproduced in Figure 6. (Their z is dimensionless temperature and their x is 1 − x in our nomenclature). The results are shown as stereoplots, the left picture being for the right eye and vice-versa. For $\beta = 8.7$ a simple limit cycle results. As β is increased to 8.81, a period doubling bifurcation occurs and the resulting oscillation is a two peak cycle. With further increases, in β there are additional period doublings until the behavior becomes chaotic. An example of the chaos obtained for $\beta = 8.995$ is shown in the last section of the figure.

Period doubling (the transition between Figure 6A and 6B, 6B and 6C etc.) occurs when a Floquet multiplier of an oscillation crosses the unit circle in the complex plane through −1. The oscillation continues to exist but it becomes unstable and nearby transients become attracted to a new stable limit cycle, whose period is initially twice the period of the old one, as illustrated in Figure 6.

Feigenbaum observed [61] the following ratio in a cascade of successive period doublings, each occurring at a parameter value μ_i (and giving birth to a period 2^i cycle):

$$\frac{\mu_i - \mu_{i-1}}{\mu_{i+1} - \mu_i} \xrightarrow[i \to \infty]{} \delta = 4.669196223$$

where δ is a *universal* constant. Since then period doubling has been found to be the route to chaos in a variety of nonlinear systems arising in several disciplines, and the ratio δ has been recovered computationally and experimentally from these systems.

Jorgensen and Aris [62] also investigated consecutive nonisothermal reactions. They considered two exothermic reactions so that $\alpha > 0$. Period doubling bifurcations to chaos again arise. An example of the chaos that they found is shown in Figure 7. (They use u, v, and w in place of 1 − x, y, θ). The authors also employed a very useful method of analyzing the behavior of nonlinear systems, viz., a Poincare section as seen in the upper right corner of the figure. Such a section is obtained by choosing a surface (in this case a plane) that intersects the chaotic attractor transversely, and by recording its points of intersection with trajectories lying on the attractor.

We now digress for a moment to comment briefly on the chaotic behavior that can occur in systems, such as chemical reactors, which are governed by ordinary differential equations. We make only a few major points; additional details can be found in texts on the subject, e.g., [63].

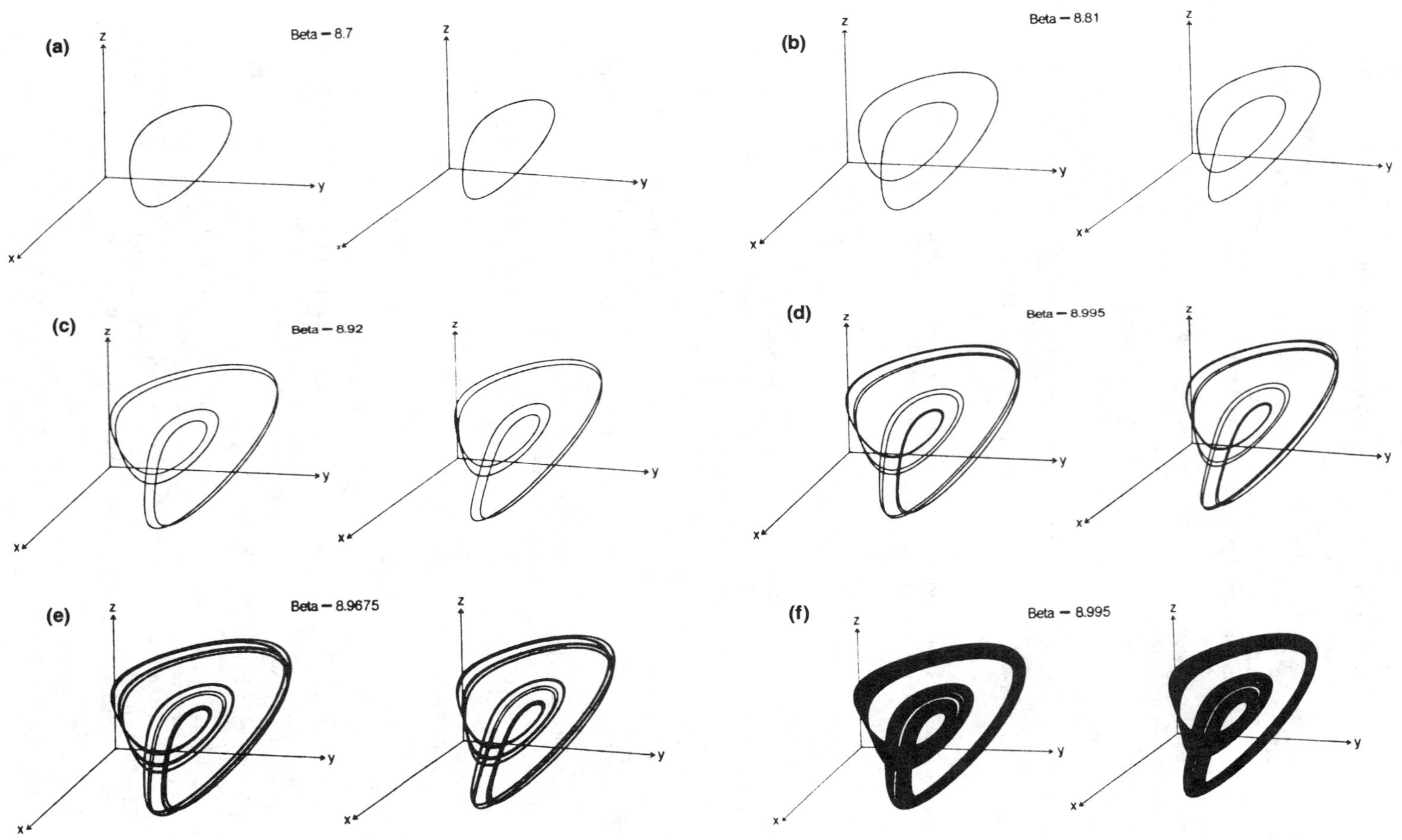
(a)
Beta — 8.7
(b)
Beta — 8.81
(c)
Beta — 8.92
(d)
Beta — 8.995
(e)
Beta — 8.9675
(f)
Beta — 8.995
x
y
z

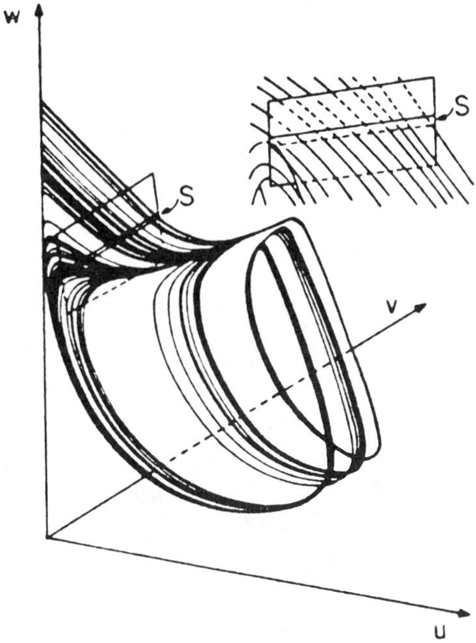

Figure 7. Chaotic behavior of two consecutive exothermic reactions. (Reprinted with permission from Ref. 62.)

Chemical reactors are governed by dissipative (as opposed to conservative) differential equations. Such systems with constant (or periodic in time) external conditions will eventually approach some attractive state (after initial transients have died down). The attracting state might be a steady state, a limit cycle, or a chaotic attractor. A chaotic attractor requires at least three dimensions since otherwise (in two dimensions) trajectories in state space would cross each other.

A measure of chaos is a quantity known as the Liapunov characteristic exponent. There are three such exponents in a third order system. These exponents are a measure of the rate at which trajectories starting on nearby points on the attractor move away from each other in each of the three directions. One of the three exponents is identically zero since there is no divergence or convergence in the direction of flow (or movement) of the trajectories. The sum of the remaining exponents is negative since the system is dissipative. One of the three is positive, however, causing exponential divergence of trajectories in the surface of the attractor, with subsequent folding. The spectrum of exponents in these systems is thus $(+, O, -)$. The dissipation in the examples being considered is fairly strong so that the chaotic attractor is almost a two dimensional surface and the Poincare cross section is almost one-dimensional. Actually their dimensions are $2 + \varepsilon$ and $1 + \varepsilon$ respectively, where ε is some small number. This is known as the fractal dimension of the attractor [64]. It is possible for ε to be somewhat larger (even for attractors for chemical reactors) so that the surface of the attractor would appear to be thicker, and the Poincare section would appear to be a somewhat fatter curve. The Poincare section can itself be cut (in a transverse direction) revealing a Cantor set structure.

There are few examples so far of chaos in nonisothermal reacting systems. Undoubtedly many more could be found. There have been examples found in isothermal reactor models. Isothermal models have not been investigated because they are richer in dynamic behavior, but rather because they are easier to analyze. We note also that experimental studies on chaos in stirred multiple reaction systems have been carried out under isothermal conditions. A discussion of such studies can be found in a review article [65]. More recently routes to chaos other than the period doubling

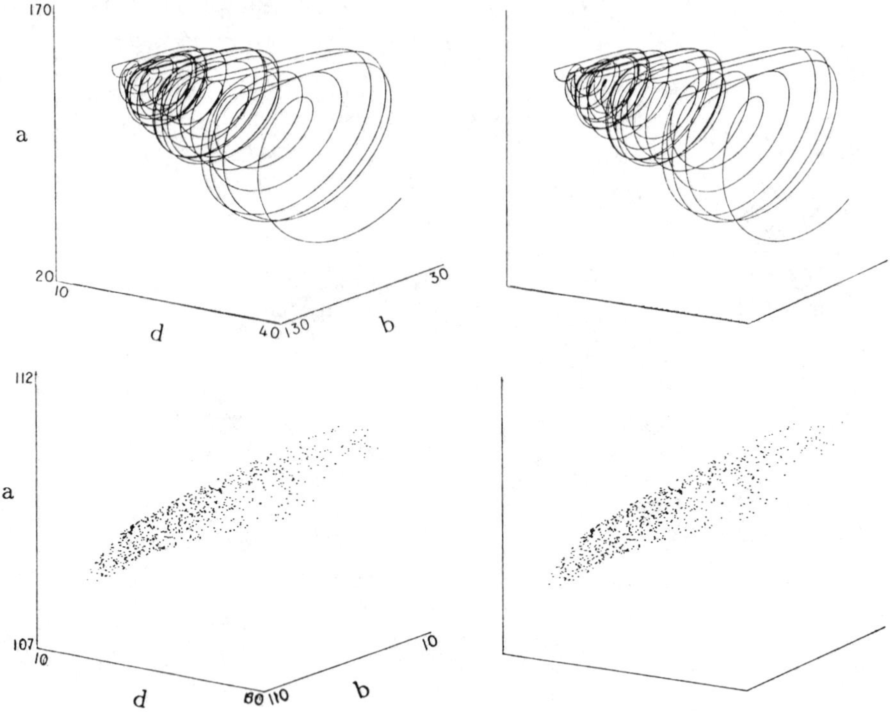

Figure 8. Higher chaotic behavior of a model chemical reaction. (a) attractor (b) Poincaré section. (Reprinted with permission from Ref. 69.)

cascade have been documented, e.g., type I Intermittency [66] and breaking of Tori [67]. Furthermore, it can be noted that multiple oscillatory states have been found in experimental studies in isothermal reactors [68].

Can multiple reaction systems in stirred reactors show even more complicated behavior? The answer is most likely yes although the evidence to date is limited to simulations of model isothermal reactions. Killory et al. [69] have shown that higher chaos can arise in a chemical reaction model. The attractor is shown in Figure 8A. There are now two directions of expansions of the trajectories in state space and thus two positive Lyapunov characteristic exponents. Because of two directions of expansion of the trajectories the Poincare section now appears to be sheet-like as can be seen in Figure 8B.

Experimental characterization of chaotic attractors and of their further transitions requires the observation of long nonrecurrent transients until certain statistical properties (attractor dimension, Lyapunov exponents) converge. Several techniques for efficiently extracting this information from long time series have been used [70, 71] along with elegant ways of representing the data [72].

One would like to be able to predict that a set of nonlinear ODEs modeling a complex reaction network will be chaotic without searching the parameter space and integrating the equations. Feinberg [73] and his co-workers have been developing a framework that can be used to determine a priori if certain types of reaction networks will not exhibit multiplicity or oscillations. Several positive results have also been obtained, but the theory is currently limited to multiple steady states and the existence of oscillations.

Systematic searches of parameter space have also been performed through singularity theory [53, 59] the Newton Polygon technique [74] or the Carleman linearization [75], but these are limited to steady state structures. There exists no a priori method for finding chaotic behavior in a system. Experience is the most valuable guide in such a quest for chaos.

PERIODICALLY FORCED CHEMICAL REACTORS

In this section we consider oscillations in a CSTR with external periodic forcing. This forcing could be produced by a variation in the flow rate, feed concentration, or coolant temperature. For example, the single exothermic reaction with periodic forcing of the coolant temperature would be governed by the following equations:

$$dx/dt = -x + Da\,(1 - x)\exp[\theta/(1 + \theta/\gamma)] \tag{13}$$

$$d\theta/dt = -\theta + B\,Da\,(1 - x)\exp[\theta/(1 + \theta/\gamma)] - \beta(\theta - \theta_c) \text{ with } \theta_c = \bar{\theta}_c + \alpha\sin(\omega t)$$

where α and ω are the dimensionless amplitude and frequency of the forcing respectively.

Motivations for studying the dynamic behavior of periodically operated CSTRs include improvement of reactor performance as well as control and stability considerations [76, 77, 78]. Since the available steady states for the operation of a reactor may be unstable or undesirable, it is interesting to examine whether the mean productivity or selectivity of a reaction carried out under non-steady state conditions will compare favorably with the available steady states. If the modulation is simply periodic in time, we expect the response (the reaction rate) to be characterized by the input frequency. This frequency provides us with a natural time scale over which to average the productivity or selectivity we want to optimize by periodic forcing: one forcing period. During the late sixties there has been an extensive research effort aimed at the optimization of some characteristic of the reactor performance by periodically varying its inputs.

An alternative approach to periodic forcing comes from consideration of frequency response methods in the control of nonlinear systems; even the simplest nonisothermal CSTR (with the irreversible exothermic A → B reaction) is notoriously nonlinear, and there exist situations in which it possesses multiple steady states, or even multiple oscillatory states, some stable and some unstable. The response of such a CSTR to a periodically varying perturbation will give us a measure of the stability of the reactor base operating state; it will provide insights as to the downstream propagation and amplification of disturbances in an array of units. Finally, even though in a nonlinear system we cannot superimpose responses due to different components in a perturbation, such studies will provide us with information on the frequencies to which the base operating state is most sensitive. Thus, the study of periodically forced chemical reactors can be considered as an important subcase of nonlinear frequency response.

The recent advances in the theory of dynamical systems have provided one more viewpoint from which to approach this subject. The fact that a number of dynamical phenomena are common to a large variety of dynamical systems, coming from apparently unrelated disciplines made it possible to identify several dynamic traits of periodically forced reactors with similar "generic" or "typical" characteristics of nonlinear oscillators. A periodically forced system provides us with an easy way to study (both experimentally and computationally) the nonlinear interaction of several frequencies [79, 80]. One of these frequencies is the input (forcing) frequency, while the others come from the unperturbed (autonomous) system itself. The fact that the amplitude and the frequency of the forcing are tunable parameters gives us more flexibility compared to the spontaneous generation of two frequencies by a system through a Hopf bifurcation of a limit cycle to a torus [23, 24]. In this latter case any operating parameter change will alter *both* frequencies in an a priori unpredictable way.

We will see that even for the simplest of nonisothermal CSTRs, a vast possibility of different dynamic behaviors are possible; these include frequency locking and quasiperiodicity; chaotic behavior, developing through period doublings or through global bifurcations; the coexistence of different periodic solutions, of periodic and quasiperiodic or even periodic and chaotic solutions. Even more spectacularly, we will demonstrate that chaotic behavior lurks in the operating space

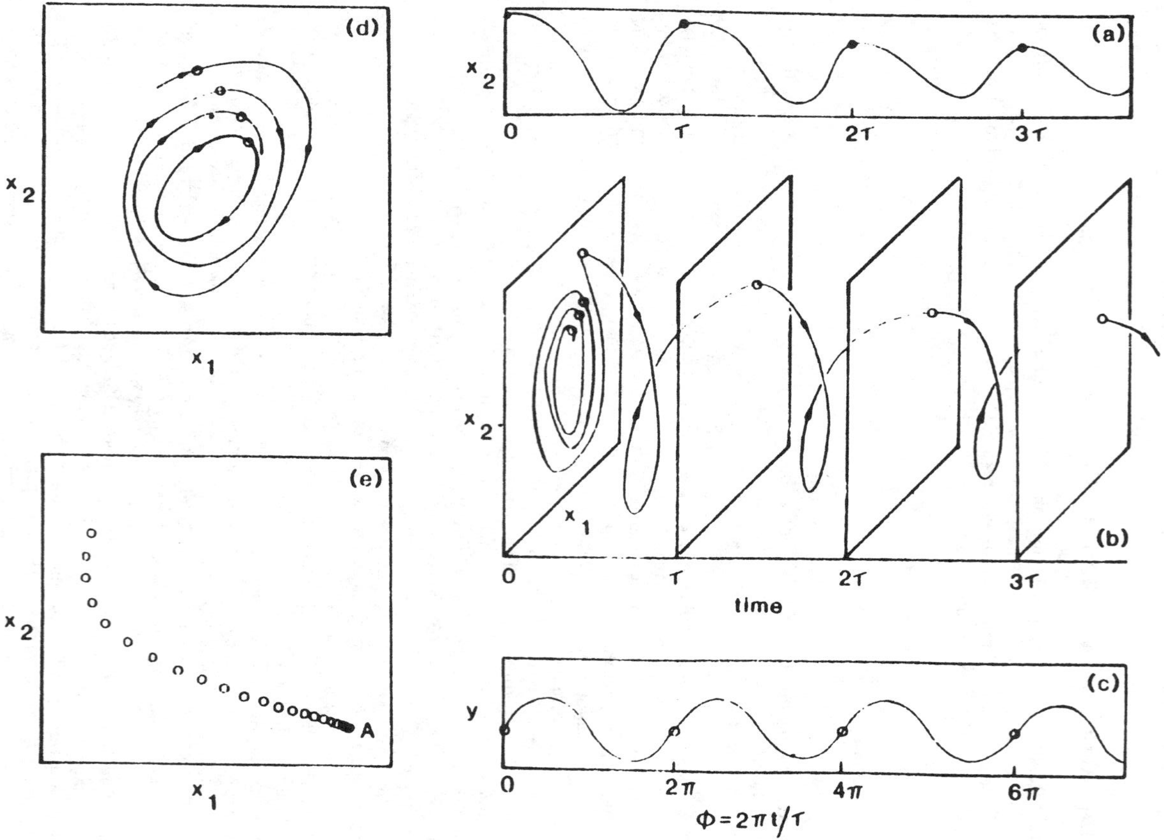

Figure 9. Schematic representation of the stroboscopic method. A transient in the variables x_1 and x_2 is observed at fixed time intervals (9a, 9b), at the same phase ϕ of the 2π-periodic forcing term (9c). The winding towards a limit cycle in the phase plane (9d) is thus reduced to th...

of almost every forced nonisothermal CSTR, and a number of techniques (experimental and theoretical) dictated by dynamical systems theory becomes necessary in order to explore and understand this apparently staggering number of new possibilities. The study of periodically forced reactors is also a first step towards understanding coupled chemical reactors, since forcing can be considered as one-way coupling.

In a periodically forced system, the simplest state is oscillatory, with the same period as the forcing; we then say that the system has been entrained by the forcing. Most of the theoretical work of the late seventies was based on a wide separation of the time scales of the forcing and the intrinsic time scales of the system, i.e. the forcing was either too fast or too slow [78]. Most of the interesting dynamics comes into play when the intrinsic and forcing time scales become comparable [81]; indeed some fairly deep nonlinear phenomena occur when the base autonomous state is an oscillation. *Any* periodic perturbation will initially (i.e., for small forcing amplitude) produce qualitatively similar responses. This similarity can be exploited by initially working at the low-forcing amplitude limit, where the behavior, even though complicated, develops in a prescribed, hierarchical way, and then study the gradual development of large forcing amplitude behavior. This is (both experimentally and computationally) a continuation technique: we start from a corner in parameter space where we know what to expect, and proceed to the real region of interest.

The fact that one frequency of a periodically forced system is given, allows us to define a "natural" Poincaré map, the stroboscopic map. This is obtained by recording the trajectory once every period of the forcing (or "strobing" it with the forcing frequency hence the expression "stroboscopic map"). An oscillation then by itself will appear as a *fixed point* of the map. The gradual spiralling approach to the oscillation will appear stroboscopically as a "hopping" towards the fixed point as can be seen in Figure 9 [82].

The stability of a trajectory is quantified by its characteristic or Floquet multipliers, which describe the rate of decay (or growth) of infinitesimally small perturbations around the limit cycle. As we discussed in earlier, there always exists a characteristic multiplier at unity. In the forced case, this multiplier corresponds to the forcing variable, so that a 2-D forced system has two free multipliers, enough to provide bifurcations to tori, period doublings and chaotic behavior.

Figure 10A is a typical "excitation diagram" for a periodically forced chemical oscillator—a forced Brusselator [83, 84]. It describes the behavior of the system as a function of the two main characteristics of the periodic forcing: its amplitude α and its frequency ω. A more appropriate second parameter is the ratio of the forcing frequency to a natural frequency of the system ω/ω_0. We are interested in the structure of the small forcing amplitude regime—exploded in figure 10b—where two types of regions are observed. The first type consists of white, cusp-like regions, with their tips meeting the $\alpha = 0$ axis at *rational* values of ω/ω_0. If the forcing variables (α and ω) are chosen in these regions then the system response is a simple oscillation whose period is an integer multiple of the period of the forcing. We then say that the forcing has *entrained* the system, and these regions are called *resonance horns* or *Arnol'd horns* [85, 86]. If their tip meets the $\alpha = 0$ axis at $\omega/\omega_0 = p/q$ where p and q are relatively prime integers, then the period of the *entrained* (subharmonic) periodic trajectory will be p times the period of the forcing. We also observe a "sea" of shaded area in which the cusp-like resonance regions are interspersed; if the operating variables are chosen in this area, the response of the forced system is *quasiperiodic*, i.e. it is characterized by two frequencies having an *irrational* ratio; one of these two frequencies is the forcing frequency, while the second is the result of the nonlinear interactions of the forcing with the system frequency. It is important to mention that a resonance exists *for every rational value* of the frequency ratio; this means that an infinity of very thin resonance regions (the larger the prime numbers p and q the thinner the region) exist, which cannot be accurately detected at the level of our computational—let alone experimental—resolution.

Figure 11 shows several views of quasiperiodic trajectories [87]; it is convenient to visualize them as winding around a doughnut-shaped surface (a torus T^2) in R^3 (the three variables for the forced CSTR being temperature, conversion and the phase ωt (mod 2π) of the forcing). The trajectory will never come back to exactly the same position again, even though it will pass repeatedly arbitrarily close to any point on the surface of the doughnut. The projection of the trajectory on a phase plane will give a space filling curve. The doughnut picture is helpful in visualizing the role of the two frequencies in the response: a main oscillatory pattern (say rotation around the parallel) representing the one frequency, is modulated by a second oscillatory pattern (rotation around the meridian)

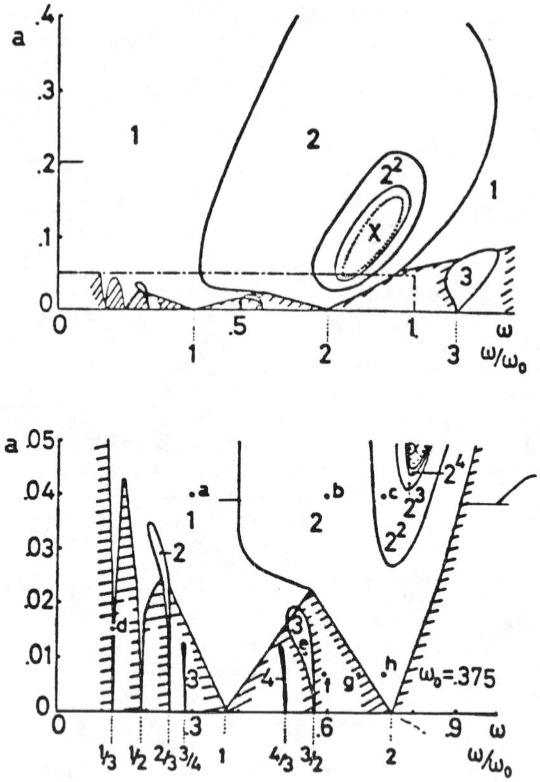

Figure 10. (a) Excitation diagram for a periodically forced Brusselator. A quasiperiodic solution exists in the shaded region and entrained periodic solutions exist in the unshaded regions. The numbers indicate the period of these frequency-locked solutions, normalized by the forcing period. (b) Enlarged figure of the lower portion of (a). The cusp-like shape of the various resonance regions close to the bottom of the figure can be clearly seen. (Reprinted with permission from Ref. 84.)

representing the second frequency. If the ratio of the two frequencies is *rational*, the trajectory will eventually repeat itself exactly (entrainment) else it will never repeat itself (quasiperiodicity). If we cut this doughnut shaped surface with a transverse plane at constant phase of the forcing (i.e., if we look at the response stroboscopically) we obtain an *invariant circle*, a closed curve. This curve is drawn by the stroboscopic phase point as it hops discontinuously on the curve. The ratio of the two frequencies (the rotation number) characterizes the entire quasiperiodic response.

Figure 12 illustrates stroboscopically the basic mechanism underlying frequency locking on a torus as we vary one parameter across a resonance region. Outside the region the system has a quasiperiodic solution winding around a doughnut-shaped torus, which appears in the stroboscopic cut as an *invariant circle*. At the onset of entrainment a pair of limit cycles (a stable node and a saddle) appear as periodic points on the invariant circle. As ω/ω_0 changes, these points move away from each other until they meet their next neighbors at the other entrainment boundary. At that point we have a turning point (saddle-node) bifurcation of periodic solutions, and the quasiperiodic

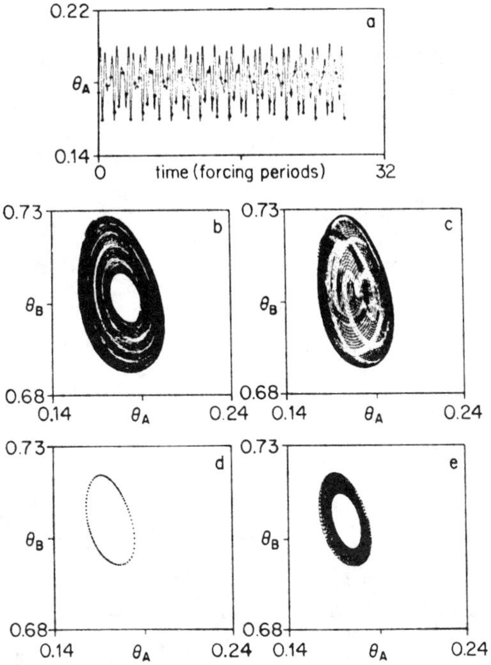

Figure 11. Views of quasiperiodic attractor. (a) Variation of one component of a quasiperiodic trajectory with time. Stroboscopic points are denoted by ◇. (b–c) Projection of the attractor on the phase plane. The hole in the middle of the doughnut may (b) or may not (c) be visible. In both cases a space-filling curve is obtained. (d) A stroboscopic section of the torus yields an invariant circle. (e) Connecting each point on the circle with its next iterate by means of a straight line yields a caustic curve tangent to all these connections. (Reprinted by permission from Ref. 87.)

attractor appears again. This phenomenon, involving the loss and rebirth of a quasiperiodic oscillation is of course a *global* phenomenon.

Algorithms for the computation of periodic solutions can be used to study some of the details of these phenomena, but they will fail in the regimes where quasiperiodic solutions exist. The necessity of methods for the accurate computation of tori, independent of whether quasiperiodic solutions wind around them or whether entrained periodic solutions are locked on them, has become apparent in the last few years. Some efforts have already been made towards that purpose [88–91]. While the concept is simple and similar with the computation of periodic trajectories, the technical details become fairly complicated for these computations. We will only state here that these algorithms are essentially following not one single system trajectory, but a one-parameter *family* of trajectories for the system equations.

We now examine some of the phenomena that occur for higher forcing amplitudes by observing what occurs for a forced Brusselator at $\alpha = 0.0055$ as we vary the forcing frequency (Figure 13, [92]). Initially the system has a smooth, globally attracting invariant circle IC (an attracting torus). At $\omega/\omega_0 = 0.906734776$ however, a pair of periodic solutions (a saddle-node) appears *outside* the invariant circle, and as ω/ω_0 changes further the saddle Σ moves away from the stable node SN (Figure 13B). This means that stable *periodic* (SN) and stable *quasiperiodic* (IC) oscillations coexist for these parameter values. The two arms $\Sigma\Gamma$ and $\Sigma\Delta$ of the stable manifold of the saddle periodic solution Σ provide the *separatrix* of the basins of attraction between the two attractors. As we further change ω/ω_0 we come to Figure 13C: the arms ΣA and $\Sigma\Gamma$ of the saddle invariant manifolds have crossed each other, the quasiperiodic attractor has disappeared and the only attractor left in the phase plane is the entrained periodic solution SN. The process by which the quasiperiodic attractor is annihilated (through its interaction with the separatrix $\Sigma\Gamma$) is complicated, and involves intervals in parameter space where infinitely many attractors and nontrivial dynamics coexist (Smale horseshoes, homoclinic tangles etc.). Some illustrations of these phenomena can be found in Ref. 92.

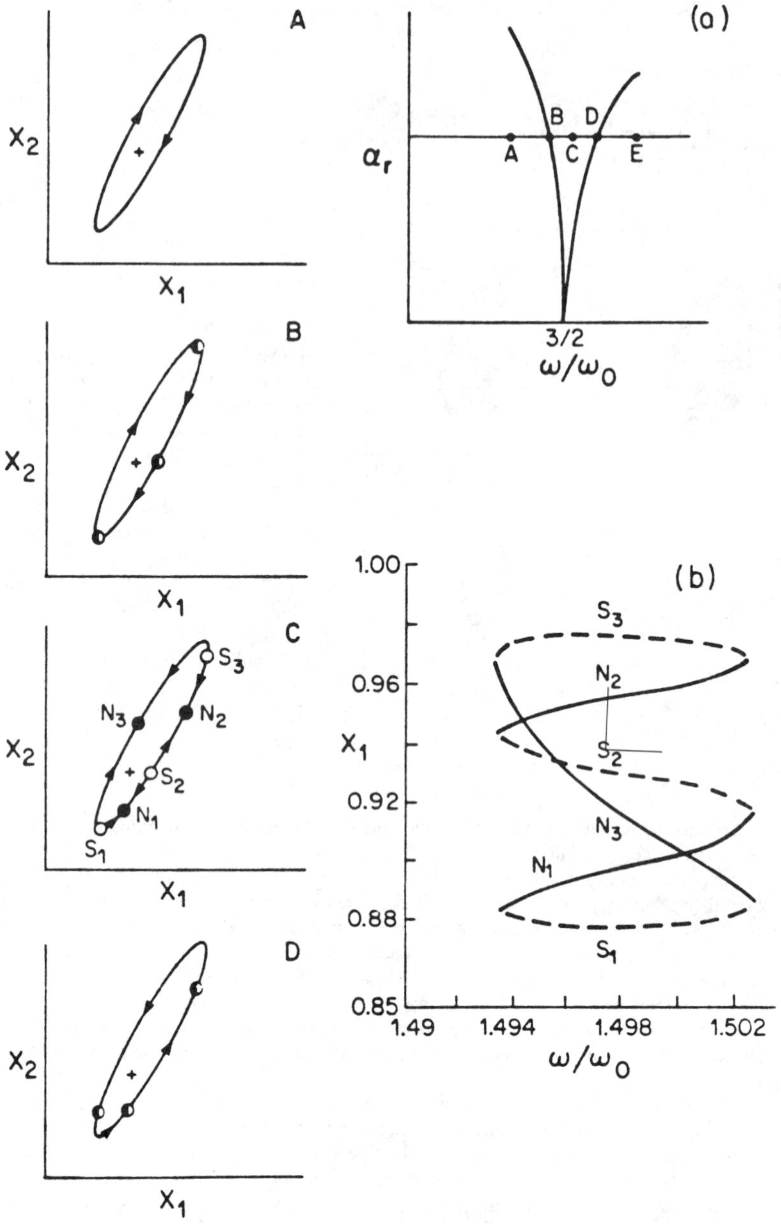

Figure 12. Frequency locking on a torus. Stroboscopic views from a 3/2 resonance region of a periodically forced CSTR. A quasiperiodic attractor (A) is lost when three pairs of periodic points appear on it (B), separate into a stable attracting period 3 and a saddle period 3 (C) and eventually collide (D) giving again birth to quasiperiodicity. The one-parameter cut is shown schematically in 12(a) and the resulting bifurcation diagram in 12(b). (Reprinted by permission from Ref. 94.)

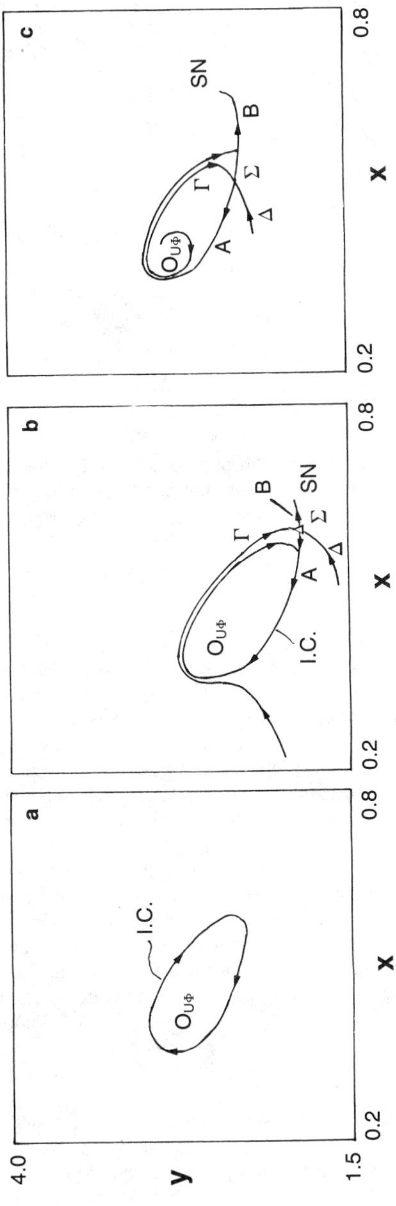

Figure 13. Variation of the forcing frequency for high forcing amplitude: Quasiperiodicity (a), coexistence of periodic and quasiperiodic solutions (b) and simple periodicity (c). The transition form (a) to (b) is a simple saddle-node bifurcation, but that from (b) to (c) is a complicated breakup of the torus that may lead to chaos. (Reprinted by permission from Ref. 92.)

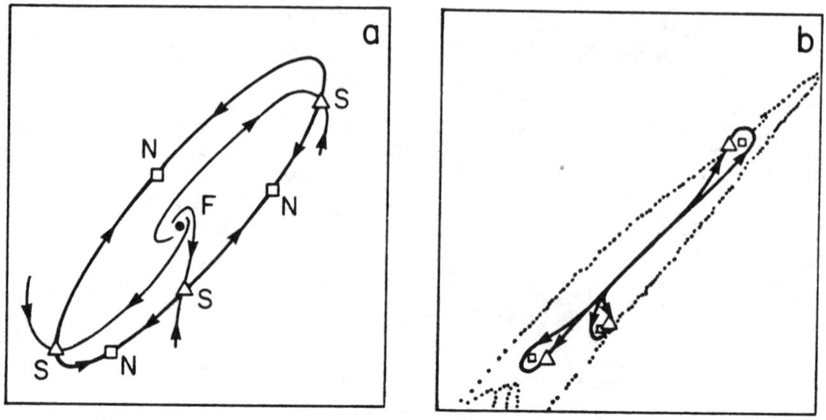

Figure 14. Smooth torus with entrained periodic solutions for a 2/3 resonance of the forced CSTR (a). At higher forcing amplitudes complicated global bifurcations break the torus leading to the coexistence of entrained periodic and chaotic attractors (b). (Reprinted by permission from Ref. 94.)

Dynamic behavior and transitions similar to the type we described above is by no means novel. It is actually quite standard in the study of maps of the plane [86] (and hence Poincaré maps of 3-D O.D.E.'s). One can show that they will occur as a torus breaking mechanism in almost every periodically forced oscillator, be it a nonlinear oscillating circuit or an oscillating CSTR whose coolant temperature we periodically vary. It may occur in a small region in a parameter space, but it definitely exists. Its operating significance is clear: it signals the coexistence of periodic and quasiperiodic responses (before the bifurcation). After the bifurcation we have only one attractor (the periodic oscillation SN). It also shows how close simple systems are to complicated temporal behavior (horseshoes, infinity of attractors etc.) [26, 93].

Figure 14 contains one more illustration of the effects of global bifurcations on the dynamics of the periodically forced CSTR as they appear on the stroboscopic phase space [94]. The two pictures have been obtained in a 3/2 resonance region; the first at small forcing amplitude (near the tip of the resonance region) shows a smooth invariant circle with a stable and a saddle period 3 solutions locked on it. The stable period 3 is the only attractor. The second picture shows a chaotic attractor (on the outside) coexisting with a stable subharmonic period 3. The basins of attraction of this "inner" period 3 are provided by the stable manifolds of the subharmonic saddle period 3 points. This snapshot has been taken higher up in the resonance region, and it developed from the first one through a sequence of global bifurcations like the ones we referred to in the previous section.

A number of systematic computational studies of periodically forced systems have been undertaken during the last few years, most of them for isothermal systems [e.g., 95, 96]. A detailed two-parameter study of the excitation diagram for the periodically forced CSTR with respect to both forcing frequency and amplitude has appeared recently [94], incorporating a one-parameter study performed earlier [97]. The results are shown in Figure 15. A maze of possible bifurcations exist, and those shown are only the *local* ones, i.e the ones related to the frequency locked oscillatory solutions. This figure is already too complex even without showing any homoclinic transition boundaries of the type we previously described. In addition to the medium forcing amplitude behavior—which involves the breaking of the low-amplitude tori and is qualitatively similar in large classes of oscillators—each individual nonlinear system exhibits its own characteristics for

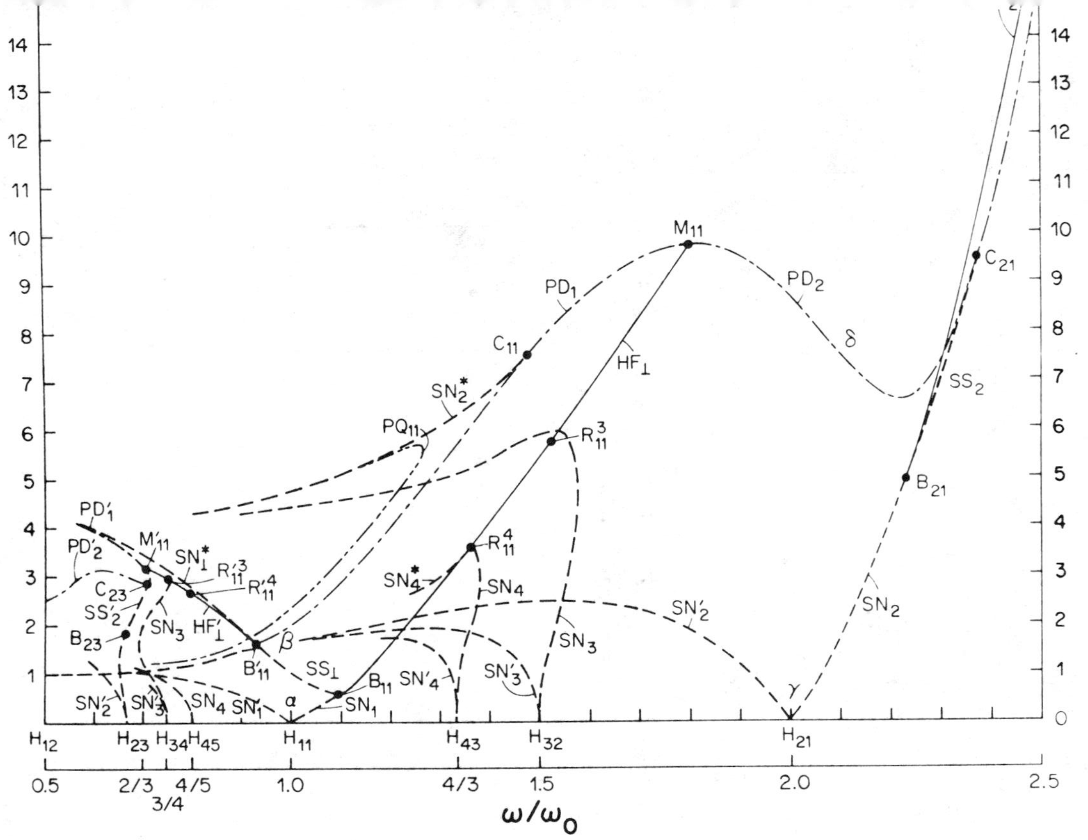

Figure 15. Bifurcations of the forced CSTR as a function of the amplitude and the frequency of the forcing. Observe the low-forcing amplitude resonance regions with their tips at H_{pq} where $\omega/\omega_0 = p/q$ (p, q relatively prime integers). Labelling of curves: SN saddle-stable node bifurcations. SS saddle-unstable node bifurcations. HF Hopf bifurcations to a torus. PD, PQ period doubling and quadrupling. A number of special codimension two points (B, M, R, C) are described in detail in the original article. (Reprinted by permission from Ref. 94.)

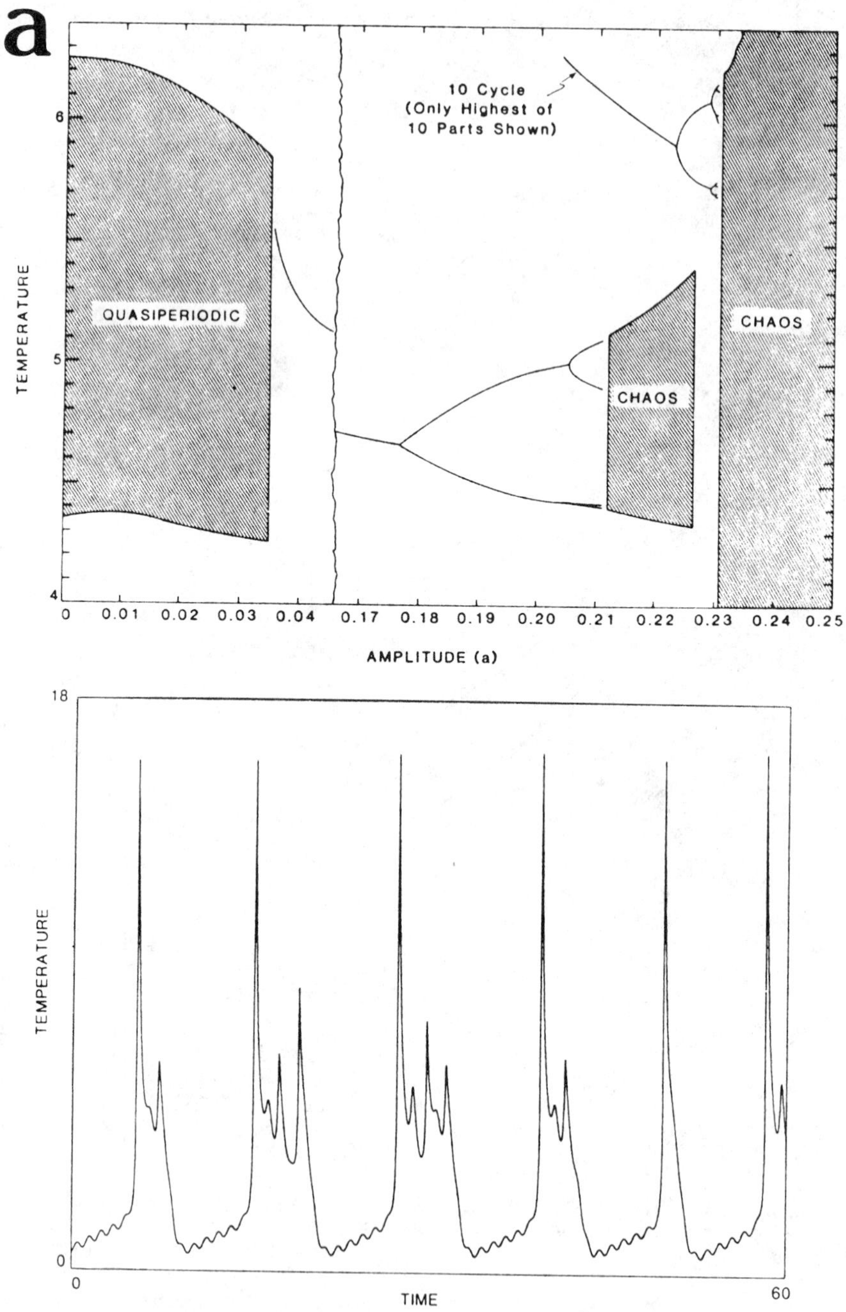

Figure 16. One-parameter bifurcation diagram of the forced CSTR with respect to the amplitude of the forcing (a). Observe the development of chaotic behavior far above the quasiperiodic regime. A representative nonperiodic temperature versus time transient is shown in (b). (Reprinted by permission from Ref. 97.)

high forcing amplitude. This can be seen in Figure 16, where far beyond the quasiperiodic regime large-amplitude chaotic time-series have been observed for the periodically forced CSTR. It appears that the study of even the simplest periodically forced reactor is far from over, in the sense that we are only now starting to acquire an understanding of the dynamical phenomena involved even in the low to medium forcing amplitude region.

These phenomena include complicated high-codimension bifurcations of periodic solutions, global bifurcations, homoclinic tangles and an entire zoo of exotic dynamics, along with the period doublings routes to chaos we saw in the previous section. The routes to chaos via global bifurcations and breakings of tori appear to underly not only chaotic dynamics in such simple lumped systems, but also the development of hydrodynamic instabilities and turbulence in a number of transport processes.

All of the experimental studies on periodically forced stirred reactors have been performed under isothermal conditions. A few of these experimental studies have been done with low-amplitude forcing. Dulos [98] has studied synchronization of a chemical oscillator by means of light pulses. Buchholz et al. [99] have imposed a sinusoidal flow rate on oscillations in a CSTR. Hudson et al. [100] have studied entrainment bands with low-amplitude forcing of a chemical oscillator. State space plots and stroboscopic maps were used to characterize some of the features of the quasi-periodic behavior outside the entrainment bands, such as the shape of the toroidal flow, frequency pulling and changes in the nonuniform slipping between phases. An example of the quasiperiodic behavior shown in cylindrical coordinates is given in Figure 17.

Experiments with large amplitude forcing of chemical oscillators have dealt largely with chaos and transitions from periodic to chaotic behavior [101, 102]. Lamba and Hudson [103] and Guevara et al. [104] have carried out experimental studies of period doubling to chaos in forced chemical and biological oscillators respectively. In the former study characteristics of the chaos as a function of a parameter were also investigated throughout the chaotic region. A bifurcation diagram showing behavior as a function of forcing period is shown in Figure 18.

Pugh et. al. [105] have investigated the effect of perturbations on the oscillatory gas-phase combustion of acetaldehyde. The feed rates of both acetaldehyde and oxygen were varied simultaneously. They observed bistability, entrainment and hysteresis as a function of the phase shift between the two perturbations.

COUPLED CSTRs

In a general sense, coupling among non-steady chemical reactors or reaction sites is potentially one of the most interesting problems of chemical reactor analysis. This category includes coupling among a large number of catalyst particles (as well as the interstices between them) in a packed bed reactor, coupling among sites on a catalyst surface, and coupling among reactor arrays and separation units in a chemical plant [106–110]. Studies of discrete reaction sites coupled by means of mass and/or heat transfer will naturally lead to the study of continuous systems in which the coupling is due to diffusion and conduction. A recent article by Pismen reviews such topics as reaction-diffusion interaction, wave propagation and pattern formation [111].

The study of coupled non-steady processes is in its early stages. We concentrate in this section on coupled non-isothermal stirred reactors. This subject has perhaps a primary importance as a paradigm for the study of other subjects which may be more complicated and possibly more relevant to industrial application.

Coupled non-steady processes behave in a very complicated manner. We note that the forced reactor is a limiting case of the coupled system since the latter reduces to the former if one reactor is unaffected by the other; the unaffected reactor might be, for example, much larger than the other. Coupled systems can thus display all the behavior seen in the forced systems such as complicated oscillations, chaos, period doubling, entrainment, quasiperiodicity, etc.

The steady state behavior of coupled cells has been considered by several investigators. Turing first studied pattern formation in coupled biological cells [112]. Theoretical studies by Tsotsis [109], Bar-Eli [113] and Kennedy and Aris [114] and experimental studies by Stuchl and Marek [115] have shown that systems of identical chemical reactors can have nonuniform steady states,

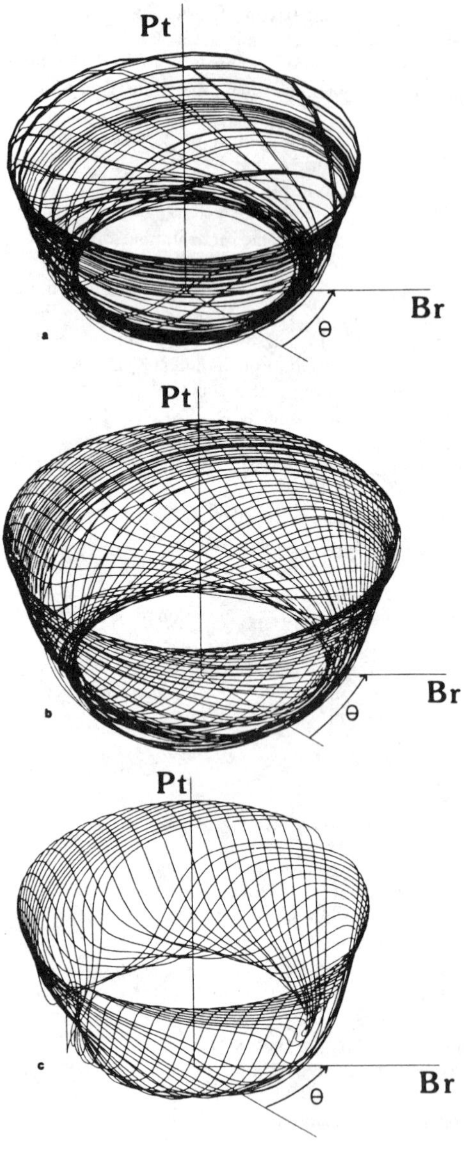

Figure 17. Experimental quasiperiodic behavior shown in cylindrical coordinates at (a) $\omega_0/\omega = 0.493$, (b) $\omega_0/\omega = 0.958$ and (c) $\omega_0/\omega = 2.063$. (Reprinted by permission from Ref. 100.)

that is a steady state can develop in which each reactor has conditions such as concentrations which are different from the other reactors.

Schreiber and Marek [116, 117] found apparently chaotic behavior with the oscillating Belousov-Zhabotinskii reaction in an experimental system of two reactors coupled by a common porous wall. Using the Brusselator model, they obtained period doubling and chaos in numerical simulations of coupled identical reactors. Nandapurkar et al. [118], also found chaos in simulations of coupled Brusselators.

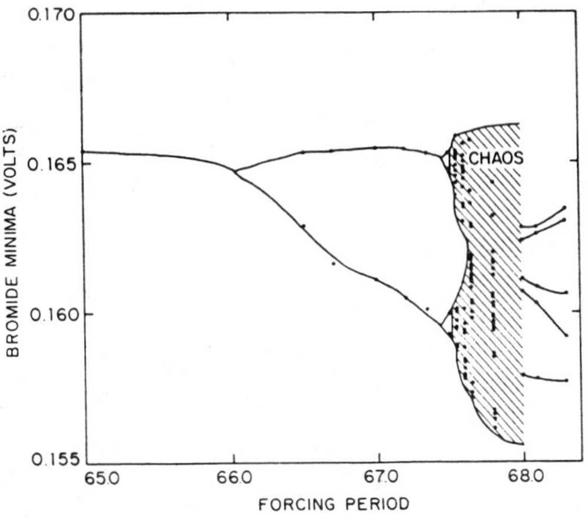

Figure 18. Experimental bifurcation diagram as a function of the forcing period for high-amplitude forcing. (Reprinted by permission from Ref. 103.)

Rössler [119] found chaos in a four-variable system consisting of two identical diffusion-coupled abstract chemical reactions. Waller and Kapral [120] numerically coupled two oscillators of a type also due to Rössler and found chaotic behavior. Ravikumar et al. [121] found complex oscillations in simulations of coupled oscillating reactors using an abstract reaction scheme. Some results on heat-transfer-coupled non-isothermal reactors were presented by Hudson et al. [122]. Bar-Eli [123] studied several examples of coupled CSTRs in which both reactors oscillate with no coupling. He found that there is often an intermediate region in the strength of the coupling where the entire system has a stable nonuniform steady state. Othmer discusses synchronization and phase-locking in coupled cells [124].

The study of coupled oscillators is an area of active research not only in the physical sciences, but also in mathematics [125–128].

We consider now two nonisothermal CSTRs coupled by exchange of mass and/or heat. A first-order, exothermic reaction is occurring in each reactor. Much of the discussion is reprinted from Mankin and Hudson [129].

We discuss first the dynamic behavior of two identical reactors, i.e., reactors with the same parameters, which are coupled by means of mass transfer. We discuss steady states, periodic oscillations, and chaos. The behavior of such identical reactors can be classified according to uniformity and symmetry. In uniform behavior the conditions in both reactors remain identical. While in nonuniform behavior instantaneous temperature and concentration differences exist. An attractor in state space may or may not be symmetric with respect to interchanging the states of the two reactors. If it is asymmetric, a mirror image attractor must also exist. Note that nonuniform steady states must be asymmetric, but nonuniform oscillatory behavior can be symmetric even though the concentrations and temperatures in the reactors are different instantaneously. This occurs if the attractor, which represents the behavior over a long period of time in x_1, θ_1, x_2, θ_2 state space, contains x, θ, x′, θ' for each x′, θ', x, θ. We also discuss reactors coupled by heat transfer; in this case, however, the reactors are not identical so that neither uniform nor symmetric states are possible.

The equations governing two coupled nonisothermal CSTRs with first-order reaction are:

$$\left.\begin{aligned}
dx_1/dt &= -x_1 + Da_1(1 - x_1)e^{\theta_1} - k_m(x_1 - x_2)\\
d\theta_1/dt &= -\theta_1 + B\,Da_1(1 - x_1)e^{\theta_1} - \beta(\theta_1 - \theta_c) - \beta_m(\theta_1 - \theta_2)\\
dx_2/dt &= -x_2 + Da_2(1 - x_2)e^{\theta_2} - k_m(x_2 - x_1)\\
d\theta_2/dt &= -\theta_2 + B\,Da_2(1 - x_2)e^{\theta_2} - \beta(\theta_2 - \theta_c) - \beta_m(\theta_2 - \theta_1)
\end{aligned}\right\}\qquad (14)$$

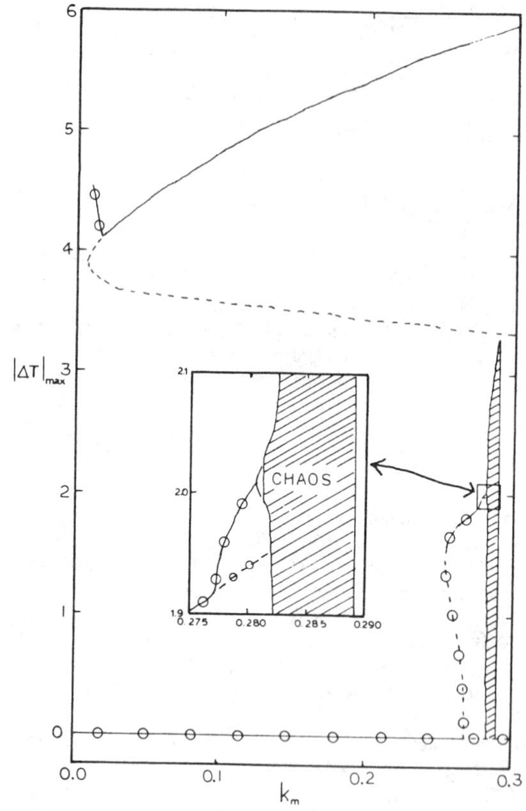

Figure 19. Bifurcation diagram for identical mass-transfer coupled reactors a function of k_m; other parameters are $Da_1 = Da_2 = 0.085$, $B = 22.0$, $\beta = 3.0$, $T_c = 0$. —— stable steady state; ----- unstable steady state; —○—stable limit cycle; --○-- unstable limit cycle. (Reprinted with permission from Ref. 129.)

These equations have the same form as Equations 1, which were written for a single reactor. The subscripts 1 and 2 denote reactor 1 and 2 respectively. The additional (last) term in each equation denotes transport between the reactors, with dimensionless interreactor mass and heat transfer coefficients k_m and β_m respectively. The dimensionless heat transfer coefficient for exchange with the coolant is still denoted by β.

Consider first the case of two identical reactors coupled by means of mass transfer only. A bifurcation diagram showing the behavior of the coupled reactors as a function of the coupling mass transfer coefficient k_m is given in Figure 19. Under oscillating conditions the following occur with increase in k_m: synchronized reactors, nonuniform limit cycles, symmetry breaking, and period doubling into chaos. An example of the chaotic behavior is given in Figure 20.

When the reactors are coupled by heat transfer, no symmetry breaking occurs. Two identical reactors always remain synchronized. If the reactors are slightly different chaos can occur with bifurcations occurring from a torus to a distorted toroidal chaotic attractor.

Planeaux and Jensen [130] have considered a very interesting related problem, viz., a nonisothermal CSTR with extraneous thermal capacitance, e.g., that of a reactor wall. This is a coupled problem in which one region, the heat capacitance, does not directly take place in the reaction but rather contributes to the dynamics by acting as storage. Chang and Schmitz [44] had studied this problem experimentally and Luss [131] and Ray and Hastings [132] had considered it in earlier modeling studies. Planeaux and Jensen showed that several dynamic phenomena occur with a reactor with extra thermal capacitance that do not occur without it; examples are bifurcations of

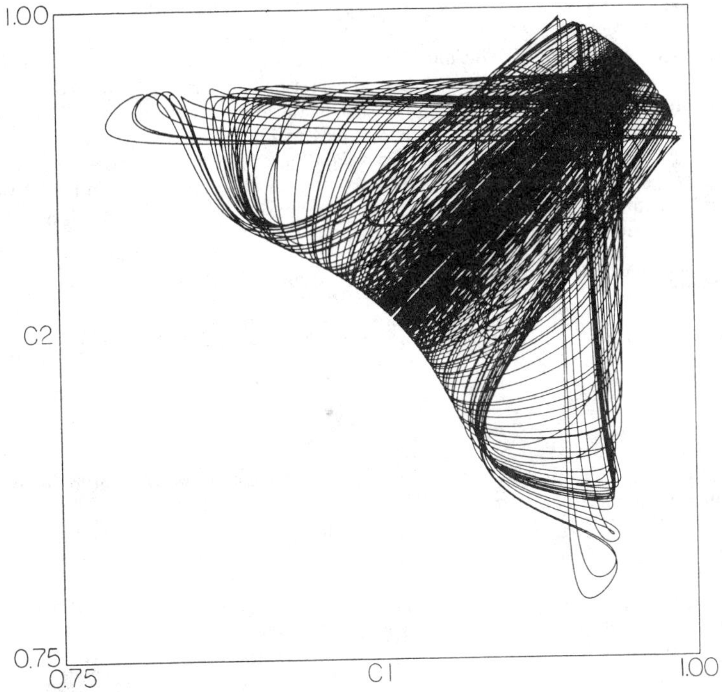

Figure 20. x_1 vs. x_2 phase plane plot of chaotic behavior at $k_m = 0.285$. (Reprinted with permission from Ref. 129.)

periodic solutions to invariant tori, isolas of periodic branches, multiple stable periodic orbits, and degenerate Hopf bifurcations.

Mankin and Hudson [133] have considered a closely related problem, viz., the dynamics of a nonisothermal catalyst particle in a surrounding fluid. Here the nonisothermal reaction occurs in the particle and the fluid serves as a non-reacting capacitance for mass. The model is meant to be a step in the analysis of the dynamics of catalytic reactors including coupling between the catalyst particles and the fluid in the interstices of the reactor. It is shown that in this simple third order system bifurcations to chaos, as well as the simultaneous occurrence of chaotic and periodic attractors, arise.

We chose to present here the transitions occurring in coupled systems as we move away from the small coupling limit towards stronger coupling. The existence of this limit is a very convenient starting point for the study of coupling phenomenology, since the behavior there has not changed much from that of the individual reactors. A number of researchers have considered the behavior of systems that do not possess such a "low coupling" limit, e.g. situations where the output of one reactor constitutes the input to the second with or without feedback through the coolant [134, 135]. Several other aspects of reactor dynamics involving CSTRs may be considered to belong to this category of coupled systems. The dynamics of heterogeneous catalytic CSTRs for example involve the coupling between two capacities (the catalytic surface and the gas phase) for storing the reactants. The dynamics of CSTRs under linearized or nonlinear feedback control may also be considered as the result of coupling between the reactor itself and the controller variables. The same nonlinear methods that have been applied throughout this discussion are being applied in the systematic study of such problems [136–141].

FINAL COMMENTS

We have tried to discuss most of the important topics dealing with the dynamics of nonisothermal CSTRs. This is a rich field and the number of important papers is rather large. We have not cited all the papers, particularly those that have been included in review articles. Rather we have concentrated on recent work on bifurcations, complex oscillations and chaos.

The nonisothermal CSTR has served as a paradigm for studies of reactor dynamics in chemical engineering. An understanding of the fundamentals in this problem is the foundation for work now in progress on the dynamics of reaction-diffusion networks, heterogeneous catalytic reactions, electrochemical reactions and polymerization.

Acknowledgment

This work was supported in part by a grant from the National Science Foundation to the University of Virginia.

NOTATION

- A heat or mass transfer area
- B dimensionless adiabatic temperature rise $[(-\Delta H)C_{Af}/\rho C_p T_f](E/RT_f)$
- c concentration
- C_p specific heat
- E activation energy
- F volumetric feed rate
- h heat transfer coefficient
- ΔH heat of reaction
- k mass transfer coefficient
- k_m dimensionless mass transfer coefficient between two reactors, k/AF
- k_0 reaction rate constant for 1st order reaction $A \rightarrow B$
- R universal gas constant
- S ratio of rate constant of reaction two to that of reaction one
- t dimensionless time t′F/V
- t′ time
- T temperature
- V reactor volume
- x conversion $c(_{Af} - c_A)/c_{Af}$
- y C_B/C_{Af}
- Da Damkohler number, $Da = \tau k_0 e^{-\gamma}$

Greek Symbols

- α ratio of heat of reaction of reaction two to that of reaction one
- β dimensionless heat transfer coefficient $hA\tau/V\rho C_p$
- β_m dimensionless heat transfer coefficient between the reactors
- γ dimensionless activation energy E/RT_f
- k ratio of activation energy for reaction two to that of reaction one
- ρ density
- τ residence time
- θ dimensionless temperature $[(T - T_f)/T_f](E/RT_f)$

Subscripts

- A species A
- c cooling medium
- f feed state
- s steady state
- 1 reactor 1
- 2 reactor 2

REFERENCES

1. Van Heerden, C., "Autothermic Processes," *Industr. Engng. Chem.* (*Industr*). 45, 1242–1247 (1953).
2. Bilous, O., and Amundson, N. R., "Chemical Reactor Stability and Sensitivity," *AIChE* 1, 513–521 (1955).

3. Aris, R., and Amundson, N. R., "An Analysis of Chemical Reactor Stability and Control-I," *Chem. Eng. Sci.*, 7, 121–131 (1958).
4. Schmitz, R. A., "Multiplicity, Stability, and Sensitivity of States in Chemically Reacting Systems—A Review," *Advan. Chem. Ser.* 148, 156–211 (1975).
5. Bailey, J. E., "Periodic Phenomena," in *Chemical Reactor Theory: A Review*, Lapidus, L., and Amundson, N. R. (ed.), Prentice-Hall, 758–813 (1977).
6. Pismen, L. M., "Kinetic Instabilities in Man-Made and Natural Reactors," *CES* 35, 1950–1978 (1980).
7. Razon, L. F., and Schmitz, R. A., Plenary Lecture, ISCRE 9, Philadelphia, May, 1986.
8. Varma, A., and Aris, R., "Stirred Pots and Empty Tubes," in *Chemical Reactor Theory: A Review*, Lapidus, L., and Amundson, N. R. (ed.), Prentice-Hall, 79–155 (1977).
9. Gavalas, G. R., *Nonlinear Differential Equations of Chemically Reacting Systems*, Springer, New York (1968).
10. Denn, M. M., *Stability of Reaction and Transport Processes*, Prentice-Hall, Englewood Cliffs, NJ (1975).
11. Perlmutter, D. D., *Stability of Chemical Reactors*, Prentice-Hall, Englewood Cliffs, NJ (1973).
12. Douglas, J. M., *Process Dynamics and Control*, Prentice-Hall, Englewood Cliffs, NJ (1972).
13. Friedly, J. C., *Dynamic Behavior of Processes*, Prentice-Hall, Englewood Cliffs, NJ (1972).
14. Hlavacek, V., ed., *Dynamics of Nonlinear Systems*, Gordon and Breach, New York, 1986.
15. *Dynamics and Modeling of Reactive Systems*, Stewart, W. E., Ray, W. H., and Conley, C. C., eds., Academic Press, New York (1980).
16. Gilles, E. D., "Stability Phenomena in Chemical Reactors." *Ber. Bunsenges. Phys. Chem.* 84, 323–333 (1980).
17. Uppal, A., Ray, W. H., and Poore, A., "On the Dynamic Behavior of Continuous Stirred Tank Reactors," *Chem. Eng. Sci.* 29, 967–985 (1974).
18. Uppal, A., Ray, W. H., and Poore, A. B., "The Classification of the Dynamic Behavior of Continuous Stirred Tank Reactors—Influence of Reactor Residence Time," *Chem. Eng. Sci.* 31, 205–214 (1976).
19. Doedel, E. J., "AUTO: A Program for the Automatic Bifurcation Analysis of Autonomous Systems," Cong. Num. 30, 265–286, 1981.
20. Kubicek, M., DERPAR ACM Trans. Math. Software, 2, 98 (1976).
21. Hassard, B. D., Kazarinoff, N. D., and Wan, Y. H., Theory and Application of Hopf Bifurcation, London Math. Soc. Lect. Note Series 41, Cambridge U. Press (1981).
22. Aluko, M., and Chang, H.-C., "PEFLOQ: An Algorithm for the Bifurcational Analysis of Periodic Solutions of Autonomous Systems," *Comp. Chem. Eng.*, 8, 355–365 (1984).
23. Iooss, G., and Joseph, D. D., "Elementary Stability and Bifurcation Theory," UTM series, Springer, NY (1980).
24. Marsden, J. E., and McCracken, M., "The Hopf Bifurcation and Its Applications," *Appl. Math. Sci.*, Vo. 19, Springer, Berlin (1976).
25. Caracotsios, M., and Stewart, W. E., "Sensitivity Analysis of Initial Value Problems with Mixed ODEs and Algebraic Equations," *Comp. Chem. Eng.*, 9, 359–365 (1985).
26. Guckenheimer, J., and Holmes, P., Nonlinear Oscillations, Dynamical Systems and Bifurcations of Vector Fields, Springer, New York (1983).
27. Andronov, A. A., Leontovic, E. A., Gordon, I. I., and Maier, A. G., "Theory of Bifurcations of Dynamical Systems on a Plane," Translated from the Russian (1967), Jerusalem (1971).
28. Keener, J. P., "Infinite Period Bifurcation and Global Solution Branches," SIAM J. Appl. Math. 41, 127–146 (1981).
29. Vaganov, D. A., Samoilenko, N. G., and Abramov, V. G., "Periodic Regimes of Continuous stirred tank reactors," *Chem. Eng. Sci.*, 33, 1133 (1978).
30. Chang, H.-C., and Calo, J. M., Exact Criteria for Uniqueness and Multiplicity of an n-th Order Chemical Reaction via a Catastrophe Theory Approach, *Chem. Eng. Sci.*, 34, 285–299 (1979).
31. Williams, D. C., and Calo, J. M., "Fine Structure of the CSTR Parameter Space," *AIChE J.*, 27, 514–516 (1981).
32. Kwong, V. K., and Tsotsis, T. T., "Fine Structure of the CSTR Parameter Space," *AIChE J.*, 29, 343–347 (1983).

33. Golubitsky, M., and Keyfitz, B., "A Qualitative Study of the Steady State Solutions for a Continuous Flow Stirred Reactor SIAM," *J. Math. Anal.*, 11, 316 (1980).
34. Balakotaiah, V., and Luss, D., Analysis of Multiplicity Patterns of a CSTR, *Chem. Eng. Commun.* 13, 111–132 (1981).
35. Balakotaiah, V., and Luss, D., "Analysis of Multiplicity Patterns of a CSTR" (Letter), 19, 185–189 (1982).
36. Balakotaiah, V., and Luss, D., "Structure of the Steady-State Solutions of Lumped-Parameter Chemically Reacting Systems," *Chem. Eng. Sci.*, 37, 1611–1623 (1982).
37. Balakotaiah, V., and Luss, D., "Dependence of the Steady State of a CSTR on the Residence time," *Chem. Eng. Sci.*, 38, 1709–1729 (1983).
38. Golubitsky, M., and Schaeffer, D. G., *Singularities and Groups in Bifurcation Theory*, Vol. 1, Springer, New York 1985.
39. Gray, P., and Scott, S. K., "Autocatalysis in Isothermal, Open Systems," *J. Chem. Phys.*, 79, 6421–6423 (1983).
40. Gray, P., and Scott, S. K., "Autocatalytic Reactions in the Isothermal CSTR: Oscillations and Instabilities in the system $A + 2B \rightarrow 3B$, $B \rightarrow C$," *Chem. Eng. Sci.*, 39, 1087–1097 (1984).
41. Aris, R., "The Mathematical Background of Chemical Reactor Analysis. II. The Stirred Tank," in *Reacting Flows*, G.S.S. Luddford (ed.), Lectures in Applied Math., Vol. 24, 75–108, 1986.
42. Hafke, C., and Gilles, E. D., "Experimentelle Untersuchungen des Dynamischen Verhaltens von Rührkesselreaktoren," *Mess., Steuern, Regeln*, 11, 204 (1968).
43. Baccaro, G. P., Gaitonde, N. Y., and Douglas, J. M., "An Experimental Study of Oscillating Reactors," *AIChE J.*, 16, 249–254 (1970).
44. Chang, M., and Schmitz, R. A., "An Experimental Study of Oscillatory States in a Stirred Reactor," *Chem. Eng. Sci.* 30, 21–34 (1975).
45. Schmitz, R. A., Bautz, R. R., Ray, W. H., and Uppal, A., "The Dynamic Behavior of a CSTR: Some Comparisons of Theory aand Experiment," *AIChE J.*, 25, 289–297 (1979).
46. Vejtasa, S. A., and Schmitz, R. A., "An Experimental Study of Steady-State Multiplicity and Stability in an Adiabatic Stirred Reactor," *AIChE J.*, 16, 410 (1970).
47. Gray, B. F., and Felton, P. G., "Low Temperature Oxidation in a Stirred Flow Reaction, Part 1. Propane," *Combust. Flame* 23, 295 (1974).
48. Griffiths, J. F., "Thermokinetic Oscillations in Homogeneous Gas-Phase Oxidations," in *Oscillations and Travelling Waves in Chemical Systems*, Field, R. J., and Burger, M. (ed.), Wiley, New York (1985).
49. Gray, P., Griffiths, J. F., and Hasko, S. M., "Ignitions, Extinctions and Thermokinetic Oscillations Accompanying the Oxidation of Ethane in an Open System," *Proc. Roy. Soc. London A*, 396, 227–255 (1984).
50. Sheintuch, M., and Luss, D., "Use of Observed Transitions for Classification of Dynamic Systems—Application to Cool Flames" preprint (1986).
51. Hlavacek, V., Kubicek, M., and Visnak, K., "Modelling of Chemical Reactors—XXVI Multiplicity and Stability Analysis of a Continuous Stirred Tank Reactor with Exothermic Consecutive Reactions $A \rightarrow B \rightarrow C$," *Chem. Eng. Sci.*, 27, 719–742 (1972).
52. Pikios, C. A., and Luss, D., "Steady-State Multiplicity of Lumped-Parameter Systems in which Two Consecutive or Two Parallel Irreversible First-Order Reactions Occur," *Chem. Eng. Sci.*, 34, 919—927 (1979).
53. Balakotaiah, V., and Luss, D., "Exact Steady-State Multiplicity Criteria for Two Consecutive or Parallel Reactions in Lumped Parameter Systems," *Chem. Eng. Sci.*, 37, 433–445 (1982).
54. Sabo, D. S., and Dranoff, J. S., "Stability Analysis of a Continous Flow Stirred Tank Reactor with Consecutive Reactions," *AIChE J.*, 16, 211 (1970).
55. Cohen, D. S., and Keener, J. P., "Multiplicity and Stability of Oscillatory States in a CSTR with Exothermic Consecutive Reactions $A \rightarrow B \rightarrow C$," *Chem. Eng. Sci.*, 31, 115–122 (1975).
56. Halbe, D. C., and Poore, A. B., "Dynamics of the Continuous Stirred Tank Reactor with Reactions $A \rightarrow B \rightarrow C$," *Chem. Eng. J.*, 21, 241–253 (1981).
57. Doedel, E. J., and Heinemann, R. F., "Numerical Computations of Periodic Solutions Branches and Oscillatory Dynamics of the Stirred Tank Reactor with $A \rightarrow B \rightarrow C$ Reactions," *Chem. Eng. Sci.*, 38, 1493–1499 (1983).

58. Jorgensen, D. V., Farr, W. W., and Aris, R., "More on the Dynamics of the CSTR with Two Consecutive Reactions," *Chem. Eng. Sci.*, 39, 1741–1752 (1984).
59. Farr, W. W., and Aris, R., "Reflections on the Multiplicity of Steady States of the Stirred Tank Reactor," *Chem. Eng. Sci.*, 41, 1385–1402 (1986).
60. Kahlert, C., Rossler, O. E., and Varma, A., "Chaos in a Continous Stirred Reactor with Two Consecutive First Order Reactions, one Exo-, One Endothermic" in *Modeling Chemical Reaction Systems*, Ebert, K., and Jaeger, W., ed., Springer, Heidelberg (1981).
61. Feigenbaum, M., "Quantitative Universality for a Class of Nonlinear Transformations," *J. Stat. Phys.*, 19, 25–52 (1978).
62. Jorgensen, D. V., and Aris, R., "On the Dynamics of a Stirred Reactor with Consecutive Reactions," *Chem. Eng. Sci.*, 38, 45–53 (1983).
63. Schuster, H. G., "Deterministic Chaos," Physik, Weinheim (1984).
64. Mandelbrot, B. B., "The Fractal Geometry of Nature," Freeman, NY (1983).
65. Hudson, J. L., and Rossler, O. E., "Chaos and Complex Oscillations in Stirred Chemical Reactors," in *Dynamics of Nonlinear Systems*, Hlavacek, V., ed., Gordon and Beach, New York (1986).
66. Pomeau, Y., Roux, J.-C., Rossi, A., Bachelert, S., and Vidal, C., "Intermittent Behavior in the Belousov-Zhabotinskii Reaction," *J. Phys. Lett.*, 42, L271 (1981).
67. Argoul, F., Arneodo, A., Richetti, P., and Roux, J.-C., "From Quasiperiodicity to Chaos in the Belousov-Zhabotinskii Reaction," Preprint (1986).
68. Lamba, P., and Hudson, J. L., "Experimental Evidence of Multiple Oscillatory States in a Continuous Reactor," *Chem. Eng. Commun.*, 32, 369–375 (1985).
69. Killory, H., Rossler, O. E., and Hudson, J. L., "Higher Chaos in a Four Variable Chemical Reaction Model," *Physics Letters A, 122*, 341 (1987).
70. Grassberger, P., and Procaceia, I., "Characterization of Strange Attractors," *Phys. Rev. Lett.*, 50, 346–349 (1983).
71. Mayer-Kress, G., "Dimensions and Entropies in Chaotic Systems," Springer, Heidelberg (1986).
72. Prackard, N. H., Crutchfield, J. P., Farmer, J. D., and Shaw, R. S., "Geometry from a Time Series," *Phys. Rev. Lett.*, 45, 712 (1980).
73. Feinberg, M., "Reaction Network Structure, Multiple Steady States, and Sustained Composition Oscillations: A Review of Some Results," in *Modelling of Chemical Reaction Systems*, Ebert, K. H., et al. eds., Springer, Berlin (1981).
74. Lyberatos, G., Kuszta, B., and Bailey, J. E., "Steady-State Multiplicity and Bifurcation Analysis via the Newton Polygon Approach," *Chem. Eng. Sci.*, 39, 947–960 (1984).
75. Tsiligiannis, C. A., and Lyberatos, G., "A Linear Algebraic Approach to Steady-State Bifurcation of Chemical Reaction Systems," *Chem. Eng. Sci.*, 42, 535–541 (1987).
76. Gaitonde, N. Y., and Douglas, J. M., "The Use of Positive Feedback Control Systems to Improve Reactor Performance," *AIChE J.*, 15, p. 902 (1969).
77. Douglas, J. M., *Process Dynamics and Control* vol. 2, Chapter 10, Prentice Hall, Englewood Cliffs, NJ (1972).
78. Bailey, J. E., "Periodic Phenomena" Chapter 12 in *Chemical Reactor Theory, A Review* Lapidus, L., and Amundson, N. R. (eds.), Prentice Hall, Englewood Cliffs, NJ (1977).
79. Minorsky, N., *Nonlinear Oscillations* Van Nostrand, New York (1962).
80. Hayashi, C., *Nonlinear Oscillations in Physical Systems* McGraw-Hill, New York (1964).
81. Sincic, D., and Bailey, J. E., "Pathological Dynamic Behavior of Forced Periodic Chemical Processes," *Chem. Eng. Sci.* 32, 281–286 (1977).
82. Kevrekidis, I. G., Schmidt, L. D., and Aris, R., "On the Dynamics of Periodically Forced Chemical Reactors" *Chem. Eng. Commun.* 30, 323–330 (1984).
83. Tomita, K., and Kai, T., "Chaotic Response of a Limit Cycle," *J. Stat. Phys.* 21, 65–86 (1979).
84. Tomita, K., "Chaotic Response of Nonlinear Oscillators," *Phys. Rep.* 86, 113–167 (1982).
85. Arnol'd, V. I., *Geometrical Methods in the Theory of Ordinary Differential Equations* Springer New York (1982).
86. Aronson, D. G., Chory, M. A., Hall, G. R., and McGehee, R. P., "Bifurcations from an Invariant Circle for Two-Parameter Families of Maps of the Plane; a Computer-Assisted Study," *Comm. Math. Phys.* 83, 303–354 (1982).

87. Kevrekidis, I. G., Schmidt, L. D., and Aris, R., "Some Common Features of Periodically Forced Reacting Systems," *Chem. Eng. Sci.* 41, 1263–1276 (1986).
88. Thoulouze-Pratt, E., "Numerical Analysis of the Behaviour of an Almost Periodic Solution to a Periodic Differential Equation, an Example of Successive Bifurcation of Invariant Tori," in *Lect. Notes in Biomath.* 49, 265–271 Springer, Berlin (1983).
89. Chan, T. N., *Numerical Bifurcation Analysis of Simple Dynamical Systems* M.C.Sc. Thesis, Concordia University (1983).
90. Kevrekidis, I. G., Aris, R., Schmidt, L. D., and Pelikan, S., "Numerical Computation of Invariant Circles of Maps," *Physica 16D*, 243–251 (1985).
91. Van Veldhuizen, E., "On a Polygonal Approximation of an Invariant Curve," *SIAM J. Sci. Stat. Comp.* to appear (1987).
92. Kevrekidis, I. G., "A Numerical Study of Global Bifurcations in Chemical Dynamic," *AIChE J.* to appear (1987).
93. Newhouse, S., "The Abundance of Wild Hyperbolic Sets and Non-Smooth Stable Sets for Diffeomorphisms," *Publ. Math. IHES* 57, 5–72 (1983).
94. Kevrekidis, I. G., Aris, R., and Schmidt, L. D., "The CSTR Forced," *Chem. Eng. Sci.* 41, (Amundson Festschrift) (1986).
95. Taylor, T. W., and Geiseler, W., "Periodic Perturbation of Limit Cycles in an Isothermal CSTR," in *Synergetics Series* 29, 122–125 (1985).
96. Rehmus, P., and Ross, J., "Periodically Perturbed Chemical Systems" in *Oscillations and Travelling Waves in Chemical Systems*, Field, R., and Burger, M. (eds.) Wiley, New York (1985).
97. Mankin, J. C., and Hudson, J. L., "Oscillatory and Chaotic Behaviour of a Forced Exothermic Chemical Reaction," *Chem. Eng. Sci.* 39, 1807–1814 (1984).
98. Dulos, E., "Synchronization of a Chemical Oscillation by Periodic Light Pulses" in *Nonlinear Phenomena in Chemical Dynamics* Vidal, C., and Pacault, A. (eds.) 140 Springer, New York (1981).
99. Buchholz, F., Freund, A., and Schneider, F. W., "Periodic Perturbation of the BZ Reaction in a CSTR; Chemical Resonance, Entrainment and Quasiperiodic Behavior" in *Temporal Order* Renzing, L., and Jaeger, N. I. (eds.) p. 116–121 Springer, New York (1985).
100. Hudson, J. L., and Lamba, P., and Mankin, J. C., "Experiments on Low-Amplitude Forcing of a Chemical Oscillator," *J. Phys. Chem.* 90, 3430–3434 (1986).
101. Nagashima, H., "Experiments on Chaotic Responses of a Forced Belousov-Zhabotinskii Reaction," *J. Phys. Soc. Japan* 51, 21 (1982).
102. Marek, M., "Periodic and Aperiodic Regimes in Forced Chemical Oscillations" in *Temporal Order* Renzig, L., and Jaeger, N. I. (eds.) 105 Springer, Berlin (1985).
103. Lamba, P., and Hudson, J. L., "Experiments and Bifurcations to Chaos in a Forced Chemical Reactor," *Chem. Eng. Sci.* 42, 1–8 (1987).
104. Guevara, M. R., Glass, L., and Shrier, A., "Phase-Locking, Period Doubling Bifurcations and Irregular Dynamics in Periodically Stimulated Cardiac Cells," *Science* 214, 1350 (1981).
105. Pugh, S. A., DeKock, B., and Ross, J., "Effects of Two-Periodic Perturbations on the Oscillatory Combustion of Acetaldehyde" *J. Chem. Phys.* 85, 879–886 (1986).
106. Jensen, K. F., and Ray, W. H., "The Role of Surface Structures in the Dynamic Behavior of Heterogeneous Catalytic Systems" in *Dynamics of Nonlinear Systems*, Hlavacek, V., ed. p. 111, Gordon and Breach, New York 1986.
107. Chang, H.-C., "The Domain Model in Heterogeneous Catalysis" *Chem. Eng. Sci.* 38, 535–546 (1983).
108. Schmitz, R. A., and Tsotsis, T. T., "Spatially Patterned States in Systems of Interacting Catalyst Particles," *Chem. Eng. Sci.* 38, 1431–1437 (1983).
109. Tsotsis, T. T., "Spatially Patterned States in Systems of Interacting Lumped Reactors" *Chem. Eng. Sci.* 38, 701–717 (1983).
110. Nandapurkar, P. J., Hlavacek, V., and Van Rompay, P., "Complex Oscillations over Isothermal Catalyst Pellet" *Chem. Eng. Sci.* 39, 1511–1516 (1984).
111. Pismen, L. M., "Symmetry Breaking and Pattern Selection", in *Dynamics of Nonlinear Systems*, Hlavacek, V. (ed.), Gordon and Breach, NY (1986).

112. Turing, A., "The Chemical Basis of Morphogenesis," *Phil. Trans. R. Soc. B237*, 37–72 (1952).
113. Bar-Eli, K., "On the Stability of Coupled Chemical Oscillators," *Physica 14D*, 242–252 (1985).
114. Kennedy, C. R., and Aris, R., "Bifurcations of a Model Diffusion-Reaction System", in *New Approaches to Nonlinear Problems in Dynamics.* (Edited by Holmes, P. J.). SIAM (1980).
115. Stuchl, I., and Marek, M., "Dissipative Structures in Coupled Cells," *J. Chem. Phys.*, 77, 2956–2963 (1982).
116. Schreiber, I., and Marek, M., "Strange Attractors in Coupled Reaction-Diffusion Cells, *Physica 5D*, 258–272 (1982).
117. Schreiber, I., and Marek, M., "Transitions to Chaos via Two-Torus in Coupled Reaction-Diffusion Cells," *Phys. Lett.*, 91, 263–266 (1982).
118. Nandapurkar, P., Hlavacek, V., Degreve, J. Janssen, R. and Van Rompay, P., "Reaction Diffusion Dissipative System—Detailed Stability Analysis-Pattern of Growth and Effect of Inhomogeneity." *Z. Naturforsch, 39A*, 899–916 (1984).
119. Rössler, O. E., "Chemical Turbulence: Chaos in a Simple Reaction-Diffusion System", *Z. Naturforsch, 31A*, 1168–1172 (1976).
120. Waller, I., and Kapral, R., "Synchronization and Chaos in Coupled Nonlinear Oscillators," *Phys. Letter, 105A*, 163–168 (1984).
121. Ravi Kumar, V., Jayaraman, B., Kulkarni, B., and Doraiswamy, L., "Dynamic Behavior of Coupled CSTRs Operating Under Different Conditions," *Chem. Engng. Sci.*, 38, 673–686 (1983).
122. Hudson, J. L., Mankin, J. C., and Rössler, O. E., "Chaos in Continuous Stirred Chemical Reactors," in *Stochastic Phenomena and Chaotic Behavior in Complex Systems* (edited by Schuster, P.), Springer Series in Synergetics (Proceedings of UNESCO Conference Flatnitz, Austria, June 1983). Springer, New York (1984).
123. Bar-Eli, K., "On the Coupling of Chemical Oscillators," *J. Phys. Chem.*, 88, 3616–3622 (1984).
124. Othmer, H. G., "Synchronization, Phase Locking and Other Phenomena in Coupled Cells," in *Temporal Order*, Rensing, L., and Jaeger, N. I. (eds.), Springer, Berlin (1985).
125. Othmer, H. G., Aronson, D. G., and Doedel, E. J., "Resonance and Bistability in Coupled Oscillators," *Phys. Letters* 113A, 349–353 (1986).
126. Ermentrout, B., "Losing Amplitude and Saving Phase" in *Nonlinear Oscillations in Biology and Chemistry*, Othmer, H. G., (ed.) p. 98–114 Springer, Berlin (1986).
127. Neu, J., "Coupled Chemical Oscillators" *SIAM J. Appl. Math.* 37, 307–315 (1979).
128. Ermentrout, B., and Kopell, N., "Frequency Plateaus in a Chain of Weakly Coupled Oscillators, I," *SIAM J. Math Anal.* 15, 215–237 (1984).
129. Mankin, J. C., and Hudson, J. L., "The Dynamics of Coupled Nonisothermal Continuous Stirred Tank Reactors," *Chem. Eng. Sci.*, 41, 2651–2661 (1986).
130. Planeaux, J. B., and Jensen, K. F., "Bifurcation Phenomena in CSTR Dynamics: A System with Extraneous Thermal Capacitance," *Chem. Eng. Sci.*, 41, 1497–1523 (1986).
131. Luss, D., "The Influence of Capacitance Terms on the Stability of Lumped and Distributed Parameter Systems," *Chem Engng. Sci.*, 29, 1832–1836 (1974).
132. Ray, W. H., and Hastings, S. P., "The Influence of the Lewis Number on the Dynamics of Chemically Reacting System," *Chem Engng. Sci.*, 35, 589–595 (1980).
133. Mankin, J. C., and Hudson, J. L., "The Dynamics of a Nonisothermal Catalyst Particle in a Surrounding Fluid," *AIChE J.*, 32, 1208–1210 (1986).
134. Svoronos, S., Aris, R., and Stephanopoulos, G., "On the Behavior of Two Stirred Tanks in Series," *Chem. Eng. Sci.* 37, 357–366 (1982).
135. Kim, S. H., and Hlavacek, V., "On the Detailed Dynamics of Coupled Continuous Stirred Tank Reactors," *Chem. Eng. Sci.* 41, 2767–2777 (1986).
136. Nowobilski, P., and Takoudis, C., "Dynamic Behavior of Chemical Reactors II. Some New Aspects in Oscillatory Heterogeneous Reacting Systems" in *Frontiers in Chemical Reaction Engineering* Doraiswamy, L. K., and Mashelkar, R. A. (eds.) Vol. 2, 352–360 (1984).
136. Chang, H.-C., "Recent Developments in the Dynamics of Heterogeneous Catalytic Reactions" in *Dynamics of Nonlinear Systems* p. 85 Hlavacek, V. (ed.) Gordon and Breach 1986.

137. Polizopoulos, I., and Takoudis, C. G., "On the Steady State Solutions of Chemically Reacting Systems-I. Applications to Single Species Surface Reactions," *Chem. Eng. Sci.* 41, 1221–1232 (1986).
138. Chang, H.-C., and Chen, L.-H., "Bifurcation Characteristics of Nonlinear Systems under Conventional PID Control," *Chem. Eng. Sci.* 39, 1127–1142 (1984).
139. Lyberatos, G., Kuszta, B., and Bailey, J. E., "Discrimination and Identification of Dynamic Catalytic Reaction Models via Introduction of Feedback," *Chem. Eng. Sci.* 40, 199–208 (1986).
140. McDermott, P. E., and Chang, H.-C., "On the Global Dynamics of an Autothermal Reactor Stabilized by Linear Feedback Control," *Chem. Eng. Sci.* 39, 1,1347–1356 (1984).
141. Prairie, M. R., and Bailey, J. E., "Application of Feedback Induced Bifurcation for Evaluating Steady State and Transient Heterogeneous Catalysis Kinetic Models," *Chem. Eng. Sci.* 41, 937 (1986).

CHAPTER 26

MODELING TUBULAR FLOW REACTORS

J. R. Too

Department of Chemical Engineering
The Catholic University of America
Washington, D.C.

CONTENTS

INTRODUCTION

Physical effects in chemical reactors are difficult to eliminate from the chemical rate processes. Non-uniformities in the velocity and temperature profiles, and interphase heat and mass transfer tend to distort the kinetic data and complicate the analyses of a reactor. In order to analyze the behavior of a chemical process, we need a mathematical representation of the physical and chemical phenomena occurring. Such a mathematical representation constitutes the model of the system, and "modeling" refers to the activities leading to the construction of the model. A proper model for a flow system is also essential to dynamic simulation, reactor design and scale-up, and process control.

We employ mathematical models to represent both chemical and physical effects. The model must represent the flow behavior of an actual reactor realistically enough to yield useful information for its design and analysis. However, a model can never represent a complete picture of reality. A simple model may be quite adequate in some instances, but a much more refined and elaborate model may be necessary in another circumstance. A good model, therefore, must recognize its own inadequacies, so that it can serve as a means to develop a more complete picture of reality. Hence, in formulating a model, we first differentiate the major factors that are significantly important from the minor factors that may be neglected. By analyzing the behavior of the reactor model and comparing it with the actual reactor, we shall be able to learn how and in which direction the improvement of the model should be attempted.

The tubular reactor is so named because the physical configuration of the reactor is normally such that the reaction takes place within a tube. Basically, the tubular reactor is a conduit of some sort through which the reactants flow and in which no attempt is made to increase the natural degree of mixing. Aris [1] has divided tubular reactors into those designed for homogeneous reactions, and those designed for a heterogeneously catalytic reaction, and hence to be packed with a catalyst. In the unpacked tubular reactor, there may be considerable variations in flow rate across the tube. For example, in a laminar flow reactor, there is a pronounced velocity gradient across the tube with zero velocity at the wall. Molecules near the center will follow high-velocity streamlines and will undergo relatively little reaction. On the other hand, the information necessary to describe velocity profile in a packed-bed reactor is usually not available. The flow profile and the radial and longitudinal diffusion are all governed by the packing. In addition, there are the problems of heat and mass transfer to and from the catalyst particles.

Hill [2] classified tubular reactors based on heat transfer requirements into three major categories:

1. Single-jacketed tubes.
2. Shell-and-tube heat exchangers.
3. Tube furnaces, in which the tubes are exposed to thermal radiation and heat transfer from combustion gases.

The single-jacketed tube reactor is the simplest type of tubular reactor to conceptualize and to fabricate. It may be used only when the heat transfer requirements are minimal because of the low surface area to volume ratio characteristic of these reactors. When the shell-and-tube configuration is used, the reaction may occur on either the tube side or the shell side. The shell-and-tube tubular reactor has a much greater area for heat transfer per unit of effective reactor volume than the single-jacketed tube. In many cases energy economics can be achieved using countercurrent flow of a hot product stream to preheat an incoming reactant stream to the temperature where the reaction occurs at an appreciable rate. Tubular furnaces are used only when it is necessary to carry out endothermic reactions at fairly high temperatures on very large quantities of feedstock. Thermal reforming reactions and other reactions used to increase the yield of gasoline from petroleum-based feedstocks are commercial scale processes that employ this type of reactor.

Because there is no back-mixing of fluid elements along the reactions of flow in a tubular reactor, there is a continuous gradient in reactant concentration in this direction. One does not encounter the step changes characteristic of multiple stirred tank reactors. Consequently, for the same feed composition and reaction temperature, the average reaction rate will generally be significantly higher in a tubular reactor than it would be in a single stirred tank or a series of stirred tanks with a total volume equal to that of the tubular reactor [2, 3]. Efficient use of reactor volume is an advantage of the tubular reactor that permits one to use it in processes which demand very large capacity.

Because variations in temperature and composition may occur in the axial direction in tubular reactors, these systems may be somewhat more difficult to control than continuous flow stirred tank reactors. However, the problems are usually not insurmountable, and we can normally obtain steady-state operating conditions which give rise to uniform product quality. Other advantages of the tubular reactor relative to stirred tanks include suitability for use at higher pressures and temperatures, thereby surmounting severe energy transfer constrains. The tubular reactor is usually employed for liquid phase reactions when relatively short residence times are needed to effect the desired chemical transformation. It is the reactor of choice for continuous gas phase operations.

The axial dispersion model has been used in a diverse variety of dispersion problems, especially, in analysis of tubular flow reactors. An excellent introduction to the axial dispersion model and to methods for measuring dispersion coefficients is given by Levenspiel [3]. A more advanced account is given by Wen and Fan [4], Nauman and Buffham [5], Froment and Bischoff [6], and Nauman [7].

DISPERSION MODELS

Dispersion models are useful mainly to represent flow in empty tubes and packed beds, which is much closer to the ideal case of plug flow than to the opposite extreme of back-mixing flow. In empty tubes, the mixing is caused by molecular diffusion and turbulent diffusion, superposed on the velocity-profile effect. In packed beds, mixing is caused both by "splitting" of the fluid streams as they flow around the particles and by the variations in velocity across the bed. The general dispersion model is given below [8]:

$$\frac{\partial C}{\partial t} + U \cdot \nabla C = \nabla \cdot (D \nabla C) + r_c \qquad (1)$$

where r_c represents the reaction rate term. The dispersion coefficient, D, is a function of both the fluid properties and the flow situation. The fluid properties have a higher effect on D at low flow rates, but almost none at high rates. The vector differential operator known as "nabla" or "del" is defined as

$$\nabla = \delta_x \frac{\partial}{\partial x} + \delta_y \frac{\partial}{\partial y} + \delta_z \frac{\partial}{\partial z} \qquad \text{(for rectangular coordinates)}$$

$$= \delta_r \frac{\partial}{\partial r} + \delta_\theta \frac{1}{r}\frac{\partial}{\partial \theta} + \delta_z \frac{\partial}{\partial z} \qquad \text{(for cylindrical coordinates)}$$

The vector ∇C (or grad C) is called the gradient of the scalar function C. The inner product of del and a vector v, sometimes called the "divergence" of v, is given below:

$$\nabla \cdot v = \frac{\partial v_x}{\partial x} + \frac{\partial v_y}{\partial y} + \frac{\partial v_z}{\partial z} \qquad \text{(for rectangular coordinates),}$$

$$= \frac{1}{r}\frac{\partial}{\partial r}(r v_r) + \frac{1}{r}\frac{\partial v_\theta}{\partial \theta} + \frac{\partial v_z}{\partial z} \qquad \text{(for cylindrical coordinates).}$$

The dispersion coefficient and the fluid velocity in Equation 1 are all functions of position. The dispersion coefficient is also in general nonisotropic, i.e., it has different values in different directions.

The first simplification is for the frequently encountered situation of symmetrical axial flow in cylindrical vessels. For this particular geometry. Equation 1 reduces to

$$\frac{\partial C}{\partial t} + u_z(r)\frac{\partial C}{\partial z} = \frac{\partial}{\partial z}\left[D_L(r)\frac{\partial C}{\partial z}\right] + \frac{1}{r}\frac{\partial}{\partial r}\left[r D_R(r)\frac{\partial C}{\partial r}\right] + r_c \qquad (2)$$

where D_L and D_R are the longitudinal (axial) and radial molecular dispersion coefficients, respectively. With D_L, D_R and u, all functions of radial position, analytical solutions of this equation are still impossible. This makes evaluation of dispersion extremely difficult; hence further simplifications are needed to permit analytical solutions to the differential equation.

If the axial and radial dispersion coefficients are each taken to be independent of position, Equation 2 can be rewritten as

$$\frac{\partial C}{\partial t} + u_z(r)\frac{\partial C}{\partial z} = D_L \frac{\partial^2 C}{\partial z^2} + D_R\left(\frac{\partial^2 C}{\partial r^2} + \frac{1}{r}\frac{\partial C}{\partial r}\right) + r_c \tag{3}$$

This mathematical description is called the *uniform dispersion model* for which an analytical solution is sometimes possible.

For the isothermal, incompressible flow of fluids under a constant flow rate and in a cylindrical vessel, D_L and D_R can be assumed to be independent of position. Equation 2 can be rewritten as

$$\frac{\partial C}{\partial t} + \bar{u}\frac{\partial C}{\partial z} = D_L \frac{\partial^2 C}{\partial z^2} + D_R\left(\frac{\partial^2 C}{\partial r^2} + \frac{1}{r}\frac{\partial C}{\partial r}\right) + r_c \tag{4}$$

where $\bar{u}$ is the mean linear velocity. This equation is used frequently for turbulent flow of fluids in pipes, flow through packed beds, flow of liquids through fluidized beds, etc. In fact, the equation has been applied to many other homogeneous and heterogeneous systems in which the flow behavior is not too far from that of plug-flow.

However, when the flow behavior deviates considerably from plug-flow such as in a stirred tank, in a bubbling fluidized bed, and in the two phase flow of a gas-liquid system, the behavior cannot always be represented by this model. This does not mean that the model cannot be used each phase when two phases are involved. Many researchers used a simplification of this model to represent gas-flow behavior in irrigated packed columns or liquid flow in extraction columns.

When radial dispersion can be neglected in comparison with axial dispersion. Equation 4 reduces to

$$\frac{\partial C}{\partial t} + \bar{u}\frac{\partial C}{\partial z} = D_L \frac{\partial^2 C}{\partial z^2} + r_C \tag{5}$$

This equation is called the *axial-dispersed plug-flow model* the *longitudinal dispersed plug-flow model*, the *Fickian form of the diffusion equation*, or sometimes simply the *dispersion model*. Usually radial dispersion can be neglected in comparison with the axial dispersion when the ratio of column diameter to length is very small and the flow is in turbulent regime. Perhaps this model is the most widely used model for chemical reactors and other contacting devices.

Initial and Boundary Conditions

Naturally, an initial condition and two boundary conditions, one at the entrance $z = 0$ and the other at the exit $z = L$, are needed to solve the dispersion equation, Equation 5. The initial condition for the axial dispersion model may be written as

$$C(z, 0) = C_0(z), \qquad 0 < z < L \tag{6}$$

which specifies the initial distribution of molecules (or particles) or mass in the reactor.

Suppose that the tube is divided into three sections, an inlet section from $z = -\infty$ to $z = 0$ (designated by subscript in), the reacting section $z = 0$ to $z = L$, and the outlet section from $z = L$ to $+\infty$ (designated by subscript out); each section may have distinct modes of mixing. Therefore, boundary conditions must be derived from the continuity relations or, more specifically, the continuity of flux and/or concentration [9, 10].

The flux is the net rate of flow of molecules or particles across a boundary. In terms of concentration, the flux based on the axial dispersion model has the form

$$J = -D\frac{\partial C}{\partial z} + \bar{u}C \tag{7}$$

which represents the net flow of mass in the positive z direction. The continuity of flux can be denoted as

$$J_- = J_+ \qquad \text{at } z = 0 \text{ or } L \text{ for all } t \tag{8}$$

For the tubular flow reactor characterized by the axial dispersion model, this condition merely states that the net flow of mass into the bounding surface must equal the net flow out of this surface; there can be no accumulation within the bounding surface since a surface has no volume. More specifically. Equation 8 may be written for the entrance and exit, respectively, as

$$-D_{in}\frac{\partial C}{\partial z} + \bar{u}C\bigg|_{0^-} = -D\frac{\partial C}{\partial z} + \bar{u}C\bigg|_{0^+} \tag{9}$$

and

$$-D\frac{\partial C}{\partial z} + \bar{u}C\bigg|_{L^-} = -D_{out}\frac{\partial C}{\partial z} + \bar{u}C\bigg|_{L^+} \tag{10}$$

The boundary conditions at the entrance may be classified into the open and closed entrances according to the capability of molecules to disperse or diffuse in the inlet section. For the closed entrance, the diffusion coefficient, D_{in}, is zero, and this boundary does not permit the molecules to diffuse back. Once the molecules (or particles) drift or connect to the entrance and pass it, they drift and diffuse to the right; they will not return to the inlet section ($-\infty < z < 0$). For this case, Equation 9 reduces to

$$\bar{u}C\bigg|_{0^-} = -D\frac{\partial C}{\partial z} + \bar{u}C\bigg|_{0^+} \tag{11}$$

The term on the left side of this equation represents the purely convective flow or drift from the inlet section into the entrance of the reacting section.

The continuity of concentration is not upheld at a strictly entrance of a tubular flow reactor represented by the axial dispersion model for which $D_{in} = 0$. Suppose that the concentration at the inlet, $C(0^-, t)$, drops instantly to zero; diffusion, with its assumed infinite propagation speed, will prevent a step change from occurring within the system. Thus, $C(0^+, t)$ cannot instantly drop to zero. Instead, it will remain positive because of backward diffusion of molecules or particles from downstream regions of the reactor [5, 11].

In contrast, diffusion can occur across the boundaries of a reactor with *open* entrance and exit. Obviously, the continuity of flux at the entrance, Equation 9, is still satisfied; furthermore, the continuity of concentration is also upheld; thus,

$$C(0^-, t) = C(0^+, t) \tag{12}$$

In summary, loss of the continuity in concentration occurs only in the hypothetical limit of $D_{in} = 0$. If it is considered that the closed entrance is realized under the condition of $D_{in} \to 0$, both the continuity of flux and that of concentration are upheld [12].

When the diffusion coefficient in the outlet section is zero ($D_{out} = 0$), we have the so-called *closed* exit; once the molecules (or particles) pass this exit, they drift or connect to the right (z-direction) and will not diffuse back to the reacting section $(0 < z < L)$. For this boundary, Equation 10 becomes

$$-D\frac{\partial C}{\partial z} + \bar{u}C\Big|_{L^-} = \bar{u}C\Big|_{L^+} \tag{13}$$

At the closed exit boundary the flow is from a mixed section to a section where there is no mixing, and thus, there is no way the composition will change across the boundary. Thus, we have continuity of concentration

$$C(L^-, t) = C(L^+, t) \tag{14}$$

TABLE 1
Boundary Conditions for Axial Dispersion Models

Type of Vessels	Axial Dispersion Model	Stochastic Axial Dispersion Model
Open-Open $D_{in} > 0$ ¦ D ¦ $D_{out} > 0$ 0 L	$C(0^-, t) = C(0^+, t)$ $J\|_{0^-} = J\|_{0^+}$ $C(L^-, t) = C(L^+, t)$ $J\|_{L^-} = J\|_{L^+}$	$C(0^-, t) = C(0^+, L)$ $J^*\|_{0^-} = J^*\|_{0^+}$ $C(L^-, t) = C(L^+, t)$ $J^*\|_{L^-} = J^*\|_{L^+}$
Open-Closed $D_{in} > 0$ ¦ D ¦ $D_{out} = 0$ 0 L	$C(0^-, t) = C(0^+, t)$ $J\|_{0^-} = J\|_{0^+}$ $C(L^-, t) = C(L^+, t)$ $\frac{\partial C}{\partial z} = 0, \quad \text{at } z = L$	$C(0^-, t) = C(0^+, t)$ $J^*\|_{0^-} = J^*\|_{0^+}$ $C(L^-, t) = C(L^+, t)$ $\frac{\partial}{\partial z}(DC) = 0, \quad \text{at } z = L$
Closed-Open $D_{in} = 0$ ¦ D ¦ $D_{out} > 0$ 0 L	$\bar{u}C\|_{0^-} = \bar{u}C - D\frac{\partial C}{\partial z}\Big\|_{0^+}$ $C(L^-, t) = C(L^+, t)$ $J\|_{L^-} = J\|_{L^+}$	$u_{in}C\|_{0^-} = -\frac{\partial}{\partial z}(DC) + uC\|_{0^+}$ $C(L^-, t) = C(L^+, t)$ $J^*\|_{L^-} = J^*\|_{L^+}$
Closed-Closed $D_{in} = 0$ ¦ D ¦ $D_{out} = 0$ 0 L	$\bar{u}C\|_{0^-} = \bar{u}C - D\frac{\partial C}{\partial z}\Big\|_{0^+}$ $C(L^-, t) = C(L^+, t)$ $\frac{\partial C}{\partial z} = 0, \quad \text{at } z = L$	$u_{in}C\|_{0^-} = -\frac{\partial}{\partial z}(DC) + uC\|_{0^+}$ $C(L^-, t) = C(L^+, t)$ $\frac{\partial}{\partial z}(DC) = 0, \quad \text{at } z = L$
	$J = \bar{u}C - D\left(\frac{\partial C}{\partial z}\right)$	$J^* = uC - \frac{\partial}{\partial z}(DC)$

Thus, Equation 13 reduces to

$$\frac{\partial C}{\partial z} = 0, \qquad \text{at } z = L \text{ for all } t \tag{15}$$

Table 1 summarizes possible combinations of the boundary conditions at the entrance and exit of the reactor. With a sufficient number of approprite initial and boundary conditions, the axial dispersion model, Equation 5, can be solved either analytically or numerically.

STOCHACTIC AXIAL DISPERSION MODEL

The axial dispersion model given in the previous section is one of the most widely employed models for representing and characterizing the performance of a tubular flow chemical reactor. In deriving this equation we mainly rely on a mass (or population) balance approach, but seldom on a probabilistic approach. More often than not probabilistic may be more appropriate than mass balance in describing and modeling the dispersion of molecules or particles in the flow reactor. This is especially so when the rate of reactant flow through the reactor is high generating turbulent eddies, or when the flow involves more than one phase inducing irregular flow patterns, or when the path of reactant flow is affected by internals or agitators rendering motion of reactant particles random.

Nauman [13] has discussed the notion of the one-dimensional simple random walk as it pertains to flow chemical reactors; he has pointed out that the simple random walk in the continuous limit on both time and displacement reduces to the dispersion equation and that the latter can be viewed as representing the probability distribution of an individual molecule on the real line (displacement axis).

It has been shown that the continuous limit of a general random walk gives rise to the stochastic diffusion or dispersion model (see, e.g., Cox and Miller [14]). The general random walk has the property that one-step transitions of a particle or molecule are permitted only to the nearest neighboring states, and the probability of moving one step up or down on a real line can be expressed in general as a function of time and position of the particle or molecule. Too et al. [15] have considered probabilistic termination of the random walk of a reactant molecule due to chemical reaction and derived the so-called stochastic axial dispersion model for an irreversible reaction as

$$\frac{\partial}{\partial t} C(z, t) + \frac{\partial}{\partial z} [\mu(z, t)C(z, t)] = \frac{1}{2}\frac{\partial^2}{\partial z^2} [\sigma^2(z, t)C(z, t)] - \lambda(z, t)C(z, t) \tag{16}$$

This equation is also known as the Kolmogorov forward diffusion equation with chemical reaction. The symbols used here have the following meaning. The instantaneous mean, $\mu(z, t)$, and the half of the instantaneous variance, $\sigma^2(z, t)$, are referred to as the drift and diffusion coefficients, respectively (see, e.g., Cox and Miller [14]). The instantaneous reaction rate, $\lambda(z, t)$ also known as the intensity of reaction (see, e.g., McQuarrie [16]; Fan et al. [17]), is closely related to the reaction rate constant. For example, $\lambda(z, t)$ is independent of $C(z, t)$ for a first-order reaction and may be expressed generally as $k_1C(z, t)$ (see, e.g., Ishida [18]; McQuarrie [16]).

By letting

$$D(z, t) = \frac{1}{2}\sigma^2(z, t) \tag{17}$$

$$u(z, t) = \mu(z, t) \tag{18}$$

and replacing the reaction term with r_C, Equation 16 can be rewritten as

$$\frac{\partial}{\partial t} C(z, t) + \frac{\partial}{\partial z} [u(z, t)C(z, t)] = \frac{\partial^2}{\partial z^2} [D(z, t)C(z, t)] + r_C \tag{19}$$

If the process is time homogeneous, the drift and diffusion coefficients and the intensity of reaction are independent of time. Thus, Equation 19 reduces to

$$\frac{\partial}{\partial t} C(z, t) + \frac{\partial}{\partial z} [u(z)C(z, t)] = \frac{\partial^2}{\partial z^2} [D(z)C(z, t)] + r_C \tag{20}$$

If the drift and diffusion coefficients are constant, i.e.,

$$D(z) = D \tag{21}$$

$$u(z) = \bar{u} \tag{22}$$

Equation 20 will reduce to the axial dispersion model, Equation 5. Note that the drift coefficient (velocity), $\bar{u}$, corresponding to the convective velocity, arises naturally whenever a group of molecules or particles move through the force field and thus their center of gravity shifts or drifts in the direction of the spatial coordinate [19, 20].

The Fickian form of the diffusion equation, Equation 5, is very similar to the Kolmogorov diffusion equation. However, these two equations reduce to an identical form only when D and u are constant. Another distinction between them is that the diffusion coefficient in the Kolmogorov diffusion equation is a derived quantity which has an explicitly physical meaning while that in the Fickian form of diffusion equation is essentially a proportionality constant relating the mass flux to the concentration gradient. The Kolmogorov diffusion equation is capable of generating a non-uniform steady reactant concentration profile as $t \to \infty$ independent of spatial and temporal dependence of the reactant diffusivity [19, 21]. Thus, the Kolmogorov diffusion model sometimes may be more versatile than the Fickian diffusion model.

The Kolmogorov diffusion equation can be extended to a three-dimensional flow reactor in a fairly straight-forward manner. When no reaction occurs, the Kolmogorov diffusion equation can characterize the residence time distribution. Under the assumption that thermal energy is totally transported by flowing molecules or particles, the results presented here may be applicable to thermal transport through an adiabatically operated reactor.

Initial and Boundary Conditions

Again, an initial condition and two boundary conditions are needed to solve the Kolmogorov diffusion equation, Equation 19. The initial condition for the stochastic axial dispersion model is the same as that given in Equation 6. Similarly, the boundary conditions must be derived from the continuity relations or, more specifically, the continuity of flux and/or concentration.

The flux is the net rate of flow of molecules or particles across a boundary. In terms of concentration, the flux based on the Kolmogorov diffusion equation has the form

$$J = -\frac{\partial}{\partial z}(DC) + uC \tag{23}$$

which can be derived using probabilistic reasoning (see, e.g., Kimura [22]); it can also be derived based on the Kolmogorov diffusion equation itself. Note that the physical significances of the fluxes based on the Kolmogorov and Fickian equations are essentially identical; they represent the net flow of molecules (particles) for the former and that of mass for the latter in the positive z direction. The continuity of flux, Equation 8, still holds for the axial dispersion model of the Kolmogorov form. This condition merely states that the net flow of molecules or particles into the boundary surface must equal the net flow out of this surface. More specifically, the continuity of flux may be written for the entrance and exit, respectively, as

$$-\frac{\partial}{\partial z}(D_{in}C) + u_{in}C\Big|_{0^-} = -\frac{\partial}{\partial z}(DC) + uC\Big|_{0^+} \tag{24}$$

and

$$-\frac{\partial}{\partial z}(DC) + uC\Big|_{L^-} = -\frac{\partial}{\partial z}(D_{out}C) + u_{out}C\Big|_{L^+} \tag{25}$$

For the closed entrance, Equation 24 reduces to

$$u_{in}C\Big|_{0^-} = -\frac{\partial}{\partial z}(DC) + uC\Big|_{0^+} \tag{26}$$

The term on the left side of this equation represents the purely convective flow or drift from the inlet section into the entrance of the reacting section. Analogous to the Fickian form, the continuity of concentration is not upheld at a strictly closed entrance of a tubular flow reactor represented by the axial dispersion model for which $D_{in} = 0$.

In contrast, diffusion can occur across the boundaries of a reactor with open entrance and exit. Obviously, the continuity of flux at the entrance, Equation 24, is still satisfied; furthermore, the continuity of concentration, Equation 12, is also upheld.

When the diffusion coefficient in the outlet section is zero ($D_{out} = 0$), we have the so-called closed exit; once the molecules (or particles) pass this exit, they drift or connect to the right (z-direction) and will not diffuse back to the reacting section ($0 < z < L$). For this boundary, Equation 25 becomes

$$-\frac{\partial}{\partial z}(DC) + uC\Big|_{L^-} = u_{out}C\Big|_{L^+} \tag{27}$$

At the closed exit boundary the flow is from a mixed section to a section where there is no mixing, and thus, there is no way the composition will change across the boundary. Thus, the continuity of concentration, Equation 14, is still upheld. Furthermore, for a relatively dilute system, the local velocities of molecules or particles are approximately equal to the linear velocity of the bulk fluid. i.e.,

$$u = u_{out} = \bar{u} \tag{28}$$

Thus, Equation 27 reduces to

$$-\frac{\partial}{\partial z}(DC) = 0, \qquad \text{at } z = L \tag{29}$$

Various combinations of the above boundary conditions as shown in Table 1 are possible at the entrance and exit of the reactor. With a sufficient number of appropriate initial and boundary conditions, the Kolmogorov diffusion equation, Equation 19, can be solved either analytically or numerically.

ENERGY BALANCE ASPECTS FOR TUBULAR REACTORS

The derivation of differential energy balance for the components of an element of fluid flowing in a reactor is considered in detail in the texts on transport processes (see, e.g., Bird et al. [23]). The general form of energy equation is given below.

$$\left\{\begin{matrix}\text{rate of}\\ \text{accumulation}\\ \text{of energy per}\\ \text{unit volume}\end{matrix}\right\} + \left\{\begin{matrix}\text{rate of}\\ \text{energy output}\\ \text{per unit volume}\\ \text{by convection}\end{matrix}\right\} = \left\{\begin{matrix}\text{rate of}\\ \text{energy input}\\ \text{per unit volume}\\ \text{by conduction}\end{matrix}\right\} + \left\{\begin{matrix}\text{rate of}\\ \text{energy generated}\\ \text{due to chemical}\\ \text{reactions}\end{matrix}\right\} \tag{30}$$

Other energy terms encountered include work of expansion or compression, viscous dissipation, energy flux by molecular diffusion, and radiation heat flux. However, these energy effects are negligible in most circumstance of interest to the designer of chemical reactors. Mathematically, Equation 30 can be written as

$$\sum M_j C_j C_{pj}\left(\frac{\partial T}{\partial t} + u \cdot \nabla T\right) = (\nabla \cdot q) + \sum(-\Delta H_j) r_j \tag{31}$$

where C_j = molar concentration of species j,
M_j = molecular weight of species j,
C_{pj} = heat capacity,
q = heat flux of conduction

For a tubular flow reactor, this equation is written, in cylindrical coordinates, as

$$\sum M_j C_j C_{pj}\left(\frac{\partial T}{\partial t} + u_r \frac{\partial T}{\partial r} + \frac{u_\theta}{r}\frac{\partial T}{\partial \theta} + u_z \frac{\partial T}{\partial z}\right)$$
$$= k\left[\frac{1}{r}\frac{\partial}{\partial r}\left(r\frac{\partial T}{\partial r}\right) + \frac{1}{r^2}\frac{\partial^2 T}{\partial \theta^2} + \frac{\partial^2 T}{\partial z^2}\right] + \sum(-\Delta H_j) r_j \tag{32}$$

where k is the thermal conductivity of the fluid (reactants). Note that when there is more than one phase, more than one energy equation has to be written, and a transfer term has to be introduced.

Non-isothermal Plug-Flow Reactors

In a plug flow reactor, there may be a variation in the temperature of the reactor contents from point to point within the reactor. Here we will confine our analysis to situations in which both the temperature and composition are uniform across the cross section of the reactor. The energy balance for the differential reactor element shown in Figure 1 is

$$\left\{\begin{matrix}\text{rate of}\\ \text{accumulation}\\ \text{of energy}\end{matrix}\right\} = \left\{\begin{matrix}\text{rate of}\\ \text{energy in by}\\ \text{convection}\end{matrix}\right\} - \left\{\begin{matrix}\text{rate of}\\ \text{energy out by}\\ \text{convection}\end{matrix}\right\} + \left\{\begin{matrix}\text{rate of}\\ \text{energy}\\ \text{generated}\\ \text{due to}\\ \text{chemical}\\ \text{reactions}\end{matrix}\right\} + \left\{\begin{matrix}\text{input rate}\\ \text{of heat}\\ \text{transfer}\\ \text{through}\\ \text{the wall}\end{matrix}\right\} \tag{33}$$

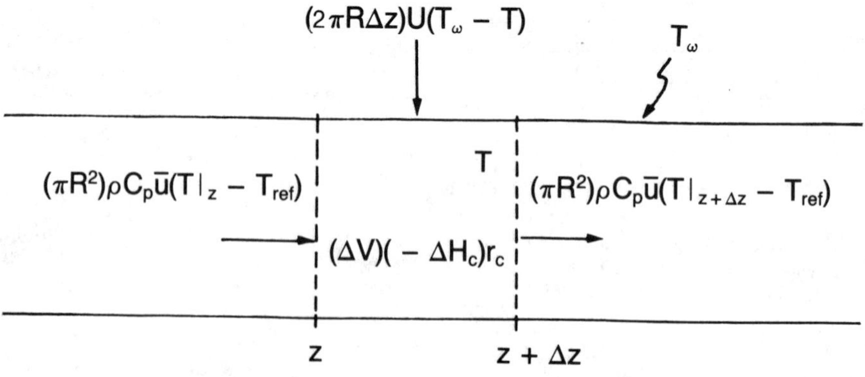

Figure 1. Non-isothermal plug-flow differential reactor element.

or

$$(\pi R^2\,\Delta z)\rho C_p\frac{\partial T}{\partial t} = (\pi R^2)\rho C_p\bar{u}(T - T_{ref})|_z - (\pi R^2)\rho C_p\bar{u}(T - T_{ref})|_{z+\Delta z}$$

$$+ (\pi R^2\,\Delta z)(-\Delta H_c)r_c + (2\pi R\,\Delta z)U(T_w - T) \tag{34}$$

where U = overall heat transfer coefficient,
T_{ref} = reference temperature where the specific enthalpy of the reactant fluid is assumed to be zero,
T_w = wall temperature

As Δz approaches 0, this equation becomes

$$\rho C_p\left[\frac{\partial T}{\partial t} + \bar{u}\frac{\partial T}{\partial z}\right] = (-\Delta H_c)r_c + 2\frac{U}{R}(T_w - T) \tag{35}$$

which is the form usually encountered. Since the reaction rate heavily depends on the temperature of the reactant, the axial dispersion model and energy balance equation must be solved simultaneously for non-isothermal flow reactors.

Non-isothermal Laminar Flow Reactors

Consider a viscous fluid with constant physical properties (k and C_p) flowing through a circular tube of radius R. For $z < 0$, the fluid temperature is uniform at T_0. To obtain the temperature distribution, we have to make a thermal energy balance over a ring-shaped element such as that shown in Figure 2, inasmuch as T is clearly a function of r and z. Energy enters and leaves this ring by thermal condition in both r- and z-directions. Also, energy will enter and leave by fluid entering and leaving the ring, the fluid carrying with it a certain amount of enthalpy.

The energy balance around the ring can be written as

$$\left\{\begin{array}{l}\text{rate of}\\ \text{accumulation}\\ \text{of energy}\end{array}\right\} + \left\{\begin{array}{l}\text{rate of}\\ \text{energy output}\\ \text{by convection}\end{array}\right\} = \left\{\begin{array}{l}\text{rate of}\\ \text{energy input}\\ \text{by conduction}\end{array}\right\} + \left\{\begin{array}{l}\text{rate of energy}\\ \text{generated due}\\ \text{to reaction}\end{array}\right\} \tag{36}$$

or in a differential form as

$$\rho C_p\frac{\partial T}{\partial t} + \rho C_p u_z\frac{\partial T}{\partial z} = -\frac{1}{r}\frac{\partial}{\partial r}(rq_r) - \frac{\partial q_z}{\partial z} - (\Delta H_c)r_c \tag{37}$$

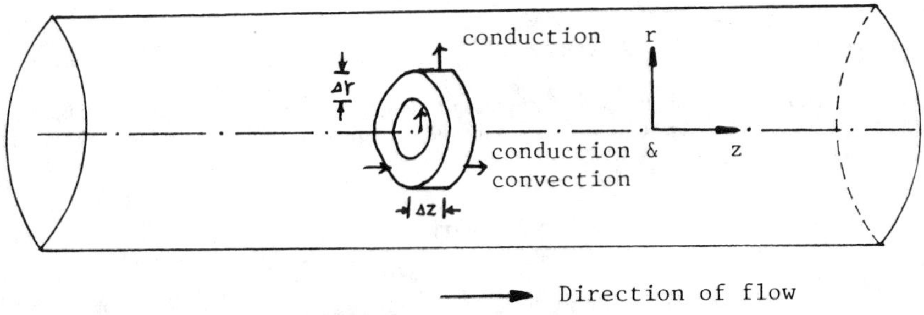

Figure 2. Annular ring over which energy balance is made in order to obtain temperature distribution in a tubular flow reactor.

Into this equation we introduce the velocity distribution for laminar flow and Fourier's law for heat conduction in both r- and z-directions:

$$u_z = 2\bar{u}\left[1 - \left(\frac{r}{R}\right)^2\right]$$

$$q_r = -k\frac{\partial T}{\partial r} \qquad q_z = -k\frac{\partial T}{\partial z} \tag{38}$$

Then, we obtain the partial differential equation

$$\rho C_p\frac{\partial T}{\partial t} + 2\rho C_p\bar{u}\left[1 - \left(\frac{r}{R}\right)^2\right]\frac{\partial T}{\partial z} = k\left[\frac{1}{r}\frac{\partial}{\partial r}\left(r\frac{\partial T}{\partial r}\right) + \frac{\partial^2 T}{\partial z^2}\right] - (\Delta H_c)r_c \tag{39}$$

Usually the heat conduction in the z-direction is small in comparison with the convective transfer term. When this term is omitted, we have

$$\rho C_p\frac{\partial T}{\partial t} + 2\rho C_p\bar{u}\left[1 - \left(\frac{r}{R}\right)^2\right]\frac{\partial T}{\partial z} = k\frac{1}{r}\frac{\partial}{\partial r}\left(r\frac{\partial T}{\partial r}\right) - (\Delta H_c)r_c \tag{40}$$

The boundary conditions are

B.C. 1. $T = T_0$ at $z = 0$ and for all r

2. $\frac{\partial T}{\partial r} = 0$ (radial symmetry) at $r = 0$ (41)

3. $-k\frac{\partial T}{\partial r} = q_1$ (a constant) at $r = R$

Two other frequently encountered approximations for the third boundary condition are

$\frac{\partial T}{\partial r} = 0$ (adiabatic operation)

(42)

$T = T_w$ (constant wall temperature)

Solving Equations 40 and 3 simultaneously subject to the appropriate boundary conditions gives the temperature and concentration as functions of time and both r and z in the tubular reactor.

Non-isothermal Turbulent Flow Reactors

The turbulent mixing that leads to flat concentration profiles will also give flat temperature profiles. Thus, $T(r, z, t) = T(z, t)$. An expression for the axial dispersion of heat analogy to Equation 5 can be written as:

$$\frac{\partial T}{\partial t} + \bar{u}\frac{\partial T}{\partial z} = E\frac{\partial^2 T}{\partial z^2} + \frac{(-\Delta H_c)r_c}{\rho C_p} + \frac{2U}{\rho C_p R}(T_w - T) \tag{43}$$

where E is axial dispersion coefficient for heat. The boundary conditions are

$$\bar{u}T_{in} = \bar{u}T - E\left.\frac{\partial T}{\partial z}\right|_{0^+} \tag{44}$$

and

$$\frac{\partial T}{\partial z} = 0 \qquad \text{at } z = L \tag{45}$$

at the inlet and outlet, respectively. Equation 43 must be solved simultaneously with Equation 5: and when r_c has an Arrhenius temperature dependence, the solution must be numerical. In many industrial reactors, the axial dispersion of heat can be neglected. When Re > 10,000, plug flow is normally a good approximation for tubular reactors [7].

HETEROGENEOUS TUBULAR REACTORS

In the previous sections, we were mainly concerned about the design of the tubular reactors for a single phase. However, many industrial processes involve reactants in more than one phase. These reactions are complicated because mass and heat transfers may occur at the interface of two different phases. A comprehensive treatment of heterogeneous catalysis and reactor design is given by Lee [24]. More specifically, interested readers will find details on the formulation and solution of model equations for tubular flow reactors by Froment and Bischoff [6], Smith [25], and Chen [26]. Here, the generalized mass and energy balances are given, and two examples of heterogeneous tubular reactors are discussed.

Consider a reactant fluid flowing through and undergoing a chemical reaction in a tube. The mass balance for component j in the fluid in a small volume element shown in Figure 2 can be made as follows:

$$\left\{\begin{matrix}\text{rate of}\\ \text{accumulation}\\ \text{of mass}\end{matrix}\right\} + \left\{\begin{matrix}\text{net rate of}\\ \text{mass output}\\ \text{by convection}\end{matrix}\right\} = \left\{\begin{matrix}\text{net rate of}\\ \text{mass input}\\ \text{by diffusion}\end{matrix}\right\} + \left\{\begin{matrix}\text{rate of}\\ \text{generation}\\ \text{due to}\\ \text{chemical}\\ \text{reaction}\end{matrix}\right\} \tag{46}$$

The differential form of this equation can be written as

$$\frac{\partial C_j}{\partial t} + \frac{\partial (uC_j)}{\partial z} = D_L\left(\frac{\partial^2 C_j}{\partial z^2}\right) + \frac{D_R}{r}\frac{\partial}{\partial r}\left(r\frac{\partial C_j}{\partial r}\right) + r_c \tag{47}$$

where D_L and D_R are the effective longitudinal and radial diffusivities, respectively. The superficial velocity based on the empty tube is usually used in dealing with the design of heterogeneous reactors.

The overall energy balance for the reactant fluid in a small volume has the same form as given in Equation 30. Assuming that T is not a function of θ because of cylindrical symmetry, Equation 32 can be written as

$$\rho C_p\left[\frac{\partial T}{\partial t} + u_z\frac{\partial T}{\partial z}\right] = k_L\frac{\partial^2 T}{\partial z^2} + \frac{k_R}{r}\frac{\partial}{\partial r}\left(r\frac{\partial T}{\partial r}\right) + \sum(-\Delta H_j)_j \tag{48}$$

where k_L and k_R are the longitudinal and radial effective thermal conductivities, respectively.

Fixed-Bed Catalytic Reactors

A fixed-bed reactor, sometimes called packed-bed reactor, consists of many cylindrical tubes filled with catalyst pellets. Reactants flow from the bottom of the reactor through the catalyst bed and are converted into products that flow out the top of the reactor. The catalysts in the reactor are stationary. Various models are extensively discussed in the books by Froment and Bischoff [6], and Chen [26].

From the generalized mass and energy balances, we obtain the following equations for two dimensional heterogeneous model. The model equations are

Fluid:

$$u_\infty \frac{\partial C}{\partial z} = \frac{D_R}{r}\frac{\partial}{\partial r}\left(r\frac{\partial C}{\partial r}\right) - k_g a_v (C - C_\infty) \tag{49}$$

$$u_\infty \rho C_p \frac{\partial T}{\partial z} = \frac{k_{R,f}}{r}\frac{\partial}{\partial r}\left(r\frac{\partial T}{\partial r}\right) + h a_v (T_\infty - T) \tag{50}$$

Solid:

$$k_g a_v (C - C_\infty) = \zeta \rho_b r_c \tag{51}$$

$$h a_v (T_\infty - T) = \zeta \rho_b (-\Delta H) r_c + \frac{k_{R,s}}{r}\frac{\partial}{\partial r}\left(r\frac{\partial T}{\partial r}\right) \tag{52}$$

subject to boundary conditions

$$C = C_0, \quad T = T_0, \quad \frac{\partial C}{\partial r} = 0 \quad \text{at } z = 0 \tag{53}$$

$$\frac{\partial T}{\partial r} = \frac{\partial T_s}{\partial r} = 0, \quad \frac{\partial C}{\partial r} = 0 \quad \text{at } r = 0 \tag{54}$$

$$\left.\begin{aligned} h_f(T_w - T) &= k_{R,f}\frac{\partial T}{\partial r} \\ h_s(T_w - T) &= k_{R,s}\frac{\partial T_s}{\partial r} \end{aligned}\right\} \quad \text{at } r = R \tag{55}$$

where
C_∞ = the concentration at the surface of the catalyst
a_v = the surface area of the catalyst per unit volume
k_g = the mass transfer coefficient
u_∞ = the superficial velocity
$k_{R,f}$ = the effective thermal conductivity in the r-direction for fluid
$k_{R,s}$ = the effective thermal conductivity in the r-direction for solid
h_s = the local heat transfer coefficient of solid
h_f = the local heat transfer coefficient of fluid
T_∞ = the surface temperature of the catalyst
ζ = the effectiveness factor

If the temperature and concentration can be assumed to be uniform through the cross-section, then we have the one-dimensional heterogeneous model. The model equations are obtained straight-forward by dropping the dependence of r on temperature and concentration. They are

Fluid:

$$-u_\infty \frac{dC}{dz} = k_g a_v (C - C_\infty) \tag{56}$$

$$u_\infty \rho C_p \frac{dT}{dz} = h a_v (T_\infty - T) - 2\frac{U}{R}(T - T_w) \tag{57}$$

Solid:

$$\rho_b r_c = k_g a_v (C - C_\infty) \tag{58}$$

$$-(\Delta H)\rho_b r_c = h a_v (T_\infty - T) \tag{59}$$

subject to the boundary conditions

$$C = C_0 \quad \text{and} \quad T = T_0 \qquad \text{at } z = 0 \tag{60}$$

Fluidized-Bed Reactors

A fluidized bed is simply a bed of solid particles, usually catalysts, with a stream of gas passing upward through the particles at a high enough rate to set them in motion. The large surface area of the solid particles make the fluidized bed desirable for mass transfer and chemical reactions involving the gas-solid interfaces. The fast recirculation of solids, due to gas bubbling, results in temperature uniformity. One of the most desirable properties of a fluidized bed operation is easy handling of solid-gas streams to or from the process.

When a chemical reaction occurs in a fluidized bed, the operation will also involve mass transfer. Examples are the catalytic cracking of petroleum, and removal of SO_2 from an air stream via a limestone process. The operation involves interaction between the incoming gas, which is usually a reactant, and the solid particles, which act as reactants or as catalysts. The understanding of the bubble phenomenon is the key to the successful modeling of the simultaneous process of mass transfer and chemical reaction.

Many models have been proposed for describing the performance of a fluidized-bed reactor [27]. Usually a simplified flow pattern of plug flow or complete mixing is assumed in representing the fluid flow behavior in one or more of the phases in these models. The examples given below show applications of the axial dispersion model to fluidized-bed reactors.

Fan and Fan [28] considered the axial dispersion in the phases for the nonlinear catalytic reactions in a bubbling fluidized bed. They have assumed that the three phases, bubble, cloud-wake and emulsion, are homogeneously distributed statistically in a fluidized bed and that each of the phases can be represented by the axial dispersion model:

$$\frac{\partial C_i}{\partial t} = D_i \frac{\partial^2 C_i}{\partial z^2} - u_i \frac{\partial C_i}{\partial z} - F_{i,i+1}(C_i - C_{i+1})\left(\frac{\eta_1}{\eta_i}\right)\left(\frac{1}{\varepsilon_i}\right) + F_{i-1,i}(C_{i-1} - C_i)\left(\frac{\eta_1}{\eta_i}\right)\left(\frac{1}{\varepsilon_i}\right) + r_i \tag{61}$$

where
i = 1 for the bubble phase
i = 2 for the cloud phase
i = 3 for the emulsion phase
$F_{i,j}$ = gas exchange coefficient between phases i and j
ε_i = void fraction of phase i
η_i = volume fraction of the fluidized-bed occupied by phase i

The initial condition is

$$C_i = C_{i0} \tag{62}$$

and the appropriate boundary conditions are

$$C_{i,in} u_i \Big|_{0^-} = C_i u_i - D_i \frac{\partial C_i}{\partial z}\Big|_{0^+} \tag{63}$$

and

$$\frac{\partial C_i}{\partial z} = 0, \qquad \text{at } z = L_{mf} \tag{64}$$

Many of the parameters in this model are closely interrelated through either the bubbling phenomenon or the mass balance. See the original work [28] for the estimation of those parameters. Since the temperature uniformity is assumed due to fast circulation of solids, no energy balance is needed.

For a bubbleless fluidized bed reactor, the flow regime is characterized by relatively uniform expansion of the bed without formation of bubbles. Thus, the bed can be approximated as an expanded packed bed. The material balance for the dispersion model in this flow regime can be represented by [29]:

$$D_L \frac{d^2C_j}{dz^2} + \frac{D_R}{r}\frac{d}{dr}\left(\frac{1}{r}\frac{dC_j}{dr}\right) - \bar{u}\frac{dC_j}{dz} + r_j = 0 \tag{65}$$

where subscript j denotes component j.

The radial dispersion coefficient, D_R, is usually much greater than the axial dispersion coefficient. For beds with large height to diameter ratio, the radial dispersion can be neglected. Hence,

$$D_L \frac{d^2C_j}{dz^2} - \bar{u}\frac{dC_j}{dz} + r_j = 0 \tag{66}$$

The estimation of the values for D_L is given in the book by Wen and Fan [4].

NUMERICAL SOLUTION TECHNIQUES

Many techniques have been developed for the numerical solution of partial differential equations. The best method depends on the specific equations being solved and on the geometry of the system. The first step in solving a partial differential equation is to discretize it. The differential equations must be replaced by an approximating, finite system of algebraic equations. Three basic discretization methods are considered here: the method of lines, finite differences and finite elements. We do not intend to give a complete description of numerical techniques for partial differential equations. Interested readers are encouraged to read the books by Davis [30], Lapidus and Pinder [31], Ames [32], Gladwell and Wait [33] and Rice [34] for more detailed discussion on this subject.

The Method of Lines

This method applies to initial value (time-dependent) problems, and it reduces a partial differential equation to a system of ordinary differential equations. The resulting system of ordinary differential equations is then solved using any available software. The method is most directly applicable to a problem of the form

$$\frac{\partial C}{\partial t} = f\left(C, r, z, \frac{\partial C}{\partial r}, \frac{\partial C}{\partial z}, \frac{\partial^2 C}{\partial r^2}, \frac{\partial^2 C}{\partial z^2}\right)$$

The idea is to make a partial discretization, to discretize the space variable(s) and leave the time variable alone.

Consider the axial dispersion model, Equation 5, with an irreversible, first-order reaction

$$\frac{\partial C}{\partial t} = D_L \frac{\partial^2 C}{\partial z^2} - \bar{u}\frac{\partial C}{\partial z} - k_1 C \tag{67}$$

Choose a mesh on the spatial interval, say, [0, L],

$$0 = z_0 < z_1 < \cdots < z_N = L \tag{68}$$

such that the approximate solution will be sought at these mesh points. A finite difference approximation for the partial derivative of concentration in the axial direction is

$$\frac{\partial C}{\partial z} \approx \frac{C(z_{i+1}, t) - C(z_{i-1}, t)}{2(\Delta z)} \approx \frac{W_{i+1} - W_{i-1}}{2(\Delta z)} \tag{69}$$

where $W_i(t) \approx C(z_i, t)$. For the second derivative, we use

$$\frac{\partial^2 C}{\partial z^2} = \frac{\partial}{\partial z}\left(\frac{\partial C}{\partial z}\right) \approx \frac{C(z_{i+1}, t) - 2C(z_i, t) + C(z_{i-1}, t)}{(\Delta z)^2}$$
$$\approx \frac{W_{i+1} - 2W_i + W_{i-1}}{(\Delta z)^2} \tag{70}$$

Substitution of these approximations into Equation 67 yields

$$\frac{dW_i}{dt} = (\alpha - \beta)W_{i+1} - (2\alpha + k_1)W_i + (\alpha - \beta)W_{i-1}, \tag{71}$$

where $i = 1, 2, \ldots, (N - 1)$
$\alpha = D_L/(\Delta z)^2$
$\beta = \bar{u}/2(\Delta z)$

We thus have a coupled set of ordinary differential equations for the unknown functions $W_i(t)$.

In this method, the boundary conditions are incorporated into the discretization in the z-direction while the initial condition is used to start the initial value problem. A standard integration scheme, such as "Runge-Kutta" or the predictor-corrector "Adams-Moulton" [35] can be used to solve for $W_i(t)$. This is usually not done because the time derivative would be treated much more accurately than the spatial derivative. Instead, we use a less sophisticated method for solving this system of equations. For instance, the "Euler-Cauchy" scheme is a simple way to solve an ordinary differential equation.

Finite Differences

The finite differences method is the most straightforward and easiest to understand. It obtains a finite system of equations from a partial differential equation by discretizing the domain; values of the approximate solution are found only at a finite set of points. The basic step for a finite difference method are as follow: first choose a mesh on the interval of interest as given in Equation 68; second form the algebraic equations required to satisfy the differential equation and the BCs by replacing derivatives with difference quotients involving only the mesh points; and last solve the algebraic system of equations. If a particular problem contains flux boundary conditions, then they can be treated using either the method of false boundaries or the integral method [30].

Explicit Scheme

Let $W_{i,j} \approx C(z_i, t_j)$ and $t_j = j\,\Delta t$. If the Euler method is used to integrate Equation 71, we obtain

$$\frac{W_{i,j+1} - W_{i,j}}{\Delta t} = (\alpha - \beta)W_{i+1,j} - (2\alpha + k_1)W_{i,j} + (\alpha - \beta)W_{i-1,j} \tag{72}$$

$i = 1, 2, \ldots, (N - 1)$ and $j = 1, 2, \ldots$

$$\text{or}\, W_{i,j+1} = (\alpha' - \beta')W_{i+1,j} + [1 - (2\alpha' + k_1')]W_{i,j} + (\alpha' - \beta')W_{i-1,j} \tag{73}$$

where $\alpha' = \alpha\,\Delta t$,
$\beta' = \beta\,\Delta t$,
$k_1' = k_1\,\Delta t$.

At $j = 0$, all the W_i's are known from the initial condition. Therefore, implementation of Equation 73 is carried out as:

1. Calculate $W_{i,j+1}$ for $i = 1, 2, \ldots, (N - 1)$, using Equation 73 with $j = 0$.
2. Repeat step 1 using the computed $W_{i,j+1}$ value to calculate $W_{i,j+2}$ and so on.

Equation 73 is called the explicit scheme or the forward difference method.

Implicit Scheme

Consider again the discretization of Equation 67. If the implicit Euler method is used to integrate Equation 71, we have

$$\frac{W_{i,j+1} - W_{i,j}}{\Delta t} = (\alpha - \beta)W_{i+1,j+1} - (2\alpha + k_1)W_{i,j+1} + (\alpha - \beta)W_{i-1,j+1} \tag{74}$$

or

$$W_{i,j} = -(\alpha' - \beta')W_{i+1,j+1} + [1 + (2\alpha' + k_1')]W_{i,j+1} - (\alpha' - \beta')W_{i-1,j+1} \tag{75}$$

Equation 74 or 75 is called the backward difference method, and it is unconditionally stable. We have gained stability over the forward difference method at the expense of having to solve a tridiagonal linear system, but the same accuracy is maintained.

Crank-Nicholson Scheme

This scheme is obtained if we center both space and time differences midway between the j-th and (j + 1)-th level. The approximations are

$$\frac{\partial C(z_i, t_{j+1/2})}{\partial t} \approx \frac{W_{i,j+1} - W_{i,j}}{\Delta t} \tag{76}$$

$$\frac{\partial C(z_i, t_{j+1/2})}{\partial z} \approx \frac{1}{2}\left[\frac{W_{i+1,j+1} - W_{i-1,j+1}}{2(\Delta z)}\right] + \frac{1}{2}\left[\frac{W_{i+1,j} - W_{i-1,j}}{2(\Delta z)}\right] \tag{77}$$

$$\frac{\partial^2 C(z_i, t_{j+1/2})}{\partial z^2} \approx \frac{1}{2}\left[\frac{W_{i+1,j+1} - 2W_{i,j+1} + W_{i-1,j+1}}{(\Delta z)^2}\right] + \frac{1}{2}\left[\frac{W_{i+1,j} - 2W_{i,j} + W_{i-1,j}}{(\Delta z)^2}\right] \tag{78}$$

Therefore, we obtain for Equation 67

$$\left\{\frac{1}{2}(\alpha' - \beta')W_{i+1,j+1} - (1 + \alpha')W_{i,j+1} + \frac{1}{2}(\alpha' - \beta')W_{i-1,j+1}\right\}$$
$$= \left\{-\frac{1}{2}(\alpha' - \beta')W_{i+1,j} - (1 - \alpha')W_{i,j} - \frac{1}{2}(\alpha' - \beta')W_{i-1,j}\right\} \tag{79}$$

This difference procedure is known as the Crank-Nicholson scheme, and it is unconditionally stable.

Finite Element Methods

The finite element method obtains a finite system of equations by discretizing the solution space: the approximate solution obtained is a finite combination of known (and selected) functions. The principle of the finite element method is the standard one for numerical methods to solve general equations. The steps in the method are [34]:

1. Select some known basis function to approximate C(z, t), say

$$C(z, t) \approx \sum_{i=1}^{n} a_i b_i(z, t)$$

where $b_i(z, t)$ are the basis functions.
2. Substitute $\sum a_i b_i(z, t)$ into the governing partial differential equation with the coefficients a_i to be determined.
3. Since step 2 is generally impossible to do exactly (one has only n unknowns available to satisfy an equation which holds for all values of z and t in some domain), select n conditions to approximate the given partial differential equation and determine the coefficients a_i to satisfy this finite system of equations.

The finite element method requires that the basis functions be finite elements, that is, functions which are zero except on a small part of the domain under consideration. The piecewise polynomials and B-splines are typical examples of finite element basis functions; the most commonly used basis elements are piecewise linear.

Software for Partial Differential Equations

Software for partial differential equations tends to be rather large. It is not easy to make it portable, and the demands of efficiency have often led to complexities in the use of the software. There is a good survey entitled "Survey of Software for Partial Differential Equations" by Machura and Sweet [36]. We do not summarize these surveys here, rather we briefly describe some widely used subprograms for solving the type of partial differential equations encountered in tubular reactor modeling.

PDEONE [37]: This algorithm implements the method of lines for initial value problems with time and one space variable of the form

$$\frac{\partial C}{\partial t} = f\left(t, z, C, \frac{\partial C}{\partial z}, \frac{\partial}{\partial z}\left(D\frac{\partial C}{\partial z}\right)\right)$$

I.C. $\quad C(z, 0) \qquad$ given

B.C. $\quad \alpha C + \beta \frac{\partial C}{\partial z} = \gamma \qquad$ at $z = a$ or b

The domain is $\{t \geqslant 0$ and $a \leqslant z \leqslant b\}$. The user must provide an ordinary differential equation solver plus subprograms to define the functions f, α, β, γ, D and C(z, 0).

PDECOL [38]: This algorithm implements the finite element method for the initial value problem with time and one space variable of the form

$$\frac{\partial C}{\partial t} = f\left(t, z, C, \frac{\partial C}{\partial z}, \frac{\partial^2 C}{\partial z^2}\right)$$

I.C. $\quad C(z, 0) \qquad$ given

B.C. $\quad h\left(C, \frac{\partial C}{\partial z}\right) = g(t), \qquad$ for $z = a$ or b

The domain is $\{t \geqslant 0$ and $a \leqslant z \leqslant b\}$. The method is based on collocation in z by piecewise polynomials.

PDETWO [39]: This is a complete set of programs for solving initial value problems with two space variables. The partial differential equation is of the form

$$\frac{\partial C}{\partial t} = f\left(t, r, z, C, \frac{\partial C}{\partial r}, \frac{\partial C}{\partial z}, \frac{\partial}{\partial r}\left(D_R \frac{\partial C}{\partial r}\right), \frac{\partial}{\partial z}\left(D_L \frac{\partial C}{\partial z}\right)\right)$$

I.C. $C(r, z, 0)$ given

B.C. $AC + B\dfrac{\partial C}{\partial r} = E$ for $a \leqslant z \leqslant b$ and $r = 0$ or R

$FC + G\dfrac{\partial C}{\partial z} = H$ for $0 \leqslant r \leqslant R$ and $z = a$ or b

The functions A, B, E, F, G, and H may depend on t, r, z and C, where D_L and D_R depends on t, r and z. The method of line is used with the 5-point star discretization of r and z and then using GEARB [40] to solve the resulting system of ordinary differential equations.

DPDES [41, 42]: This is a IMSL program which implements the method of lines to solve the initial value problem with one space variable of the form

$$\frac{\partial C}{\partial t} = f\left(z, t, C, \frac{\partial C}{\partial z}, \frac{\partial^2 C}{\partial z^2}\right)$$

I.C. $C(z, 0)$ given

B.C. $\alpha C + \beta\dfrac{\partial C}{\partial z} = \gamma(t)$ for $z = a$ or b

This problem has a general second-order operator in the space variable and linear boundary conditions; the coefficient α, and β are constant. The space variable is discretized with collocation by Hermite cubics at Gauss points; thus the lines are not equally spaced. The special version of DGEAR [42] used takes advantage of the bandedness of both the discretized f and the Jacobian of the system of differential equations.

NOTATION

a_v	surface area of the catalyst per unit volume
C	concentration
C_∞	concentration at the surface of the catalyst
C_p	heat capacity
D	diffusivity or dispersion coefficient
E	axial dispersion coefficient for heat
$F_{i,j}$	gas exchange coefficient between phases i and j
J	mass flux
$-(\Delta H)$	heat of reaction
h	local heat transfer coefficient
k	thermal conductivity of reactant fluid
k_1	first-order reaction rate constant
k_g	mass transfer coefficient
L	length of the tubular reactor
L_{mf}	height of the bed at minimum fluidization
M	molecular weight
q	energy flux
R	radius of the tube
r_c	reaction term
T	temperature of the reactant fluid
T_∞	surface temperature of the catalyst
T_w	temperature of the wall of the tubular reactor
U	overall heat transfer coefficient
u	fluid velocity
$\bar{u}$	mean linear velocity
u_∞	superficial velocity
$W_{i,j}$	approximation of $C(z_i, t_j)$

Greek Letters

δ_x	unit vector in the x-direction
ε_i	void fraction of phase i
ζ	effectiveness factor
η_i	volume fraction of the bed occupied by phase i
$\lambda(z, t)$	instantaneous reaction rate or intensity of reaction
$\mu(z, t)$	instantaneous mean or drift coefficient
ρ	mean density of reactant fluid
$\sigma^2(z, t)$	instantaneous variance

Subscript

b	bulk
f	fluid
in	inlet section
j	j-th component
L	longitudinal
o	initial condition
out	outlet section
R	radial
s	solid
w	wall of the tubular reactor

REFERENCES

1. Aris, R., *Introduction to the Analysis of Chemical Reactors*, Prentice-Hall, Englewood Cliffs, NJ, 1965.
2. Hill, C. G., *Introduction to Chemical Engineering Kinetics and Reactor Design*, Wiley, New York, 1977.
3. Levenspiel, O., Chemical Reaction Engineering, 2nd ed., Wiley, New York, 1972.
4. Wen, C. Y., and Fan, L. T., *Models for Flow Systems and Chemical Reactors*, Marcel-Dekker, New York, 1975.
5. Nauman, E. B., and Buffham, B. A., *Mixing in Continuous Flow Systems*, Wiley, New York, 1983.
6. Froment, G. F., and Bischoff, K. B., *Chemical Reaction Analysis and Design*, Wiley, New York, 1979.
7. Nauman, E. B., *Chemical Reactor Design*, Wiley, New York, 1987.
8. Levenspiel, O., and Bischoff, K. B., "Patterns of Flow in Chemical Process Vessels," in *Advances in Chemical Engineering*, ed. by Drew, T. B., Hoopers, J. W., and Vermeulen, T., Vol. 4, Academic Press, New York, 1963.
9. Nauman, E. B., and Mallikarjun, R., "Generalized Boundary Conditions for the Axial Dispersion Model," *Chem. Eng. J.*, 26, 231–237 (1983).
10. McLaughlin, H. S., Mallikarjun, R., and Nauman, E. B., "The Effect of Radial Velocities on Laminar Flow, Tubular Reactor Models," *AICHE J.*, 32, 419 (1986).
11. Choi, C. Y., and Perlmutter, D. D., "A Unified Treatment of the Inlet Boundary Condition for Dispersive Flow Models," *Chem. Eng. Sci.*, 31, 250 (1976).
12. Wehner, J. F., and Wilhelm, R. H., "Boundary Conditions of Flow Reactor," *Chem. Eng. Sci.*, 6, 89 (1956).
13. Nauman, E. B., "Residence Time Distribution in Systems Governed by the Dispersion Equation," *Chem. Eng. Sci.*, 36, 957 (1981).
14. Cox, D. R., and Miller, H. D., *The theory of Stochastic Process*, Wiley, New York, 1965.
15. Too, J. R., Fan, L. T., and Nassar, R., "A Stochastic Axial Dispersion Model for Tubular Flow Reactors," *Chem. Eng. Sci.*, 41, 2341–2346 (1986).
16. McQuarrie, D. A., "Stochastic Approach to Chemical Kinetics," *J. Appl. Prob.*, 4, 413–479 (1967).
17. Fan, L. T., Too, J. R., and Nassar, R., "Stochastic Flow Reactor Modeling: A General Continuous Time Compartmental Model with First-Order Reactions," in *Residence Time Distribution Theory in Chemical Engineering*, ed. by Petho, A., and Noble, R. D., Verlag Chemie, Weinheim, West Germany, 1982.

18. Ishida, K., "The Stochastic Model for Unimolecular Gas Reaction," *Bull. Chem. Soc., Japan*, 33, 1030 (1960).
19. Fan, L. T., and Shin, S. H., "Stochastic Diffusion Model for Non-ideal Mixing in a Horizontal Drum Mixer," *Chem. Eng. Sci.*, 34, 811 (1979).
20. Yariv, A., *An Introduction to Theory and Application of Quantum Mechanics*, Wiley, New York, 1982.
21. Fan, L. T., Shin, S. H., and Fan, L. S., "A Model for Dynamics of Expansion of Gas-Solid Fluidized Beds," *I & EC Fundamentals*, 19, 156–159 (1980).
22. Kimura, M., *Diffusion Models in Population Genetics*, Metheun, London, 1963.
23. Bird, R. B., Stewart, W. E., and Lightfoot, E. N., *Transport Phenomena*, Wiley, New York, 1960.
24. Lee, H. S., *Heterogeneous Reactor Design*, Butterworth, Boston, 1984.
25. Smith, J. M., *Chemical Engineering Kinetics*, 3rd ed., McGraw-Hill, New York, 1981.
26. Chen, N. H., *Process Reactor Design*, Allyn and Bacon, Newton, MA, 1983.
27. Chen, L. H., and Too, J. R., "Fluidized Bed Models," in *Encyclopedia of Fluid Mechanics, Vol. 4—Solids and Gas-Solids Flows*, ed. by Cheremisinoff, N. P., Gulf Publishing, Houston, TX, 1986.
28. Fan, L. S., and Fan, L. T., "Transient and Steady State Characteristics of a Gaseous Reactant in Catalytic Fluidized-Bed Reactors," *AICHE J.*, 26, 139–144 (1980).
29. Wen, C. Y., "Models for Flow Systems and Chemical Reactors," in *Residence Time Distribution Theory in Chemical Engineering*, ed. by Petho, A., and Noble, R. D., Verlag Chemie, Weinheim, West Germany, 1982.
30. Davis, M. E., *Numerical Methods and Modeling for Chemical Engineers*, Wiley, New York, 1984.
31. Lapidus, L., and Pinder, G. F., *Numerical Solution of Partial Differential Equations in Science and Engineering*, Wiley, New York, 1982.
32. Ames, W. F., *Numerical Methods for Partial Differential Equations*, Academic Press, New York, 1977.
33. Gladwell, J., and Wait, R., *A Survey of Numerical Methods for Partial Differential Equations*, Oxford University Press (1979).
34. Rice, J. R., *Numerical Methods, Software, and Analysis*, McGraw-Hill, New York, 1983.
35. Atkinson, K. E., *An Introduction to Numerical Analysis*, Wiley, New York, 1978.
36. Machura, M., and Sweet, R., "Survey of Software for Partial Differential Equations," ACM Trans. Math. Software, 6, 461 (1980).
37. Sincovec, R. F., and Madsen, N. K., Software for Nonlinear Partial Differential Equations," ACM Trans. Math. Software, 1, 232 (1975).
38. Madsen, N. K., and Sincovec, R. F., "PDECOL, General Collocation Software for Partial Differential Equations," ACM Trans. Math. Software, 5, 326 (1979).
39. Melgaard, D., and Sincovec, R., "General Software for Two Dimensional Nonlinear Partial Differential Equations," ACM Trans. Math. Software, 7, 106 (1981).
40. Hindmarsh, A. C., "GEARB: Solution of Ordinary Differential Equations Having Banded Jacobians," Lawrence Livermore Laboratory Report UCID-30059 (1975).
41. Swell, G., "IMSL Software for Differential Equations in One Space Variable," IMSL Tech. Report No. 8202 (1982).
42. International Mathematics and Statistics Libraries Inc., Sixth Floor-NBC Building, 7500 Bellaire Blvd., Houston, TX.

CHAPTER 27

SENSITIVITY ANALYSIS OF CHEMICAL REACTORS: GENERAL CONCEPTS AND APPLICATIONS

Stefan H. Ungureanu

Politechnical Institute of Iasi
Faculty of Chemical Technology
Iasi, Romania

CONTENTS

GENERAL CONCEPTS

Let us consider the mathematical model of a continuous dynamic system in the form of a vectorial state equation:

$$\dot{x}(\tau) = f(x(\tau), u(\tau), p(\tau), \tau) \tag{1}$$

with the initial condition $x(\tau_0) = x_0$ and the relationships system for calculating the output quantities:

$$y(\tau) = g(x(\tau), u(\tau), p(\tau), \tau) \tag{2}$$

where $x(\tau)$ = state vector having n elements
$u(\tau)$ = vector of control inputs (monitoring values) with ℓ elements
$p(\tau)$ = vector of parameters with m elements
f = continuous function vector satisfying the Lipschitz condition with n elements
$y(\tau)$ = output vector with r elements
g = function vector with r elements
τ = independent variable (in particular, time)

The input $u(\tau)$ causes the system described by Equation 1, if stable to pass from its initial state $x_0 = x(\tau_0)$, at the initial moment $\tau = \tau_0$, to the final state $x_f = x(\tau_f)$, at the final moment $\tau = \tau_f$, on the $x(\tau)$ trajectory—the solution of the Equation 1:

$$x(\tau) = x(x_0, u(\tau), p(\tau), \tau) \tag{3}$$

A variation of the state vector $x(\tau_1)$, with $\Delta x(\tau_1)$, and/or of the control vector $u(\tau_1)$ with $\Delta u(\tau_1)$, and/or of the parameter vector, $p(\tau_1)$ with $\Delta p(\tau_1)$, occurring at moment τ_1, $\tau_0 \leq \tau_1 \leq \tau_f$, determines the change of the state and output vector at all the moments subsequent to moment τ_1. The state and output trajectories are changed, starting from the τ_1 moment from the nominal ones, with $\Delta x(\tau)$ and $\Delta y(\tau)$, respectively.

The problem that interests us consists in the calculation of these deviations when the state, control inputs, and parameters modifications are known, without integrating each time the mathematical model. Also, of special significance are the parameters and control inputs on the hierarchical system, according to the influence of its variations on the state of the considered system, i.e. to the sensitivity of the system relative to these magnitudes.

The sensitivity of the system (Equation 1) can be investigated with respect to:

1. The state vector—particularly the initial state vector, establishing the influence of changes of the initial state on the state or output trajectories in time.
2. The control inputs vector—establishing the influence of the monitoring values changes on the state and output vectors.
3. The parameters vector—the so called "parametric sensitivity," establishing the influence of the parameters deviations on the state and output trajectories.

The general sensitivity analysis (GSA) of the systems considers two features: the direct sensitivity analysis (DSA) and the inverse sensitivity analysis (ISA).

The direct sensitivity analysis (DSA) of a system is a method for determining the influence of the small deviations of the initial state, of control inputs and parameters, from the ideal nominal values on the state trajectory and the system output in time. It considers the relative order, as regards the significance of these influences.

The matrices of sensitivity functions are calculated for that purpose.

The inverse sensitivity analysis (ISA) is an opposite problem to the one above. Starting from the measurement of the trajectory deviation of the state of a real system that is perturbed, in time, from the trajectory of the ideal model, this method determines the causes leading to this deviation—the values of changes of the initial state, of the parameters and control inputs—and is the so called "technical diagnosis" of the system.

A particular case of the general sensitivity analysis of a dynamic system consists of the *structural sensitivity analysis* (SSA), which deals with that small modifications of some parameters of a system that lead to the structural modification of the system [1, 2]. By "structural modification" we mean the fundamental change of the dynamic type (category) of a system.

APPLICATIONS OF THE GENERAL SENSITIVITY ANALYSIS TO THE CHEMICAL ENGINEERING SYSTEMS [3]

Mathematical Modeling and System Identification

The sensitivity analysis is a means for determining the required accuracy of the model and for the model simplification. The parameters to which the system state or output exhibits a low sensitivity can be considered in the model as having constant values, determined with low accuracy, which results in lowering the expenditures for modeling and identifying.

As already known, the mathematical model of a chemical industrial system consists of the mathematical models of the various component subsystems. For most chemical processes there are both simplified mathematical models of low accuracy, and very accurate but complicated models with difficult calculations. The choice of only partial models of the highest accuracy can lead to an extremely complicated and expensive general model. The sensitivity analysis of the general model with respect to all of the parameters allows the detection of those subsystems for which the considered models can be of lower accuracy [4]–[11].

Design of Engineering Systems

In designing equipment, some material sizes and constants taken from catalogues and standards will not coincide with calculated values, however small the difference is. In such situations the problem arises in what way and how much the dynamics of the process deviate from results expected from design calculations. DSA allows not only a fast answer to this question, but on the basis of the information it provides, it can also suggest convenient alternatives for the design [12]–[18]. Some conditions, with respect to which the process is very sensitive, will be chosen and kept strictly constant, while others, whose influence is smaller, can be chosen from a wider area of possibilities. The conditions that significantly influence the process can thus be chosen according to how well they reciprocally interact.

Determining the optimal safety factor is another application of DSA in designing industrial systems. With increasing system complexity and expenses, the empirical selection of the safety factor cannot be accepted any more. Based on the knowledge of the sensitivity matrices, minimum values for these safety factors can be settled on a real basis.

Exploitation of Engineering Systems

The efficient control of an industrial system implies the adequate selection of the control quantities and their suitable changes. By adequate selection means the choice of those controls that most greatly influence a process, and quantities to which the system has the highest sensitivity.

The analysis of direct sensitivity of the industrial system to all the control inputs permits a hierarchy of controls according to their influence on the system and, facilitates the selection of control inputs and the order of their use [2, 8, 10, 14, 19–27].

At the same time, the sensitivity analysis is a way for establishing the required accuracy of the control systems of the industrial systems.

The inverse sensitivity analysis, which estimates in real time the causes that deflect the working of the system from the desired trajectory (technical diagnosis) without directly measuring these causes, has applicability in the optimal system control, by means of the process computers [2, 3, 24–26, 29].

Optimization of the Engineering Systems

Often, the optimal regime calculated for the exploitation of a chemical industrial system is placed in the working range of high parametric sensitivity, which can result in small, unavoidable parametric changes causing significant deviations of the system trajectory from the calculated optimal form. In these cases it is advisable that the initial optimization problem be accompanied by the additional restrictions regarding the parametric sensitivity of the system.

Generally, the optimization parameters of the mathematical model of a chemical system are found to be somewhat inaccurate when compared to experimental data. In addition, these values modify in time, in the real system, as a consequence of external actions (material aging, soiling, etc.).

If the calculated exploitation model is placed in the range of high parametric sensitivity then, as a consequence of the inaccuracy in taking the values of some parameters, the real working regime can be found far from the optimal calculated one.

In solving the optimal problem it is necessary to compromise between optimality and sensitivity, that is the decision variables must be selected so that the calculated objective functions are less sensitive to the parameters even if the working regime is not optimal, but merely in the "neighborhood." Therefore, selecting decision variables and determining their optimal values must be based not only on optimum conditions but also on the sensitivity conditions of the system. This means that the optimization problem has two criteria: minimum cost and minimum sensitivity, or maximum yield and minimum parametric sensitivity.

The problem is solved in many ways [4, 12, 30–34] of which only two are mentioned here. [35, 36].

If the initial optimization task were:

$$\min_{u} \{J(x, u, p)\}$$

to minimize the sensitivity of objective function towards the variation of parameters without increasing essentially the optimal value of the objective function, one would proceed as follows:

1. The objective function is enlarged by introducing a sensitivity term and the task becomes:

   $$\min_{u} \{J(x, u, p) + \lambda S_p^J(x, u, p)\}$$

   where λ represents a weight factor expressing the extent to which the sensitivity of the objective function has to be diminished.
2. The original objective function is kept but additional sensitivity restrictions are introduced, the problem becoming [4]:

   $$\min_{u} \{J(x, u, p)\}$$

   $$S_p^{*J}(x, u, p) \leqslant \sigma$$

Both methods lead to an optimal value J^{opt} different from the ideal one, obtained without considering the sensitivity of the objective function, but this deviation is accepted because the optimal regime becomes more stable.

Thus, the practical application of the last method to the optimization of a tubular reactor, in which an exothermic first order irreversible reaction occurs, by considering the sensitivity of overall expenses as an objective function, and the change of overall heat transfer coefficients as parameters, indicated that sensitivity diminution by 35% resulted in an increase of the overall expenses of only 3.6% [36].

NOTATION

f	vector of functions $f(x(\tau), u(\tau), p(\tau), \tau)$, Equation 1
g	vector of functions $g(x(\tau), u(\tau), p(\tau), \tau)$, Equation 2
J	objective function
p	vector of parameters
S_p^J	matrix of sensitivity functions of objective function with respect to parameters
u	vector of control inputs
x	vector of state variables
y	vector of output variables
Δp	deviation of vector p
Δu	deviation of vector u
Δx	deviation of vector x
y	deviation of vector y
λ	weight factor
σ	matrix of small constants
τ	time

Subscripts

0	initial time
f	final time
1	any time

Superscripts

*	dimensionless

REFERENCES

1. Tomovič, R., and Vukobratovič, M., *General Theory of Sensitivity*, Sovietskoye Radio, Moscow, p. 19, 52–73 (in Russian).
2. Ungureanu, S., *Sensitivity of Technical Dynamic Systems*, Technica, Bucharest, 1988 (in press) (in Romanian).
3. Ungureanu, S., "Applications of Cybernetics Methods to Sensitivity Analysis of the Chemical Engineering Systems," *Proceedings of Symposium on Cybernetics and Consonantism*, Iasi, Romania, 1986.
4. Chang, T. M., and Wen, C. Y., "Sensitivity Analysis in Optimal Systems Based on the Maximum Principle," *Ind. Eng. Chem., Fdtls.*, 7, 422 (1968).
5. Ghibu, C., Malanca, C., and Petrila, C., "Sensitivity of Reacting Zone of a Reactor for Ammonia Synthesis Relative to Changes in the Synthesis Gas Composition," *Rev. Chim.* (*Buc.*), 23, 155 (1972) (in Romanian).
6. Ungureanu, S., and Petrila, C., "Parametric Sensitivity of a Continuous Reactor with Perfect Mixing under Dynamic Condition," *Rev. Chim.* (*Buc.*), 32, 1088 (1981) (in Romanian).
7. Ungureanu, S., Curievici, I., and Petrila, C., "Sensitivity of a Multitubular Catalytic Reactor for Strong Exothermal Processes," *Rev. Chim.* (*Buc.*), 33, 255 (1982) (in Romanian).
8. Ungureanu, S., Petrila, C., and Curievici, I., "The Sensitivity Analysis of a Chemical Reactor as a Dynamic System," *Mem. Sect. St. Acad. R.S.R., Ser. IV*, 5, 267 (1982).
9. Thomas, I. M., and Kiparissides, C., "Sensitivity Analysis of a Batch Polymerization Reactor," *J. Appl. Polym. Sci.*, 29, 2195 (1984).
10. Morbidelli, M., and Varma, A., "Parametric Sensitivity and Runaway in Tubular Reactors," *A.I.Ch.E. Journal*, 28, 705 (1982).
11. Hosten, L. H., and Froment, G. F., "Parametric Sensitivity in Co-Currently Cooled Tubular Reactors," *Chem. Eng. Sci.*, 41, 1073 (1986).
12. Watanabe, N., Nishimura, Y., and Matsubara, M., "Optimal Design of Chemical Processes Involving Parameter Uncertainty," *Chem. Eng. Sci.* 28, 905 (1973).
13. Priestley, A. J., and Agnew, J. B., "Sensitivity Analysis in the Design of a Packed Bed Reactor," *Ind. Eng. Chem. Proc. Des. Dev.*, 14, 171 (1975).
14. Welsnaere Van, R. J., and Froment, G. F., "Parametric Sensitivity and Runaway in Fixed Bed Catalytic Reactors," *Chem. Eng. Sci.*, 25, 1503 (1970).
15. Bailey, J. E., "Sensitivity Analysis for a Chemical Reaction in a Porous Catalyst with External Heat and Mass Transfer Resistance," *Chem. Eng. Sci.*, 28, 1417 (1973).
16. Václavek, V., Rajniak, P., and Ilavsky, J., "Sensitivity Analysis in Balance Computations of Complex Chemical Processes," *Che. Eng. Commun.*, 0098-6445/79/0304-0377, Gordon and Breach Science Publishers, Inc., U.S.A., 1979, p. 377.
17. Bilous, O., and Amundson, R., "Chemical Reactor Stability and Sensitivity," *A.I.Ch.E. Journal*, 2, 117 (1956).
18. Takamatsu, T., Hashimoto, I., and Ohno, H., "Optimal Design of Large Scale Complex Systems from the Viewpoint of Sensitivity Analysis," *Ind. Eng. Chem., Proc. Des. Dev.*, 9, 369 (1970).
19. Takamatsu, T., "Optimum Design and Operation of Chemical Processes from the Point of View of Sensitivity Analysis," Preprints of II-nd IFAC Symposium on Sensitivity and Adaptivity, Dubrovnik, 1968.
20. Wahrman, S., and Dayan, J., "Optimal Control for a Simple Batch Reactor Alternatives on Parametric Sensitivity," *Israel J. of Technology*, 17, 139 (1979).
21. Curievici, I., Ungureanu, S., and Petrila, C., "Sensitivity of a Nonisothermal Continuous—Stirred—Tank Reactor Relative to Its Initial State," *Bul. Inst. Politeh.*, Iasi, *XXVIII*(*XXXII*), 51 (1982).
22. Ungureanu, S., and Petrila, C., "Sensitivity Analysis of a Chemical Reactor with Respect to the Control Inputs," *Int. Chem. Eng.*, 25, 693 (1985), reprinted from *Rev. Chim.* (*Buc.*), 33, 1125 (1982).
23. Ungureanu, S., Macoveanu, M., and Petrila, C., "Investigation on Sensitivity of a Reactor for Vynil Chloride Suspension Polymerization Under Constant Temperature," *Rev. Roum. Chim.* (Buc.), 28, 763 (1983) (in German).

24. Ungureanu, S., "Technical Diagnosis of a Chemical Reactor by the Inverse Sensitivity Analysis," *Rev. Chim.* (Buc.), 35, 1097 (1984) (in Romanian).
25. Ungureanu, S., Petrila, C., and Tudose, R. Z., "General Sensitivity Analysis of the Jacketed Heat—Exchangers," *Rev. Chim.* (Buc.), 36, 527 (1985) (in Romanian).
26. Mihail, R., Maria, Gh., and Tao, L. C., "Determination of the Operating Condition for a Reactor for Nitrobenzene Hydrogenation by Means of Sensitivity Analysis," *Rev. Chim.* (Buc.), 34, 718 (1983).
27. Morbidelli, M., and Varma, A., "On Parametric Sensitivity and Runaway Criteria of Pseudo-homogeneous Tubular Reactors," *Chem. Eng. Sci.*, 40, 2165 (1985).
28. Ungureanu, S., and Petrila, C., "Application of Inverse Sensitivity Method from the Optimal Systems Theory to the Technical Diagnosis of a Chemical Reactor," *Applied Cybernetics* (Manescu, M., Florescu, M., and Niculescu-Mizil, E., coord.), Ed. Acad. R.S.R., Bucharest, 1985, p. 223–228 (in Romanian).
29. Ungureanu, S., "Method for Increasing the Accuracy of Sensitivity Analysis of a Dynamic System," Proceedings of Third National Conference on Cybernetics, Bucharest, 1985 (in Romanian).
30. Seinfeld, I., and McBridge, "Optimization with Multiple Performance Criteria," *Ind. Eng. Chem., Proc. Des. Dev.*, 9, 53 (1970).
31. Röhrer, R. A., and Sobral, M., "Sensitivity Consideration in Optimal System Design," *IEEE Trans., Autom. Contr., AC-10,* 43 (1965).
32. Chen, M. S. K., Erikson, L. E., and Fan, L. T., "Consideration of Sensitivity and Parameter Uncertainty on Optimal Process Design," *Ind. Eng. Chem., Proc. Des. Dev.*, 9, 514 (1970).
33. Nishida, N., Ichikawa, A., and Tazaki, E., "Optimal Design and Control in a Class of Distributed Parameter System Under Uncertainty," *A.I.Ch.E. Journal*, 18, 561 (1973).
34. Wen, C. Y., and Chang, T. M., "Optimal Design of Systems Involving Parameter Uncertainty," *Ind. Eng. Chem., Proc. Des. Dev.*, 7, 48 (1968).
35. Dittmar, R., and Hartman, K., "Application of Sensitivity Analysis to the Structure of the Systems of Processes and Apparatuses," *Wiss., Z.TH. Leuna-Merseburg*, 18, 26 (1976) (in German).
36. Dittmar, R., Hartman, K., and Ostrovski, G. M., "Application of Sensitivity Theory Methods to Studying and Optimization of Chemical Technological Systems," *Teor. Osn. Khim. Tech., XII*, 104 (1978) (in Russian).

CHAPTER 28

DIRECT SENSITIVITY ANALYSIS OF CHEMICAL REACTORS

S. H. Ungureanu

Politechnical Institute of Iasi
Faculty of Chemical Technology
Iasi, Romania

CONTENTS

SENSITIVITY FUNCTIONS MATRICES

Let us consider, for the beginning, the simplest but the common case of the continuous nonlinear with the nonvariant in time parameters and control inputs system, having the mathematical model:

$$\dot{x}(\tau) = f(x(\tau), u, p, \tau) \tag{1}$$

$$y(\tau) = g(x(\tau), u, p, \tau) \tag{2}$$

with the initial condition $x(\tau_0) = x_0$.

A step variation Δx_0, of the initial state vector, Δp, of the parameters vector and/or Δu, of the control vector, occurs at the initial moment τ_0.

We denote:

$\Delta_{x_{j,0}} x_i(\tau)$ = the deviation of the x_i component of the state trajectory caused by the $\Delta x_{j,0}$ perturbing component only

$$\Delta_{x_{j,0}} x_i(\tau) = x_i(x_{1,0}, x_{2,0}, \ldots, x_{j,0} + \Delta x_{j,0}, \ldots, x_{n,0}, u, p, \tau) - x_i(x_0, u, p, \tau) \tag{3}$$

$\Delta_{u_j} x_i(\tau)$ = the deviation of the x_i component of the state trajectory, caused by the Δu_j perturbing component only

$$\Delta_{u_j} x_i(\tau) = x_i(x_0, u_1, u_2, \ldots, u_j + \Delta u_j, \ldots, u_l, p, \tau) - x_i(x_0, u, p, \tau) \tag{4}$$

$\Delta_{p_j} x_i(\tau)$ = the deviation of the x_i component of the state trajectory, caused by the Δp_j perturbing component only

$$\Delta_{p_j} x_i(\tau) = x_i(x_0, u, p_1, p_2, \ldots, p_j + \Delta p_j, \ldots, p_m, \tau) - x_i(x_0, u, p, \tau) \tag{5}$$

The *state sensitivity functions matrices* are defined:

- The sensitivity functions matrices of the state relative to the initial state, $S^x_{xo}(\tau, \tau_0)$:

$$S^x_{xo}(\tau, \tau_0) = [S^{x_i}_{x_j}(\tau, \tau_0)]_0 \triangleq \left[\lim_{\Delta x_{j,o}\to 0} \frac{\Delta_{x_{j,o}} x_i(\tau)}{\Delta x_{j,o}}\right] = \left[\frac{\partial x_i}{\partial x_j}\right]_0 \qquad i = \overline{1, n};\ j = \overline{1, n} \tag{6}$$

- The sensitivity functions matrices of the state relative to the control inputs, $S^x_u(\tau)$:

$$S^x_u(\tau) = [S^{x_i}_{u_j}(\tau)] \triangleq \left[\lim_{\Delta u_j\to 0} \frac{\Delta_{u_j} x_i(\tau)}{\Delta u_j}\right] = \left[\frac{\partial x_i}{\partial u_j}\right] \qquad i = 1, n;\ j = 1, l \tag{7}$$

- The sensitivity functions matrices of the state relative to the parameters (the parametric sensitivity), $S^x_p(\tau)$:

$$S^x_p(\tau) = [S^{x_i}_{p_j}(\tau)] = \left[\lim_{\Delta p_j\to 0} \frac{\Delta_{p_j} x_i(\tau)}{\Delta p_j}\right] = \left[\frac{\partial x_i}{\partial p_j}\right] \qquad i = 1, n;\ j = 1, m \tag{8}$$

The concept of *dimensionless sensitivity functions matrices*, denoted by S^{*x}_{xo}, S^{*x}_u, S^{*x}_p, is introduced to facilitate the comparison and array of the influences of the different vector components Δx_0, Δp and Δu:

$$S^{*x}_{xo} = \left[\frac{\partial x_i}{\partial x_{j,o}} \frac{x_{j,o}}{x_i}\right] = \left[S^{x_i}_{x_{j,o}} \frac{x_{j,o}}{x_i}\right], \qquad i = \overline{1, n};\ j = \overline{1, n}$$

$$S^{*x}_u = \left[\frac{\partial x_i}{\partial u_j} \frac{u_j}{x_i}\right] = \left[S^{x_i}_{u_j} \frac{u_j}{x_i}\right], \qquad i = \overline{1, n};\ j = \overline{1, l} \tag{9}$$

$$S^{*x}_p = \left[\frac{\partial x_i}{\partial p_j} \frac{p_j}{x_i}\right] = \left[S^{x_i}_{p_j} \frac{p_j}{x_i}\right], \qquad i = \overline{1, n};\ j = \overline{1, m}$$

The *sensitivity matrices of the output relative to initial state, to control inputs and parameters* are defined in the same manner as state sensitivity matrices:

$$S^y_{xo}(\tau, \tau_0) = [S^{y_i}_{x_{j,o}}(\tau, \tau_0)] \triangleq \left[\lim_{\Delta x_{j,o}\to 0} \frac{\Delta_{x_{j,o}} y_i(\tau)}{\Delta x_{j,o}}\right] = \left[\frac{\partial y_i}{\partial x_j}\right]_0 \qquad i = \overline{1, r};\ j = \overline{1, n}$$

$$S^y_u(\tau) = [S^{y_i}_{u_j}(\tau)] \triangleq \left[\lim_{\Delta u_j\to 0} \frac{\Delta_{u_j} y_i(\tau)}{\Delta u_j}\right] = \left[\frac{\partial y_i}{\partial u_j}\right] \qquad i = \overline{1, r};\ j = \overline{1, l} \tag{10}$$

$$S^y_p(\tau) = [S^{y_i}_{p_j}(\tau)] \triangleq \left[\lim_{\Delta p_j\to 0} \frac{\Delta_{p_j} y_i(\tau)}{\Delta p_j}\right] = \left[\frac{\partial y_i}{\partial p_j}\right] \qquad i = \overline{1, r};\ j = \overline{1, m}$$

where:

$$\Delta_{xj,o} y_i(\tau) = [y_i(x(x_{1,o}, x_{2,o}, \ldots, x_{j,o} + \Delta x_{j,o}, \ldots, x_{n,o}, u, p, \tau), u, p, \tau) - y_i(x(x_0, u, p, \tau), u, 0, \tau)]$$

$$\Delta_{uj} y_i(\tau) = [y_i(x(x_0, u_1, u_2, \ldots, u_j + \Delta u_j, \ldots, u_1, p, \tau), u_1, u_2, \ldots, u_j + \Delta u_j, \ldots, u_1, p, \tau) - y_i(x(x_0, u, p, \tau), u, p, \tau)] \tag{11}$$

$$\Delta_{pj} y_i(\tau) = [y_i(x(x_0, u, p_1, p_2, \ldots, p_j + \Delta p_j, \ldots, p_m, \tau), u, p_1, p_2, \ldots, p_j + \Delta p_j, \ldots, p_m, \tau) - y_i(x(x_0, u, p, \tau), u, p, \tau)]$$

If the deviations of the state, of the control inputs and of the parameters occur at any moment $\tau_1 \neq \tau_0$, the definitions of the sensitivity matrices are the same. For instance,

$$S^x_{x_{\tau_1}} \triangleq \left[\frac{x_i}{x_j}\right]_{\tau_1}, \qquad i = \overline{1, n}; j = \overline{1, n} \tag{12}$$

The computing algorithm of these matrices is what changes.

The direct sensitivity problem (DSA) is completely solved by calculating the sensitivity functions matrices.

By denoting:

$\Delta_{x_0}x(\tau)$ = the deviation of the state trajectory caused by the initial state change, Δx_0, only

$\Delta_u x(\tau)$ = the deviation of the state trajectory caused by the change at the initial moment of the control inputs, Δu, only

$\Delta_p x(\tau)$ = the deviation of the state trajectory caused by the variation at the initial moment of the parameters, Δ_p, only; once the matrices of direct sensitivity functions are settled (Equations 6, 7, and 8) these deviations of state from the nominal trajectories can be calculated by means of the relationships:

$$\begin{aligned} \Delta_{x_0}x(\tau) &\cong S^x_{x_0} \cdot \Delta x_0 \\ \Delta_u x(\tau) &\cong S^x_u \cdot \Delta u \\ \Delta_p x(\tau) &\cong S^x_p \cdot \Delta p \end{aligned} \tag{13}$$

If the perturbing actions, Δx_0, Δu, Δp, simultaneously occur at the initial moment, the resulting deviation of the state trajectory in time is:

$$\Delta x(\tau) = \Delta_{x_0}x(\tau) + \Delta_u x(\tau) + \Delta_p x(\tau) \tag{14}$$

Relationships 13 are approximate; the exact relationship for $\Delta_{x_0}x(\tau)$, for instance, is:

$$\Delta_{x_0}x(\tau) = \left[\frac{\Delta_{x_{j,0}}x_i}{\Delta x_{j,0}} \Delta x_{j,0}\right]; \qquad i = \overline{1, n}; j = \overline{1, n} \tag{15}$$

The deviations of the system output, caused by the changes of the initial state, control inputs or parameters are computed in the same way, by relationships:

$$\begin{aligned} \Delta_{x_0}y(\tau) &\cong S^y_{x_0} \cdot \Delta x_0 \\ \Delta_u y(\tau) &\cong S^y_u \cdot \Delta u \\ \Delta_p y(\tau) &\cong S^y_p \cdot \Delta p \end{aligned} \tag{16}$$

and

$$\Delta y(\tau) = \Delta_{x_0}y(\tau) + \Delta_u y(\tau) + \Delta_p y(\tau) \tag{17}$$

respectively.

To be able to order the initial states, the control inputs and parameters by the sensitivity of the system relative to their variations the dimensionless sensitivity functions matrices 9 are computed and compared to each other.

THE SENSITIVITY EQUATIONS: THE DSA ALGORITHMS

Sensitivity Relative to Initial State and to State at Any Moment

The sensitivity of the state relative to initial state. The sensitivity matrix $S^{x}_{xo}(\tau, \tau_0)$ is computed as solution of the sensitivity equations system [1–4]:

$$\dot{S}^{x}_{xo}(\tau, \tau_0) = f_x(x_0, u, p, \tau) \cdot S^{x}_{xo}(\tau, \tau_0) \tag{18}$$

with initial condition

$$S^{x}_{xo}(\tau_0, \tau_0) = 1, \forall \tau_0 \tag{19}$$

where f_x is the Jacobian matrix of the vectorial function $f(x(\tau), u, p, \tau)$ with respect to $x(\tau)$ vector:

$$f_x = \begin{bmatrix} \frac{\partial f_1}{\partial x_1} & \frac{\partial f_1}{\partial x_2} & \cdots & \frac{\partial f_1}{\partial x_n} \\ \frac{\partial f_2}{\partial x_1} & \frac{\partial f_2}{\partial x_2} & \cdots & \frac{\partial f_2}{\partial x_n} \\ \cdots & \cdots & \cdots & \cdots \\ \frac{\partial f_n}{\partial x_1} & \frac{\partial f_n}{\partial x_2} & \cdots & \frac{\partial f_n}{\partial x_n} \end{bmatrix} \tag{20}$$

If the system is a continuous linear one, with the mathematical model:

$$\dot{x}(\tau) = A(p) \cdot x(\tau) + B(p) \cdot u \tag{21}$$

the sensitivity equation of the state relative to initial state has the particular shape:

$$\dot{S}^{x}_{xo}(\tau, \tau_0) = A(p) \cdot S^{x}_{xo}(\tau, \tau_0) \tag{22}$$

The sensitivity of the final state relative to initial state of a continuous system is obtained passing to limit in previous case, for $\tau = \tau_f$:

$$S^{x}_{xo}(\tau_f, \tau_0) = S^{x}_{xo}(\tau, \tau_0)\big|_{\tau=\tau_f} \tag{23}$$

and

$$S^{*x}_{xo}(\tau_f, \tau_0) = S^{*x}_{xo}(\tau, \tau_0)\big|_{\tau=\tau_f} \tag{24}$$

respectively.

The sensitivity of the system output with respect to initial state. If the system output is given by Equation 2:

$$y(\tau) = g(x(\tau), u, p, \tau)$$

then, the sensitivity equation of the output relative to initial state, has the evident form [4]:

$$S^{y}_{xo}(\tau, \tau_0) = g_x(\tau) \cdot S^{x}_{xo}(\tau, \tau_0) \tag{25}$$

where g_x is the Jacobian matrix of the functions g with respect to the state variables vector:

$$g_x(\tau) = \begin{bmatrix} \frac{\partial g_1}{\partial x_1} & \frac{\partial g_1}{\partial x_2} & \cdots & \frac{\partial g_1}{\partial x_n} \\ \frac{\partial g_2}{\partial x_1} & \frac{\partial g_2}{\partial x_2} & \cdots & \frac{\partial g_2}{\partial x_n} \\ \cdots & \cdots & \cdots & \cdots \\ \frac{\partial g_r}{\partial x_1} & \frac{\partial g_r}{\partial x_2} & \cdots & \frac{\partial g_r}{\partial x_n} \end{bmatrix} \tag{26}$$

For a linear relationship between system output and the state variables:

$$y(\tau) = C(p) \cdot x(\tau) + D(p) \cdot u \quad (27)$$

the sensitivity of the output is calculated by:

$$S^{y}_{x0}(\tau, \tau_0) = C(p) \cdot S^{x}_{x0}(\tau, \tau_0) \quad (28)$$

The computing algorithm of the sensitivity matrices of the state and output relative to initial state, for the continuous, linear and non-linear systems is described in the Figure 1.

The sensitivity of the final state relative to the state at any given moment. Let be the continuous linear system with the state Equation 1, as mathematical model. The control input u causes the unperturbed nominal trajectory of the state between the moments τ_0 and τ_f:

$$x(\tau) = x(x_0, u, p, \tau), \qquad \tau_0 \le \tau \le \tau_f \quad (29)$$

If at any moment τ_1, $\tau_0 \le \tau_1 \le \tau_f$, the state trajectory changes with $\Delta x(\tau_1) = \Delta x_1$, becoming $x_1 + \Delta x_1$, this variation brings about a corresponding state trajectory deviation from the moment τ_1, when the variation Δx_1 happens, to the final moment, τ_f. We denote this deviation by $\Delta_{x_1} x(\tau)$.

The sensitivity matrix $S^{x}_{x_1}(\tau)$ of the state at the moment τ, $\tau_1 \le \tau \le \tau_f$, relative to the state at moment τ_1 has to make possible to compute the state trajectory deviation, $\Delta_{x_1} x(\tau)$, by the relationship:

$$\Delta_{x_1} x(\tau) = S^{x}_{x_1}(\tau) \cdot \Delta x_1, \qquad \begin{matrix} \tau_1 \le \tau \le \tau_f \\ \tau_0 \le \tau_1 \le \tau_f \end{matrix} \quad (30)$$

Particularly, when $\tau = \tau_f$, the matrix $S^{x}_{x_1}(\tau)$ becomes $S^{x_f}_{x_1}(\tau)$.

This matrix cannot be computed by the same method as the matrix $S^{x}_{x0}(\tau)$, Equation 18.

Using the property of the invariance of the scalar product of the linear differential equations system solution and the solution of its adjoint system and changing the independent variable τ to θ by relationship:

$$\tau = \tau_f - \theta \quad (31)$$

we get the new differential equations system [4], [5]:

$$\dot{\Psi}(\theta) = f^{T}_{x}(\tau_f - \theta) \cdot \Psi(\theta) \quad (32)$$

with initial condition:

$$\Psi(\theta_0) = 1 \quad (33)$$

Once Equation 32 is integrated and the solution $\Psi(\theta)$ found, the sensitivity matrix $S^{x_f}_{x_1}(\tau)$ is computed by relationship:

$$S^{x_f}_{x_1}(\tau) = [\Psi(\theta)]^{T}\Big|_{\theta = \tau_f - \tau} \quad (34)$$

where the superscript T denotes the transposition operation.

The dimensionless sensitivity matrix of the final state with respect to the state at any given moment is calculated by the relationship similar to Equation 9:

$$S^{*x_f}_{x_1}(\tau) = \left[S^{x_{i,f}}_{x_{j,1}} \frac{x_j}{x_i} \right], \qquad i, j = \overline{1, n} \quad (35)$$

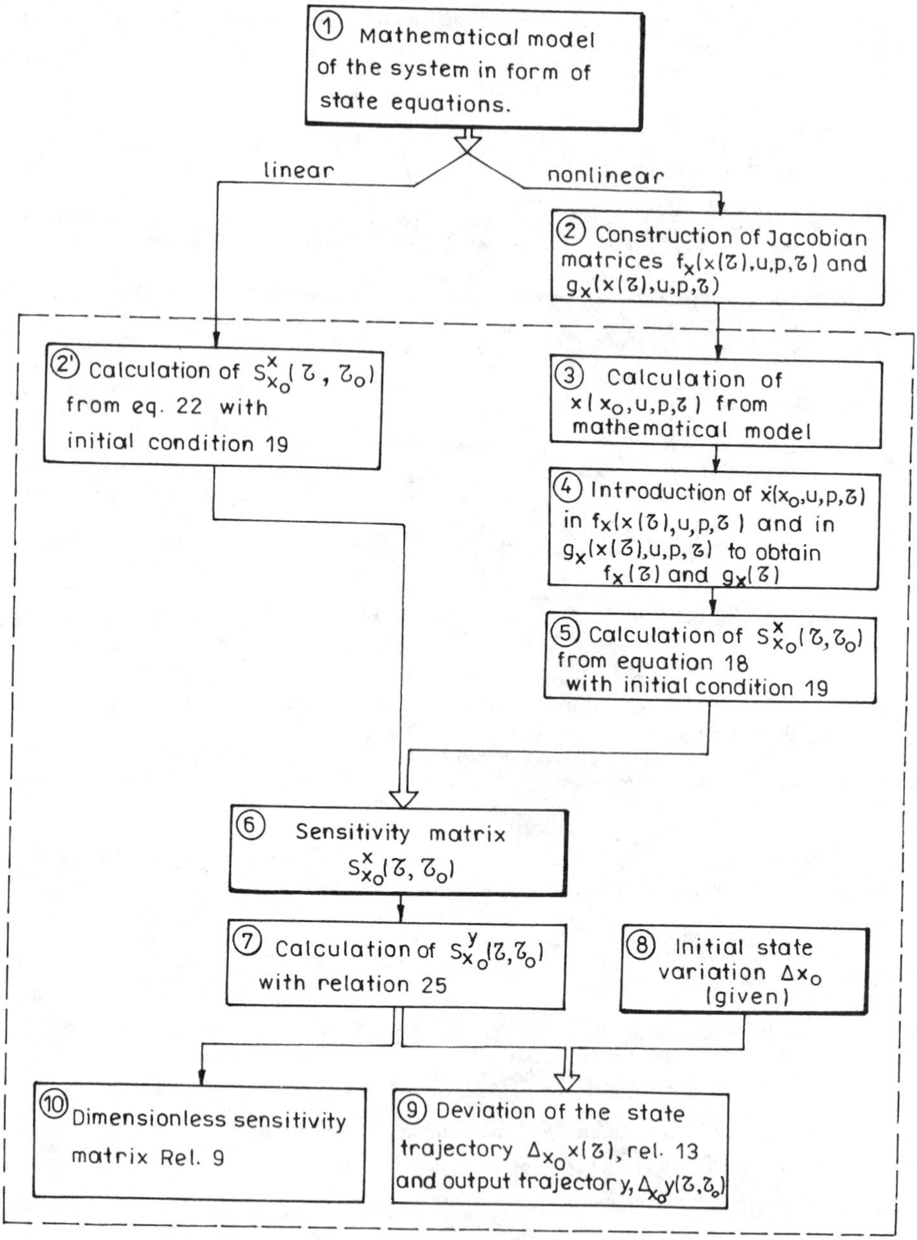

Figure 1. Logical diagram of the algorithm for analysis of the direct sensitivity of a continuous dynamic system with respect to its initial state.

The computing algorithm of the sensitivity matrix of the final state with respect to the state at any given moment, $S_{x_1}^{x_f}$, is described in the Figure 2:

Parametric Sensitivity

The sensitivity of the state with respect to the parameters with unchanging time deviations. Starting from the mathematical model of Equation 1, the solution that gives the unperturbed state trajectory, we consider the emergence at the moment τ_0 of the step variation of the parameters, a variation that forms the vector Δp.

The parametric sensitivity functions matrix of the state, $S_p^x(\tau)$, defined by Equation 8, is computed as solution of the sensitivity equation [3, 4, 6–8]:

$$\dot{S}_p^x(\tau) = f_x(x(\tau), u, p, \tau) \cdot S_p^x(\tau) + f_p \tag{36}$$

The initial condition is:

$$S_p^x(\tau_0) = 0 \tag{37}$$

In the differential equations system, Equation 36, f_x is the Jacobian matrix of the vectorial function $f(x(\tau), u, p, \tau)$ with respect to the vector $x(\tau)$, Equation 20, and f_p is the Jacobian matrix of the vectorial function $f(x(\tau), u, p, \tau)$ with respect to the vector p:

$$f_p = \begin{bmatrix} \frac{\partial f_1}{\partial p_1} & \frac{\partial f_1}{\partial p_2} & \cdots & \frac{\partial f_1}{\partial p_m} \\ \frac{\partial f_2}{\partial p_1} & \frac{\partial f_2}{\partial p_2} & \cdots & \frac{\partial f_2}{\partial p_m} \\ \cdots & \cdots & \cdots & \cdots \\ \frac{\partial f_n}{\partial p_1} & \frac{\partial f_n}{\partial p_2} & \cdots & \frac{\partial f_n}{\partial p_m} \end{bmatrix} \tag{38}$$

In the particular case of the linear continuous systems with the mathematical model given by the state Equation 21, in the parametric sensitivity Equation 36, the Jacobian matrices f_x and f_p have the shapes:

$$\begin{aligned} f_x &= A(p) \\ f_p &= A_p(p) \cdot x(\tau) + B_p(p) \cdot u \end{aligned} \tag{39}$$

where A_p and B_p are the Jacobian matrices of the vectorial functions A(p) and B(p) with respect to the parameters vector p:

$$A_p = \left[\frac{\partial A_i}{\partial p_j}\right], \quad B_p = \left[\frac{\partial B_i}{\partial p_j}\right]; \quad \begin{matrix} i = \overline{1, n} \\ j = \overline{1, m} \end{matrix} \tag{40}$$

The sensitivity of the output with respect to the parameters with unchanging time variations. Considering the computing relation of the output, Equation 2, the parametric sensitivity equation of the output gets the form:

$$S_p^y(\tau) = g_x(x(\tau), u, p, \tau) \cdot S_p^x(\tau) \tag{41}$$

in which the Jacobian matrix g_x is given by the Equation 26 and $S_p^x(\tau)$ is the parametric sensitivity matrix of the state.

In the case of the linear systems, Equation 27, Equation 41 gets the particular form:

$$S_p^y(\tau) = C(p) \cdot S_p^x(\tau) \tag{42}$$

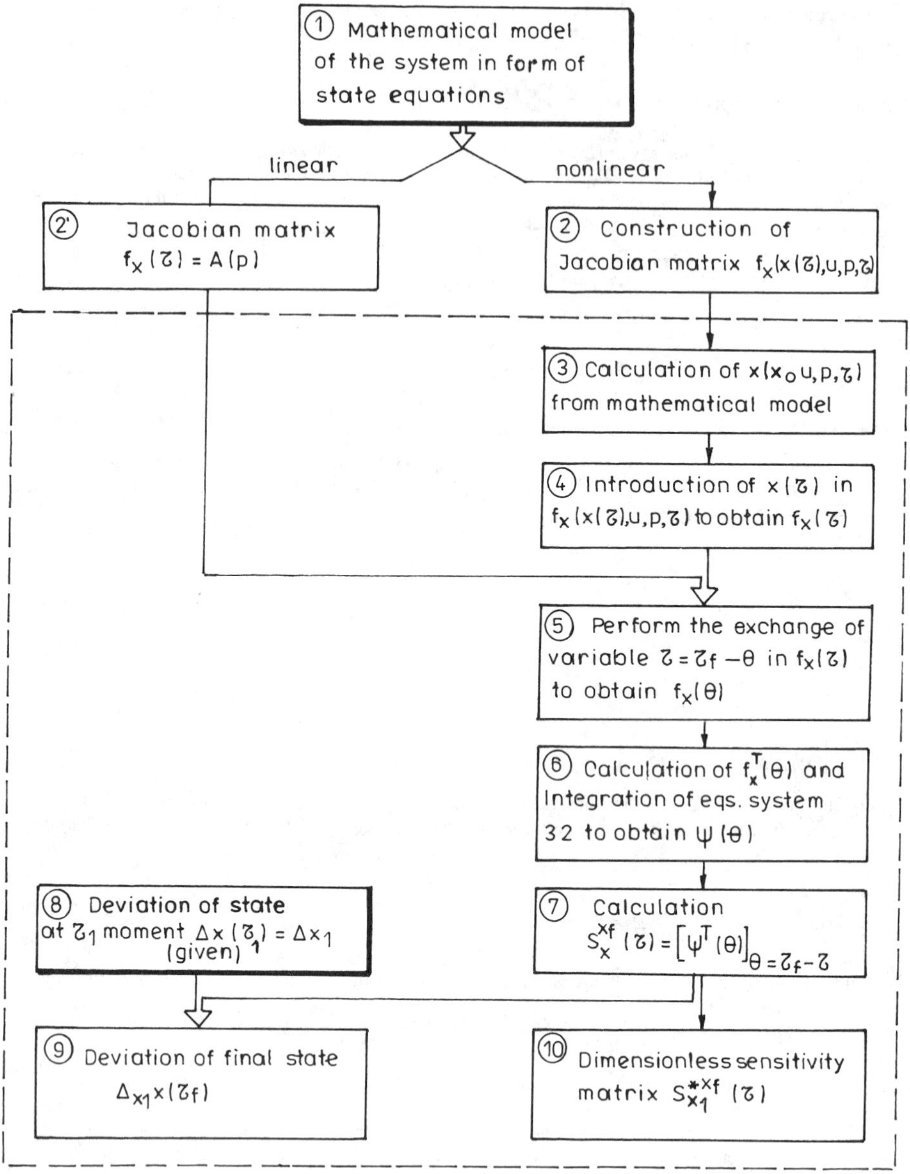

Figure 2. Logical diagram of the algorithm for analysis of the direct sensitivity of a continuous dynamic system with respect to the state at any given moment.

The computing algorithm of the parametric sensitivity of the continuous systems is described in the diagram of logic in Figure 3.

The sensitivity of the state and output with respect to the parameters with the variable time variations. The parametric sensitivity analysis of the systems in which the parameters changes are functions of time:

$$\Delta p = \Delta p(\tau) \tag{43}$$

is calculated assimilating the parameters to the control inputs with changing in time variations.
The computing algorithm is described below.

Sensitivity to Control Inputs

The sensitivity of the state and output relative to the control inputs with unchanging time variations. In the sensitivity analysis of the state and output relative to the control inputs with unchanging in time variations, these control quantities can be considered as parameters with unchanging in time variations, so that we may use the same algorithm described earlier.

The sensitivity equations are in this case [3]:

For state:

$$\dot{S}_u^x(\tau) = f_x(x(\tau), u, p, \tau) \cdot S_u^x(\tau) + f_u \tag{44}$$

with $S_u^x(\tau_0) = 0$

For output:

$$S_u^y(\tau) = g_x(x(\tau), u, p, \tau) \cdot S_u^x(\tau) \tag{45}$$

The meanings of the f_x and g_x in the Equations 44 and 45 are given by the Equations 20 and 26, respectively, while f_u is the Jacobian matrix of the vectorial function $f(x(\tau), u, p, \tau)$ with respect to vector u:

$$f_u = \begin{bmatrix} \frac{\partial f_1}{\partial u_1} & \frac{\partial f_1}{\partial u_2} & \cdots & \frac{\partial f_1}{\partial u_1} \\ \frac{\partial f_2}{\partial u_1} & \frac{\partial f_2}{\partial u_2} & \cdots & \frac{\partial f_2}{\partial u} \\ \cdots & \cdots & \cdots & \cdots \\ \frac{\partial f_n}{\partial u_1} & \frac{\partial f_n}{\partial u_2} & \cdots & \frac{\partial f_n}{\partial u} \end{bmatrix} \tag{46}$$

The sensitivity of the state and output with respect to the control inputs with changing time variations. Let us consider the mathematical model of a continuous system in the form of the state equation:

$$\dot{x} = f(x(\tau), u, p, \tau) \tag{47}$$

with the initial condition $x(\tau_0) = x_0$, in which the control inputs u, with constant nominal values, are assumed to deviate from these nominal values by variable in time quantities, $\Delta u = \Delta u(\tau)$.

In this case, for the sensitivity analysis of a system with respect to control inputs, the definitions of the sensitivity matrices are no longer valid; the sensitivity functions will be defined as functional derivatives.

The nominal control inputs u_j, $j = \overline{1, l}$, as a result of the variations appearance $\Delta u_j(\tau)$, become $u_j + \Delta u_j(\tau)$. We assume that the changing in time variations Δu_j have the general form [9, 4]:

$$\Delta u_j(\tau) = \varepsilon_j \cdot v_j(\tau), \quad j = \overline{1, l} \tag{48}$$

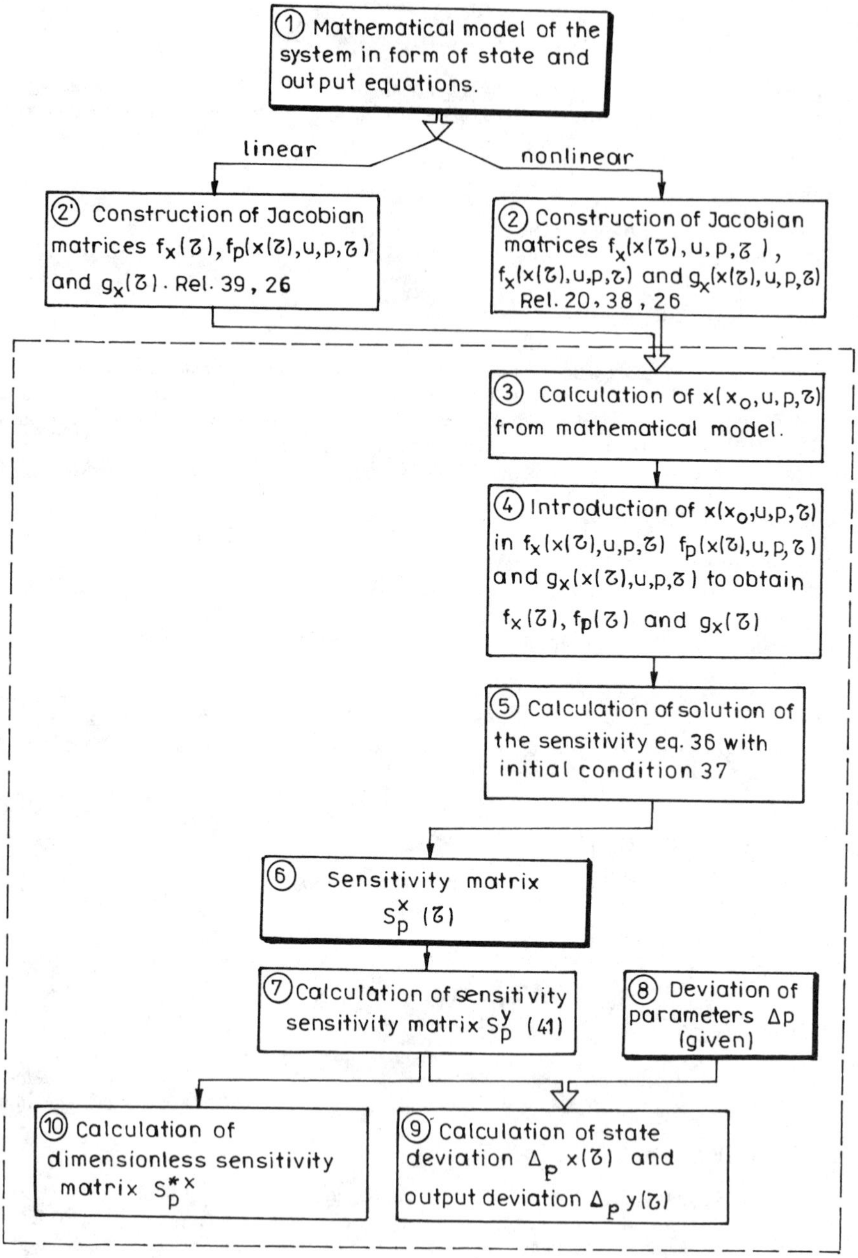

Figure 3. Logical diagram of the algorithm for analysis of the direct sensitivity of a continuous dynamic system with respect to the parameters.

Here ε_j are constants and $v_j(\tau)$ are functions of time; they are integrable and uniformly bounded.

The vector of the deviations, as a function of time, of the control inputs from the nominal (prescribed) value, $\Delta u(\tau)$, can be expressed in general form as:

$$\Delta u(\tau) = w(\tau) \cdot \varepsilon \tag{49}$$

where ε is the vector of the constants ε_j, $j = \overline{1, l}$, and $w(\tau)$ is the square matrix whose elements are the functions of time

$$w_{i,j}(\tau) = \delta_{i,j} \cdot v_j(\tau), \qquad j = \overline{1, l} \tag{50}$$

$\delta_{i,j}$ being the Kronecker delta function:

$$\delta_{i,j} = 0, i \neq j$$

$$\delta_{i,j} = 1, i = j$$

$$\delta = \begin{bmatrix} 1 & 0 & \cdots & 0 \\ 0 & 1 & \cdots & 0 \\ \vdots & \vdots & & \vdots \\ 0 & 0 & \cdots & 1 \end{bmatrix}, \qquad w = \begin{bmatrix} v_1 & 0 & \cdots & 0 \\ 0 & v_2 & \cdots & 0 \\ \vdots & \vdots & & \vdots \\ 0 & 0 & \cdots & v_l \end{bmatrix}$$

We denote by $v(\tau)$, the vector of functions of time $v_j(\tau)$, $j = 1, l$.

If u becomes $u + w(\tau) \cdot \varepsilon$, the perturbed trajectory of the state of the system, $x(\tau) + \Delta_u x(v(\tau), \varepsilon, \tau)$, is the solution of the vectorial differential equation:

$$\dot{x}(\tau) + \Delta_u \cdot x(v(\tau), \varepsilon, \tau) = f(x(\tau) + \Delta_u x(v(\tau), \varepsilon, \tau), u + w(\tau) \cdot \varepsilon, p, \tau) \tag{51}$$

The *matrix of the sensitivity functions* is defined as the matrix of the functional derivatives [4, 9]:

$$S_u^x(v(\tau), \tau) = \left[\lim_{\varepsilon_j \to 0} \frac{x_i(x_0, u_1, u_2, \ldots, u_j + \varepsilon_j \cdot v_j(\tau), \ldots, u_l, p, \tau) - x_i(x_0, u, p, \tau)}{\varepsilon_j} \right]$$

$$= \left[\frac{\partial x_i}{\partial u_j} \right], \qquad \begin{matrix} i = \overline{1, n} \\ j = \overline{1, l} \end{matrix} \tag{52}$$

For low values of the constants ε_j, the effect of the functions $v_j(\tau)$ on the variables of state of the system can be determined from the approximate relationship:

$$\Delta_u x = S_u^x(v(\tau), \tau) \cdot \varepsilon \tag{53}$$

The sensitivity functions matrix of the state with respect to the control inputs with changing in time variations, described by the functions $v_j(\tau)$, is computed as solution of the sensitivity differential equations system [4, 10]:

$$\dot{S}_u^x(v(\tau), \tau) = f_x(x(\tau), u, p, \tau) \cdot S_u^x(v(\tau), \tau) + f_u(x(\tau), u, p, \tau) \cdot w(\tau) \tag{54}$$

with the initial condition:

$$S_u^x(v(\tau_0), \tau_0) = 0 \tag{55}$$

To compute the dimensionless sensitivity, the known relationship is used:

$$S_u^{*x} = \left[S_{u_j}^{x_i} \frac{u_j}{x_i} \right], \qquad \begin{matrix} i = \overline{1, n} \\ j = \overline{1, l} \end{matrix} \tag{56}$$

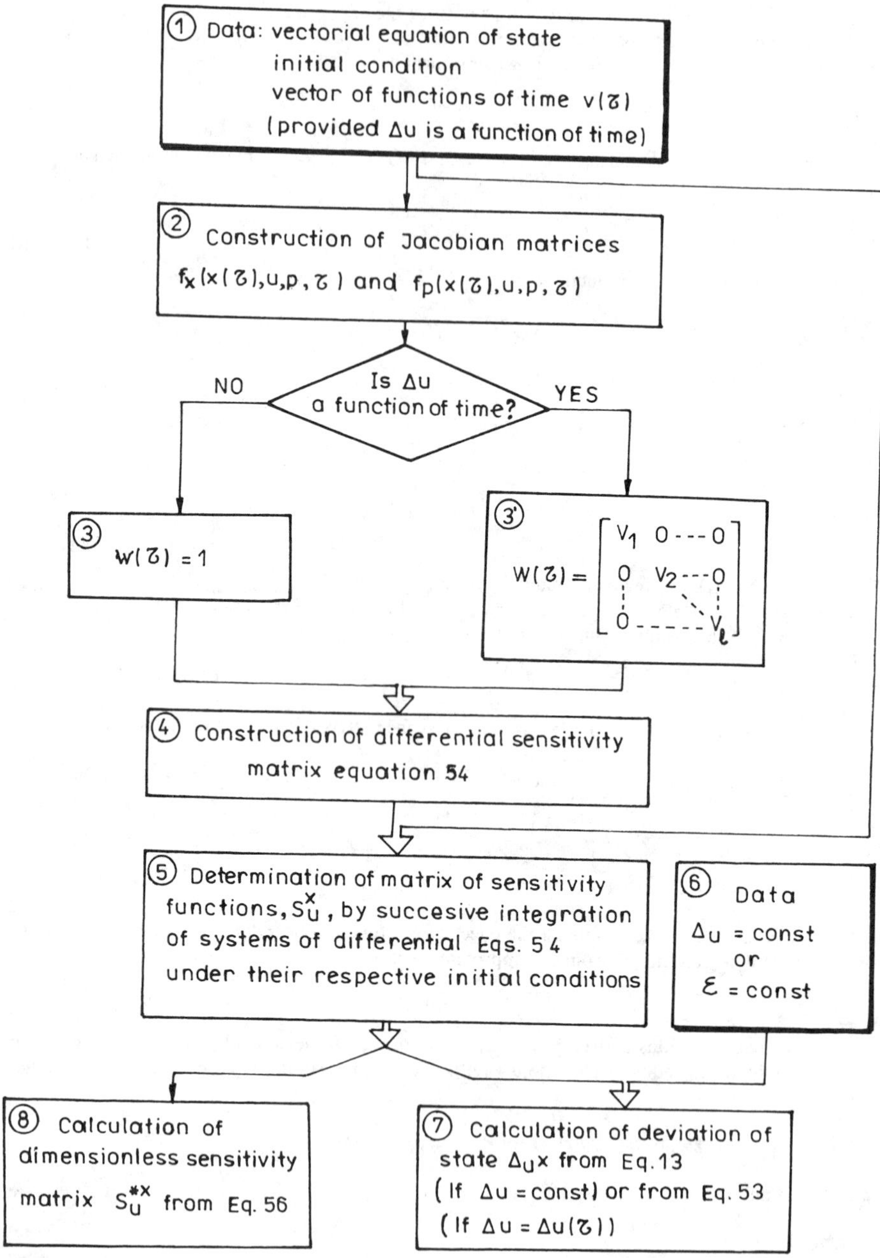

Figure 4. Logical diagram of the algorithm for analysis of the direct sensitivity of a continuous dynamic system with respect to the control inputs.

We note that, if $w(\tau) = 1$, the sensitivity equation (54), with S_u^x defined by Equation 52, reduces to Equation 44, with S_u^x defined by Equation 7, which is to say that the case discussed in this section contains, as a particular case, the one that was analysed earlier.

This leads to the general algorithm for the sensitivity analysis of a dynamic system with respect to the control inputs. This algorithm is described in the diagram of logic in Figure 4.

DSA OF CHEMICAL REACTORS AS DYNAMIC SYSTEMS

DSA of a Nonisothermal CSTR [2, 3]

The mathematical model of a nonisothermal continuous stirred tank reactor, as a lumped-parameter system, has the general form [11, 12]:

$$V \frac{dC}{d\tau} = q \cdot \Delta C + r \cdot V \tag{57}$$

$$V \cdot \rho \cdot C_p \frac{dT}{d\tau} = q \cdot \rho \cdot C_p \cdot \Delta T - K \cdot A \cdot \Delta T_m + V \cdot (-\Delta H) \tag{58}$$

where
- A = heat transfer area of the reactor
- C = concentrations
- C_p = average specific heat capacity
- K = overall heat transfer coefficient
- q = volumetric flow rate
- r = reaction rate
- T = temperature
- T_m = average (logarithmic) temperature difference
- V = reactor volume
- ΔH = heat of reaction

The state variables of the system are the chemical species concentrations (C vector) and the reaction mixture temperature, T. The inlet cooling agent flow rate and inlet reacting substances flow rates are the control variables. Finally, we may consider as parameters, the reactor's constructive and material characteristics (volume, heat transfer area, thermal conductivity of steel), inlet concentrations, and temperatures of reactants and cooling agent as design and operating characteristics (activation energy, the frequency factor, and the coefficients in the relation reaction heat versus temperature)—magnitudes whose precise measurement is often uncertain [13], [14].

The nonisothermal continuous stirred tank reactor for hexamine production was chosen as a numerical application, as we had at our disposal a model experimentally verified [13] and well suited to optimal control [12].

The reaction follows the stoichiometric relation:

$$4NH_3 + 6CH_2O \longleftrightarrow N_4(CH_2)_6 + 6H_2O$$

In the mathematical description of the process several simplifying assumptions were made. These include perfect mixing in the reactor, no heat losses, a third-order, irreversible reaction, and reaction velocity constant given by the Arrhenius equation.

Equations 57 and 58, written for this particular case, give the mathematical model:

$$\frac{dC_A}{d\tau} = \frac{q_A}{V} C_{A_i} = \frac{q_A + q_F}{V} C_A - r \tag{59}$$

$$\frac{dC_F}{d\tau} = \frac{q_F}{V} C_{F_i} - \frac{q_A + q_F}{V} C_F - 1.5r \tag{60}$$

$$\frac{dT}{d\tau} = \frac{q_A}{V} T_{A_i} + \frac{q_F}{V} T_{F_i} - \frac{q_A + q_F}{V} T + \frac{(-\Delta H)}{\rho C_p} r - \frac{KA\,\Delta T_m}{V\rho C_p} \tag{61}$$

where

$$r = k_0 \cdot C_A \cdot C_F^2 \cdot \exp\left(-\frac{E}{R \cdot T}\right)$$

$$(-\Delta H) = a_1 + a_2 \cdot T \tag{62}$$

$$T_m = \frac{T_{ro} - T_{r_i}}{\ln\left(\dfrac{T - T_{r_i}}{T - T_{ro}}\right)}$$

where a = coefficients in relationship
$(-\Delta H) = f(T)$
E = energy of activation
k_0 = frequency factor
R = gas constant
A = ammonia
F = formaldehyde
i = inlet
m = medium
0 = initial moment
r = cooling agent

Eliminating T_{ro}, the last term in Equation 61 becomes:

$$\frac{K \cdot A \cdot T_m}{V \cdot \rho \cdot C_p} = \frac{\rho_r \cdot C_r}{\rho \cdot C_p} \cdot \frac{q_r}{V}(T - T_{r_i})\left[1 - \exp\left(-\frac{K \cdot A}{\rho_r \cdot C_r \cdot q_r}\right)\right] \tag{63}$$

The state, control and parameter's vectors are:

$$x = \begin{bmatrix} x_1 \\ x_2 \\ x_3 \end{bmatrix} = \begin{bmatrix} C_A \\ C_F \\ T \end{bmatrix}; \qquad u = \begin{bmatrix} u_1 \\ u_2 \\ u_3 \end{bmatrix} = \begin{bmatrix} q_A \\ q_F \\ q_r \end{bmatrix} \tag{64}$$

$$\begin{aligned} p &= [p_1 \quad p_2 \quad p_3 \quad p_4 \quad p_5 \quad p_6 \quad p_7 \quad p_8 \quad p_9 \quad p_{10} \quad p_{11} \quad p_{12}]^T \\ &= [V \quad A \quad K \quad C_{A_i} \quad C_{F_i} \quad T_{A_i} \quad T_{F_i} \quad T_{r_i} \quad E/R \quad k_0 \quad a_1 \quad a_2]^T \end{aligned}$$

Introducing Equations 64 in the mathematical model of Equations 59–63, we obtain the form adequate to matricial Equation 1:

$$\begin{aligned} \dot{x}_1 &= \frac{u_1}{p_1} p_4 - \frac{u_1 + u_2}{p_1} x_1 - p_{10} \cdot x_1 \cdot x_2^2 \cdot \exp\left(-\frac{p_9}{x_3}\right) \\ \dot{x}_2 &= \frac{u_2}{p_1} p_5 - \frac{u_1 + u_2}{p_1} x_2 - 1.5 p_{10} x_1 x_2^2 \exp\left(-\frac{p_9}{x_3}\right) \\ \dot{x}_3 &= \frac{u_1}{p_1} p_6 + \frac{u_2}{p_1} p_7 - \frac{u_1 + u_2}{p_1} x_3 + (p_{11} + p_{12} x_3) \frac{p_{10}}{b_1} x_1 x_2^2 \cdot \exp\left(-\frac{p_9}{x_3}\right) \\ &\quad - \frac{b_2}{b_1} \frac{u_3}{p_1} (x_3 - p_8)\left[1 - \exp\left(-\frac{p_2 p_3}{b_2 u_3}\right)\right] \end{aligned} \tag{65}$$

where constants b_1 and b_2 are:

$$b_1 = \rho \cdot C_p$$

$$b_2 = \rho_r \cdot C_r$$

The mathematical model is accompanied by the initial condition:

$$x(\tau_0) = \begin{bmatrix} x_{1,0} \\ x_{2,0} \\ x_{3,0} \end{bmatrix} = \begin{bmatrix} C_{A_0} \\ C_{F_0} \\ T_0 \end{bmatrix} \tag{66}$$

The sensitivity of the state with respect to the initial state. In order to use the algorithm given in Figure 1 for the case of the nonlinear mathematical model, the components of the 3 × 3 Jacobian matrix f_x were determined from the following expressions:

$$\begin{aligned}
f_{x_{1,1}} &= \frac{u_1 + u_2}{p_1} - p_{10} x_2^2 \exp\left(-\frac{p_9}{x_3}\right) \\
f_{x_{1,2}} &= -2p_{10} x_1 x_2 \exp\left(-\frac{p_9}{x_3}\right) \\
f_{x_{1,3}} &= -p_9 p_{10} \frac{x_1 x_2^2}{x_3^2} \exp\left(-\frac{p_9}{x_3}\right) \\
f_{x_{2,1}} &= -1.5 p_{10} x_2^2 \exp\left(-\frac{p_9}{x_3}\right) \\
f_{x_{2,2}} &= -\frac{u_1 + u_2}{p_1} - 3p_{10} x_1 x_2 \exp\left(-\frac{p_9}{x_3}\right) \\
f_{x_{2,3}} &= -1.5 p_9 p_{10} \frac{x_1 x_2^2}{x_3^2} \exp\left(-\frac{p_9}{x_3}\right) \\
f_{x_{3,1}} &= (p_{11} + p_{12} x_3) \frac{p_{10}}{b_1} x_2^2 \exp\left(-\frac{p_9}{x_3}\right) \\
f_{x_{3,2}} &= 2(p_{11} + p_{12} x_3) \frac{p_{10}}{b_1} x_1 x_2 \exp\left(-\frac{p_9}{x_3}\right) \\
f_{x_{3,3}} &= -\frac{u_1 + u_2}{p_1} - \frac{b_2}{b_1}\frac{u_3}{p_1}\left[1 - \exp\left(-\frac{p_2 p_3}{b_2 u_3}\right)\right] \\
&\quad + \frac{p_{10}}{b_1} x_1 x_2^2 \left(p_{12} + \frac{p_9 p_{12}}{x_3} + \frac{p_9 p_{11}}{x_3^2}\right) \exp\left(-\frac{p_9}{x_3}\right)
\end{aligned} \tag{67}$$

The following numerical values [13] were used to integrate the mathematical model equations system (Equation 65) and the sensitivity equations system (Equation 18) with the Jacobian matrix elements (Equation 67).

$C_{A_0} = 4.06 \text{ Kmol/m}^3$

$C_{F_0} = 6.32 \text{ Kmol/m}^3$

$T_0 = 293.2°K$

$q_A = 1.5 \times 10^{-6} \text{ m}^3/\text{s}$

$q_F = 1.5 \times 10^{-6} \text{ m}^3/\text{s}$

$q_r = 2.65 \times 10^{-6} \text{ m}^3/\text{s}$

$V = 0.49 \times 10^{-3} \text{ m}^3/\text{s}$

$A = 0.05 \text{ m}^2$

$K = 837.1 \text{ J/m}^2 \text{ deg s}$

$T_{A_i} = 293.2°K$

$T_{F_i} = 293.2°K$

$T_{r_i} = 293.2°K$

$a_1 = -78.968 \times 10^6 \text{ J/Kmol NH}_3$

$a_2 = 0.50645 \times 10^6 \text{ J/Kmol NH}_3 \text{ deg}$

$E = 25.695 \times 10^6 \text{ J/Kmol}$

$R = 8315 \text{ J/Kmol deg}$

$k_0 = 1419 (\text{Kmol/m}^3)^{-2} \text{s}^{-1}$

$\rho = 1000 \text{ Kg/m}^3$

$\rho_r = 1000 \text{ Kg/m}^3$

$C_p = 4.1855 \text{ J/Kg deg}$

$C_r = 4.1855 \text{ J/Kg deg}$

Considering the CSTRs dynamics, the initial state vector components were taken as coincident to inlet values.

Hamming's modified predictor-corrector method was used to integrate the equations. Due to the significant number of differential equations, special care was taken to preserve the accuracy.

The diagrams of the component functions of the sensitivity matrix $S^x_{x0}(\tau, \tau_0)$ based on the results of the numerical integration, were drawn in Figures 5–10 [2].

These diagrams were drawn for two different time scales, due to the variation speed of the sensivity matix during the first part of the reaction.

Thus, in Figures 5–7, the first five seconds were considered, while in Figures 8–10, the next 5–600-s period was studied.

The Figures 5–10, together with Equation 13, give the possibility to compute the state vector deviation at any time in response to initial state change.

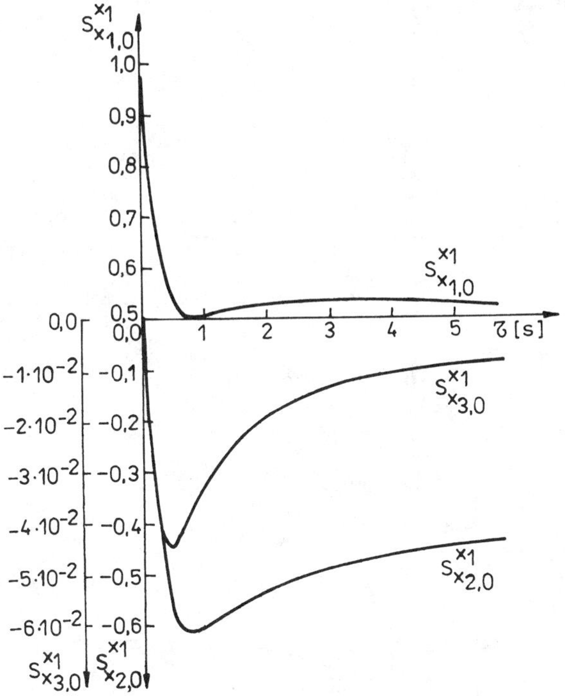

Figure 5. Sensitivity of ammonia concentration to changes in the ammonia initial concentration, $S^{x_1}_{x_{1,0}}$; the formaldehyde initial concentration, $S^{x_1}_{x_{2,0}}$; and the initial temperature $S^{x_1}_{x_{3,0}}$; within first five seconds period from the beginning of the reaction.

The results obtained were verified by integration of the mathematical model differential equations (65), first for initial condition:

$$x_0 = \begin{bmatrix} 4.06 \\ 6.32 \\ 293.2 \end{bmatrix} \tag{68}$$

and then for

$$x_0 = \begin{bmatrix} 4.10 \\ 6.40 \\ 296.0 \end{bmatrix} \tag{69}$$

to determine the influence of a $\approx 1\%$ deviation of initial state vector components on the state at any time, particularly at the end of the transient process, using the relationship:

$$\Delta_{x_0}x(\tau) = x(x_0 + \Delta x_0, u, p, \tau) - x(x_0, u, p, \tau) \tag{70}$$

The results $\Delta_{x_0}x(\tau)$ obtained in this way have very close values to those computed by means of Equation 13 and sensitivity matrix, the difference being less than 1%.

Let us consider two numerical applications of the analysis given above.

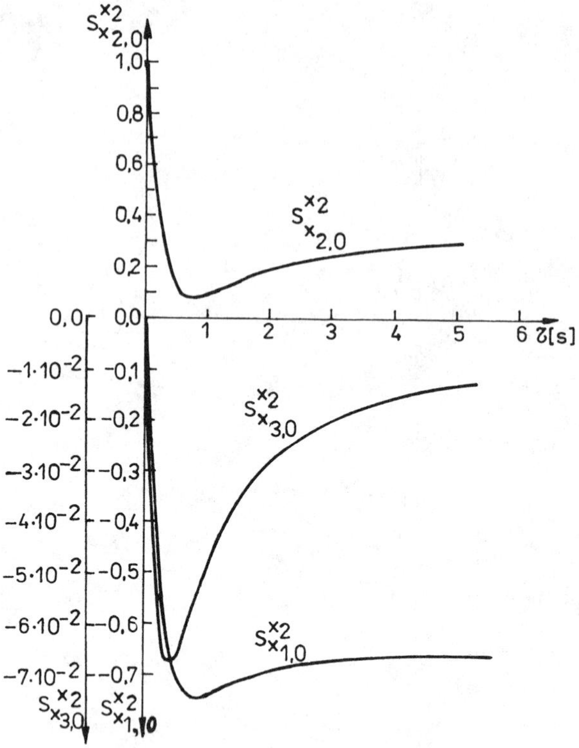

Figure 6. Sensitivity of formaldehyde concentration to changes in the ammonia initial concentration, $S^{x2}_{x1,0}$; the formaldehyde initial concentration, $S^{x2}_{x2,0}$; and the initial temperature, $S^{x2}_{x3,0}$, within first five seconds period from the beginning of the reaction.

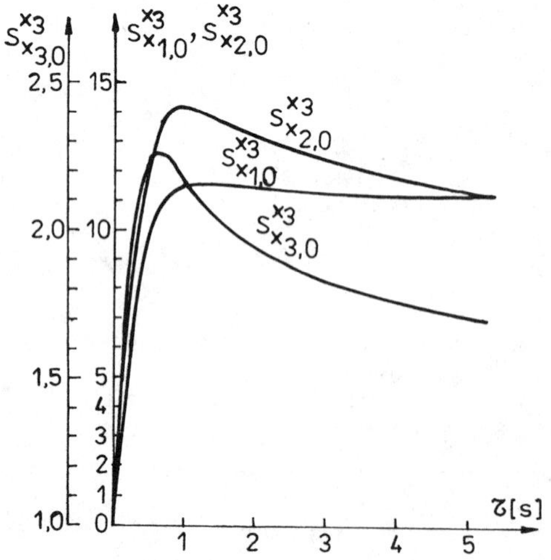

Figure 7. Sensitivity of mass reaction temperature to changes in the ammonia initial concentration, $S^{x3}_{x1,0}$; the formaldehyde initial concentration, $S^{x3}_{x2,0}$; and the initial temperature, $S^{x3}_{x3,0}$, within first five seconds period from the beginning of the reaction.

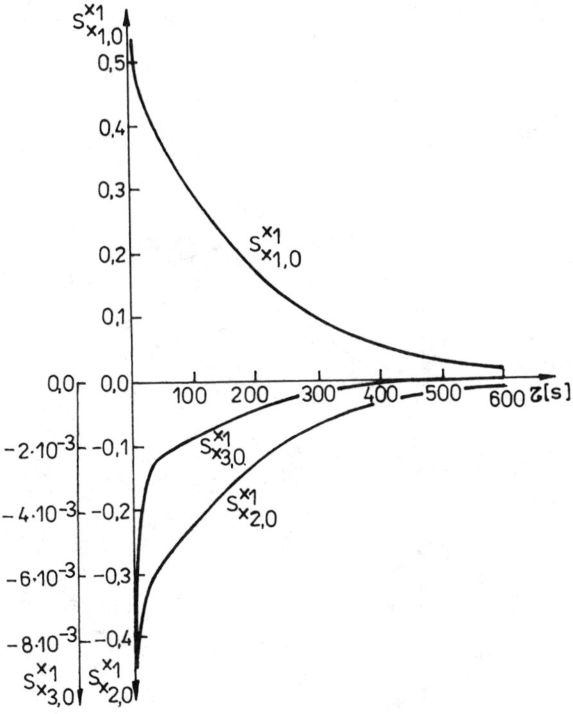

Figure 8. Sensitivity of ammonia concentration to changes in the ammonia initial concentration, $S^{x_1}_{x_{1,0}}$; the formaldehyde initial concentration, $S^{x_1}_{x_{2,0}}$; and the initial temperature, $S^{x_1}_{x_{3,0}}$, for $\tau = 5 \ldots 600$ s.

1. Consider the hexamine producing reactor operating under initial condition of Equattion 68. To compute the combined influence of a $\approx 1\%$ variation in reactants initial concentrations and initial temperature, e.g.

$$\Delta x_0 = \begin{bmatrix} 0.04 \\ 0.08 \\ 2.80 \end{bmatrix}$$

on concentrations and temperature after 300 s since initiation of the reaction, by means of Equation 13, we use the sensitivity matrix (read in Figures 8–10):

$$S^{x}_{x_0}(300, 0) = \begin{bmatrix} 0.096 & -0.067 & -0.00033 \\ -0.096 & 0.058 & -0.00050 \\ 0.460 & 0.550 & 0.077 \end{bmatrix}$$

and obtain

$$\Delta_{x_0} x(300) = \begin{bmatrix} -0.002444 \\ -0.0006 \\ 0.278 \end{bmatrix}$$

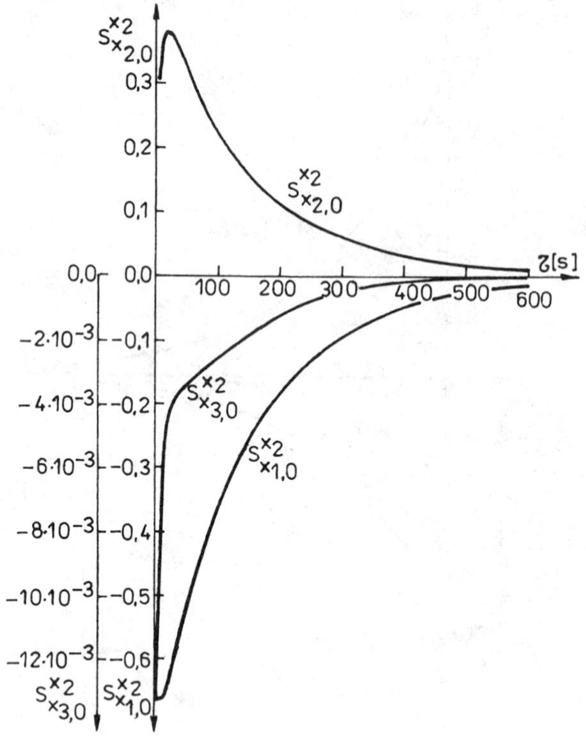

Figure 9. Sensitivity of formaldehyde concentration to changes in the ammonia initial concentration, $S^{x2}_{x1,0}$; the formaldehyde initial concentration, $S^{x2}_{x2,0}$; and the initial temperature, $S^{x2}_{x3,0}$, for $\tau = 5 \ldots 600$ s.

2. If, during the same process, the ammonia initial concentration only changes with $\approx 1\%$, Δx_0 being:

$$\Delta x_0 = \begin{bmatrix} 0.04 \\ 0 \\ 0 \end{bmatrix}$$

$\Delta_{x_0} x(300, 0)$ will be:

$$\Delta_{x_0} x(300, 0) = \begin{bmatrix} 0.00384 \\ -0.00384 \\ 0.0184 \end{bmatrix}$$

So, the sensitivity functions matrix, shown in Figures 5–10, allows one to estimate the variable influence of the initial concentrations and initial temperature variations on the concentrations and

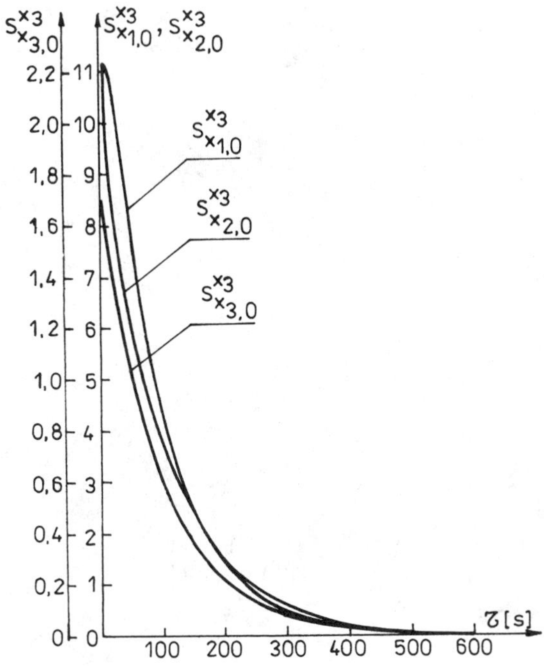

Figure 10. Sensitivity of mass reaction temperature to changes in the ammonia initial concentration, $S^{x_3}_{x_{1,0}}$; the formaldehyde initial concentration, $S^{x_3}_{x_{2,0}}$; and the initial temperature, $S^{x_3}_{x_{3,0}}$, for $\tau =$ 5 . . . 600 s.

temperature during the reaction. It also permits one to compute, for any moment of the process, the concentration and temperature deviations from nominal values, caused by the modification of initial values, without supplementary integrations of the differential equations systems.

The parametric sensitivity of the state. To compute the parametric sensitivity, the algorithm given in Figure 3 is used.

The elements of the 3 × 12 Jacobian matrix f_p are:

$$f_{p_{1,1}} = [(u_1 + u_2)x_1 - u_1 p_4]\frac{1}{p_1^2}$$

$$f_{p_{1,2}} = 0; \qquad f_{p_{1,3}} = 0$$

$$f_{p_{1,4}} = \frac{u_1}{p_1}$$

$$f_{p_{1,5}} = 0; \qquad f_{p_{1,6}} = 0; \qquad f_{p_{1,7}} = 0; \qquad f_{p_{1,8}} = 0$$

$$f_{p_{1,9}} = p_{10}\frac{x_1 x_2^2}{x_3}\exp\left(-\frac{p_9}{x_3}\right)$$

$$f_{p_{1,10}} = -x_1 x_2^2 \exp\left(-\frac{p_9}{x_3}\right)$$

$$
\begin{aligned}
&f_{p_{1,11}} = 0; \qquad f_{p_{1,12}} = 0 \\
&f_{p_{2,1}} = [(u_1 + u_2)x_2 - u_2p_5]\frac{1}{p_1^2} \\
&f_{p_{2,2}} = 0; \qquad f_{p_{2,3}} = 0; \qquad f_{p_{2,4}} = 0 \\
&f_{p_{2,5}} = \frac{u_2}{p_1} \\
&f_{p_{2,6}} = 0; \qquad f_{p_{2,7}} = 0; \qquad f_{p_{2,8}} = 0 \\
&f_{p_{2,9}} = 1.5p_{10}\frac{x_1x_2^2}{x_3}\exp\left(-\frac{p_9}{x_3}\right) \\
&f_{p_{2,10}} = -1.5x_1x_2^2\exp\left(-\frac{p_9}{x_3}\right) \\
&f_{p_{2,11}} = 0; \qquad f_{p_{2,12}} = 0 \\
&f_{p_{3,1}} = [(u_1 + u_2)x_3 - u_1p_6 - u_2p_7]\frac{1}{p_1^2} + \frac{b_2}{b_1}\frac{u_3}{p_1^2}(x_3 - p_8)\left[1 - \exp\left(-\frac{p_2p_3}{b_2u_3}\right)\right] \\
&f_{p_{3,2}} = -\frac{p_3}{b_1p_1}(x_3 - p_8)\exp\left(-\frac{p_2p_3}{b_2u_3}\right) \\
&f_{p_{3,3}} = -\frac{p_2}{b_1p_1}(x_3 - p_8)\exp\left(-\frac{p_2p_3}{b_2u_3}\right) \\
&f_{p_{3,4}} = 0; \qquad f_{p_{3,5}} = 0 \\
&f_{p_{3,6}} = \frac{u_1}{p_1} \\
&f_{p_{3,7}} = \frac{u_2}{p_1} \\
&f_{p_{3,8}} = \frac{b_2}{b_1}\frac{u_3}{p_1}\left[1 - \exp\left(-\frac{p_2p_3}{b_2u_3}\right)\right] \\
&f_{p_{3,9}} = -\frac{p_{10}}{b_1}\frac{x_1x_2^2}{x_3}(p_{11} + p_{12}x_3)\exp\left(-\frac{p_9}{x_3}\right) \\
&f_{p_{3,10}} = \frac{x_1x_2^2}{b_1}(p_{11} + p_{12}x_3)\exp\left(-\frac{p_9}{x_3}\right) \\
&f_{p_{3,11}} = \frac{p_{10}}{b_1}x_1x_2^2\exp\left(-\frac{p_9}{x_3}\right) \\
&f_{p_{3,12}} = \frac{p_{10}}{b_1}x_1x_2^2x_3\exp\left(-\frac{p_9}{x_3}\right)
\end{aligned}
\tag{71}
$$

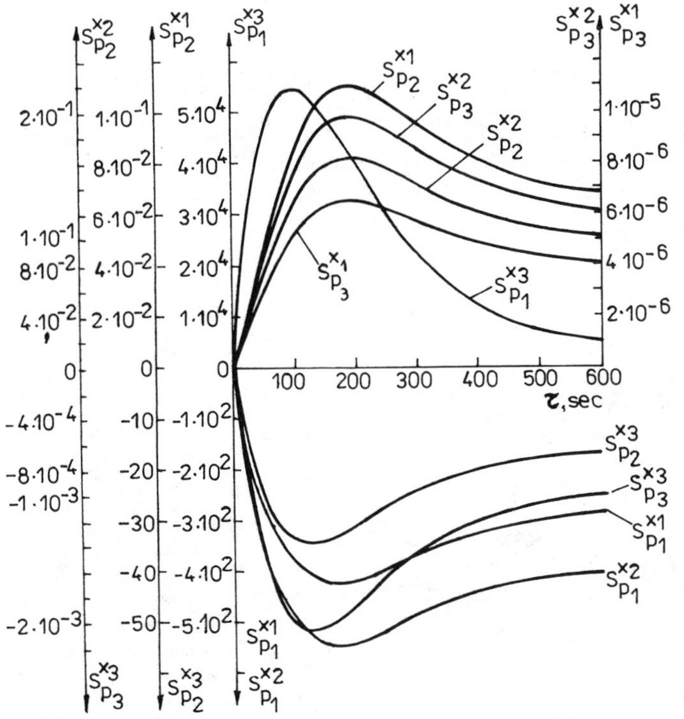

Figure 11. Sensitivities of the ammonia concentration, the formaldehyde concentration and the temperature of reacting mass, with respect to the reactor volume V, $S_{p_1}^{x_1}$, $S_{p_1}^{x_2}$, and $S_{p_1}^{x_3}$, respectively; the heat transfer area, A, $S_{p_2}^{x_1}$, $S_{p_2}^{x_2}$, and $S_{p_2}^{x_3}$, respectively; and the overall heat transfer coefficient K, $S_{p_3}^{x_1}$, $S_{p_3}^{x_3}$, and $S_{p_3}^{x_3}$; respectively. (Reprinted with permission from Ref. 7.)

Based on the results of the numerical integration of the differential equations systems (Equations 36 and 65) with the numerical values given earlier, the diagrams of the component functions of the sensitivity matrix S_p^x were drawn in Figures 11–15 [37].

To compute the influence of the initial variations of the parameters on the reacting mass concentrations and temperature 200 s from initiation of the reaction, we use the sensitivity coefficients matrix (read in Figures 11–15):

$$
S_p^x(200) = \left[\begin{matrix}
-4.18\cdot 10^2 & 1.10\cdot 10^{-1} & 6.54\cdot 10^{-6} & 2.22\cdot 10^{-1} & -1.37\cdot 10^{-1} \\
-5.42\cdot 10^2 & 1.64\cdot 10^{-1} & 9.81\cdot 10^{-6} & -2.04\cdot 10^{-1} & 1.52\cdot 10^{-1} \\
3.99\cdot 10^4 & -3.11\cdot 10 & -1.86\cdot 10^{-3} & 2.10 & 2.14
\end{matrix}\right.
$$

$$
\begin{matrix}
-9.32\cdot 10^{-4} & -9.32\cdot 10^{-4} & -1.61\cdot 10^{-3} & 3.72\cdot 10^{-4} & -8.34\cdot 10^{-5} \\
-1.40\cdot 10^{-3} & -1.40\cdot 10^{-3} & -2.41\cdot 10^{-3} & 5.58\cdot 10^{-4} & 1.26\cdot 10^{-4} \\
2.77\cdot 10^{-1} & 2.77\cdot 10^{-1} & 4.77\cdot 10^{-1} & -5.00\cdot 10^{-3} & 1.12\cdot 10^{-3}
\end{matrix}
$$

$$
\left.\begin{matrix}
-1.34\cdot 10^{-9} & -4.44\cdot 10^{-7} \\
-2.02\cdot 10^{-9} & -6.66\cdot 10^{-7} \\
3.75\cdot 10^{-7} & 1.24\cdot 10^{-4}
\end{matrix}\right]
$$

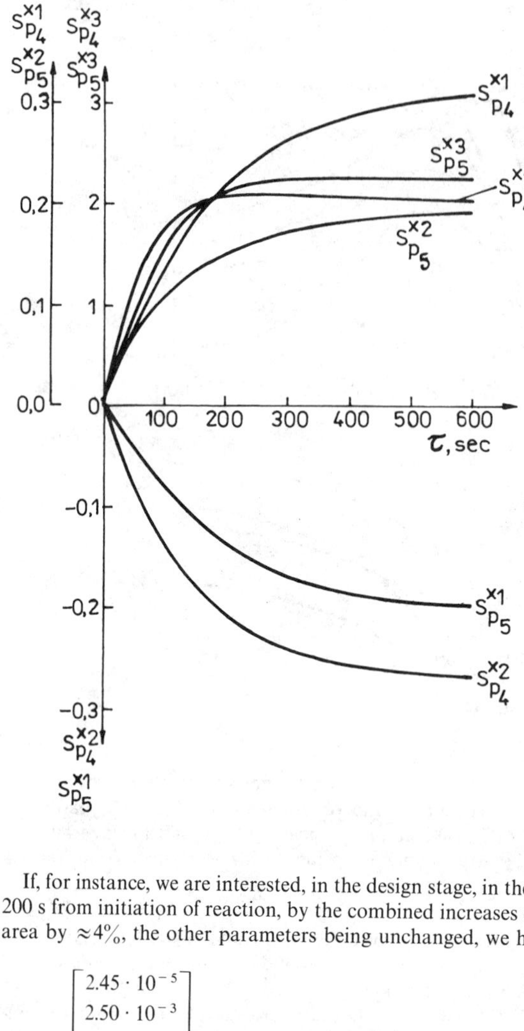

Figure 12. Sensitivities of the ammonia concentration, the formaldehyde concentration and the temperature of reacting mass, with respect to the inlet ammonia concentration, C_{A_i}, S^{x1}_{p4}, S^{x2}_{p4}, and S^{x3}_{p4}, respectively; and the inlet form-aldehyde concentration C_{F_i}, S^{x1}_{p5}, and S^{x3}_{p4}, S^{x2}_{p5}, and S^{x3}_{p5}, respectively. (Reprinted with permission from Ref. 7.)

If, for instance, we are interested, in the design stage, in the way the state variables are influenced, 200 s from initiation of reaction, by the combined increases of the volume and heat transfer reactor area by $\approx 4\%$, the other parameters being unchanged, we have:

$$\Delta p = \begin{bmatrix} 2.45 \cdot 10^{-5} \\ 2.50 \cdot 10^{-3} \\ 0 \\ 0 \\ \vdots \\ 0 \end{bmatrix}$$

Applying Equation 13, the vector of the corresponding state deviations is obtained:

$$\Delta_p x(200) = S^x_p(200) \cdot \Delta p = \begin{bmatrix} -9.97 \cdot 10^{-3} \\ -1.29 \cdot 10^{-2} \\ 0.90 \end{bmatrix}$$

that is, the ammonia concentration decreases by $9.97 \cdot 10^{-3}$ Kmol/m^3, i.e., 3.17% from the corresponding nominal value, which is 0.3055 Kmol/m^3; the formaldehyde concentration decreases by

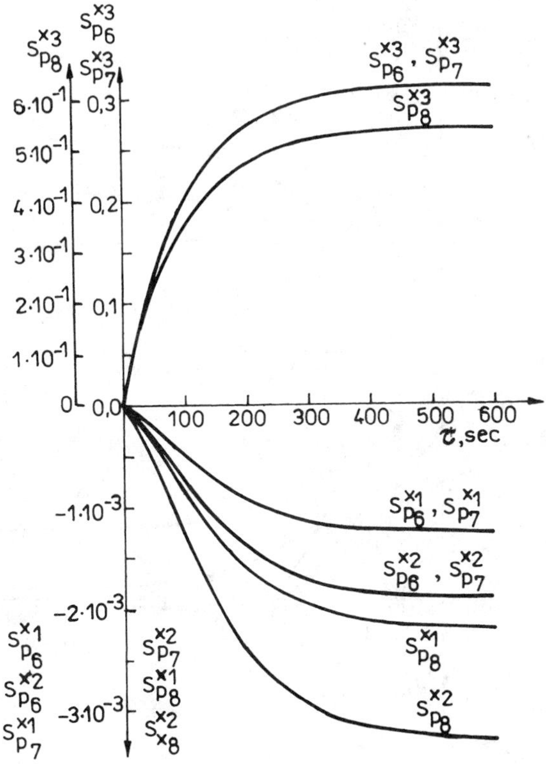

Figure 13. Sensitivities of the ammonia concentration, the formaldehyde concentration and the temperature of reacting mass, with respect to the inlet ammonia temperature, T_{A_i}, $S^{x_1}_{p_6}$, $S^{x_2}_{p_6}$ and $S^{x_3}_{p_6}$, respectively; the inlet formaldehyde temperature, T_{F_i}, $S^{x_1}_{p_7}$, $S^{x_2}_{p_7}$, and $S^{x_3}_{p_7}$, respectively; and the inlet coolant temperature, T_{r_i}, $S^{x_1}_{p_8}$, $S^{x_2}_{p_8}$, and $S^{x_3}_{p_8}$, respectively. (Reprinted with permission from Ref. 7.)

$1.29 \cdot 10^{-2}$ Kmol/m^3, i.e. 2.1% from the corresponding nominal value, which is 0.6137 Kmol/m^3; and the reaction mass temperature increases by 0.9°.

In the operation stage, we may be interested, for instance, by the influences of the ammonia concentration increase by 5% and, simultaneously, of the formaldehyde concentration decrease by 5%, in the reactor inlet stream, on the concentrations and temperature, 200 s from begining of reaction, the other parameters being unchanged, the vector of the parameters deviations is:

$$\Delta p = \begin{bmatrix} p_1 \\ p_2 \\ p_3 \\ p_4 \\ p_5 \\ p_6 \\ \vdots \\ p_{12} \end{bmatrix} = \begin{bmatrix} 0 \\ 0 \\ 0 \\ 0.203 \\ -0.316 \\ 0 \\ \vdots \\ 0 \end{bmatrix}$$

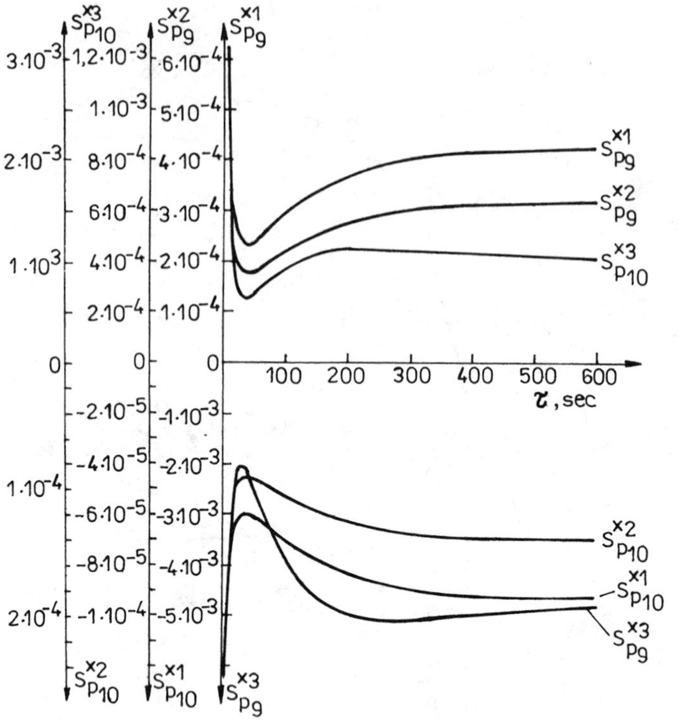

Figure 14. Sensitivities of the ammonia concentration, the formaldehyde concentration and the temperature of reacting mass with respect to the E/R ratio, $S_{p9}^{x_1}$, $S_{p9}^{x_2}$ and $S_{p9}^{x_3}$, respectively; and the frequency factor k_0, $S_{p10}^{x_1}$, $S_{p10}^{x_2}$ and $S_{p10}^{x_3}$, respectively. (Reprinted with permission from Ref. 7.)

The state vector deviation, computed by means of Equation 13, using the sensitivity matrix $S_p^x(200)$, is:

$$\Delta_p x(200) = \begin{bmatrix} 8.84 \cdot 10^{-2} \\ -8.94 \cdot 10^{-2} \\ -0.25 \end{bmatrix}$$

that is, the ammonia concentration will be $8.84 \cdot 10^{-2}$ Kmol/m^3 greater than its nominal value at $\tau = 200$ s, i.e. will increase by $\approx 29\%$; the formaldehyde concentration will decrease by $8.94 \cdot 10^{-2}$ Kmol/m^3 i.e., by 14.6% from its nominal value; and the reacting mass temperature will decrease by 0.25°.

In the same way the influence of the variation of any parameter or group of parameters that changes simultaneously on the state variables at any moment from the reaction begining can be computed.

The sensitivity of the state with respect to the control inputs with unchanging time deviations. The state sensitivity is computed by means of the algorithm given in Figure 4, for the case when the control inputs deviations, Δu, are not functions of time.

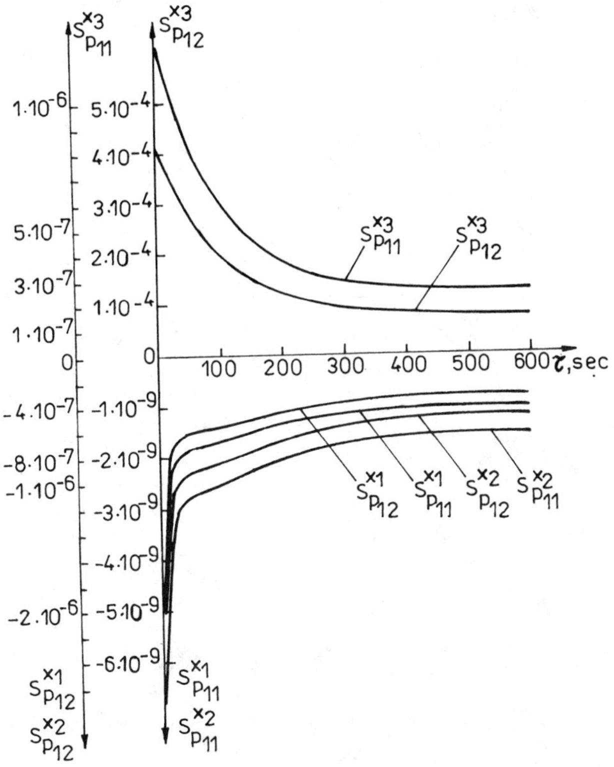

Figure 15. Sensitivities of the ammonia concentration, the formaldehyde concentration and the temperature of reacting mass with respect to the a_1 and a_2 coefficients in relation $(-\Delta H) = a_1 + a_2T$, $S^{x_1}_{p_{11}}$, $S^{x_2}_{p_{11}}$, $S^{x_3}_{p_{11}}$ and $S^{x_1}_{p_{12}}$, $S^{x_2}_{p_{12}}$, $S^{x_3}_{p_{12}}$, respectively. (Reprinted with permission from Ref. 7.)

The Jacobian matrix f_x is given by the Equations 67; the 3×3 Jacobian matrix f_u is:

$$f_u = \begin{bmatrix} \dfrac{p_4 - x_1}{p_1} & -\dfrac{x_1}{p_1} & 0 \\ -\dfrac{x_2}{p_1} & \dfrac{p_5 - x_2}{p_1} & 0 \\ \dfrac{p_6 - x_3}{p_1} & \dfrac{p_7 - x_3}{p_1} & -\dfrac{b_2}{b_1 p_1}(x_3 p_5)\left[1 - \left(\dfrac{p_2 p_3}{b_2 u_3} + 1\right)\exp\left(-\dfrac{p_2 p_3}{b_2 u_3}\right)\right] \end{bmatrix} \quad (72)$$

The diagrams of the functions components of the sensitivity matrix S^x_u, on the basis of the date obtained by numerical integration of the differential equations systems (Equations 44 and 65) using the numerical values given earlier, were drawn in Figures 16 and 17 [3].

If, for instance, we are interested in the influence of the initial variation of formaldehyde flow rate, which decreases by $0.1 \cdot 10^{-6}$ m^3/s, and of cooling agent flow rate, which simultaneously increases by $0.5 \cdot 10^{-6}$ m^3/s, on the concentrations and temperature in the reactor at 200 s from the beginning of the reaction, Figures 16 and 17 give the corresponding values of the sensitivity

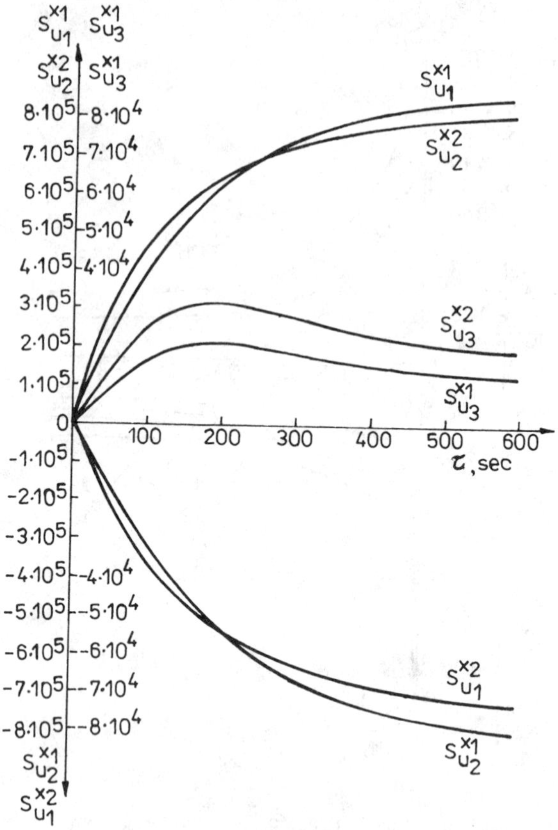

Figure 16. Sensitivities of the ammonia concentration and the formaldehyde concentration with respect to the ammonia feed-rate $S^{x_1}_{u_1}$ and $S^{x_2}_{u_1}$, respectively; the formaldehyde feed-rate, $S^{x_1}_{u_2}$ and $S^{x_2}_{u_2}$; respectively and the coolant feed-rate, $S^{x_1}_{u_3}$, and $S^{x_2}_{u_3}$, respectively.

functions:

$$S^{x}_{u}(200) = \begin{bmatrix} 6.27 \cdot 10^5 & -5.32 \cdot 10^5 & 2.12 \cdot 10^4 \\ -5.33 \cdot 10^5 & 6.49 \cdot 10^5 & 3.18 \cdot 10^4 \\ -2.31 \cdot 10^6 & 9.83 \cdot 10^5 & -6.04 \cdot 10^6 \end{bmatrix}$$

Applying Equation 13, for $\tau = 200$ s:

$$\Delta_u x(200) = S^x_u(200) \cdot \Delta u$$

where

$$\Delta u = \begin{bmatrix} \Delta q_A \\ \Delta q_F \\ \Delta q_r \end{bmatrix} = \begin{bmatrix} 0 \\ -0.1 \cdot 10^{-6} \\ 0.5 \cdot 10^{-6} \end{bmatrix}$$

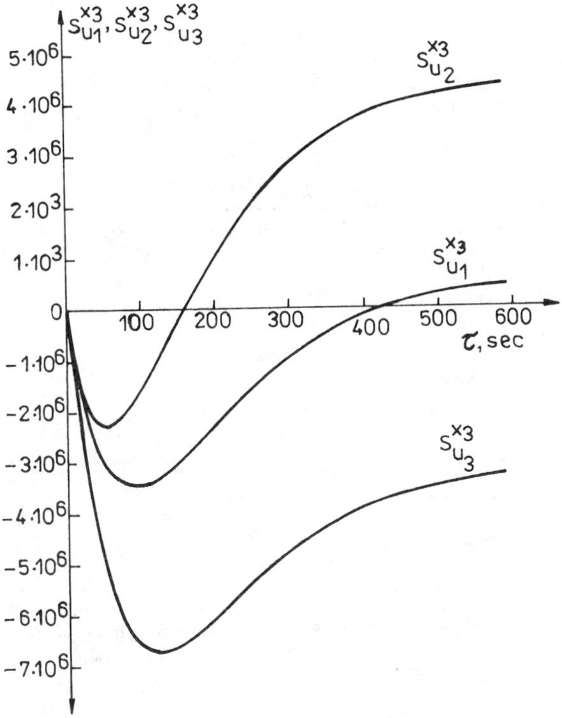

Figure 17. Sensitivity of the temperature of reacting mass with respect to the ammonia feed-rate, $S_{u_1}^{x_3}$; the formaldehyde feed-rate $S_{u_2}^{x_3}$; and the coolant feed-rate, $S_{u_3}^{x_3}$.

we get

$$\Delta_u x(200) = \begin{bmatrix} 0.0638 \\ -0.049 \\ 3.12 \end{bmatrix}$$

These results show that: the ammonia concentration increases by 0.0638 $Kmol/m^3$, the formaldehyde concentration decreases by 0.049 $Kmol/m^3$, and the mass reacting temperature increases by 3.12° with respect to the nominal corresponding values at the same moment.

The diagrams of the trajectories of dimensionless sensitivity functions of the state with respect to the control inputs, computed by means of the corresponding Equation 9, are shown in Figures 18 and 19.

These diagrams enable us to conclude the following about the sensitivity of the hexamine-producing reactor with respect to variations of flow rates of reactants and cooling agent as control inputs:

1. The concentrations of reactants are several times more sensitive to changes in inlet reactants flow-rates than to changes in the cooling agent flow-rate.
2. The mass reacting temperature is less sensitive to control inputs variations than are the concentrations of the reactants.

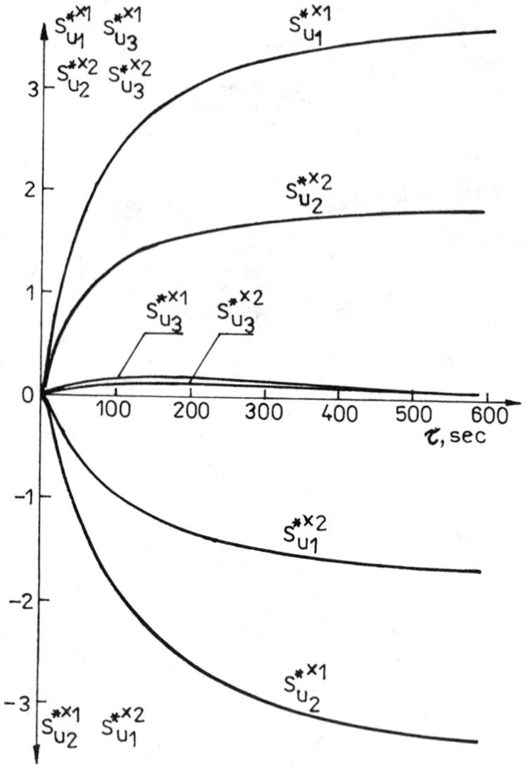

Figure 18. Dimensionless sensitivities of the ammonia concentration and the formaldehyde concentration with respect to the ammonia feed-rate $S^{x_1}_{u_1}$, and $S^{x_2}_{u_1}$, respectively; the formaldehyde feed-rate $S^{x_2}_{u_1}$ and $S^{x_2}_{u_2}$, respectively; and the coolant feed-rate $S^{x_1}_{u_3}$, and $S^{x_2}_{u_3}$, respectively.

3. The absolute values of the sensitivity of concentrations of reactants with respect to the inlet flow-rate of reactants increase in time, tending to maximal constant steady-state values; the temperature sensitivity with respect to all control inputs and sensitivity of concentrations with respect to cooling agent flow-rate variations exhibit an extreme in the first part of the transient regime.

The sensitivity of the state with respect to the control inputs with changing time variations [10]. The sensitivity of the state is computed by means of the algorithm described in Figure 4 for the case when the control inputs variations, Δu, are functions of time.

The Jacobian matrices f_x and f_u, required in sensitivity Equation 54 are given by Equations 67 and 72.

The choice of the functions of time $v_j(\tau)$, $j = \overline{1, l}$, is made by considering the hypothesis that the control input values—the ammonia, formaldehyde, and cooling agent flow rates—are automatically adjusted to the prescribed constant values. However, owing to the perturbations, and even considering the intervention of the control loop, the monitoring values will be varying with time, normally oscillating with low amplitudes around the described values. It can therefore be taken that on top of the prescribed constant value u_j of each automatically stabilized control input will be superimposed a deviation $\Delta u_j(\tau)$, having a form of variation of a periodically oscillating function.

The following sinusoidal function of time is postulated:

$$v_j = \sin\left(\frac{2\pi\tau}{T_j}\right), \qquad j = \overline{1, l} \tag{73}$$

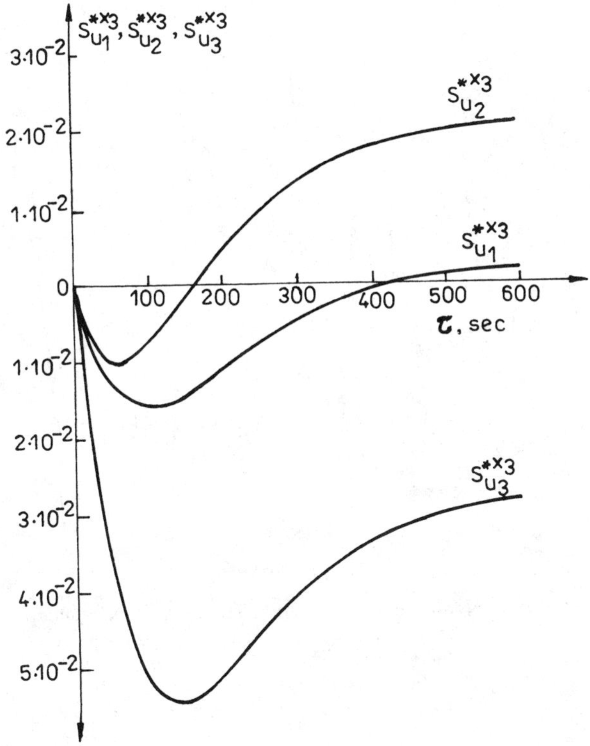

Figure 19. Dimensionless sensitivity of the temperature of reacting mass with respect to the ammonia feed-rate, $S^{x_3}_{u_1}$; the formaldehyde feed-rate, $S^{x_3}_{u_2}$; and the coolant feed-rate, $S^{x_3}_{u_3}$.

The integration of the systems of differential Equation 47, under the form of Equations 54 and 65, was performed on the computer by using the fourth-order Runge-Kutta method with the numerical data given earlier.

On the basis of results obtained by numerical integration of the above systems of differential equations, the curves of the component functions of the sensitivity matrix $S^x_u(v(\tau), \tau)$, in Figures 20–23 were traced.

The component functions of the matrix of the dimensionless sensitivities were drawn in Figures 24–26.

The graphs in Figures 20–23 permit the calculation of the deviations of the components of the state vector x, as the vector of control inputs varies with time.

- Taking as an example the calculation of the deviation of the state variables of the reactor for producing hexamine at a time $\tau = 116$ s from the start of the process, as a result of the time-variable changes in the control inputs, according to the functions expressed by Equations 48 and 73, with periods $T_j = 20$ s, $j = \overline{1, l}$, and the amplitudes:

$$\varepsilon = \begin{bmatrix} 0.2 \cdot 10^6 \\ -0.1 \cdot 10^6 \\ 0.5 \cdot 10^6 \end{bmatrix}$$

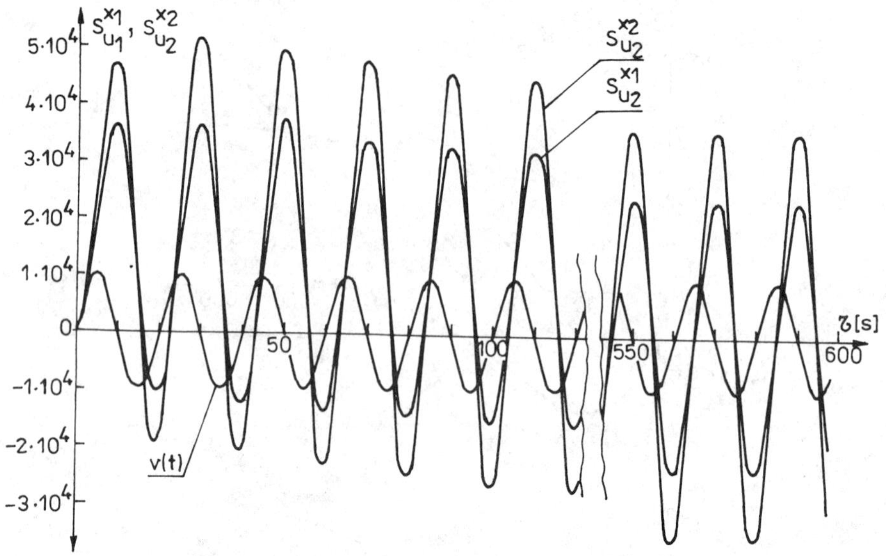

Figure 20. Sensitivity of ammonia concentration to changes in the ammonia feed-rate, $S^{x_1}_{u_1}$; and sensitivity of formaldehyde concentration to changes in the formaldehyde feed-rate, $S^{x_2}_{u_2}$, with feed-rates varying according to function $v(\tau)$. (Reprinted with permission from Ref. 10.)

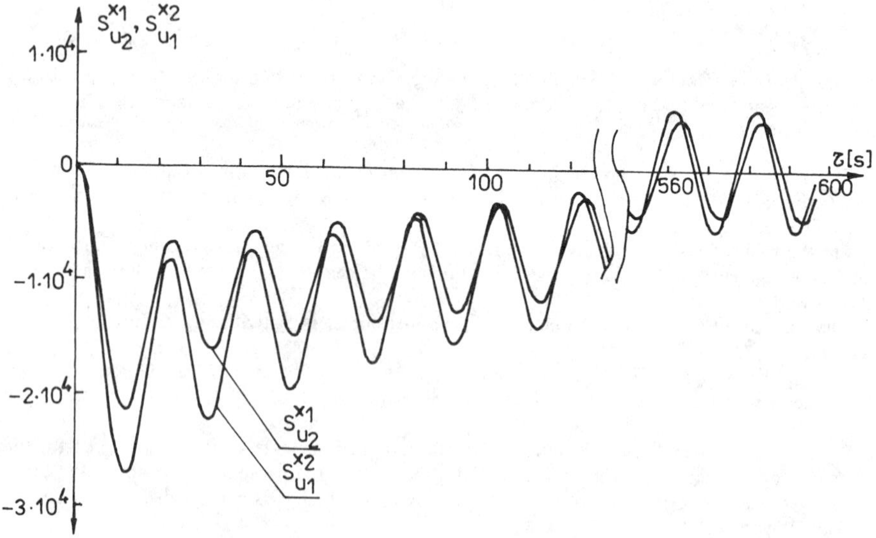

Figure 21. Sensitivity of ammonia concentration to changes in the formaldehyde feed-rate, $S^{x_1}_{u_2}$; and sensitivity of formaldehyde concentration to changes in the ammonia feed-rate, $S^{x_2}_{u_1}$, with feed-rates varying according to function $v(\tau)$. (Reprinted with permission from Ref. 10.)

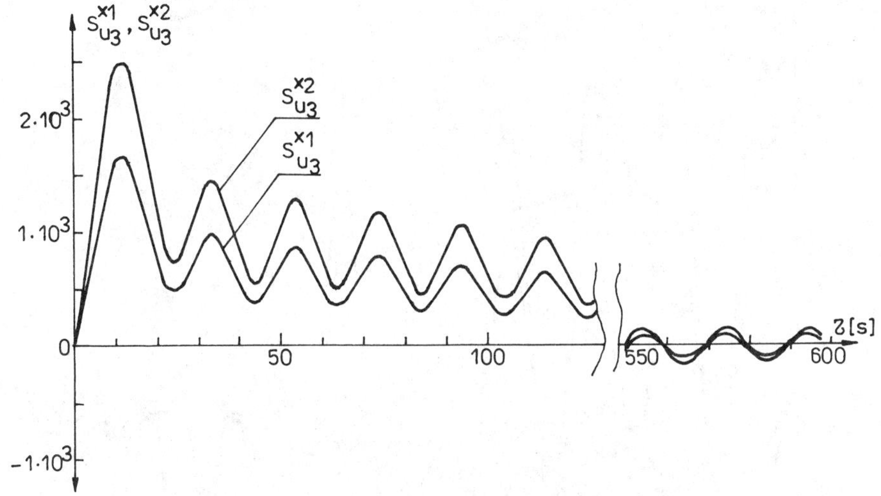

Figure 22. Sensitivities of ammonia concentration and formaldehyde concentration to changes in the coolant flow-rate, $S_{u_3}^{x_1}$ and $S_{u_3}^{x_2}$, respectively; with feed-rate varying according to function $v(\tau)$. (Reprinted with permission from Ref. 10.)

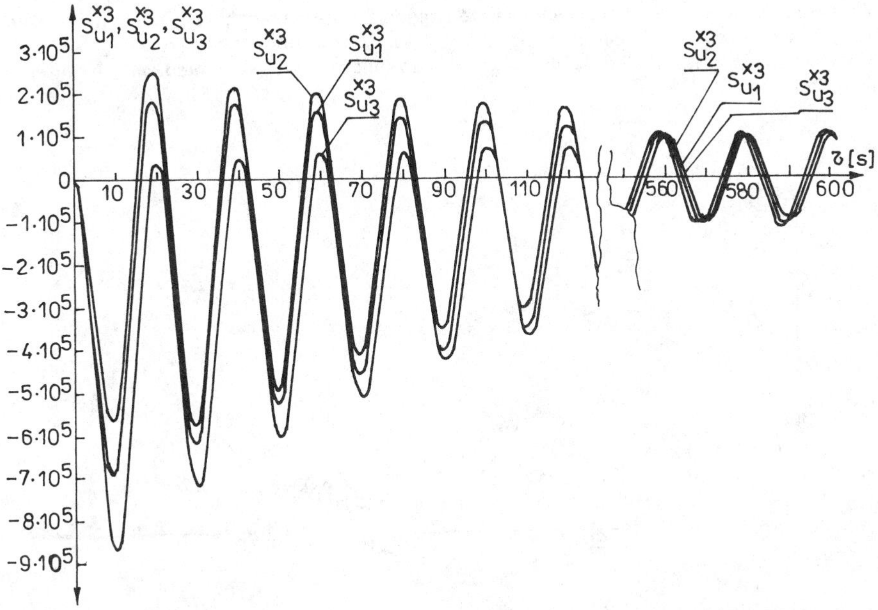

Figure 23. Sensitivities of temperature of reacting mass to changes in the ammonia feed-rate, $S_{u_1}^{x_3}$; the formaldehyde feed-rate, $S_{u_2}^{x_3}$; and the coolant feed-rate, $S_{u_3}^{x_3}$; with feed rates varying according to function $v(\tau)$. (Reprinted with permission from Ref. 10.)

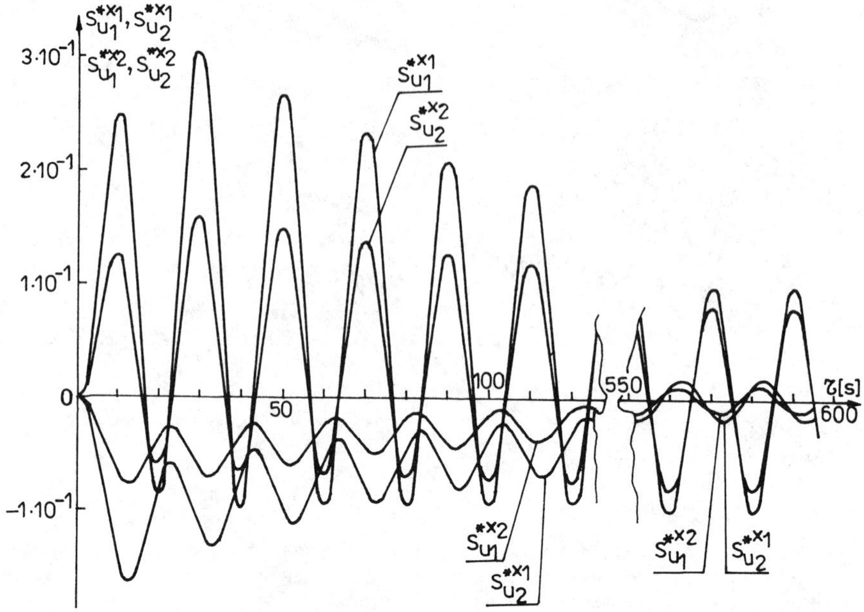

Figure 24. Dimensionless sensitivities of the ammonia and formaldehyde concentrations with respect to the ammonia feed-rate, $S_{u_1}^{x_1}$ and $S_{u_1}^{x_2}$; and formaldehyde feed-rate, $S_{u_2}^{x_1}$ and $S_{u_2}^{x_2}$, respectively; with feed rates varying according to function $v(\tau)$. (Reprinted with permission from Ref. 10.)

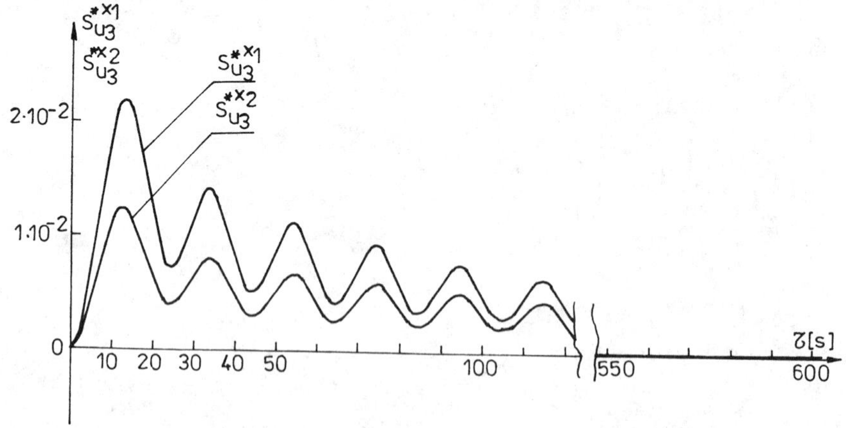

Figure 25. Dimensionless sensitivities of the ammonia concentration, $S_{u_3}^{x_1}$ and the formaldehyde concentration, $S_{u_3}^{x_2}$, with respect to the coolant feed-rate varying according to function $v(\tau)$. (Reprinted with permission from Ref. 10.)

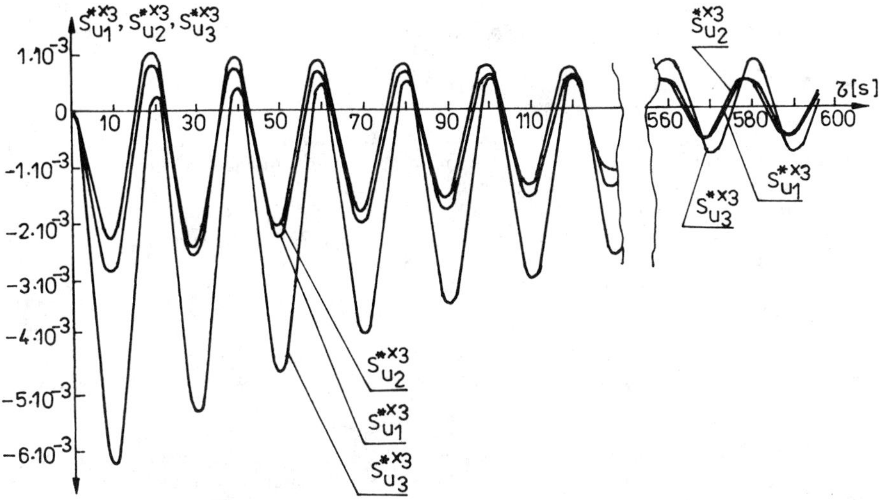

Figure 26. Dimensionless sensitivities of the temperature of the reacting mass with respect to the ammonia feed-rate, $S^{x_3}_{u_1}$; the formaldehyde flow-rate, $S^{x_3}_{u_2}$; and the coolant feed-rate, $S^{x_3}_{u_3}$; with feed rates varying according to function $v(\tau)$. (Reprinted with permission from Ref. 10.)

the following matrix of sensitivity functions is read off the graphs in Figures 20–23:

$$S^{x}_{u}(110) = \begin{bmatrix} 3.24 \cdot 10^4 & -1.02 \cdot 10^4 & 5.03 \cdot 10^2 \\ -1.30 \cdot 10^4 & 4.47 \cdot 10^4 & 7.55 \cdot 10^2 \\ -3.43 \cdot 10^5 & -2.91 \cdot 10^5 & -3.73 \cdot 10^5 \end{bmatrix}$$

Applying Equation 53, we obtain:

$$\Delta_u x(110) = \begin{bmatrix} 0.00775 \\ -0.00669 \\ -0.226 \end{bmatrix}$$

which means that the concentration of ammonia is 0.00775 Kmol/m^3 higher, the concentration of formaldehyde is 0.00669 Kmol/m^3 lower and the temperature of the reaction mass is 0.226 lower than the nominal values.

- From the graphs of the dimensionless sensitivity functions shown in Figures 24–26, the following conclusions can be drawn with regard to the sensitivity of a nonisothermal, continuous reactor with perfect mixing to changes in the rates of flow of the reactants and the coolant as the time-variable control inputs (monitoring values):

  1. Most of the sensitivity functions oscillate with dampening, and in the steady state tend to oscillate with a minimal nonzero amplitude and a period equal to that of the variation of the control inputs, but with a different phase difference.
  2. In the steady state, the concentrations of the reactants become insensitive to oscillatory changes in the rate of flow of the coolant.

The sensitivity of a reactor with respect to control inputs with constant deviations can be used as a criterion for selecting the control inputs for the particular process under consideration, while the sensitivity with respect to control inputs with time-variable deviations can be used as a measure of the required performance of the prescribed system for automatic control.

DSA of a Fixed Bed Reactor for Ammonia Synthesis

In order to analyze the sensitivity of the reaction zone of a fixed bed reactor for ammonia synthesis, around the working condition with known temperature distribution along the catalytic bed, the adjoint system method, described earlier, is applied [15].

All the numerical data required by the mathematical model of the reaction zone and the temperature and gas composition measured data correspond to a 295 at. pressure and 450 tons/day production reactor.

The Mathematical Model

Let us consider a reactor with the catalyst among the tubes, as it is shown in Figure 27.

In the mathematical description of the process several simplifying assumptions were adopted. These include:

1. The granular structure of the catalyst and the large flow rate of gases assure a perfect mixing of the reaction mass; so, the radial gradient of the concentration may be neglected.
2. The large number of tubes (499 tubes) and their uniform distribution inside the reaction zone causes the maximum distance between any catalyst particle and tube walls to be no larger than 37 mm. This fact and the great transversal mixing of the gases passing through catalyst particles allow us to neglect the transversal gradient of temperature, without significant errors.
3. Because of the large flow rate of the gases, the mass transfer due to the axial diffusion is negligible as compared to the mass transfer due to gas circulation through reactor.
4. The reactor is in a steady state, therefore without accumulation phenomena.

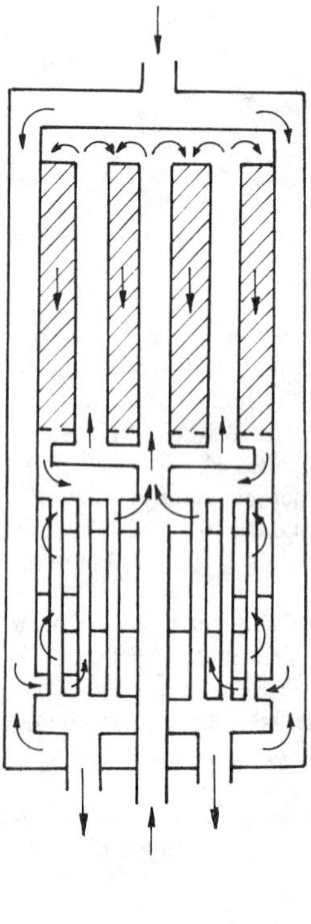

Figure 27. The fixed bed reactor for ammonia synthesis.

Considering these considerations, the independent variable in our case is not the time, τ, anymore, but a spatial coordinate, z. The reactor—in steady state with respect to time—is investigated as a "dynamic system" with respect to this spatial coordinate.

The state vector is:

$$x = \begin{bmatrix} x_A \\ x_N \\ x_H \\ x_I \\ T \end{bmatrix} \tag{74}$$

where x = molar fraction
T = temperature
A = ammonia
N = nitrogen
H = hydrogen
I = inert gas

As the first four components of the state vector have to answer the relation:

$$x_A + x_N + x_H + x_I = 1 \tag{75}$$

only three of its are independent; however Equation 74 is used due to the advantage of the symmetry.

All the magnitudes receive the subscript "0" to indicate the inlet in the reaction zone and "f" for the outlet.

The mass balance of ammonia gives the equation:

$$\dot{x}_A = -4.92 \cdot 10^{11} \exp\left(-\frac{40765}{RT}\right)\left[K_a^2 x_N f_N \frac{(x_H f_H)^{1.5}}{x_A f_A} - \frac{x_A f_A}{(x_H f_H)^{1.5}}\right] = \Phi_A(x, z) \tag{76}$$

where $K_a = K_a(T)$, equilibrium factor
R = universal gas constant
f = f(T, P), fugacity
P = pressure

The equation of the reaction

$$N_2 + 3H_2 \rightleftharpoons 2NH_3$$

leads to the relations:

$$\begin{aligned} x_N &= \frac{x_{N,0} - 0.5}{x_{A,0} + 1} x_A + \frac{0.5x_{A,0} + x_{N,0}}{x_{A,0} + 1} = \alpha_N x_A + \beta_N \\ x_H &= \frac{x_{H,0} - 1.5}{x_{A,0} + 1} x_A + \frac{1.5x_{A,0} + x_{H,0}}{x_{A,0} + 1} = \alpha_H x_A + \beta_H \\ x_I &= \frac{x_{I,0}}{x_{A,0} + 1} x_A + \frac{x_{I,0}}{x_{A,0} + 1} = \alpha_I x_A + \beta_I \end{aligned} \tag{77}$$

The measurements on reactor by means of twelve thermocouples placed in the catalyst bed at different levels were made in order to find out the temperature distribution along the reaction zone, T(z).

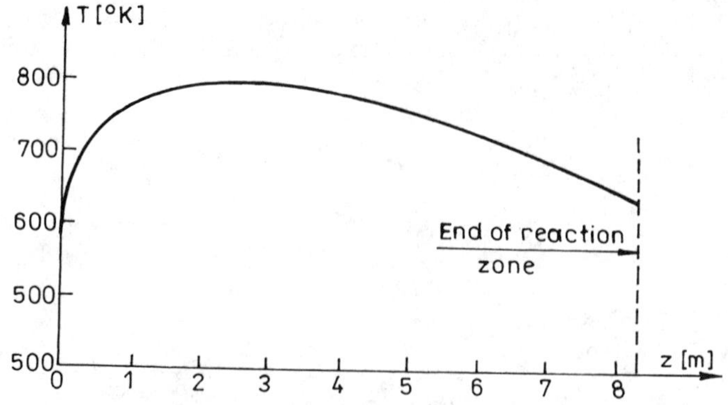

Figure 28. Distribution of the temperature along the reaction zone.

The diagram in Figure 28 was obtained, corresponding to a function:

$$T = \Phi_T(x_0, z) \tag{78}$$

Figure 29 shows the trajectory of the state variable x_A, obtained by integrating the state Equation 76, where the values of x_N, x_H, x_I, and T, given by Equations 77 and 78 were introduced.

The initial condition used to integrate was:

$$x_0 = \begin{bmatrix} 0.031 \\ 0.236 \\ 0.583 \\ 0.149 \\ 603 \end{bmatrix} \tag{79}$$

The validation of the mathematical model was made by measuring the ammonia concentrations, using the chromatography of gases, at the same time with the temperature measurements.

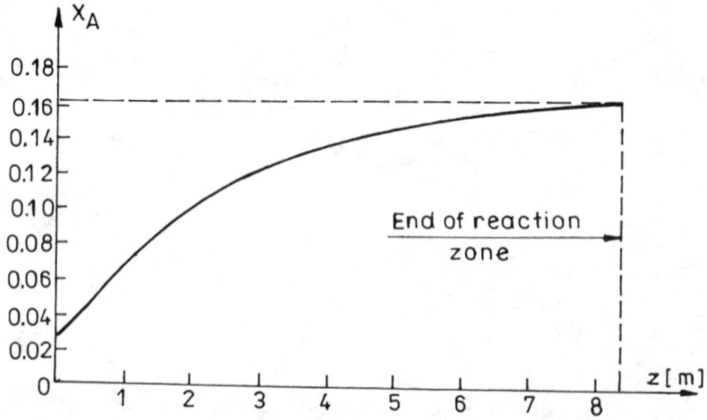

Figure 29. Distribution of the ammonia concentration along the reaction zone.

Summing up, the mathematical model of the considered process on the state equations is:

$$\begin{aligned}
\dot{x}_A &= \Phi_A(x, z) \\
\dot{x}_N &= \alpha_N \Phi_A(x, z) \\
\dot{x}_H &= \alpha_H \Phi_A(x, z) \\
\dot{x}_I &= \alpha_I \Phi_A(x, z) \\
T &= \Phi_T(x_0, z)
\end{aligned} \tag{80}$$

We assume that only the sensitivity of the molar fractions x_A, x_N, x_H, x_I, at the end of the reaction zone with respect to deviations of these fractions at different levels of the reaction zone interests us.

The value of the function $\Phi_T(x_0, z)$ is introduced in $\Phi_A(x, z)$ so, we get the state vector:

$$x = \begin{bmatrix} x_A \\ x_N \\ x_H \\ x_I \end{bmatrix}$$

The mathematical model becomes:

$$\dot{x} = f(x, z)$$

where

$$f(x, z) = \begin{bmatrix} 1 \\ \alpha_N \\ \alpha_H \\ \alpha_I \end{bmatrix} \Phi_A(x, z)$$

The Sensitivity Analysis

The DSA algorithm, described in Figure 2 is followed. From Equation 77 we obtain:

$$\frac{\partial x_A}{\partial x_N} = \frac{1}{\alpha_N}$$

$$\frac{\partial x_A}{\partial x_H} = \frac{1}{\alpha_H}$$

$$\frac{\partial x_A}{\partial x_I} = \frac{1}{\alpha_I}$$

and considering Equation 76, the Jacobian matrix f_x takes the form:

$$f_x(x, z) = \begin{bmatrix} 1 & \frac{1}{\alpha_N} & \frac{1}{\alpha_H} & \frac{1}{\alpha_I} \\ \alpha_N & 1 & \frac{\alpha_N}{\alpha_H} & \frac{\alpha_N}{\alpha_I} \\ \alpha_H & \frac{\alpha_H}{\alpha_N} & 1 & \frac{\alpha_H}{\alpha_I} \\ \alpha_I & \frac{\alpha_I}{\alpha_N} & \frac{\alpha_I}{\alpha_H} & 1 \end{bmatrix} \frac{\partial}{\partial x_A} [\Phi_A(x, z)] \tag{81}$$

The functions matrix $f_x(x, z)$ as a function of spatial coordinate z, only, is obtained by integrating the Equation 76 (Figure 29) and using Equations 77 and 81. The modified adjoint system is built through the transformation of the independent variable $z = z_f - \theta$:

$$\frac{\partial}{\partial \theta} \Psi(\theta) = f_x^T(z_f - \theta)\Psi(\theta) \tag{82}$$

with the initial condition

$$\Psi(0) = 1 \tag{83}$$

The solution of Equation 82, with initial condition of Equation 83, after the return to the primitive independent variable z, using the relation $\theta = z_f - z$, is the sensitivity matrix of the concentrations (molar fractions) x_A, x_N, x_H, x_I at the end of the reaction zone with respect to the deviations of the same concentrations at any point z_1, $0 \le z_1 \le z_f$, of the reaction zone:

$$S_x^{x_f}(z) = [\Psi^T(\theta)]_{\theta = z_f - z}$$

This matrix has the form:

$$S_x^{x_f}(z) = \begin{bmatrix} S_{x_A}^{x_{A,f}} & S_{x_N}^{x_{A,f}} & S_{x_H}^{x_{A,f}} & S_{x_I}^{x_{A,f}} \\ S_{x_A}^{x_{N,f}} & S_{x_N}^{x_{N,f}} & S_{x_H}^{x_{N,f}} & S_{x_I}^{x_{N,f}} \\ S_{x_A}^{x_{H,f}} & S_{x_N}^{x_{H,f}} & S_{x_H}^{x_{H,f}} & S_{x_I}^{x_{H,f}} \\ S_{x_A}^{x_{I,f}} & S_{x_N}^{x_{I,f}} & S_{x_H}^{x_{I,f}} & S_{x_I}^{x_{I,f}} \end{bmatrix}$$

where each element is a function of z, $0 \le z \le z_f$.

These sensitivity functions are shown in Figures 30–33.

If we wish, for instance, to compute the deviations of the ammonia, nitrogen, hydrogen, and inert gas concentrations at the reactor outlet, if at level z = 6 m a variation of the ammonia and

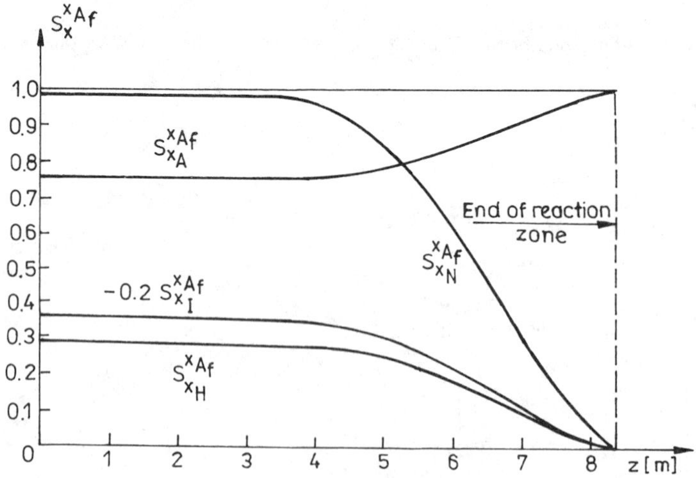

Figure 30. Sensitivities of ammonia final concentration to changes in the ammonia concentration, $S_{x_A}^{x_{A_f}}$; the nitrogen concentration, $S_{x_N}^{x_{A_f}}$; the hydrogen concentration, $S_{x_H}^{x_{A_f}}$; and the inert gas concentration, $S_{x_I}^{x_{A_f}}$.

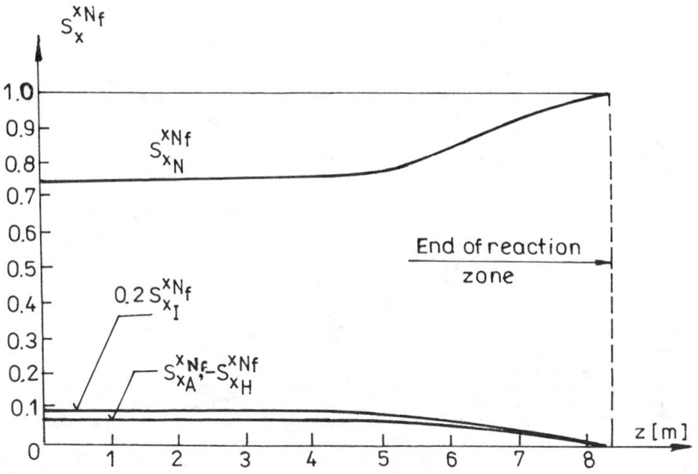

Figure 31. Sensitivities of nitrogen final concentration to changes in the ammonia concentration, $S_{xA}^{xN_f}$; the nitrogen concentration, $S_{xN}^{xN_f}$; the hydrogen concentration, $S_{xH}^{xN_f}$; and the inert gas concentration, $S_{xI}^{xN_f}$.

inert gas concentrations, $\Delta x_A(6) = 0.015$ and $\Delta x_I(6) = -0.01$, arises, the hydrogen-nitrogen concentrations ratio remaining unaltered, we proceed as follows: consider Equation 75, the corresponding variations of the nitrogen and hydrogen concentrations, at z = 6 m height, are computed.

Equation 75 is written in finite variations form:

$$\Delta x_A(6) + \Delta x_N(6) + \Delta x_H(6) + \Delta x_I(6) = 0$$

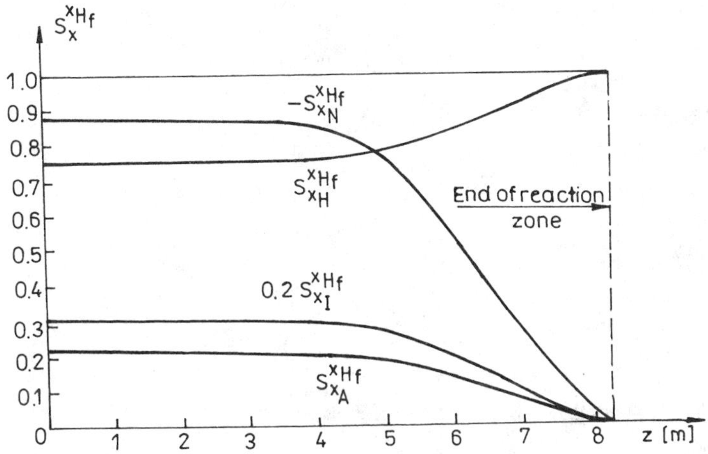

Figure 32. Sensitivities of hydrogen final concentration to changes in the ammonia concentration, $S_{xA}^{xH_f}$; the nitrogen concentration, $S_{xN}^{xH_f}$; the hydrogen concentration, $S_{xH}^{xH_f}$; and the inert gas concentration, $S_{xI}^{xH_f}$.

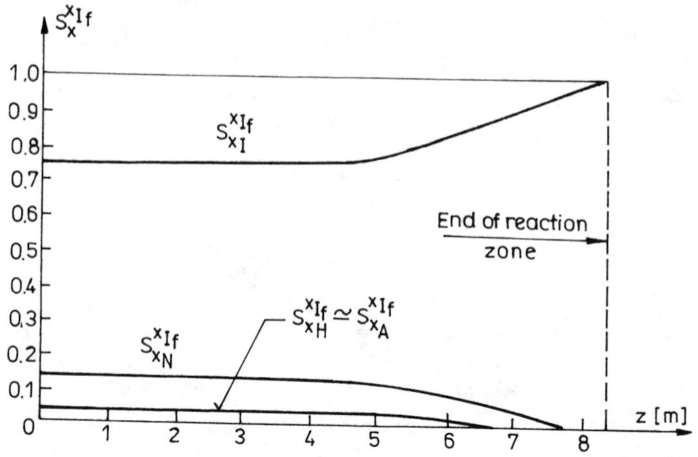

Figure 33. Sensitivities of final concentration of the inert to changes in the ammonia concentration, $S_{x_A}^{x_{I_f}}$; the nitrogen concentration, $S_{x_N}^{x_{I_f}}$; the hydrogen concentration, $S_{x_H}^{x_{I_f}}$; and the inert gas concentration, $S_{x_I}^{x_{I_f}}$.

and by introducing the numerical data:

$$0.015 + \Delta x_N(6) + \Delta x_H(6) - 0.01 = 0$$

From the constant ratio between nitrogen and hydrogen concentrations condition we get:

$$\frac{\Delta x_N(6)}{\Delta x_H(6)} = \frac{x_N(6)}{x_H(6)} = \frac{x_N(0)}{x_H(0)} = \frac{0.236}{0.583} = 0.404$$

A system of equations is composed from the last two equations:

$$\begin{cases} \Delta x_N(6) + \Delta x_H(6) = -0.005 \\ \Delta x_N(6) - 0.404\, \Delta x_H(6) = 0 \end{cases}$$

which has the solution $\Delta x_N(6) = -0.0014$ and $\Delta x_H(6) = -0.0036$.
Therefore, the $\Delta x(6)$ vector is:

$$\Delta x(6) = \begin{bmatrix} 0.015 \\ -0.0014 \\ -0.0036 \\ -0.01 \end{bmatrix}$$

The sensitivity matrix $[S_x^{x_f}(z)]_{z=6}$ is read in Figures 30–33:

$$S_x^{x_f}(6) = \begin{bmatrix} 0.83 & 0.61 & 0.17 & -1.00 \\ 0.04 & 0.83 & -0.04 & 0.35 \\ 0.13 & -0.50 & 0.83 & 0.90 \\ -0.02 & 0.09 & 0.02 & 0.83 \end{bmatrix}$$

The deviation of the state vector at $z = z_f$ is computed using Equation 30, for $\tau_1 = z_1 = 6$, $\tau = \tau_f = z_f$:

$$\Delta x(z_f) = S_x^{x_f}(6) \cdot \Delta x(6)$$

and we obtain

$$\Delta x(z_f) = \begin{bmatrix} 0.155 \\ -0.0026 \\ -0.036 \\ -0.0094 \end{bmatrix}$$

Thus, at the reactor outlet, the ammonia concentration increases by 0.155 and the nitrogen, hydrogen, and inert gas concentrations decrease by 0.0026, 0.036 and 0.0094, respectively.

Particularly, if the concentrations variations arise at the reactor inlet,

$$\Delta x_0 = \begin{bmatrix} 0.015 \\ -0.0014 \\ -0.0036 \\ -0.01 \end{bmatrix}$$

The corresponding deviations, at the outlet of the reactor will be:

$$\Delta x_f = \begin{bmatrix} 0.75 & 0.98 & 0.26 & -1.75 \\ 0.06 & 0.75 & -0.06 & 0.45 \\ 0.22 & -0.87 & 0.75 & 1.55 \\ -0.04 & 0.14 & 0.04 & 0.75 \end{bmatrix} \cdot \Delta x_0 = \begin{bmatrix} 0.026 \\ -0.0044 \\ -0.0137 \\ -0.0084 \end{bmatrix}$$

which means that the ammonia concentration will increase by 0.026 only; and the other components concentrations will decrease by 0.0044, 0.0137, and 0.0084, respectively.

The conclusions from those calculations can suggest some automatic control methods by compensation of the reactor for ammonia synthesis [15].

NOTATION

a	coefficients in Equation of $(-\Delta H)$,
A	matrix of functions of p, Equation 21; heat transfer area of the reactor,
A_p	Jacobian matrix of the functions of p, A(p), with respect to the parameters
B	matrix of functions of p, Equation 21
B_p	Jacobian matrix of the functions of p, B(p), with respect to the parameters
C	matrix of functions of p, Equation 27; concentrations
C_p	specific heat at constant pressure
C_r	specific heat of the coolant
D	matrix of functions of p, Equation 27
E	energy of activation
f	vector of functions $f(x(\tau), u, p, \tau)$, Equation 1; fugacity
f_p	Jacobian matrix of the vector of functions $f(x(\tau), u, p, \tau)$ with respect to the parameters vector
f_u	Jacobian matrix of the vector of functions $f(x(\tau), u, p, \tau)$ with respect to the control inputs vector
f_x	Jacobian matrix of the vector of functions $f(x(\tau), u, p, \tau)$ with respect to the vector of the state
g	vector of functions $g(x(\tau), u, p, \tau)$, Equation 2
g_x	Jacobian matrix of the vector of functions $g(x(\tau), u, p, \tau)$ with respect to the vector of the state
ΔH	heat of reaction
K	overall heat transfer coefficient
k_0	frequency factor

K_a equilibrium factor
p vector of parameters
P pressure
q volumetric flow rate
r rate of reaction
R universal gas constant
S^x_p sensitivity matrix of the state with respect to the parameters
S^x_u sensitivity matrix of the state with respect to the control inputs
S^x_{xo} sensitivity matrix of the state with respect to the initial state
$S^x_{x_1}$ sensitivity matrix of the state with respect to the state variables at any moment, τ_1
S^y_p sensitivity matrix of the output with respect to the parameters
S^y_u sensitivity matrix of the output with respect to the control inputs
S^y_{xo} sensitivity matrix of the output with respect to the initial state
T temperature
u vector of control inputs
v functions of time, Equation 48
V volume of reactor
w square matrix of functions of time, Equation 50
x vector of state variables
y vector of output variables
z spatial coordinate

Greek Symbols

α constants, Equation 77,
β constants, Equation 77,
δ Kronecker delta function
Δ... deviation of...
ε small constants, Equation 48
θ independent variable of the adjoint system, Equation 31
ρ density
τ time
Φ functions of z and x, Equations 76, 78,
Ψ vector of dependent variables of the adjoint system, Equation 32

Subscripts

A ammonia
f final, outlet
F formaldehyde
H hydrogen
i inlet
I inert gas
m mean value
N nitrogen
o initial, inlet
p parameters
r coolant
T temperature
u control inputs
x_0 initial state
x_1 state at any moment, τ_1

Superscripts

T transposed
x state
x_f final state
y output
* dimensionless
' derivative with respect to the independent variable (time, τ, or a spatial coordinate, z)

REFERENCES

1. Boudarel, R., Delmas, J., and Guichet, P., *Optimal Control of Processes* Dunod, Paris, 1967, vol. I, p. 132 (In French).
2. Curievici, I., Ungureanu, S., and Petrila, C., "Sensitivity of a Nonisothermal Continuous-Stirred-Tank Reactor Relative to Its Initial State," *Bul. Inst. Politeh.*, Iasi, XXVIII (XXXII), 51 (1982).

3. Ungureanu, S., Petrila, C., and Curievici, I., "The Sensitivity Analysis of a Chemical Reactor as a Dynamic System," *Mem. Sect. St., Acad. R.S.R., Ser. IV*, 5, 267 (1982).
4. Ungureanu, S., *Sensitivity of Technical Dynamic Systems*, Ed. Technica, Bucharest, 1988 (In press), (In Rom.).
5. Boudarel, R., Delmas, J., and Guichet, P., *Optimal Control of Processes* Dunod, Paris, 1967, vol. I, p. 82–88, (In French).
6. Boudarel, R., Delmas, J., and Guichet, P., *Optimal Control of Processes* Dunod, Paris, 1967, vol. I, p. 133–134 (In French).
7. Ungureanu, S., and Petrila, C., "Parametric Sensitivity of a Continuous Reactor with Perfect Mixing under Dynamic Condition," *Rev. Chim.* (*Buc.*), 32, 1088 (1981), (In Rom.).
8. Ungureanu, S., Curievici, I., and Petrila, C., "Sensitivity of a Multitubular Catalytic Reactor for Strong Exothermal Processes," *Rev. Chim.* (*Buc.*), 33, 255 (1982), (In Rom.).
9. Tomovič, R., and Vukobratovič, M., *General Theory of Sensitivity*, Sovietskoye Radio, Moscow, 1972, p. 31 (In Russ.).
10. Ungureanu, S., and Petrila, C., "Sensitivity Analysis of a Chemical Reactor with Respect to the Control Inputs," *Int. Chem. Eng.*, 25, 693 (1985), reprinted from *Rev. Chim.* (*Buc.*), 33, 1125 (1982).
11. Mihail, R., *Modeling of Chemical Reactors*, Ed. Tehnica, Bucharest, 1976, p. 271—274, (In Rom.).
12. Mihail, R., Bozga, G., and Sima, V., "Optimal Control of the Dynamic Regime of a Reactor," *Rev. Chim.* (*Buc.*), 30, 51 (1979), (In Rom.).
13. Kermode, R. I., and Stevens, W. F., "Experimental Verification of the Mathematical Model for a Continuous Stirred-Tank Reactor," *Canad. J. Chem. Eng.*, 43, 68 (1965).
14. Rase, H. F., *Chemical Reactor Design for Process Plants*, John Wiley & Sons, N.Y., London, Sydney, Toronto, vol. I, 1977, p. 418.
15. Ghibu, C., Malanca, C., and Petrila, C., "Sensitivity of Reacting Zone of a Reactor for Ammonia Synthesis to Changes in the Synthesis Gas Composition," *Rev. Chim.* (*Buc.*), 23, 155 (1972), (In Rom.).

CHAPTER 29

THE INVERSE SENSITIVITY ANALYSIS OF CHEMICAL REACTORS

S.H. Ungureanu

Politechnical Institute of Iasi
Faculty of Chemical Technology
Iasi, Romania

CONTENTS

THE INVERSE SENSITIVITY PROBLEM STATEMENT

Let the mathematical model of a nonlinear, continuous, dynamic system in the form of a vectorial state equation be:

$$\dot{x} = f(x(\tau), u, p, \tau) \tag{1}$$

having the initial condition

$$x(\tau_0) = x_0 \tag{2}$$

where, the state vector, $x(\tau)$, has n components, the control vector, u, has l components, and the parameter vector, p, has m components. We consider the case in which the control inputs and the parameters change by constant in time variations (a step change) from the initial values.

The unperturbed state trajectory is the solution of Equation 1:

$$x(\tau) = x(x_0, u, p, \tau) \tag{3}$$

We denote by q the vector obtained by the juxtaposition of the components of the vectors x_0, u and p, having $k = n + l + m$ components:

$$\begin{aligned} q &= [q_1 \quad q_2 \cdots q_k]^T \\ &= [x_{1,0} \quad x_{2,0} \cdots x_{n,0} \quad u_1 \quad u_2 \cdots u_l \quad p_1 \quad p_2 \cdots p_m]^T \end{aligned} \tag{4}$$

Equation 1 becomes:

$$\dot{x}(\tau) = x(q, \tau) \tag{5}$$

At the τ_0 moment, the modifications in step form of the initial state, Δx_0, of the control inputs, Δu, and of the parameters, Δp, arise.

We denote:

$$\Delta q = [\Delta q_1 \quad \Delta q_2 \cdots \Delta q_k]^T = [\Delta x_{1,0} \quad \Delta x_{2,0} \cdots \Delta x_{n,0} \quad \Delta u_1 \quad \Delta u_2 \cdots \Delta u_l \quad \Delta p_1 \quad \Delta p_2 \cdots \Delta p_m]^T \tag{6}$$

The perturbed trajectory of the state being

$$x(x_0 + \Delta x_0, u + \Delta u, p + \Delta p, \tau) = x(q + \Delta q, \tau) \tag{7}$$

the deviation of the state trajectory from the nominal one is given by:

$$\Delta x = x(q + \Delta q, \tau) - x(q, \tau) \tag{8}$$

The direct sensitivity analysis of the dynamic system investigates the influence of the deviations of the initial state, the control inputs and the parameters on the state and output of the system, considering these deviations known.

Synthetically, the DSA problem can be expressed as follows [1]:

$$\Delta x(\tau) = \varphi(\Delta q, \tau) \tag{9}$$

We define the *general sensitivity matrix*, $S_q^x(\tau)$, the matrix obtained by juxtaposition of the sensitivity functions matrices of the state, with respect to initial state, $S_{x_0}^x$, to control inputs, S_u^x and to parameters, S_p^x, having $n \times k$ elements, $k = n + l + m$:

$$S_q^x(\tau) = [S_{q_j}^{x_i}] = \begin{bmatrix} S_{x_{1,0}}^{x_1} & S_{x_{2,0}}^{x_1} \cdots S_{x_{n,0}}^{x_1} & S_{u_1}^{x_1} & S_{u_2}^{x_1} \cdots S_{u_l}^{x_1} & S_{p_1}^{x_1} & S_{p_2}^{x_1} \cdots S_{p_m}^{x_1} \\ S_{x_{1,0}}^{x_2} & S_{x_{2,0}}^{x_2} \cdots S_{x_{n,0}}^{x_2} & S_{u_1}^{x_2} & S_{u_2}^{x_2} \cdots S_{u_l}^{x_2} & S_{p_1}^{x_1} & S_{p_2}^{x_2} \cdots S_{p_m}^{x_2} \\ & & \cdots\cdots\cdots\cdots & & & \\ S_{x_{1,0}}^{x_n} & S_{x_{2,0}}^{x_n} \cdots S_{x_{n,0}}^{x_n} & S_{u_1}^{x_n} & S_{u_2}^{x_n} \cdots S_{u_l}^{x_n} & S_{p_1}^{x_n} & S_{p_2}^{x_n} \cdots S_{p_m}^{x_n} \end{bmatrix}$$

$$i = \overline{1, n};\ j = \overline{1, k};\ k = n + l + m \tag{10}$$

According to DSA, the Equation 9 becomes:

$$\Delta x(\tau) = S_q^x(\tau) \cdot \Delta q \tag{11}$$

The DSA problem is satisfactorily solved by computing the sensitivity functions matrices $S_{x_0}^x$, S_u^x and S_p^x, such it is shown in the previous chapter.

The problem of *inverse sensitivity analysis*, ISA, can be thus formulated [2]:

"Given (measured) the deviation in time of the trajectory of state of the real system, $\Delta x^*(\tau)$, $\tau \in [\tau_0, \tau_f]$ from the trajectory of the ideal system (corresponding to the mathematical model), let us determine the vector of initial state changes, Δx_0, of control inputs, Δu, and parameters, Δp, changes, which by simultaneous action cause this deviation."

Formally, starting from Equation 9, the ISA problem reduces itself to the solution of the equation:

$$\Delta q = \varphi^{-1}(\Delta x^*(\tau)), \qquad \tau \in [\tau_0, \tau_f] \tag{12}$$

In connection with ISA problem, we must answer the following important questions [1]:

1. Under what conditions can we solve Equation 12?
2. By what methods can we calculate the required components of the vector Δq?

Before answering these questions, we note that the ISA starts from the knowledge of the state deviation trajectory of the real system from the nominal trajectory, $\Delta x^*(\tau)$, which requires its definition.

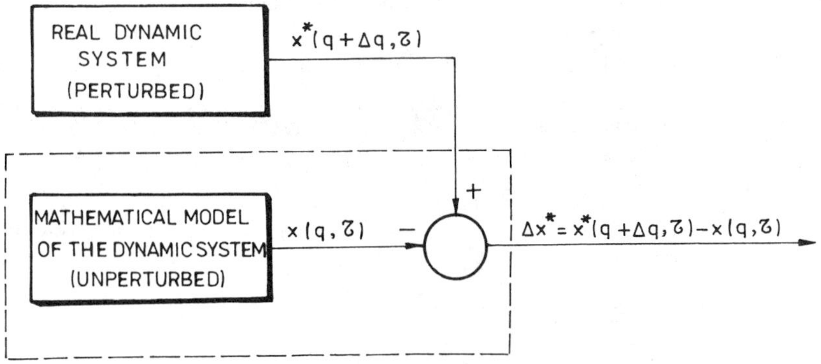

Figure 1. Determination of the difference $\Delta x^*(\tau)$.

Considering Equation 8, it means that in the study of the inverse sensitivity we must observe the state deviation of the perturbed dynamic system in real time and we must get a plot $x(q + \Delta q, q)$ as a time function. So, in order to obtain this initial information, we must have adequate measuring and recording instruments connected to the industrial system.

At the same time, we must have the state trajectory of the unperturbed ideal dynamic system, $x(q, \tau)$ in time. In fact, this trajectory is the solution of Equation 1 and can be either calculated or generated in real time, in advance on a computer. Anyway, this presupposes the knowledge of the accurate mathematical model of the system.

In this respect, the initial information for ISA are more numerous and difficult to obtain than in the DSA, because they require certain measuring devices and special computer operating as data logger and computing device.

The block diagram for obtaining the trajectory of the state deviation of real system in real time is shown in Figure 1.

SOLVING THE ISA PROBLEM: GENERAL ALGORITHM FOR TECHNICAL DIAGNOSIS

First, we notice that the solution to Equation 12 cannot be reduced to the ordinary inversion of the vectorial function $\varphi(\Delta x^*(\tau))$, because the number of Δq vector components may only accidentally—if at all—coincide with Δx^* vector components. The matrix $S_q^x(\tau)$ is not a quadratic one ($k \neq n$) in the general case, and therefore we cannot univocally determine Δq for given Δx^* from Equation 11.

However, there are some algorithms for a satisfactory solution of the ISA problem [3, 4]; such a method, based on the minimization of a criterion—a function of two variables, which varies in dependence upon the system state—is described below [2, 4, 5].

The first variable is the difference $\Delta x^*(\tau)$ obtained on the basis of calculations according to Figure 1, therefore it is the state deviation of the real system.

For the second variable, the state deviation, calculated on the basis of mathematical model, using Equation 11, is chosen.

The objective function that must be minimized is the scalar criterion:

$$J = \|\Delta x^*(\tau) - \Delta x(\tau)\|^2 \tag{13}$$

This criterion indicates the degree of closeness of the state deviation of model, due to the perturbations Δq, obtained on computer, to the state deviation of perturbed real dynamic system confronted by its unperturbed mathematical model, relative to the same modifications, Δq.

In Equation 13, by $\|\Delta x^*(\tau) - \Delta x(\tau)\|$ we denote the norm of the functions difference vector $\Delta x^*(\tau) - \Delta x(\tau)$.

Introducing the value of Δx vector, given by Equation 11 into Equation 13, we get:

$$J = \|\Delta x^* - S_q^x \cdot \Delta q\|^2 = \int_{\tau_0}^{\tau_f} (\Delta x^* - S_q^x \cdot \Delta q)^T (\Delta x^* - S_q^x \cdot \Delta q)\, d\tau \tag{14}$$

The condition of minimum for J:

$$\frac{\partial J}{\partial(\Delta q)} = 0 \tag{15}$$

leads to the equations system:

$$A \cdot \Delta q = B \tag{16}$$

where
$$\begin{aligned} A &= \int_{\tau_0}^{\tau_f} [(S_q^x)^T \cdot S_q^x]\, d\tau \\ B &= \int_{\tau_0}^{\tau_f} [(S_q^x)^T \cdot \Delta x^*]\, d\tau \end{aligned} \tag{17}$$

by the solution of which we can find the vector of deviations, Δq.

The vectorial Equation 16 has a unique solution if the rank of matrix A is equal to the dimension of vector Δq, which is $k = n + l + m$.

In the general sensitivity matrix 10, written in the form:

$$S_q^x = \begin{bmatrix} S_{q_1}^{x_1} & S_{q_2}^{x_1} & \cdots & S_{q_k}^{x_1} \\ S_{q_1}^{x_2} & S_{q_2}^{x_2} & \cdots & S_{q_k}^{x_2} \\ & \cdots\cdots & & \\ S_{q_1}^{x_n} & S_{q_2}^{x_n} & \cdots & S_{q_k}^{x_n} \end{bmatrix} \tag{18}$$

we denote the i column by S_i^x:

$$S_i^x = [S_{q_i}^{x_1} \quad S_{q_i}^{x_2} \quad \cdots \quad S_{q_i}^{x_n}]^T, \qquad i = \overline{1, k} \tag{19}$$

Using the Equation 19 denotation, matrix A, defined by Equation 17 is written:

$$A = \begin{bmatrix} \langle S_1^x, S_1^x \rangle & \langle S_1^x, S_2^x \rangle & \cdots & \langle S_1^x, S_k^x \rangle \\ \langle S_2^x, S_1^x \rangle & \langle S_2^x, S_2^x \rangle & \cdots & \langle S_2^x, S_k^x \rangle \\ & \cdots\cdots\cdots\cdots & & \\ \langle S_k^x, S_1^x \rangle & \langle S_k^x, S_2^x \rangle & \cdots & \langle S_k^x, S_k^x \rangle \end{bmatrix} = [\langle S_i^x, S_j^x \rangle] \tag{20}$$
$$i = \overline{1, k};\ j = \overline{1, k}$$

and the vector B takes the form:

$$B = \begin{bmatrix} \langle S_1^x, \Delta x^* \rangle \\ \langle S_2^x, \Delta x^* \rangle \\ \cdots\cdots \\ \langle S_k^x, \Delta x^* \rangle \end{bmatrix} = [\langle S_i^x, \Delta x^* \rangle], \qquad i = \overline{1, k} \tag{21}$$

Under the form of Equation 20, matrix A is the Gram matrix of the system of functions vector $S_1^x(\tau), S_2^x(\tau), \ldots, S_k^x(\tau)$, $\tau \in [\tau_0, \tau_f]$, where the components are defined by Equation 19.

Matrix A is not degenerated if its determinant is not equal to zero:

$$\det A \neq 0 \tag{22}$$

The determinant of matrix A is the Gram determinant of the functions vector system $S_i^x(\tau)$, $i = 1, k$, $\tau \in [\tau_0, \tau_f]$ and therefore, the condition of Expression 22 becomes:

$$G(S_1^x, S_2^x, \ldots, S_k^x) = \begin{Vmatrix} \langle S_1^x, S_1^x \rangle & \langle S_1^x, S_2^x \rangle & \cdots & \langle S_1^x, S_k^x \rangle \\ \langle S_2^x, S_1^x \rangle & \langle S_2^x, S_2^x \rangle & \cdots & \langle S_2^x, S_k^x \rangle \\ & \cdots\cdots\cdots & & \\ \langle S_k^x, S_1^x \rangle & \langle S_k^x, S_2^x \rangle & \cdots & \langle S_k^x, S_k^x \rangle \end{Vmatrix} \neq 0 \qquad (23)$$

Thus, in order to have a unique solution for ISA problem, given by Equation 12, the vectors of sensitivity functions $S_i^x(\tau)$, $i = 1, k$, must constitute a linear independent system, on the considered time period, $\tau \in [\tau_0, \tau_f]$.

Once the condition of linear independence of Equation 23 is fulfilled, the estimation of Δq vector components, which means the optimal policy that minimizes the Equation 13 is obtained by the solution of vectorial Equation 16.

The minimum value of the scalar criterion J, corresponding to the optimal policy Δq, calculated using Equation 16, is:

$$J_{min} = \min_{\Delta q} J = \frac{G(\Delta x^*, S_1^x, S_2^x, \ldots, S_k^x)}{G(S_1^x, S_2^x, \ldots, S_k^x)} \qquad (24)$$

where

$$G(\Delta x^*, S_1^x, S_2^x, \ldots, S_k^x) = \begin{Vmatrix} \langle \Delta x^*, \Delta x^* \rangle & \langle \Delta x^*, S_1^x \rangle & \langle \Delta x^*, S_2^x \rangle & \cdots & \langle \Delta x^*, S_k^x \rangle \\ \langle S_1^x, \Delta x^* \rangle & \langle S_1^x, S_1^x \rangle & \langle S_1^x, S_2^x \rangle & \cdots & \langle S_1^x, S_k^x \rangle \\ & & \cdots\cdots\cdots & & \\ \langle S_k^x, \Delta x^* \rangle & \langle S_k^x, S_1^x \rangle & \langle S_k^x, S_2^x \rangle & \cdots & \langle S_k^x, S_k^x \rangle \end{Vmatrix} \qquad (25)$$

The part placed between dotted lines represents the Gram determinant, $G(S_1^x, S_2^x, \ldots, S_k^x)$.

Figure 2 gives in succint form the ISA algorithm just shown for the case in which Equation 13 is fulfilled; the case in which this condition is not fulfilled is treated in [2, 4].

Before using the ISA algorithm, given in Figure 2, for the real industrial dynamic system, it is adequate to simulate the ISA testing algorithm, given in Figure 3, on computer in order to verify the accuracy of the technical diagnosis. [5]

In the algorithm described in Figure 3, the deviation $\Delta x^*(\tau)$ is not calculated according to block diagram in Figure 1, but it is simulated on computer, instead of the real dynamic system being used its mathematical model with given perturbation values Δq^*. These perturbation magnitudes are used as testing data for ISA method; by comparison between the Δq vector components, calculated by means of the ISA algorithm, and the testing Δq^* vector components, we are able to estimate the accuracy of the technical diagnosis of a dynamic system, by ISA method.

We notice that the ISA algorithm involves, as an important, even indispensable, step, the calculation of the sensitivity functions matrices S_{xo}^x, S_u^x and S_p^x. In Figures 2 and 3, this step is shown by the block named DSA.

ISA OF A COMPLEX CHEMICAL REACTION

The application discussed below [2] about the ISA of a chemical system, described by a simple mathematical model that could be analytically treated, is considered as a pretext to exhibit the structure and composition of a FORTRAN programs package. This package can be used for the ISA of any system.

Let us consider the chemical system corresponding to the consecutive reactions:

$$A \xrightarrow{k_1} B \xrightarrow{k_2} C$$

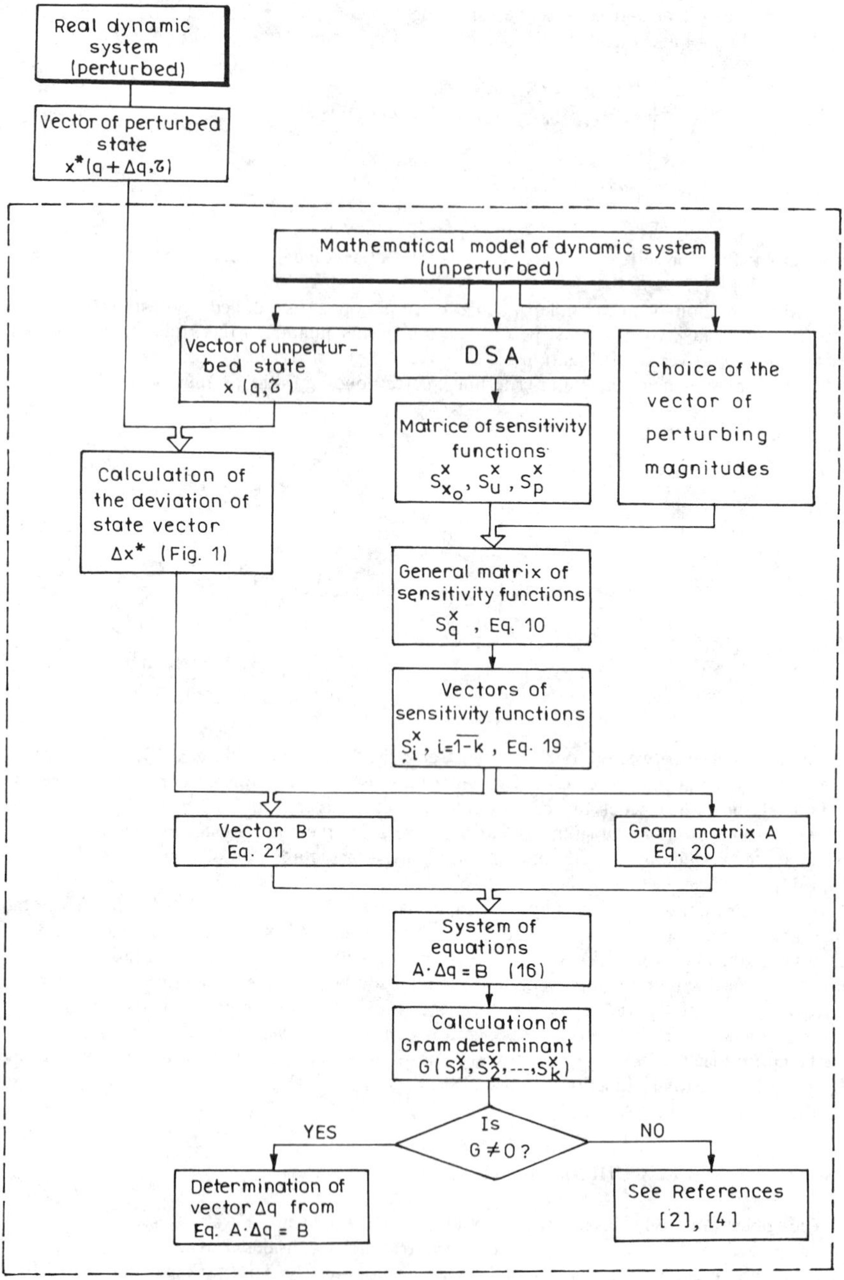

Figure 2. Logic diagram of the ISA method. (Reprinted with permission from Ref. 5.)

The mathematical model is:

$$\begin{cases} \dot{c}_A(\tau) = f_1(c_A(\tau), k_1) \\ \dot{c}_B(\tau) = f_2(c_A(\tau), c_B(\tau), k_1, k_2) \end{cases} \tag{26}$$

where

$$f_1 = -k_1 c_A$$

$$f_2 = k_1 c_A - k_2 c_B$$

with initial condition: $c_A(\tau_0) = c_{A,0}$ and $c_B(\tau_0) = c_{B,0}$

The vector of state variables is:

$$x(\tau) = \begin{bmatrix} x_1 \\ x_2 \end{bmatrix} = \begin{bmatrix} c_A \\ c_B \end{bmatrix} \tag{27}$$

and of parameters:

$$p = \begin{bmatrix} p_1 \\ p_2 \end{bmatrix} = \begin{bmatrix} k_1 \\ k_2 \end{bmatrix} \tag{28}$$

The q vector (Equation 4) has the form:

$$q = [c_{A,0} \quad c_{B,0} \quad k_1 \quad k_2]^T \tag{29}$$

The numerical nominal values of the initial state variables and of the parameters are:

$$\begin{aligned} x_{1,0} &= c_{A,0} = 0.18 \text{ Kmol/m}^3 \qquad & p_1 &= k_1 = 0.1 \text{ min}^{-1} \\ x_{2,0} &= c_{B,0} = 0 \text{ Kmol/m}^3 \qquad & p_2 &= k_2 = 0.025 \text{ min}^{-1} \end{aligned} \tag{30}$$

The unperturbed mathematical model of the dynamic system is given by the Equations 26 with the numerical data shown below.

The DSA requires the integration of the following sensitivity equations:

$$\begin{cases} \dot{S}^{c_A}_{c_{A,0}} = \dfrac{\partial f_1}{\partial c_A} S^{c_A}_{c_{A,0}} + \dfrac{\partial f_1}{\partial c_B} S^{c_B}_{c_{A,0}} = -k_1 S^{c_A}_{c_{A,0}} \\[2ex] \dot{S}^{c_A}_{c_{B,0}} = \dfrac{\partial f_1}{\partial c_A} S^{c_A}_{c_{B,0}} + \dfrac{\partial f_1}{\partial c_B} S^{c_B}_{c_{B,0}} = -k_1 S^{c_A}_{c_{B,0}} \\[2ex] \dot{S}^{c_B}_{c_{A,0}} = \dfrac{\partial f_2}{\partial c_A} S^{c_A}_{c_{A,0}} + \dfrac{\partial f_2}{\partial c_B} S^{c_B}_{c_{A,0}} = k_1 S^{c_A}_{c_{A,0}} - k_2 S^{c_B}_{c_{A,0}} \\[2ex] \dot{S}^{c_B}_{c_{B,0}} = \dfrac{\partial f_2}{\partial c_A} S^{c_A}_{c_{B,0}} + \dfrac{\partial f_2}{\partial c_B} S^{c_B}_{c_{B,0}} = k_1 S^{c_A}_{c_{B,0}} - k_2 S^{c_B}_{c_{B,0}} \end{cases} \tag{31}$$

with initial condition

$$\begin{bmatrix} S^{c_A}_{c_{A,0}}(0) & S^{c_A}_{c_{B,0}}(0) \\ S^{c_B}_{c_{A,0}}(0) & S^{c_B}_{c_{B,0}}(0) \end{bmatrix} = 1$$

and

$$
\begin{cases}
\dot{S}_{k_1}^{c_A} = \dfrac{\partial f_1}{\partial c_A} S_{k_1}^{c_A} + \dfrac{\partial f_1}{\partial c_B} S_{k_1}^{c_B} + \dfrac{\partial f_1}{\partial k_1} = -k_1 S_{k_1}^{c_A} - c_A \\[2ex]
\dot{S}_{k_2}^{c_A} = \dfrac{\partial f_1}{\partial c_A} S_{k_2}^{c_A} + \dfrac{\partial f_1}{\partial c_B} S_{k_2}^{c_B} + \dfrac{\partial f_1}{\partial k_2} = -k_1 S_{k_2}^{c_A} \\[2ex]
\dot{S}_{k_1}^{c_B} = \dfrac{\partial f_2}{\partial c_A} S_{k_1}^{c_A} + \dfrac{\partial f_2}{\partial c_B} S_{k_1}^{c_B} + \dfrac{\partial f_2}{\partial k_1} = k_1 S_{k_1}^{c_A} - k_2 S_{k_1}^{c_B} + c_A \\[2ex]
\dot{S}_{k_2}^{c_B} = \dfrac{\partial f_2}{\partial c_A} S_{k_2}^{c_A} + \dfrac{\partial f_2}{\partial c_B} S_{k_2}^{c_B} + \dfrac{\partial f_2}{\partial k_2} = k_1 S_{k_2}^{c_A} - k_2 S_{k_2}^{c_B} + c_B
\end{cases}
\tag{32}
$$

with initial condition:

$$S_{k_1}^{c_A}(0) = S_{k_2}^{c_A}(0) = S_{k_1}^{c_B}(0) = S_{k_2}^{c_B}(0) = 0$$

The fourth-order Runge-Kutta method, Gill variant, was used here to integrate the differential equations.

The corresponding FORTRAN subroutine simultaneously calculates for each integration step the values of all variables; this it gives us the possibility to call a list of these values in the main program in order to plot them.

In Program 1 we give the FORTRAN program of the integration subroutine "RKGILL," which is useful for integrating differential equations system in the form:

$$Y = f(X, Y)$$

with the following notations:

N = number of equations
H = integration step
X = independent variable at the beginning of the integration step
Y(I) = value of the solution at the beginning of the integration step
Y1(I) = value of the solution at the end of a integration step
F(I, X, Y) = a FUNCTION subprogram for each $f_i(X, Y)$.

Program 1

```
      SUBROUTINE RKGILL(N,H,X,Y,Y1,F)
      IMPLICIT DOUBLE PRECISION(H,X,Y,R,F,P)
      DIMENSION Y(N),Y1(N),R1(12),R2(12),R3(12),R4(12)
      XH=X+H/2.
      XX=X+H
      PM=1.-1./SQRT(2.)
      PP=1.+1./SQRT(2.)
      DO 1 I=1,N
    1 R1(I)=F(I,X,Y)
      DO 2 I=1,N
    2 Y1(I)=Y(I)+H*R1(I)/2.
      DO 3 I=1,N
    3 R2(I)=F(I,XH,Y1)
      DO 4 I=1,N
    4 Y1(I)=Y(I)+PM*H*R1(I)/SQRT(2.)+PM*H*R2(I)
      DO 5 I=1,N
```

```
5 R3(I)=F(I,XH,Y1)
  DO 6 I=1,N
6 Y1(I)=Y(I)-H*R2(I)/SQRT(2.)+PP*H*R3(I)
  DO 7 I=1,N
7 R4(I)=F(I,XX,Y1)
  DO 8 I=1,N
8 Y1(I)=Y(I)+H*(R1(I)+2.*PM*R2(I)+2.*PP*R3(I)+R4(I))/6.
  RETURN
  END
```

Since we will simultaneously perform the numerical integration of the unperturbed mathematical model and sensitivity equations, in order to facilitate the programming we will create the W vector, having as components the elements of state vector and sensitivity functions matrices.

The general form of vector W is

$$W = [x_1 \quad x_2 \cdots x_n \quad S^{x_1}_{x_{1,0}} \quad S^{x_1}_{x_{2,0}} \cdots S^{x_1}_{x_{n,0}} \quad S^{x_2}_{x_{1,0}} \quad S^{x_2}_{x_{2,0}} \cdots$$
$$\cdots S^{x_2}_{x_{n,0}} \cdots S^{x_n}_{x_{1,0}} \quad S^{x_n}_{x_{2,0}} \cdots S^{x_n}_{x_{n,0}} \quad S^{x_1}_{p_1} \quad S^{x_1}_{p_2} \cdots$$
$$\cdots S^{x_1}_{p_m} \quad S^{x_2}_{p_1} \quad S^{x_2}_{p_2} \cdots S^{x_2}_{p_m} \cdots S^{x_n}_{p_1} \quad S^{x_n}_{p_2} \cdots S^{x_n}_{p_m}]^T \tag{33}$$

In our case,

$$W = [c_A \quad c_B \quad S^{c_A}_{c_{A,0}} \quad S^{c_A}_{c_{B,0}} \quad S^{c_B}_{c_{A,0}} \quad S^{c_B}_{c_{B,0}} \quad S^{c_A}_{k_1} \quad S^{c_A}_{k_2} \quad S^{c_B}_{k_1} \quad S^{c_B}_{k_2}]^T \tag{34}$$

so, the system that must be integrated is:

$$\dot{W} = \begin{bmatrix} -k_1 c_A \\ k_1 c_A - k_2 c_B \\ -k_1 S^{c_A}_{c_{A,0}} \\ -k_1 S^{c_A}_{c_{B,0}} \\ k_1 S^{c_A}_{c_{A,0}} - k_2 S^{c_B}_{c_{A,0}} \\ k_1 S^{c_A}_{c_{B,0}} - k_2 S^{c_B}_{c_{B,0}} \\ -k_1 S^{c_A}_{k_1} - c_A \\ -k_1 S^{c_A}_{k_2} \\ k_1 S^{c_A}_{k_1} - k_2 S^{c_B}_{k_1} + c_A \\ k_1 S^{c_A}_{k_2} - k_2 S^{c_B}_{k_2} - c_B \end{bmatrix} \tag{35}$$

The FUNCTION subprogram F, corresponding to this system, used as input parameter in RKGILL subroutine, is given in Program 2; the notations used in the program are:

$CA = c_A$	$SAA = S^{c_A}_{c_{A,0}}$	$SBB = S^{c_B}_{c_{B,0}}$	$SB1 = S^{c_B}_{k_1}$
$CB = c_B$	$SAB = S^{c_A}_{c_{B,0}}$	$SA1 = S^{c_A}_{k_1}$	$SB2 = S^{c_B}_{k_2}$
$AK1 = k_1$	$SBA = S^{c_B}_{c_{A,0}}$	$SA2 = S^{c_A}_{k_2}$	
$AK2 = k_2$			

Program 2

```
DOUBLE PRECISION FUNCTION F(J,T,W)
IMPLICIT DOUBLE PRECISION (A-H,O-Z)
```

```
      COMMON AK1,AK2
      DIMENSION W(10)
      CA=W(1)
      CB=W(2)
      SAA=W(3)
      SAB=W(4)
      SBA=W(5)
      SBB=W(6)
      SA1=W(7)
      SA2=W(8)
      SB1=W(9)
      SB2=W(10)
      GO TO (1,2,3,4,5,6,7,8,9,10),J
    1 F=-AK1*CA
      RETURN
    2 F=AK1*CA-AK2*CB
      RETURN
    3 F=-AK1*SAA
      RETURN
    4 F=-AK1*SAB
      RETURN
    5 F=AK1*SAA-AK2*SBA
      RETURN
    6 F=AK1*SBA-AK2*SBB
      RETURN
    7 F=-AK1*SA1-CA
      RETURN
    8 F=-AK1*SA2
      RETURN
    9 F=AK1*SA1-AK2*SB1+CA
      RETURN
   10 F=AK1*SA2-AK2*SB2-CB
      RETURN
      END
```

The perturbed mathematical model has the form:

$$\begin{cases} \dot{c}_A(\tau) = -(k_1 + \Delta k^*_{1,0})c_A(\tau) = -k^*_1 c_A \\ \dot{c}_B(\tau) = (k_1 + \Delta k^*_{1,0})c_A(\tau) - (k_2 + \Delta k^*_{2,0})c_B(\tau) = k^*_1 c_A - k^*_2 c_B \end{cases} \tag{36}$$

with initial condition:

$$\begin{aligned} c_A(0) &= c_{A,0} + \Delta c^*_{A,0} = c^*_{A,0} \\ c_B(0) &= 0 \end{aligned} \tag{37}$$

For the integration of the perturbed mathematical model, in RKGILL subroutine, instead of the function F, the function-subprogram F1 will be called. The FORTRAN statement of this function is given in Program 3. The following notations were used:

$AK1P = k^*_1 \qquad CA = c_A$

$AK2P = k^*_2 \qquad CB = c_B$

Program 3

```
      DOUBLE PRECISION FUNCTION F1(J,T,X)
      IMPLICIT DOUBLE PRECISION (A-H,O-Z)
      DIMENSION X(2)
      COMMON/B1/AK1P,AK2P
      CA=X(1)
      CB=X(2)
      GO TO (1,2),J
    1 F1=-AK1P*CA
      RETURN
    2 F1=AK1*PCA-AK2P*CB
      RETURN
      END
```

The separation of the sensitivity functions general matrix, S_q^x, from the vector W, in order to calculate the state deviation using the relation $\Delta x = S \cdot \Delta q$, for each integration step, is made by means of the subroutine named WS; the FORTRAN program of this subroutine is given in Program 4.

Program 4

```
      SUBROUTINE WS(NX,NCS,NW,W,S)
      DOUBLE PRECISION S,W
      DIMENSION W(NW),S(NX,NCS)
      NP=NCS-NX
      DO 1 I=1,NX
      DO 2 J=1,NX
      IW=I*NX+J
    2 S(I,J)=W(IW)
      DO 1 K=1,NP
      J=NX+K
      IW=NX*NX+NX+(I-1)*NP+K
    1 S(I,J)=W(IW)
      RETURN
      END
```

The structure of vector W is given in Equation 34 and the form of the sensitivity general matrix is:

$$S = \begin{bmatrix} S_{q_1}^{x_1} & S_{q_2}^{x_1} & \cdots & S_{q_k}^{x_1} \\ S_{q_1}^{x_2} & S_{q_2}^{x_2} & \cdots & S_{q_k}^{x_2} \\ & \cdots\cdots & & \\ S_{q_1}^{x_n} & S_{q_2}^{x_n} & \cdots & S_{q_k}^{x_n} \end{bmatrix} = \begin{bmatrix} S_{x_{1,0}}^{x_1} & S_{x_{2,0}}^{x_1} & \cdots & S_{x_{n,0}}^{x_1} & S_{p_1}^{x_1} & S_{p_2}^{x_1} & \cdots & S_{p_m}^{x_1} \\ S_{x_{1,0}}^{x_2} & S_{x_{2,0}}^{x_2} & \cdots & S_{x_{n,0}}^{x_2} & S_{p_1}^{x_2} & S_{p_2}^{x_2} & \cdots & S_{p_m}^{x_2} \\ & & & \cdots\cdots\cdots & & & & \\ S_{x_{1,0}}^{x_n} & S_{x_{2,0}}^{x_n} & \cdots & S_{x_{n,0}}^{x_n} & S_{p_1}^{x_n} & S_{p_2}^{x_n} & \cdots & S_{p_m}^{x_n} \end{bmatrix} \tag{38}$$

In the FORTRAN Program 4 the following notations are used:

NX = the dimension of the state vector (n in text)
NCS = the number of the columns of S_q^x matrix (dimension of vector q, text "k" in)
NW = dimension of vector W, NW = n + k

In our particular case, here treated, the S_q^x matrix has two rows and four columns:

$$S = S_q^x = \begin{bmatrix} S_{c_{A,0}}^{c_A} & S_{c_{B,0}}^{c_A} & S_{k_1}^{c_A} & S_{k_2}^{c_A} \\ S_{c_{A,0}}^{c_B} & S_{c_{B,0}}^{c_B} & S_{k_1}^{c_B} & S_{k_2}^{c_B} \end{bmatrix} \tag{39}$$

If ISA refers only to a part k′ of the q vector components, in order to calculate the elements of Gram Matrix A and of vector B, Equation 16, a particular sensitivity matrix SS must be built, starting from the general sensitivity matrix, S. The matrix SS has n rows and k columns, corresponding to the considered k′ elements of vector q. This matrix is *specific* to each problem.

In the example treated by us, we consider that, always, $c_{B,0} = 0$ and therefore, $\Delta c_{B,0} = 0$ (rigorously), so that we consider three elements of q vector only, which can suffer modifications: $c_{A,0}$, k_1, and k_2. The SS matrix has n = 2 rows and k′ = 3 columns.

$$SS = \begin{bmatrix} S^{cA}_{cA,0} & S^{cA}_{k_1} & S^{cA}_{k_2} \\ S^{cB}_{cA,0} & S^{cB}_{k_1} & S^{cB}_{k_2} \end{bmatrix}$$

The perturbations vector, Δq_0^*, with values for calculation and test given, has k′ = 3 elements, and it is:

$$\Delta q_0^{\equiv} = \begin{bmatrix} \Delta c^*_{A,0} \\ \Delta k^*_{1,0} \\ \Delta k^*_{2,0} \end{bmatrix} \tag{40}$$

and the matrix SS is built by SSS subroutine, Program 5.

Program 5

```
SUBROUTINE SSS(N,NS,NSS,S,SS)
DOUBLE PRECISION S,SS
DIMENSION S(N,NS),SS(N,NSS)
SS(1,1)=S(1,1)
SS(1,2)=S(1,3)
SS(1,3)=S(1,4)
SS(2,1)=S(2,1)
SS(2,2)=S(2,3)
SS(2,3)=S(2,4)
RETURN
END
```

The components of Gram matrix A are:

$$A_{i,j} = \langle S_i^x, S_j^x \rangle = \int_{\tau_0}^{\tau_f} [S_i^x(\tau)]^T \cdot S_j^x(\tau)\, d\tau, \qquad i, j = \overline{1, k} \tag{41}$$

But

$$S_i^x(\tau) = [S_{qi}^{x_1} \quad S_{qi}^{x_2} \quad \cdots \quad S_{qi}^{x_n}]^T \quad \text{and}$$

$$S_j^x(\tau) = [S_{qj}^{x_1} \quad S_{qj}^{x_2} \quad \cdots \quad S_{qj}^{x_n}]^T \tag{42}$$

It will follow:

$$A_{i,j} = \int_{\tau_0}^{\tau_f} \sum_{l=1}^{n} [S_{qi}^{x_l}(\tau) \cdot S_{qj}^{x_l}(\tau)]\, d\tau, \qquad i, j = \overline{1, k} \tag{43}$$

In the same way, the vector B elements are:

$$B_i = \langle S_i^x, \Delta x^* \rangle = \int_{\tau_0}^{\tau_f} [S_i^x(\tau)]^T \cdot \Delta x^*\, d\tau \tag{44}$$

The vector Δx^* is:

$$\Delta x^* = [\Delta x_1^* \quad \Delta x_2^* \cdots \Delta x_n^*]^T \tag{45}$$

It will follow:

$$B_i = \int_{\tau_0}^{\tau_f} \sum_{l=1}^{n} [S_{q_i}^{x_l}(\tau) \cdot \Delta x_l^*] \, d\tau, \qquad i, j = \overline{1, k} \tag{46}$$

We introduce the notations:

$$\varphi = [\varphi_{i,j}(\tau')] = \sum_{l=1}^{n} [S_{q_i}^{x_l}(\tau) \cdot S_{q_j}^{x_l}(\tau)], \qquad i, j = \overline{1, k} \tag{47}$$

$$\Psi = [\Psi_i(\tau)] = \sum_{l=1}^{n} [S_{q_i}^{x_l}(\tau) \cdot \Delta x_l^*], \qquad i, = \overline{1, k}$$

and then

$$A_{i,j} = \int_{\tau_0}^{\tau_f} \varphi_{i,j}(\tau) \, d\tau; \qquad B_i = \int_{\tau_0}^{\tau_f} \Psi_i(\tau) \, d\tau \tag{48}$$

In order to create the matrix φ, having $k \times k$ elements, and the vector Ψ, with k elements, a subroutine FIPSI is built, Program 6. The following notations were used in this subroutine:

FI – φ DX – Δx^*

PSI – Ψ S(L, I) – $S_{q_i}^{x_l}$

Also, we consider that $\varphi_{i,j} = \varphi_{j,i}$ and adequately reduce the number of calculations.

Program 6

```
      SUBROUTINE FIPSI(N,M,S,DX,FI,PSI)
      DOUBLE PRECISION S,DX,FI,PSI
      DIMENSION S(N,M),DX(N),FI(M,M),PSI(M)
      DO 1 J=1,M
      DO 2 K=J,M
      FI(J,K)=0.
      DO 3 L=1,N
    3 FI(J,K)=FI(J,K)+S(L,J)*S(L,K)
    2 FI(K,J)=FI(J,K)
      PSI(J)=0
      DO 1 L=1,N
    1 PSI(J)=PSI(J)+S(L,J)*DX(L)
      RETURN
      END
```

Any numerical method can be used to accomplish the definite integration. In our example, we use the Trapezium Rule; the height of each trapezium coincides with integration step of the differential equations system (Equation 35), so that in the main program all calculations corresponding to each integration step, and are made both for the differential equations and for the definite integration.

The Trapezium Rule algorithm is taken in form:

$$I = \int_{\tau_0}^{\tau_f} f(\tau) \, d\tau = h\left[0.5f(\tau_0) + \sum_{k=1}^{k_f} f(\tau_0 + kh) + 0.5f(\tau_f)\right] \tag{49}$$

in which k_f corresponds to that τ, which answer to condition:

$$\tau_f - h \leq \tau \leq \tau_f$$

This condition is followed in the main FORTRAN program.

The determination of the state deviations, calculated by means of the sensitivity matrix, with the relation under the form $\Delta x = S_q^x \cdot \Delta q$, requires a matrix multiplication subroutine. The FORTRAN statements of this subroutine, called PROMAT, is given in Program 7.

The PROMAT subroutine evaluates the product between matrix A, with M rows and L columns and Matrix B, with L rows and N columns, the resulting matrix C having M rows and N columns.

Program 7

```
      SUBROUTINE PROMAT(M,L,N,A,B,C)
      DOUBLE PRECISION A,B,C
      DIMENSION A(M,L),B(L,N),C(M,N)
      DO 1 I=1,M
      DO 1 J=1,N
      C(I,J)=0
      DO 1 K=1,L
    1 C(I,J)=C(I,J)+A(I,K)*B(K,J)
      RETURN
      END
```

The verification of the compatibility and determination degree of a linear algebraic equation system as well as its solution is made by means of a subroutine called SISL [6]. This subroutine is built on the basis of the Gauss method algorithm. A subprogram for the mutual replacement of two equations, called INTERV, is used in subroutine SISL.

The FORTRAN statements of the subroutines SISL and INTERV are given in Programs 8 and 9.

```
      SUBROUTINE SISL(A,B,X,N)
      DOUBLE PRECISION A,B,X,Y
      DIMENSION A(N,N),B(N),X(N)
      N1=N-1
      DO 3 I=1,N1
      I1=I
      DO 20 I2=I,N
      IF(DABS(A(I1,I).GE.DABS(A(I2,I)))GO TO 20
      I1=I2
   20 CONTINUE
      IF(DABS(A(I1,I)).LE.1.D-50)GO TO 18
      IF(I1.EQ.I)GO TO 16
      CALL INTERV(A,B,I,I1,N)
   16 Y=A(I,I)
      DO 5 J=I,N
    5 A(I,J)=A(I,J)/Y
      B(I)=B(I)/Y
      I1=I+1
      DO 6 J=I1,N
      IF(DABS(A(J,I)).LE.1.D-50)GO)GO TO 6
      Y=A(J,I)
      DO 8 K=I,N
    8 A(J,K)=A(J,K)-Y*A(I,K)
      B(J)=B(J)-B(I)*Y
```

```
  6 CONTINUE
  3 CONTINUE
    IF(DABS(A(N,N)).LE.1.D-50)GO TO 18
    X(N)=B(N)/A(N,N)
    DO 10 I=1,N1
    NI=N-I
    X(NI)=B(NI)
    DO 11 K=1,I
    NIK=N-I+K
    X(NI)=X(NI)-A(NI,NIK)*X(NIK)
 10 CONTINUE
    WRITE(108,15) (X(I),I=1,N)
 15 FORMAT(/2X,'ROOTS= ',(7G15.7))
    GO TO 19
 18 WRITE(108,17)
 17 FORMAT(31X,'INCOMPATIBLE OR INCONSISTENT SYSTEM')
 19 RETURN
    END

    SUBROUTINE INTERV(A,B,I,K,N)
    DOUBLE PRECISION A,B,Y
    DIMENSION A(N,N),B(N)
    DO 1 J=1,N
    Y=A(I,J)
    A(I,J)=A(K,J)
  1 A(K,J)=Y
    Y=B(I)
    B(I)=B(K)
    B(K)=Y
    RETURN
    END
```

The main program accomplishes:

1. Calculates and tabulates the unperturbed system state variables, x.
2. Calculates and tabulates the perturbed system state variables, x*.
3. Calculates and tabulates all sensitivity functions.
4. Calculates and tabulates the deviations of state variables, computed by means of relations $\Delta x^* = x^* - x$ and $\Delta x = S_q^x \cdot \Delta q$.
5. Tests the possibility to perform ISA and calculate the perturbations Δq_0^* that cause the deviation Δx^*, as it is shown in Figure 3.

The following notations are used in the main program:

TAU = τ
TAUO = τ_0
H = integration step, h
IPAS = counter of steps number
NRPAS = the number of steps after which the tabulated values are printed
W = the vector $W(\tau)$
WW = the perturbed state variables vector, $x^*(\tau)$
DPP = the columnar matrix of perturbing elements Δq_0^* (calculating and testing values for ISA)
DX = state deviation vector, computed as $\Delta x^* = x^* - x$
DXC = state deviation vector, computed as $\Delta x = S_q^x \cdot \Delta q$

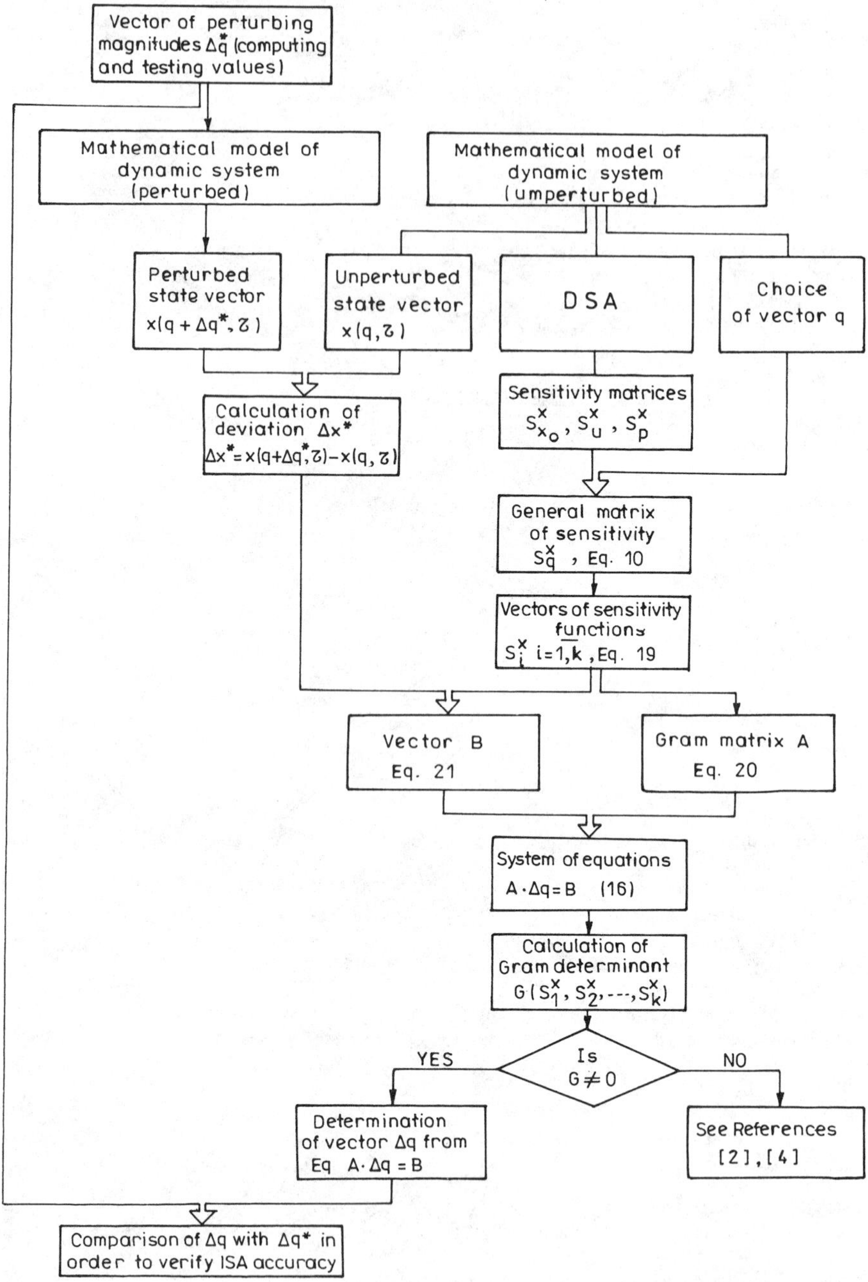

Figure 3. Logic diagram of the testing algorithm of the ISA method. (Reprinted with permission from Ref. 5.)

N = dimension of the state vector
N1 = dimension of the vector W
K = dimension of the vector Δq_0^* (total number of rows of the DPP matrix)
K1 = number of Δq_0^* vector elements, considering ISA
S = sensitivity general matrix
SS = a particular sensitivity matrix for ISA having N × K1 elements
FI = φ functions
PSI = Ψ functions
W1 = vector $W(\tau + h)$
WW1 = the vector $WW(\tau + h)$
G = the Gram Matrix A, in Equation 16
GX = B vector in Equation 16

The FORTRAN statements of the main program is given in Program 10.

Program 10

```
      IMPLICIT DOUBLE PRECISION (A-H,O-Z)
      DIMENSION W(10),W1(10),WW(2),WW1(2),S(2,4),DXC(2,1)DX(2),
      DPP(4,1)
      DIMENSION SS(2,3),FI(3,3),PSI(3),DPC(3),G(3,3),GX(3)
      COMMON AK1,AK2
      COMMON/B1/AK1P,AK2P
      EXTERNAL F,F1
      DATA W/.18,0.,1.,0.,0.,1., 4*0./
      DATA N,K,K1/2,4,3/
      DATA DPP/.02,0.,.01,.0025/
      DATA TAUO,TAUF,H/0.,220.,.2/
      DATA IPAS,NRPAS/0,5/
      AK1=.1
      AK2=.025
      N1=N*K+N
      AK1P=AK1+DPP(3,1)
      AK2P=AK2+DPP(4,1)
      TAU=TAUO
      WW(1)=W(1)+DPP(1,1)
      WW(2)=W(2)+DPP(2,1)
      DO 1 I=1,N
    1 DX(I)=WW(I)-W(I)
      CALL WS(N,K,N1,W,S)
      CALL PROMAT(N,K,1,S,DPP,DXC)
      PRINT 105,TAU,((S(I,J),J=1,4),I=1,2),DPP,W(1),W(2),WW,DX,DXC
  105 FORMAT(1X,4HTAU=,F7.2,3X,2HS,2(4(2X,E9.3),1X)/12X,3HDPP,3X,4
      (E9.31,2X)/13X,3HXA=,E12.6,3X,2HT=,E12.6/12X,4HXAD=,E12.6,2X,
      3HTD=,E12.6,2/13X,2HDX,3X,2(E10.4,2X)/,12X,3HDXC,3X,2(E10.4,2X)//)
      CALL SSS(N,K,K1,S,SS)
      CALL FIPSI(N,K1,SS,DX,FI,PSI)
      DO 3 I=1,K1
      DO 2 J=I,K1
    2 G(I,J)=.5*FI(I,J)
    3 GX(I)=.5*PSI(I)
    4 CALL RKGILL(N1,H,TAU,W,W1,F)
      CALL RKGILL(N,H,TAU,WW,WW1,F1)
      TAU=TAU+H
      DO 12 I=1,N1
```

```
12 W(I)=W1(I)
   DO 5 I=1,N
   WW(I)=WW1(I)
 5 DX(I)=WW(I)-W(I)
   CALL WS(N,K,N1,W,S)
   CALL PROMAT(N,K,1,S,DPP,DXC)
   IPAS=IPAS+1
   IF(IPAS.NE.NRPAS)GO TO 6
   PRINT 105,TAU,((S(I,J),J=1,4),I=1,2),DPP,W(1),W(2),WW,DX,DXC
   IPAS=0
 6 CALL SSS(N,K,K1,S,SS)
   CALL FIPSI(N,K1,SS,DX,FI,PSI)
   IF(TAU.GE.TAUF)GO TO 9
   DO 8 I=1,K1
   DO 7 J=I,K1
 7 G(I,J)=G(I,J)+FI(I,J)
 8 GX(I)=GX(I)+PSI(I)
   GO TO 4
 9 DO 11 I=1,K1
   DO 10 J=I,K1
   G(I,J)=H*(GX(I,J)+.5*FI(I,J))
10 G(J,I)=G(I,J)
11 GX(I)=H*(GX(I)+.5*PSI(I))
   CALL SISL(G,GX,DPC,K1)
   STOP
   END
```

In order to test the possibility of accomplishing ISA, the following data as computing and testing values are taken, besides the numerical data just mentioned:

$$\Delta q_0^* = [0.02 \quad 0.01 \quad 0.0025]^T$$

Using the FORTRAN programs package previously above, the following results were obtained:

$$\Delta q_0 = [0.01927 \quad 0.01018 \quad 0.002497]^T$$

The agreement between the testing values Δq_0^* and the computed ones Δq_0 is significant to the validity of the ISA method and the programs package we used.

NOTATION

(Excepting those in connection with the FORTRAN programs)

- A — Gram matrix, defined by Equations 17 and 20
- B — vector of functions, defined by Equations 17 and 21
- c — concentrations
- f — vector of functions $f(x(\tau), u, p, \tau)$, Equation 1; function of time, Equation 49
- G — Gram determinant, Equation 23
- h — integration step
- $i = \overline{1, k}$ — means $i = 1, 2, \ldots, k$
- J — a scalar criterion as objective function, Equation 13
- k — reaction-rate constant
- p — vector of parameters
- q — a general vector of initial state variables, control inputs and parameters, Equation 4
- $S_{c_{A,0}}^{c_A}$ — sensitivity function of the concentration c_A with respect to the initial concentration $c_{A,0}$

$S^{c_A}_{c_{B,0}}$ sensitivity function of the concentration c_A with respect to the initial concentration $c_{B,0}$

$S^{c_A}_{k_1}$ sensitivity function of the concentration c_A with respect to the reaction-rate constant k_1

$S^{c_A}_{k_2}$ sensitivity function of the concentration c_A with respect to the reaction-rate constant k_2

$S^{C_B}_{C_{AO}}$ sensitivity function of the concentration c_B with respect to the initial concentration $c_{A,0}$

$S^{C_B}_{C_{BO}}$ sensitivity function of the concentration c_B with respect to the initial concentration $c_{B,0}$

$S^{c_B}_{k_1}$ sensitivity function of the concentration c_B with respect to the reaction-rate constant k_1

$S^{c_B}_{k_2}$ sensitivity function of the concentration c_B with respect to the reaction-rate constant k_2

S^x_i, S the "i" column of the general sensitivity matrix, Equation 18 and Equation 19

S^x_p sensitivity matrix of the state with respect to the parameters

S^x_q general sensitivity matrix, Equation 10

S^x_u sensitivity matrix of the state with respect to the control inputs

$S^x_{x_0}$ sensitivity matrix of the state with respect to the initial state

SS particular matrix of sensitivity functions

u vector of control inputs

x vector of state variables

Greek Symbols

$\Delta\ldots$ deviation of . . .

τ time

φ vector of functions, Equation 9; matrix of functions, Equation 47

Ψ vector of functions, Equation 47

Subscripts

A, B, C chemical substances

min minimum

0 initial

Superscripts

T transposition (of matrix)

* refers to a real system

derivative with respect to the time, τ

REFERENCES

1. Tomovič, R., *Sensitivity Analysis of Dynamic Systems*, McGraw-Hill Book Co., N.Y., Toronto, London, 1963, p. 121.
2. Ungureanu, S., *Sensitivity of Technical Dynamic Systems*, Ed. Tehnica, Bucharest, 1988 (In press), (In Rom.).
3. Tomovič, R., *Sensitivity Analysis of Dynamic Systems*, McGraw-Hill Book Co., N.Y., Toronto, London, 1963, p. 122–129.
4. Gorodetzkij, V. I., Zaharin, F. M., Rosenwasser, E. N., and Yusupov, R. M., *Methods of Sensitivity Theory in Automatic Control*, Energija, Leningrad, 1971, p. 264–274, (In Russ.).
5. Ungureanu, S., "Technical Diagnosis of a Chemical Reactor by the Inverse Sensitivity Analysis," *Rev. Chim. (Buc.)*. 35, 1097 (1984), (In Rom.).
6. Georgescu, H., and Basca, O., *Programs in FORTRAN Language*, Albatros, Bucharest, 1975, p. 146, (In Rom.).

CHAPTER 30

LINEAR PROCESS CALCULATIONS IN COMPUTER-AIDED DESIGN

Marshall E. Findley

Chemical Engineering Department
University of Missouri—Rolla
Rolla, MO

CONTENTS

APPLICATIONS OF LINEARIZATION IN PROCESS CALCULATIONS

Most chemical and separation process calculations are non-linear, often to a considerable extent. There are some calculations that may be linear in nature, such as material and energy balances, but in the study of complete processes these types of equations must usually include variables that are determined by non-linear functions. For this reason, the application of linear mathematical techniques to the study of processes must be carefully considered to ensure their applicability. In addition, where practical, results obtained from linearization and the use of linear assumptions should be checked by more rigorous calculations. The principal benefit from the application of linear assumptions and methods to non-linear systems of equations is that it provides a relatively simple estimate for the effects of small changes. Linearization may also make it possible to obtain algebraic solutions to systems where a rigorous solution would require much more sophisticated techniques. Such estimates can be useful in decision-making, design, control, optimization, and operation in process systems.

In studying a process with mutliple units it is often desirable to be able to estimate the effects that occur in the overall process performance that are caused by changes in a certain process variable. While the effects of large changes in variables require rigorous non-linear calculations to determine overall effects, the effects of small changes can often be estimated with reasonable accuracy by linear approximations, such as the first two terms of the Taylor series applied to the resulting changes in each unit in series. With modern computer-aided design techniques, linear estimates may not be necessary or particularly useful in studying readily programmable processes. However, for special cases, it may be possible to make linear estimates more conveniently than using a design program. Such estimates can also be sufficiently accurate for many preliminary decisions or for indicating promising areas for further detailed study or for future laboratory or plant studies.

Linearization is a standard procedure used to obtain dynamic equations for process control purposes [1]. In this case, the validity of a linearization of a nonlinear relationship is restricted to a narrow range of deviations, but once adequate control is obtained, there will be only small deviations from the desired steady-state conditions. Another application of linearization in process control is determining the steady-state gain for a control loop or a series of control loops with interaction. Such considerations are important in selecting a control strategy.

In a similar way, linearization assumptions may be made in optimization studies to reduce the number of variables and reduce the complexity of the system to be optimized. The proper choices of simplifying assumptions, including linearization methods and variables to hold constant, can be very important in achieving an optimization solution in a reasonable time. In some cases, where time and effort limitations are critical, such simplification may permit an approximate optimization to be made, where otherwise no optimization would be feasible. Linearization and linear calculations are also part of some optimization techniques and convergence methods. In some optimization methods, successive linear programming is used over narrow ranges with revised linearized equations after each move [2, 3].

Linearization can be helpful in the study of the operation of existing process equipment, and many of the applications of statistics are based on linear correlations of process data, even though it may be known that the relationships involved are non-linear. The use of appropriate linearizations, the appropriate interpretation of the results, and the calculation of effects on subsequent processing can lead to a better understanding of the effects of proposed changes, and eventually to more optimum operating conditions. In addition, data obtained from linear correlations can be used to provide the values of derivatives at certain conditions, which in turn can be used to improve the mathematical models of existing processes for optimization or control purposes. The "Evolutionary Operations" technique is based on linear approximations and their use in moving a process towards a more optimum set of conditions [4].

In studying design possibilities, it is not uncommon to consider costs as proportional to throughput, energy requirements, number of stages, or similar process parameters. This linearization technique may be used even when computer-aided design programs are readily available along with much more accurate cost estimating data. Although it is much better to check such approximations by more rigorous estimates, in practice, some designers may use such estimates as the only basis for important decisions in the selection of process configurations, or in the evaluation of the feasibility of certain types of equipment. Generally, such decisions are checked to some extent in the final design, but often discarded options are not rechecked. In computer-aided design, particularly in flowsheet type programs, linear calculations or estimations are used to assist in reaching a converged set of calculations of all units. Rosen [5, 6] suggested a two-tier approach to flowsheet oriented calculations, with a linearized approximation being used to assist in the convergence of the flowsheet oriented nonlinear calculations. This has also been called a "simultaneous modular" technique [7], using both simultaneous linear solutions and nonlinear modular calculations.

In the various uses of linearization, the purposes may be somewhat different. In most cases accuracy is relatively unimportant and only a rough idea of the calculated results is necessary. For example, in selecting approaches to a process design, where further study will be made of all roughly equal alternatives, the objective is likely to be simply the elimination of alternatives that will not economically produce benefits comparable to other alternatives. In using linearization as a method of convergence in design programs, the critical factor is whether the linearization results will lead to convergence. The linear estimates themselves will always be followed by more rigorous calculations, and these will be relied on in the design. In optimization, operations studies, and process control, linearization techniques should be relatively accurate for small changes in order to achieve their purpose, but deviations in variables to which they will apply are normally small, and the accuracy is normally satisfactory for such changes.

In this discussion, linearization techniques will be considered primarily with respect to techniques that have been used to assist in design, and particularly those used to assist in convergence of flowsheet oriented computer design and simulation methods. The linearization methods can of course be applied to other cases where an approximate solution based on linear relationships is adequate for the purpose at hand.

FLOWSHEET-ORIENTED DESIGN

Many design techniques have been developed based on flowsheet oriented computer calculations. These have been developed at industrial corporations, design and construction companies, and at universities, but for the most part the calculation procedures are very similar. Their basic principles have been described in some detail by several authors [7–12].

Basically, the process structure, the data and conditions for equipment calculations, stream data, and other parameters for economic, optimization, or other calculations are maintained as arrays in a number of computer files. Many of these data must be input to specify the problem. The process structure is an input array to the program indicating the inflow streams by number to each unit, or module, and the outflow streams from each unit. Both units and streams are identified by a unit or stream number. Thus at any point in the calculations, the next equipment in the flow direction can be identified and the necessary inflows to a unit can be identified. An array for equipment, units, or modules must also be input to specify type of unit, method of calculation, and required equipment data. One or more arrays are normally used for stream data, with feed streams requiring input, and other stream data entered as it is calculated by the program. The stream arrays include data on concentrations, component flows, temperature, pressure, enthalpy, and perhaps other data. Other input arrays can be used for economic calculations, optimization procedures, and other specifications.

The programs generally contain a number of subroutines for calculations on various types of process units, and each is normally set up to calculate the outflow stream data from inflows and equipment input specifications. A series of subroutines are also available to furnish thermodynamic properties as required by the various equipment subroutines.

In the normal flowsheet procedure, once a given stream has been specified by previous calculations, the subroutine for the next unit in line is called, and the data on all entering streams are used to calculate the outflows from that unit. This in turn provides the input to the following unit. Thus the calculations proceed from fresh feed streams through the process modules in the direction of the flowsheet streams, and eventually the product streams and all recycle streams are calculated. When desired, the equipment characteristics and sizes can be used to calculate cost and economic data.

Although individual unit modules can involve very complicated and time-consuming computer calculations, such as distillation columns and non-isothermal reactors which require trial and error convergence, the major convergence problem involves the recycle streams that cannot be calculated until after all the units in a recycle loop are calculated, and, of course, the recycle loop units cannot be accurately calculated without an accurate value of the recycle stream. Thus, whenever a recycle stream is encountered, it is necessary to use an estimate for each of its properties in order to proceed with the unit calculations, and all the following unit calculations become only estimates. Repetition of the calculations around a loop with improving estimates is carried out until the calculated recycle stream and its properties converge with the estimated stream properties and the two are equal within reasonable limits. With the convergence of all component flows and all properties of all recycle streams, all calculations can be completed accurately.

Since within any recycle loop there may be individual units that require a number of repetitions to converge in each repetition of a loop calculation, and since there are often loops within loops, a moderately complex process can require considerable computation time. For optimization search programs involving flowsheet programs, many process variations must be calculated, each of which may involve numerous unit and loop repetitions to reach convergence. Thus, any improvements in convergence techniques that accelerate convergence may save considerable amounts of computer time.

Several techniques are available for reaching convergence on recycle streams. The simplest of these is the successive substitution method, in which the calculated recycle stream properties for one trial calculation are used for the estimated recycle stream properties in the following trial calculation. This procedure is essentially automatic if no other convergence technique is used, since the calculated stream properties are recorded in the stream array when calculated, and when the loop unit calculations are repeated, these stream properties will be taken from the array. For example, if F_{ren} is the estimated recycle flow on trial number n, and F_{rcn} is the calculated recycle flow from trial number n, then for trial n + 1,

$$F_{re(n+1)} = F_{rcn} \tag{1}$$

Similar substitutions are necessary for each component flow, temperature, pressure, and enthalpy, but with no other procedure specified such substitution will be carried out automatically, for all recycle streams.

Another frequently used method to accelerate convergence is the Wegstein method [13]. This method assumes a linear relationship between a specific calculated recycle stream property and the estimate of the same property that was used in the calculation. This relationship is used to determine the value of an estimate that will give an equal value of the calculated property. Thus if

$$F_{rcn} = a + bF_{ren} \tag{2}$$

the slope b can be determined from two previous trials as

$$b = (F_{rcn} - F_{rc(n-1)})/(F_{ren} - F_{re(n-1)}) \tag{3}$$

The estimate of this flow for trial number n + 1 can be calculated to make $F_{rc(n+1)} = F_{re(n+1)}$ based on the above assumptions as

$$F_{re(n+1)} = (F_{ren} - bF_{ren})/(1 - b) \tag{4}$$

This procedure can be used to change the estimated properties whenever an unconverged recycle stream is encountered in the program. In general it will provide faster convergence than the successive substitution method, but for some situations, particularly with multiple recycle loops and interaction, the procedure may be unstable, and the estimates and calculated values may diverge. For this reason, modifications of the Wegstein method that are more stable are often used.

The previous methods have a disadvantage when there are loops within loops because the inner loops may have to converge before the outer loop calculations become reliable for estimates, and the feed flows to inner loops may keep changing. The estimates have no relation to the feed rate and are functions of only the recycle data, yet in many recycle processes, the rate of recycle is proportional to the feed rate. Changes in feed rates to internal loops may cause important changes in calculated recycle rates, which the Wegstein method will erroneously attribute to changes in estimated recycle flow. For this reason, modifications of the successive substitution and Wegstein methods can be used that operate on the ratio of recycle flow to feed flow rather than on the recycle flow only. These methods have been shown to be effective in multiple loop systems [14, 15]. Using these ratios, Equation 1 becomes

$$R_{r/fe(n+1)} = R_{r/fcn} \tag{5}$$

for the successive substitution method, where $R_{r/fcn}$ represents the calculated ratio of the recycle flow to the feed flow for trial number n, and $R_{r/fe(n+1)}$ is the estimate of the ratio for trial n + 1. To get the estimated recycle flow for trial n + 1, $R_{r/fe(n+1)}$ should be multiplied by the feed rate for trial n + 1. Similarly, for the Wegstein method, variables in Equations 3 and 4 can be changed to R representing recycle flow to feed flow ratios and Equation 4 becomes

$$R_{r/fe(n+1)} = R_{r/fcn} - b_r R_{r/fen})/(1 - b_r) \tag{6}$$

where b_r is the slope of the $R_{r/fc}$ versus $R_{r/fe}$ relationship. Again $R_{r/fe(n+1)}$ should be multiplied by the feed rate to the loop for trial n + 1 to get the estimated recycle rate. There is no advantage to this procedure if the feed rate to the loop is constant, such as the fresh feed to the outermost loop. However, for inner loops with feed rates that change appreciably with each trial, the above procedures can be quite helpful with respect to stability. In applications to several processes, the successive substitution method applied to recycle to feed ratios was the most stable of the methods tried. However, it did not convergence rapidly [14, 15].

LINEARIZATION METHODS

Linearization methods have long been used as approximation methods in design, and it was logical that such methods be used to obtain estimates for the convergence of computer design programs. The Wegstein method previously discussed is a method based on linearization of the relationship between an estimated variable and the same variable calculated using the estimate. However, the Wegstein method is not based on the design or the relationships used in the calculations. A more appropriate estimate would be one based on the system being studied, and the relationships between the variables of the system. One of the first approaches to estimates based on the design structure was by Rosen [5], who suggested a two-tier calculation scheme, with one tier an approximate linear calculation of estimates and a second tier being a more rigorous calculation to check the estimates. Calculations were repeated until the two tiers checked. His method was based on the use of "split fractions," which will be discussed later.

Processes generally consist of a series of units in a desired order with a certain set of flows between units to provide the necessary changes to convert raw material to products. Most of these flows proceed from the raw material feeds toward the outflow of products, with recycle streams in the opposite direction and perhaps inflows and outflows at various intermediate points. It is not necessary in manual calculations, but the natural order of calculations is in the direction of stream flow as discussed for flowsheet programs, and the natural method of calculation for material balances is to calculate the outflow from the first unit then proceed to the second unit and calculate its outflow and continue on through the process and around the recycle loops. If this can be done with a series of relatively simple equations, the equations can be derived and written in this order, and solved simultaneously by manual algebraic manipulations. If each unit can be approximated by a linear equation, then such a solution can be readily obtained, although a problem with a large number of variables may require a computer solution. If desired, such calculations may also be performed in the reverse order to calculate the necessary feed flows or other parameters that are needed to provide desired product flow and specifications. One direct method of linearizing process flow calculations is to use an estimate for each outflow of each unit as

$$F_o = a + bF_I \tag{7}$$

with F_I the inflow to the unit. This would provide an equation for each flow in the system, other than the fresh feed flows to the process. The number of equations would equal the number of variables to be calculated, and these variables could be solved for by matrix methods. However, in the process material balances there is not just one flow per stream that must balance, but each component flow must be accounted for in each unit, and in some cases, the outflow of component A might be a function of the inflow of several components, such that an appropriate linear estimate might be

$$A_o = a + b_A A_I + b_B B_I + b_C C_I \cdots \tag{8}$$

where A, B, C, ... represent different component flows. The number of variables is then equal to the number of components times the number of streams (other than fresh feed streams), and the number of equations is the same. This leads to very large matrices even though many of the coefficients are 0 due to the fact that only a few variables are in each equation, or the system is "sparse." This approach is possible, but for large systems it may not be practical, and does not seem to have found much favor, probably because other simpler methods have proven satisfactory for most applications.

For almost all process units, any particular component outflow will be primarily dependent on the amount of inflow of that component, and there will be only slight effects due to the amount of inflow of other components. Reactors are definite exceptions to this because product outflow depends more on reactant than on product inflow. Other frequent exceptions are separation units

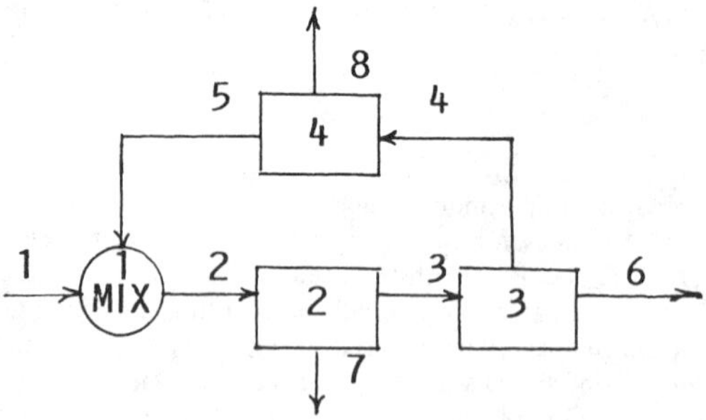

Figure 1. Example process for Equations 9–17.

where the inflow of a volatile compound can change the relative vapor and liquid outflows of other components, or solvent flow can change the amounts of outflows of other components in the extract and raffinate. However, in most separation units, if the other components are relatively constant, the outflows of a given component will be primarily dependent on the inflow of that component. If it is assumed that all component outflows from a given unit are linear functions of the same component inflow to the unit, then an equation such as Equation 7 can be applied to each component for each unit. For the convergence of 4 stages of vapor-liquid flash separation with 3 recycle streams and 16 components, Cavett showed that convergence was obtained much more rapidly when each component outflow was assumed dependent only on the inflow of that component [16]. Most other reports of convergence techniques and linear design or simulation methods have also used this assumption, with special methods applied to reactors.

An application of the above procedures to the system in Figure 1 (with no reactors) can illustrate how it can be used to estimate a recycle flow. Consider the flow of component A in stream j as A_j, and for this example, assume that for streams 2 through 5 only,

$$A_j = a_j + b_j A_{j-1} \tag{9}$$

Under these conditions,

$$A_5 = a_5 + b_5 a_4 + b_5 b_4 a_3 + b_5 b_4 b_3 A_2 \quad \text{or} \quad A_5 = k_1 + b_5 b_4 b_3 A_2 = k_1 + b_5 b_4 b_3 (A_1 + A_5) \tag{10}$$

with k_1 a combined constant. To obtain A_5 as a function of A_1,

$$A_5 = (k_1 + b_5 b_4 b_3 A_1)/(1 - b_5 b_4 b_3) = k_2 + k_3 A_1 \tag{11}$$

Other components could be analyzed similarly. Note that there is no constant needed for the mixer because the output is the sum of the inflows. Also for Figure 1, the following can be written

$$A_6 = a_6 + b_6 b_3 (k_1 + A_1)/(1 - b_5 b_4 b_3) = k_4 + k_5 A_1 \tag{12}$$

There is an equation similar to Equation 9 for each component in each unit other than a mixer or unit with inflow equal outflow. An accurate determination of the constants a and b for a given component and a given unit could be obtained by finding the partial derivative for b and the value of A_j at one value of A_{j-1} to find a, or a and b both could be obtained by finding two sets of values of A_j and A_{j-1}. This could be done by calculation, or experiments, but in either case, extensive study might be required to obtain one set of a and b values for each component in each unit. Equations 10 and 11 indicate that it could be possible to obtain sets of combined constants for a number of units in series or for a single loop, by two sets of A_2, A_5 values for the series 2 to 5, or two sets of A_1, A_5 values for the loop recycle, or A_1, A_6 values for loop output, for each component. For a small change from a base point, one can write from Equation 11

$$A_5 - A_{5b} = k_3 (A_1 - A_{1b}) \tag{13}$$

Equation 13 can be used to determine k_3 from an independent small change in A_1 and measurement or calculation of A_5. Or if k_3 is known, Equation 13 can be used to calculate A_5 or A_1 for a desired change in the other. Such relationships can be used to get reasonably accurate estimates for control or operation or design changes that are within a linear range, but for such purposes it should be kept in mind that an independent change is necessary to accurately find the value for each independent constant (or combined constant).

Special considerations are necessary for reactors because reactor products and the consumption of some reactants are not based on the amount of the same component in the inflow, but on the amount of reaction that occurs. For limiting reactants, the amount in the outflow is the amount of input times $(1 - X)$, where X is the fraction of the limiting reactant reacted. For reactants in excess, the outflow is the inflow minus the amount reacted with the limiting reactant, and for reaction products, the outflow is the amount of products produced by the reaction of the limiting reactant plus any inflow of products. Thus, except for the limiting reactant or reactants, the reactor equations are equivalent to the addition of products (based on another component) or the subtraction of non-limiting reactants (based on another component). For this situation it is better to consider the reactor as a mixer for products, adding a hypothetical stream calculated from the limiting reactant conversion as if it were a fresh feed. Similarly for non-limiting reactants, a negative feed stream based on conversion of limiting reactant can be added. The limiting reactants can also be calculated as a negative feed of the amount reacting, or they can be considered as if the reacting portion were split off in a unit in parallel with the hypothetical mixer. For example, for the reaction $aA + bB \rightarrow cC$ with A the limiting reactant, and X the fraction converted, the outflow of A would be $A_o = A_i(1 - X)$, the outflow of B would be $B_o = B_i - A_iXb/a$, and the output of C would be $C_0 = C_i + A_iXc/a$. In the above, the subscript o refers to outflow and i to inflow. When combining equations for units, the positive and negative terms can be considered as fresh feeds to the reactor considered as a mixer. Since a mixer often exists just ahead of a reactor, for all streams except the mixer to reactor stream, the hypothetical streams to the reactor can be considered as if they entered the mixer.

For convergence purposes in computer-aided process design, accuracy is not the most important criterion for linearization, so simpler methods of linearization that are revised with each new rigorous calculation [17] are used. For example, the Wegstein method may be used after each rigorous flowsheet calculation, which amounts to one independent process change even though a number of variables are changed simultaneously. Yet the Wegstein method based on one independent change is used to estimate a linear relationship for each component in each recycle loop. If there is any degree of interaction, these estimates will be inaccurate. However, these estimates are upgraded with each calculation until convergence is reached, and the estimates become accurate.

A convenient way to approximately linearize a process unit is to assume that a certain fraction of the input to the unit leaves in each of the output streams. This fraction is called the "split fraction" and is identified with a certain component in a certain stream, and the unit where the stream originates. For example, the split fraction of component A for stream 4 in Figure 1 is A_4/A_3. It is not necessary to specify the unit, since each stream originates in only one unit. Component split fractions for mixers, heat exchangers and pumps, and similar units with a single output equal to input, are all equal to one. Split fractions have been used by a number of authors for linear estimates in design [5, 6, 14, 15, 17–21] primarily because they are very convenient to use in multiple unit calculations. They are also less sensitive to small errors due to interaction than the b values for slope used in Equations 9–12. This is because they are calculated from flows rather than from changes in flows. The use of split fractions is equivalent to assuming the a values and k_1, k_2, and k_4 in Equations 9–12 are all zero, with b values equal to the split fractions. If f_{ij} is the split fraction for component i in stream j, then Equations 9–12 become

$$A_j = f_{Aj}A_{j-1} \tag{14}$$

$$A_5 = f_{A3}f_{A4}f_{A5}A_2 = f_{A3}f_{A4}f_{A5}(A_1 + A_5) \tag{15}$$

$$A_5 = f_{A3}f_{A4}f_{A5}A_1/(1 - f_{A3}f_{A4}f_{A5}) \tag{16}$$

$$A_6 = f_{A3}f_{A4}f_{A6}A_1/(1 - f_{A3}f_{A4}f_{A5}) \tag{17}$$

When split fractions are applied to a series of units, the product of all the split fractions in the series is the split fraction for the complete series, as in Equation 15. It can also be shown by algebra and Mason's rule [22], that if there is a single loop with its recycle entering between streams h and k, and only one feed, then for component i,

$$I_k = \text{product of all } f_{ij} \text{ between streams h and k times } I_h/(1 - \text{product of all } f_{ij} \text{ around the recycle loop}) \tag{18}$$

where I_k = the flow of component I in stream k

Equations 16 and 17 indicate how this is applicable to the loop shown in Figure 1. Where there is one or more feed streams entering between streams h and k in the previous situation, then the effect of each source of component i must be calculated as above and the effects added to obtain the flow of component I in stream k.

For a single recycle loop, the product of all split fractions around the loop is the fraction of the total feed of a component (fresh feed plus recycle) that is recycled, and can be called the recycle fraction of a given component for a given loop, designated here as f_{riL} for component i in loop L. Thus in Figure 1, $f_{rA1} = f_{A3}f_{A4}f_{A5}$ if the only loop is loop 1.

In any linearization where accuracy over a small range is desired, some consideration should be given to the system and types of units involved. Normally where accuracy is required, the proper application of Equation 13 would be most appropriate with an independent determination of each constant or combined constant. If a number of constants are determined simultaneously from one independent change, then split fractions would probably be more reliable.

LINEARIZATION FOR CONVERGENCE ACCELERATION

Linearization may be used in several ways to accelerate convergence in flowsheet design or simulation programs. Generally overall material balances and/or the solution of simultaneous equations are used to find the flows of recycle streams based on a linear or simplified system of equations. The constants in these equations that approximate the system can be found from the results of rigorous solutions that are obtained in a pass through the flowsheet program. For example, after the outflow from any given unit is calculated by the flowsheet program, the split fraction for each component in each output stream can be calculated by dividing the component outflow by the total inflow to the unit. If it were desired to use the relationship in Equation 9 for each unit, two rigorous calculations would be necessary to evaluate the a and b constants. From two rigorous calculations, one could try to calculate these constants for all components, but the constants would not be accurate unless all components behaved independently. In an extreme case, the inflow of a component could remain the same to a given unit for two rigorous calculations, and yet, a small change in the outflow of that component could occur due to effects of other variables. This would produce a b value of plus or minus infinity. Generally, split fractions would be less sensitive to small effects of interaction. If desired, as loop calculations are completed, or as the entire process calculations are completed, combined constants for loops, such as recycle fraction, can be calculated. After a rigorous calculation and the calculation of split fractions, all the information is available for calculating any desired streams including recycle streams. Figure 2 is a computer flow diagram showing how split fraction techniques can be used to assist convergence in flowsheet programs, with an indication of the programming necessary beyond that in the normal flowsheet type programming.

The calculation of recycle streams from split fractions can be done in several ways, including equations such as Equations 9–18 for relatively simple systems. However, for more complex multiple loop systems, it is desirable to have a consistent straightforward method of deriving the equations needed to calculate recycle streams. Two methods will be discussed for deriving such equations based on process structure and their application will be demonstrated using the process shown in Figure 3. This figure represents a reactor with three flash units used to separate a product stream and a recycle stream to the reactor. There are three recycle streams, streams 11, 10, and 9.

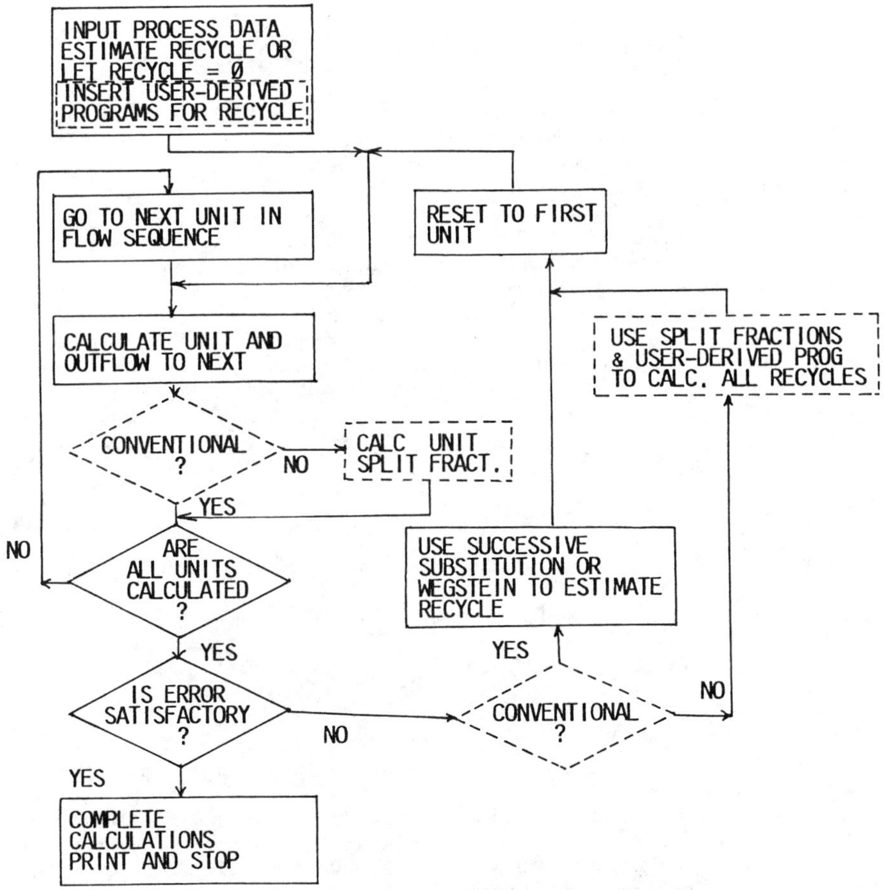

Figure 2. Computer flow diagram for using linear process calculations with split fractions to estimate recycle flows in flowsheet programs. Additional programming to use split fractions with conventional flowsheet programs ----------.

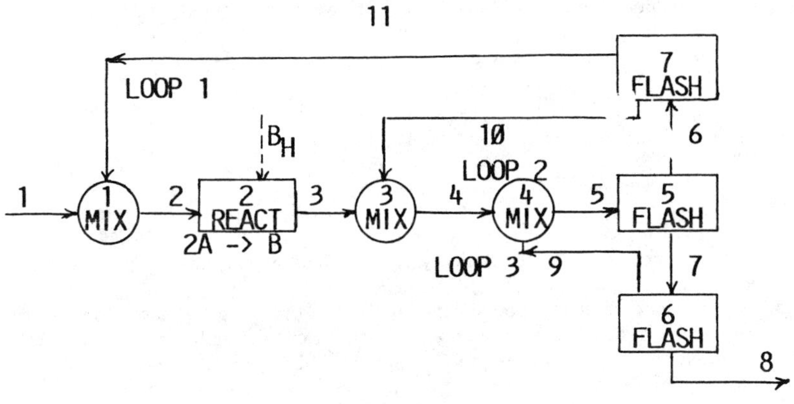

Figure 3. Example process for Equations 19–24 and 27–30.

One method to derive the necessary equations is that of Reklaitis [21]. In this approach all mixer feed streams are followed in the reverse flow direction, and split fractions are multiplied until either a fresh feed is reached or a mixer output is reached. The mixer outputs are then set equal to the sum of the derived inputs, which gives one equation for each mixer output, with mixer outputs and fresh feeds as the only variables. These equations can be solved for all the mixer outputs, and other streams can be calculated from these. In Figure 3, the mixer inputs are streams 1, 11, 3, 10, 4, and 9. Following these in the reverse direction, stream 1 is a fresh feed (and known for flowsheet calculations). For stream 11 and component A, $A_{11} = f_{A11}A_6 = f_{A11}f_{A6}A_5$. Since A_5 is a mixer output the above equation is sufficient. For stream 3, $A_3 = f_{A3}A_2$, where A_2 is a mixer output. For stream 10, $A_{10} = f_{A10}f_{A6}A_5$, and A_5 is a mixer output. Stream 4 is a mixer output, and for stream 9, $A_9 = f_{A9}f_{A7}A_5$. For mixer outputs, streams 2, 4, and 5, we can write

$$A_2 = A_1 + f_{A11}f_{A6}A_5 \tag{19}$$

$$A_4 = f_{A3}A_2 + f_{A10}f_{A6}A_5 \tag{20}$$

$$A_5 = A_4 + f_{A9}f_{A7}A_5 \tag{21}$$

If the split fractions and A_1 are known, these equations can be solved simultaneously to give

$$A_2 = A_1(1 - f_{A10}f_{A6} - f_{A9}f_{A7})/(1 - f_{A10}f_{A6} - f_{A9}f_{A7} - f_{A11}f_{A6}f_{A3}) \tag{22}$$

$$A_4 = (1 - f_{A9}f_{A7})f_{A3}A_2/(1 - f_{A10}f_{A6} - f_{A9}f_{A7}) \tag{23}$$

$$A_5 = A_4/(1 - f_{A9}f_{A7}) \tag{24}$$

The recycle streams or any other streams can be calculated from these mixer output streams by multiplying split fractions.

In the reactor in Figure 3, the split fraction for component A to stream 3, f_{A3}, is $1 - X$, where X is the conversion of A, (A is the limiting reactant). However in the reactor, component flow B_3 should not be considered as a split fraction times B_2, but instead should be $B_2 + A_2X(1/2)$. After the flow of the limiting component has been calculated, a hypothetical feed, $B_H = A_2X/2$ can be calculated and treated as if it were added at the reactor. The split fraction for B in the reactor is then hypothetically 1. Equations 19 and 21 would be the same if A were replaced by B and split fractions for B were used. Equation 20 becomes

$$B_4 = B_2 + A_2X/2 + f_{B10}f_{B6}B_5 \tag{25}$$

Solving the B version of Equations 19 and 20 and 25 gives

$$B_2 = \frac{B_1(1 - f_{B10}f_{B6} - f_{B9}f_{B7}) + A_2X/2f_{B11}f_{B6}}{1 - f_{B11}f_{B6} - f_{B10}f_{B6} - f_{B9}f_{B7}} \tag{26}$$

The B version of Equation 23 is

$$B_4 = (1 - f_{B9}f_{B7})(B_2 + A_2X/2)/(1 - f_{B10}f_{B6} - f_{B9}f_{B7}) \tag{27}$$

Equation 24 can be revised by replacing A with B and using split fractions of B. If other products were produced they could be treated similarly, and non-limiting reactants would have a negative hypothetical feed.

Another convenient method to obtain equations for multiple loop systems is Mason's rule, as outlined by Henley and Williams primarily for complex circuits and control loops [22]. This method has been applied to complex process loops by Milani [15, 23]. Since split fractions are used to multiply inputs to obtain outputs, in the same manner as linear transfer functions are used in control, the theory of control loops and linear circuits can be applied almost directly to the use of split fractions. The one major difference between control loops and recycle loops is that feedback loops for control are made to be negative, while recycle loops in processes produce positive feedback. Thus, the signs in recycle loop equations are often the opposite of those in control loop equations.

For a series of units with no recycle streams entering between streams h and k, one can write for component A,

$$A_k = \sum P_{hk} A_h \tag{28}$$

where P_{hk} is the product of all split fractions for A between stream h and stream k. If there is more than one forward path between h and k or more than one stream being added to produce k, then the effects of each feed stream, h, and each path must be determined by Equation 28 and added.

Mason's rule may be applied to a system where process recycle loops enter between a feed stream h and any following stream k, to give the following equation for A_k as a function of A_h

$$A_k = \sum P_{hk} M_{hk} A_h / N_{hk} \tag{29}$$

If there is more than one source of A outside the recycle loops entering between h and k, then A_k is the sum of Equation 29 applied to all such sources, and if there is more than one forward path from h to k, A_k is the sum of Equation 29 applied to each forward path. P_{hk} is the same as in Equation 28. N_{hk} equals 1 – (the sum of the recycle fractions of all recycle loops that affect any stream between h and k) + (the sum of the recycle fractions of non-touching loops multiplied two loops at a time) – (the sum of the recycle fractions of non-touching loops multiplied 3 loops at a time) + etc. As previously discussed, the recycle fraction of a loop is the product of all the split fractions around the loop. M_{hk} is equal to N_{hk} after deleting all terms that include loops which share a stream with the path for P_{hk}.

This rule can be applied to the process in Figure 3 to find A_2, the mixer 1 output of component A, in terms of the feed stream. $P_{1,2}$ equals 1 for the mixer and

$$N_{1,2} = 1 - f_{A3} f_{A6} f_{A11} - f_{A6} f_{A10} - f_{A7} f_{A9} \tag{30}$$

Split fractions 3, 6, and 11 are in loop 1, split fractions 6 and 10 are in loop 2, and split fractions 7 and 9 are in loop 3. There are no non-touching loops since loop 1 goes through stream 5. Since loop 1 contains stream 2, the recycle fraction of loop 1 should be deleted from $N_{1,2}$ to obtain $M_{1,2}$. Thus,

$$M_{1,2} = 1 - f_{A6} f_{A10} - f_{A7} f_{A9} \tag{31}$$

Using Equation (26),

$$A_2 = (1 - f_{A6} f_{A10} - f_{A7} f_{A9}) A_1 / (1 - f_{A3} f_{A6} f_{A11} - f_{A6} f_{A10} - f_{A7} f_{A9})$$

This is the same result as obtained in Equation 22. From stream 2 to stream 4 in Figure 3, loop 1 is not involved because it does not enter between streams 2 and 4 and it does not change either the loop 2 or loop 3 flows. Loop 2, but not 3, contains a stream in common with the path from 2 to 4, so the product for loop 2 is deleted from $N_{2,4}$ to get $M_{2,4}$ and applying Equation 29 one gets the same result as Equation 23. To get B_5 from B_4, only one loop is involved, and the result is Equation 24.

As another example, to calculate the flow of component A in stream 11,

$$P_{1,11} = f_{A3} f_{A6} f_{A11}$$

$N_{1,11}$ is the same as $N_{1,2}$, and $M_{1,11} = 1$, because the path from 1 to 11 includes parts of all three loops, and

$$A_{11} = f_{A3} f_{A6} f_{A11} A_1 / (1 - f_{A3} f_{A6} f_{A11} - f_{A6} f_{A10} - f_{A7} f_{A9}) \tag{32}$$

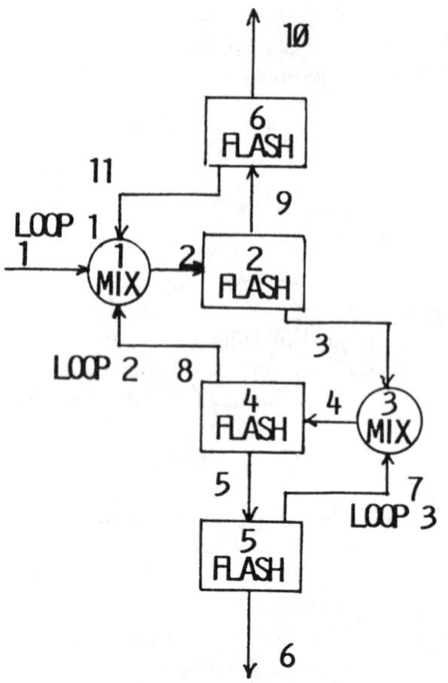

Figure 4. Example process. Calculation of component flow of A in Stream 11: $P_{1,11} = f_{A9}f_{A11}$; $N_{1,11} = 1 - f_{A9}f_{A11} - f_{A3}f_{A8} - f_{A5}f_{A7} + f_{A9}f_{A11}f_{A5}f_{A7}$ (Loop 1 and Loop 3 are non-touching); $M_{1,11} = 1 - f_{A5}f_{A7}$ (Path 1 to 11 includes parts of Loops 1 and 2, but not 3); $A_{11} = P_{1,11}M_{1,11}A_1/N_{1,11}$.

The above procedures should not be directly applied to component B in Figure 3, because of the reactor. However, except for the effect on stream 2, the hypothetical B feed from reaction could enter the same mixer as stream 1, or the reactor as a second feed, and the split fraction of the reactor would be one. We could write for B_{11} for example,

$$B_{11} = f_{B6}f_{B11}(B_1 + A_2X/2)/(1 - f_{B6}f_{B11} - f_{B6}f_{B10} - f_{B7}f_{B9}) \tag{33}$$

To get B_2, it would be necessary to consider the hypothetical reactor feed as a second feed and add $P_{1,2}M_{1,2}B_1$ to $P_{3,2}M_{3,2}A_2X/2$ and divide the sum by $N_{1,2}$ which is the same as $N_{3,2}$. $P_{1,2}$ would be one and $P_{3,2}$ would be $f_{B6}f_{B11}$, while $M_{1,2}$ would be $(1 - f_{B6}f_{B10} - f_{B7}f_{B9})$ and $M_{3,2}$ would be one since the path from 3 to 2 includes parts of all three loops. This would give the same result as Equation 26. Another example illustrating the case of non-touching loops is shown in Figure 4.

Either of the previous methods, or other methods, can be used to derive equations for the recycle loops, or for the mixer outputs, based on the split fractions. These user-derived equations can then be programmed into a subroutine to estimate flows required for convergence. Because they are based on the process structure, and use reasonably stable estimates, the convergence should be more rapid than that from a generalized convergence method. Milani has proposed a method (called LPS for Linear Process Simulation) of using rigorous flowsheet calculations with estimates of mixer outputs that proceed around each loop and provide split fractions for repeated estimates until each loop converges [23]. However, as an addition to most flowsheet programs, it is possible to estimate all the recycle flows from split fractions and user-derived equations and proceed in the normal flowsheet manner, as indicated in Figure 2, and this method is equivalent to LPS. The requirements for a program using this type of linear process calculations for convergence are first, a flowsheet oriented design or simulation program that can be modified, second, the addition of split fraction calculations to each unit subroutine for each outlet stream and component with an array for storage of these split fractions, and finally, a subroutine for user programming to estimate all recycles after a complete flowsheet sequence. The user-derived program would include calculations such as Equation 33. The comparison of estimated and calculated recycles should normally be a part of the flowsheet program. Once such a program is established, there is an additional requirement for each user to derive the recycle equations by one of the previous or other methods and program it into the estimating subroutine.

Table 1
Comparison of Linear Process Simulation Convergence with Other Convergence Methods

Process	Reference	Convergence Method	Number of process Calculations to Converge	Number of LPS[23] Calculations to Converge*
Flash with Recycle 6 comp.	[10]	Bounded Wegstein	5	5
4 Flash, 3 Mix, 3 Recycles, 16 Components	[16]	Newton's, 1 Deriv. per Estimate	16	19
Same as above	[16]	Successive Sub.	56	19
As above, 6 comp.	[23]	Succ. Sub.	24	13
Reactor, Distill. Splitter, 3 Comp.	[24]	Newton-Raphson Fibonacci	50	40

* *Linear process calculations using split fractions.*

A comparison of the above type of convergence method with some methods discussed in the literature and applied to various processes was made by Milani [14, 15, 23]. The results of comparing these methods is shown in Table 1. Although these comparisons are limited, in general they indicate that the LPS method of linearized process calculations using split fractions is probably better than successive substitution, and approximately equivalent to the other methods used. Linear process calculations are probably more easily programmed than Newton's method or the Newton-Raphson-Fibonacci method, but slightly more programming is involved than the successive substitution or bounded Wegstein method which do not require user-derived equations.

RECYCLE FRACTION METHOD

According to the equations derived in previous sections, the use of split fractions results in linear material balance equations for a series of units, for recycles and products of process loops, and for multiple loop processes. Thus, if one assumes the split fractions are constant in the units of a process, it follows that the recycle fraction of a process loop, the recycle flow of a component divided by the mixed feed of the component, should be constant even if internal loops or intersecting loops exist. On completing a rigorous flow sheet calculation, the recycle fraction can be calculated for each component in each loop. The number of recycle fraction calculations is normally much less than the number of split fraction calculations. These recycle fractions can then be used to estimate the recycle flows for each loop for the next trial.

There are some problems with the assumption that recycle fractions are constant when split fractions are constant. One problem exists with loops that have more than one point of addition of external feeds to the loop. At such a point, the recycle may not be primarily a function of the mixed feed at that point, but perhaps more a function of the mixed feed where another feed source enters. Another problem with the calculation of the recycle fraction from an unconverged flowsheet calculation is that internal loops may not have converged, which produces an inappropriate value for the recycle at an outer mixed feed. Also, reactor products and non-limiting reactants may produce effects similar to more than one feed point in some cases. Thus the use of recycle fractions may not be as satisfactory for estimating recycles as the use of linear process calculations based on user-derived equations. The user-derived equations represent a converged set of calculations if the split fractions are constant, whereas the calculation of recycle fraction from an unconverged rigorous solution is not based on a converged solution. However, as convergence is approached, the recycle fraction calculation should become increasingly accurate.

If we let A_{fL}, A_{rcL}, and A_{reL} represent the fresh feed, calculated recycle (rigorous), and estimated recycle used for the rigorous calculation, all for component flows of A in loop number L in a given trial, then the recycle fraction of A for that loop and trial may be obtained as

$$\text{Recycle fraction of A in loop L} = f_{rAL} = A_{rcL}/(A_{fL} + A_{reL}) \tag{34}$$

If this recycle fraction remains constant, and we wish to find the estimated recycle that will equal the calculated recycle on the next trial, then

$$A_{rcL} = A_{reL} = f_{rAL}(A_{fL} + A_{reL}) \quad \text{or} \quad A_{reL} = f_{rAL}A_{fL}/(1 - f_{rAL}) \tag{35}$$

Equation 34 can be used after each flowsheet calculation sequence to estimate the recycle fraction, and then Equation 35 can be used to estimate the recycle flow for the next calculation. This procedure is relatively simple, probably less complex than most modified Wegstein procedures, and does not require any user-derived equations. It is based on the process structure, but not as much so as the linear process calculations based on split fractions.

As in the methods based on split fractions, the recycle fraction for loops with reactors needs to be modified for reaction products and non-limiting reactants. Even though the products produced by reaction do not enter the process at the same point as the fresh feed for the loop, in most cases, it does not matter as far as the recycle fraction is concerned, and when there is a possible problem its importance is likely to be reduced as recycle flow estimates become more constant. Probably the best procedure for reaction products in loops with reactors is to calculate the recycle fraction as the calculated recycle component flow divided by the fresh feed plus the reaction product produced in the reactor plus the estimated recycle flow used. All terms would be from the previous rigorous calculation of reaction products. Following the estimations on the limiting reactant, the estimated reaction product for the next trial can be obtained. The recycle fraction can then be applied to the estimate for the next trial by using Equation 35, with fresh feed plus estimated reaction product substituted for A_{fL}.

When two or more fresh feeds enter a loop at different points, the recycle fraction calculated by Equation 34 at the recycle mixer is not truly a recycle fraction, and could even conceivably be greater than 1 due to the other feed. This is not likely, and should not happen as convergence is approached. If the recycle fraction should come out greater than 1 in early trials, some other method of estimating recycle (successive substitution is suggested) should be used to prevent the estimation of a negative recycle. However, such a calculated recycle fraction is a ratio of the recycle at that point to the combined feed at that point, and should become approximately constant as convergence is approached. Thus it can be useful in estimating the recycle flow for the next trial, if it is not greater than 1.

The procedure for the use of recycle fraction for recycle estimation is indicated in Figure 5, a computer flow diagram that also shows the programming that must be added to the basic flowsheeting procedures. An important point [14] is that the recycle fraction that is calculated at the end of one rigorous trial should be used with the next trial's feed rate to estimate an internal recycle as that point is reached in the next rigorous flowsheet trial. In that way, the new feed rate to the internal loop, which may be changing due to unconverged outer loops, will be used in the estimation procedure. The same principle applies when the successive substitution or Wegstein procedure is applied to recycle to feed ratio, and computer flow diagrams very similar to Figure 5 could be used for these methods. The recycle fraction method should not be expected to converge as rapidly as linear process calculations based on split fractions, but once programmed, it requires no user-derived equations. It does require some flagging or indication of mixers that require recycle estimation.

A comparison of various convergence procedures on relatively simple 2-component processes consisting of reactors, flash units, and mixers is given in Table 2. The methods compared include successive substitution of recycle to feed ratio, the Wegstein method applied to the recycle to feed ratio, and the recycle fraction method, all applied to newly calculated loop feeds [14, 15]. These methods were shown to be preferable to the same methods applied to loop feeds from previous calculations for multiple loop flowsheet calculations [14]. Also shown are the results from

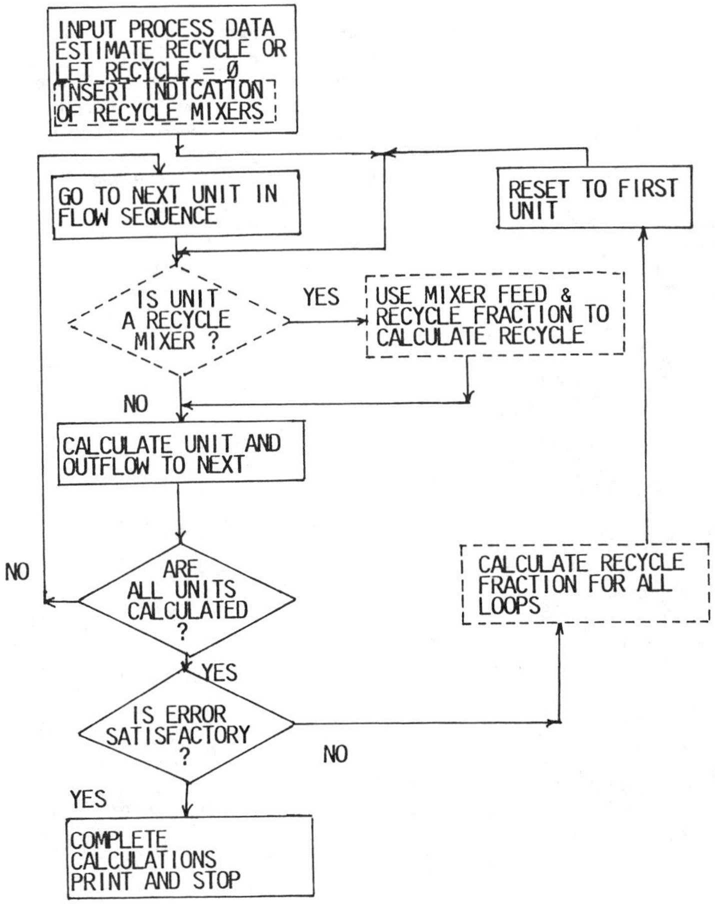

Figure 5. Computer flow diagram for using recycle fractions to assist in convergence of flow-sheet oriented process design and simulation programs. Additional programming for convergence by recycle fraction method ----------. Similar programming is suitable for convergence using recycle to feed ratio with successive substitution or Wegstein method.

linear calculations based on split fractions. In all cases, convergence was considered complete when the difference between each component recycle flow calculated and the estimate used was less than 0.1%. It can be noted that the results on Process I were appreciably different from the results on Processes II through VI. This is because Process I contained only 1 loop with a relatively large amount of recycle, and the simpler methods appeared to be adequate, while the recycle fraction method and linear process calculations method tended to become unstable. In processes II through VI, the linear process calculations produced the most rapid convergence, and the recycle fraction method was usually the best of the methods that do not require user-derived equations. In all of the cases where convergence was not reached it appeared to be due to oscillations in the calculated and estimated results, and in some of these cases, it is doubtful that convergence would have

Table 2
Comparison of Convergence Methods on Two Component Processes

Process	Number of Process Iterations to Converge to Less than 0.1% Error all Components			
	Successive Substitution on Rec./Feed	Wegstein on Recycle Feed Ratio	Recycle Fraction	Linear Process Calc. Using Split Fract.
I. Reactor Flash, 1 Recycle $2A \rightarrow B$, Rel. Vol. A = 3				
A. Conversion, X = .5 Vapor mol. fr. A, Y = .8	7	5	7	7
B. X = .5, Y = .7	9	9	>21	>21
C. X = .4, Y = .8	7	13	12	12
II. 3 Flash, 2 Mixers, 2 Recycles, Rel. Vol. A = 3				
A. Reflux ratio, R = 3 Feed mol. fr. A, Z = .5	18	11	7	5
B. R = 3, Z = .3	17	16	7	5
C. R = 2, Z = .3	14	9	7	4
III. Reactor, 2 Flash, 2 Recycles, $2A \rightarrow B$ Rel. Vol. = 3				
A. Reflux Ratio, R = 2 Conversion, X = .6	14	9	7	5
B. R = 2, X = .5	14	6	7	5
C. R = 3, X = .6	18	11	7	5
D. R = 3, X = .5	16	11	7	5
IV. Reactor, 3 Flash, 3 Recycles $2A \rightarrow B$, X = .5, R = 2 Rel. Vol. = 3	15	>21	6	2
V. Same as IV, $A \rightarrow 2B$ Rel. Vol. A = 1/3	18	>21	9	7
VI. 4 Flash, 3 Recycles, Rel. Vol. = 3				
A. Reflux ratio = 2	20	18	8	5
B. R = 3	25	>41	9	6

Feed Composition I, III, IV, V = .9 mol fract. A, VI = .5 mol fract. A

ever occurred. Only one method always reached convergence, and that was the successive substitution method applied to recycle to feed ratio. This suggests that a check on unstable convergence might be included in flowsheet programming, and when this occurs, the program should switch to the successive substitution method.

ADJUSTMENT OF PROCESS PARAMETERS

One disadvantage of flowsheet oriented computer programs is that they are generally designed only to calculate outputs from inputs, and even though it might be relatively easy to manually

Table 3
Comparison of Convergence Methods with Parameter Changes

					Convergence Method			
Process*	**Parameter Changed**	**Initial Param.**	**Final Param.**	**Desired Prod.**	**Succ. Sub.**	**Wegstein on rec/f**	**Recycle Fract.**	**LPC S. Fr.**
V	None	—	—	—	10	>21	9	7
V	Conversion	.5	.37	90 mol %	38	>41	21	14
VI A	None	—	—	—	20	18	8	5
VI A	Reflux Ratio	2	.95	80 mol %	25	>41	17	14
VI B	None	—	—	—	25	>41	9	6
VI B	Reflux Ratio	3	.95	80 mol %	25	>41	18	15

At convergence to 0.1%, the desired product concentration was achieved within 0.2%.

* *See Table 2 for Process.*

calculate in the reverse direction (calculate inflows from desired outflows), this is usually impossible in flowsheet programs without specially programmed subroutines. Neither is it possible to adjust the parameters of a unit in order to obtain certain output results, such as product flow and composition. Without special programming, data in any streams other than those involved in the unit itself cannot be utilized in a unit calculation. Certain control routines are available to force certain conditions on the flowsheet solutions, and in some cases manual calculations are possible to set equipment parameters such that a desired output will be achieved. The calculation of split fractions or recycle fractions can simplify the estimation of parameters needed to achieve a certain output result, and these can be performed at the same time as the estimation of recycle flows. In this way parameters in a process can be adjusted to obtain a desired downstream result simultaneously with the convergence procedures. This is possible with any convergence procedure, but the calculations may be more readily carried out if split fractions or recycle fractions are available, and the new estimates of recycle can be consistent with the changes in process parameters. Table 3 shows some results on the more complex processes used in Table 2 [15], in which process parameters were changed during the convergence procedures. Reactor conversion adjustments were made in one case based on material balances, and in two cases the reflux ratio in the equivalent of a simple distillation was adjusted empirically. In neither case was the use of split fractions necessary for the parameter adjustment, but the convergence along with parameter adjustment was compared using different convergence methods. In all of these 3 cases, linear calculations were best and the recycle fraction method was next best. With parameter adjustment, the Wegstein method applied to recycle to feed ratio appeared to be unstable in all cases, but successive substitution of recycle to feed ratio appeared to be satisfactory. The processes considered in Tables 2 and 3 are simple two component processes, but the convergence depends on the same type of factors as complex processes, and it may be observed that as the processes become more complex, the advantages of the linear calculations based on split fractions are equally or more significant.

Another type of parameter adjustment occurs in optimization using flowsheet oriented computer simulation or design. Lasdon [25], and Evans [17] have discussed the use of multiple level optimization using techniques such as successive linear programming and others. It seems likely that the use of split fractions and perhaps recycle fractions to approximately linearize process calculations could provide approximations useful in optimization techniques, especially for those technique such as successive linear programming. Other potential uses of split fractions and recycle fractions could occur in adaptive control where fractions determined by measurements or computer monitored data could be used to adjust control parameters. In automatic optimizing process control techniques, split fractions and recycle fractions could also prove to be useful.

REFERENCES

1. Coughanowr, D. R., and Koppel, L. B., *Process Systems Analysis and Control*, 67, McGraw-Hill, New York (1965).
2. Griffith, R. E., and Stewart, R. A., "A Nonlinear Programming Technique for the Optimization of Continuous Processing Systems," *Management Science*, 7, 379, (1961).
3. Buzby, B. R., "Technique and Experience Solving Really Big Nonlinear Programs," *Optimization Methods*, Cottle, R. W., and Karup, J. (eds.), English Universities Press, London (1974).
4. Box, G. E. P., and Draper, N. R., *Evolutionary Operations*, 105, Wiley, New York (1969).
5. Rosen, E. M., "A Machine Computation Method for Performing Material Balances," *Chem. Eng. Prog.*, 58, 10, 69–73, (1962).
6. Rosen, E. M., "Steady-State Chemical Process Simulation—State-of-the-art Review," *Computer Applications to Chemical Engineering*, ACS Symposium Series No. 124, Squires, R. G., and Reklaitis G. V. (eds.), 3–36, ACS (1980).
7. Westerberg, A. W., Hutchison, H. P., Motard, R. L., and Winter, P., *Process Flowsheeting*, Cambridge Univ. Press, Cambridge (1979).
8. Crowe, C. M., Hamielec, A. E., Hoffman, T. W., Johnson, A. I., Shannon, P. T., and Woods, D. R., *Chemical Plant Simulation*, Prentice Hall, Englewood Cliffs, N. J. (1971).
9. Motard, R. L., Shacham, M., and Rosen, E. M., "Steady-State Chemical Process Simulation," *AICHE J.*, 21, 3, 417–436, (1975).
10. Rosen E. M., and Pauls, A. C., "Computer-Aided Chemical Process Design: The FLOWTRAN System," *Comp. and Chem. Eng.*, 1, 1, 11–21 (1977).
11. Evans, L. B., Joseph, B., and Seider, W. D., "System Structures for Process Simulation," *AICHE J*, 23, 5, 658–666 (Sept. 1977).
12. Seider, W. D., "Model and Algorithm Synthesis in Process Analysis and Design," *Proceedings of 2d International Conference on Foundations of Computer-Aided Process Design*, Westerberg, A. W., and Chien, H. H. (eds.), 167. CACHE Pub., Ann Arbor, MI (1984).
13. Wegstein, J., "Accelerating Convergence of Iteraction Processes," *Comm. ACM*, 1, pp. 9, (1958).
14. Milani, S. M., and Findley, M. E., "Linear Process Calculations as Convergence Accelerators in Flowsheet-Sequenced Programs," *AICHE J*, 32, 4, 624–631 (April 1986).
15. Milani, S. M., and Findley, M. C., "Linear Process Simulation Convergence Methods for Flow Sheet Programs," *Proceedings 11th IMACS World Conf.*, Oslo, Norway (1985).
16. Cavett, R. H., "Applications of Numerical Methods to the Convergence of Simulated Processes Involving Recycle Loops," *Proc. Am. Pet. Inst.*, 43 (III), 57–76 (1963).
17. Evans, L. B., "Advances in Process Flowsheeting Systems," *Foundations of Computer-Aided Chemical Process Design*, Mah, R. S. H., and Seider, W. D. (eds.), Vol. 1, 425–469, Engineering Foundation, New York (1981).
18. Vela, M. A., "Use Split Fractions for Recycle Balances, Parts I and II," *Petrol. Refiner*, Vol. 40, 5, pp. 247; Vol. 40, 6, pp. 189 (1961).
19. Ravicz, A. E., and Norman, R. L., "Heat and Mass Balancing on a Digital Computer," *CEP*, 60, 5, pp. 71–76 (1964).
20. Hutchison, H. P., "Plant Simulation by Linear Methods," *Trans. Inst. Chem. Engrs.*, 52, pp. 287–290 (1974).
21. Reklaitis, G. V., Sood, M. K., and Woods, J. M., "Solution of Material Balances for Flow Sheets Modelled with Elementary Modules," *AICHE J*, 25, 2, pp. 209–219 (1979).
22. Henley, E. J., and Williams, R. A., *Graph Theory in Modern Engineering*, Academic Press, New York (1973).
23. Milani, S. M., "A Linear Process Simulation Method," Ph.D. Diss., Univ. of Missouri-Rolla (1983).
24. Napthali, L. M., "Process Heat and Material Balances," *CEP*, 60, 9, pp. 70–74 (1964).
25. Lasdon, L. S., "A Survey of Nonlinear Programming Algorithms and Software." *Foundations of Computer-Aided Chemical Process Design*, Mah, R. S. H., and Seider, W. D. (eds.), Vol. 1, pp. 185–217, Engineering Foundation, New York (1981).

CHAPTER 31

AN ITERATIVE COMPUTATION METHOD OF CHEMICALLY REACTING SYSTEMS WITH DISTRIBUTED STATE VARIABLES

Boleslaw Tabis

Department of Chemical Engineering
and Physical Chemistry
Technical University of Cracow, Poland

CONTENTS

INTRODUCTION

The steady states of many chemically reacting systems with distributed state variables are described by means of systems of ordinary differential equations together with corresponding boundary or initial conditions.

Such systems include a tubular reactor with axial mixing, a catalyst pellet in which contact process occurs, or a wide group of fluidized bed reactors.

Chemical processes are usually accompanied by considerable thermal effects. Therefore, it is necessary in most cases to assume their nonisothermal nature. Limit cases are sometimes analyzed, i.e., isothermal or adiabatic processes. In actual practice we usually have to deal with polytropic processes.

The polytropic process in a chemically reacting system is strongly nonlinear in character, which is mainly due to the form of kinetic terms. Therefore, the differential equations describing such processes are non-linear differential equations.

The type of boundary conditions connected with the model of the interior of the chemically reacting system depends on a physical interpretation of the process.

The chemical processes in plug flow tubular reactors require only initial conditions, so their mathematical model is the initial-value problem. The chemical reactions occurring in tubular reactors with axial mixing or in catalyst pellets are described by boundary value problems. These are usually two-point boundary value problems.

This chapter presents an iterative method of solving the whole group of nonlinear differential problems describing the behavior of chemically reacting systems with distributed state variables.

At the first stage of this method the original differential problem is transformed into a set of integral equations. Next the topological concept of homotopy has been used to solve the obtained integral equations by iteration.

The following section discusses general principles of homotopy method in solving integral equations. The method is illustrated in two subsequent sections for two examples of chemically reacting systems with distributed state variables. Also considered is a way of determining degrees of conversion and temperature profiles in a tubular polytropic homogeneous reactor and in a catalytic fluidized-bed reactor.

THE METHOD OF HOMOTOPY IN ITERATIVE SOLUTION OF INTEGRAL EQUATIONS

Definition 1. Let Y be a metric space. If f(y) and g(y) are continuous mappings of space Y into Y, then transformation h(y, t) is called homotopy between these mappings, where

$$h(y, t): Y \times [0, 1] \longrightarrow Y \tag{1}$$

besides

$$h(y, 0) = f(y) \quad \text{and} \quad h(y, 1) = g(y)$$

In Expression 1 scalar parameter t has values from the closed interval [0, 1].

Let us assume that the following single integral equation should be solved

$$y(z) = F[y(z)] \tag{2}$$

where

$$F[y(z)] = G(z, \partial z)y(\partial z) + \int_0^1 G(\xi, z)\varphi[y(\xi)]\, d\xi \tag{3}$$

and $\partial z = 0$ or $\partial z = 1$

Multiplying Equation 2 by parameter t we get

$$tF(y) - ty = 0 \tag{4}$$

Adding element y on both sides of Equation 4 we obtain

$$y = (1 - t)y + tF(y) = h(y, t) \tag{5}$$

It is easy to verify that h(y, 0) = Iy and h(y, 1) = F(y). Therefore, it is homotopy between identity operator I and original non-linear mapping F.

In the presented method of solving integral Equation 2, the simple iteration, so-called successive approximation

$$y_{k+1}(z) = F[y_k(z)] \tag{6}$$

is substituted by procedure

$$y_{k+1}(z) = h[y_k(z), t_k(z)] \tag{7}$$

in which $t_k(z)$ is a functional parameter, $t(z) \in C(0, 1)$.

Theorem 1. If Y is a Banach space, then iterative sequences generated by Equations 6 and 7 have the same limit $y^* \in Y$.

Proof. Let $y^* \in Y$ be a fixed point of operator F, i.e.

$$y^* = F(y^*) \tag{8}$$

Multiplying Equation 8 by t and adding $(1 - t)y^*$ on both sides we get

$$ty^* + (1 - t)y^* = tF(y^*) + (1 - t)y^*$$

that is

$$y^* = h(y^*, t) \tag{9}$$

which was to be proved.

Functional parameter t(z) has been determined from dependence

$$t(z) = \frac{1}{1 + |F'_y[y(z)]|} \tag{10}$$

where

$$F'_y[y(z)] = \int_0^1 G(\xi, z)\frac{\partial\varphi[y(\xi)]}{\partial y}\,d\xi \tag{11}$$

From Equation 10 of the parameter t it follows that for each fixed $z \in [0, 1]$

$$\lim_{F'_y \to 0} t(z) = 1 \tag{12}$$

and

$$\lim_{F'_y \to -\infty} t(z) = \lim_{F'_y \to \infty} t(z) = 0 \tag{13}$$

POLYTROPIC TUBULAR REACTOR WITH AXIAL MIXING

Mathematical Model of the Reactor

One of the frequently used models of nonisothermal tubular reactors is a one-dimensional model with heat and mass longitudinal dispersion [1]. The aim of this section is to give an efficient method of determining degrees of conversion and temperature profiles in a general case when in a reactor N linear independent of arbitrary stoichiometry and kinetics chemical reactions may occur.

The operation of such a reactor in a stationary state can then be described by set of N + 1 nonlinear ordinary differential equations

$$D_m\frac{d^2C_i}{dx^2} - u\frac{dC_i}{dx} - r_i(C_j, T) = 0, \qquad (i = 1, \ldots, N) \tag{14}$$

$$D_q\frac{d^2T}{dx^2} - u\rho_p c_p\frac{dT}{dx} + \sum_{i=1}^{N}(-\Delta H_i)r_i(C_j, T) - \frac{4k_q}{d_r}(T - T_q) = 0 \tag{15}$$

The Danckwerts boundary conditions generally used in such cases are

$$x = 0, \quad u(C_{if} - C_i) = -D_m \frac{dC_i}{dx} \qquad (i = 1, \ldots, N) \tag{16}$$

$$u\rho_p c_p(T_f - T) = -D_q \frac{dT}{dx} \tag{17}$$

$$x = L_r, \quad \frac{dC_i}{dx} = 0 \qquad (i = 1, \ldots, N) \tag{18}$$

$$\frac{dT}{dx} = 0 \tag{19}$$

Many papers have been devoted to producing effective numerical methods of solving a much simpler case when in the reactor there occurs a single irreversible reaction. The shooting method, also called ballistic, proposed by Lapidus [2] has proved useless because of numerical divergence, which explains some modifications of the method [3]. It is practically useless for nonlinear boundary value problems of higher order, even when fast digital computers are used. In practice it is usually applied when from among n boundary conditions, n − 1 given ones are on one boundary of integration range [4].

Hlavaček and Hofmann, analyzing the problems of steady state multiplicity in tubular reactors with longitudinal dispersion, gave in their papers [5, 6] a detailed review of numerical methods of solving a two-point boundary value problem for a single irreversible first order chemical reaction.

An extensive set of difference methods of solving two-point boundary value problems is given by Drobyshevich [7]. In this case the problem would be reduced to solving a very large system of transcendental equations, which is a strenuous task and requires fast computers of considerable central memory.

The method of orthogonal collocation was also used for solving nonlinear boundary value problems of type similar to Equations 14–19. The methods of this group, similarly to finite difference methods, lead to obtaining and next solving a system of transcendental equations [8, 9].

The works mentioned here lead to the conclusion that certain numerical methods of direct solving a system of Equations 14 and 15 with Conditions 16–19 are completely useless, others are extremely time consuming, i.e., require much computer work.

This makes it advisable to seek indirect methods of solving the problem in question.

Such a method may be a transformation of the differential problem (14–16) into a corresponding system of integral equations, and next solving this system. This is because integral operators are in general a better tool for applying various approximation methods. Roughly speaking, the idea is that integration is a "smoothing" operation, whereas the effect of a differential operator is just the opposite.

Transformation of a Differential Problem into a Set of Integral Equations

In order to apply the proposed method, Problems 14–19 will be transformed into a dimensionless form. Let us introduce the following notation

$$\alpha_i = \frac{C_{if} - C_i}{C_{if}} \quad (i = 1, \ldots, N), \qquad \theta = \frac{T - T_f}{T_f}, \qquad \theta_q = \frac{T_q - T_f}{T_f}$$

$$Pe_m = \frac{uL_r}{D_m}, \qquad Pe_q = \frac{u\rho_p c_p L_r}{D_q}, \qquad r_i(C_i, \theta) = C_{if} r_i(\alpha_i, \theta)$$

$$z = \frac{x}{L_r}, \qquad \tau = \frac{L_r}{u}, \qquad \eta_i = \frac{(-\Delta H_i)C_{if}}{\rho_p c_p T_f}, \qquad Q = \frac{4\tau k_p}{\rho_p c_p d_r}$$

Equations 14 and 15 and Boundary Conditions 16–19 are now as follows

$$\frac{1}{Pe_m}\frac{d^2\alpha_i}{dz^2} - \frac{d\alpha_i}{dz} + \tau r_i(\alpha_i, \theta) = 0, \qquad (i = 1, \ldots, N) \tag{20}$$

$$\frac{1}{Pe_q}\frac{d^2\theta}{dz^2} - \frac{d\theta}{dz} + \tau \sum_{i=1}^{N} \eta_i r_i(\alpha_i, \theta) - Q(\theta - \theta_q) = 0 \tag{21}$$

$$\alpha_i(0) - \frac{1}{Pe_m}\frac{d\alpha_i(0)}{dz} = 0 \qquad (i = 1, \ldots, N) \tag{22}$$

$$\theta(0) - \frac{1}{Pe_q}\frac{d\theta(0)}{dz} = 0 \tag{23}$$

$$\frac{d\alpha_i(1)}{dz} = 0 \qquad (i = 1, \ldots, N) \tag{24}$$

$$\frac{d\theta(1)}{dz} = 0 \tag{25}$$

Let us define the following linear differential operators

$$L_m\alpha_i := \frac{1}{Pe_m}\frac{d^2\alpha_i}{dz^2} - \frac{d\alpha_i}{dz}, \qquad (i = 1, \ldots, N) \tag{26}$$

$$L_q\theta := \frac{1}{Pe_q}\frac{d^2\theta}{dz^2} - \frac{d\theta}{dz} \tag{27}$$

and boundary conditions operators

$$B_{m,1}\alpha_i := \alpha_i(0) - \frac{1}{Pe_m}\frac{d\alpha_i(0)}{dz} \qquad (i = 1, \ldots, N) \tag{28}$$

$$B_{q,1}\theta := \theta(0) - \frac{1}{Pe_q}\frac{d\theta(0)}{dz} \tag{29}$$

$$B_{m,2}\alpha_i := \frac{d\alpha_i(1)}{dz} \qquad (i = 1, \ldots, N) \tag{30}$$

$$B_{q,2}\theta := \frac{d\theta(1)}{dz} \tag{31}$$

Then, Equations 20 and 21 and Conditions 22–25 can be written as

$$L_m\alpha_i = -\varphi_i(\alpha_i, \theta), \qquad (i = 1, \ldots, N) \tag{32}$$

$$L_q\theta = -\varphi_{N+1}(\alpha_i, \theta) \tag{33}$$

$$B_{m,j}\alpha_i = 0 \qquad (i = 1, \ldots, N;\ j = 1, 2) \tag{34a}$$

$$B_{q,j}\theta = 0 \qquad (j = 1, 2) \tag{34b}$$

where

$$\varphi_i(\alpha_i, \theta) = \tau r_i(\alpha_i, \theta) \qquad (i = 1, \ldots, N) \tag{35}$$

$$\varphi_{N+1}(\alpha_i, \theta) = \tau \sum_{i=1}^{N} \eta_i r_i(\alpha_i, \theta) - Q(\theta - \theta_q) \tag{36}$$

The use of vector notation in the dependences (32–36) gives

$$L_n y = -\Phi(y) \tag{37}$$

$$B_{n,j} y(\partial z) = 0 \tag{38}$$

where

$$y = [\alpha_1, \ldots, \alpha_N, \theta]^T \tag{39}$$

$$\Phi = [\varphi_1, \ldots, \varphi_{N+1}]^T$$

$$n = \begin{cases} m, & \text{for } i \in [1, N] \\ q, & \text{for } i = N + 1 \end{cases} \tag{40}$$

and $\partial z = 0$ or $\partial z = 1$

The method of Green function lies in finding such an operator L^{-1} for which the solution of the differential problem (37, 38) can be presented by equality

$$y = L^{-1}(-\Phi) \tag{41}$$

A way of deriving such an operator is given here. For this purpose let us define the following inner product

$$(G_n | L_n y) := \int_0^1 G_n(\xi, z) L_n y(\xi)\, d\xi \tag{42}$$

where $G_n(\xi, z)$ is the so-called Green function of differential operator L_n. It is a function determined in the square $0 \le \xi, z \le 1$.

The differential operator analyzed in this work has the following form

$$L_n = \frac{1}{Pe_n} \frac{d^2}{d\xi^2} - \frac{d}{d\xi} \qquad (n = m, q)$$

Introducing it into Equation 42 and integrating by parts, using homogeneous boundary conditions (38) give

$$\begin{aligned} \int_0^1 G_n(\xi, z) L_n y(\xi)\, d\xi &= \int_0^1 G_n(\xi, z)\left(\frac{1}{Pe_n}\frac{d^2 y}{d\xi^2} - \frac{dy}{d\xi}\right) d\xi \\ &= \frac{1}{Pe_n}\frac{\partial G_n(0, z)}{\partial \xi} y(0) - \left[G_n(1, z) + \frac{1}{Pe_n}\frac{\partial G_n(1, z)}{\partial \xi}\right] y(1) \\ &\quad + \int_0^1 y(\xi)\left(\frac{1}{Pe_n}\frac{\partial^2 G_n}{\partial \xi^2} + \frac{\partial G_n}{\partial \xi}\right) d\xi \end{aligned} \tag{43}$$

As follows from the form of the analyzed differential problem, values y(0) and y(1) are not defined, nevertheless they can be eliminated by requirements

$$\frac{\partial G_n(0, z)}{\partial \xi} = 0 \tag{44}$$

$$Pe_n G_n(1, z) + \frac{\partial G_n(1, z)}{\partial \xi} = 0 \tag{45}$$

Thus, Equation 43 can be written down by formula

$$\int_0^1 G_n(\xi, z) L y(\xi)\, d\xi = \int_0^1 y(\xi) L_n^* G_n(\xi, z)\, d\xi \tag{46}$$

where L_n^* is on operator adjoint with differential operator L_n.

If equation

$$L_n^* G_n(\xi, z) = \delta(\xi - z) \tag{47}$$

is required to be satisfied then consistently with the properties of Dirac distribution we get

$$\int_0^1 y(\xi) L_n^* G_n(\xi, z)\, d\xi = \int_0^1 y(\xi)\delta(\xi - z)\, d\xi = y(z) \tag{48}$$

which is the right side of Equation 46. The use of Equation 37 in the left side of Equation 46 gives an integral equation of basic, for the presented method importance, i.e.

$$\int_0^1 G_n(\xi, z)[-\Phi(y(\xi))]\, d\xi = y(z) \tag{49}$$

The comparison of Equations 41 and 49 leads to the conclusion that the obtained Hammerstein operator F is the searched inverse operator

$$F(y) := \int_0^1 G_n(\xi, z)[-\Phi(y(\xi))]\, d\xi \tag{50}$$

whose kernel is Green function. As could be expected, it is an integral operator. Thus the solution of the system of Equation 37 with Boundary Conditions 38 is reduced to the solution of operational equation

$$y(z) = F[y(z)] \tag{51}$$

where

$$F = \begin{bmatrix} F_1 & 0 & 0 & \dots & 0 \\ 0 & F_2 & 0 & \dots & 0 \\ \dots & \dots & \dots & \dots & \dots \\ 0 & 0 & 0 & \dots & F_{N+1} \end{bmatrix} \tag{52}$$

integral operators F_i being defined by dependences

$$F_i(\alpha_i) = \int_0^1 G_m(\xi, z)[-\varphi_i(\alpha_1(\xi), \dots, \alpha_N(\xi), \theta(\xi))]\, d\xi \qquad (i = 1, \dots, N) \tag{53}$$

$$F_{N+1}(\theta) = \int_0^1 G_q(\xi, z)[-\varphi_{N+1}(\alpha_1(\xi), \dots, \alpha_N(\xi), \theta(\xi))]\, d\xi \tag{54}$$

In order to determine Green function, i.e. the kernel of integral operator (Equation 50), Equation 47 was used

$$\frac{1}{Pe_n}\frac{\partial^2 G_n(\xi, z)}{\partial \xi^2} + \frac{\partial G_n(\xi, z)}{\partial \xi} = \delta(\xi - z) \tag{55}$$

Since $\forall_{\xi \neq z}\ \delta(\xi - z) = 0$, it is convenient to split the integral range into two parts in each which $L_n^* G_n = 0$.

The solution of Equation 55 using this property leads to dependence

$$G_n(\xi, z) = \begin{cases} A\exp(-Pe_n\xi) + B, & 0 \le \xi < z \\ C\exp(-Pe_n\xi) + D, & z < \xi \le 1 \end{cases} \tag{56}$$

To determine four constants A, B, C and D four equations are needed. Two of these are provided by Conditions 44 and 45 introduced before. Two others follow from the requirement of Green function continuity, which matches the left and right branches of function G_n at point $\xi = z$. The corresponding conditions securing the continuity will be obtained by the integration of Equation 55 in the interval from "z − 0" to "z + 0":

$$\int_{z-0}^{z+0}\left(\frac{1}{Pe_n}\frac{\partial^2 G_n(\xi, z)}{\partial \xi^2} + \frac{G_n(\xi, z)}{\partial \xi}\right) = \int_{z-0}^{z+0} \delta(\xi - z)\, d\xi \tag{57}$$

The integration gives the third equation for determination of the constants, i.e.

$$\frac{1}{Pe_n}\frac{\partial}{\partial \xi} G_n(\xi, z)\Big|_{z-0}^{z+0} + G_n(\xi, z)\Big|_{z-0}^{z+0} = 1 \tag{58}$$

The fourth equation is constituted by the condition of function $G_n(\xi, z)$ continuity at point $\xi = z$

$$G_n(\xi, z)\Big|_{z-0}^{z+0} = 0 \tag{59}$$

which also reduces to zero the second term on the left side of Equation 58.

The use of Conditions 44, 45, 58, and 59 results in a corresponding system of linear equations

$$-Pe_n A = 0 \tag{60a}$$

$$Pe_n D = 0 \tag{60b}$$

$$A\exp(-Pe_n z) - C\exp(-Pe_n z) = 1 \tag{60c}$$

$$A\exp(-Pe_n z) + B - C\exp(-Pe_n z) - D = 0 \tag{60d}$$

Its solution gives the following values of integration constants

$$A = 0, \quad B = -1, \quad C = -\exp(Pe_n z), \quad D = 0 \tag{61}$$

The Green function will finally have the form

$$G_n(\xi, z) = \begin{cases} -1, & 0 \le \xi < z \\ -\exp[Pe_n(z - \xi)], & z < \xi \le 1 \end{cases} \tag{62}$$

Introducing it into Equation 49 makes it possible to determine the state reactor y(z).

It should be stressed that the system of integral Equations 49 can have several solutions, which means that there may be realized multiple steady states in the analyzed reactor.

Application of the Method

The application of the method of homotopy in solving a system of N + 1 integral equations lies in a mechanical use of Equation 7 for each of the equations.

Let $y_{i,k}(z)$ means the k-th approximation of i-th component of state vector y. Then k + 1 approximation is determined by dependences

$$y_{i,k+1} = [1 - t_{i,k}(z)]y_{i,k}(z) + t_{i,k}(z) \int_0^1 G_n(\xi, z)\varphi_i[y_k(z)]\, d\xi \qquad (i = 1, \ldots, N + 1) \tag{63}$$

To simplify the considerations and notations, in the example below the occurrence of a single first order chemical reaction was assumed. The kinetic equation of such a single reaction (i = N = 1) has the form

$$r_A(\alpha_A, \theta) = k_0 \exp\left(-\frac{E}{RT_f(1 + \theta)}\right)(1 - \alpha_A) \tag{64}$$

where $\alpha_A = (C_{Af} - C_A)/C_{Af}$ is a degree of conversion of reference substrate A.

In Table 1 the values of the model parameters were shown for which calculations were done to determine degree of conversion and temperature profiles in the analyzed reactor.

The calculations were done by iteration using Equation 63, while topological parameter t(z) was calculated according to Equations 10 and 11. The integration was done by Simpson method, and the values of state vector y(z) at certain points in the range $z \in [0, 1]$ were stored in working tables.

Calculations were stopped when condition

$$\frac{\|y_{k+1}(z) - y_k(z)\|}{\|y_{k+1}(z)\|} < 0.002 \tag{65}$$

was fulfilled.

In Figure 1 the results of the calculations were presented.

In order to check the convergence region of the homotopy method (Equation 7) and simple iteration (Equation 6) several numerical experiments were carried out. The results are illustrated in Figure 2. It turns out that the convergence range of homotopy method covers the whole plane $(\tau, \Delta T_{ad})$, while the convergence region of simple iteration becomes narrower with the increase of the mean residence time τ or adiabatic temperature rise ΔT_{ad}. For example, the results shown in Figure 1 could not be achieved by means of a simple iteration method.

As it is known, the convergent sequence in a metric space can have only one limit. Therefore, the method of homotopy discussed here in the range of multiple steady states is convergent towards

Table 1
Values of Model Parameters for Tubular Reactor with Axial Mixing

Parameter	Value	Unit
E	6. E 04	kJ/kmol
k_0	2. E 06	1/s
Pe_m, Pe_q	10–20	—
Q	2	—
T_f	360	K
T_q	360	K
ΔT_{ad}	20–400	K
τ	5–300	s

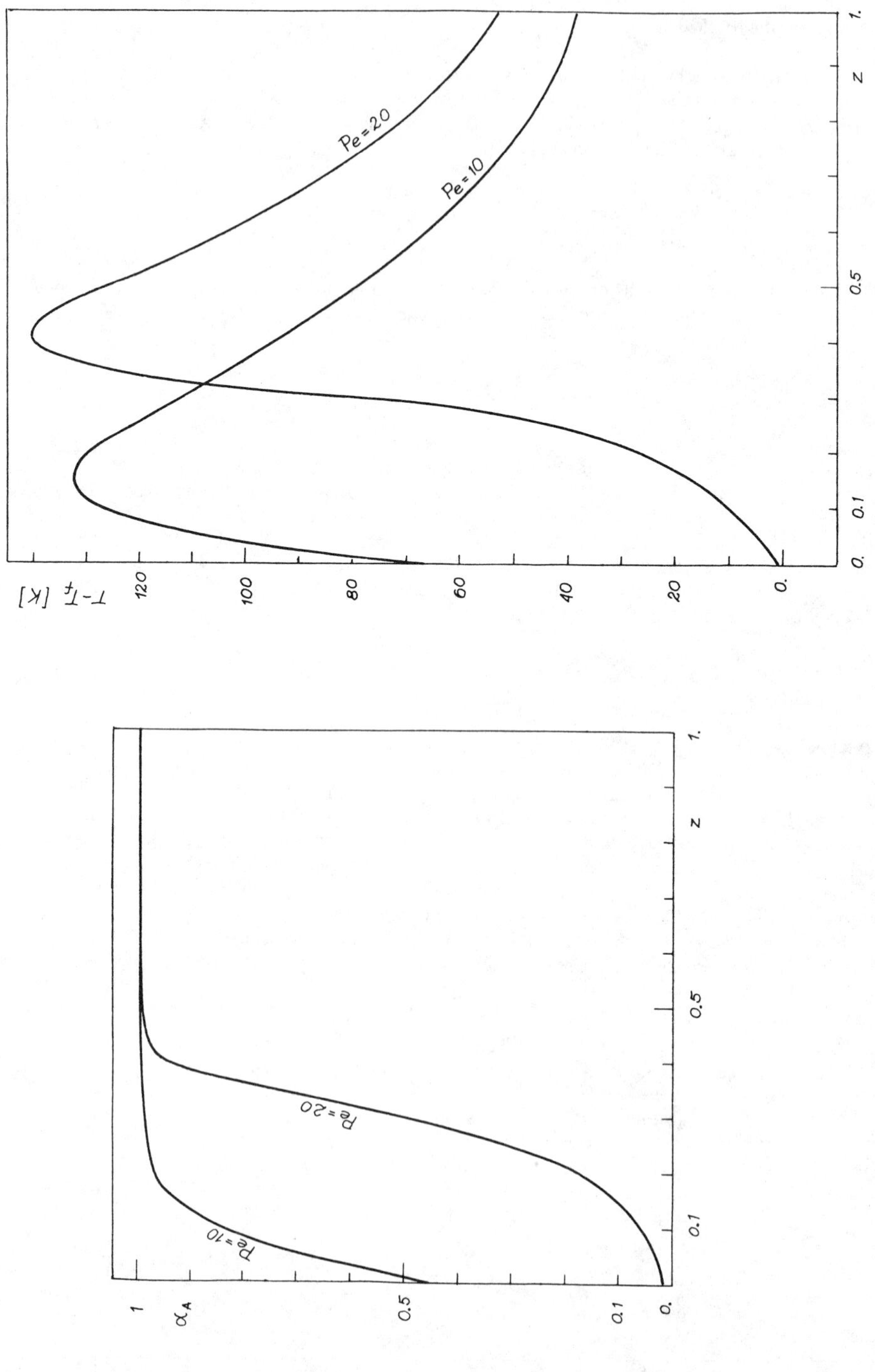

Figure 1. Degree of conversion and temperature rise profiles in polytropic tubular reactor with axial mixing for various Peclet number ($\Delta T_{ad} = 200$ K, $\tau = 60$ s).

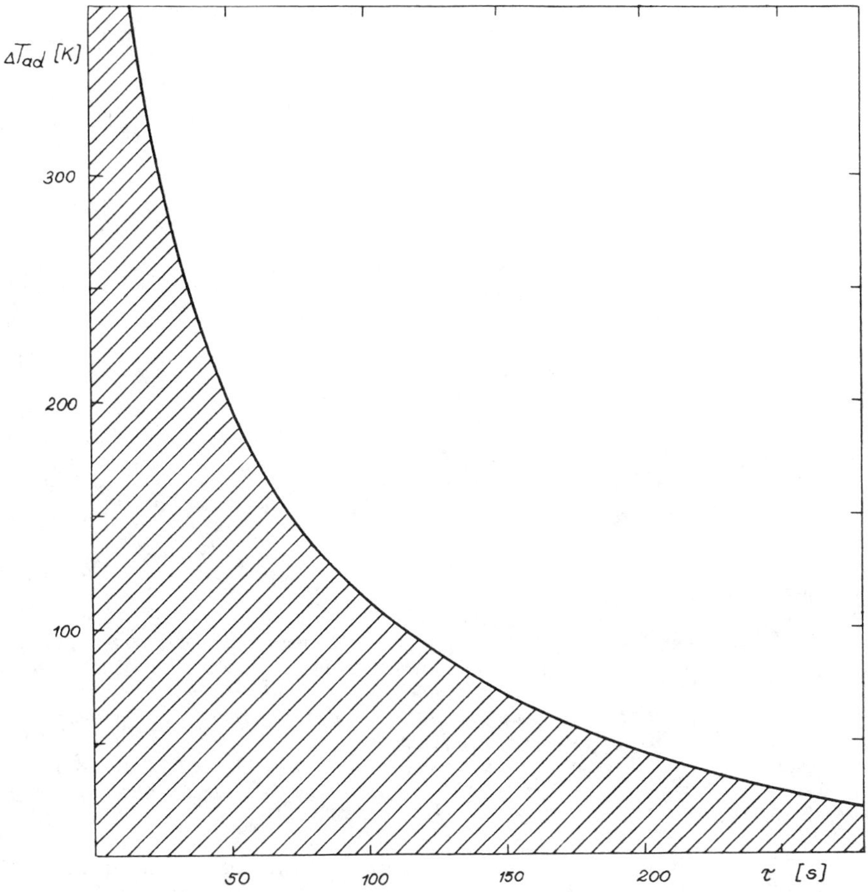

Figure 2. Convergence region of the method of simple iteration (hatched area) and that of homotopy (whole plane) for $Pe_m = Pe_q = 10$. (Values of the other parameters as in Table 1.)

one limit, which is the lower steady state. This property of the method was documented by means of numerical experiments and presented in Figure 3.

CATALYTIC FLUIDIZED BED REACTOR

Mathematical Model of the Reactor and Boundary Conditions

From among numerous models of a fluidized bed the bubble models have become the most popular. This group of models includes Rowe-Partridge [10], Calderbank-Toor [11], Kunii-Levenspiel [12], Kato-Wen [13] and Potter [14] models.

Several experiments have been carried out to verify these models. Chavarie and Grace [15] have compared the distribution of selected component concentration in the fluidized bed found experimentally with that obtained by calculations. The experimental data and the calculated ones were most compatible in case of Kunii-Levenspiel model.

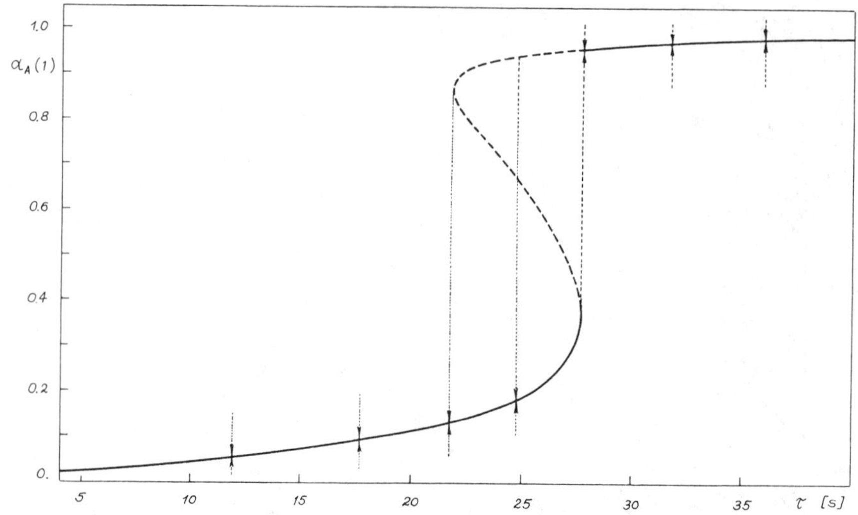

Figure 3. Illustration of convergence of homotopy method in the region of unique and multiple steady states.

The Kunii-Levenspiel model, moreover, has an important advantage from the aspect of calculation. Namely, on the basis of familiarity with physicochemical properties of the fluidizing factor and the granular material as well as the single adjustable parameter, which is the effective bubble diameter, it is possible to determine the values of the other parameters of the model. These properties of the Kunii-Levenspiel model have decided of its popularity [16].

The Kunii-Levenspiel model assumes the existence of three zones called phases: the bubble phase, the cloud and wake phase, and the emulsion phase. A structural diagram of the whole fluidized bed has been shown in Figure 4. The diagram is a basis for the derivation of a mathematical model of the reactor.

The catalytic process in a nonadiabatic fluidized bed reactor is analyzed. Considering the assumptions of Kunii-Levenspiel model and assuming occurrence of N linear independent chemical reaction pseudohomogeneous with respect to the catalyst, we obtain for the steady state

$$\frac{d\alpha_i^b}{dz} = a_2 W_1 r_i(\alpha_i^b, T^b) + B_{1i}(\alpha_i^c - \alpha_i^b) \tag{66}$$

$$\frac{dT^b}{dz} = a_3 W_1 \sum_{i=1}^{N} \Delta T_{ad,i} r_i(\alpha_i^b, T^b) + B_2(T^c - T^b) - Q_1(T^b - T_q) \tag{67}$$

$$\frac{d\alpha_i^c}{dz} = a_4 W_1 r_i(\alpha_i^c, T^c) + B_{3i}(\alpha_i^e - \alpha_i^c) - B_{4i}(\alpha_i^c - \alpha_i^b) \tag{68}$$

$$\frac{dT^c}{dz} = W_2 \sum_{i=1}^{N} \Delta T_{ad,i} r_i(\alpha_i^c, T^c) + B_5(T^e - T^c) - B_6(T^c - T^b) - Q_2(T^c - T_q) \tag{69}$$

$$\frac{d\alpha_i^e}{dz} = a_4 W_3 r_i(\alpha_i^e, T^e) - B_{7i}(\alpha_i^e - \alpha_i^c) \tag{70}$$

$$\frac{dT^e}{dz} = 0 \tag{71}$$

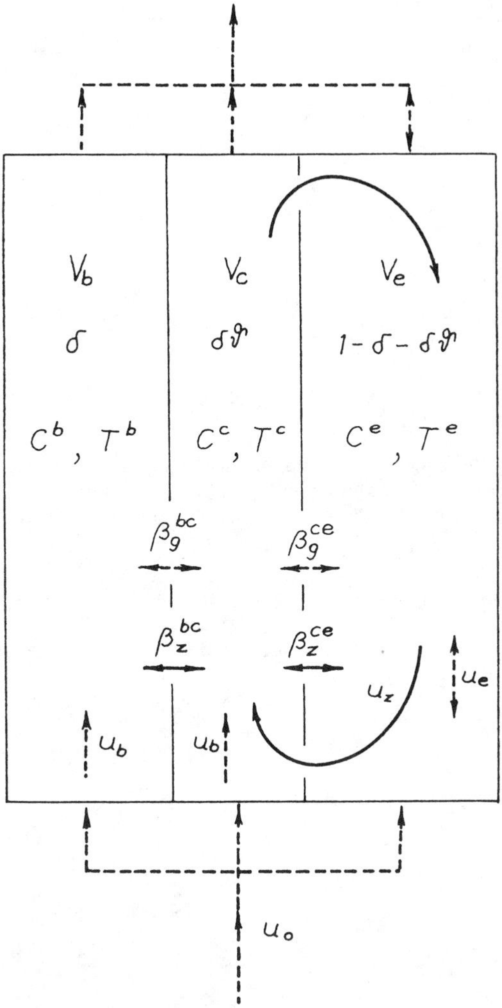

Figure 4. Structural diagram of the whole fluidized bed: movement of gas (- - - - - -); movement of solid particles (——).

where

$$\alpha_i^j = \frac{C_{if} - C_i^j}{C_{if}} \qquad (i = 1, \ldots, N; j = b, c, e)$$

$$z = \frac{x}{H}, \qquad H = \frac{H_{mf}}{1-\delta}$$

$$a_1 = \frac{\rho_z c_z}{\rho_g c_g}, \qquad a_2 = \frac{\gamma}{1-\gamma}, \qquad a_3 = \frac{\gamma}{1-\gamma+a_1\gamma}, \qquad a_4 = \frac{1-\varepsilon_{mf}}{\varepsilon_{mf}}$$

$$B_{1i} = \frac{H_{mf}\beta_{gi}^{bc}}{(1-\gamma)u_b(1-\delta)}, \qquad B_2 = \frac{H_{mf}\left(\dfrac{\alpha_q^{bc}}{\rho_g c_g} + \beta_z^{bc} a_1\right)}{(1-\gamma+a_1\gamma)u_b(1-\delta)}$$

$$B_{3i} = \frac{H_{mf}\beta_{gi}^{ce}}{\vartheta\varepsilon_{mf}u_b(1-\delta)}, \qquad B_{4i} = \frac{H_{mf}\beta_{gi}^{bc}}{\vartheta\varepsilon_{mf}u_b(1-\delta)}$$

$$B_5 = \frac{H_{mf}\left(\frac{\alpha_q^{ce}}{\rho_g c_g} + \beta_z^{ce}a_1\right)}{\vartheta(1-\delta)u_b[\varepsilon_{mf} + (1-\varepsilon_{mf})a_1]}, \qquad B_6 = \frac{H_{mf}\left(\frac{\alpha_q^{bc}}{\rho_g c_g} + \beta_z^{bc}a_1\right)}{\vartheta(1-\delta)u_b[\varepsilon_{mf} + (1-\varepsilon_{mf})a_1]}$$

$$B_{7i} = \frac{H_{mf}\delta\beta_{gi}^{ce}}{(1-\delta-\delta\vartheta)\varepsilon_{mf}u_e(1-\delta)}, \qquad Q_1 = \frac{H_{mf}a_q k_q}{(1-\gamma+a_1\gamma)u_b(1-\delta)\rho_g c_g}$$

$$Q_2 = \frac{H_{mf}a_q k_q}{(1-\delta)u_b[\varepsilon_{mf} + (1-\varepsilon_{mf})a_1]\rho_g c_g}, \qquad \Delta T_{ad,i} = \frac{(-\Delta H_i)C_{fi}}{\rho_g c_g}$$

$$W_1 = \frac{H_{mf}}{u_b(1-\delta)}, \qquad W_2 = \frac{H_{mf}(1-\varepsilon_{mf})}{(1-\delta)u_b[\varepsilon_{mf} + (1-\varepsilon_{mf})a_1]}, \qquad W_3 = \frac{H_{mf}}{u_e(1-\delta)}$$

The boundary conditions connected with the model of the reactor interior (Equations 66–71) are derived on the basis of the analysis of fluidized bed behavior on both reactor edges. There are two subsets of boundary conditions depending on the flow direction of the gas in the emulsion phase;

For $u_e > 0$ (i.e., for low fluidization ratio)

$$\alpha_i^b(0) = \alpha_i^c(0) = \alpha_i^e(0) = 0, \qquad (i = 1, \ldots, N) \tag{72}$$

$$T^b(0) = T_f \tag{73}$$

$$T^c(0) = a_5 T^b(0) + a_6 T^e \tag{74}$$

For $u_e < 0$ (i.e., for high fluidization ratio)

$$\alpha_i^b(0) = 0, \qquad (i = 1, \ldots, N) \tag{75}$$

$$\alpha_i^c(0) + a_7\alpha_i^e(0) = 0 \tag{76}$$

$$T^b(0) = T_f \tag{77}$$

$$T^c(0) = a_5 T^b(0) + a_6 T^e \tag{78}$$

$$a_8\alpha_i^b(1) + a_9\alpha_i^c(1) = \alpha_i^e(1), \qquad (i = 1, \ldots, N) \tag{79}$$

where

$$a_5 = \frac{u_0 - u_b\delta}{u_b\delta\vartheta[\varepsilon_{mf} + (1-\varepsilon_{mf})a_1]}, \qquad a_6 = \frac{(1-\delta-\delta\vartheta)[u_z(1-\varepsilon_{mf})a_1 - u_e\varepsilon_{mf}]}{u_b\delta\vartheta[\varepsilon_{mf} + (1-\varepsilon_{mf})a_1]}$$

$$a_7 = \frac{(1-\delta-\delta\vartheta)u_e}{u_b\delta\vartheta}, \qquad a_8 = \frac{1-\gamma}{1-\gamma+\vartheta\varepsilon_{mf}}, \qquad a_9 = 1 - a_8$$

The emulsion temperature T^e for the reactor operating at steady state is determined by roots of the equation

$$\sigma(T^e) = T_f + \sum_{i=1}^{N} \Delta T_{ad,i}\bar{\alpha}_i(1) - \bar{T}(1) - Q\,\Delta T_m = 0 \tag{80}$$

where

$$\bar{\alpha}_i(1) = \begin{cases} a_{10}\alpha_i^b(1) + a_{11}\alpha_i^c(1) + a_{12}\alpha_i^e(1), & \text{for } u_e > 0 \\ a_8\alpha_i^b(1) + a_9\alpha_i^c(1), & \text{for } u_e < 0 \end{cases}$$

$$\bar{T}(1) = \begin{cases} a_{10}T^b(1) + a_{11}T^c(1) + a_{12}T^e, & \text{for } u_e > 0 \\ a_8T^b(1) + a_9T^c(1), & \text{for } u_e < 0 \end{cases}$$

$$\Delta T_m = \delta \int_0^1 (T^b(z) - T_q)\,dz + \delta\vartheta \int_0^1 (T^c(z) - T_q)\,dz + (1 - \delta - \delta\vartheta)(T^e - T_q)$$

and

$$a_{10} = \frac{u_b\delta(1-\gamma)}{u_b\delta[(1-\gamma) + \vartheta\varepsilon_{mf}] + u_e(1 - \delta - \delta\vartheta)\varepsilon_{mf}}$$

$$a_{11} = \frac{u_b\delta\vartheta\varepsilon_{mf}}{u_b\delta[(1-\gamma) + \vartheta\varepsilon_{mf}] + u_e(1 - \delta - \delta\vartheta)\varepsilon_{mf}}$$

$$a_{12} = 1 - a_{10} - a_{11}, \qquad Q = \frac{H_{mf}a_q k_q}{(1-\delta)u_0\rho_g c_g}$$

The system of Equations 66–71 together with Conditions 72–74 or 75–79 is a difficult numerical problem. Numerical computations show that the Equations 66–71 have a high stiffness ratio. Moreover, for $u_e < 0$, the differential problem of Equations 66–70 with Equations 75–79 becomes an ill-conditioned problem. This leads to divergence of numerical integration procedures.

In this section, an indirect method of solving the obtained boundary value problem is proposed. In this method, first the original differential problem is transformed into a set of integral equations, next these equations are solved by a modified iterative procedure.

Transformation of a Boundary Value Problem into a Set of Integral Equations

The afore-mentioned transformation can be done in several ways. This section presents the method providing the fastest convergence in the process of iterative computation of steady states. According to this method, the system of Equations 66–70 should be transformed into the form

$$\frac{d\alpha_i^b}{dz} + B_{1i}\alpha_i^b = \varphi_n(\alpha_i^b, T^b, \alpha_i^c), \qquad (n = 1, \ldots, N) \tag{81}$$

$$\frac{dT^b}{dz} + (B_2 + Q_1)T^b = \varphi_n(\alpha_i^b, T^b, T^c), \qquad (n = N + 1) \tag{82}$$

$$\frac{d\alpha_i^c}{dz} + (B_{3i} + B_{4i})\alpha_i^c = \varphi_n(\alpha_i^b, \alpha_i^c, \alpha_i^e), \qquad (n = N + 2, \ldots, 2N + 1) \tag{83}$$

$$\frac{dT^c}{dz} + (B_5 + B_6 + Q_2)T^c = \varphi_n(\alpha_i^c, T^b, T^c, T^e), \qquad (n = 2N + 2) \tag{84}$$

$$\frac{d\alpha_i^e}{dz} + B_{7i}\alpha_i^e = \varphi_n(\alpha_i^c, \alpha_i^e, T^e), \qquad (n = 2N + 3, \ldots, 3N + 2) \tag{85}$$

In Equations 81–85 functions φ_n ($n = 1, \ldots, 3N + 2$) are non-linear residuals that remain after transposition of linear terms of the state vector onto the left side of Equations 66–70.

Using matrix notation in these dependences we receive

$$Ly(z) = \Phi[y(z)] \tag{86}$$

where

$$y = [y_1, \ldots, y_{3N+2}]^T = [\alpha_1^b, \ldots, \alpha_N^b, T^b, \alpha_1^c, \ldots, T^c, \alpha_1^e, \ldots, \alpha_N^e]^T$$

$$\Phi = [\varphi_1(y), \ldots, \varphi_{3N+2}(y)]^T$$

and

$$L = \begin{bmatrix} L_1 & 0 & \cdots & 0 \\ 0 & L_2 & \cdots & 0 \\ \cdots & \cdots & \cdots & \cdots \\ 0 & 0 & & L_{3N+2} \end{bmatrix}$$

In this kind of transformation, all the linear differential operators L_n have the same form, namely

$$L_n = \frac{d}{dz} + b_n \qquad (n = 1, \ldots, 3N + 2) \tag{87}$$

Let us define the following interior product

$$(G_n | L_n y_n) := \int_0^1 G_n(\xi, z) L_n y_n(\xi)\, d\xi \tag{88}$$

where $G_n(\xi, z)$ is a so-called Green function of differential operator L_n. It is a function determined in the square $0 \le \xi, z \le 1$.

The application of Equation 87 of operator L_n in Equation 88 and integration by parts gives

$$\begin{aligned} \int_0^1 G_n(\xi, z) L_n y_n(\xi)\, d\xi &= \int_0^1 G_n(\xi, z)\left(\frac{dy_n}{d\xi} + b_n y_n\right) d\xi \\ &= G_n(1, z)y_n(1) - G_n(0, z)y_n(0) \\ &\quad + \int_0^1 y_n(\xi)\left(b_n G_n - \frac{\partial G_n}{\partial \xi}\right) d\xi \end{aligned} \tag{89}$$

Let us next assume that

$$G_n(1, z) = 0 \qquad \text{for } y_n \text{ determined at } z = 0, \tag{90a}$$

$$G_n(0, z) = 0 \qquad \text{for } y_n \text{ determined at } z = 1, \tag{90b}$$

Using Equation 86, Equation 89 can be written as

$$\int_0^1 G_n(\xi, z)\varphi_n[y(\xi)]\, d\xi = \begin{cases} -G_n(0, z)y_n(0) + \int_0^1 y_n(\xi) L_n^* G_n(\xi, z)\, d\xi & \text{(91a)} \\ G_n(1, z)y_n(1) + \int_0^1 y_n(\xi) L_n^* G_n(\xi, z)\, d\xi & \text{(91b)} \end{cases}$$

where Equation 91a corresponds to the Equation 90a, Equation 91b to Equation 90b, while L_n^* is on operator adjoint with differential operator L_n.

If it is required to satisfy the equation

$$L_n^* G_n(\xi, z) = \delta(\xi - z) \tag{92}$$

then, consistently with Dirac distribution, we get respectively

$$y_n(z) = G_n(0, z)y_n(0) + \int_0^1 G_n(\xi, z)\varphi_n[y(\xi)]\, d\xi \qquad (n = 1, \ldots, 2N + 2) \tag{93a}$$

and

$$y_n(z) = -G_n(1, z)y_n(1) + \int_0^1 G_n(\xi, z)\varphi_n[y(\xi)]\, d\xi \qquad (n = 2N + 3, \ldots, 3N + 2) \tag{93b}$$

According to Equation 71, $T^e(z) = T^e$ = idem, so Equation 93b refers only to the degrees of conversion profiles in the emulsion phase for $u_e < 0$. The other profiles can be described by integral Equation 93a.

In order to determine the Green functions occurring in integral Equation(s) 93, Equation 92 has been used. The searched functions have been defined separately for both cases previously discussed. Thus for $y_n(0) = y_n^0$, consistent with 92, we have

$$b_n G_n(\xi, z) - \frac{\partial G_n(\xi, z)}{\partial \xi} = \delta(\xi - z), \qquad G_n(1, z) = 0 \tag{94}$$

and with given $y_n(0) = y_n^0$ function $G_n(0, z)$ has such property that

$$G_n(0, 0) = 1 \tag{95}$$

Using Laplace transformation on both sides of Equation 94 in relation to variable ξ, we get in the image space

$$b_n \bar{G}_n(s, z) - s\bar{G}_n(s, z) + G_n(0, z) = e^{-zs} \tag{96}$$

hence

$$\bar{G}_n(s, z) = \frac{G_n(0, z)}{s - b_n} - \frac{e^{-zs}}{s - b_n} \tag{97}$$

Application of inverse transformation in Equation 97 and use of Equation 95 gives

$$G_n(\xi, z) = \exp[b_n(\xi - z)][1 - 1(\xi - z)] \tag{98}$$

Whereas for $y_n(1) = y_n^1$ function $G_n(1, z)$ has such property that

$$G_n(1, 1) = -1 \tag{99}$$

Since in this case $G_n(0, 0) = 0$, proceeding as above, we get Green function in the form

$$G_n(\xi, z) = -\exp[b_n(\xi - z)]1(\xi - z) \tag{100}$$

Let us notice that the Equation(s) 93 can now be written by means of the following integral equations

$$y_n(z) = G_n(0, z)y_n(0) + \int_0^z \exp[b_n(\xi - z)]\varphi_n[y(\xi)]\, d\xi \qquad (n = 1, \ldots, 2N + 2) \tag{101a}$$

$$y_n(z) = -G_n(1, z)y_n(1) + \int_z^1 \exp[b_n(\xi - z)]\varphi_n[y(\xi)]\, d\xi \qquad (n = 2N + 3, \ldots, 3N + 2) \tag{101b}$$

Using matrix form to shorten the notation we get

$$y(z) = G(\partial z, z)y(\partial z) + \int_0^1 G(\xi, z)\Phi[y(\xi)]\, d\xi$$
$$= G(\partial z, z)y(\partial z) + V[y(z)] = F[y(z)] \qquad (102)$$

where $\partial z = 0$ or $\partial z = 1$.

Application of Homotopy Method in Fluidized Bed Reactor Computation

Let $y_{n,k}(z)$ denote k-th approximation of n-th component of a state vector y(z). Then for each determined value of emulsion temperature T^e, k + 1 approximation is defined by

For $u_e > 0$

$$y_{n,k+1}(z) = [1 - t_{n,k}(z)]y_{n,k}(z) + t_{n,k}(z)\left[G_n(0, z)y_n(0) + \int_0^z G_n(\xi, z)\varphi_n(y_k)\, d\xi\right],$$

$$(n = 1, \ldots, 3N + 2) \qquad (103)$$

For $u_e < 0$

$$y_{n,k+1}(z) = [1 - t_{n,k}(z)]y_{n,k}(z) + t_{n,k}(z)\left[G_n(0, z)y_{n,k}(0) + \int_0^z G_n(\xi, z)\varphi_n(y_k)\, d\xi\right],$$

$$(n = 1, \ldots, 2N + 2) \qquad (104a)$$

$$y_{n,k+1}(z) = [1 - t_{n,k}(z)]y_{n,k}(z) + t_{n,k}(z)\left[\int_z^1 G_n(\xi, z)\varphi_n(y_k)\, d\xi - G_n(1, z)y_{n,k}(1)\right],$$

$$(n = 2N + 3, \ldots, 3N + 2) \qquad (104b)$$

If the following condition is satisfied

$$|\sigma(T^e)| < \Delta$$

where Δ is the required accuracy of computation, then the chosen value of T^e determines the emulsion temperature with accuracy $\pm\Delta$, corresponding to the steady state. Otherwise, the corrected value T^e is assumed and computations are done along the described algorithm. To determine successive values T^e one of the methods of finding zeros of function $\sigma(T^e)$ can be used.

In Figure 5 the regions of convergence have been shown for the simple iteration method (Equation 6) and for the process using homotopy (Equation 7) in which functional parameters $t_n(z)$ have been calculated from Equations 10 and 11.

The results shown in Figure 5 have been obtained by numerical experiments that have been done for selected values of reactor operating parameters, assuming occurrence of a first order irreversible chemical reaction. The values of the model parameters are enclosed in Table 2.

It should be noted that applying the homotopy method to fluidized bed reactor computation makes it possible to determine the state vector for the regions of unique as well as multiple steady states. This means that in the region of multiple steady states it is possible to determine every steady state i.e., lower, middle, and higher steady states. This fact was illustrated in Figure 6.

CONCLUSION

A general method of determining degrees of conversion and temperature profiles in chemically reacting systems with distributed variables has been presented.

The application of this method has been illustrated using as an example a nonisothermal tubular reactor with longitudinal dispersion and nonisothermal catalytic fluidized bed reactor.

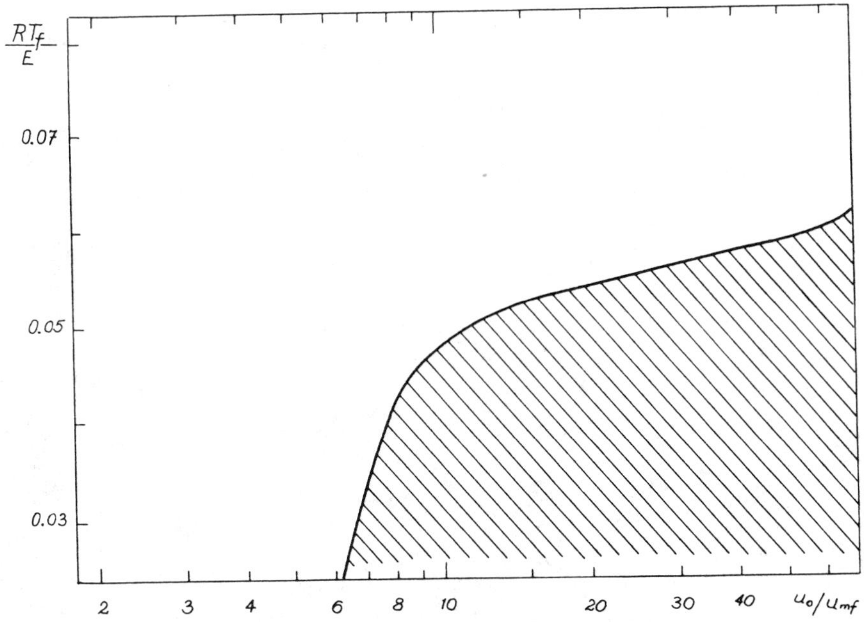

Figure 5. Convergence region of simple iteration method (hatched area) and that of homotopy (whole plane). (Parameters of the model as in Table 2.)

The analysis comprises a general case where in the chemically reacting system there may occur simultaneously a set of N linear independent chemical reactions of arbitrary stoichiometry and kinetics.

In this method first the original system of differential equations is transformed into a set of nonlinear integral equations. This stage has been presented in detail and a way of determining Green functions being kernels of the obtained integral operators has been given.

Table 2
Values of the Basic Model Parameters for Catalytic Fluidized Bed Reactor

Parameter	Value	Unit
a_1	550	—
$a_q k_q$	0.4	kJ/m^3 sK
E	7. E 04	kJ/kmol
H_{mf}	1	m
k_0	1. E 07	1/s
l_f	2–60	—
T_f	300–700	K
T_q	400	K
ΔT_{ad}	1200	K
u_{mf}	0.01	m/s
ε_{mf}	0.5	—

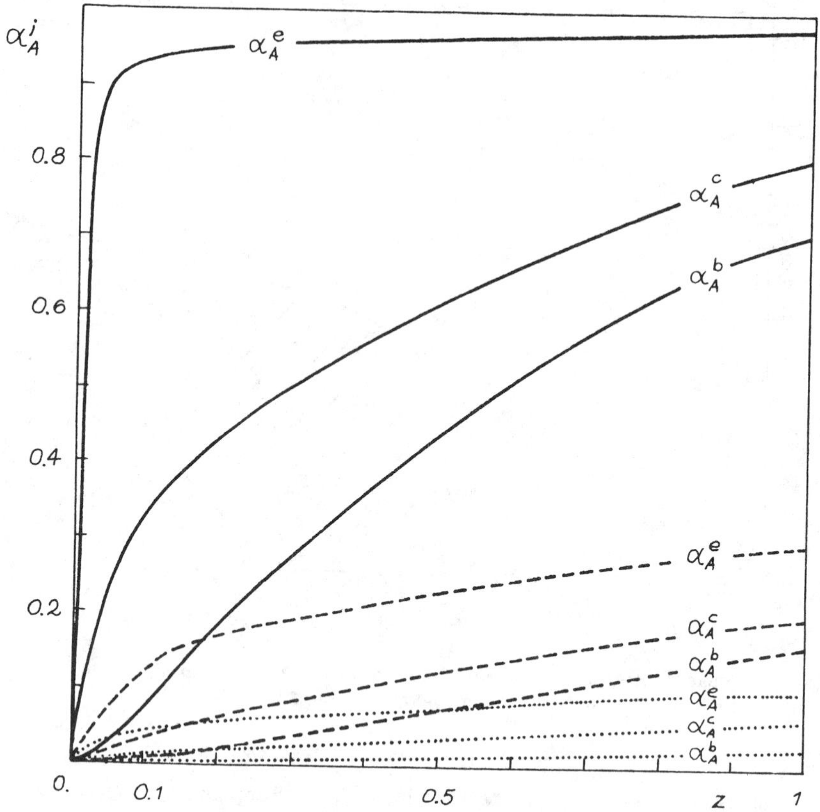

Figure 6. Degrees of conversion and temperature rise profiles in polytropic fluidized bed reactor for $I_f = 4$, $T_f = 300$ K. (Values of the other parameters as in Table 2.) ·········· lower steady state; ---------- intermediate steady state; ———— higher steady state.

In subsequent parts of the chapter an iterative method of solving a system of integral equations has been proposed. It makes use of topological concept of homotopy, the difference being that instead of a scalar parameter, a parameter that is a function of the reactor length has been used. A way of determining this parameter has been given.

To summarize, it can be stated that the presented homotopy method has the following advantages:

1. It is numerically stable.
2. It makes it possible to reduce significantly the number of net points in the range $z \in [0, 1]$ in comparison with method of direct integration of differential problems.
3. Iterative process of Equation 7 requires at least twice smaller number of iterations in comparison with Equation 6 in its convergence region.
4. It is a convergent method in a wide region of model parameters variation.
5. It has a high level of generality, i.e., it is applicable for a set of N linear independent chemical reactions of arbitrary stoichiometry and kinetics.
6. It can be used for iterative solving of both Voltera and Hammerstein nonlinear integral equations.

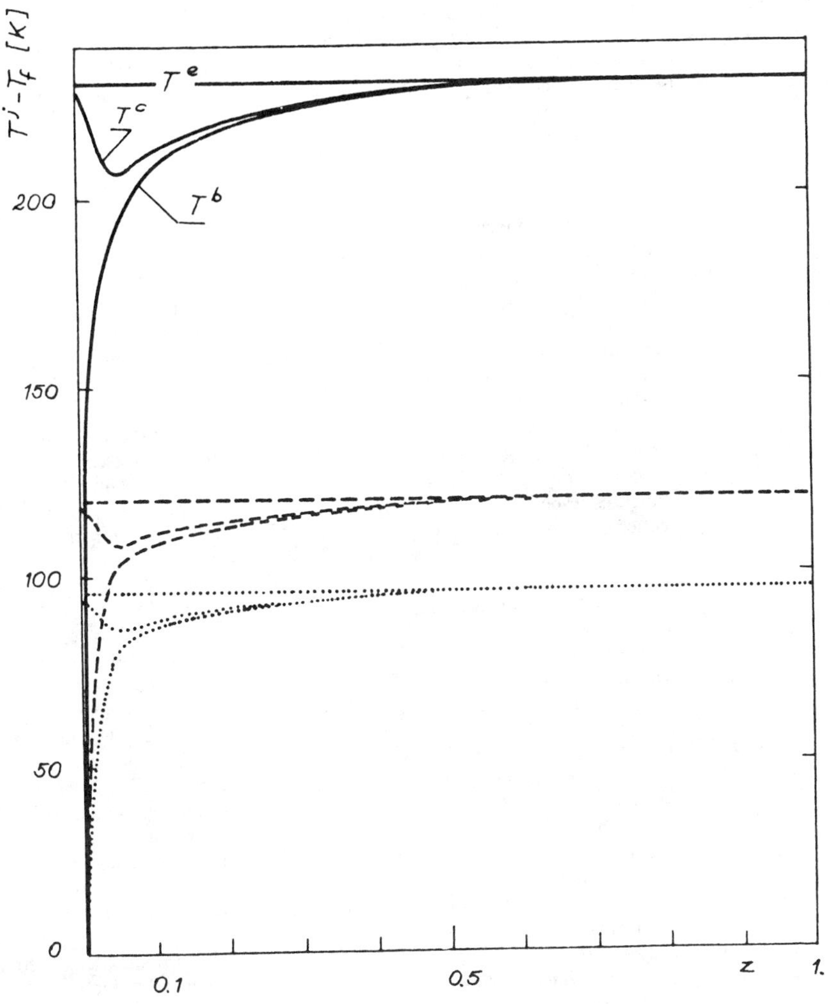

Figure 6. (Continued)

The transformation of differential problems into a set of integral equations can be justified as follows:

1. An integral equation includes the whole problem, i.e., both the description of the system interior and boundary or initial conditions as well.
2. Such transformation leads to achieving compact operators and Fredholm operators, which makes it possible to analyze the properties of these operators at a high level of generality.
3. It provides the possibility to construct uniqueness criteria of the steady states [17].
4. It allows the use of many approximation methods for solving integral equations.
5. In comparison with differential equations, integral equations are much less susceptible to numerical instability.

The practical application of the method for cases different from those discussed in the examples is reduced to the solution of an analogous system of integral equations, whose kernels are constituted by Green functions derived here. In particular cases only of the form of functions φ_i will be changed, because they depend mainly on stoichiometry and kinetics of chemical reactions occurring in a reactor.

NOTATION

a_i (i = 1, . . . , 12)	dimensionless model parameters
A_i (i = 1, . . . , N)	reference reactants
B_i (i = 1, . . . , 7)	dimensionless model parameters
B_m, B_q	boundary conditions operators connected with the model of tubular reactor with axial mixing
c_g, c_p, c_z	specific heat of gas, reaction mixture and catalyst particles respectively
C_i	concentration of reactant A_i
d_r	diameter of reactor
D_m, D_q	axial dispersion coefficients for mass and heat
E	activation energy
$G(\xi, z)$	Green function
$\bar{G}(s, z)$	image of Green function in complex space
H, H_{mf}	height of fluidized bed
ΔH_i	heat of the i-th chemical reaction
k_q	overall heat transfer coefficient
l_f	fluidization ratio, $l_f = u_0/u_{mf}$
L_n	linear differential operators
L_r	length of reactor
N	number of linear independent chemical reactions
Pe_m, Pe_q	Peclet numbers
Q, Q_i (i = 1, 2)	model parameters
r_i	rate of the i-th chemical reaction
R	gas constant
t	topological joining parameter
T	temperature in a homogeneous tubular reactor
T^j, T_f, T_q	the j-th phase, feed and cooling medium temperature, respectively
ΔT_{ad}	adiabatic temperature rise
u	mean linear velocity of fluid stream in tubular reactor
u_0	superficial gas velocity in fluidized bed reactor
u_b	rise velocity of a bubble, cloud, and wake
u_e	gas velocity within emulsion phase
u_{mf}	superficial gas velocity at minimum fluidization conditions
W_i (i = 1, . . . , 3)	model parameters
x	current coordinate of reactor length
y	state vector
z	dimensionless length coordinate of a reactor

Greek Symbols

α_i	degree of conversion of reference reactant A_i
α_q^{ij}	heat interchange coefficient between the phases i and j
β_g^{ij}, β_z^{ij}	gas and particles interchange coefficient between the phases i and j
γ	volume fraction of particles in a bubble
δ	volume fraction of bubbles in fluidized bed
ε_{mf}	void fraction of emulsion phase at minimum fluidization conditions
η	dimensionless adiabatic temperature rise
ϑ	volume of a cloud and wake per volume of a bubble
θ	dimensionless temperature in tubular reactor
λ_g	thermal conductivity of gas

ρ_g, ρ_p, ρ_z	density of gas, reaction mixture and catalyst particles, respectively
τ	mean residence time
$\delta(\xi - z)$	Dirac distribution
$1(\xi - z)$	Heaviside unit function

Superscripts

b, c, e	bubble, cloud-wake and emulsion phase, respectively

Subscripts

f	feed stream

REFERENCES

1. Aris, R., *Introduction to the Analysis of Chemical Reactors*, Prentice-Hall, Inc., Englewood Cliffs, N. Jersey 1965.
2. Lapidus, L., *Digital Computation for Chemical Engineers*, Mc Graw Hill Book Comp., Inc., New York—London 1962.
3. Kafarov, V., *Cybernetic Methods in Chemistry and Chemical Engineering*, Mir Publishers, Moscow 1976.
4. Kalitkin, N. N., *Numerical Methods*, Science Publishers, Moscow, 1978 (in Russian).
5. Hlavaček, V., Hofmann, H., "Steady State Axial Heat and Mass Transfer in Tubular Reactors: An Analysis of the Uniqueness of Solutions," *Chem. Engng Sci.*, 25, 173, 1970.
6. Hlavaček, V., Hofmann, H., "Steady State Axial Heat and Mass Transfer in Tubular Reactors: Numerical Investigation of Multiplicity," *Chem. Engng Sci.*, 25, 187, 1970.
7. Drobyshevich, V. I., Dymnikov, V. P., Rivin, G. S., *Problems of Computational Mathematics*, Science Publishers, Moscow, 1980 (in Russian).
8. Fan, L. T., Chen, G. K. C., Erickson, L. E., "Efficiency and Utility of Collocation Methods in Solving the Performance Equations of Flow Chemical Reactors with Axial Dispersion," *Chem. Engng Sci.*, 26, 379, 1971.
9. Finlayson, B. A., *Nonlinear Analysis in Chemical Engineering*, Mc Graw-Hill Inc., New York—Toronto 1980.
10. Rowe, P. N., Partridge, B. A., "Gas Flow Through Bubbles in a Fluidized Bed—I. Flow Through an Ideal Bubble," *Chem. Engng Sci.*, 18, 511, 1963.
11. Toor, F. D., Calderbank, K. P. M., "Reaction Kinetics in Gas-fluidized catalyst beds—II. Mathematical Models," *Proceedings* of Intern. Symp. on Fluidization, Eindhoven, Natherland Univ. Press, Amsterdam 1967.
12. Kunii, D., Levenspiel, O., "Bubbling Bed Model," *Ind. Engng Chem., Fundam.*, 7, 446, 1968.
13. Kato, K., Wen, C. Y., "Bubble Assembly Model for a Fluidized Bed Catalytic Reactors," *Chem. Engng Sci.*, 24, 1351, 1969.
14. Fryer, C., Potter, O. E., "A Counter-Current Back Mixing Model for Fluidized Bed Catalytic Reactors. Applicability of Simplified Solutions," *Ind. Engng Chem.*, Fundam., 11, 338, 1972.
15. Chavarie, C., Grace, J. R., "Performance Analysis of a Fluidized Bed Reactor I–III," *Ind. Engng Chem.*, Fundam., 14, 75, 1975.
16. Guigon, P., Large, J. F., Bergeugnou, M. A., "Application of the Kunii-Levenspiel Model to a Multistage Baffled Catalytic Cracking Regenerator," *The Chem. Engng Journ.*, 28, 131, 1984.
17. Tabiś, B., "Criterion for the Uniqueness of Steady States in Nonadiabatic Tubular Reactors," *Int. Chem. Engng*, 26, 746, 1986.

CHAPTER 32

REPRESENTATION OF CHEMICAL STRUCTURES BY MATRICES AND COMPUTER ALGORITHMS

A. Călușaru

Institute of Chemical Research
Bucharest, Romania

CONTENTS

INTRODUCTION

The foundation of chemistry on mathematical concepts appears as a natural idea, since all known bonded systems are formed from about 100 atoms arranged in groups, called molecules or complex ions, according to a few mathematically stated combinatorial laws. However, the chemistry evolved in a rather intuitive fashion, with the predominant consideration of the empirical data, using symbols with both literal and numerical components. This procedure could not define a universal model of chemistry, which needs the use of a mathematical treatment on the constitution and transformations of the chemical systems. In spite of the obvious suggestiveness of the classical formulas, the accumulation of an enormous set of experimental data and the fast development of computers incited chemists to find suitable procedures for a dialogue with electronic computers. In this way the foundation of the mathematical constitutional chemistry was strongly stimulated.

The basic principle is that a structural representation of a molecule, formed from covalently bonded components, can be viewed as a mathematical graph, where the atoms are the points or vertices and the covalent two-electron bonds are lines or edges of the graph. If the concept of isomerism is extended from molecules to ensembles of molecules, then the chemical reactions can be depicted also by graphs. On this basis a mathematical model of constitutional chemistry is easily conceivable. The major advantage of the representation of chemical structures and reactions in form of graphs is the possibility of their conversion into matrices, which are mathematical entities that can be introduced into the memory structure of computers. In this way it is possible to solve automatically a large set of chemical problems, by means of elements of the matrix calculus.

It is important to note that by translating chemical structures and reactions in matrix form, the whole information from the chemical formula is conserved: both the interatomic bonds and the number of unshared or nonparticipating electrons may be accounted. Thus, the chemical formulas become characteristic symbols for the mathematical language by means of which the intrinsic qualities of computers to effect matrix operations are used; only a few selection rules, derived from both the molecular structure and the chemical reaction stoichiometry are imposed. Owing to this possibility the chemistry has the advantage to be actually and potentially the best documented among the scientific branches. By conversion of the chemical entities into graphs the definition, nomenclature, codification, retrieval, enumeration, systematization etc. become possible by using a large variety of programming procedures.

The use of computers to solve the problems of chemistry, considering the construction of the algorithms, can be envisaged from two points of view. For chemical synthesis and reaction mechanisms a specific type of algorithm construction must be stated for the determination and prognosis of chemical reactions. On the other hand, for documentation purposes, another kind of algorithm principle is necessary. This last point was successfully applied in 1965 by Chemical Abstracts Service and has demonstrated its efficiency for a long period of time and for very many chemical compounds. In the case of determination and prognosis of chemical reactions, or computer-assisted synthesis design, a very long computing time is necessary for larger molecules. Although the effectiveness of these aspects is not generally established, there is no doubt that the computer programs for deductive chemistry, based on mathematical models, will reach an outstanding importance in the future.

Computer-assisted chemistry is only a part, a very useful one, of the mathematical constitutional chemistry, but this branch is also important both from a fundamental and a didactical points of view. If the reaction matrices for the typical elementary mechanisms are considered, then it may be found that the basis of any chemical reaction consists of two square 2×2 matrices, corresponding to two fundamental processes only: one polarized (with electron transfer) and another nonpolarized (radicalic), both being, however, one-electron transformations. This is not only a Taoist finding, showing the simple concept of the existence of two essences at the basis of any natural manifestation of the unmanifested reality, but it represents also a practical possibility to construct the operator of any chemical reaction with a few rules of the matrix calculus.

It may be interesting to anticipate here how the deduction of any reaction operator is possible starting from two fundamental 2×2 matrices. In order to understand this problem, a large matrix, expressing all chemical transformations can be imagined. Any individual reaction matrix is then a submatrix, which, for the simplest elementary processes, becomes a 2×2 typical matrix. Among these, only two irreducible components will be found. Conversely, with these elements, all the ten 2×2 forms of a two atoms center of reaction can be constructed by operations of inversion, addition and permutation of matrices. Further, the same operations may be used for the construction of any transformation operator, corresponding to a multi-atomic center of reaction.

In addition to the above mentioned problems, the new interpretation of chemical forms as vectors of valence states allows the finding of the unknown chemical forms as potentially new compounds and/or unstable intermediates. Obviously, in this situation new pathways for chemical synthesis and a rigorous tool for the expression of the reaction mechanism are available.

This chapter presents in an accessible form the basic principles of the mathematical constitutional chemistry, together with a few applications concerning the study of algorithms used in the computer programs for both documentation purposes and computer-assisted determination-prognosis of the chemical transformations. But it may be interesting to convey our opinion that the suggestive classical expression of chemical structure and reactions must be maintained for didactical and intuitive purposes; however, it appears now that in the near future the completion of the ancient method with the mathematical one will become unavoidable. For the older chemists this may require some accommodation time, which is why any postponement may cause unexpected problems.

CONSTITUTIONAL GRAPHS

The chemical processes are produced by the outer electron orbitals termed commonly as valence electrons. The remainder atom, formed by the nucleus and the inner orbitals, the so-called atom core or center, does not undergo modifications as a consequence of chemical reactions. In a graph molecule the points (vertices) represent the projection of the atom core on a plane; the covalent bonds are the lines (edges) of the graph.

As a mathematical entity, the graph G is a finite non empty set R(G) of points in form of unordinated pairs of points connected by lines or edges. In terms of a chemical structure this is a *simple graph.*

In a vertex of the simple graph several lines can meet, constituting the degree of the vertex. If a graph contains vertices with the same degree, it is called *regular graph.* The molecules formed by C_2 rings are regular graphs of degree 2. When the degree of a regular graph is 3, it is termed as *cubic graph.* As an example of cubic graph, the skeleton of valence isomers of annulenes can be given.

The points connected by a line or two lines meeting a point are termed as *adjacent*. A line is *incident* to the corresponding points of its extremities. If two points are considered, the sequence of points and lines between them is termed as *walk*. When all these points and lines are distinct, the sequence forms a *path.* The *distance* is the shortest path between two points. Three or more points form a connected ring; this is called circuit or cycle.

A simple graph can be formed from several parts. If no point in a part can be connected by lines with points of other parts, the graph is disconnected. The molecular graphs are always *connected.*

A cyclic graph forms *trees* if any two vertices are connected by a unique path. A tree has one center or a bicenter.

When a few vertices and/or lines are deleted from the graph G, a *subgraph* H is obtained.

But in chemistry many molecules contain atoms bonded by multiple bonds. The corresponding graph contains therefore pairs of points joined by more than one line. This kind of structure is called a *multigraph.* In other cases the lines are curved and return at the emergence point; there is therefore only one extremity of the line. The graph is termed in this case a *loop-graph.* In practice a chemical graph may contain several joining lines between two points and also lines without two distinct extremities. In this more general case the resulted form is called a *pseudograph* or *general graph.* These kinds of constitutional graphs will be exemplified taking into account some simple molecules.

CHEMICAL STRUCTURES REPRESENTED BY MATRICES [1]

Among the chemical compounds, known so far, a considerable amount (more than 90%) is formed by organic compounds or molecules containing organic ligands with covalent bonds. The corresponding graph contains points (vertices) symbolizing the atom core and lines (edges) showing covalent two-electron bonds.

For the matrix representation of a structural chemical formula the atom is considered to be composed of two parts:

1. The nucleus and the electrons of the inner orbitals that form the atomic center
2. The electrons of the outer orbitals or of valence.

In conventional formulation the molecular structure is represented by the covalent bonds between the atomic centers denoted by arbitrary symbols (the symbols of the elements) as well as by the number of valence electrons that do not participate in the bonds.

Simple Graph and Adiacency Matrix, J

As it has been already shown, a simple graph contains only points and simple lines. The corresponding adiacency matrix, noted by J is a n × n square one, with the entries $a_{ij} = 1$ for connected points and zero otherwise. Each row and column design a indexed vertex. This is why n different, but isomorfic adiacency matrices can result as a function of indexing form choosen among n possible similar variants.

In the case of a molecule, formed by n atoms (A) a square n × n matrix can be formed, in which one line and the corresponding column of i-th order design the atom A_i of the molecule. A matrix of this kind shows the covalent bonds between the atoms. The diagonal entries are always zeros, the off-diagonal entries, noted by one, indicate one or several covalent bonds and these noted by zero show the absence of the bonds. In the case of a matrix of adiacency type, similar structures can have identical matrices. Thus water and hydrogen cyanide show no difference in the form of their adiacency matrices for certain indexing of the atoms in the molecule and zero values for the diagonal entries of the matrix:

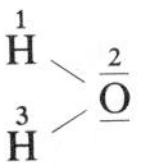

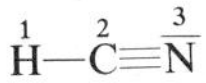

$$J(H_2O) = \begin{array}{c} \begin{matrix} H & O & H \end{matrix} \\ \begin{pmatrix} 0 & 1 & 0 \\ 1 & 0 & 1 \\ 0 & 1 & 0 \end{pmatrix} \end{array} \begin{matrix} H \\ O \\ H \end{matrix} \qquad J(HCN) = \begin{array}{c} \begin{matrix} H & C & N \end{matrix} \\ \begin{pmatrix} 0 & 1 & 0 \\ 1 & 0 & 1 \\ 0 & 1 & 0 \end{pmatrix} \end{array} \begin{matrix} H \\ C \\ N \end{matrix}$$

For different indexing of the atoms in molecule, equivalent to permutation of the order in which they correspond to the rows and columns of the matrix, isomorphic matrices are obtained, therefore matrices that can reciprocally be transformed into one another by a permutation P of the rows, followed by the same permutation P of the columns. In fact the adiacency matrix is associated with the graph of the covalent bonds. Thus in the case of formaldehyde this graph is shown in Figure 1, and the associated matrix is:

$$J(H_2CO) = \begin{array}{c} \begin{matrix} H & C & H & O \end{matrix} \\ \begin{pmatrix} 0 & 1 & 0 & 0 \\ 1 & 0 & 1 & 1 \\ 0 & 1 & 0 & 0 \\ 0 & 1 & 0 & 0 \end{pmatrix} \end{array} \begin{matrix} H \\ C \\ H \\ O \end{matrix}$$

One follows that from the point of view of the correlation between the structure and mathematic symbol represented by the matrix, the quantity of information is diminished.

All these matrices are square n × n, and both the row and the column of order i correspond to the atom A_i; the matrices are also symmetric, since the bonds are equivalent in both directions: $A_i—A_j$ and $A_j—A_i$; hence $b_{ij} = b_{ji}$.

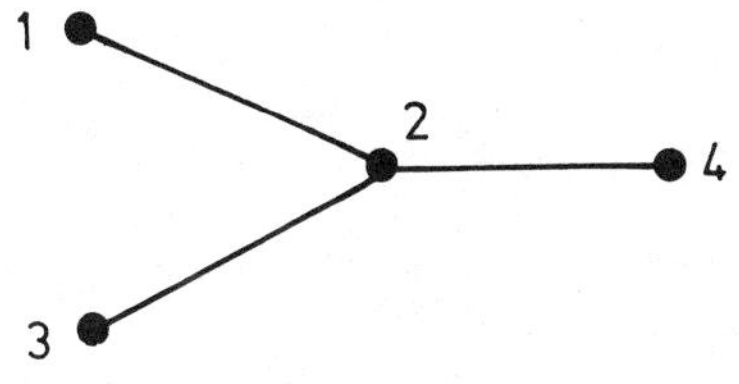

Figure 1. Simple graph of the covalent bonds for the formaldehyde molecule.

Multigraph and Connectivity Matrix, C

Another way of expressing chemical formulas is the one known by the term connectivity matrix, noted by C. In this variant the diagonal entries are occupied by usual chemical symbols of the atoms or by null elements; the off-diagonal entries show not only the presence, but also the effective number of covalent bonds between the atoms. In this way the water and the hydrogen cyanide are represented by non-isomorphic matrices, even when the main diagonal entries are zeros:

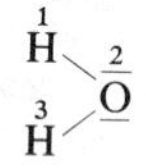

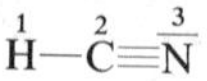

$$C(H_2O) = \begin{pmatrix} H & 1 & 0 \\ 1 & O & 1 \\ 0 & 1 & H \end{pmatrix} \qquad C(HCN) = \begin{pmatrix} H & 1 & 0 \\ 1 & C & 3 \\ 0 & 3 & N \end{pmatrix}$$

The connectivity matrix corresponds to a multigraph in which not only the simple, but also the multiple bonds are shown. For the formaldehyde molecule this multigraph is shown in Figure 2. The matrix corresponding to this multigraph is:

$$C(H_2CO) = \begin{pmatrix} H & 1 & 0 & 0 \\ 1 & C & 1 & 2 \\ 0 & 1 & H & 0 \\ 0 & 2 & 0 & O \end{pmatrix}$$

These three examples demonstrate that the connectivity matrix contains additional information in that the sum of the entries of the i-th row or column gives the number of electron pairs with which the pertinent atom participates in chemical bonding. If the diagonal entries are denoted by zeros, the following relationship holds:

$$s_i = \sum_{j=1}^{n} b_{ij} = \sum_{j=1}^{n} b_{ji} \tag{1}$$

Pseudograph and Bond and Electron Matrix, BE

As proposed in [2], more complete information is contained in the BE matrix (bond and non-participating electrons) of a set of n atoms $A = A_1, A_2, \ldots, A_n$ which constitute a molecule. This, too, is a square $n \times n$ matrix in which the i-th row and column correspond to the atomic center A_i. The off-diagonal entries are constructed in the same way as with the connectivity matrix, showing the final order of the bond from A_i to A_j, which is the same as that from A_j to A_i. The conditions $b_{ij} = b_{ji}$ and $\sum_{j=1}^{n} b_{ij} = \sum_{j=1}^{n} b_{ji}$ are again fulfilled. However, in contrast to the connectivity matrix,

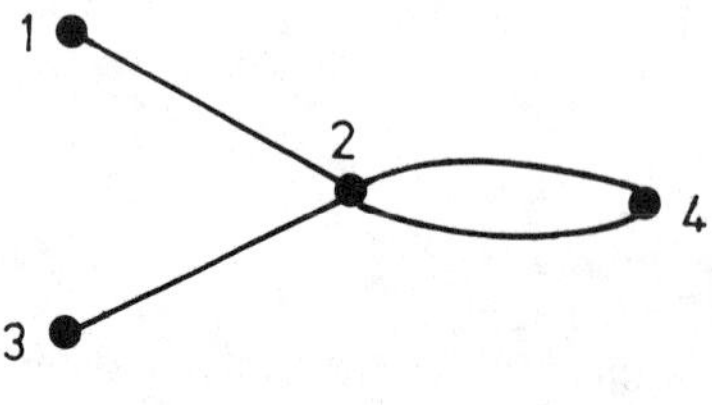

Figure 2. Multigraph for the formaldehyde molecule.

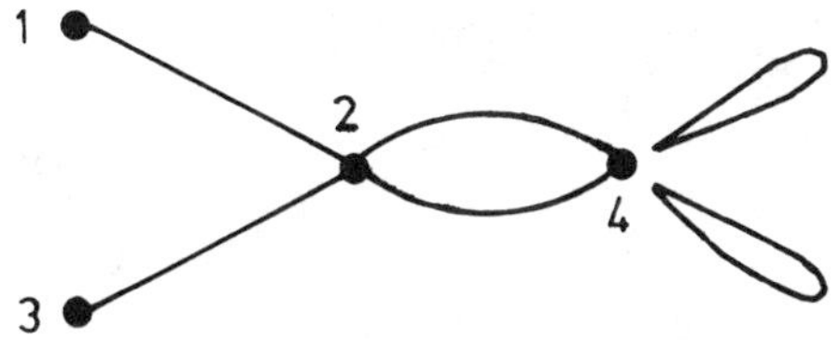

Figure 3. Pseudograph for the formaldehyde molecule.

the diagonal entries in the BE matrix are no longer occupied by atomic symbols or zeros but by the numbers of electrons not participating in the interatomic bonds. If the octet rule is taken into account, all the diagonal entries must be even for a molecule with closed valence shells and electrons with paired spins.

The BE matrices, or B, of the nitrile and isonitrile forms of hydrogen cyanide are now neither identical nor isomorphic [2]:

$$\overset{1}{\mathrm{H}}-\overset{2}{\mathrm{C}}\equiv\overset{3}{\mathrm{N}} \qquad\qquad \overset{1}{\mathrm{H}}-\overset{3}{\mathrm{N}}{}^{+}\equiv\overset{2}{\mathrm{C}}{}^{-}$$

$$B(HCN) = \begin{pmatrix} 0 & 1 & 0 \\ 1 & 0 & 3 \\ 0 & 3 & 2 \end{pmatrix} \begin{matrix} H^1 \\ C^2 \\ N^3 \end{matrix} \qquad B(HNC) = \begin{pmatrix} 0 & 0 & 1 \\ 0 & 2 & 3 \\ 1 & 3 & 0 \end{pmatrix} \begin{matrix} H^1 \\ C^2 \\ N^3 \end{matrix}$$

A zero diagonal entry indicates that the entry b_{ii} to which it refers has not nonparticipating (free) electrons. The diagonal entry $b_{33} = 2$ in the nitrile form indicates that the nitrogen atom has two nonparticipating electrons, while $b_{22} = 2$ in the isonitrile form indicates two nonparticipating electrons on the carbon atom. The off-diagonal entries $b_{12} = b_{21} = 1$ correspond to the $\overset{1}{\mathrm{H}}-\overset{2}{\mathrm{C}}$ bond; likewise, $b_{13} = b_{31} = 1$ correspond to the $\overset{1}{\mathrm{H}}-\overset{3}{\mathrm{N}}$ bond.

The BE matrix represents what is called a pseudograph or a general graph. The pseudograph is shown for formalydehyde molecule in Figure 3. The matrix corresponding to the pseudograph of Figure 3 has the form:

$$B(H_2CO) = \begin{pmatrix} 0 & 1 & 0 & 0 \\ 1 & 0 & 1 & 2 \\ 0 & 1 & 0 & 0 \\ 0 & 2 & 0 & 4 \end{pmatrix} \begin{matrix} H^1 \\ C^2 \\ H^3 \\ O^4 \end{matrix}$$

The additional information contained in the BE matrix results from the observing the rule concerning the maximum number of valence electrons that can be grouped around an atom (two for hydrogen and eight for the other atoms) and from including the total number of valence electrons corresponding to the molecule under consideration. The formal charge of an atom of the molecule can thereby also be inferred.

The octet rule (or doublet in the case of hydrogen) results from the "cross sum" $\hat{s}_i$:

$$\hat{s}_i = 2s_i - b_{ij} = \begin{cases} 2 \\ 8 \end{cases} \tag{2}$$

where s_i is the sum of the entries of the i-th row or column and b_{ii} is the diagonal entry. The number of all the valence electrons in the molecule is the sum of all the entries of the matrix:

$$S = \sum 2s_i = \sum b_{ij} \tag{3}$$

The formal charge of the atom A_i is found from the sum of the entries of the row or column minus the number of valence electrons e_i of the neutral atom under consideration:

$$\hat{e}_i = \sum b_{ij} - e_i \tag{4}$$

Thus, in the isonitrile form of hydrogen cyanide, for the second row or column (the carbon atom):

$$\hat{e}_i = \sum b_{ij} - e_i = 2 + 3 - 4 = 1 \tag{5}$$

The presence of one excess electron gives this atom a negative charge.
Similarly, for the third row or column (the nitrogen atom):

$$\hat{e}_3 = 1 + 3 - 5 = -1$$

The deficit of one electron gives the nitrogen atom a positive charge.

Synthon-Graph and Corresponding Matrices

A molecular structure can be split into simpler substructures whose recombination by known reactions can reform the target molecule [3]. It is possible to note as vertices synthons and as lines bond sets assembling these synthons. The obtained graph was called by Hendrickson *synthon-graph* [4]. In Figure 4 is shown an example of synthon graph. The steroid skeleton is divided into four parts (synthons, full lines), connected by five lines (dotted ones) [5].

The connectivity matrices are:

$$C(a) = \begin{pmatrix} 0 & 1 & 1 & 0 \\ 1 & 0 & 1 & 0 \\ 1 & 1 & 0 & 2 \\ 0 & 0 & 2 & 0 \end{pmatrix} \qquad C(b) = \begin{pmatrix} 0 & 2 & 0 & 0 \\ 2 & 0 & 1 & 2 \\ 0 & 1 & 0 & 0 \\ 0 & 1 & 0 & 0 \end{pmatrix}$$

In this way considerably simpler matrices can be used for more complex molecules.

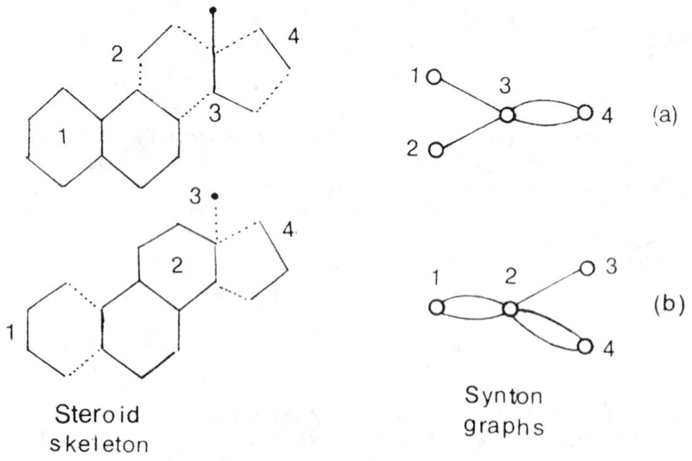

Figure 4. Synthongraph for the steroid skeleton [5].

By using synthon-graphs extended programs were composed for computer-aided design of organic synthesis [6–9]. The heuristic stage was intended for the uncovering of new possible reactions [10].

Not only a molecular structure but also a chemical reaction can be described in matrix form, by introducing some basic concepts, such as the family of the isomeric ensembles of molecules, denoted by FIEM, and the extension of the concept of isomerism.

ISOMERIC ENSEMBLES OF MOLECULES [11]

In a chemical reaction, a group of molecules, or ensemble of molecules, EM, participates as start products or educt (B) and another group of the same ensemble, EM, is obtained at the end as reaction product (E), by the redistribution of the valence electrons. Both the atomic species and the number of these species are conserved in the chemical reaction. In other words, the first and second members of the components of a chemical reaction have the same empirical formula. Therefore, the empirical formula of all the components entering into the reaction is to be considered and not the one of an isolated molecule. In general, the ensembles of molecules having the same empirical formula are called isomeric ensembles of molecules. The totality of the isomeric ensembles forms a family of isomeric ensembles of molecules, FIEM. If the entire collection of atoms is denoted by A, then all ensembles that can be formed with the same empirical formula $\langle A \rangle$ represents the family of isomeric ensembles of molecules.

The following sequence of reactions with the empirical formulas in parentheses can be taken as an example [2]:

$$HCN + Cl_2 = ClCN + HCl \qquad \langle CHCl_2N \rangle \tag{6}$$

$$NH_3 + ClCN = H_2NCN + HCl \qquad \langle CH_3ClN_2 \rangle \tag{7}$$

$$H_2HCN + H_2O = H_2NCONH_2 \qquad \langle CH_4N_2O \rangle \tag{8}$$

$$HCN + Cl_2 + NH_3 + H_2O = H_2NCONH_2 + HCl + HCl \qquad \langle CH_6Cl_2N_2O \rangle \tag{9}$$

Reaction (9) is the summation of reactions (6–8) included in the empirical formula $\langle CH_6Cl_2N_2O \rangle$. Under the condition of keeping the reaction sequence (6–8) in the same FIEM, the molecules not directly participating in that step are also written down at each step if they participate in one of the steps of the overall reaction:

$$\begin{aligned} HCN + Cl_2 + NH_3 + H_2O &\longrightarrow ClCN + HCl + NH_3 + H_2O \longrightarrow \\ &\longrightarrow H_2NCN + HCl + HCl + H_2O \longrightarrow \\ &\quad H_2NCONH_2 + HCl + HCl \end{aligned} \tag{10}$$

Obviously, the method of writing the reactions in this way is a convention by means of which all the steps are formally kept within the frame of one FIEM; the coexistence of species such as HCl and NH_3 within the limits of an actual system is not implied.

REACTION MATRIX OPERATORS [11]

Earlier, a BE matrix was shown to contain complete information concerning both the number of bonds and electrons not participating in the chemical bonds. Remembering the definition of an FIEM, the reactants (educts) and the resulting products for a chemical reaction must belong to the same FIEM, and the total number of valence electrons participating in the bonds plus the non participating ones must remain constant [2, 12].

In a BE matrix the diagonal entries b_{ii} represent the electrons non participating in chemical bonds and the off-diagonal entries b_{ij} of the i-th row and j-th column represent the bond between two covalently bonded A_i and A_j in the EM(A). BE matrices are symmetric because the A_i—A_j is the same as A_j—A_i bond, and therefore $b_{ij} = b_{ji}$.

A chemical reaction can be considered on the basis of the definitions previously given, as the conversion of one EM into another, isomeric EM by a redistribution of the valence electrons. This electron redistribution changes neither the atomic entity nor the total number of electrons. In matrix terms, a chemical reaction involves the transformation of one matrix into another matrix, in which both the indexing of the rows and columns and the sum of all matrix entries are conserved. This transformation can be represented in the most general way by the scheme:

$$\mathrm{EM(B)} \longrightarrow \mathrm{EM(E)} \tag{11}$$

The question arises of the nature of the operator that expresses this transformation, represented as follows:

$$\mathrm{B} + \mathrm{R} = \mathrm{E} \tag{12}$$

Here R is the reaction matrix operator transforming the educt matrix B in the product one E. Therefore, a chemical reaction is here represented as a matrix addition in which the sum of the entries of the transformation matrix R must be equal to zero. The action of the matrix operator R is to redistribute the electrons within the limits of a molecule (molecular isomerization) and/or of an isomeric ensemble of molecules (chemical reaction).

In consideration of the sum s of the matrix entries, the following equation can be written:

$$\mathrm{s} = \sum_{ij} \mathrm{b}_{ij} = \sum_{ij} \mathrm{e}_{ij} = \sum_{ij} \mathrm{b}_{ij} + \sum_{ij} \mathrm{r}_{ij} \tag{13}$$

in which the b_{ij} denote the entries of the educt matrix, the e_{ij} the entries of the matrix of the reaction product, and the r_{ij} are the entries of the reaction matrix operator. Equation 13 has meaning only if:

$$\sum_{ij} \mathrm{r}_{ij} = 0 \tag{14}$$

Whereas no matrix entry b_{ij} or e_{ij} can be a negative number, the entries r_{ij} are both positive and negative so that Equation 14 may be satisfied. This equation is self-evident, considering that electrons are neither created nor annihilated in a chemical reaction, the electrons merely being subject to a process of rearrangement. Since the b_{ij} entries are always positive, the question arises of the physical meaning corresponding to the assignment of the matrix entries r_{ij}. In any chemical transformation, pairs of inverse processes take place, such as the donating and accepting of electrons, the breaking and formation of bonds, cleavage into free radicals and recombination of radicals. Conventionally, a minus sign is assigned to the giving up of electrons (bond breakage, cleavage into radicals etc.) and a plus sign to the acceptance of electrons (bond formation, radical recombination etc.).

In the classical expression of chemical reactions, no symbolic correspondence element for the reaction matrix operator (R) can be found. However, the electron rearrangement occurs as a self-evident process in the chemist's or scholar's mind. This lack of any symbolic correspondence between the thought process and written expression is principally an important drawback of the classical language for the chemical reactions. As it will be shown, the R-matrix is an important element for the classification of chemical reactions, showing often that, apparently, very different reactions are in fact identical in relation with the R-matrix operator.

MATRICES FOR CHEMICAL REACTIONS [11]

As shown earlier, both first and second members of the components of the chemical reactions have the same empirical formula and are formally kept within the compass of one FIEM. In a BE matrix of a chemical compound the bond A_i—A_j is obviously the same as A_j—A_i and therefore $b_{ij} = b_{ji}$: the BE matrices are therefore symmetrical. The $n \times n$ square BE matrix can so be conceived as a vector b with n^2 elements:

$$b = (b_{11}, \ldots, b_{1n}; b_{21}, \ldots, b_{n1}, \ldots, b_{nn}) \quad (15)$$

This means that the matrices of chemical compounds are FIEM in the metric space R_2^n with n^2 coordinates on the body of the real numbers. For a chemical reaction, the educt EM(B) and the product EM(E) are two parts of the vector space R_2^n [2, 8, 13–16]. These parts are bound by the vector corresponding to the reaction matrix (R), which is the accountant for the electrons of the described reaction.

As an example, consider the following chemical reaction for the synthesis of formaldehyde cyanohydrin [12]:

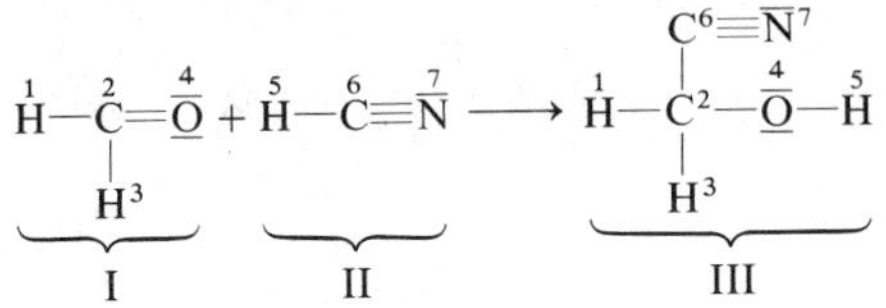
(16)

In matrix form Reaction 16 is written:

$$B_{I,II} + R_{I,II} = E_{III} \quad (17)$$

where

$$B_{I-II} = \begin{array}{c} \begin{array}{ccccccc} H^1 & C^2 & H^3 & O^4 & H^5 & C^6 & N^7 \end{array} \\ \begin{pmatrix} 0 & 1 & 0 & 0 & 0 & 0 & 0 \\ 1 & 0 & 1 & 2 & 0 & 0 & 0 \\ 0 & 1 & 0 & 0 & 0 & 0 & 0 \\ 0 & 2 & 0 & 4 & 0 & 0 & 0 \\ 0 & 0 & 0 & 0 & 0 & 1 & 0 \\ 0 & 0 & 0 & 0 & 1 & 0 & 3 \\ 0 & 0 & 0 & 0 & 0 & 3 & 2 \end{pmatrix} \end{array} \begin{array}{c} \\ H^1 \\ C^2 \\ H^3 \\ O^4 \\ H^5 \\ C^6 \\ N^7 \end{array}$$

$$E_{III} = \begin{array}{c} \begin{array}{ccccccc} H^1 & C^2 & H^3 & O^4 & H^5 & C^6 & N^7 \end{array} \\ \begin{pmatrix} 0 & 1 & 0 & 0 & 0 & 0 & 0 \\ 1 & 0 & 1 & 1 & 0 & 1 & 0 \\ 0 & 1 & 0 & 0 & 0 & 0 & 0 \\ 0 & 1 & 0 & 4 & 1 & 0 & 0 \\ 0 & 0 & 0 & 1 & 0 & 0 & 0 \\ 0 & 1 & 0 & 0 & 0 & 0 & 3 \\ 0 & 0 & 0 & 0 & 0 & 3 & 2 \end{pmatrix} \end{array} \begin{array}{c} \\ H^1 \\ C^2 \\ H^3 \\ O^4 \\ H^5 \\ C^6 \\ N^7 \end{array}$$

$$R_{I+II-III} = \begin{array}{c} \begin{array}{ccccccc} 1 & 2 & 3 & 4 & 5 & 6 & 7 \end{array} \\ \begin{pmatrix} 0 & 0 & 0 & 0 & 0 & 0 & 0 \\ 0 & 0 & 0 & -1 & 0 & +1 & 0 \\ 0 & 0 & 0 & 0 & 0 & 0 & 0 \\ 0 & -1 & 0 & 0 & +1 & 0 & 0 \\ 0 & 0 & 0 & +1 & 0 & -1 & 0 \\ 0 & +1 & 0 & 0 & -1 & 0 & 0 \\ 0 & 0 & 0 & 0 & 0 & 0 & 0 \end{pmatrix} \end{array} \begin{array}{c} \\ 1 \\ 2 \\ 3 \\ 4 \\ 5 \\ 6 \\ 7 \end{array}$$

In order to simplify the notation, the zero entries may be no longer written down.

A further example refers to the case of molecular isomerization. This case is illustrated by the isomerization of hydrogen cyanide from the nitrile form to the izonitrile one:

$$B(HC\overline{N}) + R = E(HN\overline{C}) \tag{18}$$

$$\overset{\begin{matrix} H^1 & C^2 & N^3 \end{matrix}}{\begin{pmatrix} \cdot & 1 & \cdot \\ 1 & \cdot & 3 \\ \cdot & 3 & 2 \end{pmatrix}} + \overset{\begin{matrix} 1 & 2 & 3 \end{matrix}}{\begin{pmatrix} \cdot & -1 & 1 \\ -1 & 2 & \cdot \\ 1 & \cdot & -2 \end{pmatrix}} = \overset{\begin{matrix} H^1 & C^2 & N^3 \end{matrix}}{\begin{pmatrix} \cdot & \cdot & 1 \\ \cdot & 2 & 3 \\ 1 & 3 & \cdot \end{pmatrix}} \tag{19}$$

The matrix notation is obviously applicable also in inorganic chemical reactions. Consider as an example the formation of carbonic acid from carbon dioxide and water:

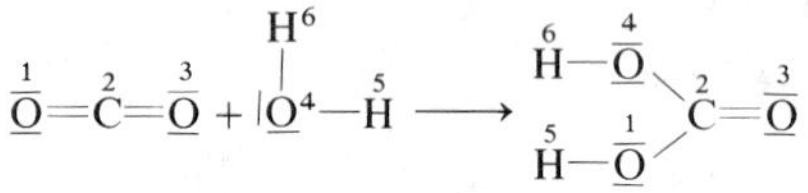

(20)

$$B(CO_2 + H_2O) + R \longrightarrow E(H_2CO_3)$$

In matrix form Reaction 20 is written:

$$\overset{\begin{matrix} O^1 & C^2 & O^3 & O^4 & H^5 & H^6 \end{matrix}}{\begin{pmatrix} 4 & 2 & 0 & 0 & 0 & 0 \\ 2 & 0 & 2 & 0 & 0 & 0 \\ 0 & 2 & 4 & 0 & 0 & 0 \\ 0 & 0 & 0 & 4 & 1 & 1 \\ 0 & 0 & 0 & 1 & 0 & 0 \\ 0 & 0 & 0 & 1 & 0 & 0 \end{pmatrix}} + \overset{\begin{matrix} 1 & 2 & 3 & 4 & 5 & 6 \end{matrix}}{\begin{pmatrix} 0 & -1 & 0 & 0 & 1 & 0 \\ -1 & 0 & 0 & 1 & 0 & 0 \\ 0 & 0 & 0 & 0 & 0 & 0 \\ 0 & 1 & 0 & 0 & -1 & 0 \\ 1 & 0 & 0 & -1 & 0 & 0 \\ 0 & 0 & 0 & 0 & 0 & 0 \end{pmatrix}}$$

$$= \overset{\begin{matrix} O^1 & C^2 & O^3 & O^4 & H^5 & H^6 \end{matrix}}{\begin{pmatrix} 4 & 1 & 0 & 0 & 1 & 0 \\ 1 & 0 & 2 & 1 & 0 & 0 \\ 0 & 2 & 4 & 0 & 0 & 0 \\ 0 & 1 & 0 & 4 & 0 & 1 \\ 1 & 0 & 0 & 0 & 0 & 0 \\ 0 & 0 & 0 & 1 & 0 & 0 \end{pmatrix}} \tag{21}$$

In the examples previously presented the direct R matrix has been used. The question arises as to what matrix to use for the transformation represented by a chemical equilibrium, given by the reaction:

$$B \rightleftarrows E \tag{22}$$

The reaction operator depends on the direction of the reaction, the convention being observed that the operator is applied to the component that is being transformed. Using the R matrix, Reaction 22 can be written in the form of two separate reactions depending on the direction of the reaction:

$$\begin{aligned} &B + R \longrightarrow E \\ &E + \overline{R} \longrightarrow B \end{aligned} \tag{23}$$

A relationship evidently exists between R and $\overline{R}$; specifically, the matrix entries R have their signs changed in $\overline{R}$. Accordingly,

$$\overline{R} = -R \tag{24}$$

in which $\overline{r}_{ij} = -r_{ij}$. As an example, consider the decomposition reaction of the cyanohydrin [17]:

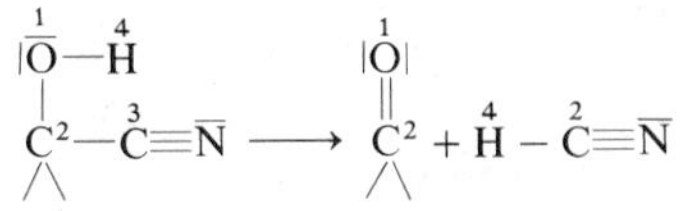

$$
\begin{array}{c}
\overset{1}{|\text{O}}-\overset{4}{\text{H}} \\
| \\
\overset{2}{\text{C}}-\overset{3}{\text{C}}\equiv\overset{}{\text{N}} \\
\diagup\;\diagdown
\end{array}
\longrightarrow
\begin{array}{c}
\overset{1}{|\text{O}|} \\
\| \\
\overset{}{\text{C}^2} + \overset{4}{\text{H}} - \overset{2}{\text{C}}\equiv\overline{\text{N}} \\
\diagup\;\diagdown
\end{array}
\tag{25}
$$

which is the reverse of Reaction 16. Here, the reaction matrix is:

$$
\overline{R} = -R =
\begin{array}{cccc}
\text{O}^1 & \text{C}^2 & \text{C}^3 & \text{H}^4
\end{array}
\left(
\begin{array}{cccc}
\cdot & 1 & \cdot & -1 \\
1 & \cdot & -1 & \cdot \\
\cdot & -1 & \cdot & 1 \\
-1 & \cdot & 1 & \cdot
\end{array}
\right)
\begin{array}{c}
\text{O}^1 \\
\text{C}^2 \\
\text{C}^3 \\
\text{H}^4
\end{array}
\tag{26}
$$

The matrix representation of chemical reactions thus calls for the express use of the matrix operator denoted by R or $\overline{R}$, which indicates and localizes the valence electron regroupings. In the usual representation of chemical reactions, an equivalent symbolic notation is not used, the role of the reaction operator remaining an intuitive concept.

CENTER OF REACTION

In the case of computer-assisted work of chemical reactions an outstanding importance must be ascribed to the study of the center of reaction in the structure of molecule, represented by the restricted group of atoms participating in the breaking and creation of chemical bonds. Taking into account this center of reaction in Reaction 16, only four atoms instead of seven are to be considered. In the R matrix of Equation 17 the rows and columns indexed as 1, 3, and 7 contain only zero entries and are therefore redundant; accordingly only the atoms indexed as 2, 4, 5, and 6 must be used. Reaction 16 is rewritten and reindexed [12]:

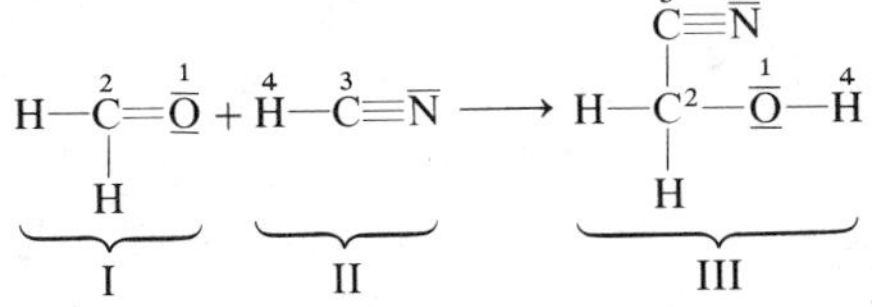

$$
\text{H}-\overset{2}{\text{C}}=\overset{1}{\overline{\text{O}}} + \overset{4}{\text{H}}-\overset{3}{\text{C}}\equiv\overline{\text{N}}
\longrightarrow
\begin{array}{c}
\overset{3}{\text{C}}\equiv\overline{\text{N}} \\
| \\
\text{H}-\overset{2}{\text{C}}-\overset{1}{\text{O}}-\overset{4}{\text{H}} \\
| \\
\text{H}
\end{array}
\tag{27}
$$

$$\underbrace{}_{\text{I}}\quad\underbrace{}_{\text{II}}\quad\underbrace{}_{\text{III}}$$

In matrix form Equation 27 is represented as follows:

$$
\begin{array}{cccc}
\text{O}^1 & \text{C}^2 & \text{C}^3 & \text{H}^4
\end{array}
\left(
\begin{array}{cccc}
4 & 2 & \cdot & \cdot \\
2 & \cdot & \cdot & \cdot \\
\cdot & \cdot & \cdot & 1 \\
\cdot & \cdot & 1 & \cdot
\end{array}
\right)
+
\begin{array}{cccc}
1 & 2 & 3 & 4
\end{array}
\left(
\begin{array}{cccc}
\cdot & -1 & \cdot & 1 \\
-1 & \cdot & 1 & \cdot \\
\cdot & 1 & \cdot & -1 \\
1 & \cdot & -1 & \cdot
\end{array}
\right)
=
\begin{array}{cccc}
\text{O}^1 & \text{C}^2 & \text{C}^3 & \text{H}^4
\end{array}
\left(
\begin{array}{cccc}
4 & 1 & \cdot & 1 \\
1 & \cdot & 1 & \cdot \\
\cdot & 1 & \cdot & \cdot \\
1 & \cdot & \cdot & \cdot
\end{array}
\right)
\tag{28}
$$

In this way a considerable simplification was obtained.

In the case of isomerization Reaction 18 no further simplification is possible since all atoms are included in the reaction center. But for reaction 21 a simpler form can be used:

$$\begin{matrix} O^1 & C^2 & O^4 & H^4 \end{matrix} \qquad \begin{matrix} 1 & 2 & 4 & 5 \end{matrix} \qquad \begin{matrix} O^1 & C^2 & O^4 & H^4 \end{matrix}$$

$$\begin{pmatrix} 4 & 2 & \cdot & \cdot \\ 2 & \cdot & \cdot & \cdot \\ \cdot & \cdot & 4 & 1 \\ \cdot & \cdot & 1 & \cdot \end{pmatrix} + \begin{pmatrix} \cdot & -1 & \cdot & 1 \\ -1 & \cdot & 1 & \cdot \\ \cdot & 1 & \cdot & -1 \\ 1 & \cdot & -1 & \cdot \end{pmatrix} = \begin{pmatrix} 4 & 1 & \cdot & 1 \\ 1 & \cdot & 1 & \cdot \\ \cdot & 1 & 4 & \cdot \\ 1 & \cdot & \cdot & \cdot \end{pmatrix}$$

For the examples, the simplification of the matrix is seen to be more significant, the larger the molecule and smaller its center of reaction. For reactions involving small molecules (Reaction 18), simplifications are no longer possible, since the rearrangement of a single atom entails the regrouping of all the atoms of the molecule. Particular importance attaches accordingly to the center of reaction.

In the reaction mechanism of a considerable number of chemical reactions both the highest occupied molecular orbital (HOMO) and the lowest unoccupied molecular orbital (LUMO) are involved. One of the most simple and most frequently encountered reaction is the water molecule self-protolysis [17]:

$$H_2O + H_2O \rightleftarrows H_3O^+ + {}^-OH \tag{30}$$

In this form it is not very clear which reacts with which, but the answer can be found when this reaction is expressed in a more thorough form:

$$\underset{\substack{| \\ H}}{H-\overset{\delta-}{\overline{O}}|} + \overset{\delta+}{H}-\underline{O}-H \rightleftarrows \underset{\substack{| \\ H}}{H-\overset{+}{\overline{O}}}-H + {}^-|\underline{O}-H \tag{31}$$

This means that the orbital HOMO of the oxygen-donor (base) reacts with LUMO on hydrogen-acceptor (acid). These are the two centers of reaction that can be found in water molecule.

Actually, R matrices are generated only by consideration of the existence of these centers. A chemical reaction can be considerably simplified if account is taken only of the atoms of the molecule that participate in the breaking and formation of bonds. Consider the example represented by the reaction:

$$H-\overline{\underline{O}}|^- + \rangle C^{\delta+}-\overline{\underline{Cl}} \rightleftarrows \rangle C^{\delta+}-\overline{\underline{O}}-H + |\overline{\underline{Cl}}|^- \tag{32}$$

with the simplified matrix representation:

$$\begin{matrix} O^1 & C^1 & Cl^3 \end{matrix} \qquad \begin{matrix} 1 & 2 & 3 \end{matrix} \qquad \begin{matrix} O^1 & C^2 & Cl^3 \end{matrix}$$

$$\begin{pmatrix} 6 & \cdot & \cdot \\ \cdot & \cdot & 1 \\ \cdot & 1 & 6 \end{pmatrix} + \begin{pmatrix} 2 & 1 & \cdot \\ 1 & \cdot & 1 \\ \cdot & -1 & 2 \end{pmatrix} = \begin{pmatrix} 4 & 1 & \cdot \\ 1 & \cdot & \cdot \\ \cdot & \cdot & 8 \end{pmatrix} \tag{33}$$

This reaction can occur in a molecule that contains an active center. If there are no active centers in such molecules, then Reaction 32 embodies the chemical transformation that characterizes the substitution of chlorine by hydroxyl, and the matrix form is of the type of Reaction 33.

A particular electron redistribution often describes a series of apparently different reactions. In matrix form this signifies the existence of the same matrix for these reactions; they are, however, distinguished by the indexing of the rows and columns.

As an example consider the following reactions [2]:

$$CH_3-\overset{\overset{1}{|\underline{O}H}}{\overset{|}{C^2H}}-\overset{\overset{3}{H}}{\overset{|}{\underline{N}^4}}-CH_3 \longrightarrow CH_3-\overset{2}{C}H=\overset{4}{\underline{N}}-CH_3 + H-\overset{1}{\underline{O}}-\overset{3}{H} \tag{34a}$$

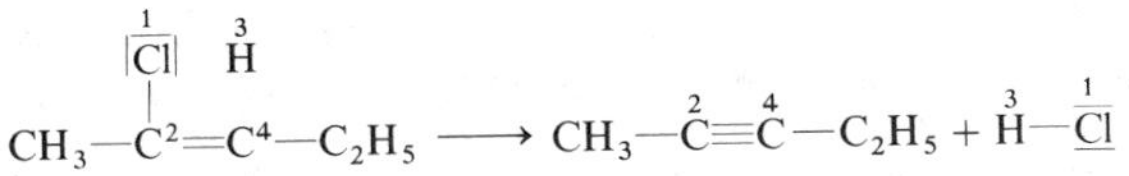

$$\overset{1}{|Cl|} \quad \overset{3}{H}$$
$$CH_3 - \underset{|}{\overset{|}{C^2}} = C^4 - C_2H_5 \longrightarrow CH_3 - \overset{2}{C} \equiv \overset{4}{C} - C_2H_5 + \overset{3}{H} - \overset{1}{Cl} \tag{34b}$$

$$\overset{1}{|Cl|} \quad \overset{3}{H}$$
$$C_3H_7 - \underset{|}{\overset{|}{C^2}}H - \underset{|}{\overset{|}{C^4}}H - C_3H_7 \longrightarrow C_3H_7 - \overset{2}{C}H = \overset{4}{C}H - C_3H_7 + \overset{3}{H} - \overset{1}{Cl} \tag{34c}$$

$$\overset{1}{|Cl|} \quad \overset{3}{H}$$
$$H - \underset{|}{\overset{|}{C^2}}H - \underset{|}{\overset{|}{C^4}}H - C_3H_7 \longrightarrow H - \overset{2}{C}H = \overset{4}{C}H - C_3H_7 + \overset{3}{H} - \overset{1}{Cl} \tag{34d}$$

For all of these, the reaction matrix is:

$$R = \begin{array}{c} \\ \\ \\ \\ \end{array} \begin{pmatrix} \cdot & -1 & 1 & \cdot \\ -1 & \cdot & \cdot & 1 \\ 1 & \cdot & \cdot & -1 \\ \cdot & 1 & -1 & \cdot \end{pmatrix} \begin{array}{c} 1 \\ 2 \\ 3 \\ 4 \end{array}$$

But, for Reaction 34a, the indexing is O^1 C^2 H^3 N^4, while, for the others, the indexing follows from the numbering of the atomic species indicated in the series of Reactions 34a–d.

PROPERTIES OF REACTION MATRIX OPERATORS

R matrices are symmetric, since $B + R = E$ represents symmetric matrices, inasmuch as they are BE matrices. For these $b_{ij} = b_{ji}$, and it follows that:

$$r_{ij} = r_{ji} \tag{35}$$

In a R matrix, negative off-diagonal entries $r_{ij} = r_{ji} = -1$ indicate the breaking of a covalent bond $A_i - A_j$ or, in general, a giving up of electrons. A negative diagonal entry r_{ii} shows the number of valence electrons that the atom A_i gives up following a chemical transformation. A positive diagonal entry shows the number of free valence electrons that the atom A_i gains in a chemical reaction.

The transformation of a B matrix by addition to an R matrix, namely, $B + R = E$ corresponds to a chemical reaction only if the following condition is fulfilled for all the matrix entries:

$$e_{ij} = b_{ij} + r_{ij} \geq 0 \tag{36}$$

This relationship arises from the requirement that a BE matrix cannot contain negative entries. Consequently, the negative entries of an R matrix must be chosen so as to satisfy the relationship:

$$|r_{ij}| \leq b_{ij} \quad \text{for} \quad r_{ij} < 0 \tag{37}$$

Another condition that must be observed at the same time is that the entries e_{ij} of the E matrix of the reaction product must have values in accord with the possible valences of the elements to which they refer. This condition allows the negative entries r_{ij} of the R matrix to match equivalent entries of the B matrix from the mathematical point of view. Accordingly, the positive entries of the R matrix are found by considering the condition:

$$\sum_{ij} r_{ij} = 0 \tag{38}$$

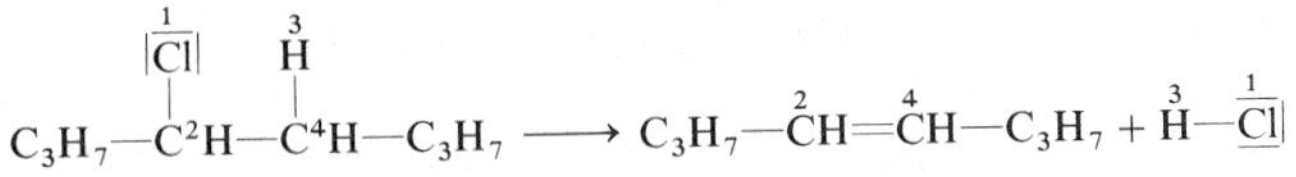

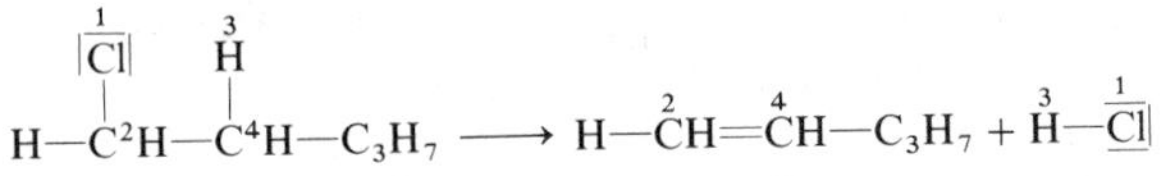

Thus, all the possible chemical reactions are found if these conditions are observed: the mathematical correspondence given by the equation $b_{ij} + r_{ij} = b_{ij}$, and r_{ij} should be in accord with the chemical valence of the element on which a bond is changed. In this way, the totality of the R matrices can be obtained, which, applied to a B matrix, leads to the discovery of E matrices of the entire family of isomeric ensembles of molecules. At the same time, the pairs of B and E matrices that will go together, both under valence condition and under the mathematical condition, can be found for a specified reaction matrix R. Accordingly, the totality of chemical reactions that share the electron redistribution entries contained in R matrix can be found, an aspect that offers interest in chemical synthesis. An example was presented earlier by Reactions 34a–d. A thorough examination of this problem is carried out in the following section.

CHEMICAL METRIC

Estimating a distance is generally based on a metric (as a gauge) that entails the geometric interpretation of the elements involved. The present case requires the geometric interpretation of a family of isomeric ensembles of molecules (FIEM). This method of interpretation is important because of possibility of finding the "shortest" pathway for the reaction and deciding which is the most probable course of the reaction among the many possible routes. For the quantitative treatment of this problem it is necessary to make use of a set of properties of vectors and to establish a broader relationship between vectors and matrices.

As a physical concept, a vector has magnitude and direction. A more complete description considers the terminus of a vector that has its origin at the origin of a system of coordinate axes. The components of a vector a are then the projections a_i of the terminus of the vector upon the coordinate axes. Rules corresponding to the mathematical operations that are carried out with vectors must be derived to operate with the components on the axes. In this sense the definition of a vector as a physical entity having magnitude and direction becomes unsatisfactory.

A vector is defined as the endpoint of a line segment passing through the origin of the coordinate system. The vector is determined completely and unambiguously in this way. By this mathematical interpretation of a vector components greater than three can be brought into consideration, which, in purely mathematical terms corresponds to a hypothetical space with any number coordinates (dimensions). On each coordinate a dimension, corresponding to the point position can be noted. The vector can therefore have a number of dimensional components equaling the set of coordinates that constitute the spatial structure necessary for the existence of the given species of vector. Thus in a plane, a vector of defined magnitude and direction is represented by two projections (a_1, a_2), and in common physical space by three projections (a_1, a_2, a_3). The number of these components can be extended further, depending on the number of coordinates of the space that is to be employed, resulting finally in an ordered series of numbers as a mathematical representation of the vector. The use of the concept of coordinate dimension (position) for each component of the vector results from the considerable advantage offered by the treatment of vectors in geometric terms and concepts. This representation of a vector in the form $(a_1, a_2, a_3, \ldots, a_n)$ is equivalent to that of a point located in a space of n coordinates in which a_i represents the dimension coordinate of the i-th axis of the space in question. From the geometric point of view, the two components of vector and point represent the same thing.

The series of numbers $(a_1, a_2, \ldots, a_n)$ can be written as a row or column and then represents a $1 \times n$ or $n \times 1$ matrix. A complete equivalence then exists between the vector or point and the matrix. Thus, the definitions of equality, addition, and multiplication by a scalar are the same for a vector as for a matrix of one row or column. Further, the scalar product of a vector row and a vector column corresponds to the definition of matrix multiplication when the first term of the multiplication is a row matrix and the second is a column matrix. However, the scalar product of two vectors is a scalar, while the product of a row matrix and column matrix is a matrix of a single entry; nevertheless, a complete equivalence exists between numbers and 1×1 matrices. The notation for the scalar product of two column or two row vectors are the same as for matrices [18].

An $n \times n$ BE matrix can be written as a series of vectors of n^2 components:

$$b = (b_{11}, \ldots, b_{1n}; b_{21}, \ldots, b_{2n}; \ldots; b_{n1}, \ldots, b_{nn}) \tag{39}$$

In this form the matrix represents a vector whose components are formed by row and/or column vectors. The BE matrix thus incorporates into a metric space R_2^n of n^2 coordinates over the field of real numbers, a FIEM that corresponds to a number of chemical processes. But the entries b_{ij} of the BE matrix can also be interpreted as Cartesian coordinates of a point P(BE) in the R^{n^2} space or as components of a vector in the same R^{n^2} space. This interpretation leads to the designation of a point P(BE) as a point of the BE matrix itself. In other words, a family of an isomeric ensemble of molecules corresponding to isomorphic matrices represents points lying on the surface of a sphere with a radius equal to the length of the vector.

A similar interpretation can be given to a reaction matrix R, which corresponds to a vector (point) in the same R^{n^2} space to which the BE matrix belongs. A chemical reaction B + R = E signifies the displacement of the point P(B) to the point P(E). The sum of the absolute values of the entries of the R matrix is:

$$D(B, E) = \sum_{ij} |b_{ij} - e_{ij}| = \sum_{ij} |r_{ij}| \tag{40}$$

This sum represents twice the number of electrons that are redistributed during the reaction, since this number appears once as a positive entry and a second time as a negative one.

The distance between the points P(B) and P(E), denoted by D(B, E) (Equation 40), is called the "chemical distance" [2]. The metric defined by D(B, E) in the R^{n^2} space is Euclidean. The chemical distance is therefore a normal distance characterized by the BE matrices that define a FIEM. If the totality of the isomorphic matrices that can be formed from the B and E matrices is considered, then this distance characterizes the distance between the surfaces of two spheres whose centers lie at the same point of the R^{n^2} space, defined by the $n \times n$ zero matrix. A segment in the R^{n^2} space is thus seen to represent the square of a number n, and the difference between two segments (squared numbers) to represent a segment of the same dimension (a squared number). In this way, D(B, E) represented by Equation 40 expresses the square of a number and, consequently, has the general form of any distance, given in the simplest form by the generalized rule of the right triangle.

As an example consider the R matrices presented in the preceding sections. The chemical distance between members of the FIEM (Reaction 16), B(formaldehyde plus hydrogen cyanide), and E(cyanohydrin) is then:

$$D(B, E) = |-1| + |-1| + |-1| + |-1| + 1 + 1 + 1 + 1 = 8$$

Similarly, for Reaction 18, D(HCN/HNC) = 8; for Reaction 20, D(CO_2 + H_2O, H_2CO_3) = 8; and for the Diels-Alder reaction or Cope rearrangement (see below), D(B, E) = 12. Further, in an elementary one-electron redox reaction, D(B, E) = 2, and in a coligation reaction, D(B, E) = 4.

In this presentation the conceptual difficulty arises from the tentative to cover with geometrical form some formless entities. This is why the procedure must be not interpreted as based on a geometrical reality, but as a suggestive means to understand an abstract notion using a gauge procedure. The previous figures for chemical distance cannot be expressed by any length unit, but must be understood as indicating the number of formed and broken bonds. D(B, E) can reach quantified values since a R-matrix contains only entire entries, whose sum is also an entire number. The simplest R-matrix is composed of a positive and a negative unit; therefore the minimal value of D(B, E) is 2. The larger values are always even.

The practical utility of the concept of chemical distance may be questioned. Evidence of the utility of this concept is found with more complicated reactions, when the way on which a particular reaction actually proceeds is not known precisely. As an example, consider arbitrary alteration of the numbering in the right member of a chemical reaction. Additional entries then appear in the reaction operator, expressing the breaking and formation of the same bonds. The center of reaction appears more complicated than it really is. This surplus of entries in the R matrix results in an increasing of D(E, B), defined as chemical distance, which has a minimum value only for the real center of reaction, therefore for the correct numbering.

When there is uncertainty about the numbering in the right member of a chemical reaction, the computer program may be started with a permutation P′ as close as possible to the minimum chemical distance [2]. Heuristic method, based on the comparision of the neighborhoods $U(A_i, A_j)$ of the atoms A_i in EM(B) with those of A_j in EM(E), have been proposed to find the approximate solution P′. Next, an arrangement of an EM(B) consistent with the atoms of EM(A) is tested, so as to superpose the correlated neighborhoods as well as possible.

Determining the minimum chemical distance permits the identification of the correct matrix, R_{min}. In simple cases the correct notation of the atoms is obvious in both members of the reaction, but this may not hold for very complicated reactions, where the center of reaction must be found [19].

MATRICES OF ONE-ELECTRON TRANSFORMATIONS IN TWO-ATOM CENTERS OF REACTION [19]

The reactions occurring in organic chemistry can be grouped considering the information on the valence state (see below) and on the bond and coordination number of the carbon atom, undergoing changes of the hybrid states according to the type of reaction mechanism. Any matrix of an overall reaction contains entries corresponding to a few types of elementary reactions. This section shows reaction matrices of some typical reaction mechanisms corresponding to a center of reaction formed from two atoms.

The one-electron transformations are the simplest ones by which a chemical reaction can be produced. In this group the charge transfer (redox) and radicalic reactions are included. Each of these two types of reactions embraces correlated pairs, corresponding either to the direction of reaction path (reciprocally inverse processes), or to the sequence of the components of the center of reaction (reciprocally permuted processes).

One-Electron Redox Reactions

The redox reactions are characterized by processes in which a charge transfer produced by electron motions occurs. An atomic species is transformed in a positive ion by the loss of one electron. In this way the atom undergoes a process of oxidative electronic dissociation; this process is designated by the symbol $1D_e$. Such a process can occur only if the electron finds a free site in another atom (ion) to which it can associate. This place is offered the most frequently by a positive ion, becoming a neutral atom by charge neutralization owing to the electron capture. This process of ion or atom association with an electron is termed as reductive association for which the symbolic notation $1A_e$ is adopted [20].

The redox reactions can be produced by means of the electrochemical devices, by the action of radicalic species and, generally, by chemical species where an atom has several electronic states.

Oxidative Dissociation ($1D_e$)

The elementary redox process in which a one-electron transfer is produced may be represented by the following general schemes:

$$\begin{aligned} &A_i^{\bullet} + A_j^{+} \longrightarrow A_i^{+} + {}^{\bullet}A_j \\ &A_i^{\bullet} + {}^{\bullet}A_j \longrightarrow A_i^{+} + \overline{A}_j^{-} \end{aligned} \qquad (41)$$

A is the atom species or reactant, included in a molecular structure.

A reaction that follows the scheme (41) is the oxidation of the ferrous ion with a radicalic species formed by water radiolysis:

$$\overset{i}{Fe}{}^{2+} + {}^{\bullet}\overset{j}{\underline{O}}{-}H \qquad \overset{i}{Fe}{}^{3+} + {}^{-}|\overset{j}{\underline{O}}{-}H \qquad (42)$$

To this reaction corresponds the reaction matrix:

$$R_1 = \begin{array}{c} \begin{matrix} \mathrm{i} & \quad \mathrm{j} \end{matrix} \\ \begin{pmatrix} -1 & 0 \\ 0 & 1 \end{pmatrix} \end{array} \begin{array}{c} \\ \mathrm{i} \\ \mathrm{j} \end{array} \qquad (1D_e)$$

which shows that an electron is transferred from A_i to A_j. The matrix entries indicate therefore the loss (−) or the gain (+) of the electron. No chemical bond is formed or broken.

Reductive Association ($1A_e$)

In the case of the reductive association the general reactions are:

$$\begin{aligned} &A_i^+ + {}^{\bullet}A_j \longrightarrow A_i^{\bullet} + A_j^+ \\ &A_i^+ + \overline{A}_j \longrightarrow A_i^{\bullet} + {}^{\bullet}A_j^+ \end{aligned} \qquad (43)$$

The following reaction can be taken as an example:

$$\overset{\mathrm{i}}{\mathrm{Ti}}{}^{4+} + {}^{\bullet}\overset{\mathrm{j}}{\mathrm{H}} \longrightarrow \overset{\mathrm{i}}{\mathrm{Ti}}{}^{3+} + \overset{\mathrm{j}}{\mathrm{H}}{}^{+} \qquad (44)$$

For these reactions the matrix is:

$$R_2 = \overline{R}_1 = \begin{array}{c} \begin{matrix} \mathrm{i} & \quad \mathrm{j} \end{matrix} \\ \begin{pmatrix} 1 & 0 \\ 0 & -1 \end{pmatrix} \end{array} \begin{array}{c} \\ \mathrm{i} \\ \mathrm{j} \end{array} \qquad (1A_e)$$

which represents the reverse (or permuted) previous matrix.

Radicalic Reactions

Radical reactions embrace breakings of covalent bonds (homolysis) and recombination of radicals produced by chemical, electrochemical and radiolytic reactions with formation of covalent bonds (coligation).

Radicalic Dissociation (D_R)

The radicalic dissociation is termed as homolysis. By this process, each species retains its electron and, consequently, no electrical charged particles are formed. The general schemes for these reactions are radicalic splittings:

$$\begin{aligned} &A_i{-}A_j \longrightarrow A_i^{\bullet} + {}^{\bullet}A_j \\ &A_i{=}A_j \longrightarrow A_i^{\bullet}{-}{}^{\bullet}A_j \end{aligned} \qquad (45)$$

A reaction of this type, encountered in radiation chemistry, is the radicalic splitting of the water molecule:

$$\overset{\mathrm{i}}{\mathrm{H}}{-}\overset{\mathrm{j}}{\overline{\mathrm{O}}}{-}\mathrm{H} \longrightarrow \overset{\mathrm{i}}{\mathrm{H}}{}^{\bullet} + {}^{\bullet}\overset{\mathrm{j}}{\overline{\underline{\mathrm{O}}}}{-}\mathrm{H} \qquad (46)$$

Another reaction of this type is the breaking of $\gt$C—H bond:

$$\gt\overset{i}{C}—\overset{j}{H} + {}^{\bullet}\underline{\overline{O}}—H \longrightarrow \gt\overset{i}{C}{}^{\bullet}— + \overset{j}{H}—\underline{\overline{O}}—H \qquad (47)$$

This rupture is effected by the action of the radical species formed in Reaction 46.
The reaction matrix corresponding to this scheme is:

$$R_3 = \begin{pmatrix} 1 & -1 \\ -1 & 1 \end{pmatrix} \begin{matrix} i \\ j \end{matrix} \qquad (D_R)$$

(columns i, j)

By this process a covalent bond is broken symmetrically and each fragment retains a non shared electron.

Radicalic Association (A_R)

The recombination of radical species, termed also as *coligation*, is the reverse of the homolysis reaction. The general schemes are therefore the followings:

$$\begin{aligned} &A_i^{\bullet} + {}^{\bullet}A_j \longrightarrow A_i—A_j \\ &A_i^{\bullet}—{}^{\bullet}A_j \longrightarrow A_i{=}A_j \end{aligned} \qquad (48)$$

These reactions are the reverses of the reactions (45). As an example, the following radical reactions are given:

$$H—\overset{i}{\underline{\overline{O}}}{}^{\bullet} + {}^{\bullet}\overset{i}{\underline{\overline{O}}}—H \qquad H—\overset{i}{\underline{\overline{O}}}—\overset{j}{\underline{\overline{O}}}—H \qquad (49)$$

and

$$\gt\overset{i}{C}{}^{\bullet}— + {}^{\bullet}\overset{j}{\underline{\overline{O}}}—H \qquad \gt\overset{i}{C}—\overset{j}{\underline{\overline{O}}}—H \qquad (50)$$

The reaction matrix is the reverse of the previous one:

$$R_4 = R_3 = \begin{pmatrix} -1 & 1 \\ 1 & -1 \end{pmatrix} \begin{matrix} i \\ j \end{matrix} \qquad (A_R)$$

(columns i, j)

The application of this operator to the matrix of radicalic species of the educt bears to formation of a covalent bond.

Relationship between Correlated Matrices

By the study of the correlated pairs of the previously studied processes, a principal difference between redox and radicalic reactions can be noticed, from the point of view of the reaction matrix.

In the case of redox reactions, the pairs of matrices appear formally as reciprocally permuted or reversed. The problem of the true correlation between them arises. The general schemes (41 and 43) show that both correlations hold. As it has been previously shown, either the matrix form of the chemical structure or the classical one, based on literal symbols, shows the number of interatomic bonds together with the number of nonparticipating electrons. But the redox reactions are polarized, since two kinds of charged particles can form or vanish: positive and negative. Therefore

Table 1
Matrices of One-Electron Transformations in Centers of Reaction Formed by Two Atoms

No.	Chemical Process	Scheme of Reaction	Symbol	Bonds −1	Bonds +1	Matrix Reaction	Matrix Correlated
Redox Reactions							
1	Oxidative dissociation	$A_i^{\bullet} + A_j^{+} \longrightarrow A_i^{+} + {}^{\bullet}A_j$ $A_i^{\bullet} + {}^{\bullet}A_j \longrightarrow A_i^{+} + \overline{A}_j$	D_e	0	0	R_1	
2	Reductive association	$A_i^{+} + {}^{\bullet}A_j \longrightarrow A_i^{\bullet} + A_j^{+}$	A_e	0	0	R_2	$\overline{R}_1$
Radicalic Reactions							
3	Radicalic dissociation (homolysis)	$A_i{-}A_j \longrightarrow A_i^{\bullet} + {}^{\bullet}A_j$ $A_i{=}A_j \longrightarrow A_i^{\bullet}{-}{}^{\bullet}A_j$ $A_i{\equiv}A_j \longrightarrow A_i^{\bullet}{=}{}^{\bullet}A_j$	D_R	1	0	R_3	
4	Radicalic association (coligation)	$A_i^{\bullet} + {}^{\bullet}A_j \longrightarrow A_i - A_j$ $A_i^{\bullet}{-}{}^{\bullet}A_j \longrightarrow A_i{=}A_j$ $A_i^{\bullet}{=}{}^{\bullet}A_j \longrightarrow A_i{\equiv}A_j$	A_R	0	1	R_4	$\overline{R}_3$

$\overline{R}$ is the reverse of matrix R

a redox reaction is in principle sensitive to a permutation operation and four different matrices may be found for these transformations. Incidentally, owing to the simplicity of these matrices, the permuted and reversed forms are identical and in this way only two types are found in practice.

In the case of radicalic reactions the matrices R_3 and R_4 appear formally also as reverse or permuted. But in constrast with redox reactions, a radicalic transformation is not polarized since no charge is exchanged by this process. The general schemes 45 and 46 show obviously a reverse type of relationship. Consequently, for the radicalic reactions, expressed by R_3 and R_4 matrices, are only reverse and not permuted processes. With other words, the nature of this relationship is determined by the structural identity (nonpolarization) of the two species of the center of reactions.

The typical elementary reactions corresponding to the one electron transformations are summarized in Table 1.

MATRICES OF TWO-ELECTRON TRANSFORMATIONS IN TWO-ATOM CENTERS OF REACTION [19]

The two-electron processes form a group transformation also in a two-atom center of reaction. The corresponding operator can be constructed by summation of two matrices, peculiar to one-electron transformations. Therefore, the problem arises about the possible combinations of these matrices. While a bielectronic redox reaction is possible, a bielectronic radical reaction has no sense, since by definition these reactions are only one-electron processes. Consequently, two matrices for the two-electron redox reactions can be constructed by doubling the one-electron ones. Further, by combination of the two redox with the two radicalic processes, four different matrices are obtained. In this way six types of two-electron processes can be expected. These reactions are often encountered, representing basic processes for organic and inorganic chemistry.

Two-Electron Redox Reactions

Essentially the two-electron redox reactions are not different from the one-electron ones. The charge transfer is produced in this case, by the displacement of two electrons. In the case of the possible mechanism by two successive one-electron reactions, the same matrix is found as in the case of a simultaneous two-electron transfer, since the center of reaction is formed in both cases by two atoms. This is why, the overall reaction matrix is given by the normal sum of the partial steps.

Oxidative Dissociation $(2D_e)$

In this group are included reactions in which two electrons are transferred from the oxidizing species to the reducing one. The general schemes of this dissociation type are the following:

$$A_i: + A_j^{2+} \longrightarrow A_i^{2+} + :A_j$$

$$A_i^- : + A_j^+ \longrightarrow A_i^+ + :A_j^- \tag{51}$$

As an example the oxidation of zinc in presence of copper ions in solution is given:

$$\overset{i}{Z}n: + \overset{j}{C}u^{2+} \longrightarrow \overset{i}{Z}n^{2+} + :\overset{j}{C}u \tag{52}$$

The reaction matrix for this process is the double of R_1:

$$R_5 = 2R_1 = \begin{array}{cc} & \begin{array}{cc} i & j \end{array} \\ \begin{pmatrix} -2 & 0 \\ 0 & 2 \end{pmatrix} & \begin{array}{c} i \\ j \end{array} \end{array} \quad (2D_e)$$

By this processes two electrons are transferred from the A_i to A_j species. The entries indicate the loss (-2) and the gain $(+2)$ of these two electrons. No covalent bond is broken or formed by this process.

Reductive Association $(2A_e)$

The general schemes of two-electron reduction of the species A_i are the following:

$$A_i^{2+} + :A_j \longrightarrow A_i: + A_j^{2+}$$

$$A_i^+ + :A_j^- \longrightarrow A_i^- : + A_j^+ \tag{53}$$

As an example the permuted Reaction 51 is given:

$$\overset{i}{C}u^{2+} + :\overset{j}{Z}n \longrightarrow \overset{i}{C}u: + \overset{i}{Z}n^{2+} \tag{54}$$

Consequently, the reaction matrix will be the previous one, reverse or permuted:

$$R_6 = 2\overline{R}_1 = \begin{array}{cc} & \begin{array}{cc} i & j \end{array} \\ \begin{pmatrix} 2 & 0 \\ 0 & -2 \end{pmatrix} & \begin{array}{c} i \\ j \end{array} \end{array} \quad (2A_e)$$

This matrix is R_2 multiplied with 2.

Electrolytic Reactions

The electrolytic reactions are a part of the larger class termed as heterolytic transformations. These processes embrace the electrofugic dissociation (D_E) and the association of ionic species with the reformation of non-charged molecules, the so called electrophilic association (A_E). Ion dissociation and association represent reverse reaction.

Electrofugic Dissociation (D_E)

One of the simplest kind of chemical reaction is the splitting of a interatomic bond with separation of electrical charges. A general scheme describing this process is the following:

$$A_i-A_j \longrightarrow \overline{A_i^-} + A_j^+ \tag{55}$$

By the breaking of the interatomic bond the corresponding electron pair passes to the species A_i, which in this way, gets a negative charge. The other species, which losses an electron, remains positively charged; this is therefore an electrofugic dissociation process. As practical examples the dissociation of hydrochloric acid is given:

$$\overset{i}{|\underline{Cl}}-\overset{j}{H} \longrightarrow \overset{i}{|\underline{Cl}|^-} + \overset{j}{H^+} \tag{56}$$

and also of acetic acid:

$$CH_3-\overset{|O|}{\overset{\|}{C}}-\overset{i}{\underline{O}}-\overset{j}{H} \longrightarrow CH_3-\overset{|O|}{\overset{\|}{C}}-\overset{i}{\underline{O}}|^- + \overset{j}{H^+} \tag{57}$$

A similar process produces when one from several bonds is broken, the atoms remaining bonded by the non splitted bonds:

$$A_i{=}A_j \longrightarrow \overline{A_i^-}-A_j^+$$
$$A_i{\equiv}A_j \longrightarrow \overline{A_i^-}{=}A_j^+ \tag{58}$$

This kind of reaction applies to the double and triple bonds between the nonsaturated organic compounds:

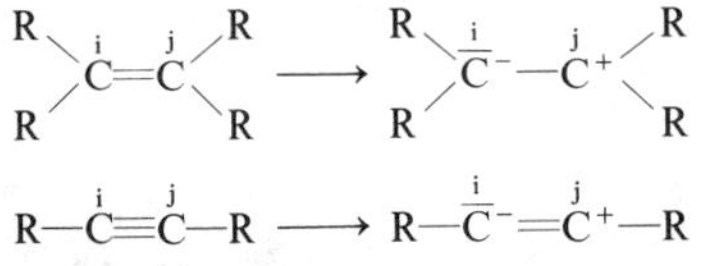

$$\overset{R}{\underset{R}{>}}\overset{i}{C}{=}\overset{j}{C}\overset{R}{\underset{R}{<}} \longrightarrow \overset{R}{\underset{R}{>}}\overset{i}{C^-}-\overset{j}{C^+}\overset{R}{\underset{R}{<}} \tag{59}$$

$$R-\overset{i}{C}{\equiv}\overset{j}{C}-R \longrightarrow R-\overset{i}{C^-}{=}\overset{j}{C^+}-R$$

Unlike reactions leading to stable compounds 54, Reaction 57 is only an intermediate step of more complex processes.

From the general schemes (55 and 58), and also from the concrete examples (56, 57, and 59), it follows that the bielectronic process of electrofugic dissociation represents the splitting of a bond with formation of charged particles: in Reaction 54 $\overline{A_i^-}$ is the reduced species and A_j^+ the oxidized one. This process can be interpreted virtually as a sum of an elementary process of radicalic dissociation, followed by an elementary process of reductive association, by the electron, transfer from the species $\cdot A_j$ to the species A_i. Reaction 55 can be written, as a stepwise process, in the form:

$$A_i-A_j \longrightarrow A_i^{\cdot} + {}^{\cdot}A_j \longrightarrow \overline{A_i^-} + A_j^+ \tag{55a}$$

The reaction matrix is therefore:

$$R_7 = R_3 + \overline{R}_1 = \begin{matrix} i & j \\ \begin{pmatrix} 1 & -1 \\ -1 & 1 \end{pmatrix} \end{matrix} + \begin{matrix} i & j \\ \begin{pmatrix} 1 & 0 \\ 0 & -1 \end{pmatrix} \end{matrix} = \begin{matrix} i & j \\ \begin{pmatrix} 2 & -1 \\ -1 & 0 \end{pmatrix} \begin{matrix} i \\ j \end{matrix} \end{matrix} \quad (D_E)$$

$$D_R \quad + \quad A_e \quad = \quad D_E$$

The addition of the martices is a commutative operation and therefore by reversing the order of the sum elements the same result is obtained. The matrix represents the operator of an electrofugic dissociation process by which a chemical bond is broken (-1) and a pair of nonparticipating electrons $(+2)$ is transferred too the species A_i.

Electrophilic Association (A_E)

The reverse of the previous process is the electrophilic association of the species carrying electrical charges. The general schemes are the followings:

$$\overline{A}_i^- + A_j^+ \longrightarrow A_i\!-\!A_j$$

$$\overline{A}_i^-\!-\!A_j^+ \longrightarrow A_i\!=\!A_j \tag{60}$$

therefore the reverses of Reactions (55 and 58).

In this class the acido-basic reactions are embraced. For example:

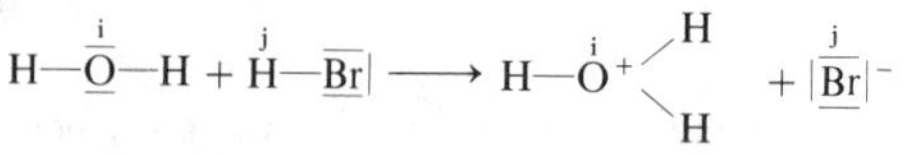

$$H\!-\!\overset{i}{\underline{O}}\!-\!H + H\!-\!\overset{j}{\underline{Br}|} \longrightarrow H\!-\!\overset{i}{O}{}^{+}\!\!\overset{\displaystyle H}{\underset{\displaystyle H}{<}} + |\overset{j}{\underline{Br}}|^{-} \tag{61}$$

In this group the Lewis acids and bases are also included.

As in the case of electrophilic association, Scheme(s) 60 and Reaction 61 can be viewed as processes virtually formed by two one-electron steps. The first process might be the electron transfer from $\overline{A}_i^-$ to A_j^+ with formation of two neutral radical species and the second process the recombination of the two radicals. The reaction matrix is therefore the sum:

$$R_8 = R_3 + R_1 = \begin{matrix} i & j \\ \begin{pmatrix} -2 & 1 \\ 1 & 0 \end{pmatrix} \begin{matrix} i \\ j \end{matrix} \end{matrix} \quad (A_E)$$

$$A_R + D_e = A_E$$

This matrix represents an electrophilic association process in which a chemical bond is formed by the mediation of a nonparticipating electron pair of the educt substrate species $\overline{A}_i$.

Heterolytic Proper Reactions

In this group are embraced the reactions of nucleofugic dissociation (D_N) and the reactions of nucleophilic association (A_N). This pair is formed from reciprocally reversed processes. In the same time there is a permutation correspondence with the electrolytic reactions. Thus the mechanism D_N is equivalent with D_E by a operation of index permutation. Likewise $A_N = {}^P A_E$. This correspondence is due to the electrical charge of the involved components; both the electrolytic and the heterolytic proper reactions are ionic, therefore polarized transformations. They are also generally termed as heterolytic reactions.

Nucleofugic Dissociation (D_N)

If the species A_i constitutes the substrate of the molecule A_i—A_j and the bond is broken on this side, the process is termed as nucleofugic dissociation or heterolysis. The reaction schemes, corresponding to this class, are the following

$$A_i\text{—}A_j \longrightarrow A_i^+ + \overline{A}_j^-$$

$$A_i{=}A_j \longrightarrow A_i^+ - \overline{A}_j^- \tag{62}$$

These reactions are permuted forms of Reactions (55 and 59). The Scheme(s) 62 can be applied to a series of a few chemical reactions encountered commonly in organic chemistry. A few examples are:

1. The breaking (heterolysis) of the bond $\overset{\diagup}{>}$C—Hal to the carbon atom:

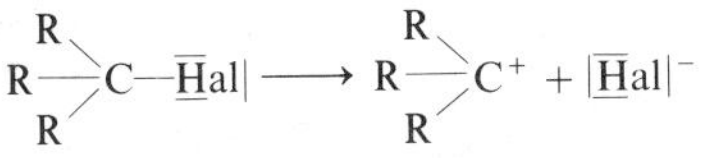

$$R\overset{R}{\underset{R}{\diagdown}}C\text{—}\overline{\underline{H}}\text{al}| \longrightarrow R\overset{R}{\underset{R}{\diagdown}}C^+ + |\overline{\underline{H}}\text{al}|^- \tag{63}$$

2. The thermal dissociation of the diazoalkans:

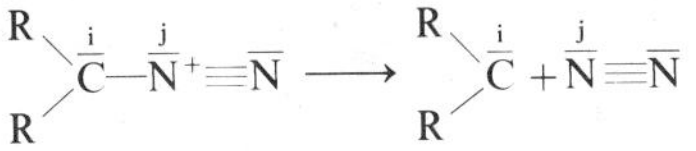

$$\overset{R}{\underset{R}{\diagdown}}\overset{i}{C}\text{—}\overset{j}{N}^+{\equiv}\overline{N} \longrightarrow \overset{R}{\underset{R}{\diagdown}}\overset{i}{C} + \overset{j}{N}{\equiv}\overline{N} \tag{64}$$

For the matrix of reaction, corresponding to this process, the Scheme(s) 68 and Reaction 63 and 64, can be considered, as in the previous cases, as the sum of two virtual processes: one of radicalic dissociation, followed by another electron transfer (D_e) from $A_i^{\cdot}$ to A_j. With this model the matrix of reaction is:

$$R_9 = R_3 + R_1 = \begin{pmatrix} 0 & -1 \\ -1 & 2 \end{pmatrix} \begin{matrix} i \\ j \end{matrix} \quad (D_N)$$

$$D_R + D_e = \qquad D_N$$

which shows the breaking of a bond on the side of the species A_i and the transfer of an electron pair to the species A_j. This matrix is the permutation form of R_7.

Nucleophilic Association (A_N)

By the reverse process represented by Equation 62, a chemical bond is formed, due to the mutual attraction of opposite electrical charges (ionic reaction). This mechanism is termed as nucleophilic (heterolytic) association. The schemes describing the reactions of this groups are the following:

$$A_i + A_j \longrightarrow A_i^- + A_j^+$$

$$A_i^+ + A_j^- \longrightarrow A_i\text{—}A_j \tag{65}$$

$$A_i^+\text{—}A_j^- \longrightarrow A_i{=}A_j$$

As an example the following reactions are taken:

$$\overset{i}{\underset{\diagup}{\searrow}}\overset{}{C^{+}}-\overset{j}{\underline{\underline{O}}}|^{-} \qquad \overset{i}{\underset{\diagup}{\searrow}}\overset{}{C}=\overset{j}{\underline{O}} \tag{66}$$

$$\begin{array}{c}Cl\\ \searrow\overset{i}{Al}-Cl + |\underline{Cl}|^{-}\\ Cl\diagup\end{array} \qquad \begin{array}{c}ClCl\\ \searrow\overset{i}{Al}^{-}\diagup\\ Cl\diagup\searrow Cl\end{array} \tag{67}$$

These processes are an intermediate step of more complex reactions.

By analogy with the previous examples, Scheme(s) 65 and the Reaction 66 and 67 might represent the sum of two virtual processes: reductive association ($1A_e$) and radicalic association (A_R). The matrix of reaction is, in this case, the following:

$$R_{10} = \overline{R}_1 + \overline{R}_3 = \begin{array}{cc} & \begin{array}{cc} i & j \end{array} \\ \begin{pmatrix} 0 & 1 \\ 1 & -2 \end{pmatrix} & \begin{array}{c} i \\ j \end{array} \end{array} \quad (A_N)$$

$$A_e + A_R = \quad A_N$$

This matrix shows the formation of a bond by the mediation of an electron pair between the bonded atomic species. R_{10} is the reverse R_9 and the permuted R_8.

Two Fundamental Matrices of Chemical Transformations

The study of elementary processes occurring in the frame of typical reaction mechanisms in two-atom centers allows one to deduce the reaction matrices corresponding to these mechanisms. The groups of reactions were presented in the previous sections as pairs of dissociation and association processes, implying, in this way, ten matrices for the typical elementary steps of five reaction couples. It has been found that *two matrices* from the couples of the one-electron processes bear, by reversion, to four ones for all one-electron transformations. By addition operations, pairs from this set, in accord with the indicated schemes, the six matrices corresponding to the two-electron processes are obtained.

Therefore it is possible to take as building blocks for the construction of any matrix of reaction, the following two matrices:

$$R_1 = \begin{array}{cc} & \begin{array}{cc} i & j \end{array} \\ \begin{pmatrix} -1 & 0 \\ 0 & 1 \end{pmatrix} & \begin{array}{c} i \\ j \end{array} \end{array} \quad (1D_e) \quad \text{and} \quad R_3 = \begin{array}{cc} & \begin{array}{cc} i & j \end{array} \\ \begin{pmatrix} 1 & -1 \\ -1 & 1 \end{pmatrix} & \begin{array}{c} i \\ j \end{array} \end{array} \quad (D_R)$$

Further the corresponding correlated pairs are formed by a reversion process:

$$R_2 = \overline{R}_1 \quad \text{and} \quad R_4 = \overline{R}_3$$

The matrices of reaction for the two-electron processes are constructed as follows:

$$R_5 = 2R_1; \qquad R_6 = 2\overline{R}_1; \qquad R_7 = \overline{R}_1 + R_3;$$

$$R_8 = R_1 + \overline{R}_3; \qquad R_9 = R_1 + R_3; \qquad R_{10} = \overline{R}_1 + \overline{R}_3.$$

The four matrices corresponding to the heterolytic reactions are also correlated by reversion and permutation relationships. As an example, if the matrix R_7 is taken as basic element, then the

Table 2
Matrices of Two-Electron Transformations in Centers of Reaction Formed by Two Atoms

No.	Chemical Process	Scheme of Reaction	Symbol	Bonds −1	Bonds +1	Matrix Reaction	Matrix Correlated
Redox Reactions							
1	Oxidative dissociation	$A_i{:} + A_j^{2+} \longrightarrow A_i^{2+} + {:}A_j$ $A_i^-{:} + A_j^+ \longrightarrow A_i^+ + {:}A_j^-$	$2D_e$	0	0	R_5	$2R_1$
2	Reductive association	$A_i^{2+} + {:}A_j \longrightarrow A_i{:} + A_j^{2+}$	$2A_e$	0	0	R_6	$2R_2$
Electrolytic Reactions							
3	Electrofugic dissociation	$A_i - A_j \longrightarrow \overline{A}_i^- + A_j^+$ $A_i{=}A_j \longrightarrow \overline{A}_i^-{-}A_j^+$ $A_i{\equiv}A_j \longrightarrow \overline{A}_i^-{=}A_j^+$	D_E	1	0	R_7	
4	Electrophilic association	$\overline{A}_i^- + A_j^+ \longrightarrow A_i - A_j$ $\overline{A}_i^-{-}A_j^+ \longrightarrow A_i{=}A_j$	A_E	0	1	R_8	$\overline{R}_7$
Heterolytic Proper Reactions							
5	Nucleofugic dissociation (heterolysis)	$A_i - A_j \longrightarrow A_i^+ + \overline{A}_j^-$ $A_i{=}A_j \longrightarrow A_i^+{-}\overline{A}_j^-$	D_N	1	0	R_9	${}^pR_7$
6	Nucleophilic association	$A_i + \overline{A}_j \longrightarrow A_i^- - A_j^+$ $A_i^+ + \overline{A}_j^- \longrightarrow A_i - A_j$ $A_i^+{-}A_j^- \longrightarrow A_i{=}A_j$ $A_i^+{=}A_j^- \longrightarrow A_i{\equiv}A_j$	A_N	0	1	R_{10}	${}^p\overline{R}_7$

$\overline{R}$ is the reverse of matrix R; ${}^pR$ is the permuted of matrix R.

following correlations can be found:

$$R_8 = \overline{R}_7; \qquad R_9 = {}^pR_7; \qquad R_{10} = {}^p\overline{R}_7$$

In the case of multi-atom center of reactions more complex operator matrices are found, but, regardless of this complexity, the matrices R_1 and R_3 serve as elementary components.

The typical reactions, corresponding to two-electron transformations are presented in Table 2.

It is worth mentioning that the system of classification of the chemical transformations embraced in this section and also a part of the adopted terminology [19] is in agreement with the ones proposed by Guthrie [21]. This symbolization system for reaction mechanisms was also proposed to the Division of Organic Chemistry, Commission of Physical Organic Chemistry, IUPAC [22]. But the classification adopted in [21] is not endowed with a rigorous mathematical base, represented by the matrix operator of the chemical reaction. The advantage of the matrix procedure is in the possibility to determine unequivocally the specificity of the reaction mechanism, and also the unique way of its realization. Only by this method has it been possible to construct any operator of reaction starting from two elementary matrices [19].

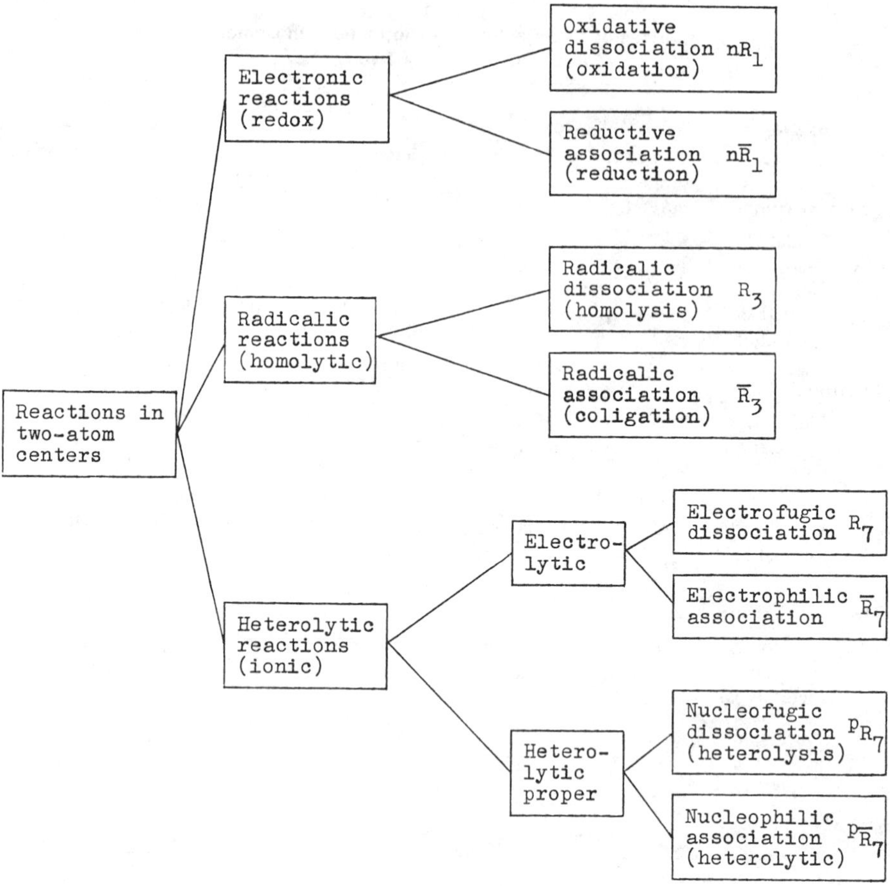

Figure 5. Typical mechanisms of the elementary steps in two-atom centers of reaction, described by means of three reaction matrices; fundamental are the matrices R_1 and R_3, since the matrix R_7 can be composed by the addition of the matrices $\bar{R}_1$ and R_3 *[19]*.

The accounting of the chemical bonds and of the nonparticipating electrons by means of reaction matrix allows a rigorous systematization not only of the effective way on which the chemical reactions are produced, but also the manner in which this development is principally possible.

A general scheme of the chemical reactions occurring in a two-atom center of reaction is given in Figure 5.

MATRICES FOR CORRELATED PAIRS IN THREE-ATOM CENTERS OF REACTION

In the previous section the reaction matrices for the elementary steps in two-atom reaction centers were deduced. These matrices can be used also in order to obtain the reaction operators for more complex reactions. The present section aims to show the systematic procedure to combine two typical elementary reactions corresponding to the succession of pairs of the correlated processes: dissociation-association and reversely.

Addition of Matrices of Elementary Processes

The typical elementary 2 × 2 matrices corresponding to the two-atom centers of reaction represent submatrices of higher order, determined by the number of atoms in the center of reaction.

A reaction matrix can also be decomposed into a sum of matrices. As an example is taken the matrix of hydrogen cyanide isomerisation from the nitrile to isonitrile form, previously mentioned, Reactions (18 and 19):

$$\begin{array}{c} \begin{matrix} i & j & k \end{matrix} \\ \begin{pmatrix} 0 & -1 & 1 \\ -1 & 2 & 0 \\ 1 & 0 & -2 \end{pmatrix} \end{array} \begin{matrix} i \\ j \\ k \end{matrix} = \begin{array}{c} \begin{matrix} i & j & k \end{matrix} \\ \begin{pmatrix} 0 & -1 & 0 \\ -1 & 2 & 0 \\ 0 & 0 & 0 \end{pmatrix} \end{array} + \begin{array}{c} \begin{matrix} i & j & k \end{matrix} \\ \begin{pmatrix} 0 & 0 & 1 \\ 0 & 0 & 0 \\ 1 & 0 & -2 \end{pmatrix} \end{array} \begin{matrix} i \\ j \\ k \end{matrix} \qquad (68)$$

$$R_I \quad = \quad R_{II} \quad + \quad R_{III}$$

The matrix R_I, for a reaction with a three-atom center is composed therefore from two bielectronic processes: the matrix R_{II}, which, on a two-atom center (i, j), is a nucleofugic dissociation process (D_N) and the matrix R_{III}, which, in a two-atom center (i, k) is a nucleophilic association process (A_N). In order to express R_I as the sum of R_9 and R_{10}, therefore a process D_NA_N, the symbol sum in square is used [20]:

$$R_I = R_9 \boxed{+} R_{10} \qquad (69)$$

This relation shows that, before the addition, R_9 and R_{10} must be transformed in adequate matrices of the same order with R_1 by introducing additional rows/columns with zero entries, as a function of the indexation of atoms in the pertinent center of reaction.

Electrophilic Substitution (S_E)

In the mechanism of electrophilic substitution two schemes are included: electrofugic dissociation (D_E) and electrophilic association (A_E) with the reaction matrices R_7 and R_8. There are two possibilities to combine these procedures: by the sequence D_EA_E termed as monomolecular electrophilic substitution (S_E1); and by the sequence A_ED_E, termed as bimolecular electrophilic substitution (S_E2).

Monomolecular Electrophilic Substitution ($S_E1 = D_EA_E$)

In a reaction of electrophilic substitution the first step is the breaking of a covalent bond by a process of electrofugic dissociation (D_E, Schemes 55 and 58) and the second step is the formation of a covalent bond by electrophilic association (A_E, Scheme 60). The general scheme is the following:

$$A_i{-}A_j + A_k^+ \xrightarrow{D_E} \bar{A}_i^- + A_j^+ + A_k^+ \xrightarrow{A_E} A_i{-}A_k + A_j^+ \qquad (70)$$

In the case of some organometallic compounds the substitution of the metal species follows the sequence:

$$H_3\overset{i}{C}{-}\overset{j}{Li} \longrightarrow \overset{j}{Li} + H_3\overset{i}{\bar{C}}^- + \overset{k}{Cd}^{2+} \longrightarrow H_3\overset{i}{C}{-}\overset{k}{Cd}^+ \qquad (71)$$

An electrophilic substitution reaction, composed by both electrofugic dissociation and electrophilic association steps can be represented also as a stepwise chemical process, as in the case of acid catalyzed polymerization:

The first step:

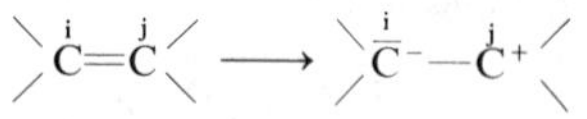

$$\overset{\backslash}{\underset{/}{C}}\overset{i}{=}\overset{j}{\underset{\backslash}{C}} \longrightarrow \overset{\backslash}{\underset{/}{C}}\overset{i}{-}\overset{j}{\underset{\backslash}{C}}{}^{+} \tag{72}$$

The second step:
(a) association of hydrogen ion

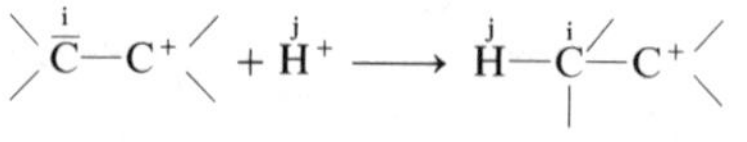

$$\overset{\backslash}{\underset{/}{C}}\overset{i}{-}\overset{j}{C}{}^{+} + \overset{i}{H}{}^{+} \longrightarrow \overset{j}{H}-\overset{i}{\underset{|}{C}}\overset{}{-}C{}^{+}$$

(b) polymerization

$$H-\overset{i}{\underset{|}{C}}-\overset{j}{\underset{|}{C}}{}^{+} + \overset{k}{\underset{|}{C}}-C^{+} \longrightarrow H-\overset{i}{\underset{|}{C}}-\overset{j}{\underset{|}{C}}-\overset{k}{\underset{|}{C}}-C^{+} \quad \text{etc.}$$

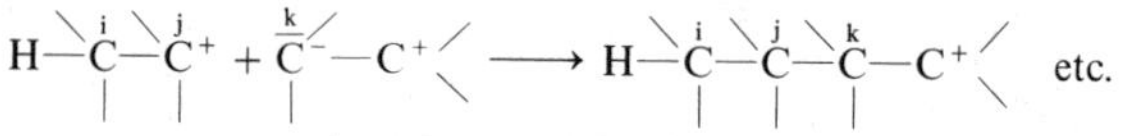

In reaction 71 the breaking of the bound $\overset{\backslash}{\underset{/}{C}}\overset{i}{-}\overset{j}{Li}$ is described by the matrix R_7, but the subsequent formation of the bond $\overset{\backslash}{C}-Cd^+$ by the matrix R_8. The reaction matrix for Schemes 70, 71, and 72 is therefore the sum of the matrices R_7 and R_8 regrouped on the three-atom center of reaction i, j, k. The matrix R_7 is ordered on the i, j indexes and has therefore the k row/column formed by zero entries; the matrix R_8 is ordered on indexes i, k and now the j row/column contains zero entries. Accordingly to Relation 79 the reaction matrix is:

$$R_{11} = \underbrace{R_7}_{\overline{R}_1 + R_3} + \underbrace{R_8}_{R_1 + \overline{R}_3}$$

$$= \begin{array}{ccc} & i & j & k \\ & \begin{pmatrix} 2 & -1 & 0 \\ -1 & 0 & 0 \\ 0 & 0 & 0 \end{pmatrix} \end{array} + \begin{array}{ccc} i & j & k \\ \begin{pmatrix} -2 & 0 & 1 \\ 0 & 0 & 0 \\ 1 & 0 & 0 \end{pmatrix} \end{array} = \begin{array}{ccc} i & j & k \\ \begin{pmatrix} 0 & -1 & 1 \\ -1 & 0 & 0 \\ 1 & 0 & 0 \end{pmatrix} \begin{array}{c} i \\ j \\ k \end{array} \end{array} \quad (D_E A_E)$$

$$D_E \quad + \quad A_E \quad = \quad D_E A_E$$

This matrix shows therefore the breaking of a bond, followed by the formation of another one. The matrix sum shows also that the process occurs by the gain of an electron pair and the loss of the same pair by the species A_i. In the final matrix form this regrouping of the electron pair is not more expressed, owing to the zero sum of the entries $2 - 2$. This drawback of reaction matrices is avoided by expressing the chemical transformation through the difference of the valence state vectors, as it will be shown in a next section.

Bimolecular Electrophilic Substitution $(S_E2 = A_E D_E)$

Compared with the previous one, this mechanism represents the permutation of the succession of the two processes, peculiar to monomolecular electrophilic substitution. There is therefore an $A_E D_E$ process, initiated by an electrophilic association, with formation of a chemical bond, followed by an electrofugic dissociation with the breaking of another bond. The electrophilic association can occur only if a charged particle can find an opposite charge or a nonoccupied electron pair to the partner atom. The general scheme is:

$$\overline{A}_i-A_k + A_j^+ \xrightarrow{A_E} A_j-A_i^+-A_k \xrightarrow{D_E} \overline{A}_i-A_j + A_k^+ \tag{73}$$

As a practical example the following reaction is taken:

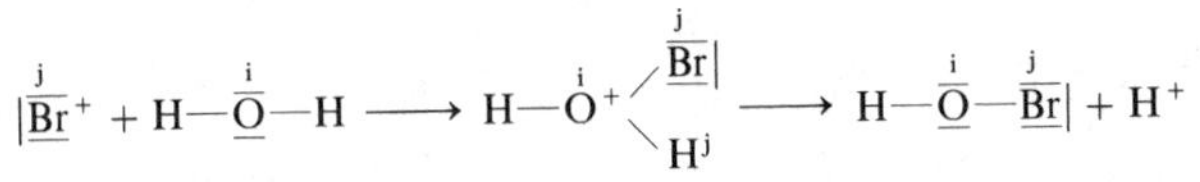

$$|\overset{j}{\overline{Br}}{}^{+} + H{-}\overset{i}{\underline{O}}{-}H \longrightarrow H{-}\overset{i}{\underline{O}}{}^{+}\overset{\overset{j}{\overline{Br}|}}{\underset{H^j}{\diagdown}} \longrightarrow H{-}\overset{i}{\underline{O}}{-}\overset{j}{\underline{Br}}| + H^{+} \tag{74}$$

The ion $|\overline{Br}{}^{+}$ is initially associated to the electron pair of the oxygen atom from the water molecule and then a hydrogen atom is eliminated by the breaking of the bond $-\underline{O}-H$.

In this case the matrix R_8 (A_E process) is ordered on the indexes i, j, but the matrix R_7 (D_E process) on i, k. The reaction matrix is therefore:

$$R_{12} = \underbrace{R_8(i,j)}_{R_1 + \overline{R}_3} + \underbrace{R_7(i,k)}_{\overline{R}_1 + R_3}$$

$$= \begin{matrix} & i & j & k \\ & \begin{pmatrix} -2 & 1 & 0 \\ 1 & 0 & 0 \\ 0 & 0 & 0 \end{pmatrix} \end{matrix} + \begin{matrix} i & j & k \\ \begin{pmatrix} 2 & 0 & -1 \\ 0 & 0 & 0 \\ -1 & 0 & 0 \end{pmatrix} \end{matrix} = \begin{matrix} i & j & k \\ \begin{pmatrix} 0 & 1 & -1 \\ 1 & 0 & 0 \\ -1 & 0 & 0 \end{pmatrix} \begin{matrix} i \\ j \\ k \end{matrix} \end{matrix} \quad (A_E D_E)$$

$$A_E \qquad + \qquad D_E \qquad = \qquad A^E D^E$$

One can notice that in Scheme 70 the indexes i, j, k may be permuted in six ways and thus six matrices are obtained as permuted forms of R_{11} matrix. One of these is the matrix R_{12} which corresponds to Scheme 73. The matrix R_{12} shows that a bond is formed and another is broken (the order is $A_E D_E$). As a matter of fact, A_i loss initially two electrons that are regained in the second step ($r_{ii} = -2 + 2 = 0$).

Nucleophilic Substitution (S_N)

The electrophilic substitution was expressed by means of matrices R_7 (mechanism D_E) and R_8 (mechanism A_E). Similarly, in nucleophilic substitution the matrices R_9 (mechanism D_N) and R_{10} (mechanism A_N) are used.

Monomolecular Nucleophilic Substitution ($S_N 1 = D_N A_N$)

The sequence in which the first step is a nucleofugic dissociation (D_N) and the second one a nucleophilic association (A_N) corresponds to the following general scheme:

$$A_i{-}A_j + \overline{A}_k^- \longrightarrow A_k{-}A_i + \overline{A}_j^- \tag{75}$$

The breaking of the covalent bond on the side of A_i species is the mechanism expressed by the matrix R_9. The next step is the association of $\overline{A}_k^-$ species to A_i^+ one formed as a intermediate product. There is, therefore, a mechanism of association to a non-occupied electron pair of the fragment $\overline{A}_k^-$ (Schemes 65), whose matrix is R_{10}.

A reaction following this mechanism is the alkene polymerization catalyzed by bases:

$$\overset{i}{C}H_2{=}\overset{j}{C}H + \overset{k}{\overline{C}}{}^{-}H_3Na^+ \longrightarrow C^+H_2{-}\overset{}{\overset{}{C}}{}^{-} - H + \overline{C}^-H_3$$
$$\underset{Ph}{|} \qquad\qquad \underset{Ph}{|}$$

$$\longrightarrow \overset{k}{C}H_3{-}\overset{i}{C}H_2{-}\overset{j}{C}{}^{-}{-}H \tag{76}$$
$$\underset{Ph}{|}$$

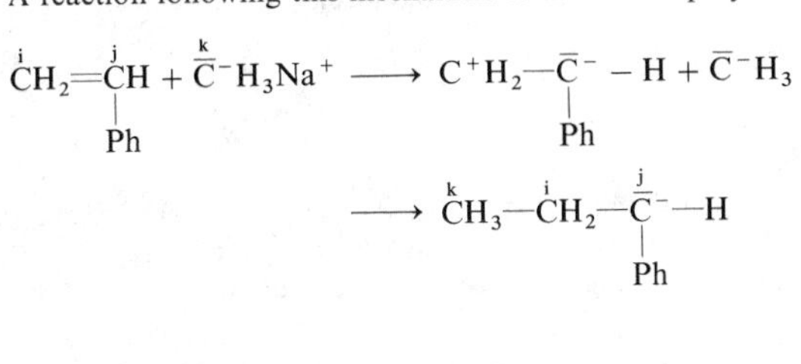

The formation of the monofluoremethane is produced according to the same mechanism:

$$\underset{CH_3}{\overset{CH_3}{\diagdown}}\overset{j}{O}{}^{+}\!\!-\!\overset{i}{C}H_3 + |\overset{k}{\underline{F}}|^{-} \longrightarrow CH_3\!-\!\overset{i}{\underline{O}}\!-\!CH_3 + \overset{i}{C}H_3\!-\!\overset{k}{\underline{F}}|$$

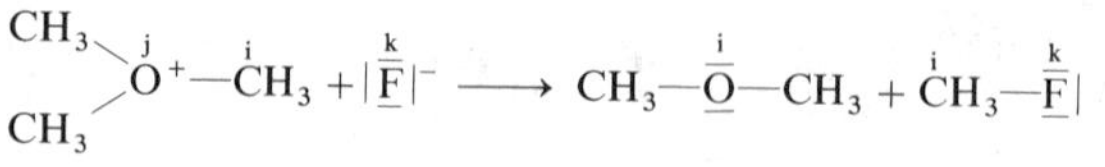

(77)

The reaction matrix, corresponding to the sequence of these mechanisms, is given by the sum:

$$R_{13} = \underbrace{R_9}_{R_1 + R_3}\ \boxed{+}\ \underbrace{R_{10}}_{R_1 + \overline{R}_3}\ =\ \begin{array}{ccc} & \begin{matrix} i & j & k \end{matrix} & \\ \begin{pmatrix} 0 & -1 & 1 \\ -1 & 2 & 0 \\ 1 & 0 & -2 \end{pmatrix} & \begin{matrix} i \\ j \\ k \end{matrix} \end{array}\quad (D_N A_N)$$

By this process a covalent bond is broken and another similar one is formed; an electron pair is gained by the species A_j, and another one is lost by the species A_k.

Bimolecular Nucleophilic Substitution $(S_N 2 = A_N D_N)$

If the order of the previous step is reversed, then the sequence $A_N D_N$ is obtained. The general scheme for this case is:

$$\overline{A}_i^{-} - A_k + \overline{A}_j^{-} \ \overset{A_N}{\longrightarrow}\ A_k - \overline{A}_i^{-} - A_j \ \overset{D_N}{\longrightarrow}\ A_i - A_j + \overline{A}_k^{-}$$

(78)

The first step is a nucleophilic association mechanism by which an electron pair from the species $\overline{A}_k^{-}$ is transferred to species A_i; in this way an intermediate product is formed. The stabilization of this compound is produced subsequently by the elimination of the species A_j after the breaking of the covalent bond with A_i.

The solvatation reaction follows this scheme. As an example the dissociation of hydrochloric acid in water is taken:

$$\overset{i}{H}\!-\!\overset{i}{\underline{C}l}| + H\!-\!\overset{k}{\underline{O}}\!-\!H \longrightarrow H\!-\!\overset{k}{O}{}^{+}\!\!\underset{H}{\overset{\overset{i}{H}}{\diagup}} + |\overset{i}{\underline{C}l}|^{-}$$

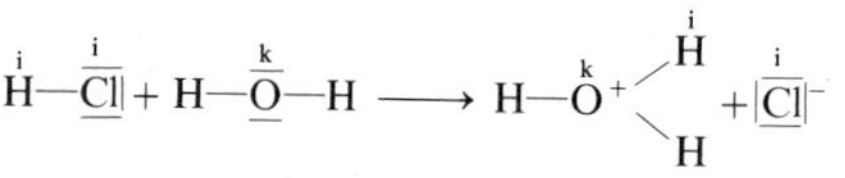

(79)

The reaction matrix is obtained by the sum:

$$R_{14} = \underbrace{R_{10}}_{\overline{R}_1 + R_3}\ \boxed{+}\ \underbrace{R_9}_{R_1 + \overline{R}_3}\ =\ \begin{array}{ccc} & \begin{matrix} i & j & k \end{matrix} & \\ \begin{pmatrix} 0 & 1 & -1 \\ 1 & -2 & 0 \\ -1 & 0 & 2 \end{pmatrix} & \begin{matrix} i \\ j \\ k \end{matrix} \end{array}\quad (A_N D_N)$$

The matrix R_{14} shows the transfer of two pairs of electrons, the formation of a covalent bond and the breaking of another bond.

Radicalic Substitution (S_R)

In the case of both the electrophilic and nucleophilic substitutions tow covalent bonds are broken on the side of the A_j or A_i species, respectively. In the mechanism of radicalic substitution the covalent bond is dissociated symmetrically according to the mechanism of homolysis.

Monomolecular Radicalic Substitution ($S_R1 = D_RA_R$)

If the first step is the radicalic dissociation (D_R) and the second one is the recombination (A_R) of the formed radicals with another preexistent radical species, then the general scheme is:

$$A_i{-}A_j + {}^{\bullet}A_k \longrightarrow A_i^{\bullet} + {}^{\bullet}A_j + {}^{\bullet}A_k \longrightarrow A_i{-}A_k + A_j \tag{80}$$

As an example the following reaction is taken:

$$H{-}\overset{i}{\underline{\overline{O}}}{-}\overset{j}{H} + {}^{\bullet}\overset{k}{\underline{\overline{O}}}{-}H \longrightarrow H{-}\overset{i}{\underline{\overline{O}}}{}^{\bullet} + {}^{\bullet}\overset{k}{\underline{\overline{O}}}{-}H + {}^{\bullet}\overset{j}{H} \longrightarrow H{-}\overset{i}{\underline{\overline{O}}}{-}\overset{k}{\underline{\overline{O}}}{-}H + {}^{\bullet}\overset{j}{H} \tag{81}$$

This is one of the reactions produced in the process of water radiolysis. Since the sequence of the steps is D_RA_R the reaction matrix is:

$$R_{15} = R_3 \boxed{+} R_4 = \begin{array}{c} \begin{matrix} i & j & k \end{matrix} \\ \begin{pmatrix} 0 & -1 & 1 \\ -1 & 1 & 0 \\ 1 & 0 & -1 \end{pmatrix} \end{array} \begin{matrix} i \\ j \\ k \end{matrix} \qquad (D_RA_R)$$

The entries of this matrix shows that a covalent bond is broken, another is formed, an electron is shared to form the bond and another electron remains unshared on the species A_j.

Bimolecular Radicalic Substitution ($S_R2 = A_RD_R$)

In this case the sequence of the reaction steps is the combination of a radical species with a molecule, followed by the radical species through a homolysis process. The general scheme is:

$$A_k^{\bullet} + A_i{-}A_j \longrightarrow A_k{-}A_i^{\bullet}{-}A_j \longrightarrow A_k{-}A_i + {}^{\bullet}A_j \tag{82}$$

The reaction of sodium hydroxide from water and metallic sodium is taken as an example:

$$H{-}\overset{i}{\underline{\overline{O}}}{-}\overset{j}{H} + {}^{\bullet}\overset{k}{Na} \longrightarrow H{-}\underline{\overline{O}}{}^{\bullet}{-}H \longrightarrow H{-}\underline{\overline{O}}{-}Na + {}^{\bullet}H \tag{83}$$

The reaction matrix is given by the sum:

$$R_{16} = R_4 \boxed{+} R_3 = \begin{array}{c} \begin{matrix} i & j & k \end{matrix} \\ \begin{pmatrix} 0 & -1 & 1 \\ -1 & 1 & 0 \\ 1 & 0 & -1 \end{pmatrix} \end{array} \begin{matrix} i \\ j \\ k \end{matrix} \qquad (A_RD_R)$$

The entries of R_{16} are the same as for the matrix R_{15}, since the radicalic processes are not polarized and therefore remain unaffected by permutation operations, i.e., by the sequence of the elementary components.

One-Electron Mediated Transfer

The double one-electron transfer can be produced by the action of the radicalic species in media containing ionic species. This group of reactions occurs in some radiolytic processes or in a series of electrochemical reactions.

Mechanism $1D_e1A_e$

The first step in this mechanism is the electron transfer from a radicalic species to a positively charged particle (D_e); the second is the reduction (A_e) of the newly formed cation by another radicalic species. The general scheme is:

$$A_j^+ + {}^{\cdot}A_i + {}^{\cdot}A_k \longrightarrow A_j^{\cdot} + {}^{\cdot}A_i + A_k^+ \tag{84}$$

In this scheme a direct transfer from $A_k^{\cdot}$ to A_j^+ is not possible, but can be mediated by the species $A_i^{\cdot}$.

The reaction matrix is obtained by the sum:

$$R_{17} = R_1 \boxed{+} R_2 = \begin{array}{c} \begin{matrix} i & j & k \end{matrix} \\ \begin{pmatrix} 0 & 0 & 0 \\ 0 & 1 & 0 \\ 0 & 0 & -1 \end{pmatrix} \end{array} \begin{matrix} i \\ j \\ k \end{matrix} \qquad (1D_e1A_e)$$

The entries of this matrix show that a species losses and another species gains the electron. The intermediate $A_i^{\cdot}$ remains unchanged at the end of the transfer process.

Mechanism $1A_e1D_e$

The general scheme in this case is the reverse of Scheme 84:

$$A_j^{\cdot} + A_i^+ \longrightarrow A_j^+ + A_i^{\cdot} + {}^{\cdot}A_k \longrightarrow A_i^+ + A_j^+ + {:}A_k^- \tag{85}$$

The first step is the reduction of the ion A_i^+ ($1A_e$) and the second one is the electron transfer from A_i to A_k, therefore the oxidation of A_i ($1D_e$). This is also a reaction that is produced in electrochemical processes or radiolysis of liquid media.

The matrix of reaction is obtained by the sun:

$$R_{18} = R_2 + R_1 = \begin{array}{c} \begin{matrix} i & j & k \end{matrix} \\ \begin{pmatrix} 0 & 0 & 0 \\ 0 & -1 & 0 \\ 0 & 0 & 1 \end{pmatrix} \end{array} \begin{matrix} i \\ j \\ k \end{matrix} \qquad (1A_e1D_e)$$

The entries of this matrix show the same processes as R_{17}, but in reversed sequence.

Two-Electron Mediated Transfer

This is a similar case to the previous one, but now two electrons are transfered. This is why in this process no radicalic species is involved, since an electron pair is yielded to cathionic species with double positive charge.

Mechanism $2D_e2A_e$

For the succession $2D_e2A_e$ of the reaction steps, the general scheme is the following:

$$A_i{:} + A_k^{2+} \longrightarrow A_k{:} + A_i^{2+} + {:}A_j \longrightarrow A_i{:} + {:}A_k + A_j^{2+} \tag{86}$$

No covalent bond is formed or broken.

The reaction matrix is obtained by the combination of two elementary processes:

$$R_{19} = R_5 \boxed{+} R_6 = \begin{array}{cc} \begin{array}{ccc} i & j & k \end{array} & \\ \begin{pmatrix} 0 & 0 & 0 \\ 0 & 2 & 0 \\ 0 & 0 & -2 \end{pmatrix} & \begin{array}{c} i \\ j \\ k \end{array} \end{array} \quad (2D_e 2A_e)$$

Consequently, two electrons are transferred from a species to another which remains finally unchanged.

Mechanism $2A_e 2D_e$

The sequence $2A_e 2D_e$ is described by the scheme:

$$A_k: + A_i^{2+} \longrightarrow A_k^{2+} + :A_i + A_j^{2+} \longrightarrow A_i^{2+} + :A_j \tag{87}$$

For this case the reaction matrix is formed by the sum:

$$R_{20} = R_6 \boxed{+} R_5 = \begin{array}{cc} \begin{array}{ccc} i & j & k \end{array} & \\ \begin{pmatrix} 0 & 0 & 0 \\ 0 & -2 & 0 \\ 0 & 0 & 2 \end{pmatrix} & \begin{array}{c} i \\ j \\ k \end{array} \end{array} \quad (2A_e 2D_e)$$

In this process the species A_i^{2+} is firstly reduced, then oxidized, mediating the two-electron transfer from $A_k:$ to A_j.

Association Rules for Elementary Processes [23]

The matrices of reactions in three-atom centers can be deduced by means of processes in two-atom centers [19]. In this group are included a series of reactions whose mechanisms are often encountered is organic chemistry: electrophilic substitution (mechanism S_E) and nucleophilic substitution (mechanism S_N). This class embraces also a series of reactions occurring especially in radiolytic and electrochemical processes: radicalic substitution (mechanism S_R) and one- or two-electron mediated transfer.

The processes grouped in the frame of one of the specified mechanisms are formed always from correlated pairs of processes occurring in two-atom centers of reaction. Thus an electrofugic dissociation process (D_E) is followed univocally by a matched process of electrophilic association (A_E) constituting a $D_E A_E$ couple. The same occurs in the case of nucleophilic substitution, where, if a nucleofugic dissociation process (D_N) occurs, the next process is one of nucleophilic association (A_N), obtaining finally the sequence $D_N A_N$.

Since the dissociation process occurs in the involved (substrat) molecule, the initiation of the reaction is not depending on the presence of the other molecular species in the system and for this reason are termed as monomolecular. For the reverse sequence $A_E D_E$ or $A_N D_N$, respectively, the reactions are initiated by the interaction of different molecular or ionic species and are therefore called bimolecular transformations. This univocal succession, formed by matched reactions is the base of the so called two electron correlated pairs [20].

It is worth mentioning that the interpretation related to the maxtrix operator of reaction founds rigorously and explicitly the classification of the set of chemical reactions.

The reaction matrices and the general schemes associated to the couples of matched processes in three-atom centers are presented in Table 3.

The chemical reactions composed by correlated pairs in three-atom centers are given in Figure 6.

Table 3
Matrices Associated to Pairs of Correlated Reactions in Centers Formed by Three Atoms

No.	Chemical Process	Scheme of Reaction	Symbol	Bonds −1	Bonds +1	Matrix of Reaction
Electrophilic Substitution (S_E)						
1	Monomolecular (S_E1)	$A_i - A_j + A_k^+ \longrightarrow$ $\overline{A_i^-} + A_j^+ + A_k^+ \longrightarrow$ $\overline{A_i} - A_k + A_j^+$	D_EA_E	1	1	$R_{11} = R_7 + R_8$ $= R_7 + \overline{R}_7$
2	Bimolecular (S_E2)	$\overline{A_i} - A_k + A_j \longrightarrow$ $A_j - A_i^+ - A_k \longrightarrow$ $\overline{A_i} - A_j + A_k^+$	A_ED_E	1	1	$R_{12} = R_8 + R_7$ $= \overline{R}_7 + R_7$
Nucleophilic Substitution (S_N)						
3	Monomolecular (S_N1)	$A_i - A_j + A_k \longrightarrow$ $A_k - A_i + \overline{A_j^-}$	D_NA_N	1	1	$R_{13} = R_9 + R_{10}$ $= {}^pR_7 + {}^p\overline{R}_7$
4	Bimolecular (S_N2)	$\overline{A_k^-} + A_i - A_j \longrightarrow$ $A_k - \overline{A_i^-} - A_j \longrightarrow$ $A_i - A_k + \overline{A_j^-}$	A_ND_N	1	1	$R_{14} = R_{10} + R_9$ $= {}^p\overline{R}_7 + {}^pR_7$
Radicalic Substitution (S_R)						
5	Monomolecular (S_R1)	$A_i - A_j + {}^{\bullet}A_k \longrightarrow$ $A_i^{\bullet} + {}^{\bullet}A_j + {}^{\bullet}A_k \longrightarrow$ $A_i - A_k + A_j$	D_RA_R	1	1	$R_{15} = R_3 + R_4$ $= R_3 + \overline{R}_3$
6	Bimolecular (S_R2)	$A_k^{\bullet} + A_i - A_j \longrightarrow$ $A_k - A_i - A_j \longrightarrow$ $A_k - A_i + {}^{\bullet}A_j$	A_RD_R	1	1	$R_{16} = R_4 + R_3$ $= \overline{R}_3 + R_3$
One-Electron Mediated Transfer						
7	Mechanism $1D_e1A_e$	$A_j^+ + {}^{\bullet}A_i + {}^{\bullet}A_k \longrightarrow$ $A_j^{\bullet} + {}^{\bullet}A_i + A_k$	$1D_e1A_e$	0	0	$R_{17} = R_1 + R_2$ $= R_1 + \overline{R}_1$
8	Mechanism $1A_e1D_e$	$A_j^{\bullet} + A_i^+ \longrightarrow$ $A_j^+ + A_i^{\bullet} + {}^{\bullet}A_k \longrightarrow$ $A_i^+ + A_j^+ + :A_k^-$	$1A_e1D_e$	0	0	$R_{18} = R_2 + R_1$ $= \overline{R}_1 + R_1$
Two-Electron Mediated Transfer						
9	Mechanism $2D_e2A_e$	$A_i: + A_k^{2+} \longrightarrow$ $A_k: + A_i^{2+} + :A_j \longrightarrow$ $A_i: + A_j^{2+}$	$2D_e2A_e$	0	0	$R_{19} = R_5 + R_6$ $= 2R_1 + 2\overline{R}_1$
10	Mechanism $2A_e2D_e$	$A_k: + A_i^{2+} \longrightarrow$ $A_k^{2+} + :A_i + A_j^{2+} \longrightarrow$ $A_i^{2+} + :A_j$	$2A_e2D_e$	0	0	$R_{20} = R_6 + R_5$ $= 2\overline{R}_1 + 2R_1$

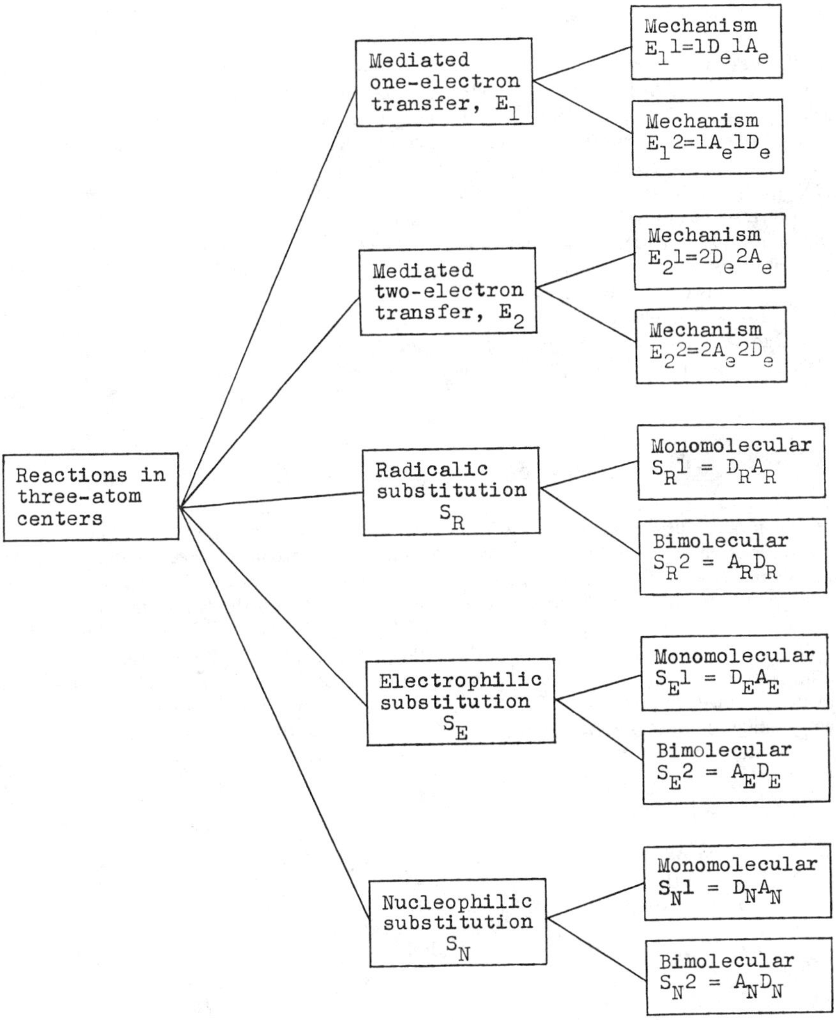

Figure 6. Typical mechanisms of the pairs of correlated elementary steps in three-atom centers of reaction. The matrices are deduced by addition of matrices R_1–R_{10} (Tables 1 and 2) [23].

MATRICES FOR MECHANISMS IN MULTI-ATOM CENTERS OF REACTION [23]

The association of the matrices corresponding to one- and two-electron transformations in centers of reaction composed by two atoms can be carried out in a center formed at least from three atoms. In this centers, maximum three elementary processes can be produced. For more complex reactions, more atoms in the center of reaction are indispensable. The number of atoms determines the order of the corresponding matrix.

Indexing Consistency of Reactant Species

In the previous section the pairs of associated processes for the reactions occurring in three-atom centers were studied. It has been shown also the way to construct these associations starting from the submatrices of the typical elementary reactions produced in two-atom centers (Tables 1 and 2). Table 3 presents the correlated processes. It follows from this table that the association can be carried out by joining correlated pairs: D_eA_e, D_RA_R, D_EA_E, D_NA_N and their permuted forms: A_eD_e, A_RD_R, A_ED_E, A_ND_N. In the case of matrix expression of the reaction operator, the permutation of a step corresponds to the same operation for two indices.

Since in three-atom center of reaction are associated at least two processes, it follows that the permutation of two indices change the left-right order in Tables 1 and 2 in the case of one reaction step only. This is why, for the indexing of the components in centers of reaction formed from three or more atoms, one must consider the order of index permutation of a step in relation to another one and to carry out the same operation in the structure of component submatrices.

As an example, the following general scheme, corresponding to the monomolecular electrophilic substitution is taken:

$$A_i{-}A_j + A_k^+ \xrightarrow{D_E} A_i^- + A_j^+ + A_k^+ \xrightarrow{A_E} A_i{-}A_k + A_j^+ \qquad (70)$$

In this process the first step is an electrofugic dissociation (D_E) and the second one an electrophilic association (A_E). The pair D_EA_E is composed from two correlated processes and the indexing on Reaction 70 is consistent with the indexing order of the submatrices in Table 2.

The reaction matrix can be written either from the elements of the educt and product, or by addition of the matrices corresponding to processes $D_E(i, j)$ and $A_E(i, k)$ [19]. The result is the matrix R_{11} (Table 3). It has been specified previously that by index permutation of Reaction 70, six matrices are obtained ($P_3 = 3! = 6$), representing permuted forms of the matrix R_{11}. It is worth mention that the intermediate products in Reaction 70 are not more pertinent for other forms, each from them yielding intermediates, as a function of the sequence of the involved elementary processes. These matrices are:

$$\begin{array}{ccc} i & j & k \\ \end{array} \qquad \begin{array}{ccc} i & j & k \\ \end{array} \qquad \begin{array}{ccc} i & j & k \\ \end{array}$$

$$\begin{pmatrix} 0 & -1 & 1 \\ -1 & 0 & 0 \\ 1 & 0 & 0 \end{pmatrix} \begin{pmatrix} 0 & 1 & -1 \\ 1 & 0 & 0 \\ -1 & 0 & 0 \end{pmatrix} \begin{pmatrix} 0 & -1 & 0 \\ -1 & 0 & 1 \\ 0 & 1 & 0 \end{pmatrix}$$

$$M(1) \qquad\qquad M(2) \qquad\qquad M(3)$$

$$\begin{array}{ccc} i & j & k \\ \end{array} \qquad \begin{array}{ccc} i & j & k \\ \end{array} \qquad \begin{array}{ccc} i & j & k \\ \end{array}$$

$$\begin{pmatrix} 0 & 1 & 0 \\ 1 & 0 & -1 \\ 0 & -1 & 0 \end{pmatrix} \begin{pmatrix} 0 & 0 & -1 \\ 0 & 0 & 1 \\ -1 & 1 & 0 \end{pmatrix} \begin{pmatrix} 0 & 0 & 1 \\ 0 & 0 & -1 \\ 1 & -1 & 0 \end{pmatrix}$$

$$M(4) \qquad\qquad M(5) \qquad\qquad M(6)$$

Among these only M(1) is consistent with Reaction 70 and with the order adopted in Tables 1 and 2; the other matrices are forms, resulting from the permutation variants of the indexes i, j, k in Reaction 70.

The situation is similar for the centers of reaction with more than three atoms, but the complexity of the problem increases with the increase of the number of the component atoms. Thus the number of the permuted forms in centers with four atoms is $P_4 = 4! = 24$ matrices, and in centers of reaction with eight atoms $P_8 = 8! = 45\,360$ matrices. But, as it will be shown later, about 51% from the reactions encountered in organic chemistry are produced in four-atom centers of reaction.

Matrices in Three-Atom Centers of Reaction

In a three-atom center of reaction, in addition to the pairs of correlated processes, studied in the previous section, reactions can be produced in which two bonds are broken and one is formed $(-2, +1)$, as well as reactions where a bond is broken and two ones are formed $(-1, +2)$ [23].

Elimination Mechanism

A general scheme in which two bonds are broken and one formed, is the following:

$$A_j\text{—}A_i\text{—}A_k \longrightarrow \overline{A}_i + A_j\text{—}A_k \tag{88}$$

In relation with the atom A_i one bond is nucleofugically and the other one electrofugically dissociated.

As an example the chloroform dissociation is taken:

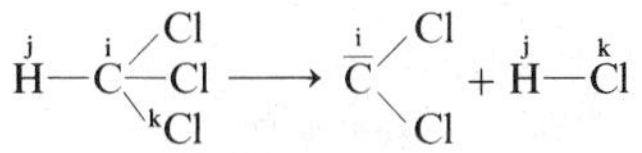

(89)

In alkaline medium, where this reaction occurs, the hydrogen is electrofugically dissociated and then associated to the oxidrilic group:

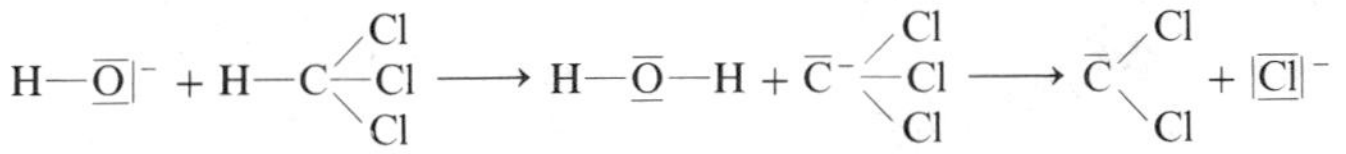

(90)

The final phase is the heterolytic elimination of $|\overline{\text{Cl}}|^-$.

Reaction 89 produces a three-atom center, but in Reaction 90 an additional component intervenes, mediating the chemical process, and the reaction develops in a four-atom center.

In the case of the System 88 and 89 the sequence $D_EA_ND_N$ is produced. Thus the bond H—C is broken on the side of the hydrogen atom, showing that a D_E process is produced against this atom. The proton attaches to the chlorine atom by a process A_N. Finally, the bond C—Cl is broken on the side of the carbon atom by a process of D_N type. For the deduction of the reaction matrix from the matrices of component processes the indexing of the atoms with which the three specified processes are related is considered in this way: $D_E(i, j)$, $A_N(j, k)$ and $D_N(i, k)$. The matrix of reaction is deduced by the sum:

$$R_{3,1} = R_7 \boxed{+} R_{10} \boxed{+} R_9 \tag{91}$$

or

$$R_{3,1} = \underbrace{\begin{pmatrix} \overset{i}{2} & \overset{j}{-1} & \overset{k}{0} \\ -1 & 0 & 0 \\ 0 & 0 & 0 \end{pmatrix}}_{D_E(i,\, j)} + \underbrace{\begin{pmatrix} \overset{i}{0} & \overset{j}{0} & \overset{k}{0} \\ 0 & 0 & 1 \\ 0 & 1 & -2 \end{pmatrix}}_{A_N(j,\, k)} + \underbrace{\begin{pmatrix} \overset{i}{0} & \overset{j}{0} & \overset{k}{-1} \\ 0 & 0 & 0 \\ -1 & 0 & 2 \end{pmatrix}}_{D_N(i,\, k)} = \underbrace{\begin{pmatrix} \overset{i}{2} & \overset{j}{-1} & \overset{k}{-1} \\ -1 & 0 & 1 \\ -1 & 1 & 0 \end{pmatrix}}_{D_EA_ND_N} \begin{matrix} i \\ j \\ k \end{matrix}$$

This matrix can be represented also as a sequence $D_E(A_ND_N)$, which shows that a matrix D_E is associated to the matrix of the pair (A_ND_N). The adopted indexation for Reaction 89 is consistent with the form M(5) from the set of the six previous shown matrices. Therefore the following sum is obtained:

$$R_{3,1} = R_7 \boxplus M(5) \tag{92}$$

that is

$$R_{3,1} = \overset{\begin{matrix} i & \;j & \;k \end{matrix}}{\begin{pmatrix} 2 & -1 & 0 \\ -1 & 0 & 0 \\ 0 & 0 & 0 \end{pmatrix}} + \overset{\begin{matrix} i & \;j & \;k \end{matrix}}{\begin{pmatrix} 0 & 0 & -1 \\ 0 & 0 & 1 \\ -1 & 1 & 0 \end{pmatrix}} = \overset{\begin{matrix} i & \;j & \;k \end{matrix}}{\begin{pmatrix} 2 & -1 & -1 \\ -1 & 0 & 1 \\ -1 & 1 & 0 \end{pmatrix}} \begin{matrix} i \\ j \\ k \end{matrix} \qquad (D_E(A_ND_N))$$

$$D_E \quad + \quad D_NA_N \quad = \quad D_E(A_ND_N)$$

The deduced matrix shows the breaking of two bonds, the formation of a bond and a nonparticipant electron pair on the species A_i.

Addition Mechanism

For the breaking of one bond and the formation of two ones, the reaction scheme is:

$$\overline{A}_i + A_j{-}A_k \longrightarrow A_j{-}A_i{-}A_k \tag{93}$$

therefore the reverse of Reaction 88.

As an example the following reaction is taken:

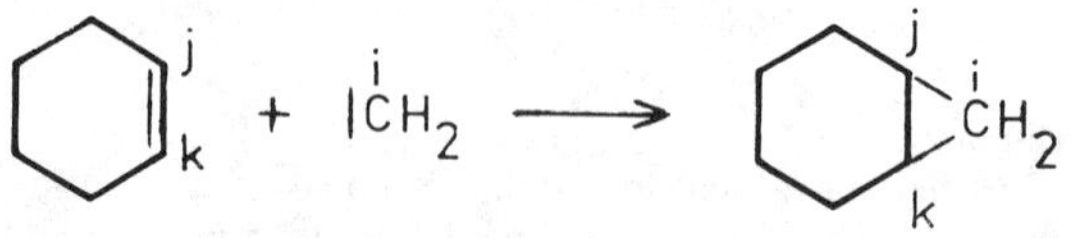

(94)

A similar mechanism is followed in Grignard type reactions:

$$\overset{j}{C}H_3{-}\overset{k}{\underline{\bar{I}}}| + :\overset{i}{Mg} \longrightarrow \overset{j}{C}H_3{-}\overset{i}{Mg}{-}\overset{k}{\underline{\bar{I}}}| \tag{95}$$

In the first stage a nucleofugic dissociation (D_N) is produced in the center $A_j{-}A_k$, then a nucleophilic association (A_N) of the species A_i, A_k and an electrophilic association of the species A_i, A_j. There is therefore a process $D_NA_NA_E$. Considering the indexing, the reaction matrix is the total of addition of the following elementary matrices:

$$R_{3,2} = R_9 \boxplus R_{10} \boxplus R_8 \tag{96}$$

that is:

$$\overset{\begin{matrix} i & \;j & \;k \end{matrix}}{\begin{pmatrix} 0 & 0 & 0 \\ 0 & 0 & -1 \\ 0 & -1 & 2 \end{pmatrix}} + \overset{\begin{matrix} i & \;j & \;k \end{matrix}}{\begin{pmatrix} 0 & 0 & 1 \\ 0 & 0 & 0 \\ 1 & 0 & -2 \end{pmatrix}} + \overset{\begin{matrix} i & \;j & \;k \end{matrix}}{\begin{pmatrix} -2 & 1 & 0 \\ 1 & 0 & 0 \\ 0 & 0 & 0 \end{pmatrix}} = \overset{\begin{matrix} i & \;j & \;k \end{matrix}}{\begin{pmatrix} -2 & 1 & 1 \\ 1 & 0 & -1 \\ 1 & -1 & 0 \end{pmatrix}} \begin{matrix} i \\ j \\ k \end{matrix} \qquad (D_E(A_ND_N))$$

$$D_N(j, k) \quad + \quad A_N(i, k) \quad + \quad A_E(i, j) \quad = \quad D_NA_NA_E$$

If this sequence is taken as a mechanism of association of D_NA_N with A_E, then, for the resulted pair, the indexing adopted in Reaction 93 is consistent with the matrix M(6):

$$R_{3,2} = M(6) \boxplus R_8$$

$$R_{3,2} = \underset{D_NA_N}{\overset{\begin{matrix} i & j & k \end{matrix}}{\begin{pmatrix} 0 & 0 & 1 \\ 0 & 0 & -1 \\ 1 & -1 & 0 \end{pmatrix}}} + \underset{A_E}{\overset{\begin{matrix} i & j & k \end{matrix}}{\begin{pmatrix} -2 & 1 & 0 \\ 1 & 0 & 0 \\ 0 & 0 & 0 \end{pmatrix}}} = \underset{(D_NA_N)A_E}{\overset{\begin{matrix} i & j & k \end{matrix}}{\begin{pmatrix} -2 & 1 & 1 \\ 1 & 0 & -1 \\ 1 & -1 & 0 \end{pmatrix}}} \quad (D_NA_N)A_E$$

The final result is therefore the breaking of a bond by nucleofugic dissociation, the formation of a bond by nucleophilic association to the nonparticipating electron pair and the formation of another bond by an electrophilic association process.

Matrices in Four-Atom Centers

The reactions occurring in four-atom centers embraces an important part of many processes encountered very often in organic chemistry.

A general reaction scheme in a four-atom center is the following:

$$A_i—A_j + A_k—A_l \longrightarrow A_i—A_k + A_j—A_l \tag{98}$$

In this reaction two bonds are broken and other two are formed. Reaction 98 shows an electrofugic dissociation (D_E) of the species A_i, A_j; the species A_i associates then electrophilically to A_k (process A_E). Further A_l is electrofugically dissociated from A_k, and this last associates nucleophilically to A_j. The sequence of the reaction steps is therefore obtained by the addition of three elementary matrices:

$$R_{4,1} = R_7 \boxplus R_8 \boxplus R_9 \boxplus R_{10} \tag{99}$$

which, in developed form, becomes:

$$\underset{D_E(i,j)}{\overset{\begin{matrix} i & j & k & l \end{matrix}}{\begin{pmatrix} 2 & -1 & 0 & 0 \\ -1 & 0 & 0 & 0 \\ 0 & 0 & 0 & 0 \\ 0 & 0 & 0 & 0 \end{pmatrix}}} + \underset{A_E(i,k)}{\overset{\begin{matrix} i & j & k & l \end{matrix}}{\begin{pmatrix} -2 & 0 & 1 & 0 \\ 0 & 0 & 0 & 0 \\ 1 & 0 & 0 & 0 \\ 0 & 0 & 0 & 0 \end{pmatrix}}} + \underset{D_N(k,l)}{\overset{\begin{matrix} i & j & k & l \end{matrix}}{\begin{pmatrix} 0 & 0 & 0 & 0 \\ 0 & 0 & 0 & 0 \\ 0 & 0 & 0 & -1 \\ 0 & 0 & -1 & 2 \end{pmatrix}}}$$

$$+ \underset{A_N(j,l)}{\overset{\begin{matrix} i & j & k & l \end{matrix}}{\begin{pmatrix} 0 & 0 & 0 & 0 \\ 0 & 0 & 0 & 1 \\ 0 & 0 & 0 & 0 \\ 0 & 1 & 0 & -2 \end{pmatrix}}} = \underset{D_EA_ED_NA_N}{\overset{\begin{matrix} i & j & k & l \end{matrix}}{\begin{pmatrix} 0 & -1 & 1 & 0 \\ -1 & 0 & 0 & 1 \\ 1 & 0 & 0 & -1 \\ 0 & 1 & -1 & 0 \end{pmatrix}}} \quad (D_EA_ED_NA_N)$$

The sequence of the steps of Reaction 98 can be taken as an association of two pairs: $D_E A_E$ and $D_N A_N$. In this case the indexation of Reaction 98 is consistent with $M(1)$ for $D_E A_E(i, j, k)$ and with $M(6)$ for $D_N A_N(j, k, l)$:

$$R_{4,1} = M(1) \boxed{+} M(6) \tag{100}$$

that is:

$$
\begin{matrix}
\begin{matrix} i & j & k & l \end{matrix} & & \begin{matrix} i & j & k & l \end{matrix} & & \begin{matrix} i & j & k & l \end{matrix} \\
\begin{pmatrix} 0 & -1 & 1 & 0 \\ -1 & 0 & 0 & 0 \\ 1 & 0 & 0 & 0 \\ 0 & 0 & 0 & 0 \end{pmatrix} & + & \begin{pmatrix} 0 & 0 & 0 & 0 \\ 0 & 0 & 0 & 1 \\ 0 & 0 & 0 & -1 \\ 0 & 1 & -1 & 0 \end{pmatrix} & = & \begin{pmatrix} 0 & -1 & 1 & 0 \\ -1 & 0 & 0 & 1 \\ 1 & 0 & 0 & -1 \\ 0 & 1 & -1 & 0 \end{pmatrix} \\
D_E A_E & + & D_N A_N & = & D_E A_E D_N A_N
\end{matrix} \qquad (D_E A_E D_N A_N)
$$

This matrix shows that two bonds are broken and other two are formed.

It is worth mentioning that a considerable number of reactions in organic chemistry follows the sequence corresponding to Reaction 98 with the matrix $R_{4,1}$. A few examples are given [20]:

The following reaction is produced according to the mechanism expressed by $R_{4,1}$:

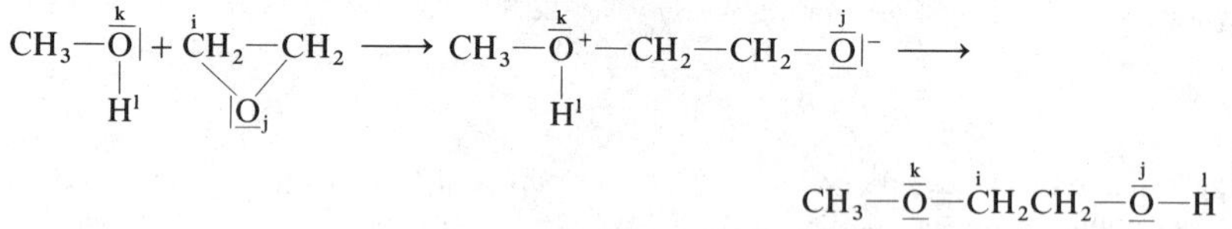

$$CH_3 - \overset{k}{\underset{H^l}{\overset{|}{O}}}| + \overset{i}{C}H_2 - \underset{|O_j}{CH_2} \longrightarrow CH_3 - \overset{k}{\overset{|}{O}}{}^+ - CH_2 - CH_2 - \overset{j}{O}|^- \longrightarrow$$

$$CH_3 - \overset{k}{\underline{O}} - \overset{i}{C}H_2 CH_2 - \overset{j}{\underline{O}} - \overset{l}{H} \tag{101}$$

Another example is represented by the olefinic monomolecular elimination (E1):

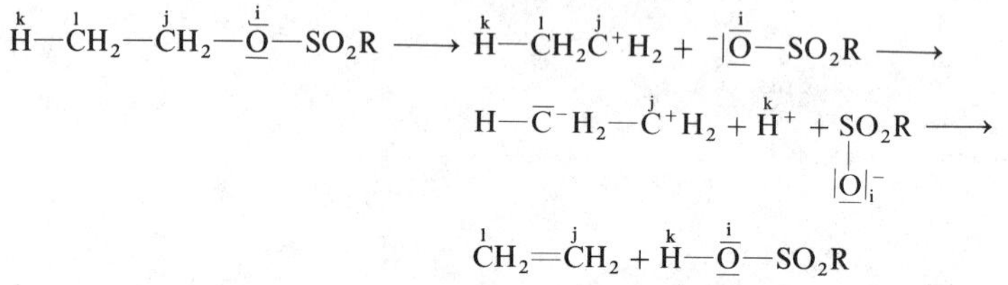

$$\overset{k}{H} - \overset{l}{C}H_2 - \overset{j}{C}H_2 - \overset{i}{\underline{O}} - SO_2 R \longrightarrow \overset{k}{H} - \overset{l}{C}H_2 \overset{j}{C}{}^+ H_2 + {}^- \overset{i}{|\underline{O}} - SO_2 R \longrightarrow$$

$$H - \overset{j}{C}{}^- H_2 - \overset{j}{C}{}^+ H_2 + \overset{k}{H}{}^+ + SO_2 R \longrightarrow$$
$$\underset{|\underline{O}|_i^-}{}$$

$$\overset{l}{C}H_2 = \overset{j}{C}H_2 + \overset{k}{H} - \overset{i}{\underline{O}} - SO_2 R \tag{102}$$

This reaction can be interpreted as a process $D_E A_E A_N D_N$. There are here two pairs of correlated processes, one representing the permuted form of the other. If the permuted indexing, shown in Reaction 102, is adopted, then the matrix of reaction is also $R_{4,1}$.

It is interesting that 51% of the reactions encountered in organic chemistry follow the mechanism corresponding to the center with four atoms [20]:

1. The mechanism of electrophilic (S_E) and nucleophilic (S_N) substitution corresponds to reactions in which participate the saturated and aromatic molecules.

2. The addition to the bonds $\overset{}{>}C = C\overset{}{<}$, $-C \equiv C-$, $>C = \overline{O}$, $>C = \overline{N}-$, and $-C \equiv \overline{N}$. In this group are included the synthesis of: azomethines, oximes, hydrazones, cyanohydrines, and of some organometallic compounds; the aldolic and benzoic condensation, etc. can be also specified.

3. Elimination reactions, especially of β-type, intermolecular cis-eliminations of Tschugaeff, Cope, etc. type.

4. Tautomer transformations of the type: ceto-emol, cyclo-oxo, oxo-lactal.

5. The transpositions: Wagner-Meerwein, Wittig, Fischer-Hepp, Hoffman-Martins, Fries, Claisen, Demianov, Amador, Beckman, Rupe; to these can be added the benzidinic and prototropic transpositions, the aminotropic exchange (S_N1', S_N2', cycle-chain) and also the intramolecular reactions: Michael's, Dieckmann's, Barton's, etc.

Matrices in Five-Atom Centers

The types of reactions in which two bonds are broken and two are formed is the case proper of processes occurring in four-atom centers. Similar reactions can take place also in five-atom centers, according to the following scheme of reaction:

$$A_i—A_j + A_k—A_l + \bar{A}_m^- \longrightarrow \bar{A}_j^- + A_i—A_k + A_k—A_m \qquad (103)$$

We can specify in this case the sequence of the elementary steps as $A_ND_ND_NA_N$. This follows from the example:

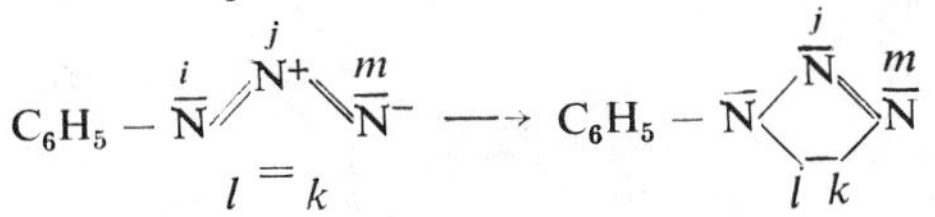

(104)

The atom k attaches to the atom j by a process A_N. A nucleofugic dissociation of the bond between the j, i species follows, with the transfer of one electron pair to j. Afterwards is produced a nucleofugic dissociation of a bond, among the two, binding the species k and l. The next step is the nucleophilic association between k and m species and also between i and l. The matrix of reaction is therefore:

$$R_{5,1} = \begin{array}{c} \begin{matrix} i & j & k & l & m \end{matrix} \\ \begin{pmatrix} 0 & -1 & 0 & 1 & 0 \\ -1 & 2 & 1 & 0 & 0 \\ 0 & 0 & 0 & -1 & 0 \\ 1 & 0 & -1 & 0 & 1 \\ 0 & 0 & 0 & 1 & -2 \end{pmatrix} \end{array} \begin{matrix} i \\ j \\ k \\ l \\ m \end{matrix} \qquad (A_ND_ND_NA_N)$$

Another general scheme of reaction in a five-atom center, in which three bonds are broken and two are formed, is the following:

$$A_i—A_j—A_m + A_k—A_l \longrightarrow \bar{A}_i^- + A_j^+—A_k + A_l—A_m \qquad (105)$$

The sequence of the five elementary processes follows the series: D_E, D_EA_E, D_NA_N. The reaction matrix is:

$$R_{5,2} = \begin{array}{c} \begin{matrix} i & j & k & l & m \end{matrix} \\ \begin{pmatrix} 2 & -1 & 0 & 0 & 0 \\ -1 & 0 & 1 & 0 & -1 \\ 0 & 1 & 0 & -1 & 0 \\ 0 & 0 & -1 & 0 & 1 \\ 0 & -1 & 0 & 1 & 0 \end{pmatrix} \end{array} \begin{matrix} i \\ j \\ k \\ l \\ m \end{matrix} \qquad (D_E, D_EA_E, D_NA_N)$$

As an example of this type the following reaction is taken:

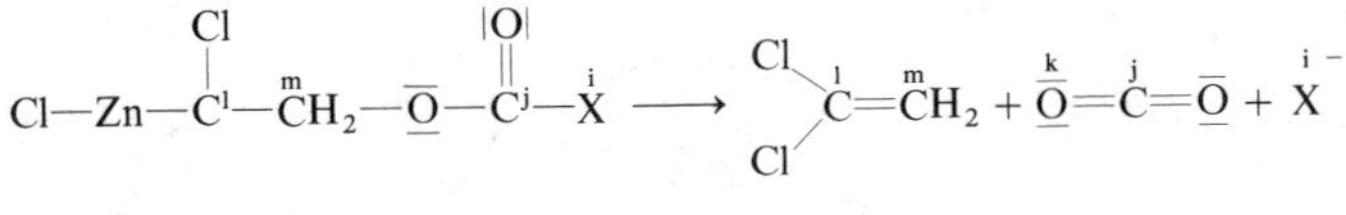

(106)

Matrices in Six-Atom Centers

The six-atom centers of reaction are exemplified by the following general scheme:

$$A_i—A_l + A_j—A_m + A_k—A_n \longrightarrow A_i—A_n + A_j—A_l + A_k—A_m \qquad (107)$$

Here three bonds are electrofugically broken and as many ones are formed by electrophilic association process. The following sequence of the steps are therefore produced: $D_EA_ED_EA_ED_EA_E$.
The matrix of reaction has the form:

$$R_{6,1.} = \begin{array}{c} \begin{array}{cccccc} i & j & k & l & m & n \end{array} \\ \begin{pmatrix} 0 & 0 & 0 & -1 & 0 & 1 \\ 0 & 0 & 1 & 1 & 0 & -1 \\ 0 & 0 & 0 & 0 & 1 & -1 \\ -1 & 1 & 0 & 0 & 1 & 0 \\ 0 & 0 & 1 & 1 & 0 & 0 \\ 1 & -1 & -1 & 0 & -1 & 0 \end{pmatrix} \end{array} \begin{array}{c} \\ i \\ j \\ k \\ l \\ m \\ n \end{array} \qquad (D_EA_ED_EA_ED_EA_E)$$

An example of reaction following this scheme is:

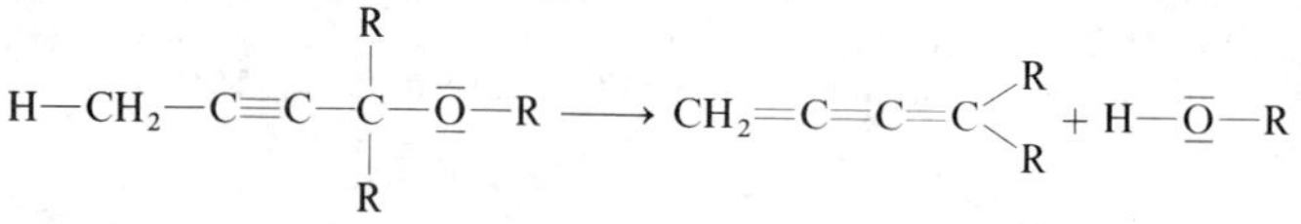

(108)

Another six-atom center scheme include only nucleophilic processes. For example:

$$A_n—A_i—A_j—A_m + A_k—A_l \longrightarrow \bar{A}_i^-—A_j^+ + A_n—A_l + A_k—A_m$$

In this case the sequence is: $D_NA_ND_ND_NA_N$; the corresponding reaction matrix is:

$$R_{6,2} = \begin{array}{c} \begin{array}{cccccc} i & j & k & l & m & n \end{array} \\ \begin{pmatrix} 2 & 0 & 0 & 0 & 0 & -1 \\ 0 & 0 & 0 & 0 & -1 & 0 \\ 0 & 0 & 0 & -1 & 0 & 1 \\ 0 & 0 & -1 & 0 & 1 & 0 \\ 0 & -1 & 0 & 1 & 0 & 0 \\ -1 & 0 & 1 & 0 & 0 & 0 \end{pmatrix} \end{array} \begin{array}{c} \\ i \\ j \\ k \\ l \\ m \\ n \end{array} \qquad (D_NA_ND_NA_ND_NA_N)$$

In six-atom centers occur important reactions for organic synthesis. In this respect the Diels-Alder reaction and Cope transposition are specified [2, 11, 20].

In Diels-Alder reaction, compounds with double conjugated bonds form a cycle by the reaction with an olefinic double bond:

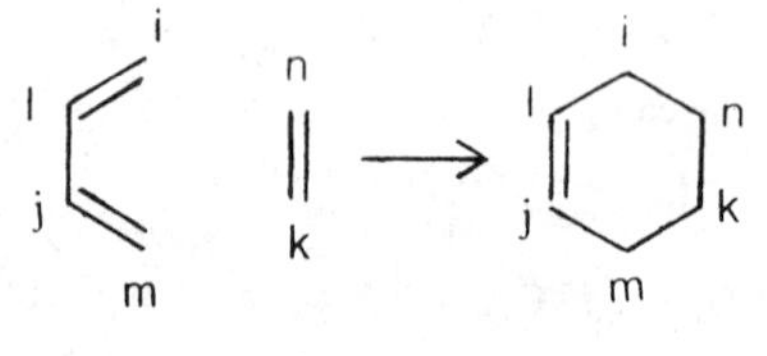

(110)

The Cope transposition is represented by the reaction:

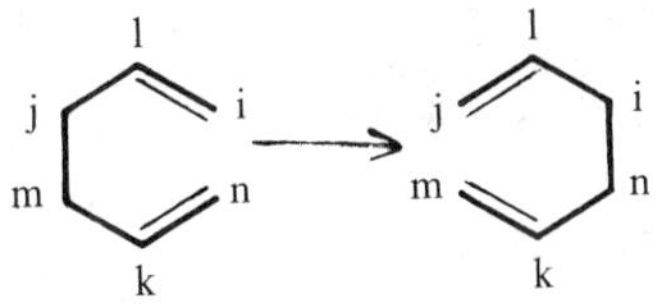

(111)

Here takes place the modification of the position of the double bonds . In both cases the reaction matrix is $R_{6,1}$ since the sequence $D_EA_ED_EA_ED_EA_E$ is fulfilled. A series of well known reactions in organic chemistry follows this reaction scheme. The following examples are taken [20, 24]: Grob's fragmentation, Blanc's reaction, Bogart's synthesis, Canizzaro's reaction, Fenton's reaction, Gabriel's elimination method, Hammick's decarboxylation of picolinic acid, Hunsdrick-Borodin's reaction, Ianovsk's reaction, Nef's synthese, Nenitzescu's reductive acylation, Openhauer's oxidation, Reverdin's reaction, Serin's reaction, cycle broadening of Tiffenau-Demjanov, Wagner-Jauregg's reaction, Wurz-Fittig's reaction, Ziegler's cyclization etc. In the case of transpositions the following types are specified [24]: pinacol-pinacoline transposition, acylation, benzilation, Nametkin's Claisen's, Cope's Fischer-Hepp's, benzidination, 5c-allylic, Favorks's, Perkin's, 1, 2 transposition by Clemensons reduction, cetenacetal transposition etc. [25–27].

In Table 4 the general schemes in centers of reaction with more than two-atoms are presented.

Table 4
General Schemes and Matrices in Multi-Atom Centers of Reaction

No.	Scheme of Reaction	Symbol	Bonds −1	Bonds −1	Matrix of Reaction
Three-Atom Centers of Reaction					
1	Elimination mechanism $A_j - A_i - A_k \longrightarrow \overline{A_i} + A_j - A_k$	$D_EA_ED_N$	2	1	$R_{3,1}$
2	Addition mechanism $\overline{A_i} + A_j - A_k \longrightarrow A_j - A_i - A_k$	$D_NA_NA_E$	1	2	$R_{3,2}$
Four-Atom Centers of Reaction					
3	$A_i - A_j + A_k - A_l \longrightarrow A_i - A_k + A_j - A_l$	$D_EA_ED_NA_N$	2	2	$R_{4,1}$
Five-Atom Centers of Reaction					
4	$A_i - A_j + A_k - A_l + \overline{A_m} \longrightarrow$ $\overline{A_i} + A_j - A_k + A_l - A_m$	$A_ND_ND_NA_N$	2	2	$R_{5,1}$
5	$A_i - A_j - A_m + A_k - A_l \longrightarrow$ $\overline{A_i} + A_j - A_k + A_l - A_m$	$D_ED_EA_ED_EA_E$	3	2	$R_{5,2}$
Six-Atom Centers of Reaction					
6	$A_i - A_j + A_k - A_l + A_m - A_n \longrightarrow$ $A_i - A_n + A_j - A_k + A_l - A_m$	$D_ED_EA_ED_EA_E$	3	2	$R_{6,1}$
7	$A_n - A_i - A_j - A_m - A_l \longrightarrow$ $\overline{A_i} - A_j + A_n - A_k + A_l - A_m$	$D_NA_ND_ND_NA_N$	3	2	$R_{6,2}$

VECTORS OF VALENCE STATES [28]

The foundation of a mathematical model for the expression of molecular structures and the modifications undergone by these formations during the chemical reactions is based on two main aspects: (1) structure and reaction matrices and (2) transformations of valence states of the atoms by electron regrouping.

Chemical Species in Molecule

Any chemical species such as an atom, ion, or radical is characterized by a particular electronic configuration that can be described by the term of valence state of the chemical species, denoted by VS (valence state). A definition of the VS, corresponding to a rigorous interpretation of this notion, was formulated in 1934 by Van Vleck [29]: the valence state is "the chemical species in molecule." We can imagine that the atom is taken off from the molecule, without change the bond orbitals and thus the atom conserves a specific valence state, which can be found in a series of molecular structures, where the specified atom is located. By the determination of chemical compounds, interpretations about the non-stationarity of a certain structure are encountered. In this case the statistic approximation of the stationary state is considered as valence state for which three are specified interactions of the electrons with the neighbor atoms in the corresponding structure.

A chemical reaction represents a reorganization of the electrons in a center of reaction, accompanied by a change of the valence states of the atoms. This is why a rigorous treatment of the problem of chemical reactions is possible only by a nonambiguous determination of the possible valence state, which can be reached by the atom included in the center of reaction. The way to produce the chemical transformation is determined exclusively by the succession of the steps making possible the electron regrouping in ensembles corresponding to a defined valence state.

Components of the Vectors of Valence States

The valence state can be completely determined by means of four components, termed as vectors of valence state, denoted VVS (Vectors of Valence State). These components are [2, 17, 25]:

f, N, n—number of the nonparticipant electrons in chemical bonds
s, S, σ—number of simple (or sigma) bonds
d, D, π—number of double (or pi) bonds
t, T, 2π—number of triple (or two pi) bonds

Among the three proposed notations, the notation (nsdt) for the vector of valence state will be used. In this way a defined valence state of any atomic species is completely and univocally described [2, 17, 20, 25].

As an example the vector of valence state (0210) in (0400), therefore, $>C= \rightarrow >C<$, is taken. The difference of these vectors (DVVS) is (0-210). By stepwise transformations of VS it is found that in order to effect this reaction, a intermediate step is necessary, as follows:

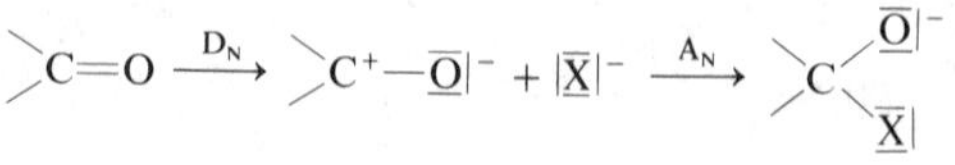

$$>C=O \xrightarrow{D_N} >C^+ - \overline{\underline{O}}|^- + |\underline{\overline{X}}|^- \xrightarrow{A_N} >C<\begin{matrix}\overline{\underline{O}}|^-\\ \underline{\overline{X}}|\end{matrix} \tag{112}$$

(0210)   (0300)   (0400)

Therefore, it is necessary to generate the intermediate state $>C^+-$ (0300), by the breaking of a bond; further, this form is stabilized by the creation of another bond by a nucleophilic association of this species with $|\underline{\overline{X}}|^-$ to form $>C<$ [23]. From the point of view of the formation of positive charge to the carbon atom, the question arises if such a process may represent a real intermediate of the reaction (112). The answer is that the double bond >C=O can be weakened under action of a positive electrical field of a cation and in this way the electron density χ at the carbon atom is diminished.

Principally, the procedure can be applied not only for known reactions; this scheme has a more general significance, which allows its application also in the case of hypothetically reactions, by observing the effective valence states and possible electron regroupings.

Possible Valence States of the Atomic Species

An atomic species can participate in a very extended series of chemical combinations. The state of the atom in a defined molecular structure is the valence state proper, as it has been previously shown. The ensemble of these compounds is the source for the empirical determination of the possible valence states of the atoms. But, instead of a specified atomic species, a symbolic one X can be considered, for the schematic representation of valence state of all chemical elements.

The vector of valence state, determined by its four components, characterizes completely a specified valence state. The vector with all the components zeros, therefore (0000), applies to the proton and the free ions of the metals; the vector (1000) shows the valence state of the hydrogen atom and alkaline metal atoms. Other examples are the following: >C= (0210), N̄≡ (2001), —C≡ (0101), >S̄= (2210), =Ẋ≡ (1111) etc. In Table 5 all valence states, practically possible, corre-

Table 5
Valence State as Site of Atomic Species in Molecule and the Vectors of the Valence States

No.		nsdt	No.		nsdt	No.		nsdt	No.		nsdt
0	X	0 0 0 0	35	X̲—	4 1 0 0	70	⋝X⋜ (with vertical bonds)	0 6 1 0	105	⋝X≡ (with vertical bonds)	0 5 0 1
1	X—	0 1 0 0	36	—X̲—	4 2 0 0	71	—Ẋ=	1 1 1 0	106	Ẋ≡	1 0 0 1
2	—X—	0 2 0 0	37	—X̲<	4 3 0 0	72	>Ẋ=	1 2 1 0	107	—Ẋ≡	1 1 0 1
3	—X<	0 3 0 0	38	>X̲<	4 4 0 0	73	⋝Ẋ=	1 3 1 0	108	>Ẋ≡	1 2 0 1
4	>X<	0 4 0 0	39	|Ẋ	5 0 0 0	74	⋝Ẋ⋜	1 4 1 0	109	⋝Ẋ≡	1 3 0 1
5	>X⋜	0 5 0 0	40	|Ẋ—	5 1 0 0	75	⋝Ẋ⋜	1 5 1 0	110	⋝Ẋ≡	1 4 0 1
6	⋝X⋜	0 6 0 0	41	|Ẋ<	5 2 0 0	76	—X̄=	2 1 1 0	111	X̄≡	2 0 0 1
7	⋝X⋜	0 7 0 0	42	|Ẋ⋜	5 3 0 0	77	>X̄=	2 2 1 0	112	—X̄≡	2 1 0 1
8	⋝X⋜	0 8 0 0	43	|X̲	6 0 0 0	78	⋝X̄=	2 3 1 0	113	>X̄≡	2 2 0 1
9	⋝X⋜	0 9 0 0	44	|X̲—	6 1 0 0	79	⋝X̄⋜	2 4 1 0	114	⋝X̄≡	2 3 0 1
10	⋝X⋜	010 0 0	45	|X̲<	6 2 0 0	80	—Ẋ̲=	3 1 1 0	115	Ẋ̲≡	3 0 0 1
11	⋝X⋜	011 0 0	46	|X̲·	7 0 0 0	81	>Ẋ̲=	3 2 1 0	116	—Ẋ̲≡	3 1 0 1

(Reprinted by permission of M. Kratochvil, J. Koča and V. Kvasnička [25]).

(Continued)

Table 5 (Continued)

No.	nsdt	No.	nsdt	No.	nsdt	No.	nsdt
12	X 012 0 0	47	X 7 1 0 0	82	X= 3 3 1 0	117	X= 3 2 0 1
13	X 1 0 0 0	48	X 8 0 0 0	83	—X= 4 1 1 0	118	X= 4 0 0 1
14	X— 1 1 0 0	49	X= 0 0 1 0	84	X= 4 2 1 0	119	—X= 4 1 0 1
15	—X— 1 2 0 0	50	=X= 0 0 2 0	85	X< 5 1 1 0	120	X= 5 0 0 1
16	—X< 1 3 0 0	51	=X< 0 0 3 0	86	=X= 0 1 2 0	121	=X= 0 0 1 1
17	>X< 1 4 0 0	52	>X< 0 0 4 0	87	=X= 0 2 2 0	122	=X= 0 1 1 1
18	>X< 1 5 0 0	53	X= 1 0 1 0	88	=X= 0 3 2 0	123	=X= 0 2 1 1
19	>X< 1 6 0 0	54	=X= 1 0 2 0	89	=X= 0 4 2 0	124	=X= 0 3 1 1
20	>X< 1 7 0 0	55	=X< 1 0 3 0	90	=X= 1 1 2 0	125	=X= 1 0 1 1
21	X 2 0 0 0	56	X= 2 0 1 0	91	=X= 1 2 2 0	126	=X= 1 1 1 1
22	X— 2 1 0 0	57	=X= 2 0 2 0	92	=X= 1 3 2 0	127	=X= 1 2 1 1
23	—X— 2 2 0 0	58	=X< 2 0 3 0	93	=X= 2 1 2 0	128	=X= 2 0 1 1
24	—X< 2 3 0 0	59	X= 3 0 1 0	94	=X= 2 2 2 0	129	=X= 2 1 1 1
25	>X< 2 4 0 0	60	=X= 3 0 2 0	95	>X= 3 1 2 0	130	=X= 3 0 1 1
26	>X< 2 5 0 0	61	X= 4 0 1 0	96	>X= 0 1 3 0	131	>X= 0 0 2 1
27	>X< 2 6 0 0	62	=X= 4 0 2 0	97	>X= 1 1 3 0	132	>X= 1 0 2 1
28	X 3 0 0 0	63	·X= 5 0 1 0	98	>X= 0 2 3 0	133	>X= 0 1 2 1
29	X— 3 1 0 0	64	X= 6 0 1 0	99	X= 0 0 0 1	134	=X= 0 1 0 2
30	—X— 3 2 0 0	65	—X= 0 1 1 0	100	=X= 0 0 0 2	135	=X= 0 2 0 2
31	—X< 3 3 0 0	66	>X= 0 2 1 0	101	—X= 0 1 0 1	136	=X= 1 0 0 2
32	>X< 3 4 0 0	67	>X= 0 3 1 0	102	>X= 0 2 0 1	137	=X= 2 0 0 2
33	>X< 3 5 0 0	68	>X< 0 4 1 0	103	>X= 0 3 0 1	138	=X= 0 0 1 2
34	X 4 0 0 0	69	>X< 0 5 1 0	104	>X= 0 4 0 1		

sponding to all chemical elements, are presented [25]. This table includes 139 forms for which the graphical symbols and the four components of the corresponding vector are shown. The limitation imposed by the number of the covalent bonds was considered with regard to the rule of the stable octet, but also the incomplete formations, suboctet structures until the maximal state nd^4 (see Reference 25 and the bibliography cited therein). Thus for the vector of valence state with the four components $(\vec{v}_1\vec{v}_2\vec{v}_3\vec{v}_4)$, the following relation holds:

$$s = v_1 + v_2 + 2v_3 + 3v_4 \leq 8 \tag{113}$$

With this reaction a few s-values are calculated: proton s = 0, carbon s = 4, sulfur in $F_3S{\equiv}N$ s = 6, iodine in IO_4^- s = 0 etc. Exceptions are the vectors (0900)–(01200), for which the coordination number is in the range 9–12 [26]. In hybride states the occurence of maximal two triple bonds for an atom is accepted [27]. In the delocalized bonds of the combinations with conjugated double bonds the vector (0210) is adopted. Similarly for the states of the type $>P^{\delta+}\cdots O^{\delta-}\cdots Me^+$ (0310) and $>C^{\delta+}\cdots O^{\delta-}\cdots Me^+$ (0210), two normal bonds are ascribed. The states $>C^+<$ and $>C^-<$ have VVS (0500).

Among the valence states, presented in Table 5, a few ones might not satisfy the relation (113) which is a limitative rule. Thus, for hydrogen, the maximal number of bond is 1, for the elements of second period is 4, for the third and fourth periods the same number is 6; the rest of elements have maximum 8 bonds. In the case of the s, p and d orbitals 9(1 + 3 + 5) bonds may exist, but the highest electron layers are always diffuse and therefore the value 9 is not limitative. It is possible that among the 139 types of valence states, some must be excluded and others are not applicable to possible structures or intermediates.

In Table 5 the first column corresponds to the order in which the symbols of the valence states were located. Any attempts to establish a significant correlation between this ordering number and a property of the vector of the valence state fails, excepting the first 13th positions, for which the ordering number is the same as the simple bonds in the vector of the atom.

For a computing program Table 5 alone is not sufficient. It may be completed with the matrix corresponding to the step of valence states for the atoms.

The problem of the valence states in case of chemical elements arises, and cannot be deduced from Table 5, and, consequently, an additional indication is necessary. This can be introduced by means of a matrix in which the vector of the valence state (VVS) is correlated with a few individual chemical elements, as it is shown in Table 6 for a series of metalloids and in Table 7 for a series of metals. In the first column the vectors from Table 5, which have no correspondence for the elements counted up, were excluded.

Conversion of Valence States in Chemical Transformations

By means of the vectors of valence state it is possible, in principle, to study the forms of a chemical species in the course of any chemical transformation. These forms can be represented in the form of graphs, including more or less extended groups of reactions, such as, for example, the graph of the totality of the nucleofugic dissociation of simple, double, and triple bonds [28]. Such a formation is a subgraph of the hypothetical graph corresponding to the totality of valence state of the atoms, termed as graph ECVSA (Electron Conversion of Valence States of the Atoms). This graph is obviously too large and too complex to be represented in complete form. This is why only more limited subgraph are used.

As an example, in Figure 7 is presented a subgraph related to the group $>C{=}O$, in which, for the carbon atom the VS is (0210) and for oxygen (0410) [20]. The lines of the graph show the pairs of valence states where the electron conversion typically needs elementary steps in the above described manner by the method of the matrix operator of reaction [19, 23]. The framed vectors express the transformations in which both atoms participate. The elementary processes by which the chemical reaction is realized are also shown. As an example, the transformation of the central

Table 6
Vectors of Valence States for Some Metalloids

VVS nsdt	H 1	B 5	C 6	N 7	O 8	F 9	Si 14	P 15	S 16	Cl 17	Br 35	I 53
0000	1											
0100	1											
0200	1	1										
0300		1	1	1			1		1			
0400		1	1	1	1		1	1	1			
0500		1	1	1			1	1	1			
0600		1	1				1	1	1			1
0700												1
1000	1											
1200		1	1									
1300			1	1			1	1				
1400			1					1	1			
2000	1											
2100		1	1				1					
2200			1	1	1		1	1				
2300			1	1	1							
2400			1		1		1	1	1	1	1	1
2500									1	1	1	1
2600												1
3000		1										
3100			1	1			1					
3200			1	1	1							
3300								1	1			
3500			1									
4000			1				1					
4100			1	1	1			1	1			
4200				1	1	1					1	1
4300					1					1	1	1
4400											1	1
5000				1	1			1	1			
5100				1	1	1			1	1	1	1
5200										1		1
6000					1	1			1	1	1	1
6100				1	1	1			1	1	1	1
6200										1		1
7000					1	1			1	1	1	1
7100										1		
8000					1	1			1	1	1	1
0010			1									
0020		1	1	1				1	1			
0030									1	1	1	1
0040									1	1	1	
1010			1	1								
1020				1								
1030										1	1	1
2010			1	1			1					1

The VVS that have no correspondents among the specified elements in this table were excluded.

(Continued)

Table 6 (Continued)

VVS / nsdt	H 1	B 5	C 6	N 7	O 8	F 9	Si 14	P 15	S 16	Cl 17	Br 35	I 53
2020								1	1	1		1
3010			1	1	1			1	1			
3020									1	1	1	1
4010				1	1	1		1	1			
4020										1		
5010									1	1		
6010										1		
0110		1	1				1					
0210		1	1	1	1		1	1	1			
0310			1				1	1	1			
0410							1	1	1			
0510							1					1
1110		1	1	1			1	1				
1210			1				1	1				
2110			1	1	1		1	1	1		1	
2210			1		1			1	1	1	1	1
2310									1	1		
2410										1		
3110					1				1			
4110					1				1	1	1	1
4210												1
0120								1	1			
0220								1	1			1
0320												1
0420							1					
2120									1	1	1	1
2220												1
0130										1	1	1
0001			1				1					
0101			1	1	1		1	1				
0201			1	1				1	1			
0301			1						1			
1001			1	1								
1101			1	1								
2001			1	1	1		1	1				
2101								1	1			

vectors is taken, therefore $\begin{pmatrix}0210\\4010\end{pmatrix}$ in $\begin{pmatrix}0300\\6100\end{pmatrix}$:

$$\rangle C{=}\overline{\underline{O}} \underset{2A_N,\,2A_E}{\overset{2D_N,\,2D_E}{\rightleftarrows}} \rangle C^{+}{-}\overline{\underline{O}}|^{-} \qquad (114)$$

$$\begin{pmatrix}0210\\4010\end{pmatrix} \qquad \begin{pmatrix}0300\\6100\end{pmatrix}$$

In this direct transformation, in relation with the carbon atom, a nucleofugic dissociation process of the double bond is produced, but in relation with the oxygen atom an electrofugic dissociation

Table 7
Vectors of Valence States for Some Metals

VVS / nsdt	Li 3	Be 4	Na 11	Mg 12	Al 13	K 19	Ca 20	Ti 22	V 23	Cr 24	Mn 25	Fe 26	Co 27	Ni 28	Cu 29	Zn 30	Ga 31
0000	1	1	1	1	1	1	1			1			1		1	1	
0100	1	1	1	1	1	1	1	1		1			1		1	1	
0200	1	1	1	1	1	1	1	1	1	1	1	1	1	1	1	1	1
0300	1	1	1	1	1	1	1	1	1	1		1	1		1	1	1
0400	1	1	1	1	1	1	1	1	1	1		1	1	1	1	1	1
0500	1			1	1		1	1	1	1	1	1	1	1	1	1	1
0600	1			1	1		1	1	1	1	1	1	1	1	1	1	
0700							1	1	1	1		1			1		
0800							1	1	1	1		1			1		
1000	1	1	1	1		1	1								1		
1100							1										
1300								1									
2000	1	1	1	1	1	1	1			1		1	1		1	1	
2100					1												
3000					1												
4000								1									1
5000									1								
6000										1							
0010					1			1					1				
0020					1				1			1					
0030										1		1					
1010								1									
0110					1												
0210					1				1	1	1						
0310									1	1		1		1			
0410									1	1		1					
0610									1								
0120									1		1						
0220												1	1				
0130												1					
0201									1								
0301										1							

The VVS that have no correspondents among the specified elements in this table were excluded.

of the same bond occurs. In the reverse transformation, the processes of dissociation are replaced with their reverses, therefore correlated association processes occur.

A reaction sequence, often encountered, is represented by the transformation:

$$\begin{array}{c} CH_3 \\ CH_3 \\ CH_3 \end{array}\!\!\!>\!\overset{i}{C}-\overset{j}{\underline{O}}\overset{+}{<}\!\begin{array}{c}H\\R\end{array} \xrightarrow{\,D_N\,} \begin{array}{c}CH_3\\CH_3\end{array}\!\!\!>\!\overset{i}{C}{}^{+}\!-CH_3 + H-\overset{j}{\underline{O}}-R + \overset{k}{X}{}^{-} \xrightarrow{\,A_N\,}$$

$$\xrightarrow{\,A_N\,} \begin{array}{c}CH_3\\CH_3\\CH_3\end{array}\!\!\!>\!\overset{i}{C}-\overset{k}{X}$$

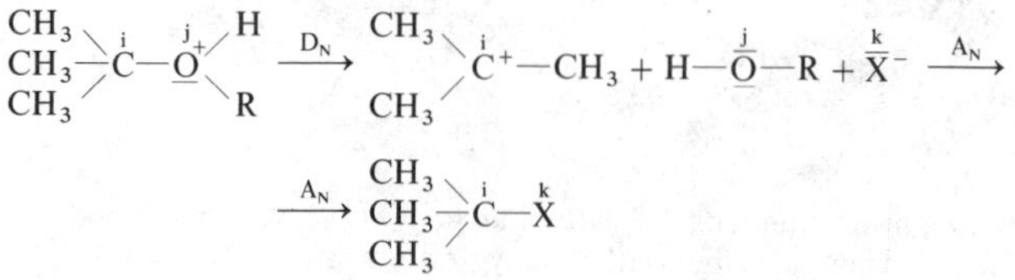

(115)

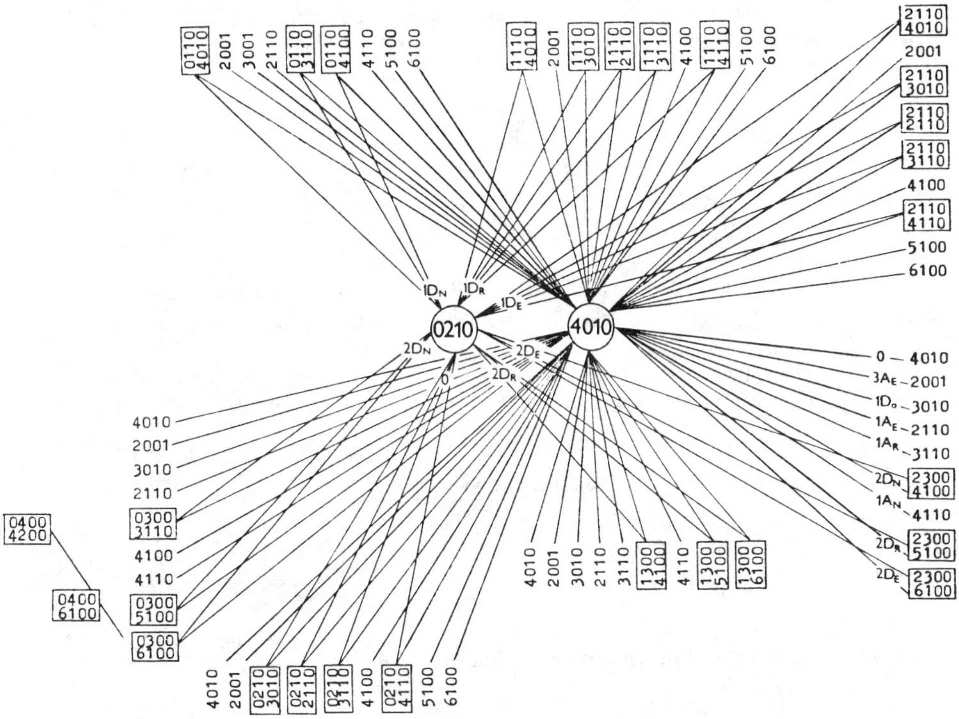

Figure 7. The subgraph of the atomic vector $\binom{0210}{4010}$ corresponding to $>$C=O; the common valence states and the ones specific to the individual atoms are shown together with the indication of elementary typical processes by which the electron conversions occur during the chemical transformations. (Reproduced with permission of the authors) [20].

This transformation must be expressed by means of the VVS as follows:

$$\begin{pmatrix} 0400 \\ 2300 \end{pmatrix} \underset{1D_E}{\overset{1D_N}{\rightleftarrows}} \begin{pmatrix} 0300 \\ 4200 \end{pmatrix}; \qquad \begin{pmatrix} 0300 \\ 2000 \end{pmatrix} \underset{1A_E}{\overset{1A_N}{\rightleftarrows}} \begin{pmatrix} 0400 \\ 0100 \end{pmatrix} \tag{116}$$

There is an association of pairs of typical mechanisms $1D_N1A_N$, therefore a nucleophilic monomolecular substitution process (S_N1), for which the matrix R_{13} was deduced [23]. This is a sum of the matrices $R_9(D_N)$ and R_{10} (A_N) [19], as it was previously shown:

$$R_{13} = \begin{array}{c} \\ \\ \end{array} \begin{matrix} & i & j & k & \\ & & & & \end{matrix}$$

$$R_{13} = \begin{pmatrix} 0 & -1 & 1 \\ -1 & 2 & 0 \\ 1 & 0 & -2 \end{pmatrix} \begin{matrix} i \\ j \\ k \end{matrix} \quad \text{(columns } i, j, k\text{)}$$

In this way the reaction matrix is correlated with the VVS, yielding a codification possibility in a computer program of the type REEL (Reorganization of Valence Electrons) [17, 20, 23].

For this kind of program, the matrix R_{13} corresponds to the mechanism S_N1.

An important problem is represented by the sequence of the elementary steps in the clarification of the overall reaction mechanism. For this purpose, using the subgraph in Figure 7, the following transformation is taken as an example [20]:

$$
\underset{\begin{pmatrix}0210\\4010\end{pmatrix}}{\overset{i}{\underset{}{>}}\overset{j}{C}=\overset{}{O}} \xrightarrow[2D_E]{2D_N} \underset{\begin{pmatrix}0300\\6100\end{pmatrix}}{\overset{}{>}C^+ - \overline{O}|^-} \xrightarrow{1A_N} \underset{\begin{pmatrix}0400\\6100\end{pmatrix}}{\overset{}{>}C\overset{\overline{O}|^-}{\underset{X}{\overset{O}{|}}}} \xrightarrow[1A_E]{O} \underset{\begin{pmatrix}0400\\4200\end{pmatrix}}{\overset{i}{>}C\overset{\overset{j}{O}-H}{\underset{\overset{k}{X}}{|}}}
$$

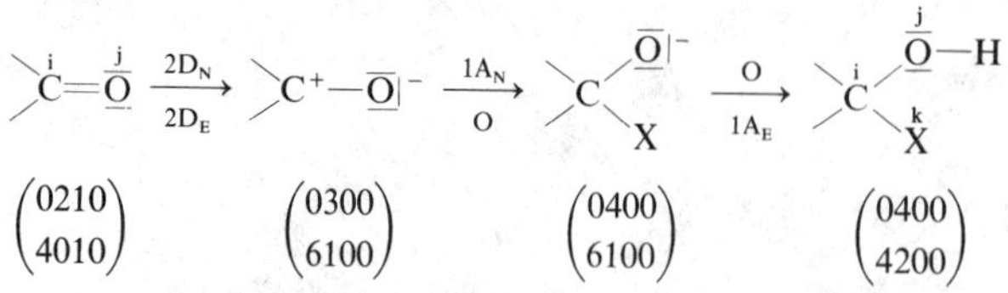

(117)

The constraint of the first step D_N can be effected by the weakness of the double bond. Thus, in the presence of a cation, the interaction $>C^{\delta+}\cdots\overline{O}^{\delta-}\cdots M^+$ is produced. The next steps occur without difficulties and so a reaction with the mechanism $2D_N1A_N$ (S_N1) for the carbon atom (indexed by i) and $2D_E1A_E$ (S_E1) for the oxygen atom (indexed by j). The nucleophilic substituent X^- is indexed with k. In order to use Scheme 117 in an example, the acetone is taken as a substrat molecule of the educt, corresponding to AV(CO) $\begin{pmatrix}0210\\4010\end{pmatrix}$ (Figure 7). As reactant molecule the nucleophilic group CN^- is taken. The educt can be written as follows:

$$
\overset{CH_3}{\underset{CH_3}{>}}\overset{j}{\underset{}{\overset{i}{C}=\overset{j}{O}}} + {}^-\overset{k}{C}\equiv\overline{N}
$$

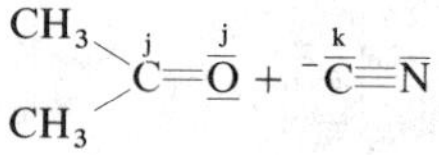

(118)

The reaction product can be deduced from the matrix form according to the scheme: $BE(E) + R = BE(P)$. The matrix R is the previous one termed as R_{13}:

$$
\begin{array}{ccc}i & j & k\end{array}
\begin{pmatrix}0 & 2 & 0\\2 & 4 & 0\\0 & 0 & 2\end{pmatrix} +
\begin{array}{ccc}1 & 2 & 3\end{array}
\begin{pmatrix}0 & -1 & 1\\-1 & 2 & 0\\1 & 0 & -2\end{pmatrix} =
\begin{array}{ccc}i & j & k\end{array}
\begin{pmatrix}0 & 1 & 1\\1 & 6 & 0\\1 & 0 & 0\end{pmatrix}\begin{array}{c}i\\j\\k\end{array}
$$

(119)

Considering the educt indexing in 118, the reaction product for the following compound is obtained:

$$
\overset{CH_3}{\underset{CH_3}{>}}\overset{i}{C}\overset{\overset{j}{\overline{O}|^-}}{\underset{\overset{k}{C}\equiv\overline{N}}{\big|}}
$$

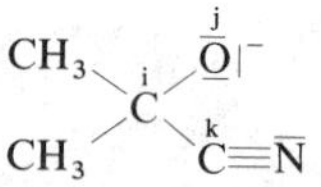

(120)

But the VVS (6100) from (120) is not the same as the VVS (4200) from (117). Therefore the compound (120) is not the compound looked for in the educt (118). In order to find the correct answer it is necessary also the step $1A_E$ for the oxygen atom in 117; thus:

$$
\underset{\begin{pmatrix}0400\\6100\end{pmatrix}}{\overset{CH_3}{\underset{CH_3}{>}}\overset{i}{C}\overset{\overset{j}{\overline{O}|^-}}{\underset{\overset{k}{C}\equiv\overline{N}}{\big|}}} + \overset{l}{H}^+ \xrightarrow{1A_E} \underset{\begin{pmatrix}0400\\4200\end{pmatrix}}{\overset{CH_3}{\underset{CH_3}{>}}\overset{i}{C}\overset{\overset{j}{O}-\overset{l}{H}}{\underset{\overset{k}{C}\equiv\overline{N}}{\big|}}}
$$

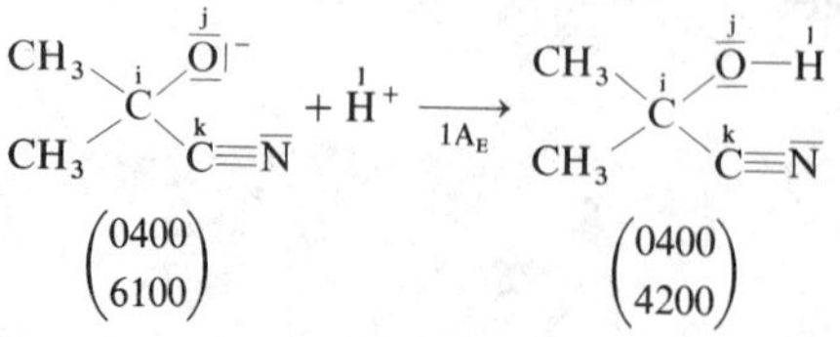

(121)

In this way it follows that by the codification of VVS, control elements are introduced, which allow one to obtain more correct answers for the determination of the product of a chemical reaction.

Vectors of Valence States and Elementary Mechanisms

In the previous sections the one- and two-electron elementary typical transformations were studied in connection with the matrix of reaction alone. It is possible also to express these elementary processes by means of the difference of vectors of valence states (DVVS). In the case of two-atom centers of reaction only the interactions between the component atoms were studied. For instance as an example of radicalic dissociation process (D_R), Schemes 45 were taken:

$$A_i{-}A_j \longrightarrow A_i^{\bullet} + {}^{\bullet}A_j \qquad (45a)$$

$$A_i{=}A_j \longrightarrow A_i^{\bullet}{-}{}^{\bullet}A_j \qquad (45b)$$

$$A_i{\equiv}A_j \longrightarrow A_i^{\bullet}{=}{}^{\bullet}A_j \qquad (45c)$$

For all these transformations the following reaction matrix holds:

$$R_3 = \begin{array}{c} \\ \end{array}\begin{pmatrix} \overset{i}{1} & \overset{j}{-1} \\ -1 & 1 \end{pmatrix}\begin{array}{c} i \\ j \end{array} \qquad (D_R)$$

Considering the vectors of valence states (Table 5) one can express each of three reactions (45) by a specific label as follows:

1. VVS of A_i: educt (0100), product (1000); DVVS (1-100)
2. VVS of A_j: educt (0100), product (1000); DVVS (1-100)
3. A covalent bond is broken (−1) during the transformation.

Reaction 45a can be expressed by DVVS as: (1-100, −1, 1-100).
In the same way:

For reaction 45b DVVS is (11-10, −1, 11-10)
For reaction 45c DVVS is (101-1, −1, 101-1

This example shows that the label expressed by DVVS is richer in information as compared with the matrix of reaction.

Owing to these more detailed possibilities of expression one can include also among the typical elementary transformations the cases where only one atom from the two-atom centers undergoes electron conversions. As an example the following set of reactions is taken:

$$-A_i{-}A_j \longrightarrow A_i^{\bullet}{-}A_j \qquad (1\text{-}100, 0, 0000) \qquad (122a)$$

$$=A_i{-}A_j \longrightarrow -A_i^{\bullet}{-}A_j \qquad (11\text{-}10, 0, 0000) \qquad (122b)$$

$$\equiv A_i{-}A_j \longrightarrow =A_i^{\bullet}{-}A_j \qquad (101\text{-}1, 0, 0000) \qquad (122c)$$

By this method it is possible to systematize all elementary conversions of the electrons in the atom vectors, as it is shown in Table 8 [30]. In this way the totality of the typical elementary processes in two-atom centers of reaction is described.

Subgraphs of the ECVSA Graph

Reaction 112 shows that the transition between two valence states is not always produced by one reorganization step of the valence electrons only. This circumstance is more important than

Table 8
Reaction Schemes and the Corresponding Elementary Conversions of Valence States of Atomic Vectors [56]

No.	Reaction Scheme	Symbol	DVVS
Redox Reactions			
1	${}^{\bullet}A_i + A_j \longrightarrow A_i + A_j{}^{\bullet}$	$1D_e$	$(-1000, 0, 1000)$
2	$\overline{A}_i + A_j \longrightarrow A_i + \overline{A}_j$	$2D_e$	$(-2000, 0, 2000)$
3	${}^{\bullet}A_i + A_j \longrightarrow A_i + A_j{}^{\bullet}$	$1D_e^1$	$(-1000, 0, 0000)$
4	$\overline{A}_i + A_j \longrightarrow A_i + \overline{A}_j$	$2D_e^1$	$(-2000, 0, 0000)$
5	$A_i + A_j{}^{\bullet} \longrightarrow A_i + A_j$	$1D_e^2$	$(0000, 0, -1000)$
6	$A_i + \overline{A}_j \longrightarrow A_i + A_j$	$2D_e^2$	$(0000, 0, -2000)$
7	$A_i + A_j{}^{\bullet} \longrightarrow {}^{\bullet}A_i + A_j$	$1A_e$	$(1000, 0, -1000)$
8	$A_i + \overline{A}_j \longrightarrow \overline{A}_i + A_j$	$2A_e$	$(2000, 0, -2000)$
9	$A_i + A_j \longrightarrow {}^{\bullet}A_i + A_j$	$1A_e^1$	$(1000, 0, 0000)$
10	$A_i + A_j \longrightarrow \overline{A}_i + A_j$	$2A_e^1$	$(2000, 0, 0000)$
11	$A_i + A_j \longrightarrow A_i + A_j{}^{\bullet}$	$1A_e^2$	$(0000, 0, 1000)$
12	$A_i + A_j \longrightarrow A_i + \overline{A}_j$	$2A_e^2$	$(0000, 0, 2000)$
Homolytic Reactions			
13	$A_i - A_j \longrightarrow A_i{}^{\bullet} + {}^{\bullet}A_j$	$1D_R$	$(1-100, -1, 1-100)$
14	$A_i{=}A_j \longrightarrow A_i{}^{\bullet}{-}{}^{\bullet}A_j$	$2D_R$	$(11-10, -1, 11-10)$
15	$A_i{\equiv}A_j \longrightarrow A_i{}^{\bullet}{=}{}^{\bullet}A_j$	$3D_R$	$(101-1, -1, 101-1)$
16	$-A_i-A_j \longrightarrow A_i{}^{\bullet}-A_j$	$1D_R^1$	$(1-100, 0, 0000)$
17	$=A_i-A_j \longrightarrow -A^{\bullet}-A_j$	$2D_R^1$	$(11-10, 0, 0000)$
18	$\equiv A_i-A_j \longrightarrow =A_i{}^{\bullet}-A_j$	$3D_R^1$	$(101-1, 0, 0000)$
19	$A_i-A_j- \longrightarrow A_i-{}^{\bullet}A_j$	$1D_R^2$	$(0000, 0, 1-100)$
20	$A_i-A_j= \longrightarrow A_i-{}^{\bullet}A_j-$	$2D_R^2$	$(0000, 0, 11-10)$
21	$A_i-A_j\equiv \longrightarrow A_i-{}^{\bullet}A_j=$	$3D_R^2$	$(0000, 0, 101-1)$
22	$A_i{}^{\bullet} + {}^{\bullet}A_j \longrightarrow A_i - A_j$	$1A_2$	$(-1100, 1, -1100)$
23	$A_i{}^{\bullet}{-}{}^{\bullet}A_j \longrightarrow A_i{=}A_j$	$2A_R$	$(-1-110, 1, -1-110)$
24	$A_i{}^{\bullet}{=}{}^{\bullet}A_j \longrightarrow A_i{\equiv}A_j$	$3A_R$	$(-10-11, 1, -10-11)$
25	$A_i-A_j \longrightarrow -A_i-A_j$	$1A_R^1$	$(-1100, 0, 0000)$
26	$-A_i-A_j \longrightarrow =A_i-A_j$	$2A_R^1$	$(-1-110, 0, 0000)$
27	$=A_i-A_j \longrightarrow \equiv A_i-A_j$	$3A_R^1$	$(-10-11, 0, 0000)$
28	$A_i-A_j \longrightarrow A_i-A_j-$	$1A_R^2$	$(0000, 0, -1100)$
29	$A_i-A_j- \longrightarrow A_i-A_j=$	$2A_R^2$	$(0000, 0, -1-110)$
24	$A_i-A_j= \longrightarrow A_i-A_j\equiv$	$3A_R^2$	$(0000, 0, -10-11)$
Heterolytic Reactions			
Electrolytic			
25	$A_i - A_j \longrightarrow \overline{A}_i + A_j$	$1D_E$	$(2-100, -1, 0-100)$
26	$A_i{=}A_j \longrightarrow \overline{A}_i-A_j$	$2D_E$	$(21-10, -1, 01-10)$
27	$A_i{\equiv}A_j \longrightarrow \overline{A}_i{=}A_j$	$3D_E$	$(201-1, -1, 001-1)$
28	$-A_i-A_j \longrightarrow \overline{A}_i-A_j$	$1D_E^1$	$(2-100, 0, 0000)$
29	$=A_i-A_j \longrightarrow -\overline{A}_i-A_j$	$2D_E^1$	$(21-10, 0, 0000)$
30	$\equiv A_i-A_j \longrightarrow =\overline{A}_i-A_j$	$3D_E^1$	$(201-1, 0, 0000)$
31	$A_i-A_j- \longrightarrow A_i-\overline{A}_j$	$1D_E^2$	$(0000, 0, 2-100)$
32	$A_i-A_j= \longrightarrow A_i-\overline{A}_j-$	$2D_E^2$	$(0000, 0, 21-10)$
33	$A_i-A_j\equiv \longrightarrow A_i-\overline{A}_j=$	$3D_E^2$	$(0000, 0, 201-1)$

(Continued)

Table 8 (Continued)

No.	Reaction Scheme	Symbol	DVVS
34	$\overline{A_i} + A_j \longrightarrow A_i - A_j$	$1A_E$	(−2100, 1, 0100)
35	$\overline{A_i}{-}A_j \longrightarrow A_i{=}A_j$	$2A_E$	(−2 − 110, 1, 0 − 110)
36	$\overline{A_i}{=}A_j \longrightarrow A_i{\equiv}A_j$	$3A_E$	(−20 − 11, 1, 00 − 1−)
37	$\overline{A_i}{-}A_j \longrightarrow {-}A_i{-}A_j$	$1A_E^1$	(−2100, 0, 0000)
38	${-}\overline{A_i}{-}A_j \longrightarrow {=}A_i{-}A_j$	$2A_E^1$	(−2 − 110, 0, 0000)
39	${=}\overline{A_i}{-}A_j \longrightarrow {\equiv}A_i{-}A_j$	$3A_E^1$	(−20 − 11, 0, 0000)
40	$A_i{-}\overline{A_j} \longrightarrow A_i{-}A_j{-}$	$1A_E^2$	(0000, 0, −2100)
41	$A_i{-}\overline{A_j}{-} \longrightarrow A_i{-}A_j{=}$	$2A_E^2$	(0000, 0, −2 − 110)
42	$A_i{-}\overline{A_j}{=} \longrightarrow A_i{-}A_j{\equiv}$	$3A_E^2$	(0000, 0, −20 − 11)
Heterolytic Proper			
43	$A_i - A_j \longrightarrow A_i + \overline{A_j}$	$1D_N$	(0 − 100, −1, 2 − 100)
44	$A_i{-}A_j \longrightarrow A_i{-}\overline{A_j}$	$2D_N$	(01 − 10, −1, 21 − 10)
45	$A_i{\equiv}A_j \longrightarrow A_i{=}\overline{A_j}$	$3D_N$	(001 − 1, −1, 201 − 1)
46	${-}A_i{-}A_j \longrightarrow A_i{-}A_j$	$1D_N^1$	(0 − 100, 0, 0000)
47	${=}A_i{-}A_j \longrightarrow {-}A_i{-}A_j$	$2D_N^1$	(01 − 10, 0, 0000)
48	${\equiv}A_i{-}A_j \longrightarrow {=}A_i{-}A_j$	$3D_N^1$	(001 − 1, 0, 0000)
49	$A_i{-}A_j{-} \longrightarrow A_i{-}A_j$	$1D_N^2$	(0000, 0, 0 − 100)
50	$A_i{-}A_j{=} \longrightarrow A_i{-}A_j$	$2D_N^2$	(0000, 0, 01 − 10)
51	$A_i{-}A_j{\equiv} \longrightarrow A_i{-}A_j{=}$	$3D_N^2$	(0000, 0, 001 − 1)
52	$A_i + \overline{A_j} \longrightarrow A_i - A_j$	$1A_N$	(0100, 1, −2100)
53	$A_i{-}\overline{A_j} \longrightarrow A_i{=}A_j$	$22A_N$	(0 − 110, 1, −2 − 110)
54	$A_i{-}\overline{A} \longrightarrow A_i{\equiv}A_j$	$3A_N$	(00 − 11, 1, −20 − 11)
55	$A_i{-}A_j \longrightarrow {-}A_i{-}A_j$	$1A_N^1$	(0100, 0, 0000)
56	${-}A_i{-}A_j \longrightarrow {=}A_i{-}A_j$	$2A_N^1$	(0 − 110, 0, 0000)
57	${=}A_i{-}A_j \longrightarrow {\equiv}A_i{-}A_j$	$3A_N^1$	(00 − 11, 0, 0000)
58	$A_i{-}A_j \longrightarrow A_i{-}A_j{-}$	$1A_N^2$	(0000, 0, 0100)
59	$A_i{-}A_j{-} \longrightarrow A_i{-}A_j{=}$	$2A_N^2$	(0000, 0, 0 − 110)
60	$A_i{-}A_j{=} \longrightarrow A_i{-}A_j{\equiv}$	$3A_N^2$	(0000, 0, 00 − 11)

it appears, since it allows one to study the occurrence of valence states corresponding to less common forms among the chemical compounds. In this way, it may be specified implicitly, with an appreciable degree of probability, that some new or compounds with doubtful occurrence, can really occur, since the correlated valence states can be recovered as points in the graph of the specified transformations.

A series of interesting cases were studied [25, 31] aiming to show the procedure of recovering valence states rarely encountered. An example is represented by etoxycarbonylcarbene, $\cdot\overline{C}{-}COOC_2H_5$ where one of the carbon atoms is in the state $\cdot\overline{C}{-}$. The problem is in this case to consider states of the carbon atom as element. It is accepted that, in its basic state, the carbon atom has two unshared electrons: $\cdot\overline{C}\cdot$. For this configuration the LUMO orbitals are located at the "low part" of the atom. In a ECVSA type graph this atom forms the knot with the valence state (4000). The problem is to determine the way in which this form can be reached starting from common valence states: (4100), (2100), (3100). For this purpose Figure 8, showing allowed transformations of the successive steps, is used. It follows from this graph that all these three forms can lead to the state (2200), further to (2300), and finally to a normal state (0210).

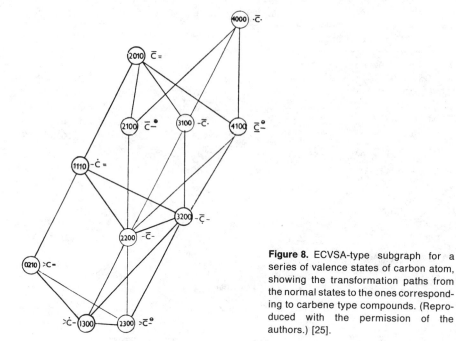

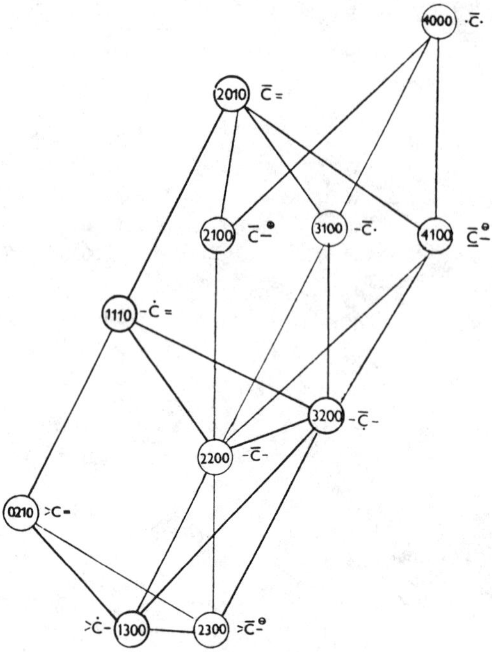

Figure 8. ECVSA-type subgraph for a series of valence states of carbon atom, showing the transformation paths from the normal states to the ones corresponding to carbene type compounds. (Reproduced with the permission of the authors.) [25].

In other cases the introduction of the still unknown valence states is necessary in order to complete the lacking points of the ECVSA graph. Thus for the point (2120) or $-\overline{Cl}\lessdot$ of the subgraph of chlorine valence states, an additional knot is necessary, which, by a heterolytic process, mediates the transition to the state (0130), therefore $\gtrdot Cl \lessdot$. In this way the occurrence of unstable intermediate valence states can be assumed: (0030) $\gtrdot Cl^{+}=$, (2030) $\gtrdot \overline{Cl}^{-}=$ and (2220) $\gtrdot \overline{Cl}^{-}\lessdot$, as it is shown in Figure 9. From this figure it follows that the state (2400) $>\overline{Cl}^{+}<$ should be located between the points (4300) $-\overline{Cl}<$ and (2500) $>\overline{Cl}\lessdot$. Support elements for this assumption could be found among the similar states of bromine and iodine atoms. But it may be established that the experimental data referred to bromine show a limited set of examples, and therefore the corresponding graph remains scarce.

The field of ECVSA subgraph is vast and interesting [25, 30, 31]. A detailed study of these subgraphs, systematized on specified elements, can lead to find new states, which, even if these states are unstable, allow to explain the necessary elementary steps by which the reaction can occur. In this way it is possible to understand hidden mechanisms and to find the necessary conditions and media that ensure the stability to obtain the defined chemical transformations. In addition, the vector of valence states can be used for elaborating algorithms for determining the centers of reactions for substrate and reactant molecules and to find in this way the reaction product of the chemical reaction.

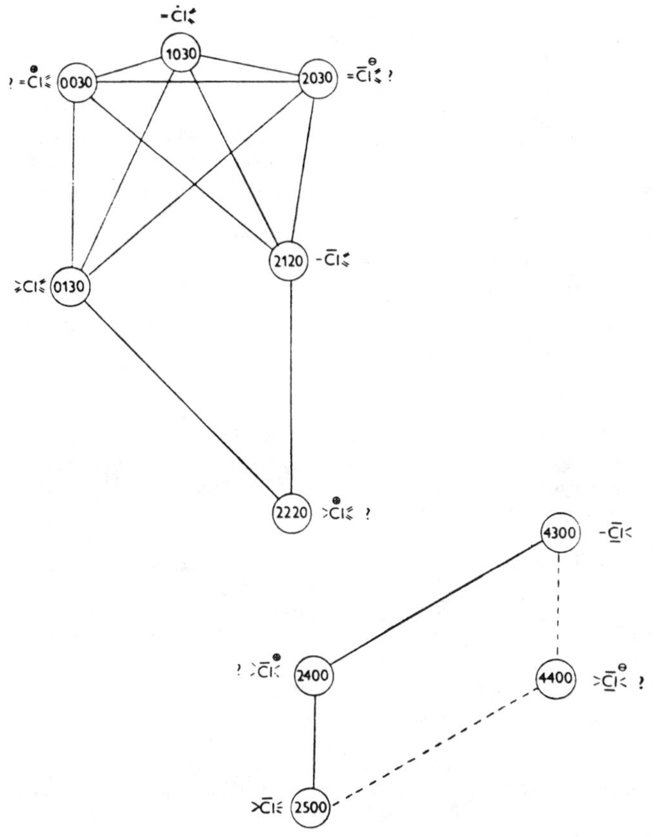

Figure 9. ECVSA-type subgraph for a series of chlorine atom valence states; here are shown also unknown in practice valence states, but unavoidable as transients for the transition between specified species by allowed conversions. (Reproduced with the permission of the authors.) [25].

TOPOLOGICAL SYMMETRY AND CANONICAL CONNECTIVITY

The constitution matrix, which represents a graph corresponding to the connectivity of the atoms in the molecule, has a form depending on the row of column assigned to the atom, i.e., on the arbitrarily chosen way of numbering the atoms. There are as many matrices as there are possibilities of numbering that can be adopted for the atoms of the molecule, but all these matrices are isomorphic, i.e., they can be transformed into one another by permutations of the rows and columns. The problems posed by the isomorphism of the graphs and matrices is, from the computational point of view, that of finding an efficient algorithm of establishing the topological equivalence of the atoms and the bonds between them [32]. The known algorithms for demonstrating the isomorphism of the graphs are very unfavorable with respect to complexity and the time needed to carry out the algorithm, demanding a prohibitive number of computational steps for solving a problem of significant size [33]. With isomorphism of constitutive matrices, the complexity of the problem can depend factorially on the size of the matrix. The number of operations required by the algorithm is then an exponential function of the size of the matrix. These are the worst kinds of algorithms, rapidly becoming inefficient with an increase in the size of the matrix [34]. Partial solutions have been given, on the basis of which various authors have expressed optimistic opinions [35]; nevertheless, a satisfactory algorithm resting on a theoretically valid basis has not yet been found for solving the problem isomorphism of the graphs [32, 33, 36]. The basic algorithm that has served as the point of departure for the cited papers is that proposed by Morgan [37] for the *Chemical Abstracts Service*, which has demonstrated its efficiency and economy for a long period of time and for a very large number of chemical compounds. The procedure developed by Morgan for storing and manipulating chemical structures in the computer at *Chemical Abstracts Service* is now examined. The concept of connectivity introduced by Morgan will be shown to have an equivalent in the minimum number of pathways from one node to the adjacent nodes in a specified graph, which can be determined from the adjacency matrix and its powers.

The Morgan Algorithm [37]

In order to verify whether a given chemical structure has been stored in computer memory, Morgan [37] developed a unique method of labeling by symbols, combining all of the information concerning a molecular structure. Indeed, a procedure was found for the generation by computer of an alphanumeric description for every structure that provides a unique description for that structure. In the initial stage, a two-dimensional projection of the chemical structure was used, but later a three-dimensional representation was also employed for differentiating stereoisomers; at the same time, the handling unknown structures and polymeric structures was kept in mind.

The structure description proposed by Morgan consists in drawing up a uniquely ordered list of the node positions of the structure, equivalent to a graph, in which the atomic symbol at each node and its mode of attachment to the other nodes of the total structure are described. The list thus drawn up is called the "connection table."

A scheme of the molecular structure is first introduced in the memory of the computer. Further, the indexing of the graph nodes, from which the hydrogen atoms are excluded is carried out in order to draw up the "compact connection table." The indexing starts with any node of the graph by the assignment of the number 1. The labeling is continued with numbers 2, 3, etc. for the joined neighbors of the starting node. The indexing operation is then carried out for the remaining non-labeled neighbors of node 2. The notation is thus continued for all points of the graph. In the case of an ion containing graph, therefore a disconnected one, the indexing is carried out until a point where all nodes are not labeled; these lasts are not joined to the already indexed nodes. Another arbitrary selection is then made to designate the preceding node.

Consider the structure consisting of four atoms:

```
A—B—C
  |
  D
```
(123)

Table 9
Connectivity Table Corresponding to Structure [123]

No.	Possible Assignments of the Nodes											
1	A	A	B	B	B	B	B	B	C	C	D	D
2	B	B	A	A	C	C	D	D	B	B	B	B
3	C	D	C	D	A	D	A	C	A	D	A	C
4	D	C	D	C	D	A	C	A	D	A	C	A

For this structure the connection table that is drawn up shows the numberings that result from the application of the previous rules (Table 9).

In the case of Structure 123 there are 24 possible numberings using the numbers 1 to 4, but only half of the possible numberings comply with the rules previously cited. This reduction becomes more significant as the complexity and size of the structure under consideration increase.

When the structure has been numbered according to the preceding rules, the connection table is formed by recording the structural relationships in five lists, as shown below.

The "From Attachment" List

Also in this case the hydrogen atoms are excluded from the graph structure. The number of the remained atoms is noted by N. The "from attachment" list contains a rank for each atom, therefore N ranks. The rank of order i corresponds to the simple attachment between the i-th node and the one other node of the graph. The rank number at the lowest numbered atom connected to the i-th node is recorded at the i-th rank. If the rank number that would be recorded at i-th rank is a greater number than i, it is left blank.

Next, consider the following structure:

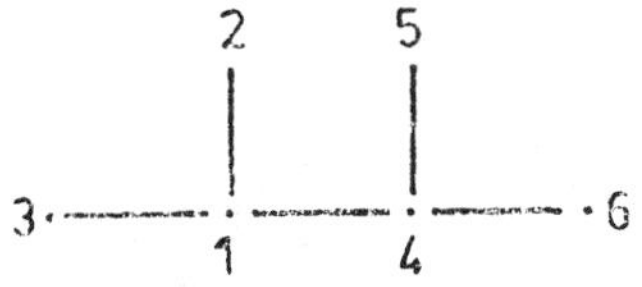

(124)

The "from attachment" list for this molecular structure is given in Table 10.

The "Ring Closure" List

This list is composed of N ranks of fixed length where N is equal to the number of cycles (rings) in the structure. Structures without cycles do not have this list. After the formation of the "from" list, one connection remains for each cycle not included in this list. These additional bonds are included in the "ring closure" list as follows.

1. For each ring closure the number of the two atoms that close the ring are recorded in the list.
2. To set up the rank, the smaller number is placed first.
3. The ranks are ordered so that the number pair of the first rank will be smaller than the second, which is less than the third, etc. Thus, 002007 003005 003006.

Table 10
From Attachment List

Rank Number	From Attachment
1	BLANK
2	001
3	001
4	001
5	004
6	004

Table 11
Ring Closure List

Rank Number	From Attachment	Ring Closure
1	BLANK	
2	001	
3	001	
4	001	
5	002	
6	002	
7	003	
8	004	
9	006	
10	007	003 005 008 009

As an example, consider the following structure:

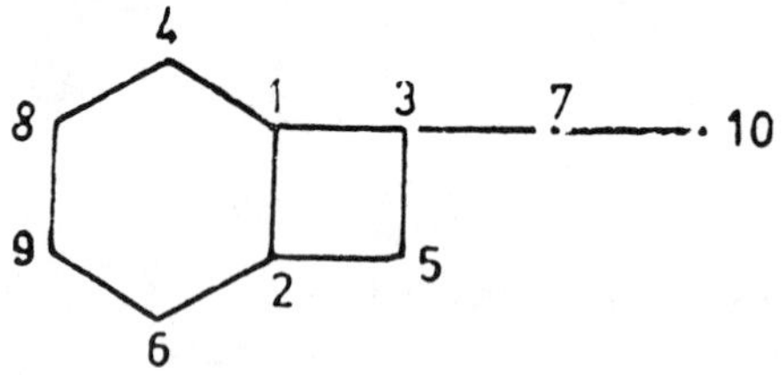

(125)

The related "from attachment" and "ring closure" lists are given in Table 11.

The combination of these two lists is sufficient for a complete description of the interconnections of the graph for the two-dimensional projection of the structure.

The "Nod Value" List

This list correlates the rank with the atomic symbol, as shown below. As in the two previous cases, this list contains a rank for each atom of the graph, therefore N ranks.

The "Line Value" List

The number N of bonds between two nodes of the graph is included in the "line value" list. The task of this table is to correlate the line value with the data contained in both "from" and "ring closure" lists for the i-th rank. Obviously, the rank number adopted by "ring closure" (Table 11) is indexed in connection with "from" list (Table 10). In this way the interatomic bonds are noted by means of an appropriate label.

The following molecular structure may be chosen as an example:

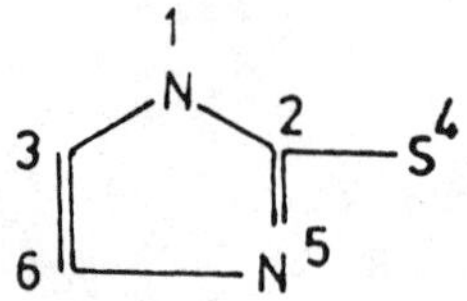

(126)

Table 12
Lists A, B, C, and D

Rank Number	From Attachment	Ring Closure	Node Value	Line Value
1	BLANK		N	BLANK
2	001		C	1
3	001		C	1
4	002		S	1
5	002		N	2
6	003		C	2
		005 006		

The data corresponding to the lists "from," "ring closure," "nod value," and "line value" are given in Table 12.

The "Modifications" List

Any modifications of the nodes and lines as previously listed above, such as the charge of ions, isotopic masses, unusual valence states, etc. are noted in this list. These modifications are registered by assigning a code number to the type of modification, followed by the node number or line number that has been modified. Accordingly, the "modifications" list refers to an extension of the techniques included in the previous lists and comprises only a few exceptions.

The system based on the connection tables is thus seen to ensure an unambiguous correlation of the two-dimensional projection of a chemical structure. However, in this form the table lacks uniqueness from the point of view of its use in the computer. The table selected for a system of storage and manipulation is one of the variants included in the family of possible forms. An unambiguous criterion is therefore established that will ensure the uniqueness of the connection table. In terms of matrix form, discussed earlier, a procedure must be established that will select one of the isomorphic matrices that uniquely characterize a chemical structure corresponding to a graph. The ordering procedure cannot depend on the order of the nodes in the input table, and for that reason the unique table is independent of both the orientation and the position of the projected structure. The achievement of uniqueness is very important, since a unique structure is then stored in the computer just once, the registry number corresponding to a unique and unambiguous identification of a chemical substance.

Any particular variant of the family set of isomorphic tables describes a given structure just as well as any other variant. Which particular one of the possible variants is selected for the unique description is therefore unimportant. As mentioned earlier, the set of isomorphic variants is finite and depends on the square of the order of the matrix that describes the graph of the structure. The unique table can be selected by generating all numbers of the set based on the characteristics involved in the description, and selecting the first member of the set as representing the unique table.

The elaboration of tables according to the procedure already described is a part of the program structure, allowing one to determine a single invariant subset among several ones, which form an isomorphic set. The possibility of selection from several variants becomes limiting as the number of atoms in molecule is increased, owing to the increase of the expensive computing time. This is why a limiting procedure must be devised in order to render the entire computing time economically acceptable. It may be possible to save computing time if the indexing procedure described for the "from attachment" list are considered during the elaboration of the computer program. In this way the selection procedure is considerably restrained. Morgan shows as an example the case of a six-atom cycle where 720 indexing variants are possible; using the rules described earlier, only 12 modes are effectively worked out. These rules represent in themselves a procedure for creating an invariant subset considerably smaller than the maximum number possible. In the next step the computer program employs certain invariant properties of the graph to reduce even further the size of the subset. These properties have been called by Morgan the "connectivity value" of each node; they include the node value given by the atomic symbol and the line value showing the number of bonds.

A second means by which the subset is reduced in size is the introduction of a partial ordering among the nodes of the graph. The selection of the next node that is to be listed, when a choice is possible, can in many cases be resolved on the basis of a priority implicit in the partial ordering. An example of the way in which such a partial ordering can be ensured is offered by the following structure:

A—B—C—D (127)

In this case there are two possibilities for ordering the nodes:

(1)		(2)	
	B		C
	C		B
	A		D
	D		A

Only nodes B and C were thus given the number 1 because of the preference prescribed by the partial ordering. In this way nodes 3 and 4 are fixed by the rules that were adopted in the numbering. A subset of two tables has thus been selected from the maximum set of 24 tables, which would have resulted without the partial ordering of the numbering. This partial ordering of the nodes based on the number of attachments to a given node does not usually reduce the number of tables in the subset sufficiently for the partitioning of the set to ensure economy of operation. This situation is linked to the observation that in organic chemistry the number of bonds to any given atom does not generally exceed five. In order to increase the effectiveness of the ordering, one possibility is the consideration of the "connectivity value" for each node based on the invariant properties of the graph. A partial ordering is then introduced among the nodes in the same way that the number of connections was used in Structure 127.

For computing the "connectivity value," each node is first assigned a connectivity value equal to the number of atoms, other than hydrogen, that are attached to that node. This number represents an invariant property of the graph. The computer calculates the number k of different connectivity values that have been assigned. An iterative process is used to compute on the basis of the preceding values a new connectivity value k′ for each node. If $k' > k$, the new values are assigned to the initial nodes, k is set equal to k′, and the process is repeated. When the situation is reached in which $k' \leq k$, the process is terminated, and the last set of values assigned to the nodes is used to introduce a partial ordering. Using this partial ordering, the size of the subset is reduced by giving preference to the node associated with the higher connectivity value at each point of selection in the process of numbering just described. The iterative process is finite for any graph for N nodes in which N is a finite number. The process terminates under the conditions described after $(N + 1)$ iterations, since there are at most N values that can be assigned to a k, and thereby allow the process to continue.

The drawing up of the subset of tables follows after the previous partial indexing of the graph nodes. But in the case when the formation of rather large blocks of possible redundant subsets must be avoided, the entire subset is not still produced.

The selection of a unique table is described below.

After generating any two tables of the subset, a preference is introduced by a so-called "alphabetizing" on the basis of the collating sequence of the computer symbols. The stored table is the preferred one. If the two tables are identical, one of them is arbitrarily selected. For the purpose of "alphabetizing," the tables are treated as a string of symbols in the order in which the lists previously cited were drawn up. Since a preference or a lack of preference is introduced into these two tables each time, no more than two complete tables need to be in the memory of the computer at any given time.

When a complete table is stored in the memory of the computer, a second table is generated, so that at each step a determination is made whether one or the other of the tables is preferable. The first step is the "from" list, by means of which the first trial selection is carried out. If the first table

Table 13
Connectivity Values Found by Computer

	A	B	C	D	E	F	
i = 0	4	1	1	1	2	1	k = 3*
i = 1	5	4	4	4	5	2	k = 3

* These values are used for partial ordering.

is found to be preferable according to the "from" list, the generation of the second table is stopped, as well as all the other tables tested up to that point.

The presence of two or more terminal atoms attached to the same atom is often encountered among chemical structures. A terminal atom is defined as an atom attached to only one atom that is not a hydrogen atom. The partial ordering described above does not then resolve the order of selection of these terminal atoms. Methods are therefore introduced by which a comparison of the tables permits the assignment of a priority.

The following structure is taken as an example:

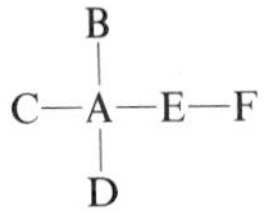

$$
\begin{array}{c}
\text{B} \\
| \\
\text{C—A—E—F} \\
| \\
\text{D}
\end{array}
\qquad (128)
$$

In this case, the partial ordering of the nodes is: $\{A\} > \{E\} > \{B, C, D, F\}$. The connectivity values found by the computer are given in Table 13.

In Structure 128, because of the partial ordering, node A is selected first and node E second. Further B, C, and D have equal priority, requiring six tables to be drawn up. Since Case 128 is common in organic structures, a more efficient selection method is necessary. To this end, the computer has to perform a preliminary selection to determine the possibility of choosing among the level of these three positions. This preliminary exploration is possible since the "form" or "ring closure" lists are not affected. As a result of this preliminary examination an implied criterion of preference is found. If the node values are equal, the preference is taken from the line values or from the node or line modifications that are introduced. By the application of this preliminary examination, the program offers the possibility of eliminating the alternatives, and for Structure 128 only a single table is generated instead of six. Aside from terminal atoms, the method of preliminary testing can be extended without affecting the ultimate selection of the unique description.

The last method for reducing the number of tables to generated is the provision for recalling, under certain conditions, priorities detected during the process of generation. Because of the nature of techniques that have been described, the size of the subset depends on the structure, leading to the situation that the same preference or lack of preference is rediscovered several times.

Consider the structure:

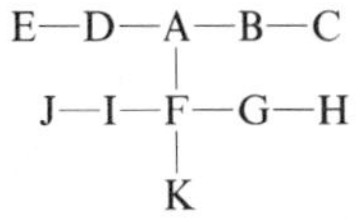

$$
\begin{array}{c}
\text{E—D—A—B—C} \\
| \\
\text{J—I—F—G—H} \\
| \\
\text{K}
\end{array}
\qquad (129)
$$

In Structure 129 the problem of priority of B or D atoms must be determined in two steps: (a) for G and I indexed third and fourth; and (b) for G and I indexed fourth and third, respectively. The efficiency would be greater if the preference were remembered as soon as detected and this information were used for the following stage. The problem that arises is that the preference is recalled only when it is independent of previous choices. This can happen under the following conditions: (a) the atom that determines the choice (A in Structure 129) must be bonded to three atoms other than hydrogen, two of which are involved in the choice; (b) the bond not involved in the choice (A—F in Structure 129) must not form a part of a cycle.

In this case, during the process of generation at that particular moment when the above-mentioned conditions are realized, the computer program divides the graph into two subgraphs by temporary removing the bond that is not involved in the choice (A—F in 129). In this situation the program operates on the subgraph involved in the choice so as to determine a preference or lack of preference between the two choices. This preference is determined by generating the set of tables that arises during the selections in the subgraph. Once this preference is determined the graph is restored, and the preference is recalled when the same choice arises again. When no priority problem is involved in the selection of the two possibilities, any one can be selected owing to the equivalence of the both variants.

The most important methods for reducing the number of tables are the following: (a) the partial ordering of the nodes by the computed "connectivity values"; and (b) the rules for numbering the nodes for the purpose of generating the tables. Both these methods alone cannot avoid the use of a prohibitively long time for calculation, even when a very short consumption would be really necessary; this is why additional methods must be supplied in order to fulfill the specified reduction.

The advantages and economy of Morgan's procedure, described above, have been demonstrated in practice in the activity carried on at *Chemical Abstracts Service* in 1965. By way of example consider the structure:

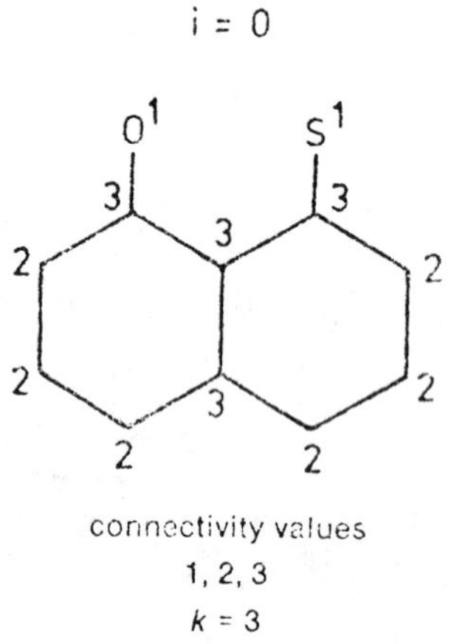

(130)

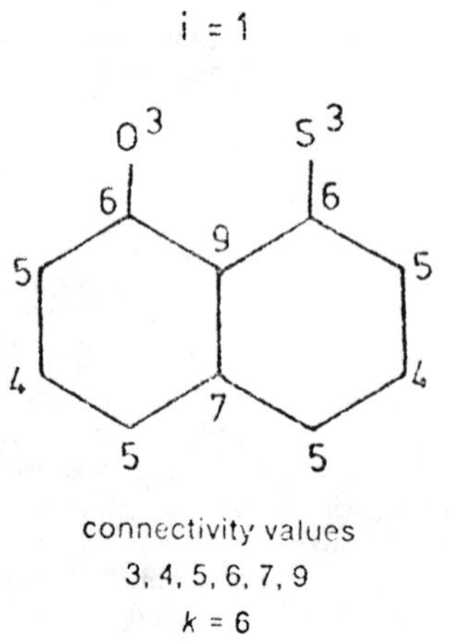

(131)

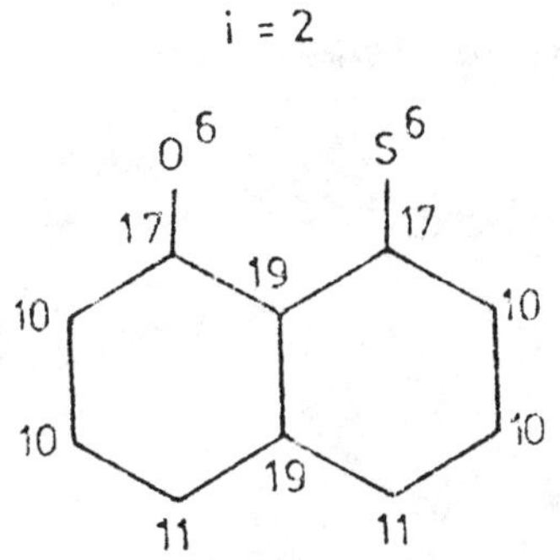

connectivity values
6, 10, 11, 17, 19
$k = 5$

(132)

The iterative process terminates after iterations, and the values assigned after the first is used to introduce the partial ordering. The subset comprises four tables. The nodes of the graph are marked as follows:

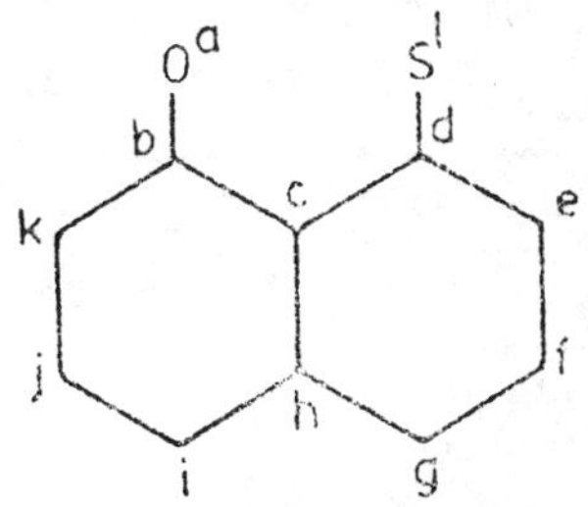

(133)

Using the indicated connectivity values, the following partial ordering is introduced:

$$\{c\} > \{h\} > \{b, d\} > \{k, e, i, g\} > \{i, f\} \tag{134}$$

The possible tables are drawn up considering the above shown partial indexing with priority for the smaller index of the nodes located between leftmost pair of braces at any site of selection. The unique table is selected from the set of four tables.

The preferred numbering and the corresponding table are shown in Table 14.

The unique table that is stored in the computer is shown in Table 15.

Morgan's algorithm has proved efficient for many years on a considerable volume of data. Despite this, Morgan's criterion for classifying the vertices can result in, although very rarely, a nonuniform convergence and can then lose information; this criterion, as has been shown, may lead to instability in the determination; and vertices that are not automorphic can receive the same extended connectivity value at every step [38]. Subsequently, an algorithm more complex than Morgan's has been proposed [39, 40], one that, consequently, demands more time for computation. However, it offers the advantage of being much more discriminating. This algorithm operates with a greater number of steps. In the first step certain invariants of the graph are selected. In the second and third steps an iterative classification of the vertices is carried out. Even with this method no invariant or combination of invariants in the first step is known, which is sufficient to establish the partitioning automorphism of a graph.

Table 14
Example of the Numbering of a Structure and the Corresponding Table

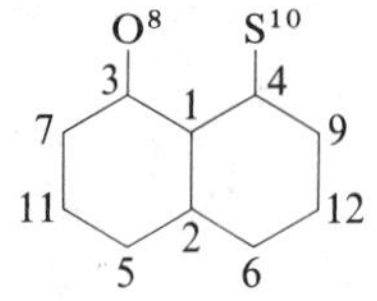

1	C	—	—
2	C	1	1
3	C	1	1
4	C	1	1
5	C	2	1
6	O	2	1
7	C	3	1
8	C	3	1
9	C	4	1
10	S	4	1
11	C	5	1
12	C	6	1
Rings	7	11	1
	9	12	1

Table 15
The Unique Table Stored in the Computer. From List

001 001 001 002 002 003 003 004 004 005 006

Ring Closure			
007	011	009	012

Node Values											
C	C	C	C	C	C	C	O	C	S	C	C

Line Values											
1	1	1	1	1	1	1	1	1	1	1	1

Consider a classification of vertices. A substantial simplification of the problem is achieved, reducing it to the construction of π_i (P_i!) permutations. Here P is the number of vertices in the i-th class [32]. A vertex classification based on cycles of 10 vertices of a regular graph can be taken as a numerical example. With this formula, the number of permutations is reduced from 10! = 3,628,800 to 4!4!2! = 1152.

Two procedures can be adopted for numbering a graph: in depth-first and in breadth-first. The first method has the advantage of reducing the material that must be stored in the memory of the computer.

This method identifies automorphisms that can be used to reduce the branches of the system represented, and does not lead to the identification of supplementary automorphisms. Permutations P_1, P_2, and P_3 show that for every pair of vertices in the graph of cyclopropane there are automorphisms. Hence, the permutations P_4, P_5 and P_6 are no longer necessary and can be reduced, considerably simplifying the ensemble under consideration. Morgan's algorithm can be modified on this basis [41].

Other methods exist by means of which permutations of a graph can be performed: a sequence of numberings is assigned to a vertex that distinguishes this vertex from all others. Actually, the rule employed in Morgan's algorithm records the previously attached vertices, i.e., the vertices adjacent to a vertex already recorded are in a different class than the nonadjacent vertices.

A combination of the above-described methods can be used to determine the partition automorphism more rigorously. Permutations are also often used to permit the construction of different connection tables. The advantage is that the number of these tables is small, permitting them to be compared easily.

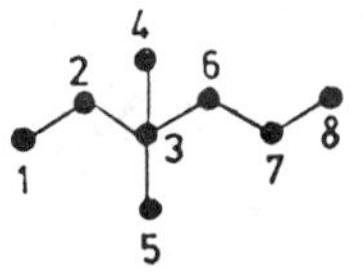

Figure 10. Numbering and rank assigned to the atoms in the computation of the extended connectivity, according to Morgan [43].

Another problem resides in recording the bonds of aromatic compounds. If a pair of vertices belongs to several bonds, the connection tables exhibit a formal difference in the resonance state with pi-electrons. The multiple bond is then replaced by a single bond, without altering the value that designates the number of two-electron covalent bonds connecting a vertex to vertices without hydrogen atoms; the difference between the resonance forms with pi-electrons is removed and at the same time the other chemical systems remain differentiated according to the number of bonds [34].

An algorithm based on the principles enumerated above has been proposed by Shelly and Munk [34]. This algorithm permits reduction of a problem involving 10! = 3,628,800 permutations to the construction of four such permutations.

In general, these algorithms are less efficient for a very few molecular graphs. Thus, of the 677,000 structures processed in 1975 by *Chemical Abstracts Services*, only 0.15% required an appreciably greater computer time. In other applications, such as the computer elucidation of structures, this disadvantage is of greater significance [42].

Extended Connectivity and the Minimum Number of Pathways in a Graph [43]

From what has been presented above, it follows that a molecular structure can be characterized on the basis of the graph represented by the skeleton of the structure, the hydrogen atoms being excluded. For organic chemistry it is sufficient in most cases to consider the lower valence, at most equal to four. For this reason, the points of the graph can be classified in four categories as a function of the number of atoms (aside from the hydrogen atoms) that are attached to the point under consideration, which in the terminology used by Morgan is called the extended connectivity of this point. The extended connectivity then represents a canonical term characterizing the chemical structure.

Razinger [43] has shown that instead of the extended connectivity the number of pathways (walks) in the graph can be used as a method of computation, leading to results identical to those obtained by Morgan's method.

The higher powers of the adiacency matrix A were examined, i.e., $A^2, A^3, \ldots, A^N$, where N is the number of points of the graph. The most important result is that the value of the extended connectivity, computed in iteration i of Morgan's method, can be deduced directly from the i-th power of A. Ratzinger took the structure of Figure 10 as an example. The powers of the adiacency matrix with the numbering of Figure 11 are as follows:

Matrix of power 1

i/j	1	2	3	4	5	6	7	8	Sum of the e_{ij} (j = 1, ... 8)
1	0	1	0	0	0	0	0	0	1
2	1	0	1	0	0	0	0	0	2
3	0	1	0	1	1	1	0	0	4
4	0	0	1	0	0	0	0	0	1
5	0	0	1	0	0	0	0	0	1
6	0	0	1	0	0	0	1	0	2
7	0	0	0	0	0	1	0	1	2
8	0	0	0	0	0	0	1	0	1

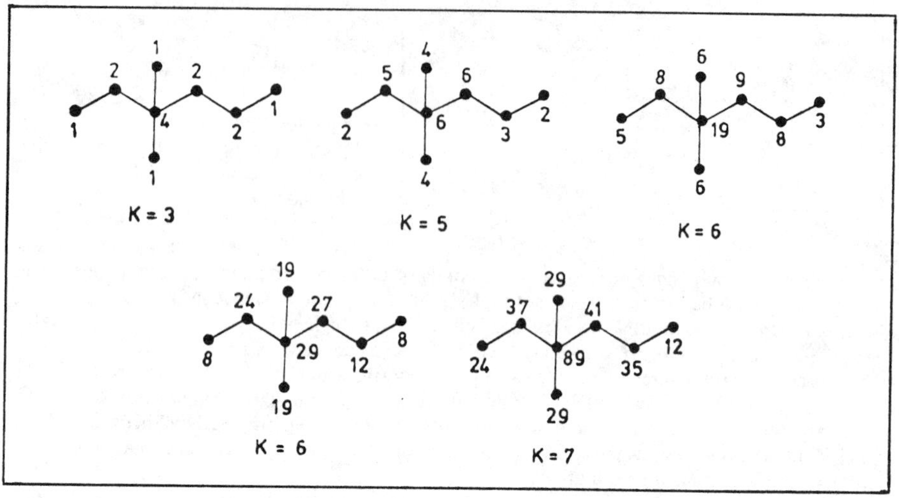

Figure 11. Numbering of the nodes of the graph for indexing the rows and columns of the adjacency matrix and its powers [43].

Matrix of power 2

i/j	1	2	3	4	5	6	7	8	Sum of the e_{ij} (j = 1, . . . 8)
1	1	0	1	0	0	0	0	0	2
2	0	2	0	1	1	1	0	0	5
3	1	0	4	0	0	0	1	0	6
4	0	1	0	1	1	1	0	0	4
5	0	1	0	1	1	1	0	0	4
6	0	1	0	1	1	2	0	1	6
7	0	0	1	0	0	0	2	0	3
8	0	0	0	0	0	1	0	1	2

Matrix of power 3

i/j	1	2	3	4	5	6	7	8	Sum of the e_{ij} (j = 1, . . . 8)
1	0	2	0	1	1	1	0	0	5
2	2	0	5	0	0	0	1	0	8
3	0	5	0	4	4	5	0	1	19
4	1	0	4	0	0	0	1	0	6
5	1	0	4	0	0	0	1	0	6
6	1	0	5	0	0	0	3	0	9
7	0	1	0	1	1	3	0	2	8
8	0	0	1	0	0	0	2	0	3

Matrix of power 4

i/j	1	2	3	4	5	6	7	8	Sum of the e_{ij} (j = 1, . . . 8)
1	2	0	5	0	0	0	1	0	8
2	0	7	0	5	5	6	0	1	24
3	5	0	18	0	0	0	6	0	29
4	0	5	0	4	4	5	0	1	19
5	0	5	0	4	4	5	0	1	19
6	0	6	0	5	5	8	0	3	27
7	1	0	6	0	0	0	5	0	12
8	0	1	0	1	1	3	0	2	8

Matrix of power 5

i/j	1	2	3	4	5	6	7	8	Sum of the e_{ij} (j = 1, . . . 8)
1	0	7	0	5	5	6	0	1	24
2	7	0	23	0	0	0	7	0	37
3	0	23	0	18	18	24	0	6	89
4	5	0	18	0	0	0	6	0	29
5	5	0	18	0	0	0	6	0	29
6	6	0	24	0	0	0	11	0	41
7	0	7	0	6	6	11	0	5	35
8	1	0	6	0	0	0	5	0	12

By means of Morgan's algorithm the values of the extended connectivity were computed, including various ranks K assigned to the atoms of the structure of the graph. These values were compared with the sum of the entries of the rows of the matrices of different powers. Identical values were found for the connectivity and the sum of the row entries, each rank K corresponding to a certain power of the connectivity matrix. The values computed with Morgan's algorithm are given in Table 16. The value of the entry e_{ij} of the k-th power of the adjacency matrix A is equal to the number

Table 16
Extended Connectivity Values Computed by Morgan's Algorithm for Various Rank Parameters K of the Nodes of the Graph

	Power of the Matrix				
	1	2	3	4	5
	Rank of the Points of the Graph				
No.	**K = 3**	**K = 5**	**K = 6**	**K = 6**	**K = 7**
1	1	2	5	8	24
2	2	5	8	24	37
3	4	6	19	29	89
4	1	4	6	19	29
5	1	4	6	19	29
6	2	6	9	27	41
7	2	3	8	12	35
8	1	2	3	8	12

of all possible pathways of length k starting from point i and ending at pooint j [44, 45]. The sum of these entries e_{ij} for all values of j (i.e., the sum of the i-th row) represents the number of all possible pathways of length k from point i to all other points of the graph. This is valid both for cyclic graphs and for trees. The concept of extended connectivity introduced by Morgan thus actually represents a graph invariant in the adjacency matrix of the graph or a power N of this matrix as a function of the rank assigned to the points of the graph. This correspondence explains why the algorithm intuitively arrived at by Morgan has been proven rationally and economically, having become the classic method on which subsequent work has been based.

ALGORITHMS FOR DETERMINING AND PREDICTING CHEMICAL REACTIONS [50]

The possibility to express the structures and chemical reactions by mathematical symbols represented by graphs, matrices, and vectors of valence states is an important advantage of chemistry, giving direct access to the facilities offered by the powerful computers to solve mathematically the most complete and diversified problems of the chemistry. One of the most important aspects is determining chemical reactions and predicting reaction products, including the heuristic aspects by which the discovery of the new reaction pathways for chemical synthesis, new valence states or compounds and, synoptic presentation of the biological structures and reactions become routine operations. The evolution was particularly difficult, sprinkled with unfulfilled hopes, trite or naive results, and puzzles by exponential-type algorithms facing strong limitations, even in the case of the most advanced devices. But the rapid evolution of computers also allowed a spectacular jump of computational and mathematical chemistry and now this branch, although still unsatisfactorily founded, can offer important opportunities for practical use.

The basic principles, presented in the previous sections, generally show the simplicity of the mathematical background and procedure involved in these problems. The complexity appears in the extension of the data, isomorphism problems, and nonstationarity of structures and interactions. But now the evolution of this field is so fast that in a few months, fundamental aspects can be changed or evolved [46–49].

The most important problem of the current chemistry is, however, determining chemical reactions. The elaboration of algorithms for this purpose implies the use of additional algorithms corresponding to the determination of the center of reaction of the substrate educt molecules and also algorithms for determining the reactants [50].

Algorithm for Determining Center of Reaction

One of the most important problems of the chemical reactions is the determining the center of reaction in the structure of substrate educt molecule. It is therefore necessary to use a computing method, based on a proper program, that automatically determines the center of reaction of any molecule.

In the literature are the algorithms necessary to determine the center of reaction [17, 32] of any molecule. Integral computing programs were also published [32]. But owing to the large extension of these programs, this section deals only with the basic principles of the algorithms used for determining the active part in the molecular structure of a chemical combination.

Extended data on the algorithm termed as RECENT (Determination of the Reaction Center) can be found in References 17 and 23. This algorithm is composed from three propositions:

1. Ordering of the molecular substructures until $n = 1$ level.
2. Finding the atom Vector (AV) for the substructure $n = 1$.
3. Determining valence state of each of the two components of the atomic vector. In order to elucidate the specific aspect of this algorithm the details characterizing each distinct proposition are presented.

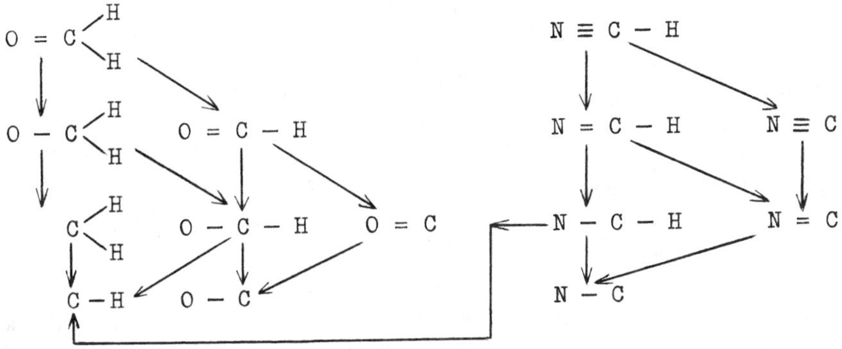

Figure 12. Decomposition of the formaldehyde and hydrogen cyanide in fragments until the level of atomic vectors [2].

1. Fragmentation of the Molecule in Ensembles of Substructures

In a previous section the correlation between a graph, a molecular structure, and the different matricial forms of the molecular graph was shown. It is well known from the graph theory that it is possible to carry out a graph fragmentation in subgraphs, until the lowest level of complexity, represented by two nodes bonded by a line. Similarly, a molecule can be successively divided in substructures, representing fragments from which the initial molecule can be recomposed. As an example, Figure 12 shows the decomposition of the formaldehyde and hydrogen cyanide [2, 32].

By fragment decomposition the center of reaction of any molecule can be found, no matter the nature or atom number constituting the center. This method is based on the fact that any reaction can be produced on a center formed from two atoms (A_i—A_j), where a regrouping of valence electrons can occur.

In order to find the center of reaction of a molecule by means of automatic procedures, based on computer programs, the algorithm GEN (Automatic Generation of Substructures) [17, 32] must be used. This algorithm contains the following propositions [32].

1. The number n of the bond contained in the initial molecule is determined.
2. The set of substructures containing n bonds is determined in a fixed ordering for both the complete molecules and the corresponding fragments, which are included in the table of substructure groups of the considered level (Structure Familes, SF).
3. The sequence of the levels is determined from higher values to the next lower ones obtained by elimination of both marginal node and line from the group of fragments in which the specified structure is contained.
4. Step 2 is repeated until the $n = 1$ value, for which the vectors are formed from two-atom groups A_i—A_j, when the process is finished.

The computing program was published in Reference 32, by means of which the fragments can be found starting from the lists of the ordered substructure sets and resulting from the dividing molecular formations. Variants, correlated with this program and the elaboration procedure can be found in References 33–35.

2. Finding the Substructures at the Atom Vector Level

By the operations shown in the first proposition a series of two-atom groups are obtained, therefore atomic vectors of the type: C—H, C—O, C=O, C—Hal, C—N, C=N, N—H, O—H,

Table 17
List of the Interatomic Bonds in Formaldehyde Molecule

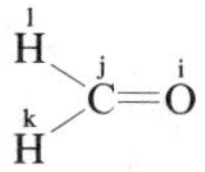	A_i	A_j	A_j	A_j	A_k	A_l	Atomic species
	A_j	A_i	A_k	A_l	A_j	A_j	Bounded atomic species
	2	3	1	1	1	1	Number of bonds
	O	C	C	C	H	H	Literal symbol
	C	O	H	H	C	C	Bounded symbol
	2	2	1	1	1	1	Number of bonds

etc. These atom vectors are stored as a standard table in the computer memory. The generation is continued further by means of tables by which the substructures are codified according to the corresponding graph. Thus, in the case of a formaldehyde molecule (Figure 12) the list of bonds is shown in Table 17.

The table of the bonds is based on the ordered atomic vector, formed by two-atom species, noted as a column. In the lower part, the element with the lowest atomic number is noted. The atomic vector is codified in this way: the first number in brackets shows the lowest atomic number, therefore that of the element noted below, afterwards the number of bonds, which join the atoms, and finally the largest atomic number.

In Table 18 a part of the atomic vectors, the most often encountered in practice is noted [17]. Among the atoms forming the vector, the following types of bonds can be found: simple (s), double (d) and triple (t). The number of the nonparticipating electrons is given by n as previously shown. In the atomic vector three kinds of bonds can exist: for $\overset{A_j}{\underset{A_i}{|}}$ a sigma-bond; for $\overset{A_j}{\underset{A_i}{||}}$ one is sigma and the other is pi; and for $\overset{A_j}{\underset{A_i}{|||}}$ one bond is sigma and two are pi.

The nature of the center of reaction is completely defined only by the determination of the hybridization type, corresponding to the bond, the coordination number of the species in the atomic vector, and the complete data concerning the valence state of the same atom.

In this case valence state of the atom is understood as a specific electron configuration resulting from the nature of the bonds of the atomic center in the molecular, radicalic or ionic state in which it is located (as shown in Table 5). Usually the valence state is determined intuitively. Thus, in the case of a molecule, for instance H—$\underline{\overline{O}}$—H, the two hydrogen atoms are adiabatically (without reorganization of the electrons) removed. The oxygen atom is in the valence state —$\underline{\overline{O}}$—, with the six outer electrons distributed as follows: two electron pairs and each from the two remained are located in bond orbitals with sp^3 hybridization.

3. Determining Valence State of Atoms

The valence state (VS) of the atom in the atomic vector is an important parameter. In the case of the center of reaction, the participation of the atom to a chemical transformation is effected by means of the frontier orbitals.

The drawing up of the table of valence states (Table 5) is based on data that are known from the set of chemical combinations and of transient states of the atom during its transformations in a chemical reaction.

Based on the data of Table 5, a method was proposed for the codification of the atomic vector [17]. According to the new procedure the notation of the atomic vectors on the base of the data from Table 5 becomes:

⋗C—$\underline{\overline{O}}$—,	⋗C—$\underline{\overline{O}}^-$	⋗C—$\overline{O}^+$	⟩C^+—$\underline{\overline{O}}$—	⟩C=$\overline{O}$	=C=$\overline{O}$	$\overline{C}$=$\overline{O}$
(4, 1, 36)	(4, 1, 44)	(4, 1, 30)	(3, 1, 36)	(66, 2, 61)	(50, 2, 61)	(56, 2, 61)

Table 18
Types of Atomic Vectors

$A_j{-}A_i$	Mark	$A_j{-}A_i$	Mark	$A_j{=}A_i$	$A_j{\equiv}A_i$	$A_j{-}A_i$	Mark	$A_j{=}A_i$
H H	(1, 1, 1)	H B	(5, 1, 1)			O O	(8, 1, 8)	(8, 2, 8)
C H	(1, 1, 6)	B B	(5, 1, 5)			F O	(8, 1, 9)	
N H	(1, 1, 7)	C B	(5, 1, 6)			F F	(9, 1, 9)	
O H	(1, 1, 8)	N B	(5, 1, 7)			H Na	(11, 1, 1)	
F H	(1, 1, 9)	O B	(5, 1, 8)			C Na	(11, 1, 6)	
P H	(1, 1, 15)	F B	(5, 1, 9)			O Na	(11, 0, 8)	
S H	(1, 1, 16)	Cl B	(5, 1, 17)			F Na	(11, 0, 9)	
Cl H	(1, 1, 17)	Br B	(5, 1, 35)			Cl Na	(11, 0, 17)	
Br H	(1, 1, 35)	C C	(6, 1, 6)	(6, 2, 6)	(6, 3, 6)	Br Na	(11, 0, 35)	
I H	(1, 1, 53)	N C	(6, 1, 7)	(6, 2, 7)	(6, 3, 7)	I Na	(11, 0, 53)	
Li Li	(2, 1, 2)	O C	(6, 1, 8)	(6, 2, 8)	(6, 3, 8)	H Mg	(12, 1, 1)	
H Li	(2, 1, 1)	F C	(6, 1, 9)			C Mg	(12, 1, 6)	
C Li	(2, 1, 6)	S C	(6, 1, 16)	(6, 2, 16)		N Mg	(12, 1, 7)	
N Li	(2, 1, 7)	Cl C	(6, 1, 17)			O Mg	(12, 1, 8)	
O Li	(2, 1, 8)	Br C	(6, 1, 35)			Mg Mg	(12, 1, 12)	
F Li	(2, 1, 9)	I C	(6, 1, 53)			Cl Mg	(12, 1, 17)	
Cl Li	(2, 1, 17)	N N	(7, 1, 7)	(7, 2, 7)	(7, 3, 7)	Br Mg	(12, 1, 35)	
H Be	(3, 1, 17)	O N	(7, 1, 8)	(7, 2, 8)		I Mg	(12, 1, 53)	
Cl Be	(3, 1, 17)	F N	(7, 1, 9)					
		C P	(15, 1, 6)	(15, 2, 6)	(15, 3, 6)	H Al	(13, 1, 1)	
		N P	(15, 1, 7)	(15, 2, 7)		C Al	(13, 1, 6)	

(Continued)

Table 18 (Continued)

$A_j \equiv A_i$	Mark	$A_j - A_i$	Mark	$A_j = A_i$	$A_j \equiv A_i$	$A_j - A_i$	Mark	$A_j = A_i$
		O P	(15, 1, 8)			N Al	(13, 1, 7)	
		F P	(15, 1, 9)			O Al	(13, 1, 8)	
		P P	(15, 1, 15)			F Al	(13, 1, 9)	
		S P	(15, 1, 16)	(15, 2, 16)		Cl Al	(13, 1, 17)	
		Cl P	(15, 1, 17)			Br Al	(13, 1, 35)	
						I Al	(13, 1, 53)	
						H Si	(14, 1, 1)	
						C Si	(14, 1, 6)	
						N Si	(14, 1, 7)	
						O Si	(14, 1, 8)	(14, 2, 8)
						F Si	(14, 1, 9)	
						Si Si	(14, 1, 14)	
						P Si	(14, 1, 15)	
						S Si	(14, 1, 16)	
						Cl Si	(14, 1, 17)	
						Br Si	(14, 1, 35)	
						I Si	(14, 1, 53)	

The first number in the brackets represents the position of the valence state of the first atom, the second number shows the number of the interatomic bonds, and the third number the position of the valence state of the second atom (after the notations adopted in Table 5).

Using also the numbers from Table 5 a special matrix can be drawn up, termed as BVS (Bond and Valence State Matrix) [17], similarly with the BE matrix (Bond and Electron Matrix). In this matrix, on diagonal, instead of the nonparticipating electrons the label of the valence state from

Table 5 is noticed. Thus for the formaldehyde molecule, the BVS matrix is:

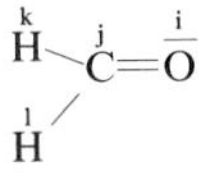

$$
\begin{array}{cccc}
i & j & k & l \\
\end{array}
$$

$$
\overset{k}{H}\diagdown\overset{j}{\underset{\diagup}{C}}=\overset{i}{O}
\qquad
\begin{pmatrix}
61 & 2 & 0 & 0 \\
2 & 66 & 1 & 1 \\
1 & 1 & 1 & 0 \\
0 & 1 & 0 & 1
\end{pmatrix}
\begin{array}{c}
i \\ j \\ k \\ l
\end{array}
$$

$$\overset{l}{H}$$

The amount of information thus becomes more consistent, but in the drawing up the matrix, conventionally noticed elements are used (Table 5, first column). This is why this matrix form can be useful especially for the elaborating computer programs. No operator of reaction can however be used with these matrices. But by this procedure a distinction can be made between molecular forms containing the same atomic vectors. For instance, for the carbonylic combinations the same vector $\diagup C=O$ (52, 2, 61) has the following variants: $=C=\overline{O}$ (50, 2, 61) and $\overline{C}=\overline{O}$ (56, 2, 61). There are in fact several structures containing AV(CO). For the vector C—Cl there are also a few forms:

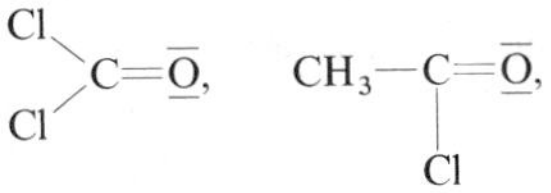

$$
\begin{array}{l}
\overset{Cl}{\underset{Cl}{\diagdown}}C=\overline{O}, \qquad CH_3-\underset{\underset{Cl}{|}}{C}=\overline{O}, \tag{135}
\end{array}
$$

The selection of the individual form from a larger series can be made by determining other atomic vectors.

Algorithm for Deduction of Chemical Reactions

A chemical reaction is a change of the center of reaction undergone by a chemical structure. The modification is expressed by the mathematical symbol in the form of the matrix operator of reaction, which accounts for the breaking or the formation of covalent bonds, and also any changes in the electronic configuration of the ensemble of the reaction.

A computer program for a chemical reaction has as a basic element the conversion of the valence states produced in the center of reaction. An attractive method is to use interactive graphs for the computer accepting diagrams of chemical structure, hand-drawn in a normal way. Among the first programs using this method is OCSS (Organic Chemical Simulation Synthesis) [51]. Subsequently, a more elaborate program was drawn up termed LHASA (Logic and Heuristics Applied to Synthetic Analysis) [52]. Based on the same graphic method, this program took into account the usual *ab initio* transformation, which must be in univocal correspondence with the matrix operator of reactions, observing the characteristic conditions of the valence states of the elements located in the center of reaction. The same starting point is the basis of EROS (Elaboration of Reactions for Organic Synthesis) [8, 16]; its variant ASSOR (Allgemeines System zur Simulation organischer Reactionen) [2, 8, 16, 53] in which the matrices R are no longer used as linear combinations of the fundamental elements; of AHMOS (Automatisierte heuristische organisch-chemischer Synthesen) [54]; of CICLOPS (Computers in Chemistry, Logic Oriented Planning of Synthese) [15, 55]; and of the program ESRE (Elementary Steps of Reorganisation of Valence Electrons) [17].

The basic principle of ESRE program is the interaction between donor and acceptor species in the case of a chemical reaction. In all chemical reactions are implied only the frontier orbitals of the atom: HOMO (Highest Occupied Molecular Orbital), LUMO (Lowest Unoccupied Molecular Orbital) and SOMO (Highest One-Electron Occupied Molecular Orbital or Radical). The problem that arises is transposing in mathematical language the modifications in frontier orbitals of the atoms of the center of reaction by the modifications of the valence states (VS). In the programming language this means introducing by an operative step the transfer of one or two electrons. As it is shown in the Table 20, the atom of an element displays very different states by the binding mode and the position occupied in the structure of the molecule where it is included. As a corollary of chemical transformations any modification of a state of an atom in a atomic vector is reflected univocally in the valence state of the second atom of the specified vector and also in the state of the other atoms that form the reaction center.

The ESRE algorithm is composed of seven propositions [17].

1. For the evolution of the allowed VS of the atom forming $AV(A_i, A_j)$, from the entire set of the MECVS (Matrices of the Elementary Conversion of Valence States of the Atom), the MECVS submatrix of the valence states, corresponding to the species A_i, is formed.
2. From the VS matrix of the species A_i is determined the subgraph of the elementary conversions of the atoms in the center of reaction, including the atom A_i: the node of subgraph shows the code of the atom VS and the vector of the difference of the VS. The stable state is distinguished from the radicalic one and from the charged species, which are now unstables, undergoing subsequent conversions.
3. For each line, binding the nodes, the difference of the vectors $VS_1 - VS_2$ is determined, representing the line evolution of the subgraph.
4. On the line of the elementary step of valence electron regrouping (ESRE) by the position "difference of the vectors of the valence states (DVVS)," the nature of ESRE is determined.
5. The characteristic ESRE notation is established. By the position "execute the next step of electron donation" the required step is established, from the first to n order, for the type of heterolytic (1) and radicalic (2) reactions and also of the redox one- (3) or two-electron (4) transformations.
6. Steps 1 and 5 of the ESRE algorithm are deduced for the second atom A_j of the specified $AV(A_i, A_j)$.
7. The operation is continued by the procedure corresponding to algorithm for the combination of the valence states of the atoms (COMB).

Each of the specified propositions implies a series of characteristic aspects that must be taken into account; in the use of this case additional algorithms are used for yielding the data needed by the elaboration of the ensemble of the computing program.

1. Choosing the Matrix of Elementary Conversion of Valence States of the Atom

Table 5 presents 139 positions related to the valence states of an atom in the frame of molecular structure where it is included. For each atom it is possible to find these forms, allowed for defined structures or as transient forms, participating in the pathway of chemical reactions. For the carbon atom 15 valence forms, more often encountered in practice, can be selected from Table 5; to these one can add also four radical states, obtaining in this way 19 nodes of the graph. For the drawing of the graph of the valence states of the carbon atom, it is necessary to settle also the sequence of transitions between these forms marking the graph lines. On this base the graph in Figure 13A was obtained. Instead of the graphical forms, as elements constituting the nodes of the graph, the code numbers of the vectors of valence states, Figure 13B, can be used. The transitions between these states are expressed by the matrix of elementary convertions of valence states of the atomic elements, presented in Table 19. The numbering is here different from the one adopted in Table 5. But, since the VVS are also included, in Table 19 the states that are in agreement with the possible forms of the oxygen in various circumstances can be found. For instance the valence states 5 (35) can pass through the forms 2 (43), 6 (36), 13 (23), and 17 (56); in brackets the corresponding states from the Table 5 are given. For the oxygen atom the states 13 (23) and 17 (56) are not stable. A few of the found states can, therefore, correspond to some instable formations, similarly to those with non-correlated charges or non-shared electrons. In this situation the process is repeated in n steps. But, customarily, instead of the individual atoms $A_i, A_j \ldots$ atomic vectors $AV(A_i, A_j)$ are used.

The conversion of valence states of an atom A_i in the atom vector is an element included in the set of the valence states $VS(A_i)$ which is drawn up empirically. In this way it is necessary for the

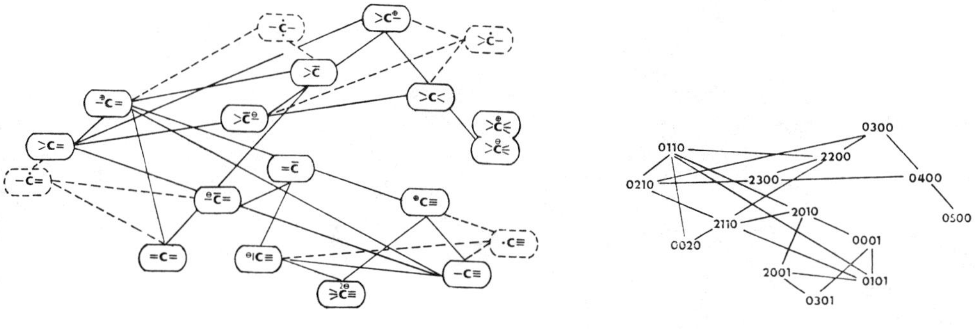

a b

Figure 13. Subgraph of the elementary electron conversions of the carbon atom valence states; (a) literal symbols; dotted frames and lines indicate radical states; (b) numerical codes of the vectors of valence states [17].

formation of this set to consider that the selected states would be in agreement with the allowed molecular orbitals of the elements forming the vector in which the species A_i is included. If allowed states, previously unknown, are found, then it is possible to draw new chemical reactions in which the selected event can occur.

In the present algorithm are studied individual vectors resulting from the fragmentation of several carbonilic compounds such as aldehydes, ketones and organic acids. An atom can be removed from the vector for which the subgraph of the corresponding valence states are drawn. After this operation the next step is included in the proposition 6 of this algorithm, elaborated for the construction of the subgraph, corresponding to the second atom A_j, which, in this case, is oxygen.

2. Drawing the Subgraph of Elementary Conversion of the Valence States of Atoms

In order to overcome the inductive stage used for drawing the matrix of the elementary transformation of valence states, it is necessary to use another step of the computing program. Instead of the graph from Figure 13, the matrix of the valence states of the atom A_i is used. All forms involved in the initial $VS(A_i)$ transformation can be recognized by the forms of the vectors of valence states. In case of heterolytic transformations Table 20 is presented for oxygen. Here the ordinal numbering is the same as in Table 19.

The initial matrix with the numerical entries (0, 1) was arranged by the use of the alphanumeric code of the type $1D_N$

3. Computing the Difference of the Valence State Vectors of the Atom as a Result of the Conversion Process.

In the submatrix of elementary conversions of valence states a column was applied for the difference of the vectors of valence states (Table 20). The electron regrouping by the conversion of valence states of the atom is simulated similarly to the real elementary transfer.

As in the previous case, by n and s the two-electron transfer was noted in the case of the two-electron heterolytic and redox reactions. An older variant, but principally accurate [17] of the difference of valence states for the instructions concerning the electron regrouping, termed as REEL, is shown in Table 21. A more modern variant of this procedure can be found in Ref. [56].

Table 19
Matrix of Elementary Conversions of Valence States of Atomic Elements

VS	v	1	2	3	4	5	6	7	8	9	10	11	12	13	14	15	16	17	18	19	20	21	22	23	24	25	26	27	28	29	30	31	32	33	34	35	36	37	38	39	40	41	42	43	44	45	46	47
8000	1			1																																												
6000	2			1		1																																										
6100	3	1	1		1		1		1																																								
6200	4			1				1		1																																						
4100	5		1				1		1									1																														
4200	6			1		1		1		1					1				1																														
4300	7				1		1										1																																
4010	8			1		1				1	1								1						1																									
4110	9				1		1		1												1																												
4001	10								1																																								
2000	11													1																1																								
2100	12											1						1														1											1														
2200	13					1								1		1				1													1									1														
2300	14						1												1				1										1	1										1												
2400	15							1											1		1														1										1											
2500	16																1															1								1										
2010	17					1								1						1							1											1								1				
2110	18						1		1										1		1	1	1																1		1	1						1			
2210	19									1						1				1				1																1			1						1		
2020	20																				1																				1								
2120	21																					1	1		1																				1	1					
2030	22																					1																											1				
2001	23								1												1																													1			
0000	24																												1																							

0100	25											1													1		1								1													
0200	26									1																1		1								1												
0300	27													1	1												1		1								1											
0400	28														1													1		1								1										
0500	29															1													1		1								1									
0600	30																1													1		1																
0700	31																														1		1															
0800	32																															1		1														
0900	33																																1															
0010	34									1																1										1								1			
0110	35																	1									1								1		1			1						1		
0210	36														1				1									1								1		1			1						1	
0310	37															1													1								1		1			1						1
0410	38																1		1											1								1										
0020	39																		1																						1							
0120	40																			1	1															1	1			1		1	1					
0220	41																					1																1			1			1				
0030	42																						1																		1			1				
0130	43																																									1	1					
0001	44																	1																	1											1		
0101	45																		1				1													1								1		1		
0201	46																			1																1									1		1
0301	47																			1																	1	1									1	

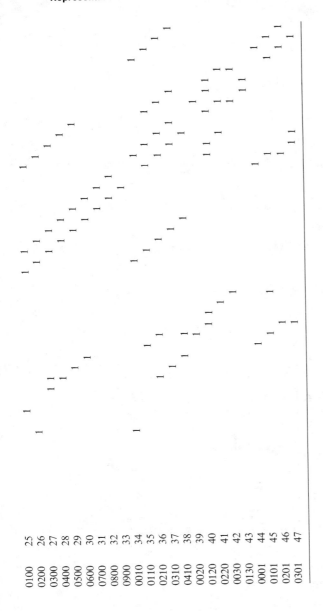

Table 20
Matrix of Elementary Conversions of Oxygen Atom and Difference of Valence States (DVVS)

	DVVS											
	1	2	3	5	6	8	9	(10)	14	18	23	$\longrightarrow$
1			$2A_E$									$8000 \longrightarrow 6100\ (-2 + 100)$
2			$2A_N$	$2A_E$								$(0 + 100), (-2 + 100)$
3	$1D_E$	$1D_N$			$2A_E$	$4A_E$						$(+2 - 100), (0 - 100), (-2 + 100), (-2 - 1 + 10)$
5		$1D_E$			$2A_N$	$4A_N$						$(+2 - 100), (0 + 100), (0 - 1 + 10)$
6			$1D_E$	$1D_N$			$4A_N$		$2A_E$	$4A_E$		$(+2 - 100), (0 - 100), (0 - 1 + 10), (-2 + 100),$ $(-2 - 1 + 10)$
8			$3D_E$	$3D_N$			$2A_N$	$6A_N$		$2A_E$	$6A_E$	$(+1 + 1 - 10), (0 + 1 - 10), (0 + 100), (00 - 1 + 1),$ $(-2 + 100), (-2 - 1 + 1)$
9					$3D_N$	$1D_N$						$(0 + 1 - 10), (0 - 100)$
(10)						$5D_N$						$(00 + 1 - 1)$
14					$1D_E$							$(+2 - 100)$
18					$3D_E$	$1D_E$						$(+2 + 1 - 10), (+2 - 100)$
23						$5D_E$						$(+20 + 1 - 1)$

4. From the Position of the Differences of Valence States (DVVS), the Nature of Elementary Steps of Electron Reorganization is Determined

The information of the modifications produced by the development of chemical reactions is presented in Table 21 in the form of 22 types of DVVS noted as pairs of correlated processes expressing the transformation in the atomic vector. The first process refers to A_i. When a bond is broken between species A_i and A_j, then the DVVS for the atom A_i is noted by −s. The same difference for the atom A_j is noted as s → n; this means that the two electrons, constituting the bonds, were caught by the species A_j. Therefore a two-electron step of nucleofugic dissociation D_N is produced; for this transformation the couple (−s, s → n), as DVVS is noted in Table 23 as (0–100). Similarly, for the formation of a bond, the notation (+s, n → s) is used, which means that the electron pair of the species A_j is transformed in a A_i—A_j bond. This process expresses a nucleophilic association, A_N, for which the DVVS is (0 + 100). The transformation of s bond is a indication of the direction of VVS in the center of reaction, $\vec{v}_1$ and $\vec{v}_2$. The oriented vectors of VS, $\vec{v}_1$, $\vec{v}_2$ and $\vec{v}_3$ show the breaking of formation of the double bonds (d), and the vectors $\vec{v}_1$, $\vec{v}_3$, $\vec{v}_4$ the same process for the triple bonds (t). Further. it is worth mentioning that the pair (s → n, −s) for the atom A_i corresponds to the associated pair (−s, s → n) for the atom A_j, which can represent the component of the reaction center of the reactant.

Table 21
Notations Used in the Procedure of Electron Regroupings (REEL)

No.	Transformation	DVVS	Symbol
Redox Reactions			
1	−n/2	(−1000)	D_e
2	n/2	(1000)	A_e
3	−n	(−2000)	D_e
4	n	(2000)	A_e
Homolytic Reactions			
5	−s, s → n/2	(1 − 100)	D_R
6	n/2 → s, s	(−1100)	A_R
7	−d, d → n/2	(11 − 10)	D_R
8	n/2 → d, d	(−1 − 110)	A_R
9	−t, t → n/2	(101 − 1)	D_R
10	n/2 → t, t	(−10 − 11)	A_R
Heterolytic Reactions			
11	−s, s → n	(0 − 100)	D_N
12	s → n, −s	(2 − 100)	D_E
13	s, n → s	(0100)	A_N
14	n → s, s	(−2100)	A_E
15	−d, d → n	(01 − 10)	D_N
16	d → n, −d	(21 − 10)	D_E
17	d, n → d	(0 − 110)	A_N
18	n → d, d	(−2 − 110)	A_E
19	−t, t → n	(001 − 1)	D_N
20	t → n, t	(201 − 1)	D_E
21	t, n → t	(00 − 11)	A_N
22	n → t, t	(−20 − 11)	A_E

5. Electron Donor Steps, Accompanied by Regrouping of Valence Electrons, are Extended

Table 21 correlates the symbol of the elementary chemical step, for instance D_N (nucleofugic dissociation), with the transformations produced in the two atoms of the center of reaction ($-s$, $s \rightarrow n$) and with the difference of the valence states (0–100).

The significance of the symbol corresponding to the elementary process arises from the nature of transformation produced in the center of reaction.

The matrix of electron regrouping, together with the typical mechanism of reaction yields the method to determine the nature of bond transformation, the kind of reaction partner with which the target molecule interacts, the step of electron donation and the donor-acceptor nature of the components of the center of reaction, including the substrate and the reactant participating in the specified transformation. In connection with the operativity of the computing program, the possibility arises of introducing limitations, by means of which, the restriction of the very large subgraph becomes possible and therefore the surplus of the operations needed for computing. For this purpose the programs yet proposed, adopted diversified procedures. Thus the program EROS [8, 16] assumed the ensemble of the educt molecule (EM_E) to be solved by a mathematical calculus, based on the use of the set of reaction matrices. In this way ensembles of solutions are found, chemically possible, among which a few solutions appear as heuristical. An important element of the program is the selection based on stoichiometry. In AHMOS [54, 57] the limitations imposed by stoichiometric examination are not adopted in order to appreciably simplify the processing of an enormous calculation ballast, when for each stage limitations are imposed on the behavior of the center of reactions and of reduced zones in its close neighborhood.

6. Propositions 1 and 5 are Used for the Second Atom (A_j) of the Atomic Vector VA(A_i, A_j).

By this step of the algorithm the same database set for A_j as for the atom A_i is obtained. Thus the necessary elements are available for the characterization of the atomic vector.

7. Correlation of the Transformations of the Valence States of the Atom with the Atomic Vector

From the data determined for the atoms A_i and A_j of the atomic vector two subgraphs of the elementary conversions of the valence states for both atoms are obtained. Obviously in the frame of the atomic vector the two components are not independent, since they are correlated by common bonds. However, here is taken into account the case in which the transformations of the valence states of the species A_i are not always involved in the change of all intermediate states of A_j. Such an example is represented by the transformation:

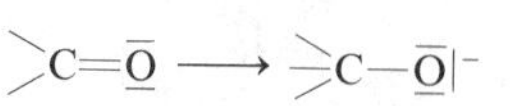

(136)

for which the step $>C{=}\overline{\underline{O}} \rightarrow -\overline{C}{=}\overline{\underline{O}}$ is necessary.

In case of finding the associations allowed from the chemical point of view of the valence states, the oriented vectors corresponding to the atom A_i, i.e. $\vec{v}_2, \vec{v}_3, \vec{v}_4$ are multiplied with the same vectors corresponding to the atom A_j: $\vec{u}_2, \vec{u}_3, u_4$. By this operation it is possible to obtain, for the association $\vec{v}_2, \vec{v}_4$, a result different from zero; in this case the combination of the two species of the atomic vector is made by a sigma bond. In the case of the association of $\vec{v}^i_3 \cdot \vec{u}^j_3 \neq 0$ the atoms in their new valence states are bonded by a pi bond, and in the case $\vec{v}^i_4 \cdot \vec{u}^j_4$ the atoms are bound through a two pi bonds. When the product of the vectors $\vec{v}^i_n \cdot \vec{u}^j_n = 0$, between the two components of the atomic vector, no bond can be found. Among the variants of the valence states can occur pairs that have no chance

Table 22
Possible Combinations in the Carbon-Oxygen Atomic Vector Expressed by Allowed Valence States

C	23	24	56	76	111	3	4	5	65	66	67	50	99	101
0														
44	1	1				1	1	1	1		1			
35	1	1					1							
36	1						1	1			1			
61			1	1					1	1	1	1		
83			1	1		1				1		1		
24	1						1							
76			1	1		1				1		1		
77					1								1	1

of being formed, for example $>C^{+}—\underline{O}^{+}=$. In general, for the atomic vector $AV\left|\begin{smallmatrix}O\\C\end{smallmatrix}\right|$, the allowed combinations between carbon and oxygen, by observing the possible valence forms, are presented in Table 22, where the numbering is the same used in Table 5.

The procedure shown in Figure 12 for the fragmentation of the molecules at the level of atomic vectors allows one to find all atomic pairs with the corresponding bonds. By the successive processing of these vectors one can deduce the complete form of the transformations in which these can participate.

The states in which the atomic vectors are bound can be grouped in the form of the so-called tree of allowed valence states [17]. A graph of this type is shown in Figure 14 for the conversion of AV(CO). In the computing program the possibility of choice of the pertinent atomic vector is included, according to the partial branches of the graph. Eight levels can be found in the graph shown in Figure 14 on which are located the allowed valence states in the vector (C, O). The first level is composed by nine branches, corresponding to electron regrouping in a typical elementary step of reaction. For the next step a new stage of reorganization is necessary. From the 9 states of the first level 18 states are thus generated on the next level by a single step of electron regrouping. This process can be expressed also by the matrix of reaction of a one- or two-electron transformation in a center with two atoms. Among the 18 states, 8 are did again and thus only 10 different states are generated. Further, from the set of structures that can be generated by a new step of valence electron regrouping, the subset of the doublets, containing the allowed states from the point of view of the chemical structures is selected. A part of the forms generated in Figure 14 corresponds to intermediate studies of real reactions, as it is, for instance, the generation of the vector $>C=\underline{O} \rightarrow —C—O^{+}$ on the first level, by a process of nucleofugic dissociation (D_E) [19]. One can specify further, according to Reference 17, the transformation of the atomic vector (C, O) in the case of carbonylation, by the reaction of carbon oxide with bases, cetens and their additional reactions that can be found for the carbonylic group $>C=\overline{\underline{O}}$. Through the intermediate species $>C^{+}—\overline{\underline{O}}|^{-}$ the nucleophilic addition is carried out to carbonyl with the stabilization of the group $—\!\!>C—\overline{\underline{O}}—$, as it happened in the case of the acid-catalyzed nucleophilic substitution of aliphatic hydrocarbons. In this respect the carbene ($\overline{C}<$) formation is specified by the substitution of oxygen with atoms of nitrogen, sulfur, selenium and by the transformation of the valence state in the group $>C=$; this reaction can be produced by breaking the bond in the vector C—O, followed by the transition of the valence state of Wittig's reaction $\geq P=\overline{\underline{O}}$. In the next step the acid-catalyzed addition reaction to the carbonyl group is produced.

All these examples show that the tree, shown in Figure 14, is particularly useful.

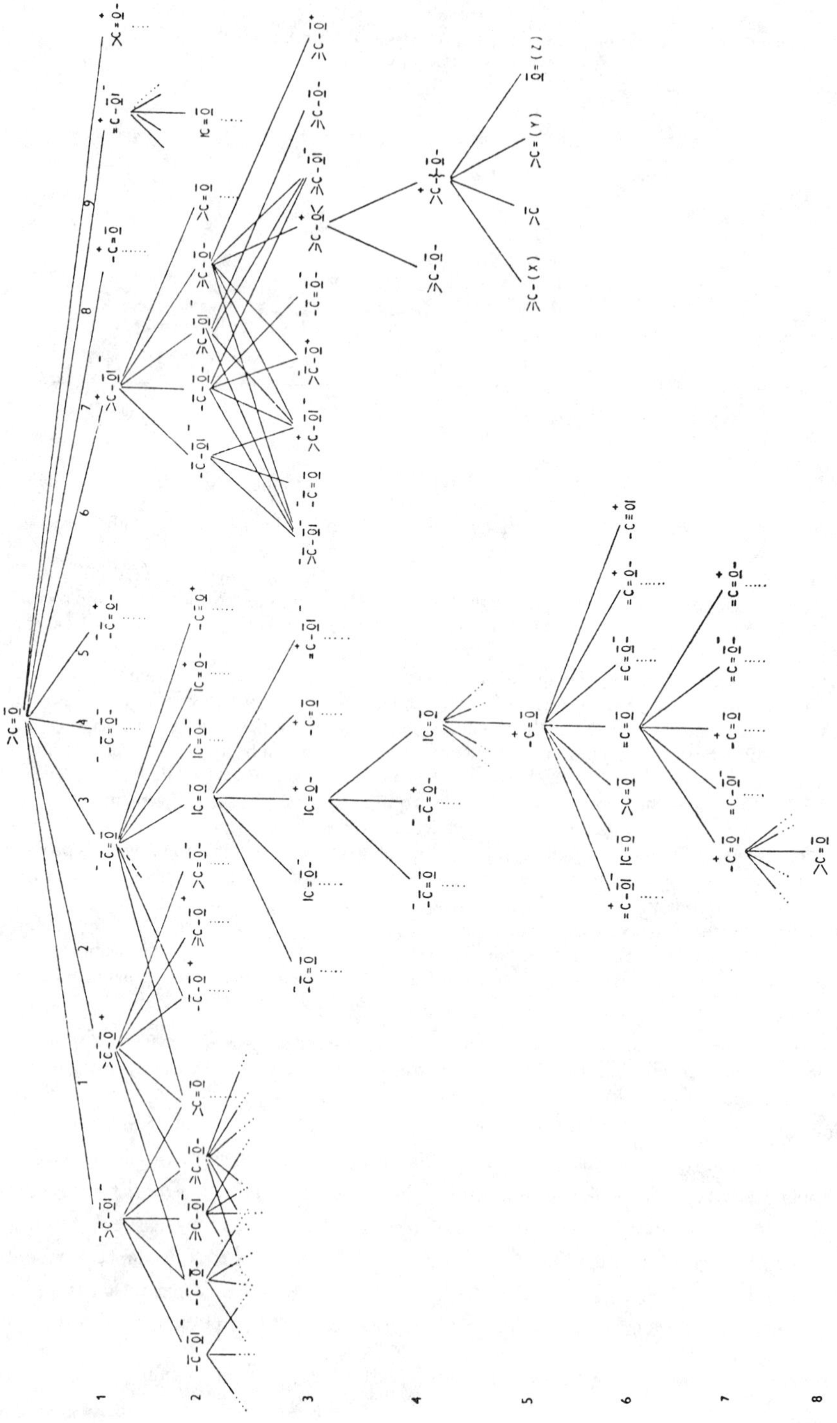

Figure 14. Tree of allowed conversions of valence states of the atomic vector C═O. (Reproduced with author's permission.) [17].

Figure 15 [56] shows a tree of the stepwise transformations of the valence states of the vector $\gt C{-}\overline{N}\lt$. In this tree the paths of several well known reactions in organic chemistry can be found. For instance the following paths are used: (a) Hoffman fragmentation of amides of carboxylic acids; (b) KaplanSchechter reduction in the synthesis of gem-dinitro-alkans; (c) von Braun splitting of amides in nitriles; (d) Birchov's reduction, sec- and tert-amids in nitrils; (e) Behrend's transposition of nitrons; (f) nitron oxidation and Schiffer bases; (g) thermolyze of imidoylhalids; (h) reduction of the nitrocompounds and (i) Curti's fragmentation of azides.

The examples in Figures 14 and 15 shown the way in which a chemical reaction can be described by a stepwise procedure, where the elementary transformation is the step of the electron regrouping process. A computer program thus offers the possibility to cover any reaction path and to find new forms of reactions or compounds.

Algorithm for Determining the Reactant

In the most general meaning, a chemical reaction expresses a interaction of the educt species, based on electron regroupings between the centers of reaction of both substrate and reactant components. In the previous section the algorithm for the determining the center of a substrate molecule was discussed. In this section an algorithm proposed for determining the reactant center of reaction is proposed. This algorithm, termed REALA [17] (from the Czech expression "Reaktivity Latek," reactivity of substances), embraces 5 propositions:

1. Drawing the electron scheme of the reactant.
2. Determining the electronegativity χ_j of the reactant atoms.
3. Determining bond polarities of $A_i{-}A_j$, $A_j{-}A_k$ from the differences $\Delta\chi_{jk}$, $\Delta\chi_{ij}$.
4. After the deduction of bond polarities, the symbols of the inductive (I) and conjugation (M) properties are found.
5. In the atomic code the arrow showing the vector direction denotes the effects I and M, correlated with the symbols of the fragmentary charges $\delta-$ and the neighboring ones $\delta+$. To the atoms with $\delta-$ in the first approximation the largest electronic density is assumed, having in the same time donor properties. To the atoms with $\delta+$ the lowest electronic densities are assumed, having acceptor properties.

In the model already presented for the determination of the substrate center of reaction are used the instructions yielded by the procedure REEL: (a) valence electron regrouping in the substrate, operation noted as P_i; (b) the variants of reaction mechanisms, noted with P_k and (c) donor-acceptor nature of the substrate center of reaction, noted with P_j. The total operations is $P_iP_kP_j$. On one hand P_k expresses an operation from a very large set of data, connected with the possible reaction mechanisms; on the other hand P_j refers to the possible centers of reaction of the reactant component, representing also a considerable set of possible components; to all these are added the problems arising in determining the substrate center of reaction by means of the P_i operation. In the matrix of ESRE procedure (Table 21) the process corresponding to the mode of regrouping of valence electrons is shown. This corresponds to a difference of the vectors of valence states of the constituent atoms, showing the first step of the possible reaction mechanism. Thus the atomic vector $-\overline{\underline{O}}-H$ can participate in a reaction of electrofugic dissociation:

$$-\overline{\underline{O}}-H \xrightarrow{D_E} -\overline{\underline{O}}|^- + H^+ \qquad (137)$$

$$VA_E\begin{pmatrix}4200\\0100\end{pmatrix} \longrightarrow VA_P\begin{pmatrix}6100\\0000\end{pmatrix}$$

The difference of the vectors of the valence states is (-2010) for oxygen, and $(0-100)$ for hydrogen.

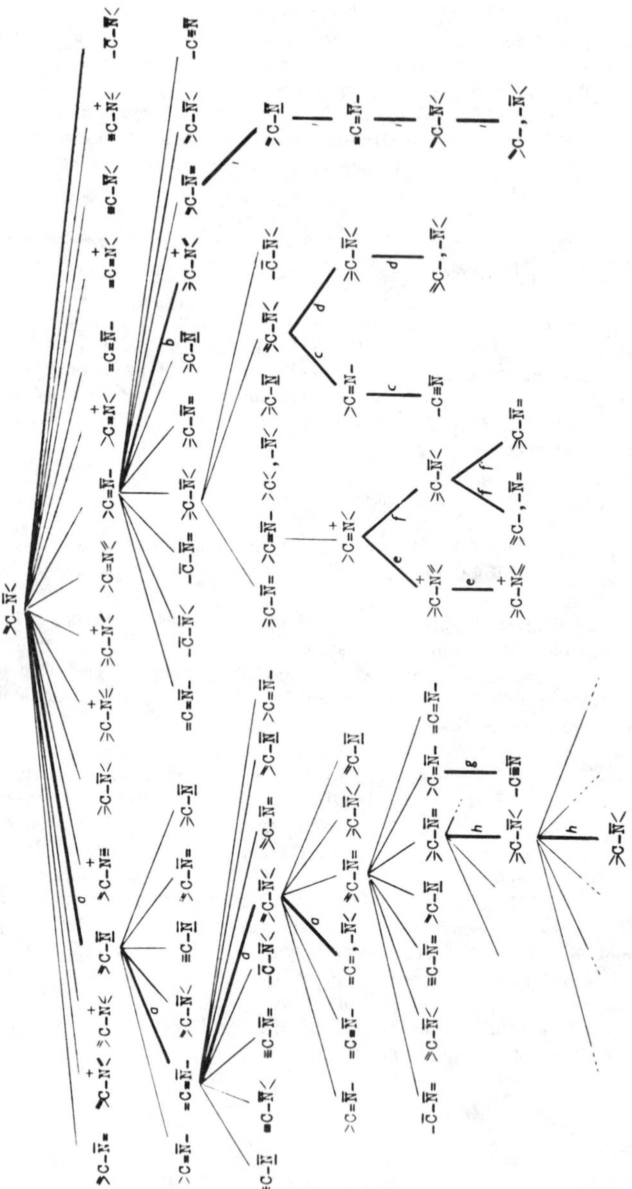

Figure 15. Tree of allowed conversions of valence states of the atomic vector $\geqslant C-\bar{N}<$. (Courtesy of J. Koča, M. Kratochvil, V. Kvasnička, L. Matyska and J. Pospíchal, [56].)

The atomic vector (SO) can participate in an electrophilic association process:

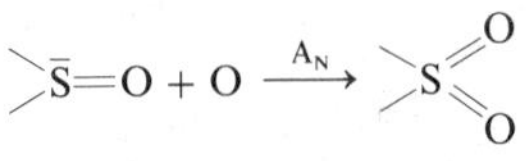

(138)

$$VA_E(2210) \longrightarrow VA_P(0220)$$

The difference of the vectors of valence state for the sulfur atom is therefore (−2010). The group peroxi, $-\underline{\overline{O}}-\underline{\overline{O}}-$, can undergo a process of radicalic dissociation:

$$-\underline{\overline{O}}-\underline{\overline{O}}- \xrightarrow{D_R} -\underline{\overline{O}}^{\bullet} + {}^{\bullet}\underline{\overline{O}}- \qquad (139)$$

$$VA_E(4200) \longrightarrow VA_P(5100)$$

The difference of the valence states is therefore (1–100). In this way any atomic vector, real, hypothetical, known or unknown in practice can be treated. The utility of a computing model, based on this principle, is therefore obvious.

It follows that when the substrate center of reaction is known, it is possible to determine also the center of reaction of the reactant starting from the indication given by the code of the difference of the vectors of valence states. The main properties connected to the center of reaction is the electrophilic, nucleophilic, or radicalic character of the component atoms. The amount of operations is determined by the size of the set including the reactants. Considering the three specified kinds of reactants one can note that, in the case of the substrate molecules, the set of radicals is on the order of tenths of individual components, but in the case of nucleophilic and electrophilic reactants the same set is on the order of hundreds. For the reactant molecules, the amount of the possible variants is considerably smaller. Here must be taken into account the known properties that restrict the possibilities of participation in occurrence of reaction, i.e. the electronic, steric and energetic factors. For a mechanism of the type of bimolecular nucleophilic substitution (S_N2), series of reactivity are specified. In aprotic media such a series is given by the sequence:

$$CN^- > AcO^- > F^- > N_3^- > Cl^- > Br^- > I^- > SCN^-$$

Obviously no electrophilic or nucleophilic group can react in the substrate center of reaction with defined donor-acceptor properties. This is why it was necessary to consider the compatibility between substrate and reactant as reaction partners. In the more complex cases, substrate molecule sets are drawn up together with the set of adequate reactants for each substrate species. The transformation of the ensembles of educt molecules in ensembles of the product ones, can be carried out with a computer using the matrices of reaction. These operations need generally short intervals for the computing time. For the selection of the ensembles that correspond to defined product molecules, selection rules, operation instructions, and procedures which included in any computing program are used. But, for the economy of computing work, it is necessary to adopt procedures that avoid as much as possible the redundance in the computation programs.

PREDICTING CHEMISTRY FROM SUBSTRUCTURES (EFFECTORS) AND TOPOLOGY

Chemistry has succeeded in identifying and synthetizing more than seven million molecular species. Each of these molecules has defined properties whose determination is included also in the task of chemical research. In conditions of accumulation of this vast amount of knowledge, the problem arises of the possibility of predicting the properties of chemical substances, starting from the molecular structure alone. This problem is old, but only now can be realized on quantitative grounds. There are several points of view from which the problem can be envisaged. Among these, two are of particular interest: (a) searching the set of effectors, defined as the molecular substructures determining one or a few properties of the molecule that contains these fragments; (b) searching the molecular topology, defining topological indices that are in close correlation with a defined molecular property.

The first point was thoroughly studied in this chapter as a base to elaborate algorithms for determining chemical reactions. But the correlation of molecular substructures as effectors with the properties (especially the pharmacological ones) of the molecules was studied in detail [46]. A similar topic is taken into account [58] for inhibitor complexes of renine [58].

The second point lies on a completely different base, an empirical one, which is not still principally founded. Starting from a interatomic distance, taken equal to one, and various modalities to calculate, cummulative distances between points in the molecular graph allow one to obtain a series of "topological indices," which, surprisingly, can be very well correlated with a molecular property. This finding, although with some alchemical savor owing to its empirical ground and oracular claim, offers, however, a powerful tool for the new branch of the mathematical chemistry termed "Predicting Chemistry" [59].

Predicting Chemistry from Effectors [50]

The main problem of predicting chemistry by using substructures, obtained as shown in Figure 12, is the possibility to activate or inhibit a specified property by the presence of a peculiar type of one or a group of molecular fragments. Properties such as toxicity, bacteriostaticity, or fungicidity are particularly interesting, owing to the major applications in many problems of the practice. These molecular fragments, able to determine specific properties of the molecules, are termed as effectors. This problem reached an outstanding interest in the last years [60–62] and seems to be very promising in the future, especially for larger molecules encountered in pharmacology and biology. In these molecules the effector can be formed by a large molecular group. For instance the elimination of the C-terminals of the histidylleucine dipeptide by the angiotensin converting enzime yields angyotensine II, the proper effector of the reninangyotensin-system [58]. The term effector is here used for a molecule composed of 10 amino acids and, therefore, a very large compound.

The deduction of substructures is carried out by means of a computer program based on a algorithm of GEN type (Automatic Generation of Substructures) [48, 63–66]. Using these substructures a series of molecules can be recomposed. Starting from a molecule with known properties, substructures are found that correlate with these properties. Once the building blocks of the searched property are known, the problem is to recompose these molecules in which the specified property is enhanced. In this way a dynamic dialogue with the computer is established. In the next step for finding the wanted property or set of properties, all necessary substructures are recomposed from the database. The problem is, therefore, to find the properties by using the substructures.

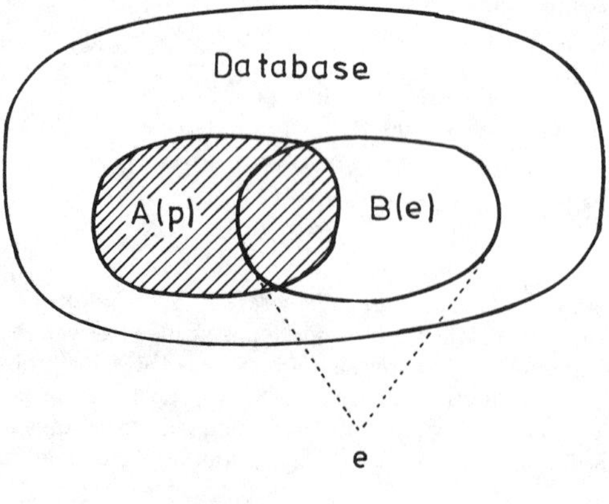

Figure 16. Substructures as possible effectors for the property p. A(p) is the set of fragments of the molecule with the property p (hatched surface); B(e) is the set of fragments of the molecule with some common substructures; e is the communication of substructure.

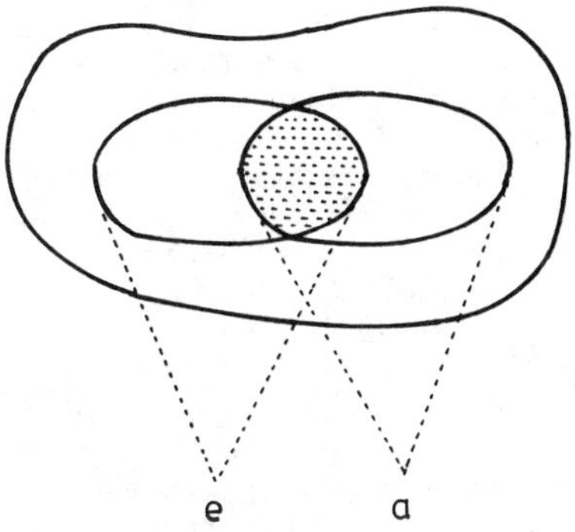

Figure 17. Synergistic effector influence of the fragments of molecule (a) in the presence of the fragments of molecule (e).

The criteria to detect effector quality of a fragment for a certain property are based on a statistical evaluation. In this case it is assumed that a decision can be taken for at least 50 molecules from database. Among these, 25 structures possess the specified quality and the remained 25 lack it.

From the molecular fragments in Figure 16 note the set A(p) of fragments obtained from the molecule having the property p. From the fragments of the effector B(e), the overlaped part on A(p) shows the common fragments that can be considered as significant for the property of interest.

The effectors maintaining the specified property, regardless of the nature of other fragments present, are termed as independent effectors. Another group is formed by the fragments that show effector activity in the presence of other effectors, as shown by the dotted surface in Figure 17. These lasts are termed as synergistic effectors. Figure 18 presents the antagonistic influence of the fragments whose presence inhibits the activity of other fragments. In this case the corresponding fragments are termed as inhibitors.

The influence shown by substructures on properties can be clearly evidentiated in the case of the larger molecules. The properties such as bacteriostatically and fungicidity can be detected by spectroscopical procedures, allowing a correlation possibility with the effector action of the molecule fragments [61, 62, 67–72].

Although the stereochemical structural aspects are not taken into account, these often represent an important influence on the molecular properties [73]. It is well known that some chromatic or fisiological effects are due not only to constitution, but also to the steric arrangement of the atoms in the structure of the molecule [74].

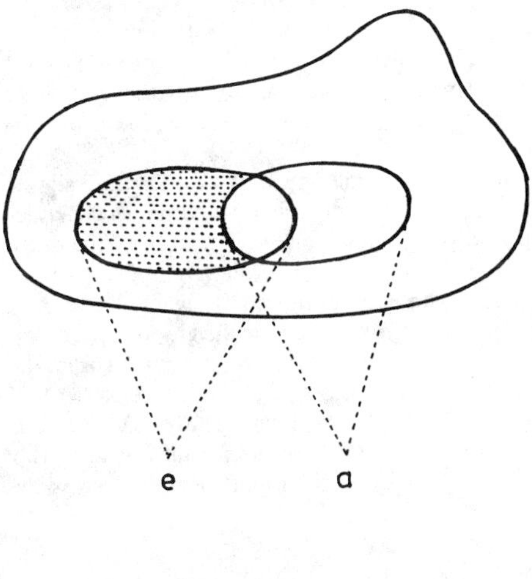

Figure 18. Inhibition effector influence of the fragments of molecule (a) in the presence of fragments of molecule (e).

In literature [46] algorithms are described for selecting substructures and their statistic evaluation. The procedure VAL refers to the value allowance for the fragments that can be processed from a set of indexed molecules. The procedure SEL is related to the most reliable substructure selection. The description of these procedures correlates with the algorithm GEN, studied in the 16th section. Also proposed were methods for hierarchical iterative selection, and algorithms for determining the most reliable (EFF), synergistic (SYN) or antagonistic (ANT) effectors. The very extended computer program can be found in Reference [46].

Predicting Chemistry from Topological Indices

A very simple idea is to consider dimensional parameters, express interconnections of the points (atoms) on a molecular graph, and correlate them with a characteristic property of the molecule. A typical procedure allows one to obtain a value termed as topological index (TI). It has been found that these indices can be calculated from a planar form of the molecular graph. This clearly shows that sometimes the spatial arrangement of the atoms, the nature and lengths of the interatomic bonds, and also angles between the lines (chemical bonds) of the graph are not parameters of influence for the correlation of TI with a molecular property. The most important parameters are number of the atoms in the molecule, reciprocal connectivity between these atoms, length of straight chains, lateral branchings, and number and combination forms of the rings.

The most important problem of the predicting topology is the determination of the method to define the index that correlates best with the physico-chemical property of interest. One can imagine a specified rule that defines a index, allowing one to obtain peculiar values for each structure. The chosen method is applied to several well studied molecules and the obtained values are plotted against several molecular properties. If a close correlation, expressed by a defined continuous line is found, then the index under consideration can be used to determine that property for a unstudied molecule or a not-yet-available structure.

Similarly to the effector method, the topological indices allow one to not only find physico-chemical constants, but also some properties of extensive applicability. It is possible to determine with this method the pharmacological activity of the drugs, anestetical properties, psychoactivity concerning action of some substances, etc. Successful applications were also found for predicting the pollutant action in the environment of some substances, the way to control and model corrosion, and production of drinks with a desired taste. One can actually ask about the limits of extension of this field and principal foundation that is able to explain how the topology is concerned in such diversified branches: Are molecules always really producers, or are they sometimes transmitters of "properties" sensorially perceivable? Here is involved the consciousness together with the concept of length, which strongly suggests its reciprocical, the wave. The problem is to know how the molecules interact with QCD (Quantum Chromo Dynamic)-vacuum [75].

A well known and commonly reputed method is to determine, as exactly as possible, the geometric, energetic, and field parameters of the molecule by using quantum mechanics procedures.

Another method is the one already specified, based on the effector properties. The most important disadvantage is the rather abusive assumption that the properties of a complex structure should be well correlated with those of the fragments, although they can be arranged in several modes, obtaining in this way several completely different molecules.

The method of topological indices, although principally still unfounded, is based on the simple assumption that rigorous correlations can be found between the empirical properties and mathematical parameters, precisely determined. In the absence of availability of theoretical rules, the problem reduces to the possibility of finding empirically the geometrical way for determining a peculiar number, and then to include it in the physico-chemical database of interest.

In practice, for a study using topological analysis it is first necessary to draw the graph of the molecule showing the points (atoms) and lines (chemical bonds). As it has been already emphasized, the reciprocical ratio between lines and the angles between them have no visible influence. Instead of this, the simple presence of the bonds between points has the essential role. This circumstance is rather surprising, because the data about relative lengths of bonds and the angles they form appear intuitively to be of particular importance. Therefore at the base of the topological analysis is the simple molecular graph, from which the topological index is deduced. The essential condition to be fulfilled by this index is to be a graph invariant, therefore its value must be independent of the position or indexing of the graph. As previously specified in describing Morgan's algorithm, the hydrogen atoms can often be omitted. Thus the carbon number characterizes a straight-chain, but cannot be used for describing branched structures, which have very different forms for an equal number of carbon atoms; it is not therefore appropriate and another type of index must be found, in order to dispose of a higher discriminating power.

The following describes a few more important topological indices.

The local graph invariants are numbers associated with each node considering the following three conditions: (a) the number assigned to a node is independent of the arbitrary indexing; (b) a node number expresses a defined topological site, and (c) isomorphic graphs have the same graph invariant.

Although nonisomorphic, a group of graphs can have the same topological index (TI); this property, termed as degeneracy, must be as low as possible in order to have a good correlational ability. As previously shown, the hydrogen atoms can be removed to obtain hydrogen-depleted graphs. An important parameter of these graphs is the distance $d_{i,j}$ between two nodes. One can draw a matrix whose entries are these distances. Such a matrix is termed as a distance matrix D, where the main diagonal entries are zeros and the off-diagonal ones entire numbers different from zero.

The most important problem is obviously the procedure to construct rules for calculating topological indices having a specified correlational ability. In general for this construction two steps are involved: (a) finding local vertex invariants (LOVIs) for the nodes of the graphs (assignment step); and (b) using a suitable mathematical procedure to obtain the necessary correlation (operational step) [76]. In the first step it is necessary to find the encoding procedure of information correlated with the property of interest. When the core atom of the graph is not involved, in this encoding the assignment is purely topological; otherwise the procedure is chemical.

Three main criteria can be used for the assignment step: distance, connectivity, and node neighbors.

Distance Sum

When distance is considered, the gauge is represented by A_i—A_j interspace. On this base the assignment of nodes in the hydrogen-depleted graph of the isopentane molecule is:

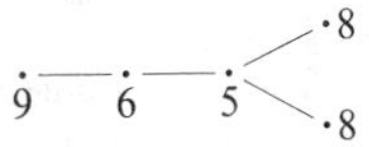

(140)

Using this assignment, several indices can be defined by the operational stage. Two variants were already proposed.

One of these, termed as the Wiener index [77], uses the relation, based on the number of atom assignment:

$$TI = \tfrac{1}{2} \sum A_i \qquad (141)$$

A suggested form to apply to this relation is given in Figure 19, where all possible distances of the graph are considered and TI = 18 is obtained. Using any arbitrary numbering, the distance matrix of the hydrogen depleted isopentan molecule is:

$$
\begin{array}{c c c}
 & \begin{array}{ccccc} 1 & 2 & 3 & 4 & 5 \end{array} & \\
D = & \begin{pmatrix} 0 & 1 & 2 & 3 & 3 \\ 1 & 0 & 1 & 2 & 2 \\ 2 & 1 & 0 & 1 & 1 \\ 3 & 2 & 1 & 0 & 2 \\ 3 & 2 & 1 & 2 & 0 \end{pmatrix} & \begin{array}{c} 1 \\ 2 \\ 3 \\ 4 \\ 5 \end{array}
\end{array}
$$

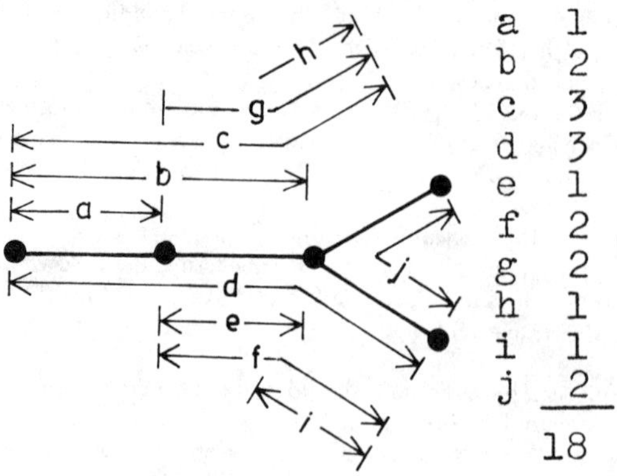

Figure 19. Calculation of Wiener index for hydrogen depleted isopentane molecule.

The Wiener topological index is given by half of the sum of all entries of this matrix, therefore TI = 36/2 = 18.

This method obtains indications about the carbon atom number and it indicates the branching of the structure. Its value is low for small molecules and increases rapidly with the increase of molecular size. For a series of hydrocarbon molecules this index correlates very well with the boiling point, viscosity, surface tension, and refractive index.

It has been found that the Wiener index is widely applicable. A good correlation was found between this index and energies of the bonding electrons in a series of molecules, for instance the spiro-type compounds, where several rings lay in perpendicular planes, with adjacent rings sharing a single vertex, and policyclic aromatic hydrocarbons with hexagonal rings that share at least one line and are located in the same plane. This correlation is of fundamental importance, since the energy levels of the bonding electrons largely determine the reactivity of the molecule and the kind of reactions in which it can participate. In this way a series of other molecular properties are also concerned by this correlation. Here are included, for example, the electrical conductivity, the electron affinity, and the frequencies of the bands of electromagnetic waves absorbed by the molecule. Thus, the Wiener index allows one to predict the molecular stability of unknown compounds.

The Wiener index can be applied also to characterize very large molecules as polymers and crystals. A method was devised to modify the calculation of Wiener index in order to determine finite values for infinite systems provided that these are composed from identical units (monomer molecule). In this way it was possible to estimate the electrical properties of the conducting or semi-conducting polymers. The other properties such as melting and boiling points for polytetrafluoroethylene, polycapramide, and polyethyleneterephtalate were accurately predicted.

In various other fields such as corrosion control, catalysis, chemisorption, etc. the Wiener index can be applied, allowing one to determine the interstitial sites that can be filled by foreign atoms. Here the following rule holds: For low values of the Wiener index the system is in its lowest energy state. The problem is reduced therefore to count the three-coordinate Wiener index for all possible states of both the crystal-lattice and foreign atoms. The low value of the Wiener indices show the most probable configurations.

These various applications of the Wiener index indicate that it correlates not only with the value of molecule or lattice site, but also with the corresponding form of the considered formation.

The second variant of operational stage, based on distance criterion for the assignment step, was proposed by Balaban [78, 79]:

$$TI_J = \frac{q}{(\mu + 1)} \sum (A_i A_j)^{-1/2} \tag{142}$$

q is the total number of edges A_i—A_j and μ the cyclomatic number. Here, instead of the individual atom, an atom pair is used. In this way the index becomes more sensitive to the branching of the molecule, a parameter of particular importance for octan number of fuel hydrocarbon molecules.

It is also possible to assign to each bond a value, as it is in the following notation:

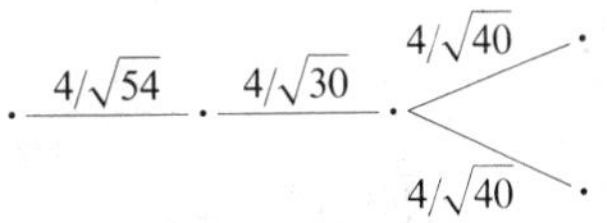
4/√54
4/√30
4/√40
4/√40

(143)

In this way TI_J can be obtained by addition. Thus, the index value for isopentane is therefore $TI_J = 2{,}539$ [76].

Vertex Degree

Instead of the distance sum, for a series of TI the vertex degree was used as a criterion for the assignment step. Thus, the isopentane is assigned as follows:

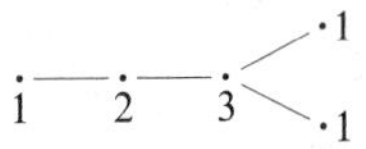
1
2
3
1
1

(144)

With this assignment several variants are used for the operational stage.
Gutman, et al. [80] proposed the relation:

$$TI_{M1} = \sum A_i^2 \tag{145}$$

In this way the value 16 was obtained for the index.
Another computing relation was proposed by Gutman and Trinajstić [81] as follows:

$$TI_{M2} = \sum A_i A_j \tag{146}$$

The value of the topological index is now 14.
A particularly useful method was found by Randić [82] using the formula:

$$TI_X = \sum (A_i A_j)^{-1/2} \tag{147}$$

obtaining the value 2,2701 in the case of isopentane molecule. Since the most important property of the index is its connection with the geometry and shape of the molecule, this method succeeded to define more sensitive topological procedures. The molecular-connectivity index introduced by Randić is the most elaborated variant among the proposed forms. Compared with the Wiener system based on distance, the Randić index expresses a topological concept of degree. As in the Morgan concept, the degree of a node is given by the number of the nodes attached to him [37]. Also in this case to each line, a value can be assigned, which is the product of the reverse of the square root of the degrees, as shown in Figure 20. Here the Randić index of a molecule is obtained by the addition of the values of graph's lines. Randić indices correlate well with a series of molecular properties, allowing one to predict drug action of molecules, toxicity and polluant action of industrial wastes, and also sensorial properties, such as taste and smell, of not yet synthetized molecules.

It has been found that the best correlations are obtained when isolated parts of the molecule are used for the calculation of the Randić indices. This suggests strongly the similarity with the concept of the effector. In this way the topological index expresses in synthetic form the concepts described previously: cannonical connectivity, combined with molecule fragmentation.

Related to these structures, instead of an index, a set of indices are obtained and thus the symplicity of a single value is substituted by the multiplicity of tabulated values.

Randić molecular connectivity indices were found to predict a large variety of physico-chemical properties, such as heat of vaporization, solubility, density, etc. Their domain of applicability was extended to detect particular biological responses by correlating the molecular structure with anesthetic, narcotic, and hallucinogenic action and also with the taste and odor of a series of molecules.

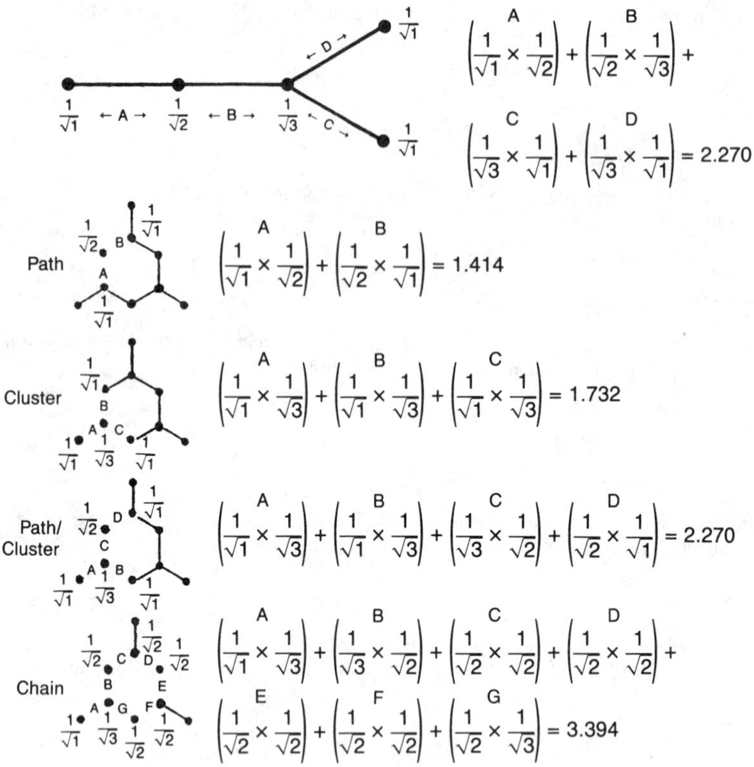

Figure 20. Examples of calculation for Randić index [59].

Node Neighbors

The third method uses for node assignment the number of neighbors. Two variants were proposed for this case.

The first procedure takes into account second neighbors [83]. The assignment of nodes is:

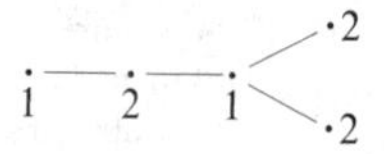

(148)

and the computing formula:

$$TI_{N2} = \frac{1}{2} \sum A_i \tag{149}$$

The topological index is 4.

The second procedure assigns the nodes of the graph considering the third neighbors [77]:

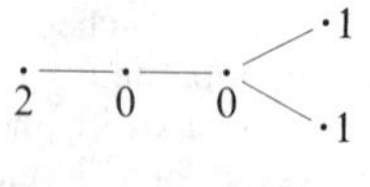

(150)

and the same computing formula:

$$TI_P = \frac{1}{2}\sum A_i \tag{151}$$

The topological index is now 2.

Other Topological Indices

More recently, correlations were found with the inhibition action for microorganism reproduction, killing certain viruses, mutagenicity, etc. In recent years applications were found for environmental studies. Topological indices were used to study the toxicity of pollutants in fauna water, air, and soil; the ability to concentrate within living organisms; and pollutant interchange between different media. The advantage of the topological indices is in this case obvious since the control and experiments in environmental media are particularly difficult and expensive. This is why the U.S. Environment Protection Agency adopted topological indices for the study of toxicity and damages produced by untested pollutants.

The problem of finding specialized indices arises when Wiener and Randić methods are not more suitable for some particular situations. Topologic methods are successful for the cases in which the overall form, size, and branching are determinant for the specified property.

A particularly difficult case was to find indices for predicting the quantity of soot produced during burning of a molecule. When the same family of molecules was investigated, the problem simplifies, but in the case of molecules from different families, the procedure becomes easily unreliable. It is necessary in this case to consider the occurrence of the double bonds or chain rings. For each molecular family an index can be calculated, and a more general form is obtained by combining the desired indices. In this way one index, the hydrogen-deficiency number, shows the amount of atom rings (Figure 21) [59]; another index is established to measure the sum of averaged-distances showing the molecular-connectivity of the studied molecules. The correlation index for soot production is obtained then by the product of the above shown indices.

An interesting attempt was to find a topological index able to predict the carcinogenicity of a molecule. In some cases this prediction is possible but the difficulty arises owing to the multistep processes involved in cancer causation. This is why such a index must include information of the chemical action of the initial molecule and also the same action produced by the molecules formed during the first interaction. A Randić type index can correlate the carcinogenic action of a molecule, but is not sufficient to determine the degree of carcinogenicity. The problem was recently solved by the combination of several common indices. The method applies for the polycyclic aromatic hydrocarbon molecules. It has been found that limited regions of this type of structure are more active in carcinogenesis, since in these sites starts the reaction chain of the totality of involved processes. Similarly, other regions are less active. By appropriate indexing of these regions and well selected relations, fairly good correlations between calculated indices and experimental values for carcinogenicity are found (Figure 22).

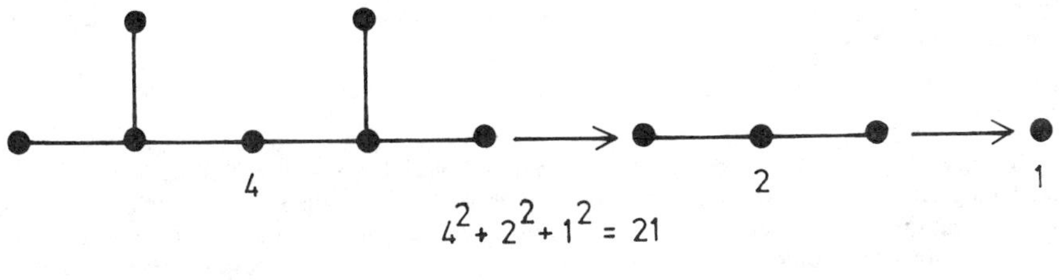

Figure 21. Hydrogen-deficiency index [59].

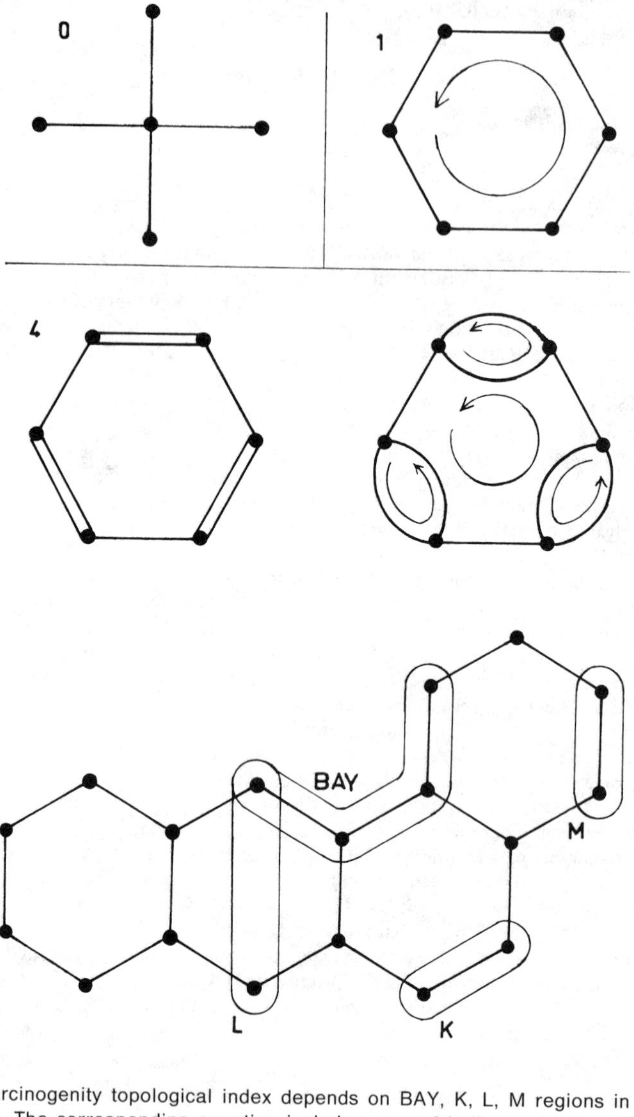

Figure 22. Carcinogenity topological index depends on BAY, K, L, M regions in a series of hydrocarbons. The corresponding equation includes several indices, structural features that can be defined in terms of these regions [59].

The area of applicability of the topological indices is very large, embracing physical, chemical, and biological properties. Although no theoretical principles are available for deduction, selection, or classification of these indices, it is possible to establish empirically the suitable index in order to solve a practical problem. Owing to the excellent correlations with the properties of interest, topological indices can be extended for very diversified predictions allowing the use of a powerful and economical tool for many practical problems.

CONCLUSION

Some fundamental aspects of a mathematical version for the chemistry were studied: molecules as graphs converted in matrices; chemical reactions as matrix operations applied to matrix molecules; drawing of reaction operators starting from two fundamental matrices; matrix form of elementary mechanisms; vector of valence states and elementary transformations; and several algorithms for elaboration of computer programs. For the problems concerning documentation and classification the new concept of connectivity was particularly interesting and proved that the connectivity matrix can be successfully used. The topological indices also address connectivity, distance, and node degree. In the case of computer programs for determining and predicting the chemical reactions, the BE matrices, more rich in information, together with the codes and trees of the valence states with elementary step of electron regrouping must be used.

All these procedures for the transposition of the classical symbols of chemistry in mathematical entities are useful for elaborating computing programs, and for a more rigorous understanding of the notions peculiar to the chemistry. The actual criteria introduced for the nomenclature of the reaction mechanisms, can be mathematically founded taking into account the conversion of the valence states and the matrices of reactions describing the typical elementary transformations. One can form a clear image of the mechanism of a chemical reaction, of stable and unstable intermediates, more or less encountered, only by the nonambiguous expression of the elementary conversion of the valence states, produced according to the rule of allowed steps, which are components of the subgraphs of atomic vectors or individual atoms. The set of these subgraphs forms the graph of the series of all chemical transformations, based on electron conversion of the valence states of atoms.

The question arises about the point of view from which the study of the chemistry is concerned in conditions of several possibilities of symbolization, i.e., if the usual literal notation must be substituted by the mathematical one. It seems to be not reasonable to consider the problem in this way. The literal symbolism is expressive and must be maintained especially in the didactic learning methods of the chemistry. The mathematical forms can, however, be set up in an indispensable chapter of systematization and ordering, the information being obtained by the literal notation. The considerable advantage of the mathematical form of expression is still enhanced by direct dialogue with computers.

Actually, a personal computer with a chemical database can be used. Thus, the systematic examination of many compounds is possible, since the databases are formed by selected subsets of I.S.I.'s Index Chemical Oneline containing four million chemical structures. This method often lets the chemist visually identify key structural determinants of activity suggesting new compounds and new pathways for chemical synthesis. In addition, a chemical database management system from Molecular Design Ltd. [84] was used to develop the processing of literature data. Chem-Base works with the IBM computer family (PC, PC X T, PC AT) and is available in the U.S. and Europe. These devices allow design of databases that allow various actions, such as drawing molecules, defining forms for data display, and carrying out database sort, search, edit operations.

The chemist working with these personal computers can use data to elaborate new sets of databases. But, sometimes, the simplest way to extend the necessary sets is to use the commercially available databases for selected topics. This possibility saves time and routine work. Moreover, the possibility to transform databases according to circumstantial necessities allows the introduction of different types of user-added data for completeness. But the use of these modern and easily available facilities becomes possible only when the mathematical principles to express the chemical symbolism are appropriated.

NOTATION

a_i	vector projection on coordinate axis
a_{ii}	diagonal entry of matrix (general)
a_{ij}	entry of matrix (general)
A	collection of molecules
A_i	indexed atomic species
$\langle A \rangle$	empirical formula of FIEM
A_e	reductive (electronic) association
A_E	electrophilic association
A_N	nucleophilic association

A_R	radicalic association
AV	atomic vector
b	square matrix as vector
b_{ii}	diagonal entry of educt matrix
b_{ij}	entry of educt matrix
B	educt matrix
BE	bond and electron matrix
C	connectivity matrix
d	number of double bonds in VVS
D	distance matrix
D(BE)	chemical distance
D_e	oxidative (electronic) dissociation
D_E	electrofugic dissociation
D_N	nucleofugic dissociation
D_R	radicalic dissociation
DVVS	difference of vectors of valence states
E	product matrix
e_i	valence electron
e_{ii}	diagonal entry of product matrix
e_{ij}	entry of product matrix
EM	ensemble of molecules
EM(B)	ensemble of educt molecules
EM(E)	ensemble of product molecules
FIEM	family of ensemble of molecules
HOMO	highest occupied molecular orbital
i	order of row or column matrix
J	adjacency matrix
LUMO	lowest unoccupied molecular orbital
MECVS	matrix of the elementary conversions of the elements
n	number of nonparticipating electrons in VVS
n	number in general (atoms, matrices); order of matrix
n	electron pair
n	level of substructure
N	power of matrix
P	permutation as value and operation
P(B, E)	matrix as point in vector space
r_{ii}	diagonal entry of reaction matrix
r_{ij}	entry of reaction matrix
R	matrix of reaction
R_2^n	metric space with n^2 coordinates (dimensions)
s	number of simple bonds in VVS
s	sum of the matrix entries
$\hat{s}$	cross sum
s_i	sum of entries of row or column
S_E	electrophilic substitution
S_E1	monomolecular electrophilic substitution
S_E2	bimolecular electrophilic substitution
S_N	nucleophilic substitution
S_N1	monomolecular nucleophilic substitution
S_N2	bimolecular nucleophilic substitution
S_R	radicalic substitution
S_R1	monomolecular radicalic substitution
S_R2	bimolecular radicalic substitution
SF	structure family
SOMO	highest one-electron occupied molecular orbital of atom or radical
TI	topological index
v_i	component of VVS (general)
VS	valence state
VVS	vector of valence state
X	nonindexed atomic species

Algorithms

AHMOS	Automatisierte Heuristische Organischer Chemischer System
ANT	Determination of Synergistic Effectors
ASSOR	Allgemeines System zur Simulation Organischer Reaktionen
CICLOPS	Computers in Chemistry Logic Oriented Planning of Synthese
COMB	Combination of Valence States of the Atoms
EROS	Elaboration of Organic Synthesis
ESRE	Elementary Step of Reorganization of Valence Electrons
GEN	Automatic Generation of Substructures
LHASA	Logic and Heuristics Applied to Synthetic Analysis
OCSS	Organic Chemical Simulation Synthesis
REALA	Reaktivity Latek (Reactivity of Substances)

RECENT Determination of the Center of Reaction
REEL Regrouping of Valence Electrons
SEL Most Reliable Substructure Selection
SYN Determination of Most Reliable Effectors

REFERENCES

1. Călușaru, A., and Volanschi, C., *Rev. Chim.* (Bucharest), 35, 307 (1984); Călușaru, A., and Volanschi, C., *Intern. Chem. Eng.*, 26, 428 (1986).
2. Ugi, I., Bauer, J., Brandt, J., Friedrich, J., Gasteiger, J., Jochum, C., and Schubert, W., *Angew. Chem. Int. Engl. Ed.*, 18, 111 (1979).
3. Corey, E. J., Johnson, A. P., and Long, A. K., *J. Org. Chem.*, 45, 2051 (1980).
4. Hendrickson, J. B., *J. Am. Chem. Soc.*, 99, 5439 (1977).
5. Balaban, A. T., *J. Chem. Inf. Comput. Sci.*, 25, 334 (1985).
6. Bersohn, M., and Esak, A., *Chem. Rev.*, 76, 269 (1976).
7. Balaban, A. T., *Math. Chem.*, 8, 159 (1980).
8. Gasteiger, J., and Jochum, C., *Top. Curr. Chem.*, 74, 93 (1978).
9. Johnson, A. P., *Chem. Ber.*, 21, 59 (1985).
10. Balaban, A. T., *Rev. Chim. Acad. Repub. Pop. Roum.*, 7, 675 (1964).
11. Călușaru, A., and Volanschi, C., *Rev. Chim.* (Bucharest), 35, 598 (1984); Călușaru, A., and Volanschi, C., *Intern. Chem. Eng.*, 26, 441 (1986).
12. Kratochvil, M., *Chem. Listy*, 75, 673 (1981).
13. Dugundji, J., and Ugi, I., *Top. Curr. Chem.*, 39, 19 (1973).
14. Ugi, I., and Gillespie, P. D., *Angew. Chem.*, 83, 980, 982 (1971).
15. Ugi, I., Gasteiger, J., Gillespie, C., and Gillespie, P. D., *IBM-Nachr.*, 24, 185 (1974).
16. Gasteiger, J., Jochum, C., Marsili, M., and Thoma, J., *Inform. Commun. Math. Chem.*, 177 (1979).
17. Kratochvil, M., *Chem. Listy*, 77, 225 (1983).
18. Bodewig, E., *Matrix Calculus*, North-Holland Publ. Comp., Amsterdam, 1959; Hadley, G., *Linear Algebra*, Addison-Wesley Publishing Comp. Inc., London, 1961.
19. Călușaru, A., *Rev. Chim.* (Bucharest), 38, 373 (1987).
20. Kratochvil, M., Koča, J., and Kvasnička, V., *Chem. Listy*, 78, 1 (1984).
21. Guthrie, R. D., *J. Org. Chem.*, 40, 402 (1975).
22. Guthrie, R. D., *System for Symbolization of Reaction Mechanisms* (Draft No. 6), Organic Chemistry Division, Commission of Physical Organic Chemistry, IUPAC Commission III. 2, December 1984.
23. Călușaru, A., *Rev. Chim.* (Bucharest), 38, 461, 653 (1987).
24. Bart, J. C. J., and Garagnani, E., *Z. Naturforsch.*, 31b, 1646 (1976).
25. Kratochvil, M., Koča, J., and Kvasnička, V., *Chem. Listy*, 79, 807 (1985).
26. Simon, A., *Angew. Chem.*, 95, 111 (1983).
27. Cotton, F. A., and Walton, F. R., *Multiple Bonds between Metal Atoms*, Wiley, N.Y. 1982.
28. Călușaru, A., *Rev. Chim.* (Bucharest), 38, 869, 965 (1987).
29. Van Vleck, J. H., *J. Chem. Phys.*, 2, 782 (1934).
30. Koča, J., Kratochvil, M., Kunz, M., Kvasnička, V., and Matyska, L., *Chemie v grafech* (in Czech), LACHEMA, Oborovy podnik, Brno, 1986.
31. Kratochvil, M., and Koča, J., *Chemie v grafech* (in Czech), LACHEMA, Oborovy podnik, Brno, 1985.
32. Read, R. C., and Corneil, D. G., *J. Graph Theory*, 1, 339 (1977).
33. Ugi, I., Gillespie, P., and Gillespie, C., *Ann. N.Y. Acad. Sci.*, 34, 416 (1972); A. V. Aho, *Acta Crystallogr.*, 33, 5 (1977).
34. Shelley, C. A., and Munk, M. E., *J. Chem. Inf. Comput. Sci.*, 19, 247 (1979).
35. Jochum, C., and Gasteiger, J., *J. Chem. Inf. Comput. Sci.*, 17, 113 (1977); 19, 49 (1979).
36. Carhart, R. E., *J. Chem. Inf. Comput. Sci.*, 18, 108 (1978); T. M. Dyott, and W. J. Howe, *J. Chem. Inf. Comput. Sci.*, 19, 187 (1979).

37. Morgan, H. L., *J. Chem. Doc.*, 5, 107 (1965).
38. Randic, R., *J. Chem. Inf. Comput. Sci.*, 15, 105 (1975).
39. Corneil, D. G., and Gotlieb, C. C., *J. Assoc. Comput. Match.*, 17, 51 (1970).
40. Shelley, C. A., and Munk, M. E., *J. Chem. Inf. Comput. Sci.*, 17, 110 (1977).
41. Wipke, W. T., and Dyott, T. M., *J. Am. Chem. Soc.*, 96, 4834 (1974).
42. Shelley, C. A., Munk, M. E., and Roman, R. V., *Anal. Chim. Acta*, 103, 245 (1978).
43. Razinger, M., *Teor. Chim. Acta*, 61, 581 (1982).
44. Harary, R., *Graph Theory*, Reading, MA, Addison-Wesley, 1969.
45. Deo, N., *Graph Theory with Application to Engineering and Computer Science*, Englewood Cliffs, N.J. Pretice-Hall, 1974.
46. Friedrich, J., and Ugi, I., *J. Chem. Research*, (S), 70 (1980); (M) 1301–1380, 1401–1497, 1501–1550 (1980).
47. Friedrich, J., and Ugi, I., *Inform. Commun. Mathem. Chem.*, No. 6, 201 (1979).
48. Brandt, J., Friedrich, J., Gasteiger, J., Jochum, C., Schubert, W., Lemmen, P., and Ugi, I., *Pure Appl. Chem.*, 50, 1303 (1978).
49. Ugi, I., Bauer, J., Brandt, J., Friedrich, J., Gasteiger, I., Jochum, C., Schubert, W., and Dugundji, J., *Inform. Commun. Mathem. Chem.*, No. 6, 159 (1979).
50. Călusaru, A., *Rev. Chim.* (Bucharest), 38, 1067 (1987); 39, 117, 309 (1988).
51. Corey, E., and Wipke, W. T., *Science*, 166, 178 (1969); E. Corey, *Pure Appl. Chem.*, 14, 19 (1967).
52. Corey, E., Wipke, W. T., Cramer III, R. D., and Hove, W. J., *J. Am. Chem. Soc.*, 26, 421 (1972).
53. Schubert, W., and Ugi, I., *Chimia*, 33, 183 (1979).
54. Weise, A., *Z. Chem.*, 19, 49 (1979).
55. Blair, J., Gasteiger, J., Gillespie, C., Gillespie, P. D., and Ugi, I., *Tetrahedron*, 30, 1845 (1974).
56. Koča, J., Kratochvil, M., Kvasnička, V., Matysky, L., and Pospichal, J., *Chem. Listy*, (in press).
57. Weise, A., *Z. Chem.*, 15, 333 (1975).
58. Raddatz, P., Schittenhelm, C., and Barnickel, G., Kontakte (Darmstadt), No. 3, 3 (1985).
59. Rouvray, D. H., *Scient. Amer.*, 225 (3) 36 (1986).
60. Ullman, J. R., *J. Am. Chem. Soc.*, 23, 31 (1976).
61. Lynch, M. F., Harrison, J. M., Town, W. G., and Ash, J. E., *Computer Handling of Chemical Structure Information*, Macdonald/Elsevier, London, New York, 1971.
62. Stuper, A. J., and Jurs, P. C., *J. Am. Chem. Soc.*, 97, 182 (1975).
63. Adamson, G. W., and Bawden, D., *J. Chem. Inf. Comput. Sci.*, 17, 164 (1977).
64. Fugman, R., Burns, W., and Vaupel, W., *Nachr. Dokum.*, 14, 179 (1963).
65. Eakin, D. R., and Hyde, E., in *Computer Representation and Manipulation of Chemical Information* (W. T. Wipke, S. R. Heller, R. J. Feldman, and E. Hyde, ed.), Wiley, New York, 1974, pp. 1–30.
66. Brandt, J., Friedrich, J., Gasteiger, J., Jochum, C., Schubert, W., and Ugi, I., in *Computers in Chemical Education and Research* (E. V. Luden, N. H. Sabelli, and A. C. Wahl, ed.), Plenum Publishing Comp., New York, 1977, pp. 337–355.
67. Brandt, J., Friedrich, J., Gasteiger, J., Jochum, C., Schubert, W., and Ugi, I., *Am. Chem. Soc. Symposium Series*, 61, 33 (1977).
68. Bond, V. B., Bowman, C. M., Lee, N. L., Peterson, D. R., and Reslock, M. H., *J. Chem. Doc.*, 11, 168 (1971).
69. Hansh, C., Leo, A., and Elkins, D., *J. Chem. Doc.*, 14, 57 (1974).
70. Kim, K. H., Harsch, C., Fukunga, J. Y., Steller, E. E., Jow, P. Y. C., Craig, P. N., and Page, J., *J. Med. Chem.*, 22, 366 (1979).
71. Oxman, M. A., Kissman, H. M., Burnside, J. M., Edge, J. R., Haberman, C. B., and Wykes, A. A., *J. Chem. Inf. Comput. Sci.*, 16, 19 (1976).
72. Kowalski, B. R., and Bender, C. F., *J. Am. Chem. Soc.*, 96, 916 (1974).
73. Chu, K. C., Feldban, R. J., Shapiro, M. B., Hasard, G. F., and Geran, R. J., *J. Med. Chem.*, 18, 539 (1975).
74. Davis, H. W., *Computer Representation of Stereochemistry of Organic Molecules*, Birkhauser Verlag, Basel and Stuttgart, 1976.
75. Caianiello, E. R., (ed.), *Physics Reports*, 137 (1) 1–144 (1986).
76. Filip, P. A., Balaban, T. S., and Balaban, A. T., *J. Math. Chem.*, 1, 61 (1987).

77. Wiener, H., *J. Am. Chem. Soc.*, 69, 17 2636 (1947); *J. Phys. Chem.*, 52, 425, 1082 (1948).
78. Balaban, A. T., *Pure Appl. Chem.*, 54, 1075 (1982).
79. Balaban, A. T., *Chem. Phys. Lett.*, 89, 399 (1982); A. T. Balaban, and P. A. Filip, *Math. Chem.*, 16, 163 (1984).
80. Gutman, I., Ruščić, B., Trinajstić, N., and Wilcox, C. F., *J. Chem. Phys.*, 62, 3399 (1975).
81. Gutman, I., and Trinajstić, N., *Chem. Phys. Lett.*, 17, 535 (1972).
82. Randić, M., *J. Am. Chem. Soc.*, 97, 6609 (1975); *Int. J. Quantum Chem. Symp.*, 5, 245 (1978).
83. Gordon, M., and Scatlebury, G. R., *Trans. Faraday Soc.*, 60, 605 (1964).
84. Garfield, E., "Index Chemicus Goes Online with Graphic Access to Three Million New Organic Compounds. Essays of an Information Scientist: The Award of Science and Other Essays," Philadelphia, I.S.I. Press, 1985, Vol. 7, pp. 194–201.

CHAPTER 33

CONTROLLER DESIGN FOR PROCESS SYSTEMS

Babatunde A. Ogunnaike

Department of Chemical Engineering
University of Lagos
Lagos, Nigeria

CONTENTS,

INTRODUCTION

The objective of this introductory section is to take up some necessary preambles regarding controller design for process systems. It is primarily concerned with introducing the role a control system plays in the overall scheme of the chemical process industry, emphasizing the need for automatic control if the global objectives of the process industry are to be met and maintained. A brief overview of the material to be fully discussed in subsequent sections is also given.

The Process System

A chemical process system, in the most general term, is an integration of processing units set up for the conversion of raw materials (and input energy) into finished product (Figure 1).

It is desirable to operate the processing units safely, while maintaining specified production rates and product quality. Process systems are by nature dynamic, by which we mean that their variables are always changing. It is therefore clear that to achieve the objectives we must monitor and be able to induce change in those key variables related to safety, product quality, and production rates. Chemical Process Control is concerned with the design of control systems that will effectively maintain the desired objectives of safety, production rates, and product quality.

The variables of a process system are usually classified as follows:

1. *Input variables*—those that independently stimulate the system and can thereby induce change in the internal conditions of the process.
2. *Output variables*—those by which one obtains information about the internal state of the process.

Furthermore, the input variables that are at our disposal to manipulate freely as we choose are called *manipulated variables*, while those that we have no control over, whose values we cannot decide at will, are called *disturbance variables* (Figure 2).

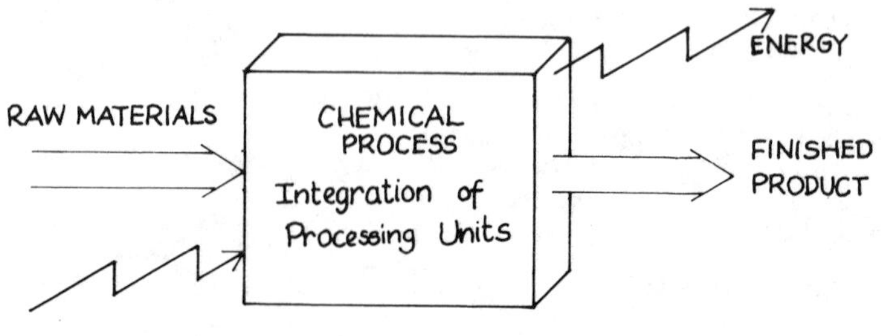

Figure 1. The chemical process system.

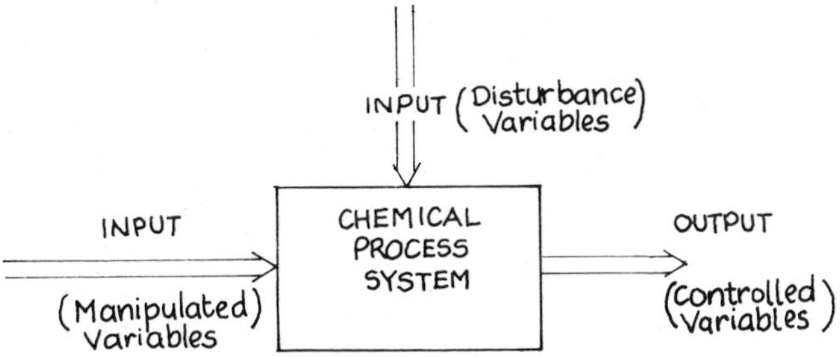

Figure 2. Component variables of a chemical process system.

To illustrate consider the stirred heating tank system shown in Figure 3, in which it is required to regulate the temperature of the liquid in the tank in the face of fluctuations in inlet temperature T_i. The flow rates in and out are constant and equal. In this case, clearly our main concern is with the temperature of the liquid in the tank; thus T is the output variable. Now, the value of this variable is affected by changes in both T_i and Q. These are therefore the input variables. However, only Q can be manipulated at will. We therefore find that T_i is a disturbance variable while Q is the manipulated variable.

The Concept of a Process Control System

In a typical chemical process the process control system is what is charged with the responsibility of monitoring outputs and taking decisions about how best to manipulate inputs so as to obtain desired output behavior. This can be done by a manual control system or an automatic or computer control system. A process control system can be configured several different ways, depending primarily on the structure of the decision-making process. To illustrate, two typical structures are shown in Figure 4.

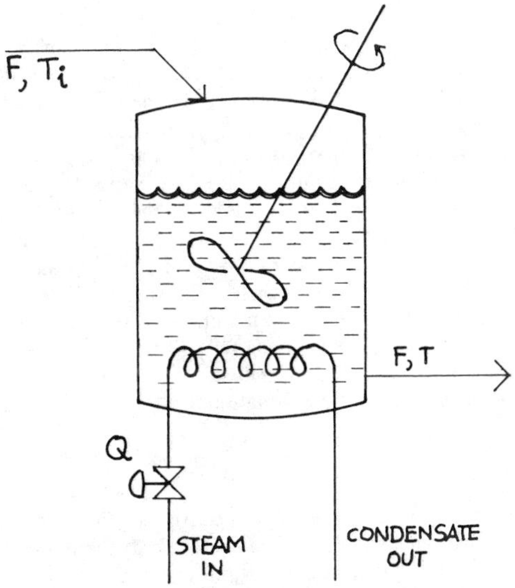

Figure 3. The stirred heating tank system.

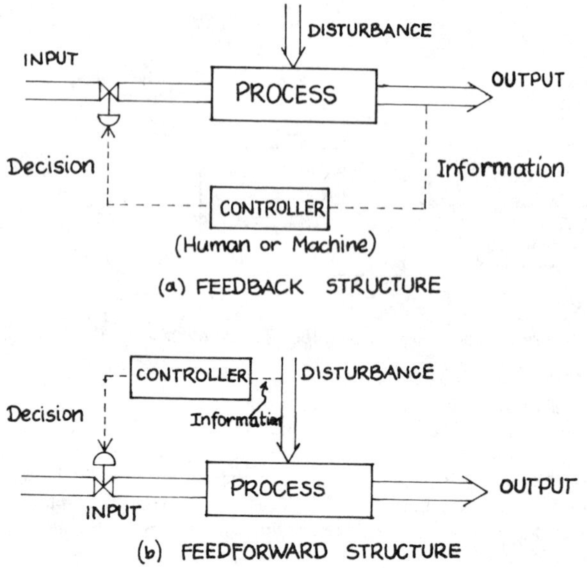

Figure 4. Some standard control system structures.

In Figure 4a, the information from the system output is being fed back to the controller; and because the controller decision is based on such "fed back" information, this is known as the feedback control structure. This is the simplest and by far the most popular control structure employed in chemical process control. Note that with this structure the effect of any disturbance entering the process must first be registered by the process output before corrective control action can be taken; i.e. controller decisions are taken "after the fact."

In Figure 4b on the other hand, information about any incoming disturbance is communicated directly to the controller so that its decision can be made "before" the process is affected. This is the feedforward control structure since the controller decision is based on information that is being "fed forward." Note that with this structure the controller is unable to ascertain the true state of the actual system output; it has no access to this information. We shall study these and other control system structures in greater detail later.

One final point of interest: Important process variables earmarked to receive the attention of the control system typically have set target values at which they are required to be maintained. These target values are called *set-points.* Maintaining these process variables at their prescribed set-points is, of course, the main objective of the process control system (manual or automatic). However, output variables deviate from their set-points either as a result of the effect of disturbances or because the set-point itself has changed. *Regulatory control* occurs when the control system's task is solely that of counteracting the effect of disturbances in order to maintain the output at its set-point. When the objective is to cause the output to track the changing set-point, we have *servo control.* Even though regulatory control is more common in the process industry than servo control, we shall discuss the principles of designing control systems for both situations.

Mathematical Description of Process Systems

The tools of mathematical analysis play an important role in the design of controllers for process systems. For one thing, to take rational control decisions we must understand the dynamic (and steady state) behavior of the process in question, i.e., we must know how outputs respond to changes in the inputs. This implies the need for a process model—the most efficient and objective means

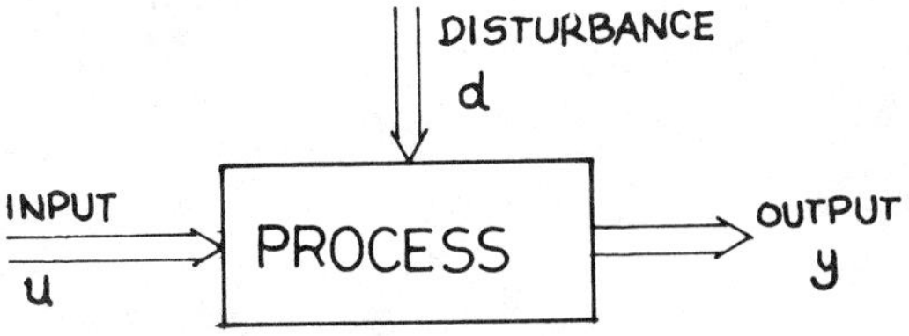

Figure 5. Schematic diagram of a process system.

of quantitatively assessing process behavior—and process models are most effectively couched in the language of mathematics.

In addition to process model development, mathematical tools also come in handy for dynamic analysis and even in the decision-making process of how best to manipulate the inputs to obtain desired output behavior. We must, however, remember that the task of control system analysis and design is not purely mathematical. It is an engineering task that is sometimes made easier by availing ourselves of the relevant tools of mathematical analysis.

It is customary to classify chemical process systems according to the nature of the models used for their mathematical description. Thus a system described by linear equations is classified as linear while the nonlinear system is the one described by nonlinear equations. Furthermore, a *lumped* parameter system (which may be linear or not) is one in which, physically, the process variables change only with time and not with spatial position. These are described by ordinary differential equations. In contrast, the process variables for *distributed* parameter systems change with spatial position as well as with time. They are usually represented by partial differential equations.

It is therefore clear that, in general, the process system may be represented mathematically in a variety of ways. Some of the most important forms that these models take are now listed below.

Consider the schematic diagram of a process system as shown in Figure 5. We shall adopt the notation of representing the output by y, the input by u, the disturbance by d, and the internal state variable (whenever needed) by x. We shall use the appropriate vector quantities **y**, **u**, **d**, and **x** whenever the variables involved are more than one.

Input/Output Transfer Function Models

For *linear* single input- single output (SISO) systems:

$$y(s) = g(s)u(s) + g_d(s)d(s) \tag{1}$$

or

$$\mathbf{y}(s) = \mathbf{G}(s)\mathbf{u}(s) + \mathbf{G_d}(s)\mathbf{d}(s) \tag{2}$$

for the multivariable counterparts.

Here, $\mathbf{G}$, $\mathbf{G_d}$, g, g_d are called transfer functions and are all in terms of the Laplace variable s.

Differential Equation (or State Space) Models

Linear "Lumped Systems"

$$\dot{\mathbf{x}} = \mathbf{Ax} + \mathbf{Bu} + \mathbf{\Gamma d} \tag{3}$$

$$\mathbf{y} = \mathbf{Cx} \tag{4}$$

Nonlinear "Lumped Systems"

$$\dot{\mathbf{x}} = \mathbf{f}(\mathbf{x}, \mathbf{u}, \mathbf{d}) \tag{5}$$

$$\mathbf{y} = \mathbf{g}(\mathbf{x}, \mathbf{u}) \tag{6}$$

where **f**( ) **g**( ) are usually nonlinear functions.

Distributed Parameter Systems

$$\frac{\partial x}{\partial t} = f(x, u, \nabla x, \nabla^2 x, \ldots) \quad (7)$$

Discrete Time (Difference Equation) Models

$$y_{k+1} = ay_k + bu_k + \psi d_k \quad (8)$$

Impulse/Step Response Models

Impulse Response

$$y_k = \sum_{i=1}^{\infty} h_i u_{k-i+1} \quad (9)$$

Step Response

$$y_k = \sum_{i=1}^{\infty} a_i z_{k-i+1} \quad (10)$$

where the model parameters are related as follows:

$$\left.\begin{aligned} z_k &= u_k - u_{k-1} \\ \text{and} \quad h_k &= a_k - a_{k-1} \Rightarrow a_k = \sum_{i=1}^{k} h_i \end{aligned}\right\} \quad (11)$$

Control Systems Design

An overview of the steps involved in successfully carrying out the task of control system design will now be given.

Step 1. Assess the process system and define control objectives.
- Why the need for control?
- Can the problem be solved only by control or is there another alternative like, for example, redesigning the process?
- What do we expect the control system to achieve?

Step 2. Select the process variables to be used in achieving the control objectives articulated in Step 1.
- Which output variables are crucial and therefore must be measured (in order to facilitate efficient monitoring of process conditions)?
- Which input variables can be manipulated (for effective regulation of the process system)?

Step 3. Select control structure.
The usual alternatives are feedback, feedforward, feedforward/feedback, and others we shall discuss later.

Step 4. Design controller.
This step can be carried out to varying degrees of sophistication but it essentially involves obtaining a control law by which, given information about the system (current and past outputs, past inputs and disturbances, sometimes even future predictions of system outputs), a control decision is determined that the controller implements by adjusting the manipulated variables accordingly.

In the upcoming sections of this article, we shall assume that the process control engineer has carried out Steps 1 and 2 for the specific problem at hand. We shall instead focus on principles to guide in dealing with the issues raised in Steps 3 and 4.

Overview and General Outline

With the possible exception of the very simple cases, the analysis, design, and implementation of control systems cannot be effectively carried out without the aid of certain tools. The following section discusses these tools as a foundation for what is to come.

The next section covers feedback controller design for single-input, single-output (SISO) systems. Attention is focused on classical techniques. The design of higher level SISO control systems such as cascade control and feedforward control are deferred until the fourth section.

Some process systems have unusual dynamics and as such are difficult to control by the same techniques used for "regular" systems. Non-minimum phase systems (i.e., time delay and inverse responding systems), as well as open-loop unstable systems, fall into this category. Strategies for effectively controlling such processes are discussed.

Next is a section that focuses on controller design when the nonlinearities of a process system are to be explicitly recognized. The importance of this is underscored by the fact that nearly all important process systems are nonlinear in nature.

Following that is a totally different approach to control system design; the approach of direct synthesis. The results of this approach are carefully compared with those obtained via the classical approach while also noting the various advantages and disadvantages of each of the two approaches.

When dealing with processes in which more than one variable is to be controlled, we are confronted with a new set of problems requiring fresh solutions. The control system design for this important group of systems (i.e., multivariable systems) is discussed.

This chapter includes a brief introduction to computer control systems and the principles of Dynamic Matrix Control (DMC), one of the more successful industrial computer control techniques. A summary and some conclusions then close the chapter.

TOOLS OF CONTROL SYSTEM ANALYSIS, DESIGN, AND IMPLEMENTATION

The Transfer Function

In its simplest sense, a transfer function relates the Laplace transform of two variables in a physical process; an input variable and an output (or response) variable. Mathematically, we mean, for example

$$y(s) = g(s)u(s) \tag{12}$$

where y(s), u(s), are, respectively the Laplace transforms of the process output variable y(t), and u(t), the input variable; g(s) is the *transfer function* relating them (Figure 6). Systems represented this way are called *single-input, single-output* (SISO) systems for obvious reasons.

For multivariable systems, by natural extension, we have a transfer function matrix G(s) that relates the vector of outputs **y**(s) to the vector of inputs **u**(s) according to

$$\mathbf{y}(s) = \mathbf{G}(s)\mathbf{u}(s) \tag{13}$$

where G is composed of elements $g_{ij}(s)$, which are transfer functions of the type in Equation 12.

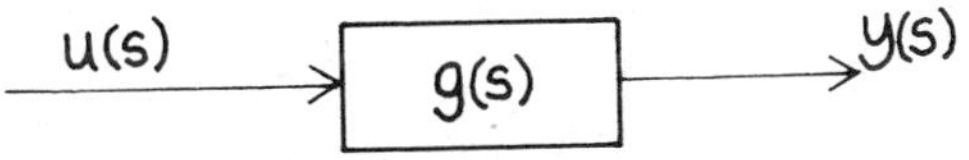

Figure 6. The transfer function.

In principle, the transfer function, contains all the information about the dynamic characteristics of a system. For observe that given any input u(t) with the transform u(s), the system response to this input is simply given by Equation 12. However, the transfer function representation is a linear one; it is therefore limited to linear systems or linearized approximations to nonlinear systems.

Transfer functions are usually obtained for process systems in one of two ways:

1. From Laplace transformation of the linear or linearized theoretical differential equation model, followed by simple algebraic manipulations of the transformed model as illustrated in Examples 1 and 2 [1, 2].
2. Experimentally, from actual plant data, using ideas of process identification [3].

Example 1. It may be shown that a possible theoretical model for the stirred mixing tank of Figure 3 is

$$\frac{dy}{dt} = -\frac{1}{\theta}y + \beta u + \frac{1}{\theta}d \tag{14}$$

where
$y = T - T_s$
$u = Q - Q_s$
$d = T_i - T_{is}$
$\beta = 1/\rho V C_p$
$\theta = V/F$, the residence time

The physical process variables are given as follows:

T = tank temperature, with a steady state value T_s

T_i = inlet fluid temperature, steady state value, T_{is}

Q = rate of heat input from the heater, steady state value Q_s

ρ, the liquid density, C_p, the liquid specific heat capacity, and V, the tank volume, are all assumed constant.

A Laplace transformation of Equation 14 now gives

$$\theta s y(s) = -y(s) + \beta\theta u(s) + d(s)$$

which rearranges to give

$$y(s) = \frac{\beta\theta}{\theta s + 1}u(s) + \frac{1}{\theta s + 1}d(s) \tag{15}$$

This may now be written as

$$y(s) = g(s)u(s) + g_d(s)d(s) \tag{16}$$

where the transfer functions are now seen to be given by

$$\left.\begin{aligned} g(s) &= \frac{\beta\theta}{\theta s + 1} \\ \text{and} \quad g_d(s) &= \frac{1}{\theta s + 1} \end{aligned}\right\} \tag{17}$$

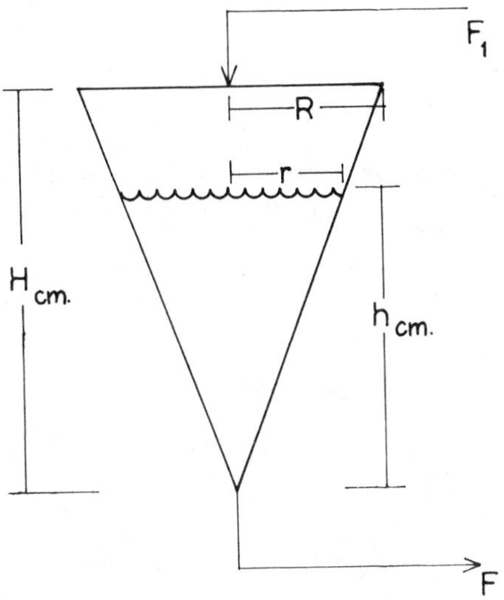

Figure 7. The conical tank system.

Example 2. Consider the conical tank system shown in Figure 7. A mathematical model for this system, as shown in Ref. [4] for the situation where the liquid flow rate out of the tank is proportional to the square root of the liquid level in the tank, is

$$\frac{dh}{dt} = -Kh^{-3/2} + F_1/\alpha h^2 \tag{18}$$

Here, the constants K and α are properties of the tank. Note that this equation is nonlinear; we therefore cannot take Laplace transforms directly.

An approximate transfer function is however obtainable using a linearized approximation of Equation 18.

According to standard linearization procedure we now carry out a Taylor-series expansion of the nonlinear terms $Kh^{-3/2}$ and $F_1/\alpha h^2$ around the steady state values h_s, F_{1s}, and retain only the linear terms (ignoring 2nd and higher order terms). The result, after some simplification, is the following linear approximation of Equation 18:

$$\frac{dy}{dt} = (3/2\ Kh_s^{-5/2} - 2F_{1s}h_s^{-3}/\alpha)y + (h_s^{-2}/\alpha)u \tag{19}$$

where $y = (h - h_s)$ and $u = (F_1 - F_{1s})$

We may now take Laplace transforms of Equation 19 to obtain

$$sy(s) = \phi y(s) + \beta u(s) \tag{20}$$

with ϕ and β respectively representing the coefficients of y and u in Equation 19. (Note that for any given steady state operating condition h_s and F_{1s}, ϕ and β take fixed, constant values.) Further simplification of Equation 20 now yields

$$y(s) = \frac{\beta}{s - \phi} u(s) \tag{21}$$

from where we see the approximate transfer function as

$$g(s) = \frac{\beta}{s - \phi} \tag{22}$$

It should be noted that this approximate g(s) is a function of the process steady state conditions around which Equation 18 was linearized, owing to the dependence of β and ϕ on h_s and F_{1s}. This is typical of nonlinear processes as will be seen later.

General Forms of Transfer Functions

Consider the general 1st order differential equation model

$$\left.\begin{aligned} a_1 \frac{dy}{dt} + a_0 y = bu \\ y(0) = 0;\ u(0) = 0 \end{aligned}\right\} \tag{23}$$

which may be rearranged to give

$$\tau \frac{dy}{dt} + y = Ku \tag{24}$$

where now $\tau = a_1/a_0$ and $K = b/a_0$ (for a_0 not zero). Taking the Laplace transform of Equation 24 and rearranging appropriately gives

$$y(s) = \frac{K}{\tau s + 1} u(s) \tag{25}$$

Now, a physical system modeled by Equation 23 is called a first-order system by virtue of it being a (linear) first-order differential equation. Also by virtue of the fact that Equation 25 results from Equation 23 we may then state that transfer functions for first-order systems take the form

$$g(s) = \frac{K}{\tau s + 1} \tag{26}$$

with characteristic parameters K and τ called, respectively, the steady state gain and the time constant for reasons we shall soon explain. Note that the transfer functions in Examples 1 and 2 are of the first order kind.

Transfer functions for second-order systems have the standard form

$$g(s) = \frac{K}{\tau^2 s^2 + 2\zeta\tau s + 1} \tag{27}$$

where the indicated characteristic parameters are:

K = steady state gain

ζ = damping coefficient

τ = reciprocal of system's frequency of natural oscillation

The meanings of these terms will become clear later.

The *most general* form for an arbitrary transfer function g(s) however, is as a ratio of two polynomials in s, viz;

$$g(s) = \frac{N(s)}{D(s)} \tag{28}$$

(with the exception of time delay systems to be discussed later). The transfer functions given above for first- and second-order systems are special cases of Equation 28. For, observe that in Equations 26 and 27 the D(s) functions are, respectively, "first" and "second" order polynomials, while N(s) is the constant K in each case (i.e., a zeroth order polynomial).

Another example is the following transfer function for an important class of systems to be discussed later:

$$g(s) = \frac{K(\eta s - 1)}{(\tau_1 s + 1)(\tau_2 s + 1)} \tag{29}$$

a "first-over-second" order type (N(s) is first order; D(s) is second order).

Now, if the order of N(s) is r and that of D(s) is n, this implies that the polynomials respectively have r and n roots. They may thus be factorized as follows:

$$N(s) = K_1(s - z_1)(s - z_2) \cdots (s - z_r) \tag{30}$$

and $$D(s) = K_2(s - p_1)(s - p_2) \cdots (s - p_n) \tag{31}$$

so that Equation 29 becomes

$$g(s) = \frac{K_1(s - z_1)(s - z_2) \cdots (s - z_r)}{K_2(s - p_1)(s - p_2) \cdots (s - p_n)} \tag{32}$$

Note: (i) for $s = z_1$, or $z_2, \ldots$ or z_r, $g(s) = 0$

and (ii) for $s = p_1$, or p_2, or $\cdots$ p_n, $g(s) = \infty$

Thus, z_i, $i = 1, 2, \ldots, r$, the roots of N(s), the numerator of g(s), are called zeroes of the transfer function while p_i, $i = 1, 2, \ldots, n$, the roots of D(s) the denominator of g(s) are called the poles of the transfer function. As we shall see shortly, crucial information regarding the dynamic behavior of process systems may be obtained by mere inspection of the nature of the poles and zeroes of their transfer functions.

Uses of Transfer Functions

In studying the dynamic behavior of process systems, we are usually interested in finding out how the output y(t) responds to changes in the input u(t). This task is most conveniently carried out with the aid of transfer functions.

According to the definition of the transfer function in Equation 12, given any u(t), once we obtain its transform, u(s), the system response to this input is immediately given by

$$y(s) = g(s)u(s)$$

from where the required y(t) is obtained by Laplace inversion.

To illustrate, we now proceed to obtain the response of first- and second-order systems to various inputs in the following set of examples.

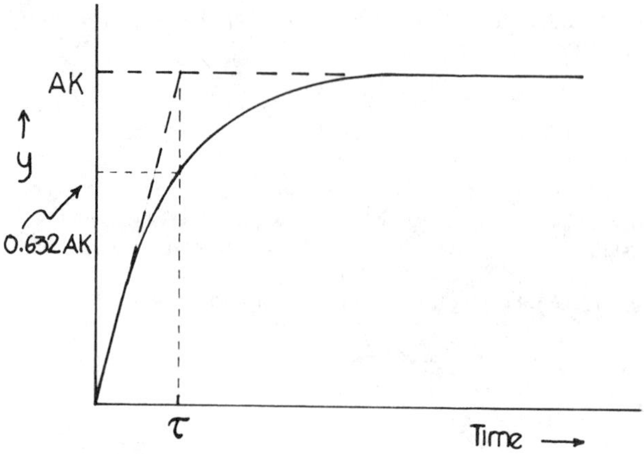

Figure 8. Step response of a first-order system.

Example 3. Step response of a first order system. Here the input step function is given by

$$u(t) = \begin{cases} 0; & t < 0 \\ A; & t \geq 0 \end{cases}$$

so that $u(s) = A/s$.

For a first-order system g(s) is as in Equation 26; therefore y(s) is given by

$$y(s) = \frac{K}{\tau s + 1} \cdot \frac{A}{s}$$

which, by partial fraction expansion becomes

$$y(s) = AK\left[\frac{1}{s} - \frac{\tau}{\tau s + 1}\right] \quad (33)$$

Laplace inversion of Equation 33 now yields the required result;

$$y(t) = AK(1 - e^{-t/\tau}) \quad (34)$$

A plot of this response is shown in Figure 8, which indicates some salient characteristics.

1. The ultimate steady state value for y(t) as $t \to \infty$, is AK. A ratio of this ultimate value for the output, to the value of the input function responsible for inducing this response is AK/A; which is exactly K; hence the designation "steady state gain."
2. By differentiating Equation 34 we may verify that

$$\left.\frac{dy}{dt}\right|_{t=0} = AK/\tau$$

and since this represents the initial rate of change of y(t), the implication is that were this rate to continue, y(t) will attain its ultimate value AK in exactly τ time units.
3. Also at $t = \tau$, the actual response value is $y(t) = 0.632$ AK.

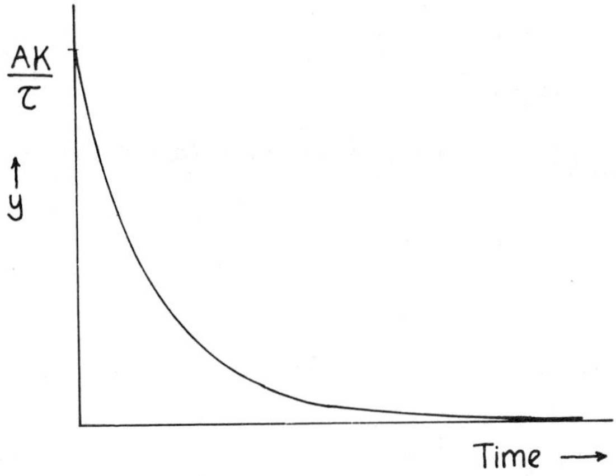

Figure 9. Impulse response of a first-order system.

Characteristics 2 and 3 give us the bases for referring to τ as the time constant. Observe that τ is a measure of the speed of response; the larger its value, the slower the response. The converse is also true.

Example 4. Impulse response of a first order system. Here $u(t) = A\,\delta(t)$ ($\delta(t)$ is the unit impulse, or dirac delta function) so that $u(s) = A$. Thus

$$y(s) = \frac{K}{\tau s + 1} \cdot A$$

which upon Laplace inversion gives

$$y(t) = \frac{AK}{\tau} e^{-t/\tau} \tag{35}$$

A sketch of this response is shown in Figure 9.

Example 5. Step response of a second order system. Since $u(s) = A/s$ for a step input of size A, and the transfer function for the second order system is as given in Equation 27, y(s) is given by

$$y(s) = \frac{K}{\tau^2 s^2 + 2\zeta\tau s + 1} \cdot \frac{A}{s} \tag{36}$$

Factorizing the denominator, we have

$$y(s) = \frac{AK/\tau^2}{s(s - r_1)(s - r_2)} \tag{37}$$

where r_1 and r_2, the roots of the quadratic term, are given by

$$r_1, r_2 = \frac{-\zeta}{\tau} \pm \frac{\sqrt{(\zeta^2 - 1)}}{\tau} \tag{38}$$

We may now observe that the type of response obtained by Laplace inversion of Equation 37 depends on the nature of the roots r_1, r_2, itself dependent on the value of the parameter ζ.

From Equation 38 we see that there are three distinct situations; $0 < \zeta < 1$, and $\zeta = 1$, and $\zeta > 1$. Let us examine each case in turn.

Case 1. $0 < \zeta < 1$, (Complex conjugate roots). It may be shown that upon inverting Equation 37 under these conditions we obtain

$$y(t) = AK\left[1 - \frac{1}{\beta} e^{-\zeta t/\tau} \sin(\beta t/\tau + \phi)\right] \tag{39}$$

$$\text{where} \quad \beta = |(\zeta^2 - 1)^{1/2} \quad \text{and} \quad \phi = \tan^{-1}(\beta/\zeta) \tag{40}$$

Qualitatively, observe that this response will be a damped sinusoid which as $t \to \infty$ attains the steady state value of AK.

Case 2. $\zeta = 1$ (Real and identical roots). In this case $r_1 = r_2 = -1/\tau$ and we find that the inversion of Equation 37 yields,

$$y(t) = AK[1 - (1 + t/\tau)e^{-t/\tau}] \tag{41}$$

Qualitatively, Equation 41 indicates an exponential approach to the ultimate value AK at $t \to \infty$.

Case 3. $\zeta > 1$ (Real and distinct roots). With r_1, and $r_2 = -\zeta/\tau \pm \beta/\tau$ (where β is as defined in Equation 40) the inversion of Equation 37 yields

$$y(t) = AK[1 - e^{-\zeta t/\tau}(\cosh \beta t/\tau + \zeta/\beta \sinh \beta t/\tau)] \tag{42}$$

having consolidated the exponential functions into the hyperbolic sine and cosine functions using the following relationships:

$$\sinh \theta = (e^{\theta} - e^{-\theta})/2$$

$$\cosh \theta = (e^{\theta} + e^{-\theta})/2$$

Equation 42 indicates, yet again, an exponential approach to the ultimate value AK but of a somewhat slower nature than that in Case 2.

A plot of each of the indicated responses is shown in Figure 10. It has become customary to refer to these responses in the following terms:

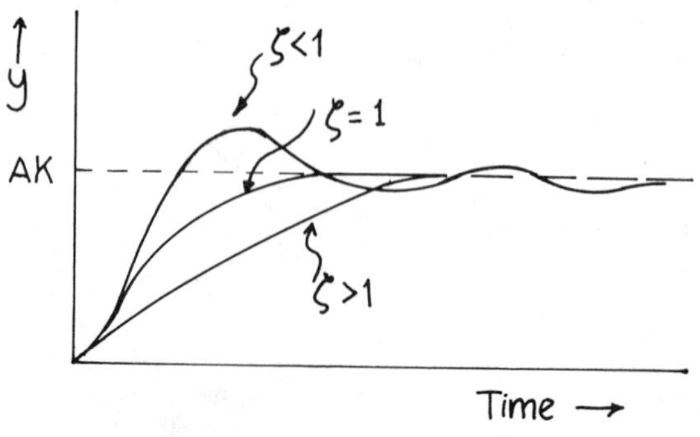

Figure 10. Step responses for second-order systems.

For $0 < \zeta < 1$ the response is said to be underdamped because of its oscillatory nature, while for $\zeta > 1$ the response is said to be overdamped owing to its more sluggish nature. When $\zeta = 1$ the response is said to be critically damped. We now see why ζ is called the damping coefficient. Observe that the larger the value of ζ the greater the damping, and the more sluggish the response. Lower values indicate less damping with more oscillatory response.

As a final point we note that when $\zeta = 0$ (i.e., no damping) the step response shown in Equation 39 becomes:

$$y(t) = AK\,[1 - \sin(t/\tau + \pi/2)] \tag{43}$$

an undamped sinusoid. The frequency of this sustained oscillation, $1/\tau$, is called the natural frequency (ω_n) of the system, hence our earlier definition of τ.

Example 6. Impulse response of a second-order system. In this case

$$y(s) = \frac{AK}{\tau^2 s^2 + 2\zeta\tau s + 1} \tag{44}$$

which, upon inversion, again yields three different types of response dictated by the value of ζ, viz;

$0 < \zeta < 1$ (Underdamped)

$$y(t) = 1/\beta e^{-\zeta t/\tau} \sin \beta t/\tau \tag{45}$$

$\zeta = 1$ (Critically damped)

$$y(t) = (te^{-t/\tau})/\tau^2 \tag{46}$$

$\zeta > 1$ (Overdamped)

$$y(t) = \frac{1}{\beta\tau} e^{-\zeta t/\tau} \sinh \beta t/\tau \tag{47}$$

These responses are plotted in Figure 11.

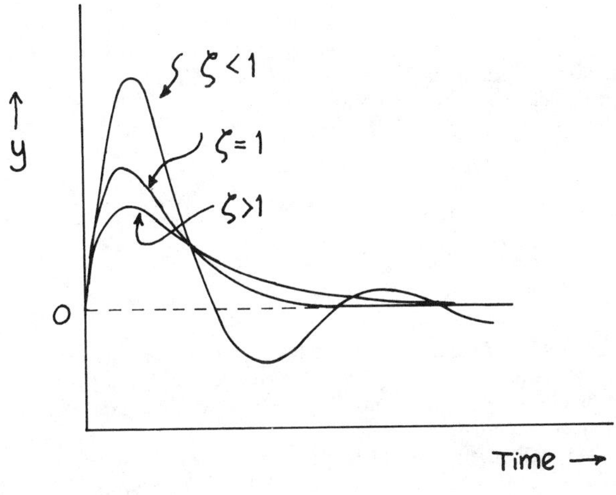

Figure 11. Impulse responses for second-order systems.

Block Diagrams

Consider now the situation in which the stirred mixing tank system shown in Figure 3 is to be operated under automatic control with the objective of maintaining the tank temperature at a given value.

In terms of the notation developed in Example 1, a feedback control system will carry out this task as follows:

1. "Measure" y, (i.e., measure T, and subtract its steady state value T_s) using a *measuring device* (say a thermocouple); the result, y_m may or may not be the same as y.
2. *Compare* measured value y_m, with desired set-point value y_d, to obtain the deviation ϵ as

$$\epsilon = y_d - y_m \tag{48}$$

3. Supply the *controller* with ϵ; to be used in obtaining the value of u (the change in the energy input to the system via the steam heating arrangement) which will be implemented on the *process.*
4. u is implemented through a *final control element* (in this case the steam valve).
5. y is again observed and the entire procedure repeated.

Notice how, according to this scheme, information flows from one component to the other in the form of a loop. Note also that the components of this feedback loop, namely; (a) the process itself, (b) the measuring device, (c) a comparator (comparing y_m and y_d), (d) the controller, and (e) the final control element, are all physical systems in their own rights, with inputs and outputs, and hence can be individually characterized by transfer functions.

For the process, with inputs u and d, and output y, the transfer function representation is as obtained in Example 1 (Equation 16), i.e.

$$y(s) = g(s)u(s) + g_d(s)d(s) \tag{49}$$

For the measuring device, the input is y, and the output is y_m. If the transfer function is designated h(s) then

$$y_m(s) = h(s)y(s) \tag{50}$$

The inputs to the comparator are y_m, and y_d, while the output is $\epsilon(s)$, and these are related as already indicated in Equation 48. The input to the controller is ϵ while the output, designated c, is the control command signal. The controller transfer function is usually designated g_c, thus

$$c(s) = g_c(s)\epsilon(s) \tag{51}$$

The input to the final control element is c(s), and the output is u(s), so that if it transfer function is g_v then

$$u(s) = g_v(s)c(s) \tag{52}$$

If we now represent *each* of the above given transfer functions with a block as in Figure 6, we end up with the block diagram shown in Figure 12. The relationship between each component of the feedback control loop is easier to visualize with such a block diagram, and subsequent analysis of the overall system is also greatly facilitated.

The block diagram in Figure 12 is said to be for a closed loop system for the simple reason that the control loop is closed; the controller is connected with the process so that information flows to the process from the controller and also from the process back to the controller, continuously in one unbroken (hence "closed") loop.

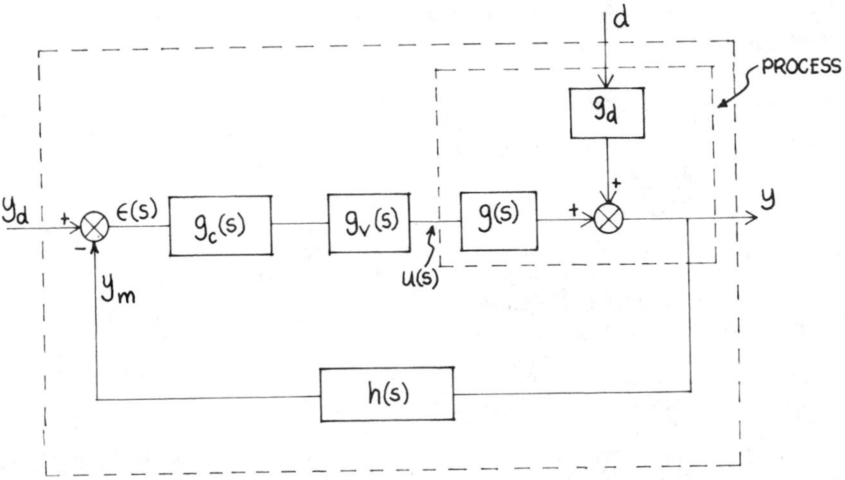

Figure 12. Typical block diagram for a feedback control system.

On the other hand, the block diagram in Figure 6 is for an open loop system. Here the controller is not connected to the process; the loop is hence open.

Closed Loop Transfer Functions

In terms of the outer box in Figure 12, observe that the overall closed loop system in reality just has two inputs, y_d and d, and one output y; indicating that the individual transfer functions for the separate components of this feedback control system may be consolidated to give composite, overall closed loop transfer functions; one relating y to y_d and the other, relating y to d.

Let us begin consolidating the transfer functions for this system by noting that even though the process, by itself, is described by Equation 49, the input u is obtained according to Equation 52; i.e., $u = g_v c$. However c itself is obtained from Equation 51, so that now, u is given by

$$u = g_v g_c \epsilon \tag{53}$$

Using Equation 48 for ϵ and Equation 50 for y_m, Equation 53 becomes

$$u = g_v g_c (y_d - hy) \tag{54}$$

Introducing Equation 54 into the process equation now completes the consolidation exercise, having eliminated every other variable except y, y_d and d.

The result is:

$$y = g\{g_v g_c (y_d - hy)\} + g_d d$$

which, when solved for y, now gives

$$y = \frac{g g_v g_c}{1 + g g_v g_c h} y_d + \frac{g_d}{1 + g g_v g_c h} d \tag{55}$$

or,

$$y(s) = \psi(s) y_d(s) + \psi_d(s) d(s) \tag{56}$$

a closed loop transfer function representation, where the closed loop *transfer functions* ψ and ψ_d are given by:

$$\psi(s) = \frac{gg_vg_c}{1 + gg_vg_ch} \tag{57}$$

and $$\psi_d(s) = \frac{g_d}{1 + gg_vg_ch} \tag{58}$$

Observe that:

1. ψ and ψ_d have identical denominators.
2. The numerator of ψ, i.e., gg_vg_c, is the product of the transfer functions in the forward path from y_d to y; while g_d, the numerator of ψ_d, is also the "product" of the transfer functions in the forward path between d and y (in this case there is only one).
3. gg_vg_ch is the product of all transfer functions in the entire loop.

We may state, therefore that for single loop feedback systems (such as that in Figure 12) the closed loop transfer functions (CLTF) are given by the general expression;

$$\text{CLTF} = \frac{\pi_f}{1 + \pi_L}$$

where π_f = product of the transfer functions in the forward path between the input (y_d or d) and the output y
π_L = product of all transfer functions in the entire loop

Reference [1] may be consulted for strategies used in handling more complicated block diagrams.

Closed Loop Transient Behavior

One of the most important implications of representing the closed loop system as in Equation 56 is that we may now, in principle, use this equation to evaluate the response of the complete closed loop system to changes in y_d or d.

Under servo control, the closed loop system behavior will be determined from

$$y(s) = \psi(s)y_d(s) \tag{59}$$

while under regulatory control,

$$y(s) = \psi_d(s)d(s) \tag{60}$$

gives the required system behavior.

The principles for obtaining closed loop transient responses are identical to those used for open loop dynamic analysis in Examples 3–6 as we shall now illustrate.

Example 7. Principles of obtaining closed loop servo response: A qualitative treatment. The response of the feedback control system in Figure 12 to a unit step change in set-point may be obtained using Equation 59, with $\psi(s)$ as given in Equation 57.

Since in this case $y_d(s)$ is 1/s, we have

$$y(s) = \frac{gg_vg_c}{1 + gg_vg_ch} \cdot \frac{1}{s} \tag{61}$$

In principle, the denominator of Equation 61 may be factorized into its roots to give,

$$y(s) = \frac{A(s)}{(s - r_1)(s - r_2)\cdots(s - r_n)}\frac{1}{s}$$

which, upon partial fraction expansion, becomes:

$$y(s) = \frac{A_0}{s} + \frac{A_1}{(s - r_1)} + \frac{A_2}{(s - r_2)} + \cdots + \frac{A_n}{(s - r_n)} \tag{62}$$

from where Laplace inversion now finally gives

$$y(t) = A_0 + A_1 e^{r_1 t} + A_2 e^{r_2 t} + \cdots + A_n e^{r_n t} \tag{63}$$

It may be shown that $r_1, r_2, \ldots, r_n$ are the roots of the equation

$$1 + g g_v g_c h = 0 \tag{64}$$

i.e., the roots of the denominator of $\psi(s)$.

In a qualitative sense, Equation 63 represents the response of the closed loop system (process + measuring device + controller + final control element) to a unit step change in y_d.

Similarly, for *regulatory control*, for any given d(s), Equation 60 is used to obtain the closed loop response with ψ_d as given in Equation 58. Note, once again, that all the information about the dynamic behavior of the *closed loop* system is contained in ψ, and ψ_d, the closed loop transfer functions.

Closed Loop Stability

That the character of the transient response obtained in Equation 63 is intimately tied in with the nature of $r_1, r_2, \ldots, r_n$ should be very clear. In particular, let us consider the following two cases:

1. If these roots all have negative real parts, we observe that as $t \to \infty$, all the exponential terms will vanish, and y will tend to a finite limiting value, A_0.
2. On the other hand, if just one of the roots, say r_i, has a positive real part, then as $t \to \infty$, the exponential term involving this r_i will become infinite; so that even though all the other exponential terms vanish, y will be infinite because of this one term.

Now, keep in mind that these transient responses are for a unit step change in the set-point. For such a bounded input (a unit step function is a bounded function), we have deduced that the output y is bounded in the former case, while it is infinite (i.e., unbounded) in the latter. In the former case the system is said to be stable while in the latter case, the system is unstable.

Although there are several different ways of defining system stability, we find that for most process control applications the bounded input, bounded output (BIBO) stability notions alluded to above will be sufficient. These notions may now be formalized as follows:

If, for a *bounded input* we find that the system output, y(t) remains *bounded* as $t \to \infty$ then the system is said to be *stable*. Otherwise, it is said to be *unstable*.

Let us note that we have been able to determine whether the system output remains bounded in response to a bounded input (the unit step function in this case) solely on the basis of the sign of the real parts of the roots of Equation 64, i.e.,

$$1 + g g_v g_c h = 0$$

This equation is therefore called the system's characteristic equation.

We may now state the following very important facts: stability analysis for a closed loop system is carried out by investigating the nature of the roots of the system's characteristic equation. In particular, a system is stable if, and only if, *all* the roots of the characteristic equation have negative, real parts. Otherwise, it is unstable.

The characteristic equation is a polynomial in the variable *s* whose order is, of course, determined by the order of the contributing transfer functions. For low-order polynomial characteristic equations, the roots are easy to find, and stability analysis is therefore easy to carry out.

For higher order polynomials, however, since finding the roots directly can be quite tedious, less tedious methods of stability analysis, which cleverly sidetrack the issue of actually calculating the roots of the characteristic equation are preferred. These methods, in particular, the Routh stability test may be found in most texts on process control [1, 2, 3, and 5].

Classical Feedback Controllers

In our discussion on closed loop systems, we mentioned the controller as being the component of the feedback loop that issues a control command signal to the process (via a final control element) based on ϵ, the deviation of the process measurement from its desired setpoint value.

How the controller calculates what control command signal to issue for any given value of ϵ depends on the type of controller in question. The classical feedback controllers are by far the most commonly encountered in normal process control applications and we shall now present the equations that describe how each one relates $\epsilon(t)$ to $c(t)$. The hardware component actually responsible for physically performing this task will be discussed along with other control instruments later.

Proportional Controller

Let $p(t)$ be the actual output signal from the controller (usually a pressure or electrical signal); and let p_s be its (constant) value when $\epsilon(t)$ is zero. Then a proportional controller operates according to

$$p(t) = K_c \epsilon(t) + p_s \tag{65}$$

The deviation of p from its "zero error" value p_s is the control command signal, i.e.,

$$c(t) = K_c \epsilon(t) \tag{66}$$

which is seen to be directly proportional to the error.

Laplace transforming Equation 66 leads immediately to

$$c(s) = K_c \epsilon(s)$$

so that the transfer function for a proportional controller is seen to be given by

$$g_c(s) = K_c \tag{67}$$

The characteristic parameter of this controller, K_c, is called the proportional gain.

Proportional–Integral (PI) Controller

In this case $p(t)$ is given by

$$p(t) = K_c \left\{ \epsilon(t) + \frac{1}{\tau_I} \int_0^t \epsilon(t)\, dt \right\} + p_s \tag{68}$$

which contains a proportional portion along with an integral of the error over time. Upon taking Laplace transforms, we obtain

$$c(s) = \left\{K_c\left(1 + \frac{1}{\tau_I s}\right)\right\}\epsilon(s) \tag{69}$$

with the transfer function as indicated in the winged brackets. The additional parameter τ_I is called the integral time constant or the reset time.

Proportional–Derivative (PD) Controller

Here the operating equation is

$$p(t) = K_c\left(\epsilon(t) + \tau_D \frac{d\epsilon}{dt}\right) + p_s \tag{70}$$

and Laplace transformation gives

$$c(s) = \{K_c(1 + \tau_D s)\}\epsilon(s) \tag{71}$$

so that, $g_c(s)$ is given by the terms in the winged brackets. The parameter τ_D is called the derivative time constant.

Proportional–Integral-Derivative (PID) Controller

The operating equation for the PID controller is

$$p(t) = K_c\left\{\epsilon(t) + \frac{1}{\tau_I}\int_0^t \epsilon(t)\,dt + \tau_D \frac{d\epsilon}{dt}\right\} + p_s \tag{72}$$

This gives, upon Laplace transformation,

$$c(s) = \left\{K_c\left(1 + \frac{1}{\tau_I s} + \tau_D s\right)\right\}\epsilon(s) \tag{73}$$

with $g_c(s)$ as indicated in the winged brackets.

The properties of each of these controllers is discussed later when attention is focused entirely on the issue of feedback controller design.

Control Instrumentation

Certain hardware components are required for the successful implementation of any control scheme. As might be deduced from the block diagram in Figure 12, these instruments essentially fall into the following categories: sensors, transmitters, controllers, and final control elements.

Sensors (same as measuring devices) are needed for acquiring information about the status of the process output variables. In most process control applications, the sensors are usually for pressure, temperature, liquid level, flow, and composition measurements. A list of the various types of sensors available for these tasks is available [2, 5, and 6].

How process information acquired by the sensor gets to the controller, and the control signal gets back to the process via the final control element, is the responsibility of the *transmitter*. Measurement and control signals may be transmitted as air pressure signals or as electrical signals. Pneumatic transmitters are required for the former, and electrical ones for the latter [2, 5].

The *controller* hardware may be pneumatic (in which case it operates on air signals) or it may be electronic (in which case it operates on electrical signals). Electronic controllers have become more common in industrial applications in recent times. A description of the hardware aspects of controllers may be found, for example, in Reference [5].

As useful as the classical controllers just mentioned are, they are restricted to relating $\epsilon(t)$ to $c(t)$ in one of the four forms discussed earlier. When, for reasons we shall see later, control laws different from those that apply for these classical feedback controllers are required, a new type of controller is called for—the digital computer.

It is virtually impossible to implement any truly advanced control technique without using the process control computer. Since, in the most general sense, a controller is simply a piece of equipment that accepts the error $\epsilon(t)$, and computes corrective control action according to a pre-specified equation, the computer is perfectly suited to play this role.

It is no longer necessary to restrict what form the control equation can take as the computer can be programmed to accept any form of equation as the control law. Furthermore, such computations are carried out at extremely high speeds. All these, coupled with the computer's large capacity for information storage make it ideal for process control applications. A good description of the digital computer in application as a process controller may be found, for example, in Reference [2].

Final control elements have the task of actually implementing, on the process, the control command issued by the controller. Most final control elements are control valves, usually pneumatic in nature (i.e., they are air driven) and, they occur in various shapes, sizes, and have several various modes of specific operation. Appendix C of Reference [5] contains a useful discussion on control valves and is recommended to the interested reader.

Finally, let us note that the need to change one type of signal to another is often unavoidable. For example, it will be necessary to change the electrical signal from an electronic controller to a pneumatic signal needed to operate a control valve. The equipment used for such signal transformations are called transducers and various types are available for various signal transformation applications. The specific kind needed for the example signal change noted above is a current-to-pneumatic (I/P) transducer. Voltage-to-pneumatic (E/P), pneumatic-to-current (P/I), pneumatic-to-voltage (P/E), etc. are other types of commonly encountered transducers.

Also, for computer control applications, it is necessary to have what are known as analog-to-digital, (A/D), and digital-to-analog, (D/A), converters. This is because, while the rest of the control loop operates on analog signals (electric or pneumatic), the computer operates digitally, giving out, and capable of recognizing, only numbers. A/D converters make the process information available in recognizable form to the computer while D/A converters make the computer information accessible to the process [2, 7].

Having thus given, in this section, a panoramic survey of some of the tools of process control systems design and implementation, we shall now proceed to take on, in the remainder of the chapter, the actual task of controller design for process systems.

FEEDBACK CONTROLLER DESIGN FOR SISO SYSTEMS

In chemical process control, the classical feedback controller plays a very important role. A surprising number of industrial control problems are of such a nature that they are adequately handled by straightforward single loop feedback control. This section is therefore devoted entirely to the issue of designing such single loop feedback control systems.

Design Principles

As earlier noted, the output of a process system may deviate from its desired set-point value as a result of either a load change, (the entrance of a disturbance) or a set-point change. In either case, the objective of the *control system* is to ensure the restoration of the system output to the desired set-point value as rapidly as possible.

The *feedback controllers* available for performing this task, P, PI, PD, PID controllers, as noted in the preceding subsection, necessarily respond differently to the same error information ϵ. Which controller type to use for a given process system thus becomes the first design issue.

Upon resolving the controller type decision, we are next confronted with the fact that the magnitude of the values chosen for the controller parameters, K_c, τ_I, τ_D, also influence the response of any particular controller to the supplied error signal ϵ. Also, different combinations of these parameter values give rise to different overall control system responses. Closely related to the issue of choosing controller parameters, therefore, is that of a-priori specification of criteria for judging overall control system performance, as this will now enable objective discrimination among competing alternative parameter value combinations.

The controller design problem is thus seen to essentially boil down to the following: *Choose the controller type, and the parameters for this choice of controller, so that your favorite performance criteria are satisfied.*

It is thus necessary to first clearly specify the criteria by which closed loop system performance may be judged, in general. This often provides sufficient information to enable us to carry out the controller type decision. The final step, and from a practical viewpoint, the most important, will be that of choosing the controller parameters so that the system response resulting from this choice meets the specified performance criteria as closely as possible.

Let us now consider some standardized performance criteria.

Performance Criteria

Even though the specific details of what is considered acceptable performance will vary from individual to individual, there are some general principles that apply universally. An effective closed loop control system is, for example, expected to be *stable*, and to be capable of causing the system output to *ultimately* attain to its desired set-point value. In addition, the approach of this system output to the desired set-point should be neither too sluggish, nor too oscillatory.

We have therefore identified three criteria for assessing general performance, viz;

1. Stability criteria

2. Steady state performance criteria

3. Dynamic response criteria

Of these, 1 and 2 are very easy to specify. The only reasonable specification for 1 is that whatever the case, the system *must* be stable. (Note that we are not here concerned with *how* stable, but that it is stable). Also, the key steady state criterion is that there be no steady state offset, i.e., no non-zero value is acceptable for ϵ at steady state.

There are various criteria for evaluating dynamic responses, ranging from the subjective types; small "overshoot," quick "rise time," very little "oscillation," quick "settling time," etc.; to the more global, and mathematically more formal "time-integral" types, which deal with the entire closed loop response trajectory from the beginning until when steady state is achieved. The most common involve minimizing the time integral functions of $\epsilon(t) = y_d - y(t)$ listed below:

Integral squared error (ISE)

$$\int_0^\infty \epsilon^2(t)\, dt$$

Integral absolute error (IAE)

$$\int_0^\infty |\epsilon(t)|\, dt$$

Integral time-weighted absolute error (ITAE)

$$\int_0^{\infty} t|\epsilon(t)|\, dt$$

Integral time weighted square error (ITSE)

$$\int_0^{\infty} t\epsilon^2(t)\, dt$$

The Controller Type Decision

Even though the controller type may be selected for various reasons it is most practical to base the selection on the general characteristics of different types of feedback controllers. These characteristics, are based on theoretical analyses of closed loop transient responses [2] and are now summarized as follows:

1. Proportional Controller: Accelerates the control system response but *leaves a non-zero steady state offset* for all processes except "pure capacity" processes.
2. Proportional + Integral Controller: Eliminates offsets but the system response becomes more sluggish and oscillatory. The added integral action tends to increase the propensity towards instability.
3. Proportional + Derivative Controller: Enjoys the *anticipatory* and *stabilizing* effect of derivative action but still leaves a non-zero steady state offset.
4. Proportional + Integral + Derivative Controller: Integral action eliminates offsets, but the oscillations normally introduced as a result are curbed by the derivative action; tends to amplify noise components of noisy signals, as a result of the presence of derivative action.

In light of these characteristics, the following guidelines may be used in selecting the most suitable controller type:

1. When offsets are not important, or when the process possesses a natural integrator (like pure capacity systems) use a P controller. Many liquid level control loops, for example, are on P control.
2. When offsets cannot be tolerated and the process is somewhat naturally fast responding, use a PI controller. A large proportion of feedback controllers in a typical plant are PI controllers.
3. When it is important to compensate for some natural sluggishness in the overall system, and the process signals are relatively noise-free use a PID controller. Temperature control loops are typically under PID control; the effect of the "lag" usually introduced by the measuring devices are compensated for by the derivative action. In contrast, flow loops or level loops are seldom on PID control; these signals are more susceptible to noise.
4. PD controllers are seldom used.

Choosing Controller Parameters (Tuning)

This crucial aspect of the overall scheme of controller design can be carried out in several ways and to varying degrees of sophistication. However, one subtle fact remains: all controller tuning methods are based, explicitly or implicitly, on some form of a-priori process characterization. This is to say that even the "instrument mechanic" who tunes the controller "by feel" [3] obviously draws upon his experience, which, in reality, contains an informal, implicit, and often fairly accurate, characterization of the process.

We will thus consider controller tuning in two categories: when reliable process models are available, and when no such models are available.

Reliable Process Models Available

Under these circumstances, the process model is used in conjunction with specified performance criteria to arrive at the set of controller parameters that satisfy the pre-specified objectives. It must be noted however, that as aptly demonstrated in [2], this procedure is usually tedious, quite often mathematically demanding and, in the long run, not particularly useful. This approach is therefore seldom used for controller tuning.

A somewhat more straightforward technique involves using only the stability criterion. In this case, once the controller type has been decided, the characteristic equation is examined, for various choices of controller parameters, to establish closed loop stability. Under this approach, a trial set of parameters will be acceptable as long as the overall closed loop system resulting from this choice is stable. Let us illustrate with the following example.

Example 8. PI controller tuning for a first-order process. Consider the closed loop system with the transfer functions as given below:

Process: $$g(s) = \frac{1}{2s + 1}$$

Controller: $$g_c(s) = K_c\left(1 + \frac{1}{\tau_I s}\right)$$

with $h(s) = 1$, $g_v(s) = 1$. The controller parameters K_c and τ_I are to be chosen such that the closed loop system is stable.

The closed loop characteristic equation,

$$1 + gg_cg_vh = 0 \tag{74}$$

in this particular case, becomes, upon introducing the given transfer functions and rearranging appropriately,

$$s^2 + \{(K_c + 1)/2\}s + K_c/2\tau_I = 0. \tag{75}$$

Consider the choice $K_c = 3$ and $1/\tau_I = 6$, for which it may be verified that the characteristic equation becomes

$$s^2 + 2s + 9 = 0 \tag{76}$$

with roots $r_1, r_2 = -1 \pm \sqrt{8}j$ which are complex conjugates with negative real parts. The conclusion therefore is that since the system is stable with this choice of parameters, they are acceptable. In fact, it may be verified that there is no positive value of K_c or τ_I for which the closed loop system becomes unstable. This implies therefore that this closed loop system, under PI control, remains stable for any choice of controller parameters.

An immediate corollary of this last example is that if we wished to, we could choose the parameters to give us a *specific type* of stable closed loop response. Recalling that the roots of the characteristic equation determine the nature of the closed loop response, observe that the specific choice $K_c = 3$ and $1/\tau_I = 6$ used above will give us a damped oscillatory response; oscillatory because of the presence of the non-zero imaginary part. As demonstrated in the next example, we may choose the controller parameters such that, for example, the closed loop response is not oscillatory.

Example 9. For the same system of Example 8, let us choose K_c and τ_I such that the roots of the characteristic equation are -4 and -3. From Equation 75 and elementary algebra of polynomials, we know that if r_1 and r_2 are the roots of Equation 75, then

$$r_1 + r_2 = -\left(\frac{K_c + 1}{2}\right) \tag{77}$$

and

$$r_1 r_2 = K_c/2\tau_I \tag{78}$$

Thus to obtain the desired roots, from Equation 77 we have

$$(K_c + 1)/2 = 7 \Rightarrow K_c = 13 \tag{79}$$

and from Equation 78 in conjunction with Equation 79, we have

$$\tau_I = \tfrac{13}{24} \tag{80}$$

We have thus obtained the PI controller parameters that give the required closed loop behavior as embodied in the pre-specified roots for the characteristic equation.

For most practical situations, very rarely does one have a process model which is so reliable. Let us consider what can be done under these circumstances.

No Reliable Process Model Available

Some general rules of thumb are available, accumulated over many years of practice [3]. Being rules of thumb, they only indicate in a more or less qualitative manner, what obtains in common practice. Less subjective is the semiempirical technique based on the *process reaction curve*, which we shall now discuss.

For the purposes of this technique, the final control element and the measuring device are lumped together with the process system to form the controlled process ensemble. In an open loop situation (when the controller is disconnected from the controlled process), a step change in the input signal to the controlled process ensemble will elicit a response in the measured variable y_m; a record of this response with time is known as the process reaction curve (PRC).

Cohen and Coon [8] noted that the process reaction curves for most controlled processes may be reasonably well approximated by the step response of a first order system with a time delay, i.e., if g_α is the combined transfer function for the controlled process ensemble (which is to say that $g_\alpha = g_v g h$), then

$$g_\alpha(s) \simeq \frac{Ke^{-t_d s}}{Ts + 1} \tag{81}$$

The values of K, T, and t_d that give a 1st order-plus-time delay step response that approximates the actual process reaction curve the closest are now used to characterize the process. These characterizing parameters are used in the controller tuning formulas derived by Cohen and Coon [8] to obtain recommended controller parameter values.

Let Θ represent the ratio of t_d, the effective time delay, to T, the effective time constant, i.e.;

$$\Theta = t_d/T \tag{82}$$

then, the Cohen and Coon recommended controller settings for various controller types are as follows:

Proportional $$K_c = \frac{1}{K\Theta}(1 + 1/3\Theta)$$

Proportional + Integral $$K_c = \frac{1}{K\Theta}(0.9 + 1/12\Theta)$$

$$\tau_I = t_d\left(\frac{30 + 3\Theta}{9 + 20\Theta}\right)$$

Proportional + Derivative

$$K_c = \frac{1}{K\Theta}(5/4 + 1/6\Theta)$$

$$\tau_D = t_d\left(\frac{6 - 2\Theta}{22 + 3\Theta}\right)$$

Proportional + Integral + Derivative

$$K_c = \frac{1}{K\Theta}(4/3 + 1/4\Theta)$$

$$\tau_I = t_d\left(\frac{32 + 6\Theta}{13 + 8\Theta}\right)$$

$$\tau_D = t_d\left(\frac{4}{11 + 2\Theta}\right)$$

The following is a procedure for employing the "process reaction curve technique" in practice:

1. *Obtain the process reaction curve.* Disconnect the controller from the controlled process. Implement a step change of size A on the controlled process via the final control element (e.g., open or close the control valve by a certain fixed amount). Record the resulting transient response of y_m, the measured output. This gives the process reaction curve, an example of which is shown in Figure 13.
2. *Estimate the characterizing parameters.*
   a. Estimate t_d.
   Draw a tangent line at the inflexion point on the process reaction curve (PRC); where this line intersects the time axis gives an estimate of the effective time delay t_d (see Figure 13)
   b. Estimate K.
   By definition of the steady state gain,

$$K = \frac{\text{ultimate value of output}}{\text{size of the step input}}$$

we have, in this case, (see Figure 13) that

$$K = y_m(\infty)/A$$

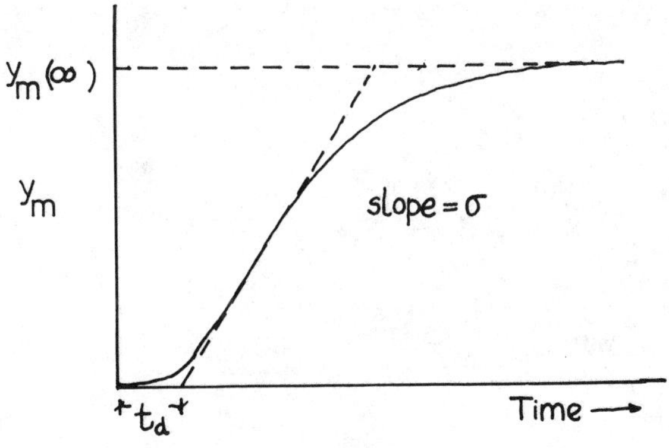

Figure 13. The process reaction curve.

c. Estimate T.
A useful but rough estimate of T is obtained as

$$T = \frac{y_m(\infty)}{\sigma}$$

where σ is the slope of the tangent line drawn at the inflexion point.

Frequency Domain Strategies

The response of a linear system to a sinusoidal input, say A sin ωt, (given enough time for all the initial transients to die out) is also a sine wave. As illustrated in Figure 14, the output sinusoid has the same frequency as the input but a different amplitude, A_0; and it is out of phase by $\phi°$. The output therefore has the form $A_0 \sin(\omega t + \phi)$. The ratio of output and input amplitudes, A_0/A, is known as the amplitude ratio, AR, and ϕ is called the phase angle.

For any given system, the AR and ϕ values will vary with ω, the frequency of the input signal. The investigation of how these quantities vary with ω, for any particular system, is the main concern of frequency response analysis.

Our interest in this sort of analysis is justified in part by the fact that the dynamics of a linear process can be entirely characterized by the AR and ϕ behavior over a range of ω values. In particular, a plot of log AR versus log ω in conjunction with that of ϕ versus log ω for any particular system together form what is known as its Bode diagram. For example, Figure 15 shows the Bode diagram for a first-order system. As we shall soon see, Bode diagrams are quite useful for control systems analysis and design.

How to generate Bode diagrams from transfer function models is routinely discussed in standard process control texts; we merely note here that given any transfer function, it is always possible to generate the corresponding Bode diagram.

A particularly useful Bode diagram is obtained from the open loop transfer function g_L of a feedback control system. Consider the feedback control system introduced in Figure 12. If the feedback loop were opened after the measuring device, as shown in Figure 16, then the response of y_m to changes in y_d is given by

$$y_m = (g_c g_v g h) y_d \tag{83a}$$

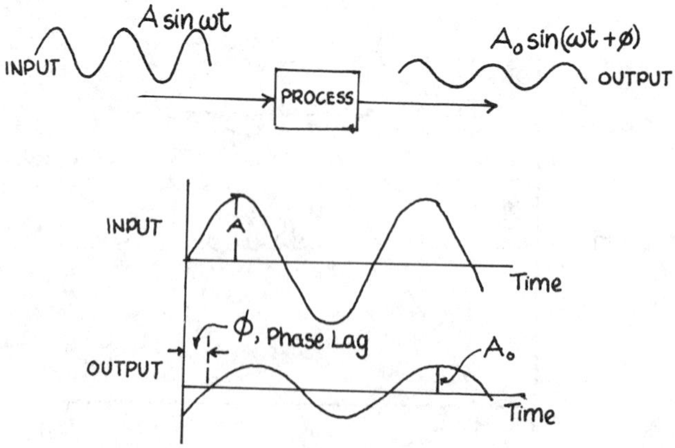

Figure 14. Frequency response of a process system.

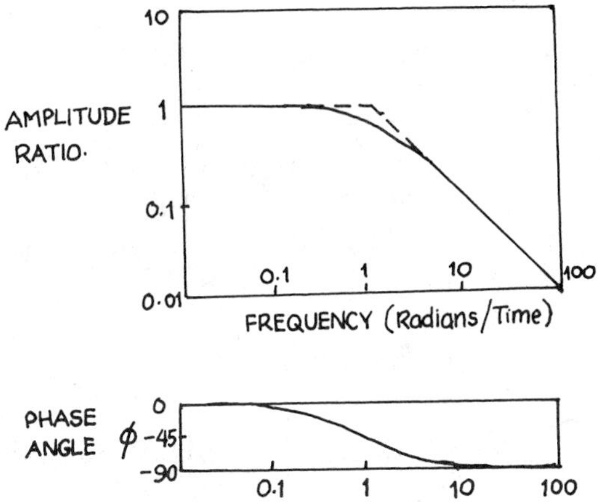

Figure 15. Bode diagram of a first order system.

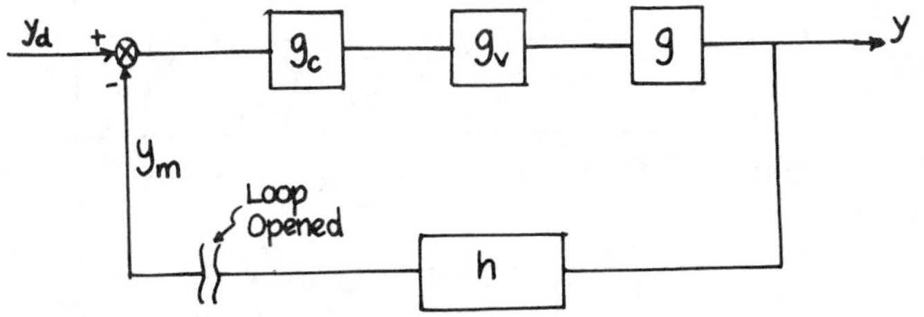

Figure 16. Block diagram of Figure 12 with loop opened.

so that the open loop transfer function between y_m and y_d is given from Equation 83a as

$$g_L = g_c g_v g h \tag{83b}$$

In general, the open loop transfer function for a feedback control system is the product of all the transfer functions in the loop.

It is important to note that the characteristic equation for the closed loop system given in Equation 64 may now be written as

$$1 + g_L = 0 \tag{84}$$

in light of the introduction of this new composite transfer function.

It is known that the open loop transfer function of a feedback control system gives rise to a Bode diagram from which we can determine the stability of the closed loop system, and which can also be used for controller parameter selection. The basis of this assertion is the Bode stability criterion:

> If the AR of the open loop transfer function of a feedback control system is greater than 1 at the crossover frequency (i.e. that frequency for which $\phi = -180°$), the system is unstable.

A formal justification of this statement is available [1]. To illustrate its application, consider the Bode diagram shown on Figure 17 for an arbitrary control system's open loop transfer function.

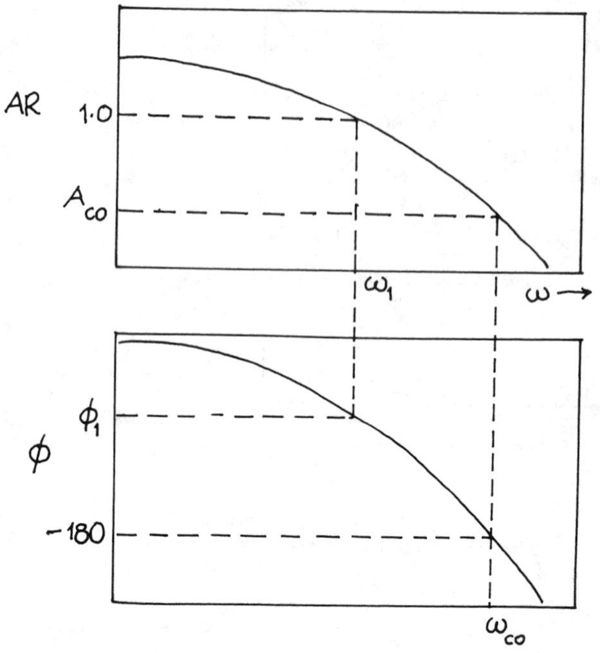

Figure 17. A general Bode diagram.

Every Bode diagram of this type has the following important characteristics:

1. Two critical points, one on each plot; the phase plot has ω_{co}, the frequency for which $\phi = -180°$, and the AR plot has the point where AR = 1.
2. The corresponding values of AR and ϕ at each of the critical points noted: A_{co} is the value of AR at the crossover frequency, ω_{co}; ϕ_1 is the value of ϕ at the point when AR = 1, the frequency here being ω_1.

Thus, according to the Bode stability criterion, if $A_{co} > 1$ then the above system is unstable. Conversely, the system is stable if $A_{co} < 1$.

Furthermore, we observe that an intuitively appealing measure of how stable a system is may be defined as how far A_{co} is from the critical value of 1, or how far ϕ_1 is from -180. We therefore define a gain margin, GM, as;

$$GM = 1/A_{co} \tag{85}$$

and a phase margin PM, as

$$PM = \phi_1 - (-180) \tag{86}$$

These are quantitative measures of stability margins; measures of how far the system is from being on the verge of instability. (Note that for a stable system, GM > 1 and PM > 0).

Conceptually, we could now use this notion of gain and phase margins for controller design. For, observe that we could conceive of a scheme by which a g_c is chosen, the Bode diagram for the resulting open loop transfer function g_L obtained, and the critical points of the Bode diagram investigated first for absolute stability, then for stability margins if the system is stable.

Regarding stability margins, it is typical, for design purposes, to choose controller parameters to give a GM of about 1.7 or a PM of about 30 [1]. Now, if the chosen g_c fails to give a control system that meets the noted stability margin specifications, another choice is made, and the resulting control system reinvestigated until a g_c is found for which the specifications are met.

In actual fact, this concept of controller design using gain and phase margin specifications is only useful for selecting K_c values for proportional-only controllers. For selecting the additional parameters required for other controller types, a time consuming, trial-and-error procedure must be followed [1, 2]. A more useful and more popular method for obtaining controller settings from Bode diagrams is now discussed.

Ziegler-Nichols Settings from Bode Diagrams

1. Choosing g_c as a proportional-only controller with K_c unspecified, obtain the Bode diagram for the open loop transfer function, g_L of the given system. It is customary in this situation to use AR/K_c as the ordinate for the amplitude plot; K_c is now merely a constant scaling factor on the ordinate.
2. From this plot obtain the value of (AR/K_c) at the crossover frequency, ω_{co}; say ξ. (Figure 18), i.e.,

$$(AR/K_c)\Big|_{\omega=\omega_{co}} = \xi \tag{87}$$

Observe from here that if

$$K_c = 1/\xi \tag{88}$$

then according to Equation 87 the value of AR at $\omega = \omega_{co}$ must equal 1.

The immediate implication is that according to the Bode stability criterion, the system will be on the verge of instability when K_c takes on the value $1/\xi$ (since for this value of K_c, we have shown that AR = 1 at the crossover frequency). This value of K_c is called the ultimate gain, K_u.

3. It can be shown that when the system is on the verge of instability, (as is the case when $K_c = K_u$), the system output oscillates perpetually as an undamped sinusoid with frequency ω_{co}. The period of this oscillation, known as the ultimate period, P_u, is given by

$$P_u = 2\pi/\omega_{co} \text{ (time/cycle)} \tag{89}$$

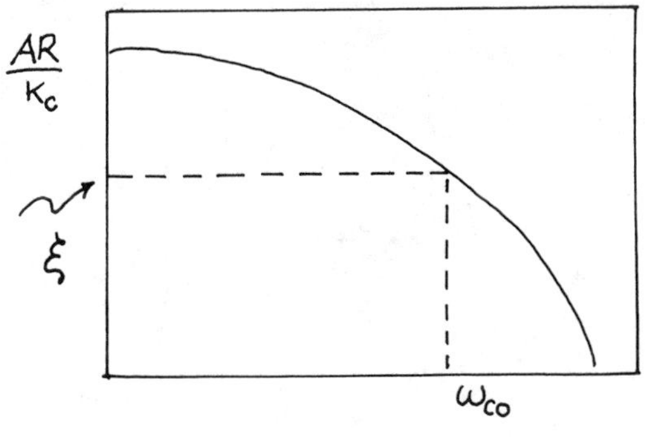

Figure 18. Obtaining ultimate gain values from AR plots.

4. With the values of the ultimate gain and period thus determined, Ziegler and Nichols [9] recommend the controller settings summarized below:

Controller Type	K_c	τ_I	τ_D
Proportional	$0.5K_u$		
Proportional-Integral	$0.45K_u$	$P_u/1.2$	
Proportional-Integral-Derivative	$0.6K_u$	$P_u/2$	$P_u/8$

It must be mentioned that Ziegler and Nichols did not suggest that the values of K_u and P_u be obtained from a Bode diagram. They assumed that no transfer function was available for the process and therefore K_u and P_u were to be determined experimentally.

The procedure for determining K_u and P_u experimentally involves operating the process in the closed loop, under proportional-only control, introducing a step change in the set-point and monitoring the system output as the value of K_c is progressively increased. The point at which sustained oscillations are observed in the system output marks the onset of instability and the K_c value at this point is recorded as K_u, the ultimate gain. The period of the sustained oscillation may be extracted from an instruments chart recording; this is P_u.

It should be clear that this method will suffer from many disadvantages; the most obvious being (a) the fact that it is quite tedious and time consuming to implement in practice; also (b) it could prove dangerous trying to operate a closed loop system at the brink of instability; where the slightest "disturbance" is likely to precipitate a crossover into actual instability.

Another method exists for obtaining the values of K_u and P_u without having to draw a Bode diagram. If the transfer function g for the process exists, then for the situation where proportional-only control is applied, the characteristic equation is given by

$$1 + K_c g_v g h = 0 \tag{90}$$

This equation gives rise to a polynomial in s, with K_c as a parameter. It is the basis of what is known as the Root Locus, which is discussed in many texts [1, 2, 3, 5] but has been omitted here primarily because of its doubtful usefulness in current times.

Recall that the roots of Equation 90 indicate whether the system in question is stable or not. We may therefore appeal to the fact that when the process is on the verge of instability, at least one pair of roots of Equation 90 *must* be precisely located on the imaginary axis, and exploit this for the purpose of finding K_u and P_u.

If the pair of roots are located at $s = \pm bj$, then by substituting this directly into Equation 90, we can then find the values of K_c and b that satisfy the equation. These values are the ultimate gain and crossover frequency, respectively; P_u is then obtained as indicated in Equation 89. Let us illustrate with an example.

Example 10. Finding K_u and P_u by "Direct Substitution." Consider a feedback control system whose component transfer functions are given as follows:

$$g(s) = \frac{1}{s+1}; \qquad g_v(s) = \frac{1}{\frac{1}{2}s+1}; \qquad h(s) = \frac{1}{\frac{1}{3}s+1}.$$

With $g_c = K_c$, the characteristic equation is given by

$$1 + \frac{K_c}{(s+1)(\frac{1}{2}s+1)(\frac{1}{3}s+1)} = 0 \tag{91}$$

and, upon further simplification, we obtain:

$$1/6s^3 + s^2 + 11/6s + (1 + K_c) = 0 \tag{92}$$

To obtain K_u and P_u for this system we now substitute $s = bj$; giving

$$-1/6jb^3 - b^2 + 11/6bj + (1 + K_c) = 0$$

If we now rearrange and collect like terms, we have:

$$(-b^3 + 11b)j + [6(1 + K_c) - 6b^2] = 0 \quad (93)$$

Comparing coefficients of both sides of Equation 93 then yields

$$\left.\begin{array}{l} -b^3 + 11b = 0 \Rightarrow b = 0 \text{ (a trivial solution)} \\ \qquad\qquad\qquad\quad \text{or } b^2 = 11 \end{array}\right\} \quad (94)$$

along with

$$6(1 + K_c) - 6b^2 = 0 \quad (95)$$

and since, from Equation 94 b^2 is 11, Equation 95 simplifies to give

$$K_c = 10.$$

Thus $K_u = 10$, and $\omega_{co} = b = \sqrt{11}$; so that $P_u = 2\pi/\sqrt{11}$.

Let us note, finally that the illustrated procedure is not easy to apply in situations when the transcendental function $e^{-\tau s}$ is involved, as will be the case for time delay systems (to be discussed later). In such situations, the Bode diagram approach is more straightforward.

In this section, we have introduced the basic principles of single loop feedback controller design. The main issues were identified as the controller type decision, and choosing controller parameters (also known as controller tuning). We introduced various criteria and techniques that are typically used for making rational decisions about what controller type to use and what parameters to use for these controllers.

It is true that a large proportion of industrial systems operate well enough under single loop feedback control. However, important situations arise in which this conventional single loop feedback control scheme proves inadequate. We shall have cause, in the ensuing sections, to deal with the issue of controller design under those circumstances in which more is required than the conventional scheme can offer.

DESIGN OF HIGHER LEVEL SISO CONTROL SYSTEMS

The control problems posed by certain process systems cannot be effectively handled by standard feedback control. In such situations, it becomes necessary to employ a higher level control strategy. This section is devoted to a discussion of the characteristics of, and controller design procedure for, these higher level control systems.

Consider the conventional feedback temperature control system shown in Figure 19 in which the temperature at the bottom of the distillation column is controlled by adjusting the steam flow rate to the reboiler. According to this scheme, the controller outputs the desired steam flow rate required to achieve good temperature regulation, but this command is actually executed in form of an appropriate valve opening which supposedly corresponds to the desired flow rate.

Observe, however, that for a given valve opening, a change in the steam supply pressure will alter the actual steam flow delivered to the reboiler; ultimately causing an unwanted alteration in the column temperature. If such fluctuations in steam supply pressure are frequent and substantial, the performance of the conventional scheme will deteriorate. Under these circumstances, a more effective control scheme is required for improved performance.

Consider the second example system shown in Figure 20; the stirred heating tank system under conventional feedback control. The objective is to regulate T, the temperature within the tank by

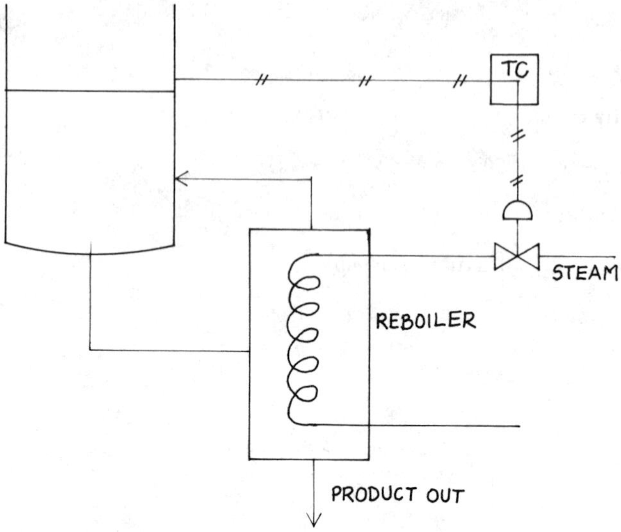

Figure 19. Distillation column bottom temperature control.

adjusting the rate of steam flow through the coil. According to the conventional scheme, any changes in T_i must first be registered as an upset in the value of T before the controller can take corrective action. Again, where the fluctuations in T_i are frequent and substantial, it appears as if an alternative scheme that can detect changes in the disturbance, T_i, and implement control action *before* an upset is registered in T, will be far more effective.

The aforementioned are examples of process systems that require control schemes of a higher level than conventional feedback control. The first process system is a typical example of those that require *cascade control* while process systems of the type considered in the second example

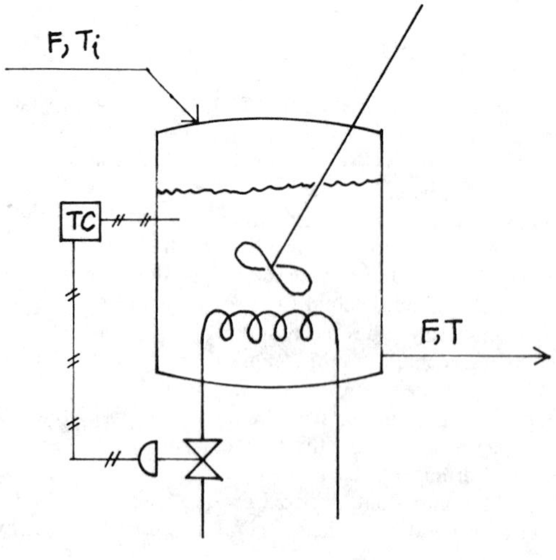

Figure 20. The stirred mixing tank control system.

require *feedforward control.* Many more examples of industrial systems requiring the application of cascade and feedforward control are available [2, 3, 5].

Cascade Control

Let us now return to the distillation column temperature control problem. Suppose we now install a flow controller (FC), in between the temperature controller (TC) and the control valve, for the sole purpose of overseeing the flow conditions; to ensure that, irrespective of fluctuations in the steam supply pressure, the desired steam flow rate is delivered to the reboiler.

Such an arrangement (see Figure 21) constitutes a cascade control configuration. Observe that under this scheme, the output of the TC (the primary controller) is the set-point for the FC (the secondary controller).

The general scenario for cascade control may now be given:

1. Process 1, our main process, has a single output y to be controlled by manipulating a single input u. This constitutes our primary control loop. However, u is subject to significant disturbances.
2. A second controller is therefore set up to regulate u by manipulating the command signal sent to the final control element; constituting a secondary control loop, for "Process 2."
3. The output of the primary controller does not go directly to the process; it becomes the set-point for a secondary controller whose job is to ensure that the process receives the input u as originally intended by the primary controller.

Figure 22 shows a block diagram of a typical cascade control system. Such a system has the following typical features:

1. There are two controllers in two nested loops; the outer (or primary) loop being where the set-point for the inner (or secondary) loop is issued. The two controllers are sometimes referred to as master and slave controllers, for the obvious reason that the one issues the command that the other is expected to implement.
2. The cascade control system is advantageous only if the inner loop (which must contain the "entrance point" of a disturbance) responds faster than the outer loop.

Closed Loop Characteristics of Cascade Control

To analyze the overall behavior of the cascade control system, let us first consolidate the block diagram of Figure 22 by dealing first with the inner loop.

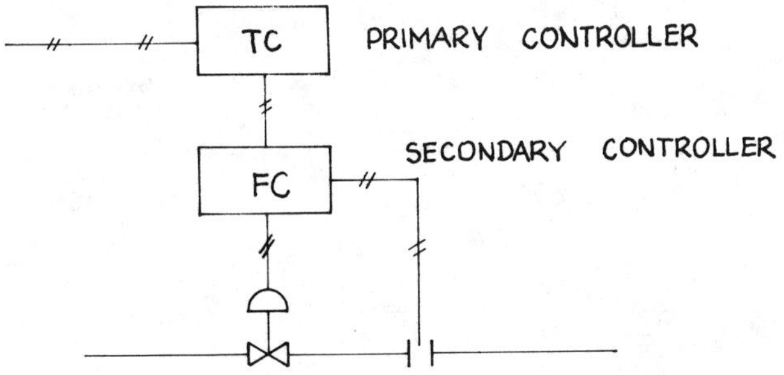

Figure 21. Cascade control configuration.

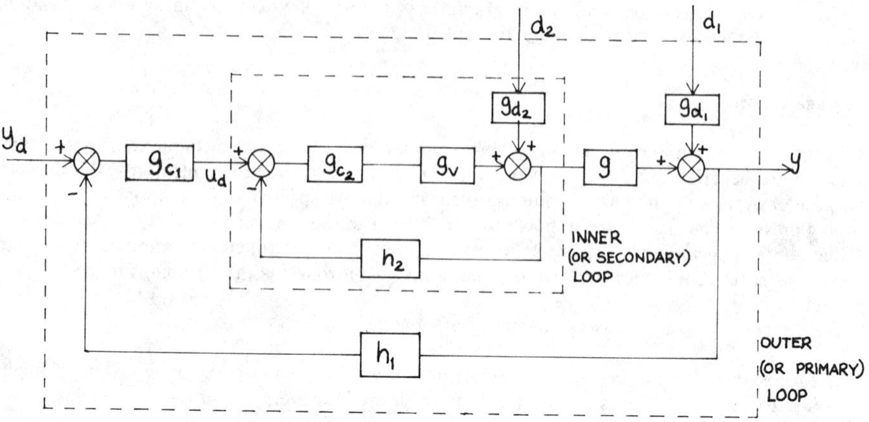

Figure 22. Typical block diagram of a cascade control system.

It is easy to see that the closed loop relationship for the inner loop elements is

$$u = \frac{g_{c_2} g_v}{1 + g_{c_2} g_v h_2} u_d + \frac{g_{d_2}}{1 + g_{c_2} g_v h_2} d_2 \tag{96a}$$

or

$$u = g_1^* u_d + g_2^* d_2 \tag{96b}$$

where g_1^*, and g_2^* are obtained directly from Equation 96; so that the block diagram is consolidated to give that shown in Figure 23.

From here, the overall closed loop transfer function representation is now immediately obtained as:

$$y = \frac{g g_{c_1} g_1^*}{1 + g g_{c_1} g_1^* h_1} y_d + \frac{g g_2^*}{1 + g g_{c_1} g_1^* h_1} d_2 + \frac{g_{d_1}}{1 + g g_{c_1} g_1^* h_1} d_1 \tag{97}$$

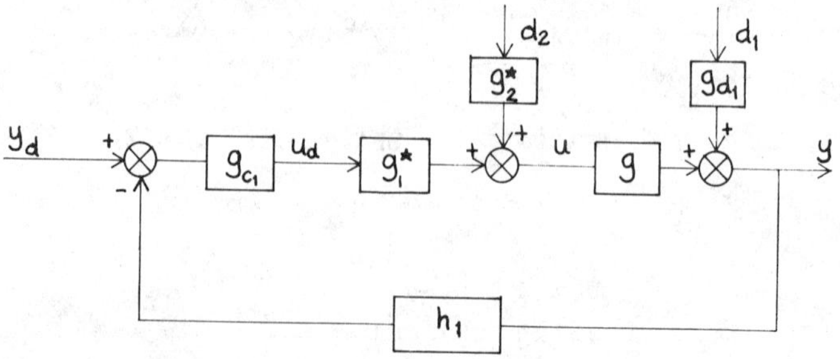

Figure 23. Consolidated block diagram for the cascade control system.

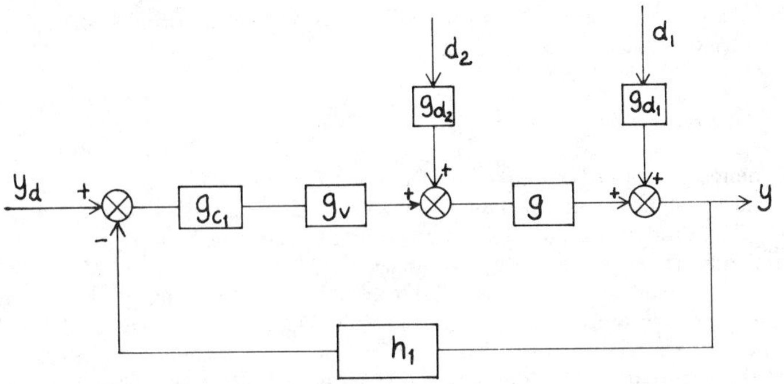

Figure 24. Block diagram for system without cascade control.

Now, the corresponding system without cascade control will have the block diagramatic representation shown in Figure 24, for which the closed loop transfer function representation is easily obtained as:

$$y = \frac{gg_{c_1}g_v}{1 + gg_{c_1}g_vh_1} y_d \frac{gg_{d_2}}{1 + gg_{c_1}g_vh_1} d_2 + \frac{g_{d_1}}{1 + gg_{c_1}g_vh_1} d_1 \quad (98)$$

A careful comparison of Equations 97 and 98 now reveals the effects of cascade control on closed loop performance:

$$g_v \text{ is replaced by } g_1^* = \frac{g_{c_2}g_v}{1 + g_{c_2}g_vh_2}$$

$$g_{d_2} \text{ is replaced by } g_2^* = \frac{g_{d_2}}{1 + g_{c_2}g_vh_2}$$

Let us now observe that:

as the magnitude of g_{c_2} increases, $g_1^* \rightarrow 1$ and $g_2^* \rightarrow 0$;

with the attendant consequences that the overall effect of the disturbance, d_2 on u (and hence on the process system), is "wiped out"; since, according to Equation 97 the above conditions imply $u \rightarrow u_d$.

The conclusion therefore is that for a fast inner loop (this is the real implication of having a high magnitude for g_{c_2}), the overall cascade system is less vulnerable to the effects of fluctuations in d_2 than the equivalent system under conventional feedback control.

Controller Tuning

It is clear that the controller tuning exercise for a cascade control system must proceed in two stages:

1. The inner loop is usually tuned "very tightly" (i.e., use as high a proportional gain value as the control loop will tolerate without going unstable) to give the fast inner loop response required for effective cascade control. This must be done first.
2. The outer loop is then tuned, with the inner loop in operation, using any of the methods discussed in the previous section.

A detailed discussion of cascade control applications on two industrial systems is available in Chapter 8 of Reference [5].

Feedforward Control

The basic philosophy of feedforward control is depicted in Figure 25; i.e., measure the disturbance, d, directly, and *appropriately* adjust the manipulated variable, u, to compensate for any observed changes in d. Thus, for the example stirred mixing tank system of Figure 20, T_i is measured and the steam rate adjusted to compensate for changes in T_i.

Let us note the main difference between this scheme and conventional feedback. With feedforward, compensation for the entrance of a disturbance is possible before the effect is felt by the process; while with the feedback scheme, corrective action can only be taken after the process has registered the effect of the disturbance. The immediate implication is that perfect disturbance rejection, an absolute impossibility with feedback control, is in fact theoretically possible with feedforward control.

Design of Feedforward Controllers

As we might rightly suspect, feedforward controllers are designed with the aid of process models. Consider, therefore the following general transfer function model for a process system by itself (no controller attached yet);

$$y(s) = g(s)u(s) + g_d(s)d(s) \tag{99}$$

The objective is for y(s) to equal $y_d(s)$ at all time, irrespective of changes in d(s). The design problem is therefore simply to derive the u(s) which achieves this objective. Observe now that this translates, algebraically, to the problem of solving Equation 99 for u upon setting $y = y_d$. Setting y to y_d in Equation 99 therefore, and solving for u immediately gives:

$$u(s) = \left\{\frac{1}{g(s)}\, y_d - \frac{g_d(s)}{g(s)}\, d(s)\right\} \tag{100}$$

or $$u(s) = g_{st}(s)y_d - g_{ff}(s)d(s) \tag{101}$$

This is the controller equation for the feedforward scheme; the block diagramatic representation is shown in Figure 26.

Let us note the following about the feedforward control scheme from the Equations 100 and 101:

1. The scheme can, in principle, be used for both set-point tracking (the servo problem), and disturbance rejection (the regulator problem). Observe that for servo problems (d = 0), the

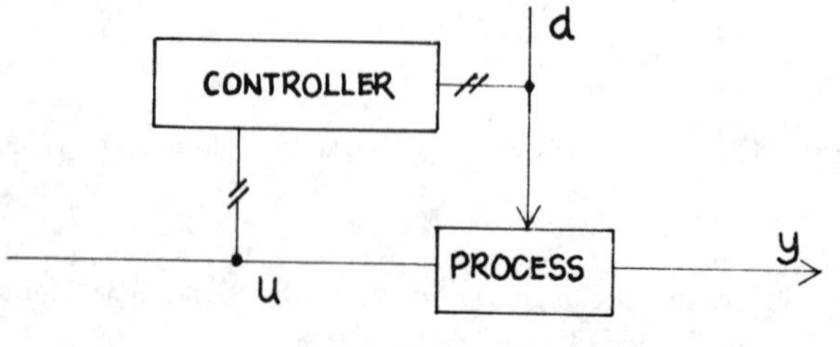

Figure 25. The feedforward control scheme.

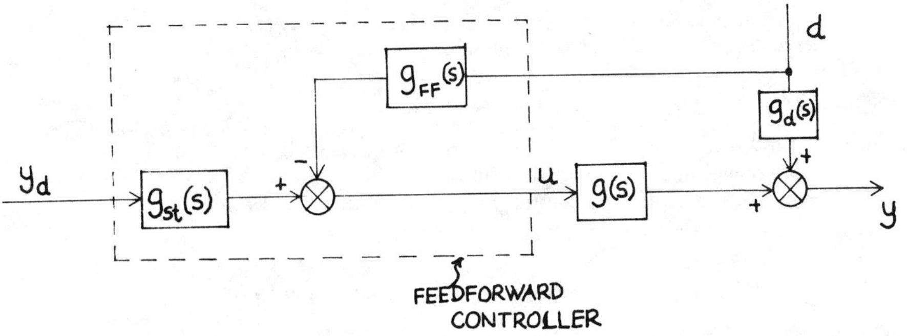

Figure 26. The feedforward controller.

controller equation is:

$$u(s) = g_{st}(s)y_d(s) \tag{102}$$

while for the regulator problem ($y_d = 0$),

$$u(s) = -g_{ff}(s)d(s) \tag{103}$$

2. In either case (set-point tracking or disturbance rejection), the controller has no access to information on the status of y, the real variable to be controlled. Attention is focused instead on the potential cause of the upset (viz, changes in y_d or d), while relying on the accuracy of g(s) and $g_d(s)$ (in representing the true dynamic behavior of the actual process system) to ensure that the desired behavior is obtained, even though y itself is not monitored by the controller.

Before commenting on the merits and demerits of such a scheme, let us first consider the following examples.

Example 11. Design of a Feedforward Controller for the Stirred Mixing Tank of Figure 20. In Example 1, we obtained the transfer function model for this process system in the Equation 99 form, with:

$$g(s) = \frac{\beta\theta}{\theta s + 1} \tag{104}$$

and $\quad g_d(s) = 1/(\theta s + 1)$ (105)

(recall Equation 17).

According to the design procedure given, the equation for the feedforward controller therefore is:

$$u(s) = \frac{\theta s + 1}{\beta\theta} y_d(s) - \frac{1}{\beta\theta} d(s) \tag{106}$$

In terms of "standard" controller types, this implies that a PD controller (with $K_c = 1/\beta\theta$ and $\tau_D = \theta$), but whose input is y_d, (and not $\epsilon = y_d - y$ as would be the case in feedback control) is required for set-point tracking, while a purely proportional controller with $K_c = 1/\beta\theta$, whose input is d, (again, not ϵ) will suffice for disturbance rejection.

It is important to re-emphasize the point that these are not feedback controllers; the structural similarities with standard feedback controllers pointed out above are purely coincidental.

Let us investigate, more closely, the performance of the above derived feedforward controller.

Example 12. The set-point tracking properties of the controller of Example 11. We wish to investigate the controller performance and the overall behavior of the Example 11 system in response to a step change of magnitude A in the set-point y_d.

According to Equation 106, the controller equation for set-point tracking is

$$u(s) = \frac{1}{\beta\theta}(1 + \theta s)y_d(s),$$

and since, in this case, $y_d(s) = A/s$, we have:

$$u(s) = \frac{A}{\beta\theta s} + \frac{A}{\beta}. \tag{107}$$

The overall system response is now obtained from:

$$y(s) = \frac{\beta\theta}{\theta s + 1}u(s),$$

using Equation 107 for u(s); this immediately gives

$$y(s) = \frac{A}{\theta s + 1}\left(\frac{1}{s} + \theta\right) \tag{108}$$

We may now rearrange Equation 108 straightforwardly to give:

$$y(s) = A/s \tag{109}$$

which, inverted back to time, gives the result:

$$y(t) = A. \tag{110}$$

The implication of this result is that the system output, y(t) tracks the desired set-point perfectly. It is easy to show, in general, that regardless of the particular form y_d is required to take, this feedforward scheme always gives the result that $y = y_d$ for all time.

We shall now investigate the disturbance rejection properties of the feedforward controller.

Example 13. The disturbance rejection properties of the controller of Example 11. According to Equation 106, the controller equation for disturbance rejection is simply

$$u(s) = -1/\beta\theta\, d(s)$$

which is inverted back to time straightforwardly to give

$$u(t) = -1/\beta\theta\, d(t). \tag{111}$$

Recalling from Example 1 the physical quantities that β and θ represent, Equation 111 becomes:

$$u(t) = -F\rho C_p d(t) \tag{112}$$

If now d(t) were to increase from zero to a value δ (i.e., T_i increases from T_{is} to $T_{is} + \delta$), the controller in Equation 112 recommends that the energy input to the process through the steam heating arrangement, be reduced by the factor $F\rho C_p\delta$.

Observe now that since F is the volumetric flow rate of liquid into the tank, $F\rho C_p\delta$ is precisely that amount of additional energy brought into the system as a result of the increase in T_i. The result, therefore, is an exact counterbalancing of the disturbance effect by the prescribed control action. This leaves the tank temperature entirely unaffected by whatever fluctuations the inlet temperature T_i may experience; a situation of perfect disturbance rejection.

As attractive as feedforward control may appear to be, there are, however, some significant drawbacks from which the scheme suffers:

1. It is not useful if d cannot be measured.
2. Even when d is measurable, the scheme requires a perfect process model to achieve its objectives.
3. Even in the unrealistic event that a perfect process model exists, the derived transfer function for g_{ff}, i.e. g_d/g, may present any of the following problems: (a) it may be too complicated to be realizable in time; or (b) if g_d and g both have time delay elements and the time delay associated with g_d is *less* than that associated with g then g_{ff} will contain a term in $e^{\alpha s}$, requiring a prediction. Such a g_{ff} is said to be physically unrealizable since, *at time t*, it requires the knowledge of the value that d will take α time units into the future, i.e. $d(t + \alpha)$. It is, of course, impossible to predict this exactly.

All these facts notwithstanding, feedforward control has proved to be a very powerful process control scheme [3]. For one reason, many process disturbances are indeed measurable. For another, even when the available process models are imperfect, and/or the derived g_{ff} is too complicated, it is known that reasonably good performance can still be obtained using devices called lead/lag units. Let us justify this last statement.

If we assume the popular first-order-plus-time-delay transfer function as a general approximate representation for most g and g_d elements, (recall the Cohen and Coon "process reaction curve" technique for approximate process dynamic characterization), this leads to a g_{ff} having the following generalized form:

$$g_{ff} = \frac{K_d e^{-\alpha_1 s}}{\tau_d s + 1} \cdot \frac{\tau s + 1}{K e^{-\alpha s}} \tag{113}$$

and for α_1 approximately equal to α, we have

$$g_{ff} \simeq k\,\frac{\tau s + 1}{\tau_d s + 1} \tag{114}$$

The transfer function in Equation 114 has the form of a lead/lag unit, with lead time constant τ and lag time constant τ_d. This offers an objective explanation for the effectiveness of lead/lag units in the implementation of feedforward control schemes even in situations when the dynamic behavior of the processes in question are poorly modelled.

Lead/lag units are commercially available as analog instruments, and, as indicated in Equation 114, by adjusting the values for τ, τ_d and k on the equipment, it is possible to obtain an acceptable approximation to the exact feedforward controller calculated as indicated in Equation 100.

In conclusion, let us note that even though our discussion on feedforward controller design has so far been based on linear transfer function models, in fact, by its very nature, feedforward control is not in any way limited only to linear systems. An interesting discussion of nonlinear feedforward control is available in Chapter 13 of Reference [3].

Feedback-Augmented Feedforward Control

It is common in the chemical industry to augment a feedforward scheme with feedback compensation: the basic premise being to complement the excellent disturbance rejection properties of the feedforward controller with the "ruggedness" of the feedback controller.

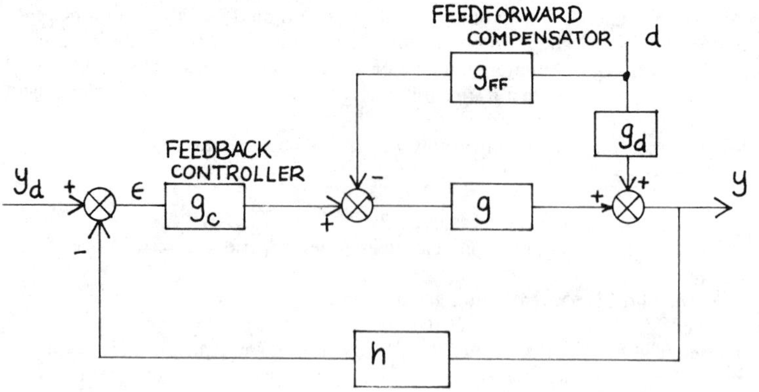

Figure 27. Block diagram for feedforward/feedback system.

We thus have a situation in which feedforward control is used to contain the effects of large, and frequent disturbances, while the feedback controller takes care of the errors introduced as a result of the inevitable imperfections of feedforward control and/or other unmeasurable disturbances.

The block diagram for this feedforward/feedback scheme is shown in Figure 27. The dual objective here is to choose g_{ff} for perfect disturbance rejection, and to choose g_c so that the closed loop system is stable. Upon simple block diagram manipulations on Figure 27, we obtain the equivalent block diagram of Figure 28, from where the closed loop transfer functions are easily obtained as

$$y(s) = \frac{gg_c}{1 + gg_ch} y_d + \frac{g_d - g_{ff}g}{1 + gg_ch} d \tag{115}$$

From here, we observe immediately that if we now choose g_{ff} as

$$g_{ff} = g_d/g \tag{116}$$

the effect of d on y is theoretically eliminated.

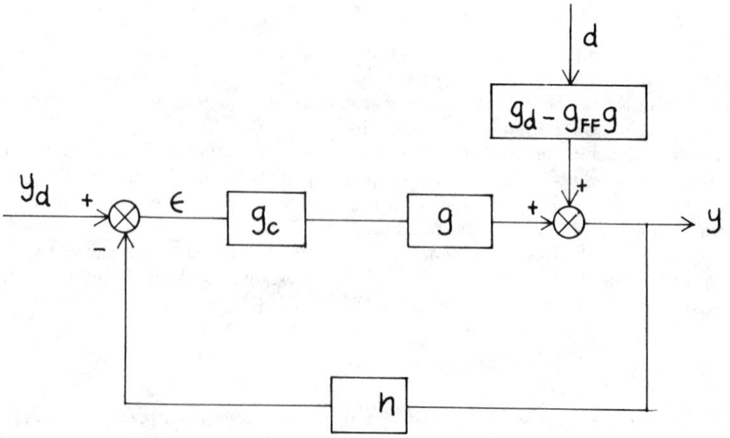

Figure 28. Equivalent block diagram for system in Figure 27.

The following are some important points to note about the feedforward/feedback scheme:

1. The overall system stability is determined by the roots of the characteristic equation,

$$1 + gg_c h = 0 \tag{117}$$

which has nothing to do with g_{ff}. The implication is that the stability of the feedback loop remains unaltered by the addition of feedforward compensation.

2. When g_d and g are known perfectly, perfect compensation is possible. In the more realistic situations where this is not the case, and/or the disturbances are (partially or completely) unmeasurable, the feedback loop picks up the resultant error and eliminates it with time.

In this section, we have introduced situations in which the performance of the conventional feedback controller will be inadequate. The higher level controllers required in such situations were then discussed. We have restricted ourselves to a discussion of cascade control, feedforward control, and feedforward/feedback control. Other somewhat more specialized schemes such as ratio control, override control, auctioneering control, split range control, etc. are discussed in References [2, 3, 5].

CONTROLLER DESIGN FOR NON-MINIMUM PHASE AND OPEN LOOP UNSTABLE SYSTEMS

The open loop dynamic behavior of certain processes are so different from what normally obtains for most other processes that they pose rather unique controller design problems. Strategies for effectively controlling such processes must necessarily consider the unusual open loop dynamic behavior they exhibit. This section discusses the dynamic characteristics of such systems, the control problems they create, and the controller design strategies specifically tailored to handle their unusual control problems.

Introduction

In our discussion so far, we have tacitly assumed that, by itself, in the open loop (before the controller is attached), the process system to be controlled exhibits no unusual dynamic behavior. For such a system, if the input variable were, for example, increased from an initial steady state value of F_1 to a new value of say $F_1 + \Delta F$, the dynamic behavior is considered not unusual if the output variable responds as depicted in Figures 29a and b; i.e., the output satisfies the following conditions:

1. It responds fairly instantaneously.
2. Heads *directly* for a new steady state value without first taking an excursion in the opposite direction before turning around to eventually head in the "right" direction.
3. Finally *settles* down to a new steady state value (which may be higher, or lower than the initial steady state value).

Mathematically, this means that, in the general transfer function model representation,

$$y(s) = g(s)u(s) + g_d(s)d(s) \tag{118}$$

the transfer function, g(s), is not "unusual" in form. What makes a transfer function form "unusual" will be made clear shortly; for now we just note that the controller design techniques discussed so far will be adequate only for those systems for which g(s) is not "unusual." Recall that conventional feedback is adequate when neither the transfer functions nor the inputs u, and d, suffer from any "unusual problems"; cascade control improves on conventional feedback when the process input, u is subject to unwanted, external disturbances; and feedforward (or feedforward/feedback) is recommended when d is subject to large and frequent changes.

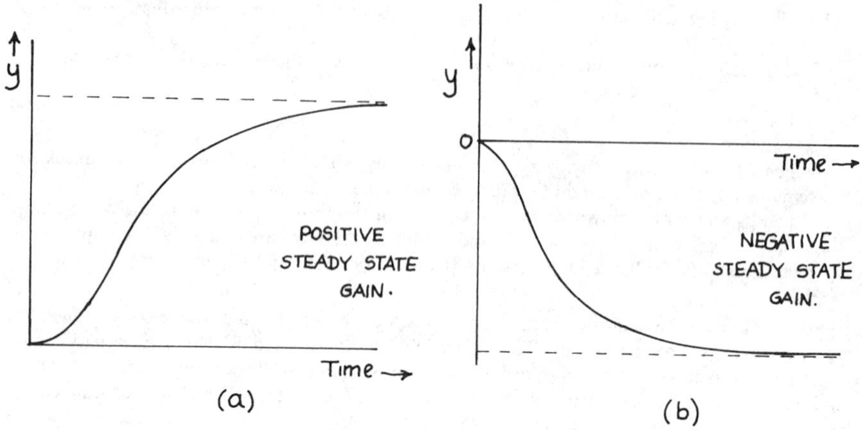

Figure 29. Step responses for processes with "normal" open loop dynamics: (a) system with positive steady state gain; (b) system with negative steady state gain.

However, when the transfer function g(s) is unusual in form, (indicating that the dynamic behavior of the process itself is unusual), the design techniques so far discussed will quite often prove inadequate, since they contain no specific provisions for handling problems posed by those processes that exhibit unusual dynamic behavior in the open loop.

Unusual Dynamics in Chemical Processes

There are three main types of unusual dynamic behavior exhibited by chemical process systems: time delay, inverse response, and open loop instability; respectively identified in a transfer function model by the presence of an exponential term, a right-half plane zero, and a right-half plane pole, which are never present for "normal" systems.

When the step response of a process system is as depicted in Figure 30a, i.e., it exhibits an initial, noticeable period of no response, we have a time delay (or dead time) process.

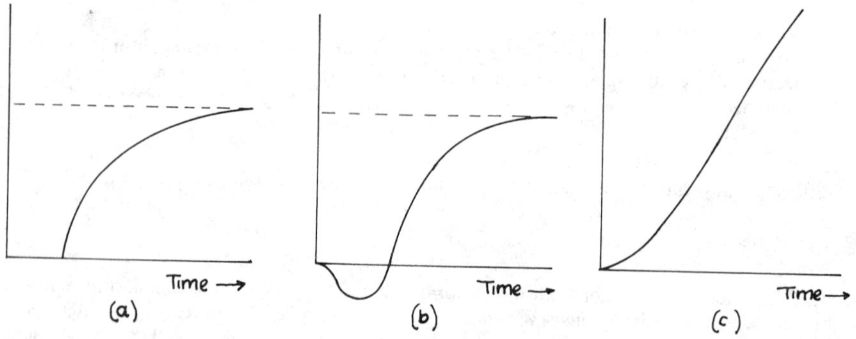

Figure 30. Step responses for processes with unusual dynamics: (a) time delay system, (b) inverse responding system, (c) open loop unstable system.

A time delay process thus violates the first condition just noted for normal dynamic behavior: it does not respond instantaneously to input changes. Unfortunately, most chemical process systems possess time delays of varying magnitudes. The most important reasons for such a situation are

1. Fluids have to be transported through various lengths of pipes; the time to traverse the pipe length constituting the time delay.
2. Sampling and analysis delays are introduced by measuring devices such as gas chromatographs, etc.

An inverse responding (IR) system violates the second condition for normal dynamic behavior in that, even though its step response eventually ends up heading in the direction of the new steady state, it starts out initially heading in the opposite direction, away from the new steady state; changing direction somewhere during the course of time. Such a response is depicted in Figure 30b. Examples of physical process systems that exhibit this unusual dynamic behavior include the drum boiler and the base of a distillation column [2, 3].

Time delay and IR systems are sometimes collectively referred to as non-minimum phase (NMP) systems; a term whose origin and justification lies in the domain of electrical engineering.

A system for which the step response is unbounded, i.e., the output increases (or decreases) indefinitely with time, as depicted in Figure 30C, is said to be open loop unstable, for obvious reasons. The open loop unstable (OLU) system thus violates the third condition noted above; its output fails to settle down to a new steady state value in response to a step change in the input. The most well known process system that exhibits open loop instability is the exothermic chemical reactor.

The unique control problems presented by these systems, and the controller design techniques available for handling these problems will now be considered.

Time Delay Systems

Control Problems

When a time delay element is present in a feedback control loop, the following obvious control problems arise:

1. With a delay in the measuring device, the controller is compelled to take control action based on delayed, hence obsolete, process information that is usually not representative of the current situation within the process.
2. The effect of this obviously inadequate control action will not be immediately felt by the process when, in addition there is *input delay*; compounding the problem even further.

It is easy to see how such a situation can provoke instability.

Mathematically, the transfer function for a time delay system involves a term in $e^{-\alpha s}$. For example, a first-order system having a time delay of α time units has the following transfer function form:

$$g(s) = \frac{Ke^{-\alpha s}}{\tau s + 1} \tag{119}$$

or $\quad g(s) = g^*(s)\, e^{-\alpha s}$

where $g^*(s)$ represents the "normal" first order transfer function form. It is well known, from frequency response arguments, that the $e^{-\alpha s}$ term is a real source of closed loop instability [2], making it difficult for a conventional feedback controller to function acceptably. In the closed loop, a general time delay system with transfer function $g(s) = g^*(s)\, e^{-\alpha s}$ has the characteristic equation:

$$1 + g_c g_v h g^* e^{-\alpha s} = 0 \tag{120}$$

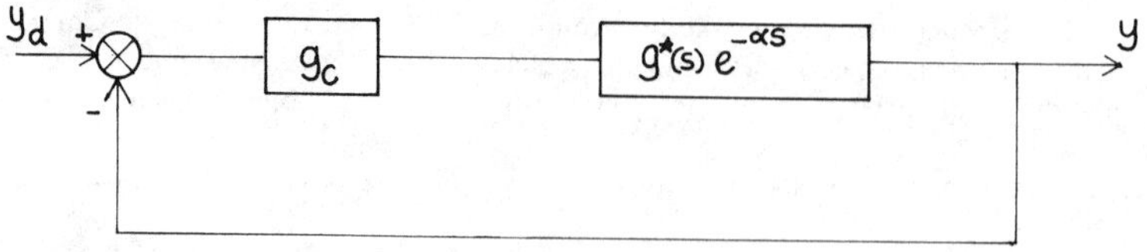

Figure 31. Block diagram of time delay system under conventional feedback control.

We now note that to retain closed loop stability, the presence of the transcendental function in the characteristic equation demands a reduction in the value of the proportional gain, K_c; meaning that the closed loop response will now be more sluggish.

It thus appears that with conventional feedback control, to have closed loop stability we must sacrifice the speed of response.

Controller Design Techniques

Conventional feedback control. When the time delay is not too large, it is known that the conventional feedback controller using Ziegler-Nichols, or Cohen and Coon settings performs acceptably well. In this case closed loop stability can be achieved without sacrificing too much of the speed of response. With larger time delays, smaller controller gains are required and the resultant sacrifice in closed loop performance often proves unacceptable.

Time delay compensator. Consider the block diagram of Figure 31 for a time delay system under conventional feedback control. For simplicity, we have lumped g_v and h into the process model represented as $g(s) = g^*(s)\,e^{-\alpha s}$. The characteristic equation for such a closed loop system is:

$$1 + g_c g^* e^{-\alpha s} = 0 \tag{121}$$

which contains the troublesome $e^{-\alpha s}$ term.

Now consider the block diagram of Figure 32 where a minor feedback loop has been introduced around the conventional controller, as shown. Let us define $y^*(s)$ as follows:

$$y^*(s) = g^*(s)u(s) \tag{122}$$

Since the actual y is given by

$$y(s) = g^*(s)e^{-\alpha s}u(s) \tag{123}$$

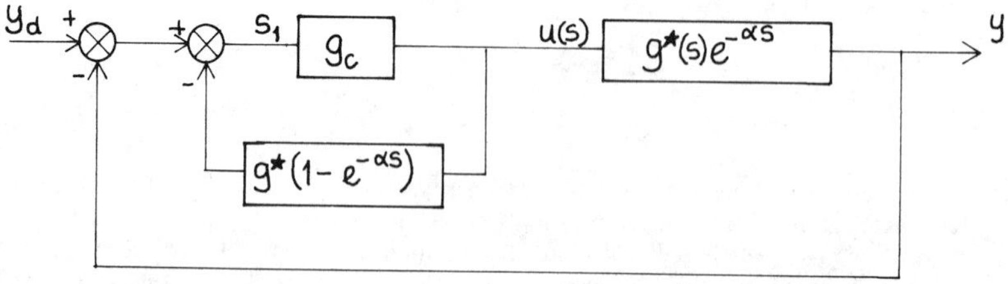

Figure 32. Block diagram incorporating the Smith predictor.

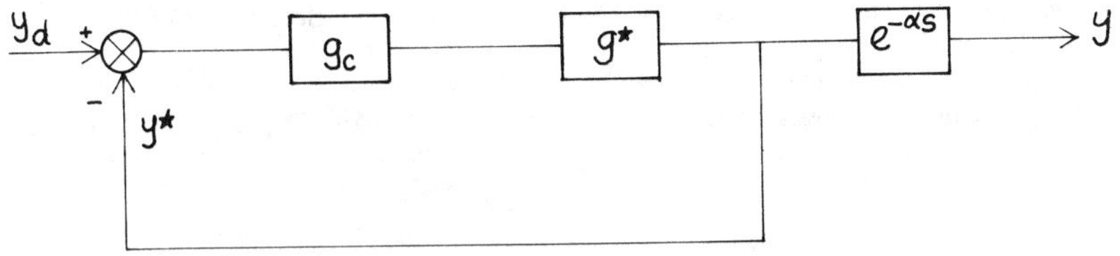

Figure 33. Equivalent block diagram for system incorporating the Smith predictor.

then $y^*(s)$ is the output of the "undelayed" version of the process output $y(s)$. Observe that the signal s_1 reaching the controller is given by

$$s_1 = y_d - y(s) - [y^*(s) - y(s)] \tag{124}$$

or $$s_1 = y_d - y^* \tag{125}$$

implying, as a result that the block diagram of Figure 32 is equivalent to that shown in Figure 33. It is now clear that the net result of the introduction of the minor loop is therefore to eliminate the time delay factor from the feedback loop where it causes stability problems, and "move" it outside the loop where it has no effect on closed loop system stability.

The characteristic equation is now seen to be:

$$1 + gg^* = 0 \tag{126}$$

which no longer contains the time delay element, and therefore allows the use of higher controller gain values without placing the closed loop stability in jeopardy.

This control scheme is due to Smith [10, 11] and the minor loop of Figure 32 is generally known as the Smith Predictor. It is important to note the following points about this specialized conrol scheme:

1. The effective action of the compensator is to feed the signal y^* to the controller instead of y.
2. By its definition in Equation 122, and from Equation 123, $y^*(s) = e^{\alpha s}y(s)$, implying that $y^*(t) = y(t + \alpha)$. We may hence observe that y^* is a prediction of $y(t)$, α time units ahead, hence the name Smith Predictor.
3. The scheme will work perfectly only if the process model is perfectly known; modeling errors will affect its performance.
4. In those chemical process systems for which the time delays are due to fluid flow through long pipes, the time delays observed for such processes will vary with the fluid flow rate; an increase in flow rate giving rise to lower time delays, and vice-versa. The Smith Predictor scheme is for static time delays and may therefore not perform as well for such systems, especially if the time variations of the time delays are significant.

Inverse Responding Systems

Control Problems

The major problem created by the inverse responding system is the confusing scenario it presents to the automatic controller: for, having taken the proper action that will eventually yield the desired result, the controller is first given the impression that it in fact took the wrong action. The "uninformed" controller, in reacting to this illogical state of affairs, is liable to further compound the problem. It is therefore not difficult to see that such a system's closed loop stability stands in real jeopardy.

The transfer function representation for an IR process has at least one zero in the right half of the complex plane (commonly referred to as a right-half plane (RHP) zero). For example, the transfer function

$$g(s) = \frac{K(1 - \eta s)}{(\tau_1 s + 1)(\tau_2 s + 1)} \tag{127}$$

has a zero at $s = +1/\eta$; hence it will be inverse responding, as illustrated in the following example.

Example 14. Step response of an Inverse responding system. The response of the system whose transfer function is given by

$$g(s) = \frac{(1 - 5s)}{(5s + 1)(3s + 1)} \tag{128}$$

to a unit step input is obtained from

$$y(s) = g(s) \cdot 1/s$$

and upon introducing Equation 128, carrying out the indicated partial fraction expansion, and then inverting back into time, we obtain:

$$y(t) = 1 - 5e^{-t/5} + 4e^{-t/3} \tag{129}$$

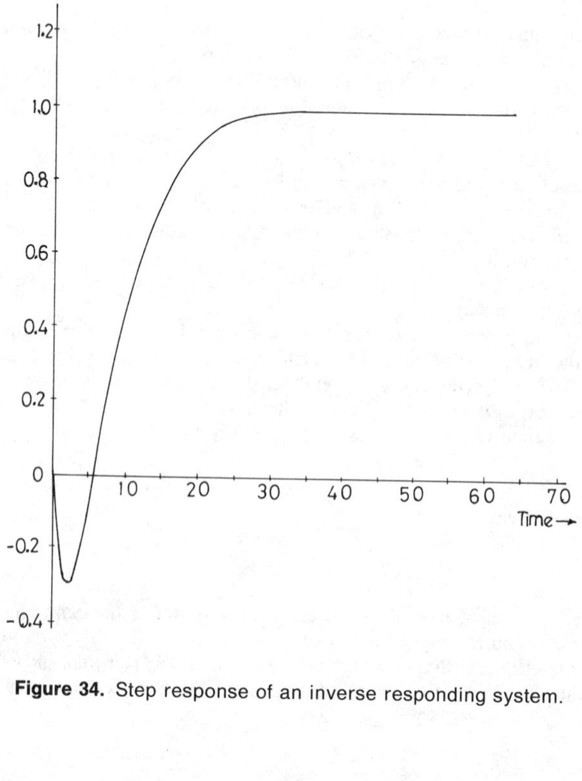

Figure 34. Step response of an inverse responding system.

A plot of this response is shown in Figure 34 where the inverse responding characteristics are very clearly seen.

Controller Design Techniques

Typically, IR systems are controlled using either conventional PID control or an inverse response compensator, similar in nature to the time delay compensator discussed.

Conventional PID control. Because the derivative mode of the PID controller endows it with some "anticipatory" character, this controller is able to somewhat cope with controlling the IR system by anticipating the "wrong way behavior" and appropriately accommodating it.

As demonstrated by Waller and Nygardas [12] the Ziegler-Nichols settings for PID controllers yield acceptable control of IR systems. (Later we will uncover another justification for the fact that, of all conventional controllers, only the PID type can be used to control IR systems with any degree of success).

Inverse response compensator. The same principles behind the time delay compensator discussed above has been extended to IR systems by Iinoya and Altpeter [13]. What we shall now present is a slightly different, and more general version of what is available in References [2, 13].

Consider the block diagram shown in Figure 35a for the conventional feedback control of an IR system with transfer function representation $g(s) = g^0(s)K(1 - \eta s)$; where g^0 represents that portion of the transfer function left after factoring out the steady state gain K, and the problematic right-half plane zero. For example, for the transfer function in Equation 128 (see Example 14), $K = 1$ and $g^0(s) = 1/(5s + 1)(3s + 1)$.

Now consider the situation in Figure 35b in which a minor loop is introduced as shown, with the transfer function g′ given by $g' = g^0(s)\lambda s$. The objective here is to choose the quantity λ such

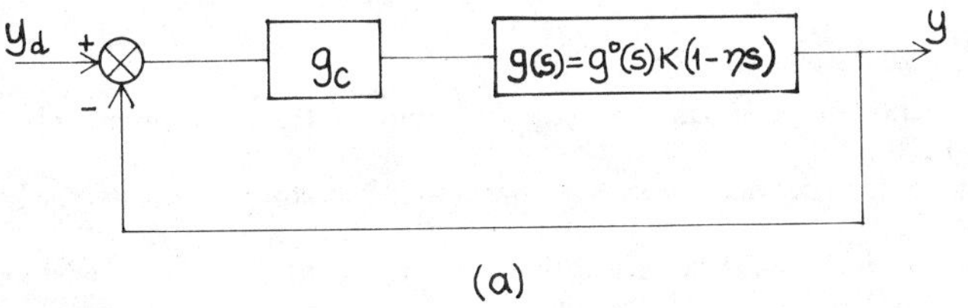

Figure 35a. Conventional feedback control of an inverse responding system.

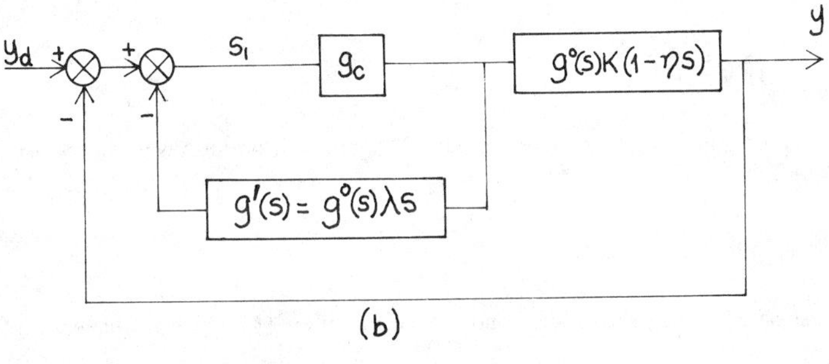

Figure 35b. Block diagram incorporating the inverse response compensator.

that the signal reaching the controller appears to be from a "normal" system; in this context, one which does not exhibit inverse response.

Let $y'(s) = g'(s)u(s)$; i.e the signal from the minor loop. Then the signal reaching the controller, s_1, is given by:

$$s_1 = y_d - y(s) - y'(s)$$

or
$$s_1 = y_d - \{g(s) + g'(s)\}u(s) \tag{130}$$

Now let
$$g^*(s) = g(s) + g'(s) \tag{131}$$

and
$$y^*(s) = g^*(s)u(s) \tag{132}$$

then Equation 130 becomes:

$$s_1 = y_d - y^* \tag{133}$$

As a result of Equation 133, observe that we now have a situation in which, as far as the controller is concerned, it thinks it is interfaced with the apparent process which generates the signal y^*, and whose transfer function, $g^*(s)$, is as given in Equation 131.

Now, introducing the expressions for g and g′ into Equation 131 gives

$$g^*(s) = g^0(s)K(1 - \eta s) + g^0(s)\lambda s$$

or
$$g^*(s) = g^0(s)\{K + (\lambda - K\eta)s\} \tag{134}$$

Observe that if we now choose λ such that (for $K > 0$)

$$\lambda \geq K\eta \tag{135}$$

the transfer function of the apparent process generating y^*, the signal reaching the controller, no longer has a RHP zero.

Thus the minor loop provides a corrective signal which effectively eliminates the inverse response from the feedback loop.

Let us note, in conclusion that, once again as with the Smith Predictor, model inaccuracies will affect the performance of this compensator.

Example 15. An IR Compensator for the Example 14 system. For this process, we observe that $K = 1$, $\eta = 5$, and

$$g^0(s) = \frac{1}{(5s + 1)(3s + 1)} \tag{136}$$

Thus, the transfer function $g'(s)$ required for the IR compensation loop is given by:

$$g'(s) = \frac{\lambda s}{(5s + 1)(3s + 1)} \tag{137}$$

where λ must be chosen to satisfy the condition in Equation 135 which in this case translates to mean,

$$\lambda \geq 5 \tag{138}$$

Observe now that for the specific choice of $\lambda = 7$, the transfer function of the apparent system, $g^*(s)$, is easily verified to be given by

$$g^*(s) = \frac{(2s + 1)}{(5s + 1)(3s + 1)} \tag{139}$$

for which there is now no longer a RHP zero.

Open Loop Unstable Systems

The transfer function that describes an open loop unstable system has at least one pole in the right half of the complex plane. Thus while a right-half plane zero indicates inverse response behavior, the presence of a right-half plane pole in a transfer function indicates instability.

The most popular control technique is stabilization by conventional feedback; by which we mean that classical controllers are used, with the parameters chosen such that the resultant closed loop system is stable. Let us illustrate with some examples.

Example 16. Proportional feedback control stabilization of a first-order open loop unstable system. The process transfer function in this case is given by:

$$g(s) = \frac{K}{\tau s - 1} \tag{140}$$

and for proportional only control, with $g_v = 1$, $h = 1$, the characteristic equation is given by

$$1 + gg_c = 1 + \frac{KK_c}{\tau s - 1} = 0$$

which gives

$$\tau s - 1 + KK_c = 0$$

an equation with only one root at

$$s = (1 - KK_c)/\tau \tag{141}$$

Thus, observe that this root will be negative so long as

$$K_c > 1/K. \tag{142}$$

The implication therefore is that K_c values that satisfy Equation 142 will stabilize the otherwise open loop unstable system.

Example 17. Closed loop stabilization of a first-order OLU system with a PI controller. Let us consider the possibility of stabilizing the Example 16 system using a PI controller.

In this case, since $g_c = K_c(1 + 1/\tau_I s)$, the characteristic equation becomes, upon some elementary rearrangement,

$$\tau\tau_I s^2 + (KK_c - 1)\tau_I s + KK_c = 0 \tag{143}$$

Observe now that the roots of this quadratic will all be negative provided the coefficients of s^2, s, and the constant term, are all positive. Thus, the system is stabilized provided $KK_c > 1$, or, $K_c > 1/K$; the same stabilizing condition obtained for P control.

In this section we have focused attention on those process systems that exhibit unusual dynamic behavior in the open loop, and, as a result, are difficult to control by conventional means. The non-minimum phase systems (time delay and inverse responding systems) were shown to require compensators introduced in a minor loop around a conventional controller for satisfactory control system performance. The open loop unstable system on the other hand was shown to require closed loop stabilization by conventional feedback control. The usual controller design procedure was then seen to involve finding those parameters of the classical controller that will make the closed loop system stable.

CONTROLLER DESIGN FOR NONLINEAR SYSTEMS

All physical systems exhibit nonlinear behavior to varying degrees. Yet, the bulk of existing control systems design and analysis techniques are for linear control systems—perhaps for the understandable reason that linear systems are much easier to deal with.

To be sure, a substantial number of chemical process systems are only mildly nonlinear and therefore can be adequately approximated by linear models. However, there are enough severely nonlinear process systems of importance to motivate a special treatment of the problems of nonlinear control systems design. This section examines the rapidly developing field of nonlinear process control.

That nonlinear dynamics are inevitable in most chemical processes is a fact that needs no justification. However, chemical process control has traditionally focused almost entirely on the analysis and control of linear systems. This state of affairs is often justified by appealing to the fortunate circumstance that many process systems are in fact only mildly nonlinear. In such cases, it is possible to treat the process system as approximately linear and thus employ linear analysis and design techniques with satisfactory results.

Nevertheless, quite a few important process systems are severely nonlinear. For such systems, linear controller design techniques often prove inadequate and alternatives must be considered.

Nonlinear Controller Design Philosophies

Controller design for nonlinear systems may be carried out along the lines indicated by any one of the following four schemes:

1. *Local linearization* involves linearizing the modeling equations around a steady state and applying linear control systems design results. It is obvious that the controller performance will deteriorate as the process moves further away from the steady state around which the model was linearized.
2. *Local linearization with adaptation* seeks to improve on scheme 1 by recognizing the presence of nonlinearities and consequently providing the controller a means for systematically adapting whenever the adequacy of the linear approximation becomes questionable.
3. *Exact linearization by variable transformation* is a scheme by which a system that is nonlinear in its original variables is converted to one that is *exactly linear* in a different set of variables by the use of appropriate transformations; controller design may then be carried out for the transformed system with great facility since it is now linear.
4. "*Special purpose*" *procedures:* usually custom made for specific processes or specific types of nonlinearities [3, 7].

We shall now consider each of these schemes in turn, keeping in mind that within the available space we can only hope to provide at best a panoramic overview. (We shall, however, not discuss the "special purpose" techniques because of their highly specialized nature. The given references should be consulted for more information).

Linearization and the Classical Approach

In the context of process dynamics and control, linearization is a term used in general for the process by which a nonlinear system is approximated by a linear one; i.e., the system's mathematical representation, the nonlinear process model is somehow approximated with a linear one.

The most popular technique for obtaining these linear approximations is based on Taylor series expansions of the nonlinear aspects of the process model, as demonstrated below.

Any function f(x), under certain conditions that are always satisfied by realistic process system models, can be expressed in the following power series around the point $x = x_0$:

$$f(x) = f(x_0) + \left(\frac{df}{dx}\right)_{x=x_0}(x - x_0) + \left(\frac{d^2f}{dx^2}\right)_{x=x_0}\frac{(x - x_0)^2}{2!} + \cdots + \cdots + \left(\frac{d^nf}{dx^n}\right)_{x=x_0}\frac{(x - x_0)^n}{n!} + \cdots \tag{144}$$

If we now ignore second and higher order terms, Equation 144 becomes

$$f(x) \simeq f(x_0) + f'(x_0)(x - x_0) \tag{145}$$

which is now linear. Observe that if $(x - x_0)$ is small, the higher order terms will be even smaller and the linear approximation is satisfactory. The implication of this linearization process is depicted in Figure 36. The approximation is exact at $x = x_0$, remains satisfactory so long as x is close to x_0, and deteriorates as x moves further away from x_0; the rate of this deterioration being directly related to the severity of the nonlinearity of f(x). The above is easily extended to situations when f( ) is a function of more than one variable [2].

This purely mathematical idea will now be applied to nonlinear process control problems. Consider the general nonlinear process model

$$\frac{d\xi}{dt} = F(\xi, \mu) \tag{146}$$

where F( ) is an arbitrary nonlinear function of the *two variables* ξ, the process output, and μ, the process input. A Taylor series expansion of F( ) around the point (ξ_0, μ_0) gives:

$$\frac{d\xi}{dt} = F(\xi_0, \mu_0) + \left(\frac{\partial F}{\partial \xi}\right)_{(\xi_0,\mu_0)}(\xi - \xi_0) + \left(\frac{\partial F}{\partial \mu}\right)_{(\xi_0,\mu_0)}(\mu - \mu_0) + \text{higher order terms.} \tag{147}$$

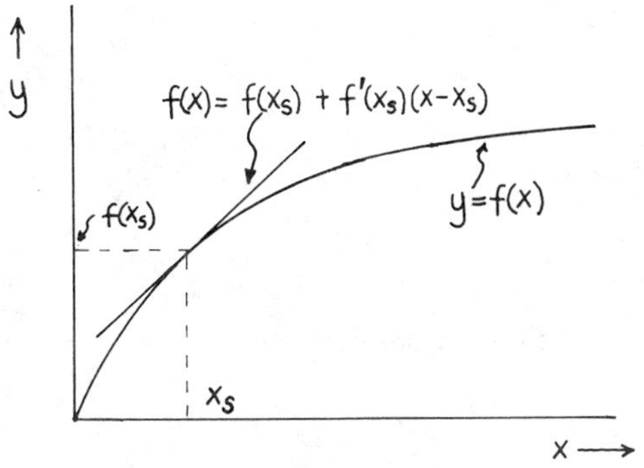

Figure 36. Nonlinear function and linearized approximation.

ignoring the higher order terms now gives the linear approximation:

$$\frac{d\xi}{dt} = F(\xi_0, \mu_0) + A(\xi_0, \mu_0)(\xi - \xi_0) + B(\xi_0, \mu_0)(\mu - \mu_0) \tag{148}$$

where $A(\ ) = \left(\frac{\partial F}{\partial \xi}\right)_{(\xi_0, \mu_0)}$

and $B(\ ) = \left(\frac{\partial F}{\partial \mu}\right)_{(\xi_0, \mu_0)}$

both functions of ξ_0 and μ_0. It is now customary to express Equation 148 in terms of deviation variables: say, $y = (\xi - \xi_0)$; and $u = (\mu - \mu_0)$, and if the linearization point (ξ_0, μ_0) is chosen to be a steady state process operating point, then observe from Equation 146 that by definition of a steady state, $d\xi/dt$ will be zero, and hence $F(\xi_0, \mu_0)$ is also zero, so that Equation 148 becomes

$$\frac{dy}{dt} = Ay + Bu \tag{149}$$

where, for simplicity, the arguments have been dropped from A and B.

A transfer function model corresponding to Equation 149 may now be obtained by the usual procedure; the result is:

$$y(s) = \left\{\frac{B(\xi_0, \mu_0)}{s - A(\xi_0, \mu_0)}\right\} u(s) \tag{150}$$

with the transfer function as indicated in the winged brackets.

The classical approach now involves designing a controller on the basis of the approximate transfer function indicated in Equation 150, using standard linear control systems design strategies. The adequacy of such a control scheme is clearly dependent on how good an approximation Equation 150 is, which in turn is dependent on the severity of the nonlinearities involved in the function $F(\xi, \mu)$.

Example 2 illustrates how to obtain approximate transfer function representations for nonlinear systems. The following is a simpler example, in which the nonlinear portion of the model is a function of only one variable. Other examples may be found [2].

Example 18. Approximate linear model for a flow system. In Reference [4], the mathematical model for the liquid level in a cylindrical tank was given as

$$A_c \frac{dh}{dt} = F_1 - Ch^{1/2} \tag{151}$$

which is nonlinear because it contains the square root of h. The linear approximation for this model is now obtained by linearizing this nonlinear function.

A Taylor series expansion of $h^{1/2}$ around the steady state h_s gives:

$$h^{1/2} = h_s^{1/2} + \tfrac{1}{2}h_s^{-1/2}(h - h_s) + \text{higher order terms} \tag{152}$$

Ignoring the higher order terms and introducing the linear approximation into Equation 151 for $h^{1/2}$ gives:

$$A_c \frac{dh}{dt} = F_1 - Ch_s^{1/2} - \tfrac{1}{2}Ch_s^{-1/2}(h - h_s) \tag{153}$$

Introducing the deviation variables $y = (h - h_s)$, and $u = (F_1 - F_{1s})$, and realizing that under steady state conditions ($dh/dt = 0$), Equation 151 implies that $F_{1s} = Ch_s^{1/2}$, Equation 153 reduces to:

$$A_c \frac{dy}{dt} = u - \frac{1}{K} y \tag{154}$$

from where, taking the usual Laplace transforms, we obtain the approximate transfer function representation:

$$y(s) = \frac{K}{\tau s + 1} u(s) \tag{155}$$

where $\tau = A_c K$, and $K = (2h_s^{1/2}/C)$

It should be noted, finally, that K, and hence τ, are functions of h_s so that the apparent steady state gain and time constant exhibited by this system will be different at each operating steady state condition.

Adaptive Control Principles

A control system designed for the Example 18 system using the approximate linear transfer function of Equation 155 will function acceptably as long as the level, h is maintained at, or close to the steady state value h_s. Under these conditions, $(h - h_s)$ will be small enough to make the linear approximation adequate. However, if the level is required to change over a wide range, the further away from h_s the level gets, the poorer the linear approximation.

The main problem with this scheme therefore is that it ignores the fact that the characteristics of the approximate model must change as the process moves away from h_s, if the approximate model is to remain reasonably accurate. The immediate implication is that the controller designed on the basis of this changing approximate model must also have its parameters appropriately adjusted if it is to remain effective.

The adaptive control scheme is one in which the parameters of the controller are adjusted (in an automatic fashion) to keep up with the changes in the process system characteristics. It is intuitively obvious that this scheme will be a significant improvement over the classical scheme.

There are various types of adaptive control schemes, differing mainly in the way the controller parameters are adjusted. The programmed (or scheduled) adaptive control scheme is one in which, as a result of *a-priori* knowledge and easy quantification of what is responsible for the changes in the process characteristics, the commensurate changes required in the controller parameters are programmed (or scheduled) ahead of time. As changes are observed in the process characteristics, such information is sent to the controller, and its parameters adjusted according to the preprogrammed adjustment mechanism. Let us illustrate with an example.

Example 19. Programmed adaptive control of a catalytic reactor: A qualitative discussion. Let us consider the situation in which the effect of catalyst decay on the dynamic behavior of a catalytic reactor control system is to change the effective steady state gain of the process according to the equation:

$$K = K_0 - \alpha_1 t - \alpha_2 t^2 \tag{156}$$

where t is the age of the catalyst, in days.

If all the other elements of the control loop, g_v, h, have negligible dynamics, (i.e., their transfer functions are equal to 1, for all intents and purposes) then the overall gain in the control loop is KK_c. If we now wish to keep this overall gain at its initial value of K_0K_{c0}, then observe that this would require K_c to change according to

$$K_c = \frac{K_0 K_{co}}{K_0 - \alpha_1 t - \alpha_2 t^2} \tag{157}$$

This equation is therefore the required controller gain adjustment mechanism for this particular process.

It should not be difficult to see that programmed adaptive control can only be applied on very few systems; since for the vast majority of processes, the mechanism responsible for the changes in system characteristics are usually not so well known. In the more realistic situations in which the process is not so well known as to permit the use of programmed adaptive control, there are the self-adaptive schemes, in which the measured value of the process output is used to deduce the required controller parameter adaptation.

There are two basic types of self-adaptive schemes; model reference adaptive control (MRAC) and the self-tuning regulator (STR). With MRAC, the process output is compared with the output of a reference model, and the observed error, l_m, is used by an adaptation scheme to adjust the controller parameters in such a way as to ultimately reduce ϵ_m to zero. The details of how to design and implement the MRAC scheme fall outside the intended scope of this section; such information may be found in References [14] and [15].

The STR scheme consists of using the process output to recursively reestimate the parameters of the approximate model chosen to represent the process. These new model parameters are then used to recalculate the corresponding controller parameter values so that the overall control system satisfies some prespecified objectives. The details of this scheme are available in the standard STR reference: Åström and Wittenmark [16]. General information about the vast field of adaptive control may be found in Reference [17].

Variable Transformations

Consider the following modeling equations for a simple isothermal CSTR in which the *second order* reaction A → B occurs:

$$\tau \frac{dC_A}{dt} = -(C_A + k\tau C_A^2) + C_{Af} \tag{158}$$

where τ = reactor residence time
k = the reaction rate constant
C_A = the concentration of A in the reactor
C_{Af} = concentration of A in the feed stream

By virtue of the presence of the squared term C_A^2, Equation 158 is nonlinear.

Let us now introduce the following variable transformation:

$$z = \frac{C_A}{(1 + k\tau C_A)} \tag{159}$$

From elementary calculus, we know that

$$\frac{dz}{dt} = \frac{dz}{dC_A} \cdot \frac{dC_A}{dt} \tag{160}$$

so that Equation 160 becomes, upon introducing Equations 159 and 160, and rearranging:

$$\frac{dz}{dt} = -\frac{1}{\tau} \frac{C_A}{(1 + k\tau C_A)} + \frac{1}{\tau} \frac{C_{Af}}{(1 + k\tau C_A)} \tag{161}$$

and now, if we define another new variable, v, as

$$v = \frac{C_{Af}}{(1 + k\tau C_A)} \tag{162}$$

then Equation 161 becomes

$$\frac{dz}{dt} = -\frac{1}{\tau} z + \frac{1}{\tau} v \tag{163}$$

which is linear in the variables z and v.

The implication here is that even though the reactor control system is nonlinear in its original variables C_A and C_{Af}, it is in fact linear in the transformed variables z and v given respectively in Equations 159 and 162.

According to a control scheme discussed in Reference [4], linear controller design techniques can now be carried out for the transformed system in Equation 163. The transformed output, z is derived from the actual process output C_A using Equation 159; the controller designed for this transformed system accepts z and produces a value for v, the transformed system input. Using Equation 162, we may now deduce the actual input C_{Af} to be implemented on the *real* system as:

$$C_{Af} = (1 + k\tau C_A)v \tag{164}$$

This technique of controller design for nonlinear systems via variable transformations is based on the hypothesis that a system that is nonlinear in its original variables is linear in some transformation of these original variables. Constructive methods for finding the appropriate transformations and practical guidelines to facilitate design may be found in Reference [4]. Other techniques of variable transformation are available [18–21].

In this section, we have considered the situation where the process system's nonlinearities are to be explicitly recognized and we have outlined the various techniques that may be used to design effective control systems.

The classical approach of local linearization followed by linear controller design, adequate for mildly nonlinear systems, is ineffective when the nonlinearities are severe; the adaptive control schemes, or the variable transformation technique are recommended in this case.

Special purpose design techniques, which we did not discuss, have been reported for some specific nonlinear systems and the given references should be consulted by the interested reader.

CONTROLLER DESIGN BY DIRECT SYNTHESIS

So far, the feedback controller design issue has been approached from the classical viewpoint; i.e. first decide on the controller type (P, PI, PD, or PID) then, following prescribed design guidelines, choose the controller parameters.

There is an alternative approach: by which, given the transfer functions of all the other components of the feedback control loop, the controller required to produce a pre-specified closed loop behavior is directly synthesized. Designing controllers by this direct synthesis method is the objective in this section.

Fundamental Principles of Direct Synthesis

Consider the block diagram of Figure 37 in which all the other transfer functions in the loop apart from that of the controller have been consolidated into one, g(s) (i.e., g(s) is the composite transfer function for the process + measurement device + final control element). In this case, the

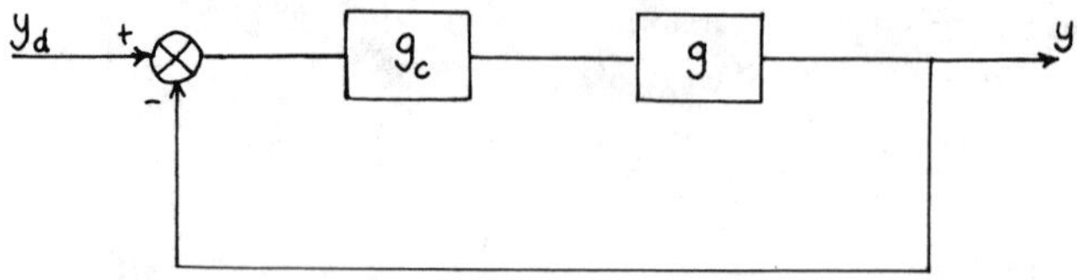

Figure 37. Simplified block diagram of feedback control system.

closed loop transfer function is given by:

$$y(s) = \frac{gg_c}{1 + gg_c} y_d(s) \tag{165}$$

Suppose now that we require the closed loop behavior to be:

$$y(s) = q(s)y_d(s) \tag{166}$$

where q(s) is a specific, predetermined transfer function of our choice. The controller synthesis problem is now posed as follows: What g_c is required to produce the pre-specified closed loop behavior represented by the transfer function q(s)? In other words, given g and q, find the g_c required if the system's closed loop transfer function is to exactly equal q.

Noting that the system's closed loop behavior of Equation 165 will be as we desire it to be in Equation 166 if, and only if,

$$q = \frac{gg_c}{1 + gg_c} \tag{167}$$

the controller synthesis problem then reduces to solving Equation 167 for g_c; giving the result:

$$g_c = \frac{1}{g} \frac{q}{1 - q} \tag{168}$$

the controller synthesis formula, from which, given g, we may derive the controller g_c required for obtaining any desired closed loop behavior, q.

Observe that there are no restrictions on the form this controller can take; for this reason, we may also expect that there will be no guarantees that the controller will be implementable in all cases. However, we shall see that in some of the most important cases, the synthesized controller takes on familiar, easily implementable forms.

Specifying the Desired Closed Loop Behavior

The type of controller synthesized using Equation 168 clearly depends on the nature of q, representing the desired closed loop response. Acceptable closed loop responses in general are expected to have the following features:

1. No steady state offset.
2. Quick, stable response having little or no overshoot.
3. Mathematical quantification of the overall response should be as easy (uncomplicated) as possible.

Although there are various forms of q(s) that possess these characteristics, perhaps the simplest form is the following:

$$q(s) = \frac{1}{\theta s + 1} \tag{169}$$

implying that the desired closed loop response is that of a first order system with time constant θ, and unity steady state gain.

Observe the following about this choice of q:

1. Closed loop stability is not an issue.
2. Because the steady state gain is 1, $y = y_d$ at steady state, hence there will be no offsets.
3. θ determines the speed of response, and this parameter is at the disposal of the control engineer to choose.
4. No overshoot.
5. It is simple and easy to specify (the only adjustable parameter is θ).

For this choice of q, it is a trivial exercise to show that the controller synthesis formula (Equation 168) simplifies to:

$$g_c = \frac{1}{\theta s}\frac{1}{g} \tag{170}$$

We may now investigate the various types of controllers prescribed by Equation 170 for various types of process systems.

Synthesis for Low Order Systems

Pure Gain Processes

For these process systems, the transfer function representation is

$$y(s) = Ku(s) \tag{171}$$

In this case, Equation 170 gives rise to

$$g_c = \frac{1}{K\theta s} \tag{172}$$

a purely integral controller with integral time constant $\tau_I = K\theta$.

Pure Capacity Processes

The transfer function representation here is:

$$g(s) = \frac{K}{s} \tag{173}$$

so that the required synthesized controller, from Equation 170 is:

$$g_c = \frac{1}{K\theta} \tag{174}$$

a purely proportional controller with proportional gain $K_c = K\theta$.

This confirms the fact that under proportional feedback control, pure capacity systems exhibit no steady state offset.

First Order Processes

In this case, with a process transfer function

$$g(s) = \frac{K}{\tau s + 1} \tag{175}$$

Equation 170 gives, as the required controller,

$$g_c = \frac{\tau s + 1}{K\theta s}$$

This may be rearranged to take the more familiar form

$$g_c = \frac{\tau}{K\theta}\left(1 + \frac{1}{\tau s}\right) \tag{176}$$

which is immediately recognizable as a PI controller with $K_c = \tau/K\theta$ and $\tau_I = \tau$.

Second Order Processes

Here, we have:

$$g(s) = \frac{K}{\tau^2 s^2 + 2\zeta\tau s + 1} \tag{177}$$

and Equation 170 gives the required controller as:

$$g_c = \frac{\tau^2 s^2 + 2\zeta\tau s + 1}{K\theta s} \tag{178}$$

which upon rearrangement into a more familiar form, gives:

$$g_c = \frac{2\zeta\tau}{K\theta}\left(1 + \frac{1}{2\zeta\tau s} + \frac{\tau}{2\zeta} s\right) \tag{179}$$

a PID controller with the indicated parameters.

The most significant implications of the foregoing are twofold:

1. Once the desired speed of the closed loop response is specified (i.e., a value is chosen for θ), for any of the simple low-order processes considered, both the controller type and the controller parameters required to achieve the specified closed loop objectives are immediately given in the derived expressions, in terms of the transfer function model parameters, and θ.
2. For simple low-order processes, we observe that the direct synthesis approach prescribes nothing outside of the familiar collection of classical feedback controllers.

It should be clear that for higher order transfer functions, for the same q as in Equation 169, the synthesized controllers are bound to take on more esoteric forms. We will not pursue this aspect further since it is not of practical interest. What is of practical interest is that the dynamics of most higher order process systems are usually approximated by a first-order-plus-time-delay transfer function. We shall therefore consider this class of transfer functions next.

Synthesis for Time Delay Systems

In order to focus attention on the essentials we shall consider that the system in question is represented by the transfer function

$$g(s) = \frac{Ke^{-\alpha s}}{\tau s + 1} \tag{180}$$

even though the discussion to follow may be straightforwardly generalized to other forms of time delay systems.

In this case retaining the same q we have made use of so far (see Equation 169) means having to derive the required controller from Equation 170. The result is:

$$g_c = \frac{(\tau s + 1)e^{+\alpha s}}{K\theta s} \tag{181}$$

which we notice immediately to be unrealizable, since it requires a prediction. (This is the implication of the positive exponential term).

However, it should not surprise us that the controller we have just derived is unrealizable. The demand to have a time delay system respond, in the closed loop, instantaneously as a regular first order system, is entirely unrealistic. We therefore find that this choice of q fails to consider that inevitable, peculiar dynamic behavior characteristic of time delay systems, i.e., their inherent inability to respond instantaneously.

A more realistic choice for q is:

$$q = \frac{e^{-\alpha s}}{\theta s + 1} \tag{182}$$

in which due recognition is now given to the inevitability of an initial delay period in which no response can be expected, i.e., we still require the same first order response only delayed by the appropriate amount of time.

We must now rederive the controller synthesis formula, using Equation 182 for q in Equation 168: the result is

$$g_c = \frac{\tau s + 1}{K} \cdot \frac{1}{\theta s + 1 - e^{-\alpha s}} \tag{183}$$

a controller that is now realizable in principle, even though not in the form of the familiar classical controllers.

We shall shortly show that Equation 183, realized exactly as is, is identical to a Smith Predictor plus a PI controller. For now, we show that using various approximations for the exponential term in Equation 183 simplifies the controller to the classical PI and PID forms.

Using a first order Taylor series approximation for $e^{-\alpha s}$, i.e.

$$e^{-\alpha s} \cong 1 - \alpha s \tag{184}$$

Equation 184 becomes

$$g_c = \frac{\tau s + 1}{K(\theta + \alpha)s} \tag{185}$$

which rearranges to yield

$$g_c = \frac{\tau}{K(\theta + \alpha)}\left(1 + \frac{1}{\tau s}\right) \tag{186}$$

a PI controller with the indicated parameters.

It is interesting to note that in the limit as $\theta \to 0$ (i.e., infinitely fast closed loop response), whereas for the equivalent system without delay (see Equation 176) this requires $K_c \to \infty$, observe from Equation 186 that for the time delay system there is a limiting K_c value; $\tau/K\alpha$. Furthermore, this limiting value gets smaller as the time delay gets larger; all of which is in perfect keeping with experience.

It can be shown [5] that a PID controller results when a 1st order Padé approximation is used for $e^{-\alpha s}$; i.e.

$$e^{-\alpha s} \cong \frac{1 - \alpha s/2}{1 + \alpha s/2}$$

Let us now take on the issue of implementing Equation 184. Control action is to be determined in this case using:

$$u(s) = \frac{\tau s + 1}{K} \cdot \frac{1}{\theta s + 1 - e^{-\alpha s}}\,\epsilon(s) \tag{187}$$

which may be rearranged to give

$$K(\theta s + 1 - e^{-\alpha s})u(s) = (\tau s + 1)\epsilon(s) \tag{188}$$

or
$$\frac{K\theta s}{\tau s + 1}\,u(s) + \frac{K}{\tau s + 1}\,u(s) = \frac{Ke^{-\alpha s}}{\tau s + 1}\,u(s) + \epsilon(s) \tag{189}$$

Now, let us recall from an earlier discussion that for $y(s) = [(Ke^{-\alpha s})/(\tau s + 1)]u(s)$, we defined $y^*(s) = [K/(\tau s + 1)]u(s)$, the output of the fictitious, equivalent system with no delay. This being the case, Equation 189 then becomes:

$$\frac{K\theta s}{\tau s + 1}\,u(s) = y^*(s) - y(s) + \epsilon(s)$$

so that u(s) is now given by:

$$u(s) = \frac{\tau s + 1}{K\theta s}\,\{y^*(s) - y(s) + \epsilon(s)\}$$

or, finally:

$$u(s) = \frac{\tau}{K\theta}\left(1 + \frac{1}{\tau s}\right)\{y^*(s) - y(s) + \epsilon(s)\} \tag{190}$$

Upon examining Equation 190 closely we observe immediately that this is a PI controller operating on a signal composed of $\epsilon(s)$, the feedback error signal, augmented by the signal $y^* - y$, the signal from the minor loop of the Smith Predictor strategy (Figure 32); confirming our earlier assertion.

Synthesis for Inverse Responding Systems

The fact that the general controller synthesis formula in Equation 168 requires the inverse of the process model (regardless of our choice of q) should make us cautious in applying it. Processes with unusual dynamics have unusual transfer function models whose inverses often tend to be even more problematic.

The "realization" problem we initially encountered with the time delay system stemmed from taking the inverse of the $e^{-\alpha s}$ term, leading to the predictive $e^{+\alpha s}$ term. Introducing a "more realistic" q amounted, mathematically speaking, to a means of "neutralizing" the unrealizable term.

Now, the transfer function of an inverse responding system has at least one zero in the right half plane (RHP). Upon taking the inverse of this transfer function, the RHP zero becomes a RHP pole; with the immediate implication that the synthesized controller, which must contain this inverse (along with the other terms involving q), will be *unstable*.

Thus the issue with inverse responding systems is that if q is chosen as in Equation 169, the controller synthesized therefrom (Equation 170) will simply be unstable; not unrealizable as with the time delay system. Again, the problem has arisen from demanding an unrealistic closed loop response from a system with peculiar dynamic characteristics; an inverse responding system is by nature incapable of responding as indicated by Equation 169. The solution therefore lies in modifying q to take a more realistic form; again, as with the time delay system.

Once more, to focus attention on essentials, we shall consider the IR systems in question to be of the form:

$$g(s) = \frac{K(1 - \eta s)}{(\tau_1 s + 1)(\tau_2 s + 1)} \tag{191}$$

Choosing the following transfer function form for q:

$$q(s) = \frac{(1 - \eta s)}{(1 + \eta s)} \cdot \frac{1}{\theta s + 1} \tag{192}$$

a variation on the "standard" form in Equation 169 in which we have now accorded due recognition to the inevitability of inverse response (note the preservation of the RHP pole), upon rederiving the required controller (using Equation 192 for q in Equation 168), we obtain:

$$g_c = \frac{\tau_1 + \tau_2}{K(2\eta + \theta)} \left\{ 1 + \frac{1}{(\tau_1 + \tau_2)s} + \frac{\tau_1 \tau_2}{(\tau_1 + \tau_2)} s \right\} \left\{ \frac{1}{\phi s + 1} \right\} \tag{193}$$

$$\text{with} \quad \phi = \frac{\eta\theta}{2\eta + \theta} \tag{194}$$

This controller is clearly a PID controller, but with an additional term. It is easy to show that this additional term is the transfer function of a first order filter having a filter time constant ϕ.

The implication therefore is that the direct synthesis method, using the modified, more realistic q of Equation 192, prescribes the use of a PID controller (with the indicated parameters) along with a first-order filter for use in controlling the inverse responding system of Equation 191. Earlier we indicated that PID controllers had been found useful for controlling IR systems. The above results now provide another justification for this fact, for observe that in the event that either η, or θ, or both, are small, then $\phi \to 0$ and the synthesized controller becomes a regular PID controller.

In this section, we have introduced a totally different approach to the issue of controller design. This new approach allows the control engineer to specify the closed loop behavior desired of the process; and from this, the controller required to obtain the prespecified closed loop behavior is directly synthesized.

We have shown that for low order processes, the synthesized controllers take the familiar forms of the classical controllers; while for those processes with unusual dynamics (i.e., time delay and inverse responding systems) they take on more esoteric forms that still reduce to the classical forms upon introducing certain simplifications.

MULTIVARIABLE SYSTEMS

When a process system has only one input variable to be used in controlling one output variable, the controller design problem can be handled, fairly conveniently, by the methods we have discussed so far.

In several important situations, however, the system under consideration has multiple inputs and multiple outputs; making it multivariable in nature. Many non-trivial issues, not encountered hitherto in our discussions for single-input-single-output systems, are raised when effective controllers are to be designed for these multivariable systems.

This section will provide an introduction to the nature of multivariable systems, the unique control problems they present, and how these problems are typically handled.

The Nature of Multivariable Process Systems

A multivariable (MV) system is one with multiple inputs, $u_1, u_2, \ldots, u_m$, and multiple outputs, $y_1, y_2, \ldots, y_n$; where m is not necessarily equal to n. It could be a single process system, or an aggregate of many process units in an entire plant [2].

Up until now, because we have had to deal only with SISO systems, the question of what input to use in controlling what output did not arise at all, since there was just one of each. But now, with m inputs and n outputs, we are faced with a new problem: which input variable should be used to control which output variable? This is the input-output pairing problem.

Now, each u_i to y_j "pairing" gives a control configuration; and for a two-input, two-output system (referred to as a 2 × 2 system) we have two such configurations,

$$\begin{array}{lcl} u_1 - y_1 & \text{and} & u_1 - y_2 \\ u_2 - y_2 & & u_2 - y_1 \end{array}$$

For a 3 × 3 system, it can be shown that there are 6 such configurations; and in general, for an N × N system, there are, in fact, N! possible input-output pairing configurations.

We know, of course, that our controllers have to be set up according to only one of these configurations. Furthermore, one would intuitively expect one of the configurations to yield "better overall control system performance" than the others. How then to choose among these possibilities?

We thus see that the first problem of just deciding on what input to pair with what output is not at all trivial.

Another important consideration is the following: even after somehow arriving at the conclusion that u_i is best used to control y_j, we are faced with the very pertinent question: Can u_i control y_j in isolation, i.e., in addition to affecting y_j, its assigned output, will u_i also affect other outputs? Unfortunately, the answer, in virtually all cases, is YES; and this, the interaction problem, is recognized as the other main problem with the control of multivariable systems.

Clearly, MV systems pose more complicated control problems than do SISO systems.

Multivariable System Models

Owing to the multivariable nature of the equations that are typically used to represent the dynamic behavior of MV systems, these models are more conveniently written in vector-matrix form.

MV system models occur most commonly either in the state space form, or in the transfer function form.

State space model. The linear multivariable system is represented in the state space as:

$$\left.\begin{aligned}\dot{\mathbf{x}} &= \mathbf{A}\mathbf{x} + \mathbf{B}\mathbf{u} + \mathbf{\Gamma}\mathbf{d}\\ \mathbf{y} &= \mathbf{C}\mathbf{x}\end{aligned}\right\} \tag{195}$$

where $\mathbf{x} \equiv$ n-dimensional vector of state variables
$\mathbf{u} \equiv$ m-dimensional vector of input (control) variables
$\mathbf{y} \equiv \ell$-dimensional vector of output variables
$\mathbf{d} \equiv$ k-dimensional vector of disturbance variables

and **A**, **B**, **C**, and **Γ** are matrices of *conformable order* with the respective multiplying vectors.

Transfer function models. Analogous to the SISO transfer function model, for a MV system we have:

$$\mathbf{y}(s) = \mathbf{G}(s)\mathbf{u}(s) + \mathbf{G}_d(s)\mathbf{d}(s) \tag{196}$$

where, for an m-input, ℓ-output system, **G** is an $\ell \times m$ transfer function matrix with elements

$$\mathbf{G}(s) = \begin{bmatrix} g_{11}(s) & g_{12}(s) & \cdots & g_{1m}(s) \\ g_{21}(s) & g_{22}(s) & \cdots & g_{2m}(s) \\ \vdots & & & \\ g_{\ell 1}(s) & g_{\ell 2}(s) & \cdots & g_{\ell m}(s) \end{bmatrix} \tag{197}$$

$\mathbf{G}_d$ is an $\ell \times k$ transfer function matrix consisting of similar transfer function elements.

Now, it is possible to convert Equation 195 to a transfer function representation. By taking Laplace transforms and rearranging appropriately, we obtain:

$$\mathbf{y}(s) = [\mathbf{C}(s\mathbf{I} - \mathbf{A})^{-1}\mathbf{B}]u(s) + [\mathbf{C}(s\mathbf{I} - \mathbf{A})^{-1}\mathbf{\Gamma}]\mathbf{d}(s) \tag{198}$$

and by comparison with Equation 196 the relationship between the transfer functions **G**, $\mathbf{G}_d$ and the state space matrices are obvious.

The reverse problem of deducing the equivalent state space model from the transfer function model, (typically known as the realization problem) is not by any means trivial and it lies outside the intended scope of this section. The interested reader is referred to Reference [7] for the important details.

Multivariable Block Diagrams

In the same vein as with SISO systems, MV systems may be represented with block diagrams. Figure 38A shows an example block diagram for an m-input, ℓ-output (k-disturbance) system: where the multiple lines are used to indicate the multiplicity of the variables involved.

Such a block diagram is often "simplified" to the type shown in Figure 38B, where it is enough that the blocks contain transfer function matrices, and that the signals are designated as vectors, to set it apart from the SISO counterpart to which it bears potentially confusing similarities. Such a block diagram is quite useful for overall closed loop analysis.

Alternatively, the block diagrams can be "expanded" to emphasize the individual effects of *each* element of **G**(s) on each output. For example a 2 × 2 system may be represented as in Figure 38C, which shows, very clearly, the interactive effects of u_1 on y_2, and of u_2 on y_1. This block diagram type is useful for interaction analysis and decoupler design, as we shall see later.

Closed loop behavior. From the more compact block diagram (Figure 38B), it is easy to show that the closed loop relationship between **y**, $\mathbf{y}_d$, and **d** is:

$$\mathbf{y}(s) = (\mathbf{I} + \mathbf{G}\mathbf{G}_c)^{-1}\mathbf{G}\mathbf{G}_c\mathbf{y}_d(s) + (\mathbf{I} + \mathbf{G}\mathbf{G}_c)^{-1}\mathbf{G}_d\mathbf{d}(s) \tag{199}$$

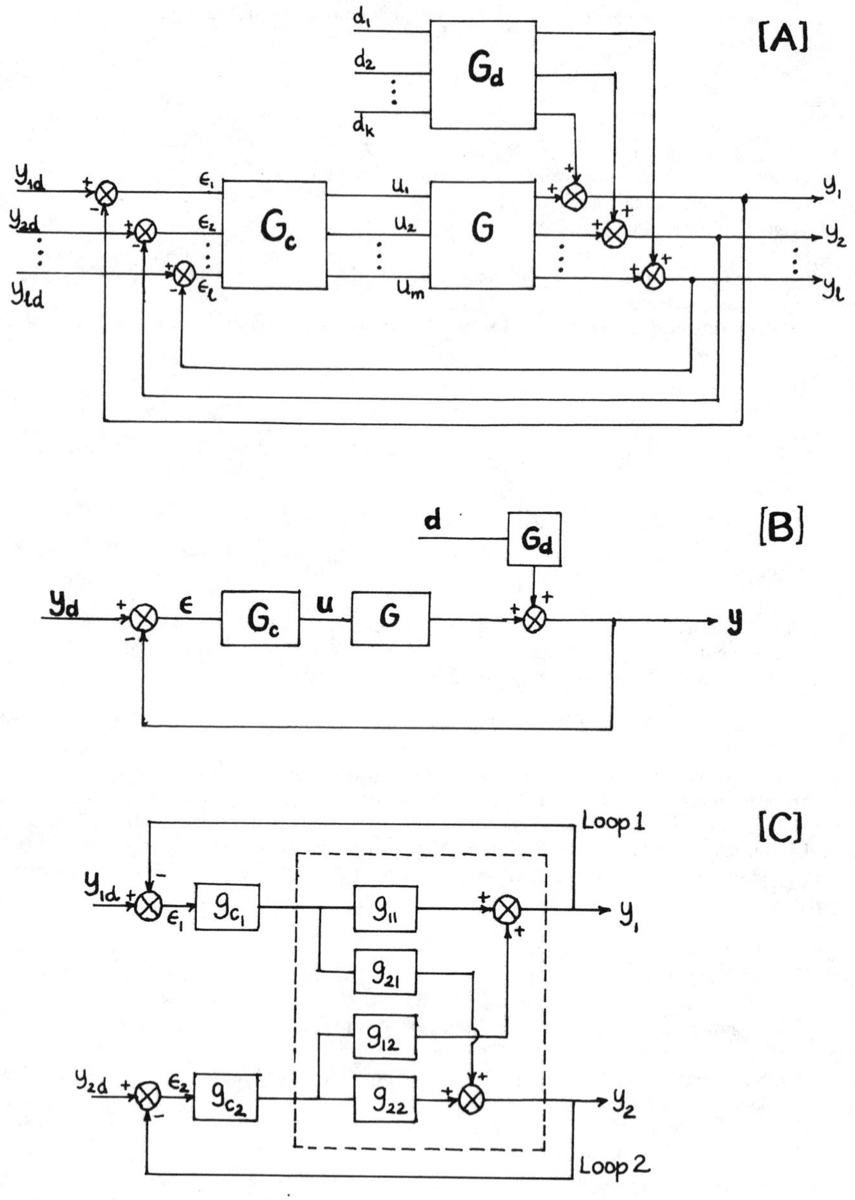

Figure 38. Three types of multivariable block diagrams.

and, just as in the SISO case, when, for closed loop stability we inspected the roots of the characteristic equation;

$$1 + gg_ch = 0 \tag{200}$$

we state, without formal proof, that for the stability analysis of the MV closed loop system, the characteristic equation is:

$$|\mathbf{I} + \mathbf{G}\mathbf{G}_c\mathbf{H}| = 0 \tag{201}$$

(when a measuring device transfer function matrix **H** is involved). Here, | | denotes the determinant of the included matrix.

The conditions required for closed loop stability are, once again, that all the roots of this characteristic equation lie in the left half of the complex plane.

Interaction Analysis

Consider, as an example, the transfer function model for a 2 × 2 system, which in its expanded form is given by the following equations:

$$\left.\begin{aligned} y_1 &= g_{11}u_1 + g_{12}u_2 \\ y_2 &= g_{21}u_1 + g_{22}u_2 \end{aligned}\right\} \tag{202}$$

from where we are able to see how each input variable is capable of influencing each output variable. Here, we have a situation in which if u_1 were assigned to y_1, and u_2 to y_2, each of these control loops will experience interactions from the other loop; loop 1 (the $u_1 - y_1$ loop) will experience interaction from loop 2 (the $u_2 - y_2$ loop) via the g_{12} element since it is by this that y_1 is influenced by y_2. Loop 2 experiences its interaction from loop 1 via the g_{21} element. If the pairing were switched, the interactions will now come about via the g_{11} and g_{22} elements.

It seems reasonable that, as long as we intend to use two single loop controllers, we should pair the input and output variables such that the resulting interaction is "minimum." This immediately demands a means for quantifying interactions.

One of the most widely used measures of interaction is the *Relative Gain Array* (RGA), (also called the *Bristol Array*) first discussed by Bristol [22]. The elements of this array provide guidelines for selecting which manipulated variable to pair with which controlled variable in order to achieve minimum interaction at steady state.

The RGA. This array consists of elements λ_{ij}, defined as follows:

$\lambda_{ij} \equiv$ the relative gain between output y_i and input u_j,

and it is the dimensionless ratio of two static (steady state) gains.

$$\lambda_{ij} = \frac{(\partial y_i/\partial u_j)_{\text{all loops open}}}{(\partial y_i/\partial u_j)_{\text{all loops closed except for the } u_j \text{ loop}}} \tag{203}$$

A detailed discussion about the genesis of this quantity, and how it is a useful measure of interaction can be found in Reference [22], or in McAvoy [23]. We merely note the following properties of λ_{ij}:

1. $\sum_j \lambda_{ij} = \sum_i \lambda_{ij} = 1$

   In other words, the elements of the Bristol Array across any row or down any column, sum up to 1.

2. λ_{ij} is dimensionless, therefore neither the units, nor the absolute values actually taken by the variables u_j, y_i affect it.
3. The value of λ_{ij} is a measure of the steady state interaction to expect the system to experience if u_j is paired with y_i. In particular, $\lambda_{ij} = 1$ implies that u_j affects y_i without interacting with, or eliciting interaction from, other control loops. By the same token, $\lambda_{ij} = 0$ implies u_j has absolutely no effect on y_i.

It is in light of this last statement that the following considerations are needed in using the Bristol Array for effective loop pairing:

1. In the ideal situation, the array takes the form:

$$\Lambda = \begin{bmatrix} 1 & & & 0 \\ & 1 & & \\ & & \ddots & \\ 0 & & & 1 \end{bmatrix} \tag{204}$$

   or, that each row and each column contains one, and only one, non-zero element whose value is unity. This indicates a situation of absolute non-interacting control.
2. When $\lambda_{ij} > 0$ and close to 1, the indicated i, j pairing is desirable;
3. When $\lambda_{ij} < 0$, the i, j pairing will either result in instability, or produce inverse response: it should be avoided.

Before taking a specific example to illustrate the use of this array, let us consider the issue of how the array is actually obtained in practice.

Calculating the RGA. With the exception of the most trivial cases, calculating the elements λ_{ij} using the definition in Equation 203 is often quite tedious. It is customary to use the following matrix method, which is applicable for all situations in which a transfer function matrix model exists for the MV system in question.

Let $\mathbf{K} = \mathbf{G}(0)$, i.e., $\mathbf{G}(s)$ evaluated at $s = 0$. This is the matrix of steady state gains for the process in question. Let its elements be k_{ij}.

Let

$$\mathbf{R} = (\mathbf{K}^{-1})^T \tag{205}$$

i.e., the transpose of the inverse of the matrix of steady state gains. Let the elements of $\mathbf{R}$ be r_{ij}. Then, λ_{ij} is given by:

$$\lambda_{ij} = k_{ij}r_{ij} \tag{206}$$

We shall now take an illustrative example.

Example 20. Loop pairing for a binary distillation column using the RGA. The transfer function matrix representation for a methanol/water distillation unit reported in several references [7, 24, 25] takes the form shown in Equation 196 with y_1 as the overhead mole fraction of methanol, y_2 as the bottoms mole fraction of methanol; u_1 is the overhead reflux flow rate, u_2 is the bottoms steam flow rate, and d is the column feed flow rate. The transfer function matrices $\mathbf{G}$ and $\mathbf{G}_d$ are thus, respectively, 2×2 and 2×1 in dimension.

To decide on the "best" $y_i - u_j$ pairing requires only the $\mathbf{G}(s)$ matrix, which is now reproduced below:

$$\mathbf{G}(s) = \begin{bmatrix} \dfrac{12.8e^{-s}}{16.7s + 1} & \dfrac{-18.9e^{-3s}}{21s + 1} \\ \dfrac{6.6e^{-7s}}{10.9s + 1} & \dfrac{-19.4e^{-3s}}{14.4s + 1} \end{bmatrix} \tag{207}$$

In this case, **G**(0) is obtained as:

$$\mathbf{G}(0) = \mathbf{K} = \begin{bmatrix} 12.8 & -18.9 \\ 6.6 & -19.4 \end{bmatrix} \tag{208}$$

so that its inverse is given by:

$$\mathbf{K}^{-1} = \begin{bmatrix} .157 & -.153 \\ .053 & -.1036 \end{bmatrix} \tag{209}$$

from where, upon taking the transpose of this matrix, we obtain:

$$\mathbf{R} = \begin{bmatrix} .157 & .053 \\ -.153 & -.1036 \end{bmatrix} \tag{210}$$

A term-by-term multiplication of k_{ij} and r_{ij} yields:

$$\Lambda = \begin{bmatrix} 2.0 & -1.0 \\ -1.0 & 2.0 \end{bmatrix} \tag{211}$$

The interpretation of this RGA is that a $(u_1 - y_1)/(u_2 - y_2)$ configuration is recommended over the other alternative. Thus, the reflux flow rate (u_1) is to be used to control the overhead mole fraction of methanol (y_1) while the bottoms mole fraction of methanol (y_2) is to be regulated by the bottom steam flow rate (u_2). Let us note that this recommended configuration makes physical sense.

Other examples may be found in References [2] and [23], while discussions on how to obtain and interprete RGA's for nonsquare systems are contained in Reference [26]. Let us now make the following final comments about Bristol's RGA: (a) It requires only steady state information, making it easy to use; (b) however, it ignores dynamic factors that can often be the most influential, [23].

Multiple Single Loop Designs

To control the N variables of an N × N multivariable system using N individual controllers requires, first of all, a judicious assignment of inputs to outputs. Bristol's RGA, has been presented above as the most widely used tool for making this assignment.

However, after this input/output assignment, the task of actually designing each of these N individual controllers still remains; a task that must be carried out in full recognition of the fact that the RGA-suggested pairing is merely that which gives the minimum possible interaction out of all the available alternatives: the interactions are still very present; they have not been eliminated.

As is noted by most practicing control engineers, the task of single loop designs for multivariable systems follows a more-or-less trial and error procedure of tuning each loop independently, with others under manual control, and readjusting the tuning when all the controllers are later on restored to jointly operate under automatic control [27].

Decoupling

It should be reiterated that even though the RGA provides an input/output pairing scheme with the minimum interaction, there are situations where this "minimum" is still substantial. Under such circumstances, the strong interactions between the loops make good control system performance virtually impossible.

It is possible to improve the control system performance by applying the principles of decoupling. The main objective is to introduce additional "blocks" in between the single loop controllers and the process for the sole purpose of compensating for interactions, as depicted in Figure 39.

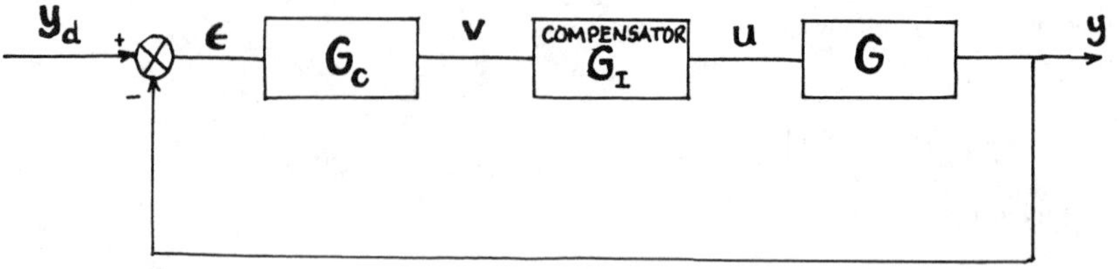

Figure 39. Multivariable controller incorporating interaction compensator.

In the ideal situation, the decoupler causes the control loops to act as if totally independent of each other; reducing the controller tuning task to that of tuning several, noninteracting controllers; thus making it possible to use the SISO controller design techniques. The decoupler design problem is that of choosing the elements of the matrix $\mathbf{G}_1$ shown in Figure 39 to satisfy usually one of the following objectives:

1. Eliminate interactions from *all loops* for all time (known as Dynamic Decoupling).
2. Eliminate only steady state interactions (Steady State or Static Decoupling); this allows dynamic interactions, and is usually easier to design for, since it is less ambitious than dynamic decoupling.
3. Eliminate interactions (dynamically, or only at steady state) in only a subset of the loops (Partial Decoupling; this focuses attention on the critical loops only; leaving those with weak interactions to act without the aid of decoupling).

Decoupler Design

There are several ways by which decouplers can be designed; the principles are, however, all basically the same. We shall illustrate, first, the principles of simplified decoupling, so-called, using a 2 × 2 example and the block diagram shown in Figure 40.

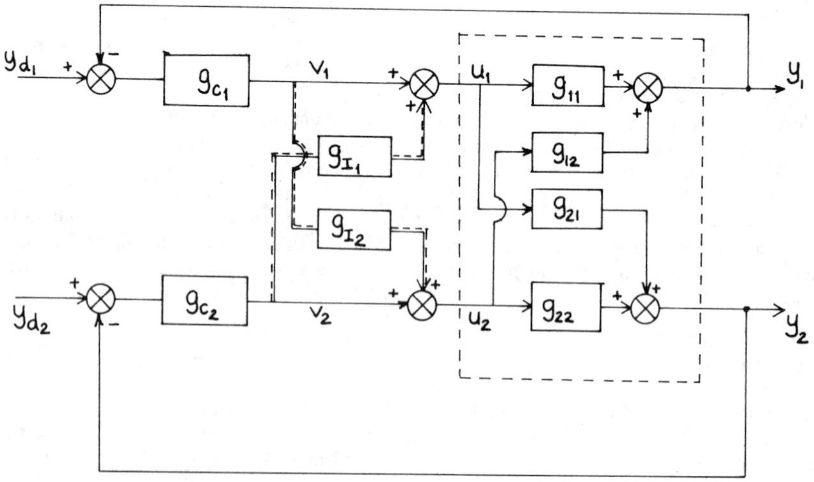

Figure 40. Multivariable 2 × 2 system incorporating simplified decoupling.

Let us now observe the following important aspects of this diagram:

1. We have adopted a new notation: the controller outputs are now designated as v_1 and v_2, while the control action implemented on the process remain as u_1 and u_2. This distinction becomes necessary because the output of the controllers and the control action implemented on the process no longer have to be the same.
2. Without the compensator, for a 1-1/2-2 pairing i.e., $(u_1 - y_1)/(u_2 - y_2)$ we have that $u_1 = v_1$ and $u_2 = v_2$; so that:

$$\left.\begin{aligned} y_1 &= g_{11}u_1 + g_{12}u_2 \\ y_2 &= g_{21}u_1 + g_{22}u_2 \end{aligned}\right\} \tag{212}$$

   and the interactions persist; since u_2 affects y_1 through the g_{21} element and u_1 affects y_2 through g_{12}.

Now, with the compensator, through g_{I_2}, loop 2 is "informed" of changes in v_1 so that u_2—what the system actually feels—is adjusted accordingly. Similarly, g_{I_1} does the same for loop 1, adjusting u_1 with v_2 information. What should g_{I_1} and g_{I_2} be if the effects of the loop interactions are to be neutralized?

Let us consider loop 1, under this new arrangement incorporating the interaction com ensators: here,

$$y_1 = g_{11}u_1 + g_{12}u_2 \tag{213}$$

but now, and

$$\left.\begin{aligned} u_1 &= v_1 + g_{I_1}v_2 \\ u_2 &= v_2 + g_{I_2}v_1 \end{aligned}\right\} \tag{214}$$

so that Equation 213 becomes:

$$y_1 = (g_{11} + g_{12}g_{I_2})v_1 + (g_{11}g_{I_1} + g_{12})v_2 \tag{215}$$

It is now enough, in order to eliminate the effect of v_2 on y_1, for us to choose g_{I_1} such that the term $g_{11}g_{I_1} + g_{12}$ vanishes; this clearly requires:

$$g_{I_1} = -\frac{g_{12}}{g_{11}} \tag{216}$$

A similar procedure carried out for loop 2 leads to the fact that to make y_2 entirely free of v_1 requires:

$$g_{I_2} = -\frac{g_{21}}{g_{22}} \tag{217}$$

These are the decouplers needed to compensate for the effect of loop interactions in the example 2 × 2 system of Figure 40.

It is now easy to ascertain that the overall system equations, upon introducing Equations 216 and 217 become:

$$y_1 = \left(g_{11} - \frac{g_{12}g_{21}}{g_{22}}\right)v_1 \tag{218}$$

and

$$y_2 = \left(g_{22} - \frac{g_{12}g_{21}}{g_{11}}\right)v_2 \tag{219}$$

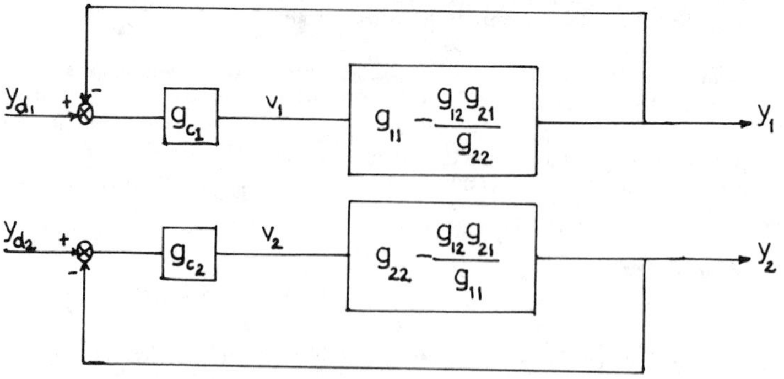

Figure 41. Equivalent block diagram for system in Figure 40 with compensator implemented as in Equations 216 and 217.

and v_1 now affects only y_1; with v_2 affecting only y_2. The equivalent block diagram is now shown in Figure 41 where the two loops now appear to act independently.

The matrix method of decoupler design is outlined below:

1. Referring back to Figure 39, we observe that without the compensator,

$$\mathbf{y} = \mathbf{G}\mathbf{u} \qquad (\mathbf{u} = \mathbf{v}) \tag{220}$$

and because **G** is not diagonal, the interactions persist.

2. With compensation, we have

$$\mathbf{y} = \mathbf{G}\mathbf{G}_I\mathbf{v} \tag{221}$$

3. We may now choose $\mathbf{G}_I$ such that:

$$\mathbf{G}\mathbf{G}_I = \mathbf{D} \tag{222}$$

where **D** is some diagonal matrix. With this choice, decoupling is attained in Equation 221 by virtue of **D** being diagonal.

4. The condition in Equation 222 requires therefore that $\mathbf{G}_I$ be given by:

$$\mathbf{G}_I = \mathbf{G}^{-1}\mathbf{D} \tag{223}$$

It should be clear that the obtained compensator depends on what is chosen for **D**. A commonly employed choice for **D** is:

$$\mathbf{D} = \mathrm{Diag}\{\mathbf{G}(s)\} \tag{224}$$

i.e., the diagonal elements of **G**(s) are retained as the elements of the diagonal matrix **D**. Other choices of **D** are, of course, permissible.

General Comments About Decoupling

1. Perfect decoupling is only possible if the process models are perfect. This is hardly ever the case.
2. The ideal decouplers derived in Equations 216 and 217 are similar to feedforward controllers; ratios of transfer functions are involved in each case.

3. As a result of step 2, ideal decouplers are subject to the same problems of realization we had earlier enumerated for feedforward controllers; particularly when time delays are involved in the transfer function elements.
4. The decoupler designed by the matrix method suffers from the handicap of requiring the inversion of an $N \times N$ matrix containing transfer function elements. This can be quite tedious for $N > 3$.
5. Because of some of the problems noted, some simplifications are often called for. For example, requiring decoupling only at steady state relieves us of the burden of dealing with full transfer functions; the resulting decouplers are merely constant numbers. The disadvantages are quite obvious, but it is often better to have something less rigorous than the more rigorous dynamic versions that are nonimplementable, and hence useless.

This section has been concerned with introducing the important topic of multivariable dynamics and control. We have identified the fact that loop pairing, and interactions among control loops are the main issues in multivariable systems. Bristol's relative gain array was introduced as the most widely used tool for quantifying loop interactions, and consequently, for input/output pairing. When loop interactions remain significant even after correct loop pairing, decoupling has been presented as a useful alternative.

INTRODUCTION TO SAMPLED-DATA SYSTEMS AND COMPUTER CONTROL

The drive for improved control has led to the development of several advanced control schemes that cannot be implemented by the standard, analog control hardware. The multivariable decouplers discussed earlier is a typical case in point.

The use of the digital computer to implement advanced control schemes has become so widespread that virtually all new plants are designed to operate under computer control in one form or the other.

The treatment of computer control systems in this section is necessarily sketchy; since considerably more information than space will allow are available on the subject. Thus, only a panoramic view is presented; with pertinent references provided at appropriate places during the discussion.

Computers and Process Control

Reduced to its most fundamental essence, a controller is no more than a device which, given information about the error signal ϵ from a process, computes the control action required to reduce the observed error, using a predetermined control "law." Classical feedback controllers have the specific, "three-mode" control "laws" discussed earlier. Viewed in this light, it becomes clear that the digital controller is perfectly suited to do the job of a controller, and with greater flexibility, for the following reasons:

1. The control "law" no longer has to be restricted to the "three-mode" form that the classical controllers are constrained to take; any control law, no matter how unconventional, or complicated, can be programmed on a computer.
2. The required computations, no matter how complex, are carried out at very high speeds.
3. A tremendous capacity for mass storage of information is available.
4. The cost of digital computers has reduced rather drastically in the last few years.

All these factors make computer applications in the on line implementation of process control schemes almost inevitable.

Idiosyncracies of Computer Control

Computers by nature deal in "digitized" entities: integer numbers. Thus, even though signals from a process may be continuous (e.g., voltage signals from a thermocouple) the computer can

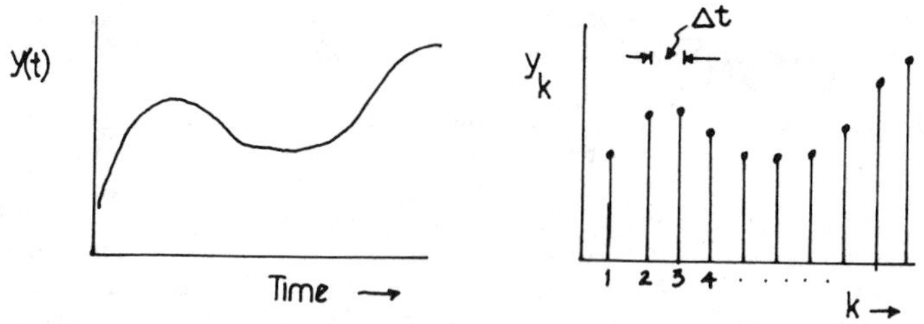

Figure 42. A continuous signal discretized.

only access this information in digital form. This requires the use of an analog-to-digital (A/D) converter. The continuous signal y(t) is therefore sampled, at a predetermined frequency, to give the "sampled" data, y_k, obtained at the kth time interval (Figure 42).

The use of the computer therefore introduces a new perception of the system; a quantized view, in which the system is no longer seen as giving out continuous information; only discrete information, at finite intervals of time.

On the other side of the coin is the fact that the computer also gives out information at discrete points in time. This must now be "made continuous" before implementing on the real process. A digital-to-analog (D/A) converter is used for this purpose; to reconstruct some form of a continuous signal from the discrete information sent from the computer. The key elements of the D/A converters are referred to as *holds*, and they are discussed further [2, 28, 29].

As a result of the effects of using the computer for data acquisition and control action implementation, computer control systems are also known as sampled-data (or discrete-time) systems. Such systems must now be described, mathematically, in a manner that reflects their character of giving out, and receiving, information only at discrete points in time. We shall discuss this shortly.

Further information about the computer components, hardware and software required for data acquisition, computation, data storage and retrieval, control implementation, etc. are available [2, 7, 28].

Tools of Dynamic Analysis of Sampled-Data Systems

Discrete Time Models

Because of the discrete character bestowed on the process system by virtue of its being interfaced with the digital computer, it is more appropriate, and perhaps more convenient, to use a discrete time model for its mathematical representation.

A very general discrete time model takes the form:

$$y_k = a_1 y_{k-1} + a_2 y_{k-2} + \cdots + a_n y_{k-n} + b_1 u_{k-1} + b_2 u_{k-2} + \cdots + b_n u_{k-n} \tag{225}$$

where y_k = sampled value of y(t) obtained at the kth sample time
u_k = control action to be implemented at the kth sample time
a_i, b_i = constants, or dependent on k.

For the specific case of a first order system, the discrete time model is:

$$y_k = a_1 y_{k-1} + b_1 u_{k-1} \tag{226}$$

Such discrete time models are typically obtained in one of two ways:

1. Discretization of a continuous (differential equation) model.
2. Empirically, by fitting a discrete time model to (discrete time) plant data.

A process system is very rarely modelled in the discrete form from first principles. Reference [29] may be consulted for further information about obtaining discrete time models.

Other Tools of Dynamic Analysis

In continuous time dynamic analysis, the Laplace transform is known to be particularly useful; providing, among other things, compact, transfer function representations. In discrete time analysis, the equivalent is the z-transform. The equivalent of the s-domain transfer function is the pulse transfer function. Detailed discussions on z-transforms, pulse transfer functions, and how they are used in studying the dynamic behavior of sampled-data systems, are available in several texts [2, 3, 28, 30], but particularly noteworthy is the treatment in Reference [29].

Design of Digital Controllers

There are two fundamental approaches to the design of controllers for discrete-time systems:

1. Carry out controller design for the continuous time system, and discretize the resulting continuous controller.
2. Use discrete-time design techniques; these give rise directly to discrete controllers.

The first approach considers the system to be fundamentally continuous; that the observed discrete behavior is artificially induced by the computer.

When one takes this approach, we find that all the results we have earlier discussed become applicable; only that the controllers must now be given in discretized form. It is therefore not surprising that many industrial computer control schemes operate on the discrete forms of the classical, analog (continuous) P, PI, or PID controllers.

Recall that the equation for the (continuous time) PID controller was given as:

$$u(t) = K_c\left\{\epsilon(t) + \frac{1}{\tau_I}\int_0^t \epsilon(t)\,dt + \tau_D\frac{d\epsilon}{dt}\right\} \tag{227}$$

This may be approximated in discrete time by using the appropriate approximations for the indicated operations of integration and differentiation. In particular, approximating the "area under the curve" represented by the integral as a sum of k rectangular strips of equal width Δt, and using a finite difference approximation for the derivative, Equation 227 becomes:

$$u_k = K_c\left\{\epsilon_k + \frac{\Delta t}{\tau_I}\sum_{i=1}^{k}\epsilon_i + \frac{\tau_D}{\Delta t}(\epsilon_k - \epsilon_{k-1})\right\} \tag{228}$$

This is known as the position form of the discrete PID controller. From this we can derive what is known as the velocity form, given as:

$$\Delta u_k = u_k - u_{k-1} = K_c\left(1 + \frac{\Delta t}{\tau_I} + \frac{\tau_D}{\Delta t}\right)\epsilon_k - K_c\left(1 + \frac{2\tau_D}{\Delta t}\right)\epsilon_{k-1} + K_c\frac{\tau_D}{\Delta t}\epsilon_{k-2} \tag{229}$$

The velocity form is also sometimes written as:

$$\Delta u_k = K_c\left\{(\epsilon_k - \epsilon_{k-1}) + \frac{\Delta t}{\tau_I}\epsilon_k + \frac{\tau_D}{\Delta t}(\epsilon_k - 2\epsilon_{k-1} + \epsilon_{k-2})\right\} \tag{230}$$

See Isermann [30] for other discrete forms for the classical PID controller.

The discrete form of the PI controller is obtained by setting τ_D to zero above, yielding:

$$u_k = K_c\left(\epsilon_k + \frac{\Delta t}{\tau_I}\sum_{i=1}^{k}\epsilon_i\right) \tag{231}$$

or, in the velocity form:

$$\Delta u_k = K_c\left\{(\epsilon_k - \epsilon_{k-1}) + \frac{\Delta t}{\tau_I}\epsilon_k\right\} \tag{232}$$

The discrete P controller is given from here as:

$$u_k = K_c\epsilon_k \tag{233}$$

or, in the velocity form,

$$\Delta u_k = K_c(\epsilon_k - \epsilon_{k-1}) \tag{234}$$

With the second approach, the system is accepted as discrete, and appropriately treated as such. Controller design from this point of view leads directly to discrete controllers that are often not of the classical type and are often more complex. A discussion of such techniques lies outside the intended scope of this section. References [2, 28, 29 and 30] should be consulted for more on this important aspect.

In this section, we have provided a rapid introduction to the elements of computer control; pointing out the discrete state of affairs introduced by the computer's "view" of the process, and the necessity for discrete time models to be used for dynamic analysis. The other tools of dynamic analysis, such as z-transforms and pulse transfer functions were mentioned.

Controller design was presented primarily in the form of discretization of the familiar continuous controllers designed according to the principles laid down for continuous systems. The alternative approach to controller design, in which the discrete nature of the process is explicitly considered, was not discussed. The given references should be consulted for the omitted details.

AN INTRODUCTION TO DYNAMIC MATRIX CONTROL

It is generally believed that over 80% of industrial control loops are of the type that operate comfortably under conventional control. However, the challenging problems posed by the remaining 20% or so, are usually accompanied with economic incentives strong enough to motivate the development and implementation of more advanced control schemes needed to take care of these problems.

Very few computer control techniques have had the industrial success of Shell's Dynamic Matrix Control (DMC). It therefore seems appropriate to conclude this chapter by introducing DMC in this final section.

The universal drive for more efficient use of energy in the chemical process industry has resulted in the imposition of stricter demands on control systems. To be considered effective, the control system must cope with the problems caused by time delays, interaction between system variables, and inherent system nonlinearities. In addition, it must be capable of handling constraints in the input as well as the output variables, while remaining robust in the face of modeling errors [31].

The steps taken by the Shell Oil Company, (U.S.A.) towards tackling the above stated problems led to the development of the DMC technique which first appeared in the open literature in Reference [32], in 1979, after having been applied with notable success on industrial processes since 1973.

The DMC technique is discussed in this section in its most basic form. Deeper discussions of the implications of the DMC philosophy are available in Garcia and Morari [33] while a discussion of the DMC framework from the perspective of its statistical parallels are available in Ogunnaike [34].

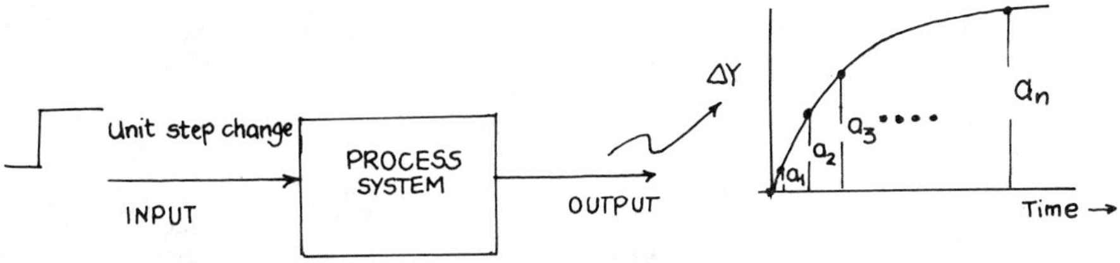

Figure 43. The unit step response function.

The DMC Technique

The following discussion of the DMC technique is summarized from Reference [31], with permission.

Let $\mathbf{a} = [a_1, a_2, \ldots, a_n]^T$ represent the unit step response function of a dynamical system, i.e., the elements of a represent the *change* observed in the system output, at n, consecutive, equally spaced, discrete time instants after implementing a unit change in the input variable (see Figure 43).

Now let x_i represent the *change* in the input variable at time instant i (called a control move in DMC parlance). Initially, before the implementation of any control moves, let the predicted system output be $\mathbf{Y}^0 = [Y_1^0, Y_2^0, \ldots, Y_n^0]^T$ where Y_1^0 need not be equal to Y_j^0 (i not equal to j).

How an arbitrary sequence of m control moves, $\mathbf{x} = [x_1, x_2, \ldots, x_m]^T$ will cause the system to change from the initial $\mathbf{Y}^0$ to some new state $\mathbf{Y}$ may now be deduced. Assuming linearity, so that the principle of superposition applies, the new state $\mathbf{Y} = [Y_1, Y_2, \ldots, Y_n]^T$ will be given by the following [32]:

$$\left.\begin{aligned} Y_1 &= Y_1^0 + a_1x_1 \\ Y_2 &= Y_2^0 + a_2x_1 + a_1x_2 \\ &\vdots \\ Y_m &= Y_m^0 + a_mx_1 + a_{m-1}x_2 + \cdots + a_1x_m \\ Y_{m+1} &= Y_{m+1}^0 + a_{m+1}x_1 + a_mx_2 + \cdots + a_2x_m \\ &\vdots \\ Y_n &= Y_n^0 + a_nx_1 + a_{n-1}x_2 + \cdots + a_{n-m+1}x_m \end{aligned}\right\} \tag{235}$$

This may be rewritten as:

$$\mathbf{y} = \mathbf{Ax} \tag{236}$$

where $\mathbf{y} = \mathbf{Y} - \mathbf{Y}^0$ is a change in the system output, and

$$\mathbf{A} = \begin{bmatrix} a_1 & 0 & 0 & \cdots & 0 \\ a_2 & a_1 & 0 & \cdots & 0 \\ \vdots & & & & \vdots \\ a_m & a_{m-1} & a_{m-2} & \cdots & a_1 \\ a_{m+1} & a_m & a_{m-1} & \cdots & a_2 \\ \vdots & & & & \\ a_n & a_{n-1} & a_{n-2} & \cdots & a_{n-m+1} \end{bmatrix} \tag{237}$$

is called the system's dynamic matrix.

Assuming that the system's dynamics are adequately represented by Equation 236, the control problem then becomes that of judiciously choosing, and implementing the sequence of control moves $\{x_1, x_2, \ldots, x_m\}$ such that the system output is caused to move to, and remain at, the desired value Y^*.

The DMC approach to the control problem is as follows:

1. In the absence of control moves (i.e., $\mathbf{x} = \mathbf{0}$), the system output is predicted to remain as $\{Y_1^0, Y_2^0, \ldots, Y_n^0\}$ over the prediction horizon of n time intervals. However, the desired situation is for Y_i to be Y^* for all i. The difference between the desired and currently predicted outputs (in the absence of control action) we shall call $\mathbf{e}$, the "error prediction vector," i.e., $\mathbf{e} = [e_1, e_2, \ldots, e_n]^T$, with $e_i = Y^* - Y_i^0$.
2. Given $\mathbf{e}$, if $\mathbf{x}$ is chosen such that

$$\mathbf{Ax} = \mathbf{e} \tag{238}$$

holds exactly, the system output would be transformed from $\mathbf{Y}^0$ to $\mathbf{Y}^*$, since from Equation 236, $\mathbf{Y}$ becomes $\mathbf{Y}^0 + \mathbf{e}$ which by definition of $\mathbf{e}$ is $\mathbf{Y}^*$.
3. However, Equation 238 usually contains an overdetermined set of equations (since $m < n$, usually), i.e., Equation 238 has fewer unknowns than equations, in which case no solution exists. We may nevertheless find a vector $\mathbf{x}$ that minimizes the vector norm $\|\mathbf{Ax} - \mathbf{e}\|$, i.e.,

$$\min_{x} \phi = (\mathbf{Ax} - \mathbf{e})^T(\mathbf{Ax} - \mathbf{e}) \tag{239}$$

This, of course, yields the "least squares" solution to Equation 238:

$$\mathbf{x} = (\mathbf{A}^T\mathbf{A})^{-1}\mathbf{A}^T\mathbf{e} \tag{240}$$

A control sequence $\mathbf{x}$ thus chosen minimizes the squared deviation of the system output from the desired state over the n-interval prediction horizon.
4. In practice, penalty against excessive control action is often incorporated into the optimization objective (Equation 239) to read:

$$\min_{x} \phi = (\mathbf{Ax} - \mathbf{e})^T(\mathbf{Ax} - \mathbf{e}) + K^2(\mathbf{x}^T\mathbf{x}) \tag{241}$$

with the result:

$$\mathbf{x} = (\mathbf{A}^T\mathbf{A} + K^2\mathbf{I})^{-1}\mathbf{A}^T\mathbf{e} \tag{242}$$

Thus, given $\mathbf{A}$, the system model, and $\mathbf{e}$, information about the system state, and K, a tuning parameter, Equation 242 represents the "control law" used by the DMC scheme.

Let us note, however, that because of unavoidable prediction inaccuracies, it is not advisable to implement the entire sequence $\{x_1, x_2, \ldots, x_m\}$, as calculated from Equation 242, over the next m intervals in automatic succession. This is because over the m time intervals required to completely implement the entire $\mathbf{x}$ sequence, unavoidable plant/model mismatch, and other unmodeled disturbances often cause the actual plant state to differ from the predictions that were used to compute $\mathbf{x}$. This set of precomputed control moves is, therefore, inherently incapable of reflecting the changes that would subsequently occur after the computation.

The DMC strategy is to implement only the first move, x_1, and then update the error prediction vector at each time instant; using the currently available system measurements adjusted for the effect of implementing x_1. The remaining details of this "feedback error update" structure, along with other additional considerations may be found in References [32, 34, 35, 36].

Additional Features of DMC

In addition to those basic features discussed, it should be noted that the DMC scheme extends quite straightforwardly to multivariable systems. In actual fact, as is evident from the original publications, [32, 36] DMC was developed specifically for multivariable systems.

The scheme is also capable of handling constraints in both output and input variables. This is achieved by posing the optimization problem as a linear program, or a quadratic program. The details of these aspects of DMC are available in Reference [37].

When the process time delays and steady state gains change with time, as is usually the case in industrial systems, it is not enough to rely on the feedback error update scheme within the DMC framework to handle the problems created by this non-stationarity of the process [31, 38]. However, with some surprisingly simple modifications, DMC will handle these situations with comparable ease. Several simulation examples to demonstrate this fact, using realistic systems with substantial industrial flavor, are available [31, 38].

We have presented a short summary of the highly successful Dynamic Matrix Control (DMC) technique in this section; outlining the standard procedure and referring to several other additional features and extensions.

The control scheme has been analyzed rigorously in several publications, and the reasons for its success are fairly well understood; namely the mode of representing the system mathematically, (this enhances robustness); it uses a process model inverse as its controller, which, according to Reference [33] gives rise to the ideal controller. Also, according to Reference [34], within the DMC framework resides a collection of the same principles upon which certain, time-proven statistical concepts are based.

Several other reports containing the numerous successful applications of DMC on various real industrial systems are available in proprietary Shell publications.

CONCLUSION

The main thrust of this chapter has been the design of effective controllers for process systems. Since it is next to impossible to carry out controller design in a proper manner without the tools of dynamic analysis, these were first briefly reviewed.

Many control loops in industry can be designed according to the classical methods discussed. Beyond these rather straightforward control systems, the next level of difficulty comes about when there are problematic disturbances. Systems whose control variables are subject to such disturbances are candidates for cascade control; for the other types of disturbances, feedforward control is the recommended technique. It should be noted that cascade and feedforward control are very popular control techniques in the chemical process industry.

Processes with unusual, and hence problematic, dynamics require careful attention. It is known that when the apparent time delay is very significant, even with the "best" PID controller tuning, the performance can still be very poor. The situation with inverse responding systems is equally bad. That time delay, and inverse response compensators have not gained as much acceptance in industrial practice is primarily due to their notorious sensitivity to modeling errors. Newer techniques like Carcia and Morari's Internal Model Control (IMC) [33] indicate how the issue of robustness in the face of modeling errors can be tackled in a more direct manner thus giving rise to improved behavior for systems with the Smith Predictor type of structure. These ideas are also contained in the so-called inferential control structure [2, 48, 49].

For open loop unstable systems, not much is available in the open literature beyond stabilization by feedback. Some new results on the direct synthesis approach, paying particular attention to the fact that the process model is only an approximation (and often a poor one) of the real process behavior, are available [39].

Accepting the fact that one can no longer ignore the nonlinearities of most process systems has fueled much of the research efforts of the 1980s. Apart from the classical approach, our discussion highlighted just one area of current research interest; that of linearizing transformations. Much of the available material on nonlinear control can be obtained from the references supplied in the main body of the chapter. In addition to these, the extension of IMC to nonlinear systems, as contained in Economou [41], will make particularly interesting reading for those with the appropriate mathematical preparation.

The discussion on multivariable (MV) systems was kept at the introductory level. Attention was focused more on interactions, loop pairing, and decoupling. The more involved issue of what to do with MV systems having multiple delays can be found in several publications, [7, 25, 41, 42, 43]. Simulation testings of some recent, unpublished, but encouraging results on MV controller design by direct synthesis are available [44].

The process systems of the future will operate under computer control, almost exclusively. This important subject matter, of course, cannot be disposed of in the few pages available within a panoramic chapter of this nature. It is highly recommended that the supplied references be consulted to obtain a balanced picture of the state of affairs in this area.

There are several aspects of controller design not featured in this chapter. We have not included, for example, any discussions on state estimation; that aspect that deals with how to carry out controller design when either the process outputs are not available for measurement, or the available measurements are corrupted with noise. Most process systems have measurable outputs, and noise corruption of measurements has not been a major headache for most control loops. Nevertheless the subject matter is important, and Reference [7], among others, has a particularly lucid presentation on the subject of State Estimation and Stochastic Control; the only impediment being, perhaps, the limited statistical preparation of most process control engineers.

We have also not explicitly dealt with the issue of controller design for distributed parameter systems; those systems whose mathematical models occur in the form of partial differential equations; systems like heat exchangers, fixed bed reactors, etc. whose output variables depend both on time, and at least one spatial variable. The traditional view is that these systems are required to be controlled only at a finite number of spatial points; in other words, a discretized, lumped approximation is just as appropriate. Taking this view, which Ray [7] refers to as early lumping, these systems are reduced to the same category of systems we have discussed in the main body of the chapter.

This fact notwithstanding, some new results on the application of the predictive/optimizing principles of DMC to distributed parameter systems are available in Reference [45], while an interesting discussion on the application of the direct synthesis approach may be found in Reference [46].

The issue of controller design when the process system's model has significant uncertainties was also not discussed, even though it has taken on prominence recently. In Reference [47], one can find several articles that give a fairly accurate picture of the current state of affairs as regards this very important issue, and, for that matter, the main issue of this chapter; controller design for process systems. It is highly recommended.

REFERENCES

1. Coughanowr, D. R., and Koppel, L. B., *Process Systems Analysis and Control*, McGraw-Hill, New York, 1965.
2. Stephanopoulos, G., *Chemical Process Control—An Introduction to Theory and Practice*, Prentice-Hall, Englewood Cliffs, New Jersey, 1985.
3. Luyben, W. L., *Process Modeling, Simulation and Control For Chemical Engineers*, McGraw-Hill, New York, 1973.
4. Ogunnaike, B. A., "Controller Design for Nonlinear Processes via Variable Transformations," *I. & E.C. Proc. Des. Dev.*, 25 (1), 241 (1986).
5. Smith, C. A., and Corripio, A. B., *Principles and Practice of Automatic Process Control*, John Wiley and Sons, Inc., New York, 1985.
6. Considine, D. M., and Ross, S. D., *Handbook of Applied Instrumentation*, McGraw-Hill, New York, 1964.

7. Ray, W. H., *Advanced Process Control*, McGraw-Hill, New York, 1981.
8. Cohen, G. H., and Coon, G. A., "Theoretical Considerations of Retarded Control," *Trans. ASME*, 75, 827 (1953).
9. Ziegler, J. G., and Nichols, N. B., "Optimum Settings for Automatic Controllers," *Trans. ASME*, 64, 759 (1942).
10. Smith, O. J. M., "Closer Control of Loops with Dead Time," *Chem. Eng. Prog.*, 53, 217 (1957).
11. Smith, O. J. M., "A Controller to Overcome Dead Time," *ISA J.*, 6 (2), 28 (1959).
12. Waller, K. V. T., and Nygardas, C. G., "On Inverse Response in Process Control," *I. & E.C. Fundamentals*, 14 (3), 221 (1975).
13. Iinoya, K., and Altpeter, R. J., "Inverse Response in Process Control," *Ind. Eng. Chem.*, 54 (7), 39 (1962).
14. Whitaker, H. P., Yamron, J., and Kezer, A., "Design of Model-Reference Adaptive Control Systems for Aircrafts," *Report R-164*, Instrumentation Laboratory, MIT, Cambridge, Mass. (1958).
15. Landau, I. D., *Adaptive Control—The Model Reference Approach*, Marcel-Dekker, Inc., New York, 1979.
16. Åström, K. J., and Wittenmark, B., "On Self Tuning Regulators," *Automatica*, 9, 185 (1973).
17. Narendra, K. S., and Monopoli, R. V., (eds.) *Applications of Adaptive Control*, Academic Press, Inc., New York, 1980.
18. Hoo, K., and Kantor, J. C., "An Exothermic Reactor is Feedback Equivalent to a Linear System," *Chem. Eng. Comm.*, 37, 1 (1985).
19. Hunt, L. R., Su, R., and Meyer, G., "Design for Multi-Input Nonlinear Systems" in *Differential Geometry Control Theory*, (R. W. Brockett, R. S. Millman, H. J. Sussmann, eds.) Birkhäuser, U.S.A. (1983).
20. Su, R., "On the Linear Equivalents of Nonlinear Systems," *Systems and Control Letters*, 2 (1), 48 (1982).
21. Reboulet, C., and Champetier, C., "A New Method for Linearizing Nonlinear Systems: The Pseudolinearization," *Int. J. Control*, 40 (4), 631 (1984).
22. Bristol, E. H., "On a New Measure of Interaction for Multivariable Process Control," *IEEE Trans. Auto. Cont.*, AC-11, 133 (1966).
23. McAvoy, T. J., *Interaction Analysis*, ISA Monograph Series, ISA, Research Triangle Park, N.C., 1983.
24. Wood, R. K., and Berry, M. W., "Terminal Composition Control of a Binary Distillation Column," *Chem. Eng. Sci.*, 28, 1707 (1973).
25. Ogunnaike, B. A., and Ray, W. H., "Multivariable Controller Design for Linear Systems Having Multiple Time Delays," *AIChE. J.*, 25 (6), 1043 (1979).
26. Ogunnaike, B. A., *Dynamics and Control of Chemical Processes*, Unpublished Lecture Notes, (1985).
27. Shinskey, F. G., *Distillation Control for Productivity and Energy Conservation*, McGraw-Hill, New York, 1977.
28. Deshpande, P. B., and Ash, R. H., *Elements of Computer Control—With Advanced Control Applications*, ISA, Research Triangle Park, NC, 1981.
29. Seborg, D. E., Edgar, T. F., Mellichamp, D. A., *Process Dynamics and Control*, John Wiley and Sons, Inc., New York, 1986.
30. Isermann, R., *Digital Control Systems*, Springer-Verlag, New York, (1981).
31. Ogunnaike, B. A., and Adewale, K. E. P., "Dynamic Matrix Control for Processes with Time Varying Parameters," *Chem. Eng. Comm.*, 47 (4), 295 (1986).
32. Cutler, C. R., and Ramaker, B. L., "Dynamic Matrix Control—A Computer Control Algorithm," *AIChE 86th National Meeting*, April 1979.
33. Garcia, C. E., and Morari, M., "Internal Model Control, 1. A Unifying Review and Some New Results," *I. & E.C. Proc. Des. Dev.*, 21, 308 (1982).
34. Ogunnaike, B. A., "Dynamic Matrix Control: A Non-Stochastic Industrial Process Control Technique with Parallels in Applied Statistics," *I. & E.C. Fundamentals*, 25, 712 (1986).
35. Cutler, C. R., "Dynamic Matrix Control: An Optimal Multivariable Control Algorithm with Constraints," Ph.D. Thesis, University of Houston, Texas, 1983.

36. Prett, D. M., and Gillette, R. D., "Optimization and Constrained Multivariable Control of a Catalytic Cracking Unit," *AIChE 86th National Meeting*, April 1979.
37. Morshedi, A. M., Cutler, C. R., Fitzpatrick, T. J., and Skrovanek, T. A., "A Method of Controlling a Process Combining the Quadratic/Linear Programming Method of Optimization with Dynamic Matrix Control," U.S. Patent Applied for. (Application No. K-8838).
38. Adewale, K. E. P., "Dynamic Matrix Control for Processes with Time-Varying Parameters: Simulated Application to Industrial Type Processes," M.Sc. Thesis, University of Lagos, Nigeria, 1983.
39. Ojo-Osagie, C. O., "Controller Synthesis for Processes with Unusual Dynamics," B.Sc. Thesis, University of Lagos, Nigeria, 1987.
40. Economou, C. G., "An Operator Theory Approach to Nonlinear Controller Design," Ph.D. Thesis, California Institute of Technology, Pasadena California, 1985.
41. Ogunnaike, B. A., "Control Systems Design for Multivariable Systems with Multiple Time Delays," Ph.D. Thesis, University of Wisconsin-Madison, 1981.
42. Jerome, N. F., and Ray, W. H., "High Performance Multivariable Controller Strategies for Systems Having Time Delays," *AIChE. J.* (in press).
43. Holt, B. R., and Morari, M., "Time Delay Compensation: Discussion and Multivariable Extension," *Automatica*, (in press).
44. Bamgbose, A. O., "Design of Robust Multivariable Controllers by Direct Synthesis: Simulation Applications," M.Sc. Thesis, University of Lagos, Nigeria, 1987.
45. Anumonwo, E. C., "Identification and Predictive-Optimizing Control of Distributed Parameter Systems," Ph.D. Thesis, University of Lagos, Nigeria, 1987.
46. Williams, A. O. F., "Studies in Dynamics Analysis and Controller Design by Direct Synthesis for Distributed Parameter Systems," Ph.D. Thesis, University of Lagos, Nigeria, (expected, 1988).
47. Morari, M., and McAvoy, T. J., (eds.) *Chemical Process Control—CPC III*, (Proceedings of the Third International Conference on Chemical Process Control, Asilomar, Jan 1986) Elsevier, New York, 1987.
48. Weber, R., and Brosilow, C., "The Use of Secondary Measurements to Improve Control," *AIChE. J.*, 18, 614 (1972).
49. Brosilow, C., and Tong, M., "The Structure and Dynamics of Inferential Control Systems," *AIChE. J.*, 24, 492 (1978).

CHAPTER 34

METHOD OF SENSITIVITY ANALYSIS IN CHEMICAL KINETICS

A. A. Levitskii, T. M. Grigor'eva, Ju. A. Kolbanovskii, L. S. Polak, and R. L. Tatuzov

A. V. Topchiev Institute of Petrochemical Synthesis
Academy of Sciences of the USSR
Moscow, USSR

CONTENTS

INTRODUCTION

Sensitivity analysis for chemical kinetics is used to study the influence of the changes in the parameters (rate constants, initial conditions, etc.) on model predictions. Historically the sensitivity of chemical kinetics equations to rate constant variation seems to appear for the first time in [1].

The analysis of chemical kinetics system sensitivity to variation of initial conditions and other parameter values is one of possible approaches to the problem of choosing significant features of the model. The precise definition of the notion "significant feature" is required.

Each mathematical model of physical or chemical process is naturally created and used for some particular parameter range typical for this process. "Complete" mathematical models of this type usually lead to systems too large to deal with.

Application of equations presented as a model of a particular chemical process is restricted only by the initial conditions. Note that this model may be "sufficiently complete," "unsufficiently complete," or "excessive." The last means that the model includes not only significant features but also unsignificant ones. The main problem of sensitivity analysis is to divide these two kinds of features.

By the significant feature of the model we mean an equation that is necessary (but not sufficient) for the description of the process with given accuracy (usually with the accuracy of the experiment) in the adopted parameter change range. Accordingly, an insignificant model feature is an equation that in the given range of parameter changes may be eliminated from the system without decrease of precision of the phenomenon description.

We shall call an "insufficiently complete" model such a system of equations where just one of the significant features is missing, and a "sufficiently complete" model a system of equations containing all the significant features and none of the insignificant ones.

In most cases, especially in chemistry and physical chemistry, we must deal with "excessive" models. Obviously, to consider everything that seems important is simpler and more foolproof than to select something relying on intuitive reasons. This problem arises in selecting the most probable chemical reaction mechanism from several possible ones.

The reader well acquainted with the problem of applied mathematics may notice the fact that the terms "significant" and "insignificant" features are typical in image processing. The coincidence is not accidental. In fact, if a mathematical model of chemical process is thought of as its image, the formalism of image processing may be used. With this degression we want to emphasize the close connection between various problems of applied mathematics.

Computational models of chemical process are usually based on differential or algebraic equations:

$$\vec{y} = f(t, \vec{y}, \vec{k}) \tag{1}$$

where $\vec{y}$ = n-vector of solutions
t = time
$\vec{k}$ = m-vector of parameters

For a more exact study of the process one must use a greater number of complex equations.

Solving these equations requires not only subtle techniques but also great expense in memory, time, etc. In this case it may be useful to reduce the number of model simulations on computer retaining all data that are sufficient for adequate description of the process.

Since values of model parameters cannot be determined exactly or may be varied to study different modes of real systems, it would be interesting to know the measure of the solution sensitivity to parameter variation. The developed model can be used for description of the real system only if it is known which of the estimated characteristics are sensitive to parameter variation, and how.

Let us assume parameter k_j to vary slightly about its nominal value k_j^0 and use the first order components of truncated Taylor series to estimate y_i:

$$y_i(t, \vec{y}, \vec{k}) \approx y_i(t, \vec{y}, \vec{k}^0) + \sum_{j=1}^{m} \frac{\partial y_i}{\partial k_j} \Delta k_j \tag{2}$$

First order parametric derivatives of solution vector components that have been studied [3–5] are called first-order sensitivity coefficients. $\partial y_i/\partial k_j$ is the first-order coefficient of sensitivity of solution component i to variation of parameter j. In many works on sensitivity analysis the significant part of the effort has gone into development of powerful prediction schemes or the named coefficients [5–12]. Interpretation of system sensitivity in terms of first-order coefficients is known as local sensitivity analysis, and constitutes a deterministic approach to the model.

Although sensitivity coefficients dy_i/dk_j provide direct information on the influence of slight variations of each parameter around its nominal value on the solution vector component they can't reflect the influence of simultaneous considerable change of all parameters on system behavior. Global sensitivity analysis must be employed here since it has no restrictions on parameter change and parameter interrelations.

LOCAL METHODS OF SENSITIVITY ANALYSIS

Usually models for chemical kinetics problems turn out to be a set of ordinary first order differential equations:

$$dy_i/dt = f_i(t, \vec{y}, \vec{k}) \tag{3a}$$

Initial conditions for this system are as follows:

$$\vec{y}(0) = \vec{y}_0 \tag{3b}$$

Here functions f_i, $i = 1, 2, \ldots, n$, depend not only on $\vec{y}$ and variable t, but on parameter m-vector $\vec{k}$ as well. Usually, system based on Equation 3 describes the evolution of some substances, and vector $\vec{k}$ defines the rate coefficients of chemical reactions under consideration.

Stepwise Parameter Variation

The simplest procedure in calculating the first-order sensitivity coefficients is to use stepwise parameter variation. In this case parameters are given one by one the value from a certain diapazon, while other parameters remain fixed. The parameter set formed in this way is used for solving Equation(s) 3.

This method is very convenient for the programmer since no additional programs must be written: one may use those elaborated for solving Equation(s) 3. However, it appears to require excessive computational costs: the model that estimates n output functions depending on m parameters has to solve Equation 3 nz^m times, where z is the number of values for each parameter. For $m = 20$ and $z = 3$ stepwise parameter variation in sensitivity analysis requires that stiff differential equations must be solved 3,486,784,401 times. In such a situation just listing the received results would be a serious problem.

Direct Method

Alternative to stepwise parameter variation method is to consider sensitivity coefficients as dynamic variables and deriving a set of so-called sensitivity (differential) equations, which compose a Cauchi problem. Let's introduce a new variable.

$$\beta_{ij} = \partial y_i/\partial k_j$$

Equation 3 may be differentiated with respect to the parameters k. We assume that the derivatives of the functions f are continuous and so obtain differential equations for sensitivity coefficients:

$$\frac{\partial \beta_{ij}}{\partial t} = \frac{\partial f_i}{\partial k_j} + \sum_{l=1}^{m} \frac{\partial f_i}{\partial y_l} \beta_{lj} \qquad \begin{matrix} i = 1, \ldots, n \\ j = 1, \ldots, m \end{matrix} \tag{4a}$$

$$\beta_{ij}(0) = 0 \tag{4b}$$

Equation 4 is a system of m × n-dimensional ordinary differential equations

$$\frac{\partial \vec{\beta}_j}{\partial t} = J(t)\vec{\beta}_j(t) + b_j(t) \qquad j = 1, \ldots, m \tag{5a}$$

$$\vec{\beta}_j(0) = 0 \tag{5b}$$

where $\vec{\beta}_j$ = n-vector $[\beta_{1j}, \ldots, \beta_{nj}]$
$J(t)$ = n × n Jacobian matrix with $\{\partial f_i/\partial x_l\}$ elements
b_j = n-vector $[\partial f_1/\partial k_j, \ldots, \partial f_n/\partial k_j]$.

Let us note that each vector Equation 5 is independent of the others. Equation 5 must be solved together with Equation 3 to obtain J(t) and b(t) values. One of two strategies is applied to solve Equations 3 and 5.

1. Equations 3 and 5 are solved simultaneously. This requires a solution of a system of 2n ordinary differential equations to be calculated m times.
2. Equation 3 is solved first. The solution is interpolated to calculate J(t) and b(t). Then solutions for the Equation 5 are calculated m times. This requires (m + 1) calculations of a solution for a system of n ordinary differential equations.

In the most cases the initial condition (Equation 5b) is zero-vector. If parameter k is the initial condition for Equation 3, then

$$\vec{\beta}_j(0) = \vec{\delta}_j$$

where $\vec{\delta}$ is vector with all components having the zero value while the i-th component has the value 1.

Equations describing higher order sensitivities are obtained by taking consecutive derivatives of Equation 3 with respect to parameters. The complete form of these equations is given in [7]. For their solving a great number of stiff systems has to be integrated simultaneously.

Green Function Method

When m > n the more effective approach than direct method can be proposed for obtaining $\vec{\beta}_j$. Observing that Equation 5 is a nonhomogeneous linear differential equation with time dependent coefficients, its solution can be expressed by the Green's function (matrix) associated with them [7–9]. Note that all the m linear nonhomogeneous differential equations from Equation 5 differ from one another only by the nonhomogeneous terms $\partial f_i/\partial k_j$, and thus there is only one Green's function (matrix) to be found.

The solution of linear nonhomogeneous differential equation can be obtained in terms of a linear integral transform of the nonhomogeneous term f_i with respect to the kernel $\vec{K}(t, \tau)$:

$$\vec{\beta}_j(t) = \int_0^t \vec{K}(t, \tau)\vec{b}_j(\tau)\, d\tau \tag{6}$$

where the Green function K(t, τ) satisfies:

$$\vec{K}'(t, \tau) - J(t)\vec{K}(t, \tau) = (t - \tau)\vec{1} \tag{7a}$$

$$\vec{K}(0, \tau) = 0 \tag{7b}$$

Obviously,

$$\vec{K}(t, \tau) = 0, \qquad t < \tau \tag{8}$$

and

$$\vec{K}'(t, \tau) - J(t)\vec{K}(t, \tau) = 0 \tag{9a}$$

$$\vec{K}(t, \tau) = 1 \qquad t \geq \tau \tag{9b}$$

Let's pick for integral estimation, a set of N + 1 points $\{\tau_i\}$. Within each subinterval $\{\tau_i, \tau_{i+1}\}$ Equation 9a is solved with $\tau = \tau_i$ while initial condition is $K(\tau_i, \tau_i) = 1$, k = 0, 1, . . . , N − 1. It results in $\vec{K}(\tau_{i+1}, \tau_i)$ evaluation. The desired Green's function can then be expressed as

$$\vec{K}(\tau_N, \tau_i) = \vec{K}(\tau_N, \tau_{N-1})\vec{K}(\tau_{N-1}, \tau_{N-2}) \cdots \vec{K}(\tau_{k+1}, \tau_k) \qquad k = 0, 1, \ldots, N-1 \tag{10}$$

Further improvement of this method is connected with expression of Green's function as

$$\vec{K}(t, \tau) = G(t)G^{-1}(\tau) \tag{11}$$

of adjoint matrix $\vec{K}^{+}(\tau, t)$ may be used instead of $\vec{K}(t, \tau)$.

The important advantage of this approach is that higher order sensitivity coefficient calculation needs no additional computation of solution for any differential equations, since all the required values are determined by numerical integrating [7].

Some authors [10] propose to express the kernel $\vec{K}(t, \tau)$ as

$$K(t + \Delta t, t) = \exp\left(\int_{t}^{t+\Delta t} J(S)\, dS\right) \tag{12}$$

This formula is a first-order approximation of the exact series solution given by Magnus [11]. This is so-called AIM (Analytically Integrated Magnus method) algorithm.

An attempt to make equitable comparisons between rival techniques for local sensitivity analysis is presented in [5]. Although no method is optimal in every situation, the AIM algorithm appears to be generally more efficient than other methods.

Principal Component Analysis

Let's assume that time evolution of sensitivity coefficients (1) has been calculated by one of the described methods. However, the obtained results can be hardly used to gain information on parameter interaction. A rather formalized and slightly heuristic procedure is proposed in [12]. There the problem is discussed in terms of eigenvalues and eigenvectors of matrix S^TS, where S denotes the array of normalized sensitivity coefficients.

The effect a variation in the rate coefficients has on the calculated behavior of a reaction mechanism may be quite naturally expressed in terms of a following function:

$$Q(k) = \sum_{j=1}^{q} \sum_{i=1}^{m} \left[\frac{y_{ij}(k) - y_{ij}(k^0)}{y_{ij}(k^0)}\right]^2 \tag{13}$$

where $y_{ij} = y_i(t_j, k)$, $i = 1, 2, \ldots, m$. Let's expand Q(k) into its Taylor series about the point k^0:

$$Q(k) \approx Q(k^0) + G^T(k^0)\,\Delta k + \tfrac{1}{2}(\Delta k)^T H(k^0)(\Delta k) \tag{14}$$

where $\Delta k = k - k^0$
G = gradient vector
H = Hessian matrix of Q, defined by $[G]_i = dQ/dk_i$
and $[H]_{ij} = d^2Q/dk_i\, dk_j$, respectively

Obviously, $Q(k^0) = 0$ and $G(k^0) = 0$, since the point k^0 is a minimum of Q(k). Thus:

$$Q(k) = \tfrac{1}{2}(\Delta k)^T H(k^0)(\Delta k) \simeq (\Delta k)^T S^T S(\Delta k), \tag{15}$$

where the last approximate equality can be derived by the well-known Gauss approximation [24].

Equation (15) is a quadratic function of the variations Δk_i, $i = 1, 2, \ldots, m$. At any fixed ε the inequality $Q(k) < \varepsilon$ defines an ellipsoid in the parameter space with principal axes not necessarily being along the components of k.

The full picture of parameter dependence is obtained by diagonalization (singular decomposition) of the matrix S^TS:

$$S^TS = U \times \Lambda \times U^T \tag{16}$$

where Λ is a diagonal matrix formed by the eigenvalues of S^TS and U denotes the matrix of normed eigenvectors u_i, $i = 1, 2, \ldots, m$. The new set of the parameters

$$\bar{\alpha} = U^T\bar{k} \tag{17}$$

called the principal components allows Equation 15 to be written as follows

$$Q(k) = \sum_{i=1}^{m} \lambda_i \|\Delta\alpha_i\|^2 \tag{18}$$

where λ_i are eigenvalues of S^TS and $\|\alpha_i\|$ is the norm of eigenvectors.

In order to demonstrate the advantages of the described technique consider the particular case of the only eigenvalue λ_1 to be nonzero. Further let the corresponding eigenvector to have the following form:

$$u_1 = (u_{11}, u_{12}, \ldots, u_{12}, 0, 0, \ldots, 0) \tag{19}$$

Then the largest effect on y is brought about by a change in parameters $k_1, k_2, \ldots, k_2$. The nonzero values of eigenvector components define the relative contribution of respective parameters.

Thus, principal component analysis offers an effective tool for extracting useful kinetic information from the derived sensitivity tables. Eigenvectors reveal strongly interacting reaction sequences and the corresponding eigenvalues measure the significance of separate parts of the kinetic mechanism. The authors of this method suggest following applications of their method [12].

First, if the parameters are rate coefficients of primitive chemical stages and normalized sensitivity coefficients, such information may be used to select the minimum reaction set.

Second, to reveal dependencies among the parameters principal components must be calculated. This results in confirming or denying the validity of quasi-steady-state assumptions under the considered experimental conditions.

Third, the identification of parameter-parameter interactions provides answers as to how inaccuracies in known parameters affect the ability to use the mechanism for determining unknown parameters and how a large variation of parameter estimates can be expected.

Global Sensitivity Analysis

The general sensitivity problem [4] is to determine probability density of function $\vec{y}(t)$ when probability densities of preselected parameters k and initial conditions $\vec{y}_0$ are known. Actually the problem can be always reduced to study of function depending on the initial conditions since parameter vector can be joined to the main system in the following way:

$$d\vec{k}/dt = 0 \tag{20a}$$

$$\vec{k}(0) = \vec{k}_0 \tag{20b}$$

Therefore, it is sufficient to consider the problem of determining probability density of function y(t) while probability densities of initial conditions y_0 and the following system are given:

$$dy/dt = f(\vec{y}, t) \tag{21a}$$

$$\vec{y}(0) = \vec{y}_0 \tag{21b}$$

Assume function f to satisfy existence and uniqueness conditions of the solution of Equation 21 for each $x \in R^n$ and for each $t \in [0, \infty]$. Let P_0 to be probability distribution of y_0, i.e., $P_0(B) = \int_B p_0(x_0)\, dx_0$. Let's denote probability density of y(t) as $p_y(y, t)$. The problem is now to estimate P_y if p_0 and f are known.

The previously described approach enables us to write the following equations for probability density:

$$\partial P(y, t)/\partial t + \nabla y(P(y, t)f(y, t)) = 0 \tag{22a}$$

$$P(\vec{y}, 0) = P_0(\vec{y}) \tag{22b}$$

However solution of Equation 22 is usually rather difficult since these differential equations are frequently stiff and their numerical integration requires large computational costs.

Mostly density probability p is unknown and the only given thing is the nominal parameter value and its range of variation. In this case the wisest course would be to consider parameter values from this range, estimate function changes, and calculate averaged (in certain sense) sensitivity coefficients.

In [16] the natural approach to calculate mean values of derivative of function y with respect to parameters is offered. Consider the dispersion of the studying function in the selected parameter range:

$$\sigma^2 = \langle y^2 \rangle - \langle y \rangle^2 \tag{23}$$

Let us average y over all but one variables:

$$\langle y \rangle_i = \int \cdots \int y \, dk_j \cdots dk_{i-1} \, dk_{i+1} \cdots dk_m \tag{24}$$

and consider the dispersion of the resulting single-variable function $\langle y \rangle_i$:

$$\sigma_i^2 = \int \langle y \rangle_i^2 \, dk_i - \langle y \rangle^2, \qquad i = 1, \ldots m, \tag{25}$$

Quantity S_i defined by the expression

$$S_i = \sigma_i^2/\sigma^2 \tag{26}$$

is called global sensitivity coefficient and measure averaged sensitivity of y over parameter uncertainties.

The connection between local sensitivity and integral sensitivity expressions can easily be observed for the following reasons. Let us decompose our function f to a truncated Taylor series with respect to parameters and consider only the first-order members:

$$f(\vec{k}) = f(\vec{k}_0) + \sum_{i=1}^{m} \frac{\partial f}{\partial k_i} \Delta k_i \tag{27}$$

The expression obtained defines surfaces in the parameter space. Values S_i can be easily calculated for them.

$$S_i^2 = (\partial f/\partial k_i)^2 \tag{28}$$

Thus global sensitivity coefficients are the squares of local sensitivity coefficients if only ranges of uncertainties are sufficiently small.

Similar to the sensitivity of a function to a single parameter varying coefficients S_{ij} describing sensitivity to the simultaneous parameter variation can be defined.

FAST-Method of Sensitivity Analysis

The effective routine to estimate the Equation 26 has been presented by the authors of the FAST-method (FAST—Fourier Amplitude Sensitivity Test) [13–16]. The main idea of this procedure is simultaneous variation in all parameters according to the following equations:

$$k_i = G_i(\sin w_i s), \qquad i = 1, \ldots, m \tag{29}$$

If the values of frequencies w_i are chosen to be incommensurate, the curve generated by the set of Equation 29 will cover parameter space exactly for variation of s over the range $-\infty < s < +\infty$. It means that for any point in parameter space and any small ε such value of parameter s can be selected so that the distance from the presented point to the curve is less than ε.

Two problems arise in realization of this approach by means of modern computer. First, since computer numbers are all finite it is not suitable to use the infinite limits of the parameter (s in this case) variation range. Second, since a computer can operate only with rational numbers the incommensurate frequencies can't be used.

Because of these problems the authors of the FAST-method present the use of integer frequencies chosen to fit some specific tests. Thus all parameters become the functions of s periodic on $(0, 2\pi)$ and can be Fourier analyzed.

In this case global sensitivity coefficients can be defined as the Fourier coefficients of the harmonics defined by Equation 29:

$$S_i^2 = C_{w_i}^2 \Big/ \sum_{l=1}^{m} C_{w_e}^2 \tag{30}$$

The calculation of Fourier coefficients of s dependent function is obviously the replacing of multidimensional integral (Equation 26) by a single dimension integration along the curve defined by Equation 29. According to the Weyl theorem [17], conversion is legitimate when the curve fills the integration space exactly.

Two types of errors are considered by the authors of FAST-method while they analyze the developed procedure application. The approximation of integral by a finite summation leads to an error in the estimation of its value. Besides in case of integer frequencies w_i the curve doesn't cover the space of investigation exactly.

One can easily overcome errors of the first type by increasing the number of integration points or using quadrature higher order formulae; but the situation with errors of the second type is more difficult. The authors of the FAST-method have paid great attention to this problem and have developed special recommendations on the appropriate choice of integer frequencies for different pair combinations of values {dimension, number of required points} for better space covering by the curve [15].

A variation of argument with frequency w for nonlinear functions leads to the fact that Fourier coefficients have nonzero values for harmonics of w as well. Therefore it is useful to examine harmonics of the fundamental frequencies $\{w_i\}$ of parameter variations to calculate sensitivity coefficients. On the account of these reasons Equation 30 can be rewritten as:

$$S_i = \frac{\sum_{p=1}^{\infty} (C_{pw_i}^2 + C_{-pw_i}^2)}{\sum_{j=1}^{\infty} (C_j^2 + C_{-j}^2)} \tag{31}$$

The advantage of FAST-method is that its realization is simple and that relatively few trial points are used to estimate an integral (Equation 26). An appropriate choice of frequencies used for parameter variation is important. It is a way to obtain a more uniform distribution of parameter curve points in the space of parameters.

However, if the accuracy of calculations must be increased it is necessary to increase variation parameter frequencies to obtain more uniform distribution of points. Unfortunately, earlier calculated function values can't be used, and that constitutes one of the main shortcomings of FAST-method.

In [16] the authors of FAST-method present further developments of the described approach. For example, they recommend a different basis in the decomposition of the function under investigation, that is to substitute Equation 29. Such attempts probably will really result in certain modernization of the technique, but are hardly able to remove its shortcomings just pointed out.

Estimation of Multiple Integrals in Global Sensitivity Analysis

Many mathematical modeling problems presume estimation of multiple integrals of rather large dimensions. In this connection special mathematical methods that aim to minimize the number of test points without increasing the error of calculation were developed. In order to explain the advantage of these techniques let us examine the following example.

Given the function $f(x(x_1, \ldots, x_m)$ of m variables the quantity of integral

$$I = \int f(x_1, \ldots, x_m)\, dx_1 \cdots dx_m \tag{32}$$

must be estimated, where m-dimensional cube can be taken as region of integration without a generality limitation.

Multiple integrals of large dimensions are calculated by the Monte-Carlo method, its essence being function evaluation in points with random coordinates. The square of dispersion of integral quantity appears to decrease in inverse proportion to the number of points. Thus, the calculation error decreases as $1/\sqrt{N}$, where N is number of integration points. Thus, it shows no direct dependency on space dimension. Attention should be drawn to the fact that computer application of the Monte-Carlo method needs some random point generator algorithm. These random numbers are controlled by special tests—the test for uniform distribution being in this case the most important one.

Studies connected with creating the algorithms of random uniformly distributed point generation have led to unexpected results. Use of specially formed sequences of uniformly distributed points may lead to decrease of calculation error to nearly 1/N [19]. Note that such uniformly distributed sequences are those that are used by the Fast-method of sensitivity analysis uses for evaluation of integrals (Equation 26).

I. M. Sobol has elaborated an algorithm for one class of sequences containing uniformly distributed points and has estimated their discrepancies [19–20]. These are so-called LP-sequences [19]. We consider LP_τ-sequences to be most suitable for such integral calculations. The order of convergence rate in integral estimation by these sequences is about $\ln^{m-1} N/N$, which is better than $1/N^{1-\varepsilon}$ for any ε, however small. We'll give a brief description of algorithm for calculation of coordinates of LP_τ-points.

Consider matrix of numbers v_{ij} which are called directive. If m is space dimensionality and maximum number of test points N_{max} satisfies the correlation

$$N_{max} \leq 2^m \tag{33}$$

than matrix size becomes $n \times m$. Let's calculate coordinates of the point with index i. Consider binary representation of number i:

$$i = e_k e_{k-1} \cdots e_2 e_1 \tag{34}$$

where $e_j I \leq j \leq k$ are corresponding binary digits. In this case j-th coordinate of i-th point will be

$$x = e_1 v_{1j} \otimes e_2 v_{2j} \otimes \cdots \otimes e_k v_{kj} \tag{35}$$

Henceforth sign $\otimes$ is used for modulo two addition (exclusive "or"). The values of directive numbers v_{ij} for $m = 50$ and $n = 20$ are cited in [21].

The effective procedures of global sensitivity analysis can be derived from application of Monte-Carlo methods to estimate integrals (Equation 26). The weakest point in this approach is the evaluation of the first integral from Equation 25 where the function to be integrated itself is the square of integral that has to be calculated, too.

In this case direct numerical integration has no since, because quantities $\langle y \rangle_i$ and $\int \langle y \rangle_i^2 \, dk_i$ are to be calculated separately, i.e., uniform net is needed. An attempt to improve integration accuracy results in astronomical increase in number of points.

To avoid this difficulty one may use the following expression:

$$\left(\int g(x)\,dx\right)^2 = \left(\int g(z_1)\,dz_1\right)\left(\int g(z_2)\,dz_2\right) = \iint g(z_1)g(z_2)\,dz_1\,dz_2 \tag{36}$$

Such an interpretation reduces the problem to integration inside several regions and can yield some decrease of calculational costs; but since several integrations (number of iterations depends on number of parameters) are to be carried out all at once, the total quantity of calculations remains relatively large.

This "brute force" method is unsuitable for integral sensitivity analysis. Instead we propose the function under study to be substituted by another having analytical presentation and differing from the given one as slight as possible.

Polynomial Approximation

We propose in [22] the following procedure, called PSI-method (PSI—Polynomial Sensitivity Investigation). In the space of parameter uncertainties random and equally distributed points are dropped. Usually this space is a multidimensional parallelepiped. The more "equally" the points are distributed the more precise calculations can be made. To our opinion points of LP_τ-sequence are most suitable for this procedure.

Required function is calculated (e.g., Equation 3 is solved) for the set of parameters defined by selected points. Obtained values are used to build the polynomial function by the least square method. Such polynomials define certain hypersurfaces in multidimensional space. Expressions for them are rather simple, so integrals (Equation 26) can be found analytically. Calculated integral values combine global sensitivity coefficients.

The previous description makes it clear that first-order polynomials can't help in analysis of sensitivity to simultaneous varying of parameter combination, since the plane defined by linear polynomials has zero value for such sensitivities.

It is interesting to note that the Fast-method, including only first harmonics and linear polynomial procedure, is drawn to the same expression when the number of points increases.

Higher order polynomials allow the peculiarities of the approximated functions to be described more thoroughly and to calculate the quantity measuring dependency of function varying to simultaneous parameter variation.

The numerical experiments demonstrate that polynomials of too high order are hard to use since the correct polynomial building requires too many points. Besides the higher order of polynomial more local extrema may appear. These extrema are likely related to real function conduct. We use only first- and second-order polynomials in our calculations.

Simple realization of PSI-method is its indubitable merit. The user needs nothing more than a routine for the least squares methods and a random number generator, which are contained in any program package. (A relatively simple procedure based on Sobol algorithm and whose text is given in the Addendum is recommended instead of standard random generator if greater accuracy is needed.)

In our opinion one more advantage of the proposed technique is its clearness and transparency of presentation. The "magic" connection between such values, as for example Fourie amplitudes and sensitivity coefficients, in the FAST-method is realized on abstract level of formula terms. But scientists intuitively desire to imagine the studied function geometrically as a surface (the simplest one is the plane).

It should be noted, however, that obtained sensitivity coefficients are applied not to the given function itself but rather to its approximation. That is why the approximation is to be as adequate as possible. The described procedure is undoubtedly not the only possible one. Use of polynomials is not obligatory. They are simplest for the least squares method to be applied to, and handling them is mostly suitable.

Generally, if a priori some peculiarities of the function are known, they are to participate in selection of approximating functions. Another worthwhile way of improving this technique is to divide parameter space into areas of modest size, calculate sensitivity coefficients for this region, and consider the resulting sensitivity as a sum (in a some strictly defined sense) of the areas sensitivities. While the areas volume is decreasing, the calculational error converges to zero.

The use of polynomial approximation to select a minimal reaction set seems to be the most sensible field of application. A detailed description is presented in the next section.

Polynomial approximation can be a base for solving the problem of kinetic parameters fitting. Moreover, PSI-method may be useful in such traditional branches of sensitivity investigation as process controling and checking the reliability of obtained data with respect to parameter uncertainties.

APPLICATIONS

The wide variety of questions arising while simulating physical, chemical, and other phenomena can be answered by the help of sensitivity analysis. Three major classes of applications can be identified based on the type of manipulation involved in the treatment of the sensitivity coefficients.

The first category includes applications that use the elementary sensitivities (dy/dk, d^2y/dk^2, d^3y/dk^3) directly. Most in this group of analysis are conceptually simple. We'll just list the corresponding items: (a) ranking of most/least important reactions; (b) identification of governing/least important reactions; (c) quantification of extent and sources of errors; (d) mapping of parameter space; (e) fitting model to kinetic data; and (f) identification of steepest descent/ascent direction of optimization routines.

The nonclassical branches of sensitivity analysis are intended to study the interface between modeling and experiments more explicitly. Feature sensitivity analysis considers cases in which the experimental observable is not the function y(t), but rather some feature of y(t), such as amplitude, period, etc.

Sometimes it is necessary to not know sensitivity coefficients, but some modifications that can provide reasonable information on the correlation between experiment and simulation. Effective techniques for calculating such things as dk/dy or d^2k/dy^2 used to reveal interdependence between parameters are described in Reference [9]. This approach should be distinguished from classical sensitivity analysis, where parameters are considered to be independent a priori.

The application of local sensitivity analysis (direct method) to the Chapman mechanism for atmospheric ozone kinetics is presented in Reference [6]. A scheme of 4 reactions is considered. Three types of parametric sensitivity are illustrated. They are: sensitivity to the initial conditions, the photodissociation rates being held constant at their appropriate daily averaged values, and diurnally varying rates.

The results of this analysis show the sensitivity distinctions between two last cases. Asymptotic states appeared to be quite different for these two types of calculations. This implies a need for closer examination of constant solar flux approximation that are commonly used in atmospheric applications.

Methane oxidation kinetics was successfully analyzed by the global FAST-method. The model consisted of a set of 23 coupled rate equations involving 23 rate coefficients varied over a 50% range of uncertainty about the nominal values. The output functions were the species concentrations (CH_4, CH_3, CH_2O, CHO, CO, CO_2, H_2O, O, H, OH) at different times ($1_{10^{-7}}$ to $1_{10^{-2}}$ sec).

Their analysis showed that only about 5–7 reactions strongly affect the concentrations of that species. Thus, the analysis provides an important example of how sensitivity analysis can be used to simplify complex models by segregating the "important" and "unimportant" component equations.

SELECTION OF THE MOST PROBABLE REACTION MECHANISM

A sensitivity analysis has decisive importance in the selection of the most probable mechanism of a complex chemical reaction when several alternatives exist. The selection of the most probable mechanism may be formulated as the problem of minimizing the number of elementary steps appearing in the mechanism of a chemical reaction that are necessary and sufficient for describing a chemical process. This problem was first considered by Gargarin et al. [2]. However, that procedure did not use a computer to minimize the number of steps.

Let us now consider the algorithm that we propose for selecting the most probable mechanism for a complex multistep chemical process on the basis of a sensitivity analysis of equations of chemical kinetics.

We shall assume that:

1. There is quantitive information on the kinetics of the process that was obtained experimentally or by any other means and must be described by the most probable reaction mechanism sought.
2. The original mechanism under consideration, for which the minimization of the number of steps is carried out, includes the steps of the most probable mechanism, possibly with rate constants differing from the true constants.

In addition:

1. The reaction products (the components of the first group) whose concentrations significantly (by approximately an order of magnitude) exceed the concentrations of the other reaction products are picked out on the basis of the information on the kinetics of the process, and all remaining components (regardless of whether they are experimentally detected or not) are assigned to the second group.
2. All the steps in the mechanism under consideration are also divided into two groups. The steps whose products include components of the first group are assigned to the first group, and all the remaining steps are assigned to the second group.
3. The first iteration of the sensitivity analysis is carried out with normalization of the sensitivity coefficients within each of the two groups of steps just described, and the most important steps, whose sensitivity coefficients are significantly (by an order of magnitude) greater than all the others, are picked out. If there is a number of such steps, all of them are picked out. Then the next iteration of the sensitivity analysis, in which the previously singled out most important steps are not considered (but they are, of course, considered in the solution of the straightforward kinetic problem), is carried out, etc.

   The question is where to stop the iterations, which ultimately give back the original complete mechanism. For a completely automated procedure the answer can be obtained by solving the straightforward kinetic problem with the inclusions of only the most important steps selected after the first, second, and so forth iterations in the shortened mechanism. The iterative analysis of the sensitivity is assumed to be completed when the solution of the straightforward problem after a given iteration fits the experimental data.
4. Now it is necessary to verify whether there are any "extra" steps among the steps selected. For example, in some cases if the only step remains after n iterations, it would be necessarily selected in the successive iterations. (In the following example, viz., the selection of the most probable mechanism for the oxidation of nitrogen, only step 6 appeared in group 1 in the third iteration.) For such verification the straightforward kinetic problem is solved without the last step(s) included in the shortened mechanism. The solution is obtained alternatively for each of the groups. If the exclusion of any steps does not cause a change in the solution of the straightforward kinetic problem within the range of the experimental error, the steps are not included in the most probable mechanism. Similar additional verification should also be performed for the preceding iteration(s) in the group whether the correction just indicated was made.

The selection of the most probable mechanism ends at this point, if the complete mechanism describes the experiment, i.e., when there is no basis to assert that a particular value of a rate constant is erroneous.

When the complete mechanism of the process does not fit the experiment, the iteration procedure (steps 1–4) is carried out until coincidence of the complete and shortened mechanism produces solutions within the range of experimental accuracy.

The problem of evaluating the parameters is solved for the shortened reaction mechanism picked out, i.e., the set of rate constants providing the best description of the experiment is sought. The iteration procedure for sensitivity analysis is applied to the original complete reaction mechanism with the new set of rate constants, etc.

RESULTS OF CALCULATIONS FOR CONCRETE MECHANISM

The method described for the selection of the most probable reaction mechanism was applied to the analysis of the process of the high-temperature nitrogen oxidation. Table 1 presents the elementary steps of the process and their rate constants. All the elementary steps of the process were divided into two groups, according to the proposed approach. For this mechanism the only principal reaction product is NO.

According to the algorithm described, an investigation of the sensitivity of the concentration of NO to alteration of the rate constants in every group of steps was carried out by the polynomial-approximation method (the variation of the rate constants was carried out within $+2$ orders of magnitude). NO concentration was measured at steady state of the system.

The first iteration of the sensitivity analysis showed that the step 1 in group 2 and step 7 in group 1 were the most significant steps (see Table 1), and the second iteration showed that among the remaining steps, step 8 and step 9 in group 1, were the most significant. Table 2 presents a comparison of the results of the solution of the straightforward steps 1 and 7–9. In this case, it may be asserted even without the solution of the straightforward kinetic problem that one or two iterations are not enough for the selection of the most probable mechanism, because NO can accumulate until the reactants are completely exhausted (i.e., the thermodynamical equilibrium is violated), since there is no step involving the decomposition of NO in the scheme containing the steps indicated.

Three iterations are sufficient for a sensitivity analysis, since the mechanism consisting of steps 1, 2, and 6–10 describes all the laws of the process exactly (Table 2).

Let us now apply the procedure prescribed in paragraph 4 to this mechanism. The exclusion of step 6 (group 1), which was included in the last iteration, does not influence the solution of the straightforward kinetic problem (see Table 2). Therefore, this step should be excluded from the most probable mechanism. After this, the application of step 4 of the algorithm to steps 2 and 10 (group 2) is meaningless, since it would lead to the unsatisfactory results in the second iteration. However, according to step 4 of the algorithm, we should now solve the straightforward kinetic problem again without one of the steps in group 1. This is step 9. The solution of the straightforward kinetic problem with consideration of steps 1, 2, 7, 8, and 10 does not make it possible to describe the experiment.

Thus, the step-by-step application of the formal procedure prescribed by steps 1–4 of the algorithm makes it possible to find a most probable mechanism consisting of steps 1, 2, and 7–10 for the nitrogen oxidation, which corresponds completely to the known Zel'dovich mechanism [21].

The prescribed example illustrates the advantages of the provided technique, which are efficiency, high level of formalization, and universality.

In spite of wide opportunities of the method, some questions yet remaining open should be pointed out. It concerns mainly complex problems of mathematical modeling of various processes. In particular these problems arise when chemical reactions are connected with heat and/or mass transfer. Then direct use of the proposed algorithm is impossible since heat transfer and chemical reaction rates can't be compared because of their different units.

CHEMICAL REACTIONS CHARACTERISTIC TIMES

Very often tempering is the stage defining the aim products in modern kinetic experiments and chemical technology of gas phased thermal processes. Tempering means the decrease of temperature

Table 1
Mechanism of the Oxidation of Nitrogen ($N_2:O_2 = 1:1$, $P = 10^2$ kPa, $T = 3,000$ K)

N	Stage	No. of Group	Rate Const. (sm^3/mole s) (sm^6/mole^2 s)	Sensitivity Coefficients			Inclusion of Step in Most Probable Mechanism
				1 Iteration	2 Iteration	3 Iteration	
1	$O_2 + M \longrightarrow O + O + M$	2	$3.2_{10^{6}}$	0.799	—	—	yes
2	$O + O + M \longrightarrow O_2 + M$	2	$5.3_{10^{14}}$	$0.358_{10^{-1}}$	$0.4_{10^{-4}}$	0.439	yes
3	$N_2 + M \longrightarrow N + N + M$	2	$1.4_{10^{-1}}$	$0.273_{10^{-2}}$	$0.6_{10^{-5}}$	$0.1_{10^{-6}}$	no
4	$N + N + M \longrightarrow N_2 + M$	2	$3.6_{10^{14}}$	$0.168_{10^{-1}}$	$0.5_{10^{-6}}$	$0.1_{10^{-6}}$	no
5	$NO + M \longrightarrow N + O + M$	2	$3.0_{10^{5}}$	$0.134_{10^{-1}}$	$0.3_{10^{-6}}$	$0.1_{10^{-6}}$	no
6	$N + O + M \longrightarrow NO + M$	1	$3.3_{10^{15}}$	$0.567_{10^{-2}}$	$0.7_{10^{-5}}$	1.0	no
7	$O + N_2 \longrightarrow NO + N$	1	$2.2_{10^{8}}$	0.945	—	—	yes
8	$NO + N \longrightarrow O + N_2$	2	$1.6_{10^{13}}$	$0.867_{10^{-1}}$	0.989	—	yes
9	$N + O_2 \longrightarrow NO + O$	1	$2.8_{10^{12}}$	$0.493_{10^{-1}}$	1.0	—	yes
10	$NO + O \longrightarrow N + O_2$	2	$1.3_{10^{10}}$	$0.450_{10^{-1}}$	$0.7_{10^{-4}}$	0.561	yes

Table 2
Comparison of the Results of Calculation for Various Mechanisms (Concentration, mole/sm³)

Component	1 Iteration Stages 1, 7	2 Iteration Stages 1, 7, 8, 9	3 Iteration Stages 1, 2, 6–10	Complete Scheme Stages 1–10	Stages 1, 2, 7–10	Stages 1, 2, 7, 8, 10
N_2	0	$0.766_{10^{-6}}$	$0.198_{10^{-5}}$	$0.198_{10^{-5}}$	$0.198_{10^{-5}}$	$0.196_{10^{-5}}$
O_2	$0.446_{10^{-7}}$	0	$0.192_{10^{-5}}$	$0.192_{10^{-5}}$	$0.192_{10^{-5}}$	$0.197_{10^{-5}}$
N	$0.203_{10^{-5}}$	$0.655_{10^{-11}}$	$0.284_{10^{-10}}$	$0.284_{10^{-10}}$	$0.284_{10^{-10}}$	$0.134_{10^{-6}}$
O	$0.194_{10^{-5}}$	$0.153_{10^{-5}}$	$0.109_{10^{-6}}$	$0.109_{10^{-6}}$	$0.109_{10^{-6}}$	$0.110_{10^{-6}}$
NO	$0.203_{10^{-5}}$	$0.253_{10^{-5}}$	$0.107_{10^{-6}}$	$0.107_{10^{-6}}$	$0.107_{10^{-6}}$	$0.229_{10^{-10}}$

from the reaction temperature to some lower one, which defines the stability of aim products in order to maintain the unstable concentrations.

It is obvious that the efficiency of tempering is a function of temperature decrease rate dT/dt. But the rate can't be simply chosen, the rate of stages where the aim product may be spent must be considered and the part of aim product η to be reserved must be chosen. (Later we shall discuss the problem of choice of this part). Apparently, $\eta < 1$ since $dT/dt \rightarrow \infty$ while $\eta \rightarrow 1$.

Therefore, the question concerning unisothermic kinetics is formulated, i.e., what the velocity of tempering (dT/dt) must be to receive the given value of η for given chemical system. Direct comparison of tempering rate with the rate of chemical reaction where aim product may change is impossible since they are measured in different units.

That is why it is reasonable to compare the characteristic times of tempering processes (τ^*) and chemical reactions (τ), and therefore appropriate definitions must be formulated.

Let us call the characteristic time of elementary gas-phased chemical reaction (τ_k) number k

$$\sum_i \alpha_{ik} A_{ik} \rightarrow \sum_j \beta_{jk} B_{jk}$$

where α_{ik}, β_{jk} = stoichiometric coefficients, value

$$\tau_k = [B_k]/W_k$$

where W_k = reaction rate
B_k = product generated in the stage k and has maximum (relative to other products) concentration

We understand the characteristic time of tempering to be:

$$\tau^* = T/V^*$$

where T = current value of temperature in the process of tempering
V^* = dT/dt is current value of tempering speed

Obviously, τ_k and τ^* are functions of time and the relation:

$$\tau_0^* = T_0/V_0^*$$

governs characteristic time of tempering under the initial temperature and tempering speed.

If the characteristic time of aim product decay τ_p is defined as the minimum number of characteristic times of reactions, then the condition of maintaining a reasonable part of product on the output of the tempering device is the following:

$$\tau_p \gg \tau^*$$

As mentioned, the question of what the tempering speed must be depends on specific properties of reaction system and chosen value of v*. These data are exactly just what determine how strong the inequality $\tau_p \gg \tau^*$ must be in every particular case.

Let us look for particular model example. We'll examine the mechanism of generation and decay of nitrogen oxides that was frequently used by different investigators (Table 3). In the examined case the maximum of equilibrium aim product (nitrogen oxide) concentration is reached at T = 3,000–3,500 K and P = 1–10 atm [1]; the nitrogen oxide completely decays by means of slow cooling. The state composition of the system for T = 3,000 K and P = 1 atm is the following (concentrations are given in M/sm^3):

N	O	NO	O	N
$1,8_{10^{-6}}$	$1,65_{10^{-6}}$	$2,02_{10^{-7}}$	$2,92_{10^{-7}}$	$3,75_{10^{-11}}$

Calculations were performed in the following way: for a pressure of 1 atm and temperature of 3,000 K a system of chemical kinetics equations was integrated until a state composition (see above) fitting the data of thermodynamic calculations was reached. Then constant speed of tempering was given and the system of chemical kinetics equations was integrated under unisothermic conditions. Under the examined conditions speeds of the stages (4) and (6) (Table 3) where nitrogen oxide decays are

$$W_4 = 1,2_{10^{-4}}; \qquad W_6 = 7,93_{10^{-4}}\ MO\pi b \cdot C^{-1} \cdot CM^{-3}$$

and the characteristic times are

$$\tau_4 = 1,5_{10^{-2}}; \qquad \tau_6 = 2,I_{10^{-3}}$$

Thus, τ_p defined as stated above is equal to τ_6. If it is assumed that

$$\tau^* = \alpha T_0/v^* = \tau_p \qquad \alpha \gg 1$$

then

$$v^* = \alpha T_0/\tau^*$$

Table 3
Mechanism of the Oxidation of Nitrogen

N	Stages	lg(A)*	n	E_a, $\frac{kkal}{mole}$
1	$O_2 + M \longrightarrow O + O + M$	18.6	−1	118.0
2	$O + O + M \longrightarrow O + M$	18.2	−1	0
3	$O + N_2 \longrightarrow NO + N$	13.9	0	75.5
4	$N + NO \longrightarrow O + N_2$	13.2	0	0
5	$N + O_2 \longrightarrow O + NO$	13.0	0	7.5
6	$O + NO \longrightarrow N + O_2$	9.5	−1	39.1

* *Coefficient A: For bimolecular stages is measured in $sm^3\ mole^{-1}\ s^{-1}$.*
For trimolecular stages—in $sm^6\ mole^{-2}\ s^{-1}$.

Table 4
Simulation of Tempering Process

α	1	5	10	30	100
V*, K/c	$1,4_{10^6}$	$7,2_{10^6}$	$1,4_{10^7}$	$4,3_{10^7}$	$1,4_{10^8}$
$\eta = \dfrac{[NO]_{T=300}}{[NO]_{T=3000}}$	73, 3	93, 6	95, 5	98, 0	99, 5

Table 4 shows the results of tempering process simulating: first line—values of α; second line—values of required tempering speed; third line—part of aim product remained after tempering process performing ($\eta\%$).

While α rises from 1 to 10 the remaining part of the aim product is seen to increase exponentially and practically reaches saturation. It seems that a value of $\alpha = 1$ will be reasonable estimation of tempering speed for most real processes.

In addition it must be noticed that if τ_p is known, then the value of initial tempering speed may be determined (rather exactly) wtihout special calculations by accepting of $\alpha = 10$ for the first estimation.

In the examined case $V_0^* = 1.43 \cdot 10^7\ K \cdot s^{-1}$. This shows that investigators now possess a simple and reliable method for practical aims—a preliminary estimation of necessary tempering speed.

The introduced notion of characteristic time of elementary chemical reaction appears to be rather useful in searching for the most probable chemical reaction mechanism too. In the expanded mechanism of nitrogen oxidation the elementary stage hierarchy was built as a base of comparison for τ_K. The most important stages detected are shown in Table 1. As can be concluded from the results of many independent studies, these reactions compose the most probable mechanism of the process.

Moreover, the introduced notion of characteristic time of chemical reaction that appeared to be very useful in considering chemical reaction kinetics together with tempering rate undoubtedly may be used also in the joint analysis of chemical kinetics reactions, equations of diffusion, and other processes with rate units different from that of gas phase chemical reaction.

ADDENDUM—FORTRAN PROGRAM FOR GLOBAL SENSITIVITY ANALYSIS BY THE PSI-METHOD

The program for previously described technique consists of several modules. Some must be supplied by the user since their texts depend on the specific problem to be solved. The following modules are problem independent:

- PLANE—routine for sensitivity coefficients calculating.
- DESOLV—solution of matrix equation, used in the least square method.
- AKOEF—function, calculating integral expressions evaluating sensitivity coefficients for polynomials found.
- LPTAU—provides coordinates of points uniformly distributed in the hypercube (LP_τ-sequence).

Note: maximum space dimensionality used in this program is 10. Number of integration points shouldn't exceed 1,024. Such restrictions arise from the fact that only the first $10 \times 10 = 100$ direct numbers are defined in the array NR of LPTAU module. Values of NR elements for larger dimensions (up to 50) and greater numbers of iteration points (about 1,000,000) are given in Reference [15]. If the user for any reason doesn't want to apply LP_τ-sequences, he should delete LPTAU the procedure call and use one of standard random numbers generator instead, as it is shown in comments (lines, indicated by C-character).

The user is to program the main routine defining values of necessary variables, array dimensions, tolerance, etc. The main procedure calls to module PLANE. The call is written as follows:

CALL PLANE (NMIN,NMAX,NX,NY,COEFF,SUM,NREAL,FUN)

Arguments for this routine have the following meanings:

NMIN—minimum number of points.
NMAX—maximum number of points.
NX—dimensionality of parameter space.
NY—number of functions to be studied.
COEFF—array of NX NY dimension, where the relative sensitivity coefficients are stored.
SUM—NY-dimensioned array of normalizing factors, characterizing absolute sensitivity for every function.
NREAL—number of points needed for sensitivity analysis (finish condition is determined by the IFNSH routine, see later).
FUN—routine for calculating the values of exploring functions at the parameter values given (main routine must contain description EXTERNAL FUN); the routine name may be any allowed for FORTRAN language name.

Module FUN is also provided by user. This procedure is called from module PLANE and has 4 parameters:

NX—dimensionality of parameter space.
X—array, containing parameter values.
NY—number of functions to be studied.
Y—array, where function values are stored.

Note: the parameters are assumed to be distributed in the interval $(-1, 1)$ and thus real parameter values must be renormalized if they have the different range of variations.

Module PLANE finishes its work when either number of employed points goes beyond the value set (NMAX), or some given condition is satisfied. One more user defined routine describes the condition satisfying. It is named IFNSH and uses the following arguments:

NX—dimensionality of parameter space.
NY—number of functions to be studied.
COEFF—sensitivity coefficients.
SUM—normalizing factors.

Module IFNSH is called by the routine PLANE after each point from the parameter space has been processed. If the defined condition is satisfied, calculations are finished and current sensitivity coefficients together with several used points are transferred to the main procedure. In the opposite case the program continues its work considering the next point. If the number of points becomes greater than NMAX module, PLANE returns control to the main routine. Values of sensitivity coefficients are accepted to be those, that where evaluated at the previous step. Variable NREAL is set to -1 in this case.

The following example illustrates the use of the package. Routine FUN calculates values of two different functions dependent of five parameters. We have picked such functions as test ones:

$$f_1 = 5x_1 + 4x_2 + 3x_3 + 2x_4 + x_5$$
$$f_2 = x_1 + 2x_2 + 3x_3 + 4x_4 + 5x_5$$

The following condition for routine IFNSH check was chosen

$$\sum_{ij} /\sigma_{ij}^{(n)} - \sigma_{ij}^{(n+1)}/ < \varepsilon$$

where σ_{ij} = coefficient of global sensitivity of the i-th function to the j-th parameter variation.

```
C***********************************************************
      DIMENSION COEFF(5,2),SUM(2)
      EXTERNAL FUN
      COMMON /ERROR/ EPS
      DATA EPS/1.E-7/
      NMIN=64
      NMAX=128
      CALL PLANE(NMIN,NMAX,5,2,COEFF,SUM,NREAL,FUN)
      PRINT 2,NREAL
      PRINT 3
      DO 1 II=1,2
        PRINT 4,SUM(II),(COEFF(I,II),I=1,5)
1     CONTINUE
2     FORMAT(5X,''NREAL-'',I6)
3     FORMAT(4X,''T O T A L '',20X,''Sensitivity coeff''/)
4     FORMAT(2X,G11.3,2X,6G11.3)
      END
C***********************************************************
      SUBROUTINE PLANE(NMIN,NMAX,NPP,NPY,COEFF,SUM,NREAL,FUNCT)
      EXTERNAL FUNCT
      REAL COEFF(NPP,NPY),SUM(NPY)
      INTEGER NMIN,NMAX,NPP,NPY
      DOUBLE PRECISION A(40,40),B(40,40),Q(40,40),SC1(40),C(40)
      DIMENSION AMX(40)
      DIMENSION IPS(40)
      DIMENSION X(40)
      DIMENSION Y(40)
      LOGICAL IFNSH
C... SET POLYNOM POWER TO 2
      N=2
C... CALCULATE NUMBER OF POLYNOM PARAMETERS
      NP=NPP+1
C... CALCULATE NUMBER OF MEMBERS OF SUM IN POLYNOM
      NPN=N*NPP+1
C... SET MATRIXES TO ZERO
      DO 13 J=1,NPN
        DO 12 II=1,NPY
          Q(J,II)=0
12      CONTINUE
        DO 10 II=1,NPN
          A(J,II)=0
10      CONTINUE
13    CONTINUE
      AMX(1)=1
      DO 1 I=1,NMAX
        CALL LPTAU(I-1,NPP,X)
C... FOR LARGE DIMENSIONS DELETE PREVIOUS LINE
C        AND PERFORM THE NEXT CYCLE
C           DO 8 J=1,NPP
C             X(J)=RAND(0)
```

```
C8          CONTINUE
        CALL FUNCT(NPP,X,NPY,Y)
        DO 11 J=1,NPP
          XX=2*X(J)-1
          XXX=1
          DO 21 JK=1,N
            NPK=NPP*(JK-1)+1
            XXX=XXX*XX
            AMX(J+NPK)=XXX
21        CONTINUE
11      CONTINUE
        DO 2 J=1,NPN
          XX=AMX(J)
          DO 7 II=1,NPY
            Q(J,II)=Q(J,II)+XX*Y(II)
7         CONTINUE
          DO 3 II=1,NPN
            A(J,II)=A(J,II)+XX*AMX(II)
3         CONTINUE
2       CONTINUE
        IF (I.LT.NMIN) GOTO 1
C... SAVE MATRIX A
         DO 5 IK=1,NPN
         DO 5 J=1,NPN
           B(IK,J)=A(IK,J)
5        CONTINUE

C... GET SENSITIVITY COEFFICIENTS
        DO 9 II=1,NPY
          ISW=1
          IF (II.NE.1) ISW=0
          CALL DESOLV(ISW,40,NPN,A,IPS,SC1,Q(1,II),C,IINI)
          SUM(II)=0
          DO 4 IK=2,NP
            SUM(II)=SUM(II)+AKOEF(C,NPP,IK,N)
4         CONTINUE
          DO 6 IK=2,NP
            COEFF(IK-1,II)=AKOEF(C,NPP,IK,N)/SUM(II)
6         CONTINUE
9       CONTINUE

C... CHECK FO EXIT
        NREAL=I
        IF (IFNSH(NPP,NPY,COEFF,SUM) RETURN

C... RESTORE MATRIX A
        DO 115 IK=1,NPN
        DO 115 J=1,NPN
          A(IK,J)=B(IK,J)
115     CONTINUE

C... END THE MAIN CYCLE
1      CONTINUE

       NREAL=-1
       RETURN
       END
```

```
C*******************************************************************
      SUBROUTINE LPTAU(I,N,Q)
      DIMENSION Q(N)
      LOGICAL START,NUM
      COMMON /NRT/NR(50,20),NRS(50,20),NUM(20),IP2(20),ISTART
     =,IQO(50),PP2
      DATA NR /1,1,1,1,1,1,1,1,1,1,40*0,
     =1,3,1,3,1,3,1,3,3,1,40*0,
     =1,5,7,7,5,1,3,3,7,5,40*0,
     =1,15,11,5,3,1,7,9,13,11,40*0,
     =1,17,13,7,15,9,31,9,3,27,40*0,
     =1,51,61,43,51,59,47,57,35,53,40*0,
     =1,85,67,49,125,25,109,43,89,69,40*0,
     1,255,79,147,141,89,173,43,9,25,40*0,
     1,257,465,439,177,321,181,225,235,103,40*0,
     1,771,721,1013,759,835,949,113,929,615,40*0,
     50*0,
     50*0,
     50*0,
     50*0,
     50*0,
     50*0,
     50*0,
     50*0,
     50*0,
     50*0/
      DATA IQO /50*0/
      DATA NUM /20*.FALSE./
      DATA START /.TRUE./
C... TEST FOR PARAMETERS' CORRECTNESS
      IF (N.GT.10 .OR. N.LE.0) PRINT 13
      IF (N.GT.10 .OR. N.LE.0) STOP
13    FORMAT(5X,''ERROR FROM LPTAU: ILLEGAL DIMENSION'')
      IF (I.GT.1023 .OR. I.LT.0) PRINT 14
      IF (I.GT.1023 .OR. I.LT.0) STOP
14    FORMAT(5X,''ERROR FROM LPTAU: ILLEGAL POINT #'')

      IF (.NOT.START) GOTO 7
        START=.FALSE.
        PP2=1
        DO 6 J=20,1,-1
          IP2(J)=PP2
          PP2=PP2*2
6       CONTINUE
        PP2=1./PP2
        DO 8 J=1,20
          DO 8 J1=1,50
            NR(J1,J)=NR(J1,J)*IP2(J)
            IF (J.NE.1) GOTO 10
              NRS(J1,J)=NR(J1,J)
            GOTO 8
10          CONTINUE
            NRS(J1,J)=IXOR(NRS(J1,J-1),NR(J1,J))
8       CONTINUE
```

```
7     CONTINUE
        IF (I.NE.0) GOTO 4
          DO 5 J=1,N
            Q(J)=0.
5         CONTINUE
          RETURN

4       CONTINUE
          DO 11 J=1,20
            NUM(J)=.NOT.NUM(J)
            IF (NUM(J)) GOTO 9
11        CONTINUE
9         CONTINUE
          DO 12 J1=1,N
            IQO(J1)=IXOR(IQO(J1),NRS(J1,J))
            Q(J1)=IQO(J1)*PP2
12        CONTINUE
        RETURN
      END

C*****************************************************************
      SUBROUTINE FUN(N,X,M,Y)
      DIMENSION X(N), Y(M)

      Y(1)=X(1)+2.*X(2)+3.*X(3)+4.*X(4)+5.*X(5)
      Y(2)=5.*X(1)+4.*X(2)+3.*X(3)+2.*X(4)+X(5)

      RETURN
      END

C*****************************************************************
      SUBROUTINE DESOLV(ISW,NDIM,N,A,IPVT,WORK,B,C,IER)
      DOUBLE PRECISION A(NDIM,N),B(N),WORK(N),C(N),COND,CONDP1
      INTEGER ISW,IPVT(NDIM),NDIM,N

      DOUBLE PRECISION COND,CONDP1
      INTEGER I

      IF (ISW.EQ.0) GOTO 3
        CALL DECOMP(NDIM,N,A,COND,IPVT,WORK)
        CONDP1=COND+1
        IF (CONDP1.NE.COND) IER=1
        IF (CONDP1.EQ.COND) IER=2
3     CONTINUE
      DO 1 I=1,N
        WORK(I)=B(I)
1     CONTINUE
      CALL SOLVE(NDIM,N,A,WORK,IPVT)
      DO 2 I=1,N
        C(I)=WORK(I)
2     CONTINUE
      RETURN
      END

C*****************************************************************
      SUBROUTINE DECOMP(NDIM,N,A,COND,IPVT,WORK)
      INTEGER NDIM,N
```

```
      DOUBLE PRECISION A(NDIM,N),COND,WORK(N)
      INTEGER IPVT(N)

      DOUBLE PRECISION EK,T,ANORM,YNORM,ZNORM
      INTEGER NM1,I,J,K,KP1,KB,KM1,M

      IPVT(N)=1
      IF (N.EQ.1) GOTO 80
      NM1=N-1
C  CALCULATE 1-NORM OF MATRIX A
      ANORM=0
      DO 10 J=1,N
        T=0
        DO 5 I=1,N
          T=T+ABS(A(I,J))
5       CONTINUE
        IF (T.GT.ANORM) ANORM=T
10    CONTINUE
C  GAUSS
      DO 35 K=1,NM1
        KP1=K+1
C  FIND MAIN ELEMENT
        M=K
        DO 15 I=KP1,N
          IF (ABS(A(I,K)).GT.ABS(A(M,K))) M=I
15      CONTINUE
        IPVT(K)=M
        IF (M.NE.K) IPVT(N)=-IPVT(N)
        T=A(M,K)
        A(M,K)=A(K,K)
        A(K,K)=T
        IF (T.EQ.0) GOTO 35
        DO 20 I=KP1,N
          A(I,K)=-A(I,K)/T
20      CONTINUE
        DO 30 J=KP1,N
          T=A(M,J)
          A(M,J)=A(K,J)
          A(K,J)=T
          IF (T.EQ.0) GOTO 30
          DO 25 I=KP1,N
            A(I,J)=A(I,J)+A(I,K)*T
25        CONTINUE
30      CONTINUE
35    CONTINUE
C  FIND COND
      DO 50 K=1,N
        T=0
        IF (K.EQ.1) GOTO 45
        KM1=K-1
        DO 40 I=1,KM1
          T=T+A(I,K)*WORK(I)
40      CONTINUE
45      EK=1
        IF (T.LT.0) EK=-1.
        IF (A(K,K).EQ.0) GOTO 90
        WORK(K)=-(EK+T)/A(K,K)
```

```
50     CONTINUE
       DO 60 KB=1,NM1
         K=N-KB
         T=0
         KP1=K+1
         DO 55 I=KP1,N
           T=T+A(I,K)*WORK(K)
55       CONTINUE
         WORK(K)=T
         M=IPVT(K)
         IF (M.EQ.K) GOTO 60
         T=WORK(M)
         WORK(M)=WORK(K)
         WORK(K)=T
60     CONTINUE
       YNORM=0
       DO 65 I=1,N
         YNORM=YNORM+ABS(WORK(I))
65     CONTINUE
       CALL SOLVE(NDIM,N,A,WORK,IPVT)
       ZNORM=0
       DO 70 I=1,N
         ZNORM=ZNORM+ABS(WORK(I))
70     CONTINUE
C  ESTIMATE COND
       COND=ANORM*ZNORM/YNORM
       IF (COND.LT.1) COND=1.
       RETURN
C  CASE OF MATRIX 1*1
80     COND=1.
       IF (A(1,1).NE.0) RETURN
90     COND=1.E30
       RETURN
       END

C************************************************************
       SUBROUTINE SOLVE(NDIM,N,A,B,IPVT)
       INTEGER NDIM,N,IPVT(N)
       DOUBLE PRECISION A(NDIM,N),B(N)

       DOUBLE PRECISION T
       INTEGER NM1,K,KP1,M,I,KB,KM1

C  DIRECT PATH
       IF (N.EQ.1) GOTO 50
       NM1=N-1
       DO 20 K=1,NM1
         KP1=K+1
         M=IPVT(K)
         T=B(M)
         B(M)=B(K)
         B(K)=T
         DO 10 I=KP1,N
           B(I)=B(I)+A(I,K)*T
10       CONTINUE
20     CONTINUE
```

```
C  REVERSED PATH
      DO 40 KB=1,NM1
        KM1=N-KB
        K=KM1+1
        B(K)=B(K)/A(K,K)
        T=-B(K)
        DO 30 I=1,KM1
          B(I)=B(I)+A(I,K)*T
30      CONTINUE
40    CONTINUE
50    B(1)=B(1)/A(1,1)
      RETURN
      END

C***********************************************************
      FUNCTION AKOEF(COEFF,NPP,IK,N)
      DOUBLE PRECISION COEFF(1)
      SUM=0.
      II=IK
      DO 1 I=1,N
        A=I
        B=1./(2*A+1)
        CC=A+1.
        IF (MOD(I,2).EQ.1) GOTO 2
          B=A**2*B/CC**2
2       CONTINUE
        SUM=SUM+COEFF(II)**2*B
        II=II+NPP
1     CONTINUE
      AKOEF=SUM
      RETURN
      END

C***********************************************************
      LOGICAL FUNCTION IFNSH(NPP,NPY,COEFF,SUM)
      REAL COEFF(NPP,NPY),SUM(NPY)

      LOGICAL FIRST
      COMMON /OLD/ FIRST,CCO(1000),SUMO(100)
      COMMON /ERROR/ EPS

      DATA FIRST/.TRUE./

      IF (.NOT.FIRST) GOTO 1
      FIRST=.FALSE.
      DO 2 I=1,NPY
        SUMO(I)=SUM(I)
        N=NPP*(I-1)
        DO 2 J=1,NPP
          CCO(N+J)=COEFF(J,I)
2     CONTINUE
      IFNSH=.FALSE.
      RETURN

1     CONTINUE
      ERR=0
      DO 3 I=1,NPY
```

```
          SUMO(I) = SUM(I)
          N = NPP * (I-1)
          DO 3 J=1,NPP
            ERR = ERR + ABS(CCO(N+J) - COEFF(J,I))
            CCO(N+J) = COEFF(J,I)
3       CONTINUE

        IF (ERR.LE.EPS) IFNSH = .TRUE.
        IF (ERR.GT.EPS) IFNSH = .FALSE.

        RETURN
        END
```

References

1. Bukhman, F. A., Melamed, V. G., Polak, L. S., Khait, Yu. L., and Chervochkin, E. N., in *Application of Computational Mathematics in Chemical and Physical Kinetics* [in Russian], Nauka, Moscow (1969), p. 12.
2. Gagarin, S. G., Kolbanovskii, Yu. A., and Polak, L. S., in *Application of Computational Mathematics in Chemical and Physical Kinetics* [in Russian], Nauka, Moscow (1969), p. 82.
3. Tomovic R., and Vukobratovic, M., *General Sensitivity Theory*, American Elsevier, New York (1972).
4. Tilden, J. W., Costanza, V., McRae, G. J., and Seinfeld, J. H., *Modeling of Chemical Reaction Systems*, Springer-Verlag, Berlin-Heidelberg-New York (1981), p. 69.
5. Kramer, M. A., Rabitz, H., Calo, J. M., and Kee, R. J., *Int. J. Chem. Kinet.*, 16, No. 5, 559 (1984).
6. Dickinson, R. P., and Gelinas, R. J., "Sensitivity Analysis of Ordinary Differential Equation Systems," *J. Comput. Phys.*, 21, No 2, 123 (1976).
7. Hwang, J.-T., Dougherty, E. P., Tabitz, S., and Rabitz, H., "The Green's Function Method of Sensitivity Analysis in Chemical Kinetics," *J. Chem. Phys.* 69, NO. 11, 5180 (1978).
8. Hwang, J.-T., and Rabitz, H., "The Green's Function's Method in Quantum Dynamics *J. Chem. Phys.*, 70, No. 10, 4609 (1979).
9. Dougherty, E. P., Hwang, J.-T., and Rabitz, H., "Further Developments and Applications of the Green's Function Method of Sensitivity Analysis in Chemical Kinetics," *J. Chem. Phys.*, 71, No. 4, p. 1794 (1979).
10. Kramer, M. A., Calo, J. M., and Rabitz, H., *Appl. Math. Modeling*, 11, p. 1237 (1979).
11. Magnus, W., *Commun. Pure Appl. Math.*, 7, p. 649 (1954).
12. Vajda, S., Valko, P., and Turanyi, T., "Principal Component Analysis of Kinetic Models," *Int. J. Chem. Kinet.*, 17, No. 1, 55 (1985).
13. Cukier, R. I., Fortuin, C. M., Shuler, K. E., Petschek, A. G., Shraibly, J. H., "Study of the Sensitivity of Coupled Reaction Systems to Uncertainties in Rate Coefficients: I. Theory," *J. Chem. Phys.*, 59, No. 8, 3873 (1973).
14. Shraibly, J. H., and Shuler, K. E., "Study of the Sensitivity of Coupled Reaction Systems to Uncertainties in Rate Coefficients. II. Applications," *J. Chem. Phys.*, 59, No. 8, 3879 (1973).
15. Cukier, R. I., Shraibly, J. H., and Shuler, K. E., "Study of the Sensitivity of Coupled Reaction Systems to Uncertainties in Rate Coefficients. III. Analysis of the Approximations," *J. Chem. Phys.*, 63, No. 3, 1140 (1975).
16. Cukier, R. I., Levine, H. B., and Shuler, K. E., Nonlinear Sensitivity Analysis of Multiparameter Model Systems," *J. of Comput. Phys.*, 26(No. 1, 1 (1978).
17. Weyl, H., *Amer. J. Math.*, 60, p. 889 (1938).
18. Sobol, I. M., *Numerical Monte-Carlo Methods* [in Russian], Nauka, Moscow (1973).
19. Sobol, I. M., *Multidimensional Quadrature Formulas and Haar Functions* [in Russian], Nauka, Moscow (1969), p. 196.
20. Sobol, I. M., "On the Systematic Search in a Hypercube, SIAM," *J. Numer. Anal.*, 16, No. 5, 790 (1979).

21. Sobol, I. M., and Statnikov, R. B., *Selection of Optimal Parameters in Problem with Many Criteria* [in Russian], Nauka, Moscow (1981), p. 94.
22. Grigor'eva, T. M., Kolbanovskii, Ju. A., Levitskii, A. A., Polak, L. S., and Tatuzow, R. L., *Kinet. Katal.*, 26, No. 6, 1307, (1985).
23. Gear, C. W., "DIFSUB for Solution of Ordinary Differential Equations," *Com. ACM*. 14, p. 176 (1971).
24. Bard, Y., *Nonlinear Parameter Estimation*, Academic, New York (1974).
25. Boni, A. A., and Penner, R. C., *Combust. Sci. Technol.* 1976, 15, p. 99 (1976).

CHAPTER 35

PRINCIPLES OF FAULT DIAGNOSIS

Peter Andow

KBC Process Automation
Chilworth Research Centre
Southampton, United Kingdom

CONTENTS

INTRODUCTION

Modern process plants are typically large and complex. There have been increasing pressures to reduce product costs, improve product quantity, reduce pollution, and improve safety. These pressures all serve to constrain plant operations ever more tightly. Plant design has tended toward larger plants with fewer streams, continuous operation (where possible), and increasingly automated operation.

An unwanted side effect is that the penalty for plant failure is often high. Many plants have large inventories of hazardous materials. High pressures and temperatures are common. Plant failures are comparatively rare, but the consequences of failure are high. The public at large is also far more aware of the industry and its more spectacular failures. Modern life would be almost unrecognizable without the products that our industry produces. The benefits for society are therefore clear, but they must be balanced against the risks imposed by our plants. If we can reduce the risks, then we are more able to reap the benefits. Fault diagnosis is one tool that we can use to reduce the risks.

What do we mean by "fault diagnosis?" For the purpose of this chapter it will be taken to mean the whole activity (by plant operators) of detecting faults and of taking action to prevent them from causing major failures. Notice that this does not include the after-the-event or "post-mortem" diagnostic activity. We are interested here in preventing failures, not in analyzing them when it's too late. (Post-mortem analysis is of course important—and should be reflected in changes in design, operation and management—but it is not the subject of this chapter).

The material presented will also be strongly oriented to *continuous* plants and will concentrate on the *chemical* industry. The general concepts are, however, clearly applicable to batch and semi-batch plants and also to other industries.

Fault diagnosis is essentially an operational activity. In order to put it into its proper perspective and to define its limitations we need to see how it relates to other activities in the plant life cycle. For this reason we will look at the role of fault diagnosis in some of the more well-known accidents.

CASE HISTORIES

The public's attention has been captured by several of the more catastrophic failures: Flixborough (U.K.) in 1974, Seveso (Italy) in 1976, Three Mile Island (U.S.A.) in 1979, and Bhopal (India) in 1984. These are only some of the more spectacular disasters, but they do serve to illustrate both the potential and the limitations of improved fault diagnosis.

Flixborough

Flixborough is a small village a few miles from the town of Scunthorpe and southwest of the city of Hull. At Flixborough a badly-designed temporary by-pass line failed—see Lees [1]. The line had been designed and installed when the site was operating without a competent mechanical engineer. The line contained two bends to align it to the vessels concerned. The line could not withstand the forces that occurred because of the flow around these bends.

A large quantity of cyclohexane was released, found a source of ignition, and resulted in a large, unconfined vapor cloud explosion. The explosion killed 28 people—18 in the control room. No members of the public were killed, although 53 lesser injuries were reported. Nearly 2,000 buildings were damaged to some extent—although many only had broken windows. To put this into context, this death toll is an order of magnitude higher than the annual average for the whole of the U.K. chemical industry. This accident was easily the worst in the U.K. chemical industry in modern times.

The Flixborough fatalities would have been even worse if the accident had happened on a weekday instead of on a Saturday. The consequences could also have been much worse if the plant had been closer to large residential areas.

The circumstances of the accident are also notable from another viewpoint. The Flixborough plant was the only one of its kind in the country. The company operating it had only this one plant—one with a major hazard process. There was, therefore, very little in the way of support available when the senior mechanical engineer left the company. This combination of circumstances is rather unusual. In spite of this, Flixborough was a watershed for the U.K. chemical industry and led to major changes in safety legislation. (It should be noted, however, that the better companies were already very safety-conscious and, coincidentally, a major European meeting on safety had taken place in the week preceding the explosion).

The accident highlights the importance of design—even superb diagnostic performance would not have prevented Flixborough. The accident also highlights the need for professional engineering management and the support structure that is needed for safe operation of a major hazard site.

At Flixborough fault diagnosis (in the sense outlined earlier) was not relevant—the failure was in the design of the temporary bypass. There is no particular reason to suggest that any operator action could have detected the failure in time to take action.

There are many other lessons that can be learned from Flixborough, but, for the purpose of this chapter, a further point to note is that the temporary pipe introduced a catastrophic failure mode into the plant. Normally, we design such that any single failure is either non-hazardous or very unlikely. We do expect failures to occur, but we design our plants such that they are tolerant of failure. A single failure will then lead to a deterioration in the overall safety of the plant. Subsequent failures move the plant closer to the point where a catastrophic event will occur.

The accident also reminds us that any design can be compromised by ad-hoc modifications.

Seveso

Seveso is a small town about fifteen miles from Milan. At Seveso a reactor producing trichlorophenol had control problems that led to a much larger than normal production of an unwanted, hazardous by-product—2,3,7,8-tetrachlorodibenzoparadioxin (TCDD). The reactor temperature and pressure built up. A safety relief valve then lifted (as it was designed to do) and released a quantity of gas to the atmosphere. It is estimated that this gas contained 2 kg of TCDD, which is one of the most poisonous substances known to man. It can be absorbed into the body by ingestion, inhalation, or skin contact. The main symptom is chloracne (an acne-like skin effect). Other symptoms include skin burns and damage to internal organs and the nervous system.

After the release emergency action was taken inside the works to protect personnel. The company had problems warning the local community because the local authorities were difficult to contact on the day of the accident (it was a Saturday). Little action was taken for several days. Animals near the plant consumed contaminated vegetation and began to die. On the fourth day a child became ill. A state of emergency was declared on the following day. The local population naturally became alarmed as various symptoms appeared. Eventually, 17 days after the release, 250 people were evacuated from the area. A local highway was still in use causing further spread of pollution. It was finally realized that a large area had been contaminated, so more evacuations were ordered. Over forty factories were in the contaminated area. Several points should be noted:

1. The protective system did work as intended. The relief valve opened to protect the vessel.
2. One important lesson is not to vent to atmosphere if the material being vented could (in some circumstances) be hazardous.
3. The consequences were made much worse by the delay in evacuation and isolation of the plant.

Three Mile Island

The accident at the Three Mile Island (TMI) nuclear power plant was caused by water escaping through a partially open valve that should have been closed [2]. This caused the reactor pressure to drop low enough for a steam bubble to form and push more water out of the reactor, eventually partially exposing the core, and damaging the fuel. Water was escaping for over two hours before the basic cause was recognized. During this period the automatic protective systems tried to pump water into the reactor, but the operators stopped these systems from operating. We can draw several lessons from TMI:

1. The operators stopped the protective systems because they were convinced that there was already *too much* water in the reactor when, in fact, there was too little. They were misled by a high level reading in the pressurizer (water was leaving via this vessel). The pressurizer level was normally used to indicate the reactor level, but under the leak conditions prevailing this inference was completely wrong.
2. At the subsequent inquiry into the accident much was made of the fact that such an important measurement as reactor level had to be inferred in this way. Clearly, we should try to measure the variable that we really want. If inferred values are used, then the assumptions used in the inference must be made clear to the operators.
3. A great many alarms occurred during the accident. Most seemed only to add to the confusion. Notice particularly that the alarms were on display for a long time before the fault was correctly diagnosed.
4. The protective systems were overridden by the operators. The "last line of defense" was useless. Good engineering of protective systems is wasted in these circumstances. We often go to great lengths to remove "common mode failures" from our protective systems. In this case the common mode was the operator who didn't recognize the need for more water—and then overrode the protective system that did recognize the need for more water.
5. One of the indications that also caused problems was a panel indication of the position of the leaking valve. In fact the indication was really of the *command* signal to the valve. The indication was read as "valve closed" instead of the (more correct) "valve should be closed." This kind of error is not new. It is easier to provide an indication of the command signal—and perhaps this is better than no indication at all. When an indication is not a feedback signal, it must be made absolutely clear.

Bhopal

The disaster at Bhopal occurred when methyl-iso-cyanate (MIC) escaped from an intermediate storage tank. The escape was apparently caused by a reaction of MIC with water. The tank temperature gradually rose until a runaway caused more and more MIC to vaporize. The plant had been designed to cope with MIC release. The protective systems were in a poor state of repair and failed to cope. Between 2,000 and 3,000 people were killed and another 200,000 injured. The high number of fatalities is partly because the plant attracted people to a previously unpopulated area—but this in no way excuses the fact that the accident happened at all. Particular lessons that should be learned from this disaster are:

1. Protective systems must be kept in a state of good repair. Engineered safeguards are totally useless if company management does not insist on good maintenance—and ensure that it has been carried out.
2. Complex protective systems may not be appropriate for developing countries.
3. A critical measurement (tank temperature) was not properly appreciated by the operators.

From these 4 case studies we see that fault diagnosis is not always a significant factor. Good fault diagnosis could have prevented the accidents at TMI and Bhopal. Other factors were more important at Flixborough and Seveso.

FAULT MANAGEMENT

It has already been noted that we are interested in failures where there are several contributory factors. This will generally mean that there will also be time for operator intervention. Typically the profile of such a fault will involve the following stages:

1. Detection of some abnormal condition.
2. Diagnosis of the basis cause.
3. Formulation of a plan for correction (if possible).
4. Execution of the plan.

These stages are shown in Figure 1. Notice that we are primarily concerned with step 2. Diagnosis must be carried out while further events occur at the plant. Generally there will be an evolving pattern of abnormal conditions:

1. Displays will show that some variables are high or low or changing rapidly or, perhaps, not changing when they should be.
2. Control loops may start to counteract the abnormality.
3. Alarms displays may start to flash and audible alarms will occur.
4. Protective systems may intervene to shut parts or all of the plant down.

Fault diagnosis often seems easy in retrospect ("20/20 hindsight"). By contrast, at the time of the fault, it may seem extremely difficult. In order to appreciate the problems of diagnosis it must also be recognized that there are a whole series of other factors that complicate the diagnostic task:

1. Initially the operator may believe that the fault is due to one of the many minor disturbances that regularly occur.
2. The fault may appear to be simply a failed instrument.
3. There may be maintenance activities on the plant that give rise to various unusual indications.
4. On most plants there are large numbers of "alarms" on display even during normal operation. Further alarms are not therefore particularly surprising. Any new fault is superimposed on this pattern of alarms. Diagnosis will require that the 2 (or more) sets of alarms are recognized— and that new alarms are associated with the appropriate set.
5. The operator may already be heavily loaded with other tasks.
6. For many faults the protective systems will prevent serious damage to the plant. Protective systems do not cater to all possible events (and they can fail themselves).
7. The operator does not know if corrective action is possible or necessary until after he has diagnosed the fault.
8. The operator also knows that for some faults early corrective action will be less costly (and may avoid a plant shutdown). The operator is therefore under pressure to diagnose the fault as early as possible. The time for diagnosis is also fault-dependent. This means that he does not know how long he has for diagnosis until diagnosis is complete.
9. The operator may be under considerable pressure to maintain production if at all possible. Plant trips may also "stress" the plant in addition to the direct costs of shutdown.
10. The pattern of abnormal indications may not be unique even when all the indications have occurred. In the early stages of the fault the pattern is even less likely to be unique.
11. Only a few critical indications are likely to be relevant to a particular fault. In practice these will be hidden among all the other indications and warnings that the operator receives. The operator does not know which indications are critical until *after* the diagnosis.
12. The better operators may have a natural talent for diagnosis, but this is unusual. Training is therefore important. Few operators receive diagnostic training, even though diagnosis may be a very important part of the job.

This is not an exhaustive list, but does serve to illustrate why fault diagnosis can be a difficult task.

THE IMPORTANCE OF DESIGN

Fault diagnosis is clearly an activity that is performed during plant operation. Poor design will cause or worsen many operational problems. In this section we examine some of those aspects of plant design that may affect fault diagnosis.

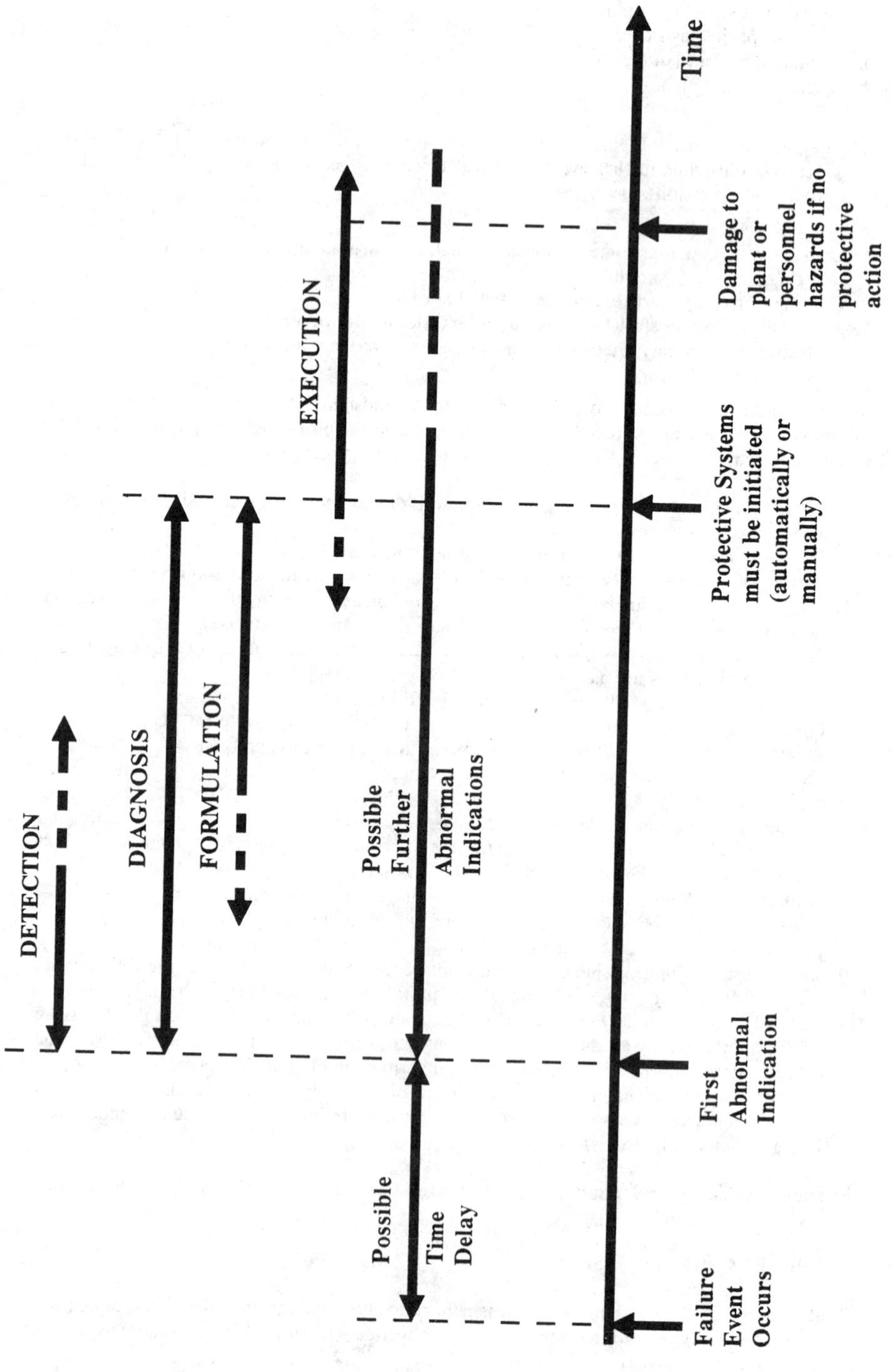

Figure 1. Profile of a fault.

Process and Plant Design

Many of the problems of plant operation arise from a design that is *inherently* difficult to operate or *inherently* unsafe. If a plant is inherently difficult to operate, then faults are more likely to occur or will be more diffidult to correct. If a plant is inherently unsafe then the consequences of poor fault diagnosis are more serious. How often are such factors considered at the design stage? Kletz [3] has produced an excellent book on inherently safe plants. Applying his ideas to Flixborough we see that a major factor was the large inventory of hazardous material involved. If we really cannot avoid having such materials in our plants, then we should at least try to minimize the quantities involved.

It should also be noted that after the Bhopal incident it was decided that the best way to dispose of the materials on site was to restart the process and make more MIC, but to use it immediately rather than store it as an intermediate, thereby reducing the inventory of hazardous material. It is always attractive to have intermediate storage in plants for operational reasons, but do the benefits really outweigh the problems when the material stored is MIC?

During design we should also use techniques such as HAZOP (Hazard and Operability study) Kletz [4]. HAZOP helps to ensure that we eliminate or reduce design errors before the plant is built. One of the benefits of HAZOP that is directly relevant here is that it helps to ensure that the operator will be able to observe deviations from the design intention. For instance, if a fault can cause a low flow rate (and there is a serious consequence), then HAZOP will draw attention to the need for a low-flow indication (or alarm or trip). An unwanted side effect is that the number of indications displayed to the operator increases.

By applying the principles of inherently safe design and use of HAZOP (or some equivalent technique), we will reduce or eliminate plant hazards, and thereby reduce the need for good fault diagnosis.

Design of Monitoring and Control Systems

The design of the plant instrumentation is particularly important for fault diagnosis. Of equal importance is the role of the human operator as a component in the monitoring and control system—yet this aspect of design rarely receives the attention that it deserves. On many modern plants the instrumentation takes care of a large part of the traditional operator's task. This has reduced the need for large operating teams. A major task for operators within this environment is fault diagnosis. This task may even be the main reason for having human operators present on the plant. It is therefore clear that the needs and limitations of the human operator should be major factors in the design of the control room and its instrumentation systems.

Designing for Diagnosis

If one's primary task is diagnosis, then it is even more apparent that the design should be "optimized" with this in mind. In practice it is seen that control systems are often very poor from this viewpoint. Control room ergonomics leaves much to be desired. From a diagnostic point of view it is useful to look in particular at the design of alarm systems. Kragt [5] has examined the alarms systems on operating plants and found many failings. Observation of other systems shows that many have similar failings to those observed by Kragt. It is not unusual to find some or all of the following poor features:

1. A very large number of distinct alarm indications. Most plants have several hundred alarms and several thousand is not unusual.
2. Many of the alarms seem to be of doubtful value. Modern "distributed" systems encourage the use of extra alarms by making it so easy to add software-based alarms to every analogue signal.
3. Many plants have no design criteria for alarm systems.

Design of Alarm Systems

Good design often involves design codes that effectively embody design criteria. Process plant alarms systems need criteria, just like any other aspect of the plant. Plamping and Andow [6] show that similar procedures can also be developed for alarm systems. As yet though, there is no well-established and accepted procedure for alarm system design.

In the absence of such a procedure it is still possible to establish a checklist of questions to stimulate the designer:

1. What is the overall function of the alarm system? Is it intended merely to act as an indication that abnormal events are occurring or is it intended as a diagnostic aid? (Sometimes alarm systems are primarily used for control purposes—to indicate that an adjustment needs to be made on a control loop. This is quite different from the kind of system that will be good for diagnostic purposes).
2. If the system is to be used for diagnosis, how often will a correct diagnosis be expected from the operator?
3. Has there been any systematic attempt to ensure that the operator is able to use the system to discriminate adequately between alternative failures?
4. Will the system give the operator adequate time to perform diagnosis?
5. Does the plant provide suitable means for corrective action following diagnosis? (If it doesn't, alarms are of little value, except for evacuation purposes).
6. Does the operator need any job aids to help him perform the diagnostic task? (Or will it be completely automated?)
7. Is there a target frequency for the maximum arrival rate of all alarms during "normal" operation?
8. Is there a target frequency for the maximum arrival rate of individual alarms?
9. Is there any systematic attempt to specify individual alarms on a rational basis (type of alarm, number of limits, limit settings, alarm priority, hysteresis, type of annunciator device)?

It is not easy to answer these questions properly—a good design requires attention to detail. The questions presented here are to stimulate thought. If we expect our operators to run plants efficiently and safely then we must engineer our protective systems carefully.

PROCESS OPERATION

All process plants of any size are continually subjected to disturbances. If the plant has been well-designed (as suggested earlier) then the impact of these disturbances will be smaller:

1. The plant designers will have identified sources of disturbances and the design may incorporate buffering vessels, although we should avoid high-hazard materials in these vessels.
2. Control systems will cope with other frequently-occurring faults.
3. The operators will be trained to deal with disturbances that cannot be effectively handled by the control systems, or with disturbances that require reconfiguration of the control systems.

Even on batch plants, modern control systems are now able to relieve the operator of many traditional tasks.

It might then appear that the operator has very little to occupy his time. In practice this is rarely true—even on well-designed plants the operators are usually continually occupied. What do the operators actually do?

The Role of Operators

The previous comments apply mainly to modern plants. On older plants the operators spend much of their time on *control* activities. They make regular adjustments to the plant. Pumps are stopped and started manually—or start/stop sequences are initiated manually. Valves are opened and closed by manual action at the plant, or by operator action from the control room.

On more modern plants (which we are more concerned with here), the situation is quite different:

1. The operator will be continually monitoring the plant to check that it is functioning as intended.
2. He recognizes disturbances as they enter the plant.
3. He ensures that the control systems function correctly as disturbances pass through the plant.

A large part of the operator's job is likely to be concerned with these monitoring activities.

Operators often perform tasks as part of a data collection system. (Sometimes such tasks are invented by management to keep the operators busy—which is probably counter-productive). Data collection may also entail interaction with laboratory analysis staff.

Many modern control systems also support the operator when control systems are reconfigured to cope with new operating conditions (such as feedstock changes or product specification changes). The operator may initiate and/or monitor the reconfiguration and may be actively involved in some parts of it.

On many plants the operator will also be involved with other activities, such as the effects of maintenance work. He may be responsible for "permits to work" on the plant. He may also make and receive telephone and/or radio calls to or from other parts of the plant complex, often acting in a *coordinating* and/or *supervisory* role in these activities.

Consideration of these activities shows why there is no strong move towards completely automated plants—the so-called "unmanned control room". Even if a plant were "completely" automated, there would still be failures of the automatic equipment. We can design so that some failures are automatically detected, but we *cannot* do this for all failure modes (this will be discussed later). For the forseeable future there will be some diagnostic and/or maintenance activity performed by humans—at least until robotics is much more advanced than it is now.

Even when we automate control tasks to a high level we are always tempted to leave the operator with ultimate responsibility—just in case we made a mistake in the design or neglected something.

This is not necessarily wrong—but we pay dearly for this philosophy when we construct a control room. The control process performed in a modern distributed system typically involves hundreds or thousands of distinct measurements. The control schemes are increasingly sophisticated. In addition to the conventional 3-term control we increasingly use cascade and ratio loops, feedforward control, multivariable control, dead-time compensation, etc.

We do this because there are clear benefits and, perhaps more importantly, because computers are able to rapidly process the large volumes of data involved. We also tend to automate those tasks that are easy to describe algorithmically—but this also means that we are leaving the more nebulous tasks for the man, or woman.

This is only a very cursory view of the role of the operator. See Johannsen [7], Swain [8], and Rasmussen [9] for more detailed consideration of this neglected area.

The Problems of Diagnosis

The problems begin when we then try to display the computer's activities in a "transparent" way to the (comparatively) slow human operator. If the operator is ultimately responsible, then we usually need an elaborate control room with complex and expensive display systems. We try to design the displays and controls using sound ergonomic principles. We try to make the systems as simple to use as possible—but we do this against a background of increasing complexity inside the computer.

Fault Detection

When a disturbance or fault occurs, the operator must first *detect* it. In the broadest terms, he does this by noticing a deviation from the expected performance of the plant. This may be either deviation from the steady state when no deviation is expected, or deviation from an expected transient response (no response, slow response, fast response, wrong response shape).

In either case it is seen that the operator is effectively comparing the actual response of the process with some "model" behavior (although the model may not be a mathematical model in the normal sense). The discrepancy between expectation and reality must be noticed against the background of other possible events on the plant. The operator's model may also be rather "fuzzy"—his predicted response may actually be best envisaged as a whole range of possible responses, between upper and lower bounds.

The action of control systems may also hide the fault from the operator. For example, a small leak from a reactor can exist for a long time and only be detected by a low level alarm in a make-up tank.

It must also be recognized that some faults will not give rise to any symptoms until some other event occurs. For example, an impulse line in a protective system may be accidentally crushed—and will not be evident until the protective system is tested or needed.

Fault Diagnosis

Diagnosis really begins when some deviation from expectation has been detected. If a fault occurs regularly, then a good operator will rapidly learn to recognize its symptoms. If the operator has been trained in diagnosis, then he may be able to cope with a significant number of distinct faults [10]. This kind of training is rare. (A good operator may even have a natural talent for diagnosis, and be able to cope with novel faults). Difficulties arise when:

1. The symptoms are similar to a known fault but not quite the same. It is tempting to "recognize" the familiar fault and ignore contradictory evidence. Once the operator has diagnosed a fault incorrectly, it is unlikely that he will change his mind (the "mind set" phenomenon).
2. Other faults already exist on the plant (there are often many active "alarms" even during normal operation). The operator must then disentangle the two (or more) sets of symptoms.
3. The plant is being operated in an unusual way—perhaps simply a different steady state from that normally used. The operator's lack of experience of the unusual conditions will mean that his model of expected behavior will be more fuzzy. The plant behavior may also be highly non-linear in some conditions—particularly when operating at or near some physical constraint. His knowledge and expectations of behavior under fault conditions may be poor.
4. The fault condition *structurally* alters the plant behavior. For example, a heat exchanger tube leak that causes a loss of pressure and consequent boiling.
5. The fault is rare or novel. Some faults are unlikely to occur during the life of the plant and yet may have serious consequences.

Diagnostic Aids

Diagnosis is often difficult. The large number of indications available to the operator make it even more difficult. We use alarms to focus his attention on significant deviations. Unfortunately, we often use too many alarms [11]. The operator cannot "focus" his attention on a large number of distinct variables. It was suggested earlier that good alarm system design is important. It is emphasized here that improving the quality of alarms is almost certainly the single most important contribution to the diagnostic problem. Diagnostic training is also very important, and will be particularly productive if the alarm system is also well-designed.

Diagnostic aids fall into three categories:

1. Aids primarily designed for other purposes that are also useful in diagnosis.
2. Paper-based aids designed specifically for diagnosis.
3. Computer-based aids designed specifically for diagnosis.

The first category is concerned primarily with statistical aids for process identification [12]. These aids are useful in diagnosis because they help the operator identify faulty instruments (faulty instruments are a major cause of problems in diagnosis). These aids use techniques like Kalman filtering to produce a more accurate display of the process parameters. These aids may also use specific checks on mass balances and energy balances, which are commonly used for data reconciliation. This kind of aid is very useful as a platform on which diagnosis can be based. It is even better if a diagnosis-specific aid is used as well. The main problem with this kind of aid is that it does not usually include any specific targets for diagnostic performance.

The second category consists mainly of procedures for use in specific situations. Typically, there will be a tree-structured analysis that derives the causes of particular combinations of fault conditions. When a fault occurs the operator is led through a series of questions concerning parameter indications and/or alarms until a particular diagnosis is given.

The main problem with this kind of aid is that it is based on a pre-determined set of faults. All such diagnostic systems use some "cut-off" frequency. Any fault with a lower frequency than the cut-off is considered to be too improbable to be considered. As circumstances change the likelihood of such faults can change dramatically. Some faults that appeared very unlikely at the design stage may suddenly become quite likely. Paper-based aids are thus very prone to changes in circumstances. In order to be at all effective they need to be carefully maintained. Even if they are well-maintained they will still be susceptible to low-frequency faults (when an unlikely fault actually occurs we would like to be able to give some diagnostic support—it's not much use to print out a message to the effect that the fault being considered is unknown and must therefore be a low-frequency one).

The third category of system is the one that has received most attention recently. There have been a whole series of publications on computer-based fault diagnosis [13–16]. In principle the idea is very simple:

1. When a fault occurs, it will produce a pattern of symptoms.
2. These patterns are predicted for a whole series of faults.
3. The faults and patterns are then stored in a computer.
4. The symptom pattern at any stage of plant operation is then compared to the stored patterns until a match is found, and hence the fault has been diagnosed.

The computer may be on-line to the process or be used in a stand-alone mode. There are obvious advantages to an on-line system, but more complex software is needed.

In practice several problems arise. Various diagnostic methodologies have been proposed. These two aspects of diagnosis will now be considered separately.

Diagnostic Problems

Computer-based fault diagnosis is not new. Systems for use in process plants and on nuclear power stations were reported twenty years ago [17, 18]. Various problems have been found:

1. We set out to predict fault patterns for a single fault acting in isolation. As noted earlier, we often find that there are many alarms etc. on display even at "steady state." To be realistic our system must be able to work when a new fault is superimposed onto an existing set of abnormal indications.
2. It may not be easy to predict fault symptoms with confidence. For example, faults such as pipe break can have multiple possible symptom patterns, depending on position and size of leak. In some plants (such as pressurized water reactors) these faults are very important.
3. It may be necessary to include time delays and/or the *sequence* of fault symptoms in the pattern. This complicates the analysis considerably and yet may be needed in order to discriminate between similar faults.
4. Instrument faults are fairly common. On a large plant there will often be several failed measuring devices. The pattern of symptoms obtained will obviously change if a measuring device fails.
5. Symptom patterns are very susceptible to the alarm limits chosen. A fault pattern may specify a high temperature . If the high alarm limit is set at 350 K the pattern will not match if the temperature only rises to 349 K. This can be very deceptive.

6. We cannot cater to every fault on an a priori analysis basis. An infinite number of failure conditions can occur—but most are *extremely* unlikely. We usually aim to cover all the faults that are predicted to occur more often than some pre-set frequency. In the U.K. a common criterion is that any event that could cause a fatality must not occur more than once in 30,000 years [4]. In practice any rational a priori analysis must use some similar basis. The logic of this is inescapable—we spend our effort on the most likely faults. In practice it means that our support system has an in-built "cliff edge." We give the operator full support right up to the edge of the cliff, and then give him none at all for faults with which he is likely to be less familiar. There is also the problem that some unforseen change in plant circumstances will make our probabilistic basis completely wrong—some of the faults that were expected to be very unlikely are now much more probable to occur.

DIAGNOSTIC METHODS

There is an important contribution to fault diagnosis from work using linear systems theory for filtering and parameter estimation [19]. This work clearly has relevance for fault diagnosis since it provides a better view of the process. Filtering and parameter estimation are particularly useful where signal noise or slow instrument drift is significant. It is also useful in problems where kinetic performance is important, such as problems involving catalytic activity and "hot spots."

It may observed that this latter type of problem is often characterized by parameters that are difficult or impossible to measure using conventional process instrumentation. In this chapter it will be assumed that filtering and estimation techniques will be applied when appropriate. This does not remove the need for, or preclude the use of, diagnosis, which will then be based on a more accurate picture of the process. Filtering and parameter estimation is therefore considered to be important in that they are tools that provide a platform on which to perform diagnosis. The techniques that we will consider are more appropriate where many parameters *are* measured (some measurements will, however, be faulty). The kind of fault that is most likely to be of interest is where some discrete event causes a gross change in the process (such as a pump failure or a line blockage or a leak). We are also interested in parameter disturbances that propagate through a large plant causing other parameters to deviate from their normal values.

The techniques used in diagonsis are many and varied. They may be broadly classed in two categories, although there is an obvious overlap between the two: logic-based methods and fuzzy-logic methods.

With logic-based methods we effectively use statements of the form:

if X and Y then Z

meaning

if X is true and Y is true then Z is true

This kind of formalism is attractive for use in fault diagnosis because many scientists and engineers can express diagnostic logic in this way. X, Y, and Z will normally represent fault conditions (such as *cooling water pump failed*) or deviations in parameter values (such as *feed flow high*). Our statements are really expressions of causal logic. The example could therefore be interpreted as:

Z can be caused by the combination of X and Y

Notice that we use "can be" in this interpretation. This is important because there will normally be other possible causes of Z. The logic statement predicts that the coincidence of X and Y will cause Z, but that the existence of Z does not prove that X and Y have occurred.

The logic statements can involve more that two conditions. They can also include "or" and "not" operators to express complex logic:

if (A and B) or (C and D and not (E)) then P

The events A, B, C, D, and E may themselves be expressed by means of other statements, for example:

if I or J then A

if J or (K and L) then B

It soons becomes quite difficult to "read" what the *set* of logic statements means. There are a variety of logic diagrams that may be used as an aid to expressing this type of logic.

Fault Trees

The most common type of logic diagram is the fault tree [20]. Fault trees are widely used in safety and reliability analyses. They are constructed by working backwards from the "top event." The top event is the failure event of interest (such as *reactor overpressure*). We work backwards from the top event that we want to avoid looking for the possible causes. For a more detailed treatment of fault tree construction see the Appendix to this chapter. Some fault trees are very complex. However, complex the tree appears the end result is equivalent to a single complex logic statement. Various computer-based aids are available to help construct fault trees [21]. The net result of the 3 statements given may be expressed as a fault tree (see Figure 2) or may be expressed as a more complex logic statement:

if ((I or J) and (J or (K and L)) or (C and D and not (E)) then P

This may in turn be expressed as a series of alternate causes of P:

if I and J then P (1)

if I and K and L then P (2)

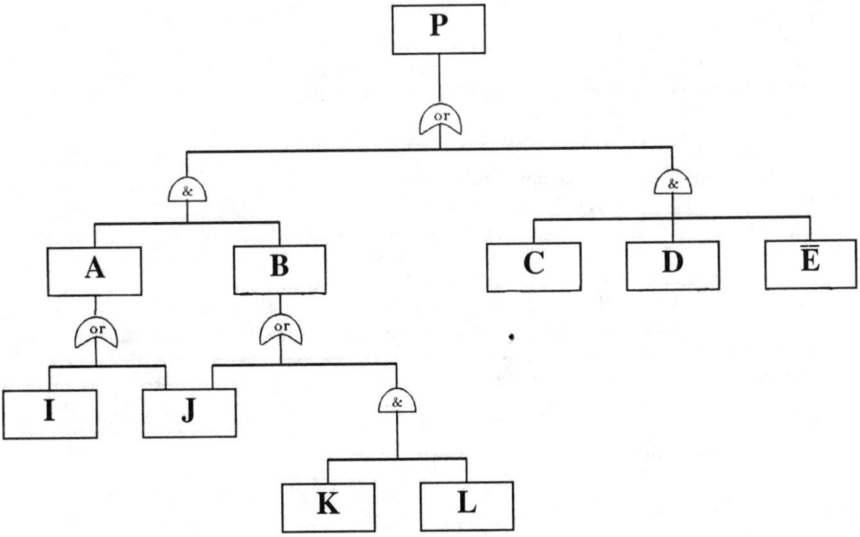

Figure 2. Fault tree.

if J then P (3)

if J and K and L then P (4)

if C and D and not (E) then P (5)

Sometimes, as in the example, the resulting statements contain inconsistencies. For example statement 3 above says that J by itself causes P. Statements 1 and 4 are then superfluous. (This does not necessarily mean that the individual statements are wrong). In the jargon of fault tree analysis statements 1 to 5 are the "cut sets" of the fault tree. Statements 2, 3, and 5 are the "minimum cut sets" of the fault tree. A minimum cut set is a set of events that causes P and is not itself a super set of some other cut set of the fault tree. The Appendix to this chapter includes an algorithm for finding minimum cut sets from a list of cut sets. It is immediately obvious that a complex fault tree (one that can contain dozens of "and," "or," and "not" gates) can contain many cut sets. The cut sets are important because they are the failure mechanisms of the system. Computer codes are available to help analyse fault trees to find cut sets and minimum cut sets [22].

It is also clear that the alternative failure mechanisms have different frequencies of occurrence. The frequency of each failure mechanism depends on the events I, J etc. The computer codes referred to can quantify a fault tree so that the overall frequency is calculated. The contribution of each minimum cut set can also be found. This enables the important failure events to be rapidly identified—even in a very complex fault tree.

Fault trees provide a means for linking new deviations (or failures) to previous events. They are useful for mapping the propagation of a fault through the plant. They provide a "template" that we can attempt to match to a pattern of symptoms. From a diagnostic viewpoint, a fault tree is not very useful if we can only use it when the (undersirable) top event has occurred. For diagnostic purposes it is, therefore, more appropriate that the top events are conditions that occur some time *before* the condition that we are trying to avoid. We will refer to this kind of event as a "critical event." Our overall pattern of events is then:

Minor Failure(s) ⇒ Critical Event(s) ⇒ Major Failure(s)

Our fault trees now relate the critical events to minor failures. When a critical event occurs, the operator uses the appropriate fault tree to find the cause. How does the fault tree fit in with our 4-step fault management process? Examining the steps individually:

1. Detection—the fault tree does not really help much in this step. Any alarms or indications that do occur may appear in many trees. We could scan them all to locate the particular symptom observed, but this would be time-consuming and unproductive. (The particular abnormal condition will only appear in one of them if it leads to one of the previously forseen critical events.)
2. Diagnosis—the fault tree was designed for this step. A good fault tree for the critical event will contain one branch that will match against the particular set of conditions (provided that the actual cause was recognized by the analyst as being reasonably likely, i.e., will occur more often than the "cut-off" frequency).
3. Formulation—the fault tree will not help directly with this step. It gives the cause, which may suggest the best corrective action, but this is up to the operator and is not contained in the fault tree itself.
4. Execution—the fault tree does not help here.

We could also use fault trees that link critical events to "major failure" events. We would still need to search through this second level of fault trees finding those trees in which the particular critical event occurred. This might be a practical approach on many plants, but is still not ideal.

What we really need is a logic diagram that works forwards from the critical event. The "Event Tree" is designed for this task.

Event Trees

The event tree is very much like a fault tree except that it works forwards from a critical event evaluating the possible alternative scenarios that could occur. The event tree branches each represent one scenario. The number of possible branches is dependent on the number of backup systems and/or protective systems and/or operator actions that are appropriate in some circumstance following the critical event.

A simple event tree is shown in Figure 3. In this tree the critical event is GRID POWER FAILS. The plant has an emergency diesel generator that should start automatically. The plant operating instructions allow the plant to be operated for two hours without grid power. If grid power has not been restored at the end of theis period, the plant must be shut down. This is also expected to take up to two hours, and so a total of four hours of emergency duty is required from the diesel generator. The event tree contains the two failure events *diesel fails to start* and *diesel fails to run for 4 hours.* Notice that the event tree contains "success" paths as well as failures—unlike the fault tree. Notice also that only relevant failure events are considered on each path. If the diesel generator fails to start, there is no point in considering *diesel fails to run for 4 hours.* Notice also that the event tree contains a variety of different outcomes. This can be useful in diagnostic terms because it can give the operator a view of just how serious the critical event can be if it is not handled properly. It also shows him how to "steer" the plant to the best outcome in the given circumstances.

Figure 4 also contains frequency and probability data. The initial frequency (of *grid power fails*) is assumed. The two probabilities are derived from the following simple reliability caluclation. The data values used are based on data given by Lees [1]. The particular values chosen are reasonably realistic and also keep the example simple:

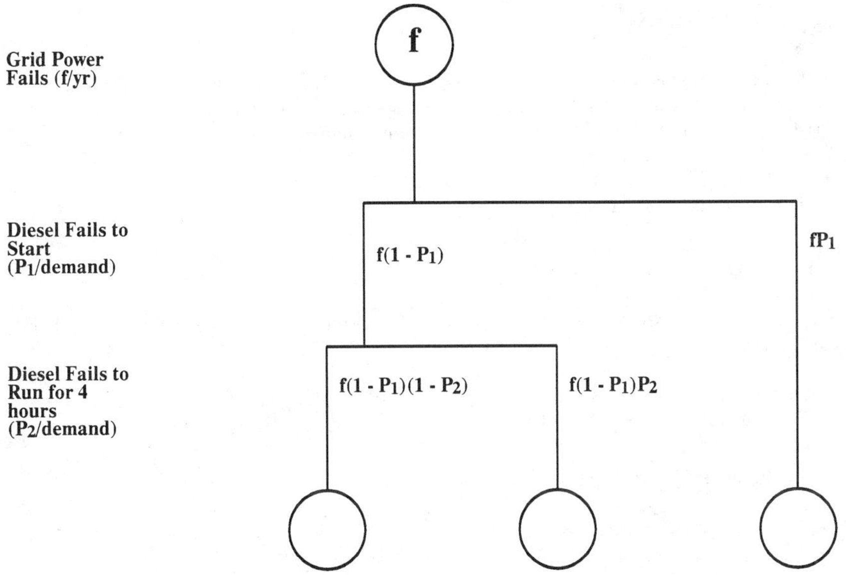

Figure 3. Event tree.

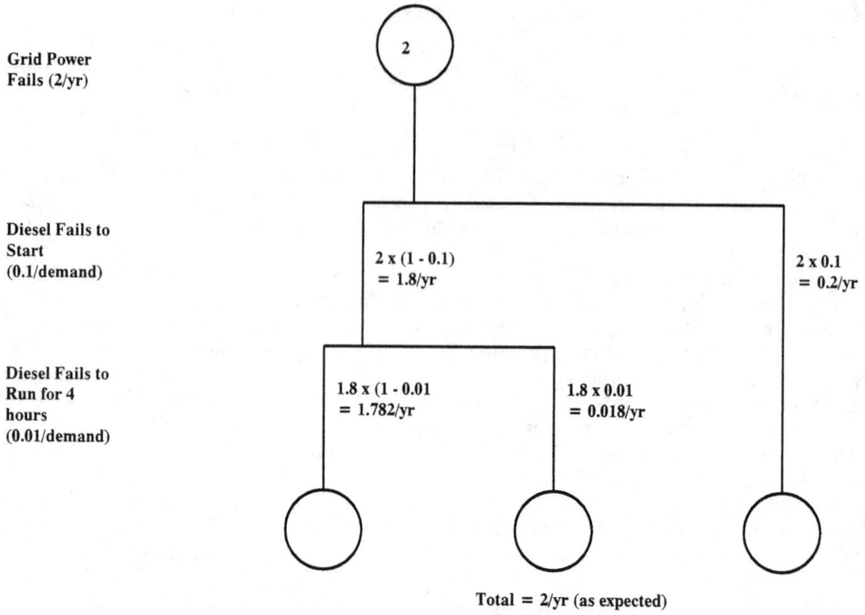

Figure 4. Event tree quantification.

Problem

A diesel generator is used to provide emergency power. It is normally on "cold" standby. The failure rate on cold standby is 2/yr. It is tested 10 times per year. When needed it should run for at least 4 hours. The running failure rate is 0.0025/hr. What is:

a) The probability of "fail to start"?
b) The probability of "fail to run for 4 hours"?

Solution

See Kletz [4] or McCormick [33] for formulae commonly used in safety and reliability calculations.

a) Standby failure rate = Fs = 2/yr.
Test interval = T = 0.1 yr

Using:
Fractional dead time, $FDT = 0.05 * Fs * T$
$= 0.5 * 2 * 0.1$
or: $FDT = 0.1$

This is the probability of "Fail to start".
Answer: a) P("Fail to start") = 0.1/demand

b) Running failure rate = Fr = 0.0025/hr
Running time = 4 hr.

Using:
Unreliability $F(t) = Fr * t$
$= 0.0025 * 4$
or: $F(t) = 0.01$/demand

This is the probability of "Fail to run for 4 hours."
Answer: b) P("Fail to run for 4 hours") = 0.01/demand
These values are used in the event tree of Figure 4.

How does the event tree fit into our four-step fault management process? Examining the steps individually:

1. Detection—the event tree does not really help us particularly. The critical event that is used as the basis of the tree will not often coincide with the first indication of a fault condition. Even for the example chosen, where *grid power fails* might well be alarmed, there are likely to be several indications (such as *pump discharge pressure low*) that would appear at about the same time. A "first-up" alarm feature might be useful in this case. This particularly critical event is of course one that would be quite easy to detect in most plants—not least because it may suddenly become very quiet.
2. Diagnosis—the event tree doesn't help at all during this step.
3. Formulation—the event tree is very good at this stage. It shows the possible scenarios following on from the critical event for various combinations of subsequent failures. It shows the "best" result that can be achieved as well as more serious consequences. It highlights the important systems and operator actions.
4. Execution—the event tree helps considerably at this stage. The operator will normally try to follow the "best" path. If further problems occur, then the tree will indicate what the options (if any) and consequences are.

The event tree therefore has some advantages and some disadvantages, when compared to the fault tree. It is quite clear that the two techniques complement each other. They could be used together with the "critical event" as the transition point from using the fault tree (for diagnosis) to the event tree (for formulation and execution of corrective action). Alternatively we could use a cause consequence diagram that combines the advantages of both techniques.

Cause Consequence Diagrams

The cause consequence diagram combines the features of the fault tree and the event tree (although it is not simply the two joined together). Figure 5 shows an example of a cause consequence diagram (CCD).

The diagram contains one or more "critical events." By convention we draw causes at the top of the diagram and consequences at the bottom. The diagram also contains "decision boxes" that indicate success or failure for various possible failure events and/or operator actions. The diagram also includes time delays—in contrast to the fault tree and event tree, which do not include time explicitly. Notice that the decision boxes are used to include success paths in the diagram—like the event tree. Small fault trees may also be linked to the decision boxes to show why systems may fail. The CCD clearly combines many of the advantages of the fault tree and the event tree. It is the "richest" of the more well-known logic diagrams, but is correspondingly the most time-consuming to produce. The CCD is useful for steps 2, 3, and 4 (diagnosis, formulation and execution) of the fault management cycle—but is not of much help in step 1 (detection).

All 3 logic diagrams so far examined have the common feature that they strongly focus on particular final events (fault tree) or initial events (event tree) or intermediate critical events (CCD). A problem with this approach is that these events have to be identified in order for the logic diagram to be constructed. Techniques such as HAZOP (noted earlier) may be useful in this context. There is however some attraction in the use of a more general type of logic diagram, such as the directed graph, which does not require such rigorous definition of critical events.

Legend for Figure 7

A. Main power supply fails

B. Local power distribution fault

C. Main power system failure

D. Power-fail detection monitor works correctly (causing emergency diesel start sequence initiation

E. Operator initiates emergency diesel start sequence

F. Emergency diesel generator starts

G. Emergency diesel generator runs for required period

H. Back-up battery system (for control power only) works correctly

J. Main motor power available

K. Control power available

L. No power available

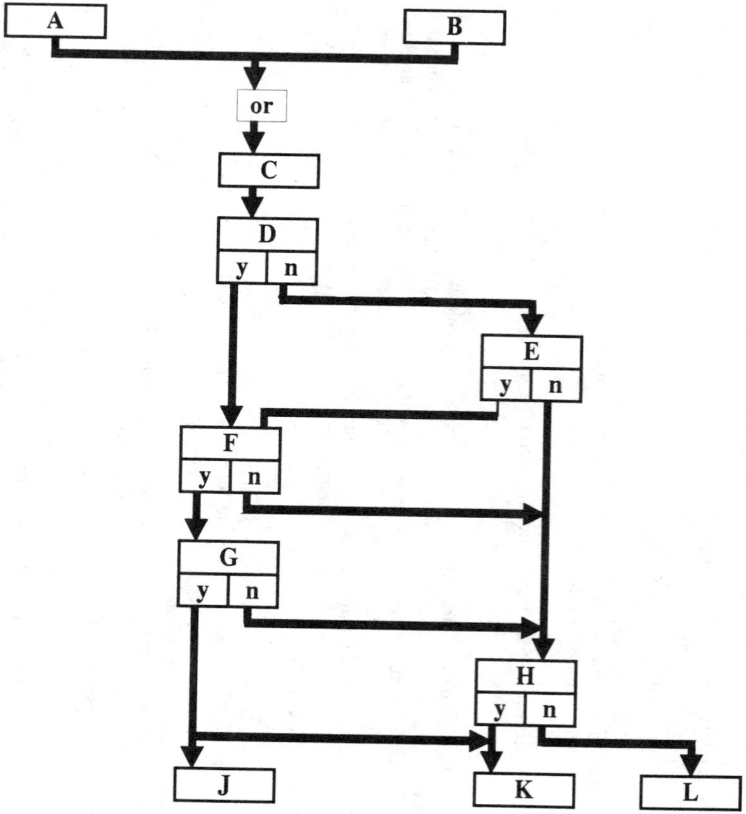

Figure 5. Cause consequence diagram.

Directed Graphs

A directed graph is a logic diagram that uses "nodes" to represent system variables or failure events and "edges" (also known as "arcs") to show the causal links between the nodes. Figure 6 shows a header tank with flows in and out. Figure 7 shows the corresponding digraph. Note that the edges are labeled to indicate the failure condition represented. Note also that the "strength" of the edge is also included. A strength of 1 indicates that a small deviation at one node will cause a small deviation at the next node. A strength of 10 indicates that a small deviation at one node will cause a large deviation at the next node.

Although the digraph may soon become quite complex, it is much more flexible than say, a fault tree, which has to be constructed for a specific failure event. The penalty is that the digraph does not show the exact mapping of failure states. For a fault tree to show this it must be inferred from the graph. In particular, any loops in the graph must be carefully noted when tracing causal paths. Lapp and Powers [23] describe a method that uses digraphs containing multiple loops as the basis of fault tree construction. The Lapp and Powers method uses a recursive algorithm (because of the need to cater to nested loops) and hence is really only suitable for computer-based fault diagnosis. Andow and Lees [24] describe applications in real-time fault diagnosis. More recently, O'Shima et al. [25] have developed the technique and describe some examples in detail.

A drawback with all of the logic diagrams so far described is that it is not always easy to specify the exact failure state. This is where fuzzy logic is attractive.

Fuzzy Logic

If we have a high reactor temperature, what do we really mean by "high"? The meaning is clear in linguistic terms—we usually mean "significantly highr than normal." Do we mean 10 degrees or 20 degrees? Assume for the moment that an appropriate limit between normal and high is 15

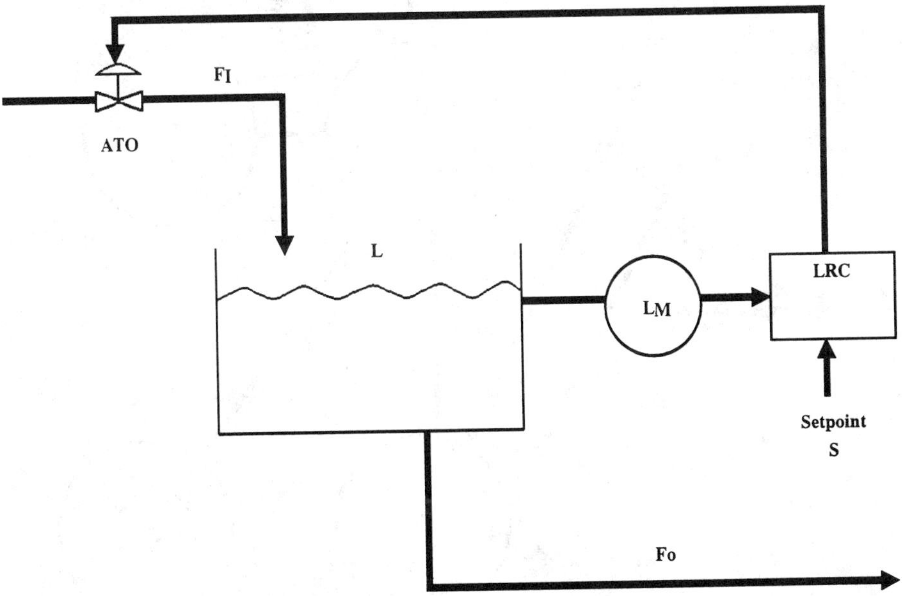

Figure 6. Header tank.

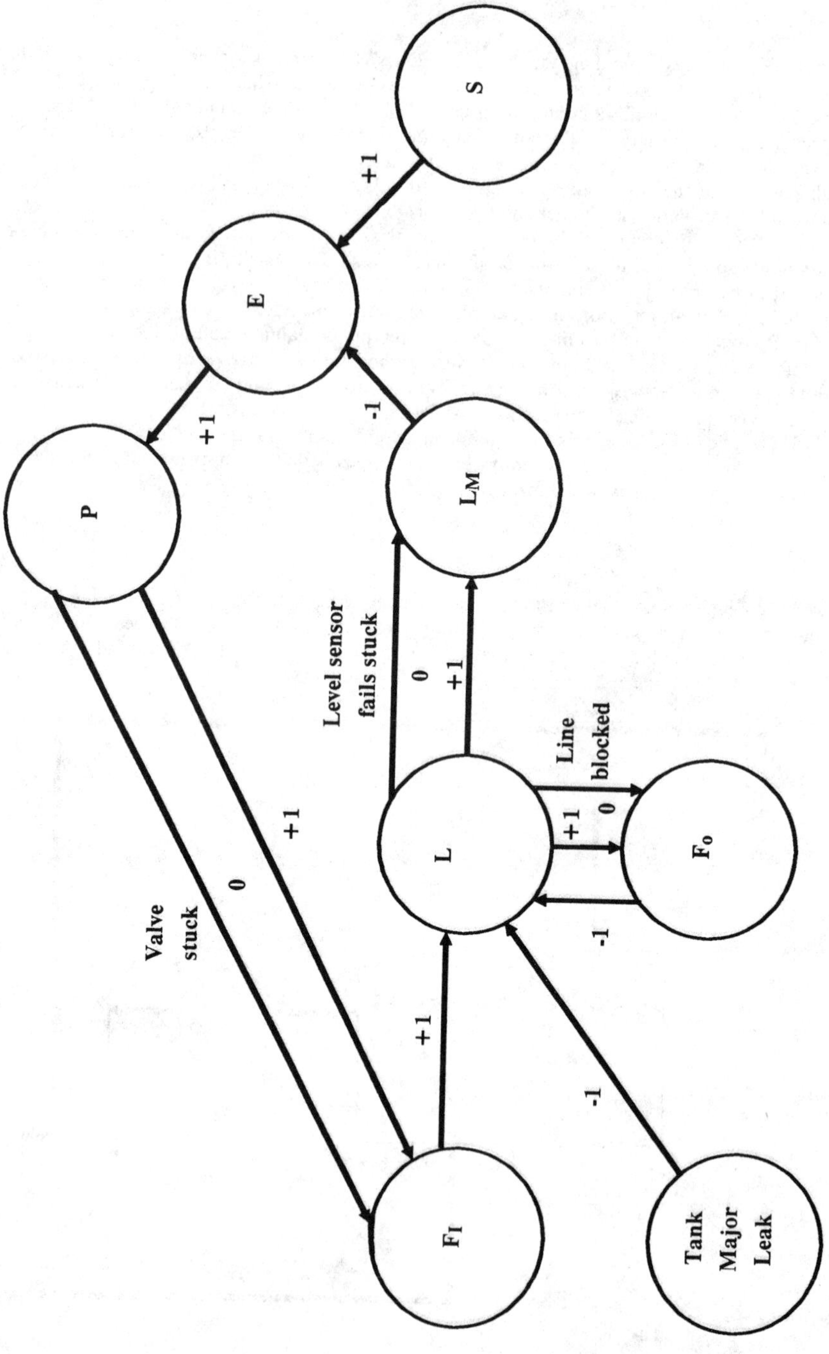

Figure 7. Digraph of header tank.

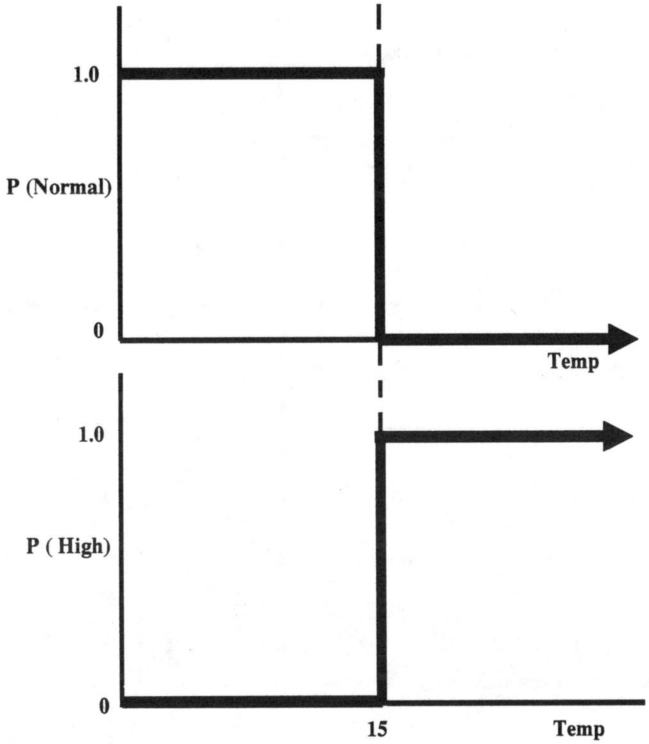

Figure 8. Discrete logic.

degrees higher. We now have the unsatisfactory situation that a deviation of 14.5 degrees is still normal but 15.5 degrees is suddenly high. In reality the transition between normal and high is not that rapid, and our logic models are not that precise. It is often undesirable to have such a sudden transition between states. We could of course use an intermediate state (such as disturbed high), but this does not really solve the problem—it justs adds one more arbitrary limit value. This is the essence of the "discretization problem"—choosing a sensible number of distinct states and setting meaningful boundary values between them. Fuzzy logic helps to overcome this problem by allowing a gradual transition between states. When we say (with conventional logic) that 15.5 degrees is high then this can be interpreted as:

The probability of being in the high state is 1.0.

Correspondingly,

The probability of being in the normal state is 0.0.

This is shown in Figure 8. By contrast, fuzzy logic allows us to define a transition point (in this case 15 degrees) where both high and normal have equal probabilities—of 0.5. We can also define a region in which the probability of being high moves gradually from 0.0 to 1.0. This is shown in Figure 9.

This must be closer to physical reality. We see that some temperatures (a little above normal) are "slightly" high, with a gradual increase in the "degree of highness" as the temperature increases. The penalty for this improved representation is an increase in complexity.

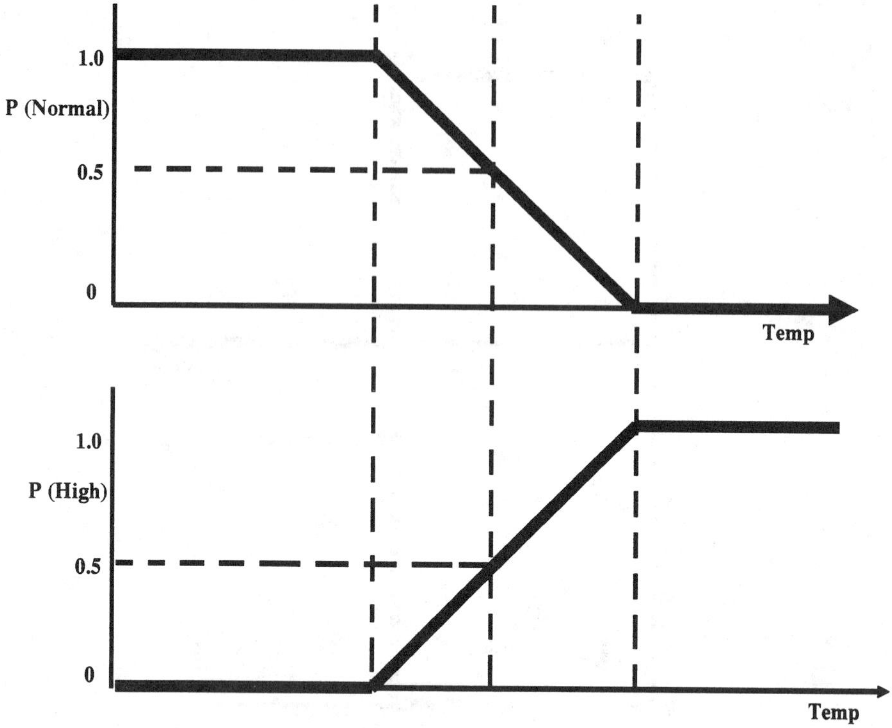

Figure 9. Fuzzy logic.

When used to interpret a temperature anywhere is our transition region, the fuzzy logic interpretation tells us that there are two possible states (normal and high) with distinct probabilities. We need to evaluate the possible causes of both of these states. In this discussion we have only considered two states of one variable. When we start to evaluate causes of deviations, we encounter several variables and some variables will have three (or more) possible states. The complexity of the analysis increases considerably. There is also a more difficult task in defining the fuzzy interactions between combinations of variables—which we need to do for failure analysis. In practical terms, we also need to cope with this increased complexity when we communicate the results of a fuzzy logic diagnosis with operators. For the present it appears that fuzzy logic is technically the best technique, but the increased complexity is certainly a barrier to widespread acceptance. Most of the reported work on fault diagnosis does not use fuzzy logic.

See Dohnal [26] for a broader discussion of the use of Fuzzy Logic.

SUMMARY

This chapter has examined many aspects of process design and operation that impact on fault diagnosis. Many criticisms have been made of current practices. These criticisms could be interpreted in a very negative way. The intention here is not to criticize designers and operators of plants, but to recognize that the whole engineering profession has much to learn in some of these areas.

We have much to learn about diagnosis and how the human operator can best be used in diagnostic tasks. In other areas, such as plant design, our store of knowledge is much richer, but we need to ensure that we apply that knowledge more effectively.

In the space available here we concentrate on the broader aspects of fault diagnosis, and examine the underlying problems and possible solution strategies. We have looked at tools that may be used to represent and manipulate diagnostic knowledge. These generic aspects of fault diagnosis underpin all practical diagnostic applications. The details of implementation are not considered here—they cannot be reasonably treated in the space available. There is no discussion at all of important practical topics such as diagnostic displays, but see Goodstein [27]. We have similarly avoided considering specific computational techniques used in machine-aided diagnosis. It would be attractive to include such topics, and perhaps that will be possible in a later volume.

The interest in fault diagnosis has increased considerably during the last decade, and yet there is still no generally-agreed theoretical basis or methodology. Recently, there has been an enormous surge of interest in "expert systems" [28–32]. One of the classic application areas of expert systems is fault diagnosis—and this partially accounts for the surge of interest. Another important factor in this increased awareness (of the need for diagnosis) is that modern distributed control systems do most of the "ordinary" monitoring and control tasks very well. Attention is then focused on less immediate problems, such as fault diagnosis. It is hoped that this increased attention will yield a better theoretical understanding of the problems of diagnosis and of the tools and techniques needed to solve those problems.

We have tried to show (by means of the case studies) that fault diagnosis is important but by no means the only avenue for improvement. Attention to detail at the design state is crucial, particularly in the specification and definition of alarm systems. Selection and training of process plant operators is also a neglected area.

In terms of techniques, it appears that the cause consequence diagram has many attractions for fault logic representation and that fuzzy logic will eventually be predominant for diagnostic calculations. A combination of the two techniques would be very powerful. Expert systems also appear to be a very useful tool. They do not give us anything new, but they do provide a very convenient framework in which to express and manipulate our ideas.

APPENDIX—FAULT TREE CONSTRUCTION AND ANALYSIS

A fault tree is a logic diagram showing the different ways that a system can fail in terms of a defined final failure event (e.g., a diagram showing all of the causes of the final event *vessel failure*).

As with all logic diagrams there is also the advantage that the process of drawing the diagram requires a good understanding of system behavior—the safety analyst scrutinizes the systems under study; this is a very valuable side-effect of analysis.

Since the analysis is in terms of a final failure, the tree finds the causes of failure by working backwards from the top event. (This means that the method is a "top down" technique). There are many possible states of a system: normal working states, states (including component failures) that do not lead to a top event, and states (including component failures) that do lead to the top event.

The purpose of a fault tree is to focus attention only on those events (or combinations of events) that lead to the top event. The tree does not include representations of other states—in particular, it does not include "success" states.

A fault tree is also a pictorial aid; it is intended to clarify the representation of failure mechanisms. A well-constructed fault tree can show failure mechanisms clearly, even for a complex system.

The systematic nature of the fault tree technique also helps to ensure that the analysis is complete. It is much more difficult to ensure completeness without the discipline and framework of a formal technique. For examples of Fault Trees see McCormick [33].

Fault Tree Construction

In spite of its name a fault tree often looks more like a "root" than a "tree"—it is usually drawn down the page, with the "top" event at the top of the page and the branches of the tree spreading out down the page.

Several stages may be formally identified:

1. Understand the system behavior.
2. Define the event of interest (the "top" event).
3. Find the logical combinations of events that could cause the top event. The logic is defined using *or* and *and* gates—or n-out-of-m gates for redundant systems.
4. Continue finding causes of events until all branches of the tree end in easy-to-understand "base" events.

These steps are not always as easy to carry out as may first appear. In particular steps 3 and 4 can be very time-consuming and error-prone.

For this reason Lawley [20] makes the distinction between (a) the sequence of events that would lead to the top event if no protection were provided, and (b) the protective systems and/or operator actions that are intended to prevent the top event occuring.

The fault tree may be constructed by first making the "cause tree" corresponding to (a). The effects of protective systems or operator actions as given in (b) can then be added afterwards. This two-step method does make fault tree construction simpler. The practical effect of this method is to first construct the tree mostly containing *or* gates. The protective systems and operator actions are then seen largely in tems of adding *and* gates to the tree. A further benefit of this approach is that it often happens that one protective system or operator action naturally counteracts a whole group of causes in the original tree. This is easily recognized as the *and* gates are added—the resulting tree may then be tidier as a result. This is not purely a cosmetic benefit—the whole purpose of a graphic aid is to make the result easier to read.

Summary of Steps in Construction

1. Define the top event carefully and write it at the top of the page.
2. Think of the prerequisites of the top event. Try to think in small steps. Don't jump straight from the top event to basic causes. Usually, there will be several causes; these alternatives are specified by using an *or* gate.

   If two events must coincide in order for a cause to be valid, then an *and* gate is used to combine them.

   If there are many different ways in which the top event may occur, then it will probably help to divide them up into several groups of similar types. Each group will then be an input to an *or* gate immediately below the top event.

   Try to find all the prerequisites of the top event before moving on to the next event. It helps to focus on one event at a time.

   Look out for common-mode failure causes (like utility failures or environmental events such as fire) that may affect several different items of equipment at the same time or in the same way. These will need to be separated out from causes that are genuinely independent and dealt with in a separate branch of the tree.
3. Select a new event and find its prerequisites as in step 2. Repeat this process until all events in the tree are "base" events that do not need to be further subdivided.
4. Check that the tree logic is correct. Pick particular causes out of the tree and verify that they really would cause the top event to occur.
5. Add the operator actions that may also help to reduce the top event rate.
6. Add the protective system events that guard against the "cause tree" sequences.

Fault Tree Analysis

The analysis process is relatively straightforward compared to that of construction, but can still be time-consuming for a large tree.

What do we want from the analysis? In general, we want to find the failure mechanisms (*What happens?*) and the failure rates (*How often* does it happen?) In practice many safety analyses concentrate almost exclusively on the second of these. In this case "direct quantification" of the tree may be used.

Direct Quantification

This is the simplest and most obvious method of analysis:

1. Each basic failure rate is noted alongside the appropriate event box on the fault tree.
2. The analyst traces forwards along the branches of the fault tree using simple arithmetic and reliability engineering calculations to combine values at logic gates. It is customary to use approximations in this evaluation process, and hence the answer obtained is not "exact." However, it should be noted that these approximations are conservative (i.e., lead to an overestimate of the overall failure rate).
3. This process is continued until all events in the tree are quantified; the final one found will be that of the "top" event.

This method of fault tree analysis has the advantage of being very easy to "read." The graphic nature of the tree helps understanding, and the numbers are imposed directly on the tree. It is then very easy to identify the dominant failure mechanisms (if any). The individual failure mechanisms are never defined explicitly, although they are of course all available for inspection in the fault tree itself.

Problems with Direct Quantification

For complex systems direct quantification may not be suitable. The reasons for this are two-fold:

1. The tree itself is more complex and hence the advantage of working with a "simple" graphic representation is not so obvious. In particular, the tree may extend over many sheets of paper and is therefore not simple to "read."
2. The mathematics used to evaluate the tree is more complex for highly-redundant systems (such as those encountered in nuclear power applications). There is more use of n-out-of-m reliability calculations and (very often) a concern that direct quantification will lead to errors because of failure to recognize common-mode effects (see later notes).

In such cases it may be more useful to formally identify the individual failure mechanisms before evaluating the failure rates.

These are the basic reasons why direct quantification is not always suitable. We will now examine these reasons in more detail—in particular it is necessary to look more closely at the mathematical aspects.

The fault tree contains the set of failure mechanisms (we hope that it contains the "complete" set). Why should we want to define the individual mechanisms?

For a simple fault tree there is no need. For a more complex tree it often happens that one or both of the following complications occur:

1. There are common-mode failures (such as power supply failure) that will cause several components to fail at the same time. This invalidates the "independent failures" assumption commonly used in probabilistic analysis. Unless this was recognized during fault tree construction, it is likely that the structure of the tree is unsuited for direct quantification. (Even if common mode was recognized during construction, it may be very difficult, or impossible, to construct a useful tree that takes several different types of common mode into account).
2. Even in simple systems it may happen that a particular item is implicitly assumed to be working in one branch of a tree (the "working O.K." branch). Elsewhere in the tree, in another branch which at sometime will be "and'd" with the "working O.K." branch, the same item is explicitly defined to be failed. The fault tree may hide this conflict of working and failed states

of the same item. The combination of events implied by the *and* gate is automatically treated as a failure mode of the fault tree (if direct quantification is used), and yet it is quite obvious that the "failure mode" cannot be real.

This kind of inconsistency may be easier to deal with if the failure mechanisms are found from the fault tree. They can then be examined individually and quantified directly.

Finding the Failure Mechanisms

We will now concentrate on obtaining a table, with one line for each failure mechanism, directly from a fault tree.

1. Start the table by writting down the top event as the first line of the table. (For some top events this will already be a combination of events and will include one or more logic gates). Each event forms one column of the table.
2. Consider the first event in the row. Three distinct cases occur:
   a) If the event is a base event, leave it "as is."
   b) If the event has an *and* gate below it in the fault tree, rewrite the line with this event replaced by all of the input events to the and gate. (This will leave the same number of lines in the table but will increase the number of columns in this particular line).
   c) If the event has an *or* gate below it in the fault tree, replace the line by a series of lines where each line contains just one of the events below the *or* gate, in addition to all of the events that were already in the original line.
3. Repeat step 2 for all other events in the row.
4. Repeat steps 2 and 3 for all rows until every row of the table contains base events only.

This procedure is much easier to carry out than to describe. The result is a table where each row represents a distinct failure mechanism, and each column in a row represents one failure event.

The number of rows therefore gives the number of failure mechanisms. Each row is also known as a "cut set" of the fault tree. For a fault tree representing failures in a simple system this will be sufficient. For a complex system (particularly one with cross-linked "trains" of equipment) it is likely that some of the rows will be supersets of other rows. In practical terms this is meaningless. A set of events in one row will cause system failure. What do additional failures cause? Each row containing a superset should be deleted from the table. The remaining rows are known as "minimum cut sets" of the fault tree.

Evaluating the Failure Mechanisms

Each mechanism is now represented by one row in our table of mechanisms. The events in one mechanism must all co-exist for the top event to occur. The frequency or probability of a particular mechanism is therefore obtained by use of arithmetic for *and* gate logic.

The overall top-event rate is approximated by adding together all of the rates for the individual failure mechanisms. This is equivalent to using *or* gate logic.

In an ideal world a fault tree would be "complete and correct." But what does this mean?

Completeness

Do we really expect every possible event, no matter how unlikely, to be included in our fault tree? In practice we will normally try to include all events that have any reasonable chance of occurring. This means that we are really using a probabilistic approach where we ignore very unlikely events.

Consider for example an analysis of hazardous waste transportation by means of a road tanker. We would probably include hazards caused by:

1. Random failures of the vehicle components.
2. Driver error or illness.
3. Problems caused by other vehicles and their drivers.
4. Bad and/or "freak" weather conditions.
5. Problems caused by pedestrians and/or animals.

We might even consider terrorist action, but would we consider the possibility of the tanker colliding with an aircraft making an emergency landing on the road? We know that such an incident could happen, but we would normally assume that the chance of it happening was so low that it could be assumed to be negligible.

There are nearly always events like this that are ignored. The analysis will still be useful. The safety analyst should, however, always be aware of such events, in case they are more likely in particular circumstances, such as when an existing fault tree is applied to a "similar" plant without careful review.

Correctness

We always hope that our work is correct. Various methods of improvement are possible:

1. We must check our fault trees carefully. An obvious mechanism for this is simply to use independent review, if possible.
2. It may also help to critically examine individual failure mechanisms—they may look fine in a completed fault tree—do they really cause system failure? (This is a further advantage of listing all the failure mechanisms.)
3. It may also be useful to try to check well-known (or expected) fault conditions against those predicted by the tree—they should all be included somewhere.
4. When the plant is actually in operation we should also make sure that we collect real operating event data so that this can be checked against the fault tree. In this context note that we do not need to wait for the top event to occur. We can use "near misses" or lesser fault sequences that do not propagate as far as the top event for checking the tree.

When to Use Fault Trees

We use a fault tree to analyze a specific hazard. We do not draw a tree for every hazard found during, say, HAZOP [4]. The fault tree is only used where detailed analysis is necessary.

The fault tree is only appropriate where the final hazard is defined. If the initial failure is important, we should use an alternative method (like the event tree).

Is the Top Event a Probability or Frequency?

We have so far avoided any detailed discussion of the type of result required. Is it a frequency or a probability? This is deliberate in that the essential process of fault tree construction is very similar for both types of analysis.

In practice, however, we must define the top event carefully, and this will mean that we will know at this point whether we need a frequency (e.g., How often will the pump fail?) or a probability (e.g., What is the chance that the pump will fail on demand?). These considerations define the units of the top event failure. All of the events (or combinations of events) in a "cause tree" will have the same units. Protective system failures and failures to take operator action will be in terms of probability (i.e., a pure chance). It is important that these considerations are carefully noted in order to avoid errors. It is very easy to come to a wrong conclusion because of units inconsistency. It is recommended that the units be stated with every value used in the quantification process.

Common Mode Failure

A major cause of errors in fault tree analysis is due to failure to recognize common mode events. In physical terms common mode failure will cause two nominally independent failures to occur at the same time (e.g., two "independent" pumps both failing when the common power supply fails. In mathematical terms common mode failure means that, say, two probabilities are multiplied together (thereby producing a smaller result) when one of them should really be treated as if its value was 1.0. In the final result this leads to an optimistic result (i.e., an underestimate of the failure rate).

This is a serious problem. It is not intended to cover this topic here, but the safety analyst should be aware of common mode failure at all times.

REFERENCES

1. Lees, F. P., *Loss Prevention in the Process Industries*, Butterworths (1980).
2. Kletz, T. A., "Three Mile Island: Lessons on Human Factors," *Phys. Bull.* 34 (1983).
3. Kletz, T. A., "Cheaper, Safer Plants or Wealth and Safety at Work," *I. Chem. E.* (1983).
4. Kletz, T. A., "HAZOP and HAZAN" (2nd Edition), *I. Chem. E.* (1986).
5. Kragt, H., and Bonten, J., "Evaluation of a conventional process alarm System in a Fertilizer Plant," *IEEE Trans. SMC-13*, 586 (1983).
6. Plamping, K., and Andow, P. K., "The Design of Process Alarm Systems," *Trans. Inst.* MC, 5 (1983).
7. Johannsen, G., Rijnsdorp, J. E., and Tamura, H., "Matching User Needs and Technologies of Displays and Graphics," *Proc. Analysis, Design, and Evaluation of Man-Machine Systems*, Varese, Italy (1985).
8. Swain, A. D., "Relative Advantages of People and Machines in Process Industries," *Proc. International Symposium on Preventing Major Chemical Accidents*, Washington (1987).
9. Rasmussen, J., "Approaches to Control the Effects of Human Error on Chemical Plant Safety," *Proc. International Symposium on Preventing Major Chemical Accidents*, Washington (1987).
10. Marshall, E. G., Scanlon, K. E., Shepherd, A., and Duncan, K. D., "Panel Diagnosis Training for Major-Hazard Continuous-Process Installations," *Chem. Engr.* (1981).
11. Kortlandt, D., and Kragt, H., "Ergonomics in the Struggle Against Alarm Inflation in Process Control Systems—Many Questions, Few Answers," *Journal A*, 19 (3) (1978).
12. Himmelblau, D. M., *Fault Detection and Diagnosis in Chemical and Petrochemical Processes*, Elsevier, Amsterdam (1978).
13. Andow, P. K., "Alarms: Fewer Is Better," *CHEMTECH* (1986).
14. Andow, P. K., "Real-Time Analysis of Process Plant Alarms Using a Minicomputer," *Computers and Chemical Engng.*, 4 (1980).
15. Visuri, P. J., Thomassen, B. B., and Owre, F. A., "Handling of Alarms with Logic," OECD Halden Reactor Project Report no. HWR 24 (1981).
16. Henley, E. J., "Applications of Expert Systems to Fault Diagnosis," *Proc. of AIChE National Meeting*, San Francisco (1984).
17. Barth, J., and Maarleveld, A., "Operational Aspects of o DDC System," *Proc. of The Applications of Automation in The process Industries, I. Chem. E.*, (1965).
18. Welbourne, D., "Alarm Analysis and Display at Wylfa Nuclear Power Station," *Proc. IEE*, 115 (1968).
19. Watanabe, K., and Himmelblau, D. M., "Fault Diagnosis in Non-linear Chemical Processes, Part 2—Application to a Chemical Reactor," *AIChE J.*, 29, 243 (1983).
20. Lawley, H. G., "Safety Technology in the Chemical Industry: A Problem in Hazard Analysis with Solution," *Reliab. Engng.*, Vol. 1, No. 2 (1980).

21. Kelly, B. E., and Lees, F. P., "The Propagation of Faults in Process Plants," *Reliab. Engng.*, 16 (special issue) (1986).
22. Vesely, W. E., and Narum, R. E., "PREP and KITT: Computer Codes for the Automatic Evaluation of a Fault Tree," Idaho Nuclear Corp. Report IN-1349 for USAEC (undated).
23. Lapp, S. A., and Powers, G. J., "Computer-Aided Synthesis of Fault Trees," *IEEE Trans. Reliab.* (1977).
24. Andow, P. K., and Lees, F. P., "Process Computer Alarm Analysis: Outline of a Method Based on List Processing," *Trans. I. Chem. E.*, 53 (1975).
25. O'Shima, E., Tsuge, Y., Shiozaki, J., and Matsuyama, H., "Feasibility Test of Fault Diagnosis Algorithm," *Proc. AICHE National Meeting*, San Francisco (1984).
26. Dohnal, M., "Fuzzy Set Theory: Basic Concepts and applications," *Proc. of CEF '87—The Use of Computers in Chemical Engineering*, Giadini Naxos, Sicily (1987).
27. Goodstein, L. P., "Computer-Based Operating Aids," Proc. of "Design '82," *I. Chem. E.*, (1982).
28. Kramer, M., "Integration of Heuristic and Model-Based Inference in Chemical Process Fault Diagnosis," *Proc. of IFAC Workshop on Fault Detection and Safety in Chemical Plants*, Kyoto, Japan (1986).
29. Rowan, D. A., "Chemical Plant Fault Diagnosis Using Expert Systems Technology: A case study," *Proc. of IFAC Workshop on Fault Detection and Safety in Chemical Plants*, Kyoto, Japan (1986).
30. Andow, P. K., "Fault Diagnosis Using Intelligent Knowledge Based Systems," *Chem. Eng. Res. Des. 63*, 368 (1985).
31. Andow, P. K., "Goal based control systems," *Proc. of IFAC Workshop on Fault Detection and Safety in Chemical Plants*, Kyoto, Japan (1986).
32. Andow, P. K., and Galluzzo, M., "Process Plant Safety and Artificial Intelligence," *Proc. of CEF '87—The Use of Computers in Chemical Engineering*, Giadini Naxos, Sicily (1987).
33. McCormick, N. J., *Reliability and Risk Analysis*, Academic Press (1981).

CHAPTER 36

FAULT DIAGNOSIS ANALYSIS FOR CHEMICAL PLANTS

J. Shiozaki

Yamatake Honeywell Co., Ltd., Tokyo, Japan

H. Matsuyama

Department of Chemical Engineering
Kyushu University, Japan

and

E. O'Shima

Research Laboratory of Resources Utilization
Tokyo Institute of Technology, Japan

CONTENTS

STRUCTURE OF FAULT DIAGNOSIS SYSTEM

The fault diagnosis system for chemical plants generally comprises the following three subsystems; measuring, signal-processing, and inferring subsystems. The measuring subsystem measures state variables of the plant to be diagnosed and transforms them into electrical signals. The signal-processing subsystem extracts characteristic symptoms of the failure in the plant from the signals. The inferring subsystem derives candidates for the origin of failure from the symptoms.

Among them, the inferring subsystem requires some techniques specific to fault diagnosis, though the measuring and signal-processing subsystems can be constructed by use of common techniques developed in the other fields, such as process control and system identification.

INFERRING SUBSYSTEM

Approaches for making the inferring subsystem are classified into two groups: experience oriented and logic oriented. The former files all the experienced symptoms of failures and the corresponding causes in the database and searches the cause corresponding to the observed symptom in it. The latter uses a model representing cause-effect relationships in the plant to be diagnosed and searches the chains of cause-effect relationships that can explain the observed symptom.

The experience oriented approach is more suitable for chemical plants whose models are difficult to be made because of technical or economical reasons. The fault diagnosis system for the batch process, for instance, is a good candidate for this approach because it is not reasonable to prepare models one by one corresponding to operating conditions for a wide variety of products produced by the batch process.

The logic oriented approach is particularly useful for finding causes of symptoms that have never been faced, though it requires a comprehensive model of the cause-effect relationships in the plant to be diagnosed. This approach is more suitable for the continuous process than the batch process because the cause-effect relationships in the continuous process are easier to analyze.

FAULT DIAGNOSIS OF BATCH PROCESS

Since the state of the batch process varies with time, the symptom should be extracted from the time-varying information. Kutsuwa et al. [1] have proposed an algorithm for the fault diagnosis of the batch process using a pattern recognition technique for extracting the symptom from trajectories of time-varying state variables. They have taken the experience oriented approach to the inferring subsystem because of the reason mentioned.

Since the present method is one of experience oriented methods, it requires the following two presumptions:

1. Sufficient operation data are accumulated for the process to be diagnosed.
2. The diagnostic result is examined with the use of the additional information every time after the on-line diagnosis.

Preparation of Standard Pattern

Suppose that abnormal states caused by N kinds of causal events have been experienced in the process to be diagnosed and J_n ($n = 1, 2, \ldots, N$) sets of data (trajectories of the measured variables) have been accumulated for abnormal states caused by the n-th causal event.

The accumulated data for the abnormal states caused by each of causal events should be previously transformed into the standard patterns for the said causal event.

Let

$x_0^{i(j)}(k\,\Delta t)$ $\quad (i = 1, 2, \ldots, I;\ j = 1, 2, \ldots, J_0;\ k = 1, 2, \ldots, K)$

be the value of the i-th measured variable at $t = k\,\Delta t$ in the j-th data of the normal state

and let

$x_n^{i(j)}(k\,\Delta t)$ $\quad (i = 1, 2, \ldots, I;\ j = 1, 2, \ldots, J_n;\ k = 1, 2, \ldots, K;\ n = 1, 2, \ldots, N)$

be the value of the same variable at $t = k\,\Delta t$ in the j-th data of the abnormal state due to the n-th causal event,

where Δt = the sampling interval
I = number of measured variables
J_0 = number of data for the normal state
K = number of sampling.

The operation data for the normal state are averaged to make the standard trajectory x_0^i (k Δt) for the i the measured variable (i = 1, 2, . . . , I).

$$x_0^i\,(k\,\Delta t) = \sum_{j=1}^{J_0} x_0^{i(j)}(k\,\Delta t)/J_0 \tag{1}$$

Then the deviation $y_n^{i(j)}(k\,\Delta t)$ from the standard trajectory is defined as

$$y_n^{i(j)}\,(k\,\Delta t) = x_n^{i(j)}(k\,\Delta t) - x_0^i(k\,\Delta t) \tag{2}$$

and a set of data is represented by vector $y^{i(j)}$ defined as

$$y_n^{i(j)} = [y_n^{i(j)}\,(\Delta t),\, y_n^{i(j)}\,(2\,\Delta t), \ldots, y_n^{i(j)}\,(K\,\Delta t)]^T \tag{3}$$

where superscript T represents the transpose. Normalizing the vector $y_n^{i(j)}$, we have

$$R_n^{i(j)} = y_n^{i(j)}/|y_n^{i(j)}| \tag{4}$$

The standard pattern $P_n^{(j)}$ for the n-th causal event transformed from the j-th data is defined by a vector given as follows:

$$P_n^{(j)} = [w^1(R_n^{1(j)})^T, w^2(R_n^{2(j)})^T, \ldots, w^I(R_n^{I(j)})^T]^T \tag{5}$$

where w^i denotes the weight for the i-th variable and is determined so as to make the distance between standard patterns for the same causal events to be as close as possible, and the distance between those for the different causal events to be as far as possible and to satisfy the following condition:

$$\sum_{i=1}^{I} (w^i)^2 = 1 \tag{6}$$

Since the patterns are defined as normalized vectors, the distance between two patterns is defined by an angle between them. For simplicity of computation, we use the inner product of the two patterns as the representation of the distance because the relation between the angle and the inner product is a monotone decreasing function. Then the problem of determining the weights in Equation 5 is formulated as the following maximize-minimize problem:

$$\underset{w^i}{\text{Maximize-}}\ \underset{m,\,n\,(m \neq n)}{\text{Minimize}}\ [(P_n^{(j)})^T P_n^{(k)} - (P_n^{(j)})^T P_m^{(h)}] \quad (\text{for } j, k = 1, 2, \ldots, J_n;\ h = 1, 2, \ldots, J_m) \tag{7}$$

$$\text{Subject to} \sum_{i=1}^{I} (w^i)^2 = 1 \tag{8}$$

This problem is easily reduced to a linear programming problem as follows:

$$\text{Maximize } z^0$$

$$\text{Subject to } z^0 \geqq \sum_{i=1}^{I} (R_n^{i(j)})^T (R_n^{i(k)} - R_m^{i(h)}) z^i$$

$$(\text{for } j, k = 1, 2, \ldots, J_n;\ h = 1, 2, \ldots, J_m)$$
$$(\text{for } n, m = 1, 2, \ldots, N;\ m = n) \tag{9}$$

$$\sum_{i=1}^{I} z^i = 1 \tag{10}$$

$$z^i \geqq 0 \qquad (\text{for } i = 0, 1, \ldots, I) \tag{11}$$

Then the weight w^i is given by

$$w^i = (z^i)^{1/2} \qquad (\text{for } i = 1, 2, \ldots, I) \tag{12}$$

After the weights in Equation 5 are determined, the standard patterns defined by Equation 5 represent points on the surface of (I × K)-dimensional sphere with unit radius.

Algorithm for Fault Diagnosis

The trajectories of the measured variables obtained from the operating plant are transformed by use of the same procedure as mentioned. Let x^i (k Δt) (i = 1, 2, . . . , I; k = 1, 2, . . . , K) be the value of the i-th variable at t = k Δt. Then, deviation y^i(k Δt) is given as

$$y^i(k\,\Delta t) = x^i(k\,\Delta t) - x_0^i(k\,\Delta t) \tag{13a}$$

and vector y^i is defined as

$$y^i = [y^i(\Delta t), y^i(2\,\Delta t), \ldots, y^i(K\,\Delta t)]^T \tag{13b}$$

Normalizing the vector y^i, we have

$$R^i = y^i/|y^i| \tag{14}$$

The pattern P given by

$$P = [w^1(R^1)^T, w^2(R^2)^T, \ldots, w^I(R^I)^T]^T \tag{15}$$

is called the "observed pattern."

The standard patterns corresponding to the same causal event are considered to exist in the same region on the surface of the (I × K)-dimensional sphere, which is called the "region corresponding to the n-th causal event." Hence, when the observed pattern exists in the region corresponding to the n-th causal event, we can conclude that the n-th causal event is a candidate for the origin of failure currently faced. Figure 1A shows a schematical example for the 2-dimensional case.

In a practical case, however, a set of standard patterns corresponding to the same causal event cannot determine the region on the surface of the (I × K)-dimensional sphere because the number of operation data is much smaller than the dimension of the sphere. Hence, the region corresponding to the n-th causal event is defined as the intersection between the surface of the (I × K)-dimensional sphere and the minimal (I × K)-dimensional cone that contains all the standard patterns corresponding to the n-th causal event in it. The region corresponding to the n-th causal event by this definition can be represented by a vector S_n satisfying the following conditions:

$$\text{Minimize } S_n$$

$$\text{Subject to } (P_n^{(j)})^T S_n \geqq 1 \qquad (\text{for } j = 1, 2, \ldots, J_n) \tag{16}$$

This vector is called the "representative vector" for the n-th causal event. As schematically shown in Figure 1B, the direction of the representative vector for an arbitrary causal event coincides with the axis of the cone, which defines the region corresponding to the causal event, and all the tangential lines at the boundary points of the region intersect with one another at the ending point of the representative vector.

The necessary and sufficient condition for an observed pattern P to exist in the region corresponding to the n-th causal event is that it satisfies

$$P^T S_n \geqq 1 \qquad (n = 1, 2, \ldots, N) \tag{17}$$

Figure 1C schematically explains Condition 17.

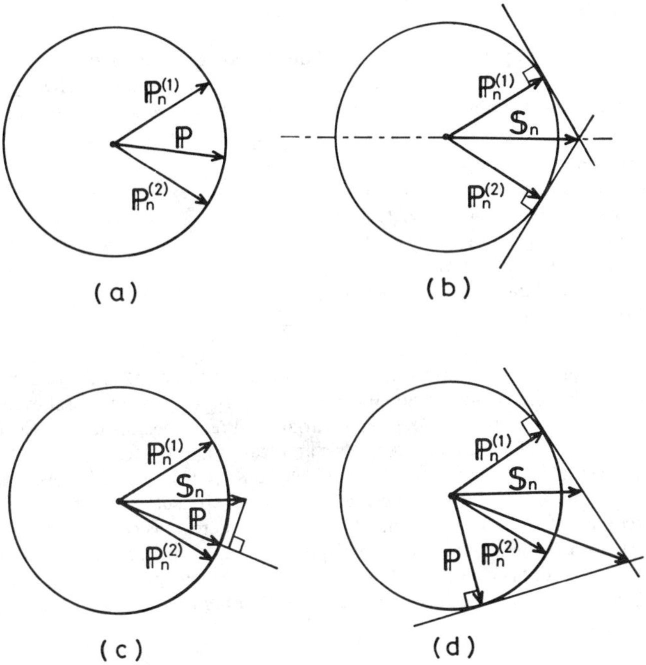

Figure 1. Explanation of the fault diagnosis by use of the pattern recognition.

Then the problem of the fault diagnosis of the batch process is formulated as follows:

Problem: For a given observed pattern, enumerate causal events that satisfy Equation 17.

The algorithm for fault diagnosis based on the formulation is very simple because it requires only the calculation of the inner products of vectors.

Learning

We call it a "wrong diagnosis" when the inner product between the observed pattern and the representative vector for the true origin of failure is less than unity. Then the representative vector for the true origin of failure should be so improved as to represent the minimal cone that contains the observed pattern as well as the original cone. The improvement of the representative patterns is called "learning."

Without loss of generality, let S_n be the representative vector to be improved. Then the improved representative vector S'_n is given as:

$$S'_n = (aP + bS_n)/(a + bP^TS_n) \quad (18)$$

where
$a = r + 1$
$b = u(u - rv)$
$r = -(1 - u^2)^{1/2}/(1 - v^2)^{1/2}$
$u = P^TS_n/|S_n|$
$v = 1/|S_n|$

Figure 1D shows the relation among the observed pattern, original and improved representative vectors.

Feasibility Study

Kutsuwa et al. [1] have applied the above-mentioned method to a laboratory-scale batch reactor where an esterfication of methanol and acetic acid occurs with the use of H_2SO_4 as a catalyst. In the experiments, the failures caused by the following 7 causal events were generated artificially:

1. Higher temperature set for jacket water.
2. Lower temperature set for jacket water.
3. Higher initial concentration of CH_3OH.
4. Lower initial concentration of CH_3OH.
5. Earlier injection of H_2SO_4 into the reactor.
6. Later injection of H_2SO_4 into the reactor.
7. Leakage of jacket water into the reactor.

Three variables—the reactor temperature, jacket temperature and pH in the reactor—were sampled every 20 seconds. The 300-dimensional standard pattern for each of causal events was made from 100 sets of sampled values of these three variables. Eight experiments for each of artificial causal events were performed repeating diagnosis and learning.

Though the effect of learning was demonstrated by their experimental results, they could not completely prevent the wrong diagnosis even after seven experiments for each of causal events.

In order to completely prevent the wrong diagnosis, all the regions corresponding to the causal events should be properly determined by use of a large number of operational data for the abnormal states, which is usually difficult in a practical case. Hence, this method should be supported by a simulator that can supplement the operational data for the abnormal states possible to occur in the process to be diagnosed.

FAULT DIAGNOSIS OF CONTINUOUS PROCESS

The inferring subsystem for the continuous process can be made through the experience oriented approach as well as the logic oriented approach. Expert systems may well be applied to the experience oriented approach, where the experiences of human operators are compiled in the knowledge-base. The knowledge-base made only from the experiences of human operator may not be complete enough to cover all the possible failures because failures scarcely occur in a well-controlled process. As stated in the section on the fault diagnosis of the batch process, the shortage of data of the abnormal states is fatal to the experience oriented approach. The logic oriented approach is superior to the experience oriented one provided that we can obtain a model comprehensive enough to explain any kind of failures in the plant to be diagnosed.

Representations of Model and Symptom

The directed graph (or digraph) is useful in representing the cause-effect relationships among state variables, where the node corresponds to a state variable and the branch represents the immediate influence between two variables. The signed digraph (SDG) is defined by giving the signs + and − to the branch of the digraph in order to distinguish the positive and negative influences (or reinforcement and suppression), respectively.

Each state variable is assumed, for simplicity, to take only three different ranges—high, normal and low—which are, respectively, designated by the signs +, 0, and −. The combination of signs designated to all the nodes corresponding to state variables is called a "pattern," which is the symptom representing the state of the process.

Example 1. In order to apply the present concept to practical problems, the SDG for a tank system in Figure 2A is given as Figure 2B, where F_0, F_1, F_2 denote flow rates and L_1, L_2 represent

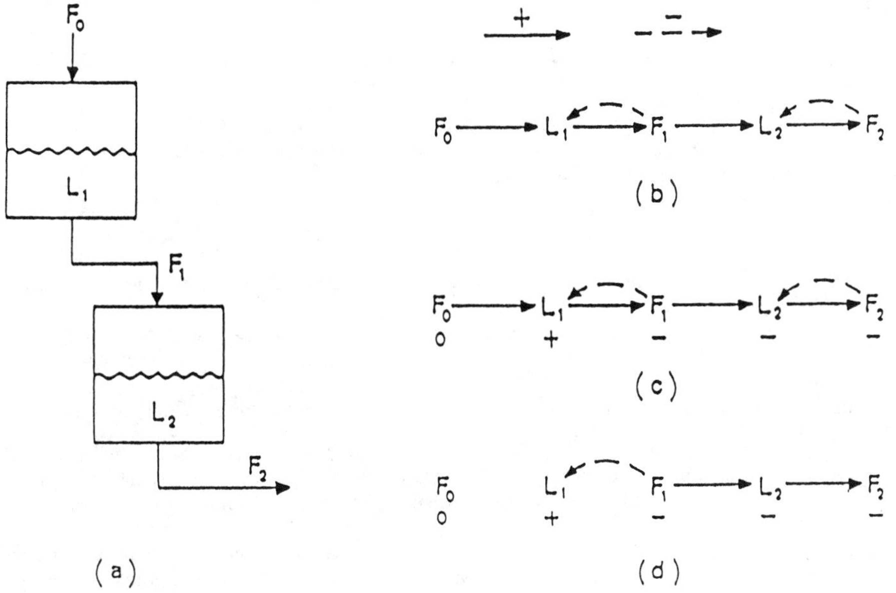

Figure 2. Explanation of the fault diagnosis by use of the signed digraph.

levels of the tanks. The abnormal decrease of F_1 caused by the blockage of the pipe between the tanks, for example, would give rise to the pattern shown in Figure 2C.

Algorithm of Fault Diagnosis

If all the state variables are measured, each of the variables should show either normal or abnormal value. The node in the SDG corresponding to the state variable that shows an abnormal value is defined as a "valid" node. The branch corresponding to the immediate influence that is transmitting the abnormality is defined as a "consistent" branch. In other words, a valid node is such a node that has a nonzero sign, and a consistent branch is such a branch whose sign is equal to the product of the signs of its initial and terminal nodes.

The subgraph of the SDG consisting of only but all the valid nodes and consistent branches is called a "cause-effect (CE)" graph. The CE graph is a mathematical representation of the propagation of the failure, and its maximal strongly connected components are composed of the candidates for the origin of failure. Hence, the problem of fault diagnosis can be formulated as a problem of searching the maximal strongly connected components of the CE graph and the nodes in them are candidates for the origin of failure.

A strongly connected component is a set of nodes in a digraph, in which there exists at least one directed path from one to the other and vice versa for an arbitrary pair of nodes. A strongly connected component is called a "maximal," if it has no branch inwardly incident to it. The algorithm proposed by Tarjan [2] is now regarded as one of the most efficient for searching the maximal strongly connected components.

Example 2. Figure 2D shows the CE graph obtained from the SDG in Figure 2B for the pattern in Figure 2C. The maximal strongly connected component in this case is $F_1(-)$, which shows the decrease of the flow rate caused by the blockage in the pipe between two tanks.

Improvement of Algorithm

In order to apply the present method to a practical plant, the following problems should be overcome:

1. There exist many unmeasured state variables in the plant to be diagnosed.
2. It is difficult to determine thresholds for distinguishing the normal and abnormal values of the measured variables.

Treatment of Unmeasured Variables

The nodes in the SDG are classified into two groups; observed nodes corresponding to measured variables and unobserved nodes corresponding to unmeasured variables. A set of signs of the observed nodes is called "partial pattern." Numerous different CE graphs are generated from a given SDG and a partial pattern by supplementing any one of the signs +, 0, and − to each unobserved node of the SDG.

In order to restrict the locations of the origins of failure as far as possible, the following presumption is adopted:

Presumption: It is presumed that there exists only one origin of failure, because the probability of the strictly simultaneous occurrence of more than one independent failure is considered to be extremely small.

Under this presumption, the CE graph to represent propagation of failure should have only one maximal strongly connected component, which is to be called the "rooted CE graph." Then the problem of fault diagnosis is formulated as follows:

Problem: For a given SDG and a partial pattern of the observed nodes, enumerate the rooted CE graphs by supplementing arbitrary signs to all the unobserved nodes in the SDG. The nodes in the maximal strongly connected components of the enumerated CE graphs are candidates for the origin of failure.

Example 3. In the tank system shown in Figure 2A, suppose that level L_2 and flow rates F_0 and F_1 are not measured.

The abnormal decrease of F_1 caused by the blockage of the pipe between the tanks, for example, would give rise to the partial pattern shown in Figure 3A. Only a rooted CE graph shown in Figure 3B can be obtained by supplementing signs to the unobserved nodes, which shows that the origin of failure is the decrease of the flow rate caused by the blockage in the pipe between the tanks.

The origin of failure may not be uniquely identified in some cases because of the lack of the information on the signs of the unobserved nodes. In such cases, a set of candidates for the origin of failure is given instead of a unique origin.

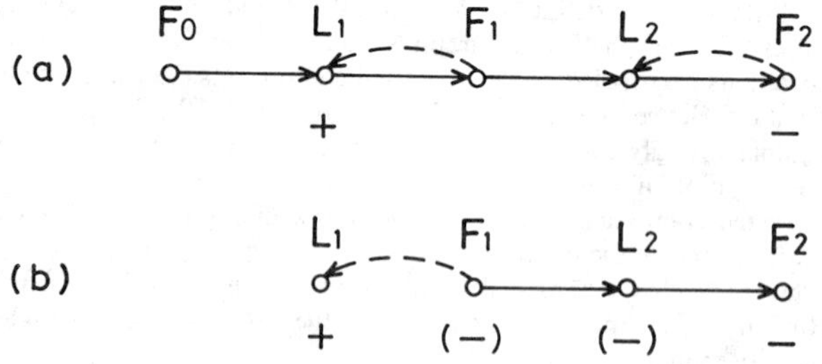

Figure 3. Partial pattern and the CE graph corresponding to it for the blockage of the pipe between two tanks.

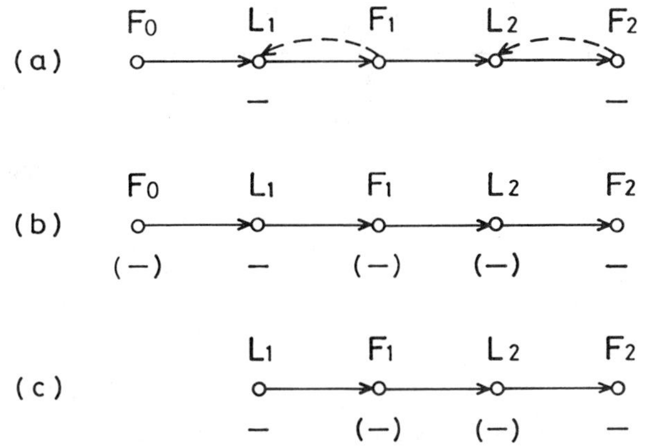

Figure 4. Partial pattern and the CE graphs corresponding to it for the abnormal decrease of the feed flow rate.

The abnormal decrease of the feed flow rate F_0 would give rise to the partial pattern shown in Figure 4A, and two rooted CE graphs, shown in Figures 4B and C, are obtained by supplementing signs to the unobserved nodes. The candidates for the origin of failure are $F_0(-)$ and $L_1(-)$, which are contained in the maximal strongly connected components of these CE graphs. We can conclude that the diagnosis is properly made since the true origin of failure, F_0, is contained in the set of candidates.

The algorithms for fault diagnosis based on the previous formulation has been proposed by Iri et al. [3, 4] and has been further improved by Shiozaki et al. [5].

Difficulty in Determining Thresholds

The lower and upper thresholds c^- and c^+ are needed for dividing the value of measured variable x into three ranges. The observed node corresponding to x is given the sign + when $x > c^+$, 0 when $c^- \leqq x \leqq c^+$, and − when $x < c^-$. A correct diagnosis may not be made if there is a poor balance among the thresholds for the measured variables.

Example 4. In the tank system shown in Figure 2A, suppose that level L_2 and flow rates F_0 and F_1 are not measured.

If the range between the lower and upper thresholds for level L_1 is too wide as compared with that for flow rate F_2, then the partial pattern resulting from a decrease of the feed flow rate F_0 will be given as in Figure 5A. Only the rooted CE graph shown in Figure 5B is obtained by supplementing signs to the unobserved nodes, which is a wrong diagnosis because the true origin of failure is overlooked.

In order to prevent the wrong diagnosis shown in Example 4, one may intend to set the ranges between the lower and upper thresholds for measured variables as narrow as possible. Too narrow ranges, however, result in a wrong diagnosis.

Example 5. In the tank system shown in Figure 2A, suppose that level L_2 and flow rates F_0 and F_1 are not measured. The decrease of level L_2 caused by the leakage at the second tank would give rise to the partial pattern shown in Figure 6A when the thresholds are properly determined.

If the range between the lower and upper thresholds for L_1 is too narrow, however, a perturbation of the level in the first tank may go across the lower threshold and may give the sign − to L_1. The resulting partial pattern is shown in Figure 6B. Only two rooted CE graphs shown in Figure

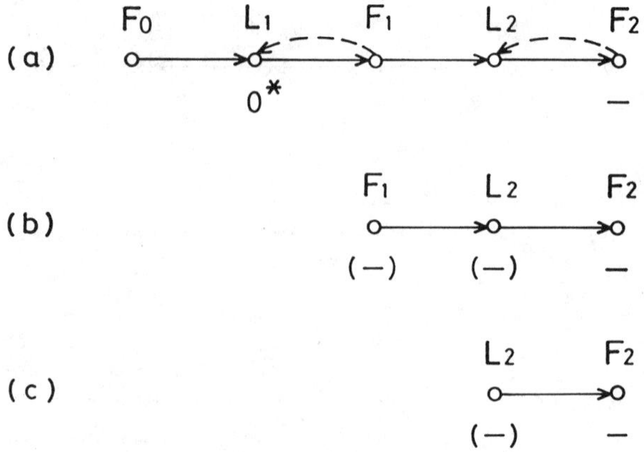

Figure 5. Improper partial pattern and the CE graph corresponding to it for the abnormal decrease of the feed flow rate when the threshold for the level of the first tank not properly determined.

6C and D can be obtained for this partial pattern, which gives a wrong diagnosis that the abnormal decrease of the feed flow rate $F_0(-)$ or the leakage at the first tank L_1 is the origin of failure.

As demonstrated in Examples 4 and 5, there exists no safe side in determining the threshold for the measured variable. In order to avoid this difficulty, the concept of a "five-range pattern" is introduced. Four thresholds $b^+ > a^+ > a^- > b^-$ are set for each of the measured variables. Thresholds b^+ and b^- are called "outer thresholds," while a^+ and a^- are called "inner thresholds." The

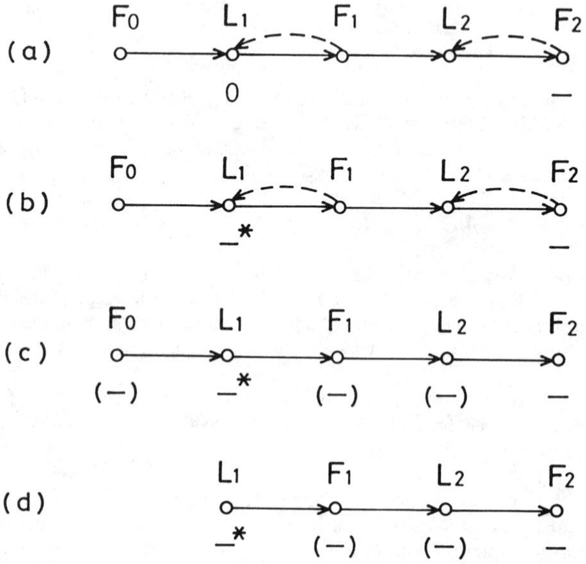

Figure 6. Proper and improper partial patterns and the CE graphs corresponding to the improper pattern for the leakage at the second tank.

sign of the observed node corresponding to variable x is given as + if $x > b^+$; +? if $a^+ < x \leqq b^+$; 0 if $a^- \leqq x \leqq a^+$; −? if $b^- \leqq x < a^-$; and "−" if $x < b^-$. These signs are collectively called "five-range signs" and the combination of five-range signs is called a "five-range pattern."

Two new signs +? and −? are called "indistinct signs." The sign +? indicates uncertainty as to whether it is 0 or +, while the sign −? indicates uncertainty as to whether it is 0 or −. Signs 0 and + are called as distinct signs corresponding to +?, while signs 0 and − are called distinct signs corresponding to −?.

With the use of the five-range pattern, the problem of fault diagnosis can be formulated as follows:

Problem: For a given SDG and a partial five-range pattern of the observed nodes, enumerate the rooted CE graphs by supplementing arbitrary signs to all the unobserved nodes and corresponding distinct signs to all the observed nodes with indistinct signs in the SDG. The nodes in the maximal strongly connected components of the enumerated CE graphs are candidates for the origin of failure.

Shiozaki et al. [6] have proposed an efficient algorithm for fault diagnosis with the use of the five-range pattern.

Even when it is difficult to determine the thresholds because of the shortage of the information, there exist safe sides in determining those for the five-range pattern. The outer side is the safe side for outer thresholds b^+ and b^- and the inner side is the safe side for inner thresholds a^+ and a^-. In other words, the more widely the ranges for the indistinct signs are set, the more possibly we can prevent the wrong diagnosis though the number of candidates increases.

Example 6. For the cases in Examples 4 and 5, sufficiently wide ranges for indistinct signs for L_1 give the same five-range pattern as shown in Figure 7A. Four rooted CE graphs shown in Figure 7B, C, D, and E can be obtained for this five-range pattern and hence the set of candidates is given as $F_0(-)$, $L_1(-)$, $F_1(-)$, and $L_2(-)$, in which the true origins F_0 for Example 4 and L_2 for Example 5 are contained.

Feasibility Study

An experimental investigation with the use of a pilot plant has been performed by Tsuge et al. [7] in order to verify the applicability of the above-mentioned algorithm for fault diagnosis. The main aspects include evaluation of:

1. Memory capacity needed to store the diagnostic program and the signed digraph.
2. Manhours for the construction of the signed digraph for a practical plant.
3. A method for determining the thresholds for measured variables.
4. Speed and accuracy of the fault diagnosis program.
5. Usefulness of the information given by off-line sensors in fault diagnosis.

A diagnostic system has has been constructed by using an analog/digital converter and an Apple II microcomputer. When a distinct abnormal sign + or − is detected in the five-range pattern generated by data from the on-line sensors, the diagnostic program starts to search the origin of failure and human operators starts to gather data from the off-line sensors that are used to verify the usefulness of the off-line information. The program has been written by GAME (General Algorithmic Micro Expression) and requires about 20KB.

The signed digraph for the pilot plant to be diagnosed contains 90 nodes (including 13 on-line observed nodes and 8 off-line observed nodes) and 196 branches, and required 3KB memory capacity to be stored and 2 man-months to be made.

The normal values of the measured variables were set at the average values during the steady state operation. The inner thresholds were set at the maximum deviations from the normal values. The outer thresholds were determined as the deviations of the indicators for which operators feel confident that the plant was operating abnormally.

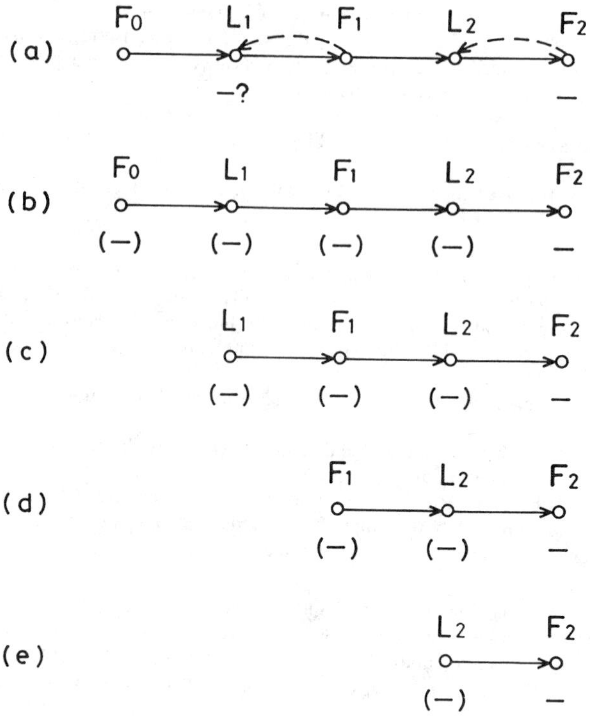

Figure 7. Five-range partial pattern and the CE graphs corresponding to it for both of the decrease of the feed flow rate and the leakage at the second tank.

In the experiments, the abnormal state caused by 11 origins were generated artificially, among which 8 origins were malfunctions of on-line sensors. The remaining 3 were:

1. TS(−): the decrease of the temperature of the warm water that controls the reactor temperature.
2. FP(−): the malfunction of the feed pump for the reactant liquid.
3. PU(+): the increase of the feed pressure of the reactant gas.

In none of the experiments was a pattern produced that could not explain the origin of failure. This is considered to prove the capability of the used method of determining thresholds.

In each experiment the true origin was contained in the set of candidates, and the diagnosis using only the on-line information was finished within 2 minutes, while the diagnosis using both the on-line and off-line information was finished faster. Considering the difference in processing speeds between an Apple II and a computer for process control, the speed of the present algorithm is very satisfactory.

Though the diagnosis using only the on-line information gave several tens of candidates for the origin of failure, the number of candidates was considerably reduced when the off-line information was used, except in two cases TS(−) and FP(−). This is because the blockages in the pipes could not be removed from the set of candidates since the instrumentation of this pilot plant could give little information on pressures and flow rates of gases and liquids in pipelines.

CONCLUSION

Methods of fault diagnosis for two typical processes, batch and continuous, are proposed.

For the batch process, an experience oriented method with the use of pattern recognition techniques is recommended since the symptom of the failure in it is characterized by the trends of the measured variables. It is not reasonable to make models of cause-effect relationships in the batch process, one by one, corresponding to operating conditions for a wide variety of its products, though the method requires either a large number of operation data for the process to be diagnosed or a powerful simulator that can simulate all the failures possible to occur in it.

For the continuous process, a logic oriented method by use of the signed digraph is recommended because its feasibility has already been demonstrated by the experiments with the use of a pilot plant.

REFERENCES

1. Kutsuwa, Y., Kojima, K., and Matsuyama, H., "Fault Diagnosis of a Batch Process by Use of Pattern-Recognition Technique," *Kagaku Kogaku Ronbunshu,* to be printed.
2. Tarjan, R. E., "Depth-First Search and Linear Graph Algorithm," *SIAM J. Computing,* 1, 146 (1972).
3. Iri, M., Aoki, K., O'Shima, E., and Matsuyama, H., "An Algorithm for Diagnosis of System Failures in the Chemical Process," *Computers and Chem. Eng.,* 3, 489 (1979).
4. Iri, M., Aoki, K., O'Shima, E., and Matsuyama, H., "A Graphical Approach to the Problem of Locating the Origin of System Failure," *J. Operations Research Soc. Japan,* 23, 295 (1980).
5. Shiozaki, J., Matsuyama, H., O'Shima, E., and Iri, M., "An Improved Algorithm for Diagnosis of System Failures in the Chemical Process," *Computers and Chem. Eng.,* 9, 285 (1985).
6. Shiozaki, J., Matsuyama, H., Tano, K., O'Shima, E., "Fault Diagnosis of Chemical Processes by the Use of Signed Directed Graphs. Extention to Five-Range Patterns of Abnormality," *Kagaku Kogaku Ronbunshu,* 10, 233 (1984) English translation, *International J. Chem. Eng.,* 25, 651 (1985).
7. Tsuge, Y., Shiozaki, J., Matsuyama, H., O'Shima, E., Iguchi, Y., Fuchigami, M., and Matsushita, M., "Feasibility Study of a Fault Diagnosis System for Chemical Plants," *Kagaku Kogaku Ronbunshu,* 10, 240 (1984) English translation, *International J. Chem. Eng.,* 25, 660 (1985).

INDEX

A

E

F

T

U

V

W

X

Z